Chinese-English
English-Chinese
Information Technology Glossary
With Abbreviations Commonly Used in Telecommunications

SECOND EDITION, REVISED AND ENLARGED

Bruce G. Hyman

Chinese-English
English-Chinese
Information Technology Glossary
With Abbreviations Commonly Used in Telecommunications

SECOND EDITION, REVISED AND ENLARGED

Bruce G. Hyman

2005
Dunwoody Press

Chinese-English English-Chinese Information Technology Glossary, Second Edition, Revised and Enlarged

All inquiries should be directed to:
Dunwoody Press
6564 Loisdale Ct, Suite 900
Springfield, VA 22150
USA

ISBN: 1-931546-16-9
Library of Congress Catalog Card Number: 2005936321
Printed and bound in the United States of America

Table of Contents

Preface to the Second Edition

As I noted in the First Edition, the obsolescence of any hard copy reference work in the information technology and telecommunications fields is guaranteed. Since the publication of the First Edition, with its emphasis on wireless telecommunication technologies, the fields of digital and optical telecommunications have seen the most remarkable development and deployment all over the world, but nowhere so rapidly and pervasively as in China. China is also experiencing a convergence of three major electronic technologies --computers, telecommunications and cable television-- and the consequent development of new services and means of distribution. This of course has consequence for translators, localizers and lexicographers, as we struggle to keep pace with the technical developments and the new words and concepts that arise.

In working on this Second Edition, I have been fortunate to have the assistance of other translators who have contributed many more terms in their specialty fields. They have helped us all with their contributions. I believe that the benefits of this glossary to translators and localizers will increase as the number of terms and the breadth of technologies expand. I encourage all translators who use this book to contribute to the translation profession and to the development of the information technology field by collecting related new terms and sending them to me in care of Dunwoody Press.

While I have made every attempt to check all the terms and correct the many errors in the First Edition, there are undoubtedly some that have escaped me. I hope the new pinyin conversion program has eliminated the pinyin misspellings. There may still be some odd-looking renditions in either Chinese or English, and some of that is because I have tried to incorporate the terms exactly as I find them in the Chinese literature. I don't think I can assume to standardize terminology for the Chinese, and indeed they have in many cases not yet determined the standard terms for many new concepts. This book is therefore published in the spirit of assisting translators by giving you terms you might encounter in your own work. You need to use the terms with caution, and assure that the correct ones are selected based on the context in which you are working. In many cases, I have added a brief contextual explanation to the terms. The retention of English abbreviations in the Chinese terms and their English equivalents is deliberate, due to the variety of Chinese renditions of standard terms (see 'Asynchronous Transfer Mode' as an example).

On a technical note, the major change in this edition is the use of tone marks on the Pinyin Romanization, thanks to a new computer program called "Hanzi to Pinyin" from CJKware, that automatically converts the characters. I also upgraded my computer to Microsoft Windows XP for greater ease of the character input and for compatibility with Unicode fonts. The problem of word division (separation of characters into logical conceptual groupings) remains. The renderings in this book are done with some applied logic, but they may not be perfect.

I want to thank Tom Creamer and the people at Dunwoody Press for their continuing encouragement of this project. My special thanks and appreciation go to my wife Alice, who helped greatly with the typing of long lists of nearly incomprehensible English terms, and who suffered through my countless hours at the computer.

Bruce G. Hyman
Oakton, Virginia
10 March 2005

Preface to the First Edition

This glossary was compiled in the hope that it will assist translators who are working with Chinese materials in the information technology fields. It is presented three ways: Chinese to English, alphabetized by pinyin romanization; alphabetized English to Chinese; and alphabetically by English abbreviation. Since the focus is on terminology used in the Peoples Republic of China, a market of considerable interest to American telecommunications vendors, pinyin romanization and simplified characters are used. The glossary was arranged in table format and thus can be sorted on any of the four columns. It was compiled on a PC using Microsoft Windows ME with Microsoft Office 2000, using the Chinese Input Method Editor. Character input was in pinyin with GB2312 encoding. The character font is *Simsun.*

In some cases the combination or division of syllables in pinyin results in some terms being out of order with respect to the strict order of the Chinese characters, for example *bianma quanshu* comes before *bianmaqi.* There are also duplicate or multiple entries for some terms with different Chinese renditions. This occurs because the Chinese themselves have not yet standardized some of the terms, and also because different technologies use the terms differently. For example, the GSM telephony world may use a term differently from the ISDN world or the computer world. I have included as many variants as possible, so that translators can select the best term for the particular context. I hope this is not too inconvenient.

The Chinese also use many English abbreviations in their writing, since much writing on advanced telecommunications and information technology appears first in English. The Recommendations of the International Telecommunication Union (ITU) in Switzerland also are filled with abbreviations, and each document generally has a glossary of their expansions. The inclusion of the section sorted by English abbreviation should thus help identify terms used when Chinese authors omit an expansion of the term. A word of caution, however: here, too, there are sometimes multiple expansions of an abbreviation, depending on the subject matter, so context is critically important.

While this is primarily a telecommunications glossary, because of the convergence of computer technology and telecommunications it is perhaps better described as a glossary of Information Technology. The glossary thus encompasses terms used in computer hardware and software, digital telecommunications, wireless and mobile telecommunications, fiber optic cable technology, and the mushrooming field of antenna theory, among others.

The rapid development of information technology, as the world goes digital, makes this small glossary incomplete as of the date it is published. Keeping up with new concepts and terms, in English as well as other languages, is a full-time pursuit, and I can only hope that users of this material will continue to add to it as they encounter new terms. I have used ***Newton's Telecom Dictionary***, 16th Edition, as the standard reference for English terminology. I recommend the use of other dictionaries for common terminology, including ***Han-Ying Zonghe Kexue Jishu Cihui,*** Second Edition 1997, published by *Kexue Chubanshe* in Beijing.

Bruce G. Hyman
Oakton, Virginia
July 2001

Additional Reference Works Used in This Edition

Mouly, Michel and Marie-Bernadette Pautet. *The GSM System for Mobile Communications*. Published by the Authors, 1992.

Bates, Regis J. and Donald W. Gregory. *Voice and Data Communications Handbook*. New York: McGraw-Hill, 2000.

汉英综合科学技术词汇, *Comprehensive Chinese-English Dictionary of Science and Technology* (2nd Edition). Beijing: Sciences Press, 1997.

新世纪汉英科技大词典. Beijing: Publishing House of Electronics Industry, 1997.

Leon-Garcia, Alberto and Indra Widjaja. *Communication Networks, Fundamental Concepts and Key Architectures*. Boston: McGraw-Hill, 2000.

Rutao, Wang, et al. *English-Chinese and Chinese-English Dictionary of Computer*, 英汉双向计算机词典. Shanghai: Shanghai Jiaotong University Press, 2002.

Part 1
Chinese-English

Alphabetically by Pinyin Romanization with Chinese Characters and English Abbreviations

A

A 层位	A céngwèi	A horizon	
A 接口	A jiēkǒu	A interface	
A 类（放大级的）	A lèi (fàngdà jíde)	Class A (of an amplifying stage)	
A 类工作站	A lèi gōngzuòzhàn	Class A workstation	
A 律	A lǜ	A-law	
A 律编码	A lǜ biānmǎ	A-law encoding	
A 码元	A mǎyuán	A element	
A&B 比特信令	A&B bǐtè xìnling	A&B bit signaling	
AAL 协议控制信息	AAL xiéyì kòngzhì xìnxī	AAL protocol control information	AAL-PCI
AAL 协议数据单元	AAL xiéyì shùjù dānyuán	AAL protocol data unit	AAL-PDU
AAL 业务接入点	AAL yèwù jiērù diǎn	AAL service access point	AAL-SAP
AAL 业务数据单元	AAL yèwù shùjù dānyuán	AAL service data unit	AAL-SDU
AAL5 上的点到点协议	AAL5-shàngde diǎn dàodiǎn xiéyì	Point-to-point protocol over AAL5	PPPOA
AARP 探测数据包	AARP tàncè shùjù bāo	AARP probe packets	
阿贝比长仪	Ā-bèi bǐ cháng yí	Abbe comparator	
阿贝常数	Ā-bèi chángshù	Abbe constant	
阿贝棱镜	Ā-bèi léngjìng	Abbe prism	
阿贝数	Ā-bèi shù	Abbe number	
阿贝正弦条件	A-bèi zhèngxián tiáojiàn	Abbe's sine condition	
阿贝折射率计	Ā-bèi zhéshèlǜ jì	Abbe refractometer	
阿贝尔积分	A-bèi'ěr jīfēn	Abel's integral	
阿比林计划	Ābǐlín jìhuà	Abilene Project (US high-speed Internet project)	
AB 类	AB-lèi	Class AB (of an amplifying stage)	
Ada 语言	Ada yǔyán	Ada (computer language)	
ADSL 局端发送接收单元	ADSL júduān fāsòng jiēshōu dānyuán	ADSL transceiver unit, central office end	ATU-C
ADSL 开销控制信道	ADSL kāixiao kòngzhì xìndào	ADSL overhead control channel	AOC
ADSL 收发单元	ADSL shōufā dānyuán	ADSL transceiver unit	ATU
ADSL 远端传输单元	ADSL yuǎnduān chuánshū dānyuán	ADSL transmission unit-remote	ATU-R
ADSL 远端发送接收单元	ADSL yuǎnduān fāsòng jiēshōu dānyuán	ADSL transceiver unit, remote terminal end	ATU-T
ADSL 终端设备	ADSL zhōngduān shèbèi	ADSL termination unit	
ADSL 中央传输单元	ADSL zhōngyāng chuánshū dānyuán	ADSL transmission unit-central	ATU-C
阿尔卡特	Ā-ěr-kǎ-tè	Alcatel (French company)	
阿尔卡特运营环境因特网系统	Ā-ěr-kǎ-tè yùnyíng huánjìng Yīntèwǎng xìtǒng	Alcatel Carrier Environment Internet System	ACEIS
阿尔卡特中国公司	Ā-ěr-kǎ-tè Zhōngguó gōngsī	Alcatel China Ltd.	
阿尔派电子（中国）有限公司	Ā-ěr-pài diànzǐ (Zhōngguó) yǒuxiàn gōngsī	Alpine Electronics (China) Co. Ltd.	
AF 保护比	AF bǎohù bǐ	AF protection ratio	
AF 信号干扰比	AF xìnhào gānrǎo bǐ	AF signal-to-interference ratio	
AGC 恢复时间	AGC huīfù shíjiān	AGC recovery time	
AGC 启动时间	AGC qǐdòng shíjiān	AGC attack time	
埃	Āi	Angstrom	
爱达利公司	Ài-dá-lì gōngsī	Vodatel (UK company)	

爱德科克阵天线	Ài-dé-kē-kè zhèn tiānxiàn	Adcock array antenna	
爱尔福德环形天线	Ài-ěr-fú-dé huánxíng tiānxiàn	Alford loop antenna	
爱尔兰	Ai'ěrlán	Erlang	
爱国者	Àiguózhě	Aigo (Chinese-made MP3 player)	
爱国者	Àiguózhě	Patriot (US anti-missile missile)	
爱国者数字信息链	Àiguózhě shùzì xìnxī liàn	Patriot digital information link (US military)	PADIL
爱捷特	Ài-jié-tè	Aztech (Singapore company)	
爱克工业集团	Ài-kè gōngyè jítuán	Acome (French company)	
爱克发	Ài-kè-fā	Agfa (Belgian company)	
艾雷斯科技有限公司	Àiléisī kējì yǒuxiàn gōngsī	I-LACS Technology Co. Ltd, Chinese maker of milspec laptop computers	
艾丽斯	Ài-lì-sī	Inland Revenue Integrated System	IRIS
爱立信	Ài-lì-xìn	Ericsson (Norwegian company)	
爱立信蜂窝数据转换器	Ài-lì-xìn fēngwō shùjù zhuǎnhuànqì	Ericsson cellular data converter	ECDC
爱立信工程工具	Ài-lì-xìn gōngchéng gōngjù	Ericsson Engineering Tool	EET
艾伦偏差	Ài-lún piānchā	Allan deviation	ADEV
艾媒体	Ài-méitǐ	IMedia (US company)	
爱普生	Ài-pǔ-shēng	Epson (Japanese company)	
爱特信有限公司	Ài-tè-xìn yǒuxiàn gōngsī	ITC Corp. (US-China JV with MIT)	
阿基米德平面螺旋天线	Ājīmǐdé píngmiàn luóxuán tiānxiàn	Plane Archimedes spiral antenna	
阿利伯克	Ālì Bókè	Arleigh Burke (US Navy destroyer class)	
ALOHA 系统	ALOHA xìtǒng	ALOHA system	
按半周进行的多周期控制	Àn bànzhōu jìnxíngde duōzhōuqī kòngzhì	Multicycle controlled by half-cycle	
按半周的多周控制	An bànzhōude duōzhōu kòngzhì	Multi-cycle control (by half-cycles)	
暗敷设在顶板内	Àn fūshè zài dǐngbǎn-nèi	Concealed in roof slab	CC
暗敷设在梁内	Àn fūshè zài liáng-nèi	Concealed in beam	BC
暗敷设在室面内	Àn fūshè zài shìmiàn-nèi	Concealed in ceiling	CC
暗敷设在珠内	Àn fūshè zài zhū-nèi	Concealed in column	CLC
按内容编址的存储器	Àn nèiróng biānzhǐde cúnchǔqì	Content addressable memory	CAM
按内容的寻址的存储器	Àn nèiróngde xúnzhǐde cúnchǔqì	Content addressable storage	CAS
暗入口	Àn rùkǒu	Trap door	
按上下文编址的分段顺序存储器	Àn shàngxiàwén biānzhǐde fēnduàn shùnxù cúnchǔqì	Context addressed segment sequential memory	CASSM
按申请分配-多址联接	Àn shēnqǐng fēnpèi-duō zhǐ liánjiē	Demand assignment multiple access	DAMA
按位	Àn wèi	Bitwise	
按位拷	Àn wèi kǎo	Bitwise copy	
按位运算	Àn wèi yùnsuàn	Bitwise operation	
按需求分配时分多重存取	Àn xūqiú fēnpèi shífēn duōzhòng cúnqǔ	Demand-assignment time division multiple access	DA-TDMA
按需要集成的网络	Àn xūyào jíchéngde wǎngluò	Integrated on-demand network	ION
按要求的电信业务	Àn yāoqiúde diànxìnyèwù	Demand telecommunication service	
按引用传递	Àn yǐnyòng chuándì	Pass by reference	
按值传递	Àn zhí chuándì	Pass by value	
按组编码	Àn zǔbiān mǎ	Encode by group	
安德鲁天线公司	Ān-dé-lǔ tiānxiàn gōngsī	Andrew Antenna Corp (UK company)	
暗电流	Àndiànliú	Dark current	
安定化光源	Āndìnghuà guāngyuán	Stabilized light source	

按键电话系统	Ànjiàn diànhuà xìtǒng	Key telephone system	KTS
按键电话机	Ànjiàn diànhuàjī	Push-button telephone set	
按键式拨号	Ànjiànshì bō hào	Touch-tone dialing	
安捷伦科技（中国）有限公司	Ān-jié-lún kējì (Zhōngguó) yǒuxiàn gōngsī	Agilent Technologies Co. Ltd. (China)	
安捷伦科技软件有限公司	Ān-jié-lún kējì ruǎnjiàn yǒuxiàn gōngsī	Agilent Technologies Software Co. Ltd.	
案例分析	Ànlì fēnxī	Case study	
案例推理	Ànlì tuīlǐ	Case-based reasoning	CBR
安立达通信设备有限公司	Ānlìdá tōngxìn shèbèi yǒuxiàn gōngsī	Elitech Datacom Co. Ltd., Shenzhen	
按钮	Ànniǔ	Buttons	
按钮话机	Ànniǔ huàjī	Push-button telephone set	
安全	Ānquán	Security	
安全保密环境	Ānquán bǎomì huánjìng	Security environment	SE
安全保密政策	Ānquán bǎomì zhèngcè	Security policy	
安全保密组	Ānquán bǎomì zǔ	Security group (GSM MoU)	SG
安全标签	Ānquán biāoqiān	Security label (IPsec)	
安全标志	Ānquán biāozhì	Safety marking	
安全标识号	Ānquán biāozhì hào	Security identifier	SID
安全参数索引	Ānquán cānshù suǒyǐn	Security parameter index (IPsec)	SPI
安全操作系统	Ānquán cāozuò xìtǒng	Secure operating system	
安全策略	Ānquán cèlüè	Security policy (IPsec)	
安全策略数据库	Ānquán cèlüè shùjùkù	Security policy database	SPD
安全测试	Ānquán cèshì	Security testing	
安全超文本传输协议	Ānquán chāowénběn chuánshū xiéyì	Secure hypertext transfer protocol	HTTPS
安全插座层	Ānquán chāzuò céng	Secure socket layer	SSL
安全传输层协议	Ānquán chuánshū céng xiéyì	Transport layer security protocol	TLS
安全措施（公共信道信令中）	Ānquán cuòshī (gōnggòng xìndào xìnlìng zhōng)	Security arrangements (in common channel signaling)	
安全电路和装置	Ānquán diànlù hé zhuāngzhì	Safety circuit and device	
安全电子交易	Ānquán diànzi jiāoyì	Secure electronic transfer	SET
安全电子结算协议	Ānquán diànzǐ jiésuàn xiéyì	Secure electronic payment protocol	SEPP
安全电子事务处理	Ānquán diànzǐ shìwù chǔlǐ	Secure electronic transaction	SET
安全电子支付过程	Ānquán diànzǐ zhīfù guòchéng	Secure electronic payment process	SEPP
安全地线	Ānquán dìxiàn	Safety ground wire	
安全多用途网际邮件扩展协议	Ānquán duōyòngtú wǎngjì yóujiàn kuòzhǎn xiéyì	Secure multi-purpose Internet mail extensions	S/MIME
安全多用途因特网邮件扩展协议	Ānquán duōyòngtú Yīntèwǎng yóujiàn kuòzhǎn xiéyì	Secure multi-purpose Internet mail extension	S/MIME
安全服务	Ānquán fúwù	Security service (IPsec)	
安全概率	Ānquán gàilǜ	Probability of safety	
安全隔离变压器	Ānquán gélí biànyāqì	Safety isolating transformer	
安全工作站	Ānquán gōngzuòzhàn	Security work station	SWS
安全管理	Ānquán guǎnlǐ	Security management	SM
安全管理实体	Ānquán guǎnlǐ shítǐ	Security management entity	SME
安全管理信息库	Ānquán guǎnlǐ xìnxīkù	Security management information base	SMIB
安全管理系统	Ānquán guǎnlǐ xìtǒng	Security management system, security administration system	SMS

安全管理中心	Ānquán guǎnlǐ zhōngxīn	Security management center	SMC
安全关联	Ānquán guānlián	Security association	SA
安全关联捆绑	Ānquán guānlián kǔnbǎng	Security association bundle	
安全关联数据库	Ānquán guānlián shùjùkù	Security association database	SAD
安全规范	Ānquán guīfàn	Security specifications	
安全过滤器	Ānquán guòlǜqì	Security filter	
安全故障管理	Ānquán gùzhàng guǎnlǐ	Security fault management	
安全 Hash 算法	Ānquán hash suànfǎ	Security hash algorithm	SHA
安全交互策略	Ānquán jiāohù cèlüè	Secure interaction policy	
安全交换协议	Ānquán jiāohuàn xiéyì	Secure exchange protocol	
安全交易业务单元	Ānquán jiāoyì yèwù dānyuán	Security exchange service element	SESE
安全级别	Ānquán jíbié	Security class (IPsec)	
安全距离	Ānquán jùlí	Safe distance	
安全开关	Ānquán kāiguān	Safety switch	
安全控制开关	Ānquán kòngzhì kāiguān	Safety control switch	SCS
安全联盟	Ānquán liánméng	Security association	SA
安全模式	Ānquán móshì	Safe mode (in computers)	
安全模式	Ānquán móshì	Security mode (telecom usage)	
安全内核	Ānquán nèihé	Security kernel	
安全配置管理	Ānquán pèizhì guǎnlǐ	Secure configuration management	
安全评估	Ānquán pínggū	Security evaluation (IPsec)	
安全评估	Ānquán pínggū	Security evaluation	
安全散列算法	Ānquán sànliè suànfǎ	Secure hash algorithm	SHA
安全色	Ānquán sè	Safety color	
安全审计	Ānquán shěnjì	Security audit (IPsec)	
安全审计路踪	Ānquán shěnjì lùzōng	Security audit trail (IPsec)	
安全审计事件	Ānquán shěnjì shìjiàn	Security audit event (IPsec)	
安全授权	Ānquán shòuquán	Security delegation (in SQL Server)	
安全速率	Ānquán sùlǜ	Insured rate	
安全套接层	Ānquán tàojiē céng	Secure socket layer	SSL
安全套接字层	Ānquán tàojiē zìcéng	Secure socket layer (CORBA term)	SSL
安全特低电压	Ānquán tèdī diànyā	Safety extra-low voltage	SELV
安全特性	Ānquán tèxìng	Security feature	
安全特征	Ānquán tèzhēng	Security features	
安全通路	Ānquán tōnglù	Secure path (IPsec)	
安全突发量	Ānquán tūfāliàng	Insured burst	
安全网关	Ānquán wǎngguān	Security gateway	SG
安全文字	Ānquán wénzì	Security context (IPsec)	
安全需求	Ānquán xūqiú	Security requirements	
安全业务	Ānquán yèwù	Safety service	
安全业务量	Ānquán yèwùliàng	Insured traffic	
安全因子	Ānquán yīnzǐ	Safety factor	
安全帐户管理器	Ānquán zhànghù guǎnlǐqì	Security account manager	SAM
安全指数	Ānquán zhǐshù	Safety index	
安全中间件	Ānquán zhōngjiān jiàn	Secure middleware	
安全周边	Ānquán zhōubiān	Security perimeter	

安全周界	Ānquán zhōujiè	Security boundary	
安全状态	Ānquán zhuàngtài	Secure state (IPsec)	
安全自动化	Ānquán zìdònghuà	Safety automation	
安全阻抗	Ānquán zǔkàng	Safety impedance	
安全的无线接入	Ānquánde wúxiàn jiērù	Secure wireless access	
安全性	Ānquánxìng	Security, safety	
安全性断言标记语言	Ānquánxìng duànyán biāojì yǔyán	Security assertion markup language	SAML
安全性管理	Ānquánxìng guǎnlǐ	Security management	SM
安盛咨询	An-shèng zīxún	Andersen Consulting	
安时计	Ānshí jì	Ampere-hour meter	
暗示性权限	Ànshì xìng quánxiàn	Implied permission	
安信达	Ān-xìn-dá	Ashton-Tate (US company purchased by Borland)	
按需拨号	Ànxū bōhào	Dial-on-demand	
按需拨号路由	Ànxū bōhào lùyóu	Dial-on-demand routing	DDR
按序存取方式	Ànxù cúnqǔ fāngshì	Sequential access method	SAM
按需点播视频	Ànxū diǎnbō shìpín	Video-on-demand	VOD
按需点播音频	Ànxū diǎnbō yīnpín	Audio-on-demand	AOD
按需分配	Ànxū fēnpèi	Demand assignment	
按需分配带宽	Ànxū fēnpèi dàikuān	Bandwidth-on-demand	BoD
按需分配多地址	Ànxū fēnpèi duōdìzhǐ	Demand assignment multiple access	DAMA
按需分配多址	Ànxū fēnpèi duōzhǐ	Demand assignment multiple access	DAMA
按需分配控制器	Ànxū fēnpèi kòngzhìqì	Demand assignment controller	DAC
按需分配协议	Ànxū fēnpèi xiéyì	Demand assignment protocol	DAP
按需分配信令传送和交换（设备）	Ànxū fēnpèi xìnlìng chuánsòng hé jiāohuàn (shèbèi)	Demand assignment signaling and switching (unit)	DASS
按需分配系统	Ànxū fēnpèi xìtǒng	Demand assignment system	
按序距离矢量	Ànxù jùlí shǐliàng	Ad hoc on-demand distance vector	AODV
按压	Ànyā	Click (on a computer mouse)	
安装	Ānzhuāng	Install (verb)	
安装程序初始化文件	Ānzhuāng chéngxù chūshǐhuà wénjiàn	Setup initialization file	
安装配置	Ānzhuāng pèizhì	Secure shell protocol (ITU-T usage)	SSH
安装线	Ānzhuāng xiàn	Hook-up wire	
奥罗管	Ào luó guǎn	Orotron (mm wave device)	
奥村计算法	Ào-cūn jìsuàn fǎ	Okumura model (to calculate RF path loss in urban area)	
奥林巴斯	Ào-lín-bā-sī	Olympus	
奥美嘉	Ào-měi-jiā	Aomega (US company)	
奥米加表	Àomǐjiā biǎo	Omegameter (in SMT)	
奥普泰	Ào-pǔ-tài	Optel	
凹陷型包层光纤	Āoxiànxíng bāocéng guāngxiān	Depressed clad fiber	
澳洲电信	Àozhōu diànxìn	Telstra	
阿帕网	Ā-pà wǎng	Advanced Research Projects Agency network (US)	ARPANET
APDU 命令	APDU mìnglìng	Command APDU	C-APDU
AppleTalk 地址解析协议	AppleTalk dìzhǐ jiěxī xiéyì	AppleTalk address resolution protocol	AARP
AppleTalk 会话协议	AppleTalk huìhuà xiéyì	AppleTalk session protocol	ASP
AppleTalk 回声协议	AppleTalk huíshēng xiéyì	AppleTalk echo protocol	AEP
AppleTalk 回应协议	AppleTalk huíyìng xiéyì	AppleTalk echo protocol	AEP

AppleTalk 基于更新的路由选择协议	AppleTalk jīyú gēngxīnde lùyóu xuǎnzé xiéyì	AppleTalk update-based routing protocol	AURP
AppleTalk 链路访问协议	AppleTalk liànlù fǎngwèn xiéyì	LocalTalk link access protocol (Apple use)	LLAP
AppleTalk 事务协议	AppleTalk shìwù xiéyì	AppleTalk transaction protocol	ATP
AppleTalk 数据流协议	AppleTalk shùjù liú xiéyì	AppleTalk data stream protocol	ADSP
AppleTalk 文件协议	AppleTalk wénjiàn xiéyì	AppleTalk filing protocol	AFP
AppleTalk 以太网接口	AppleTalk yǐtàiwǎng jiēkǒu	AppleTalk Ethernet interface	EtherTalk
AppleTalk 远程访问	AppleTalk yuǎnchéng fǎngwèn	AppleTalk remote access	ARA
阿奇文件搜寻站	Ā-qí wénjiàn sōuxúnzhàn	Archie file search engine	
Arc 标准栅格图	Arc biāozhǔn zhàgé tú	Arc standard raster graph	ASRG
Arc 空间数据库引擎	Arc kōngjiān shùjùkù yǐnqíng	Arc spatial database engine	ArcSDE
Arc 自动服务器	Arc zìdòng fúwùqì	Arc automation server	
Arc/Info 公共设施管理器	Arc/Info gōnggòng shèshī guǎnlǐqì	Arc/Info facility manager	ArcFM
Arc/Info 工具模块	Arc/Info gōngjù mókuài	Arc/Info Tools	
Arc/Info 宏语言	Arc/Info hóng yǔyán	Arc/Info macro language	AML
ASE 子系统	ASE zixìtǒng	ASE sub-system	ASES
ASP 发展环境	ASP fāzhǎn huánjìng	Ecosystem for ASP	
AT 封包连接介面	AT fēngbāo liánjiē jièmiàn	Advanced technology attachment packet interface	ATAPI
阿特伯界限	Ā-tè-bó jièxiàn	Atterberg limit	
ATM 层连接	ATM céng liánjiē	ATM layer connection	
ATM 传送功能	ATM chuánsòng gōngnéng	ATM transfer capability	ATC
ATM 反向复用	ATM fǎnxiàng fùyòng	ATM inverse multiplexing	AIMUX
ATM 固定比特率	ATM gùdìng bǐtè lǜ	ATM deterministic bit rate	
ATM 块传送	ATM kuài chuánsòng	ATM block transfer	ABT
ATM 链路	ATM liànlù	ATM link	
ATM 匹配层	ATM pǐpèi céng	ATM adaptation layer	AAL
ATM 匹配层类型 2	ATM pǐpèi céng lèixíng 2	ATM adaptation layer type 2	AAL2
ATM 适配层	ATM shìpèi céng	ATM adaptation layer	AAL
ATM 适配层公用部分	ATM shìpèi céng gōngyòng bùfen	ATM adaptation layer common part	CP-AAL
ATM 适配层业务特定部分	ATM shìpèi céng yèwù tèdìng bùfen	ATM adaptation layer service specific part	SSP-AAL
ATM 适配层公共部分	ATM shìpèicéng gōnggòng bùfen	ATM adaptation layer,common part	CP-AAL
ATM 无线接入通信系统	ATM wúxiàn jiērù tōngxìn xìtǒng	ATM wireless access communication system	AWACS
ATM 无源光网络	ATM wúyuán guāng wǎngluò	ATM passive optical network	APON
ATM 信令适配层	ATM xìnlìng shìpèi céng	Signaling ATM adaptation layer	SAAL
ATM 业务数据单元	ATM yèwù shùjù dānyuán	ATM service data unit	ATM-SDU
ATM 业务量描述语	ATM yèwùliáng miáoshù yǔ	ATM traffic descriptor	
ATM 终端系统地址	ATM zhōngduān xìtǒng dìzhǐ	ATM end system address	AESA
ATM 上的多协议	ATM-shàngde duō xiéyì	Multi-protocol over asynchronous transfer mode	MPOA
ATM 上的多协议(技术)	ATM-shàngde duō xiéyì (jìshù)	Multi-protocol over ATM (technology)	MPoA
ATM 上的多协议规范	ATM-shàngde duō xiéyì guīfàn	Multi-protocol over ATM	MPOA
ATM 上的经典 IP 规范	ATM-shàngde jīngdiǎn IP guīfàn	Classical IP over ATM	IPOA
ATM 上的 PPP	ATM-shàngde PPP	Point-to-point protocol over asynchronous transfer mode	PPPoA
ATM 上的网际协议	ATM-shàngde wǎngjì xiéyì	IP over ATM	IPoA
AU 指针调整事件	AU zhǐzhēn tiáozhěng shìjiàn	Administrative unit pointer justification event	AUPJE
A 形底座	A-xíng dǐzuò	A-bedplate	

B

B 接口	B jiēkǒu	B interface	
B 类（放大级的）	B lèi (fàngdà jíde)	Class B (of an amplifying stage)	
靶板	Bǎ bǎn	Painter (radar term)	
八比特组	Bā bǐtè zǔ	Octet	
八比特组串类型	Bā bǐtè zǔ chuàn lèixíng	Octet string type	
八比特组数据流协议	Bā bǐtè zǔ shùjùliú xiéyì	Octet stream protocol	OSP
八叉树	Bā chā shù	Octtree	
八位位组	Bā wèi wèizǔ	Octet (in digital data)	
八位位组计数	Bā wèi wèizǔ jìshù	Octet counting	
八位字节	Bā wèi zìjié	Octet byte	
八位组	Bā wèizǔ	Octet	
靶场测量雷达	Bǎchǎng cèliáng léidá	Missile-range-instrumentation radar	
白边	Bái biān	White edge	
白平衡	Bái pínghéng	White balance (digital photography)	
白噪声	Bái zàoshēng	White noise	
白噪声发生器	Bái zàoshēng fāshēngqì	White noise generator	
白板	Báibǎn	Whiteboard	
拜访公用陆地移动通信网络	Bàifǎng gōngyòng lùdì yídòng tōngxìn wǎngluò	Visited public land mobile network	VPLMN
拜访 MSC	Bàifǎng MSC	Visited MSC	VMSC
拜访 PLMN	Bàifǎng PLMN	Visited PLMN	VPLMN
拜访位置寄存器	Bàifǎng wèizhì jìcúnqì	Visitor location register	VLR
拜访移动业务交换中心	Bàifǎng yídòng yèwù jiāohuàn zhōngxīn	Visited mobile switching center	VMSC
百分点	Bǎifēndiǎn	Percentage point[s]	
柏克利因特网名域服务	Bǎi-kè-lì Yīntèwǎng míngyù fúwù	Berkeley Internet Naming Domain Service (software)	BINDS
摆脱电流阈值	Bǎituō diànliú yùzhí	Threshold of let-go current	
百万分之几	Bǎiwàn fēn zhī jǐ	Parts per million	PPM
百万分率	Bǎiwàn fēnlǜ	Parts per million	PPm
百万个像素/秒	Bǎiwàn gè xiàngsù/miǎo	Million pixels per second	MPPS
百万条指令/秒	Bǎiwàn tiáo zhǐlìng/miǎo	Million instructions per second	MIPS
百万次浮点运算/秒	Bǎiwàncì fúdiǎn yùnsuàn/miǎo	Million floating point operations per second	MEGAFLOP
白页	Báiyè	White page	
八进制移相键控	Bājìnzhì yíxiāng jiànkòng	Octal phase shift keying	8PSK
八进制的	Bājìnzhìde	Octal	
巴伦	Bā-lún	Balun (balanced-unbalanced transformer)	
八木天线	Bāmù tiānxiàn	Yagi antenna	
版别	Bǎn bié	Printing sort	
板存储地址	Bǎn cúnchǔ dìzhǐ	Flat addressing	
半刚性同轴线	Bàn gāngxìng tóngzhóu xiàn	Semi-rigid coaxial line	
半功率点的发射光束角	Bàn gōnglǜ diǎnde fāshè guāngshù jiǎo	Emission beam angle between half-power points	
半功率点波瓣宽度	Bàn gōnglǜdiǎn bōbàn kuāndù	Half-power beamwidth (3 dB beamwidth)	
版号	Bǎn hào	Plate number	
半绝缘隐埋式异质结（激光器）	Bàn juéyuán yǐnmáishì yìzhìjié (jīguāngqì)	Semi-insulated buried heterostructure (laser)	SIBH

半偶极子	Bàn ǒujízi	Half dipole, half doublet	
半双工传输	Bàn shuānggōng chuánshū	Half-duplex transmission	
半速率	Bàn sùlǜ	Half rate	HR
半速率话音业务信道	Bàn sùlǜ huàyīn yèwù xìndào	Half rate speech traffic channel	TCH/HS
半速率数据业务信道	Bàn sùlǜ shùjù yèwù xìndào	Half rate data traffic channel	TCH/H
半速率业务信道	Bàn sùlǜ yèwù xìndào	Half rate traffic channel	TCH/H
半涂银面镜	Bàn túyín miànjìng	Half-silvered mirror	
半永久链路层	Bàn yǒngjiǔ liànlù céng	Semi-permanent link layer	SPLL
板自动拨入	Bǎn zìdòng bōrù	Board inward dialing	BID
半自动交换	Bàn zìdòng jiāohuàn	Semi-automatic switching	
版本数据	Bǎnběn shùjù	Versioned data	
半变异函数	Bànbiànyì hánshù	Semi-variogram	
半波板	Bànbō bǎn	Half-wave plate (in a waveguide)	
半波偶极子	Bànbō ǒujízi	Half-wave dipole	HWD
半波桥式整流器	Bànbō qiáoshì zhěngliúqì	Half-wave bridge rectifier	HWBR
半导体成测插座	Bàndǎotǐ chéngcè chāzuò	Integrated circuit test sockets (semiconductor mfg)	
半导体存储器	Bàndǎotǐ cúnchǔqì	Semiconductor memory	
半导体工业协会	Bàndǎotǐ gōngyè xiéhuì	Semiconductor Industry Association	SIA
半导体光放大器	Bàndǎotǐ guāng fàngdàqì	Semiconductor optical amplifier	SOA
半导体光放大器	Bàndǎotǐ guāng fàngdàqì	Semiconductor laser amplifier	SLA
半导体管沟深度蚀刻	Bàndǎotǐ guǎngōu shēndù shíkè	Deep trench silicon etch (semiconductor mfg)	
半导体集成电路	Bàndǎotǐ jíchéng diànlù	Semiconductor integrated circuit	
半导体激光器	Bàndǎotǐ jīguāngqì	Semiconductor laser	
半导体可见光激光模组	Bàndǎotǐ kějiànguāng jīguāng mózǔ	Semiconductor visible laser module	
半导体图案处理曝光	Bàndǎotǐ tú'àn chǔlǐ bàoguāng	Semiconductor lithography	
半导体研磨加工设备	Bàndǎotǐ yánmó jiāgōng shèbèi	Semiconductor polishing machine	
半导体整修	Bàndǎotǐ zhěngxiū	Semiconductor trimming	
半导体真空蒸镀设备	Bàndǎotǐ zhēnkōng zhēngdù shèbèi	Semiconductor vacuum evaporation equipment	
斑点	Bāndiǎn	Macula	
半叠盖式包装箱	Bàndiégàishì bāozhuāngxiāng	Packing boxes for half folding	
半幅全宽	Bànfú quán kuān	Full width at half maximum	FWHM
半幅值全宽	Bànfúzhí quán kuān	Full width half maximum	FWHM
半刚电缆	Bàngāng diànlǎn	Semi-rigid cable	
绑定	Bǎngdìng	Binding	
绑定更新	Bǎngdìng gēngxīn	Binding update	
绑定请求	Bǎngdìng qǐngqiú	Binding request	
绑定应答	Bǎngdìng yìngdá	Binding acknowledgement	BA
邦加球	Bāng-jiā qiú	Poincare sphere	PS
办公文档结构	Bàngōng wéndàng jiégòu	Office document architecture	ODA
办公自动化	Bàngōng zìdònghuà	Office automation	OA
半公共环境	Bàngōnggòng huánjìng	Semi-public environment	SPE
半功率波束	Bàngōnglǜ bōshù	Half-power bandwidth	HPBW
棒图	Bàngtú	Bar graph	
傍轴光线	Bàngzhóu guāngxiàn	Paraxial ray	
帮助文件	Bāngzhù wénjiàn	Help file	
棒状介质天线	Bàngzhuàng jièzhì tiānxiàn	Dielectric rod antenna	DRA

棒状线	Bàngzhuàng xiàn	Rod line	
帮助台软件	Bāngzhùtái ruǎnjiàn	Help desk software	
半加法度量	Bànjiāfǎ dùliàng	Semi-additive measure	
半角字符	Bànjiǎo zìfú	Half angle character (single byte character)	
半加器	Bànjiāqì	Half adder	HA
板金模块	Bǎnjīn mókuài	Plate module	
半径	Bànjìng	Radius	
版面	Bǎnmiàn	Type area	
板面芯片	Bǎnmiàn xìnpiàn	Chip on board (in SMT)	COB
版权	Bǎnquán	Copyright	©
版权保护	Bǎnquán bǎohù	Copyright protection	
半群结构	Bànqún jiégòu	Semigroup structure	
半色调	Bànsèdiào	Halftone	
板上集成缓存	Bǎn-shàng jíchéng huǎncún	Cache on board	COB
板上控制器	Bǎn-shàng kòngzhìqì	On-board controller	OBC
版式	Bǎnshì	Setting	
半双工	Bànshuānggōng	Half duplex	HDX
半双工操作	Bànshuānggōng cāozuò	Semi-duplex operation	
半双工传输模块	Bànshuānggōng chuánshū mókuài	Half duplex transmission module	HDTM
半双工传输系统	Bànshuānggōng chuánshū xìtǒng	Half duplex transmission system	HDTS
半双工链路接入规程	Bànshuānggōng liànlù jiērù guīchéng	Link access procedure- half-duplex	LAPX
半双工通道	Bànshuānggōng tōngdào	Half duplex channel	HDC
半速	Bànsù	Half-rate	HR
半速率信道	Bànsùlǜ xìndào	Half-rate traffic channel	Lm
搬移区块	Bānyí qūkuài	Block move	
板载调试器	Bǎnzài tiáoshìqì	Onboard debugger	
半占空	Bànzhànkōng	Half-cycle	
板状垫片	Bǎnzhuàng diànpiàn	Plate gasket	
板状节理	Bǎnzhuàng jiélǐ	Platy joint	
板状天线	Bǎnzhuàng tiānxiàn	Panel antenna	
板状线	Bǎnzhuàng xiàn	Slab line	
半自动代视觉丝印机	Bànzìdòng dài shìjué sīyìnjī	Semi-automatic screen printer with visual	
半自动呼叫接续	Bànzìdòng hūjiào jiēxù	Semi-automatic call connection	
半自动化数字化	Bànzìdònghuà shùzìhuà	Semi-automated digitizing	
半字节	Bànzìjié	Nibble (half a byte)	
包	Bāo	Packet	
包标题	Bāo biāotí	Packet header	PH
包传输通道	Bāo chuánshū tōngdào	Packet transmission channel	PTC
包传输协议	Bāo chuánshū xiéyì	Packet transfer protocol	PTP
包出错率	Bāo chūcuò lǜ	Packet error rate	PER
报错码	Bào cuò mǎ	Error reporting code	
包多路复用器	Bāo duōlù fùyòngqì	Packet multiplexer	PMX
包方式	Bāo fāngshì	Packet mode	PM
包方式终端	Bāo fāngshì zhōngduān	Packet-mode terminal	PMT
包过滤	Bāo guòlǜ	Packet filtering	
包过滤式防火墙	Bāo guòlǜshì fánghuǒqiáng	Packet-filter firewall	

包级过滤	Bāo jí guòlǜ	Packet-level filtering	
包级协议	Bāo jí xiéyì	Packet-level protocol	PLP
包交换公共数据网	Bāo jiāohuàn gōnggòng shùjù wǎng	Packet switched public data network	PSPDN
包交换公众数据网	Bāo jiāohuàn gōngzhòng shùjù wǎng	Packet switched public data network	PSPDN
包交换数据	Bāo jiāohuàn shùjù	Packet switched data	PSD
包交换协议	Bāo jiāohuàn xiéyì	Inter-network packet exchange	IPX
报片	Bào piàn	Fragment	
保偏光纤	Bǎo piān guāngxiàn	Polarization maintaining fiber	
报室	Bào shì	Reporting office	BF
包式虚拟电路	Bāo shì xūnǐ diànlù	Packetized virtual circuit	PVC
薄四方扁平封装	Báo sìfāng biǎnpíng fēngzhuāng	Thin quad flat pack	
报尾	Bào wěi	Trailer	
包无线电	Bāo wúxiàndiàn	Packet radio	
包装配与拆卸	Bāo zhuāngpèi yǔ chāixiè	Packet assembly and disassembly	PAD
包自适应路径选择	Bāo zìshìyìng lùjìng xuǎnzé	Packet adaptive routing	PAR
包总线管理接口	Bāo zǒngxiàn guǎnlǐ jiēkǒu	Packet bus management interface	PBMI
保安系统	Bǎo'ān xìtǒng	Security system	
保安自动化系统	Bǎo'ān zìdònghuà xìtǒng	Safety automation system	SAS
保安器	Bǎo'ānqì	Protector	
保安性	Bǎo'ānxìng	Fail-safe	
报表栏	Bàobiǎo lán	Reporting group	
包层	Bāocéng	Cladding	
包层不圆度	Bāocéng bùyuándù	Cladding ellipticity (FOC term)	
包层模消除器	Bāocéng mó xiāochúqì	Cladding mode stripper	
包层直径	Bāocéng zhíjìng	Cladding diameter (FOC term)	
包层中心	Bāocéng zhōngxīn	Cladding center	
包层/涂层同心度误差	Bāocéng/ túcéng tóngxīndù wùchā	Cladding/coating concentricity (FOC term)	
保持	Bǎochí	Hold	
保持模式	Bǎochí móshì	Holdover mode	Ho
保持状态	Bǎochí zhuàngtài	Holdover mode	Ho
保存	Bǎocún	Save (computer command)	
保存点	Bǎocún diǎn	Save point (for database)	
保存全部	Bǎocún quánbù	Save all (computer command)	
保存为	Bǎocún wéi	Save as (WP command)	
保存与转发数据库	Bǎocún yǔ zhuǎnfā shùjùkù	Store-and-forward database	
爆发性技术	Bàofāxìng jìshù	Disruptive technology	
报告	Bàogào	Report	
曝光设备	Bàoguāng shèbèi	Exposure source	
饱和电抗器	Bǎohé diànkàngqì	Saturable reactor	SR
饱和模型	Bǎohé móxíng	Saturated model	
饱和通量密度	Bǎohé tōngliàng mìdù	Saturated flux density	
饱和度	Bǎohédù	Saturation	
保护比	Bǎohù bǐ	Protection ratio	
保护倒换	Bǎohù dǎohuàn	Protection switching	
保护倒换持续时间	Bǎohù dǎohuàn chíxù shíjiān	Protection switching duration	PSD
保护倒换间隔时间	Bǎohù dǎohuàn jiàngé shíjiān	Protection switching duration	PSD

保护倒换计数	Bǎohù dǎohuàn jìshù	Protection switching count	PSC
保护倒换事件	Bǎohù dǎohuàn shìjiàn	Protection switching event	PSE
保护导体	Bǎohù dǎotǐ	Protective conductor	
保护等候时间	Bǎohù děnghòu shíjiān	Hold-off time (SDH)	
保护电路	Bǎohù diànlù	Protective circuit	
保护电容器	Bǎohù diànróngqì	Capacitor for voltage protection	
保护段	Bǎohù duàn	Protection section	
保护和中性公用线	Bǎohù hé zhōngxìng gōngyòng xiàn	Protection earth and neutral	PEN
保护环	Bǎohù huán	Protection ring	
保护缓冲容量	Bǎohù huǎnchōng róngliàng	Protection buffer size	PBSZ
保护监测点	Bǎohù jiāncèdiǎn	Protected monitoring point	
保护间隙	Bǎohù jiànxì	Protective gap	
保护寄存器	Bǎohù jìcúnqì	Protection register	PRT
保护继电器	Bǎohù jìdiànqì	Protective relay	
保护接地	Bǎohù jiēdì	Protective ground	PG
保护链路转换	Bǎohù liànlù zhuǎnhuàn	Protection link switching	
保护率	Bǎohù lǜ	Protection ratio	
保护路径	Bǎohù lùjìng	Protection trail	
保护时段	Bǎohù shíduàn	Guard period	
保护时隙	Bǎohù shíxì	Guard period	GP
保护通道	Bǎohù tōngdào	Protection path	
保护网络连接	Bǎohù wǎngluò liánjiē	Protection network connection	
保护线	Bǎohù xiàn	Protection earth wire	PE
保护裕量	Bǎohù yùliàng	Protection margin	
保护质量	Bǎohù zhìliàng	Quality protection	QOP
保护转换	Bǎohù zhuǎnhuàn	Protection switching	
保护子网连接	Bǎohù zìwǎng liánjiē	Protection sub-network connection	
保护性忙音多路存取	Bǎohù-xìng mángyīn duōlù cúnqǔ	Conservative busy tone multiple access	C-BTMA
保护用电流互感器	Bǎohù-yòng diànliú hùgǎnqì	Protective current transformer	
保护用电压互感器	Bǎohù-yòng diànyā hùgǎnqì	Protective voltage transformer	
保价包裹手续费	Bǎojià bāoguǒ shǒuxùfèi	Insured parcel commission fee	
保价函件	Bǎojià hánjiàn	Insured correspondence	
保价函件保价费	Bǎojià hánjiàn bǎojiàfèi	Insurance charge for correspondence	
保价信封	Bǎojià xìnfēng	Envelope for insured letter	
保价信函	Bǎojià xìnhán	Insured letter	
报警电话	Bàojǐng diànhuà	Alarm reporting telephone	ART
报警汇总画面	Bàojǐng huìzǒng huàmiàn	Alarm summary panel	
报刊变动手续费	Bàokān biàndòng shǒuxùfèi	Procedures fee for newspapers and periodicals changing	
报刊出版详情登记表	Bàokān chūbǎn xiángqíng dēngjìbiǎo	List of publishing in detail	
报刊代订、代投折扣率	Bàokān dàidìng、dàitóu zhékòulǜ	Rebated rate for handling subscription and delivery	
报刊代号	Bàokān dàihào	Code number of newspapers and periodicals	
报刊订阅单	Bàokān dìngyuè dān	Application form of subscription	
报刊订阅清单	Bàokān dìngyuè qīngdān	Detailed items list of subscription	
报刊发行费	Bàokān fāxíng fèi	Fee for distribution of newspapers and periodicals	
报刊发行费率	Bàokān fāxíng fèilǜ	Circulation rate of postal distribution	
报刊发行起点费	Bàokān fāxíng qǐdiǎn fèi	Minimal charging of postal circulation	

报刊发行站	Bàokān fāxíng zhàn	Mandatory news service station	
报刊发行站收订	Bàokān fāxíng zhàn shōu dìng	Subscription in the distribution branch station	
报刊改寄	Bàokān gǎijì	Changing address of delivery for newspapers and periodicals	
报刊简明目录	Bàokān jiǎnmíng mùlù	Brief catalogue of newspapers and periodicals	
报刊目录	Bàokān mùlù	Catalogue of newspapers and periodicals	
报刊退订	Bàokān tuìdìng	Breaking off for subscription	
报刊退订、改寄手续费	Bàokān tuìdìng、gǎijì shǒuxùfèi	Procedures fee of breaking off or changing address	
报刊退款	Bàokān tuìkuǎn	Return payments of newspapers and periodicals	
报刊退款单	Bàokān tuìkuǎndān	Bill of refund	
报刊续订通知单	Bàokān xùdìng tōngzhīdān	Subscription form	
报刊延期出版损失补偿费	Bàokān yánqī chūbǎn sǔnshī bǔchángfèi	Fee for publishing delay of newspapers and periodicals	
报刊印数通知单	Bàokān yìnshù tōngzhīdān	Printing list	
报刊增版、增刊发行费	Bàokān zēngbǎn、zēngkān fāxíngfèi	Charging of additional publishing	
报刊赠阅、交换手续费	Bàokān zèngyuè、jiāohuàn shǒuxùfèi	Procedures fee of presentation or exchanging newspapers and periodicals	
报矿信函	Bàokuàng xìnhán	Letter for reporting mineral deposits	
宝兰	Bǎo-lán	Borland (US software company)	
保留间隔	Bǎoliú jiàngé	"Keep alive" interval	
保留模式	Bǎoliú móshì	Retained mode	
保留未用	Bǎoliú wèi yòng	Reserve for future use	RFU
保留字	Bǎoliúzì	Reserved word	
暴露区	Bàolù qū	Exposed zone	
包络	Bāoluò	Envelope (of a signal)	
包络负反馈	Bāoluò fùfǎnkuì	Envelope negative feed-back	
包络时延	Bāoluò shíyán	Envelope delay	
包络速度	Bāoluò sùdù	Envelope velocity	
包络线解调	Bāoluò xiàn jiětiáo	Envelope demodulation	
包络延时失真	Bāoluò yánshí shīzhēn	Envelope delay distortion	
保密保护命令	Bǎomì bǎohù mìnglìng	Privacy protected command (in FTP)	
保密变换	Bǎomì biànhuàn	Privacy transformation	
保密换算	Bǎomì huànsuàn	Privacy transformation (IPsec)	
保密控制协议	Bǎomì kòngzhì xiéyì	Encryption control protocol	ECP
保密数字通信音频终端	Bǎomì shùzì tōngxìn yīnpín zhōngduān	Digital secure voice terminal	DSVT
保密通信	Bǎomì tōngxìn	Secure communication	
保密协议标识符	Bǎomì xiéyì biāozhì fú	Baseline protocol indicator	BPI
保密协议密钥管理请求消息	Bǎomì xiéyì mìyào guǎnlǐ qǐngqiú xiāoxi	Baseline privacy key management-request	BPKM-REQ
保密协议密钥管理响应消息	Bǎomì xiéyì mìyào guǎnlǐ xiǎngyìng xiāoxi	Baseline privacy key management -response	BPKM-RSP
保密音频系统	Bǎomì yīnpín xìtǒng	Secure voice system	SVS
保密增强	Bǎomì zēngqiáng	Privacy amplification (in quantum cryptography)	
保密性	Bǎomì-xìng	Confidentiality	
薄膜封装	Báomó fēngzhuāng	Tape carrier package	TCP
薄膜集成电路	Báomó jíchéng diànlù	Thin-film integrated circuit	
薄膜晶体管	Báomó jīngtǐguǎn	Thin film transistor	TFT
薄膜滤波器	Báomó lǜbōqì	Thin film filter	TFF

包容	Bāoróng	Containment	
保实®单模光纤	Bǎo-shí ® dānmó guāngxiān	POSH® single mode optical fiber	POSH®
包头	Bāotóu	Packet header (IPsec)	
报头错误控制	Bàotóu cuòwù kòngzhì	Header error control	HEC
报文	Bàowén	Message (in telegraph and data communication)	
报文处理过程说明	Bàowén chǔlǐ guòchéng shuōmíng	Message processing procedure specification	MPPS
报文等待指示	Bàowén děngdài zhǐshì	Message-waiting indication	MWI
报文泛滥	Bàowén fànlàn	Message flooding	
报文分组	Bàowén fēnzǔ	Packet	
报文分组组装器/拆卸器	Bàowén fēnzǔ zǔzhuāngqì/chāixièqì	Packet assembler/disassembler	PAD
报文格式描述语言	Bàowén géshi miáoshù yǔyán	Packet format description language	PFDL
报文鉴别代码	Bàowén jiànbié dàimǎ	Message authentication code	MAC
报文交换	Bàowén jiāohuàn	Message switching	
报文交换数据服务	Bàowén jiāohuàn shùjù fúwù	Message switching data service	MSDS
报文开始	Bàowén kāishǐ	Start of message	SOM
报文链	Bàowén liàn	Packet chaining	
报文排队接口	Bàowén páiduì jiēkǒu	Message queuing interface	MQI
报文认证码	Bàowén rènzhèng mǎ	Message authentication code	MAC
报文输出描述符	Bàowén shūchū miáoshùfú	Message output descriptor	MOD
报文优先等级	Bàowén yōuxiān děngjí	Message priority	
报文语言终端	Bàowén yǔyán zhōngduān	Packet voice terminal	PVT
报文摘要	Bàowén zhāiyào	Message digest	
报文摘要算法	Bàowén zhāiyào suànfǎ	Message digest algorithm	MDA
报文转发多路复用器	Bàowén zhuǎnfā duōlù fù yòngqì	Message switching multiplexer	MSM
保险丝	Bǎoxiǎnsī	Fuse	F
保险丝	Bǎoxiǎnsī	Safety fuse	SF
保险丝装置	Bǎoxiǎnsī zhuāngzhì	Fuse unit	FU
包销	Bāoxiāo	Contract selling	
薄型背照式电荷耦合器件	Báoxíng bèizhàoshì diànhè ǒuhé qìjiàn	Thin backside illuminated charge coupled device	BT-CCD
保形涂层硫化	Bǎoxíng túcéng liúhuà	Conformal coat cure (semiconductor mfg)	
报讯	Bàoxùn	Alarm	
保证比特率	Bǎozhèng bǐtè lǜ	Guaranteed bit rate	GBR
保证证实	Bǎozhèng zhèngshí	Hold acknowledge	
报知	Bàozhī	Compromised (as a security breach)	
包装	Bāozhuāng	Packet assembly (data communications)	PA
包装	Bāozhuāng	Packing	
包装器	Bāozhuāng qì	Wrapper	
包装识别	Bāozhuāng shíbié	Binding identity	BID
包装重量	Bāozhuāng zhòngliàng	Package weight	
包装资源单位	Bāozhuāng zīyuán dānwèi	Capsule resource unit	CRU
巴特查里亚距离	Bā-tè-chá-lǐ-yà jùlí	Bhattacharyya distance	BD
BCCH 配置	BCCH pèizhì	BCCH allocation	BA
BCP 后面板	BCP hòumian bǎn	BCP back board	BCBB
BDA 中国	BDA Zhōngguó	BDA China (US firm in Beijing that tracks China telecom market)	
贝	Bèi	Bel	B
被测试实现体	Bèi cèshì shíxiàn tǐ	Instrument under test	IUT

背瓣	Bèibàn	Back lobe	
背板	Bèibǎn	Backplane	
背板式插座	Bèibǎnshi chāzuò	Backboard insertion socket	
背包问题	Bēibāo wèntí	Knapsack problem	
被测单元	Bèicè dānyuán	Tested unit	
被测单元	Bèicè dānyuán	Under unit test	UUT
被测对象	Bèicè duìxiàng	Instrument under test	IUT
被测器件	Bèicè qìjiàn	Device under test	DUT
被测设备	Bèicè shèbèi	Equipment under test (ITU-T Recommendation O.161)	EUT
被测设备	Bèicè shèbèi	Device under test	DUT
被测实现	Bèicè shíxiàn	Implication under test	IUT
被测网络	Bèicè wǎngluò	Network under test	
被测系统	Bèicè xìtǒng	System under test	
被测试系统	Bèicèshì xìtǒng	System under test	SUT
被触发事务	Bèichùfā shìwù	Triggered transaction	
北电网络	Běidiàn wǎngluò	Nortel networks	
被动搭线窃听	Bèidòng dāxiàn qiètīng	Passive wiretapping (IPsec)	
被动地址自动配置	Bèidòng dìzhǐ zìdòng pèizhì	Passive address auto configuration, stateful address auto-configuration	
被动窃听	Bèidòng qiètīng	Passive wiretapping	
被动威胁	Bèidòng wēixié	Passive threat	
被动式红外传感器	Bèidòngshì hóngwài chuángǎnqì	Passive infrared detector	PID
贝尔试验室	Bèi'ěr shìyànshì	Bell Labs	
贝尔通信研究所	Bèi'ěr tōngxìn yánjiūsuǒ	Bell Communications Research Lab	BELLCORE
贝尔行政管理网络通信系统	Bèi'ěr xíngzhèng guǎnlǐ wǎngluò tōngxìn xìtǒng	Bell Administrative Network Communications System	BANCS
贝尔运营公司	Bèi'ěr yùnyíng gōngsī	Bell operating company	BOC
北方电讯有限公司	Běifāng Diànxùn yǒuxiàn gōngsī	Nortel, Northern Telecom (Canada company)	
被访移动业务交换中心	Bèifǎng yídòng yèwù jiāohuàn zhōngxīn	Visited mobile service switching center	VMSC
备份	Bèifèn	Backup, reserve, spare	
备份规程	Bèifèn guīchéng	Backup procedure	
备份和恢复	Bèifèn hé huīfù	Backup and restore (in SQL Server)	
备份集	Bèifèn jí	Backup set	
备份计划	Bèifèn jihuà	Backup plan	
备份媒体	Bèifèn méitǐ	Backup media	
备份媒体池	Bèifèn méitǐ chí	Backup media pool	
备份设备	Bèifèn shèbèi	Backup device	
备份文件	Bèifèn wénjiàn	Backup file	
备份域控制器	Bèifèn yù kòngzhìqì	Backup domain controller	BDC
贝佛莱日天线	Bèi-fó-lái-rì tiānxiàn	Beverage antenna	
背负式	Bēifù-shì	Backpack-type	
被管单元	Bèiguǎn dānyuán	Managed element	
被管对象	Bèiguǎn duìxiàng	Managed object	
被管对象定义指南	Bèiguǎn duìxiàng dìngyì zhǐnán	Guidelines for the definition of managed objects	GDMO
被管对象类	Bèiguǎn duìxiàng lèi	Managed-object class	MOC
被管对象类别	Bèiguǎn duìxiàng lèibié	Managed object class	

被管对象实例	Bèiguǎn duìxiàng shílì	Managed object instance	
被管对象的属性	Bèiguǎn duìxiàngde shǔxìng	Managed object attribute	
被管目标代理	Bèiguǎn mùbiāo dàilǐ	Managed-object agent	MOA
被管实体	Bèiguǎn shítǐ	Managed entity	
被管（开放）系统	Bèiguǎn xìtǒng	Managed system	
被管元素	Bèiguǎn yuánsù	Managed element (network management term)	
背光源	Bèiguāng yuán	Backlight	
被管理域	Bèiguǎnlǐ yù	Managed domain	
被呼地址修改通知	Bèihū dìzhǐ xiūgǎi tōngzhī	Called address modified notification	
被呼用户优先	Bèihū yònghù yōuxiān	Priority for called subscriber	
被呼叫站标识符	Bèihūjiào zhàn biāoshífú	Called station identifier	CED
被检测的	Bèijiǎncède	Monitored	MON
被叫	Bèijiào	Terminating call	TC
被叫号码	Bèijiào hàomǎ	Called party number	
被叫呼叫控制器	Bèijiào hūjiào kòngzhìqì	Called party call controller	
被叫计费	Bèijiào jìfèi	Reverse charging	REV
被叫集中付费业务	Bèijiào jízhōng fùfèi yèwù	Freephone	FPH
被叫控制释放	Bèijiào kòngzhì shìfàng	Called party release	
被叫识别	Bèijiào shíbié	Connected line identity	COLI
被叫识别提供补充业务	Bèijiào shíbié tígōng bǔchōng yèwù	Connected line identification presentation supplementary service	COLP
被叫识别限制补充业务	Bèijiào shíbié xiànzhì bǔchōng yèwù	Connected line identification restriction supplementary service	COLR
被叫线识别显示	Bèijiào xiàn shíbié xiǎnshì	Connected line identification presentation	COLP
被叫线识别限制	Bèijiào xiàn shíbié xiànzhì	Connected line identification restriction	COLR
被叫线路标识	Bèijiào xiànlù biāozhì	Called line identity	CLI
被较应答	Bèijiào yìngdá	Answer message (ISUP message)	ANM
被叫用户	Bèijiào yònghù	Called party (in telecommunication)	
被叫拥护不挂机信号	Bèijiào yōnghù bùguàjī xìnhào	Called subscriber held signal	CSH
被叫终端	Bèijiào zhōngduān	Called terminal	
被叫子地址	Bèijiào zidìzhǐ	Called party sub-address	
被叫方编号	Bèijiàofāng biānhào	Called party number	
被接线路识别显示	Bèijiē xiànlù shíbié xiǎnshì	Connected line identification presentation	COLP
被接线路识别限制	Bèijiē xiànlù shíbié xiànzhì	Connected line identification restriction	COLR
被接地	Bèijiēdì	Grounded	
被接地的导体	Bèijiēdìde dǎotǐ	Grounded conductor	
背景	Bèijǐng	Background	
北京爱立信通信系统有限公司	Běijīng ài-lì-xìn tōngxìn xìtǒng yǒuxiàn gōngsī	Beijing Ericsson Communication System Co. Ltd.	
背景彩色	Bèijǐng cǎisè	Background color (WP command)	
背景差错块	Bèijǐng chācuò kuài	Background block error	BBE
背景差错块比	Bèijǐng chācuò kuài bǐ	Background block error ratio	BBER
北京高鸿通信技术有限公司	Běijīng gāohóng tōngxìn jìshù yǒuxiàn gōngsī	Beijing Gaohong Telecommunications Technology Co. Ltd.	
北京康德国际经济咨询公司	Běijīng kāngdé guójì jīngjì zīxún gōngsī	Beijing Concord International Economic Consulting Co. Ltd.	
背景块差错秒比	Bèijǐng kuài chācuò miǎo bǐ	Background block errored second ratio	BBESR

背景块误码	Bèijǐng kuài wùmǎ	Background block error	BBE
背景块误码比	Bèijǐng kuài wùmǎ bǐ	Background block error ratio	BBER
北京朗讯科技光缆有限公司	Běijīng Lǎng-xùn kējì guānglǎn yǒuxiàn gōngsī	Beijing Lucent Technologies Fiber Optic Co. Ltd.	BFOC
背景误块	Bèijǐng wùkuài	Background block error	BBE
背景误块比	Bèijǐng wùkuài bǐ	Background block error ratio	BBER
背景误块秒比	Bèijǐng wùkuài miǎo bǐ	Background bit error ratio	BBER
背景音响	Bèijǐng yīnxiǎng	Background sound	BGS
北京邮电大学	Běijīng yóudiàn dàxué	Beijing University of Post & Telecommunications	
背景噪声	Bèijǐng zàoshēng	Background noise	BGN
背景噪音降低	Bèijǐng zàoyīn jiàngdī	Background noise reduction	BNR
背景噪音调节	Bèijǐng zàoyīn tiáojié	Background noise conditioning	BNC
贝克曼	Bèi-kè-màn	Bachman	
被控变量	Bèikòng biànliàng	Controlled variable	
贝里尼-托西天线	Bèi-lǐ-ní--tuō-xī tiānxiàn	Bellini-Tosi antenna	
北美大地基准面	Běiměi dàdì jīzhǔnmiàn	North American Datum (GIS)	NAD
北美平等接入	Běiměi píngděng jiērù	North American equal access	NAEA
北美数字蜂窝系统	Běiměi shùzì fēngwō xìtǒng	North America Digital cellular System	ADC；DAMPS
北欧移动电话系统	Běi'ōu yídòng diànhuà xìtǒng	Nordic Mobile Telephone System	NMT
倍频	Bèipín	Frequency multiplication	
倍频本地振荡器	Bèipín běndì zhèndàngqì	Frequency multiplication local oscillator	
倍频程	Bèipínchéng	Octave	
倍频程滤波器	Bèipínchéng lǜbōqì	Octave filter	
被屏蔽主机网关	Bèipíngbì zhǔjī wǎngguān	Screened host gateway	
被屏蔽子网	Bèipíngbì zìwǎng	Screened sub-network	
倍频器	Bèipínqì	Frequency multiplier	
北桥芯片	Běiqiáo xìnpiàn	North Bridge chip	NBC
被切换到的第三方 MSC	Bèiqiēhuàndàode dìsānfāng MSC	The MSC to which the MS is handed over in a subsequent handover	MSC-B'
被切换到的 MSC	Bèiqiēhuàndàode MSC	The MSC to which the MS is handed over in a basic handover	MSC-B
贝塞孔耦合器	Bèi-sāi kǒng ǒuhéqì	Bethe hole coupler	
贝塞尔曲线	Bèi-sāi-ěr qūxiàn	Bezier curve	
背散射电子象	Bèisǎnshè diànzǐ xiàng	Backscattered electron image	
背射天线	Bèishè tiānxiàn	Back reflector antenna, backfire antenna	
备忘录	Bèiwànglù	Memorandum of understanding	MoU
备纤	Bèixiàn	Standby fiber	
背斜	Bèixié	Anticline	
背斜谷	Bèixié gǔ	Anticlinal valley	
背压	Bèiyā	Back Pressure	
贝叶理论	Bèi-yè lǐlùn	Bayesian theory	
贝叶斯估计	Bèi-yè-sī gūjì	Bayesian estimate	
贝叶斯网络	Bèi-yè-sī wǎngluò	Bayesian network	
贝叶斯信息准则	Bèi-yè-sī xìnxī zhǔnzé	Bayesian information criterion	BIC
北鹰科技有限公司	Běiyīng kējì yǒuxiàn gōngsī	Northern Eagle Technology Corp. (US company)	NET
备用	Bèiyòng	Spare	SP
备用 C 通路	Bèiyòng C tōnglù	Stand-by communication channel	

备用点	Bèiyòng diǎn	Spare point	
备用工作方式	Bèiyòng gōngzuò fāngshì	Spare mode	
备用关系	Bèiyòng guānxi	Back-up relationships	
备用监视器存在	Bèiyòng jiānshìqì cúnzài	Standby monitor presence	SMP
备用冗余	Bèiyòng rǒngyú	Stand-by redundancy	
备用时间	Bèiyòng shíjiān	Stand-by time	
备用通信设备	Bèiyòng tōngxìn shèbèi	Auxiliary communications facility (military usage)	ACF
备用信令链路	Bèiyòng xìnlìng liànlù	Reserve signaling link	
备用照明	Bèiyòng zhàomíng	Backup lighting	BUL
备用状态	Bèiyòng zhuàngtài	Stand-by state	
备余量	Bèiyúliàng	Margin	
被整流的直流	Bèizhěngliúde zhíliú	Rectified alternating current	RAC
被重载的操作符	Bèizhòngzàide cāozuò fú	Overloaded operator	
备注	Bèizhù	Memo	
本埠函件	Běnbù hánjiàn	Local correspondence	
本地操作控制台	Běndì cāozuò kòngzhìtái	Local operations control station	LOC
本地代理	Běndì dàilǐ	Home agent	HA
本地单元	Běndì dānyuán	Local unit	LU
本地登录标识	Běndì dēnglù biāozhì	Local login identification	
本地订阅	Běndì dìngyuè	Local subscription	
本地端局	Běndì duānjú	Local switch	LS
本地多点分配业务	Běndì duōdiǎn fēnpèi yèwù	Local multipoint distribution service	LMDS
本地多点通信系统	Běndì duōdiǎn tōngxìn xìtǒng	Local multipoint communication system (Canadian term for LMDS)	LMCS
本地多维数据集	Běndì duōwéi shùjùjí	Local data cube	
本地方式	Běndì fāngshì	Local mode	
本地访问和传输区域	Běndì fǎngwèn hé chuánshū qūyù	Local access and transport area	LATA
本地分发服务器	Běndì fēnfā fúwùqì	Local distributor	
本地服务器	Běndì fúwùqì	Local server	
本地高容量 IPC 处理器	Běndì gāo róngliàng IPC chǔlǐqì	Local high capacity IPC processor	LHIP
本地功能能力	Běndì gōngnéng nénglì	Local function capabilities	LFC
本地公用陆地移动通信网络	Běndì gōngyòng lùdì yídòng tōngxìnwǎng luò	Local public land mobile communications network	LPLMN
本地管理业务点	Běndì guǎnlǐ yèwù diǎn	Local management service point	LMSP
本地环路无线电	Běndì huánlù wúxiàndiàn	Radio in the local loop	RLL
本地交换公司	Běndì jiāohuàn gōngsī	Local exchange carrier	LEC
本地交换局	Běndì jiāohuàn jú	Local central office	LCO
本地交换网	Běndì jiāohuàn wǎng	Local exchange	LE
本地交换运行系统	Běndì jiāohuàn yùnxíng xìtǒng	Local exchange operation system	LE-OpS
本地交换运营商	Běndì jiāohuàn yùnyíng shāng	Local exchange carrier	LEC
本地交换中心	Běndì jiāohuàn zhōngxīn	Local exchange center	
本地交换子系统	Běndì jiāohuàn zixìtǒng	Local switching sub-system	LSS
本地交换机	Běndì jiāohuànjī	Local switch	LS
本地交换机	Běndì jiāohuànjī	Local exchange	LE
本地交换局	Běndì jiāohuànjú	Local exchange	LE
本地交换局	Běndì jiāohuànjú	Local switch	LS
本地节点时钟	Běndì jiédiǎn shízhōng	Local node clock	LNC

本地接入及传动区	Běndì jiērù jí chuánsòng qū	Local access and transport area	LATA
本地计费生成软件	Běndì jìfèi shēngchéng ruǎnjiàn	Local charging generator software	LCG
本地基准参考	Běndì jīzhǔn cānkǎo	Local primary reference	LPR
本地客户接口结构	Běndì kèhù jiēkǒu jiégòu	Native client interface architecture	NCIA
本地控制	Běndì kòngzhì	Local control	LC
本地码	Běndì mǎ	Native code	
本地 PLMN	Běndì PLMN	Location PLMN	LPLMN
本地识别名	Běndì shíbié míng	Local distinguished name	LDN
本地时区	Běndì shíqū	Local time zone	LTZ
本地时钟参考	Běndì shízhōng cānkǎo	Local time reference	LTR
本地通信互联网	Běndì tōngxìn hùliánwǎng	Local communication interconnection network	LCIN
本地通信网络	Běndì tōngxìn wǎngluò	Local communication network	LCN
本地通信网	Běndì tōngxìnwǎng	Local communications network	LCN
本地网	Běndì wǎng	Local area network	LAN
本地网络服务器	Běndì wǎngluò fúwùqì	Local network server	
本地网络管理中心	Běndì wǎngluò guǎnlǐ zhōngxīn	Local network management center	LNMC
本地维护终端	Běndì wéihù zhōngduān	Local craft terminal	LCT
本地维护终端	Běndì wéihù zhōngduān	Local maintenance terminal	LMT
本地线路时钟分配	Běndì xiànlù shízhōng fēnpèi	Local line clock distribution	LLCK
本地线路自动检验列行程序	Běndì xiànlù zìdòng jiǎnyàn lièxíng chéngxù	Local line automatic (testing) routine	LLAR
本地小区标识符	Běndì xiǎoqū biāozhì fú	Local cell identifier	LCI
本地系统环境	Běndì xìtǒng huánjìng	Local system environment	LSE
本地移动用户身份	Běndì yídòng yònghù shēnfen	Local mobile station identity	LMSI
本地移动用户识别号	Běndì yídòng yònghù shíbié hào	Local mobile subscriber identity	LMSI
本地移动台识别	Běndì yídòngtái shíbié	Local mobile station identity	LMSI
本地移动台识别码	Běndì yídòngtái shíbié mǎ	Local mobile station identity	LMSI
本地映像生成器	Běndì yìngxiàng shēngchéngqì	Native image generator	NGEN
本地用户服务器	Běndì yònghù fúwùqì	Home subscriber server	HSS
本地邮政属性	Běndì yóuzhèng shǔxìng	Local postal attributes	
本地载波接收	Běndì zàibō jiēshōu	Local carrier reception	
本地载波解调	Běndì zàibō jiětiáo	Local carrier demodulation	
本地在用	Běndì zàiyòng	Locally active	
本地振荡器	Běndì zhèndàngqì	Local oscillator	
本底质谱	Běndǐ zhìpǔ	Background mass spectrum	
本地终端仿真器	Běndì zhōngduān fǎngzhēnqì	Local terminal emulator	LTE
本地终端模拟器	Běndì zhōngduān mónǐqì	Local terminal emulator	
本地主基准源	Běndì zhǔ jīzhǔn yuán	Local primary reference source	LPR
本地主持者	Běndì zhǔchízhě	Local conductor	
本地组	Běndì zǔ	Local group	
本地的	Běndìde	Native	
本迪克斯公司	Běn-dí-kè-sī gōngsī	Bendix (US company)	
本端自动消息记帐	Běnduān zìdòng xiāoxi jìzhàng	Local automatic message accounting	LAMA
泵组	Bèng zǔ	Pump unit	
崩溃	Bēngkuì	Crash (i.e. computer or system crash)	
泵浦光纤放大器	Bèngpǔ guāngxiān fàngdàqì	Pumped fiber optic amplifier	

泵浦激光器	Bèngpǔ jīguāngqì	Pumped laser	
泵浦源	Bèngpǔ yuán	Pump source	
本国目的代码	Běnguó mùdì dàimǎ	National destination code	
本机操作	Běnjī cāozuò	In-local	
本机操作模式	Běnjī cāozuò móshì	Native mode usage	NMU
本机格式	Běnjī géshi	Native format	
本机记录	Běnjī jìlù	Local record	
本机码	Běnjī mǎ	Native code	
本机模式	Běnjī móshì	Native mode	
奔腾芯片	Bēn-téng xìnpiàn	Pentium® chip	
本土化软件	Běntǔhuà ruǎnjiàn	Localize software	
本位键	Běnwèi jiàn	Home key	
本征态	Běnzhēngtài	Eigenket (in quantum cryptography)	
比幅单脉冲雷达	Bǐ fú dān màichōng léidá	Amplitude-comparison monopulse radar	
避雷计	Bì léi jì	Lightning arrester	LA
边	Biān	Edge	
边标记	Biān biāojì	Edge flags	
边导模隔离器	Biān dǎo mó gélíqì	Edge-guide mode isolator	
边独享展开	Biān dúxiǎng zhǎnkāi	Edge-exclusive expansion (CAD/CAM)	
边发射发光管	Biān fāshè fāguāng guǎn	Edge light emitting diode	ELED
边分享展开	Biān fēnxiǎng zhǎnkāi	Edge-dividing expansion (CAD/CAM)	
边共享展开	Biān gòngxiǎng zhǎnkāi	Edge-sharing expansion (CAD/CAM)	
边聚合	Biān jùhé	Edge aggregation (CAD/CAM)	EA
边染色	Biān rǎnsè	Edge coloring	
边删除	Biān shānchú	Edge deletion (CAD/CAM)	ED
边生成	Biān shēngchéng	Edge generation (CAD/CAM)	EG
鞭天线	Biān tiānxiàn	Whip antenna	
边信息	Biān xìnxī	Side information (video term)	
边瓣抑制	Biānbàn yìzhì	Side lobe suppression	
辨别名	Biànbiémíng	Distinguished name	
变长单向确认	Biàncháng dānxiàng quèrèn	Variable length one-way acknowledgement	
变长双向确认	Biàncháng shuāngxiàng quèrèn	Variable length two-way acknowledgement	
编程	Biānchéng	Programming	
编程语言	Biānchéng yǔyán	Compiler language	
边带	Biāndài	Sideband	
边带非线性串扰	Biāndài fēixiànxìng chuànrǎo	Sideband non-linear crosstalk	
边带峰值功率	Biāndài fēngzhí gōnglǜ	Peak sideband power	PSP
边带干扰	Biāndài gānrǎo	Sideband interference	
边带线性串扰	Biāndài xiànxìng chuànrǎo	Sideband linear crosstalk	
边带寻址	Biāndài xúnzhǐ	Sideband addressing	SBA
边带寻址端口	Biāndài xúnzhǐ duānkǒu	Sideband address port	SAP
边带抑制度	Biāndài yìzhìdù	Sideband suppression	
便道	Biàndào	Minor road	
变点式列印	Biàndiǎn-shì liè yìn	Variable dot (printer term)	VD
变电站	Biàndiànzhàn	Transformer station	
变动系数	Biàndòng xìshù	Coefficient of variation	

蝙蝠翼盘	Biānfúyì pán	Bat-wing panel	
蝙蝠翼形天线	Biānfúyìxíng tiānxiàn	Bat-wing antenna	
编号处理子系统	Biānhào chǔlǐ zixìtǒng	Number handling sub-system	NHS
编号方式	Biānhào fāngshì	Type of number	TON
编号计划	Biānhào jìhuà	Numbering plan	NP
编号计划标识符	Biānhào jìhuà biāozhì fú	Numbering plan identifier	NPI
编号计划范围	Biānhào jìhuà fànwéi	Numbering plan area	NPA
编号计划指示符	Biānhào jìhuà zhǐshì fú	Numbering plan indicator	NPI
编号制度	Biānhào zhìdù	Numbering plan	
变换	Biànhuàn	Transform	
变换规则	Biànhuàn guīzé	Conversion rule	
变换域	Biànhuàn yù	Transformation domain	
编辑	Biānjí	Editing	
编辑菜单	Biānjí càidān	Edit menu (WP command)	
编辑处理	Biānjí chǔlǐ	Editing process	
边角辐射	Biānjiǎo fúshè	Boundary radiation	
边界	Biānjiè	Boundary	
边界	Biānjiè	Edge	
边界保护	Biānjiè bǎohù	Border protection	
边界边集	Biānjiè biān jí	Boundary edge set	
边界标志	Biānjiè biāozhì	Boundary monument	
边界标志交换路由器	Biānjiè biāozhì jiāohuàn lùyóu qì	EDGE label switching router	
边界测量法定义组件	Biānjiè cèliángfǎ dìngyì zǔjiàn	Metes bounds (GIS)	
边界多边形	Biānjiè duōbiānxíng	Universe polygon	
边界函数	Biānjiè hánshù	Boundary function	
边界检查	Biānjiè jiǎnchá	Bounds checking	
边界结点图	Biānjiè jiédiǎn tú	Edge-node graph	
边界接合	Biānjiè jiēhé	Boundary junction	
边界类型	Biānjiè lèixíng	Boundary type	
边界连接	Biānjiè liánjiē	Edge join	
边界路由协议	Biānjiè lùyóu xiéyì	Border gateway protocol	BGP
边界扫描测试	Biānjiè sǎomiáo cèshì	Boundary scan test	
边界扫描寄存器	Biānjiè sǎomiáo jìcúnqì	Border scanning register	BSR
边界条件	Biānjiè tiáojiàn	Boundary condition	
边界网关	Biānjiè wǎngguān	Border gateway	BG
边界网关协议	Biānjiè wǎngguān xiéyì	Border gateway protocol	BGP
边界网关组播协议	Biānjiè wǎngguān zǔbō xiéyì	Border gateway multicast protocol	BGMP
边界文件	Biānjiè wénjiàn	Band	
边界效应	Biānjiè xiàoyìng	Boundary effects	
边界要素	Biānjiè yàosù	Boundary element	
边界要素法	Biānjiè yàosù fǎ	Boundary element method	
边界中介系统	Biānjiè zhōngjiè xìtǒng	Border intermediate system	BIS
边界层	Biānjiècéng	Boundary layer	
变极化馈电器	Biànjíhuà kuìdiànqì	Changed polarization feed	
边境交货	Biānjìng jiāohuò	Delivered at frontier	
编辑器	Biānjíqì	Editor	

边框	Biānkuàng	Border	
遍历	Biànlì	Traverse	
遍历二叉树	Biànlì èr chā shù	Traversing binary tree	
遍历图	Biànlì tú	Traversing graph	
编连	Biānlián	Build (noun, usually a computer application, short for compile and connect 编译和连接)	
变量	Biànliàng	Variable (a quantity)	
编码	Biānmǎ	Coding, code	
编码	Biānmǎ	Encoding	
编码标记变换	Biānmǎ biāojì biànhuàn	Coded mark inversion	CMI
编码标记协议标识符	Biānmǎ biāojì xiéyì biāozhìfú	SNAP-encoded tag protocol identifier snap	STPID
编码传号反转码	Biānmǎ chuánhào fǎnzhuǎn ma	Coded mark inversion	CMI
编码传输	Biānmǎ chuánshū	Code transmission	
编码规则	Biānmǎ guīzé	Encoding rules	
编码过程	Biānmǎ guòchéng	Encoding process	
编码合成传输信道	Biānmǎ héchéng chuánshū xìndào	Coded composite transport channel	CCTrCH
编码解码器	Biānmǎ jiěmǎqì	Coder-decoder	CODEC
编码矩形	Biānmǎ jǔxíng	Coding rectangle	
编码律	Biānmǎ lǜ	Encoding law	
编码视频比特流	Biānmǎ shìpín bǐtè liú	Coded video bit stream (video term)	
编码数据串	Biānmǎ shùjù chuàn	Encoded data string	
编码顺序	Biānmǎ shùnxù	Coded order (video term)	
编码调制技术	Biānmǎ tiáozhì jìshù	Code modulation technology	
编码违列	Biānmǎ wéiliè	Coding violation	CV
编码效率	Biānmǎ xiàolǜ	Coding efficiency	
编码信号	Biānmǎ xìnhào	Coded signal (in multi-frequency signaling)	
编码信息类型	Biānmǎ xìnxī lèixíng	Encoded information type	EIT
编码约束长度	Biānmǎ yuēshù chángdù	Encoding constraint length	
编码增益	Biānmǎ zēngyì	Coding gain	
编码正交频分复用	Biānmǎ zhèngjiāo pínfēn fùyòng	Coded orthogonal frequency division multiplexing	COFDM
编码字符集	Biānmǎ zìfú jí	Coded character set	
变码器	Biànmǎqì	Transcoder	
编码器	Biānmǎqì	Coder, encoder	
编码器时序脉冲	Biānmǎqì shíxù màichōng	Coder sequential pulse	CSP
编码器输出	Biānmǎqì shūchū	Encoder output	
编码器总工作时间	Biānmǎqì zǒng gōngzuò shíjiān	Encoder overall operating time	
边模抑制	Biānmó yìzhì	Edge mode suppression	
边摸抑制比	Biānmō yìzhìbǐ	Side mode suppression ratio	SMSR
变频车	Biànpín chē	Carriage for frequency converting	
变频方式	Biànpín fāngshì	Frequency conversion format	
变频损耗	Biànpín sǔnhào	Frequency conversion loss	
变频损耗	Biànpín sǔnhào	Converter conversion loss	
扁萍带缆	Biǎnpíng dàilǎn	Ribbon cable	
扁平率	Biǎnping lǜ	Flattening	
变频器	Biànpínqì	Frequency converter, frequency changer	
变迁	Biànqiān	Transition (in Petri net)	

变容二极管	Biànróng èrjíguǎn	Variable capacitance (varactor) diode	
边射阵	Biānshè zhèn	Broadside array	
变数	Biànshù	Variable	
变速率	Biànsù lǜ	Variable-rate	
变体票品	Biàntǐ piàopǐn	Deformed postage item	
变体引擎	Biàntǐ yǐnqíng	Mutation engine	
变位	Biànwèi	Transposition (in switching)	
变维矢量量化	Biànwéi shǐliàng liànghuà	Variable dimension vector quantization	VDVQ
便携	Biànxié	Portable	
便携电话	Biànxié diànhuà	Portable telephone	
便携电台	Biànxié diàntái	Portable station	
编写复制脚本	Biānxiě fùzhì jiǎoběn	Replication scripting	
便携设备	Biànxié shèbèi	Portable equipment	
便携式载体设备	Biànxiéshì zàitǐ shèbèi	Portable vehicle equipment	
变形	Biànxíng	Deformation	
变形	Biànxíng	Morphing (in image processing)	
变形赫夫门码	Biànxíng hè-fū-mén mǎ	Modified Huffman code	MHC
变形交替传号反转	Biànxíng jiāotì chuánhào fǎnzhuǎn	Modified alternate mark inversion	
变形时延	Biànxíng shíyán	Distortion delay	
变形系数	Biànxíng xìshù	Deformation coefficient	
边沿检测	Biānyán jiǎncè	Edge detection	
边沿网关	Biānyán wǎngguān	Border gateway	BG
编译	Biānyì	Compile	
编译程序	Biānyì chéngxù	Compiler (computer program)	COMP
编译程序的生成程序	Biānyì chéngxùde shēngchéng chéngxù	Compiler generator	
变异函数	Biànyì hánshù	Variogram	
编译和连接	Biānyì hé liánjiē	Build (noun, usually a computer application)	
编译码器	Biānyì mǎqì	Codec (coder-decoder)	
编译码器	Biānyì mǎqì	Coder and decoder (the C in BORSCHT)	
编译期	Biānyì qī	Compile time	
编译时	Biānyì shí	Compile time	
变异算子	Biànyì suànzǐ	Mutation operator	
编译器	Biānyìqì	Compiler	
变元	Biànyuán	Argument	
边缘	Biānyuán	Edge	
边缘出节点	Biānyuán chū jiédiǎn	Egress LSR	
边缘处理	Biānyuán chǔlǐ	Edge crisping	
边缘到边缘伪线路仿真	Biānyuán dào biānyuán wěixiànlù fǎngzhēn	Pseudo wires edge-to-edge emulation	PWE3
边缘抖动	Biānyuán dǒudòng	Edge jitter	
边缘钢轨系统	Biānyuán gāngguǐ xìtǒng	Edge rail system (semiconductor mfg)	
边缘汇聚	Biānyuán huìjù	Edge aggregation	
边缘检测	Biānyuán jiǎncè	Edge detection	
边缘检测滤波器	Biānyuán jiǎncè lǜbōqì	Edge detection filter	
边缘交换机	Biānyuán jiāohuànjī	Edge switch	
边缘就绪	Biānyuán jiùxù	Edge-prepared	
边缘卡	Biānyuán kǎ	Edge card	

边缘卡控制	Biānyuán kǎ kòngzhì	Edge card control	ECC
边缘抗锯齿失真	Biānyuán kàng jùchǐ shīzhēn	Edge anti-aliasing (video term)	
边缘路由器	Biānyuán lùyóuqì	Edge router	ER
边缘拼接	Biānyuán pīnjiē	Edge join	
边缘匹配	Biānyuán pǐpèi	Border matching	
边缘匹配	Biānyuán pǐpèi	Edge matching	
边缘锐度	Biānyuán ruìdù	Edge sharpness	
边缘设备	Biānyuán shèbèi	Border element	BE
边缘设备	Biānyuán shèbèi	Edge device	ED
边缘特征	Biānyuán tèzhēng	Edge feature	
边缘网关	Biānyuán wǎngguān	Border gateway	
边缘元素	Biānyuán yuánsù	Edge element	
边缘增强	Biānyuán zēngqiáng	Edge enhancement	
编择	Biānzé	Compile (verb)	
变址	Biànzhǐ	Indexing	
编制	Biānzhì	Compile, edit	
编址分组系统	Biānzhǐ fēnzǔ xìtǒng	Addressed packet system	APS
变址寄存器	Biànzhǐ jìcúnqì	Index register	IXR
鞭状天线	Biānzhuàng tiānxiàn	Whip antenna	
表	Biǎo	Table	
表级约束	Biǎo jí yuēshù	Table-level constraint (for database)	
表扫描	Biǎo sǎomiáo	Table scan	
表锁	Biǎo suǒ	Table lock (for database)	
表约束	Biǎo yuēshù	Table constraint (in SQL Server)	
标称	Biāochēng	Mark, label (verb); nominal (adjective)	
标称电压	Biāochēng diànyā	Nominal voltage	
标称改正力	Biāochēng gǎizhènglì	Nominal margin (of a type of apparatus)	
标称功率	Biāochēng gōnglǜ	Nominal power	NOM_PWR
标称黑（白）	Biāochēng hēi (bái)	Nominal black (white)	
标称呼通概率	Biāochēng hūtōng gàilǜ	Nominal calling probability	
标称均方根	Biāochēng jūn fānggēn	Nominal root-mean square	NRMS
标称零色散波长	Biāochēng líng sèsàn bōcháng	Nominal zero dispersion wavelength (FOC term)	
标称塞入率	Biāochēng sāirùlǜ	Nominal stuffing rate	
标称特性阻抗	Biāochēng tèxìng zǔkàng	Nominal characteristic impedance	
标称调整率	Biāochēng tiáozhěnglǜ	Nominal justification rate	
标称页	Biāochēng yè	Nominal page	
标称值	Biāochēng zhí	Nominal value	
标称中心频率	Biāochēng zhōngxīn pínlǜ	Nominal center frequency	
标尺	Biāochǐ	Draft mode (WP command)	
标尺测量单位	Biāochǐ cèliáng dānwèi	Scaled measurement unit	SMU
表达式	Biǎodá shì	Expression	
表达式折叠	Biǎodáshì zhédié	Expression folding	
标的	Biāodì	Target	
标定误差	Biāodìng wùchā	Calibrated error	
标度变换	Biāodù biànhuàn	Scale conversion	
标度盘	Biāodùpán	Dial	

标高	Biāogāo	Mark up (in price) (verb and noun)	MU
表格	Biǎogé	Table (WP command)	
表格格式数据流	Biǎogé géshi shùjù liú	Tabular data stream	TDS
表格区	Biǎogé qū	Table area	
表格识别	Biǎogé shíbié	Form recognition	
标号	Biāohào	Label	
标号字段	Biāohào zìduàn	Label field	
标记	Biāojì	Label	
标记	Biāojì	Flag	
标记	Biāojì	Token (in software)	
标记	Biāojì	Marker	
标记打开	Biāojì dǎkāi	Mark up	
标记点	Biāojì diǎn	Label point	
标记堆栈	Biāojì duīzhàn	Label stack	LS
标记分发协议	Biāojì fēnfā xiéyì	Label distribution protocol	LDP
标记分配协议	Biāojì fēnpèi xiéyì	Label distribution protocol (IETF usage)	LDP
标记关闭	Biāojì guānbì	Mark down	
标记管理	Biāojì guǎnlǐ	Label management (system)	LMS
标记交换	Biāojì jiāohuàn	Tag switch	
标记交换路径	Biāojì jiāohuàn lùjìng	Label switching path	LSP
标记交换路由器	Biāojì jiāohuàn lùyóuqì	Label switch router	LSR
标记交换路由器	Biāojì jiāohuàn lùyóuqì	Tag switch router	TSR
标记控制信息	Biāojì kòngzhì xìnxī	Tag control information	TCI
标记通信	Biāojì tōngxìn	Tagged traffic	
标记协议标识符	Biāojì xiéyì biāozhì fú	Tag protocol identifier	TPID
标记协议信息	Biāojì xiéyì xìnxī	Tag protocol information	TPI
标记信息库	Biāojì xìnxīkù	Label information base	LIB
标记语言	Biāojì yǔyán	Markup language	
标记栈控制字	Biāojì zhàn kòngzhì zì	Marker stack control word	MSCW
标记字段	Biāojì zìduàn	Flag field	
标量聚合	Biāoliàng jùhé	Scalar aggregate	
标量型函数	Biāoliàngxíng hánshù	Scalar functions (in SQL Server)	
表面	Biǎomiàn	Surface	
表面安装	Biǎomiàn ānzhuāng	Surface mounting	
表面安装设备	Biǎomiàn ānzhuāng shèbèi	Surface mount device	SMD
表面波	Biǎomiàn bō	Surface wave	
表面波波导	Biǎomiàn bō bōdǎo	Surface-wave waveguide	
表面波大小	Biǎomiàn bō dàxiǎo	Surface wave magnitude	
表面波天线	Biǎomiàn bō tiānxiàn	Surface wave antenna	SWA
表面传输阻扰	Biǎomiàn chuánshū zǔrǎo	Surface transfer impedance	STI
表面处理	Biǎomiàn chǔlǐ	Surface treatment (semiconductor mfg)	
表面处理技术	Biǎomiàn chǔlǐ jìshù	Surface processing technology	
表面处理技术	Biǎomiàn chǔlǐ jìshù	Surface mount technology	
表面活性剂	Biǎomiàn huóxìngjì	Surfactant (in SMT)	
表面静电	Biǎomiàn jìngdiàn	Surface static electricity	
表面模型	Biǎomiàn móxíng	Surface model	

表面贴装技术	Biǎomiàn tiēzhuāng jìshù	Surface mount technology	
表面转移阻抗	Biǎomiàn zhuǎnyí zǔkàng	Surface transfer impedance (of a coaxial line)	
表面阻抗	Biǎomiàn zǔkàng	Surface impedance (of an isotropic material)	
表面组装器件	Biǎomiàn zǔzhuāng qìjiàn	Surface mount device (electronics mfg)	SMD
表面组装元件	Biǎomiàn zǔzhuāng yuánjiàn	Surface mount component (electronics mfg)	SMC
标签	Biāoqiān	Tag, label	
标签边缘路由器	Biāoqiān biānyuán lùyóuqì	Label edge router	LER
标签打印机	Biāoqiān dǎyìnjī	Label printer	
标签分配协议	Biāoqiān fēnpèi xiéyì	Label distribution protocol	LDP
标签合并	Biāoqiān hébìng	Label merge	
标签交换	Biāoqiān jiāohuàn	Tag switching	
标签交换	Biāoqiān jiāohuàn	Label switching	LS
标签交换边沿路由器	Biāoqiān jiāohuàn biānyán lùyóuqì	Label edge router	LER
标签交换路径	Biāoqiān jiāohuàn lùjìng	Label switch path	LSP
标签交换路由器	Biāoqiān jiāohuàn lùyóuqì	Label switch router	LSR
标签名	Biāoqiān míng	Tag name	
标签图像文件格式	Biāoqiān túxiàng wénjiàn géshi	Tagged image file format	TIFF
表情符	Biǎoqíng fú	Smiley ☺, :-)	
表情符号	Biǎoqíng fúhào	Emoticon	
表示	Biǎoshì	Represent (verb)	
表示层	Biǎoshì céng	Presentation layer	
表示层协议	Biǎoshì céng xiéyì	Presentation layer protocol (in ISO's OSI)	PP
表示服务	Biǎoshì fúwù	Presentation service	PS
表示服务访问点	Biǎoshì fúwù fǎngwèn diǎn	Presentation service access point	PSAP
表示服务数据单元	Biǎoshì fúwù shùjù dānyuán	Presentation service data unit	PSDU
表示功能	Biǎoshì gōngnéng	Presentation function	PF
表示连接端点	Biǎoshì liánjiē duāndiǎn	Presentation connection end point	PCEP
表示上下文	Biǎoshì shàngxiàwén	Presentation context	
表示协议机	Biǎoshì xiéyì jī	Presentation protocol machine	PPM
表示协议控制信息	Biǎoshì xiéyì kòngzhì xìnxī	Presentation protocol control information	PPCI
表示协议数据单元	Biǎoshì xiéyì shùjù dānyuán	Presentation protocol data unit	PPDU
表述	Biǎoshù	Represent	
标题开始	Biāotí kāishǐ	Start of header	SOH
表现	Biǎoxiàn	Represent	
标验码	Biāoyàn mǎ	Check (in SS7)	CK
标志	Biāozhì	Flag (video term)	
标志	Biāozhì	Label	
标识	Biāozhì	Identity	ID
标识	Biāozhì	Identifier	ID
标志	Biāozhì	Marking	
标志段	Biāozhì duàn	Flag (in a data packet)	F
标志分配协议	Biāozhì fēnpèi xiéyì	Label distribution protocol	LDP
标志交换路径	Biāozhì jiāohuàn lùjìng	Label switching path	LSP
标志交换路由器	Biāozhì jiāohuàn lùyóuqì	Label switching router	LSR
标识可达图	Biāozhì kědátú	Symbolic reachability graph (in stochastic process algebra)	
标识连接	Biāozhì liánjiē	Identity link	

标识列	Biāozhì liè	Identity column	
标志码	Biāozhì mǎ	Flag (in SS7)	F
标识属性	Biāozhì shǔxìng	Identity property	
标志位插索	Biāozhì wèi chāsuǒ	Flag hunting	
标识信息	Biāozhì xìnxī	Characteristic information	CI
标志语义模型	Biāozhì yǔyì móxíng	Denotational semantic model	
标识符	Biāozhìfú	Identifier (in software)	
标志器	Biāozhìqì	Marker	MKR
标注磁盘	Biāozhù cípán	Label a disk (verb)	
标注局内切换	Biāozhù júnèi qiēhuàn	Note internal handover	
标准包	Biāozhǔn bāo	Standard pack	
标准标记	Biāozhǔn biāojì	Standard label	
标准并行口	Biāozhǔn bìngxíng kǒu	Standard parallel port	SPP
标准差	Biāozhǔn chà	Standard deviation	
标准插头	Biāozhǔn chātóu	Standard plug	
标准单模光纤	Biāozhǔn dānmó guāngxiān	Standard single mode fiber	SSMF
标准定位服务	Biāozhǔn dìngwèi fúwù	Standard positioning service (in GPS)	SPS
标准定位业务	Biāozhǔn dìngwèi yèwù	Standard positioning service	SPS
标准二进制补码	Biāozhǔn èrjìnzhì bǔ mǎ	Complementary straight binary code	CSB
标准反应谱	Biāozhǔn fǎnyìng pǔ	Standard design response spectrum	
标准辐射源	Biāozhǔn fúshèyuán	Standard source	
标准光源	Biāozhǔn guāngyuán	Standard light source	
标准规范化标记语言	Biāozhǔn guīfànhuà biāojì yǔyán	Standard generalized markup language	SGML
标准呼通概率	Biāozhǔn hūtōng gàilǜ	Standard calling probability	
标准间隔	Biāozhǔn jiàngé	Standard interval	
标准建模语言	Biāozhǔn jiànmó yǔyán	Unified modeling language	UML
标准交换格式	Biāozhǔn jiāohuàn géshi	Standard interchange format	SIF
标准界面	Biāozhǔn jièmiàn	Standard interface	
标准库	Biāozhǔn kù	Standard library	
标准码试验信号	Biāozhǔn mǎ shìyàn xìnhào	Standard code test signal	SCTS
标准描述协议	Biāozhǔn miáoshù xiéyì	Standard description protocol	SDP
标准模拟天线	Biāozhǔn mónǐ tiānxiàn	Standard artificial antenna	
标准模板库	Biāozhǔn múbǎn kù	Standard template library	
标准频率	Biāozhǔn pínlǜ	Standard frequency	
标准频率和时间信号	Biāozhǔn pínlǜ hé shíjiān xìnhào	Standard frequency and time signals	SFTS
标准频率和时间信号电台	Biāozhǔn pínlǜ hé shíjiān xìnhào diàntái	Standard frequency and time signal station	
标准频率和时间信号业务	Biāozhǔn pínlǜ hé shíjiān xìnhào yèwù	Standard frequency and time signal service	
标准普及标记语言	Biāozhǔn pǔjí biāojì yǔyán	Standard generalized markup language	SGML
标准清晰度电视	Biāozhǔn qīngxīdù diànshì	Standard definition television	SDTV
标准时间参照系	Biāozhǔn shíjiān cānzhàoxì	Ordinal temporal reference system	
标准时间信号发射	Biāozhǔn shíjiān xìnhào fāshè	Standard-time-signal emission	
标准世界时	Biāozhǔn shìjièshí	Coordinated Universal Time	
标准适配器	Biāozhǔn shìpèiqì	Standard adaptor	
标准试验调制	Biāozhǔn shìyàn tiáozhì	Standard test modulation	
标准输出功率	Biāozhǔn shūchū gōnglǜ	Standard power output	
标准输入信号	Biāozhǔn shūrù xìnhào	Standard input signal	

标准输入信号电平	Biāozhǔn shūrù xìnhào diànpíng	Standard input-signal level	
标准输入信号频率	Biāozhǔn shūrù xìnhào pínlǜ	Standard input-signal frequency	
标准属性	Biāozhǔn shǔxìng	Standard attribute	
标准调制	Biāozhǔn tiáozhì	Standard modulation	
标准通信平台	Biāozhǔn tōngxìn píngtái	Standard communications platform	SCP
标准通用标记语言	Biāozhǔn tōngyòng biāojì yǔyán	Standard generalized markup language	SGML
标准通用标示语言	Biāozhǔn tōngyòng biāoshì yǔyán	Standard general markup language (in SQL Server)	SGML
标准头	Biāozhǔn tóu	Standard header	
标准网络连接协议	Biāozhǔn wǎngluò liánjiē xiéyì	Standard network access protocol	SNAP
标准纬线	Biāozhǔn wěixiàn	Standard parallel (GIS)	
标准线规	Biāozhǔn xiànguī	Standard wire gauge (UK)	SWG
标准信躁比	Biāozhǔn xìn zào bǐ	Standard signal to noise	
标准型	Biāozhǔn xíng	Normalization type	NZ
标准性能评估测试有限公司	Biāozhǔn xìngnéng pínggū cèshì yǒuxiàn gōngsī	Standard Performance Evaluation Corporation	SPEC
标准页面描述语言	Biāozhǔn yèmiàn miáoshù yǔyán	Standard page description language	SPDL
标准准确度校正	Biāozhǔn zhǔnquèdù jiàozhèng	Adjustment standard accuracy	
标准资源记率格式	Biāozhǔn zīyuán jìlǜ géshi	Standard resource record format	SRRF
标准化	Biāozhǔnhuà	Normalization, standardize	
标准化测试畸变度	Biāozhǔnhuà cèshì jībiàn dù	Degree of standardized distortion	
标准化段测量	Biāozhǔnhuà duàn cèliáng	Measuring normalizing block	
标准化选项	Biāozhǔnhuà xuǎnxiàng	Standardized option	
标准化栅格图形	Biāozhǔnhuà zhàgé túxíng	Standardized raster graphic	SRG
必备属性	Bìbèi shǔxìng	Mandatory attribute	
笔表射束天线	Bǐbiǎo shèshù tiānxiàn	Pencil-beam antenna	
别名	Biémíng	Alias, nickname	
别名登录项	Biémíng dēnglù xiàng	Alias entry	
别名地址	Biémíng dìzhǐ	Alias address	
别名服务器	Biémíng fúwùqì	Alias server	
闭合	Bìhé	Closure	
闭合区	Bìhé qū	Closed area	
闭合用户群	Bìhé yònghù qún	Close user group	CUG
闭合用户群补充业务	Bìhé yònghù qún bǔchōng yèwù	Closed user group supplementary service	CUG SS
闭合用户群联结码	Bìhé yònghù qún liánjié mǎ	Closed user group interlock code	
闭合用户群组	Bìhé yònghù qúnzǔ	Closed user group	CUG
闭合自动路由恢复系统	Bìhé zìdòng lùyóu huīfùxì tǒng	Close-in automatic route-restoral system	CARRS
闭环传递函数	Bìhuán chuándì hánshù	Closed loop transfer function	
闭环带宽	Bìhuán dàikuān	Closed-loop bandwidth	
闭环电压增益	Bìhuán diànyā zēngyì	Closed loop voltage gain	
闭环控制	Bìhuán kòngzhì	Closed-loop control	
闭环控制系统	Bìhuán kòngzhì xìtǒng	Closed-loop control system	
闭环零点	Bìhuán língdiǎn	Closed loop zero	
闭环系统频率特性	Bìhuán xìtǒng pínlǜ tèxìng	Closed-loop system frequency characteristic	
比较级	Bǐjiào jí	Comparative form	
比较器	Bǐjiào qì	Comparators	CM
比较统计地图	Bǐjiào tǒngjì dìtú	Cartogram	

比较线圈	Bǐjiào xiànquān	Comparator coil	
笔记本电脑	Bǐjìběn diànnǎo	Notebook computer	
笔记型电脑	Bǐjìxíng diànnǎo	Notebook computer	
壁龛式	Bìkān shì	Wall niche type	
避雷器	Bìléiqì	Lightning arrester	
避雷器	Bìléiqì	Surge arrester	
比例环节（放大环节）	Bǐlì huánjié (fàngdà huánjié)	Proportional element (amplification element)	
比例积分(控制器)	Bǐlì jīfēn (kòngzhìqì)	Proportional-integral (controller)	PI
比例积分微分(控制器)	Bǐlì jīfēn wēifēn (kòngzhìqì)	Proportional-integral-differential (controller)	PID
比例尺	Bǐlìchǐ	Scale	
比利时电信	Bǐ-lì-shí diànxìn	Belgacom, the Belgian Telecommunications Authority	
比率单调分析	Bǐlǜ dāndiào fēnxī	Rate monotonic analysis (in CORBA)	RMA
闭路电视	Bìlù diànshì	Closed circuit television	CCTV
闭路电压	Bìlù diànyā	Closed circuit voltage	
并串变换器	Bìng chuàn biànhuànqì	Parallel to serial converter	
并馈	Bìng kuì	Parallel feed	
饼图	Bǐng tú	Pie graph	
病毒	Bìngdú	Virus	
病毒防护区	Bìngdú fánghù qū	Virus resistant domain (Linux)	
病毒软件	Bìngdú ruǎnjiàn	Virus software	
并发	Bìngfā	Concurrency	
并发操作冲突	Bìngfā cāozuò chōngtū	Concurrent operating conflict	
并发处理器	Bìngfā chǔlǐqì	Concurrent processors	
并发管理	Bìngfā guǎnlǐ	Concurrency management	
并发计算	Bìngfā jìsuàn	Concurrent computing	
并发机制	Bìngfā jīzhì	Concurrency	
并发控制	Bìngfā kòngzhì	Concurrency control	
并发连结数	Bìngfā liánjié shù	Concurrent connections	
并发推动	Bìngfā tuīdòng	Concurrent push	
并合电脑	Bìnghé diànnǎo	Hybrid computer	
并馈垂直天线	Bìngkuì chuízhí tiānxiàn	Shunt-fed vertical antenna	
并联校正网络	Bìnglián jiàozhèng wǎngluò	Parallel feedback compensation network	
并联链接卷积码	Bìnglián liànjiē juànjīmǎ	Parallel concatenated convolutional code	PCCC
并联谐振频率	Bìnglián xiézhèn pínlǜ	Parallel resonant frequency	PRF
并行	Bìngxíng	Parallel	
并行编译	Bìngxíng biānyì	Parallel compiling	
并行编译器	Bìngxíng biānyìqì	Parallel compiler	
并行传输	Bìngxíng chuánshū	Parallel transmission	
并行处理	Bìngxíng chǔlǐ	Parallel processing	
并行调度	Bìngxíng diàodù	Parallel scheduling	
并行迭代匹配	Bìngxíng diédài pǐpèi	Parallel iterative matching	PIM
并行干扰消除	Bìngxíng gānrǎo xiāochú	Parallel interference cancellation	PIC
并行工程	Bìngxíng gōngchéng	Concurrent engineering	CE
并行接口	Bìngxíng jiēkǒu	Parallel port	
并行接口	Bìngxíng jiēkǒu	Parallel interface	
并行计算	Bìngxíng jìsuàn	Parallel computing	

并行联机	Bìngxíng liánjī	Peer-to-peer network	
并行频率跳变	Bìngxíng pínlǜ tiàobiàn	Parallel frequency hopping	PFH
并行视频服务器	Bìngxíng shìpín fúwùqì	Parallel video server	
并行实时操作系统	Bìngxíng shíshí cāozuò xìtǒng	Concurrent real time operating system	CROS
并行时域多路存取算法	Bìngxíng shíyù duōlù cúnqǔ suànfǎ	Concurrent time domain multiple access	CTDMA
并行输入输出	Bìngxíng shūrù shūchū	Parallel input output	PIO
并行算法	Bìngxíng suànfǎ	Parallel algorithm	
并行算法程序设计语言/数字系统设计语言	Bìngxíng suànfǎ chéngxù shèjì yǔyán/shùzì xìtǒng shèjì yǔyán	Concurrent algorithmic programming language/digital system design language	CAP/DSDL
并行通信	Bìngxíng tōngxìn	Parallel communications	
并行通信接口	Bìngxíng tōngxìn jiēkǒu	Parallel communication interface	PCI
并行图像配置	Bìngxíng túxiàng pèizhì	Parallel graphics configuration	PGC
并行信道	Bìngxíng xìndào	Parallel channel	
并行虚拟计算机	Bìngxíng xūnǐ jìsuànjī	Parallel virtual machine	PVM
并行遗传算法	Bìngxíng yíchuán suànfǎ	Parallel genetic algorithm	
并行指令代码	Bìngxíng zhǐlìng dàimǎ	Parallel instruction code	PIC
并行终端	Bìngxíng zhōngduān	Parallel terminal	
并行注释	Bìngxíng zhùshì	Parallel annotation	
并行自动呼叫	Bìngxíng zìdòng hūjiào	Parallel automatic calling	
并行性	Bìngxíngxìng	Parallelism	
饼状图	Bǐngzhuàng tú	Pie chart	
比瑞利	Bǐ-ruì-lì	Pirelli (FOC manufacturer)	
B-ISDN 网络终端	B-ISDN wǎngluò zhōngduān	Network termination for B-ISDN	B-NT
B-ISDN 终端设备	B-ISDN zhōngduān shèbèi	Terminal equipment for B-ISDN	B-TE
B-ISDN 终端适配器	B-ISDN zhōngduān shìpèiqì	Terminal adaptor for B-ISDN	B-TA
B-ISDN 专用小交换机	B-ISDN zhuānyòng xiǎo jiāohuànjī	Private branch exchange for B-ISDN	B-ISDN PBX
闭塞	Bìsè	Busied out; blocked	
闭塞信号	Bìsè xìnhào	Blocking signal	BLO
闭塞证实信号	Bìsè zhèngshí xìnhào	Blocking-acknowledgement signal	BLA
笔式绘图仪	Bǐshì huìtúyí	Pen plotter	
笔输式电脑	Bǐshū-shì diànnǎo	Pen-based-input computer	
闭锁除直接到归属 PLMN 国家外国际呼叫	Bìsuǒ chú zhíjiē dào guīshǔ PLMN guójiā-wài guójì hūjiào	Barring of outgoing international calls except those direct to the home PLMN	BOIC-exHC
闭锁除直接到 PLMN 归属国以外的国际出呼叫	Bìsuǒ chú zhíjiē dào PLMN guīshǔ guó yǐwàide guójì chū hūjiào	Barring of outgoing international calls except those directed to the home PLMN country	BOIC-exHC
闭锁出局国际呼叫	Bìsuǒ chūjú guójì hūjiào	Barring of outgoing international calls	BOIC
闭锁 GPRS 互通文件	Bìsuǒ GPRS hùtōng wénjiàn	Barring of GPRS interworking profile(s)	BGIWP
闭锁国际出呼叫	Bìsuǒ guójì chū hūjiào	Barring of outgoing international calls	BOIC
闭锁码	Bìsuǒ mǎ	Interlock code (CUG SS)	IC
闭锁全部出呼叫	Bìsuǒ quánbù chū hūjiào	All barring of outgoing call	BO
闭锁所有出呼叫	Bìsuǒ suǒyǒu chū hūjiào	Barring of all outgoing calls	BAOC
闭锁所有出局呼叫	Bìsuǒ suǒyǒu chūjú hūjiào	Barring of all outgoing calls	BAOC
闭锁所有附加业务出呼叫	Bìsuǒ suǒyǒu fùjiā yèwù chū hūjiào	Barring of all outgoing calls supplementary service	BAOC
闭锁所有附加业务入呼叫	Bìsuǒ suǒyǒu fùjiā yèwù rù hūjiào	Barring of all incoming calls supplementary service	BAIC
闭锁所有国际呼出业务	Bìsuǒ suǒyǒu guójì hūchū yèwù	Barring of all outgoing international calls	BOIC
闭锁所有呼入业务	Bìsuǒ suǒyǒu hūrù yèwù	Barring of all incoming calls	BAIC

闭锁所有入呼叫	Bìsuǒ suǒyǒu rù hūjiào	Barring of all incoming calls	BAIC
闭锁所有入局呼叫	Bìsuǒ suǒyǒu rùjú hūjiào	Barring of all incoming calls	BAIC
闭锁用户群	Bìsuǒ yònghù qún	Closed user group	CUG
闭锁在 PLMN 归属国家外漫游时的入呼叫	Bìsuǒ zài PLMN guīshǔ guójiā wài mànyóu shíde rù hūjiào	Barring of incoming calls when roaming outside the home PLMN country	BIC-Roam
比特	Bǐtè	Bit	
比特并行	Bǐtè bìngxíng	Bit parallel	
比特差错比	Bǐtè chācuò bǐ	Bit error ratio	BER
比特差错率	Bǐtè chācuò lǜ	Bit error rate	BER
比特串	Bǐtè chuàn	Bit string	
比特串类型	Bǐtè chuàn lèixíng	Bit string type	
比特错误率	Bǐtè cuòwù lǜ	Bit error rate	BER
比特丢失率	Bǐtè diūshī lǜ	Bit loss rate	BLR
比特号码	Bǐtè hàomǎ	Bit number	BN
比特间插奇偶校验	Bǐtè jiānchā jī'ǒu jiàoyàn	Bit interleaved parity	BIP
比特间插奇偶性	Bǐtè jiānchā jī'ǒu xìng	Bit interleaved parity	BIP
比特交叉奇偶校验	Bǐtè jiāochā jī'ǒu jiàoyàn	Bit interleaved parity check	BIP
比特交织奇偶性	Bǐtè jiāozhī jī'ǒu xìng	Bit interleaved parity	BIP
比特奇偶校验码	Bǐtè jī'ǒu jiàoyàn mǎ	Bit interleaved parity check	BIP
比特流	Bǐtè liú	Bit stream	
比特率	Bǐtè lǜ	Bit rate	
比特率定位信号	Bǐtè lǜ dìngwèi xìnhào	Bit-rate allocation signal	BAS
比特率容差	Bǐtè lǜ róngchā	Bit rate tolerance	
比特能量与噪声谱密度比	Bǐtè néngliàng yǔ zàoshēng pǔ mìdù bǐ	Bit energy to noise spectral density ratio	
比特数	Bǐtè shù	Number of bits	
比特网	Bǐtè wǎng	Bitnet	
比特误码率	Bǐtè wùmǎ lǜ	Bit error rate	BER
比特序列独立性	Bǐtè xùliè dúlìxìng	Bit sequence independence	
比特间插奇偶校验	Bǐtè-jiān chā jī'ǒu jiàoyàn	Bit interleaved parity check	BIP
比特间插奇偶校验 N 位码	Bǐtè-jiān chā jī'ǒu jiàoyàn N wèi mǎ	Bit interleaved parity check N code	BIP-N
比特间插奇偶性	Bǐtè-jiān chā jī'ǒu xìng	Bit interleaved parity	BIP
比相单脉冲雷达	Bǐxiāng dān màichōngléidá	Phase-comparison monopulse radar	
笔形波束天线	Bǐxíng bōshù tiānxiàn	Pencil beam antenna	PBA
必需回叫	Bìxū huíjiào	Required callback	
必要带宽	Bìyào dàikuān	Necessary bandwidth	
闭域网	Bìyù wǎng	Closed user network	
币值音	Bìzhí yīn	Coin-value tone	
壁装式	Bìzhuāng shì	Wall mounted type	W
B 距离	B-jùlí	Bhattacharyya distance	BD
B 类工作站	B-lèi gōngzuòzhàn	Class B workstation	
波	Bō	Wave	
波变形	Bō biànxíng	Wave transformation	
铂电阻温度计	Bó diànzǔ wēndùjì	Platinum resistance thermometer	PRT
波干涉	Bō gānshè	Wave interference	
波极化	Bō jíhuà	Wave polarization	
波数	Bō shù	Wave number	

波旋转式隔离器	Bō xuánzhuǎnshì gélíqì	Wave rotation isolator	
波旋转式环行器	Bō xuánzhuǎnshì huánxíngqì	Wave rotation circulator	
拨最后的号码	Bō zuìhòude hàomǎ	Last number dialed	LND
波阻抗	Bō zǔkàng	Wave impedance	
波瓣畸变	Bōbàn jībiàn	Lobe distortion	
波表合成	Bōbiǎo héchéng	Wave table synthesis	WT
波长	Bōcháng	Wavelength	
波长变换	Bōcháng biànhuàn	Wavelength conversion	WC
波长变换交叉连接器	Bōcháng biànhuàn jiāochā liánjiēqì	Wavelength interchanging optical cross-connect	
波长变换器	Bōcháng biànhuànqì	Wavelength converter	
波长重复度	Bōcháng chóngfùdù	Wavelength repeatability	
波长分割多路复用	Bōcháng fēngē duōlù fùyòng	Wavelength division multiplexing	WDM
波长分配	Bōcháng fēnpèi	Wavelength allocation	WA
波长隔离度	Bōcháng gélídù	Wavelength isolation	I
波长交叉连接	Bōcháng jiāochā liánjiē	Wavelength cross-connect	WXC
波长可调激光源	Bōcháng kětiáo jīguāng yuán	Tunable wavelength laser diode	
波长连续限制	Bōcháng liánxù xiànzhì	Wavelength continuity constraint	
波长路由网	Bōcháng lùyóu wǎng	Wavelength routed network	
波长路由器	Bōcháng lùyóuqì	Lambda router	
波长密集型复用技术	Bōcháng mìjíxíng fùyòng jìshù	Dense wavelength division multiplex	DWDM
波长热漂移	Bōcháng rè piāoyí	Thermal wavelength drift	
波长缩短因子	Bōcháng suōduǎn yīnzǐ	Wavelength reduction factor	
波长通道连接	Bōcháng tōngdào liánjiē	Wavelength path connect	WPC
波长通道链路	Bōcháng tōngdào liànlù	Wavelength path link	WPL
波长通道值	Bōcháng tōngdào zhí	Wavelength path ID	WPI
波长相关损耗	Bōcháng xiāngguān sǔnhào	Wavelength-dependent loss	WDL
波长选路开关	Bōcháng xuǎnlù kāiguān	Wavelength router switch	WRS
波长选路网	Bōcháng xuǎnlù wǎng	Wavelength routed network	
波长选择光交叉连接器	Bōcháng xuǎnzé guāng jiāochā liánjiēqì	Wavelength-selective optical cross-connect	
波长重用	Bōcháng zhòngyòng	Wavelength reuse	
波长转换板	Bōcháng zhuǎnhuàn bǎn	Wavelength converter	
波长转换器	Bōcháng zhuǎnhuànqì	Optical transponder unit	OTU
波导	Bōdǎo	Waveguide	
波导棒	Bōdǎo bàng	Waveguide post	
波导波长	Bōdǎo bōcháng	Guide wavelength	
波导波长	Bōdǎo bōcháng	Waveguide wavelength	
波导窗	Bōdǎo chuāng	Waveguide window	
波导垫片	Bōdǎo diànpiàn	Waveguide gasket	
波导垫圈	Bōdǎo diànquān	Waveguide shim	
波导端缝隙天线	Bōdǎo duān fèngxì tiānxiàn	Waveguide terminating slot antenna	
波导法兰	Bōdǎo fǎlán	Waveguide flange	
波导光探测二极管	Bōdǎo guāng tàncè èrjíguǎn	Waveguide photo diode	WGPD
波导光栅选路器	Bōdǎo guāngshān xuǎnlùqì	Waveguide grating router	WGR
波导合成	Bōdǎo héchéng	Wave guide synthesis	WG
波道减	Bōdào jiǎn	Channel removal	
波道间隔	Bōdào jiàngé	Wave channel interval	

波导截止频率	Bōdǎo jiézhǐ pínlǜ	Waveguide cut-off frequency	
波导开关	Bōdǎo kāiguān	Waveguide switch	
波导空腔	Bōdǎo kōngqiāng	Waveguide cavity	
波导滤波器	Bōdǎo lǜbōqì	Waveguide filter	
波导模	Bōdǎo mó	Waveguide mode	
波道配置	Bōdào pèizhì	Channel allocation	
波导色散	Bōdǎo sèsàn	Waveguide dispersion	
波导调节器	Bōdǎo tiáojiéqì	Waveguide tuner	
波导弯头	Bōdǎo wāntóu	Waveguide corner	
波导隙缝天线	Bōdǎo xìfèng tiānxiàn	Slotted waveguide (antenna)	
波导型二氧化碳激光	Bōdǎo xíng èryǎnghuàtàn jīguāng	Waveguide CO_2 laser	
波道信号自发辐射噪声系数	Bōdào xìnhào zìfā fúshè zàoshēng xìshù	Channel signal-spontaneous noise figure	
波道噪声系数	Bōdào zàoshēng xìshù	Channel noise figure	
波道增	Bōdào zēng	Channel addition	
波道增益	Bōdào zēngyì	Channel gain	
波德	Bō-dé	Baud	
博德图	Bó-dé tú	Bode diagram	
波动方程式	Bōdòng fāngchéngshì	Wave equation	
波动强度	Bōdòng qiángdù	Cymomotive force	c. m. f
波动气流	Bōdòng qìliú	Fluctuating flow	
波段	Bōduàn	Band	
波段比	Bōduàn bǐ	Band ratio	
波段覆盖	Bōduàn fùgài	Wave coverage	
波段扩展	Bōduàn kuòzhǎn	Band-spreading	
博多语言	Bó-duō yǔyán	Baudot language	
波分多路复用	Bōfēn duōlù fùyòng	Wavelength division multiplex	WDM
波分复用	Bōfēn fùyòng	Wavelength division multiplexing	WDM
波分复用器	Bōfēn fùyòngqì	Wavelength division multiplexer	WDM
波峰因数	Bōfēng yīnshù	Crest factor	
波峰焊	Bōfēnghàn	Wave soldering	
拨号	Bōhào	Dial (verb and noun)	
拨号备份	Bōhào bèifèn	Dial backup	
拨号存取信息检索系统	Bōhào cúnqǔ xìnxī jiǎnsuǒ xìtǒng	Dial access Information retrieval system	DAIRS
拨号错误概率	Bōhào cuòwù gàilǜ	Dialing mistake probability	
拨号辅助设备	Bōhào fǔzhù shèbèi	Dial backup unit	DBU
拨号后延迟	Bōhào hòu yánchí	Post-dialing delay	
拨号交换机	Bōhào jiāohuànjī	Dial exchange	
拨号结束	Bōhào jiéshù	End of dialing	EOD
拨号开关	Bōhào kāiguān	Dial switch (thumbwheel switch)	
拨号控制管理	Bōhào kòngzhì guǎnlǐ	Call control manager	CCM
拨号连接	Bōhào liánjiē	Dial-up connection	
拨号脉冲	Bōhào màichōng	Dial/dialed pulse	DP
拨号脉冲入局记发器	Bōhào màichōng rùjú jìfāqì	Dial pulse incoming register	DPIR
拨号请求路由	Bōhào qǐngqiú lùyóu	Dial-on-demand routing	DDR
拨号上网	Bōhào shangwǎng	Dial-up networking	DUN

拨号网络	Bōhào wǎngluò	Dial-up network	
拨号线路	Bōhào xiànlù	Dial-up line	
拨号系统	Bōhào xìtǒng	Dial system	DS
拨号选路	Bōhào xuǎnlù	Dial-on-demand routing	DDR
拨号音	Bōhào yīn	Dial tone	DT
拨号音信号	Bōhào yīn xìnhào	Dial tone signal	
拨号音延迟	Bōhào yīn yánchí	Dial tone delay	
拨号用户远程认证服务	Bōhào yònghù yuǎnchéng rènzhèng fúwù	Remote access dial-in user service	RADIUS
拨号制 B 交换台	Bōhào zhì B jiāohuàntái	Dial system B-switchboard	DSB
拨号终端	Bōhào zhōngduān	Dial-up terminal	
拨号盘	Bōhàopán	Dial (noun)	D
拨号盘备用自动应答设备	Bōhàopán bèiyòng zìdòng yìngdá shèbèi	Dial backup auto answer unit	DBAAU
拨号前时间监视	Bōhào-qián shíjiān jiānshì	Pre-dialing time supervision	
拨接	Bōjiē	Dial-up connection	
博客日记	Bókè rìjì	Blog (web log)	
伯克利软件分配代号	Bó-kè-lì ruǎnjiàn fēnpèi dàihào	Berkeley software distribution	BSD
玻璃产生机	Bōli chǎnshēngjī	Glass generator (FOC mfg)	
玻璃分相法	Bōli fēnxiàng fǎ	Phase separated glass (FOC mfg)	PSG
玻璃光纤	Bōli guāngxiān	Glass optical fiber	GOF
玻璃光纤齿咬防护	Bōli guāngxiān chǐyǎo fánghù	Fiberglass rodent protection	FRP
玻璃基板	Bōli jībǎn	Glass substrate	
玻璃激光	Bōli jīguāng	Glass laser	
玻璃面镜	Bōli miànjìng	Glass mirror	
玻璃破碎传感器	Bōli pòsuì chuángǎnqì	Glass break sensor	GBS
玻璃陶瓷陶管	Bōli táocí táoguǎn	Glass-ceramic ferrules	GCF
玻璃纤维增强塑胶	Bōli xiānwéi zēngqiáng sùjiāo	Fiberglass reinforced plastic	FRP
玻璃/陶瓷面镜	Bōli/táocí miànjìng	Glass-ceramic mirror	
剥落	Bōluò	Peeling	
拨码开关	Bōmǎ kāiguān	Thumb switch	
薄膜	Bómó	Thin film	
薄膜度量系统	Bómó dùliàng xìtǒng	Thin-film metrology system (semiconductor mfg)	
薄膜混合集成电路	Bómó hùnhé jíchéng diànlù	Thin film hybrid integrated circuit	
波尼韦尔卫星公司	Bō-ní-wéi-ěr wèixīng gōngsī	Bonneville Satellite Corp. (US)	
波谱分辨力	Bōpǔ fēnbiàn lì	Spectral resolution (GIS)	
波群	Bōqún	Wave grouping	
波数	Bōshù	Wave number	
波束成型	Bōshù chéngxíng	Beam forming	
波束覆盖区	Bōshù fùgàiqū	Beam footprint (of a satellite antenna)	
波束可控天线系统	Bōshù kěkòng tiānxiàn xìtǒng	Steerable-beam antenna system	SBAS
波束利用系数	Bōshù lìyòng xìshù	Coefficient of beam utilization	CBU
波束偏转	Bōshù piānzhuǎn	Beam deflection	
波束形状损耗	Bōshù xíngzhuàng sǔnhào	Beam-shape loss	
波束圆锥角	Bōshù yuánzhuī jiǎo	Beam conical angle	
博斯-乔赫里-霍克文黑木码	Bó-sī—Qiáo-hè-lǐ—Huò-kè-wén-hēi-mù mǎ	Bose-Chaudhuri-Hocquenghem code	BCH
泊送过程	Bó-sòng guòchéng	Poisson process	

播送通知	Bōsòng tōngzhī	Play announcement	PA
波特	Bōtè	Baud	
波特率	Bōtèlǜ	Baud rate	
箔条	Bótiáo	Chaff	
波纹边片状垫片	Bōwén biān piànzhuàng diànpiàn	Knurled plate gasket	
波纹喇叭	Bōwén lǎba	Corrugated horn	
波纹喇叭天线	Bōwén lǎba tiānxiàn	Corrugated horn antenna	
波线理论	Bōxiàn lǐlùn	Ray theory	
波形	Bōxíng	Waveform	
波形编码	Bōxíng biānmǎ	Waveform coding	
波形插值	Bōxíng chāzhí	Waveform interpolation	
波形监视器	Bōxíng jiānshìqì	Waveform monitor	WFM
波形内插	Bōxíng nèichā	Waveform interpolation	WI
波压	Bōyā	Wave pressure	
玻印迁矢量	Bō-yìn-qiān shǐliàng	Poynting vector	
BSC 时钟分配集成板	BSC shízhōng fēnpèi jíchéngbǎn	BSC clock distribution board assembly	BCDA
BSC 主处理器后面板	BSC zhǔ chǔlǐ qì hòumian bǎn	BSC main processor back panel	BMBP
BSC 时钟机架面板	BSCshízhōng jījià miànbǎn	BSC clock rack panel	BCBP
BSM 初始化和维护	BSM chūshǐhuà hé wéihù	BSM initialization and maintenance	BIM
BSS 操作维护应用部分	BSS cāozuò wéihù yìngyòng bùfen	Base station operation and maintenance application part	BSSOMAP
BTS 测量	BTS cèliáng	BTS measurement	BMEA
BTS 测试处理器	BTS cèshì chǔlǐqì	BTS test processor	BTP
BTS 高容量 IPC 处理器	BTS gāo róngliàng IPC chǔlǐqì	BTS high capacity IPC processor	BHIP
BTS 故障管理	BTS gùzhàng guǎnlǐ	BTS fault management	BFM
BTS 互联后面板	BTS hù lián hòumian bǎn	BTS interconnect back board	BIBB
BTS 呼叫控制	BTS hūjiào kòngzhì	BTS call control	BCO
BTS 控制处理器	BTS kòngzhì chǔlǐ qì	BTS control processor	BCP
BTS 控制和接口集成板	BTS kòngzhì hé jiēkǒu jíchéngbǎn	BTS control and interface board assembly	BCIA
BTS 控制和维护	BTS kòngzhì hé wéihù	BTS control and maintenance	BCM
BTS 控制和维护模块	BTS kòngzhì hé wéihù mókuài	BTS control and maintenance block	BCMB
BTS 配置和资源管理	BTS pèizhì hé zīyuán guǎnlǐ	BTS configure and resource management	BRM
BTS 数据存取	BTS shùjù cúnqǔ	BTS data access	BDA
BTS 通信互联网络	BTS tōngxìn hùliánwǎng luò	BTS communication interconnect network	BCIN
BTS 消息路由器	BTS xiāoxi lùyóu qì	BTS message router	BMR
BTS 系统时间	BTS xìtǒng shíjiān	BTS system time	BSTM
BTS 诊断	BTS zhěnduàn	BTS diagnosis	BDIA
BTS 正常运行管理器	BTS zhèngcháng yùnxíng guǎnlǐqì	BTS sanity management	BSMN
BTS 状态处理	BTS zhuàngtài chǔlǐ	BTS status handling	BSH
BTS 资源分配	BTS zīyuán fēnpèi	BTS resource allocation	BRA
不重发的差错检测	Bù chóngfāde chācuò jiǎncè	Error detection without repetition	
不重新协商消息	Bù chóngxīn xiéshāng xiāoxi	No re-negotiation message (IPsec TLS)	
补兑	Bǔ duì	Make up a deficiency of payment	
不连续干扰	Bù liánxù gānrǎo	Discontinuous interference	
不受控会议	Bù shòukòng huìyì	Non-conducted conference	
不提供数据通路信号	Bù tígōng shùjù tōnglù xìnhào	Data path not provided signal	DPN
不安全温度	Bù'ānquán wēndù	Unsafe temperature	

不变性	Bùbiànxìng	Invariant (noun)	
步长	Bùcháng	Metric	
补偿幅-相偏移键控	Bǔcháng fú—xiāng piānyí jiànkòng	Offset amplitude-phase shift keying	OAPSK
补偿配置	Bǔcháng pèizhì	Tweaking	
补偿网络	Bǔcháng wǎngluò	Compensating network (of an antenna)	
补偿微压计	Bǔcháng wēiyājì	Compensated micromanometer	
补偿型延长导线	Bǔcháng xíng yáncháng dǎoxiàn	Compensating extension lead	
补偿直接日射强度表	Bǔcháng zhíjiē rìshè qiángdù biǎo	Compensated pyrheliometer	
补偿器	Bǔchángqì	Compensator	
补充标志	Bǔchōng biāozhì	Supplementary marking	
补充基本功能	Bǔchōng jīběn gōngnéng	Additional elementary functions	AEF
补充逻辑相互连接单元	Bǔchōng luójì xiānghù liánjiē dānyuán	Supplemental logic interconnect cell	
补充信息	Bǔchōng xìnxī	Supplementary information	SI
补充业务	Bǔchōng yèwù	Supplementary service	SS
补充业务 CAMEL 签约信息	Bǔchōng yèwù CAMEL qiānyuē xìnxī	Supplementary service camel subscription	SS-CSI
补充业务处理	Bǔchōng yèwù chǔlǐ	Supplementary service handling	SH
补充业务登记	Bǔchōng yèwù dēngjì	Supplementary service registration	
补充业务互连	Bǔchōng yèwù hùlián	Supplementary service interworking	
补充业务检查	Bǔchōng yèwù jiǎnchá	Supplementary service check	SSCHK
补充业务控制串	Bǔchōng yèwù kòngzhì chuàn	Supplementary service control string	SSC
补充业务控制字符串	Bǔchōng yèwù kòngzhì zìfúchuàn	Supplementary service control string	SSC
补充业务无应答呼叫前转	Bǔchōng yèwù wúyìngdá hūjiào qiánzhuǎn	Call forwarding on no reply supplementary service	CFNRy
补充业务询问	Bǔchōng yèwù xúnwèn	Supplementary service interrogation	
补充业务应用协议数据单元	Bǔchōng yèwù yìngyòng xiéyì shùjù dānyuán	Supplement service application protocol data unit	SS APDU
不等臂混合线圈	Bùděng bì hùnhé xiànquān	Unequal-arm hybrid coil	
不等时	Bùděngshí	Anisochronism	
不等时传输	Bùděngshí chuánshū	Anisochronous transmission	
不等于	Bùděngyú	Not equal	NE
补丁	Bǔdīng	Patch	
不定期检查	Bùdìngqī jiǎnchá	Casual inspection	
不对称端子电压	Bùduìchèn duānzi diànyā	Asymmetrical terminal voltage	
不对称控制	Bùduìchèn kòngzhì	Asymmetrical control	
不对称流量控制	Bùduìchèn liúliàng kòngzhì	Asymmetric flow control	AFC
不对称数字订阅线路	Bùduìchèn shùzì dìngyuè xiànlù	Asymmetric digital subscriber line	ADSL
不对称数字用户线	Bùduìchèn shùzì yònghù xiàn	Asymmetric digital subscriber line	ADSL
不对称算法	Bùduìchèn suànfǎ	Asymmetric algorithm (IPsec)	
不对称调幅	Bùduìchèn tiáofú	Asymmetric amplitude modulation	AAM
不对易	Bùduìyì	Non-commuting	
布尔表达式	Bù-ěr biǎodá shì	Boolean expression	
布尔操作符	Bù-ěr cāozuò fú	Boolean operator	
布尔代数	Bù-ěr dàishù	Boolean algebra	
布尔赋值语句	Bù-ěr fùzhí yǔjù	Boolean assignment statement	BAS
布尔算子	Bù-ěr suànzi	Boolean operator	
布尔运算	Bù-ěr yùnsuàn	Boolean operation	

布尔型	Bù-ěr-xíng	Boolean	
部分传递函数	Bùfen chuándì hánshù	Partial transfer function	PTF
部分带宽	Bùfen dàikuān	Fractional bandwidth	
部分光分路器	Bùfen guāng fēnlùqì	Partial optical splitter	
部分恒定角速度	Bùfen héngdìng jiǎosùdù	Partial constant angular velocity	PCAV
部分环回	Bùfen huánhuí	Partial loop back	
部分句法分析	Bùfen jùfǎ fēnxī	Partial parsing	
部分路径索引	Bùfen lùjìng suǒyǐn	Partial path index (in XML)	PPI
部分生成符集	Bùfen shēngchéngfú jí	Partial generator set	
部分失效	Bùfen shīxiào	Partial failure	
部分 T1 电路	Bùfen T1 diànlù	Fractional T1 circuit	
部分网格	Bùfen wǎnggé	Partial mesh	
部分稳定氧化锆	Bùfen wěndìng yǎnghuà gào	Partially stabilized zirconia	
部分纹理下载	Bùfen wénlǐ xiàzài	Partial texture download	
部分相关	Bùfen xiāngguān	Partial period correlation	PPC
部分响应符号间干扰和无跳动编移正交相移键控	Bùfen xiǎngyìng fúhào jiān gānrǎo hé wú tiàodòng biānyí zhèngjiāo xiāngyí jiànkòng	Partial response inter-symbol-interference and jitter free offset quadrature phase shift keying	PR-IJF-OQPSK
部分响应频率调制	Bùfen xiǎngyìng pínlǜ tiáozhì	Partial response frequency modulation	PRFM
部分信息反馈	Bùfen xìnxī fǎnkuì	Partial information feedback	PIF
部分序列号协议数据单元	Bùfen xùlièhào xiéyì shùjù dānyuán	Partial sequence numbers protocol data unit	PSNP
部分有效面积	Bùfen yǒuxiào miànjī	Partial effective area (of an antenna for a given polarization and direction)	
部分增益	Bùfen zēngyì	Partial gain (of an antenna)	
不感知游标	Bùgǎnzhī yóubiāo	Insensitive cursor	
布告板服务	Bùgàobǎn fúwù	Bulletin board service	BBS
布告栏系统	Bùgàolán xìtǒng	Bulletin board system	BBS
不够安全消息	Bùgòu ānquán xiāoxi	Insufficient security message (IPsec TLS)	
不归零反相	Bùguīlíng (fǎnxiāng)	Non-return to zero (inverted)	NRZI
不归零电平	Bùguīlíng diànpíng	Non-return to zero-level	NRZL
不归零码	Bùguīlíng mǎ	Non-return to zero (NRZ) coding	
不归零制	Bùguīlíng zhì	Non-return to zero	NRZ
不规则分割法	Bùguīzé fēngē fǎ	Irregular tessellation	
不规则畸变	Bùguīzé jībiàn	Fortuitous distortion	
不规则三角网	Bùguīzé sānjiǎo wǎng	Triangular irregular network	TIN
不规则形式	Bùguīzé xíngshì	Irregular form	
不合格判定	Bùhégé pàndìng	Fail verdict	
不合理信息	Bùhélǐ xìnxī	Unreasonable message	
步话机	Bùhuàjī	Walkie-talkie	
不挥发存储器	Bùhuīfā cúnchǔqì	Non-volatile memory	
不挥发存储器	Bùhuīfā cúnchǔqì	Non-volatile memory	NVM
捕获	Bǔhuò	Capture	
捕获触发器	Bǔhuò chùfāqì	Capture trigger	
捕获区	Bǔhuò qū	Capture area	
捕获效应	Bǔhuò xiàoyìng	Capture effect	
簿记	Bùjì	Bookkeeping	
部件对象模型	Bùjiàn duìxiàng móxíng	Component object model	
部件互连语言	Bùjiàn hùlián yǔyán	Component interconnection language	CIL

部件目标模型	Bùjiàn mùbiāo móxíng	Component object model	COM
部件延性系数	Bùjiàn yánxìng xìshù	Member ductility factor	
不间断电源设备	Bùjiànduàn diànyuán shèbèi	Uninterruptible power supply	UPS
不间断色调	Bùjiànduàn sèdiào	Continuous tone	
不兼容	Bùjiānróng	Incompatibility	
不交轴光线	Bùjiāozhóu guāngxiàn	Skew ray	
步进起止系统	Bùjìn qǐzhǐ xìtǒng	Stepped start-stop system (of data transmission)	
步进选择器	Bùjìn xuǎnzéqì	Step-by-step selector	
步进应力试验	Bùjìn yìnglì shìyàn	Step stress test	
步进式马达	Bùjìnshì mǎdá	Stepping motor	
步进制	Bùjìnzhì	Step by step	SXS
步进制交换机	Bùjìnzhì jiāohuànjī	Step by step switch	SXS
步进制市话局	Bùjìnzhì shìhuà jú	Step by step switch local exchange	
布局处理	Bùjú chǔlǐ	Layout process	
布局分类	Bùjú fēnlèi	Layout category	
布局结构	Bùjú jiégòu	Layout structure	
布局客体	Bùjú kètǐ	Layout object	
布局客体类别	Bùjú kètǐ lèibié	Layout object class	
布局流	Bùjú liú	Layout stream	
布局式样	Bùjú shìyàng	Layout style	
不均衡层次结构	Bùjūnhéng céngcì jiégòu	Unbalanced hierarchy	
不可及呼叫前转补充业务	Bùkě jí hūjiào qiánzhuǎn bǔchōng yèwù	Call forwarding on mobile subscriber not reachable supplementary service	CFNRc
不可操作	Bùkěcāozuò	Inoperable	INOP
不可重复读取	Bùkěchóngfù dúqǔ	Non-repeatable read	
不可触摸	Bùkěchùmō	Non-tangible	
不可抵赖签名方案	Bùkědǐlài qiānmíng fāng'àn	Undeniable signature scheme (IPsec)	
不可懂串音	Bùkědǒng chuànyīn	Unintelligible crosstalk	
不可否认	Bùkěfǒurèn	Non-repudiation	
不可感知性	Bùkěgǎnzhī xìng	Imperceptibility	
不可及呼叫前转	Bùkějí hūjiào qiánzhuǎn	Call forwarding not reachable	CFNRc
不可见线	Bùkějiàn xiàn	Invisible line	
不可纠正块	Bùkějiūzhèng kuài	Uncorrectable block	
不可靠帧率	Bùkěkào zhèng lǜ	Unreliable frame rate	UFR
不可用秒	Bùkěyòng miǎo	Unavailable second	UAS
不可用时间	Bùkěyòng shíjiān	Unavailable time, down time	UAT
不可用性	Bùkěyòng xìng	Unavailability	
不可用状态	Bùkěyòng zhuàngtài	Down state	
布拉格光纤光栅	Bù-lā-gé guāngxiān guāngshān	Bragg optic fiber grating	
布缆	Bùlǎn	Cabling	
不连续多基频模式	Bùliánxù duōjīpín móshì	Discrete multitone	DMT
不连续发送（机制）	Bùliánxù fāsòng (jīzhì)	Discontinuous transmission (mechanism)	DTX
不连续接收（机制）	Bùliánxù jiēshōu (jīzhì)	Discontinuous reception (mechanism)	DRX
布林代数	Bù-lín dàishù	Boolean algebra	
布林值	Bù-lín zhí	Boolean value	
布里渊散射	Bù-lǐ-yuān sǎnshè	Brillouin scattering	
部门成员	Bùmén chéngyuán	Sector member (for ITU)	

部门联网	Bùmén liánwǎng	Inter-departmental net	IDNet
不能对应传送请求	Bùnéng duìyìng chuánsòng qǐngqiú	Service request not honored	SNH
不能工作时间	Bùnéng gōngzuò shíjiān	Disabled time	
不能工作状态	Bùnéng gōngzuò zhuàngtài	Disabled state; outage	
不平衡操作的异步响应类别	Bùpínghéng cāozuòde yìbù xiǎngyìng lèibié	Unbalanced asynchronous class	UAC
不平衡操作的正常响应类别	Bùpínghéng cāozuòde zhèngcháng xiǎngyìng lèibié	Unbalanced normal class	UNC
不平衡电压	Bùpínghéng diànyā	Asymmetrical voltage	
不平衡同轴馈线/平衡天线变换器	Bùpínghéng tóngzhóu kuìxiàn/ pínghéng tiānxiàn biànhuànqì	Pawsey stub (device to connect an unbalanced coaxial feeder to a balanced antenna)	
不平衡正交相移键控	Bùpínghéng zhèngjiāo xiāngyí jiànkòng	Unbalanced quadrature phase shift keying	UQPSK
不齐整层次结构	Bùqízhěng céngcì jiégòu	Ragged hierarchy	
不确定度	Bùquèdìngdù	Uncertainty	
不确定性函数	Bùquèdìngxìng hánshù	Non-deterministic functions (in SQL Server)	
不确认式信息传送服务	Bùquèrènshì xìnxī chuánsòng fúwù	Unacknowledged information transfer service	UITS
不认识的用户	Bùrènshide yònghù	Unknown subscriber	
不熔湿的	Bùróngshīde	Nonwetting (in SMT)	
布氏硬度试验	Bù-shì yìngdù shìyàn	Brinell hardness test	
不适用	Bùshìyòng	Not used, not applicable	N/A
不适置的目标 BS	Bùshìzhìde mùbiāo BS	Invalid target BS	
部首查字	Bùshǒu chá zì	Radical lookup (WP command)	
不受控滑动	Bùshòukòng huádòng	Uncontrolled slip	
不受限制数字信息	Bùshòuxiànzhì shùzì xìnxī	Unrestricted digital information	UDI
部署	Bùshǔ	Deploy	
补数	Bǔshù	Complement	
步谈机	Bùtánjī	Portable mobile station (walkie-talkie)	
步跳	Bùtiào	Hop	
不提供承载业务	Bùtígōng chéngzài yèwù	Bearer service not provided	
不提供电信业务	Bùtígōng diànxìn yèwù	Teleservice not provided	
不提供数字通路信号	Bùtígōng shùzì tōnglù xìnhào	Digital path not provided signal	DPN
不同边缘入节点	Bùtóng biānyuán rù jiédiǎn	Ingress label switch router	
不同型号光纤（缆）连接器转接座	Bùtóng xínghào guāngxiān (lǎn) liánjiēqì zhuǎnjiēzuò	Inter-type optical fiber (cable) connector adapter	
不透时环回	Bùtòu shíhuánhuí	Non-transparent loop back	
不投递	Bùtóudì	Non-delivery	
不透明的	Bùtòumíngde	Not transparent	NT
不完全参数校验	Bùwánquán cānshù jiàoyàn	Incomplete parameter checking	
不完全水清洗	Bùwánquán shuǐ qīngxǐ	Semi-aqueous cleaning (in SMT)	
不完全的拨号	Bùwánquánde bōhào	Incomplete dialing	
不稳定流	Bùwěndìng liú	Unsteady varied flow	
布线	Bùxiàn	Wiring, cabling	
布线程序控制	Bùxiàn chéngxù kòngzhì	Wired-program control	
不相干度	Bùxiānggān dù	Irrelevancy	
不相关抖动	Bùxiāngguān dǒudòng	Uncorrelated jitter	
布线图	Bùxiàntú	Artwork (in SMT)	

不锈钢阶梯网状带	Bùxiùgāng jiētī wǎngzhuàng dài	Stainless steel ladder mesh belt (semiconductor mfg)	
不锈钢内炉, 带文氏孔	Bùxiùgāng nèi lú, dài wén-shì kǒng	Stainless steel internal oven, with venturi apertures (semiconductor mfg)	
不影响功能性维护	Bùyǐngxiǎng gōngnéngxìng wéihù	Function-permitting maintenance	
不一致	Bùyīzhì	Non-conformance	
不一致测试	Bùyīzhì cèshì	Discordancy test	
不圆度	Bùyuándù	Non-circularity	
不允许漫游	Bùyǔnxǔ mànyóu	Roaming not allowed	
不占用空中通道的呼叫启动	Bùzhànyòng kōngzhōng tōngdàode hūjiào qǐdòng	Off-air call setup	OACSU
不整合	Bùzhěng hé	Unconformity	
不整合面	Bùzhěng hé miàn	Unconformity plane	
不正确信号	Bùzhèngquè xìnhào	Incorrect signal	
不支持群集的应用程序	Bùzhīchí qúnjíde yìngyòng chéngxù	Cluster-unaware application	
不支持的证书消息	Bùzhīchíde zhèngshū xiāoxi	Unsupported certificate message (IPsec TLS)	
不重要的地址部分	Bùzhòngyàode dìzhǐ bùfen	Non-significant address part	NAP
步骤对象	Bùzhòu duìxiàng	Step object	
捕捉带	Bǔzhuō dài	Pull-in range	
捕捉带宽	Bǔzhuō dàikuān	Pull-in banwidth	
捕捉区	Bǔzhuō qū	Capture area (of a terrestrial receiving station)	
捕捉时间	Bǔzhuō shíjiān	Pull-in time	
B 型显示器	B-xíng xiǎnshìqì	B scope	
B 样条曲线	B-yàng tiáoqūxiàn	B-spline	

C

C 接口	C jiēkǒu	C interface	
C 类（放大级的）	C lèi (fàngdà jíde)	Class C (of an amplifying stage)	
C 语言	C yǔyán	C language	
擦除的 SID 帧率	Cāchúde SID zhèng lǜ	Erased silence descriptor rate	ESIDR
擦除的有效 SID 帧率	Cāchúde yǒuxiào SID zhèng lǜ	Erased valid silence descriptor rate	EVSIDR
菜单	Càidān	Menu	
菜单按钮	Càidān ànniǔ	Menu button	
菜单条	Càidān tiáo	Menu bar	
财户到财户	Cáihù dào cáihù	Account to account	
财户到现金	Cáihù dào xiànjīn	Account to cash	
财户汇款	Cáihù huìkuǎn	Remitting in account	
采集	Cǎijí	Acquisition	
材料清单	Cáiliào qīngdān	Bill of materials	BoM
材料色散	Cáiliào sèsàn	Material dispersion	
彩墨带	Cǎimòdài	Color ribbon	
彩色分离	Cǎisè fēnlí	Color separation	
彩色合成	Cǎisè héchéng	Color composite	
彩色激光数位影印机	Cǎisè jīguāng shùwèi yǐngyìnjī	Laser digital color copy machine	
彩色激光印表机	Cǎisè jīguāng yìn biǎojī	Laser color printer	
彩色滤光片	Cǎisè lǜguāngpiàn	Color filter	
彩色全电视信号	Cǎisè quán diànshì xìnhào	Color video broadcast signal	CVBS
彩色图像监控器	Cǎisè túxiàng jiānkòngqì	Color graphic adapter	CGA

彩色图形适配器	Cǎisè túxíng shìpèiqì	Color graphic adapter	CGA
财务管理系统	Cáiwù guǎnlǐ xìtǒng	Financial management system	FMS
财务组	Cáiwù zǔ	Finance group (CMM)	FG
采样	Cǎiyàng	Sampling	
采样定理	Cǎiyàng dìnglǐ	Sampling theorem	
采样间隔	Cǎiyàng jiàngé	Sampling resolution	
采样频率	Cǎiyàng pínlǜ	Sampling frequency	
采样速率	Cǎiyàng sùlǜ	Sample rate, sampling rate	
采样周期	Cǎiyàng zhōuqī	Sampling period	
采样字适应算法	Cǎiyàng zìshìyìng suànfǎ	Sampling adaptive algorithm	SAA
采用反向估计的自适应量化	Cǎiyòng fǎnxiàng gūjìde zìshìyìng liànghuà	Adaptive quantization with backward estimation	AQBE
采用仪表的弯曲实验	Cǎiyòng yíbiǎode wānqū shíyàn	Instrumented bend test	IBT
采用正向评判的自适应量化	Cǎiyòng zhèngxiàng píngpànde zìshìyìng liànghuà	Adaptive quantization with forward estimation	AQFE
材质填充率	Cáizhì tiánchōng lǜ	Texel fill rate (measured in Mpix/sec)	
CAMEL 业务环境	CAMEL yèwù huánjìng	CAMEL service environment	CSE
CAMEL 应用部分	CAMEL yìngyòng bùfen	CAMEL application part	CAP CAMEL
参铥光纤放大器	Cān diū guāngxiān fàngdàqì	Thulium doped fiber amplifier	TDFA
残差激励线性预测编码	Cánchā jīlì xiànxìng yùcè biānmǎ	Residual excitation linear prediction coding	RELP
残差语音域	Cánchā yǔyīn yù	Residual speech domain	
参考	Cānkǎo	Refer, reference	
参考边带功率	Cānkǎo biāndài gōnglǜ	Reference sideband power	
参考差错率	Cānkǎo chācuò lǜ	Reference error ratio	
参考场	Cānkǎo cháng	Reference field (video term)	
参考带宽	Cānkǎo dàikuān	Reference bandwidth	BWr
参考当量	Cānkǎo dāngliàng	Reference equivalent	
参考点	Cānkǎo diǎn	Reference point	
参考电压	Cānkǎo diànyā	Reference voltage	
参考负荷	Cānkǎo fùhè	Reference load	
参考行	Cānkǎo háng	Reference line	
参考结构	Cānkǎo jiégòu	Reference configuration	
参考可用场强	Cānkǎo kěyòng chǎngqiáng	Reference usable field-strength	
参考宽带	Cānkǎo kuāndài	Reference broadband	BWr
参考灵敏度	Cānkǎo língmǐndù	Reference sensitivity	
参考模型	Cānkǎo móxíng	Reference model	
参考配置	Cānkǎo pèizhì	Reference configuration	
参考频率	Cānkǎo pínlǜ	Reference frequency	
参考区	Cānkǎo qū	Reference area	
参考事件	Cānkǎo shìjiàn	Reference event	RE
参考实例	Cānkǎo shílì	Reference example	
参考实现	Cānkǎo shíxiàn	Reference implementation	
参考时钟	Cānkǎo shízhōng	Reference clock	
参考视轴	Cānkǎo shìzhóu	Reference borseight (of an antenna)	
参考输出功率	Cānkǎo shūchū gōnglǜ	Reference output power	
参考天线	Cānkǎo tiānxiàn	Reference antenna	

参考椭球体	Cānkǎo tuǒqiútǐ	Reference ellipsoid	
参考帧	Cānkǎo zhèng	Reference frame (video term)	
参考钟	Cānkǎo zhōng	Reference clock	
参考阻抗	Cānkǎo zǔkàng	Reference impedance	
参量	Cānliàng	Parameter	
参量放大器	Cānliàng fàngdàqì	Parameter amplifier	
参量估计	Cānliàng gūjì	Parameter estimation	
参量检测器	Cānliàng jiǎncèqì	Parameter detector	
参量上变频器	Cānliàng shàng biànpínqì	Parametric up-converter	
参量下变频器	Cānliàng xià biànpínqì	Parametric down-converter	
残留边带	Cánliú biāndài	Vestigial sideband	VSB
残留边带调幅	Cánliú biāndài tiáofú	Vestigial sideband amplitude modulation	VSBAM
残留差错率	Cánliú chācuò lǜ	Residual error rate	
残留错帧率	Cánliú cuòzhèng lǜ	Residual frame error rate	RFER
参数	Cānshù	Argument, parameter	
参数	Cānshù	Parameter	
参数标识符	Cānshù biāozhì fú	Parameter identifier	PI
参数管理帧	Cānshù guǎnlǐ zhèng	Parameter management frame	PMF
参数化	Cānshù huà	Parameterize	
参数列表	Cānshù lièbiǎo	Parameter list	
参数有效性检查	Cānshù yǒuxiàoxìng jiǎnchá	Parameter validity check (CAD/CAM)	PVC
参数有效性条件	Cānshù yǒuxiàoxìng tiáojiàn	Parameter validity condition (CAD/CAM)	PVC
参数振荡器	Cānshù zhèndàngqì	Parametric oscillator	
参数值	Cānshù zhí	Parameter value	PV
参数组标识符	Cānshù zǔ biāozhì fú	Parameter group identifier	PGI
参数化绘图	Cānshùhuà huìtú	Parametric drawing	
残余边带发射	Cányú biāndài fāshè	Vestigial-sideband emission	
残余边带调制	Cányú biāndài tiáozhì	Residual margin modulation	
残余边带调制	Cányú biāndài tiáozhì	Vestigial sideband modulation	
残余边带振幅调制	Cányú biāndài zhènfú tiáozhì	Residual margin amplitude modulation	
残余比特差错率	Cányú bǐtè chācuò lǜ	Residual bit error rate	RBER
残余错帧率	Cányú cuò zhèng lǜ	Residual frame error rate	RFER
残余电流	Cányú diànliú	Residual current	
残余激励线性预测编码	Cányú jīlì xiànxìng yùcè biānmǎ	Residual excitation linear predictive coding	RELP
残余强度	Cányú qiángdù	Residual strength	
参与矢量	Cānyù shǐliàng	Participation vector	
残余衰减	Cányú shuāijiǎn	Residual attenuation	
残余衰减量	Cányú shuāijiǎn liàng	Residual attenuation	
残余误码率	Cányú wùmǎ lǜ	Residual bit error rate	RBER
参与系数	Cānyù xìshù	Participation factor	
参照键	Cānzhào jiàn	Referencing key	
参照空间	Cānzhào kōngjiān	Reference space	
参照完整性	Cānzhào wánzhěngxìng	Referential integrity (in SQL Server)	
槽道	Cáodào	Conduit	
草稿状态	Cǎogǎo zhuàngtài	Draft mode (WP command)	
槽位	Cáowèi	Slot (on computer chassis)	

操纵变量	Cāozòng biànliàng	Manipulated variable	
操纵杆	Cāozònggǎn	Joystick	
操纵器	Cāozòngqì	Manipulator (part of C++ iostream)	
操作	Cāozuò	Action	
操作分析	Cāozuò fēnxī	Operational analysis	OA
操作符	Cāozuò fú	Operator (computational)	
操作管理和维护	Cāozuò guǎnlǐ hé wéihù	Operations, administration and maintenance	OAM
操作管理维护和指配	Cāozuò guǎnlǐ wéihù hé zhǐpèi	Operations, administration, maintenance and provisioning	OAM&P
操作管理中心	Cāozuò guǎnlǐ zhōngxīn	Operations management center	OMC
操作和维护	Cāozuò hé wéihù	Operations and maintenance	O&M; OM
操作检测	Cāozuò jiǎncè	Manipulation detection (IPsec)	
操作寄存器	Cāozuò jìcúnqì	Function register	
操作控制中心	Cāozuò kòngzhì zhōngxīn	Operational control center	
操作设计与分析	Cāozuò shèjì yǔ fēnxī	Operational design and analysis	ODA
操作适合性宣言	Cāozuò shìhé xìng xuānyán	Implementation conformance statement	
操作数据地址寄存器	Cāozuò shùjù dìzhǐ jìcúnqì	Operand address register	OAR
操作维护单元（板）	Cāozuò wéihù dānyuán (bǎn)	Operations and maintenance unit (board)	OMU
操作维护分系统	Cāozuò wéihù fēn xìtǒng	Operations and maintenance sub-system	OMS
操作维护后面板	Cāozuò wéihù hòumian bǎn	Operating and maintenance back panel	OMBP
操作维护链路	Cāozuò wéihù liànlù	Operation and maintenance link	OML
操作维护应用部分	Cāozuò wéihù yìngyòng bùfen	Operations and maintenance application part	OMAP
操作维护中心	Cāozuò wéihù zhōngxīn	Operation and maintenance center	OMC
操作位置	Cāozuò wèizhì	Active position	
操作位置复位	Cāozuò wèizhì fùwèi	Active position home	
操作系统	Cāozuò xìtǒng	Operating system	OS
操作系统功能	Cāozuò xìtǒng gōngnéng	Operating system function	OSF
操作系统功能或协调功能	Cāozuò xìtǒng gōngnéng huò xiétiáo gōngnéng	Operation system function or mediation function	OSF/MF
操作系统或协调装置	Cāozuò xìtǒng huò xiétiáo zhuāngzhì	Operation system or mediation device	OS/MD
操作系统命令语言	Cāozuò xìtǒng mìnglìng yǔyán	Operating system command languages	OSCL
操作与管理	Cāozuò yǔ guǎnlǐ	Operation and management	OAM
操作与维护链路	Cāozuò yǔ wéihù liànlù	Operations and maintenance link	OML
操作与维护中心	Cāozuò yǔ wéihù zhōngxīn	Operations and maintenance center	OMC
操作支持系统	Cāozuò zhīchí xìtǒng	Operations support system	OSS
操作支援系统	Cāozuò zhīyuán xìtǒng	Operation support system	OSS
操作状态位	Cāozuò zhuàngtài wèi	Operational status bit	OSB
操作子系统	Cāozuò zixìtǒng	Operation sub-system	OSS
操作,管理和维护中心	Cāozuò, guǎnlǐ hé wéihù zhōngxīn	Operations, administration and maintenance center	OAMC
操作、维护和管理	Cāozuò, wéihù hé guǎnlǐ	Operations, administration and maintenance	OA&M
操作码	Cāozuòmǎ	Operation code	OP
操作码字段	Cāozuòmǎ zìduàn	Operation field	
操作数	Cāozuòshù	Operand	
操作数字段	Cāozuòshù zìduàn	Operand field	
操作台	Cāozuòtái	Operator's console	
操作员确定闭锁	Cāozuòyuán quèdìng bìsuǒ	Operator determined barring	ODB
操作员远程拨号	Cāozuòyuán yuǎnchéng bōhào	Operator distance dialing	ODD

CCP 测量	CCP cèliáng	CCP measurement	CMEA
CCP 处理器承载器	CCP chǔlǐqì chéngzàiqì	CCP processor loader	CPL
CCP 故障管理	CCP gùzhàng guǎnlǐ	CCP fault manager	CFM
CCP 呼叫控制	CCP hūjiào kòngzhì	CCP call control	CCC
CCP 数据存取	CCP shùjù cúnqǔ	CCP data access	CDA
CCP 消息处理	CCP xiāoxi chǔlǐ	CCP message handling	CMH
CCP 系统承载器	CCP xìtǒng chéngzàiqì	CCP system loader	CSL
CCP 诊断	CCP zhěnduàn	CCP diagnostics	CDIA
CCP 正常运行承载器	CCP zhèngcháng yùnxíng chéngzàiqì	CCP sanity loader	CSM
CCP 正常运行管理器	CCP zhèngcháng yùnxíng guǎnlǐqì	CCP sanity manager	CSMN
CCP 状态处理	CCP zhuàngtài chǔlǐ	CCP status handling	CSH
CCP 资源分配	CCP zīyuán fēnpèi	CCP resource allocation	CRA
CCP 资源管理器	CCP zīyuán guǎnlǐqì	CCP resource manager	CRM
CD 盘加图形	CD pán jiā túxíng	Compact disk plus graphics	CD + G
CDMA BTS 基本架	CDMA BTS jīběn jià	BTS CDMA base rack	BCBR
CDMA BTS 扩展架	CDMA BTS kuòzhǎn jià	BTS CDMA extended rack	BCER
CDMA 发展集团	CDMA fāzhǎn jítuán	CDMA Development Group (North America)	CDG
CDMA 发展组织	CDMA fāzhǎn zǔzhī	CDMA development group	CDG
CDMA 数字信道子系统	CDMA shùzì xìndào zixìtǒng	CDMA digital channel sub-system	CDCS
CDMA 调制与解调模块	CDMA tiáozhì yǔ jiětiáo mókuài	CDMA modulation and demodulation block	CMDB
CDMA 信道元件	CDMA xìndào yuánjiàn	CDMA channel element assembly	CCEA
CDPD 网络实体标识符服务用户证实	CDPD wǎngluò shítǐ biāozhìfú fúwù yònghù zhèngshí	CDPD network entity identifier authentication service user	CNA-SU
CDPD 网络实体标识符证实协议	CDPD wǎngluò shítǐ biāozhìfú zhèngshí xiéyì	CDPD network entity identifier authentication protocol	CNA-P
测波高仪	Cè bōgāoyí	Wave gauge	
侧波束角	Cè bōshù jiǎo	Lateral beam angle	
测地控制	Cèdì kòngzhì	Geodetic control	
测定试验	Cèdìng shìyàn	Determination test	
测地仪	Cèdìyí	Geoscope	
策恩德光纤传感器	Cè-ēn-dé guāngxiān chuángǎnqì	Zehnder fiber optic sensor	
测高雷达	Cègāo léidá	Height-finding radar	
测高法	Cègāofǎ	Hypsometry	
测高学	Cègāoxué	Hypsography	
侧沟	Cègōu	Gutter	
测井仪	Cèjǐngyí	Logger, logging instrument	
测距	Cèjù	Ranging	
测距响应消息	Cèjù xiǎngyìng xiāoxi	Ranging response message	RNG-RSP
测控	Cèkòng	Measurement and control (telecom) ; tracking and control (satellites)	
测链参照	Cèliàn cānzhào	Chainage referencing	
测链参照地物	Cèliàn cānzhào dìwù	Chainage referencing features	
测链参照区段	Cèliàn cānzhào qūduàn	Chainage referencing section	
测链支距	Cèliàn zhījù	Chainage offset	
测量	Cèliáng	Measurement	MEA
测量	Cèliáng	Survey (GIS)	
测量报告	Cèliáng bàogào	Measurement report	MR

测量层次	Cèliáng céngcì	Geodesic hierarchy	
测量单位	Cèliáng dānwèi	Unit of measurement	
测量点	Cèliáng diǎn	Measurement point	MP
测量和统计数据 I/O 模块	Cèliáng hé tǒngjì shùjù I/O mókuài	Measurements and statistics data I/O block	MSDIO
测量结果	Cèliáng jiéguǒ	Measurement result	
测量设备	Cèliáng shèbèi	Measurement equipment	
测量线	Cèliáng xiàn	Measuring line	
测量学	Cèliángxué	Surveying	
策略服务器	Cèlüè fúwùqì	Policy database (for QoS)	
策略决定点	Cèlüè juédìng diǎn	Policy decision point	PDP
策略强加点	Cèlüè qiángjiā diǎn	Policy enhancement point	PEP
策略,保护,检测,响应	Cèlüè, bǎohù, jiǎncè, xiǎngyìng	Policy, protection, detection, response	P2DR
测面法	Cèmiànfǎ	Planimetry	
参差四相伪噪声调制	Cēncī sìxiāng wěizàoshēng tiáozhì	Staggered quadriphase pseudo-noise modulation	SQPNM
参差四相相移键控	Cēncī sìxiāng xiāngyí jiànkòng	Offset-keyed quadriphase phase shift keying	OQPSK
参差正交部分响应调制	Cēncī zhèngjiāo bùfen xiǎngyìng tiáozhì	Staggered quadrature partial response (modulation)	SQPR
参差正交重叠上升余弦(调制)	Cēncī zhèngjiāo chóngdié shàngshēng yúxián (tiáozhì)	Staggered quadrature overlapped raised cosine (modulation)	SQORC
层	Céng	Layer	
层标题	Céng biāotí	Layer header	
层 2 管理连接	Céng èr guǎnlǐ liánjiē	Layer 2 management link	L2ML
层二隧道协议	Céng èr suìdào xiéyì	Layer 2 tunneling protocol	L2TP
层 2 中继	Céng èr zhōngjì	Layer 2 relay	L2R
层2转发	Céng èr zhuǎnfā	Layer 2 relay	L2R
层管理	Céng guǎnlǐ	Layer management	
层管理实体	Céng guǎnlǐ shítǐ	Layer management entity	LME
层接口	Céng jiēkǒu	Layer interface	
层链路	Céng liànlù	Layer link (for ATM)	
层网络	Céng wǎngluò	Layer network	
层 1	Céng yī	Layer 1	L1
层次	Céngcì	Level	
层次故障树分析	Céngcì gùzhàng shù fēnxī	Hierarchy fault tree analysis	
层次结构	Céngcì jiégòu	Hierarchy	
层次式数据	Céngcì shì shùjù	Hierarchical data	
层次视频组播	Céngcì shìpín zǔbō	Layered video multicast	
层次数据结构	Céngcì shùjù jiégòu	Hierarchical data structure	
层次数据库	Céngcì shùjùkù	Hierarchical database	
层次化可扩展可靠组播	Céngcìhuà kěkuòzhǎn kěkào zǔbō	Hierarchical scalable reliable multicast	HSRM
层的服务	Céngde fúwù	Layer service	
层的服务提供者	Céngde fúwù tígòngzhě	Layer service provider	
层的管理实体标识符	Céngde guǎnlǐ shítǐ biāozhìfú	Layer management entity identifier	LMEI
层叠格式表	Céngdié géshi biǎo	Cascading style sheets	CSS
层叠视窗	Céngdié shìchuāng	Cascade (Windows command)	
层间流	Céngjiānliú	Interflow	
层绞	Céngjiǎo	Stranded (optical fiber type)	
层例	Cénglì	Level	

层流	Céngliú	Laminar flow	
层状绝缘扁平电缆	Céngzhuàng juéyuán biǎnpíng diànlǎn	Laminated flat cable	LFC
CEPT 数字中继接口	CEPT shùzì zhōngjì jiēkǒu	CEPT digital trunk interface	CDIT
测试	Cèshì	Test (the T in BORSCHT)	
测试处理器	Cèshì chǔlǐqì	Test processor	
测试存取口	Cèshì cúnqǔ kǒu	Test access port	TAP
测试点	Cèshì diǎn	Testing point	
测试方式	Cèshì fāngshì	Means of test	MOT
测试管理	Cèshì guǎnlǐ	Test management	TM
测试管理协议	Cèshì guǎnlǐ xiéyì	Test management protocol	TMP
测试管理器	Cèshì guǎnlǐqì	Test manager	TSM
测试和控制系统	Cèshì hé kòngzhì xìtǒng	Test and control system	TCS
测试控制	Cèshì kòngzhì	Test control	TC
测试控制接口	Cèshì kòngzhì jiēkǒu	Test control interface	TCI
侧视雷达	Cèshì léidá	Side-looking radar	SLR
测试模式选择[总线]	Cèshì móshì xuǎnzé (zǒngxiàn)	Test mode selector [bus]	TMS
测试目的	Cèshì mùdì	Test purpose	
测试判定	Cèshì pàndìng	Test verdict	
测试设备	Cèshì shèbèi	Test equipment	
测试时钟输入[总线]	Cèshì shízhōng shūrù (zǒngxiàn)	Test clock input [bus]	TCK
测试数据输出[总线]	Cèshì shùjù shūchū (zǒngxiàn)	Test data output [bus]	TDO
测试数据输入[总线]	Cèshì shùjù shūrù (zǒngxiàn)	Test data input [bus]	TDI
测试信号识别	Cèshì xìnhào shíbié	Test signal identification	TSID
测试移动台	Cèshì yídòngtái	Test mobile	TM
测试中的实现	Cèshì zhòngdì shíxiàn	Implementation under test	IUT
测试中的系统	Cèshì zhòngdì xìtǒng	System under test	SUT
测试总线分配集成板	Cèshì zǒngxiàn fēnpèi jíchéngbǎn	Test bus distributor board assembly	TBDA
测试组结构和测试目的	Cèshì zǔ jiégòu hé cèshì mùdì	Test suite structure and test purposes	TSS&TP
测试版	Cèshìbǎn	Beta version	
测试版软件	Cèshìbǎn ruǎnjiàn	Beta software	
测试下的实现	Cèshì-xiàde shíxiàn	Implementation under test	IUT
测试下的系统	Cèshì-xiàde xìtǒng	System under test	SUT
测速电桥	Cèsù diànqiáo	Tachometer bridge	
测速雷达	Cèsù léidá	Doppler radar	
侧向流动	Cèxiàng liúdòng	Lateral flow	
侧压	Cèyā	Lateral pressure	
侧压力	Cèyālì	Crush load	
侧音参考当量	Cèyīn cānkǎo dāngliàng	Side tone reference equivalent	
侧音屏蔽平定值	Cèyīn píngbì píngdìng zhí	Side tone masking rating	STMR
侧音消耗	Cèyīn xiāohào	Sidetone loss	
CGI 脚本文件	CGI jiǎoběn wénjiàn	Common gateway interface (CGI) script	
差	Chà	Subtraction	
差温探测器	Chà wēn tàncèqì	Rate of rise thermal detector	RORTD
差斜率	Chà xiélǜ	Difference slope	
差信号	Chà xìnhào	Difference signal	
差增益	Chà zēngyì	Difference gain	

插/分复用器	Chā/fēn fùyòngqì	Add drop multiplexer	ADM
插板集成	Chābǎn jíchéng	Slice (format of digital modularized radio)	
插槽	Chācáo	Slot	
差错	Chācuò	Error	ERR
差错（误码）概率	Chācuò (wù mǎ) gàilǜ	Probability of error	PE
差错比	Chācuò bǐ	Error ratio	
差错处理	Chācuò chǔlǐ	Error handling	EH
差错二进制数字	Chācuò èrjìnzhì shùzì	Erroneous binary digit	
差错检测	Chācuò jiǎncè	Error detection	
差错检测比特	Chācuò jiǎncè bǐtè	Error check bit	E
差错检测码	Chācuò jiǎncè mǎ	Error detection code	EDC
差错控制	Chācuò kòngzhì	Error control	
差错控制编码	Chācuò kòngzhì biānmǎ	Error control coding	
差错块	Chācuò kuài	Errored block	EB
差错漏检率	Chācuò lòujiǎnlǜ	Residual error rate	
差错率	Chācuò lǜ	Error rate	
差错码组	Chācuò mǎzǔ	Erroneous block	
差错秒	Chācuò miǎo	Errored second	ES
差错秒（开业务状态）	Chācuò miǎo (kāiyè wù zhuàngtài)	Errored second (in-service condition)	ES
差错秒（停业务状态）	Chācuò miǎo (tíngyè wù zhuàngtài)	Errored second (out-of-service condition)	
差错秒比	Chācuò miǎo bǐ	Errored second ratio	ESR
差错时间段监视	Chācuò shíjiānduàn jiānshì	Error interval monitor	EIM
差错数字	Chācuò shùzì	Erroneous digit	
差错突发	Chācuò tūfā	Error burst	
差错突发长度	Chācuò tūfā chángdù	Error burst length	
差错字符	Chācuò zìfú	Erroneous character	
差动保护	Chādòng bǎohù	Differential protection	
差动二进制移相键控	Chādòng èrjìnzhì yíxiāng jiànkòng	Differential binary phase shift keying	DBPSK
差动前置放大器	Chādòng qiánzhì fàngdàqì	Differential preamplifier	
差动线圈	Chādòng xiànquān	Differential coil	
差动式双工	Chādòng-shì shuānggōng	Differential duplex	
差额请领制度	Chā'é qǐnglǐng zhìdù	Balance rule	
差分编码	Chāfēn biānmǎ	Differential encoding	
差分编码四相相移键控	Chāfēn biānmǎ sìxiāng xiāngyí jiànkòng	Differentially encoded, quadriphase shift keying	DQPSK
差分编码移相键控	Chāfēn biānmǎ yíxiāng jiànkòng	Differential-encoded phase shift keying	DEPSK
差分编码正交移相键控	Chāfēn biānmǎ zhèngjiāo yíxiāng jiànkòng	Differentially encoded quadrature phase-shift keying	DQPSK
差分服务模型	Chāfēn fúwù móxíng	Difference service model	DiffServ
差分攻击	Chāfēn gōngjī	Differential attack	
差分接口	Chāfēn jiēkǒu	Differential interface	
差分脉冲编码调制	Chāfēn màichōng biānmǎ tiáozhì	Differential pulse code modulation	DPCM
差分脉码调制	Chāfēn màimǎ tiáozhì	Differential pulse code modulation	DPCM
差分曼彻斯特编码	Chāfēn Màn-chè-sī-tè biānmǎ	Differential Manchester encoding	
差分密码分析法	Chāfēn mìmǎ fēnxīfǎ	Differential cryptanalysis	
差分耦合器	Chāfēn ǒuhéqì	Differential coupler	
差分全球定位系统	Chāfēn quánqiú dìngwèi xìtǒng	Difference global positioning system	DGPS

差分全球卫星导航系统	Chāfēn quánqiú wèixīng dǎoháng xìtǒng	Differential global navigation satellite system	DGNSS
差分群迟延	Chāfēn qún chíyán	Differential group delay	DGD
差分群时延	Chāfēn qún shíyán	Differential group delay	DGD
差分时钟	Chāfēn shízhōng	Differential timing	
差分四相相移键控	Chāfēn sìxiāng xiāngyí jiànkòng	Differential quadriphase shift keying	DQPSK
差分跳频	Chāfēn tiàopín	Differential frequency hopping	DFH
差分调制	Chāfēn tiáozhì	Differential modulation	
差分相干脉码调制	Chāfēn xiānggān màimǎ tiáozhì	Differentially coherent pulse code modulation	DCPCM
差分相干移相键控	Chāfēn xiānggān yíxiāng jiànkòng	Differentially coherent phase shift keying	DCPSK
差分相移	Chāfēn xiāngyí	Differential phase-shift	
差分相移键控	Chāfēn xiāngyí jiànkòng	Differential phase shift keying	DPSK
差分业务	Chāfēn yèwù	Differentiated service	DS
差分移相键控	Chāfēn yíxiāng jiànkòng	Differential phase shift keying	DPSK
差分正交相移键控	Chāfēn zhèngjiāo xiāngyí jiànkòng	Differential quadrature phase shift keying	DQPSK
差分正交移相键控	Chāfēn zhèngjiāo yíxiāng jiànkòng	Differential quaternary phase shift keying	DQPSK
查号业务	Cháhào yèwù	Directory name service	DNS
查号台	Cháhàotái	Information desk	
拆箱	Chāi xiāng	Unboxing	
拆箱转换	Chāi xiāng zhuǎnhuàn	Unboxing	
拆除信号	Chāichú xìnhào	Clear-back signal	CBK
拆封	Chāifēng	Decapsulation	
拆封代理	Chāifēng dàilǐ	Decapsulating agent (in IP)	
拆开	Chāikāi	Disconnect	DISC
拆线	Chāixiàn	Disconnect	
拆线	Chāixiàn	Clearing	
拆线信号	Chāixiàn xìnhào	Clear-forward signal	CLF
拆装子层	Chāizhuāng zicéng	Segmentation and reassembly sub-layer	SAR
插件	Chājiàn	Plug-in board	
插件	Chājiàn	Add-in	
插脚	Chājiǎo	Pin (on a plug or insertion chip)	
插接站	Chājiē zhàn	Docking station	
插卡	Chākǎ	Paddle card	
插孔	Chākǒng	Plug seat	
插口	Chākǒu	Socket	SO
插框	Chākuàng	Insertion-frame	
插框组件	Chākuàng zǔjiàn	Insertion-frame component	
差模电压	Chàmó diànyā	Differential mode voltage	
差模跟踪	Chàmó gēnzōng	Differential mode tracking	
差模耦合器	Chàmó ǒuhéqì	Differential mode coupler	
掺磷光纤	Chān lín guāngxiàn	Chalcogenide glass optical fiber	
掺镨光纤放大器	Chān pǔ guāngxiān fàngdàqì	Praseodymium-doped fiber amplifier	PDFA
掺稀土光纤放大器	Chān xītǔ guāngxiān fàngdàqì	Rare earth optical amplifier	
掺铒氟化光纤放大器	Chān'ěr fúhuà guāngxiān fàngdàqì	Erbium-doped fluoridized fiber amplifier	EDFFA
掺铒光纤放大器	Chān'ěr guāngxiān fàngdàqì	Erbium-doped fiber amplifier	EDFA
掺铒光纤激光器	Chān'ěr guāngxiān jīguāngqì	Erbium-doped fiber laser	
产出率	Chǎnchūlǜ	Yield (in SMT)	

掺碲的 EDFA	Chāndìde EDFA	Tellurium-doped EDFA	T-EDFA
长半径	Cháng bànjìng	Semi-major axis	
长波长半导体激光模组	Cháng bōcháng bàndǎotǐ jīguāng mózǔ	Long wavelength semiconductor laser module	
长单位数据	Cháng dānwèi shùjù	Long unit data (in SS7)	LUDT
长单位数据传输	Cháng dānwèi shùjù chuánshū	Long unit data transmission	LUDT
长单位数据传输业务	Cháng dānwèi shùjù chuánshū yèwù	Long unit data transmission service	LUDTS
场发射显示器	Cháng fāshè xiǎnshìqì	Field emitter display	FED
长桥	Cháng qiáo	Long Bridge	
场矢量	Cháng shǐliàng	Field vector	
场矢量极化	Cháng shǐliàng jíhuà	Field vector polarization	
场效应晶体管	Cháng xiàoyìng jīngtǐguǎn	Field effect transistor	FET
长字指令	Cháng zì zhǐlìng	Long-word instruction	
长波	Chángbō	Long wave	
长波光纤	Chángbō guāngxiān	Long wavelength optical fiber	LWL
长波红外	Chángbō hóngwài	Long wave infrared (semiconductor mfg)	
长波形可移动输入红外线	Chángbō-xíng kěyídòng shūrù hóngwàixiàn	Amplitude shift keyed infrared	ASK IR
场地出租	Chǎngdì chūzū	Collocation	
长度比特	Chángdù bǐtè	Length bit	LTH
长度指示	Chángdù zhǐshì	Length indicator	LI
常规电视	Chángguī diànshì	Existing quality television	
常规多维数据集	Chángguī duōwéi shùjùjí	Regular data cube	
常规畸变度	Chángguī jībiàn dù	Conventional degree of distortion	
常规视觉处理器	Chángguī shìjué chǔlǐqì	Generic visual perception processor	GVPP
常规突发脉冲序列	Chángguī tūfā màichōng xùliè	Normal burst	NB
常规维度	Chángguī wéidù	Regular dimension	
长话交换局	Chánghuà jiāohuànjú	Toll switch office	TS
常见问题	Chángjiàn wèntí	Frequently asked questions	FAQ
场控晶闸管	Chángkòng jīngzháguǎn	Field-controlled thyristor	
常量	Chángliàng	Constant (noun)	
场量	Chángliàng	Field quantity	
常量分析	Chángliàng fēnxī	Macro analysis	
长码	Chángmǎ	Code length	
长期变化	Chángqī biànhuà	Secular variation	
长期抖动指示器	Chángqī dǒudòng zhǐshìqì	Long-term flicker indicator	
长期观测	Chángqī guāncè	Long-period observation	
长期频率稳定度	Chángqī pínlǜ wěndìngdù	Long-term frequency stability	
长期预报	Chángqī yùbào	Long-range forecasting	
场强	Chǎngqiáng	Field strength	
场强测试分析	Chǎngqiáng cèshì fēnxī	Field-strength test analysis	
场强计	Chǎngqiáng jì	Field strength meter	FSM
场强灵敏度	Chǎngqiáng língmǐndù	Field intensity sensibility	
场强-距离乘积	Chǎngqiáng--jùlí chéngjī	Cymomotive force; field strength-distance product	CMF
场强-距离乘积	Chǎngqiáng--jùlí chéngjī	Field strength-distance product; cymomotive force	CMF
厂商	Chǎngshāng	Vendor	
常设电路业务	Chángshè diànlù yèwù	Permanent circuit service	
长途半自动插入	Chángtú bànzìdòng chārù	Semiautomatic toll offering	

长途电话交换中心	Chángtú diànhuà jiāohuàn zhōngxīn	Toll center	TC
长途电话记录和计算设备	Chángtú diànhuà jìlù hé jìsuàn shèbèi	Toll recording and computing equipment	TRACE
长途电话中继线	Chángtú diànhuà zhōngjìxiàn	Intertoll trunk	ITT
长途电缆无人站	Chángtú diànlǎn wúrénzhàn	Long distance unmanned cable station	CLW
长途电缆线路	Chángtú diànlǎn xiànlù	Long distance cable line	CXD
长途电路	Chángtú diànlù	Trunk circuit	
长途电路网	Chángtú diànlù wǎng	Trunk circuit network	
长途干线中继光通讯系统	Chángtú gànxiàn zhōngjì guāng tōngxùn xìtǒng	Long-haul terrestrial optical communication system	
长途光缆线路	Chángtú guānglǎn xiànlù	Long distance optical cable line	CXG
长途交换传真设备	Chángtú jiāohuàn chuánzhēn shèbèi	Toll switch-facsimile equipment	TS-FX
长途交换机	Chángtú jiāohuànjī	Toll switch	TS
长途交换局	Chángtú jiāohuànjú	Toll switch	TS
长途明线线路	Chángtú míngxiàn xiànlù	Long distance open line	CXM
长途区号	Chángtú qūhào	Trunk code	
长途通知音	Chángtú tōngzhīyīn	Toll offering tone	
长途直拨	Chángtú zhíbō	Direct distance dialing	DDD
长途中继线接续设备	Chángtú zhōngjìxiàn jiēxù shèbèi	Trunk block connector	TBC
长途终局话务员	Chángtú zhōngjú huàwùyuán	Terminating toll operator	TX
长途局	Chángtújú	Toll switch	TS
长途台	Chángtútái	Long distance console	CT
长线天线	Chángxiàn tiānxiàn	Long-wire antenna	
长线型振荡器	Chángxiàn-xíng zhèndàngqì	Long-line oscillator	
场移	Chángyí	Field displacement	
场移式隔离器	Chángyíshì gélíqì	Field-displacement isolator	
常用信令链路	Chángyòng xìnlìng liànlù	Regular signaling link	
场致发光显示板	Chǎngzhì fāguāng xiǎnshìbǎn	Electroluminescent display panel	
常驻程序区域	Chángzhù chéngxù qūyù	Resident program area	
常驻段	Chángzhù duàn	Root segment	
常驻任务	Chángzhù rènwu	Resident task	
掺铌光纤放大器	Chānní guāngxiān fàngdàqì	Niobium-doped fiber amplifier	NDFA
产品保证可信度评估程序	Chǎnpǐn bǎozhèng kěxìndù pínggū chéngxù	Product Assurance Confidence Evaluator (TRW Inc.)	PACE
产品规范	Chǎnpǐn guīfàn	Product specification	
产品基线	Chǎnpǐn jīxiàn	Product baseline	
产品模型数据交换标准	Chǎnpǐn móxíng shùjù jiāohuàn biāozhǔn	Standard for the exchange of product model data	STEP
产品模型数据转换标准	Chǎnpǐn móxíng shùjù zhuǎnhuàn biāozhǔn	Standard for the exchange of product model data	STEP
产品齐套性	Chǎnpǐn qítàoxìng	Product interoperability	
产品热领域应用	Chǎnpǐn rè lǐngyù yìngyòng	Product thermal field application (semiconductor mfg)	
产品生命周期管理	Chǎnpǐn shēngmìng zhōuqī guǎnlǐ	Product lifecycle management	
产品数据管理	Chǎnpǐn shùjù guǎnlǐ	Product data management	PDM
产品信息管理	Chǎnpǐn xìnxī guǎnlǐ	Product information management	PIM
产品一致性声明	Chǎnpǐn yīzhìxìng shēngmíng	Supplier's declaration of conformity	SdoC
超(负荷)运行位	Chāo (fùhè) yùnxíng wèi	Overrun bit	OR
超标量体系结构	Chāobiāoliàng tǐxì jiégòu	Superscalar	
超标量渲染	Chāobiāoliàng xuànrǎn	SuperScaler rendering (video term)	
超长光传输	Chāocháng guāng chuánshū	Ultra long-haul fiber	ULH

超长光传输技术	Chāocháng guāng chuánshū jìshù	Ultra long-haul optical transmission technology	ULHOTT
超长指令字	Chāocháng zhǐlìng zì	Very long instruction word	VLIW
超长波	Chāochángbō	Ultra-longwave	
超长波通信	Chāochángbō tōngxìn	Myriametric wave communication	
超大规模集成	Chāodàguīmó jíchéng	Very large scale integration	VLSI
超大规模集成电路	Chāodàguīmó jíchéng diànlù	Very large scale integrated circuit	VLSI
超大型维度	Chāodàxíng wéidù	Very large dimension	
超低频	Chāodīpín	Ultra-low frequency	ULF
超地平对流层传播	Chāodìpíng duìliúcéng chuánbō	Transhorizon tropospheric transmission	
超地平无线接力系统	Chāodìpíng wúxiàn jiēlì xìtǒng	Transhorizon radio-relay system	
超短脉冲光源	Chāoduǎn màichōng guāngyuán	Ultra-short pulse source	
超短波	Chāoduǎnbō	Ultra-shortwave	
超额突发量	Chāo'é tūfā liáng	Excess burst size	Be
超额突发速率	Chāo'é tūfā sùlǜ	Excess burst rate	EBR
超额信息速率	Chāo'é xìnxī sùlǜ	Excess information rate	EIR
超方向性	Chāofāngxiàngxìng	Superdirectivity	
超辐射发光管	Chāofúshè fāguāng guǎn	Super-luminescence diode	
超辅射发光管	Chāofúshè fāguāng guǎn	Super light emitting diode	SLED
超高数据传输速率的数字用户线路	Chāogāo shùjù chuánshū sùlǜde shùzì yònghù xiànlù	Very-high-data-rate digital subscriber line	VDSL
超高频	Chāogāopín	Super high frequency	SHF
超高速集成电路	Chāogāosù jíchéng diànlù	Very high speed integrated circuit	
超高速数字用户线	Chāogāosù shùzì yònghù xiàn	Ultra-high-speed digital subscriber line	UDSL
超高速数字用户线	Chāogāosù shùzì yònghù xiàn	Very high-speed digital subscriber line	VDSL
超高速直接内存存取	Chāogāosù zhíjiē nèicún cúnqǔ	Ultra direct memory access	Ultra DMA
超高帧	Chāogāozhèng	Hyperframe	
超固结比	Chāogùjié bǐ	Over consolidation ratio	OCR
超级带宽架构	Chāojí dàikuān jiàgòu	Super bandwidth infrastructure	SBI
超级端口结构	Chāojí duānkǒu jiégòu	Ultra port architecture	UPA
超级分发	Chāojí fēnfā	Superdistribution	
超级类别	Chāojí lèibié	Superclass	
超级链接	Chāojí liànjiē	Hyperlink	
超级南桥芯片	Chāojí nánqiáo xìnpiàn	Super South Bridge chip	SSB
超级喷射器	Chāojí pēnshèqì	Super Jet (cable blower)	
超级平面连接	Chāojí píngmiàn liánjiē	Super plane connection	SPC
超级任天堂 16 位游戏机	Chāojí rèntiāntáng 16 wèi yóuxìjī	Nintendo Super Famicom (computer game)	SFC
超级音乐 CD	Chāojí yīnyuè CD	Super audio CD	SACD
超级用户	Chāojí yònghù	Root user, super user	
超级永久性存储器	Chāojí yǒngjiǔxìng cúnchǔqì	Super permanent memory	XPM
超级智能音频集成电路	Chāojí zhìnéng yīnpín jíchéng diànlù	Super intelligent sound ASIC	
超级终端	Chāojí zhōngduān	Hyper terminal (application in Microsoft Windows)	
超卡软件	Chāokǎ ruǎnjiàn	Hypercard software	
超空间	Chāokōngjiān	Hyperspace	
超宽带	Chāokuāndài	Ultra-wideband	
超宽带光纤放大器	Chāokuāndài guāngxiān fàngdàqì	Ultra-wideband optical fiber amplifier	UWOA
超类	Chāolèi	Super-cluster	

超联	Chāolián	Hyperlink	
超量突发	Chāoliàng tūfā	Excess burst	Be
超联结	Chāoliánjié	Hyperlink	
超连接	Chāoliánjiē	Hyperlink	
超立方体	Chāolìfāngtǐ	Hypercube	
超媒体	Chāoméitǐ	Hypermedia	
超媒体对象管理	Chāoméitǐ duìxiàng guǎnlǐ	Hypermedia object management (in common information model)	HMOM
超媒体管理模式	Chāoméitǐ guǎnlǐ móshì	Hypermedia management schema (in common information model)	HMMS
超媒体管理协议	Chāoméitǐ guǎnlǐ xiéyì	Hypermedia management protocol (in common information model)	HMMP
超媒体模型	Chāoméitǐ móxíng	Hypermedia model	
超密脚距	Chāomì jiǎojù	Ultra-fine-pitch (in SMT)	
超密度	Chāomìdù	Super density	SD
超密集波分复用	Chāomìjí bōfēn fùyòng	Ultra-dense wavelength division multiplexing	UDWDM
超诺突发量	Chāonuò tūfāliàng	Excess burst size	Be
超频	Chāopín	Overclock	
超频道	Chāopíndào	Hyperband	
超前不等时并行畸变度	Chāoqián bùděngshí bìngxíng jībiàndù	Degree of early anisochronous parallel distortion	
超奇异椭圆曲线	Chāoqíyì tuǒyuán qūxiàn	Super-singular elliptic curve (cryptology)	
超群	Chāoqún	Supergroup	
超群链路	Chāoqún liànlù	Supergroup link	
超群组链路	Chāoqún zǔ liànlù	Supergroup assembly link	
超绕杆天线	Chāoràogǎn tiānxiàn	Super-turnstile antenna	
超时	Chāoshí	Time-out	TMO
超时概率	Chāoshí gàilǜ	Probability of timeout	
超视距	Chāoshìjù	Beyond line of sight	BLOS
超视距雷达	Chāoshìjù léidá	Over-the-horizon radar	
超视距无线电中继系统	Chāoshìjù wúxiàndiàn zhōngjì xìtǒng	Trans-horizon radio-relay system	
抄送	Chāosòng	Carbon copy	
超速率数据接口板	Chāosùlǜ shùjù jiēkǒu bǎn	High-speed-rate data interface board	HSL
超同步卫星	Chāotóngbù wèixīng	Super-synchronous satellite	
超图	Chāotú	Hypergraph	
超图模型	Chāotú móxíng	Hypergraph model	
超图数据模型	Chāotú shùjù móxíng	Hypergraph data model	
超椭圆曲线	Chāotuǒyuán qūxiàn	Hyperelliptic curve (cryptology)	
超外差式接收	Chāowàichā-shì jiēshōu	Superheterodyne reception	
超微半导体	Chāowēi bàndǎotǐ	Advanced Micro Devices (US computer company)	AMD
超微科技	Chāowēi kējì	Advanced Micro Devices	AMD
超文本	Chāowénběn	Hypertext	
超文本标记语言	Chāowénběn biāojì yǔyán	Hypertext markup language	HTML
超文本标识语言	Chāowénběn biāozhì yǔyán	Hypertext markup language	HTML
超文本传输协议	Chāowénběn chuánshū xiéyì	Hypertext transfer protocol	HTTP
超文本传送协议	Chāowénběn chuánsòng xiéyì	Hypertext transfer protocol	http
超文本传送协议服务器	Chāowénběn chuánsòng xiéyì fúwùqì	Hypertext transfer protocol server	HTTPS
超文本缓存协议	Chāowénběn huǎncún xiéyì	Hypertext cache protocol	HTCP
超文本链接标示语	Chāowénběn liànjiē biāoshì yǔ	Hypertext markup language (in SQL Server)	HTML

超文本应用程序	Chāowénběn yìngyòng chéngxù	Hypertext application	HTA
超文本组合语言	Chāowénběn zǔhé yǔyán	Hypertext markup language	HTML
超稳定自适应递归滤波器	Chāowěndìng zìshìyìng dìguī lǜbōqì	Hyperstable adaptive recursive filter	HARF
超小口径卫星地面接收站	Chāoxiǎo kǒujìng wèixīng dìmiàn jiēshōu zhàn	Ultra aperture terminal	UAT
超小型封装	Chāoxiǎoxíng fēngzhuāng	Thin small outline package	TSOP
超小型机成天线	Chāoxiǎoxíng jīchéng tiānxiàn	Sub-miniature integrated antenna	SIA
超小型天线终端	Chāoxiǎoxíng tiānxiàn zhōngduān	Very small aperture satellite terminal	VSAT
超小型终端移动卫星通信系统	Chāoxiǎoxíng zhōngduān yídòng wèixīng tōngxìn xìtǒng	Ultra small terminal mobile satellite communication system	MSAT
超音波	Chāoyīnbō	Ultrasonic wave	
超越概率	Chāoyuè gàilǜ	Probability of exceedance	
超越信息速率	Chāoyuè xìnxī sùlǜ	Excess information rate	EIR
超再生	Chāozàishēng	Super-regeneration	
超再生接收机	Chāozàishēng jiēshōujī	Super-regenerator receiver	
超窄频滤光镜	Chāozhǎi pínlǜ guāngjìng	Ultra narrowband filter (optical)	
超帧	Chāozhèng	Superframe	
巢状类别	Cháozhuàng lèibié	Nested class	
超主群	Chāozhǔqún	Super mastergroup	
超主群段	Chāozhǔqún duàn	Super mastergroup section	
超主群链路	Chāozhǔqún liànlù	Super mastergroup link	
差拍干扰	Chāpāi gānrǎo	Beat jamming	
差拍式接收	Chāpāi-shì jiēshōu	Beat reception	
差频失真	Chàpín shīzhēn	Difference frequency distortion	
插入	Chārù	Insert	
插入	Chārù	Patch (verb)	
插入	Chārù	Intrusion	
插入菜单	Chārù càidān	Insert menu (WP command)	
插入查询	Chārù cháxún	Insert query	
插入错误	Chārù cuòwù	Insertion error	
插入单元	Chārù dānyuán	Plugged unit	
插入后的强拆	Chārù hòude qiáng chāi	Breakdown after intrusion	
插入排序	Chārù páixù	Insertion sort	
插入扫描	Chārù sǎomiáo	Incorporated sweep	
插入式光纤(缆)连接器	Chārù shì guāngxiān (lǎn) liánjiē qì	Insertion optical fiber (cable) connector	
插入损耗	Chārù sǔnhào	Insertion loss	IL
插入相移	Chārù xiāngyí	Insertion phase shift	
插入新表格	Chārù xīn biǎogé	Insert new table (WP command)	
插入一行	Chārù yīháng	Insert row (WP command)	
插入音	Chārù yīn	Intrusion tone	
插入用户数据	Chārù yònghù shùjù	Insert subscriber data	
插入增益	Chārù zēngyì	Insertion gain	
插入值查询	Chārù zhí cháxún	Insert values query	
插入状态	Chārù zhuàngtài	Insert mode (WP command)	
插入/分出复接设备	Chārù/fēnchū fù jiē shèbèi	Add/drop multiplexer	ADM
查索	Chásuǒ	Finger	
插索	Chāsuǒ	Coupling, cabled	

插头	Chātóu	Plug	
插头外壳	Chātóu wàiké	Plug body	
插线板	Chāxiànbǎn	Patch panel	
插箱	Chāxiāng	Plugged box	
查寻	Cháxún	Find (WP command)	
查询	Cháxún	Inquiry (noun), poll (verb)	
查询	Cháxún	Polling	
查询窗口	Cháxún chuāngkǒu	Query window	
查询访问码	Cháxún fǎngwèn mǎ	Inquiry access code	IAC
查询分析器	Cháxún fēnxīqì	Server query analyzer (in SQL Server)	
查寻工具	Cháxún gōngjù	Search bar (WP command)	
查询函数	Cháxún hánshù	Query function	
查询扩充	Cháxún kuòchōng	Query expansion	
查询生成器	Cháxún shēngchéngqì	Query builder	
查询系统	Cháxún xìtǒng	Polling system	
查询优化	Cháxún yōuhuà	Query optimization	
查询优化器	Cháxún yōuhuà qì	Query optimizer	
查询语言	Cháxún yǔyán	Query language	
查询表	Cháxúnbiǎo	Look up table	LUT
查询点	Cháxúndiǎn	Query point (CAD/CAM)	
查询器	Cháxúnqì	Search engine	
查询图模型	Cháxúntú móxíng	Query graph model	QGM
差压	Chàyā	Differential pressure	
差异	Chāyì	Divergence, discrepancy	
差异备份	Chāyì bèifèn	Differential backup	
差异数据库备份	Chāyì shùjùkù bèifèn	Differential database backup	
查找	Cházhǎo	Search, searching	
查找	Cházhǎo	Finding	
查找表	Cházhǎo biǎo	Lookup table (for database)	
查找恶意呼叫	Cházhǎo èyì hūjiào	Malicious call tracing	
插针	Chāzhēn	Pin, inserted pin, connector pin	
插针体	Chāzhēntǐ	Ferrule	
插值	Chāzhí	Interpolation (in digital photography)	
插枝攻击	Chāzhī gōngjī	Value insertion attack	
差转机	Chàzhuǎnjī	Transponder	
插座	Chāzuò	Receptacle	
插座	Chāzuò	Socket	SK
车辆定位	Chēliàng dìngwèi	Vehicle location	
衬底	Chèndǐ	Substrate (semiconductor mfg)	
成本保险加运费付至	Chéngběn bǎoxiǎn jiā yùnfèi fù zhì	Cost, insurance and freight	CIF
成本加运保费	Chéngběn jiā yùnbǎo fèi	Cost, insurance and freight	CIF
成本加运费	Chéngběn jiā yùnfèi	Cost and freight	C/F
乘除差错率	Chéngchú chācuò lǜ	Residual error rate	
成对不等性码	Chéngduì bùděngxìng mǎ	Paired-disparity code	
成对字符组间距	Chéngduì zìfú zǔ jiānjù	Pairwise kerning	
惩罚时间	Chéngfá shíjiān	Penalty time	PT

成分	Chéngfèn	Construct (noun)	
乘积码形状增益矢量量化	Chéngjī mǎxíng zhuàng zēngyì shǐliàng liànghuà	Product codeform state gain vector quantization	PSGVQ
乘积项	Chéngjī xiàng	Product-term	
乘积形式解	Chéngjī xíngshì jiě	Product form solution	PFS
乘积阵天线系统	Chéngjī zhèn tiānxiàn xìtǒng	Multiplicative array antenna system	MAAS
程控长市合一	Chéngkòng cháng shì héyī	Program controlled combined city/toll office	CCS
程控长话交换	Chéngkòng chánghuà jiāohuàn	Program controlled toll switch	CCJ
程控市话交换	Chéngkòng shìhuà jiāohuàn	Program controlled city switch	CSJ
程控市话用户集中器	Chéngkòng shìhuà yònghù jízhōngqì	Subscriber line concentrator	
程控市话局	Chéngkòng shìhuàjú	Stored program controlled local exchange	
程控数字自动交换机	Chéngkòng shùzì zìdòng jiāohuànjī	Program controlled digital automatic branch exchange	
承诺速率测量时间间隔	Chéngnuò sùlǜ cèliáng shíjiān jiàngé	Committed rate measurement interval	Tc
承诺突发量	Chéngnuò tūfā liàng	Committed burst size	Bc
承诺信息速率	Chéngnuò xìnxī sùlǜ	Committed information rate	CIR
承诺的时间间隔	Chéngnuòde shíjiān jiàngé	Committed time interval	Tc
承诺的突发大小	Chéngnuòde tūfā dàxiǎo	Committed burst size	Bc
成批处理	Chéngpī chǔlǐ	Batch processing	
成批数据交换业务	Chéngpī shùjù jiāohuàn yèwù	Batch data exchange service	BDES
城市地理信息系统	Chéngshì dìlǐ xìnxī xìtǒng	Urban geographic information system	
城市和区域信息系统协会	Chéngshì hé qūyù xìnxī xìtǒng xiéhuì	Urban and Regional Information Systems Association	URISA
城市级清算和处理中心	Chéngshì jí qīngsuàn hé chǔlǐ zhōngxīn	City-level clearance and processing center	CCPC
城市交通管制系统	Chéngshì jiāotōng guǎnzhì xìtǒng	Urban traffic control system	
城市信息系统	Chéngshì xìnxī xìtǒng	Urban information system	
承受力	Chéngshòulì	Bearing capacity	
承受力系数	Chéngshòulì xìshù	Bearing capacity factor	
成象	Chéngxiàng	Formation of image, imagery	
成像处理	Chéngxiàng chǔlǐ	Imaging process	
成像次序	Chéngxiàng cìxù	Imaging order	
成形处理	Chéngxíng chǔlǐ	Imaging process	
成形次序	Chéngxíng cìxù	Imaging order	
程序	Chéngxù	Procedure, program	
程序	Chéngxù	Program	P
程序包	Chéngxù bāo	Package	
程序编写	Chéngxù biānxiě	Programming	
程序产生器	Chéngxù chǎnshēngqì	Program generator	
程序存贮器扫描	Chéngxù cúnzhùqì sǎomiáo	Program memory sweep	
程序多线控制器	Chéngxù duōxiàn kòngzhìqì	Programmed multi-line controller	PMLC
程序分段和重编	Chéngxù fēnduàn hé chóngbiān	Segmentation and reassembly	SAR
程序记数器	Chéngxù jìshùqì	Program counter	P
程序记数器保存积存器	Chéngxù jìshùqì bǎocún jīcúnqì	Program counter save register	PCS
程序块	Chéngxù kuài	Program block	
程序敏感性故障	Chéngxù mǐngǎnxìng gùzhàng	Program-sensitive fault	
程序入口点	Chéngxù rùkǒu diǎn	Program entry point	
程序设计	Chéngxù shèjì	Programming	
程序设计环境	Chéngxù shèjì huánjìng	Programming environment	
程序设计系统	Chéngxù shèjì xìtǒng	Programming system	

程序瘫痪	Chéngxù tānhuàn	Program crash	
程序调试系统	Chéngxù tiáoshì xìtǒng	Program debugging system	PDS
程序优化	Chéngxù yōuhuà	Program optimization	
程序员	Chéngxù yuán	Programmer	
程序指令	Chéngxù zhǐling	Program command	
程序指纹	Chéngxù zhǐwén	Program fingerprint	
程序状态字	Chéngxù zhuàngtài zì	Program status word	PSW
程序员用分极较糊图形标准	Chéngxùyuán-yòng fēnjí jiàohú túxíng biāozhǔn	Programmer's hierarchical interactive graphics standard	PHIGS
城域服务区	Chéngyù fúwùqū	Municipal service area	
城域网	Chéngyù wǎng	Metropolitan area network	MAN
成员	Chéngyuán	Member	
成员变量	Chéngyuán biànliàng	Member variable	
成员变量	Chéngyuán biànliàng	Data member	
成员初始值列表	Chéngyuán chūshǐ zhí lièbiǎo	Member initialization list	
成员对象	Chéngyuán duìxiàng	Member object (GIS term)	
成员函数	Chéngyuán hánshù	Member function	
成员键列	Chéngyuán jiàn liè	Member key column	
成员名列	Chéngyuán mínglìè	Member name column	
成员取用运算子	Chéngyuán qǔyòng yùnsuàn zi	Member access operator	
成员属性	Chéngyuán shǔxing	Member property	
成员委派	Chéngyuán wěipài	Member delegation	
成员组	Chéngyuán zǔ	Member group	
承载独立呼叫控制协议	Chéngzài dúlì hūjiào kòngzhì xiéyì	Bearer Independent Call Control protocol	BICC
承载分组信号的 SDH	Chéngzài fēnzǔ xìnhàode SDH	Packet over SDH	POS
承载互通功能	Chéngzài hùtōng gōngnéng	Bearer interworking function	BIWF
承载控制功能	Chéngzài kòngzhì gōngnéng	Bearer control function	BCF
承载控制节点功能	Chéngzài kòngzhì jiédiǎn gōngnéng	Bearer node control function	BCF-N
承载控制网关功能	Chéngzài kòngzhì wǎngguān gōngnéng	Bearer gateway control function	BCF-G
承载控制转接功能	Chéngzài kòngzhì zhuǎnjiē gōngnéng	Bearer transmission control function	BCF-T
承载能力	Chéngzài nénglì	Bearer capability	BC
承载能力标示单元	Chéngzài nénglì biāoshì dānyuán	Bearer capability identity element	BC_IE
承载能力信息单元	Chéngzài nénglì xìnxī dānyuán	Bearer capability information element	BCIE
承载偶联传送	Chéngzài ǒulián chuánsòng	Bearer association transport	BAT
承载容量信息单元	Chéngzài róngliàng xìnxī dānyuán	Bearer capacity information element	BCIE
承载通道连接	Chéngzài tōngdào liánjiē	Bearer channel connection	BCC
承载通路	Chéngzài tōnglù	Load-carrying channel	
承载通路连接	Chéngzài tōnglù liánjiē	Bearer channel connection	BCC
承载通路连接控制	Chéngzài tōnglù liánjiē kòngzhì	Bearer channel connection control	BCC
承载无关的呼叫控制	Chéngzài wúguānde hūjiào kòngzhì	Bearer-independent call control	BICC
承载信道	Chéngzài xìndào	Bearer channel	B-channel
承载业务	Chéngzài yèwù	Bearer service	BS
承载者标识码	Chéngzàizhě biāozhì mǎ	Carrier identification code	CIC
成帧	Chéngzhèng	Framing	
成帧接口	Chéngzhèng jiēkǒu	Framed interface	
成组路由选择指示符	Chéngzǔ lùyóu xuǎnzé zhǐshìfú	Collective routing indicator	CRI

成组信令	Chéngzǔ xìnlìng	*En-bloc* signaling	
沉埋隧道	Chénmái suìdào	Submerged tunnel	
沉砂	Chénshā	Sedimentation	
撤消	Chèxiāo	Undo (WP command)	
撤销	Chèxiāo	Revoke	
撤消	Chèxiāo	Withdrawal	
撤消操作	Chèxiāo cāozuò	Purge operation	
车载电台	Chēzài diàntái	Vehicle station	
迟绑定	Chí bǎngdìng	Late binding	
尺标	Chǐbiāo	Ruler	
赤道轨道	Chìdào guǐdào	Equatorial orbit (of a satellite)	
迟后写	Chíhòu xiě	Write-behind (in SAMBA)	
池化	Chíhuà	Pooling	
持久性	Chíjiǔxìng	Persistence	
持卡人校验信息	Chíkǎrén jiàoyàn xìnxī	Card holder verification	CHV
齿孔度数	Chǐkǒng dùshu	Perforation	
持续故障	Chíxù gùzhàng	Persistent fault	
持续时间	Chíxù shíjiān	Duration	
持续时间调制	Chíxù shíjiān tiáozhì	Duration time modulation	DTM
持续数据传输率	Chíxù shùjù chuánshū lǜ	Sustained data transfer rate	
持续信元速率	Chíxù xìnyuán sùlǜ	Sustainable cell rate	SCR
持续性	Chíxùxìng	Persistence	
迟延线	Chíyán xiàn	Delay line	
重拨	Chóng bō	Redial	
重采样	Chóng cǎiyàng	Resampling	
充油电缆	Chōng yóu diànlǎn	Oil-filled cable	OFC
充电	Chōngdiàn	Charge (as a battery)	
充电电感	Chōngdiàn diàngǎn	Charging inductor	
充电电路	Chōngdiàn diànlù	Charging circuit	
充电时间常数	Chōngdiàn shíjiān chángshù	Electric charge time constant (of a detector)	
充电效率	Chōngdiàn xiàolǜ	Charge efficiency	
充电终止电压	Chōngdiàn zhōngzhǐ diànyā	End-of charge voltage	
充电率	Chōngdiànlǜ	Charge rate	
重叠	Chóngdié	Overlay (GIS)	
重叠	Chóngdié	Overlap (in facsimile)	
重叠发送	Chóngdié fāsòng	Overlap sending	
重叠覆盖	Chóngdié fùgài	Overlay coverage	
重叠模式	Chóngdié móshì	Overlay model	OM
重叠信令	Chóngdié xìnlìng	Overlap signaling	
重定时	Chóngdìngshí	Retiming	
重定时器	Chóngdìngshíqì	Retimer	
重定向	Chóngdìngxiàng	Redirect, re-direction	
重定向服务器	Chóngdìngxiàng fúwùqì	Redirect server	RDS
重定向请求分组	Chóngdìngxiàng qǐngqiú fēnzǔ	Redirect request packet	RDR
重定向确认分组	Chóngdìngxiàng quèrèn fēnzǔ	Redirect confirm packet	RDC
虫毒	Chóngdú	Worm	

重发测试	Chóngfā cèshì	Repeat test	
重发超时	Chóngfā chāoshí	Repeat timeout	RTO
重发信号	Chóngfā xìnhào	Signal repetition	
重发周期	Chóngfā zhōuqī	Repetition cycle	
重放攻击	Chóngfàng gōngjī	Replay attack (IPsec)	
充分必要条件	Chōngfèn bìyào tiáojiàn	Necessary and sufficient condition	
重复拆线信号	Chóngfù chāixiàn xìnhào	Repeated clear forward signal	
重复动作损伤	Chóngfù dòngzuò sǔnshāng	Repetitive strain injury	RSI
重复接地	Chóngfù jiēdì	Iterative ground	
重复码	Chóngfù mǎ	Repetition code	
重复脉冲 Q 开关	Chóngfù màichōng Q kāiguān	Repetitively pulsed Q-switching	
重复信号	Chóngfù xìnhào	Repeated signal	
重复语句	Chóngfù yǔjù	Repeat statement	
重复指示	Chóngfù zhǐshì	Repeat indicator	
重复字段	Chóngfù zìduàn	Repeating fields	
重复字段组	Chóngfù zìduàn zǔ	Repeating field groups	
重复性	Chóngfù-xìng	Repeatability	
重构	Chónggòu	Re-factoring	
冲激脉冲	Chōngjī màichōng	Impulse	
冲击切性	Chōngjī qiēxing	Shock toughness	
冲击响应	Chōngjī xiǎngyìng	Impulse response	
重建	Chóngjiàn	Reconstruction, restoration	
重建图像	Chóngjiàn túxiàng	Reconstructed picture (video term)	
重建样值	Chóngjiàn yàngzhí	Reconstructed sample	
重建帧	Chóngjiàn zhèng	Reconstructed frame (video term)	
重连通图	Chóngliántōng tú	Biconnected graph	
充气电缆	Chōngqì diànlǎn	Gas filled cable	GFC
充气天线罩	Chōngqì tiānxiàn zhào	Inflation radome	
重试间隔	Chóngshì jiàngé	Retry interval	
虫蚀寻径	Chóngshí xúnjìng	Wormhole routing	
冲突分析	Chōngtū fēnxī	Conflict analysis	
冲突检测	Chōngtū jiǎncè	Conflict detection	
冲突解决策略	Chōngtū jiějué cèlüè	Conflict resolution strategy	
冲洗	Chōngxǐ	Flush, purge	
重新绑定状态	Chóngxīn bǎngdìng zhuàngtài	Rebinding state	
重新定义	Chóngxīn dìngyì	Override	
重新分配	Chóngxīn fēnpèi	Redistribution	
重新分页	Chóngxīn fēnyè	Re-paginate (WP command)	
重新格式化	Chóngxīn géshihuà	Reformatting	
重新规范化	Chóngxīn guīfànhuà	Renormalization	
重新开始	Chóngxīn kāishǐ	Resume	
重新开始拒绝	Chóngxīn kāishǐ jùjué	Resume reject	
重新开始证实	Chóngxīn kāishǐ zhèngshí	Resume acknowledge	
重新启动	Chóngxīn qǐdòng	Reboot	
重新启动键	Chóngxīn qǐdòng jiàn	Reset button/key	
重新组装	Chóngxīn zǔzhuāng	Reassembly	

重邮器	Chóngyóuqì	Remailer	
重整形	Chóngzhěngxíng	Reshaping	
重置	Chóngzhì	Resetting	
重置规程	Chóngzhì guīchéng	Reset procedure	
重置性	Chóngzhìxing	Resettability	
重组工程	Chóngzǔ gōngchéng	Re-engineering	
重做	Chóngzuò	Redo (WP command)	
抽组	Chōu zǔ	To mobilize, to select people to form groups	
臭虫	Chòuchóng	Bug	
稠密图	Chóumì tú	Dense graph	
抽取	Chōuqǔ	Extract	
抽头	Chōutóu	Tap (cryptology)	
抽象	Chōuxiàng	Abstraction	
抽象测试法	Chōuxiàng cèshì fǎ	Abstract test method	ATM
抽象测试模块	Chōuxiàng cèshì mókuài	Abstract test module	
抽象测试实例	Chōuxiàng cèshì shílì	Abstract test case	
抽象测试套	Chōuxiàng cèshì tào	Abstract test suite	ATS
抽象测试项	Chōuxiàng cèshì xiàng	Abstract test case	
抽象窗口工具库	Chōuxiàng chuāngkǒu gōngjù kù	Abstract Windows Toolkit	
抽象服务原语	Chōuxiàng fúwù yuányǔ	Abstract service primitive	ASP
抽象级	Chōuxiàng jí	Abstraction level	
抽象基类	Chōuxiàng jī lèi	Abstract base class	ABC
抽象句表记法	Chōuxiàng jùbiǎo jìfǎ	Abstract syntax notation	ASN
抽象句法	Chōuxiàng jùfǎ	Abstract syntax	
抽象句法表示法 1	Chōuxiàng jùfǎ biǎoshì fǎ 1	Abstract syntax notation 1	ASN.1
抽象句法符号	Chōuxiàng jùfǎ fúhào	Abstract syntax notation	ASN
抽象类	Chōuxiàng lèi	Abstract class	
抽象逻辑结构图	Chōuxiàng luójí jiégòutú	Abstract logic structure diagram	
抽象数据类型	Chōuxiàng shùjù lèixíng	Abstract data type	
抽象物	Chōuxiàng wù	Abstraction	
抽象性	Chōuxiàng xìng	Abstraction	
抽象业务原语	Chōuxiàng yèwù yuányǔ	Abstract service primitive	ASP
抽象语法编码	Chōuxiàng yǔfǎ biānmǎ	Abstract syntax notation	ASN
抽象语法标记	Chōuxiàng yǔfǎ biāoji	Abstract syntax notation	ASN
抽象语法定义	Chōuxiàng yǔfǎ dìngyì	Abstract syntax notation	ASN
抽象语法记法	Chōuxiàng yǔfǎ jìfǎ	Abstract syntax notation	ASN
抽样	Chōuyàng	Sample, specimen	
抽样率	Chōuyàng lǜ	Sampling rate	
除操作	Chú cāozuò	Quotient operator	
出接口	Chū jiēkǒu	Outgoing interface	oif
除至归属公共陆地移动通信网国家外,闭锁国际出呼叫	Chú zhì guīshǔ gōnggòng lùdì yídòng tōngxìnwǎng guójiā wài, bìsuǒ guójì chū hūjiào	Barring of outgoing international calls except those directed to the home PLMN country	BOIC-exHC
除至归属 PLMN 国家外,闭锁国际出呼叫	Chú zhì guīshǔ PLMN guójiā wài, bìsuǒ guójì chū hūjiào	Barring of outgoing international calls except those directed to the home PLMN country	BOIC-exHC

除直接到归属 PLMN 国家外的呼叫外,闭锁国际出呼叫	Chú zhíjiē dào guīshǔ PLMN guójiā wàide hūjiào wài, bìsuǒ guójì chū hūjiào	Barring of outgoing international calls except those directed towards the home PLMN country	BOIC-exHC
串并行变换	Chuàn bìngxíng biànhuàn	Serial-parallel conversion	
串并行转换器	Chuàn bìngxíng zhuǎnhuànqì	Serial-to-parallel converter, deserializer	
传地址	Chuán dìzhǐ	Pass by reference	
穿金属管敷设	Chuān jīnshǔguǎn fūshè	Run in metallic tubing	MT
穿蛇皮管敷设	Chuān shépíguǎn fūshè	Run in flexible metal conduit	FMC
穿硬聚乙烯管敷设	Chuān yìng jùyǐxī guǎn fūshè	Run in rigid PVC conduit	PC
穿阻燃半硬聚乙烯管敷设	Chuān zǔrán bànyìng jùyǐxī guǎn fūshè	Run in flame-retardant semi-rigid PVC conduit	FPC
穿/并变换	Chuān/bìng biànhuàn	Serial/parallel conversion	S/P
船边交货	Chuánbiān jiāohuò	Free alongside ship	
串并变换器	Chuàn-bìng biànhuànqì	Serial to parallel converter	
传播	Chuánbō	Transmission, propagation	
传播常数	Chuánbō chángshù	Propagation constant	
船舶电台	Chuánbó diàntái	Ship station	
船舶地球站	Chuánbó dìqiúzhàn	Ship earth station	
传播方向	Chuánbō fāngxiàng	Direction of propagation	
传播模	Chuánbō mó	Mode of propagation (in a transmission line)	
传播时间	Chuánbō shíjiān	Propagation time	
传播时延	Chuánbō shíyán	Propagation delay	
传播误差	Chuánbō wùchā	Propagation error	
传播信道	Chuánbō xìndào	Propagation channel	
传播性能	Chuánbō xìngnéng	Propagation performance	
传播系数	Chuánbō xìshù	Propagation coefficient	
传播延迟	Chuánbō yánchí	Propagation delay	
船舶移动业务	Chuánbó yídòng yèwù	Ship movement service	
船舶应急发信机	Chuánbó yìngjí fāxìnjī	Ship's emergency transmitter	
传达	Chuándá	Transmission	
传达系数	Chuándá xìshù	Transfer function	
串道	Chuàndào	Cross-talk (IPsec)	
传导发射	Chuándǎo fāshè	Conducted emission (in Mil-Std-461E)	
传导干扰	Chuándǎo gānrǎo	Conducted interference	
传导敏感度	Chuándǎo mǐngǎndù	Conducted susceptibility	
传导杂散发射	Chuándǎo zásǎn fāshè	Conducted spurious emission	
传递闭包	Chuándì bìbāo	Transitive closure	
传递方式	Chuándì fāngshì	Transfer mode	
传递函数	Chuándì hánshù	Transfer function	
传递能力	Chuándì nénglì	Bearer capability	BC
传递时间	Chuándì shíjiān	Transfer time	
传递顺序	Chuándì shùnxù	Pass order	
传感器	Chuángǎnqì	Sensor	
传感器	Chuángǎnqì	Transducer	
传感器定标	Chuángǎnqì dìngbiāo	Sensor calibration	
传感器分辨率	Chuángǎnqì fēnbiànlǜ	Sensor resolution	
传感器失衡	Chuángǎnqì shīhéng	Detector imbalance	

窗格式透镜	Chuānggé-shì tòujìng	Egg crate lens	
窗格式透镜	Chuānggé-shì tòujìng	Multi-cellular lens	
窗户,图标,菜单,光标	Chuānghu, túbiāo, càidān, guāngbiāo	Windows, icons, menu and cursor	WIMC
窗户,图标,菜单,光标	Chuānghu, túbiāo, càidān, guāngbiāo	Windows, icons, menu and pointer	WIMP
创建	Chuàngjiàn	Create, creation	
创建 DOS 主分区	Chuàngjiàn DOS zhǔ fēnqū	Create primary DOS partition	
创建扩展 DOS 分区	Chuàngjiàn kuòzhǎn DOS fēnqū	Create extended DOS partition	
窗口	Chuāngkǒu	Window	
窗口尺寸	Chuāngkǒu chǐcùn	Windows size	
窗口过程	Chuāngkǒu guòchéng	Window procedure	
窗口函数	Chuāngkǒu hánshù	Window function	
窗口界面	Chuāngkǒu jièmiàn	Forms interface	
闯入	Chuǎngrù	Crack (break into, hack into)	
窗体	Chuāngtǐ	Form	
创新科技	Chuàngxīn kējì	Creative Technology (US company)	
串行	Chuànháng	Serial	
串行 ATA	Chuànháng ATA	Serial ATA (asynchronous terminal adapter)	SATA
串行并行转换电路	Chuànháng bìngxíng zhuǎnhuàn diànlù	SERializing/DESerializing circuitry	SERDES
串行存在检查	Chuànháng cúnzài jiǎnchá	Serial presence detect	SPD
串行计算	Chuànháng jìsuàn	Sequential computing	
串行码	Chuànháng mǎ	Serial code	
串行时标发送	Chuànháng shíbiāo fāsòng	Serial clock transmit	SCT
串行时钟外部传输	Chuànháng shízhōng wàibù chuánshū	Serial clock transmit external	SCTE
串行数据传输	Chuànháng shùjù chuánshū	Serial data transmission	SDT
串行数据总线	Chuànháng shùjù zǒngxiàn	Serial data trunk	
串行输入输出	Chuànháng shūrù shūchū	Serial input/output	SIO
串行输入输出处理器	Chuànháng shūrù shūchū chǔlǐqì	Serial input output handler	SIOH
串行隧道	Chuànháng suìdào	Serial tunnel	STUN
串行通信控制器	Chuànháng tōngxìn kòngzhìqì	Serial communication controller	SCC
串行通信总线	Chuànháng tōngxìn zǒngxiàn	Serial telecommunications Bus	ST-BUS
串行外围接口	Chuànháng wàiwéi jiēkǒu	Serial peripheral interface	SPI
串行维特比解码器	Chuànháng wéi-tè-bǐ jiěmǎqì	Serial Viterbi decoder	SVD
串行线路接口协议	Chuànháng xiànlù jiēkǒu xiéyì	Serial line interface protocol	SLIP
串行线路网际协议	Chuànháng xiànlù wǎngjì xiéyì	Serial line Internet protocol	SLIP
串行细胞自动机	Chuànháng xìbāo zìdòngjī	Sequential cellular automata (cryptology)	SCA
串行运算	Chuànháng yùnsuàn	Serial arithmetic	
串行自动呼叫	Chuànháng zìdòng hūjiào	Serial automatic calling	
串行化图	Chuànhánghuà tú	Serialization graph	SG
传号反转码	Chuánhào fǎnzhuǎn mǎ	Coded mark inversion	CMI
传号交替变换码	Chuánhào jiāotì biànhuàn mǎ	Alternate mark inversion	AMI
传号状态	Chuánhào zhuàngtài	Mark condition (in Morse code)	
串话	Chuànhuà	Crosstalk	
传换控制	Chuánhuàn kòngzhì	Transfer control	
串级	Chuànjí	Cascade	
穿孔工具	Chuānkǒng gōngjù	Punch tool	
串口逻辑	Chuànkǒu luójí	Serial port logic	

串联	Chuànlián	Concatenation	
串联号码	Chuànlián hàomǎ	Serial number	SNR
串联加载天线	Chuànlián jiāzài tiānxiàn	Series-loaded antenna	
串联连接监视	Chuànlián liánjiē jiānshì	Tandem connection monitor	TCM
串联连接开销	Chuànlián liánjiē kāixiao	Tandem connection overhead	TCOH
串联连接远端缺陷指示	Chuànlián liánjiē yuǎnduān quēxiàn zhǐshì	Tandem connection remote defect indicator	TC-RDI
串联连接远端误差指示	Chuànlián liánjiē yuǎnduān wùchā zhǐshì	Tandem connection remote error indicator	TC-REI
串联连接终端设备	Chuànlián liánjiē zhōngduān shèbèi	Tandem connection terminating element	TCTE
串联连接踪迹	Chuànlián liánjiē zōngjī	Tandem connection trace	TCT
串列网络	Chuànliè wǎngluò	Bus network	
串流	Chuànliú	Streaming	
串扰	Chuànrǎo	Crosstalk, directivity	
串扰	Chuànrǎo	Interference	
串扰隔离度	Chuànrǎo gélídù	Crosstalk isolation	
船上交货	Chuánshàng jiāohuò	Delivered ex-ship	DES
船上交货	Chuánshàng jiāohuò	Free on board	FOB
船上通信电台	Chuánshàng tōngxìn diàntái	On-board communication station (on a ship)	
传声器	Chuánshēngqì	Microphone	
传声器噪声	Chuánshēngqì zàoshēng	Microphone noise	
传输	Chuánshū	Transmission, transport	
传输保密	Chuánshū bǎomì	Transmission security	
传输波	Chuánshū bō	Transmitted wave (in a transmission line)	
传输层安全	Chuánshū céng ānquán	Transport layer security	TLS
传输层安全协议	Chuánshū céng ānquán xiéyì	Transmission layer security protocol	TSP
传输层安全性	Chuánshū céng ānquánxìng	Transport layer security	TLS
传输层协议	Chuánshū céng xiéyì	Transfer layer protocol	TP
传输层协议	Chuánshū céng xiéyì	Transport layer protocol (in ISO's OSI)	TP
传输层协议	Chuánshū céng xiéyì	Transport layer protocol	
传输带宽滤波器	Chuánshū dàikuān lǜbōqì	Transmit band pass filter	TBPF
传输服务存取点	Chuánshū fúwù cúnqǔdiǎn	Transmission service access point	TCAP
传输服务存取点	Chuánshū fúwù cúnqǔdiǎn	Transport service access point	TSAP
传输合并器	Chuánshū hébìngqì	Transmit combiner assembly	TCOA
传输恢复	Chuánshū huīfù	Transmission restoration	
传输恢复功能	Chuánshū huīfù gōngnéng	Transmission restoration function	
传输恢复控制功能	Chuánshū huīfù kòngzhì gōngnéng	Transmission restoration control function	
传输恢复设备	Chuánshū huīfù shèbèi	Transmission restoration equipment	
传输恢复系统	Chuánshū huīfù xìtǒng	Transmission restoration system	
传输会聚	Chuánshū huìjù	Transmission convergence	TC
传输会聚子层	Chuánshū huìjù zicéng	Transmission convergence sub-layer	TC
传输接口转换器	Chuánshū jiēkǒu zhuǎnhuànqì	Transmission interface converter	XIC
传输结束	Chuánshū jiéshù	End of transmission	EOT
传输结束断开	Chuánshū jiéshù duànkāi	Disconnect end of transmission	DEOT
传输结束字符	Chuánshū jiéshù zìfú	End of transmission character	
传输集群	Chuánshū jíqún	Transmission trunking	
传输矩阵	Chuánshū jǔzhèn	Transfer matrix	

传输控制规程	Chuánshū kòngzhì guīchéng	Transmission control protocol	TCP
传输控制规约/网间规约	Chuánshū kòngzhì guīyuē/wǎng jiān guīyuē	Transmission control protocol/ Internet protocol	TCP/IP
传输控制协议	Chuánshū kòngzhì xiéyì	Transmission control protocol	TCP
传输控制协议/互联网协议	Chuánshū kòngzhì xiéyì/hùliánwǎng xiéyì	Transport control protocol/Internet protocol	TCP/IP
传输控制协议/互通协议	Chuánshū kòngzhì xiéyì/hùtōng xiéyì	Transmission control protocol/Interwork protocol	TCP/IP
传输控制协议/网间协议	Chuánshū kòngzhì xiéyì/wǎng- jiān xiéyì	Transmission control protocol/Inter-network protocol	TCP/IP
传输控制协议/网际互连协议	Chuánshū kòngzhì xiéyì/wǎngjì hùlián xiéyì	Transmission control protocol/Internet protocol	TCP/IP
传输控制协议/网际协议	Chuánshū kòngzhì xiéyì/wǎngjì xiéyì	Transmission control protocol/Internet protocol	TCP/IP
传输控制字符	Chuánshū kòngzhì zìfú	Transmission control characters	TCC
传输链路	Chuánshū liànlù	Transmission link	
传输邻接	Chuánshū línjiē	Transmission contiguity	
传输路由	Chuánshū lùyóu	Transmission route	
传输路由分集	Chuánshū lùyóu fēnjí	Transmission route diversity	
传输媒介请求	Chuánshū méijiè qǐngqiú	Transmission medium requirement	TMR
传输媒体	Chuánshū méitǐ	Transmission medium	
传输媒体要求	Chuánshū méitǐ yāoqiú	Transmission medium requirement	
传输媒质层	Chuánshū méizhì céng	Transmission media layer (STM term)	
传输能力	Chuánshū nénglì	Transmission capability	
传输频率特性	Chuánshū pínlǜ tèxìng	Transmission frequency characteristic	TFCC
传输前端架	Chuánshū qiánduānjià	Transmit front end shelf	TFES
传输设备	Chuánshū shèbèi	Transmission equipment	TE
传输时间间隔	Chuánshū shíjiān jiàngé	Transmission time interval	TTI
传输适配层接口	Chuánshū shìpèicéng jiēkǒu	Transport adapter layer interface	TALI
传输损耗	Chuánshū sǔnhào	Transmission loss	
传输通道	Chuánshū tōngdào	Transmission path	
传输通道级	Chuánshū tōngdào jí	Transmission path level	
传输通路	Chuánshū tōnglù	Transmission path	TP
传输通路	Chuánshū tōnglù	Transmission channel	
传输通路端点	Chuánshū tōnglù duāndiǎn	Transmission path endpoint	TPE
传输通路级	Chuánshū tōnglù jí	Transmission path level	
传输网	Chuánshū wǎng	Transmission network	
传输网络选择	Chuánshū wǎngluò xuǎnzé	Transmission network selection	
传输线	Chuánshū xiàn	Transmission line	
传输协议数据单元	Chuánshū xiéyì shùjù dānyuán	Transfer protocol data unit	TPDU
传输协议特定传输汇聚层	Chuánshū xiéyì tèdìng chuánshū huìjù céng	Transmission protocol-specific TC layer	TPS-TC
传输信道	Chuánshū xìndào	Transmission channel	
传输信道	Chuánshū xìndào	Transport channel	
传输性能	Chuánshū xìngnéng	Transmission performance	
传输性能评定值	Chuánshū xìngnéng píngdìng zhí	Transmission performance rating	
传输系数	Chuánshū xìshù	Transfer coefficient	
传输系统的监视与控制	Chuánshū xìtǒngde jiānshì yǔ kòngzhì	Surveillance and control of transmission system	SCOTS
传输帧自适应	Chuánshū zhèng zìshìyìng	Transmission frame adaptation	
传输线适配器	Chuánshūxiàn shìpèiqì	Transmission line adapter	
传送	Chuánsòng	Transfer	

传送	Chuánsòng	Transport	
传送层	Chuánsòng céng	Transport layer	TL
传送处理功能	Chuánsòng chǔlǐ gōngnéng	Transport processing function	
传送电路仿真	Chuánsòng diànlù fǎngzhēn	Circuit emulation over transport	CEOT
传送地址	Chuánsòng dìzhǐ	Transport address	
传送抖动	Chuánsòng dǒudòng	Transferred jitter	
传送服务接入点	Chuánsòng fúwù jiērù diǎn	Transport service access point	TSAP
传送格式	Chuánsòng géshi	Transport format	TF
传送格式集	Chuánsòng géshi jí	Transport format set	TFS
传送格式指示器	Chuánsòng géshi zhǐshìqì	Transport format indicator	TFI
传送格式组合	Chuánsòng géshi zǔhé	Transport format combination	TFC
传送格式组合集	Chuánsòng géshi zǔhé jí	Transport format combination set	TFCS
传送格式组合指示器	Chuánsòng géshi zǔhé zhǐshìqì	Transport format combination indicator	TFCI
传送功能	Chuánsòng gōngnéng	Transfer function	TF
传送功能	Chuánsòng gōngnéng	Transport function	TF
传送功能-运行系统	Chuánsòng gōngnéng--yùnxíng xìtǒng	Transfer function-operating system	TF-OS
传送功能-运行系统功能	Chuánsòng gōngnéng--yùnxíng xìtǒng gōngnéng	Transfer function-operating system function	TF-OSF
传送进程	Chuánsòng jìnchéng	Transmittal	
传送句法	Chuánsòng jùfǎ	Transfer syntax	
传送控制块	Chuánsòng kòngzhì kuài	Transport control block	TCB
传送控制协议	Chuánsòng kòngzhì xiéyì	Transport control protocol	TCP
传送媒体	Chuánsòng méitǐ	Transport media	TM
传送媒体综合框架	Chuánsòng méitǐ zōnghé kuàngjià	Delivery media integrated framework	DMIF
传送模式	Chuánsòng móshì	Transfer mode	
传送能力	Chuánsòng nénglì	Transfer capability	
传送平面	Chuánsòng píngmiàn	Transport plane	TP
传送实体	Chuánsòng shítǐ	Transport entity	
传送顺序号	Chuánsòng shùnxù hào	Transport serial number	TSN
传送通道	Chuánsòng tōngdào	Transport path	TP
传送网	Chuánsòng wǎng	Transport network	
传送网络层	Chuánsòng wǎngluò céng	Transport network layer	
传送协议数据单元	Chuánsòng xiéyì shùjù dānyuán	Transport protocol data unit	TPDU
传送信道	Chuánsòng xìndào	Transport channel	TrCH
传送信令网关	Chuánsòng xìnlìng wǎngguān	Transport signaling gateway	T-SGW
传送信息	Chuánsòng xìnxī	Pass-along message (ISUP message)	PAM
传送系统	Chuánsòng xìtǒng	Transfer system	
传送邮件	Chuánsòng yóujiàn	Send e-mail (WP command)	
传送增频变频器板	Chuánsòng zēngpín biànpínqì bǎn	Transmit up-converter board	TUCB
传送终端功能	Chuánsòng zhōngduān gōngnéng	Transport terminal function	TTF
传送后的重复帧	Chuánsòng-hòude chóngfù zhèng	Delivered duplicate frame	
传送后的出错帧	Chuánsòng-hòude chūcuò zhèng	Delivered errored frame	
传送后的失序帧	Chuánsòng-hòude shīxù zhèng	Delivered out-of-sequence frame	
传统进化类算法	Chuántǒng jìnhuà lèi suànfǎ	Conventional evolutionary algorithm	CEA
穿通调制	Chuāntōng tiáozhì	Punch-through modulation	PTM
穿通因数	Chuāntōng yīnshù	Punch-through factor	PTF
穿透损耗	Chuāntòu sǔnhào	Penetration loss	

串型	Chuànxíng	Streaming mode	
串形线路接口协议	Chuànxíng xiànlù jiēkǒu xiéyì	Serial line interface protocol (IETF usage)	SLIP
串音参考当量	Chuànyīn cānkǎo dāngliàng	Crosstalk reference equivalent	
船用收音机	Chuányòng shōuyīnjī	Ship radio	
穿越	Chuānyuè	Pass through, cut across	
传载	Chuánzài	Posting	
传真	Chuánzhēn	Facsimile	FAX
传真分组装拆设施	Chuánzhēn fēnzǔ zhuāngchāi shèshī	Facsimile packet assembly/disassembly	FPAD
传真适配器	Chuánzhēn shìpèiqì	Fax adaptor	FA
传真通信	Chuánzhēn tōngxìn	Facsimile communication	CZ
传真业务	Chuánzhēn yèwù	Facsimile service	
传真终端	Chuánzhēn zhōngduān	Facsimile terminal; facsimile machine	
出版订购者	Chūbǎn dìnggòuzhě	Publishing subscriber (in SQL Server)	
初充电	Chūchōngdiàn	Initial charge (of a battery)	
储存寿命	Chǔcún shòumìng	Storage life	
出错信息	Chūcuò xìnxī	Error message	
触电电流	Chùdiàn diànliú	Shock current	
初动	Chūdòng	First motion	
出度	Chūdù	Outdegree	
除法	Chúfǎ	Division method	
触发电路	Chùfā diànlù	Trigger circuit	
触发电路	Chùfā diànlù	Trigger circuit	
触发 DP 请求	Chùfā DP qǐngqiú	Trigger DP-request	TDP-R
触发 DP 通知	Chùfā DP tōngzhī	Trigger DP-notification	TDP-N
触发更新	Chùfā gēngxīn	Triggered update	
触发检测点 - 请求	Chùfā jiǎncè diǎn-qǐngqiú	Trigger detection point-request	TDP-R
触发检测点 - 通知	Chùfā jiǎncè diǎn-tōngzhī	Trigger detection point-notification	TDP-N
触发检出点	Chùfā jiǎnchū diǎn	Trigger detection point	TDP
触发检出点——请求	Chùfā jiǎnchū diǎn-qǐngqiú	Trigger detection point-request	TDP-R
触发检出点——通知	Chùfā jiǎnchū diǎn-tōngzhī	Trigger detection point-notification	TDP-N
触发事务	Chùfā shìwù	Triggering transaction	
触发器	Chùfāqì	Flip-flop	FF
触发器	Chùfāqì	Trigger (for database)	
触发器模型	Chùfāqì móxíng	Trigger model	
初呼振铃	Chūhū zhènlíng	First ringing	
垂射天线阵	Chuíshè tiānxiànzhèn	Broadside array antenna	BAA
垂直表面激光发射器	Chuízhí biǎomiàn jīguāng fāshèqì	Vertical cavity surface emitting laser	VCSEL
垂直成分	Chuízhí chéngfèn	Vertical component	
垂直单极子	Chuízhí dānjízi	Vertical monopole, vertical unipole (antenna)	
垂直电缆	Chuízhí diànlǎn	Backbone cable (in building)	BC
垂直方向性图	Chuízhí fāngxiàngxìng tú	Vertical directivity pattern	
垂直分区	Chuízhí fēnqū	Vertical partitioning	
垂直共振腔面射型	Chuízhí gòngzhènqiāng miàn shè xíng	Vertical cavity surface emitting laser diode	VCSEL
垂直基准	Chuízhí jīzhǔn	Vertical datum	
垂直空白间隔	Chuízhí kòngbái jiàngé	Vertical blanking interval	VBI
垂直空白间隙	Chuízhí kòngbái jiànxì	Vertical blanking interval (video)	VBI

垂直流	Chuízhí liú	Vertical flow	
垂直区间数据传输	Chuízhí qūjiān shùjù chuánshū	Vertical interval data transmission	VIDT
垂直冗余检验	Chuízhí rǒngyú jiǎnyàn	Vertical redundancy check	VRC
垂直扫描频率	Chuízhí sǎomiáo pínlǜ	Vertical scan rate	
垂直扫描频率	Chuízhí sǎomiáo pínlǜ	Vertical refresh rate (video)	VRR
垂直筛选	Chuízhí shāixuǎn	Vertical filtering	
垂直输送	Chuízhí shūsòng	Vertical transport	
垂直探测法	Chuízhí tàncèfǎ	Vertical sounding	
垂直调变	Chuízhí tiáo biàn	Vertical interpolation	
垂直压缩	Chuízhí yāsuō	Vertical aggregation	
垂直移动	Chuízhí yídòng	Vertical movement	
垂直支承力	Chuízhí zhīchénglì	Vertical bearing capacity	
垂直子系统	Chuízhí zi xìtǒng	Riser backbone sub-system	RBS
初级方向图	Chūjí fāngxiàngtú	Primary pattern	
初级分布线路	Chūjí fēnbù xiànlù	Primary distribution link	
初级辐射器	Chūjí fúshèqì	Primary radiator	
初级拓扑	Chūjí tuòpū	Preliminary topology	
出界包处理	Chūjiè bāo chǔlǐ	Outbound packet processing (IPsec)	
出境控制信道	Chūjìng kòngzhì xìndào	Outbound control channel	OCC
出局初级接线器架	Chūjú chūjí jiēxiànqì jià	Outgoing primary switch frame	OGPSWF
出局电路群	Chūjú diànlù qún	Outgoing circuit group	
出局发码器	Chūjú fāmǎqì	Outgoing sender	OS
出局发送链路	Chūjú fāsòng liànlù	Outgoing sending link	OSL
出局直接拨号	Chūjú zhíjiē bōhào	Direct outward dialing	DOD
出口	Chūkǒu	Outlet	
除了指向本地 PLMN 国家之外的 BOIC	Chúle zhǐxiàng běndì PLMN guójiā zhīwàide BOIC	BOIC except those directed to the home PLMN country	BOIC-exHC
处理	Chǔlǐ	Process (verb), processing (noun)	
出力	Chūlì	Power, exertion (power grid term)	
处理单元	Chǔlǐ dānyuán	Processing unit	
处理接入信令	Chǔlǐ jiērù xìnlìng	Process access signaling	
处理摸块	Chǔlǐ mōkuài	Process module	
处理 USSD 请求	Chǔlǐ USSD qǐngqiú	Process unstructured SS data request	PSSR
处理增益	Chǔlǐ zēngyì	Processing gain	PG
处理机	Chǔlǐjī	Processor	
处理机控制存储存取	Chǔlǐjī kòngzhì cúnchǔ cúnqǔ	Processor controlled memory access	PCMA
处理机控制的数字交换机	Chǔlǐjī kòngzhìde shùzì jiāohuànjī	Processor-controlled digital exchange	PDX
处理机间共用总线	Chǔlǐjī-jiān gòngyòng zǒngxiàn	Inter-processor common bus	IPBUS
处理器	Chǔlǐqì	Handler	
处理器承载器	Chǔlǐqì chéngzàiqì	Processor loader	PL
处理器和测试设备接口	Chǔlǐqì hé cèshì shèbèi jiēkǒu	Processor and test equipment interface	PTEI
处理器内部通信接口	Chǔlǐqì nèibù tōngxìn jiēkǒu	Processor inter-communication interface	PICI
处理器通信控制集成板	Chǔlǐqì tōngxìn kòngzhì jíchéngbǎn	Processor communication control board assembly	PCCA
处理器信息 ROM	Chǔlǐqì xìnxī ROM	Processor information ROM	PIROM
处理器序列号	Chǔlǐqì xù lièhào	Processor serial number	PSN
处理器装载数据	Chǔlǐqì zhuāngzài shùjù	Processor load data	PLD

处理器间通信	Chǔlǐqì-jiān tōngxìn	Inter-processor communication	IPC
储留函数法	Chǔliú hánshù fǎ	Storage function method	
储留系数	Chǔliú xìshù	Coefficient of storage	
纯噪声干扰	Chún zàoshēng gānrǎo	Pure-noise jamming	
唇式传声器	Chúnshì chuánshēngqì	Lip microphone	
除去	Chúqù	Detach	
出入控制系统	Chūrù kòngzhì xìtǒng	Access control system	ACS
出入口	Chūrùkǒu	Gateway	
出射角	Chūshè jiǎo	Angle of emergence	
出射/入射角	Chūshè/rùshè jiǎo	Exit/entrance angle	
初始程序输入器	Chūshǐ chéngxù shūrùqì	Initial program loader	IPL
初始程序装入程序	Chūshǐ chéngxù zhuāngrù chéngxù	Initial program loader	IPL
初始点	Chūshǐ diǎn	Initial point	
初始地址消息	Chūshǐ dìzhǐ xiāoxi	Initial address message	IAM
初始地址信息	Chūshǐ dìzhǐ xìnxī	Initial address information	
初始功率	Chūshǐ gōnglǜ	Initialization power	INIT_PWR
初始结点	Chūshǐ jiédiǎn	Initial node	
初始密钥	Chūshǐ mìyào	Primary key (cryptography)	
初始设备制造厂	Chūshǐ shèbèi zhìzàochǎng	Original equipment manufacturer	OEM
初始条件	Chūshǐ tiáojiàn	Initial condition	
初始位置	Chūshǐ wèizhì	Home position	
初始向量	Chūshǐ xiàngliàng	Initial vector	IV
初始信号单元	Chūshǐ xìnhào dānyuán	Initial signal unit	ISU
初始域标识	Chūshǐ yù biāozhì	Initial domain identifier	IDI
初始域部分	Chūshǐ yù bùfen	Initial domain part	IDP
初始值列表	Chūshǐ zhí lièbiǎo	Initialization list	
初始化	Chūshǐhuà	Initialize	INIT
初始化	Chūshǐhuà	Initialization	
初始化地址消息	Chūshǐhuà dìzhǐ xiāoxi	Initialize address message	
初始化和维护	Chūshǐhuà hé wéihù	Initialization and maintenance	BIM
初始化快照	Chūshǐhuà kuàizhào	Initialization snapshot	
初始化列表	Chūshǐhuà lièbiǎo	Initialization list	
初始化媒体	Chūshǐhuà méitǐ	Initialization media	
初始化请求	Chūshǐhuà qǐngqiú	Request for initialization	RQI
初始化图形交换规程	Chūshǐhuà túxíng jiāohuàn guīchéng	Initial graphics exchange specification	IGES
初始化文件	Chūshǐhuà wénjiàn	Initialization file; .INI file	
初始者	Chūshǐzhě	Initiator	
触头	Chùtóu	Contact head	
出现电位	Chūxiàn diànwèi	Appearance potential	
初学者通用符号指令码	Chūxuézhě tōngyòng fúhào zhǐlìng mǎ	Beginner's All-purpose Symbolic Instruction Code	BASIC
除震台	Chúzhèntái	Vibration isolator	
出中继	Chūzhōngjì	Outgoing trunk	OGT
磁波荡器	Cí bōdàngqì	Wiggler (mm wave device)	
磁测井仪	Cí cèjǐngyí	Magnetic logger	
词处理软件	Cí chǔlǐ ruǎnjiàn	Word processing software	WP
磁光调变器	Cí guāng tiáobiànqì	Magneto-optic modulator	

磁激电仪	Cí jī diàn yí	Magnetic induced polarization instrument	
磁聚焦	Cí jùjiāo	Magnetic focus	
磁脉冲调制器	Cí màichōng tiáozhìqì	Magnetic pulse modulator	
磁偏转	Cí piānzhuǎn	Magnetic deflection	
磁偏转管	Cí piānzhuǎn guǎn	Magnetic deflection CRT	
磁屏蔽	Cí píngbì	Magnetic shield	
次群速率接入	Cì qún sùlǜ jiērù	Primary rate of access	
磁调滤波器	Cí tiáo lǜbōqì	Magnetic tuning filter	
磁调制开关	Cí tiáozhì kāiguān	Magnetic modulating switch	
磁异常	Cí yìcháng	Magnetic anomaly	
磁场辐射发射	Cíchǎng fúshè fāshè	Magnetic field radiated emissions (Mil-Std-461E, RE101)	
磁场辐射敏感度	Cíchǎng fúshè mǐngǎndù	Magnetic field radiated susceptibility (Mil-Std-461E, RS101)	
磁场感应器	Cíchǎng gǎnyìngqì	Magnetic sensors	MS
磁场屏蔽室	Cíchǎng píngbìshì	Magnetically shielded room	MSR
磁场计	Cíchǎngjì	Magnetic field meter	
磁带	Cídài	Magnetic tape	
磁带备份	Cídài bèifèn	Tape backup	
磁带驱动器	Cídài qūdòngqì	Tape drive	
词典语言	Cídiǎn yǔyán	Lexical language	
词法空间	Cífǎ kōngjiān	Lexical space	
磁鼓	Cígǔ	Magnetic drum	M/D
磁化矢量	Cíhuà shǐliàng	Magnetization vector	
次级分布线路	Cìjí fēnbù xiànlù	Secondary distribution link	
瓷夹敷设	Cíjiā fūshè	Secured by porcelain clip	PL
磁矩	Cíjǔ	Magnetic moment	M
磁卡阅读机	Cíkǎ yuèdújī	Magnetic card reader	
磁控管灯丝电压控制电路	Cíkòngguǎn dēngsī diànyā kòngzhì diànlù	Magnetron filament voltage controlling circuit	
磁力变化	Cílì biànhuà	Magnetic changes	
磁盘	Cípán	Magnetic disk	
磁盘操作系统	Cípán cāozuò xìtǒng	Disk operating system	DOS
磁盘存储器	Cípán cúnchǔqì	Disk storage device	DSD
磁盘存贮	Cípán cúnzhù	Disk storage	
磁盘单元	Cípán dānyuán	Disk unit	DKU
磁盘单元后面板	Cípán dānyuán hòumian bǎn	Disk unit back panel	DKBP
磁盘调度算法	Cípán diàodù suànfǎ	Disk dispatch arithmetic	
磁盘唤醒	Cípán huànxǐng	Suspend to disk	STD
磁盘镜像	Cípán jìngxiàng	Disk mirroring	
磁盘空间	Cípán kōngjiān	Disk space	
磁盘控制软件	Cípán kòngzhì ruǎnjiàn	DiscWizard	
磁盘块再分配	Cípán kuài zàifēnpèi	Disk block sub-allocation	
磁盘束	Cípán shù	Just a bunch of disks	JBOD
磁盘条纹	Cípán tiáowén	Striping (RAID technology)	
磁盘映射	Cípán yìngshè	Disk mapping	
磁盘自检程序	Cípán zìjiǎn chéngxù	Drive self test	DST
瓷瓶敷设	Cípíng fūshè	Wiring on porcelain knob	K

磁区	Cíqū	Cluster	
磁条	Cítiáo	Magnetic stripes	
磁铁	Cítiě	Magnet	
磁通传感器	Cítōng chuángǎnqì	Magnetic flux transducer/sensor	
磁头	Cítóu	Magnetic head	
磁头集合	Cítóu jíhé	Head disk assembly	HDA
磁心	Cíxīn	Magnetic core	
磁心存储器	Cíxīn cúnchǔqì	Core memory	
磁芯天线	Cíxīn tiānxiàn	Magnetic core antenna	
次要告警	Cìyào gàojǐng	Minor alarm	
磁针偏差	Cízhēn piānchā	Magnetic declination	
磁滞	Cízhì	Magnetic hysteresis	
瓷珠敷设	Cízhū fūshè	Wiring on porcelain insulator	K
磁阻磁头	Cízǔ cítóu	Magneto-resistive head	
词组简码输入	Cízǔ jiǎnmǎ shūrù	Shorthand	
CLP 为 0 和 1 的总的信元丢失率	CLP wéi 0 hé 1de zǒngde xìnyuán diūshī lǜ	Cell loss rate (CLR) for the aggregate cell stream containing both cell loss priority (CLP)=0 and CLP=1 cells	CLR0+1
CLP 为 0 信元的信元丢失率	CLP wéi 0 xìnyuánde xìnyuán diūshī lǜ	Cell loss rate (CLR) for high priority cells (only those with CLP=0)	CLR0
Commodore 公司的动态全视视盘	Commodore gōngsīde dòngtài quánshì shìpán	Commodore dynamic total vision	CDTV
从迂回路由来	Cóng yūhuí lùyóu lái	Alternative routing from	ARF
从迂回路由去	Cóng yūhuí lùyóu qù	Alternative routing to	ART
从处理机	Cóngchǔlǐjī	Slave processor	
从机	Cóngjī	Slave machine	
从时钟	Cóngshízhōng	Slave clock	
从属失效	Cóngshǔ shīxiào	Secondary failure	
从钟	Cóngzhōng	Slave clock	
CPU 过热预防系统	CPU guòrè yùfáng xìtǒng	Automatic CPU overheat prevention system	ACOPS
粗波分复用	Cū bōfēn fùyòng	Coarse wavelength division multiplexing	CWDM
粗颗粒	Cū kēlì	Coarse-grained	
簇控制功能	Cù kòngzhì gōngnéng	Cluster control function	CCF
簇索引	Cù suǒyǐn	Clustered index (in SQL Server)	
窜改	Cuàngǎi	Tampering (IPsec)	
篡改	Cuàngǎi	Tampering (IW attack)	
粗糙集	Cūcāo jí	Rough set	
粗糙集理论	Cūcāo jí lǐlùn	Rough sets theory	
猝发	Cùfā	Burst	
猝发差错	Cùfā chācuò	Burst error	
猝发错误通道	Cùfā cuòwù tōngdào	Burst error channel	BEC
猝发导通控制	Cùfā dǎotōng kòngzhì	Burst firing control	
猝发点火控制	Cùfā diǎnhuǒ kòngzhì	Burst firing control	
催办	Cuībàn	Expedite (in groupware document handling)	
脆弱性	Cuìruòxìng	Vulnerability	
脆弱型水印	Cuìruòxíng shuǐyìn	Fragile watermark	
粗精测系统	Cū-jīng cè xìtǒng	Coarse-fine measurement system	

存储保护	Cúnchǔ bǎohù	Memory protection	
存储保护侵犯错误	Cúnchǔ bǎohù qīnfàn cuòwù	Memory protect violation error	
存储备份	Cúnchǔ bèifèn	Memory backup	
存储并转发	Cúnchǔ bìng zhuǎnfā	Store-and-forward	
存储程序	Cúnchǔ chéngxù	Stored program system	
存储程序控制	Cúnchǔ chéngxù kòngzhì	Stored program control	SPC
存储程序控制交换机	Cúnchǔ chéngxù kòngzhì jiāohuànjī	Stored program controlled switching system	
存储地址分配	Cúnchǔ dìzhǐ fēnpèi	Memory address allocation	
存储地址寄存器	Cúnchǔ dìzhǐ jìcúnqì	Memory address register	MAR
存储分配	Cúnchǔ fēnpèi	Memory allocation	
存储分配管理程序	Cúnchǔ fēnpèi guǎnlǐ chéngxù	Memory allocation manager	MAM
存储服务代理	Cúnchǔ fúwù dàilǐ	Storage service agent	
存储过程	Cúnchǔ guòchéng	Stored procedure (for database)	
存储过程的调用	Cúnchǔ guòchéngde diàoyòng	Stored procedure invocation (in SQL Server)	
存储寄存器	Cúnchǔ jìcúnqì	Memory register	MR
存储局域网络	Cúnchǔ júyù wǎngluò	Storage area network	SAN
存储控制	Cúnchǔ kòngzhì	Access control (to computer memory)	AC
存储控制装置	Cúnchǔ kòngzhì zhuāngzhì	Memory control unit	MCU
存储类资源	Cúnchǔ lèi zīyuán	Storage-class resource	
存储连网行业协会	Cúnchǔ liánwǎng hángyè xiéhuì	Storage Networking Industry Association	SNIA
存储码	Cúnchǔ mǎ	Access code (to computer memory)	AC
存储区域网络	Cúnchǔ qūyù wǎngluò	Storage area network	SAN
存储区域网络及其协议	Cúnchǔ qūyù wǎngluò jíqí xiéyì	Storage area network and SAN protocols (IETF, ANSI and ISO usage)	SAN
存储体	Cúnchǔ tǐ	Bank (unit of memory)	
存储虚拟化	Cúnchǔ xūnǐhuà	Storage virtualization	
存储域网	Cúnchǔ yù wǎng	Storage-area network	SAN
存储周期	Cúnchǔ zhōuqī	Access cycle (to computer memory)	AC
存储转发	Cúnchǔ zhuǎnfā	Store and forward	
存储转发时间	Cúnchǔ zhuǎnfā shíjiān	Latency	
存储转发式图像传输	Cúnchǔ zhuǎnfā-shì túxiàng chuánshū	Store and forward video transfer	
存储资源管理	Cúnchǔ zīyuán guǎnlǐ	Storage resource management	SRM
存储的上游邻站地址	Cúnchǔde shàngyóu línzhàn dìzhǐ	Stored upstream neighbor station address	SUA
存储器	Cúnchǔqì	Memory	
存储器存取控制器	Cúnchǔqì cúnqǔ kòngzhìqì	Memory access controller	MAC
存储器错误	Cúnchǔqì cuòwù	Storage error	SE
存储器导向器	Cúnchǔqì dǎoxiàngqì	Storage director	
存储器缓冲寄存器	Cúnchǔqì huǎnchōng jìcúnqì	Memory buffer register	MBR
存储器交替	Cúnchǔqì jiāotì	Memory interleave	
存储器寄存器指数	Cúnchǔqì jìcúnqì zhǐshù	Memory register exponent	MRE
存储器接口	Cúnchǔqì jiēkǒu	Memory interface	
存储器数据寄存器	Cúnchǔqì shùjù jìcúnqì	Storage data register	SDR
存储器网	Cúnchǔqì wǎng	Storage network, storage area network	SAN
存档	Cúndàng	Filing	
存档数据	Cúndàng shùjù	Archival data	
存档文件	Cúndàng wénjiàn	Archive file	
存根	Cúngēn	Stub (CORBA term)	

存根区域	Cúngēn qūyù	Stub area	
存根网络	Cúngēn wǎngluò	Stub network	
存活率	Cúnhuólǜ	Survivability	
存活期	Cúnhuóqī	Time to live	TTL
存取	Cúnqǔ	Access (computer term)	
存取方法	Cúnqǔ fāngfǎ	Access method	
存取键	Cúnqǔ jiàn	Storage key	SKEY
存取键	Cúnqǔ jiàn	Access key	AKEY
存取控制	Cúnqǔ kòngzhì	Access control	
存取控制表	Cúnqǔ kòngzhì biǎo	Access control list	ACL
存取控制器	Cúnqǔ kòngzhìqì	Access controller	
存取权识别	Cúnqǔ quán shíbié	Access rights identity	ARI
存取权限	Cúnqǔ quánxiàn	Access rights	
存取时间	Cúnqǔ shíjiān	Access time (computer)	
存取信令	Cúnqǔ xìnling	Access signaling	AS
存取性	Cúnqǔxìng	Availability	
存在点	Cúnzài diǎn	Point of presence	POP
存贮响应 FIR 数字滤波器	Cúnzhù xiǎngyìng FIR shùzì lǜbōqì	Stored response FIR digital filter	FIR-SRDF
存贮转发式服务	Cúnzhù zhuǎnfāshì fúwù	Store and forward service	
存贮器空间	Cúnzhùqì kōngjiān	Storage space	
错误	Cuòwù	Error, bug	
错误报警任务	Cuòwù bàojǐng rènwu	Error alert task	EAT
错误处理	Cuòwù chǔlǐ	Error processing	
错误冻结	Cuòwù dòngjié	Error freezing	
错误恢复处理	Cuòwù huīfù chǔlǐ	Error recovery	
错误检波码字节	Cuòwù jiǎnbō mǎ zìjié	Error detection code byte	EDC
错误检测	Cuòwù jiǎncè	Error checking	
错误检测	Cuòwù jiǎncè	Error detection	
错误检测码	Cuòwù jiǎncè mǎ	Error detection code	
错误检查修正	Cuòwù jiǎnchá xiūzhèng	Error checking and correction	ECC
错误检验与校正	Cuòwù jiǎnyàn yǔ jiàozhèng	Error checking and correction	ECC
错误校正码	Cuòwù jiàozhèng mǎ	Error correcting (or checking) code	ECC
错误校正模式	Cuòwù jiàozhèng móshì	Error correction mode (for facsimile)	ECM
错误路由	Cuòwù lùyóu	Mis-routing	
错误日志	Cuòwù rìzhì	Error log (for database)	
错误时段监视器	Cuòwù shíduàn jiānshìqì	Error interval monitor	EIM
错误信息	Cuòwù xìnxī	Error message	
错误应答	Cuòwù yìngdá	Negative acknowledgement	NACK
错误指示	Cuòwù zhǐshì	Error indication	AI
错误状态	Cuòwù zhuàngtài	Error status	
错误状态号	Cuòwù zhuàngtài hào	Error state number	
错账冲正	Cuòzhàng chōngzhèng	Modification of wrong account	
粗体	Cūtǐ	Bold (WP command)	
C 型弹簧管	C-xíng tánhuáng guǎn	C-type spring tube	

D

D 信道链路接入规程	D xìndào liànlù jiērù guīchéng	Link access procedure on D channel	LAPD
D4 成帧技术	D4 chéngzhèng jìshù	D4 framing	
打包和拆包	Dǎbāo hé chāibāo	Packet assembly and disassembly	PAD
大保实®单模光纤	Dàbǎoshí® dānmó guāngxiān	LAPOSH® single mode optical fiber	LAPOSH®
大比例尺	Dàbǐlìchǐ	Large scale	
打出去的长途电话电路	Dǎchūqùde chángtú diànhuà diànlù	Outgoing trunk call circuit	OGTC
大地参照系	Dàdì cānzhàoxì	Geodetic reference system	
大地基准	Dàdì jīzhǔn	Geodetic datum	
大地基准面	Dàdì jīzhǔn miàn	Datum	
大地控制点	Dàdì kòngzhì diǎn	Geodetic control point	
大地控制网	Dàdì kòngzhì wǎng	Geodetic control network	
大地水准参照	Dàdì shuǐzhǔn cānzhào	Geoidal reference	
大地水准面	Dàdì shuǐzhǔn miàn	Geoid	
大地椭球体	Dàdì tuǒqiú tǐ	Spheroid	
大地原点	Dàdì yuándiǎn	Geodetic origin	
大地坐标	Dàdì zuòbiāo	Geodetic coordinate	
大地坐标系	Dàdì zuòbiāo xì	Geodetic coordinate system	
大动态线形接收机	Dàdòngtài xiànxíng jiēshōujī	Large dynamic range linear receiver	
答复无法投递通知单费	Dáfù wúfǎtóudì tōngzhīdān fèi	Charge for reply to advice of non-delivery	
大功率速调管	Dàgōnglǜ sùtiáoguǎn	High power klystron	HPK
大功率微波部件	Dàgōnglǜ wēibō bùjiàn	High power microwave assembly	HPMA
大规模集成电路	Dàguīmó jíchéng diànlù	Large scale integrated circuit	LSI
大黄蜂	Dàhuángfēng	Super Hornet (U.S. F/A-18 aircraft)	
大话务量模拟测试	Dàhuàwùliàng mónǐ cèshì	Large traffic simulation test	
带标号的复用	Dài biāohàode fùyòng	Labeled multiplexing	
带标号的接口结构	Dài biāohàode jiēkǒu jiégòu	Labeled interface structure	
带标号的确定性信道	Dài biāohàode quèdìngxìng xìndào	Labeled deterministic channel	
带标号的统计信道	Dài biāohàode tǒngjì xìndào	Labeled statistical channel	
带标号的信道	Dài biāohàode xìndào	Labeled channel	
带成功结果的常规操作	Dài chénggōng jiéguǒde chángguī cāozuò	Normal operation with successful outcome	
带非介入监视的子网连接保护	Dài fēijièrù jiānshìde zìwǎng liánjiē bǎohù	Sub-network connection protection with non-intrusive monitoring	SNC/N
带附加信息的初始地址消息	Dài fùjiā xìnxīde chūshǐ dìzhǐ xiāoxi	Initial address with additional information	IAI
带光放大器的发送机	Dài guāng fàngdàqìde fāsòngjī	Optically amplified transmitter	OAT
带光放大器的接收机	Dài guāng fàngdàqìde jiēshōujī	Optically amplified receiver	OAR
带固有监视的子网连接保护	Dài gùyǒu jiānshìde zi wǎng liánjiē bǎohù	Sub-network connection with inherent monitoring	SNC/I
带和盘	Dài hé pán	Tape-and-reel (in SMT)	
带活动检测的主动授权业务	Dài huódòng jiǎncède zhǔdòng shòuquán yèwù	Unsolicited grant service with activity detection	UGS-AD
带类型注解的汇编器	Dài lèixíng zhùjiěde huìbiānqì	Type-annotated assembler	TAAS
带碰撞检测的数字侦听多址访问	Dài pèngzhuàng jiǎncède shùzì zhēntīng duōzhǐ fǎngwèn	Digital sense multiple access with collision detection	DSMA/CD

带碰撞检测的载波侦听多址访问	Dài pèngzhuàng jiǎncède zàibō zhēntīng duōzhǐ fǎngwèn	Carrier-sense multiple access with collision detection	CSMA/CD
带视览丝印机	Dài shì lǎn sīyìnjī	Screen printer (PCB manufacture)	
带抑制器点火分配器转子	Dài yìzhìqì diǎnhuǒ fēnpèiqì zhuànzǐ	Suppression distributor rotor	
戴在头上的耳机或听筒	Dài zài tóushàngde ěrjī huò tīngtǒng	Headset	HS
带载波调制的脉冲宽度	Dài zàibō tiáozhìde màichōng kuāndù	Pulse width with carrier modulation	PWCM
代表点	Dàibiǎo diǎn	Representative point	
代表角色	Dàibiǎo juésè	Agent role	
带电部分	Dàidiàn bùfen	Live part	
戴尔电脑集团	Dài-ěr diànnǎo jítuán	Dell Computer Corp.	
待尔发	Dài-ěr-fā	Delphi (an ISP)	
待复原	Dàifùyuán	Parked	
代换攻击	Dàihuàn gōngjī	Substitution attack (cryptography)	
代价因子	Dàijià yīnzǐ	Work factor	
带间传输	Dài-jiān chuánshū	Interband transmission	
带宽	Dàikuān	Bandwidth	
带宽代理	Dàikuān dàilǐ	Bandwidth broker	
带宽分配	Dàikuān fēnpèi	Bandwidth allocation	
带宽分配控制协议	Dàikuān fēnpèi kòngzhì xiéyì	Bandwidth allocation control protocol	BACP
带宽分配协议	Dàikuān fēnpèi xiéyì	Bandwidth allocation protocol	BAP
带宽接入服务器	Dàikuān jiērù fúwùqì	Broadband access server	BAS
带宽酒店	Dàikuān jiǔdiàn	"Bandwidth Hotel"	
带宽拒绝	Dàikuān jùjué	Bandwidth reject	
带宽扩展比	Dàikuān kuòzhǎn bǐ	Bandwidth expansion ratio	
带宽批发	Dàikuān pīfā	Bandwidth assignment	
带宽请求	Dàikuān qǐngqiú	Bandwidth request	
带宽请求拒绝	Dàikuān qǐngqiú jùjué	Bandwidth reject	BRJ
带宽确认	Dàikuān quèrèn	Bandwidth confirm	
带宽时间	Dàikuān shíjiān	Bandwidth time	BT
带宽时延乘积	Dàikuān shíyán chéngjī	Bandwidth delay product	BDP
带宽压缩技术	Dàikuān yāsuō jìshù	Bandwidth compression technique	BCT
带宽预留	Dàikuān yùliú	Bandwidth reservation	
代理	Dàilǐ	Agent, proxy	A
代理发现	Dàilǐ fāxiàn	Agent discovery (in mobile IP)	
代理服务器	Dàilǐ fúwùqì	Proxy server	
代理广播扩展	Dàilǐ guǎngbō kuòzhǎn	Agent advertisement extension	AAE
代理广播消息	Dàilǐ guǎngbō xiāoxi	Agent advertisement (message)	
代理广告	Dàilǐ guǎnggào	Agent advertisement (in mobile IP)	
代理轮询	Dàilǐ lúnxún	Proxy polling	
代理配置	Dàilǐ pèizhì	Surrogate configuration	
代理请求	Dàilǐ qǐngqiú	Agent request	AR
代理请求消息	Dàilǐ qǐngqiú xiāoxi	Agent solicitation (message)	
代理探索器	Dàilǐ tànsuǒqì	Proxy explorer	
代理通告	Dàilǐ tōnggào	Agent advertisement	AA
代理通信	Dàilǐ tōngxìn	Agent communication	
代领人	Dàilǐng rén	Payee's authorized representative	

代理商	Dàilǐshāng	Agent	
代码	Dàimǎ	Code	
代码变换	Dàimǎ biànhuàn	Code conversion	
代码表	Dàimǎ biǎo	Code table	
代码标记转换	Dàimǎ biāojì zhuǎnhuàn	Code mark inversion	CMI
代码访问安全	Dàimǎ fǎngwèn ānquán	Code access security	
代码缓冲器	Dàimǎ huǎnchōngqì	Code buffer	CB
代码集	Dàimǎ jí	Code set	
代码激励线性预测	Dàimǎ jīlì xiànxìng yùcè	Code excited linear prediction	CELP
代码扩充	Dàimǎ kuòchōng	Code extension	
代码模数发生器	Dàimǎ móshù fāshēngqì	Code modulus generator	CMG
代码违约	Dàimǎ wéiyuē	Code violation	
代码页	Dàimǎ yè	Code page	
代码转换	Dàimǎ zhuǎnhuàn	Code conversion, transcoding	
代码转换器	Dàimǎ zhuǎnhuànqì	Transcoder	TC
代码走查	Dàimǎ zǒuchá	Coding walk-through	
代码组合	Dàimǎ zǔhé	Code combination	
代码化中断原因	Dàimǎhuà zhōngduàn yuányīn	Coded interrupt cause	CIC
待命	Dàimìng	Standby (verb, command)	
带内	Dài-nèi	In-band	
带内导频单边带	Dài-nèi dǎopín dānbiāndài	Pilot tone in-band single sideband	
带内寄生信号	Dài-nèi jìshēng xìnhào	Spurious in-band signal	
带内聚簇	Dài-nèi jùcù	Intraband clustering	
带内谐波	Dài-nèi xiébō	In-band harmonic	
带内信令	Dài-nèi xìnlìng	In-band signaling	
带内噪声	Dài-nèi zàoshēng	In-band noise	
带内传输	Dài-nèi zhuànshū	Intraband transmission	
代数编码理论	Dàishù biānmǎ lǐlùn	Algebraic coding theory	ACT
代数编译程序	Dàishù biānyì chéngxù	Algebraic compiler	ACOM
代数码激励线性预测	Dàishù mǎ jīlì xiànxìng yùcè	Algebraic code excited linear prediction	ACELP
代数码本激励线性预测编码	Dàishù mǎběn jīlī xiànxìng yùcè biānmǎ	Algebraic code excited linear prediction	ACELP
代数拓朴	Dàishù tuòpò	Algebraic topology	
代替同步伙伴	Dàitì tóngbù huǒbàn	Alternate synchronization partners (in SQL Server)	
带通	Dàitōng	Bandpass	
带通滤波器	Dàitōng lǜbōqì	Bandpass filter	BF
带通滤波器/隔离器	Dàitōng lǜbōqì/gélíqì	Bandpass filter isolator	BPFI
带外	Dài-wài	Out-of-band	
带外发射	Dài-wài fāshè	Out-of-band emission	
带外辐射	Dài-wài fúshè	Out-of-band emission	OBE
带外攻击	Dài-wài gōngjī	Out-of-band attack (IPsec)	
带外功率	Dài-wài gōnglǜ	Out-of-band power	
带外频谱	Dài-wài pínpǔ	Out-of-band spectrum	
带外衰减	Dàiwài shuāijiǎn	Attenuation outside a channel	
带外信令	Dài-wài xìnlìng	Out-of-band signaling	
代销	Dàixiāo	Sale entrusted by publishing house	

待用	Dàiyòng	Quiescent, standby	
代用数据	Dàiyòng shùjù	Surrogate data	
带有长期预测的规则脉冲激励线性预测编码	Dàiyǒu chángqī yùcède guīzé màichōng jīlì xiànxìng yùcè biānmǎ	Regular pulse excitation linear predictive coding with long-term prediction	RPE-LTP
带有附加信息的初始地址消息	Dàiyǒu fùjiā xìnxīde chūshǐ dìzhǐ xiāoxi	Initial address message with additional information	IAI
带有碰撞检测的优先载波读出多路存取	Dàiyǒu pèngzhuàng jiǎncède yōuxiān zàibō dúchū duōlù cúnqǔ	Prioritized carrier-sense multiple access with collision detection	PCSMA/CD
带有时钟变量的线性时序逻辑	Dàiyǒu shízhōng biànliàngde xiànxìng shíxù luóji	Linear temporal logic with clocks	LTLC
带有一信号的后续地址消息	Dàiyǒu yī xìnhàode hòuxù dìzhǐ xiāoxi	Subsequent address message with one signal	SAO
带有远程分发者的中心出版者	Dàiyǒu yuǎnchéng fēnfā zhěde zhōngxīn chūbǎnzhě	Central publisher with remote distributor (in SQL Server)	
带状光缆	Dàizhuàng guānglǎn	Ribbon fiber cable	
带状线	Dàizhuàngxiàn	Stripline	
搭接片	Dājiēpiàn	Strap	
打卡	Dǎkǎ	Punch card	
打开连接端口对话	Dǎkāi liánjiē duānkǒu duìhuà	Open connection port dialog	OCPD
打开逻辑通道	Dǎkāi luóji tōngdào	Open logical channel	OLC
打开逻辑通道拒绝	Dǎkāi luóji tōngdào jùjué	Open logical channel reject	OLCR
打开逻辑通道确认	Dǎkāi luóji tōngdào quèrèn	Open logical channel acknowledge	OLCA
大口式光纤连接器	Dàkǒushì guāngxiān liánjiēqì	Bayonet fiber optic connector	BFOC
大块二进制数据目标	Dàkuài èrjìnzhì shùjù mùbiāo	Binary large object	BLOB
大块二进制数据目标标识	Dàkuài èrjìnzhì shùjù mùbiāo biāozhì	Binary large object identifier	BLOBID
大括号	Dàkuòhào	Brace (curly brace) { }	
大量焊	Dàliàng hàn	High mass soldering (semiconductor mfg)	
大力士监控卡	Dàlìshì jiānkòng kǎ	Hercules graphic adapter	
大楼综合定时供给设备	Dàlóu zōnghé dìngshí gōngjǐ shèbèi	Building integrated timing supply	BITS
大楼综合定时供给系统	Dàlóu zōnghé dìngshí gōngjǐ xìtǒng	Building integrated timing system	BITS
大楼内综合定时源	Dàlóu-nèi zōnghé dìngshí yuán	Building integrated timing supply	BITS
大门传感器	Dàmén chuángǎnqì	Door contacts	DC
氮分子激光	Dàn fènzi jīguāng	Nitrogen laser	
氮锡焊接	Dàn xī hàn jiē	Nitrogen soldering	
单音脉冲的单音频率	Dān yīn màichōngde dānyīn pínlǜ	Tone frequency of tone pulse	
单偶联对象	Dān'ǒulián duìxiàng	Single association object	SAO
单偶联控制功能	Dān'ǒulián kòngzhì gōngnéng	Single association control function	SACF
单板	Dānbǎn	Single board	
单板计算机	Dānbǎn jìsuànjī	Single board computer	SBC
单板设计	Dānbǎn shèjì	Single board design	
担保实验室	Dānbǎo shíyànshì	Underwriters Laboratories Inc. (US)	UL
单边接触内存模组	Dānbiān jiēchù nèicún mózǔ	Single inline memory module	SIMM
单边连接器	Dānbiān liánjiēqì	Single edge connector	SEC
单边带	Dānbiāndài	Single sideband	SSB
单边带发射	Dānbiāndài fāshè	Single sideband emission	
单边带发射机	Dānbiāndài fāshèjī	Single sideband (SSB) transmitter	

单边带解调	Dānbiāndài jiětiáo	Single sideband demodulation	
单边带调幅	Dānbiāndài tiáofú	Single sideband amplitude modulation	SSBAM
单边带调频	Dānbiāndài tiáopín	Single sideband frequency modulation	SSFM, SSBFM
单边带调相	Dānbiāndài tiáoxiàng	Single sideband phase modulation	SSPM
单边带调制	Dānbiāndài tiáozhì	Single sideband modulation	SSB
单边带信号发生器	Dānbiāndài xìnhào fāshēngqì	Single sideband signal generator	
单变量分析	Dānbiànliàng fēnxī	Univariate analysis	
单播	Dānbō	Unicast	
单波长解决方案	Dānbōcháng jiějué fāng'àn	Single wavelength solution	SWS
单波长系统	Dānbōcháng xìtǒng	Single channel system (optical)	SCS
单参函数	Dāncān hánshù	Unary function (in computer programming)	
单层紧度	Dāncéng jǐndù	Single sheet density	
单插	Dānchā	Unicast	
单厂商网络	Dānchǎngshāng wǎngluò	Single-vendor network	
单成分信号	Dānchéngfèn xìnhào	Single-component signal (in AC signaling)	
单词	Dāncí	Word	
单词清晰度	Dāncí qīngxīdù	Word articulation	
单磁道时间	Dāncídào shíjiān	Single track seek time	
单错校正（码）	Dāncuò jiàozhèng (mǎ)	Single error correcting (codes)	SEC
单导线传输线	Dāndǎoxiàn chuánshūxiàn	Single-wire line	
单点定位	Dāndiǎn dìngwèi	Single point positioning	
单点广播地址	Dāndiǎn guǎngbō dìzhǐ	Unicast address	
单点故障源	Dāndiǎn gùzhàng yuán	Single point of failure	SPOF
单点接触集中器	Dāndiǎn jiēchù jízhōngqì	Single attachment concentrator	
单地址编码	Dāndìzhǐ biānmǎ	Single address code	SAC
单独操作试验	Dāndú cāozuò shìyàn	Single operation test	SOT
单独存储与正向读出	Dāndú cúnchǔ yǔ zhèngxiàng dúchū	Individual store and forward readout	ISF
单独读出	Dāndú dúchū	Absolute read-out	
单端输入	Dānduān shūrù	Single-ended input	
单端同步	Dānduān tóngbù	Single-ended synchronization	
单端网络	Dānduān wǎngluò	One-port network	
单段消息	Dānduàn xiāoxi	Single segment message	SSM
单端口	Dānduānkǒu	One-port	
单端口网络	Dānduānkǒu wǎngluò	One-port network	
当被呼移动用户不回答时的呼叫转移	Dāng bèihū yídòng yònghù bù huídá shíde hūjiào zhuǎnyí	Call forwarding when called mobile subscriber does not reply	CFNRy
当被呼移动用户忙时的呼叫转	Dāng bèihū yídòng yònghù máng shíde hūjiào zhuǎn	Calling forwarding on mobile subscriber busy	CFB
当漫游出归属 PLMN 国家后，闭锁入呼叫	Dāng mànyóu chū guīshǔ PLMN guójiā hòu, bìsuǒ rù hūjiào	Barring of incoming calls when roaming outside the home PLMN country supplementary service	BIC-Roam
当漫游出归属 PLMN 国家后，闭锁所有入局呼叫	Dāng mànyóu chū guīshǔ PLMN guójiā hòu, bìsuǒ suǒyǒu rùjú hūjiào	Barring of all incoming calls roam	BAIC-Roam
当漫游出归属 PLMN 国家时，闭锁入呼叫	Dāng mànyóu chū guīshǔ PLMN guójiā shí, bìsuǒ rù hūjiào	Barring of incoming calls when roaming outside the home PLMN country	BIC-Roam
当漫游到原籍PLMN国家以外时禁止所有入呼	Dāng mànyóu dào yuánjí PLMN guójiā yǐwài shí jìnzhǐ suǒyǒu rùhū	Barring of incoming calls when roaming outside the home PLMN country	BIC-Roam

当且仅当	Dāng qiě jǐn dāng	If and only if	
当无线信道拥挤时的呼叫转移	Dāng wúxiàn xìndào yōngjǐ shíde hūjiào zhuǎnyí	Calling forward on mobile subscriber not reachable	CENRc
当移动用户不可及前转补充业务	Dāng yídòng yònghù bùkějí qiánzhuǎn bǔchōng yèwù	Call forwarding on mobile subscriber not reachable supplementary service	CFNRc
当移动用户忙时呼叫转发	Dāng yídòng yònghù mángshí hūjiào zhuǎnfā	Call forwarding on mobile subscriber busy	CFB
当用户忙时呼叫转发	Dāng yònghù mángshí hūjiào zhuǎnfā	Call forwarding on subscriber busy	CFB
档案	Dàng'àn	Archive	
档案搜索软件	Dàng'àn sōusuǒ ruǎnjiàn	Archie (Internet search engine)	
档次稍低	Dàngcì shāodī	Degraded, down-graded	
单个差错	Dāngè chācuò	Single error	
单个畸变度	Dāngè jībiàndù	Degree of individual distortion (of a particular significant instant)	
单个用户的鉴别钥匙	Dāngè yònghùde jiànbié yàoshi	Individual subscriber authentication key	Ki
当机	Dāngjī	Hang (computer program malfunction)	
档距	Dàngjù	Span (of cable)	
单工	Dāngōng	Simplex	
单工操作	Dāngōng cāozuò	Simplex operation	
单工无线电话机	Dāngōng wúxiàn diànhuàjī	Simplex radio telephone	
单工线路	Dāngōng xiànlù	Simplex circuit	SPX
当前布局位置	Dāngqián bùjú wèizhì	Current layout position	
当前读状态	Dāngqián dú zhuàngtài	Current read state (IPsec)	
当前服务的基站	Dāngqián fúwùde jīzhàn	Current serving base station	
当前速率	Dāngqián sùlǜ	Current rate	
当前写状态	Dāngqián xiě zhuàngtài	Current write state (IPsec)	
当前信道	Dāngqián xìndào	Current channel	
当前信元速率	Dāngqián xìnyuán sùlǜ	Current cell rate	CCR
挡圈钳	Dǎngquānqián	Internal ring pliers, snap ring pliers	
单呼	Dānhū	Single call	
氮化镓	Dànhuà jiā	Gallium nitride	GaN
氮化铝	Dànhuà lǚ	Aluminum nitride	AlN
单击	Dānjī	Single click (of a computer mouse)	
单极点	Dānjí diǎn	Single pole	
单机对称控制	Dānjī duìchèn kòngzhì	Single phase symmetrical control	
单级设备	Dānjí shèbèi	Single-level device	
单极天线	Dānjí tiānxiàn	Unipole antenna	UA
单基地雷达	Dānjīdì léidá	Monostatic radar	
单节点互连	Dānjiédiǎn hùlián	Single node interconnection (in SDH)	
单结晶制造设备	Dānjiéjīng zhìzào shèbèi	Single crystal growing equipment	
单极化天线	Dānjíhuà tiānxiàn	Single-polarized antenna	
单极化纤维	Dānjíhuà xiānwéi	Single-polarization fiber	SPF
单精度	Dānjīngdù	Single precision	
单极子天线	Dānjízi tiānxiàn	Monopole antenna, unipole antenna	
单链表	Dānliàn biǎo	Single linked list	
单连集线器	Dānlián jíxiànqì	Single-attached concentrator	SAC
单连接集中器	Dānliánjiē jízhōngqì	Single-attached concentrator	SAC

单链路规程	Dānliànlù guīchéng	Single link procedure	SLP
单流传输	Dānliú chuánshū	Single current transmission	
单路单突发	Dānlù dāntūfā	Single channel per burst	SCPB
单路单载波	Dānlù dānzàibō	Single channel per carrier	SCPC
单路调制解调器	Dānlù tiáozhì jiětiáoqì	Single channel modem	SCM
单路音频电报	Dānlù yīnpín diànbào	Single channel voice frequency telegraphy	SCVFT
单路转发器	Dānlù zhuǎnfāqì	Single channel transponder	SCT
单路由探测包	Dānlùyóu tàncè bāo	Single-route explorer packet	
丹麦电信	Dān-mài diànxìn	TeleDenmark	
单脉冲雷达	Dānmàichōng léidá	Monopulse radar	
单脉冲雷达接收机	Dānmàichōng léidá jiēshōujī	Monopulse radar receiver	
单脉冲天线	Dānmàichōng tiānxiàn	Monopulse antenna	
单码流	Dānmǎliú	Single stream	
单模波分复用器	Dānmó bōfēn fùyòngqì	Single mode wavelength division multiplexer	SWDM
单模单窗宽带分光器	Dānmó dānchuāng kuāndài fēnguāngqì	Single mode single window broadband coupler	SWBC
单模单窗宽带树型分光器	Dānmó dānchuāng kuāndài shùxíng fēnguāngqì	Single mode single window broadband tree coupler	SWTC
单模单窗宽带星型分光器	Dānmó dānchuāng kuāndài xīngxíng fēnguāng qì	Single mode single window broadband star coupler	SWSC
单模分光器	Dānmó fēnguāngqì	Single mode fiber coupler	SMFC
单模光纤	Dānmó guāngxiān	Single mode optical fiber	
单模双窗宽带分光器	Dānmó shuāngchuāng kuāndài fēnguāngqì	Single mode two window broadband coupler	TWBC
单模双窗宽带树型分光器	Dānmó shuāngchuāng kuāndài shùxíng fēnguāngqì	Single mode two window broadband tree coupler	TWTC
单模双窗宽带星型分光器	Dānmó shuāngchuāng kuāndài xīngxíng fēnguāngqì	Single mode two window broadband star coupler	TWSC
单模树型分光器	Dānmó shùxíng fēnguāngqì	Single mode tree coupler	SMTC
单模突变型光纤	Dānmó tūbiànxíng guāngxiān	Single mode stepped index optical fiber	
单模纤维	Dānmó xiānwéi	Single mode fiber	SMF
单模星型分光器	Dānmó xīngxíng fēnguāngqì	Single mode star coupler	SMSC
单模态光纤连接器	Dānmótài guāngxiān liánjiēqì	Single mode fiber optic connector	
单目广播	Dānmù guǎngbō	Unicast	
单偶联体	Dānǒuliántǐ	Single association object	SAO
单片集成电路	Dānpiàn jíchéng diànlù	Monolithic integrated circuit	
单片计算机	Dānpiàn jìsuànjī	Computer-on-a-chip	
单偏振隔离器	Dānpiānzhèn gélíqì	Single polarization fiber isolator	SPFI
单频接收电平	Dānpín jiēshōu diànpíng	Single frequency receiving level	
单频双工	Dānpín shuānggōng	Single frequency duplex	
单频网	Dānpín wǎng	Single frequency network	
单频信号	Dānpín xìnhào	Simple signal (in AC signaling)	
单频信令	Dānpín xìnlìng	Single frequency signaling	
单频噪声	Dānpín zàoshēng	Single frequency noise	
单色	Dānsè	Monochrome	
单色激光数位影印机	Dānsè jīguāng shùwèi yǐngyìnjī	Digital monochrome laser copy machine	
单色激光印表机	Dānsè jīguāng yìnbiǎojī	Monochrome laser printer	
单色适配器	Dānsè shìpèiqì	Monochrome adapter (video term)	MDA
单色显示监控器	Dānsè xiǎnshì jiānkòngqì	Monochrome display adapter	MDA
单式计次	Dānshì jìcì	Single metering	

单束光缆	Dānshù guānglǎn	Single bundle cable	
单双光纤头	Dānshuāng guāngxiān tóu	Collimator pigtail	
单数据率 SDRAM	Dānshùjù lǜ SDRAM	Single data-rate SDRAM	SDR SDRAM
单数据消息格式	Dānshùjù xiāoxī géshi	Single data message format	SDMF
单通道单脉冲雷达	Dāntōngdào dānmàichōng léidá	Single channel monopulse radar	
单通道多纹理	Dāntōngdào duōwénlǐ	Single pass multi-texturing (video term)	
单透镜	Dāntòujìng	Simple (single) lens	
单位	Dānwèi	Single bit	
单位标尺	Dānwèi biāochǐ	Unit scaling	
单位冲激响应，	Dānwèi chōngjī xiǎngyìng	Unit impulse response	
单位间隔	Dānwèi jiàngé	Unit interval	UI
单维基准	Dānwéi jīzhǔn	Unidimensional datum	
单位脉冲响应	Dānwèi màichōng xiǎngyìng	Unit pulse response	
单位码元	Dānwèi mǎyuán	Unit element	
单位体积重量	Dānwèi tǐjī zhòngliàng	Unit weight	
单稳线路	Dānwěn xiànlù	One-shot multi-vibrator	
单稳态触发电路	Dānwěntài chùfā diànlù	Monostable trigger circuit	
单稳态电路	Dānwěntài diànlù	Monostable circuit	
单线数字用户线路	Dānxiàn shùzì yònghù xiànlù	Single-line digital subscriber line	SDSL
单线程	Dānxiànchéng	Single-threaded	
单线对高比特率数字用户线	Dānxiànduì gāobǐtèlǜ shùzì yònghù xiàn	Single-pair high bit-rate digital subscriber line	SHDSL
单线对高速数据用户线	Dānxiànduì gāosù shùjù yònghù xiàn	Single pair high-speed digital subscriber line	SHDSL
单相	Dānxiàng	Single phase	
单相不对称控制	Dānxiàng bùduìchèn kòngzhì	Single phase asymmetrical control	
单向传输	Dānxiàng chuánshū	Uni-directional transmission	
单相对称控制	Dānxiàng duìchèn kòngzhì	Single phase symmetrical control	
单向功能算法	Dānxiàng gōngnéng suànfǎ	One-way function algorithm	O-ALG
单相关对象	Dānxiàng guān duìxiàng	Single association object	SAO
单相关控制功能	Dānxiàng guān kòngzhì gōngnéng	Single association control function	SACF
单向广播地址	Dānxiàng guǎngbō dìzhǐ	Unicast addressing	UA
单向控制	Dānxiàng kòngzhì	Unidirectional control	
单向路径/连接类型	Dānxiàng lùjìng/liánjiē lèixíng	Uni-directional trail/connection type	
单向逻辑信道出	Dānxiàng luóji xìndào chū	One-way logical channel outgoing	
单向逻辑信道入	Dānxiàng luóji xìndào rù	One-way logical channel incoming	
单向通道倒换环	Dānxiàng tōngdào dǎohuàn huán	Uni-directional path switch ring	UPSR
单向通信	Dānxiàng tōngxìn	One-way communication	OWC
单向信任	Dānxiàng xìnrèn	One-way trust	
单相中性点接地电抗器	Dānxiàng zhōngxìngdiǎn jiēdì diànkàngqì	Single-phase neutral grounding reactor	
单线制数字用户线	Dānxiànzhì shùzì yònghù xiàn	Single digital subscriber line	SDSL
单写多读	Dānxiě duōdú	Write-one read many	WORM
单芯光缆	Dānxīn guānglǎn	Single fiber cable	
单芯光缆连接器	Dānxīn guānglǎn liánjiēqì	Single fiber cable connector	
单芯融接机	Dānxīn róngjiējī	Optical fiber fusion splicer	
单信道地面和机载无线电分系统	Dānxìndào dìmiàn hé jīzài wúxiàndiàn fēnxìtǒng	Single channel ground and airborne radio system (US military)	SINCGARS

单信道无绳电话机	Dānxìndào wúshéng diànhuàjī	Single channel cordless telephone	
单信道无线电接入	Dānxìndào wúxiàndiàn jiērù	Single channel radio access (an Alcatel-Telletra system)	SCRA
单信号法	Dānxìnhào fǎ	Single-signal method	
单信号率定时	Dānxìnhào lǜ dìngshí	Single message rate timing	SMRT
单选按钮	Dānxuǎn ànniǔ	Radio button	
单一登录	Dānyī dēnglù	Single sign-on	
单一信号单元	Dānyī xìnhào dānyuán	Lone signal unit	LSU
单一值分解技术	Dānyī zhí fēnjiě jìshù	Singular value decomposition	
单一指令多数据流扩展	Dānyī zhǐlìng duō shùjùliú kuòzhǎn	Streaming SIMD extensions	SSE
单一化	Dānyīhuà	Oneness	
单音	Dānyīn	Tone	
单音拨号的接收机	Dānyīn bōhàode jiēshōujī	Tone dial receiver	TDR
单音脉冲	Dānyīn màichōng	Tone pulse	
单音脉冲持续时间	Dānyīn màichōng chíxù shíjiān	Tone pulse duration	
单音脉冲上升时间	Dānyīn màichōng shàngshēng shíjiān	Tone pulse rise time	
单音脉冲下降时间	Dānyīn màichōng xiàjiàng shíjiān	Tone pulse decay time	
单音脉冲的单音频率	Dānyīn màichōngde dānyīn pínlǜ	Tone frequency of tone pulse	
单音制	Dānyīnzhì	Individual tone system	
单用户固定台	Dānyònghù gùdìng tái	Fixed subscriber unit	FSU
单用户模式	Dānyònghù móshì	Single-user mode	
单用户帐号	Dānyònghù zhànghào	Single user account	SUA
单元	Dānyuán	Cell	
单元电缆段	Dānyuán diànlǎn duàn	Elementary cable section	
单元分隔	Dānyuán fēngé	Unit separator	US
单元管理系统	Dānyuán guǎnlǐ xìtǒng	Element management system	EMS
单元管理层拓扑结构	Dānyuán guǎnlǐcéng tuòpū jiégòu	Element management layer topology configurator	EML-TC
单元管理者	Dānyuán guǎnlǐzhě	Element manager	EM
单元集	Dānyuán jí	Cell set	
单元间隔	Dānyuán jiàngé	Unit interval	UI
单元流	Dānyuán liú	Element stream	ES
单元室	Dānyuán shì	Element cell	
单元再生段	Dānyuán zàishēng duàn	Elementary regenerator section	
单元中继段	Dānyuán zhōngjì duàn	Elementary repeater section	
单元自动机	Dānyuán zìdòngjī	Cellular automata	CA
单元体模型	Dānyuántǐ móxíng	Cellular model (CAD/CAM)	
单载波单路	Dānzàibō dānlù	Single channel per carrier	SCPC
单值	Dānzhí	Unique values	
单指令多数据流	Dānzhǐlìng duō shùjùliú	Single instruction multiple data	SIMD
单指向性传声器	Dānzhǐxiàng-xìng chuánshēngqì	Unidirectional microphone	UM
单字节扩展	Dānzìjié kuòzhǎn	Single byte expansion	SBE
单纵模	Dānzòngmó	Single-longitudinal mode	SLM
单纵模激光器	Dānzòngmó jīguāngqì	Single longitudinal mode laser	SLM
到交换单元	Dào jiāohuàn dānyuán	To switch unit	TSU
倒 L 形天线	Dǎo L-xíng tiānxiàn	Inverted-L antenna	
到忙用户的呼叫完成	Dào máng yònghùde hūjiào wánchéng	Completion of calls to busy subscribers	CCBS
倒 V 形天线	Dǎo V-xíng tiānxiàn	Inverted-V antenna	

道至道时间	Dào zhì dào shíjiān	Single track seek time	
导出	Dǎochū	Export	
导出增量调制	Dǎochū zēngliàng tiáozhì	Derived delta modulation	DDM
导磁板	Dǎocí bǎn	Concentrating flux plate	
导磁套	Dǎocí tào	Concentrating flux sleeve	
导磁体	Dǎocí tǐ	Magnetic conductor	
到达方向	Dàodá fāngxiàng	Direction of arrival	DOA
到达角度	Dàodá jiǎodù	Angle of arrival	AOA
到达时差	Dàodá shíchā	Time difference of arrival	TDOA
到达时间	Dàodá shíjiān	Time of arrival	TOA
到达时间差	Dàodá shíjiān chà	Time-difference of arrival	TDOA
导弹飞行工具	Dǎodàn fēixíng gōngjù	Missile flight tool (software)	MFT
导弹连数据链	Dǎodàn lián shùjù liàn	Missile battery data link (US military)	MBDL
导电部分	Dǎodiàn bùfen	Conductive part	
导电墨水	Dǎodiàn mòshuǐ	Conductive ink (in SMT)	
导电体	Dǎodiàn tǐ	Electric conductor	
导电率	Dǎodiànlǜ	Electrical conductivity	
导电性环氧树脂	Dǎodiànxìng huányǎng shùzhī	Conductive epoxy (in SMT)	
道尔夫-契比雪夫阵	Dào-ěr-fū--qì-bǐ-xuě-fū zhèn	Dolph-Chebyshev array	
道尔夫-切比雪夫阵列天线	Dào-ěr-fū—qiē-bǐ-xuě-fū zhènliè tiānxiàn	Dolph-Chebyshev array antenna	
道格拉斯算法	Dào-gé-lā-sī suànfǎ	Douglas-Peucker algorithm	
导管	Dǎoguǎn	Guiding sleeve	
导轨	Dǎoguǐ	Track, guide	
导轨炮	Dǎoguǐ páo	Railgun	
导航	Dǎoháng	Navigation	
导航模型	Dǎoháng móxíng	Navigation model	
倒换	Dǎohuàn	Changeover	
倒换开始时间	Dǎohuàn kāishǐ shíjiān	Switching start time	
倒换时间测试	Dǎohuàn shíjiān cèshì	Switching time measurement	
倒换信号	Dǎohuàn xìnhào	Changeover signal	COO
倒换证实信号	Dǎohuàn zhèngshí xìnhào	Changeover acknowledge signal	COA
倒换的传播	Dǎohuànde chuánbō	Propagation of switching (SDH)	
倒回	Dǎohuí	Changeback	
导览器	Dǎolǎnqì	Navigator	
捣乱呼叫识别	Dǎoluàn hūjiào shíbié	Malicious call identification	MCI
导纳	Dǎonà	Admittance	
导纳圆图	Dǎonà yuántú	Polar impedance diagram; Smith chart (polar admittance diagram)	
倒排文件	Dàopái wénjiàn	Inverted file	
导频	Dǎopín	Pilot frequency	
导频跌落	Dǎopín diēluò	Pilot fall-down	
导频同步/接入信道	Dǎopín tóngbù/jiērù xìndào	Pilot synchronization/access channel	PAC
导频信道	Dǎopín xìndào	Pilot channel	
导频引导	Dǎopín yǐndǎo	Pilot beacon	
导入	Dǎorù	Import	
导入媒体池	Dǎorù méitǐ chí	Import media pool	

导体	Dǎotǐ	Conductor	
导通端口	Dǎotōng duānkǒu	Conduction port	
导通故障信号	Dǎotōng gùzhàng xìnhào	Continuity-failure signal	CCF
导通检验	Dǎotōng jiǎnyàn	Continuity check	
导通消息	Dǎotōng xiāoxi	Continuity signal	COT
导通信号	Dǎotōng xìnhào	Continuity signal	COT
倒相干扰	Dǎoxiāng gānrǎo	Inverse conical scan jamming	
导向气球	Dǎoxiàng qìqiú	Pilot balloon	
倒相调制	Dǎoxiàng tiáozhì	Phase reversal modulation	PRM
倒相调制	Dǎoxiāng tiáozhì	Phase inversion modulation	
导向槽	Dǎoxiàngcáo	Guiding groove	
导行波	Dǎoxíng bō	Guided wave (in a transmission line)	
刀型天线	Dāoxíng tiānxiàn	Blade antenna	
导致网络定位请求	Dǎozhì wǎngluò dìngwèi qǐngqiú	Network induced location request	NI-LR
倒装芯片	Dàozhuāng xìnpiàn	Flip chip (in SMT)	
大屏幕显示	Dàpíngmù xiǎnshì	Large screen display	
大气无线电噪声	Dàqì wúxiàndiàn zàoshēng	Atmospheric radio noise	
大气吸收损耗	Dàqì xīshōu sǔnhào	Atmospheric absorption loss	
大气噪声	Dàqì zàoshēng	Atmospheric noise	
大区划	Dàqūhuà	Macro-zoning	
大区域同步码分多址接入	Dàqūyù tóngbù mǎfēn duōzhǐ jiērù	Large area synchronous code division multiple access	LAS-CDMA
大容量存储控制器	Dàróngliàng cúnchǔ kòngzhìqì	Mass storage controller	MSC
大容量存储器	Dàróngliàng cúnchǔqì	Bulk memory	
大容量移动电话系统	Dàróngliàng yídòng diànhuà xìtǒng	High capacity mobile telephone system (Japan)	HCMTS
大容量正色散位移单模光纤	Dàróngliàng zhèng sèsàn wèiyí dānmó guāngxiān	Large effective area non-zero dispersion-shifted optical fiber	
大唐电信多媒体中心	Dàtáng diànxìn duōméitǐ zhōngxīn	Datang Telecom Multimedia Center	
大唐电信科技股份有限公司	Dàtáng diànxìn kējì gǔfèn yǒuxiàn gōngsī	Datang Telecom Technology Co. Ltd.	
大五码	Dàwǔ mǎ	Big-5 code	
达西法则	Dá-xī fǎzé	Darcy's law	
达西公式	Dá-xī gōngshì	Darcy's formula	
搭线法	Dāxiàn fǎ	Wiretap	
大写锁定	Dàxiě suǒdìng	Caps lock	
大写转换	Dàxiě zhuǎnhuàn	Up-casing	
大写字母	Dàxiě zìmǔ	Upper case	
大型复杂系统	Dàxíng fùzá xìtǒng	Large complicated systems	LCS
大型企业	Dàxíng qǐyè	Large enterprises	LE
大型纹理	Dàxíng wénlǐ	Large texture (video)	
大信号增益输出稳定性	Dàxìnhào zēngyì shūchū wěndìngxìng	Large-signal output stability	
大芯数光缆	Dàxīnshù guānglǎn	High fiber count cable	
大西洋海底电缆	Dàxīyáng hǎidǐ diànlǎn	Atlantic cable	AC
大学士	Dàxuéshì	BrushWriter (Chinese software)	
打印	Dǎyìn	Print (WP command)	
打印报表	Dǎyìn bàobiǎo	Printing reports	
打印喷墨头	Dǎyìn pēn mò tóu	Ink jet printer head (semiconductor mfg)	

打印设备的通用串行总线级标准	Dǎyìn shèbèide tōngyòng chuànháng zǒngxiàn jí biāozhǔn	Universal serial bus device class definition for printing devices	USBDCDPD
打印设置	Dǎyìn shèzhì	Print setup	
打印隐蔽	Dǎyìn yǐnbì	Print suppress (IPsec)	
打印预览	Dǎyìn yùlǎn	Print preview	
打印预视	Dǎyìn yùshì	Print preview	
打印机	Dǎyìnjī	Printer	
打印机访问协议	Dǎyìnjī fǎngwèn xiéyì	Printer access protocol (Apple usage)	PAP
打印机接口	Dǎyìnjī jiēkǒu	Printer port	
打印机控制语言	Dǎyìnjī kòngzhì yǔyán	Printer control language	PCL
打印机驱动程式	Dǎyìnjī qūdòng chéngshì	Printer driver	
打印机字型	Dǎyìnjī zìxíng	Printer font	
打印机作业语言	Dǎyìnjī zuòyè yǔyán	Printer job language	PJL
大有效面积光纤	Dàyǒuxiào miànjī guāngxiān	Large effective area optical fiber	
大宇	Dàyǔ	Daewoo Corp. (Korean company)	
大众传媒	Dàzhòng chuánméi	Mass communication	
大众呼叫	Dàzhòng hūjiào	Mass call	MAS
大众呼叫业务	Dàzhòng hūjiào yèwù	Mass calling service	MAS
打字锁定键	Dǎzì suǒdìng jiàn	CapsLock key	
大宗函件	Dàzōng hánjiàn	Bulk-posted correspondence	
大宗汇款	Dàzōng huìkuǎn	Bulk remittance	
DECnet 路由选择协议	DECnet lùyóu xuǎnzé xiéyì	DECnet routing protocol	DRP
DECT 认证模型	DECT rènzhèng móxíng	DECT authentication module	DAM
德国电信	Déguó Diànxìn	Deutsche Telekom	
德国工业标准	Déguó gōngyè biāozhǔn	Deutsche Industrie Norm	DIN
德洛内三角	Dé-luò-nèi sānjiǎo	Delaunay triangulation	
德-模定理	Dé-mó dìnglǐ	deMorgan's theorem	
德-模尔根定理	Dé-mó-ěr-gēn dìnglǐ	deMorgan's theorem	
等额现金请领制	Děng'é xiànjīn qǐnglǐng zhì	Equal cash rule	
等步的	Děngbùde	Isochronous	
等测图	Děngcè tú	Isometric map	
等长电码	Děngcháng diànmǎ	Equal length code	
等待恢复	Děngdài huīfù	Wait to restore	WTR
等待恢复时间	Děngdài huīfù shíjiān	Wait to restore time	WTR
等待时间	Děngdài shíjiān	Latency	
等待时间	Děngdài shíjiān	Waiting time	
等待指示	Děngdài zhǐshì	Wait indicator	
等电平远端串音	Děngdiànpíng yuǎnduān chuànyīn	Equal level far end crosstalk	ELFEXT
等电平远端串音衰减功率和	Děngdiànpíng yuǎnduān chuànyīn shuāijiǎn gōnglǜ hé	Equal level far end crosstalk attenuation power sum	PSELFEXT
等电位连接	Děngdiànwèi liánjiē	Bonding	
等电位连接	Děngdiànwèi liánjiē	Equipotential bonding	
等电位连接导体	Děngdiànwèi liánjiē dǎotǐ	Equipotential bonding conductor	
等电位远端串扰	Děngdiànwèi yuǎnduān chuànrǎo	Equal level far end crosstalk	ELFEXT
等幅电报	Děngfú diànbào	Continuous wave telegraph	
等高平面位置显示器	Děnggāo píngmiàn wèizhì xiǎnshìqì	Constant altitude plane position indicator	PPI

等高距	Děnggāojù	Contour interval (GIS)	
等高线	Děnggāoxiàn	Contour (GIS)	
等高线标注	Děnggāoxiàn biāozhù	Contour tagging	
等高线间距	Děnggāoxiàn jiānjù	Contour interval	
等号操作符	Děnghào cāozuòfú	Equality operator	
等级	Děngjí	Rank	
登记	Dēngjì	Login, register (verb)	
等积地图投影	Děngjī dìtú tóuyǐng	Homolosine map project (GIS)	
等级改变	Děngjí gǎibiàn	Classmark change	
登记呼叫	Dēngjì hūjiào	Register call	
登记口令	Dēngjì kǒuling	Register password	
等级嵌块动态	Děngjí qiànkuài dòngtài	Hierarchical patch dynamics	
登记请求消息	Dēngjì qǐngqiú xiāoxi	Register request message	REG-REQ
登记确认消息	Dēngjì quèrèn xiāoxi	Register acknowledge message	REG-ACK
登记任务请求	Dēngjì rènwu qǐngqiú	Registration task request	
登记 SS	Dēngjì SS	Register SS	
等积投影	Děngjī tóuyǐng	Equiareal projection (GIS)	
登记响应消息	Dēngjì xiǎngyìng xiāoxi	Register response message	REG-RSP
等级钟	Děngjí zhōng	Layer clock	LC
登记周期	Dēngjì zhōuqī	Registration interval	REGINT
等价	Děngjià	Equivalence	
等价关系	Děngjià guānxi	Equivalence relation	
等价谓词	Děngjià wèicí	Equivalence predicate	
等角螺旋天线	Děngjiǎo luóxuán tiānxiàn	Equiangular spiral antenna	
等角平面螺旋天线	Děngjiǎo píngmiàn luóxuán tiānxiàn	Plane equiangular spiral antenna	
等角投影	Děngjiǎo tóuyǐng	Conformal projection	
等角投影	Děngjiǎo tóuyǐng	Equiangle projection (GIS)	
登记的公用陆地移动通信网	Dēngjìde gōngyòng lùdì yídòng tōngxìnwǎng	Registered public land mobile network	RPLMN
等距分类	Děngjù fēnlèi	Equal interval classification	
等距投影	Děngjù tóuyǐng	Equidistant projection (GIS)	
等距离投影	Děngjùlí tóuyǐng	Equidistant projection (GIS)	
等宽	Děngkuān	Monospace	
等离子表面改质机	Děnglízǐ biǎomiàn gǎizhìjī	Plasma surface modification machine (semiconductor mfg)	
等离子改良的化学汽相沉积法	Děnglízǐ gǎiliángde huàxué qìxiāng chénjīfǎ	Plasma modified chemical vapor deposition	PMCVD
等离子光阻去除机	Děnglízǐ guāngzǔ qùchújī	Plasma photoresist stripper (semiconductor mfg)	
等离子刻蚀机	Děnglízi kèshíjī	Plasma etcher (semiconductor mfg)	
等离子蚀刻机	Děnglízǐ shíkèjī	Plasma etcher (semiconductor mfg)	
等离子显示板	Děnglízǐ xiǎnshì bǎn	Plasma display panel	
等离子体化学汽相沉积法	Děnglízǐtǐ huàxué qìxiāng chénjīfǎ	Plasma chemical vapor deposition (FOC mfg)	PCVD
等离子体激活化学气相沉积	Děnglízǐtǐ jīhuó huàxué qìxiāng chénjī	Plasma-activated chemical vapor deposition (for FOC)	PCVD
等离子体增强化学汽相沉积	Děnglízǐtǐ zēngqiáng huàxué qìxiāng chénjī	Plasma enhanced chemical vapor deposition	PECVD
登录	Dēnglù	Login, logon	

登录安全模式	Dēnglù ānquán móshì	Login security mode (for database)	
登录服务器	Dēnglù fúwùqì	Login server	
登录脚本	Dēnglù jiǎoběn	Logon script	
登录脚本路径	Dēnglù jiǎoběn lùjìng	Logon script path	
登录权限	Dēnglù quánxiàn	Logon rights	
等面积投影	Děngmiànjī tóuyǐng	Equal area projection (GIS)	
等偏角图表	Děngpiānjiǎo túbiǎo	Isogonic chart (GIS)	
等偏角线	Děngpiānjiǎo xiàn	Isogonic line	
等强度线射束天线	Děngqiángdù xiàn shèshù tiānxiàn	Contoured-beam antenna	
等权网	Děngquán wǎng	Democratic network	
等时	Děngshí	Isochronism, isochronous	
等时传输	Děngshí chuánshū	Isochronous transmission	
等时畸变度	Děngshí jībiàndù	Degree of isochronous distortion	
等时调制	Děngshí tiàozhì	Isochronous modulation	
等时信号	Děngshí xìnhào	Isochronous signal	
等时以太网	Děngshí yǐtàiwǎng	Isoethernet	
等维	Děngwéi	Equivalent dimensionality	
等位编号	Děngwèi biānhào	Uniform numbering	
等相位面	Děngxiàngwèi miàn	Equiphase surface	
等向性	Děngxiàngxìng	Isotropy	
等效（点）噪声温度（线性双端口网络的）	Děngxiào (diǎn) zàoshēng wēndù (xiànxìng shuāng duān kǒu wǎngluòde)	Equivalent (spot) noise temperature (of a linear two-port network)	
等效半径	Děngxiào bànjìng	Equivalent radius (of a conductor)	
等效半径	Děngxiào bànjìng	Equivalent radius (of a multi-wire element)	
等效比特率	Děngxiào bǐtèlǜ	Equivalent bit rate	
等效地球半径	Děngxiào dìqiú bànjìng	Equivalent earth radius	
等效二进制数	Děngxiào èrjìn zhìshù	Equivalent binary content	
等效辐射功率	Děngxiào fúshè gōnglǜ	Equivalent radiated power	ERP
等效负载	Děngxiào fùzài	Dummy load	
等效各向同性辐射功率	Děngxiào gèxiàng tóngxìng fúshè gōnglǜ	Equivalent isotropically radiated power (in a given direction)	EIRP
等效全向辐射功率	Děngxiào quánxiàng fúshè gōnglǜ	Equivalent isotropic radiated power	EIRP
等效视数	Děngxiào shìshù	Equivalent number of looks (radar)	ENL
等效四线系统	Děngxiào sìxiàn xìtǒng	Equivalent four-wire system	EFWS
等效卫星链路噪声温度	Děngxiào wèixīng liànlù zàoshēng wēndù	Equivalent satellite link noise temperature	
等效卫星线路躁声温度	Děngxiào wèixīng xiànlù zàoshēng wēndù	Equivalent satellite link noise temperature	
等效噪声	Děngxiào zàoshēng	Equivalent noise	EN
等效噪声电压（单端口网络的）	Děngxiào zàoshēng diànyā	Equivalent noise voltage (of a one-port network)	
等效噪声电阻	Děngxiào zàoshēng diànzǔ	Equivalent noise resistance (of a one-port network)	
等效噪声输入	Děngxiào zàoshēng shūrù	Equivalent noise input	ENI
等压线	Děngyāxiàn	Isobar	
等增益合并	Děngzēngyì hébìng	Equivalent gain consolidation	EGC
等增益控制	Děngzēngyì kòngzhì	Equality gain control	EGC
等值剪切模型	Děngzhí jiǎnqiē móxíng	Equivalent shear model	
等值面	Děngzhí miàn	Isosurface	

等值区域图	Děngzhí qūyù tú	Choropleth map (GIS)	
等值线型化方法	Děngzhí xiànxínghuà fāngfǎ	Equivalent linearization method	
等值线	Děngzhíxiàn	Isarithm	
等值线	Děngzhíxiàn	Isoline	
等值线法	Děngzhíxiàn fǎ	Isoline method	
等值线图	Děngzhíxiàn tú	Choropleth	
等值线图	Děngzhíxiàn tú	Isarithmic map	
等值线图	Děngzhíxiàn tú	Isoline map	
等值线图	Děngzhíxiàn tú	Isopleth map	
等值线图	Děngzhíxiàn tú	Isogram	
德西特电报转换器	Dé-xī-tè diànbào zhuǎnhuànqì	Desieter telegraph translation	
德州仪器	Dézhōu yíqì	Texas Instruments	TI
第 232 号推荐标准	Dì 232 hào tuījiàn biāozhǔn	Recommended Standard 232	RS-232
地回幻线电路	Dì huíhuànxiàn diànlù	Ground phantom circuit	
第 n 次谐波比	Dì n-cì xiébō bǐ	Nth harmonic ratio	
第 N 级同步传送模块	Dì N-jí tóngbù chuánsòng mókuài	Synchronous transport module-N	STM-N
第 2 范式	Dì'èr fànshì	Second normal form	2NF
第二公共导频信道	Dì'èr gōnggòng dǎopín xìndào	Secondary common pilot channel	S-CPICH
第二公共控制物理信道	Dì'èr gōnggòng kòngzhì wùlǐ xìndào	Secondary common control physical channel	S-CCPCH
第二同步码	Dì'èr tóngbùmǎ	Secondary synchronization code	SSC
第二维纳滤波器解	Dì'èr wéinà lǜbōqì jiě	Second Wiener filter solution	SWFS
第二相邻信道	Dì'èr xiānglín xìndào	Second adjacent channel	
第二层（数据链路层）	Dì'èrcéng (shùjù liànlù céng)	Layer 2 (data link later)	L2
第二层管理链路	Dì'èrcéng guǎnlǐ liànlù	Layer 2 management link (OSI data link layer)	L2ML
第二层链路管理	Dì'èrcéng liànlù guǎnlǐ	Layer 2 management link	L2ML
第二层隧道协议	Dì'èrcéng suìdào xiéyì	Layer 2 tunneling protocol (Cisco usage)	L2TP
第二层中继	Dì'èrcéng zhōngjì	Layer 2 relay	L2R
第二层转发协议	Dì'èrcéng zhuǎnfā xiéyì	Layer 2 forwarding protocol (Cisco usage)	L2F
第二代	Dì'èrdài	Second generation	2G
第二代可下载音色	Dì'èrdài kěxiàzài yīnsè	Downloadable sounds level 2	DLS-2
第二代数字无绳电话系统	Dì'èrdài shùzì wúshéng diànhuà xìtǒng	Digital cordless telephone system second generation	CT-2
第二代无绳电话系统	Dì'èrdài wúshéng diànhuà xìtǒng	Cordless telephone system second generation	CT-2
第二类电缆	Dì'èrlèi diànlǎn	Category 2 cabling	Cat-2
第二类逻辑链路控制	Dì'èrlèi luóji liànlù kòngzhì	Logical link control, type 2	LLC2
地耦合干扰	Dì'ǒuhé gānrǎo	Ground-coupled interference	
垫	Diàn	Bead (in a coaxial line)	
点	Diǎn	Dot (in Morse code)	
点波束天线	Diǎn bōshù tiānxiàn	Spot beam antenna	
点采样技术	Diǎn cǎiyàng jìshù	Point sampling	
点操作符	Diǎn cāozuò fú	Dot operator (in graphics)	
电擦写可编程只读存储器	Diàn cāxiě kěbiānchéng zhǐdú cúnchǔqì	Electrically erasable programmable ROM	EEPROM
电长度	Diàn chángdù	Electrical length (of a waveguide element or component)	
点到点	Diǎn dào diǎn	Point-to-point	PP, P2P
点到点隧道协议	Diǎn dào diǎn suìdào xiéyì	Point-to-point tunneling protocol	PPTP
点到点协议	Diǎn dào diǎn xiéyì	Point-to-point protocol	PPP
点到多点	Diǎn dào duōdiǎn	Point-to-multipoint	

点对点传输协议	Diǎn duì diǎn chuánshū xiéyì	Point-to-point protocol	PPP
点对点短消息业务	Diǎn duì diǎn duǎn xiāoxi yèwù	Short message service point to point	SMS PP
点对点连接	Diǎn duì diǎn liánjiē	Point-to-point connection	
点对点面向连接网络业务	Diǎn duì diǎn miànxiàng liánjiē wǎngluò yèwù	Connection-mode network service	FTP-CONS PTP
点对点面向连接网络业务	Diǎn duì diǎn miànxiàng liánjiē wǎngluò yèwù	Point-to-point-connection network service	PTP-CONS
点对点隧道协议	Diǎn duì diǎn suìdào xiéyì	Point-to-point tunneling protocol	PPTP
点对点通道协议	Diǎn duì diǎn tōngdào xiéyì	Point-to-point tunneling protocol	PPTP
点对点通信	Diǎn duì diǎn tōngxìn	Point-to-point communication	
点对点通信协议	Diǎn duì diǎn tōngxìn xiéyì	Point-to-point protocol	PPP
点对点无连接网络业务	Diǎn duì diǎn wúliánjiē wǎngluò yèwù	Point-to-point connectionless-mode network service	PTP-CLNS
点对点协议	Diǎn duì diǎn xiéyì	Point-to-point protocol	PPP
点对点业务	Diǎn duì diǎn yèwù	Point-to-point service	PTP
点对地区通信	Diǎn duì dìqū tōngxìn	Point-area communication	
点对多点广播业务	Diǎn duì duōdiǎn guǎngbō yèwù	Point-to-multipoint multicasting	PTM-M
点对多点连接	Diǎn duì duōdiǎn liánjiē	Point-to-multipoint connection	
点对多点群呼业务	Diǎn duì duōdiǎn qúnhū yèwù	Point-to-multipoint group call	PTM-G
点对多点通信	Diǎn duì duōdiǎn tōngxìn	Point-to-multipoint communication	
点对多点业务	Diǎn duì duōdiǎn yèwù	Point-to-multipoint service	PTM
点对多点组播业务	Diǎn duì duōdiǎn zǔbō yèwù	Point-to-multipoint multicast	DAC
点对区域通信	Diǎn duì qūyù tōngxìn	Point-to-area communication	
点覆盖	Diǎn fùgài	Vertex cover	
电回波损耗	Diàn huíbō sǔnhào	Electric echo loss	EEL
点距	Diǎn jù	Dot pitch	
电可擦可编程序的只读存储器	Diàn kěcā kěbiān chéngxùde zhǐdú cúnchǔqì	Electrically erasable programmable read only memory	EEPROM
电可擦可编程只读存储器	Diàn kěcā kěbiānchéng zhǐdú cúnchǔqì	Electrically erasable programmable read-only memory	EEPROM
电可改存储器	Diàn kěgǎi cúnchǔqì	Electrically alterable storage	
电快速瞬变脉冲群	Diàn kuàisù shùnbiàn màichōng qún	Electrical fast transient/burst	EFT/B
点扩散函数	Diǎn kuòsàn hánshù	Point spread function	
点目标	Diǎn mùbiāo	Point target	
电屏蔽	Diàn píngbì	Electric shield	
点染色	Diǎn rǎnsè	Vertex coloring	
点生成算法	Diǎn shēngchéng suànfǎ	Point-generating algorithm	
电时分复用	Diàn shífēn fùyòng	Electrical time division multiplexing	ETDM
点十进制表示法	Diǎn shíjìnzhì biǎoshì fǎ	Dotted-decimal notation	
电网络	Diàn wǎngluò	Electrical network	
电小天线	Diàn xiǎo tiānxiàn	Electronically small antenna	
点序列	Diǎn xùliè	Dotting sequence	
点噪声温度（单端口网络的）	Diǎn zàoshēng wēndù (dān duānkǒu wǎngluòde)	Spot noise temperature (of a one-port network)	
点噪声系数（线性双端口装置的）	Diǎn zàoshēng xìshù (xiànxìng shuāng duān kǒu zhuāngzhìde)	Spot noise figure (of a linear two-port device)	
点噪声系数（线性双端口网络的）	Diǎn zàoshēng xìshù (xiànxìng shuāng duānkǒu wǎngluòde)	Spot noise factor (of a linear two-port network)	F(f)

点噪声因数（线性双端口装置的）	Diǎn zàoshēng yīnshù (xiànxìng shuāng duān kǒu zhuāngzhìde)	Spot noise factor (of a linear two-port device)	
点指向字符串	Diǎn zhǐxiàng zìfúchuàn	Point directive character string	
电/光转变	Diàn/guāng zhuǎnbiàn	Electrical/optical conversion	E/O
电/光转换	Diàn/guāng zhuǎnhuàn	Electronic/optical conversion	E/O
电报	Diànbào	Telegram, telegraph	DB
电报电码	Diànbào diànmǎ	Telegraph code	
电报电码表	Diànbào diànmǎ biǎo	Telegraph alphabet	
电报技术	Diànbào jìshù	Telegraphy	
电报技术	Diànbào jìshù	Telegraphy	
电报调制	Diànbào tiáozhì	Telegraph modulation	
电报信号	Diànbào xìnhào	Telegraph signal	
电报噪声	Diànbào zàoshēng	Telegraph noise	
电报终端	Diànbào zhōngduān	Telegraph terminal	
电波暗室	Diànbō ànshì	Anechoic enclosure	
点播电视	Diǎnbō diànshì	Video on demand	VOD
点播电影	Diǎnbō diànyǐng	Movie on demand	MOD
电波衰落	Diànbō shuāiluò	Radio wave fading	
点播消息	Diǎnbō xiāoxi	Message on demand	MOD
电测井	Diàncèjǐng	Electrical logging	
电场	Diànchǎng	Electric field	
电场辐射发射	Diànchǎng fúshè fāshè	Electric field radiated emissions (Mil-Std-461E, RE102)	
电场辐射敏感度	Diànchǎng fúshè mǐngǎndù	Electric field radiated susceptibility (Mil-Std-461E, RS103)	
电场强度	Diànchǎng qiángdù	Electric field strength	
电池低压报警	Diànchí dīyā bàojǐng	Low battery alarm	
电池低压关机	Diànchí dīyā guānjī	Low battery cut-off	
电池功率	Diànchí gōnglǜ	Battery power	
电池容量	Diànchí róngliàng	Battery capacity	
电传电报自动报文交换系统	Diànchuán diànbào zìdòng bàowén jiāohuàn xìtǒng	Automatic teletype message switching (system)	ATMS
电传图文（业务）	Diànchuán túwén (yèwù)	Telematics (services)	
电传业务	Diànchuán yèwù	Teleservice	TS
电传机	Diànchuánjī	Teleprinter	
电垂	Diànchuí	Sag	
电磁	Diàncí	Electromagnetic	
电磁发射	Diàncí fāshè	Electromagnetic emission	
电磁辐射	Diàncí fúshè	Electromagnetic radiation	
电磁干扰	Diàncí gānrǎo	Electromagnetic interference	EMI
电磁干扰安全裕度	Diàncí gānrǎo ānquán yùdù	Electromagnetic interference safety margin	
电磁感应	Diàncí gǎnyìng	Electromagnetic induction	
电磁光谱	Diàncí guāngpǔ	Electromagnetic spectrum	
电磁环境	Diàncí huánjìng	Electromagnetic environment	
电磁环境电平	Diàncí huánjìng diànpíng	Ambient electromagnetic level	
电磁兼容电平	Diàncí jiānróng diànpíng	Electromagnetic compatibility level	
电磁兼容裕量	Diàncí jiānróng yùliàng	Electromagnetic compatibility margin	
电磁兼容性	Diàncí jiānróngxìng	Electromagnetic compatibility	EMC

电磁勘查	Diàncí kānchá	Electromagnetic survey	
电磁脉冲	Diàncí màichōng	Electromagnetic pulse	EMP
电磁脉冲干扰	Diàncí màichōng gānrǎo	Electromagnetic pulse jamming	
电磁敏感度	Diàncí mǐngǎndù	Electromagnetic susceptibility	
电磁敏感性	Diàncí mǐngǎnxìng	Electromagnetic sensibility	EMS
电磁敏感性	Diàncí mǐngǎnxìng	Electromagnetic susceptibility	
电磁模	Diàncí mó	Electromagnetic mode	
电磁能量	Diàncí néngliàng	Electromagnetic energy	
电磁耦合	Diàncí ǒuhé	Electromagnetic coupling	
电磁屏蔽	Diàncí píngbì	Electromagnetic screen	
电磁屏蔽	Diàncí píngbì	Electromagnetic shielding	
电磁骚扰	Diàncí sāorǎo	Electromagnetic disturbance	
电磁通扰	Diàncí tōngrǎo	Electromagnetic disturbance	
电磁污染	Diàncí wūrǎn	Electromagnetic pollution	
电磁噪声	Diàncí zàoshēng	Electromagnetic noise	
电磁波	Diàncíbō	Electromagnetic wave	
电磁波反射	Diàncíbō fǎnshè	Reflection of electromagnetic wave	
电磁波饶射	Diàncíbō ráoshè	Diffraction of electromagnetic wave	
电磁波散射	Diàncíbō sǎnshè	Scattering of electromagnetic wave	
电磁波色射	Diàncíbō sèshè	Dispersion of electromagnetic wave	
电磁波吸收	Diàncíbō xīshōu	Absorption of electromagnetic wave	
电磁波折射	Diàncíbō zhéshè	Refraction of electromagnetic wave	
电磁场	Diàncíchǎng	Electromagnetic field	
电导	Diàndǎo	Conductance	
电导率	Diàndǎolǜ	Conductivity	
电导仪	Diàndǎoyí	Conductivity meter	
电的人机接口	Diànde rénjī jiēkǒu	Electrical man machine interface	EMMI
电的视轴	Diànde shìzhóu	Electrical boresight (of an antenna)	
电动单行程选择器	Diàndòng dānxíngchéng xuǎnzéqì	Motor uniselector	
电动势	Diàndòngshì	Electromotive force	emf
电镀零件	Diàndù língjiàn	Electroplating part	
电度表	Diàndùbiǎo	Watt-hour meter	
点分符号	Diǎnfēn fúhào	Dotted notation	
点符	Diǎnfú	Dot character (.)	
电腐蚀	Diànfǔshí	Electrical erosion	
电腐蚀	Diànfǔshí	Galvano-cautery, electrocorrosion	
电铬显示器	Diàngè xiǎnshìqì	Electrochromic display	ECD
电光光学晶体	Diànguāng guāngxué jīngtǐ	Electro-optic crystal	
电光偏折器	Diànguāng piānzhéqì	Electro-optic deflector	
电光扫瞄器	Diànguāng sǎomiáoqì	Electro-optic scanner	
电光调变器	Diànguāng tiáobiànqì	Electro-optic modulator	
电光信号转换器	Diànguāng xìnhào zhuǎnhuànqì	Electrical/optical signal converter	E/O
电荷连接设备	Diànhè liánjiē shèbèi	Charge coupled device	CCD
电荷耦合器件	Diànhè ǒuhé qìjiàn	Charge coupled device	CCD
电荷耦合器件对消器	Diànhè ǒuhé qìjiàn duìxiāoqì	Charge coupled device canceller	
电荷中和	Diànhè zhōnghé	Charge neutralization	

电话查号与通告系统	Diànhuà cháhào yǔ tōnggào xìtǒng	Directory assistance and messaging system	DAMSYS
电话答录	Diànhuà dálù	Telephone answering	
电话服务应用程序接口	Diànhuà fúwù yìngyòng chéngxù jiēkǒu	Telephony services application programming interface	TSAPI
电话服务器	Diànhuà fúwùqì	Telephone server	
电话公司	Diànhuà gōngsī	Telephone company	TELCO
电话管理信息系统	Diànhuà guǎnlǐ xìnxī xìtǒng	Telephone management information system	TMIS
电话号码	Diànhuà hàomǎ	Directory number	DN
电话汇款	Diànhuà huìkuǎn	Telephonic remittance	
电话回路	Diànhuà huílù	Telephone circuit	
电话会议	Diànhuà huìyì	Tele-conference	
电话间	Diànhuà jiān	Telephone booth	
电话技术	Diànhuà jìshù	Telephony	
电话控制协议	Diànhuà kòngzhì xiéyì	Telephone control protocol	TCP
电话控制协议	Diànhuà kòngzhì xiéyì	Telephony control specification	TCS
电话聊天室	Diànhuà liáotiān shì	Tele-chat room	
电话设备控制主机	Diànhuà shèbèi kòngzhì zhǔjī	Telephony device control master	TDCM
电话设备控制总线	Diànhuà shèbèi kòngzhì zǒngxiàn	Telephony device control bus	TD-BUS
电话设备系统库模块	Diànhuà shèbèi xìtǒngkù mókuài	Telephony device system library block	TDSL
电话设备主机后面板	Diànhuà shèbèi zhǔjī hòumianbǎn	Telephony device master back panel	TMBP
电话通知系统	Diànhuà tōngzhī xìtǒng	Voice broadcast	
电话投票	Diànhuà tóupiào	Televoting	VOT
电话应答机	Diànhuà yìngdájī	Telephone answering machine	TAM
电话应用程序接口	Diànhuà yìngyòng chéngxù jiēkǒu	Telephone application programming interface	TAPI
电话用户部分	Diànhuà yònghù bùfen	Telephone user part (SS7)	TUP
电话语音识别	Diànhuà yǔyīn shíbié	Phone query	
电话终端	Diànhuà zhōngduān	Telephone terminal	
电话中继局	Diànhuà zhōngjì jú	Telephone repeater station	TRS
电话自动计费系统	Diànhuà zìdòng jìfèi xìtǒng	Automatic call accounting	ACA
电话机	Diànhuàjī	Telephone set	
电话式电路	Diànhuàshì diànlù	Telephone type circuit	
电话线网络收发器	Diànhuàxiàn wǎngluò shōufāqì	Phoneline network transceiver	PNT
电话型电路	Diànhuà-xíng diànlù	Telephone-type circuit	
电话型信道	Diànhuà-xíng xìndào	Telephone-type channel	
点火分配器抑制器	Diǎnhuǒ fēnpèiqì yìzhìqì	Distributor spark suppressor	
电击	Diànjī	Electric shock	
点迹	Diǎnjì	Plot (verb)	
点击	Diǎnjī	Click (using a computer mouse)	
点击拨号	Diǎnjī bōhào	Click to dial	
点击传真	Diǎnjī chuánzhēn	Click to fax	CTF
点击发传真	Diǎnjī fā chuánzhēn	Click to fax	
电激发光显示器	Diànjī fāguāng xiǎnshìqì	Electroluminescence display	ELD
点击方式	Diǎnjī fāngshì	Point and click	
点击发送传真	Diǎnjī fāsòng chuánzhēn	Click to fax	CTF
点迹过滤	Diǎnjì guòlǜ	Plot filter	
点击回送传真	Diǎnjī huísòng chuánzhēn	Click to fax back	
点击数	Diǎnjī shù	Hits (number of)	

电键	Diànjiàn	Key (in switching)	
电键喀呖声	Diànjiàn kā-lì shēng	Telegraph key clicks	
电浆电视	Diànjiāng diànshì	Plasma display panel (PDP) television	
电浆显示器	Diànjiāng xiǎnshìqì	Plasma display panel	PDP
电键盘	Diànjiànpán	Keyboard	
电教馆	Diànjiào guǎn	Educational television hall	
点进次数	Diǎnjìn cìshù	Click-through	
点进率	Diǎnjìn lǜ	Click-through rate	
电抗加载移相器	Diànkàng jiāzài yíxiāngqì	Reactive loading phase shifter	
电抗式衰减器	Diànkàng-shì shuāijiǎnqì	Reactive attenuator	
电控可变光衰减器	Diànkòng kěbiàn guāng shuāijiǎnqì	Electrically variable optical attenuator	EVOA
电控转向天线	Diànkòng zhuǎnxiàng tiānxiàn	Electrically steerable antenna	
电缆槽	Diànlǎn cáo	Cable chute	
电缆单位	Diànlǎn dānwèi	Cable unit	
电缆电话	Diànlǎn diànhuà	Cable phone	CAP
电缆电视	Diànlǎn diànshì	Cable television	CATV
电缆端口	Diànlǎn duānkǒu	Cable port	
电缆附加器	Diànlǎn fùjiāqì	Cable adapter	
电缆敷设车	Diànlǎn fūshè chē	Carriage for cabling	
电缆沟	Diànlǎn gōu	Cable chute	
电缆故障探测器	Diànlǎn gùzhàng tàncèqì	Cable fault locator	CFL
电缆和电源线阻尼正弦瞬变传导敏感度	Diànlǎn hé diànyuánxiàn zǔní zhèngxián shùnbiàn chuándǎo mǐngǎndù	Power cable and power lead damped sinusoidal transient conducted susceptibility (Mil-Std-461E, CS116)	
电缆接口组件	Diànlǎn jiēkǒu zǔjiàn	Cable interface unit	CIU
电缆接入点	Diànlǎn jiērù diǎn	Cable access point	CAP
电缆宽带论坛	Diànlǎn kuāndài lùntán	Cable broadband forum	CBF
电缆盘	Diànlǎn pán	Cable drum	
电缆牵引圈	Diànlǎn qiānyǐn quān	Fish tape	
电缆桥架敷设	Diànlǎn qiáojià fūshè	Installed in cable tray	CT
电缆手推车	Diànlǎn shǒutuīchē	Cable drum hand cart	
电缆束注入传导敏感度	Diànlǎn shù zhùrù chuándǎo mǐngǎndù	Bulk cable injection conducted susceptibility (Mil-Std-461E, CS114)	
电缆束注入脉冲激励传导敏感度	Diànlǎn shù zhùrù màichōng jīlì chuándǎo mǐngǎndù	Bulk cable injection impulse excitation conducted susceptibility (Mil-Std-461E, CS115)	
电缆数据业务接口规范	Diànlǎn shùjù yèwù jiēkǒu guīfàn	Data over cable service interface specification	DOCSIS
电缆调制解调器	Diànlǎn tiáozhì jiětiáoqì	Cable modem	
电缆调制解调器终端系统	Diànlǎn tiáozhì jiětiáoqì zhōngduān xìtǒng	Cable modem termination system	CMTS
电缆替代协议	Diànlǎn tìdài xiéyì	Cable replacement protocol	CRP
电缆网上的数据接口规范	Diànlǎn wǎngshàngde shùjù jiēkǒu guīfàn	Data over cable system interface standard	DOCSIS
电缆载波	Diànlǎn zàibō	Cable carrier wave	LZ
电缆张力传感器	Diànlǎn zhānglì chuángǎnqì	Cable tension transducer	
电缆终端配线架	Diànlǎn zhōngduān pèixiànjià	Cable termination frame	CTF
电力调节设备	Diànlì tiáojié shèbèi	Power conditioning equipment	
电离层	Diànlícéng	Ionosphere	
电离层波	Diànlícéng bō	Ionospheric wave	
电离层传播	Diànlícéng chuánbō	Ionospheric propagation	

电离层反射	Diànlícéng fǎnshè	Ionospheric reflection	
电离层反射传播	Diànlícéng fǎnshè chuánbō	Ionosphere reflection propagation	
电离层散射	Diànlícéng sǎnshè	Ionospheric scatter	
电离层散射传播	Diànlícéng sǎnshè chuánbō	Ionosphere scatter propagation	
电离层骚扰	Diànlícéng sāorǎo	Ionosphere disturbance	
电离层相对透明度仪	Diànlícéng xiāngduì tòumíngdùyí	Relative ionosphere transparency meter	
电离层吸收	Diànlícéng xīshōu	Ionosphere absorption	
电离层折射	Diànlícéng zhéshè	Ionosphere refraction	
电流均衡器	Diànliú jūnhéngqì	Current equalizer	
电流探头	Diànliú tàntóu	Current probe	
电流增益	Diànliú zēngyì	Current gain	
电流-电压变换器	Diànliú/diànyā biànhuànqì	Current to voltage converter	I / V
电流表	Diànliúbiǎo	Ammeter	
电流型逻辑电路	Diànliú-xíng luóji diànlù	Current mode logic	CML
电力线架空光缆	Diànlìxiàn jiàkōng guānglǎn	Optical cables along electrical power lines	OCEPL
电力线接入	Diànlìxiàn jiērù	Powerline access	PLA
电力线宽带	Diànlìxiàn kuāndài	Powerline broadband	PLB
电力线通信	Diànlìxiàn tōngxìn	Powerline telecommunications	PLT
电力线载波	Diànlixiàn zàibō	Powerline carrier	PLC
电力线载波论坛	Diànlixiàn zàibō lùntán	Powerline carrier forum	PLCF
电路	Diànlù	Circuit	
电路板回流器	Diànlù bǎn huíliúqì	Printed circuit board diverter (in component assembly process)	
电路测试机	Diànlù cèshìjī	Circuit tester (in SMT)	
电路传递方式	Diànlù chuándì fāngshì	Circuit transfer mode	
电路传送模式	Diànlù chuánsòng móshì	Circuit transfer mode	
电路等级	Diànlù děngjí	Circuit grade	
电路方式承载业务	Diànlù fāngshì chéngzài yèwù	Circuit mode bearer service	CMBS
电路仿真业务	Diànlù fǎngzhēn yèwù	Circuit emulation service	CES
电路非衡重杂音	Diànlù fēihéngzhòng záyīn	Unweighted circuit noise	
电路副控制站	Diànlù fùkòngzhìzhàn	Circuit sub-control station	
电路复原消息	Diànlù fùyuán xiāoxi	Circuit reset signal	RSC
电路复原信号	Diànlù fùyuán xìnhào	Reset circuit signal	RSC
电路跟踪	Diànlù gēnzōng	Circuit tracing	
电路号码	Diànlù hàomǎ	Circuit number	
电路监视消息	Diànlù jiānshì xiāoxi	Circuit supervision message	CCM
电路监视信号	Diànlù jiānshì xìnhào	Circuit supervision signal	CCS
电路交换	Diànlù jiāohuàn	Circuit switching	CS
电路交换公共数据网	Diànlù jiāohuàn gōnggòng shùjù wǎng	Circuit switched public data network	CSPDN
电路交换公用数据网	Diànlù jiāohuàn gōngyòng shùjù wǎng	Circuit switched public data network	CSPDN
电路交换数据	Diànlù jiāohuàn shùjù	Circuit switched data	CSD
电路交换数据传输业务	Diànlù jiāohuàn shùjù chuánshū yèwù	Circuit switched data transmission service	
电路交换网	Diànlù jiāohuàn wǎng	Circuit switched network	CSN
电路交换网关	Diànlù jiāohuàn wǎngguān	Circuit switched gateway	CS-GW
电路交换网络	Diànlù jiāohuàn wǎngluò	Switched circuit network	SCN
电路交换业务	Diànlù jiāohuàn yèwù	Circuit switched service	CS
电路接入点	Diànlù jiērù diǎn	Circuit access points	

电路控制站	Diànlù kòngzhì zhàn	Circuit control station	
电路模拟接入卡	Diànlù mónǐ jiērù kǎ	Circuit emulation access card	CEMAC
电路配置监测器	Diànlù pèizhì jiāncèqì	Circuit configuration monitor	CCM
电路群	Diànlù qún	Circuit group	
电路群闭塞请求	Diànlù qún bìsè qǐngqiú	Circuit group blocking request (ISUP message)	CGB
电路群闭塞认可	Diànlù qún bìsè rènkě	Circuit group blocking acknowledgement (ISUP message)	CGBA
电路群复原消息	Diànlù qún fùyuán xiāoxi	Circuit group reset message	GRS
电路群复原证实消息	Diànlù qún fùyuán zhèngshí xiāoxi	Circuit group reset-acknowledgement message	GRA
电路群监视消息	Diànlù qún jiānshì xiāoxi	Circuit group supervision message	GRM
电路群解闭	Diànlù qún jiěbì	Circuit group unblock	
电路群解闭证实	Diànlù qún jiěbì zhèngshí	Circuit group unblocking acknowledge	
电路群拥塞信号	Diànlù qún yōngsè xìnhào	Circuit group congestion signal	CGC
电路群阻塞	Diànlù qún zǔsè	Circuit group block	
电路群阻塞证实	Diànlù qún zǔsè zhèngshí	Circuit group blocking acknowledge	
电路识别码	Diànlù shíbié mǎ	Circuit identification code	CIC
电路识别码表	Diànlù shíbiémǎ biǎo	Circuit identity code list	
电路网管理消息	Diànlù wǎng guǎnlǐ xiāoxi	Circuit network management message group	CNM
电路有效测试	Diànlù yǒuxiào cèshì	Circuit validation test	CVT
电路质量监测系统	Diànlù zhìliàng jiāncè xìtǒng	Circuit quality monitoring system	CQMS
电路中断器	Diànlù zhōngduànqì	Circuit interrupter	CI
电路状态指示器	Diànlù zhuàngtài zhǐshìqì	Circuit condition indicator	CCI
电路组	Diànlù zǔ	Circuit pool	
电路组表	Diànlù zǔ biǎo	Circuit pool list	
电路层网络	Diànlù-céng wǎngluò	Circuit layer network	
电脑电话集成	Diànnǎo diànhuà jíchéng	Computer telephony integration	CTI
电脑服务网	Diànnǎo fúwù wǎng	CompuServe (an ISP)	
电脑辅助培训	Diànnǎo fǔzhù péixùn	Computer-based training	CBT
电脑恐惧症	Diànnǎo kǒngjùzhēng	Cyberphobia	
电脑迷	Diànnǎo mí	Nerd, technonerd	
电脑修复中心	Diànnǎo xiūfù zhōngxīn	Computer recovery center	
电脑友伴	Diànnǎo yǒubàn	Computer Associate	CA
垫片程序	Diànpiàn chéngxù	Shim program (used between two interface programs)	
电平调节	Diànpíng tiáojié	Level modulation	LM
电屏蔽	Diànpíngbì	Electric shielding	
电气工程师协会	Diànqì gōngchéngshī xiéhuì	Institution of Electrical Engineers (UK)	IEE
电气工业中央协会	Diànqì gōngyè zhōngyāng xiéhuì	Zentralverband der Electrotechnischen Industrie (Germany)	ZVEI
电气间隙	Diànqì jiànxì	Clearance	
电气勘查	Diànqì kānchá	Electrical prospecting	
电气事故	Diànqì shìgù	Electric accident	
电气与电子工程师协会	Diànqì yǔ diànzǐ gōngchéngshī xiéhuì	Institute of Electrical and Electronic Engineers	IEEE
电气装置	Diànqì zhuāngzhì	Electrical installation	FD
电钳装	Diànqiánzhuāng	Auto-clamp assembly (surface mount technology)	
电桥	Diànqiáo	Hybrid junction	
电热调解器	Diànrè tiáojiěqì	Thermistor	
电容平衡	Diànróng pínghéng	Capacitance balance	

电容式传感器	Diànróng-shì chuángǎnqì	Capacitive transducer/sensor	
电扫描雷达	Diànsǎomiáo léidá	Electronic scanning radar	
电扫描天线	Diànsǎomiáo tiānxiàn	Electronic scanning antenna	
电声技术	Diànshēng jìshù	Telephony	
电蚀	Diànshí	Electrical corrosion, erode by electricity	
电视	Diànshì	Television	
电视电话	Diànshì diànhuà	Videophone	
电视电脑	Diànshì diànnǎo	Television-capable personal computer	TVPC
电视广播	Diànshì guǎngbō	Television broadcasting	
电视会议	Diànshì huìyì	Video conference	
电视会议服务	Diànshì huìyì fúwù	Video conference service	
电视会议终端	Diànshì huìyì zhōngduān	Video conference terminal	
电视教育馆	Diànshì jiàoyù guǎn	Educational television hall	
电视接收地面站	Diànshì jiēshōu dìmiànzhàn	Television receive only ground station	TVRO
电视数据	Diànshì shùjù	Teletext	TTX
电视文字广播系统	Diànshì wénzì guǎngbō xìtǒng	Teletext broadcast system	
电台	Diàntái	Station (a radio station)	
电台磁方位	Diàntái cí fāngwèi	Magnetic bearing of station	
电台方位	Diàntái fāngwèi	Bearing of station	
电台航向	Diàntái hángxiàng	Heading of station	
电台接口	Diàntái jiēkǒu	Radio adapter port	RAP
电调衰减器	Diàntiáo shuāijiǎnqì	Electric control attenuator	
电梯式查找（寻道）算法	Diàntī-shì cházhǎo (xúndào) suànfǎ	Elevator seeking algorithm	
电网去耦系数	Diànwǎng qù'ǒu xìshù	Mains decoupling factor	
电文	Diànwén	Teletext	
电文编号	Diànwén biānhào	Message numbering	
电文队列	Diànwén duìliè	Message queue	
电文格式	Diànwén géshi	Message format	
电文交换	Diànwén jiāohuàn	Message switching	
电文交换网络	Diànwén jiāohuàn wǎngluò	Message switching network	
电文结束代码	Diànwén jiéshù dàimǎ	End-of-message code	
电文路由选择	Diànwén lùyóu xuǎnzé	Message routing	
电文头段	Diànwén tóuduàn	Header segment	
电写	Diànxiě	Telewriting	
电写图像	Diànxiě túxiàng	Telewriting image	
电信	Diànxìn	Telecommunications	
电信传输研究所	Diànxìn chuánshū yánjiūsuǒ	Research Institute of Telecommunications Transmission (MII)	
电信电路	Diànxìn diànlù	Telecommunications circuit	
电信公司服务区	Diànxìn gōngsī fúwùqū	Carrier service area	CSA
电信公司营运服务区	Diànxìn gōngsī yíngyùn fúwùqū	Carrier service area	CSA
电信工业协会	Diànxìn gōngyè xiéhuì	Telecommunication Industries Association (US)	TIA
电信管理论坛	Diànxìn guǎnlǐ lùntán	Telecommunications Management Forum, TeleManagement Forum	TMF
电信管理网	Diànxìn guǎnlǐ wǎng	Telecommunications management network	TMN
电信管理网管理功能	Diànxìn guǎnlǐ wǎng guǎnlǐ gōngnéng	Telecommunications Management network-management function	TMN MF
电信管理网管理业务	Diànxìn guǎnlǐ wǎng guǎnlǐ yèwù	Telecommunications Management network-management service	TMN MS

电信管理网管理业务成分	Diànxìn guǎnlǐ wǎng guǎnlǐ yèwù chéngfèn	Telecommunications Management network-management service components	TMN MSC
电信管理网络	Diànxìn guǎnlǐ wǎngluò	Telecommunications Management network	TMN
电信管理局	Diànxìn guǎnlǐjú	Department of Telecommunications Administration (MII)	
电信规划研究院	Diànxìn guīhuà yánjiūyuàn	Academy of Telecommunications Research and Planning (MII)	
电信会议	Diànxìn huìyì	Teleconferencing	
电信间	Diànxìn jiān	Telecommunications closet	TC
电信建筑中的端口	Diànxìn jiànzhù-zhòngde duānkǒu	Ports in telecommunications buildings	
电信接入点基站	Diànxìn jiērùdiǎn jīzhàn	Telepoint base station	
电信接入点业务	Diànxìn jiērùdiǎn yèwù	Telepoint service	
电信技术协会	Diànxìn jìshù xiéhuì	Telecommunication Technology Association	TTA
电信科学技术研究院	Diànxìn kēxué jìshù yánjiūyuàn	China Academy of Telecommunications Technology	CATT
电信通道	Diànxìn tōngdào	Telecommunication path	
电信网	Diànxìn wǎng	Telecommunications network	
电信网用户	Diànxìn wǎng yònghù	Telecommunications network user	
电信信息组网结构	Diànxìn xìnxī zǔwǎng jiégòu	Telecommunications information networking architecture	TINA
电信研究院	Diànxìn yánjiūyuàn	Academy of Telecommunications Research (MII)	
电信业务	Diànxìn yèwù	Telecommunications service	
电信业务	Diànxìn yèwù	Teleservice	TS
电信业务电路	Diànxìn yèwù diànlù	Traffic circuit	
电信业务属性	Diànxìn yèwù shǔxìng	Telecommunications service attribute	
电信业务运载设备	Diànxìn yèwù yùnzài shèbèi	Traffic-carrying device	
电信引出端	Diànxìn yǐnchū duān	Telecommunications outlet	TO
电信政策办公室	Diànxìn zhèngcè bàngōngshì	Office of Telecommunications Policy (US)	OTP
电信支撑网	Diànxìn zhīchēng wǎng	Telecommunications supporting networks	TSN
电信支握网	Diànxìn zhīwò wǎng	Telecom supporting network	
电信中心	Diànxìn zhōngxīn	Telecommunication center	
电信主管部门	Diànxìn zhǔguǎn bùmén	Telecommunications administration	
电信总线	Diànxìn zǒngxiàn	Telecommunications bus	TBUS
典型安装	Diǎnxíng ānzhuāng	Typical installation (of software)	
典型波形内插	Diǎnxíng bōxíng nèichā	Prototype waveform interpolation	PWI
点型纹理混和	Diǎnxíng wénlǐ hùnhé	Dot texture blending (video term)	
典型相关分析	Diǎnxíng xiāngguān fēnxī	Canonical correlation analysis	
电吸收分布反馈	Diànxīshōu fēnbù fǎnkuì	Electricity absorption - distributed feedback	EA-DFB
电吸收调制	Diànxīshōu tiáozhì	Electricity absorption modulation	EAM
电吸收调制激光器	Diànxīshōu tiáozhì jīguāngqì	Electroabsorption modulated laser	EML
电吸收调制器	Diànxīshōu tiáozhìqì	Electroabsorption modulator	EAM
电讯媒体	Diànxùn méitǐ	Telemedia	
电压变化	Diànyā biànhuà	Voltage change	
电压变化持续时间	Diànyā biànhuà chíxù shíjiān	Duration of a voltage change	
电压变化发生率	Diànyā biànhuà fāshēng lǜ	Rate of occurrence of voltage change	
电压变化时间间隔	Diànyā biànhuà shíjiān jiàngé	Voltage change interval	
电压波动	Diànyā bōdòng	Voltage fluctuation	
电压波动波形	Diànyā bōdòng bōxíng	Voltage fluctuation waveform	
电压波动幅度	Diànyā bōdòng fúdù	Magnitude of a voltage fluctuation	
电压波动量	Diànyā bōdòng liáng	Voltage fluctuation magnitude	

电压不平衡	Diànyā bùpínghéng	Voltage imbalance	
电压低切断	Diànyā dī qiēduàn	Switchover on low voltage (of a battery)	
电压反射系数	Diànyā fǎnshè xìshù	Voltage reflection coefficient	
电压分解	Diànyā fēnjiě	Voltage resolving	
电压控制晶体振荡器	Diànyā kòngzhì jīngtǐ zhèndàngqì	Voltage controlled crystal oscillator	VCXO
电压浪涌	Diànyā làngyǒng	Voltage surge	
电压识别认证	Diànyā shíbié rènzhèng	Voltage identification definition	VID
电压瞬时跌落	Diànyā shùnshí diēluò	Voltage dip	
电压调整模块	Diànyā tiáozhěng mókuài	Voltage regulator module	VRM
电压骤降	Diànyā zhòujiàng	Voltage dip	
电压驻波比	Diànyā zhùbōbǐ	Voltage standing wave ratio	VSWR
电压－电流变换器	Diànyā/diànliú biànhuànqì	Voltage to current converter	V/I
电压 / 频率转换	Diànyā/pínlǜ zhuǎnhuàn	Voltage-to-frequency conversion	V/F
电压表	Diànyābiǎo	Voltmeter	
电涌	Diànyǒng	Surge	
电源	Diànyuán	Power supply	DY
电源车	Diànyuán chē	Power carriage	
电源持续工作能力	Diànyuán chíxù gōngzuò nénglì	Continuous operation ability of the power supply	
电源电压变化试验	Diànyuán diànyā biànhuà shìyàn	Change of power line voltage	
电源电压调整率	Diànyuán diànyā tiáozhěnglǜ	Line regulation	
电源丢失	Diànyuán diūshī	Loss of power	
电源管理系统	Diànyuán guǎnlǐ xìtǒng	Power management system	PMS
电源开关	Diànyuán kāiguān	Power switch (on electronic equipment)	
电源抗扰性	Diànyuán kàngrǎoxìng	Mains immunity	
电源控制电路	Diànyuán kòngzhì diànlù	Power control circuit	
电源控制系统	Diànyuán kòngzhì xìtǒng	Supply control system	SCS
电源拉偏测试	Diànyuán lāpiān cèshì	Power supply bias test	
电源连续工作能力	Diànyuán liánxù gōngzuò nénglì	Continuous operating ability of the main power	
电源母	Diànyuán mǔ	Power supply motherboard	PWB
电原配电架	Diànyuán pèidiànjià	Power supply distribution frame	PDF
电源去耦系数	Diànyuán qù'ǒu xìshù	Mains decoupling factor	
电源骚扰	Diànyuán sāorǎo	Mains-borne disturbance	
电源调节	Diànyuán tiáojié	Power conditioning	
电源系统	Diànyuán xìtǒng	Power system	PWS
电源要求	Diànyuán yāoqiú	Power requirement	
电源支架	Diànyuán zhījià	Power tray	
电源线传导发射	Diànyuánxiàn chuándǎo fāshè	Power lead conducted emissions (Mil-Std-461E, CE101)	
电源线传导敏感度	Diànyuánxiàn chuándǎo mǐngǎndù	Power lead conducted susceptibility (Mil-Std-461E, CS101)	
电源线尖峰信号（时域）传导发射	Diànyuánxiàn jiānfēng xìnhào (shí yù) chuándǎo fāshè	Power lead peak signal (time domain) conducted emissions (Mil-Std-461E, CE107)	
电源线尖峰信号传导敏感度	Diànyuánxiàn jiānfēng xìnhào chuándǎo mǐngǎndù	Power lead peak signal conducted susceptibility (Mil-Std-461E, CS106)	
电源线天线	Diànyuánxiàn tiānxiàn	Mains antenna	
点阵衍射图制作技术	Diǎnzhèn yǎnshètú zhìzuò jìshù	Lattice diffraction graph fabrication	
点阵式打印机	Diǎnzhèn-shì dǎyìnjī	Dot matrix printer	
点阵图	Diǎnzhèntú	Bitmap	

点值法	Diǎnzhí fǎ	Dot method (GIS)	
点状符号	Diǎnzhuàng fúhào	Point symbol, marker	
电子按键电话系统	Diànzǐ ànjiàn diànhuà xìtǒng	Electronic key telephone system	EKTS
电子白板	Diànzǐ báibǎn	Electronic white board	
电子传单	Diànzǐ chuándān	Electronic bonding	
电子串号	Diànzǐ chuànhào	Electronic serial number	ESN
电子串号	Diànzǐ chuànhào	Electronic sequence number	ESN
电子电话交换系统	Diànzǐ diànhuà jiāohuàn xìtǒng	Electronic telephone switching system	ETSS
电子电气工程学会	Diànzǐ diànqì gōngchéng xuéhuì	Institute of Electrical and Electronics Engineers	IEEE
电子电信咨询委员会	Diànzǐ diànxìn zīxún wěiyuánhuì	Advisory Committee on Electronics and Telecommunications	ACET
电子地图集	Diànzǐ dìtújí	Electronic atlas	
电子对抗	Diànzǐ duìkàng	Electronic countermeasures	ECM
电子干扰	Diànzǐ gānrǎo	Electronic jamming	
电子工程师协会	Diànzǐ gōngchéngshī xiéhuì	Electronic Engineers Association	EEA
电子公告栏	Diànzǐ gōnggào lán	Bulletin board system	BBS
电子攻击	Diànzǐ gōngjī	Electronic attack (IW)	EA
电子工业联合会	Diànzǐ gōngyè liánhéhuì	Electronic Industries Association	EIA
电子工业协会	Diànzǐ gōngyè xiéhuì	Electronic Industries Association	EIA
电子海图	Diànzǐ hǎitú	Electronic chart	
电子号码	Diànzǐ hàomǎ	Electronic numbering	ENUM
电子话音处理	Diànzǐ huàyīn chǔlǐ	Electronic voice processing	
电子货币	Diànzǐ huòbì	Cybercash	
电子交叉点	Diànzǐ jiāochādiǎn	Electronic crosspoint	
电子交换程序设计语言	Diànzǐ jiāohuàn chéngxù shèjì yǔyán	Electronic switching programming language	ESPL
电子集成	Diànzǐ jíchéng	Electronic integration, e-integration	
电子集成驱动器	Diànzǐ jíchéng qūdòngqì	Integrated drive electronics	IDE
电子记事本	Diànzǐ jìshìběn	Digital diary	
电子距离测量设备	Diànzǐ jùlí cèliáng shèbèi	Electronic distance measuring device	EDMD
电子控制的电话交换局	Diànzǐ kòngzhìde diànhuà jiāohuànjú	Electronically-controlled telephone exchange	ECX
电子密本	Diànzǐ mìběn	Electronic code book	ECB
电子密匙交换	Diànzǐ mìshi jiāohuàn	Electronic key exchange	
电子频移	Diànzǐ pínyí	Electron frequency drift	
电子钱	Diànzǐ qián	Cybercash, digicash	
电子前线基金会	Diànzǐ qiánxiàn jījīnhuì	Electronic Frontier Foundation	EFF
电子扫描振荡器	Diànzǐ sǎomiáo zhèndàngqì	Electronic sweep generator	ESG
电子扫描仪	Diànzǐ sǎomiáoyí	Electrostatic line scanner	
电子商务	Diànzǐ shāngwù	Electronic commerce, e-commerce	EC
电子商务	Diànzǐ shāngwù	E-business	
电子设计自动化	Diànzǐ shèjì zìdònghuà	Electronic design automation	
电子市场	Diànzǐ shìchǎng	E-marketplace	
电子束	Diànzǐ shù	Electron beam	
电子鼠	Diànzǐ shǔ	Mouse	
电子数据处理器	Diànzǐ shùjù chǔlǐqì	Electronic data processing center	EDPC
电子数据交换	Diànzi shùjù jiāohuàn	Electronic data interchange	EDI
电子数字综合计算机	Diànzǐ shùzì zōnghé jìsuànjī	Electrical numerical integrator & calculator	ENIAC
电子伪装	Diànzǐ wěizhuāng	Electronic camouflage	

电子现金	Diànzǐ xiànjīn	E-cash, digital currency	
电子信函业务	Diànzi xìnhán yèwù	Messaging service	
电子新闻收集	Diànzǐ xīnwén shōují	Electronic news gathering	ENG
电子信箱	Diànzǐ xìnxiāng	Electronic mail	E-mail
电子系统工程	Diànzǐ xìtǒng gōngchéng	Electronic system engineering	
电子序号	Diànzǐ xùhào	Electric sequence number	ESN
电子序列号	Diànzǐ xùlièhào	Electronic serial number	ECN
电子邮件	Diànzi yóujiàn	Electronic mail, e-mail	
电子游戏	Diànzǐ yóuxì	Arcade game	
电子娱乐展览会	Diànzǐ yúlè zhǎnlǎnhuì	Electronic entertainment expo	E3
电子侦察	Diànzǐ zhēnchá	Electronic reconnaissance	
电子支票	Diànzǐ zhīpiào	Electronic check, e-check	
电子支援	Diànzǐ zhīyuán	Electronic support (in electronic warfare)	
电子注聚焦	Diànzǐ zhù jùjiāo	Electronic beam focusing	
电子自动调谐	Diànzǐ zìdòng tiáoxié	Electronic automatic tuning	
电子组装	Diànzǐ zǔzhuāng	Electronic packaging	
电子管间歇振荡器	Diànzǐguǎn jiànxiē zhèndàngqì	Blocking-tube oscillator	BTO
电子束落区	Diànzǐshù luò qū	Beam landing area (video term)	BLA
电子战	Diànzǐzhàn	Electronic warfare	EW
电子战模拟试验场	Diànzǐzhàn mónǐ shìyànchǎng	Electronic warfare (EW) simulation test range	
电阻	Diànzǔ	Resistance, resistor	
电阻晶体管逻辑电路	Diànzǔ jīngtǐguǎn luójì diànlù	Resistor transistor logic circuit	RTL
电阻温度传感器	Diànzǔ wēndù chuángǎnqì	Resistance temperature detector	RTD
电阻温度计	Diànzǔ wēndùjì	Resistance thermometer	
电阻抗特性	Diànzǔkàng tèxìng	Electrical impedance characteristics	EIC
电阻式衰减器	Diànzǔ-shì shuāijiǎnqì	Resistive attenuator	
电阻性	Diànzǔxìng	Resistive (adj.)	
电阻性点火分配器电刷	Diànzǔxìng diǎnhuǒ fēnpèiqì diànshuā	Resistive distributor brush	
吊顶内敷设	Diào dǐng-nèi fūshè	In hollow spaces of ceiling	
调侧	Diáocè	Commission (verb), put into commission	
掉电	Diàodiàn	Power loss, outage	LPR
掉电请求	Diàodiàn qǐngqiú	Request to power down	REQPDN
调度	Diàodù	Scheduling	
调度（程序）	Diàodù (chéngxù)	Dispatch (program)	
调度程序	Diàodù chéngxù	Scheduler	
调度电话	Diàodù diànhuà	Dispatch telephone	D
调度算法	Diàodù suànfǎ	Scheduling algorithm	
调度器	Diàodùqì	Dispatcher	
调度器	Diàodùqì	Scheduler (for QoS)	
调度台	Diàodùtái	Dispatch desk	
调度台控制器	Diàodùtái kòngzhìqì	Dispatch station controller	DCS
掉话	Diàohuà	Dropped call	
掉话率	Diàohuà lǜ	Voice dropout rate	
调用	Diàoyòng	Call (noun, in computer use, invoking a program or subroutine, in telecom use, initiating a protocol or subroutine)	
调用	Diàoyòng	Invoke	

调用操作符	Diàoyòng cāozuò fú	Call operator	
调用跟踪	Diàoyòng gēnzōng	Invoke trace	
调用级接口	Diàoyòng jí jiēkǒu	Call-level interface	CLI
调用识别码	Diàoyòng shíbiémǎ	Invoke ID	
调用信息处理	Diàoyòng xìnxī chǔlǐ	Call information processing	CIP
调用的应用	Diàoyòngde yìngyòng	Invoked application	
底板	Dǐbǎn	Back plane	
底板	Dǐbǎn	Bay (computer term)	
地板或地板下敷设	Dìbǎn huò dìbǎn-xià fūshè	Laid in floor or under floor	
低比特率	Dībǐtè lǜ	Low bit rate	
地波	Dìbō	Ground wave	
低层功能	Dīcéng gōngnéng	Low layer function	LLF
低层管理实体	Dīcéng guǎnlǐ shítǐ	Low layer management entity	LLME
低层兼容	Dīcéng jiānróng	Lower layer compatibility	LLC
低层兼容性	Dīcéng jiānróngxìng	Low layer compatibility	LLC
底层结构	Dǐcéng jiégòu	Infrastructure	IF
底层网	Dǐcéng wǎng	Underlying network	
低层消息函数	Dīcéng xiāoxi hánshù	Low-level message function	
底层一致性	Dǐcéng yīzhìxìng	Low layer uniformity	
底场	Dǐchǎng	Bottom field	
低等级业务控制点	Dīděngjí yèwù kòngzhìdiǎn	Low order service control point	LSCP
低电平输出电压	Dīdiànpíng shūchū diànyā	Low-level output voltage	
低电平输出电流	Dīdiànpíng shūchūdiànliú	Low-level output current	
低电平调制	Dīdiànpíng tiáozhì	Low-power modulation	
低电压差动信号	Dīdiànyā chādòng xìnhào	Low voltage differential signal	LVDS
低电压光圈阴极管	Dīdiànyā guāngquān yīnjíguǎn	Low voltage small aperture grid with impregnated cathode	L-SAGIC
低定位概率	Dīdìngwèi gàilǜ	Low probability of position fix	LPPF
低地球轨道	Dīdìqiú guǐdào	Low earth orbit	LEO
低地址低字节	Dīdìzhǐ dīzìjié	Little-endian (data storage format)	
低地址段	Dīdìzhǐ duàn	Low address part	LAP
低地址高字节顺序	Dīdìzhǐ gāozìjié shùnxù	Big-endian (data storage format)	
叠辗转开解	Dié zhǎnzhuǎn kāijiě	Stack unwinding	
迭层	Diécéng	Stacking	
叠层工艺法	Diécéng gōngyì fǎ	Laminated object manufacturing	LOM
迭代	Diédài	Iterate, iteration	
迭代分组密码	Diédài fēnzǔ mìmǎ	Iterative block cipher	
迭代函数系统	Diédài hánshù xìtǒng	Iteration function system	IFS
迭代匹配调度算法	Diédài pǐpèi diàodù suànfǎ	Iterative matching scheduling algorithm	
迭代隧道	Diédài suìdào	Iterative tunneling	
迭代运算	Diédài yùnsuàn	Iterative operation	IO
迭代的	Diédàide	Iterative	
迭代器	Diédàiqì	Iterator	
叠加	Diéjiā	Stacking	
叠加	Diéjiā	Overlay (GIS)	
叠加图	Diéjiā tú	Drape	
跌落试验	Diēluò shìyàn	Impact test	

第二级数据复用器	Dì'èrjí shùjù fùyòngqì	Second data multiplexer	
叠印	Diéyìn	Overprint	
地方贝尔运营公司	Dìfang Bèi-ěr yùnyíng gōngsī	Regional Bell operating company	RBOC
地方自治	Dìfāng zìzhì	Home rule	
地方坐标系	Dìfang zuòbiāo xì	Local coordinate system	
地方的预约信息段识别	Dìfangde yùyuē xìnxī duàn shíbié	Regional subscription zone identity	RSZI
低辐射	Dīfúshè	Low emissivity	
低功率信标	Dīgōnglǜ xìnbiāo	Low-power beacon	
低功率振荡器	Dīgōnglǜ zhèndàngqì	Low power oscillator	LOP
递归	Dìguī	Recursive	
递归分区	Dìguī fēnqū	Recursive partitioning	
递归函数	Dìguī hánshù	Recursive function	
递归系统卷积码	Dìguī xìtǒng juànjīmǎ	Recursive systematic convolutional code	RSC
递归最小二乘	Dìguī zuìxiǎo èrshèng	Recursive least square	RLS
递归最小平方	Dìguī zuìxiǎo píngfāng	Recursive least square	RLS
低轨道	Dīguǐdào	Low earth orbit	LEO
低轨道卫星系统	Dīguǐdào wèixīng xìtǒng	Low earth orbit satellite mobile communication system	
地回双幻线电路	Dìhuí shuānghuànxiàn diànlù	Earth-return double phantom circuit	
低级	Dījí	Inferior, subordinate	
地籍图	Dìjí tú	Cadastral map	
低级信令转换点	Dījí xìnlìng zhuǎnhuàn diǎn	Low level signal transfer point	LSTP
低级信令转接点	Dījí xìnlìng zhuǎnjiē diǎn	Low level signal transfer point	LSTP
低级语言	Dījí yǔyán	Low level language	
低级中断请求	Dījí zhōngduàn qǐngqiú	Low level interrupt request	LLIR
低检测概率	Dījiǎncè gàilǜ	Low probability of detection	LPD
递交后的重复帧	Dìjiāo hòude chóngfù zhèng	Delivered duplicate frames	
递交后的出错帧	Dìjiāo hòude chūcuò zhèng	Delivered errored frames	
递交后的失序帧	Dìjiāo hòude shīxù zhèng	Delivered out-of-sequence frames	
低阶	Dījiē	Lower order	LO
低阶接口	Dījiē jiēkǒu	Lower order interface	LOI
低阶连接监控	Dījiē liánjiē jiānkòng	Lower order connection supervision	LCS
低阶连接监视	Dījiē liánjiē jiānshì	Lower order connection supervision	LCS
低阶通道	Dījiē tōngdào	Lower order path	LP
低阶通道保护	Dījiē tōngdào bǎohù	Lower order path protection	LPP
低阶通道层	Dījiē tōngdào céng	Lower order path layer	LOPL
低阶通道串联连接监视	Dījiē tōngdào chuànlián liánjiē jiānshì	Lower order path tandem connection monitor	LTCM
低阶通道串联连接监视器	Dījiē tōngdào chuànlián liánjiē jiānshìqì	Lower order tandem connection monitor	LO-TCM
低阶通道串联连接适配	Dījiē tōngdào chuànlián liánjiē shìpèi	Lower order path tandem connection adaptation	LTCA
低阶通道串联连接终端	Dījiē tōngdào chuànlián liánjiē zhōngduān	Lower order path tandem connection termination	LTCT
低阶通道监控未装载终端	Dījiē tōngdào jiānkòng wèizhuāngzài zhōngduān	Lower order path supervisory unequipped termination	LSUT
低阶通道接收缺陷指示	Dījiē tōngdào jiēshōu quēxiàn zhǐshì	Lower order path receive defect indicator	LP-RDI
低阶通道开销	Dījiē tōngdào kāixiao	Lower order path overhead	LPOH
低阶通道开销监视	Dījiē tōngdào kāixiao jiānshì	Lower order path overhead monitoring	LPOM
低阶通道开销监视器	Dījiē tōngdào kāixiao jiānshìqì	Lower order path overhead monitor	LPOM
低阶通道连接	Dījiē tōngdào liánjiē	Lower order path connection	LPC

低阶通道路踪识别失配	Dījiē tōngdào lùzōng shíbié shīpèi	Lower order path trace identification mismatch	LP-TIM
低阶通道适配	Dījiē tōngdào shìpèi	Lower order path adaptation	LPA
低阶通道网络连接	Dījiē tōngdào wǎngluò liánjiē	Lower order path network connection	LOP NC
低阶通道未装载	Dījiē tōngdào wèizhuāngzài	Lower order path unequipped	LP-UNEQ
低阶通道远端缺陷指示	Dījiē tōngdào yuǎnduān quēxiàn zhǐshì	Lower order path remote defect indication	LP-RDI
低阶通道远端失效指示	Dījiē tōngdào yuǎnduān shīxiào zhǐshì	Remote failure indication of lower order path	LP-RFI
低阶通道远端误码指示	Dījiē tōngdào yuǎnduān wùmǎ zhǐshì	Remote error indication of lower order path	LP-REI
低阶通道终端	Dījiē tōngdào zhōngduān	Lower order path termination	LPT
低阶虚容器	Dījiē xūróngqì	Lower order virtual container	LOVC
低截获概率	Dījiéhuò gàilǜ	Low probability of intercept	LPI
地克型辐射计	Dì-kè-xíng fúshèjì	Dicke radiometer	
地-空路径传播	Dì-kōng lùjìng chuánbō	Earth-space path propagation	
低空搜索雷达	Dīkōng sōusuǒ léidá	Low-altitude surveillance radar	
地-空通信设备	Dì-kōng tōngxìn shèbèi	Ground/air communication equipment	
地块	Dìkuài	Land parcel	
地块标识号	Dìkuài biāozhìhào	Parcel identification numbers	
抵赖性	Dǐlàixìng	Repudiation (IPsec)	
地理标记语言	Dìlǐ biāojì yǔyán	Geography markup language	GML
地里信息系统	Dìli xìnxī xìtǒng	Geographical information system	GIS
地理坐标网	Dìlǐ zuòbiāo wǎng	Geographic graticule (GIS)	
帝盟	Dì-méng	Diamond (MP3 manufacturer)	
低密聚乙烯	Dīmì jùyǐxī	Low density polyethylene	LDPE
地面电路	Dìmiàn diànlù	Terrestrial circuit	
地面电台	Dìmiàn diàntái	Terrestrial station	
地面固定无线接入	Dìmiàn gùdìng wúxiàn jiērù	Terrestrial fixed wireless access	TFWA
地面连线用户	Dìmiàn liánxiàn yònghù	Landline subscriber	
地面通道	Dìmiàn tōngdào	Terrestrial channel	TC
地面网	Dìmiàn wǎng	Ground mat	
地面无线接入	Dìmiàn wúxiàn jiērù	Terrestrial wireless access	TWA
地面无线电通信	Dìmiàn wúxiàndiàn tōngxìn	Terrestrial radio communication	
地面移动接入	Dìmiàn yídòng jiērù	Terrestrial mobile access	TMA
地面站	Dìmiànzhàn	Earth station	
地名录	Dìmíng lù	Gazetteer	
定方位	Dìng fāngwèi	Orientation	
顶板	Dǐngbǎn	Vertex plate (of a paraboloidal reflector)	
定标	Dìngbiāo	Calibrate	
定比码	Dìngbǐmǎ	Constant ratio code	
顶部	Dǐngbù	Crown	
顶部加载垂直天线	Dǐngbù jiāzài chuízhí tiānxiàn	Top-loaded vertical antenna	
定长	Dìngcháng	Fixed-length	
定长编码	Dìngcháng biānmǎ	Block code	
定长单向确认	Dìngcháng dānxiàng quèrèn	Fixed length one-way acknowledgement	
定长记录	Dìngcháng jìlù	Fixed-length records	F
定长双向确认	Dìngcháng shuāngxiàng quèrèn	Fixed-length two-way acknowledgement	
顶点	Dǐngdiǎn	Vertex	
定点表示法	Dìngdiǎn biǎoshì fǎ	Fixed point representation	FPR

顶点聚合	Dǐngdiǎn jùhé	Vertex aggregation (CAD/CAM)	VA
顶点展开	Dǐngdiǎn zhǎnkāi	Vertex expansion (CAM/CAM)	VE
顶端加载天线	Dǐngduān jiāzài tiānxiàn	Top-loaded antenna	
顶级聚集标识符	Dǐngjí jùjí biāozhìfú	Top level aggregation identifier	TLAID
顶级域	Dǐngjí yù	Top-level domain	
定量的	Dìngliàngde	Quantitative	
定流	Dìngliú	Steady flow	
定期频率预报	Dìngqī pínlǜ yùbào	Periodical frequency forecast	
定期维护	Dìngqī wéihù	Scheduled maintenance	
定时超前	Dìngshí chāoqián	Timing advance	
定时抽取	Dìngshí chōuqǔ	Timing extraction	
定时点	Dìngshí diǎn	Timing point	TP
定时电路	Dìngshí diànlù	Timing circuit	TIM
定时攻击	Dìngshí gōngjī	Timing attack	
定时和频率模块	Dìngshí hé pínlǜ mókuài	Timing and frequency block	TFB
定时环	Dìngshí huán	Timing loop	
定时恢复	Dìngshí huīfù	Timing recovery	
定时检测表	Dìngshí jiǎncè biǎo	Timing detection table	TDT
定时接收机自主完善性监测	Dìngshí jiēshōujī zìzhǔ wánshànxìng jiāncè	Timing receiver autonomous integrity monitoring	TRAIM
定时脉冲	Dìngshí màichōng	Timing pulse	
定时提前	Dìngshí tíqián	Timing advance	TA
定时提前量	Dìngshí tíqiánliàng	Timing advance	TA
定时提取	Dìngshí tíqǔ	Timing recovery	
定时同步消息	Dìngshí tóngbù xiāoxi	Timing synchronization message	SYNC
定时相位	Dìngshí xiàngwèi	Timing phase	
定时信号	Dìngshí xìnhào	Timing signal	
定时信息	Dìngshí xìnxī	Timing information	TI
定时预分配多路存取	Dìngshí yù fēnpèi duōlù cúnqǔ	Timed pre-assigned multiple access	TPMA
定时器	Dìngshíqì	Timer	
定时器超时	Dìngshíqì chāoshí	Timing period expired	
定时器重启	Dìngshíqì chóngqǐ	Timing period restarted	
定位	Dìngwèi	Alignment	
定位	Dìngwèi	Orientation	
定位参照系	Dìngwèi cānzhàoxì	Locational reference	
定位测量单元	Dìngwèi cèliáng dānyuán	Location measurement unit	LMU
定位差错率监视	Dìngwèi chācuòlǜ jiānshì	Alignment error rate monitor	AERM
定位点	Dìngwèi diǎn	Position point	
定位抖动	Dìngwèi dǒudòng	Alignment jitter	
定位范围	Dìngwèi fànwéi	Orientation range	
定位服务器	Dìngwèi fúwùqì	Location server, position server	
定位更新	Dìngwèi gèngxīn	Positioned update	
定位光纤束	Dìngwèi guāngxiānshù	Aligned bundle	
定位接口结构	Dìngwèi jiēkǒu jiégòu	Positioned interface structure	
定位精度	Dìngwèi jīngdù	Positional accuracy, locational accuracy	
定位拒绝	Dìngwèi jùjué	Location reject	LRJ

定位请求	Dìngwèi qǐngqiú	Location request	LRQ
定位区	Dìngwèi qū	Positioning area	
定位确认	Dìngwèi quèrèn	Location confirm	LCF
定位套	Dìngwèi tào	Position sleeve	
定位销	Dìngwèi xiāo	Position keying	
定位信道	Dìngwèi xìndào	Positioned channel	
定位系统	Dìngwèi xìtǒng	Positioning system	
定位业务	Dìngwèi yèwù	Localization service	LCS
定位业务	Dìngwèi yèwù	Location services	LCS
定位业务服务器	Dìngwèi yèwù fúwùqì	Location services server	LCSS
定位业务客户	Dìngwèi yèwù kèhù	Location services client	LCSC
定位仪	Dìngwèiyí	Locator	
定温控测器	Dìngwēn kòngcèqì	Fixed temperature heat detector	FTHD
定向互导	Dìngxiàng hùdǎo	Directional mutual conductance	
定向呼叫字符	Dìngxiàng hūjiào zìfú	Call-directing character	CDC
定向连接网络协议	Dìngxiàng liánjiē wǎngluò xiéyì	Connection-oriented network protocol	CONP
定向连接网络业务	Dìngxiàng liánjiē wǎngluò yèwù	Connection-oriented network service	CONS
定向能武器	Dìngxiàng néng wǔqì	Directed energy weapon	DEW
定向耦合器	Dìngxiàng ǒuhéqì	Directional coupler	
定向树	Dìngxiàng shù	Directed tree	
定向天线	Dìngxiàng tiānxiàn	Directional antenna	
定向天线阵	Dìngxiàng tiānxiàn zhèn	Directional (antenna) array	DA
定向调入字符	Dìngxiàng tiáorù zìfú	Call-directing character	CDC
定向陀螺仪位置	Dìngxiàng tuóluóyí wèizhì	Directional gyroscope position	DGP
定向信息中间件	Dìngxiàng xìnxī zhōngjiān jiàn	Message-oriented middleware	MOM
定向载波控制多路存取	Dìngxiàng zàibō kòngzhì duōlù cúnqǔ	Directional carrier sense multiple access	D-CSMA
定型号码	Dìngxíng hàomǎ	Type approval code	TAC
定型试验	Dìngxíng shìyàn	Type test	
定性的	Dìngxìngde	Qualitative	
定义	Dìngyì	Definition	
定义常数	Dìngyì chángshù	Define constant (assembler term)	DC
定义常数二字	Dìngyì chángshù èr zì	Define constant double	DCD
定义常数浮动	Dìngyì chángshù fúdòng	Define constant floating	DCF
定义常数字符	Dìngyì chángshù zìfú	Define constant character	DCC
定义事件控制字组	Dìngyì shìjiàn kòngzhì zì zǔ	Define event control block	DFECB
订阅	Dìngyuè	Subscription	
订阅服务器	Dìngyuè fúwùqì	Subscription server	
订阅数据库	Dìngyuè shùjùkù	Subscription database	
定则	Dìngzé	Formulary (IPsec)	
定帧	Dìngzhèng	In-frame (SDH)	IF
定帧字节	Dìngzhèng zìjié	Framing byte (STM term)	
定制	Dìngzhì	Custom	
定值论法	Dìngzhí lùnfǎ	Deterministic method	
顶置盒	Dǐngzhìhé	Palmtop	
顶置盒	Dǐngzhìhé	Set top box	STB
丁字尺	Dīngzìchǐ	T square	

低频	Dīpín	Low frequency	LF
低频放大器	Dīpín fàngdàqì	Low frequency amplifier	LFA
低频滑环	Dīpín huáhuán	Low frequency slip ring	
低频减载	Dīpín jiǎnzài	Low frequency load shedding	
地平面天线	Dìpíngmiàn tiānxiàn	Ground-plane antenna	
地球大气层的主要部分	Dìqiú dàqìcéngde zhǔyào bùfen	Major portion of the earth's atmosphere	
地球电台	Dìqiú diàntái	Earth station	
地球低轨卫星	Dìqiú dīguǐ wèixīng	Low earth orbit satellites	LEO
地球静止卫星	Dìqiú jìngzhǐ wèixīng	Geostationary satellite	
地球静止卫星轨道	Dìqiú jìngzhǐ wèixīng guǐdào	Geostationary satellite orbit	
地球同步卫星	Dìqiú tóngbù wèixīng	Geosynchronous satellite	
地球站	Dìqiúzhàn	Earth station	
低气压实验	Dīqìyā shíyàn	Low atmospheric pressure test	
地区	Dìqū	District	
地区码	Dìqū mǎ	Area code	
地区通信网	Dìqū tōngxìnwǎng	Area communications network	ACN
地区自动电路交换机	Dìqū zìdòng diànlù jiāohuànjī	Regional automatic circuit exchange	RACE
DirectX 纹理压缩	DirectX wénlǐ yāsuō	Direct X texture compression (video term)	DXTC
第 3 范式	Dìsān fànshì	Third normal form	3NF
第三团体	Dìsān tuántǐ	Third party	TP
第三版电子邮局协议	Dìsānbǎn diànzǐ yóujú xiéyì	Post office protocol version 3	POP3
第三层	Dìsāncéng	Layer 3	L3
第三代伙伴组织计划	Dìsāndài huǒbàn zǔzhī jìhuà	Third generation partnership projects	3GPP
第三代兴趣小组	Dìsāndài xìngqu xiǎozǔ	Third generation interest group	3GIG
第三代移动通信	Dìsāndài yídòng tōngxìn	Third generation mobile telephone	3G
第三代移动通信技术试验专家组	Dìsāndài yídòng tōngxìn jìshù shìyàn zhuānjiāzǔ	China 3G Technical Experts Group	3GTEG
第三方	Dìsānfāng	Third party	
第三方付费	Dìsānfāng fùfèi	Third party payment/billing	
第三方拷贝	Dìsānfāng kǎobèi	Third party copy	TPC
第三方业务提供者	Dìsānfāng yèwù tígòngzhě	Third party service provider	TSP
第三号邮局协议	Dìsānhào yóujú xiéyì	Post office protocol 3	POP3
第三纪	Dìsānjì	Tertiary	
第三级供电	Dìsānjí gōngdiàn	Tertiary power supply	
第三类电缆	Dìsānlèi diànlǎn	Category 3 cabling	Cat-3
低色散斜率光纤	Dīsèsàn xiélǜ guāngxiān	Low dispersion slope optical fiber	
地势	Dìshì	Relief	
地势图	Dìshì tú	Hypsometric map	
地市局	Dìshìjú	District exchange center	
低时延码激励线性预测	Dīshíyán mǎ jīlì xiànxìng yùcè	Low-delay - code excited linear prediction	LD-CELP
低时延码激励线性预测编码	Dīshíyán mǎ jīlì xiànxìng yùcè biānmǎ	Low-delay - code excited linear prediction coding	LD-CELP
地鼠	Dìshǔ	Gopher (Internet search engine)	
低数据率传输	Dīshùjùlǜ chuánshū	Low data rate transmission	LDRT
低输入网络连接节点	Dīshūrù wǎngluò liánjiē jiédiǎn	Low-entry networking node	LEN node

第四版因特网信息存取协议	Dìsìbǎn Yīntèwǎng xìnxī cúnqǔ xiéyì	Internet message access protocol version 4	IMAP4
第四代语言	Dìsìdài yǔyán	Fourth generation language	4GL
第四类电缆	Dìsìlèi diànlǎn	Category 4 cabling	Cat-4
第四类运输层协议	Dìsìlèi yùnshū céng xiéyì	Transport-level protocol 4	TP4
低速交换	Dīsù jiāohuàn	Slow Switching	
低速数据	Dīsù shùjù	Low-speed data	LSD
低速数据通道	Dīsù shùjù tōngdào	Low-speed data channel	LDC
低速线路卡	Dīsù xiànlù qiǎ	Low-speed line card	LSC
低速度带	Dīsùdù dài	Low velocity zone	
低损耗同轴电缆	Dīsǔnhào tóngzhóu diànlǎn	Low-loss coaxial cable	
低溯源概率	Dīsùyuán gàilǜ	Low probability of signal exploitation	LPSE
低通功能	Dītōng gōngnéng	Low pass function	LPF
低通滤波器	Dītōng lǜbōqì	Low pass filter	LPF
底图	Dǐtú	Base map	
地图变形	Dìtú biànxíng	Map distortion	
地图标高	Dìtú biāogāo	Map hypsographic	
地图比例尺	Dìtú bǐlìchǐ	Map scale	
地图测量学	Dìtú cèliángxué	Cartometry	
地图层	Dìtú céng	Map coverage	
地图查询	Dìtú cháxún	Map query	
地图传输	Dìtú chuánshū	Cartographic communication	
地图代数	Dìtú dàishù	Map algebra	
地图单位	Dìtú dānwèi	Map units	
地图动画	Dìtú dònghuà	Map animation	
地图分析	Dìtú fēnxī	Cartographic analysis	
地图符号库	Dìtú fúhàokù	Map symbol base	
地图符号学	Dìtú fúhàoxué	Cartographic semiology	
地图规范	Dìtú guīfàn	Map specification	
地图合并	Dìtú hébìng	Map conflation	
地图接边	Dìtú jiēbiān	Map adjustment	
地图精度	Dìtú jīngdù	Map accuracy	
地图句法	Dìtú jùfǎ	Cartographic syntax	
地图模拟	Dìtú mónǐ	Cartographic modeling	
地图配准	Dìtú pèizhǔn	Map registration (in GIS)	
地图匹配	Dìtú pǐpèi	Map matching	
地图人文要素	Dìtú rénwén yàosù	Map cultural feature	
地图设计	Dìtú shèjì	Map design	
地图数据	Dìtú shùjù	Map data	
地图数据库	Dìtú shùjùkù	Cartographic database	
地图数字化	Dìtú shùzìhuà	Map digitization	
地图投影	Dìtú tóuyǐng	Map projection	
地图文献	Dìtú wénxiàn	Map document	
地图现势性	Dìtú xiànshìxìng	Verisimilitude	
地图系列	Dìtú xìliè	Map series	
地图信息	Dìtú xìnxī	Cartographic information	

地图信息系统	Dìtú xìnxī xìtǒng	Cartographic information system	
地图页面转换	Dìtú yèmiàn zhuǎnhuàn	Map-to-page transformation	
地图元素	Dìtú yuánsù	Map element	
地图语法	Dìtú yǔfǎ	Cartographic syntax	
地图语言	Dìtú yǔyán	Cartographic language	
地图语义	Dìtú yǔyì	Cartographic semantics	
地图注记	Dìtú zhùjì	Lettering annotation	
地图自动配准	Dìtú zìdòng pèizhǔn	Automatic map registration (in GIS)	
地图组	Dìtú zǔ	Map section	
地图坐标原点	Dìtú zuòbiāo yuándiǎn	Map coordinate origin	
地图册	Dìtúcè	Atlas	
地图集成	Dìtújí chéng	Map integration	
地图库	Dìtúkù	Map library	
地图学	Dìtúxué	Cartography	
丢包测量	Diūbāo cèliáng	Packet dropout measurement	
丢弃许可	Diūqì xǔkě	Discard eligibility (in frame relay)	DE
丢弃指示	Diūqì zhǐshì	Discard eligibility	DE
丢失错误位	Diūshī cuòwù wèi	Lost error bit	LEB
丢失呼叫保持	Diūshī hūjiào bǎochí	Lost call hold	LCH
丢失呼叫清除	Diūshī hūjiào qīngchú	Lost call cleared	LCC
丢失扫描线	Diūshī sǎomiáo xiàn	Dropped scan line	
丢失数据问题	Diūshī shùjù wèntí	Missing data problem	
丢失损耗	Diūshī sǔnhào	Collapsing loss	
丢失帧	Diūshī zhèng	Lost frame	
丢失帧	Diūshī zhèng	Lost frames	
丢失指示	Diūshī zhǐshì	Discard eligibility (in frame relay)	DE
丢帧率	Diūzhèng lǜ	Frame loss rate	
地外文明探索	Dìwài wénmíng tànsuǒ	Search for extra-terrestrial intelligence	SETI
低外差式接收机	Dīwàichāi-shì jiēshōujī	Infradyne receiver	
低位址锁定	Dīwèizhǐ suǒdìng	Lower address latch	
低温试验	Dīwēn shìyàn	Low temperature test	
低温度天线	Dīwēndù tiānxiàn	Low temperature antenna	
敌我识别雷达	Díwǒ shíbié léidá	Identifier friend or foe	IFF
第 5 类报文摘要	Dìwǔlèi bàowén zhāiyào	Message digest 5	MD5
地线	Dìxiàn	Grounding wire	
地线复合光缆	Dìxiàn fùhéguāng lǎn	Optical power grounded waveguide optical fiber	OPGW
地心坐标系	Dìxīn zuòbiāo xì	Geocentric coordinate system	
地形	Dìxíng	Land form, topography	
地形表达	Dìxíng biǎodá	Terrain representation	
地形测绘雷达	Dìxíng cèhuì léidá	Mapping radar	
地形调查	Dìxíng diàochá	Investigation of land form	
地形叠加	Dìxíng diéjiā	Topographical overlay	
地形分类	Dìxíng fēnlèi	Land form classification	
地形分析	Dìxíng fēnxī	Terrain analysis	
地形建模	Dìxíng jiànmó	Terrain modeling	
地形可视化	Dìxíng kěshìhuà	Topographic visualization	

地形匹配	Dìxíng pǐpèi	Terrain-matching	
地形匹配制导	Dìxíng pǐpèi zhìdǎo	Terrain contour matching	TCM
地形数据	Dìxíng shùjù	Topographic database	
地形特征	Dìxíng tèzhēng	Topographic feature	
地形通视分析	Dìxíng tōngshì fēnxī	Terrain intervisibility calculation	
地形图	Dìxíng tú	Topographic map	
地形线	Dìxíng xiàn	Formlines	
地形制图	Dìxíng zhìtú	Topographic mapping	
地形学	Dìxíngxué	Geomorphology	
地学处理	Dìxué chǔlǐ	Geo-processing	
地学目标	Dìxué mùbiāo	Geo-object	
地学信息	Dìxué xìnxī	Geo-information	
低循环疲劳	Dīxúnhuán píláo	Low cycle fatigue	
低压	Dīyā	Low pressure	
低压减载	Dīyā jiǎnzài	Low voltage load shedding	
低烟	Dīyān	Low-smoke	
低烟无卤阻燃	Dīyān wúlǔ zǔrán	Low smoke zero halogen (FOC)	LSZH
低延迟	Dīyánchí	Reduced latency	
低延迟动态随机存取存储器	Dīyánchí dòngtài suíjī cúnqǔ cúnchǔqì	Reduced latency dynamic random access memory	RLDRAM
第 1 范式	Dìyī fànshì	First normal form	1NF
第一维纳滤波器解	Dìyī wéinà lǜbōqì jiě	First Wiener filter solution	FWFS
第一层（物理层）	Dìyīcéng (wùlǐ céng)	Layer 1 (physical layer)	L1
第一级数据复用器	Dìyījí shùjù fùyòngqì	First level data multiplexer	
第一级中断处理程序	Dìyījí zhōngduàn chùlǐ chéngxù	First level interrupt handler	FLIH
第一阶段无线传输技术	Dìyījiēduàn wúxiàn chuánshū jìshù	First generation radio transmission technology	1XRTT
第一类电缆	Dìyīlèi diànlǎn	Category 1 cabling	Cat-1
第一类网络终端	Dìyīlèi wǎngluò zhōngduān	Network terminal type 1	NT1
第一人称游戏	Dìyīrénchēng yóuxì	First person game (computer game)	FPP
低约束时延	Dīyuēshù shíyán	Low constrained delay	LCD
低噪声电缆	Dīzàoshēng diànlǎn	Low-noise cable	LNC
低噪声放大器	Dīzàoshēng fàngdàqì	Low-noise amplifier	LNA
低噪声天线	Dīzàoshēng tiānxiàn	Low-noise antenna	
低噪音放大器	Dīzàoyīn fàngdàqì	Low-noise amplifier	LNA
低噪音微波放大器	Dīzàoyīn wēibō fàngdàqì	Low-noise microwave amplifier	
地址	Dìzhǐ	Address	
地址编码	Dìzhǐ biānmǎ	Address coding	
地址比较寄存器	Dìzhǐ bǐjiào jìcúnqì	Address compare register	ACR
地址不全信号	Dìzhǐ bùquán xìnhào	Address incomplete signal	ADI
地址产成单元	Dìzhǐ chǎnchéng dānyuán	Address generation unit (CPU term)	
地址常数	Dìzhǐ chángshù	Address constant	
地址查询	Dìzhǐ cháxún	Whois (computer query)	
地址池	Dìzhǐ chí	Address pool	
地址地理编码	Dìzhǐ dìlǐ biānmǎ	Address geocoding	
地址定序	Dìzhǐ dìngxù	Address sequencing	
地址范围定义块	Dìzhǐ fànwéi dìngyì kuài	Address range definition block	ARDB

地址翻译存储器	Dìzhǐ fānyì cúnchǔqì	Address translation memory	ATM
地址分配方案	Dìzhǐ fēnpèi fāng'àn	Address allocation plan	AAP
地址函数	Dìzhǐ hánshù	Address function	ADDR
地址加法器	Dìzhǐ jiāfǎqì	Address adder	AAD
地址接收完毕	Dìzhǐ jiēshōu wánbì	Address complete message (ISUP message)	ACM
地址解析	Dìzhǐ jiěxī	Address resolution	
地址解析服务器	Dìzhǐ jiěxī fúwùqì	Address resolution server	ARS
地址解析回答	Dìzhǐ jiěxī huídá	Location confirm	LCF
地址解析拒绝	Dìzhǐ jiěxī jùjué	Location reject (packet protocol)	LRJ
地址解析请求	Dìzhǐ jiěxī qǐngqiú	Location request	LRQ
地址解析确认	Dìzhǐ jiěxī quèrèn	Location confirm	LCF
地址解析协议	Dìzhǐ jiěxī xiéyì	Address recoding protocol	ARP
地址解析协议	Dìzhǐ jiěxī xiéyì	Address resolution protocol	ARP
地址解折协议	Dìzhǐ jiězhé xiéyì	Address relief protocol	ARP
地址进位	Dìzhǐ jìnwèi	Address carry	AC
地址可选项	Dìzhǐ kěxuǎn xiàng	Destination options	
地址空间	Dìzhǐ kōngjiān	Address space	
地址控制向量	Dìzhǐ kòngzhì xiàngliàng	Address control vector	ACV
地址控制器	Dìzhǐ kòngzhìqì	Address control unit	ACU
地址类型	Dìzhǐ lèixíng	Type of address	TOA
地址类型/编号方案标识符	Dìzhǐ lèixíng/ biānhào fāng'àn biāozhì fú	Type of address /numbering plan identifier	TOA/NPI
地址模板	Dìzhǐ múbǎn	Address template	AT
地址匹配	Dìzhǐ pǐpèi	Address matching	
地址区	Dìzhǐ qū	Address area	
地址全消息	Dìzhǐ quán xiāoxi	Address complete message	ACM
地址全信号	Dìzhǐ quán xìnhào	Address-complete signal	
地址全信号（不计费）	Dìzhǐ quán xìnhào (bùjì fèi)	Address-complete signal (with no charge)	
地址全信号（计费）	Dìzhǐ quán xìnhào (jì fèi)	Address-complete signal (with charge)	
地址识别比特	Dìzhǐ shíbié bǐtè	Address identification bit	A
地址识别符	Dìzhǐ shíbié fú	Address identifier	
地址收全消息	Dìzhǐ shōuquán xiāoxi	Address completion message	ACM
地址数据选通	Dìzhǐ shùjù xuǎntōng	Address data strobe	ADS
地址探测器	Dìzhǐ tàncèqì	Addressable detector	AD
地址探测器	Dìzhǐ tàncèqì	Address detector	AD
地址位序列改变	Dìzhǐ wèi xùliè gǎibiàn	Address bit permutating	ABP
地址显示子系统	Dìzhǐ xiǎnshì zixìtǒng	Address display sub-system	ADS
地址性质表示语	Dìzhǐ xìngzhì biǎoshì yǔ	Nature of address indicator	NAI
地址信号	Dìzhǐ xìnhào	Address signal	
地址信息	Dìzhǐ xìnxī	Address information	
地址选择	Dìzhǐ xuǎnzé	Address selection	ADSEL
地址掩码	Dìzhǐ yǎnmǎ	Address mask	
地址译码器	Dìzhǐ yìmǎqì	Address decoder	AD
地址映射表	Dìzhǐ yìngshè biǎo	Address mapping list	AML
地址映射表	Dìzhǐ yìngshè biǎo	Address mapping table	AMT
地址引起的错误	Dìzhǐ yǐnqǐde cuòwù	Address over error	
地址运算器	Dìzhǐ yùnsuànqì	Address arithmetic unit	AAU

地址指示器的特性	Dìzhǐ zhǐshìqìde tèxìng	Nature of address indicator	NAI
地址转换缓冲器	Dìzhǐ zhuǎnhuàn huǎnchōngqì	Address translation buffer	ATB
地址字段	Dìzhǐ zìduàn	Address field	AF
地址字段扩展	Dìzhǐ zìduàn kuòzhǎn	Address field extension	EA
地址字节	Dìzhǐ zìjié	Address byte	AB
地址总线	Dìzhǐ zǒngxiàn	Address bus	
地指数攻击	Dìzhǐshù gōngjī	Low exponent attack	
地轴架式–文氏强制对流红外回流炉	Dìzhóujiàshi-wén-shì qiángzhì duìliú hóngwài huíliú lú	Floor standing - Venturi forced convection infrared reflow oven (semiconductor mfg)	
Dm 信道上链路接入协议	Dm xìndàoshàng liànlù jiērù xiéyì	Link access protocol on Dm channel	LAPDm
Dm 信道上的链路访问协议	Dm-xìndào-shàngde liànlù fǎngwèn xiéyì	Link access protocol on the Dm channel	LAP-Dm
洞	Dòng	Hole	
动目标检测器	Dòng mùbiāo jiǎncèqì	Moving target detector	MTD
动目标显示	Dòng mùbiāo xiǎnshì	Moving target indicator	MTI
动目标显示雷达	Dòng mùbiāo xiǎnshì léidá	Moving targets indication radar	MTI
氡浓度	Dōng nóngdù	Radon concentration	
动吸振器	Dòng xīzhènqì	Tuned mass damper	
动画	Dònghuà	Animation	
动画图形	Dònghuà túxíng	Animated graphics	
动画专家组	Dònghuà zhuānjiāzǔ	Motion Picture Experts Group	MPEG
动力反应解析	Dònglì fǎnyìng jiěxī	Dynamic response analysis	
动力分析	Dònglì fēnxī	Dynamic analysis	
动力的地基刚性	Dònglide dìjī gāngxìng	Dynamic sub-grade stiffness	
动力学理论	Dònglixué lǐlùn	Dynamics theory	
动能拦截	Dòngnéng lánjié	Kinetic energy intercept	
动态绑定	Dòngtài bǎngdìng	Dynamic binding	
动态包传输	Dòngtài bāo chuánshū	Dynamic packet transport	DPT
动态包过滤	Dòngtài bāo guòlǜ	Active packet filtering	
动态编码光栅全息	Dòngtài biānmǎ guāngshān quánxī	Dynamic code grating holography	
动态标记	Dòngtài biāojì	Dynamic labels	
动态波道配置	Dòngtài bōdào pèizhì	Dynamic channel allocation	DCA
动态补偿	Dòngtài bǔcháng	Motion compensation (video term)	
动态超文本标记语言	Dòngtài chāowénběn biāojì yǔyán	Dynamic hypertext markup language	DHTML
动态超文本置标语言	Dòngtài chāowénběn zhìbiāo yǔyán	Dynamic hypertext markup language	DHTML
动态重组	Dòngtài chóngzǔ	Dynamic regrouping	
动态磁盘	Dòngtài cípán	Dynamic disk	
动态存储分配	Dòngtài cúnchǔ fēnpèi	Dynamic memory allocation	DMA
动态存储器接口	Dòngtài cúnchǔqì jiēkǒu	Dynamic memory interface	DMI
动态带宽分配	Dòngtài dàikuān fēnpèi	Dynamic bandwidth allocation	DBA
动态单纵模	Dòngtài dānzòngmó	Dynamic single-longitudinal mode	DSLM
动态调式系统	Dòngtài diàoshì xìtǒng	Dynamic debugging system	DDS
动态调用接口	Dòngtài diàoyòng jiēkǒu	Dynamic invocation interface (CORBA term)	DII
动态地址解析	Dòngtài dìzhǐ jiěxī	Dynamic address resolution	
动态范围	Dòngtài fànwéi	Dynamic range (of a signal)	
动态范围控制	Dòngtài fànwéi kòngzhì	Dynamic range control	
动态分段	Dòngtài fēnduàn	Dynamic segmentation	

动态分组传送	Dòngtài fēnzǔ chuánsòng	Dynamic packet transmission	DPT
动态分组传送	Dòngtài fēnzǔ chuánsòng	Dynamic packet transport	
动态工作范围	Dòngtài gōngzuò fànwéi	Dynamic operating range (of equipment)	
动态规划	Dòngtài guīhuà	Dynamic programming	DP
动态骨架调用	Dòngtài gǔjià diàoyòng	Dynamic skeleton invocation (CORBA term)	DSI
动态过滤	Dòngtài guòlǜ	Dynamic filter (in SQL Server)	
动态缓冲器	Dòngtài huǎnchōngqì	Dynamic buffer	
动态话务量超载控制	Dòngtài huàwùliáng chāozài kòngzhì	Dynamic overload traffic control	
动态恢复	Dòngtài huīfù	Dynamic recovery (for database)	
动态结构化查询语言语句	Dòngtài jiégòuhuà cháxún yǔyán yǔjù	Dynamic structured query language (SQL) statements (for database)	
动态聚焦	Dòngtài jùjiāo	Dynamic focus lens (video term)	DFL
动态聚焦电极	Dòngtài jùjiāo diànjí	Dynamic focusing electrode	
动态聚焦线圈	Dòngtài jùjiāo xiànquān	Dynamic focusing coil	
动态可扩展分辨率	Dòngtài kě kuòzhǎn fēnbiànlǜ	Dynamic extended resolution	DxR
动态快照	Dòngtài kuàizhào	Dynamic snapshot (for database)	
动态框架接口	Dòngtài kuàngjià jiēkǒu	Dynamic skeleton interface (CORBA term)	DSI
动态连接	Dòngtài liánjiē	Live-Link ©	
动态连接管理	Dòngtài liánjiē guǎnlǐ	Dynamic connection management	DCM
动态链接库	Dòngtài liànjiēkù	Dynamic link library	DLL
动态链路库	Dòngtài liànlùkù	Dynamic link library	DLL
动态莫尔全息	Dòngtài mò-ěr quánxī	Dynamic moll holography	
动态模糊	Dòngtài móhu	Motion blur (video term)	
动态模糊集	Dòngtài móhu jí	Dynamic fuzzy set	
动态模拟	Dòngtài mónǐ	Dynamic simulation	
动态配件	Dòngtài pèijiàn	Dynamic assembly	
动态平面描影	Dòngtài píngmiàn miáoyǐng	Dynamic flat shading (video term)	DFS
动态频率分配	Dòngtài pínlǜ fēnpèi	Dynamic frequency allocation	
动态企业建模	Dòngtài qǐyè jiànmó	Dynamic enterprise modeling	DEM
动态全地区通信系统	Dòngtài quán dìqū tōngxìn xìtǒng	Dynamic Total Area Communications System (UK)	DYNATACS
动态全息合成制作	Dòngtài quánxī héchéng zhìzuò	Dynamic holography synthesis fabrication	
动态取责分离	Dòngtài qǔzé fēnlí	Dynamic separation of duties	DSD
动态筛选	Dòngtài shāixuǎn	Dynamic filter (for database)	
动态数据鉴别	Dòngtài shùjù jiànbié	Dynamic data authentication	
动态数据交换	Dòngtài shùjù jiāohuàn	Dynamic data exchange	DDX
动态四极镜	Dòngtài sìjí jìng	Dynamic quadrapole lens	DQL
动态随机存储器	Dòngtài suíjī cúnchǔqì	Dynamic random access memory	DRAM
动态随机存取存储器	Dòngtài suíjī cúnqǔ cúnchǔqì	Dynamic random access memory	DRAM
动态锁定	Dòngtài suǒ dìng	Dynamic locking (for database)	
动态索引结构	Dòngtài suǒyǐn jiégòu	Dynamic indexing structure	
动态宿主配置协议	Dòngtài sùzhǔ pèizhì xiéyì	Dynamic host configuration protocol	DHCP
动态同步传送模式	Dòngtài tóngbù chuánsòng móshì	Dynamic synchronous transfer mode	DTM
动态图形	Dòngtài túxíng	Dynamic graphics	
动态网络规划技术	Dòngtài wǎngluò guīhuà jìshù	Dynamic network planning technique	DYNET
动态信道分配	Dòngtài xìndào fēnpèi	Dynamic channel allocation	
动态信道分配	Dòngtài xìndào fēnpèi	Dynamic channel assignment	
动态压缩	Dòngtài yāsuō	Dynamic compression	

动态业务改变请求消息	Dòngtài yèwù gǎibiàn qǐngqiú xiāoxi	Dynamic service change request message (for data over cable- docsis)	DSC-REQ
动态业务改变确认消息	Dòngtài yèwù gǎibiàn quèrèn xiāoxi	Dynamic service change acknowledgement message	DSC-ACK
动态业务改变响应消息	Dòngtài yèwù gǎibiàn xiǎngyìng xiāoxi	Dynamic service change response message	DSC-RSP
动态业务删除请求消息	Dòngtài yèwù shānchú qǐngqiú xiāoxi	Dynamic service deletion request message	DSD-REQ
动态业务删除响应消息	Dòngtài yèwù shānchú xiǎngyìng xiāoxi	Dynamic service deletion response message	DSD-RSP
动态业务增加请求消息	Dòngtài yèwù zēngjiā qǐngqiú xiāoxi	Dynamic service addition request message	DSA-REQ
动态业务增加确认消息	Dòngtài yèwù zēngjiā quèrèn xiāoxi	Dynamic service addition acknowledgement request message	DSA-ACK
动态业务增加响应消息	Dòngtài yèwù zēngjiā xiǎngyìng xiāoxi	Dynamic service addition response message	DSA-RSP
动态一致性要求	Dòngtài yīzhìxìng yāoqiú	Dynamic conformance requirement	
动态游标	Dòngtài yóubiāo	Dynamic cursor (for database)	
动态优先级	Dòngtài yōuxiānjí	Dynamic priority	
动态源路由	Dòngtài yuán lùyóu	Dynamic source routing	DSR
动态再定义字符集	Dòngtài zàidìngyì zìfú jí	Dynamically redefinable character set	DRCS
动态噪声限制器	Dòngtài zàoshēng xiànzhìqì	Dynamic noise limiter	DNL
动态增益均衡器	Dòngtài zēngyì jūnhéngqì	Dynamic gain equalizer	DGE
动态装配件	Dòngtài zhuāngpèijiàn	Dynamic assembly	
动态主机分配协议	Dòngtài zhǔjī fēnpèi xiéyì	Dynamic host configuration protocol	DHCP
动态主机控制协议	Dòngtài zhǔjī kòngzhì xiéyì	Dynamic host control protocol	DHCP
动态主机配置协议	Dòngtài zhǔjī pèizhì xiéyì	Dynamic host configuration protocol	DHCP
动态自动增益控制特性	Dòngtài zìdòng zēngyì kòngzhì tèxìng	Dynamic automatic gain control (AGC) characteristic	
动态资源分配控制	Dòngtài zīyuán fēnpèi kòngzhì	Dynamic resource allocation control	DRAC
动态 Z 轴缓冲区	Dòngtài Z-zhóu huǎnchōngqū	Dynamic Z-buffering (video term)	
动铁芯	Dòngtiěxīn	Armature	
动作调用	Dòngzuò diàoyòng	Action invocation	
动作角色扮演游戏	Dòngzuò juésè bànyǎn yóuxì	Action role play games (computer game)	ARPG
动作类游戏	Dòngzuò lèi yóuxì	Action game	
动作指示符	Dòngzuò zhǐshì fú	Action indicator	Ai
DOS 外壳	DOS wàiké	DOS shell	
抖动	Dǒudòng	Jitter	
抖动	Dǒudòng	Dithering (video term)	
抖动测量滤波器	Dǒudòng cèliáng lǜbōqì	Jitter measurement filter	
抖动发生器	Dǒudòng fāshēngqì	Jitter generator	
抖动和漂移	Dǒudòng hé piāoyí	Jitter and wander	FW
抖动接收器	Dǒudòng jiēshōuqì	Jitter receiver	
抖动容限	Dǒudòng róngxiàn	Jitter tolerance	
抖动特性	Dǒudòng tèxìng	Jitter attribute	
抖动增益	Dǒudòng zēngyì	Jitter gain	
抖色处理	Dǒusè chǔlǐ	Dithering	
DSL 传话音	DSL chuánhuà yīn	Voice over DSL	VoDSL
DTE 拨入	DTE bōrù	Dial-in by the DTE	
D 通路上的链路接入程序	D-tōnglù shàngde liànlù jiērù chéngxù	Link access procedures on the D-channel	LAPD
D 通路上的链路接入规程	D-tōnglù-shàngde liànlù jiērù guīchéng	Link access procedure on the D-channel	LAPD
镀涂层测试	Dù túcéng cèshì	Plating and coating testing	
段	Duàn	Section (in SDH)	
短半径	Duǎn bànjìng	Semi-minor axis	

短波长半导体激光模组	Duǎn bōcháng bàndǎotǐ jīguāng mózǔ	Short wavelength semiconductor laser module	
端到端传输	Duān dào duān chuánshū	End-to-end transmission	
端到端信令	Duān dào duān xìnlìng	End-to-end signaling	
端电容器	Duān diànróngqì	End capacitor	
端对端加密	Duān duì duān jiāmì	End-to-end encryption (IPsec)	
端对端身份验证	Duān duì duān shēnfen yànzhèng	End-to-end authentication	
端对端协议	Duān duì duān xiéyì	Peer-to-peer protocol	PPP
端对端信用值	Duān duì duān xìnyòngzhí	End-to-end credit	
段寄存器	Duàn jìcúnqì	Segment register	SR
段接口协议	Duàn jiēkǒu xiéyì	Segment interface protocol	SIP
端接体	Duān jiētǐ	Terminal body	
端接体尺寸	Duān jiētǐ chǐcùn	Terminal body size	
端接体组件	Duān jiētǐ zǔjiàn	Terminus	
端局	Duān jú	End office	EO
端局交换机	Duān jú jiāohuànjī	Local switch	LS
短开槽耦合器	Duǎn kāicáo ǒuhéqì	Short slot coupler	
段开销	Duàn kāixiao	Section overhead	SOH
段控制位	Duàn kòngzhì wèi	Segment control bits	SCB
段类型	Duàn lèixíng	Segment type	ST
段描述子块	Duàn miáoshù zikuài	Segment descriptor block	SDB
段描述符	Duàn miáoshùfú	Segment descriptor	SDT
段偏移	Duàn piānyí	Segment deflection	
段识别符	Duàn shíbiéfú	Segment identifier	SID
短消息	Duǎn xiāoxi	Short message	SM
短消息传递层	Duǎn xiāoxi chuándì céng	Short message transfer layer	SM-TL
短消息传送层	Duǎn xiāoxi chuánsòng céng	Short message transfer layer	SM - TL
短消息传送层	Duǎn xiāoxi chuánsòng céng	Short message transport layer	SM-TL
短消息点对点协议	Duǎn xiāoxi diǎn duì diǎn xiéyì	Short message point to point protocol	SMPP
短消息点对点协议	Duǎn xiāoxi diǎn duì diǎn xiéyì	Short message peer to peer protocol	SMPP
短消息交换中心	Duǎn xiāoxi jiāohuàn zhōngxīn	Short message switching center	SMSC
短消息控制实体	Duǎn xiāoxi kòngzhì shítǐ	Short message control entity	SMC
段消息实体	Duàn xiāoxi shítǐ	Short message entity	SME
短消息数据链路层	Duǎn xiāoxi shùjù liànlù céng	Short message data link layer	SM - DLL
短消息网关	Duǎn xiāoxi wǎng guān	Short message gateway	SMG
短消息小区广播	Duǎn xiāoxi xiǎoqū guǎngbō	Short message service cell broadcast	SMSCB
短消息小区广播业务中心	Duǎn xiāoxi xiǎoqū guǎngbō yèwù zhōngxīn	Short message service-cell broadcast service center	SMS-CBSC
短消息系统	Duǎn xiāoxi xìtǒng	Short message system	
短消息业务	Duǎn xiāoxi yèwù	Short message service	SMS
短消息业务小区广播	Duǎn xiāoxi yèwù xiǎoqū guǎngbō	Short message service cell broadcast	SMS-CB
短消息业务中心	Duǎn xiāoxi yèwù zhōngxīn	Short message service center	SMSC
短消息业务/点到点	Duǎn xiāoxi yèwù/diǎn dàodiǎn	Short message service/point-to-point	SMS/PP
短消息应用层	Duǎn xiāoxi yìngyòng céng	Short message application layer	SM-AL
短消息终端	Duǎn xiāoxi zhōngduān	Short message terminal equipment	SMTE
短消息终端	Duǎn xiāoxi zhōngduān	Short message termination	SMTE
短消息中继层	Duǎn xiāoxi zhōngjì céng	Short message relay layer	SM-RL
短消息中继实体	Duǎn xiāoxi zhōngjì shítǐ	Short message relay entity	SMR

短消息中继协议	Duǎn xiāoxi zhōngjì xiéyì	Short message relay protocol	SM-RP
短消息中心	Duǎn xiāoxi zhōngxīn	Short message center	SMC, SC
短消息中心受理台	Duǎn xiāoxi zhōngxīn shòulǐ tái	Short message center acceptance console	
短信号	Duǎn xìnhào	Short signal	
端系统	Duān xìtǒng	End system	ES
端系统标识符	Duān xìtǒng biāozhìfú	End system identifier	ESI
端用户	Duān yònghù	End user	
段终端	Duàn zhōngduān	Section termination	
短柱	Duǎn zhù	Short column	
短字指令	Duǎn zì zhǐlìng	Short-word instruction	
短波传播	Duǎnbō chuánbō	Short wave propagation	
短波光纤	Duǎnbō guāngxiān	Short wavelength optical fiber	SWL
短波天线	Duǎnbō tiānxiàn	Short wave antenna	TX
短波通信	Duǎnbō tōngxìn	Short wave communication	
短波信号消逝	Duǎnbō xìnhào xiāoshì	Shortwave fade-out	SWF
段的边界	Duànde biānjiè	Section boundary	
断点	Duàndiǎn	Breakpoint	
端点	Duāndiǎn	End point	
端点标识符	Duāndiǎn biāozhìfú	End point identifier	EID
端点别名	Duāndiǎn biémíng	End point alias	
端点段	Duāndiǎn duàn	Termination point fragment	TPF
短接	Duǎnjiē	Short	
端接器	Duānjiēqì	Terminator (cap on cable)	
端局	Duānjú	Local switch, end office	
短句尺寸型	Duǎnjù chǐcùnxíng	Short word size type	SWS
断开	Duànkāi	Disconnect	DISC
断开板	Duànkāi bǎn	Off deck	
断开方式	Duànkāi fāngshì	Disconnected mode	DM
断开激励器	Duànkāi jīlìqì	Switch off exciter	
断开连接	Duànkāi liánjiē	Disconnect	
断开的	Duànkāide	Disconnected	
端口	Duānkǒu	Port, terminal	
端口访问实体	Duānkǒu fǎngwèn shítǐ	Port access entity	PAE
端口及核心功能	Duānkǒu jí héxīn gōngnéng	Port and core function	PCF
端口及核心功能-运行系统	Duānkǒu jí héxīn gōngnéng--yùnxíng xìtǒng	Port and core function-operating system	PCF-OS
端口及核心功能-运行系统功能	Duānkǒu jí héxīn gōngnéng--yùnxíng xìtǒng gōngnéng	Port and core function-operating system function	PCF-OSF
端口镜像	Duānkǒu jìngxiàng	Port mirroring	
端口捆绑	Duānkǒu kǔnbǎng	Port bundling	
端口名	Duānkǒu míng	Port name	
端口旁路电路	Duānkǒu pánglù diànlù	Port bypass circuit	PBC
端口日志	Duānkǒu rìzhì	Port log	
端口日志查看	Duānkǒu rìzhì chákàn	Port log dump	
端口扫描	Duānkǒu sǎomiáo	Port scanning	
端口映射	Duānkǒu yìngshè	Port mapping	
端口级管理程序	Duānkǒu-jí guǎnlǐ chéngxù	Port level manager	PLM

断连	Duànlián	Disconnect	DISC
断连模式	Duànlián móshì	Disconnect mode	
短路	Duǎnlù	Short-circuit	
短路保护	Duǎnlù bǎohù	Short-circuit protection	
短路电流	Duǎnlù diànliú	Short-circuit current	
短路终端	Duǎnlù zhōngduān	Short-circuit termination	
段落	Duànluò	Paragraph (WP command)	
段落结束标志	Duànluò jiéshù biāozhì	Paragraph mark (WP command)	
断路器	Duànlùqì	Circuit breaker	
端面光洁度	Duānmiàn guāngjiédù	End finish	
短期抖动指示器	Duǎnqī dǒudòng zhǐshìqì	Short-term flicker indicator	
短期频率稳定度	Duǎnqī pínlǜ wěndìngdù	Short-term frequency stability	
短期预报	Duǎnqī yùbào	Short-range forecast	
短期预报	Duǎnqī yùbào	Short-term prediction	
端射阵	Duānshèzhèn	End-fire array	
短时间中断	Duǎnshíjiān zhōngduàn	Short interruption (of supply voltage)	
短缩地址	Duǎnsuō dìzhǐ	Abbreviated address	AA
端头	Duāntou	Head end	
段脱机设备	Duàntuōjī shèbèi	Spooling device	SP
断线钳	Duànxiàn qián	Bolt cutter	
断相保护	Duànxiāng bǎohù	Open-phase protection	
短信业务	Duǎnxìn yèwù	Short message service	SMS
断续比	Duànxù bǐ	Break-make ratio	
断续故障	Duànxù gùzhàng	Intermittent fault	
断续振铃	Duànxù zhènlíng	Intermittent ringing	
断言	Duànyán	Assert(ion)	
断言应答	Duànyán yìngdá	Assert acknowledge	AA
短语	Duǎnyǔ	Phrase	
端子电压	Duānzi diànyā	Terminal voltage	
端子干扰电压	Duānzi gānrǎo diànyā	Terminal interference voltage	
堆	Duī	Heap, stack	
对分段数据净荷的 CRC	Duì fēnduàn shùjù jìnghéde CRC	Cyclical redundancy check for fragmented data load (in DOCSIS)	FCRC
对管理目标定义的指南	Duì guǎnlǐ mùbiāo dìngyìde zhǐnán	Guidelines for the definition of managed objects	GDMO
对忙时用户的再呼叫	Duì mángshí yònghùde zài hūjiào	Completion of call to busy subscribers	CCBS
堆排序	Duī páixù	Heap sort	
对遇忙用户完成呼叫	Duì yùmáng yònghù wánchéng hūjiào	Completion of call busy subscriber	CCBS
对找不到移动用户的呼叫转移	Duì zhǎobudào yídòng yònghùde hūjiào zhuǎnyí	Call forwarding on mobile subscriber not reachable	CFNRc
对滞后呼叫前转的最佳路由选择	Duì zhìhòu hūjiào qiánzhuǎnde zuìjiā lùyóu xuǎnzé	Optimal routing for late call forwarding	ORLCF
对比度	Duìbǐdù	Contrast	
对策	Duìcè	Countermeasures	
兑超	Duìchāo	Payment overrun	
对称保密协议	Duìchèn bǎomì xiéyì	Symmetric security protocol (IPsec)	
对称端子电压	Duìchèn duānzi diànyā	Symmetrical terminal voltage	
对称多重处理	Duìchèn duōchóng chǔlǐ	Symmetric multi-processing	SMP

对称二次调制	Duìchèn èrcì tiáozhì	Symmetric quadratic frequency modulation	SQFM
对称二元码	Duìchèn èryuán mǎ	Symmetrical binary code	
对称辐射单元	Duìchèn fúshè dānyuán	Symmetrical radiating element	
对称加密算法	Duìchèn jiāmì suànfǎ	Symmetric encryption algorithm (IPsec)	
对称交换宽带	Duìchèn jiāohuàn kuāndài	Symmetric switched broadband	SSB
对称矩阵	Duìchèn jǔzhèn	Symmetric matrix	
对称密码算法	Duìchèn mìmǎ suànfǎ	Symmetric cryptographic algorithm (IPsec)	
对称输出	Duìchèn shūchū	Balanced output	
对称数字用户线	Duìchèn shùzì yònghù xiàn	Symmetrical digital subscriber line	SymDSL
对称天线	Duìchèn tiānxiàn	Symmetrical antenna	
对称渲染架构	Duìchèn xuànrǎn jiàgòu	Symmetric rendering architecture	SRA
对称式多重处理架构	Duìchèn-shì duōchóng chǔlǐ jiàgòu	Symmetric multi-processing	SMP
对称式多处理	Duìchèn-shì duōchǔlǐ	Symmetric multi-processing	SMP
堆存储方式	Duīcúnchǔ fāngshì	Heap structure (in SQL Server)	
对等	Duìděng	Peer	
对等操作	Duìděng cāozuò	Peering	
对等关系	Duìděng guānxi	Peer relationships	
对等计算	Duìděng jìsuàn	Peer-to-peer computing	
对等实体	Duìděng shítǐ	Peer entities	
对等实体认证	Duìděng shítǐ rènzhèng	Peer entity authentication (IPsec)	
对等通信	Duìděng tōngxìn	Peer-to-peer communication	
对地不平衡阻抗	Duìdì bùpínghéng zǔkàng	Unbalanced impedance about ground	
对地电压	Duìdì diànyā	Voltage to ground	
对地观测系统	Duìdì guāncè xìtǒng	Earth observation system	EOS
对地过电压	Duìdì guòdiànyā	Over-voltage to earth	
对地静止轨道	Duìdì jìngzhǐ guǐdào	Geostationary orbit	
对地静止轨道	Duìdì jìngzhǐ guǐdào	Geostationary earth orbit	GEO
对地静止卫星	Duìdì jìngzhǐ wèixīng	Geostationary satellite	
对地静止卫星轨道	Duìdì jìngzhǐ wèixīng guǐdào	Geostationary satellite orbit	
对地同步卫星	Duìdì tóngbù wèixīng	Geosynchronous satellite	
堆叠	Duīdié	Tiered	
对方计费	Duìfāng jìfèi	Reverse charging	REV
对分天线	Duìfēn tiānxiàn	Split antenna	
兑付	Duìfù	Payment	
兑付局	Duìfù jú	Payment office	
对话	Duìhuà	Session	
对话方式	Duìhuà fāngshì	Conversational mode	
对话框	Duìhuà kuàng	Dialog box (in a GUI)	
对话栏	Duìhuà lán	Dialog box	
对话密钥	Duìhuà mìyào	Session key	
对极几何	Duìjí jǐhé	Epipolar geometry	
对讲电话机	Duìjiǎngdiànhuàjī	Intercom telephone set	
对绞线	Duìjiǎo xiàn	Twisted pair	TP
对角线	Duìjiǎoxiàn	Diagonal	
对接式光纤（缆）连接器	Duìjiē-shì guāngxiān (lǎn) liánjiēqì	Butting optical fiber (cable) connector	
对抗	Duìkàng	Countermeasure	

对空台	Duìkōng tái	Aeronautical station	
队列	Duìliè	Queue	
队列调度	Duìliè diàodù	Queue scheduling	
对流	Duìliú	Convection	
对流层	Duìliúcéng	Troposphere	
对流层波道	Duìliúcéng bōdào	Troposphere duct	
对流层传播	Duìliúcéng chuánbō	Tropospheric propagation	
对流层散射	Duìliúcéng sǎnshè	Tropospheric scatter	
对流层散射传播	Duìliúcéng sǎnshè chuánbō	Troposphere scatter propagation	
对流形回音	Duìliúxíng huíyīn	Convective echo	
对齐	Duìqí	Justification (WP command)	
对齐	Duìqí	Align	
对齐模板	Duìqí múbǎn	Align template	
对时	Duìshí	Time synch	
对数	Duìshù	Logarithm, logarithmic	
对数传输矩阵	Duìshù chuánshū jǔzhèn	Logarithmic transfer matrix	
对数放大器	Duìshù fàngdàqì	Logarithmic amplifier	
对数检波器	Duìshù jiǎnbōqì	Logarithmic detector	
对数接收机	Duìshù jiēshōujī	Logarithmic receiver	
对数几率比	Duìshù jīlǜ bǐ	Log-odds ratio	
对数偶极子阵列天线	Duìshù ǒujízi zhènliè tiānxiàn	Log periodic dipole array antenna	
对数频率特性	Duìshù pínlǜ tèxìng	Logarithmic frequency characteristic	
对数视频放大器	Duìshù shìpín fàngdàqì	Logarithmic video amplifier	
对数压缩扩展脉码调制	Duìshù yāsuō kuòzhǎn màimǎ tiáozhì	Pulse code modulation-logarithmic companded	PCM-LOG
对数正态	Duìshù zhèngtài	Log-normal	
对数正态分布	Duìshù zhèngtài fēnbù	Log-normal distribution	
对数中频放大器	Duìshù zhōngpín fàngdàqì	Logarithmic intermediate frequency amplifier	
对数周期偶极子天线阵	Duìshù zhōuqī ǒujízi tiānxiàn zhèn	Log periodic dipole array	LPDA
对数周期天线	Duìshù zhōuqī tiānxiàn	Log periodic antenna	LPA
对数-快时间常数电路	Duìshù-kuài shíjiān chángshù diànlù	Log-FTC (fast time constant) circuit	
对谈程序	Duìtán chéngxù	Talk program	
队头	Duìtóu	Front (of a queue)	
对头连接	Duìtou liánjiē	Butt joint	
队头阻塞	Duìtóu zǔsè	Head of line blocking	
对外贸易加工区	Duìwài màoyì jiāgōng qū	Foreign trade processing zone	
对外贸易区	Duìwài màoyì qū	Foreign trade zone	FTZ
队尾	Duìwěi	Rear (of a queue)	
对象	Duìxiàng	Object	
对相	Duìxiāng	Phasing (in facsimile)	
对象变量	Duìxiàng biànliàng	Object variable	
对象表达	Duìxiàng biǎodá	Object rendering	
对象标识符	Duìxiàng biāozhìfú	Object identifier	
对象参照	Duìxiàng cānzhào	Object references	
对象池化	Duìxiàng chíhuà	Object pooling	
对象定义语言	Duìxiàng dìngyì yǔyán	Object definition language	ODL
对象复合	Duìxiàng fùhé	Object generalization	

对象管理结构	Duìxiàng guǎnlǐ jiégòu	Object management architecture	OMA
对象管理体系结构	Duìxiàng guǎnlǐ tǐxì jiégòu	Object management architecture	OMA
对象管理组	Duìxiàng guǎnlǐ zǔ	Object management group	OMG
对象管理组织	Duìxiàng guǎnlǐ zǔzhī	Object management group	OMG
对象关系模型	Duìxiàng guānxi móxíng	Object relationship model	
对象过程方法	Duìxiàng guòchéng fāngfǎ	Object-process methodology	OPM
对象过程图	Duìxiàng guòchéng tú	Object-process diagram	OPD
对象交换	Duìxiàng jiāohuàn	Object exchange	OBEX
对象交换模型	Duìxiàng jiāohuàn móxíng	Object exchange model	OEM
对象交换协议	Duìxiàng jiāohuàn xiéyì	Object exchange protocol (in Bluetooth)	OBEX
对象几何	Duìxiàng jǐhé	Object geometry	
对象激活	Duìxiàng jīhuó	Object activation	
对象类	Duìxiàng lèi	Object class	
对象类别	Duìxiàng lèibié	Object class	
对象的连接与嵌入	Duìxiàng liánjiē yǔ qiànrù	Object linking and embedding	OLE
对象联系模型	Duìxiàng liánxì móxíng	Object relationship model	
对象描述	Duìxiàng miáoshù	Representation	
对象模型	Duìxiàng móxíng	Object model	
对象模型技术	Duìxiàng móxíng jìshù	Object modeling technique	OMT
对象模型开发工具	Duìxiàng móxíng kāifā gōngjù	Object model development tool	OMDT
对象模型模板	Duìxiàng móxíng múbǎn	Object model template	OMT
对象请求代理	Duìxiàng qǐngqiú dàilǐ	Object request broker	ORB
对象请求代理间的实时协议	Duìxiàng qǐngqiú dàilǐ jiānde shíshí xiéyì	Real-time inter-ORB (object request broker) protocol	RTIOP
对象请求代理器	Duìxiàng qǐngqiú dàilǐqì	Object request broker	ORB
对象权限	Duìxiàng quánxiàn	Object permission	
对象实例	Duìxiàng shílì	Object instance	
对象数据流图	Duìxiàng shùjùliú tú	Object dataflow graph	ODG
对象所有者	Duìxiàng suǒyǒuzhě	Object owner	
对象推操作	Duìxiàng tuī cāozuò	Object push profile	
对象相关性	Duìxiàng xiāngguānxìng	Object dependencies	
对相信号	Duìxiāng xìnhào	Phasing signal	
对象引用	Duìxiàng yǐnyòng	Objects-by-reference	
对象支持	Duìxiàng zhīchí	Object supports	OS
对象注册	Duìxiàng zhùcè	Object registration	
对象组	Duìxiàng zǔ	Object group	OG
对消比	Duìxiāo bǐ	Cancellation ratio	
对应 N-实体	Duìyìng N-shítǐ	Correspondent (N)-entities	
对映站	Duìyìng zhàn	Mirror site	
堆栈	Duīzhàn	Stack	
堆栈底部	Duīzhàn dǐbù	Bottom of stack	
对账	Duìzhàng	Verification of account	
对准抖动	Duìzhǔn dǒudòng	Alignment jitter	
独立	Dúlì	Autonomy, autonomous, independent	
独立边带	Dúlì biāndài	Independent sideband	ISB
独立波段文件	Dúlì bōduàn wénjiàn	Independent waveband file	

独立磁盘冗余阵列	Dúlì cípán rǒngyú zhènliè	Redundant array of inexpensive disks	RAID
独立电话公司	Dúlì diànhuà gōngsī	Independent telephone company	ITC
独立分散循环网络	Dúlì fēnsàn xúnhuán wǎngluò	Autonomous decentralized loop network	ADL-Net
独立服务器	Dúlì fúwùqì	Stand-alone server	
独立故障	Dúlì gùzhàng	Independent fault	
独立集	Dúlì jí	Independent set	
独立频移键控/跳频	Dúlì pínyí jiànkòng/tiàopín	Independent frequency shift keying/frequency hopping	I-FSK/FH
独立软件供应商	Dúlì ruǎnjiàn gōngyìngshāng	Independent software vendors	ISVs
独立软件购买者	Dúlì ruǎnjiàn gòumǎizhě	Independent software vendors	ISV
独立软件提供者	Dúlì ruǎnjiàn tígòngzhě	Independent software vendor	ISV
独立失效	Dúlì shīxiào	Primary failure	
独立同步供给设备	Dúlì tóngbù gōngjǐ shèbèi	Standalone synchronization supply equipment	SASE
独立线圈	Dúlì xiànquān	Absolute coil	
独立信息处理	Dúlì xìnxī chǔlǐ	Separate message approach	
独立硬件购买者	Dúlì yìngjiàn gòumǎizhě	Independent hardware vendor	IHV
独立于承载的呼叫控制	Dúlì yú chéngzàide hūjiào kòngzhì	Bearer independent call control	BICC
独立于协议的组播协议	Dúlì yú xiéyìde zǔbō xiéyì	Protocol-independent multicast	PIM
独立专用控制信道	Dúlì zhuānyòng kòngzhì xìndào	Stand-alone dedicated control channel	SDCCH
独立组播协议	Dúlì zǔbō xiéyì	Protocol-independent muticast	PIM
独立组播协议密集模式	Dúlì zǔbō xiéyì mìjí móshì	Protocol-independent multicast dense mode	PIM DM
独立组播协议稀疏模式	Dúlì zǔbō xiéyì xīshū móshì	Protocol-independent multicast sparse mode	PIM SM
独立坐标系	Dúlì zuòbiāo xì	Independent coordinate system	
度量	Dùliàng	Metric	
度量	Dùliàng	Measurement	
度量服务器	Dùliàng fúwùqì	Metric server	
度量空间	Dùliàng kōngjiān	Metric space	
度量值	Dùliàng zhí	Measure	
度量值表达	Dùliàng zhí biǎodá	Metric representation	
独立的	Dúlìde	Stand-alone	
独立的标识位置寄存器	Dúlìde biāozhì wèizhì jìcúnqì	Standalone home location register	SHLR
独立的原始位置寄存器	Dúlìde yuánshǐ wèizhì jìcúnqì	Standalone home location register	SHLR
独立型同步设备	Dúlì-xíng tóngbù shèbèi	Stand alone synchronization equipment	SASE
独立型同步设备	Dúlì-xíng tóngbù shèbèi	Stand-alone synchronization equipment	SASE
读码器	Dúmǎqì	Code reader (often short for bar code reader)	
镀膜材料	Dùmó cáiliào	Coating materials	
镀膜加工	Dùmó jiāgōng	Coating (process)	
镀膜设备	Dùmó shèbèi	Coating equipment	
多成分信号（交流信令中）	Duō chéngfèn xìnhào (jiāoliú xìnlìng zhōng)	Multi-component signal (in ac signaling)	
多导线单元	Duō dǎoxiàn dānyuán	Multi-conductor element	
多导线单元	Duō dǎoxiàn dānyuán	Multi-wire element	
多等级优先占用	Duō děngjí yōuxiān zhànyòng	Multi-level precedence and preemption	MLPP
多对多关系	Duō duì duō guānxi	Many-to-many relationship	
多对一关系	Duō duì yī guānxi	Many-to-one relationship	
多声明表值型函数	Duō shēngmíng biǎozhíxíng hánshù	Multi-statement table-valued functions (in SQL Server)	
多偶联控制功能	Duō'ǒulián kòngzhì gōngnéng	Multiple association control function	MACF

多倍仪	Duōbèiyí	Multiplier	
躲避	Duǒbì	Shunning, evasion	
多边形	Duōbiānxíng	Polygon	
多边形叠加	Duōbiānxíng diéjiā	Polygon overlay	
多边形分割	Duōbiānxíng fēngē	Polygon partitioning	
多边形化简	Duōbiānxíng huà jiǎn	Simplifying polygons	
多边形结构	Duōbiānxíng jiégòu	Polygon structure	
多边形融合	Duōbiānxíng rónghé	Polygonal fusion	
多边形属性表	Duōbiānxíng shǔxìng biǎo	Polygon attribute table	
多边形线	Duōbiānxíng xiàn	Polygon line	
多边形转换与光源处理	Duōbiānxíng zhuǎnhuàn yǔ guāngyuán chǔlǐ	Polygon transformation and lighting (video term)	T&L
多边形-弧段拓扑数据结构	Duōbiānxíng—húduàn tuòpū shùjù jiégòu	Polygon-arc topology	
多边形内点识别	Duōbiānxíng-nèi diǎn shíbié	Point-in-polygon operation	
多播	Duōbō	Multicast	
多播地址	Duōbō dìzhǐ	Multicast addressing	MA
多播地址动态客户端分配协议	Duōbō dìzhǐ dòngtài kèhùduān fēnpèi xiéyì	Multicast address dynamic client allocation protocol	MADCAP
多播地址解析服务	Duōbō dìzhǐ jiěxī fúwù	Multicast address resolution service	MARS
多播服务器	Duōbō fúwùqì	Multicast server	
多播呼叫	Duōbō hūjiào	Multicast call	
多播媒体访问控制地址	Duobō méitǐ fǎngwèn kòngzhì dìzhǐ	Multicast media access control address	
多播密钥管理协议	Duōbō mìyào guǎnlǐ xiéyì	Multicast key management protocol	MKMP
多播群	Duōbō qún	Multicast group	
多播数据报	Duōbō shùjù bào	Multicast datagram	
多播业务	Duōbō yèwù	Multicast service	
多播主干网	Duōbō zhǔgàn wǎng	Multicast backbone	MBONE
多波长传送网	Duōbōcháng chuánsòng wǎng	Multi-wavelength transmission network	
多波长光网络	Duōbōcháng guāng wǎngluò	Multi-wavelength optical network	
多波长光源	Duōbōcháng guāngyuán	Multi-wavelength laser source	
多波长解决方案	Duōbōcháng jiějué fāng'àn	Multiple wavelength solution	MWS
多波长激光器	Duōbōcháng jīguāngqì	Multi-wavelength laser diode	
多波长系统	Duōbōcháng xìtǒng	Multi-channel system (optical)	MCS
多波道增益变化	Duōbōdào zēngyì biànhuà	Multi-channel gain variation	
多波道增益变化比	Duōbōdào zēngyì biànhuà bǐ	Multi-channel gain-change ratio	
多波道增益变化差	Duōbōdào zēngyì biànhuà chà	Multi-channel gain-change difference	
多波道增益斜率	Duōbōdào zēngyì xiélǜ	Multi-channel gain tilt	
多波段多点分发服务	Duōbōduàn duōdiǎn fēnfā fúwù	Multi-channel multipoint distribution service	MMDS
多波段遥感	Duōbōduàn yáogǎn	Multi-spectral remote sensing (GIS)	
多波束合成网络	Duōbōshù héchéng wǎngluò	Multi-beam forming network	
多波束天线	Duōbōshù tiānxiàn	Multi-beam antenna	MBA
多步归并排序	Duōbù guībìng páixù	Polyphase merging sort	
多层交换机	Duōcéng jiāohuànjī	Multi-layer switch	
多层面镜	Duōcéng miànjìng	Multi-layer mirror	
多层协议	Duōcéng xiéyì	Multi-layer protocol	MLP

多层皱纹金属带被覆同轴对	Duōcéng zhòuwén jīnshǔdài bèifù tóngzhóu duì	Corrugated laminated coaxial	CLOAX
多厂商网络	Duōchǎngshāng wǎngluò	Multi-vendor network	
多成分影像光纤	Duōchéngfèn yǐngxiàng guāngxiān	Non-silica imaging fiber optic bundle	
多程序段	Duōchéngxù duàn	More segments	MS
多尺度数据库	Duōchǐdù shùjùkù	Multi-scale database	
多重表达	Duōchóng biǎodá	Multiple representations	
多重地址转换	Duōchóng dìzhǐ zhuǎnhuàn	Multiple address translation	
多重反射	Duōchóng fǎnshè	Multiple reflection	
多重复用方式	Duōchóng fùyòng fāngshì	Multiple frequency reuse pattern	MRP
多重回归分析	Duōchóng huíguī fēnxī	Multiple regression analysis	
多重继承	Duōchóng jìchéng	Multiple inheritance	
多重链表	Duōchóng liàn biǎo	Multi-linked list	
多重链表文件	Duōchóng liàn biǎo wénjiàn	Multi-list file	
多重启动	Duōchóng qǐdòng	Multiple boot	
多重输入	Duōchóng shūrù	Multiple input	
多重用户号码	Duōchóng yònghù hàomǎ	Multiple subscriber number	MSN
多重子奈奎斯特抽样编码	Duōchóng zi nài-kuí-sī-tè chōuyàng biānmǎ	Multiple sub-Nyquist sampling encoding	MUSE
多重时帧	Duōchòngshí zhèng	Multiple timeframe	
多窗口图文界面	Duōchuāngkǒu túwén jièmiàn	Multi-window graphical interface	
多串口	Duōchuànkǒu	Multi-port	
多处理机任务	Duōchǔlǐjī rènwu	Multi-processor task	
多处理器规范	Duōchǔlǐqì guīfàn	Multi-processor specification	MPS
多次调制	Duōcì tiáozhì	Multiple modulations	
多带激励	Duōdài jīlì	Multi-band excitation	MBE
多带激励编码	Duōdài jīlì biānmǎ	Multi-band excitation	MBE
多代理系统	Duōdàilǐ xìtǒng	Multi-agent system	MAS
多单元可控天线	Duōdānyuán kěkòng tiānxiàn	Multi-unit steerable antenna	MUSA
多单元消息	Duōdānyuán xiāoxi	Multi-unit message	MUM
多道程序设计	Duōdào chéngxù shèjì	Multi-channel programming	
多点	Duōdiǎn	Multipoint	
多点播发	Duōdiǎn bōfā	Multicast	
多点传送远程通信存取方法	Duōdiǎn chuánsòng yuǎnchéng tōngxìn cúnqǔ fāngfǎ	Multi-leaving telecommunications access method	MTAM
多点处理器	Duōdiǎn chǔlǐqì	Multipoint processor	MP
多点处理器及多点控制单元	Duōdiǎn chǔlǐqì jí duōdiǎn kòngzhì dānyuán	Multi-processor and multi-control unit	MP&MCU
多点到点树	Duōdiǎn dào diǎn shù	Multipoint to point tree	MPT
多点干扰	Duōdiǎn gānrǎo	Multipoint jamming	
多点广播路由	Duōdiǎn guǎngbō lùyóu	Multicast routing	
多点会议单元	Duōdiǎn huìyì dānyuán	Multipoint conferencing unit	MCU
多点接入	Duōdiǎn jiērù	Multipoint access	
多点控制单元	Duōdiǎn kòngzhì dānyuán	Multipoint control unit	MCU
多点控制器	Duōdiǎn kòngzhìqì	Multipoint controller	MC
多点漏洞	Duōdiǎn lòudòng	Multimode vulnerability	
多点命令服务	Duōdiǎn mìnglìng fúwù	Multipoint command service	MCS

多点命令会议	Duōdiǎn mìnglìng huìyì	Multipoint command conference	MCC
多点命令相称性数据传输	Duōdiǎn mìnglìng xiāngchènxìng shùjù chuánshū	Multipoint command symmetrical data transmission	MCS
多点命令协商	Duōdiǎn mìnglìng xiéshāng	Multipoint command negotiation	MCN
多点视频分配系统	Duōdiǎn shìpín fēnpèi xìtǒng	Multipoint video distribution system	MVDS
多点视频分配业务	Duōdiǎn shìpín fēnpèi yèwù	Multipoint video distribution service	MVDS
多点通信服务	Duōdiǎn tōngxìn fúwù	Multipoint communication service	MCS
多点通信服务接入点	Duōdiǎn tōngxìn fúwù jiērùdiǎn	Multipoint communication service access point	MCSAP
多点委托	Duōdiǎn wěituō	Multicast delegate	
多点线路	Duōdiǎn xiànlù	Multi-drop line	
多电平编码调制	Duōdiànpíng biānmǎ tiáozhì	Multi-level coded modulation	MLCM
多电平调制	Duōdiànpíng tiáozhì	Multi-level modulation	
多电平正交调幅	Duōdiànpíng zhèngjiāo tiáofú	Multi-level quadrature amplitude modulation (QAM)	
多端网络	Duōduān wǎngluò	Multi-port network	
多端口可编程序通信接口	Duōduānkǒu kěbiān chéngxù tōngxìn jiēkǒu	Multi-port programmable communications interface	MPCI
多端口天线	Duōduānkǒu tiānxiàn	Multi-port antenna	
多尔夫-契比舍夫天线阵	Duō-ěr-fū—Qì-bǐ-shè-fū tiānxiàn zhèn	Dolph-Chebyshev array antenna	DCAA
多方多媒体会话控制	Duōfāng duōméitǐ huìhuà kòngzhì	Multi-party multimedia session control	MMUSIC
多方会话	Duōfāng huìhuà	Multi-party	MPTy
多方呼叫	Duōfāng hūjiào	Multi-party call	MPTY
多方通话	Duōfāng tōnghuà	Multi-party telecommunication	MPTY
多方通信附加业务	Duōfāng tōngxìn fùjiā yèwù	Multi-party supplementary services	
多访问权终端	Duōfǎngwènquán zhōngduān	Multiple access rights terminal	
多分转站网	Duōfēn zhuǎnzhàn wǎng	Multidrop network	
多服务光纤接入平台	Duōfúwù guāngxiān jiērù píngtái	Multi-service fiber access platform	
多服务器队列	Duōfúwùqì duìliè	Multiserver queue	
多幅移键控	Duōfúyí jiànkòng	Multiple amplitude shift keying	MASK
多复用模式	Duōfùyòng móshì	Multi-reuse patterns	MRP
多工	Duōgōng	Multiplexing	
多工化	Duōgōng huà	Multiplexing	
多工步成形	Duōgōngbù chéngxíng	Multi-step forming	
多工具集成	Duōgōngjù jíchéng	Multi-tool integration	
多功能复合事务机	Duōgōngnéng fùhé shìwùjī	Multi-function product	MFP
多功能宽带通信系统	Duōgōngnéng kuāndài tōngxìn xìtǒng	Multi-function broadband communication system	MBCS
多功能设备	Duōgōngnéng shèbèi	Multi function device	MFD
多功能数字信号服务	Duōgōngnéng shùzì xìnhào fúwù	Multi-function digital signaling service	MDSS
多功能外围设备	Duōgōngnéng wàiwéi shèbèi	Multi-function peripheral	MFP
多功能终端适配器	Duōgōngnéng zhōngduān shìpèiqì	Multi-function terminal adapter	MTA
多工器	Duōgōngqì	Multiplexer	
多工器分流	Duōgōngqì fēnliú	Multiplexing	
多工运作	Duōgōngyùn zuò	Multi-threading	
多工作业	Duōgōngzuò yè	Multi-tasking	
多光谱合成图像	Duōguāngpǔ héchéng túxiàng	Multi-spectral composite imagery	
多光谱扫描仪	Duōguāngpǔ sǎomiáo yí	Multi-spectral scanner	
多回路控制系统	Duōhuílù kòngzhì xìtǒng	Multi-loop control system	
多呼叫处理装置	Duōhūjiào chǔlǐ zhuāngzhì	Multiple call processing unit	MCPU

多级安全	Duōjí ānquán	Multi-level security (IPsec)	
多级处理	Duōjí chǔlǐ	Multilevel processing	
多级多链路 ppp	Duōjí duōliànlù PPP	Multi-class multi-link point to point protocol	MCML
多级互连网络	Duōjí hùlián wǎngluò	Multi-stage interconnection network	MIN
多级脉码调制，极化 调制（脉冲源）	Duōjí màimǎ tiáozhì, jíhuà tiáozhì (màichōng yuán)	Multi-level pulse code modulation, polarization modulated (pulse source)	M-PCM-PM(PS)
多级脉码调制，强度 调制（脉冲源）	Duōjí màimǎ tiáozhì, qiángdù tiáozhì (màichōng yuán)	Multi-level pulse code modulation, intensity modulated (pulse source)	M-PCM-IM(PS)
多级设备	Duōjí shèbèi	Multi-level device	
多级体系	Duōjí tǐxì	Multi-tier architecture	
多级卫星链路	Duōjí wèixīng liànlù	Multi-satellite link	
多级相移键控	Duōjí xiāngyí jiànkòng	Multi-level phase shift keying	MPSK
多加入模式	Duōjiārù móshì	Non-participating mode	
多基地雷达	Duōjīdì léidá	Multi-static radar	
多径	Duōjìng	Multipath	
多径传播	Duōjìng chuánbō	Multipath propagation	
多径传播函数	Duōjìng chuánbō hánshù	Multipath propagation function	
多径分集	Duōjìng fēnjí	Multipath diversity	
多径干扰	Duōjìng gānrǎo	Multi-path interference	
多径 Rayleigh 衰落 信道	Duōjìng Rayleigh shuāiluò xìndào	Multi-path Rayleigh fading channels	
多径时延	Duōjìng shíyán	Multipath delay	
多径衰落	Duōjìng shuāiluò	Multipath fading	
多径效应	Duōjìng xiàoyìng	Multipath effect	
多进制扩频	Duōjìnzhì kuòpín	Multinary spread spectrum	
多进制正交幅度调制	Duōjìnzhì zhèngjiāo fúdù tiáozhì	Multinary quadrature amplitude modulation	MQAM
多计算机系统	Duōjìsuànjī xìtǒng	Multi-computer system	
多孔透镜	Duōkǒng tòujìng	Perforated lens	
多馈线天线	Duōkuìxiàn tiānxiàn	Multi-feed antenna	MFA
多喇叭馈电器	Duōlǎba kuìdiànqì	Multi-horn feed	
多量子阱	Duōliàngzǐ jǐng	Multi-quantum well	MQW
多量子阱分布反馈激光器	Duōliàngzǐ jǐng fēnbù fǎnkuì jīguāngqì	Multiple quantum well distributed feedback laser device	MQW-DFB-LD
多量子阱激光器	Duōliàngzǐ jǐng jīguāngqì	Multiple quantum well laser device	MQW-LD
多量子阱器件	Duōliàngzǐ jǐng qìjiàn	Multiple quantum well device	MQW
多连接表达式	Duōliánjiē biǎodá shì	Multi-join expression	
多链接点到点协议	Duōliànjiē diǎn dào diǎn xiéyì	Multi-link point-to-point protocol	PPP
多连接端点标识符	Duōliánjiē duāndiǎn biāozhì fú	Multi-connection endpoint identifier	
多链路拨号	Duōliànlù bōhào	Multi-link dialing	
多链路规程	Duōliànlù guīchéng	Multi-link procedure	MLP
多领域数据库	Duōlǐngyù shùjùkù	Multi-disciplinary database	
多路传输	Duōlù chuánshū	Multiplex	
多路传输包网络	Duōlù chuánshū bāo wǎngluò	Multiplexed packet network	MPN
多路多点分配业务	Duōlù duōdiǎn fēnpèi yèwù	Multi-channel multipoint distribution service	MMDS
多路分用	Duōlù fēnyòng	Demultiplex	DX
多路复接	Duōlù fùjiē	Multiplexing	
多路复用	Duōlù fùyòng	Multiplex	MUX

多路复用分组网络	Duōlù fùyòng fēnzǔ wǎngluò	Multiplexed packet network	MPN
多路复用和多路分用	Duōlù fùyòng hé duōlù fēnyòng	Multiplex and demultiplex	MULDEX
多路复用接口	Duōlù fùyòng jiēkǒu	Multiplex interface	
多路复用链路	Duōlù fùyòng liànlù	Multiplex link	
多路复用调制系统	Duōlù fùyòng tiáozhì xìtǒng	Multiplex modulation system	MMS
多路复用器	Duōlù fùyòngqì	Multiplexer	MUX
多路接入	Duōlù jiērù	Multiple access	MA
多路进入交换系统	Duōlù jìnrù jiāohuàn xìtǒng	Multiple access switching system	MASS
多路耦合器	Duōlù ǒuhéqì	Multi-coupler (of an antenna)	
多路衰减模拟器	Duōlù shuāijiǎn mónǐqì	Multi-path fading simulator	
多路数据传输接口	Duōlù shùjù chuánshū jiēkǒu	Multi-stream data transmission interface	MDTI
多路数据链接控制器	Duōlù shùjù liànjiē kòngzhìqì	Multiple data link controller	MDLC
多路微波分配系统	Duōlù wēibō fēnpèi xìtǒng	Multi-channel microwave distribution system	MMDS
多路信道	Duōlù xìndào	Multiplexer channel	
多路旋转关节	Duōlù xuánzhuǎn guānjié	Multi-channel rotary joint	
多路音频电报	Duōlù yīnpín diànbào	Multi-channel voice-frequency telegraphy	MCVFT
多路移频键控	Duōlù yípín jiànkòng	Multiple frequency shift keying	MFSK
多路语音频率	Duōlù yǔyīn pínlǜ	Multi-channel voice frequency	MCVF
多路增益	Duōlù zēngyì	Multiplexing gain	
多路转换接口适配器	Duōlù zhuǎnhuàn jiēkǒu shìpèiqì	Multiplex interface adapter	MIA
多路转换器	Duōlù zhuǎnhuànqì	Multiplexer	MPX
多路径多播	Duōlùjìng duōbō	Multi-path multicast	
多路径衰落失真	Duōlùjìng shuāiluò shīzhēn	Multi-path fading distortion	MPF
多路径误差	Duōlùjìng wùchā	Multi-path error	
多路径自选路由	Duōlùjìng zìxuǎn lùyóu	Multi-path self-routing	MPSR
多码	Duōmǎ	Multi-code	
多脉冲干扰	Duōmàichōng gānrǎo	Multi-pulse jamming	
多脉冲激励线性预测编码	Duōmàichōng jīlì xiànxìng yùcè biānmǎ	Multi-pulse excitation linear predictive coding	MPE-LPC
多脉冲线性预测编码	Duōmàichōng xiànxìng yùcè biānmǎ	Multi-pulse linear prediction code	MPLPC
多媒体	Duōméitǐ	Multimedia	
多媒体本地网	Duōméitǐ běndì wǎng	Multimedia local network	
多媒体操作	Duōméitǐ cāozuò	Multimedia action	
多媒体插座	Duōméitǐ chāzuò	Multimedia outlet	MMO
多媒体单元	Duōméitǐ dānyuán	Multimedia unit	MMU
多媒体和超媒体信息编码专家组	Duōméitǐ hé chāoméitǐ xìnxī biānmǎ zhuānjiāzǔ	Multimedia and hypermedia information coding expert group	MHEG
多媒体交流团	Duōméitǐ jiāoliú tuán	Multimedia interactive group	
多媒体结构化查询语言	Duōméitǐ jiégòuhuà cháxún yǔyán	Structured query language / multimedia	SQL/MM
多媒体扩展指令集	Duōméitǐ kuòzhǎn zhǐlìng jí	Multimedia extensions	MMX
多媒体描述	Duōméitǐ miáoshù	Multimedia description	
多媒体启动工具	Duōméitǐ qǐdòng gōngjù	Multimedia enabling tool	
多媒体视频文件	Duōméitǐ shìpín wénjiàn	Multimedia video file	MMVF
多媒体数字监控系统	Duōméitǐ shùzì jiānkòng xìtǒng	Multimedia digital surveillance system	
多媒体同步规范	Duōméitǐ tóngbù guīfàn	Multimedia synchronization specification	
多媒体通信	Duōméitǐ tōngxìn	Multimedia communications	
多媒体通讯	Duōméitǐ tōngxùn	Multimedia communications	

多媒体外设路由器	Duōméitǐ wàishè lùyóuqì	Multimedia periphery router	MPRouter
多媒体信号处理装置	Duōméitǐ xìnhào chǔlǐ zhuāngzhì	Multimedia signal processing equipment	MPE
多媒体信息服务	Duōméitǐ xìnxī fúwù	Multimedia messaging service	MMS
多媒体信息网关	Duōméitǐ xìnxī wǎngguān	Multimedia message gateway	MMG
多媒体业务	Duōméitǐ yèwù	Multimedia service	
多媒体业务分布	Duōméitǐ yèwù fēnbù	Multimedia distribution service	MDS
多媒体邮件	Duōméitǐ yóujiàn	Multimedia mailing	MMM
多媒体邮件传送协议	Duōméitǐ yóujiàn chuánsòng xiéyì	Multimedia mail transfer protocol	MMTP
多面镜	Duōmiànjìng	Polygonal mirror	
多模波导	Duōmó bōdǎo	Multimode waveguide	
多模多喇叭馈电器	Duōmó duōlǎba kuìdiànqì	Multimode - multi-horn feed	
多模光纤	Duōmó guāngxiān	Multimode optical fiber	MMF
多模渐变型光纤	Duōmó jiànbiànxíng guāngxiān	Multimode graded index optical fiber	
多模馈电器	Duōmó kuìdiànqì	Multimode feed	
多模喇叭天线	Duōmó lǎba tiānxiàn	Multimode horn antenna	
多模天线	Duōmó tiānxiàn	Multimode antenna	
多模突变型光纤	Duōmó tūbiànxíng guāngxiān	Multimode stepped index optical fiber	
多模网络	Duōmó wǎngluò	Multimode network	
多模态多心光纤连接器	Duōmótài duōxīn guāngxiān liánjiēqì	Multimode, multi-channel fiber optic connector	
多模态石英系光缆	Duōmótài shíyīng xì guānglǎn	Multimode silica fiber optic cable	
多目广播	Duōmù guǎngbō	Multicast	
多目广播边界网关协议	Duōmù guǎngbō biānjiè wǎngguān xiéyì	Multicast border gateway protocol	MBGP
多目标并列选择机制	Duōmùbiāo bìngliè xuǎnzéjī zhì	Multi-objective proportional selection scheme	
多目标遗传规划	Duōmùbiāo yíchuán guīhuà	Multi-objective genetic programming	MOGP
多目标优化	Duōmùbiāo yōuhuà	Multi-objective optimization	
多旁瓣抑制系统	Duōpángbàn yìzhì xìtǒng	Multiple sidelobe cancellation system	MSLC
多频按键	Duōpín ànjiàn	Multi-frequency press button	MFPB
多频拨号	Duōpín bōhào	Multi-frequency dialing	MFD
多频拨号记存发送器	Duōpín bōhào jìcún fāsòngqì	Multi-frequency dial register sender	MDRS
多频互控板	Duōpín hùkòngbǎn	Multi-frequency control board	MFC
多频键控呼叫	Duōpín jiànkòng hūjiào	Touch-calling multi-frequency	TCMF
多频输出发送器	Duōpín shūchū fāsòngqì	Multi-frequency output sender	MFOS
多频小区报告	Duōpín xiǎoqū bàogào	Multi-band cell reporting	MBCR
多频信令	Duōpín xìnlìng	Multi-frequency signaling	
多频信令系统	Duōpín xìnlìng xìtǒng	Signaling system multi-frequency	SSMF
多频移频键控	Duōpín yípín jiànkòng	Multiple frequency shift keying	MFSK
多频带激励	Duōpíndài jīlì	Multiband excitation	MBE
多频带天线	Duōpíndài tiānxiàn	Multiple band antenna	
多频段多模式无线电台	Duōpínduàn duōmóshì wúxiàndiàntái	Multiband multimode radio (a US system)	MBMMR
多普勒	Duō-pǔ-lè	Doppler	
多普勒雷达	Duō-pǔ-lè léidá	Doppler radar	
多普勒频偏校正	Duō-pǔ-lè pínpiān jiàozhèng	Doppler frequency deviation correction	
多普勒频移	Duō-pǔ-lè pínyí	Doppler shift	
多普勒声纳	Duō-pǔ-lè shēngnà	Doppler sonar	
多枪管	Duōqiāngguǎn	Multi-gun cathode ray tube (CRT)	
多任务	Duōrènwu	Multi-tasking	

多色激光	Duōsè jīguāng	Multi-color laser	
多色图像阵列	Duōsè túxiàng zhènliè	Multi-color graphics array	MCGA
多射束天线	Duōshèshù tiānxiàn	Multi-beam antenna, multi-pattern antenna	
多实例	Duōshílì	Multiple instances	
多时隙操作	Duōshíxì cāozuò	Multi-slot operation	
多时相图像	Duōshíxiàng túxiàng	Multi-temporal image	
多数表决判定	Duōshù biǎojué pàndìng	Majority voting (SDH term)	
多束光缆	Duōshù guānglǎn	Multiple bundle cable	
多束速调管	Duōshù sùtiáoguǎn	Multi-beam klystron	MBK
多数投票	Duōshù tóupiào	Plurality voting	
多输入多输出	Duōshūrù duō shūchū	Multi-input multi-output	MIMO
多输入输出	Duōshūrù shūchū	Multi-input multi-output	MIMO
多宿主机	Duōsù zhǔjī	Multi-homed host	
多速率单一线对数字用户环路	Duōsùlǜ dānyī xiànduì shùzì yònghù huánlù	Multirate single pair digital subscriber loop	MSDSL
多速率电路交换	Duōsùlǜ diànlù jiāohuàn	Multirate circuit switching	
多速率对称数字用户环路	Duōsùlǜ duìchèn shùzì yònghù huánlù	Multirate symmetrical digital subscriber loop	MSDSL
多速率对称数字用户线	Duōsùlǜ duìchèn shùzì yònghù xiàn	Multirate symmetrical digital subscriber line	MSDSL
多速率同步数据	Duōsùlǜ tóngbù shùjù	Multi-speed-rate data (type of interface board)	MSRD
多态性	Duōtàixìng	Polymorphism	
多态性	Duōtàixìng	Allomorphism	
多跳路径	Duōtiào lùjìng	Multihop path	
多跳卫星链路	Duōtiào wèixīng liànlù	Multi-hop satellite link	
多通道	Duōtōngdào	Multi-channel	MCH
多通道局域网	Duōtōngdào júyùwǎng	Multi-channel local area network	MLAN
多突发模式控制器	Duōtūfā móshì kòngzhìqì	Multiple burst mode controller	MBMC
多维表达式	Duōwéi biǎodá shì	Multi-dimensional expressions	MDX
多维尺度	Duōwéi chǐdù	Multi-dimensional scaling	
多维等级分析	Duōwéi děngjí fēnxī	Multi-dimensional scaling analysis	
多维结构	Duōwéi jiégòu	Multi-dimensional structure	
多维联机分析处理	Duōwéi liánjī fēnxī chǔlǐ	Multi-dimensional online analytical processing	MOLAP
多维数据	Duōwéi shùjù	Multi-dimensional data	
多维数据集	Duōwéi shùjùjí	Data cube	
多维数据集	Duōwéi shùjùjí	Cube (for database)	
多维数据集角色	Duōwéi shùjùjí juésè	Data cube role	
多维数据集文件	Duōwéi shùjùjí wénjiàn	Data cube file	
多维数组	Duōwéishù zǔ	Multi-dimensional array	
多卫星链路	Duōwèixīng liànlù	Multi-satellite link	
多文档界面	Duōwéndàng jièmiàn	Multi-documentation interface	MDI
多线程	Duōxiànchéng	Multi-threading	
多线程服务器应用程序	Duōxiànchéng fúwùqì yìngyòng chéngxù	Multi-threaded server application	
多项呼叫代理	Duōxiàng hūjiào dàilǐ	Multi-call agent	
多相流	Duōxiàng liú	Multi-phase flow	
多项逻辑回归	Duōxiàng luójì huíguī	Multinomial logic regression	
多相移相键控	Duōxiàng yíxiāng jiànkòng	Multiple phase shift keying	MPSK
多相关控制功能	Duōxiàngguān kòngzhì gōngnéng	Multiple association control function	MACF

多项式	Duōxiàngshì	Polynomial	
多项式变换	Duōxiàngshì biànhuàn	Polynomial transformation	
多线路服务器	Duōxiànlù fúwùqì	Multi-thread server	MTS
多谐发生器	Duōxié fāshēngqì	Multi-vibrator	
多协议	Duōxiéyì	Multi-protocol	
多协议边缘网关协议	Duōxiéyì biānyuán wǎngguān xiéyì	Multiprotocol border gateway protocol	MBGP
多协议标答交换	Duōxiéyì biāodá jiāohuàn	Multi-protocol label switching	MPLS
多协议标号交换	Duōxiéyì biāohào jiāohuàn	Multi-protocol label switching	MPLS
多协议标记交换	Duōxiéyì biāojì jiāohuàn	Multi-protocol label switching	MPLS
多协议标签交换	Duōxiéyì biāoqiān jiāohuàn	Multi-protocol label switching	MPLS
多协议标签协议	Duōxiéyì biāoqiān xiéyì	Multi-protocol label switching	MPLS
多协议标志交换	Duōxiéyì biāozhì jiāohuàn	Multi-protocol label switching	MPLS
多协议波长交换	Duōxiéyì bōcháng jiāohuàn	Multi-protocol wavelength switching	MPIS
多协议扩展的 BGP 协议	Duōxiéyì kuòzhǎnde BGP xiéyì	Multi-protocol extension for BGP-4	BGP-MP
多协议通信控制器	Duōxiéyì tōngxìn kòngzhìqì	Multi-protocol communications controller	MPCC
多协议 λ 交换	Duōxiéyì λ jiāohuàn	Multi-protocol wavelength switching	MPLambdaS
多芯光缆	Duōxīn guānglǎn	Multi-fiber cable	
多芯光缆连接器	Duōxīn guānglǎn liánjiēqì	Multi-fiber cable connector	
多芯光纤	Duōxīn guāngxiān	Multi-core fiber	
多心光纤连接器	Duōxīn guāngxiān liánjiēqì	Multi-channel fiber optic connector	
多信道	Duōxìndào	Multi-channel	MCH
多信道多点分配业务	Duōxìndào duōdiǎn fēnpèi yèwù	Multi-channel multipoint distribution service	MMDS
多信道微波分配系统	Duōxìndào wēibō fēnpèi xìtǒng	Multi-channel microwave distribution system	MMDS
多信道选取	Duōxìndào xuǎnqǔ	Multi-channel access	MCA
多信道载波电话系统	Duōxìndào zàibō diànhuà xìtǒng	Multi-channel carrier telephone system	MCCTS
多信道自动拨号移动通信系统	Duōxìndào zìdòng bōhào yídòng tōngxìn xìtǒng	Multiple-channel mobile communication system with automatic dialing	
多信号类级	Duōxìnhào lèijí	Multiple signal classification	MUSIC
多芯片模块	Duōxìnpiàn mókuài	Multi-chip module (electronics mfg)	MCM
多心式光缆	Duōxīnshì guānglǎn	Multi-fiber fiber optic cable	
多虚拟存储器分布库	Duōxūnǐ cúnchǔqì fēnbù kù	Multiple virtual storage distribution library	MVSDLIB
多样性	Duōyàngxìng	Diversity	
多业务传输节点	Duōyèwù chuánshū jiédiǎn	Multi-service transmission platform	MSTP
多业务传输平台	Duōyèwù chuánshū píngtái	Multi-service transport platform	MSTP
多业务分组传输平台	Duōyèwù fēnzǔ chuánshū píngtái	Multi-service packet transmission platform	MXP
多业务分组环	Duōyèwù fēnzǔ huán	Multi-service packet ring	MPR
多业务供应平台	Duōyèwù gōngyìng píngtái	Multi-service provisioning platform	
多业务汇接点	Duōyèwù huìjiēdiǎn	Multi-service confluence point	MSCP
多业务交换论坛	Duōyèwù jiāohuàn lùntán	Multi-service switching forum	MSF
多业务接入节点	Duōyèwù jiērù jiédiǎn	Multi-service access nodes	MAN
多业务接入模块	Duōyèwù jiērù mókuài	Multi-service access module	MSA
多业务接入平台	Duōyèwù jiērù píngtái	Multi-service access platform	MSAP
多业务接入网	Duōyèwù jiērù wǎng	Multi-service access network	MSAN
多业务接入点	Duōyèwù jiērùdiǎn	Multi-service access point	MSAP
多业务链路层	Duōyèwù liànlùcéng	Multi-service link layer	
多业务配置平台	Duōyèwù pèizhì píngtái	Multiple service provisioning platform	MSPP

多业务平台	Duōyèwù píngtái	Multi-service platform	MP
多业务提供平台	Duōyèwù tígōng píngtái	Multi-service provider platform	MSPP
多业务网关	Duōyèwù wǎngguān	Multi-service gateway	MSG
多影像透镜	Duōyǐngxiàng tòujìng	Multiple image lens	
多用户	Duōyònghù	Multiple user dimension	MUD
多用户	Duōyònghù	Multi-user	
多用户	Duōyònghù	Multi-party	MPTY
多用户单元	Duōyònghù dānyuán	Multi-subscriber unit	
多用户分布	Duōyònghù fēnbù	Multiple subscriber profile	MSP
多用户分时（计算机系统）	Duōyònghù fēnshí (jìsuànjī xìtǒng)	Multi-subscriber time shared (computer system)	MSTS
多用户号码	Duōyònghù hàomǎ	Multi-subscriber number	MSN
多用户检测	Duōyònghù jiǎncè	Multi-user detection	MUD
多用户线路	Duōyònghù xiànlù	Multi-subscriber profile	MSP
多用户信道	Duōyònghù xìndào	Multi-user channel	
多用户信息插座	Duōyònghù xìnxī chāzuò	Multi-user information outlet	MIO
多用户移动台	Duōyònghù yídòngtái	Multi-user mobile station	MUMS
多用途地籍簿	Duōyòngtú dìjíbù	Multi-purpose cadastre	
多用途因特网邮件扩展	Duōyòngtú Yīntèwǎng yóujiàn kuòzhǎn	Multi-purpose internet mail extension	MIME
多用途的网际邮件扩充协议	Duōyòngtúde wǎngjì yóujiàn kuòchōng xiéyì	Multipurpose Internet mail extensions	MIME
多优先队列	Duōyōuxiān duìliè	Multiple priority queue	MPQ
多优先级	Duōyōuxiān jí	Multiple priority levels	
多域网络	Duōyù wǎngluò	Multiple domain network	
多元变量分析	Duōyuán biànliàng fēnxī	Multi-variate analysis	
多元回归	Duōyuán huíguī	Multiple regression	
多元可控阵	Duōyuán kěkòng zhèn	Multiple-unit steerable array (antenna)	MUSA
多元空间数据库	Duōyuán kōngjiān shùjùkù	Multi-variate spatial database	
多元业务量处理	Duōyuán yèwùliàng chǔlǐ	Integrated traffic handling	
多余度	Duōyúdù	Redundancy	
多载波脉冲位置调制	Duōzàibō màichōng wèizhì tiáozhì	Multi-carrier pulse position modulation	MPPM
多载波调制	Duōzàibō tiáozhì	Multi-carrier modulation	MCM
多站访问单元	Duōzhàn fǎngwèn dānyuán	Multi-station access unit	MAU
多站智能用户电报装置	Duōzhàn zhìnéng yònghù diànbào zhuāngzhì	Multi-station teletex installation	
多折合偶极子	Duōzhéhé ǒujízi	Multiple folded dipole	
多振幅最小移位键控	Duōzhènfú zuìxiǎo yíwèi jiànkòng	Multi-amplitude minimum shift keying	MAMSK
多帧	Duōzhèng	Multi-frame	MF
多帧操作	Duōzhèng cāozuò	Multiple frame operation	
多帧传输	Duōzhèng chuánshū	Multiple frame transmission	
多帧模式	Duōzhèng móshì	Multi-frame mode	
多址干扰	Duōzhǐ gānrǎo	Multiple access interference	MAI
多址呼叫	Duōzhǐ hūjiào	Multi-address call	
多址联接	Duōzhǐ liánjiē	Multiple access	
多值相移键控	Duōzhí xiāngyí jiànkòng	Multiple phase shift keying	MPSK
多重处理器规范	Duōzhòng chǔlǐqì guīfàn	Multi-processor specification	MPS
多重处理器架构	Duōzhòng chǔlǐqì jiàgòu	Multi-processor architecture	MPA

多重分辨率组合	Duōzhòng fēnbiànlǜ zǔhé	Multi-resolution mesh (video term)	
多重继承	Duōzhòng jìchéng	Multiple inheritance	
多重境深	Duōzhòng jìng shēn	Depth of field	DOF
多重链路点对点协议	Duōzhòng liànlù diǎn duì diǎn xiéyì	Mult-link point-to-point protocol	MultiPPP
多重散光聚焦系统	Duōzhòng sǎnguāng jùjiāo xìtǒng	Multi-astigmatism lens system (video term)	MALS
多种商业组群	Duōzhǒng shāngyè zǔqún	Multi-business group	MBG
多重纹理	Duōzhòng wénlǐ	Multi-texture (video term)	
多重星座调制	Duōzhòng xīngzuò tiáozhì	Multiple quadrature amplitude modulation	MQAM
多重子奈奎斯特抽样编码	Duōzhòng ziNài-kuí-sī-tè chōuyàng biānmǎ	Multiple sub-Nyquist sampling encoding	MUSE
多终端公务电路	Duōzhōngduān gōngwù diànlù	Multi-terminal service circuit	
多轴应力状态	Duōzhóu yìnglì zhuàngtài	Multi-axial stress condition	
多主系统	Duōzhǔ xìtǒng	Multi-master system	
多状态调制	Duōzhuàngtài tiáozhì	Multi-state modulation	
多字节扩展	Duōzìjié kuòzhǎn	Multi-byte expansion	MBE
多纵模	Duōzòngmó	Multi-longitude mode	MLM
多纵模激光器	Duōzòngmó jīguāngqì	Multi-longitudinal mode laser	MLM
读片机	Dúpiànjī	Card reader	
镀青铜	Dùqīngtóng	Bronzing, bronze plating	
读取单元	Dúqǔ dānyuán	Fetch element	
渡越时间调制	Dùyuè shíjiān tiáozhì	Transit-time modulation	TTM
独资企业	Dúzī qǐyè	Wholly foreign owned/funded enterprise	
D 信道上的链路接入协议	D-xìndào shàngde liànlù jiērù xiéyì	Link access protocol on D channel	LAPD
D 信道上的链路访问协议	D-xìndào-shàngde liànlù fǎngwèn xiéyì	Link access protocol on the D channel	LAP-D
D 形阀	D-xíng fá	D-valve	
D-星号	D-xīng hào	D-star	

E

E 主平面	E zhǔ píngmiàn	E principal plane	
EDGE 电路交换传输 模式	EDGE diànlù jiāohuàn chuánshū móshì	EDGE circuit switched data	ECSD
EDGE 分组交换传输 模式	EDGE fēnzǔ jiāohuàn chuánshū móshì	EDGE general packet radio service	EGPRS
额定带宽	Édìng dàikuān	Rated bandwidth	
额定负载	Édìng fùzài	Normal load	
额定抗拉强度	Édìng kànglā qiángdù	Rated tensile strength	RTS
额定拉断力	Édìng lāduànlì	Rated tensile strength	RTS
额定射频输出功率	Édìng shèpín shūchū gōnglǜ	Rated radio-frequency output power	
额定使用范围	Édìng shǐyòng fànwéi	Rated operating range	
额定输出功率	Édìng shūchū gōnglǜ	Rated output power (of a transmitter)	
额定输光功率	Édìng shūguāng gōnglǜ	Rated optical output power	
额定音频输出功率	Édìng yīnpín shūchū gōnglǜ	Rated audio-frequency output power	
额定值	Édìngzhí	Rating	
额定值	Édìngzhí	Rated value	
E-H 面调节器	E-H miàn tiáojiéqì	E-H tuner	
恶劣公平系数	Èliè gōngping xìshù	Worst-case fairness index	
扼流法兰	Èliú fǎlán	Choke flange	
扼流活塞	Èliú huósāi	Choke piston	
扼流连接	Èliú liánjiē	Choke joint	

扼流器	Èliúqì	Choke	
E 面扇形喇叭天线	E-miàn shànxíng lǎba tiānxiàn	E-plane sectoral horn antenna	
E 面透镜	E-miàn tòujìng	E-plane lens	
E 面 T 形环行器	E-miàn T-xíng huánxíngqì	E-plane T circulator	
E 面 T 形接头	E-miàn T-xíng jiētóu	E-plane T-junction	
E 面弯波导	E-miàn wān bōdǎo	E-plane waveguide bend	
E-面弯头	E-miàn wāntóu	E-plane corner	
E 面 Y 形环行器	E-miàn Y-xíng huánxíngqì	E-plane Y circulator	
E-面 Y 形接头	E-miàn Y-xíng jiētóu	E-plane Y junction	
耳参考点	Ěr cānkǎo diǎn	Ear reference point	ERP
铒固体激光	Ěr gùtǐ jīguāng	Erbium laser	
二/十进制代码	Èr/shíjìnzhì dàimǎ	Binary coded decimal	BCD
二倍最小功率点	Èrbèi zuìxiǎo gōnglǜ diǎn	Twice minimum power points	
二变量相关	Èrbiànliàng xiāngguān	Bi-variate correlation	
二部图	Èrbù tú	Bipartite graph	
二层传送协议	Èrcéng chuánsòng xiéyì	Layer 2 transport protocol	L2TP
二叉查找树	Èrchā cházhǎo shù	Binary search tree	
二叉排序树	Èrchā páixù shù	Binary sort tree	
二叉树	Èrchā shù	Binary tree	
二次 AC 电压	Èrcì AC diànyā	Alternating current (AC) secondary voltage	
二次 AC 接口	Èrcì AC jiēkǒu	Alternating current (AC) secondary interface	
二次被覆层	Èrcì bèifù céng	Second coating	
二次被覆光纤	Èrcì bèifù guāngxiān	Second coating optical fiber	
二次 DC 电压	Èrcì DC diànyā	Direct current (DC) secondary voltage	
二次 DC 接口	Èrcì DC jiēkǒu	Direct current (DC) secondary interface	
二次对消器	Èrcì duìxiāoqì	Double canceller	
二次反射	Èrcì fǎnshè	Second reflection	
二次反射法	Èrcì fǎnshè fǎ	Double bounce technique	
二次辐射	Èrcì fúshè	Secondary radiation	
二次供电	Èrcì gōngdiàn	Secondary power supply	
二次监视雷达	Èrcì jiānshì léidá	Secondary surveillance radar	SSR
二次开发接口	Èrcì kāifā jiēkǒu	Secondary development interface (similar in function to API)	
二次雷达	Èrcì léidá	Secondary radar	
二次流	Èrcì liú	Secondary flow	
二次配线网	Èrcì pèixiànwǎng	Secondary distribution network	SDN
二次群	Èrcì qún	DS-2 (2nd digital standard transmission rate = 8Mbps)	
二次设计	Èrcì shèjì	Secondary design	
二次数字复用器	Èrcì shùzì fùyòngqì	Secondary digital multiplexer	
二次数字载波	Èrcì shùzì zàibō	Secondary digital carrier	SDC
二次下电	Èrcì xiàdiàn	Secondary power switchover (to secondary battery)	
二次增量调制	Èrcì zēngliàng tiáozhì	Derived delta modulation	DDM
二单元	Èrdānyuán	Two-cell	
二地址系统	Èrdìzhǐ xìtǒng	Two-address system	
二端网络	Èrduān wǎngluò	Two-terminal network	
二分查找	Èrfēn cházhǎo	Binary search	
二分法搜索	Èrfēnfǎ sōusuǒ	Dichotomizing search	

耳机	Ěrjī	Earphone	
耳机插座	Ěrjī chāzuò	Earphone socket (on radio)	
耳机额定阻抗	Ěrjī édìng zǔkàng	Rated impedance of earphone	
二级环	Èrjí huán	Secondary ring	
二级时钟	Èrjí shízhōng	Stratum 2 clock	
二级通道协议	Èrjí tōngdào xiéyì	Layer 2 tunneling protocol	L2TP
二阶矩偏振模色散差分群时延	Èrjiē jǔ piānzhèn mó sèsàn chāfēn qún shíyán	Second moment polarization mode dispersion differential group delay	
二阶失真	Èrjiē shīzhēn	Second order distortion	
二阶相关多路存取	Èrjiē xiāngguān duōlù cúnqǔ	Second order coherent multiple access	SOCMA
二阶效应	Èrjiē xiàoyìng	Second order effect	
二阶最小方乘法	Èrjiē zuìxiǎo fāngchéngfǎ	Two-stage least squares	
二极管	Èrjíguǎn	Diode	D
二极管激光器	Èrjíguǎn jīguāngqì	Diode laser	
二机管晶体管逻辑电路	Erjīguǎn jīngtǐguǎn luóji diànlù	Diode transistor logic circuit	DTL
二极管开关	Èrjíguǎn kāiguān	Diode switch	DS
二进检测	Èrjìn jiǎncè	Binary detection	
二进位型	Èrjìnwèi-xíng	Bit type	
二进制	Èrjìnzhì	Binary	
二进制备记数法	Èrjìnzhì bèijì shùfǎ	Binary notation	
二进制编码的八进制	Èrjìnzhì biānmǎde bājìnzhì	Binary coded octal	BCO
二进制编码的十进制	Èrjìnzhì biānmǎde shíjìnzhì	Binary coded decimal	BCD
二进制比特	Èrjìnzhì bǐtè	Binary digit, bit	
二进制不对称通道	Èrjìnzhì bùduìchèn tōngdào	Binary asymmetric channel	BAC
二进制大对象	Èrjìnzhì dà duìxiàng	Binary large object	
二进制大目标	Èrjìnzhì dà mùbiāo	Binary large object	BLOB
二进制对称信道	Èrjìnzhì duìchèn xìndào	Binary symmetric channel	BSC
二进制分割	Èrjìnzhì fēngē	Binary segmentation	
二进制浮点运算	Èrjìnzhì fúdiǎn yùnsuàn	Binary floating point arithmetic	BFPA
二进制符号	Èrjìnzhì fúhào	Binary figure	
二进制校验字符	Èrjìnzhì jiàoyàn zìfú	Binary check character	BCC
二进制记录	Èrjìnzhì jìlù	Binary logging	
二进制码	Èrjìnzhì mǎ	Binary code	
二进制码频移键控	Èrjìnzhì mǎ pínyí jiànkòng	Binary code frequency shift keying	BCFSK
二进制频移键控	Èrjìnzhì pínyí jiànkòng	Binary frequency shift keying	BFSK
二进制数	Èrjìnzhì shù	Binary number	
二进制数级回退机制	Èrjìnzhì shùjí huítuì jīzhì	Binary exponential backoff system (in mobile IP)	
二进制数位	Èrjìnzhì shùwèi	Binary digit, bit	
二进制数字	Èrjìnzhì shùzì	Binary figure	
二进制速率	Èrjìnzhì sùlǜ	Binary rate	
二进制调频差动相干相移键控	Èrjìnzhì tiáopín chādòng xiānggān xiāngyí jiànkòng	Binary frequency modulated differentially coherent phase shift keying	B-FMDCPSK
二进制同步控制	Èrjìnzhì tóngbù kòngzhì	Binary synchronous control	BSC
二进制同步通信	Èrjìnzhì tóngbù tōngxìn	Binary synchronous communication	BSC
二进制位	Èrjìnzhì wèi	Binary digit, bit	
二进制文件	Èrjìnzhì wénjiàn	Binary file	

二进制文件传输	Èrjìnzhì wénjiàn chuánshū	Binary file transfer	
二进制相干相移键控	Èrjìnzhì xiānggān xiāngyí jiànkòng	Binary coherent phase shift keying	BCPSK
二进制相移键控	Èrjìnzhì xiāngyí jiànkòng	Binary phase shift keying	BPSK
二进制系统间传输标准	Èrjìnzhì xìtǒng-jiān chuánshū biāozhǔn	Binary Intersystem transmission standard	BITS
二进制增量调制	Èrjìnzhì zēngliàng tiáozhì	Binary delta modulation	BDM
二路功率分配器	Èrlù gōnglǜ fēnpèiqì	Two-way power divider	2WPD
二路平衡归并排序	Èrlù pínghéng guībìng páixù	Balance two-way merging sort	
二频制	Èrpín zhì	Two-frequency system	
二十进制码	Èrshí jìnzhì mǎ	Binary-coded decimal (BCD) code	
二-十进制交换器	Èr-shíjìnzhì jiāohuànqì	Binary-decimal converter	BDC
二十六进制转换	Èrshíliù jìnzhì zhuǎnhuàn	Binary-to-hexadecimal conversion	
二态	Èrtài	Two-condition	
儿童在线保护法	Értóng zàixiàn bǎohù fǎ	Child Online Protection Act (US)	
二维	Èrwéi	Two-dimensional	2D
二维副本	Èrwéi fùběn	Two-dimensional manifold	
二维奇偶验码	Èrwéi jī'ǒu yàn mǎ	Horizontal and vertical parity check code	
二维模型	Èrwéi móxíng	Two-dimensional model	
二维平面阵	Èrwéi píngmiàn zhèn	Two-dimensional flat surface array	
二位字节	Èrwèi zìjié	Doublet byte	
二位元文件	Èrwèiyuán wénjiàn	Binary file	
二纤单向通道保护环	Èrxiān dānxiàng tōngdào bǎohù huán	Two-fiber unidirectional path protection ring	
二线交换	Èrxiàn jiāohuàn	Two-wire switching	
二线模拟接口	Èrxiàn mónǐ jiēkǒu	Two-wire analog interface	
二纤双向复用段共享保护环	Èrxiān shuāngxiàng fùyòng duàn gòngxiǎng bǎohù huán	Two-fiber multiplex section shared protection ring	
二纤双向通道保护环	Èrxiān shuāngxiàng tōngdào bǎohù huán	Two-fiber bi-directional path protection ring	
二线制	Èrxiàn zhì	Two-wire system	
二相编码	Èrxiàng biānmǎ	Biphase coding	
二相差分相移键控	Èrxiāng chàfēn xiàngyí jiànkòng	Binary differential phase shift keying	BDPSK
二相相移键控	Èrxiàng xiàngyí jiànkòng	Binary phase shift keying	BPSK
二相移相键控	Èrxiàng yíxiàng jiànkòng	Binary phase shift keying	BPSK
二项式分布	Èrxiàngshì fēnbù	Binomial distribution	
二项式扭波导	Èrxiàngshì niǔ bōdǎo	Binomial twist waveguide	
二项式弯头	Èrxiàngshì wāntóu	Binomial corner	
二氧氟化硅	Èryǎng fúhuà guī	Flourided silicon oxide	Si02F
二氧化碳激光	Èryǎnghuàtàn jīguāng	Carbon dioxide (CO_2) laser	
二氧化碳激光加工机	Èryǎnghuàtàn jīguāng jiāgōngjī	Carbon dioxide (CO_2) laser processing equipment	
二氧化碳系统	Èryǎnghuàtàn xìtǒng	Carbon dioxide extinguishing system	CDES
二元操作符	Èryuán cāozuò fú	Binary operator	
二元对称信道	Èryuán duìchèn xìndào	Binary symmetric channel	
二元合作	Èryuán hézuò	Binary collaboration	
二元逻辑回归	Èryuán luóji huíguī	Binary logistic regression	
二值图像	Èrzhí túxiàng	Binary image (GIS)	
二轴稳定系统	Èrzhóu wěndìng xìtǒng	Bi-axial stable system	
二字指令	Èrzì zhǐlìng	Two-word instruction	
ETSI 技术报告	ETSI jìshù bàogào	ETSI technical report	ETR

Euler 回路/中国邮路	Euler huílù/ Zhōngguó yóulù	Eulerian cycle / Chinese postman	
额外开销	Éwài kāixiao	Overhead	
额外业务信号	Éwài yèwù xìnhào	Extra traffic signal	
额外帧速率	Éwài zhèng sùlǜ	Extra frame rate	EFR
额外帧率	Éwài zhènglǜ	Extra frame rate	EFR
恶意呼叫检验补充业务	Èyì hūjiào jiǎnyàn bǔchōng yèwù	Malicious call identification supplementary service	MCI
恶意呼叫识别	Èyì hūjiào shíbié	Malicious call identification	MCI

F

发报刊局	Fā bàokān jú	Newspaper and periodical distribution office	
发参数	Fā cānshù	Send parameters	
发鉴权信息	Fā jiànquán xìnxī	Send authentication information	
发结束信号	Fā jiéshù xìnhào	Send end signal	
发路由信息	Fā lùyóu xìnxī	Send routing information	
发报机	Fābàojī	Telegraph transmitter	
发报机畸变	Fābàojī jībiàn	Transmitter distortion	
发布	Fābù	Publication	
发布保持期	Fābù bǎochí qī	Publication retention period	
发布表	Fābù biǎo	Publishing table	
发布服务器	Fābù fúwùqì	Publisher	
发布数据库	Fābù shùjùkù	Publication database	
发布里-珀罗饱和吸收器	Fā-bù-lǐ--pò-luó bǎohé xīshōu qì	Fabry-Perot saturable absorber	FPSA
法布里--珀罗激光二极管	Fǎ-bù-lǐ--pò-luó jīguāng èrjíguǎn	Fabry-Perot laser diode	FP-LD
法布里 - 泊罗腔激光器	Fǎ-bù-lǐ--pó-luó qiāng jīguāngqì	Fabry-Perot cavity laser device	FP-LD
发电机组	Fādiàn jīzǔ	Power generation set	
发电机	Fādiànjī	Generator	G
发端	Fāduān	Originating	
发端(信息)编号发送器	Fāduān (xìnxī) biānhào fāsòngqì	Originating number sender	ONS
发端(信息)编号寄存器	Fāduān (xìnxī) biānhào jìcúnqì	Originating number register	ONR
发端 CAMEL 签约信息	Fāduān CAMEL qiānyuē xìnxī	Originating CAMEL subscription information	O - CSI
发端端局交换机	Fāduān duānjú jiāohuànjī	Originating local exchange	OLE
发光二极管	Fāguāng èrjíguǎn	Light emitting diode	LED
发光二极体	Fāguāng èrjítǐ	Light emitting diode	LED
发光二极体传真机	Fāguāng èrjítǐ chuánzhēnjī	Light emitting diode facsimile	
发光二极体晶圆	Fāguāng èrjítǐ jīngyuán	Light emitting diode wafer	
发光二极体显示系统	Fāguāng èrjítǐ xiǎnshì xìtǒng	Light emitting diode display system	
发光二极体显示器	Fāguāng èrjítǐ xiǎnshìqì	Light emitting diode display	
发光管	Fāguāng guǎn	Light emitting diode	LED
发光光纤	Fāguāng guāngxiān	Luminescent fiber	
发光现象	Fāguāng xiànxiàng	Luminous phenomenon	
发光度	Fāguāngdù	Luminosity	
法国标准	Fǎguó biāozhǔn	Norme Francaise (French standards organization)	NF
法国电信公司	Fǎguó diànxìn gōngsī	France Telecom Corp.	
法国信息工作人员协会	Fǎguó xìnxī gōngzuò rényuán xiéhuì	Association Francaise des Informaticiens (French association of persons in the information industry)	AFIN
发话话务	Fāhuà huàwù	Originating traffic	
发货至客户	Fāhuò zhì kèhù	Time to customer (regarding delivery of goods)	

发卡机	Fākǎ jī	Ticket dispenser	TD
阀控式	Fákòng-shì	Valve regulated	
阀控式密封型电池	Fákòng-shì mìfēng xíng diànchí	Valve-regulated lead acid battery	VRLA
法拉弟效应	Fǎ-lā-dì xiàoyìng	Faraday effect	
法拉第旋转效应隔离器	Fǎ-lā-dì xuánzhuǎn xiàoyìng gélíqì	Faraday rotation isolator	
法拉第旋转式环行器	Fǎ-lā-dì xuánzhuǎn-shì huánxíngqì	Faraday rotation circulator	
法兰类型	Fǎlán lèixíng	Flange type	
法兰连接	Fǎlán liánjiē	Flange joint	
法兰组件	Fǎlán zǔjiàn	Flange assembly	
法律网络	Fǎlǜ wǎngluò	LawsNet ©	
法律上标准	Fǎlǜ-shàng biāozhǔn	*de Jure* standard	
发码器	Fāmǎqì	Code sender	
阀门	Fámén	Trap	
反电子欺骗	Fǎn diànzǐ qīpiàn	Anti-spoofing	
反对称双正交小波	Fǎn duìchēng shuāng zhèngjiāo xiǎobō·	Anti-symmetric biorthogonal wavelet	
反概率接收机	Fǎn gàilǜ jiēshōujī	Inverse probability receiver	
反概率准则	Fǎn gàilǜ zhǔnzé	Inverse probability criterion	
反共振	Fǎn gòngzhèn	Anti-resonance	
泛克里津插值法	Fàn kè-lǐ-jīn chāzhí fǎ	Universal Kriging	
反迫击炮雷达	Fǎn pǎijīpào léidá	Counter-mortar radar	
反斯托克斯线	Fǎn Sī-tuō-kè-sī xiàn	Anti-Stokes line	
反 T-R 盒	Fǎn T-R hé	Anti T-R cell	
泛欧数字蜂窝移动通信系统	Fàn'ōu shùzì fēngwō yídòng tōngxìn xìtǒng	Pan-European digital cellular land mobile telecommunication system	
泛欧数字无绳电话系统	Fàn'ōu shùzì wúshéng diànhuà xìtǒng	Digital European cordless telephone	DECT
泛欧数字无绳通信系统	Fàn'ōu shùzì wúshéng tōngxìn xìtǒng	Digital European Cordless Telecommunication system	DECT
泛欧洲数字集群标准	Fàn'Ōuzhōu shùzì jíqún biāozhǔn	Trans-European trunked radio	TETRA
翻版	Fānbǎn	Pirated (software)	
翻扳机	Fānbānjī	Board flipper (in component assembly process)	
返波管	Fǎnbōguǎn	Backward wave tube	
反差扩展	Fǎnchā kuòzhǎn	Contrast stretching	
反吹	Fǎnchuī	Back-flushing	
范杜伦码	Fàn-dù-lún mǎ	Van duuren code	
反峰阻尼电路	Fǎnfēng zǔní diànlù	Inverse damping circuit	
反复弯曲	Fǎnfù wānqū	Reverse bend, reverse bending	
反复的	Fǎnfùde	Iterative	
反复射导弹	Fǎnfùshè dǎodàn	Anti-radiation missile	ARM
防电磁泄漏	Fáng diàncí xièlòu	Protect against electromagnetic leakage (TEMPEST)	
仿函数	Fǎng hánshù	Functor	
方括号	Fāng kuòhào	Bracket (square bracket) [ ]	
方幂模	Fāng mìmó	Modular exponentiation	
防消息伪造	Fáng xiāoxi wěizào	Protection against message falsification (IPsec)	
防烟雾	Fáng yānwù	Smog-proof (one of the "three proofings")	
妨碍功能性维护	Fáng'ài gōngnéngxìng wéihù	Function-preventing maintenance	
方案论证	Fāng'àn lùnzhèng	Proof of concept	
防爆电话机	Fángbào diànhuàjī	Explosion-proof telephone set	

防病毒软件	Fángbìngdú ruǎnjiàn	Anti-virus software	
方舱	Fāngcāng	Shelter	
方差	Fāngchà	Variance	
方差元素估计	Fāngchà yuánsù gūjì	Variance component estimation	
防拆	Fángchāi	Tamper resistance	
防潮	Fángcháo	Moisture protection; protect against moisture (one of the "Six protects")	
防尘	Fángchén	Dust-protected	
方程项	Fāngchéng xiàng	Equation item	
防重放保护	Fángchóngfàng bǎohù	Anti-replay protection (IPsec)	
防篡改	Fángcuàngǎi	Anti-tampering (IPsec)	
防错码	Fángcuòmǎ	Error protection code	
放大	Fàngdà	Amplification, zoom	
放大自发辐射	Fàngdà zìfā fúshè	Amplified spontaneous emission	ASE
放大自激辐射信号	Fàngdà zìjī fúshè xìnhào	Amplified spontaneous emission	AME
放大自激发射噪声	Fàngdà zìjīfāshè zàoshēng	Amplified spontaneous emission noise	ASEN
放大/分配集成件	Fàngdà/fēnpèi jíchéngjiàn	Amplifier/divider assembly	IADA
放大率	Fàngdàlǜ	Magnification rate	
防盗报警	Fángdào bàojǐng	Intruder alarm	IA
放大器	Fàngdàqì	Amplifier	A
放大器偏压电流	Fàngdàqì piānyā diànliú	Amplifier bias current	ABC
放大器线性动态范围	Fàngdàqì xiànxìng dòngtài fànwéi	Amplifier linear dynamic range	
防滴	Fángdī	Protected against dropping water	
放电	Fàngdiàn	Discharge	
放电灯	Fàngdiàn dēng	Discharge lamp	
放电电压	Fàngdiàn diànyā	Discharge voltage	
放电深度	Fàngdiàn shēndù	Discharge depth	
放电时间常数	Fàngdiàn shíjiān chángshù	Electrical discharge time constant (of a detector)	
放电特性曲线	Fàngdiàn tèxìng qūxiàn	Discharge characteristic curve	
放电率	Fàngdiànlǜ	Discharge rate	
防毒	Fángdú	Protect against viruses (one of the "Six protects")	
防反射涂层	Fángfǎnshè túcéng	Anti-reflection coating	
防辐射	Fángfúshè	Protect against emissions (one of the Three protects)	
防腐蚀	Fángfǔshí	Corrosion protection	
防干扰	Fánggānrǎo	Protect against interference or jamming (one of the Three protects)	
方格背景	Fānggé bèijǐng	Cell shading (WP command)	
方格边框	Fānggé biānkuàng	Cell border (WP command)	
方格合并	Fānggé hébìng	Merge cells (WP command)	
方格划分	Fānggé huàfēn	Split cell (WP command)	
方格网	Fānggé wǎng	Grid square	
防护周期	Fánghù zhōuqī	Guard period	GP
防火阀	Fánghuǒ fá	Fire resistant damper	FRD
防火卷帘	Fánghuǒ juànlián	Fire resistant shutter	FRS
防火墙	Fánghuǒqiáng	Firewall	
防火墙安全会话转换协议	Fánghuǒqiáng ānquán huìhuà zhuǎnhuàn xiéyì	Protocol for sessions traversal across firewall securely (IETF usage)	Socks
防护罩	Fánghùzhào	Protective cover	

防溅	Fángjiàn	Protected against splashing	
房间系数	Fángjiān xìshù	Room coefficient	RC
防静	Fángjìng	Protect against static (one of the “Six protects”)	
防静电	Fángjìngdiàn	Protect against static (one of the Three protects)	
访客量	Fǎngkèliàng	User sessions	
防空化阀	Fángkōnghuà fá	Anti-cavitation valve	
防雷	Fángléi	Protect against lightning (one of the “Six protects”)	
防雷	Fángléi	Lightning protection	
芳纶	Fānglún	Kevlar	
芳纶纤维	Fānglún xiānwéi	Aramid fiber	
防漫水	Fángmànshuǐ	Protected against the effects of immersion	
防霉	Fángméi	Mold proof	
防霉喷涂层	Fángméi pēntú céng	Mildew-proof spray coating	
返工	Fǎngōng	Rework (in SMT)	
方平包装	Fāngpíng bāozhuāng	Quad flat pack (electronics mfg)	QFP
放弃呼叫	Fàngqì hūjiào	Abandon call	
放弃序列	Fàngqì xùliè	Abort sequence	
防潜水	Fángqiánshuǐ	Protected against submersion	
防窃听	Fángqiètīng	Anti-eavesdropping (IPsec)	
防窃听装置	Fángqiètīng zhuāngzhì	Counter-audio device	
仿射变换	Fǎngshè biànhuàn	Affine transformation	
防湿保存箱	Fángshī bǎocún xiāng	Moisture-proof packaging	
房室给排水	Fángshì gěi páishuǐ	Building plumbing	FS
房室建筑	Fángshì jiànzhù	Building construction	FJ
房室结构	Fángshì jiégòu	Building structure	FG
方式状态寄存器	Fāngshì zhuàngtài jìcúnqì	Mode status register	MSR
防鼠	Fángshǔ	Protect against rats (one of the “Six protects”)	
方位标志	Fāngwèi biāozhì	Bearing marker	
方位角	Fāngwèi jiǎo	Azimuth	
防卫数据网	Fángwèi shùjù wǎng	Defense data network	DDN
方位投影	Fāngwèi tóuyǐng	Azimuthal projection (GIS)	
方位轴	Fāngwèi zhóu	Aximuth axis	
访问	Fǎngwèn	Access (database and networking term)	
访问安全性	Fǎngwèn ānquánxìng	Access security	
访问表	Fǎngwèn biǎo	Access list	
访问单元	Fǎngwèn dānyuán	Access unit	AU
访问点	Fǎngwèn diǎn	Access point (database usage)	AP
访问调查	Fǎngwèn diàochá	Hearing survey	
访问服务器专用对象集	Fǎngwèn fúwùqì zhuānyǒng duìxiàng jí	ActiveX data object	ADO
访问关键字	Fǎngwèn guānjiàn zì	Access key	
访问过载等级	Fǎngwèn guòzài děngjí	Access overload class	ACCOLC
访问函数	Fǎngwèn hánshù	Access function	
访问级别	Fǎngwèn jíbié	Access level	
访问技术	Fǎngwèn jìshù	Access technology	
访问集中器	Fǎngwèn jízhōngqì	Access concentrator (VPN/networking term)	
访问拒绝消息	Fǎngwèn jùjué xiāoxi	Access denied message (IPsec tLS)	

访问控制	Fǎngwèn kòngzhì	Access control	AC
访问控制表	Fǎngwèn kòngzhì biǎo	Access control list	ACL
访问控制机制	Fǎngwèn kòngzhì jīzhì	Access control mechanism (IPsec)	
访问控制项	Fǎngwèn kòngzhì xiàng	Access control entry	ACE
访问控制信息	Fǎngwèn kòngzhì xìnxī	Access control information	ACI
访问类别	Fǎngwèn lèibié	Access category	
访问类型	Fǎngwèn lèixíng	Access type	
访问令牌	Fǎngwèn lìngpái	Access token	
访问路径	Fǎngwèn lùjìng	Access path	
访问目录	Fǎngwèn mùlù	Access directory	
访问期	Fǎngwèn qī	Access period	
访问请求地址	Fǎngwèn qǐngqiú dìzhǐ	Access request address	AR-ADDR
访问权	Fǎngwèn quán	Access privilege	
访问时间	Fǎngwèn shíjiān	Access time	
访问突发	Fǎngwèn tūfā	Access burst	AB
访问位置寄存器	Fǎngwèn wèizhì jìcúnqì	Visitor location register	VLR
访问协议	Fǎngwèn xiéyì	Access protocol	AP
访问业务请求	Fǎngwèn yèwù qǐngqiú	Access service request	ASR
访问用户位置寄存器	Fǎngwèn yònghù wèizhì jìcúnqì	Visitor location register	VLR
访问组	Fǎngwèn zǔ	Access group	
方向分割复用	Fāngxiàng fēngē fùyòng	Direction division multiplexing	DDM
方向键	Fāngxiàng jiàn	Arrow key, direction key	
方向角	Fāngxiàng jiǎo	Direction angle (GIS)	
方向控制阀	Fāngxiàng kòngzhì fá	Direction-control valve	
方向零点	Fāngxiàng língdiǎn	Directional null	
方向零点天线	Fāngxiàng língdiǎn tiānxiàn	Directional-null antenna	
方向滤波器	Fāngxiàng lǜbōqì	Directional filter	
方向梯度矢量	Fāngxiàng tīdù shǐliàng	Directional gradient vector	
方向性	Fāngxiàngxìng	Directionality	DL
方向性	Fāngxiàngxìng	Directivity (of a directional coupler)	
方向性光源	Fāngxiàngxìng guāngyuán	Directional light	
方向性系数	Fāngxiàngxìng xìshù	Directivity of an antenna	
方向性增益	Fāngxiàngxìng zēngyì	Directive gain	
防写保护	Fángxiě bǎohù	Write-protect	
防盐	Fángyán	Protect against salt (one of the “Six protects”)	
防蚁缆	Fángyǐ lǎn	Termite-proof cable	
放音设备	Fàngyīn shèbèi	Tape deck equipment	TKEQ
放音中继	Fàngyīn zhōngjì	Tape deck trunk	TKT
仿真平衡线	Fǎngzhēn pínghéng xiàn	Artificial balancing line	
仿真天线	Fǎngzhēn tiānxiàn	Dummy antenna	
仿真头	Fǎngzhēn tóu	Artificial head	
仿真嘴	Fǎngzhēn zuǐ	Artificial mouth	
仿真耳	Fǎngzhēn'ěr	Artificial ear	
仿真器	Fǎngzhēnqì	Emulator	
防震台	Fángzhèntái	Vibration isolator	
仿制	Fǎngzhì	Mimicking (IPsec)	

仿制电脑	Fǎngzhì diànnǎo	Clone computer	
防蛀性	Fángzhùxìng	Mothproof	
泛化的	Fànhuàde	Generic	
返回	Fǎnhuí	Return	
返回	Fǎnhuí	Homing	
返回参数	Fǎnhuí cānshù	Return parameters	
返回地址	Fǎnhuí dìzhǐ	Return address	
返回类型	Fǎnhuí lèixíng	Return type	
返回路径	Fǎnhuí lùjìng	Return path	
返回码	Fǎnhuí mǎ	Return code	
返回位置	Fǎnhuí wèizhì	Home position	
返回正常通道说明信号	Fǎnhuí zhèngcháng tōngdào shuōmíng xìnhào	Change back declaration signal	CBD
返回正常信道应答	Fǎnhuí zhèngcháng xìndào yìngdá	Change back acknowledgement	CBA
返回值	Fǎnhuí zhí	Return value	
反汇编器	Fǎnhuìbiānqì	Disassembler	
反极信号	Fǎnjí xìnhào	Reverse signal	REV
反馈	Fǎnkuì	Feedback	
反馈发射分集	Fǎnkuì fāshè fēnjí	Feedback transmit diversity	FBTD
反馈控制系统	Fǎnkuì kòngzhì xìtǒng	Feedback control system	
反馈调频	Fǎnkuì tiáopín	Feedback frequency modulation	FBFM
反馈信息	Fǎnkuì xìnxī	Feedback information	FBI
反垃圾邮件	Fǎnlājī yóujiàn	Anti-spam	
泛滥	Fànlàn	Inundation	
反量化	Fǎnliànghuà	Dequantization (video term)	
繁忙排队/自动回叫	Fánmáng páiduì/zìdòng huíjiào	Busy queuing /callback	
泛美卫星公司	Fànměi wèixīng gōngsī	Pan American Satellite Corp. (US)	PanAmSat
反潜机	Fǎnqián jī	Anti-submarine aircraft	
反潜巡逻及	Fǎnqián xúnluó jí	Anti-submarine patrol aircraft	
反色散光纤	Fǎnsèsàn guāngxiān	Reverse dispersion fiber	
反射	Fǎnshè	Reflection	
反射波	Fǎnshè bō	Reflected wave	
反射场	Fǎnshè cháng	Reflected sound	RS
反射单元	Fǎnshè dānyuán	Reflector element (of an antenna)	
反射电流	Fǎnshè diànliú	Reflected current	
反射端口	Fǎnshè duānkǒu	Reflection port (FOC)	
反射功率	Fǎnshè gōnglǜ	Reflection power	
反射光栅	Fǎnshè guāngshān	Reflection grating	
反射滤模器	Fǎnshè lǜmóqì	Reflection mode filter	
反射衰减	Fǎnshè shuāijiǎn	Return loss	RL
反射衰减	Fǎnshè shuāijiǎn	Return loss	RL
反射损耗	Fǎnshè sǔnhào	Return loss	RL
反射损耗	Fǎnshè sǔnhào	Reflection loss	
反射贴图	Fǎnshè tiētú	Reflection mapping (video term)	
反射卫星	Fǎnshè wèixīng	Reflecting satellite	
反射系数	Fǎnshè xìshù	Reflection coefficient, reflectance	
反射折射透镜	Fǎnshè zhéshè tòujìng	Catadioptric lens	

反射计	Fǎnshèjì	Albedograph	
反射计	Fǎnshèjì	Reflectometer	
反身关系	Fǎnshēn guānxi	Reflexive relationship	
反射器	Fǎnshèqì	Reflector (of an antenna)	
反射器天线	Fǎnshèqì tiānxiàn	Reflector antenna	
反射形星状光纤耦合器	Fǎnshè-xíng xīngzhuàng guāngxiān ǒuhéqì	Reflection-type star optical coupler	
反射阵天线	Fǎnshèzhèn tiānxiàn	Reflective array antenna; reactive reflector antenna	
反时针偏振电磁波	Fǎnshízhēn piānzhèn diàncíbō	Anticlockwise polarized electromagnetic wave	
泛搜索	Fànsōusuǒ	Flooding search	
范围	Fànwéi	Range	
范围查询	Fànwéi cháxún	Range query	
反向	Fǎnxiàng	Contradirectional	
反向	fǎnxiàng	Reverse direction (in a circulator or isolator)	
反向波	Fǎnxiàng bō	Backward wave	
反向地址解析协议	Fǎnxiàng dìzhǐ jiěxī xiéyì	Reverse address resolution protocol	RARP
反向地址判别协议	Fǎnxiàng dìzhǐ pànbié xiéyì	Reverse address resolution protocol	RARP
反向辐射天线	Fǎnxiàng fúshè tiānxiàn	Backfire antenna	
反向复用板	Fǎnxiàng fùyòng bǎn	Inverse multiplexing access	IMA
反向隔离	Fǎnxiàng gélí	Reverse isolation	
反向工程	Fǎnxiàng gōngchéng	Reverse engineering	
反向光电	Fǎnxiàng guāngdiàn	Reverse photocurrent	
反向话音信道	Fǎnxiàng huàyīn xìndào	Reverse voice channel	RVC
反响话音信道	Fǎnxiǎng huàyīn xìndào	Return voice channel	RVC
反向键	Fǎnxiàng jiàn	Backspace	
反向接口	Fǎnxiàng jiēkǒu	Contradirectional interface	
反向控制信道	Fǎnxiàng kòngzhì xìndào	Reverse control channel	RECC
反向链	Fǎnxiàng liàn	Backward chaining	
反向链路	Fǎnxiàng liànlù	Reverse link	
反向链路功率控制	Fǎnxiàng liànlù gōnglǜ kòngzhì	Reverse link power control	
反向路径转发	Fǎnxiàng lùjìng zhuǎnfā	Reverse path forwarding	RPF
反向路径转换	Fǎnxiàng lùjìng zhuǎnhuàn	Reverse path forwarding	RPF
反向路径组播	Fǎnxiàng lùjìng zǔbō	Reverse path multicasting	RPM
反向码分多址信道	Fǎnxiàng mǎfēn duōzhǐ xìndào	Reverse code division multiple access channel	
反向散乱波	Fǎnxiàng sànluàn bō	Back scattering wave	
反向搜索	Fǎnxiàng sōusuǒ	Reverse lookup	
反向损耗	Fǎnxiàng sǔnhào	Reversal loss	
反向损耗	fǎnxiàng sǔnhào	Reverse loss (in a circulator or isolator)	
反响误差控制	Fǎnxiǎng wùchā kòngzhì	Reverse error control	REC
反向信道	Fǎnxiàng xìndào	Reverse channel	
反向振荡节距	Fǎnxiàng zhèndàng jiéjù	Reverse oscillation lay (FOC)	ROL
反斜线	Fǎnxiéxiàn	Backslash \	
翻新	Fānxīn	Refurbish (semiconductor mfg)	
反压	Fǎnyā	Backpressure	
反压筑土工程	Fǎnyā zhùtǔ gōngchéng	Counterweight fill works	
反压式双工	Fǎnyāshì shuānggōng	Opposition duplex	
翻译单元	Fānyì dānyuán	Translation unit	

翻译旁视缓冲器	Fānyì pángshì huǎnchōngqì	Translate look-side buffer	TLB
翻译桥接	Fānyì qiáojiē	Translational bridging	
反应式离子蚀刻法	Fǎnyìngshì lízǐ shíkè fǎ	Reactive ion etch	RIE
反隐身技术	Fǎnyǐnshēn jìshù	Anti-stealth technology	
反转	Fǎnzhuǎn	Toggle	
反转离散余弦变换	Fǎnzhuǎn lísàn yúxián biànhuàn	Inverse discrete cosine transform	IDCT
反转路径转发	Fǎnzhuǎn lùjìng zhuǎnfā	Reverse path forwarding	RPF
反转脉冲	Fǎnzhuǎn màichōng	Inverse pulse	
反转双缓存	Fǎnzhuǎn shuāng huǎncún	Flip double buffered (video)	
反转芯片针脚栅格阵列	Fǎnzhuǎn xìnpiàn zhēnjiao zhàgé zhènliè	Flip chip pin grid array	FCPGA
反装置	Fǎnzhuāngzhì	Deinstall, uninstall	
反装置器	Fǎnzhuāngzhìqì	Uninstaller	
发票制	Fāpiào zhì	Invoice rule	
发起方	Fāqǐ fāng	Originator	
发起切换的主控 MSC	Fāqǐ qiēhuànde zhǔkòng MSC	The controlling MSC on which the call was originally established	MSC-A
法人签名密钥	Fǎrén qiānmíng mìyào	Corporate signing key (IPsec)	
发射	Fāshè	Emanation (IPsec)	
发射	Fāshè	Emission	
发射	Fāshè	Transmit	TX
发射安全	Fāshè ānquán	Emanation security (IPsec)	
发射电平	Fāshè diànpíng	Emission level (of a disturbance source)	
发射功率控制	Fāshè gōnglǜ kòngzhì	Transmit power control	TPC
发射类别	Fāshè lèibié	Class of emission	
发射频段	Fāshè pínduàn	Frequency transmission band	
发射限值	Fāshè xiànzhí	Emission limit	
发射裕量	Fāshè yùliàng	Emission margin	
发射主通道接口参考点	Fāshè zhǔtōngdào jiēkǒu cānkǎodiǎn	Source main path interface reference point	MPI-S
发射机	Fāshèjī	Emitter	E
发射机	Fāshèjī	Transmitter	
发射机边带频谱	Fāshèjī biāndài pínpǔ	Transmitter sideband spectrum	
发射机电源板	Fāshèjī diànyuán bǎn	Transmitter power supply board	PWT
发射机额定输出功率	Fāshèjī édìng shūchū gōnglǜ	Rated output power of transmitter	
发射机合路器	Fāshèjī hélùqì	Transmitter combiner	
发射机冷却系统	Fāshèjī lěngquè xìtǒng	Transmitter cooling system	
发射机启动时间	Fāshèjī qǐdòng shíjiān	Transmitter attack time	
发射机效率	Fāshèjī xiàolǜ	Transmitter frequency	
发射机杂散噪声	Fāshèjī zásǎn zàoshēng	Spurious transmitter noise	
发射机最大允许频偏	Fāshèjī zuìdà yǔnxǔ pínpiān	Transmitter maximum permissible frequency deviation	
发射机最大允许相偏	Fāshèjī zuìdà yǔnxǔ xiāngpiān	Transmitter maximum permissible phase deviation	
发射机之间的互调	Fāshèjī-zhījiānde hùtiáo	Inter-transmitter intermodulation	
发生器	Fāshēngqì	Producer	
发射器	Fāshèqì	Emitter	E
发射台	Fāshètái	Transmitting station	
发送	Fāsòng	Transmit	Tx
发送参考当量	Fāsòng cānkǎo dāngliàng	Sending reference equivalent	

发送参考相移键控	Fāsòng cānkǎo xiàngyí jiànkòng	Transmitted reference-phase shift keying	TRPSK
发送非对称性	Fāsòng fēiduìchènxìng	Transmission asymmetry	TA
发送分割（音频信令中）	Fāsòng fēngē (yīnpín xìnlìng zhōng)	Splitting of the outgoing line (in voice frequency signaling)	
发送结束	Fāsòng jiéshù	End of transmission	EOT
发送客观响度评定值	Fāsòng kèguān xiǎngdù píngdìngzhí	Transmit objective loudness result	TOLR
发送块	Fāsòng kuài	Transmit block	
发送劣化	Fāsòng lièhuà	Transmit degrade	TD
发送路由信息	Fāsòng lùyóu xìnxī	Send routing information	SRI
发送路由信息证实	Fāsòng lùyóu xìnxī zhèngshí	Send routing information acknowledgment	SRIack
发送失效	Fāsòng shīxiào	Transmit fail	TF
发送数据	Fāsòng shùjù	Send data	SD
发送数据请求消息	Fāsòng shùjù qǐngqiú xiāoxi	Send data request message (in multicast)	
发送数据条件	Fāsòng shùjù tiáojiàn	Send data condition	SDC
发送完全	Fāsòng wánquán	Sending complete	
发送响度评定值	Fāsòng xiǎngdù píngdìngzhí	Sending loudness rating	
发送相对当量	Fāsòng xiāngduì dāngliáng	Relative equivalent for sending	
发送消息	Fāsòng xiāoxi	Send message	SM
发送序列号	Fāsòng xùlièhào	Send sequence number	SSN
发送专用信息音信号	Fāsòng zhuānyòng xìnxī yīnxìnhào	Send special-information tone signal	SST
发送机	Fāsòngjī	Transmitter	Tx
发送器	Fāsòngqì	Emitter	E
发送器（信令中）	Fāsòngqì (xìnlìng zhōng)	Sender (in signaling)	
发现概率	Fāxiàn gàilǜ	Detection probability	
发现完成	Fāxiàn wánchéng	Discovery complete	
发现/跟踪	Fāxiàn/gēnzōng	Find me/follow me	
法向应力	Fǎxiàng yìnglì	Normal stress	
发信机/发射	Fāxìnjī/ Fāshè	Transmitter/transmission	Tx
发信机的连续骚扰	Fāxìnjīde liánxù sāorǎo	Transmitter continuous disturbance	CT
发信机的瞬态骚扰	Fāxìnjīde shùntài sāorǎo	Transmitter transient disturbance	TT
发音	Fāyīn	Pronunciation	
发音系统	Fāyīn xìtǒng	Pronunciation system	
发源点编码	Fāyuándiǎn biānmǎ	Origination point code	OPC
FDM 发送器组件	FDM fāsòngqì zǔjiàn	FDM transmitter module	FTM
FEC 至 NHLFE 的映射	FEC zhì NHLFE de yìngshè	FEC to NHLFE map	FTN
非	Fēi	Not	NOT
“非”门	Fēi mén	NOT gate	
非 DWORD 排列	Fēi DWORD páiliè	Non-DWORD-aligned (audio term)	NDA
非 GPRS 提示标志	Fēi GPRS tíshì biāozhì	Non-GPRS alert flag	NGAF
非 SDH 网元	Fēi SDH wǎng yuán	Non-SDH network element	NNE
非英特尔架构	Fēi Yīng-tè-ěr jiàgòu	Non-Intel ®	NI
非包式数字终端设备	Fēibāo-shì shùzì zhōngduān shèbèi	Non-packet digital terminal equipment	NPDTE
非标准	Fēibiāozhǔn	Non-standard	NS
非标准数据	Fēibiāozhǔn shùjù	Non-standard data	
非必备属性	Fēibìbèi shǔxìng	Non-mandatory attribute	
非参量检测器	Fēicānliàng jiǎncèqì	Non-parameter detector	
非参数检验	Fēicānshù jiǎnyàn	Non-parametric test	

非常驻区	Fēichángzhù qū	Non-resident area	
非常驻任务	Fēichángzhù rènwu	Non-resident task	
非持续载波传感多路存取	Fēichíxù zàibō chuángǎn duōlù cúnqǔ	Non-persistent carrier sensing multiple access	NCSMA
非重叠覆盖	Fēichóngdié fùgài	Non-underlay coverage	
废除	Fèichú	Revoke	
非簇索引	Fēicù suǒyǐn	Non-clustered index (in SQL Server)	
非存根区	Fēicúngēn qū	Non-stub area	
非打印周期	Fēidǎyìn zhōuqī	Non-print cycle	
非等步的	Fēiděngbùde	Anisochronous	
非登记的访问	Fēidēngjìde fǎngwèn	Non-registered access	
非电信中心	Fēidiànxìn zhōngxīn	Other than telecommunication centers	
非递归滤波器	Fēidìguī lǜbōqì	Non-recursive filtering	
非定期维护	Fēidìngqī wéihù	Unscheduled maintenance	
非对称加密	Fēiduìchèn jiāmì	Asymmetric encryption	
非对称加密算法	Fēiduìchèn jiāmì suànfǎ	Asymmetric crypto algorithm	
非对称滤波器	Fēiduìchèn lǜbōqì	Anti-symmetric filter	AFL
非对称双路通信	Fēiduìchèn shuānglù tōngxìn	Asymmetric communications	AC
非对称数据交换	Fēiduìchèn shùjù jiāohuàn	Asymmetric data exchange	ADX
非对称数字用户环路	Fēiduìchèn shùzì yònghù huánlù	Asymmetric digital subscriber loop	ADSL
非对称数字用户线路	Fēiduìchèn shùzì yònghù xiànlù	Asymmetric digital subscriber line	ADSL
非法参数消息	Fēifǎ cānshù xiāoxi	Illegal parameter message (IPsec TLS)	
非法尝试次数	Fēifǎ chángshì cìshù	Wrong attempt counter	WAC
非法代码	Fēifǎ dàimǎ	Illegal code	
非法地址错误	Fēifǎ dìzhǐ cuòwù	Illegal address error	
非法进入	Fēifǎ jìnrù	Piggy back entry	
非发展项目	Fēifāzhǎn xiàngmù	Non-developmental item	NDI
非分组终端	Fēifēnzǔ zhōngduān	Non-packet Terminal	NPT
非否认协议	Fēifǒurèn xiéyì	Non-repudiation	
非复用寻址总线模式	Fēifùyòng xúnzhǐ zǒngxiàn móshì	Non-multiplexed address bus mode	
非更改	Fēigēnggǎi	Unmodified	NO-MODIFY
非工作时间	Fēigōngzuò shíjiān	Non-operating time	
非工作状态	Fēigōngzuò zhuàngtài	Non-operating state	
非广播多接入	Fēiguǎngbō duōjiērù	Non-broadcast multiple access	NBMA
非广播式多路访问	Fēiguǎngbō-shì duōlù fǎngwèn	Non-broadcast multi-access	NBMA
非关联失效	Fēiguānlián shīxiào	Non-relevant failure	
非规范的格式标识符	Fēiguīfànde géshi biāozhì fú	Non-canonical format indication	NCFI
非归零码	Fēiguīlíng mǎ	Non-return to zero coding	NRZ
非规则数字记录系统	Fēiguīzé shùzì jìlù xìtǒng	Non-algorithmic digital record systems	NDRS
非过程监督系统	Fēiguòchéng jiāndū xìtǒng	Non-process monitor system	NPMS
非衡重杂音	Fēihéngzhòng záyīn	Unweighted noise	
非话业务呼叫	Fēihuàyèwù hūjiào	Non-voice service call	
非挥发性存储器	Fēihuīfāxìng cúnchǔqì	Non-volatile memory	
非回复（保护）运行	Fēihuífù (bǎohù) yùnxíng	Non-revertive (protection) operation	
非混杂模式	Fēihùnzá móshì	Non-promiscuous	
非活动共享机制	Fēihuódòng gòngxiǎng jīzhì	Inactive sharing mechanism (in CSCW)	
非互易极化旋转器	Fēihùyì jíhuà xuánzhuǎnqì	Non-reciprocal polarization rotator	

非互易移相器	Fēihùyì yíxiàngqì	Non-reciprocal phase shifter	
非互易圆极化移相器	Fēihùyì yuán jíhuà yíxiàngqì	Non-reciprocal circular polarized phase shifter	
非零散位移光纤	Fēiíngsǎn wèiyí guāngxiān	Non-zero-dispersion shift fiber	NZ-DSF
非加感电缆	Fēijiāgǎn diànlǎn	Unload cable	
非监督分类	Fēijiāndū fēnlèi	Unsupervised classification (GIS)	
非交换 IDSN 连接单元	Fēijiāohuàn ISDN liánjiē dānyuán	Non-switched ISDN connection element	
非交换连接	Fēijiāohuàn liánjiē	Non-switched connection	
非交换连接单元	Fēijiāohuàn liánjiē dānyuán	Non-switched connection element	
非结构补充业务数据	Fēijiégòu bǔchōng yèwù shùjù	Unstructured supplementary service data	USSD
非结构元素	Fēijiégòu yuánsù	Non-structural element	
非结构化补充服务请求	Fēijiégòuhuà bǔchōng fúwù qǐngqiú	Unstructured supplementary services request	USSR
非结构化补充服务数据	Fēijiégòuhuà bǔchōng fúwù shùjù	Unstructured supplementary services data	USSD
非结构化补充服务通知	Fēijiégòuhuà bǔchōng fúwù tōngzhī	Unstructured supplementary services notification	USSN
非结构化补充数据业务	Fēijiégòuhuà bǔchōng shùjù yèwù	Unstructured supplementary service data	USSD
非接入层	Fēijiērù céng	Non-access stage	NAS
非介入监视	Fēijièrù jiānshì	Non-intrusive monitoring	
非金属缆	Fēijīnshǔ lǎn	Non-metallic cable	
非机械式光开关	Fēijīxiè-shì guāng kāiguān	Non-mechanical optical switch	
非聚集索引	Fēijùjí suǒyǐn	Non-clustered index	
非均匀编码	Fēijūnyún biānmǎ	Non-uniform encoding	
非均匀成核热化学反应	Fēijūnyún chénghé rèhuàxué fǎnyìng	Heterogeneous nucleating thermochemical reaction (FOC mfg)	HNTD
非均匀量化	Fēijūnyún liànghuà	Non-uniform quantizing	
非均匀有理 B 样条	Fēijūnyún yǒulǐ B-yàng tiáo	Non-uniform rational B-splines	NURBS
非空间数据	Fēikōngjiān shùjù	Aspatial data	
非连接报文管理器	Fēiliánjiē bàowén guǎnlǐqì	Unconnected message manager	UCMM
非连通图	Fēiliántōng tú	Unconnected graph	
非联网汇兑网点	Fēiliánwǎng huìduì wǎngdiǎn	Off-line remittance service counter	
非连续传输	Fēiliánxù chuánshū	Discontinuous transmission	DTX
非连续反余弦变换	Fēiliánxù fǎnyúxián biànhuàn	Inverse discrete cosine transform	IDCT
非连续发射	Fēiliánxù fāshè	Discontinuous transmission	DTX
非连续发射允许	Fēiliánxù fāshè yǔnxǔ	Discontinuous transmission permission	
非连续发信	Fēiliánxù fāxìn	Discontinuous transmission	DTX
非连续干扰	Fēiliánxù gānrǎo	Discontinuous interference	
非连续接收	Fēiliánxù jiēshōu	Discontinuous reception	DRX
非劣解	Fēiliè jiě	Non-inferior solution	
非零色散光纤	Fēilíng sèsàn guāngxiān	Non-zero dispersion fiber	NZDF
非零色散位移光纤	Fēilíng sèsàn wèiyí guāngxiān	Non-zero dispersion-shifted optical fiber	NZDSF
飞利浦	Fēi-lì-pǔ	Philips (Netherlands company)	
菲利斯	Fēi-lì-sī	Plessey (UK company)	
费率	Fèilǜ	Tariff	
菲律宾卫星公司	Fēi-lǜ-bīn wèixīng gōngsī	Philippine Communications Satellite Corp.	Philcomsat
费马原理	Fèi-mǎ yuánlǐ	Fermat's principle	
非盲提取	Fēimáng tíqǔ	Non-blind retrieval	
飞秒	Fēimiǎo	Femto-second	
菲涅尔反射	Fēi-niè-ěr fǎnshè	Fresnel reflection	
菲涅尔反射损耗	Fēi-niè-ěr fǎnshè sǔnhào	Fresnel reflection loss	

菲涅耳区	Fēi-niè-ěr qū	Fresnel region	
菲涅尔透镜	Fēi-niè-ěr tòujìng	Fresnel lens	
菲涅耳透镜天线	Fēi-niè-ěr tòujìng tiānxiàn	Fresnel lens antenna; zone-plate lens antenna	
非屏蔽对绞电缆	Fēipíngbì duìjiǎo diànlǎn	Unshielded twisted pair cables	
非屏蔽对线电缆	Fēipíngbì duìxiàn diànlǎn	Unshielded twisted pair cable	UTP
非屏蔽双绞线	Fēipíngbì shuāngjiǎo xiàn	Unshielded twisted pair	UTP
非平稳性	Fēipíngwěn xìng	Non-stationary nature	
非破坏读出	Fēipòhuài dúchū	Non-destructive read-out	
非破坏只读	Fēipòhuài zhǐ dú	Non-destructive read-only	NDRO
非强占优先规则	Fēiqiángzhàn yōuxiān guīzé	Non-preemptive priority queuing discipline	
非抢占式	Fēiqiǎngzhàn-shì	Non-preemptive	
非强制性还原	Fēiqiángzhìxìng huányuán	Non-authoritative restore	
非请求消息处理器	Fēiqǐngqiú xiāoxi chǔlǐqì	Unsolicited message handler	UMH
非球面镜	Fēiqiú miànjìng	Aspheric mirror	
非球面透镜	Fēiqiú miàntòujìng	Aspherical lens	
非期望的数据值	Fēiqīwàngde shùjù zhí	Unexpected data value	
非确保工作过程	Fēiquèbǎo gōngzuò guòchéng	Non-assured operations	
非确定性故障	Fēiquèdìngxìng gùzhàng	Non-determinate fault	
非色散位移光纤	Fēisèsàn wèiyí guāngxiān	Non-dispersion shifted optical fiber	
菲识别型 DTE 业务	Fēishíbiéxíng DTE yèwù	Non-identified DTE service	
非实时	Fēishíshí	Non-real time	NRT
非实时查询业务	Fēishíshí cháxún yèwù	Non-real time polling service	NrtPS
非实时可变比特率	Fēishíshí kěbiàn bǐtè lǜ	Non-real time variable bit rate	nrt-VBR
非时域数据	Fēishíyù shùjù	Atemporal data	
非时域数据库	Fēishíyù shùjùkù	Atemporal database	
非受激单元	Fēishòujī dānyuán	Non-driven element	
非受控代码	Fēishòukòng dàimǎ	Unmanaged code	
非受控 DTE 未准许好	Fēishòukòng DTE wèi zhǔnxǔ hǎo	Uncontrolled DTE not ready	
非受控滑动	Fēishòukòng huádòng	Uncontrolled slip	
非授权存取	Fēishòuquán cúnqǔ	Unauthorized access	
非数据集时钟	Fēishùjùjí shízhōng	Non-data-set clocking	NDSC
非顺从流	Fēishùncóng liú	Non-conformant traffic	
非弹性	Fēitánxìng	Anelasticity	
非调谐天线	Fēitiáoxié tiānxiàn	Aperiodic antenna	AA
非同步脉冲干扰	Fēitóngbù màichōng gānrǎo	Non-synchronous pulse jamming	
非同步网	Fēitóngbù wǎng	Non-synchronized network	
非同等错误保护	Fēitóngděng cuòwù bǎohù	Unequal error protection	UEP
非退避方式	Fēituìbì fāngshì	Non-saving system	
非托管代码	Fēituōguǎn dàimǎ	Unmanaged code	
非图形数据	Fēitúxíng shùjù	Non-graphic data	
非危险故障	Fēiwēixiǎn gùzhàng	Non-critical fault	
非危险失效	Fēiwēixiǎn shīxiào	Non-critical failure	
非稳态随机过程	Fēiwěntài suíjī guòchéng	Non-stationary random process	
非现场维护	Fēixiànchǎng wéihù	Off-site maintenance	
非相干动目标显示	Fēixiānggān dòng mùbiāo xiǎnshì	Non-coherent moving target indicator (MTI)	
非相干频移键控调制	Fēixiānggān pínyí jiànkòng tiáozhì	Non-coherent frequency shift keyed modulation	NCFSK

非相干载波键控	Fēixiānggān zàibō jiànkòng	Non-coherent carrier keying	NCCK
非相关干扰	Fēixiāngguān gānrǎo	Non-coherent jamming/Interference	
非向量中断	Fēixiàngliàng zhōngduàn	Non-vectored interrupt	NVI
非线性	Fēixiànxìng	Non-linearity	
非线性处理器	Fēixiànxìng chǔlǐqì	Non-linear processor	NLP
非线性电路	Fēixiànxìng diànlù	Nonlinear circuit	
非线性光纤环	Fēixiànxìng guāngxiān huán	Non-linear optical loop	
非线性光纤环路镜	Fēixiànxìng guāngxiān huánlù jìng	Non-linear optical fiber loop mirror	NOLM
非线性光纤环行镜	Fēixiànxìng guāngxiān huánxíng jìng	Non-linear optical loop mirroring	NOLM
非线性光学晶体	Fēixiànxìng guāngxué jīngtǐ	Non-linear crystal	
非线性规划	Fēixiànxìng guīhuà	Non-linear programming	NP
非线性校正	Fēixiànxìng jiàozhèng	Non-linear correction	
非线性结构	Fēixiànxìng jiégòu	Non-linear structure	
非线形控制系统	Fēixiànxíng kòngzhì xìtǒng	Non-linear control system	
非线性时间序列预测	Fēixiànxìng shíjiān xùliè yùcè	Non-linear time series prediction	
非线性失真	Fēixiànxìng shīzhēn	Non-linear distortion	NLD
非线性失真	Fēixiànxìng shīzhēn	Non-linearity distortion	
非线性数字调制	Fēixiànxìng shùzì tiáozhì	Non-linear digital modulation	
非线性送代算法	Fēixiànxìng sòngdài suànfǎ	Non-linear recurrence algorithm	
非线性调频	Fēixiànxìng tiáopín	Non-linear frequency modulation	NLFM
非线性调频脉冲压缩	Fēixiànxìng tiáopín màichōng yāsuō	Non-linear frequency modulated pulse compression	
非线性微分方程	Fēixiànxìng wēifēn fāngchéng	Non-linear differential equation	NDE
非线性效应	Fēixiànxìng xiàoyìng	Non-linearity effect	
非线性有限元方法	Fēixiànxìng yǒuxiàn yuán fāngfǎ	Non-linear finite element method	
非线形振动	Fēixiànxíng zhèndòng	Non-linear vibration	
飞行情报服务	Fēixíng qíngbào fúwù	Flight information service (civil aviation)	FIS
非修理产品(装备)	Fēixiūlǐ chǎnpǐn (zhuāngbèi)	Non-repaired item	
非压缩性	Fēiyāsuōxìng	Incompressibility	
非叶	Fēiyè	Non-leaf	
非叶成员	Fēiyè chéngyuán	Non-leaf member	
非易失存储器	Fēiyìshī cúnchǔqì	Non-volatile storage or memory	
非易失随机存取存储器	Fēiyìshī suíjī cúnqǔ cúnchǔqì	Non-volatile random access memory	NVRAM
费用分担	Fèiyòng fēndān	Share of expenses	
费用风险分析	Fèiyòng fēngxiǎn fēnxī	Cost-risk analysis	
费用显示器	Fèiyòng xiǎnshìqì	Fee indicator	FI
费用效益分析	Fèiyòng xiàoyì fēnxī	Cost effectiveness analysis	
非站点线路	Fēizhàndiǎn xiànlù	Non-line-of-site	NLOS
非占空呼叫建立	Fēizhànkōng hūjiào jiànlì	Off-air call setup	OACSU
非正常帧计数	Fēizhèngcháng zhèng jìshù	Abnormal frame count	AFC
非证实服务	Fēizhèngshí fúwù	Unconfirmed service	
非证实信息传送方式	Fēizhèngshí xìnxī chuánsòng fāngshì	Unacknowledged information transfer mode	
非证实型服务	Fēizhèngshíxíng fúwù	Unconfirmed-service	
飞针式	Fēizhēn-shì	Flying probe (PCB manufacture)	
非直联信令方式	Fēizhílián xìnlìng fāngshì	Non-associated signaling	
非智能型	Fēizhìnéngxíng	Dumb	
非执行董事	Fēizhíxíng dǒngshì	Non-executive director	

非种子路由器	Fēizhǒngzǐ lùyóuqì	Non-seed router	
非周期	Fēizhōuqī	Non-periodic, aperiodic	
非周期环栅阵	Fēizhōuqī huán zhàzhèn	Aperiodic circular grid array	
非周期环节	Fēizhōuqī huánjié	Aperiodic element	
非周期信号	Fēizhōuqī xìnhào	Non-periodic signal	
非转发地址	Fēizhuǎnfā dìzhǐ	Non-forwarding address	NFA
非撞击式打印机	Fēizhuàngjī-shì dǎyìnjī	Non-impact printer	
非专用控制信道	Fēizhuānyòng kòngzhì xìndào	Non-dedicated control channel	
非专作控制信道	Fēizhuānzuò kòngzhì xìndào	Non-dedicated control channel	
非自适应运动补偿算法	Fēizìshìyìng yùndòng bǔcháng suànfǎ	Non-adaptive motion compensation algorithm	NAMC
非阻塞互连网络	Fēizǔsè hùlián wǎngluò	Non-blocking interconnection network	
芬（兰）俄（国）光缆线路	Fēn (lán) é (guó) guānglǎn xiànlù	Finland-Russia optical cable line (built 1993)	FRL
芬俄光通路	Fēn é guāng tōnglù	Finland-Russia optical gateway	FROG
分页符	Fēn yè fú	Page break (WP term)	
分/插复用设备	Fēn/chā fùyòng shèbèi	Add/drop multiplexer	ADM
分/插交叉连接	Fēn/chā jiāochā liánjiē	Add/drop cross-connection	
分贝	Fēnbèi	Decibel	dB
分贝/毫瓦	Fēnbèi/háowǎ	Decibels per milliwatt	dB/m
分辨带宽	Fēnbiàn dàikuān	Resolution bandwidth	RWB
分辨力	Fēnbiànlì	Resolution	
分辨力	Fēnbiànlì	Resolution	
分辨率	Fēnbiànlǜ	Resolution	
分辨率	Fēnbiànlǜ	Discrimination ratio (of an antenna between two received waves)	
分辨率带宽	Fēnbiànlǜ dàikuān	Resolution bandwidth	RBW
分波段编码	Fēnbōduàn biānmǎ	Sub-band coding	SBC
分布标题	Fēnbù biāotí	Distribution header	
分布布拉格反射	Fēnbù Bùlāgé fǎnshè	Distributed Bragg reflection	DCA
分布参数网络	Fēnbù cānshù wǎngluò	Distributed parameter network	
分布处理网络	Fēnbù chǔlǐ wǎngluò	Distributed processing network	DPN
分布电阻抑制器	Fēnbù diànzǔ yìzhìqì	Distributed resistive suppressor	
分布调度多路存取	Fēnbù diàodù duōlù cúnqǔ	Distributed scheduling multiple access	DSMA
分布反馈	Fēnbù fǎnkuì	Distributed feedback	
分布反馈公平排队算法	Fēnbù fǎnkuì gōngping páiduì suànfǎ	Distributed feedback fair queuing	DF^2Q
分布反馈激光器	Fēnbù fǎnkuì jīguāngqì	Distributed feedback laser	DFB
分布反馈型激光器	Fēnbù fǎnkuìxíng jīguāngqì	Distributed feedback laser diode	DFB-LD
分布管理程序	Fēnbù guǎnlǐ chéngxù	Distributed management task force	DMTF
分布过程控制系统	Fēnbù guòchéng kòngzhì xìtǒng	Distributed process control system	DPCS
分布交互仿真	Fēnbù jiāohù fǎngzhēn	Distributed interactive simulation	DIS
分布拒绝服务攻击	Fēnbù jùjué fúwù gōngjī	Distributed denial of service attack	DDoS
分布路线	Fēnbù lùxiàn	Distribution link	
分布排队双总线	Fēnbù páiduì shuāng zǒngxiàn	Distributed queue dual bus	DQDB
分布式应用	Fēnbù shì yìngyòng	Distributed application	
分布时分多重存取	Fēnbù shífèn duōzhòng cúnqǔ	Distributed time division multiple access	DTDMA
分布数组描述	Fēnbù shù zǔ miáoshù	Distributed array descriptor (Fortran)	DAD
分布协调功能	Fēnbù xiétiáo gōngnéng	Distributed coordination function (IEEE 802.11 protocol)	DCF

分布移去算法	Fēnbù yíqù suànfǎ	Stepwise removal algorithm	SRA
分布最大干扰移去算法	Fēnbù zuìdà gānrǎo yíqù suànfǎ	Stepwise maximum interference removal algorithm	SMIRA
分布作振荡器	Fēnbù zuò zhèndàngqì	Extended interaction oscillator	EIO
分布作用放大器	Fēnbù zuòyòng fàngdàqì	Extended interaction amplifier	EIA
分布式	Fēnbùshì	Distributive	
分布式查询	Fēnbùshì cháxún	Distributed query (for database)	
分布式处理	Fēnbùshì chǔlǐ	Distributed processing	
分布式处理环境	Fēnbùshì chǔlǐ huánjìng	Distributed processing environment	DPE
分布式代理环境	Fēnbùshì dàilǐ huánjìng	Distributed agent environment	DAE
分布式队列双总线	Fēnbùshì duìliè shuāng zǒngxiàn	Distributed queue dual bus	DQDB
分布式分析结构	Fēnbùshì fēnxī jiégòu	Distributed analysis structure	
分布式公共对象模型	Fēnbùshì gōnggòng duìxiàng móxíng	Distributed common object model	
分布式功能	Fēnbùshì gōngnéng	Distributed function	
分布式功能平面	Fēnbùshì gōngnéng píngmiàn	Distributed functional plane	DFP
分布式共享内存映射	Fēnbùshì gòngxiǎng nèicún yìngshè	Distributed shared memory mapping	
分布式关系数据库管理系统	Fēnbùshì guānxì shùjùkù guǎnlǐ xìtǒng	Distributed relational DBMS	DRDBMS
分布式关系数据库结构	Fēnbùshì guānxì shùjùkù jiégòu	Distributed relational database structure	DRDS
分布式关系型数据库	Fēnbùshì guānxi xíng shùjùkù	Distributed relational database	
分布式环形计算机网络	Fēnbùshì huánxíng jìsuànjī wǎngluò	Distributed loop computer network	DLCN
分布式环形信息通信规约	Fēnbùshì huánxíng xìnxī tōngxìn guīyuē	Distributed loop message communication protocol	DLMCP
分布式互联网应用结构	Fēnbùshì hùliánwǎng yìngyòng jiégòu	Distributed internet application architecture	DNA
分布式计算环境	Fēnbùshì jìsuàn huánjìng	Distributed computing environment	DCE
分布式拒绝服务攻击	Fēnbùshì jùjué fúwù gōngjī	Distributed denial of service attack	DDoS
分布式开放的电信结构	Fēnbùshì kāifàngde diànxìn jiégòu	Open distribution telecom architecture	ODTA
分步式控制	Fēnbùshì kòngzhì	Distributed control	
分布式垃圾收集	Fēnbùshì lājī shōují	Distributed garbage collection	
分布式连接管理	Fēnbùshì liánjiē guǎnlǐ	Distributed connection management	DCM
分布式排队双总线	Fēnbùshì páiduì shuāng zǒngxiàn	Distributed queue dual bus	
分布式入侵检测系统	Fēnbùshì rùqīn jiǎncè xìtǒng	Distributed intrusion detection system	DIDS
分布式实时数据库	Fēnbùshì shíshí shùjùkù	Distributed real-time database	DRTDB
分布式事务协调器	Fēnbùshì shìwù xiétiáo qì	Distributed transaction coordinator (in SQL Server)	DTC
分布式事务协调器资源	Fēnbùshì shìwù xiétiáoqì zīyuán	Distributed transaction coordinator resource	
分布式双环路计算机网络	Fēnbùshì shuāng huánlù jìsuànjī wǎngluò	Distributed double-loop computer network	DDLCN
分布式数据	Fēnbùshì shùjù	Distributed data	
分布式数据管理	Fēnbùshì shùjù guǎnlǐ	Distributed data management	DDM
分布式数据网	Fēnbùshì shùjù wǎng	Distributed data network	DDN
分布式数据库	Fēnbùshì shùjùkù	Distributed database	
分布式通信体系	Fēnbùshì tōngxìn tǐxì	Distributed communication architecture	DCA
分布式网间应用程序	Fēnbùshì wǎngjiān yìngyòng chéngxù	Distributed interNet application	DNA
分布式网络	Fēnbùshì wǎngluò	Scatternet	
分布式微波通信系统	Fēnbùshì wēibō tōngxìn xìtǒng	Distributed microwave communication system	
分布式消息队列	Fēnbùshì xiāoxi duìliè	Distributed message queue	DMQ
分布式系统	Fēnbùshì xìtǒng	Distributed system	
分布式演化算法	Fēnbùshì yǎnhuà suànfǎ	Distributed evolutionary algorithm	

分布式移动通信系统	Fēnbùshì yídòng tōngxìn xìtǒng	Distributed mobile communication system	
分布式因特网应用程序	Fēnbùshì Yīntèwǎng yìngyòng chéngxù	Distributed Internet application	DNA
分布式主动实时数据库	Fēnbùshì zhǔdòng shíshí shùjùkù	Distributed active real-time database	DARTDB
分布式组件对象模型	Fēnbùshì zǔjiàn duìxiàng móxíng	Distributed component object model	DCOM
分槽环	Fēncáo huán	Slotted ring	
分层	Fēncéng	Layering	
分层	Fēncéng	Delamination (in SMT)	
分层分类	Fēncéng fēnlèi	Hierarchical classification	
分层空时结构	Fēncéng kōng shí jiégòu	Bell layered space-time architecture	BLAST
分层设色法	Fēncéng shèsè fǎ	Hypsometric tending method (GIS)	
分层设色图	Fēncéng shèsè tú	Hypsometric map	
分层通信结构	Fēncéng tōngxìn jiégòu	Hierarchical communications architecture	
分层小区结构	Fēncéng xiǎoqū jiégòu	Hierarchical cell structure	HCS
分层小区技术	Fēncéng xiǎoqū jìshù	Hierarchical cell structure	HCS
分层星形拓扑	Fēncéng xīngxíng tuòpū	Hierarchical star topology	
分层系统	Fēncéng xìtǒng	Layer system	
分岔	Fēnchà	Bifurcation	
分插复用器	Fēnchā fùyòngqì	Add/drop multiplexer	ADM
分地印刷发行	Fēndì yìnshuā fāxíng	Printing and distribution in other cities	
分段	Fēnduàn	Segment, segmenting, segmentation (of packet data)	
分段和重装	Fēnduàn hé chóngzhuāng	Segmentation and reassembly	SAR
分段和重装子层	Fēnduàn hé chóngzhuāng zicéng	Segmentation and reassembly sub-layer	SARS
分段和重组	Fēnduàn hé chóngzǔ	Segmentation and reassembly	SAR
分段加载天线	Fēnduàn jiāzài tiānxiàn	Sectional loaded antenna	
分段消息	Fēnduàn xiāoxi	Segmentation message (ISUP)	SGM
分段与组装	Fēnduàn yǔ zǔzhuāng	Segmentation and reassembly	SAR
分段帧	Fēnduàn zhèng	Fragmented frame	FRAG
分发版	Fēnfā bǎn	Distribution (of a software version)	
分发保持期	Fēnfā bǎochí qī	Distribution retention period	
分发表	Fēnfā biǎo	Distribution list	DL
分发表扩充	Fēnfā biǎo kuòchōng	Distribution list expansion	
分发表名	Fēnfā biǎo míng	Distribution list name	
分发代理	Fēnfā dàilǐ	Distribution agent (in SQL Server)	
分发服务器	Fēnfā fúwùqì	Distributor	
分发数据库	Fēnfā shùjùkù	Distribution database	
峰包功率	Fēng bāo gōnglǜ	Peak envelope power (of a radio transmitter)	PX
峰-峰值频率偏移。	Fēng/fēngzhí pínlǜ piānyí.	Peak-to-peak (frequency) deviation	
封闭通道	Fēngbì tōngdào	Blocked passage	
封闭通道类型	Fēngbì tōngdào lèixíng	Blocked passage type	
封闭通道位置	Fēngbì tōngdào wèizhì	Blocked passage location	
封闭用户群	Fēngbì yònghù qún	Closed user group	CUG
风道	Fēngdào	Air duct	
分割	Fēngē	Compartmentalization (IPsec)	
分割	Fēngē	Partitioning, separation	
分割	Fēngē	Separation	
分割错误	Fēngē cuòwù	Segmentation error	

分隔点	Fēngé diǎn	Divided junction	
分隔符	Fēngé fú	Delimiter, separator	
分割线	Fēngē xiàn	Breakline	
分割/组装	Fēngē/Zǔzhuāng	Segmentation/reassembly	
峰-峰	Fēng—Fēng	Peak-to-peak	
峰-峰检波电路	Fēng—Fēng jiǎnbō diànlù	Peak-to-peak detector circuit	
峰峰值	Fēng-fēng zhí	Peak to peak	Pk-Pk
峰化电感	Fēnghuà diàngǎn	Peaking inductor	
烽火通信科技股份有限公司	Fēnghuǒ tōngxìn kējì gǔfèn yǒuxiàn gōngsī	FiberHome Telecommunication Technologies Co. Ltd.	
风机	Fēngjī	Blower	
风机盘管	Fēngjī pánguǎn	Fan coil unit	FCU
风积振动	Fēngjī zhèndòng	Aeolian vibration	
风景日戳	Fēngjǐng rìchuō	Landscape date mark	
蜂鸣器	Fēngmíngqì	Buzzer	BZ
分光比	Fēnguāng bǐ	Coupling ratio	CR
分光端口	Fēnguāng duānkǒu	Tap port (FOC)	
分光光度计	Fēnguāng guāngdùjì	Spectrophotometry (semiconductor mfg)	
分光晶体	Fēnguāng jīngtǐ	Dispersive crystal	
分光器	Fēnguāngqì	Tap coupler (FOC)	
分光器/滤波型波分复用器	Fēnguāngqì/lǜbōxíng bōfēn fùyòngqì	Tap coupler/filter wavelength division multiplexer	TWDM
蜂窝电信工业协会	Fēngwō diànxìn gōngyè xiéhuì	Cellular Telecommunications Industry Association (US)	CTIA
蜂窝地理服务区	Fēngwō dìlǐ fúwùqū	Cellular geographic service area	CGSA
蜂窝鉴权及话音加密	Fēngwō jiànquán jí huàyīn jiāmì	Cellular authentication and voice encryption	CAVE
蜂窝配置	Fēngwō pèizhì	Cell allocation	CA
蜂窝手持机	Fēngwō shǒuchíjī	Cellular handset	
蜂窝数字分组数据	Fēngwō shùzì fēnzǔ shùjù	Cellular digital packet data	CDPD
蜂窝通信工业协会	Fēngwō tōngxìn gōngyè xiéhuì	Cellular Telecommunications Industry Association	CTIA
蜂窝网络管理器	Fēngwō wǎngluò guǎnlǐqì	Cellular network administrator	CAN
蜂窝网络管理器界面	Fēngwō wǎngluò guǎnlǐqì jièmiàn	Cellular network administrator interface	CNAI
蜂窝无线电话服务	Fēngwō wúxiàn diànhuà fúwù	Cellular radiotelephone service	CRS
蜂窝信息加密算法	Fēngwō xìnxī jiāmì suànfǎ	Cellular message encryption algorithm	CEMA
蜂窝系统	Fēngwō xìtǒng	Cellular system	
蜂窝式移动通信系统	Fēngwō-shì yídòng tōngxìn xìtǒng	Cellular mobile system	CMS
蜂窝式移动通信系统	Fēngwō-shì yídòng tōngxìn xìtǒng	Cellular mobile radio	CMR
蜂窝式移动无线电话业务	Fēngwō-shì yídòng wúxiàn diànhuà yèwù	Cellular mobile radiotelephone service	CMRS
缝隙天线	Fèngxì tiānxiàn	Slot antenna	
风险	Fēngxiǎn	Risk	
风险分析	Fēngxiǎn fēnxī	Risk analysis	
风险管理	Fēngxiǎn guǎnlǐ	Risk management	
风险评价	Fēngxiǎn píngjià	Risk assessment	
风险投资公司	Fēngxiǎn tóuzī gōngsī	Venture capital company	
风险信息准则	Fēngxiǎn xìnxī zhǔnzé	Risk information criterion	
蜂音	Fēngyīn	Buzz, crackle	
蜂音器	Fēngyīnqì	Buzzer	BZ
峰值	Fēngzhí	Peak value	

峰值包络功率	Fēngzhí bāoluò gōnglǜ	Peak envelope power (of a transmitter)	
峰值包络检波	Fēngzhí bāoluò jiǎnbō	Peak envelope detection	
峰值电压	Fēngzhí diànyā	Peak voltage	
峰值对平均值比率	Fēngzhí duì píngjūnzhí bǐlǜ	Peak to average ratio	PAR
峰值隔离度	Fēngzhí gélídù	Peak isolation	
峰值功率	Fēngzhí gōnglǜ	Peak power	
峰值功率等级	Fēngzhí gōnglǜ děngjí	Peak power class (of a mobile station)	
峰值检波器	Fēngzhí jiǎnbōqì	Peak detector	
峰值码域误差	Fēngzhí mǎyù wùchā	Peak code domain error	PCDE
峰值相位偏移	Fēngzhí xiàngwèi piānyí	Peak phase deviation	
峰值限制	Fēngzhí xiànzhì	Peak limiting	
峰值信噪比	Fēngzhí xìn zào bǐ	Peak signal-to-noise ratio	PSNR
峰值信元速率	Fēngzhí xìnyuán sùlǜ	Peak cell rate	PCR
峰值系数	Fēngzhí xìshù	Crest factor	
峰值音量比率	Fēngzhí yīnliàng bǐlǜ	Peak loudness rating	
峰值因数	Fēngzhí yīnshù	Crest factor	
峰值因子	Fēngzhí yīnzǐ	Peak factor	
峰值-波纹系数	Fēngzhí-bōwén xìshù	Peak-ripple factor	
封装	Fēngzhuāng	Encapsulation	
封装安全负载	Fēngzhuāng ānquán fùzài	Encapsulating security payload (in IPSec)	ESP
封装安全荷	Fēngzhuāng ānquán hé	Encapsulating security payload	ESP
封装安全净荷	Fēngzhuāng ānquán jìnghé	Encapsulating security payload	ESP
封装安全载荷（协议）	Fēngzhuāng ānquán zàihè (xiéyì)	Encapsulating security payload (protocol)	ESP
封装桥接	Fēngzhuāng qiáojiē	Encapsulation bridging	
粉红噪声	Fěnhóng zàoshēng	Pink noise	
分集	Fēnjí	Diversity	
分机	Fēnjī	Extension (extra telephone set)	
分级编址按序存取法	Fēnjí biānzhǐ ànxù cúnqǔ fǎ	Hierarchical indexed sequential access method	HISAM
分级抽象计算机	Fēnjí chōuxiàng jìsuànjī	Hierarchical abstract computer	HAC
分级叠加功能	Fēnjí diéjiā gōngnéng	Stepped overlay function	
分级递阶网路	Fēnjí dìjiē wǎnglù	Hierarchical network	
分集度	Fēnjí dù	Order of diversity	
分级复联	Fēnjí fùlián	Grading	
分集改善因数	Fēnjí gǎishàn yīnshù	Diversity improvement factor	
分集合并器	Fēnjí hébìngqì	Diversity combiner	
分集间隔	Fēnjí jiàngé	Diversity separation	
分级结构	Fēnjí jiégòu	Hierarchical structure	
分机结构	Fēnjī jiégòu	Sub-assembly	
分集接收	Fēnjí jiēshōu	Diversity receiver	
分集接收	Fēnjí jiēshōu	Diversity reception	
分级控制	Fēnjí kòngzhì	Hierarchical control	
分集控制单元	Fēnjí kòngzhì dānyuán	Diversity control unit	DCU
分集切换	Fēnjí qiēhuàn	Diversity handover	DHO
分级同步网络	Fēnjí tóngbù wǎngluò	Hierarchically synchronized network	HSN
分级网络结构	Fēnjí wǎngluò jiégòu	Hierarchical network architecture	HNA
分集小区接收板	Fēnjí xiǎoqū jiēshōu bǎn	Diversity cell receiver board	DCRB

分级系统	Fēnjí xìtǒng	Hierarchy system	
分级再启动	Fēnjí zàiqǐdòng	Hierarchical restart	
分集增益	Fēnjí zēngyì	Diversity gain	
分级直接存取法	Fēnjí zhíjiē cúnqǔ fǎ	Hierarchical direct access method	HDAM
分级主干网	Fēnjí zhǔgàn wǎng	Collapsed backbone	
分解	Fēnjiě	Decomposition	
分接电缆	Fēnjiē diànlǎn	Drop cable	
分解精化	Fēnjiě jīnghuà	Partition refinement	
分接点	Fēnjiēdiǎn	Drop (noun)	
分接器	Fēnjiēqì	Demultiplexer	
分界线	Fēnjièxiàn	Demarcation	
分开	Fēnkāi	Detach	DET
分开存取和灵活发送的路由选择	Fēnkāi cúnqǔ hé línghuó fāsòngde lùyóu xuǎnzé	Split access and flexible egress routing	SAFER
分开接地	Fēnkāi jiēdì	Isolated ground	
分块	Fēnkuài	Deblocking	
分块查找	Fēnkuài cházhǎo	Block search	
芬兰俄国光通路	Fēnlán éguó guāng tōnglù	Finland-Russia optical gateway	FROG
分类	Fēnlèi	Classification	
分类方案	Fēnlèi fāng'àn	Classification scheme	
分类关系	Fēnlèi guānxi	Group relationship	
分类规则	Fēnlèi guīzé	Classification rule	
分类精度	Fēnlèi jīngdù	Classification accuracy	
分类码	Fēnlèi mǎ	Classification code	
分类其	Fēnlèi qí	Classifier (for QoS)	
分类图	Fēnlèi tú	Classification map	
分类误差	Fēnlèi wùchā	Classification error	
分类影像	Fēnlèi yǐngxiàng	Classified image	
分类的最小代价路径优先	Fēnlèide zuìxiǎo dàijià lùjìng yōuxiān	Classified minimum cost path first	CCPF
分类器	Fēnlèiqì	Classifier (IPsec)	
分离	Fēnlí	Detach	DET
分离棱镜	Fēnlí léngjìng	Split prism	
分离指示	Fēnlí zhǐshì	Detach indication	
分离器	Fēnlíqì	Splitter	
分流器	Fēnliúqì	Multiplexer	
分路放大器	Fēnlù fàngdàqì	Branch amplifier	BA
分路机/设备	Fēnlù jī/shèbèi	Drop and insert equipment	
分路滤波器	Fēnlù lǜbōqì	Channel separating filter	CSF
分路滤波器	Fēnlù lǜbōqì	Branching filter	
分路熔丝	Fēnlù róngsī	Branch fuse	
分路器	Fēnlùqì	Splitter, tap coupler (FOC)	
分路器板	Fēnlùqì bǎn	Splitter board	SPL
分路器电源板	Fēnlùqì diànyuán bǎn	Splitter power supply board	PWF
分路器框背板	Fēnlùqì kuàng bèibǎn	Splitter unit motherboard	SUB
粉末涂层外部结构	Fěnmò túcéng wàibù jiégòu	Powder coated external frame (semiconductor mfg)	
分派	Fēnpài	Dispatch	

分派标识符	Fēnpài biāozhì fú	Dispatch identifier	DISPID
分配	Fēnpèi	Allotment (of a radio frequency or channel)	
分配	Fēnpèi	Distribution	
分配	Fēnpèi	Allocate	
分配	Fēnpèi	Assignment	
分配处理器子系统	Fēnpèi chǔlǐqì zixìtǒng	Distributed processor sub-system	DPS
分配单位大小	Fēnpèi dānwèi dàxiǎo	Allocation unit size	
分配点	Fēnpèi diǎn	Distribution point	
分配放大器	Fēnpèi fàngdàqì	Distribution amplifier	DA
分配架	Fēnpèi jià	Distribution frame	
分配架	Fēnpèi jià	Distribution shelf	DISS
分配交换台	Fēnpèi jiāohuàntái	Distribution switchboard	DSB
分配命令	Fēnpèi mìnglìng	Assignment command	
分配模型	Fēnpèi móxíng	Allocation model	
分配完成	Fēnpèi wánchéng	Assignment complete	
分配网络地址	Fēnpèi wǎngluò dìzhǐ	Assign network address	ANA
分配业务	Fēnpèi yèwù	Distribution service	
分配应用	Fēnpèi yìngyòng	Distribution application	
分配中心	Fēnpèi zhōngxīn	Distribution hub	
分配资源点	Fēnpèi zīyuán diǎn	Assignment source point	ASP
分配器	Fēnpèiqì	Allocator	
分配型业务	Fēnpèixíng yèwù	Distributed service	
分批进样	Fēnpī jìnyàng	Batch inlet	
分片	Fēnpiàn	Fragment, fragmentation	
分片攻击	Fēnpiàn gōngjī	Fragment attack	
分频	Fēnpín	Frequency division	
分品	Fēnpǐn	Grading	
分频器	Fēnpínqì	Frequency divider	FD
分区	Fēnqū	Partition	
分区	Fēnqū	Zoning	
分区编码	Fēnqū biānmǎ	District coding	
分区传输路径	Fēnqū chuánshū lùjìng	Sectorized transmission path	
分区分时计费业务	Fēnqū fēnshí jìfèi yèwù	Cell and time discount service	
分区更新	Fēnqū gēngxīn	Split-horizon update	
分区启动扇区	Fēnqū qǐdòng shànqū	Partition boot sector	
分区首色图	Fēnqū shǒusè tú	Choropleth map (GIS)	
分区透镜	Fēnqū tòujìng	Zoned lens; stepped lens	
分区信息表	Fēnqū xìnxī biǎo	Partition information table	PIT
分散	Fēnsàn	Dispersion	
分散测试系统	Fēnsàn cèshì xìtǒng	Discrete component tester (semiconductor mfg)	
分散处理	Fēnsàn chǔlǐ	Decentralized processing	
分散定位	Fēnsàn dìngwèi	Distributed channel assignment	
分散队列双总线	Fēnsàn duìliè shuāng zǒngxiàn	Distributed queue, dual bus	DQDB
分散交换的操作系统	Fēnsàn jiāohuànde cāozuò xìtǒng	Operating system for distributed switching	OSDS
分散控制	Fēnsàn kòngzhì	Distributed control	
分散控制方式	Fēnsàn kòngzhì fāngshì	Decentralized control	

分散曲线	Fēnsàn qūxiàn	Dispersion curve	
分散搜索	Fēnsàn sōusuǒ	Scatter search	
分散网	Fēnsàn wǎng	Scatternet	
分散剂	Fēnsànji	Dispersant (in SMT)	
分散式多点	Fēnsàn-shì duōdiǎn	Decentralized multipoint	
分散式控制	Fēnsàn-shì kòngzhì	Distributed control	
分散式帧定位信号	Fēnsànshì zhèng dìngwèi xìnhào	Distributed frame alignment signal	
分散性波动	Fēnsàn-xìng bōdòng	Dispersed wave	
分散性瑞利波	Fēnsàn-xìng Ruì-lì bō	Dispersive Rayleigh wave	
分时	Fēnshí	Time sharing	
分时发分集	Fēnshí fāfēnjí	Time switched transmit diversity	TSTD
分时共享	Fēnshí gòngxiǎng	Time-sharing	
分时模拟网络	Fēnshí mónǐ wǎngluò	Time-division analog network	TDAN
分时系统	Fēnshí xìtǒng	Time-sharing system	
分时执行系统	Fēnshí zhíxíng xìtǒng	Time-sharing executive system	TSES
分时隙 E1	Fēnshíxì E1	Channelized E1	
分束器	Fēnshùqì	Beam splitter	
分数维模型	Fēnshùwéi móxíng	Fractal dimension model	
分数位平面	Fēnshùwèi píngmiàn	Fractional bit-plane	
粉碎机	Fěnsuìjī	Shredder	
分同步卫星	Fēntóngbù wèixīng	Sub-synchronous satellite	
粉涂层硫化	Fěntúcéng liúhuà	Powder coat cure (semiconductor mfg)	
分维	Fēnwéi	Fractal dimension	
分位数	Fènwèi shù	Quantile	
分位值	Fènwèizhí	Fractile	
分析服务器	Fēnxī fúwùqì	Analysis server	
分析管	Fēnxī guǎn	Analyzer tube	
分析引擎	Fēnxī yǐnqíng	Analysis engine	
分线盒	Fēnxiàn hé	Junction box	
分享保护环	Fēnxiǎng bǎohù huán	Shared protection ring	
分销商	Fēnxiāo shāng	Distributor	
分谐波	Fēnxiébō	Subharmonic	
分谐频	Fēnxiépín	Sub-frequency	
分形	Fēnxíng	Fractal	
分形编码	Fēnxíng biānmǎ	Fractal encoding	
分形几何	Fēnxíng jǐhé	Fractal geometry	
分形行为	Fēnxíng xíngwéi	Fractal behavior	
分用	Fēnyòng	Demultiplexing	
分用器	Fēnyòngqì	Demultiplexer	
分支	Fēnzhī	Branch, tributary	
分支处理单元	Fēnzhī chǔlǐ dānyuán	Branch processing unit	BPU
分支点	Fēnzhī diǎn	Breakout	
分支光缆	Fēnzhī guānglǎn	Breakout cable	
分支光缆	Fēnzhī guānglǎn	Branched cable	
分支目标缓冲	Fēnzhī mùbiāo huǎnchōng	Branch target buffer/cache	BTB/C
分支线	Fēnzhī xiàn	Spur feeder	

分支预测	Fēnzhī yùcè	Branch prediction	
分支预测表	Fēnzhī yùcè biǎo	Branch prediction table	
分支式电桥	Fēnzhī-shì diànqiáo	Branch hybrid junction	
分支式天线收发开关	Fēnzhī-shì tiānxiàn shōufā kāiguān	Branch antenna transceiver switch	
分装	Fēnzhuāng	Disassembly	
分装段和重组	Fēnzhuāng duàn hé chóngzǔ	Segmentation and reassembly	SAR
分子束外延	Fènzi shù wàiyán	Molecular beam epitaxy	MBE
分组	Fēnzǔ	Packet	
分组	Fēnzǔ	Segmenting	
分组按同步数字体系传送	Fēnzǔ àn tóngbù shùzì tǐxì chuánsòng	Packet over synchronous digital hierarchy (SDH)	POS
分组伴随控制信道	Fēnzǔ bànsuí kòngzhì xìndào	Packet accompanying control channel	PACCH
分组本地介入	Fēnzǔ běndì jièrù	Packet local access	
分组编码规则	Fēnzǔ biānmǎ guīzé	Packet encoding rules	PER
分组层参考事件	Fēnzǔ céng cānkǎo shìjiàn	Packet layer reference event	PE
分组层控制处理器	Fēnzǔ céng kòngzhì chǔlǐqì	Packet layer control processor	PLCP
分组层协议	Fēnzǔ céng xiéyì	Packet layer protocol	PLP
分组差错率	Fēnzǔ chācuò lǜ	Packet error rate	PER
分组拆装	Fēnzǔ chāizhuāng	Packet assembly/disassembly	PAD
分组插入率	Fēnzǔ chārù lǜ	Packet insertion rate	PIR
分组承载业务	Fēnzǔ chéngzài yèwù	Packet mode bearer service	PMBS
分组传递方式	Fēnzǔ chuándì fāngshì	Packet transfer mode	
分组传输模式	Fēnzǔ chuánshū móshì	Packet transfer mode	
分组传送模式	Fēnzǔ chuánsòng móshì	Packet transfer mode	
分组处理	Fēnzǔ chǔlǐ	Packet handling	
分组处理接口	Fēnzǔ chǔlǐ jiēkǒu	Packet handling interface	PHI
分组处理模块	Fēnzǔ chǔlǐ mókuài	Packet handler module	PHM
分组处理器	Fēnzǔ chǔlǐqì	Packet handler	PH
分组处理器功能	Fēnzǔ chǔlǐqì gōngnéng	Packet handler function	PHF
分组处理器接口	Fēnzǔ chǔlǐqì jiēkǒu	Packet handler interface	PHI
分组错误率	Fēnzǔ cuòwù lǜ	Packet error rate	PER
分组代码	Fēnzǔ dàimǎ	Block code	
分组电路倍增设备	Fēnzǔ diànlù bèizēng shèbèi	Packet circuit multiplication equipment	PCME
分组定时控制信道—上行	Fēnzǔ dìngshí kòngzhì xìndào yī shàngxíng	Packet timing control channel/uplink	PTCCH/U
分组定时控制信道—下行	Fēnzǔ dìngshí kòngzhì xìndào yīxià xíng	Packet timing control channel/downlink	PTCCH/D
分组丢失率	Fēnzǔ diūshī lǜ	Packet loss rate	PLR
分组方式终端	Fēnzǔ fāngshì zhōngduān	Packet-mode terminal	PMT
分组公共控制信道	Fēnzǔ gōnggòng kòngzhì xìndào	Packet common control channel	PCCCH
分组公平排队算法	Fēnzǔ gōngping páiduì suànfǎ	Packet fair queuing	PFQ
分组广播控制信道	Fēnzǔ guǎngbō kòngzhì xìndào	Packet broadcast control channel	PBCCH
分组过滤	Fēnzǔ guòlǜ	Packet filtering	
分组交换	Fēnzǔ jiāohuàn	Packet switched or switching	PS
分组交换公共数据网	Fēnzǔ jiāohuàn gōnggòng shùjù wǎng	Packet switched public data network	PSPDN
分组交换共用数据网	Fēnzǔ jiāohuàn gòngyòng shùjù wǎng	Packet switched public data network	PSPDN
分组交换节点	Fēnzǔ jiāohuàn jiédiǎn	Packet-switching node	PSN
分组交换数据传输业务	Fēnzǔ jiāohuàn shùjù chuánshū yèwù	Packet switched data transmission service	

分组交换数据网	Fēnzǔ jiāohuàn shùjù wǎng	Packet switched data network	PSDN
分组交换数字数据网	Fēnzǔ jiāohuàn shùzì shùjù wǎng	Packet switched digital data network	DATAPAC
分组交换网络	Fēnzǔ jiāohuàn wǎngluò	Packet switched network	PSN
分组交换协议	Fēnzǔ jiāohuàn xiéyì	Packet switching protocol	PSP
分组交换中心	Fēnzǔ jiāohuàn zhōngxīn	Group switching center	GSC
分组交换机	Fēnzǔ jiāohuànjī	Packet switch	PAC
分组校检码	Fēnzǔ jiàojiǎn mǎ	Packet check code (IPsec)	
分组接入应答信道	Fēnzǔ jiērù yìngdá xìndào	Packet access grant channel	PACCH
分组接入允许信道	Fēnzǔ jiērù yǔnxǔ xìndào	Packet access grant channel	PAGCH
分组接入准许信道	Fēnzǔ jiērù zhǔnxǔ xìndào	Packet access grant channel	PAGCH
分组进入事件	Fēnzǔ jìnrù shìjiàn	Packet entry event	
分组集中器	Fēnzǔ jízhōngqì	Packet centralization equipment	PCE
分组空闲模式	Fēnzǔ kòngxián móshì	Packet idle mode	
分组控制单元	Fēnzǔ kòngzhì dānyuán	Packet control unit	PCU
分组控制功能	Fēnzǔ kòngzhì gōngnéng	Packet controlled function	PCF
分组框	Fēnzǔ kuàng	Group box	
分组离开事件	Fēnzǔ líkāi shìjiàn	Packet exit event	
分组临时移动用户识别码	Fēnzǔ línshí yídòng yònghù shíbié mǎ	Packet temporary mobile subscription identity	P-TMSI
分组路由选择地址	Fēnzǔ lùyóu xuǎnzé dìzhǐ	Packet routing address	PRA
分组码	Fēnzǔ mǎ	Block code	
分组密码	Fēnzǔ mìmǎ	Block cipher	
分组模式承载业务	Fēnzǔ móshì chéngzài yèwù	Packet mode bearer service	PMBS
分组时间提前信道	Fēnzǔ shíjiān tíqián xìndào	Packet timing advance control channel	PTCCH
分组时间提前量控制信道	Fēnzǔ shíjiān tíqiánliàng kòngzhì xìn dào	Packet time advance control channel	PTCCH
分组数据传递信道	Fēnzǔ shùjù chuándì xìndào	Packet data transfer channel	PDTCH
分组数据传输信道	Fēnzǔ shùjù chuánshū xìndào	Packet data traffic channel	PDTCH
分组数据单元	Fēnzǔ shùjù dānyuán	Packet data unit	PCU
分组数据服务节点	Fēnzǔ shùjù fúwù jiédiǎn	Packet data serving node	PDSN
分组数据会聚协议	Fēnzǔ shùjù huìjù xiéyì	Packet data convergence protocol	PDCP
分组数据控制功能	Fēnzǔ shùjù kòngzhì gōngnéng	Packet data control function	PCF
分组数据网	Fēnzǔ shùjù wǎng	Packet data network	
分组数据网络	Fēnzǔ shùjù wǎngluò	Packet data network	PDN
分组数据协议	Fēnzǔ shùjù xiéyì	Packet data protocol	PDP
分组数据信道	Fēnzǔ shùjù xìndào	Packet data channel	PDCH
分组数据业务网络	Fēnzǔ shùjù yèwù wǎngluò	Packet data service network	PDSN
分组数据业务信道	Fēnzǔ shùjù yèwù xìndào	Packet data traffic channel	PDTCH
分组随机接入信道	Fēnzǔ suíjī jiērù xìndào	Packet random access channel	PRACH
分组随路控制信道	Fēnzǔ suílù kòngzhì xìndào	Packet associated control channel	PACCH
分组通信 I/F 集成卡	Fēnzǔ tōngxìn I/F jíchéng kǎ	Packet communication I/F card assembly	PCIA
分组通知信道	Fēnzǔ tōngzhī xìndào	Packet notification channel	PNCH
分组 turbo 码	Fēnzǔ turbo mǎ	Block turbo codes	BTC
分组无线网	Fēnzǔ wúxiàn wǎng	Packet radio network	
分组线路板	Fēnzǔ xiànlù bǎn	Packet line card	PLC
分组寻呼信道	Fēnzǔ xúnhū xìndào	Packet paging channel	PPCH
分组循环分散定位	Fēnzǔ xúnhuán fēnsàn dìngwèi	Block cyclic distributed channel assignment	
分组业务信道	Fēnzǔ yèwù xìndào	Packet traffic channel	PTCH

分组移动管理	Fēnzǔ yídòng guǎnlǐ	Packet mobile management	PMM
分组移动台临时识别号	Fēnzǔ yídòngtái línshí shíbié hào	Packet temporary mobile station identity	P-TMSI
分组因特网查询进程	Fēnzǔ Yīntèwǎng cháxún jìnchéng	Packet Internet groper	PING
分组因特网探索程序	Fēnzǔ Yīntèwǎng tànsuǒ chéngxù	Packet Internet groper	PING
分组域媒体网关	Fēnzǔ yù méitǐ wǎngguān	Packet switched media gateway	PS-MGW
分组预约多址	Fēnzǔ yùyuē duō zhǐ	Packet reservation multiple access	PRMA
分组终端	Fēnzǔ zhōngduān	Packet terminal	PT
分组中继	Fēnzǔ zhōngjì	Packet trunking	
分组装/卸	Fēnzǔ zhuāng/xiè	Packet assembler/disassembler	PAD
分组装拆包	Fēnzǔ zhuāngchāi bāo	Packet assembly/disassembly	PAD
分组装拆设备	Fēnzǔ zhuāngchāi shèbèi	Packet assembly/disassembly equipment	PAD
分组装拆设施	Fēnzǔ zhuāngchāi shèshī	Packet assembly/disassembly facility	
分组组装与拆卸	Fēnzǔ zǔzhuāng yǔ chāixiè	Packet assembly and disassembly	
分组组装/分解设备	Fēnzǔ zǔzhuāng/fēnjiě shèbèi	Packet assembler/disassembler	PAD
分组包识别	Fēnzǔbāo shíbié	Packet identification	PID
FLIR 系统公司	FLIR xìtǒng gōngsī	FLIR Systems, Inc	FSI
佛累和费区	Fó-lěi-hé-fèi qū	Fraunhofer region (far-field region)	
否定的口令检验	Fǒudìngde kǒulìng jiǎnyàn	Negative password check	
否认	Fǒurèn	Denial (IPsec)	
否认	Fǒurèn	Repudiation (IPsec)	
否认字符	Fǒurèn zìfú	Negative acknowledge	NAK
氟材料	Fú cáiliào	Fluoromaterial (semiconductor mfg)	
父处理	Fù chǔlǐ	Parenting	
父代	Fù dài	Parent	
父对象	Fù duìxiàng	Parent object	
负过程	Fù guòchéng	Subtractive process (in SMT)	
复函数方程	Fù hánshù fāngchéng	Complex functional equation	
辅节点	Fǔ jiédiǎn	Secondary node	
父类	Fù lèi	Parent class	
复四相调制	Fù sìxiāng tiáozhì	Complex quaternary phase shift modulation	CQM
复调谐天线	Fù tiáoxié tiānxiàn	Multiple-tuned antenna	MTA
复调制干扰	Fù tiáozhì gānrǎo	Complex modulated jamming	
复信号	Fù xìnhào	Complex signal	
父域	Fù yù	Parent domain	
副瓣	Fùbàn	Secondary lobe, minor lobe	
附板	Fùbǎn	Applique	
副瓣电平	Fùbàn diànpíng	Minor lobe level	
福布斯	Fú-bù-sī	Forbes (US magazine)	
浮充充电	Fúchōng chōngdiàn	Floating charge	
浮充电压峰值	Fúchōng diànyā fēngzhí	Floating voltage peak value	
附带的相位调制	Fùdàide xiàngwèi tiáozhì	Incidental phase modulation	IPM
弗丹自动重发系统	Fú-dān zìdòng chóngfā xìtǒng	Automatic repetition Verdan system	
浮点	Fúdiǎn	Floating point	
浮点表示法	Fúdiǎn biǎoshì fǎ	Floating point representation	
浮点操作/秒	Fúdiǎn cāozuò/ miǎo	Floating point operations per second	FLOP
浮点乘	Fúdiǎn chéng	Floating point multiplication	FMUL

浮点除	Fúdiǎn chú	Floating point division	FDIV
复电处理	Fùdiàn chǔlǐ	Power recovery processing	
浮点加	Fúdiǎn jiā	Floating point addition	FADD
浮点减	Fúdiǎn jiǎn	Floating point subtraction	FSUB
浮点通信库	Fúdiǎn tōngxìn kù	Floating point communications library	
浮点运算单元	Fúdiǎn yùnsuàn dānyuán	Floating point unit	FPU
浮动菜单	Fúdòng càidān	Tear-off menu	
浮动模式	Fúdòng móshì	Floating mode	
幅度	Fúdù	Amplitude	A
幅度反射系数	Fúdù fǎnshè xìshù	Amplitude reflection coefficient	
幅度分层	Fúdù fēncéng	Amplitude quantizing	
幅度概率分布	Fúdù gàilǜ fēnbù	Amplitude probability distribution	APD
幅度检波	Fúdù jiǎnbō	Amplitude detection	
幅度解调	Fúdù jiětiáo	Amplitude demodulation	
幅度量化控制	Fúdù liànghuà kòngzhì	Amplitude quantized control	
幅度频率失真	Fúdù pínlǜ shīzhēn	Amplitude/frequency distortion	
幅度频率特性	Fúdù pínlǜ tèxìng	Amplitude/frequency characteristic	
幅度谱	Fúdù pǔ	Amplitude spectrum	
幅度失真	Fúdù shīzhēn	Amplitude distortion	
幅度失真	Fúdù shīzhēn	Amplitude distortion	
幅度特性	Fúdù tèxìng	Amplitude characteristic	
幅度调制	Fúdù tiáozhì	Amplitude modulation	AM
幅度相位变换	Fúdù xiāngwèi biànhuàn	Amplitude phase conversion	APC
负反馈	Fùfǎnkuì	Negative feedback	
复反射系数，	Fùfǎnshè xìshù,	Complex reflection coefficient	
副反射器	Fùfǎnshèqì	Sub-reflector	
复费率	Fùfèi lǜ	Multi-charge rate	
付费音	Fùfèi yīn	Pay tone (in a pay telephone)	
覆盖	Fùgài	Coverage, overlay	
覆盖结构程序	Fùgài jiégòu chéngxù	Overlay structure program	
覆盖描述语言	Fùgài miáoshù yǔyán	Overlay description language	ODL
覆盖区	Fùgài qū	Coverage area (of a space station)	
覆盖层	Fùgàicéng	Cladding (in SMT)	
负功能特征	Fùgōngnéng tèzhēng	Negative functional feature (CAD/CAM)	
负关联规则	Fùguānlián guīzé	Negative association rule	
符号	Fúhào	Symbol	
符号	Fúhào	Token (in software)	
符号表	Fúhào biǎo	Symbol table	
符号表示法	Fúhào biǎoshì fǎ	Symbology	
符号操作	Fúhào cāozuò	Symbolic manipulation	
符号差错率	Fúhào chācuò lǜ	Symbol error rate	SER
符号环境	Fúhào huánjìng	Symbol environment	
符号回归	Fúhào huíguī	Symbolic regression	
符号名	Fúhào míng	Symbolic name	
符号输入	Fúhào shūrù	Symbol input (WP command)	
符号位	Fúhào wèi	Sign bit	

符号响应	Fúhào xiǎngyìng	Signed response	SRES
符号化	Fúhàohuà	Symbolization	
符号化服务	Fúhàohuà fúwù	Encoding service	
符号化识别码	Fúhàohuà shíbié mǎ	Symbolization identification code (in RTP)	
符号间干扰	Fúhào-jiān gānrǎo	Intersymbol interference	ISI
符号率	Fúhàolǜ	Symbol rate	
复合	Fùhé	Composition	
复核	Fùhé	Rechecking	
负荷	Fùhè	Payload (SDH term)	
负荷保持时间	Fùhè bǎochí shíjiān	Duration of load	
复合波形调制干扰	Fùhé bōxíng tiáozhì gānrǎo	Complex waveform modulated jamming	
复合不锈钢管型	Fùhé bùxiùgāng guǎnxíng	Composite stainless tube type (FOC)	
复合地线光缆	Fùhé dìxiàn guānglǎn	Optical fiber composite ground wire	OPGW
负荷分担	Fùhè fēndān	Load sharing (in common channel signaling)	
复合功能	Fùhé gōngnéng	Compound function	
复合光纤	Fùhé guāngxiān	Compound fiber	
复合键	Fùhé jiàn	Composite key (for database)	
复合交换	Fùhé jiāohuàn	Compound switching	
复合交会方式	Fùhé jiāohuì fāngshì	Composite intersection type	
复合矩形喇叭天线	Fùhé jǔxíng lǎba tiānxiàn	Compound rectangular horn antenna	
复合控制系统	Fùhé kòngzhì xìtǒng	Combination-loop control system	
符荷模块	Fúhé mókuài	Payload module	
负荷能力	Fùhè nénglì	Capability	
负荷容量	Fùhè róngliàng	Load capacity	
复合三价差拍	Fùhé sān jiàchā pāi	Composite triple beat	CTB
复合商业组群	Fùhé shāngyè zǔ qún	Business group complex	BGC
复合数据消息格式	Fùhé shùjù xiāoxi géshi	Multiple data message format	MDMF
复合损耗	Fùhé sǔnhào	Transducer gain (of a two-port network)	
复合锁相解调器	Fùhé suǒxiàng jiětiáoqì	Compound phase locked demodulator	CPLD
复合索引	Fùhé suǒyǐn	Composite index (for database)	
复合信号	Fùhé xìnhào	Compound signal (in AC signaling)	
复合信号拨号	Fùhé xìnhào bōhào	Composite signal dialing	CSD
负荷业务量性能	Fùhè yèwù liáng xìngnéng	Trafficability performance	
复合音	Fùhé yīn	Complex sound	
复合元素	Fùhé yuánsù	Compound element	
复合圆形喇叭天线	Fùhé yuánxíng lǎba tiānxiàn	Compound circular horn antenna	
复合语句	Fùhé yǔjù	Compound statement	
复合增益	Fùhé zēngyì	Composite gain (of a two-port network)	
复合装甲	Fùhé zhuāngjiǎ	Composite armor	
负荷转移	Fùhè zhuǎnyí	Load transfer	
复合坐标参照系	Fùhé zuòbiāo cānzhàoxì	Compound coordinate reference system	
负荷-偏差关系模型	Fùhè—piānchā guānxi móxíng	Model of the load-deflection relation	
氟化聚酸亚胺材料	Fúhuà jùsuān yà'àn cáiliào	Fluorated polyimide (FOC mfg)	FULPI
氟化物光纤	Fúhuàwù guāngxiān	Fluoride fiber	FF
负极	Fùjí	Negative electrode	
附加	Fùjiā	Append	

附加白高斯噪声	Fùjiā bái gāo-sī zàoshēng	Additive white Gaussian noise	AWGN
附加保护	Fùjiā bǎohù	Supplementary protection	
附加单元接口	Fùjiā dānyuán jiēkǒu	Attachment unit interface	AUI
附加符号	Fùjiā fúhào	Additional character	
附加高斯白噪声	Fùjiā gāo-sī bái zàoshēng	Additive white Gaussian noise	AWGN
附加绝缘	Fùjiā juéyuán	Supplementary insulation	
附加损耗	Fùjiā sǔnhào	Excess loss	
附加损耗	Fùjiā sǔnhào	Extra loss	EL
附加指配	Fùjiā zhǐpèi	Additional assignment	
附加资源计算机网络	Fùjiā zīyuán jìsuànjī wǎngluò	Attached resource computer network	ARCnet
附加的低层功能	Fùjiāde dīcéng gōngnéng	Additional low layer function	ALLF
附加的高层功能	Fùjiāde gāocéng gōngnéng	Additional high layer function	AHLF
附加的全局功能	Fùjiāde quánjú gōngnéng	Additional global function	AGF
辅件	Fǔjiàn	Auxiliary attachment	
福建万利达电子有限公司	Fújiàn wàn-lì-dá diànzǐ yǒuxiàn gōngsī	Fujian Malata Electronics Co. Ltd.	
复接	Fùjiē	Multiple	
复接段	Fùjiē duàn	Multiplex section	MS
复接段开销	Fùjiē duàn kāixiao	Multiplex section overhead	MSOH
复接设备	Fùjiē shèbèi	Multiplexer	MUX
复接器	Fùjiēqì	Multiplexer	
复接器 / 分接器	Fùjiēqì/fēnjiēqì	Multiplexer/demultiplexer	MUX/DEMUX
复接制	Fùjiēzhì	Multiple connection system	
副控制站	Fùkòngzhìzhàn	Sub-control station	
付款交单	Fùkuǎn jiāodān	Document against payment	D/P
弗朗和费区	Fú-lǎng-hé-fèi qū	Fraunhofer region	
富兰克林天线	Fù-lán-kè-lín tiānxiàn	Franklin antenna	
傅立叶变换	Fù-lì-yè biànhuàn	Fourier transform	
付立叶分析	Fù-lì-yè fēnxī	Fourier analysis	
付立叶谱	Fù-lì-yè pǔ	Fourier spectrum	
傅利叶透镜	Fù-lì-yè tòujìng	Fourier lens	
负离子	Fùlízǐ	Negative ion	
福禄克网络公司	Fú-lù-kè wǎngluò gōngsī	Fluke Networks Corp.	
负逻辑	Fùluóji	Negative logic	
负脉冲塞入	Fùmàichōng sāirù	Negative pulse stuffing	
负码速调整	Fùmǎsù tiáozhěng	Negative justification	
负摩擦	Fùmócā	Negative friction	
附票	Fùpiào	Attached tab	
幅频失真	Fú-pín shīzhēn	Amplitude-frequency distortion	AFD
幅频特性	Fú-pín tèxìng	Amplitude/frequency characteristic	
幅频响应	Fú-pín xiǎngyìng	Amplitude-frequency response	AFR
幅频一致性	Fú-pín yīzhìxìng	Amplitude-frequency equalization	
复频谱	Fùpínpǔ	Complex spectrum	
辐射	Fúshè	Radiation	
敷设	Fūshè	Lay, install (pipe, cable, etc.)	
辐射 0-线绘图法	Fúshè 0-xiàn huìtú fǎ	Radial 0-line plotting	
辐射瓣	Fúshè bàn	Radiation lobe	

辐射测量计座	Fúshè cèliángjì zuò	Bolometer mount	
辐射测试场地	Fúshè cèshì chǎngdì	Radiation test site	
辐射成象	Fúshè chéngxiàng	Radiation imaging	
辐射单元	Fúshè dānyuán	Radiating element	
辐射电阻	Fúshè diànzǔ	Radiation resistance (of an antenna)	
辐射度图	Fúshè dù tú	Radiance map	
辐射方向图	Fúshè fāngxiàngtú	Radiation pattern	
辐射方向图的数学表达式	Fúshè fāngxiàngtúde shùxué biǎodá shì	Radiation pattern (mathematical representation)	
辐射方向图的图示法	Fúshè fāngxiàngtúde túshìfǎ	Radiation pattern (graphical representation)	
辐射发射	Fúshè fāshè	Radiated emission	
辐射分辨力	Fúshè fēnbiànlì	Radiation resolution (GIS)	
辐射干扰	Fúshè gānrǎo	Radiated interference	
辐射隔离装置	Fúshè gélí zhuāngzhì	Radiant protection unit	
辐射隔离度	Fúshè gélídù	Degree of radiant protection	
辐射校正	Fúshè jiàozhèng	Radiometric correction (GIS)	
辐射激发的光线放大	Fúshè jīfāde guāngxiàn fàngdà	Light amplification by stimulated emission of radiation	LASER
辐射近场区	Fúshè jìncháng qū	Radiating near field region	
辐射距	Fúshè jù	Radial distance	
辐射冷却	Fúshè lěngquè	Radiative cooling	
辐射亮度	Fúshè liàngdù	Radiance	
辐射敏感度	Fúshè mǐngǎndù	Radiated susceptibility	
辐射偶极子盘	Fúshè ǒujízi pán	Panel of radiating dipoles	
辐射强度	Fúshè qiángdù	Radiation intensity, radiant intensity	
辐射区	Fúshè qū	Radiated area	
辐射热测定器	Fúshè rè cèdìngqì	Bolometer	
辐射热计	Fúshè rèjì	Bolometer	
辐射实验场地	Fúshè shíyàn chǎngdì	Radiation test site	
辐射衰减	Fúshè shuāijiǎn	Radiation damping	
辐射特性图	Fúshè tèxìngtú	Radiation characteristic pattern	
辐射图包络	Fúshè tú bāoluò	Radiation pattern envelope	RPE
辐射雾	Fúshè wù	Radiation fog	
辐射效率	Fúshè xiàolǜ	Radiation efficiency (of an antenna)	
辐射杂散发射	Fúshè zásǎn fāshè	Radiated spurious emission	
辐射阻抗	Fúshè zǔkàng	Radiation impedance	
辐射能	Fúshènéng	Radiant energy	
辐射式测量计	Fúshè-shì cèliángjì	Bolometer	
辐射式功率计	Fúshè-shì gōnglǜjì	Bolometric power meter	
辐射源	Fúshèyuán	Emitter (of electromagnetic disturbance)	
复式线路自动呼叫系统	Fùshì xiànlù zìdòng hūjiào xìtǒng	Multi-line automatic calling system	MACS
负失配	Fùshīpèi	Negative mismatching	
富士通	Fù-shì-tōng	Fujitsu (Japan company)	
富士通网络传输系统公司	Fùshìtōng wǎngluò chuánshū xìtǒng gōngsī	Fujitsu Network Transmission Systems Inc. (Japan)	FNTS
富士通网络交换	Fùshìtōng wǎngluò jiāohuàn	Fujitsu Network Switching (Japan)	FNS
复述	Fùshù	Restatement	
附属对象	Fùshǔ duìxiàng	Dependent object (GIS term)	
复数功率	Fùshù gōnglǜ	Complex power (in a transmission line)	

附属硬件	Fùshǔ yìngjiàn	Accessory hardware	
附属用途	Fùshǔ yòngtú	Accessory use	
附属式架空光缆	Fùshǔ-shì jiàkōng guānglǎn	Optical attached aerial cable	OPAC
附网存储	Fùwǎng cúnchǔ	Network attached storage	NAS
复位	Fùwèi	Reset	
复位程序	Fùwèi chéngxù	Reset procedure	
复位响应	Fùwèi xiǎngyìng	Answer to reset	ATR
复位信号	Fùwèi xìnhào	Reset signal	RST
复位应答	Fùwèi yìngdá	Answer to reset	ATR
负温度系数	Fùwēndù xìshù	Negative temperature coefficient	NTC
服务	Fúwù	Service	
服务补丁	Fúwù bǔding	Service pack	
服务层网	Fúwù céng wǎng	Server layer network	
服务层信号劣化	Fúwù céng xìnhào lièhuà	Server signal degrade	SSD
服务层信号失效	Fúwù céng xìnhào shīxiào	Server signal fail	SSF
服务产业	Fúwù chǎnyè	Service industry	
服务呈现点	Fúwù chéngxiàn diǎn	Point of presence	
服务代理	Fúwù dàilǐ	Service broker (in VPN)	
服务等级	Fúwù děngjí	Degree of service	
服务等级	Fúwù děngjí	Grade of service	GOS
服务等级目标	Fúwù děngjí mùbiāo	Service-level objective	SLO
服务等级协议	Fúwù děngjí xiéyì	Service-level agreement	SLA
服务等级信号音	Fúwù děngjí xìnhào yīn	Class-of-service tone	
服务电路模块	Fúwù diànlù mókuài	Service circuit module	SCM
服务调度器	Fúwù diàodùqì	Service scheduler (in CORBA)	
服务定位协议	Fúwù dìngwèi xiéyì	Service location protocol	SLP
服务端	Fúwù duān	Server	
服务端游标	Fúwù duān yóubiāo	Server cursor (for database)	
服务访问点	Fúwù fǎngwèn diǎn	Service access point	SAP
服务访问点标识符	Fúwù fǎngwèn diǎn biāozhì fú	Service access point indicator	SAPI
服务访问电识别符	Fúwù fǎngwèn diàn shíbiéfú	Service access point identifier	SAPI
服务发现和应用配置	Fúwù fāxiàn hé yìngyòng pèizhì	Service discovery and application profile	SDAP
服务 GPRS 支持节点	Fúwù GPRS zhīchí jiédiǎn	Service GPRS support node	SGSN
服务管理	Fúwù guǎnlǐ	Service management	SM
服务管理和运营	Fúwù guǎnlǐ hé yùnyíng	Service management and operations	
服务关系	Fúwù guānxi	Service relationships	
服务弧	Fúwù hú	Service arc	
服务级管理	Fúwù jí guǎnlǐ	Service-level management	SLM
服务件革命	Fúwù jiàn gémìng	Serviceware revolution	
服务级别协定	Fúwù jíbié xiédìng	Service-level agreement	SLA
服务节点	Fúwù jiédiǎn	Service node	SN
服务节点 / 智能外围设备	Fúwù jiédiǎn/zhìnéng wàiwéi shèbèi	Service node/intelligent peripheral	SN / IP
服务接口 V.11	Fúwù jiēkǒu V.11	Service interface V.11	Q.1
服务接入点	Fúwù jiērù diǎn	Service access point	SAP
服务接入点标识	Fúwù jiērù diǎn biāozhì	Service access point indicator	SAPI
服务接入点识别符	Fúwù jiērù diǎn shíbiéfú	Service access point identifier	SAPI

服务接入点识别器	Fúwù jiērù diǎn shíbiéqì	Service access point identifier	SAPI
服务基站	Fúwù jīzhàn	Serving base station	
服务拒绝	Fúwù jùjué	Denial of service (IPsec)	
服务可保持性	Fúwù kěbǎochíxìng	Service retainability	
服务可得到性	Fúwù kědédàoxìng	Service accessibility	
服务类别	Fúwù lèibié	Class of service	CoS
服务类型	Fúwù lèixíng	Type of service	TOS
服务类型标识	Fúwù lèixíng biāozhì	Service profile identifier	SPID
服务贸易总协定	Fúwù màoyì zǒng xiédìng	General Agreement on Trade in Services	GATS
服务票据	Fúwù piàojù	Service ticket	ST
服务品质协议	Fúwù pǐnzhì xiéyì	Service [quality] level agreement	SLA
服务启动	Fúwù qǐdòng	Service activator	
服务水平协议	Fúwù shuǐpíng xiéyì	Service-level agreement	SLA
服务数据单元	Fúwù shùjù dānyuán	Service data unit	SDU
服务搜索	Fúwù sōusuǒ	Service discovery	SD
服务搜索数据库	Fúwù sōusuǒ shùjùkù	Service discovery database	SDDB
服务提供部门	Fúwù tígōng bùmén	Service provider	
服务提供商	Fúwù tígōng shāng	Service provider	SP
服务提供者	Fúwù tígòngzhě	Service provider	
服务网络	Fúwù wǎngluò	Serving network	SN
服务完善性	Fúwù wánshànxìng	Service integrity	
服务无线网络分系统	Fúwù wúxiàn wǎngluò fēnxìtǒng	Serving radio network sub-system	SRNS
服务无线电网络控制器	Fúwù wúxiàndiàn wǎngluò kòngzhìqì	Serving radio network controller	SRNC
服务小区	Fúwù xiǎoqū	Serving cell	
服务信道	Fúwù xìndào	Service channel	SC
服务选择服务器	Fúwù xuǎnzé fúwùqì	Service selection server	SSS
服务要素	Fúwù yàosù	Element of service	
服务移动数据中介系统	Fúwù yídòng shùjù zhōngjiè xìtǒng	Serving mobile data intermediate system	
服务易行性	Fúwù yìxíngxìng	Service operability	
服务用户	Fúwù yònghù	Service-user	
服务元素	Fúwù yuánsù	Service element	
服务原语	Fúwù yuányǔ	Service primitive	
服务支持性	Fúwù zhīchíxìng	Service supportability	
服务质量	Fúwù zhìliàng	Quality of service	QOS
服务状况	Fúwù zhuàngkuàng	Service status	
服务准备时间	Fúwù zhǔnbèi shíjiān	Service provisioning time	
服务组成管理	Fúwù zǔchéng guǎnlǐ	Service configuration management	Ser.CM
服务器	Fúwùqì	Server	
服务器操作系统	Fúwùqì cāozuò xìtǒng	Server operating system	SOS
服务器方包含	Fúwùqì fāng bāohán	Server side include	SSI
服务器名称	Fúwùqì míngchēng	Server name	
服务器群集	Fúwùqì qúnjí	Server cluster	
服务器消息块	Fúwùqì xiāoxi kuài	Server message block	SMB
服务器信号劣化	Fúwùqì xìnhào lièhuà	Server signal degrade	SSD
服务器信号失效	Fúwùqì xìnhào shīxiào	Server signal fail	SFF
服务器信息块	Fúwùqì xìnxī kuài	Server message block	SMB

服务器信息块协议	Fúwùqì xìnxī kuài xiéyì	Server message block protocol (IBM use)	SMB
服务器游标	Fúwùqì yóubiāo	Server cursor (for database)	
服务区	Fúwùqū	Service area	
服务者	Fúwùzhě	Server	
幅相变换	Fú-xiāng biànhuàn	Amplitude phase conversion	APC
幅相键控	Fú-xiāng jiànkòng	Amplitude phase keying	APK
幅相误差	Fú-xiàng wùchā	Amplitude-phase error	
覆写	Fùxiě	Override	
赋形射束天线	Fùxíng shèshù tiānxiàn	Shaped-beam antenna	
复选按钮	Fùxuǎn ànniǔ	Check button	
复选标记	Fùxuǎn biāojì	Checkmark √	
复选框	Fùxuǎn kuàng	Check box	
负压水头	Fùyā shuǐtóu	Negative-pressure head	
敷氧化层的	Fūyǎnghuà céngde	Oxide-coated	O
俯仰角	Fǔyǎngjiǎo	Pitch angle	
幅移键控	Fúyí jiànkòng	Amplitude shift keying	ASK
浮影图	Fúyǐngtú	Hologram	
复印机	Fùyìnjī	Copier	
负印量差	Fùyìnliáng chà	Negative printing amount percent	
复用	Fùyòng	Multiplexing	
复用标志	Fùyòng biāozhì	Multiplexing identification	MID
复用标识	Fùyòng biāozhì	Multiplexing identification	MID
复用段	Fùyòng duàn	Multiplex section	MS
复用段保护	Fùyòng duàn bǎohù	Multiplex stage protection	MSP
复用段保护	Fùyòng duàn bǎohù	Multiplex section protection	MSP
复用段保护环	Fùyòng duàn bǎohù huán	Multiplex segment shared protection ring	MSPring
复用段告警指示	Fùyòng duàn gàojǐng zhǐshì	Multiplex section alarm indication signal	MS-AIS
复用段告警指示信号	Fùyòng duàn gàojǐng zhǐshì xìnhào	Multiplex section alarm indication signal	MS-AIS
复用段共享保护环	Fùyòng duàn gòngxiǎng bǎohù huán	Multiplex section-shared protection ring	MS-SPRing
复用段接收缺陷指示	Fùyòng duàn jiēshōu quēxiàn zhǐshì	Multiplex segment receive defect indicator	MS-RDI
复用段开销	Fùyòng duàn kāixiao	Multiplex section overhead	MSOH
复用段适配	Fùyòng duàn shìpèi	Multiplex section adaptation	MSA
复用段数据通信通道	Fùyòng duàn shùjù tōngxìn tōngdào	Multiplex section data communications channel	MS-DCC
复用段网络连接	Fùyòng duàn wǎngluò liánjiē	Multiplex section network connection	MS-NC
复用段远端差错指示	Fùyòng duàn yuǎnduān chācuò zhǐshì	Multiplex section remote error indication	MS-REI
复用段远端差错指针	Fùyòng duàn yuǎnduān chācuò zhǐzhēn	Multiplex section remote error indicator	MS-REI
复用段远端接收失效	Fùyòng duàn yuǎnduān jiēshōu shīxiào	Multiplex segment far-end receive expiration	MS-FERE
复用段远端缺陷指示	Fùyòng duàn yuǎnduān quēxiàn zhǐshì	Multiplex section remote defect indication	MS-RDI
复用段远端误码指示	Fùyòng duàn yuǎnduān wùmǎ zhǐshì	Multiplex section remote error indication	MS-REI
复用段终端	Fùyòng duàn zhōngduān	Multiplex section termination	MST
复用段终端功能	Fùyòng duàn zhōngduān gōngnéng	Multiplex section termination function	MST
复用段终端元	Fùyòng duàn zhōngduān yuán	Multiplex section terminating element	MSTE
复用段终结	Fùyòng duàn zhōngjié	Multiplex section termination	MST
复用段自动保护倒换	Fùyòng duàn zìdòng bǎohù dǎohuàn	Multiplex section automatic protection switching	MS-APS
复用分用器	Fùyòng fēnyòngqì	Multiplexer-demultiplexer	Muldex
复用集合比特率	Fùyòng jíhé bǐtè lǜ	Multiplex aggregate bit rate	

复用信号	Fùyòng xìnhào	Multiplex signal, multiplexed signal	
复用转换器	Fùyòng zhuǎnhuànqì	Transmultiplexer	TMUX
复用器	Fùyòngqì	Multiplexer	MUX
浮游结构物	Fúyóu jiégòu wù	Floating structure	
赋予票据的票据	Fùyǔ piàojùde piàojù	Ticket granting ticket	TGT
复原	Fùyuán	Rehabilitation	
复原	Fùyuán	Retrieve	
复原请求	Fùyuán qǐngqiú	Restore request	RESRE
复原证实	Fùyuán zhèngshí	Restore confirm	RESCO
复杂对象	Fùzá duìxiàng	Complex object	
复杂多边形	Fùzá duōbiānxíng	Complex polygon	
复杂面	Fùzá miàn	Complex surface	
复杂三角形计数	Fùzá sānjiǎoxíng jìshù	High triangle count (video)	
复杂指令集计算	Fùzá zhǐlìng jí jìsuàn	Complex instruction set computing	CISC
复杂指令集计算机	Fùzá zhǐlìng jí jìsuànjī	Complex instruction set computer	CISC
复杂指令系统计算机	Fùzá zhǐlìng xìtǒng jìsuànjī	Complex instruction set computer	CISC
负载	Fùzài	Load	
负载断路控制板	Fùzài duànlù kòngzhì bǎn	Load disconnect control panel	
负载分配	Fùzài fēnpèi	Load sharing	
负载快速响应	Fùzài kuàisù xiǎngyìng	Fast response to load (semiconductor mfg)	
负载力矩	Fùzài lìjǔ	Load moment	
负载耐力系数设计法	Fùzài nàilì xìshù shèjì fǎ	Load and resistance factor design method	
负载平衡	Fùzài pínghéng	Load balancing	
负载特性交叠	Fùzài tèxìng jiāodié	Crossover of load characteristic	
负载调整率	Fùzài tiáozhěnglǜ	Load regulation	
负载效应	Fùzài xiàoyìng	Load effect	
负载系数	Fùzài xìshù	Load factor	
负载因子	Fùzài yīnzǐ	Load factor	LF
负载增量分析	Fùzài zēngliàng fēnxī	Incremental loading analysis	
负载指示	Fùzài zhǐshì	Load indication	
负载指数	Fùzài zhǐshù	Load index	
负载最小优先算法	Fùzài zuìxiǎo yōuxiān suànfǎ	Least load first algorithm	LLF
副载波	Fùzàibō	Sub-carrier	
副载波多址接入	Fùzàibō duōzhǐ jiērù	Sub-carrier multiple access	SCMA
副载波复用	Fùzàibō fùyòng	Sub-carrier multiplexing	SCM
副载波调制	Fùzàibō tiáozhì	Sub-carrier frequency modulation	SCM
负载波振荡器	Fùzàibō zhèndàngqì	Sub-carrier oscillator	SCO
辅站	Fǔzhàn	Secondary station	
复帧	Fùzhèng	Multi-frame	
复帧丢失	Fùzhèng diūshī	Loss of multi-frame	LOM
幅值	Fúzhí	Amplitude	
赋值	Fùzhí	Assign	
复制	Fùzhì	Copy (WP command)	
复制	Fùzhì	Reproduction	
复制	Fùzhì	Replication	
复制比	Fùzhì bǐ	Reproduction ratio	

赋值操作符	Fùzhí cāozuòfú	Assignment operator	
复制冲突查看器	Fùzhì chōngtū chákàn qì	Replication conflict viewer	
复制冲突观察器	Fùzhì chōngtū guānchágì	Replication conflict viewer (in SQL Server)	
复制监视器	Fùzhì jiānshìqì	Replication monitor	
复制拓扑	Fùzhì tuòpū	Replication topology	
复制为	Fùzhì wéi	Copy as (WP command)	
幅值细化	Fúzhí xìhuà	Magnitude refinement	
赋值语句	Fùzhí yǔjù	Assignment statements (in SQL Server)	
幅值-相位仪	Fúzhí—xiàngwèiyí	Amplitude-phase meter	
辅助存储单元	Fǔzhù cúnchǔ dānyuán	Auxiliary storage unit	ASU
辅助存储器	Fǔzhù cúnchǔqì	Auxiliary memory	
辅助存储器子程序	Fǔzhù cúnchǔqì zǐchéngxù	Bulk sub-routine	
辅助电路	Fǔzhù diànlù	Secondary circuit	
辅助电源	Fǔzhù diànyuán	Auxiliary power source	APS
辅助地址	Fǔzhù dìzhǐ	Helper address	
辅助技术程序	Fǔzhù jìshù chéngxù	Assistive technology program	
辅助机箱控制器	Fǔzhù jīxiāng kòngzhìqì	Auxiliary crate controller	
辅助开关	Fǔzhù kāiguān	Auxiliary switch	ASW
辅助控制单元	Fǔzhù kòngzhì dānyuán	Auxiliary control element	ACE
辅助控制信道	Fǔzhù kòngzhì xìndào	Associated control channel	ACCH
辅助控制器总线	Fǔzhù kòngzhìqì zǒngxiàn	Auxiliary controller bus	
辅助逻辑设备单元	Fǔzhù luójì shèbèi dānyuán	Secondary logical unit	SLU
辅助偏转板	Fǔzhù piānzhuǎn bǎn	Auxiliary deflection plate	
辅助偏转线圈	Fǔzhù piānzhuǎn xiànquān	Auxiliary deflection coil	
辅助请求指令	Fǔzhù qǐngqiú zhǐlìng	Assist request instruction	ARI
辅助请求指示	Fǔzhù qǐngqiú zhǐshì	Assist request instruction	ARI
辅助设备	Fǔzhù shèbèi	Ancillary equipment	AE
辅助时钟板	Fǔzhù shízhōng bǎn	Auxiliary clock board	ACK
辅助输出信号	Fǔzhù shūchū xìnhào	Auxiliary output signal	
辅助数据	Fǔzhù shùjù	Ancillary data	
辅助数据处理设备	Fǔzhù shùjù chǔlǐ shèbèi	Auxiliary data processing equipment	ADPE
辅助数据处理系统	Fǔzhù shùjù chǔlǐ xìtǒng	Auxiliary data processing system	ADPS
辅助数据获取	Fǔzhù shùjù huòqǔ	Secondary data capture	
辅助输入接口	Fǔzhù shūrù jiēkǒu	Auxiliary input	
辅助显示装置（单元）	Fǔzhù xiǎnshì zhuāngzhì (dānyuán)	Auxiliary display unit	ADU
辅助业务控制	Fǔzhù yèwù kòngzhì	Assistance service control	ASC
辅助执行语句	Fǔzhù zhíxíng yǔjù	Auxiliary executable statement	
附着	Fùzhuó	Attach	ATT
附着分离允许	Fùzhuó fēnlí yǔnxǔ	Attach and detach permission	
附着力	Fùzhuólì	Adhesion (in SMT)	
浮子	Fúzi	Floater	
父子类连接	Fùzǐ lèi liánjiē	Parent-child linkage	
负阻放大器	Fùzǔ fàngdàqì	Negative resistance amplifier	
负阻效应	Fùzǔ xiàoying	Negative resistance effect	
负阻振荡	Fùzǔ zhèndàng	Negative resistance oscillation	
副作用	Fùzuòyòng	Side effect	

G

Chinese	Pinyin	English	Abbr.
G/T 比	G/T bǐ	G/T ratio	
盖环	Gài huán	Bezel ring	
改变呼叫特性请求	Gǎibiàn hūjiào tèxìng qǐngqiú	Call modification request (ISUP message)	CMR
改变密码说明协议	Gǎibiàn mìmǎ shuōmíng xiéyì	ChangeCipherSpec protocol (IPsec)	
概观	Gàiguān	General overview	
改号通知	Gǎihào tōngzhī	Changing number acknowledge	CAN
概化	Gàihuà	Generalization	
改汇	Gǎihuì	Redirection of remittance	
改进编码技术的研究计划	Gǎijìn biānmǎ jìshùde yánjiū jìhuà	Project for advancement of coding technique	PACT
改进多频带激励	Gǎijìn duō píndài jīlì	Improved multi-band excitation	IMBE
改进化学汽相沉积法	Gǎijìn huàxué qìxiàng chénjī fǎ	Modified chemical vapor deposition	MCVD
改进谱减法	Gǎijìn pǔ jiǎnfǎ	Improved spectral subtraction	ISS
改进同相正交调制	Gǎijìn tóngxiàng zhèngjiāo tiáozhì	Improved in-phase quadrature modulation	IIQ
改进的多带激励编码	Gǎijìnde duōdài jīlì biānmǎ	Improved multi-band excitation	IMBE
改进的分组交换无线电网络	Gǎijìnde fēnzǔ jiāohuàn wúxiàndiàn wǎngluò	Improved packet radio network	IPR
改进的陆地无线电话系统	Gǎijìnde lùdì wúxiàn diànhuà xìtǒng	Improved Land Radio Phone (Japan)	ILRP
改进的旁瓣抑制	Gǎijìnde pángbàn yìzhì	Improved sidelobe suppression	ISLS
改进的相位修改协议	Gǎijìnde xiàngwèi xiūgǎi xiéyì	Modified phase modification synchronization (in CORBA)	MPM
改良式汽相沉积法	Gǎiliáng-shì qìxiàng chénjī fǎ	Modified vapor phase deposition (FOC mfg)	MVPD
概率	Gàilǜ	Probability	
概率分布	Gàilǜ fēnbù	Probability distribution	
概率分布函数	Gàilǜ fēnbù hánshù	Probability distribution function	
概率进程代数	Gàilǜ jìnchéng dàishù	Probabalistic process algebra	
概率论	Gàilǜ lùn	Probabilistic theory	
概率论方法	Gàilǜ lùn fāngfǎ	Probabilistic method	
概率密度函数	Gàilǜ mìdù hánshù	Probability density function	
概率图	Gàilǜ tú	Probability map	
概率误差	Gàilǜ wùchā	Probable error	
概率相似	Gàilǜ xiāngsì	Probability bisimulation	
概率信息	Gàilǜ xìnxī	Probabilistic information	
概率译码	Gàilǜ yìmǎ	Probabalistic decoding (crypt.)	
概念	Gàiniàn	Construct (noun)	
概念发明	Gàiniàn fāmíng	Concept formation	
概念节点	Gàiniàn jiédiǎn	Concept node	
概念模型	Gàiniàn móxíng	Conceptual model	
概念设计	Gàiniàn shèjì	Conceptual design	
概念数据模式	Gàiniàn shùjù móshì	Conceptual schema	
概念数据模式语言	Gàiniàn shùjù móshì yǔyán	Conceptual schema language	
概念数据模型	Gàiniàn shùjù móxíng	Conceptual data model	
概念形式	Gàiniàn xíngshì	Conceptual formalism	
概念验证	Gàiniàn yànzhèng	Proof-of-concept (for hardware)	POC
概念级设计	Gàiniàn-jí shèjì	Concept-level design	
改善	Gǎishàn	Improvement	

改善修复	Gǎishàn xiūfù	Improving restoration works	
改投	Gǎitóu	Redirection	
改向名字显示	Gǎixiàng míngzì xiǎnshì	Redirecting name display	RND
改正力	Gǎizhènglì	Margin (of a receiver or terminal)	
干密度	Gān mìdù	Dry density	
钢护套	Gāng hùtào	Steel sheath	
钢塑带	Gāng sù dài	Copolymer steel tape	
刚管脉冲调制器	Gāngguǎn màichōng tiáozhìqì	Hard tube pulse modulator	
钢管桩	Gāngguǎn zhuāng	Steel-pipe pile	
刚好准时	Gānghǎo zhǔnshí	Just-in-time	JIT
港口操作业务	Gǎngkǒu cāozuò yèwù	Port operations service (seaport)	
港口电台	Gǎngkǒu diàntái	Port station (seaport)	
港口管理系统	Gǎngkǒu guǎnlǐ xìtǒng	Harbor management system	
港口交通管理系统	Gǎngkǒu jiāotōng guǎnlǐ xìtǒng	Harbor traffic control system	
纲目结构	Gāngmù jiégòu	Schema	
钢丝钳	Gāngsīqián	Linemans pliers	
钢索敷设	Gāngsuǒ fūshè	Supported by messenger wire	M
感光剂	Gǎnguāngjì	Sensitizer (chemical)	
港务网	Gǎngwù wǎng	Portnet	
刚性架构	Gāngxìng jiàgòu	Rigid frame	
干扰	Gānrǎo	Jamming, interference	
干扰允许值	Gānrǎo yǔnxǔ zhí	Limit of interference	
干扰包	Gānrǎo bāo	Chaff package	
干扰保护比	Gānrǎo bǎohù bǐ	Interference protection ratio	
干扰参数	Gānrǎo cānshù	Jamming parameter	
干扰场强	Gānrǎo chǎngqiáng	Interference field strength	
干扰词	Gānrǎo cí	Noise word	
干扰电流	Gānrǎo diànliú	Interference current	
干扰电压	Gānrǎo diànyā	Interference voltage	
干扰功率	Gānrǎo gōnglǜ	Interference power	
干扰功率密度	Gānrǎo gōnglǜ mìdù	Jamming power density	
干扰偶极子	Gānrǎo ǒujízi	Chaff dipole	
干扰强度	Gānrǎo qiángdù	Jamming strength	
干扰顺从度测试	Gānrǎo shùncóngdù cèshì	Interference compliance test	ICT
干扰调制样式	Gānrǎo tiáozhì yàngshì	Jamming modulation type	
干扰物	Gānrǎo wù	Chaff	
干扰物模拟器	Gānrǎo wù mónǐqì	Chaff simulator	
干扰限值（允许值）	Gānrǎo xiànzhí (yǔnxǔ zhí)	Limit of interference (permissible value)	
干扰消除系统	Gānrǎo xiāochú xìtǒng	Interference cancellation system	ICS
干扰信号	Gānrǎo xìnhào	Interfering signal	
干扰信号带宽	Gānrǎo xìnhào dàikuān	Jamming signal bandwidth	
干扰信号码功率	Gānrǎo xìnhào mǎ gōnglǜ	Interference signal code power	ISCP
干扰压制区	Gānrǎo yāzhì qū	Jamming blanketed zone	
干扰压制系数	Gānrǎo yāzhì xìshù	Jamming blanket factor	
干扰抑制	Gānrǎo yìzhì	Interference suppression	
干扰抑制点火电缆	Gānrǎo yìzhì diǎnhuǒ diànlǎn	Interference suppression ignition cable	

干扰抑制器	Gānrǎo yìzhìqì	Interference suppressor	
干扰源	Gānrǎo yuán	Interference source	
干扰云	Gānrǎo yún	Chaff cloud	
干扰机	Gānrǎojī	Jammer	
干涉合成孔径雷达	Gānshè héchéng kǒngjìng léidá	Interferometric synthetic aperture radar	
干涉滤光镜	Gānshè lǜguāngjìng	Interference filter (optical)	
干涉增益	Gānshè zēngyì	Coherent gain	
感生电压	Gǎnshēng diànyā	Induced voltage	
干涉性复盖层	Gānshè-xìng fùgài céng	Interference overlay (coverage)	
干涉仪	Gānshèyí	Interferometer (noun) , interferometric (adj)	IF
甘特图	Gān-tè tú	Gantt chart/graph	
感温探测器	Gǎnwēn tàncèqì	Heat detector	HD
干线	Gànxiàn	Trunk line	
干线电缆	Gànxiàn diànlǎn	Trunk cable	
干线放大器	Gànxiàn fàngdàqì	Trunk amplifier	TA
干线卡	Gànxiàn kǎ	Trunk card	
干线媒体网关	Gànxiàn méitǐ wǎngguān	Trunk media gateway	TMG
干线耦合单元	Gànxiàn ǒuhé dānyuán	Trunk coupling unit	TCU
干线升降	Gànxiàn shēngjiàng	Trunk up-down	TUD
干线子复用器板	Gànxiàn zifùyòngqì bǎn	Sub-multiplexer highway board	SMHW
感烟探测器	Gǎnyān tàncèqì	Smoke detector	SD
感应场	Gǎnyìng cháng	Induction field	
感应场区	Gǎnyìng cháng qū	Induction field (region)	
感应近场区	Gǎnyìng jìncháng qū	Reactive near-field region	
感应手套	Gǎnyìng shǒutào	Sensor glove	
感应移相器	Gǎnyìng yíxiàngqì	Induction phase shifter	
干燥充气机	Gānzào chōngqìjī	Dry-air filling machine	
感知	Gǎnzhī	Perception	
感知电流阈值	Gǎnzhī diànliú yùzhí	Threshold of perception current	
感知游标	Gǎnzhī yóubiāo	Sensitive cursor	
感知语音	Gǎnzhī yǔyīn	Perceived speech	
高掺锗光纤	Gāo chānzhě guāngxiān	High Ge-doped optical fiber	
高电子迁移率晶体管	Gāo diànzǐ qiānyílǜ jīngtǐguǎn	High electron mobility transistor	HEMT
高地球轨道	Gāo dìqiú guǐdào	High earth orbit	HEO
高阈值逻辑电路	Gāo yù zhí luójidiànlù	High threshold logic	HTL
高保真语音	Gāobǎozhēn yǔyīn	High quality voice	HV
高保真度	Gāobǎozhēndù	High fidelity	HIFI
高保真度调幅	Gāobǎozhēndù tiáofú	High fidelity amplitude modulation	HIFAM
高比特数字用户链路	Gāobǐtè shùzì yònghù liànlù	High-bit-rate digital subscriber link	HDSL
高比特率数字订阅线路	Gāobǐtèlǜ shùzì dìngyuè xiànlù	High bit rate DSL	HDSL
高比特率数字用户线	Gāobǐtèlǜ shùzì yònghù xiàn	High bit-rate digital subscriber line	HDSL
高波	Gāobō	High-angle ray	
高层测试	Gāocéng cèshì	Upper tester	UT
高层功能	Gāocéng gōngnéng	High layer function	HLF
高层兼容性	Gāocéng jiānróngxìng	High layer compatibility	HLC
高层链路控制	Gāocéng liànlù kòngzhì	High-level link control	HDLC

高层数据链路控制	Gāocéng shùjù liànlù kòngzhì	High-level data link control	HDLC
高层协议	Gāocéng xiéyì	Upper level protocol	ULP
高层一致性	Gāocéng yīzhìxìng	High layer uniformity	
高次模	Gāocì mó	Higher-order mode	
高次型	Gāocì xíng	Higher mode	
高档用户	Gāodàng yònghù	Power user	
高等级业务控制点	Gāoděngjí yèwù kòngzhìdiǎn	High-level service control point	HSCP
高电平输出电流	Gāodiànpíng shūchū diànliú	High-level output current	
高电平输出电压	Gāodiànpíng shūchū diànyā	High-level output voltage	
高电平调制	Gāodiànpíng tiáozhì	High-level modulation	
高电压技术	Gāodiànyā jìshù	High voltage technique	
高度激励线性生产编码	Gāodù jīlì xiànxìng shēngchǎn biānmǎ	Pitch excited linear productive coding	PELPC
高端	Gāoduān	High end	
高分瓣率电视	Gāofēnbànlǜ diànshì	High definition TV	HDTV
高分辨率可见光影像系统	Gāofēnbiànlǜ kějiàn guāng yǐngxiàng xìtǒng	High resolution visible image system	HRVIS
高峰内存使用	Gāofēng nèicún shǐyòng	Peak memory usage	
高功率放大单元	Gāogōnglǜ fàngdà dānyuán	High power amplifier unit	HPAU
高功率放大器	Gāogōnglǜ fàngdàqì	High power amplifier block	HPAB
高功率耦合器	Gāogōnglǜ ǒuhéqì	High power duplexer unit	HPDU
高功率调制	Gāogōnglǜ tiáozhì	High-power modulation	
高级编程接口	Gāojí biānchéng jiēkǒu	Advanced programming interface	API
高级程序中断控制器	Gāojí chéngxù zhōngduàn kòngzhìqì	Advanced programmable interrupt controller	APIC
高级程序间通信	Gāojí chéngxù-jiān tōngxìn	Advanced program-to-program communication (IBM protocol)	APPC
高级对等网络	Gāojí duìděng wǎngluò	Advanced peer to peer networking	APPN
高级二-十进制交换代码	Gāojí èr-shíjìnzhì jiāohuàn dàimǎ	Advanced binary-coded decimal interchange code	ABCDIC
高级个人通信系统	Gāojí gèrén tōngxìn xìtǒng	Advanced personal communication system	APCS
高级加密标准	Gāojí jiāmì biāozhǔn	Advanced encryption standard	AES
高级接口请求	Gāojí jiēkǒu qǐngqiú	High level interface request	HLIR
高级局域网	Gāojí júyùwǎng	Advanced local area network	ALAN
高级连续仿真语言	Gāojí liánxù fǎngzhēn yǔyán	Advanced continuous simulation language	ACSL
高级灵活接入复用系统	Gāojí línghuó jiērù fùyòng xìtǒng	Advanced flexible access multiplex system	AFMS
高级免费电话业务	Gāojí miǎnfèi diànhuà yèwù	Advanced freephone service	AFS
高级能源管理	Gāojí néngyuán guǎnlǐ	Advanced power management	APM
高级配置和电源接口	Gāojí pèizhì hé diànyuán jiēkǒu	Advanced configuration and power interface	ACPI
高级软件技术与算法	Gāojí ruǎnjiàn jìshù yǔ suànfǎ	Advanced software technology and algorithms	ASTA
高级 SCSI 编程接口	Gāojí SCSI biānchéng jiēkǒu	Advanced SCSI program interface	ASPI
高级时差检测技术	Gāojí shíchā jiǎncè jìshù	Enhanced observed time difference	EOTD
高级实时处理系统	Gāojí shíshí chǔlǐ xìtǒng	Advanced real-time processing system	
高级实体管理系统	Gāojí shítǐ guǎnlǐ xìtǒng	High-level entity management system	HEMS
高级双重内嵌式内存模块	Gāojí shuāngchóng nèiqiàn-shì nèicún mókuài	Advanced dual in-line memory modules	ADIMM
高级数据处理	Gāojí shùjù chǔlǐ	Advanced data processing	ADP
高级数据光控制系统	Gāojí shùjù guāng kòngzhì xìtǒng	Advanced digital opticai control system	ADOCS
高级数据控制	Gāojí shùjù kòngzhì	High level data control	HLDC
高级数据链跏控制规程	Gāojí shùjù liànchí kòngzhì guīchéng	High-level data link control	HDLC
高级数据链路控制	Gāojí shùjù liànlù kòngzhì	High-level data link control	HDLC

高级数据链路控制规程	Gāojí shùjù liànlù kòngzhì guīchéng	High-level data link control	HDLC
高级数据链路控制规程	Gāojí shùjù liànlù kòngzhì guīchéng	High level data link control (HDLC) procedure	
高级数据链路控制协议	Gāojí shùjù liànlù kòngzhì xiéyì	High-level data link control protocol	HDLC
高级数据链路通道	Gāojí shùjù liànlù tōngdào	High level data link channel	HDLC
高级数据通信控制协议	Gāojí shùjù tōngxìn kòngzhì xiéyì	Advanced data communication control protocol	ADCCP
高级数据系统	Gāojí shùjù xìtǒng	Advanced data system	ADS
高级体系结构	Gāojí tǐxì jiégòu	High-level architecture	HLA
高级通信功能	Gāojí tōngxìn gōngnéng	Advanced communications function	ACF
高级通信业务	Gāojí tōngxìn yèwù	Advanced communication service	
高级图形端口	Gāojí túxíng duānkǒu	Advanced graphics port	AGP
高级图形系统	Gāojí túxíng xìtǒng	Advanced graphics system	AGS
高级网络和服务	Gāojí wǎngluò hé fúwù	Advanced networks and services	ANS
高级网络集成	Gāojí wǎngluò jíchéng	Advanced network integration	ANI
高级网络系统结构	Gāojí wǎngluò xìtǒng jiégòu	Advanced network system architecture	ANSA
高级网络综合	Gāojí wǎngluò zōnghé	Advanced network integration	ANI
高级文本管理系统	Gāojí wénběn guǎnlǐ xìtǒng	Advanced text management system	ATMS
高级信号处理	Gāojí xìnhào chǔlǐ	Advanced signal processing	ASP
高级信令转换点	Gāojí xìnlìng zhuǎnhuàn diǎn	High-level signal transfer point	HSTP
高级信令转接点	Gāojí xìnlìng zhuǎnjiēdiǎn	High-level signaling transfer point	HSTP
高级研究规划局网络	Gāojí yánjiū guīhuàjú wǎngluò	Advanced Research Projects Agency network (US)	ARPANET
高级研究计划局	Gāojí yánjiū jìhuàjú	Advanced Research Projects Agency (US)	ARPA
高级研究计划局网络	Gāojí yánjiū jìhuàjú wǎngluò	Advanced Research Projects Agency Network	ARPAnet
高级研究计划署	Gāojí yánjiū jìhuàshǔ	Advanced Research Projects Agency (US)	ARPA
高级研究计划署网络	Gāojí yánjiū jìhuàshǔ wǎngluò	Advanced Research Projects Agency network (US)	ARPANET
高级移动电话服务	Gāojí yídòng diànhuà fúwù	Advanced mobile phone service	AMPS
高极移动电话系统	Gāojí yídòng diànhuà xìtǒng	Advanced mobile phone system	AMPS
高级移动电话系统	Gāojí yídòng diànhuà xìtǒng	Advanced mobile telephone system	AMTS
高级移动电话业务	Gāojí yídòng diànhuà yèwù	Advanced mobile phone service	AMPS
高级远程信息处理系统	Gāojí yuǎnchéng xìnxī chǔlǐ xìtǒng	Advanced teleprocessing system	ATS
高级语言	Gāojí yǔyán	High-level language	
高级制导系统	Gāojí zhìdǎo xìtǒng	Advanced guidance system	AGS
高级智能网	Gāojí zhìnéng wǎng	Advanced intelligent network	AIN
高集成总线	Gāojíchéng zǒngxiàn	High integrated bus	HIB
高机动多用途轮试车	Gāojīdòng duōyòngtú lúnshìchē	High Mobility Multi-purpose Wheeled Vehicle (US military vehicle popularly called Humvee)	HMMWV
高阶	Gāojiē	High order, higher order	HO
高阶接口	Gāojiē jiēkǒu	Higher order interface	HOI
高阶连接监控	Gāojiē liánjiē jiānkòng	Higher order connection supervision	HCS
高阶连接监视	Gāojiē liánjiē jiānshì	Higher order connection supervision	HCS
高阶数据链路（连接）控制	Gāojiē shùjù liànlù (liánjiē) kòngzhì	High level data link control	HDLC
高阶通道	Gāojiē tōngdào	Higher order path	HP
高阶通道保护	Gāojiē tōngdào bǎohù	Higher order path protection	HPP
高阶通道层	Gāojiē tōngdào céng	Higher order path layer	HOPL
高阶通道串联连接监控	Gāojiē tōngdào chuànlián liánjiē jiānkòng	Higher order tandem connection monitor	HO-TCM
高阶通道串联连接监视	Gāojiē tōngdào chuànlián liánjiē jiānshì	Higher order path tandem connection monitor	HTCM
高阶通道串联连接适配	Gāojiē tōngdào chuànlián liánjiē shìpèi	Higher order path tandem connection adaptation	HTCA

高阶通道串联连接终端	Gāojiē tōngdào chuànlián liánjiē zhōngduān	Higher order path tandem connection termination	HTCT
高阶通道监控未装装载终	Gāojiē tōngdào jiānkòng wèizhuāng zhuāngzài zhōng	Higher order path supervision unequipped termination	HSUT
高阶通道监控未装载终端	Gāojiē tōngdào jiānkòng wèizhuāngzài zhōngduān	Higher order path supervisory unequipped termination	HSUT
高阶通道接入点标识符	Gāojiē tōngdào jiērùdiǎn biāozhì fú	Higher order path access point identifier	HOAPID
高阶通道接收缺陷指示	Gāojiē tōngdào jiēshōu quēxiàn zhǐshì	High-level path receive defect indicator	HP-RDI
高阶通道净荷标记失配	Gāojiē tōngdào jìnghé biāojì shīpèi	Higher order path payload label mismatch	HP-PLM
高阶通道开销	Gāojiē tōngdào kāixiao	Higher order path overhead	HPOH
高阶通道开销监视	Gāojiē tōngdào kāixiao jiānshi	Higher order path overhead monitor	HPOM
高阶通道连接	Gāojiē tōngdào liánjiē	Higher order path connection	HPC
高阶通道路踪识别失配	Gāojiē tōngdào lùzōng shíbié shīpèi	Higher order path trace identification mismatch	HP-TIM
高阶通道适配	Gāojiē tōngdào shìpèi	Higher order path adaptation	HPA
高阶通道网络连接	Gāojiē tōngdào wǎngluò liánjiē	Higher order path network connection	HOP NC
高阶通道未装载	Gāojiē tōngdào wèizhuāngzài	Higher order path unequipped	HP-UNEQ
高阶通道远端错误指示	Gāojiē tōngdào yuǎnduān cuòwù zhǐshì	Higher order path-remote error indication	HP-REI
高阶通道远端缺陷指示	Gāojiē tōngdào yuǎnduān quēxiàn zhǐshì	Higher order path remote defect indication	HP-RDI
高阶通道远端误码指示	Gāojiē tōngdào yuǎnduān wùmǎ zhǐshì	Higher order path remote error indication	HP-REI
高阶通道终端	Gāojiē tōngdào zhōngduān	Higher order path termination	HPT
高解像	Gāojiě xiàng	High resolution graphics	
高阶虚容器	Gāojiē xūróngqì	Higher order virtual container	HOVC
高阶组装器	Gāojiē zǔzhuāngqì	Higher order assembler	HOA
高解析图像	Gāojiěxī túxiàng	High resolution graphics	
高解析 X 射线检测系统	Gāojiěxī X shèxiàn jiǎncè xìtǒng	High resolution X-ray inspection system (semiconductor mfg)	
告警	Gàojǐng	Alarm	ALM
告警	Gàojǐng	Bell	BEL
告警等级	Gàojǐng děngjí	Alarm severity	
告警过滤	Gàojǐng guòlǜ	Alarm filtering	
告警核对	Gàojǐng héduì	Alarm alignment	
告警监视	Gàojǐng jiānshì	Alarm surveillance	AS
告警接入控制集成板	Gàojǐng jiērù kòngzhì jíchéngbǎn	Alarm access control board assembly	AACA
告警接收机	Gàojǐng jiēshōujī	Warning receiver	
告警控制处理	Gàojǐng kòngzhì chǔlǐ	Alarm control process	ACP
告警控制集成板	Gàojǐng kòngzhì jíchéngbǎn	Alarm control board assembly	
告警面板控制集成单元	Gàojǐng miànbǎn kòngzhì jíchéng dānyuán	Alarm panel control unit assembly	APCU
告警面板控制模块	Gàojǐng miànbǎn kòngzhì mókuài	Alarm panel control block	APC
告警秒	Gàojǐng miǎo	Alarm seconds	ALS
告警屏蔽	Gàojǐng píngbì	Alarm inhibition	
告警确认	Gàojǐng quèrèn	Alarm acknowledgement	
告警日志	Gàojǐng rìzhì	Alarm log	
告警锁定	Gàojǐng suǒdìng	Alarm lock	
告警统计	Gàojǐng tǒngjì	Alarm statistics	
告警显示	Gàojǐng xiǎnshì	Alarm display	ALD
告警预投入	Gàojǐng yù tóurù	Alarm standby	
告警语句	Gàojǐng yǔjù	Alarm statement	AS
告警指示信号	Gàojǐng zhǐshì xìnhào	Alarm indication signal	AIS

告警状况	Gàojǐng zhuàngkuàng	Alarm status	
高精度计算	Gāojīngdù jìsuàn	Arbitrary precision arithmetic	
高可用集群多处理机	Gāokěyòng jíqún duō chǔlǐjī	High availability cluster multi-processor	HACMP
高利用率长途台间中继线	Gāolìyòng lǜ chángtútái-jiān zhōngjìxiàn	High usage inter-toll trunk	HUT
高洛德描影	Gāo-luò-dé miáo yǐng	Gouraud shading (video)	
高密	Gāomì	High density	HD
高密电视	Gāomì diànshì	High definition television	HDTV
高密兼容数码	Gāomì jiānróng shùmǎ	High definition compatible digital	HDCD
高密聚乙烯	Gāomì jùyǐxī	High density polyethylene	HDPE
高密度	Gāomìdù	High density	HD
高密度二进制 3 型码	Gāomìdù èrjìnzhì san xíng mǎ	High density binary-3	HDB3
高密度固定业务	Gāomìdù gùdìng yèwù	High density fixed service	HDFS
高密度互补金属氧化物半导体	Gāomìdù hùbǔ jīnshǔ yǎnghuàwù bàndǎotǐ	High density complementary metal oxide semiconductor (CMOS)	HCMOS
高密度双极性码	Gāomìdù shuāngjíxìng mǎ	High density bipolar coding	HDB
高密度数据	Gāomìdù shùjù	High density data	HDD
高密度数据系统	Gāomìdù shùjù xìtǒng	High density data system	HDDS
高模数玻璃纤维	Gāomóshù bōli xiānwéi	High modulus glass fiber	HMGF
高耐热、轻薄型塑胶球状矩阵封装	Gāonàirè、qīngbó-xíng sùjiāo qiúzhuàng jǔzhèn fēngzhuāng	High thermal, low profile, plastic ball grid array	HL-PBGA
高能吸水剂	Gāonéng xīshuǐjì	Super absorbent	
高频	Gāopín	High frequency	HF
高频放大器	Gāopín fàngdàqì	High frequency amplifier	HFA
高频数据链	Gāopín shùjù liàn	High frequency data link	HFDL
高频提升	Gāopín tíshēng	High frequency boost	
高频增益控制	Gāopín zēngyì kòngzhì	High frequency gain control	
高频中继配线架	Gāopín zhōngjì pèixiànjià	High frequency repeater distribution frame	HFRDF
高频制频率时的发射频偏	Gāopínzhì pínlǜshíde fāshè pínpiān	High frequency transmitting frequency deviation	
高清晰度电视	Gāoqīngxīdù diànshì	High definition television	HDTV
高容量干线无线电	Gāoróngliàng gànxiàn wúxiàndiàn	High capacity trunk radio	HCTR
高容量 IPC 处理器	Gāoróngliàng IPC chǔlǐqì	High capacity IPC processor	BHIP
高容量 IPC 后面板	Gāoróngliàng IPC hòumian bǎn	High capacity IPC back panel	HIBP
高容量软盘	Gāoróngliàng ruǎnpán	High-capacity floppy disk	HiFD
高容量中继无线电	Gāoróngliàng zhōngjì wúxiàndiàn	High capacity trunk radio	HCTR
高数据速率数字用户线	Gāoshùjùsùlǜ shùzì yònghù xiàn	High-data-rate digital subscriber line	HDSL
高斯白噪声	Gāo-sī bái zàoshēng	Gaussian white noise	
高斯地图投影	Gāo-sī dìtú tóuyǐng	Gauss map projection	
高斯分布	Gāo-sī fēnbù	Gaussian distribution	
高斯函数	Gāo-sī hánshù	Gaussian function	
高斯混合模型	Gāo-sī hùnhé móxíng	Gaussian mixture model	GMM
高斯近似法	Gāo-sī jìnsìfǎ	Gaussian approximation method	
高斯滤波频移键控	Gāo-sī lǜbō pínyí jiànkòng	Gaussian frequency shift keying	GAP
高斯滤波最小移频键控	Gāo-sī lǜbō zuìxiǎo yípín jiànkòng	Gaussian filtered minimum-shift keying	GMSK
高斯平面坐标系	Gāo-sī píngmiàn zuòbiāo xì	Gauss plane coordinate system	
高斯频移键控	Gāo-sī pínyí jiànkòng	Gaussian frequency shift keying	GFSK
高斯误差	Gāo-sī wùchā	Gaussian error	

高斯信道	Gāo-sī xìndào	Gaussian channel	
高斯噪声	Gāo-sī zàoshēng	Gaussian noise	
高斯最小键移	Gāo-sī zuìxiǎo jiànyí	Gaussian minimum-shift keying	GMSK
高斯最小频移键控	Gāo-sī zuìxiǎo pínyí jiànkòng	Gaussian minimum shift keying	GMSK
高斯最小移频键控	Gāo-sī zuìxiǎo yípín jiànkòng	Gaussian minimum-shift keying	GMSK
高斯坐标	Gāo-sī zuòbiāo	Gaussian coordinate	
高斯-傅里叶变换	Gāo-sī—Fù-lǐ-yè biànhuàn	Gauss-Fourier transform	GFT
高斯型通带波导阵列光栅复用/解复用器	Gāo-sī-xíng tōngdài bōdǎo zhènliè guāngshān fùyòng/jiě fùyòngqì	Gaussian passband arrayed waveguide grating multiplexer/demultiplexer	
高速包交换	Gāosù bāo jiāohuàn	On-the-fly packet switching	
高速背板	Gāosù bèibǎn	High-speed serial backplane	
高速 C 总线服务单元	Gāosù C zǒngxiàn fúwù dānyuán	High-speed C bus service unit	HCBS
高速串行接口	Gāosù chuànháng jiēkǒu	High-speed serial interface	HSSI
高速串行数据连接	Gāosù chuànháng shùjù liánjiē	High-speed serial data connection	HSSDC
高速电路交换数据	Gāosù diànlù jiāohuàn shùjù	High-speed circuit switched data	HSCSD
高速多层协议	Gāosù duō céng xiéyì	High-speed multi-layer protocol	H-MLP
高速公路	Gāosù gōnglù	Highway	HW
高速缓冲存储控制器	Gāosù huǎnchōng cúnchǔ kòngzhìqì	High-speed cache controller	
高速缓冲存储器	Gāosù huǎnchōng cúnchǔqì	High-speed cache memory	
高速缓存控制器	Gāosù huǎncún kòngzhìqì	High-speed cache controller	
高速缓存老化数据清除	Gāosù huǎncún lǎohuà shùjù qīngchú	High-speed cache aging	
高速缓存器	Gāosù huǎncúnqì	High-speed cache	
高速 IPC 处理器集成板	Gāosù IPC chǔlǐqì jíchéngbǎn	High-speed IPC processor assembly	HIPA
高速 IPC 节点集成板	Gāosù IPC jiédiǎn jíchéngbǎn	High-speed IPC node board assembly	HINA
高速局域网	Gāosù júyùwǎng	High-speed local area network	HSLAN
高速数据	Gāosù shùjù	High-speed data	HSD
高速数据链路规程	Gāosù shùjù liànlù guīchéng	High-speed data link control	HDLC
高速数据链路控制	Gāosù shùjù liànlù kòngzhì	High-speed data link control	HDLC
高速数字交换机	Gāosù shùzì jiāohuànjī	High-speed digital switch	HDS
高速数字用户回路	Gāosù shùzì yònghù huílù	High bit-rate digital subscriber line	HDSL
高速数字用户线	Gāosù shùzì yònghù xiàn	High data-rate digital subscriber line	HDSL
高速网页广播	Gāosù wǎngyè guǎngbō	Turbo webcast	
高速下行包数据接入	Gāosù xiàxíng bāo shùjù jiērù	High-speed downlink packet access	HSPDA
高速下行分组接入	Gāosù xiàxíng fēnzǔ jiērù	High-speed downlink packet access	HSDPA
高速下行链路分组接入	Gāosù xiàxíng liànlù fēnzǔ jiērù	High speed downlink packet access	HSDPA
高速新闻广播	Gāosù xīnwén guǎngbō	Turbo newscast	
高速寻呼编码体制	Gāosù xúnhū biānmǎ tǐzhì	High-speed pager coding standard (in the PRC)	FLEX
高速寻呼联网协议	Gāosù xúnhū liánwǎng xiéyì	Inter-paging networking protocol	IPNP
高速因特网业务	Gāosù Yīntèwǎng yèwù	Turbo Internet	
高速用户电报业务	Gāosù yònghù diànbào yèwù	Supertelex service, high speed telex	
高速率电路交换数据	Gāosùlǜ diànlù jiāohuàn shùjù	High-speed circuit switched data	HCSD
高调制频率时的发射频偏	Gāotiáozhì pínlǜ-shíde fāshè pínpiān	Transmission frequency derivation of a highly modulated frequency	
高通	Gāo-tōng	Qualcomm (US company)	
高通滤波器	Gāotōng lǜbōqì	High pass filter	HPF
高椭圆轨道（高轨）	Gāotuǒyuán guǐdào (gāo guǐ)	Highly elliptical orbit	HEO
高外差式接收机	Gāowàichāi-shì jiēshōujī	Supradyne receiver	

高位地址部分	Gāowèi dìzhǐ bùfen	Upper address part	UAP
高温超导过滤波器	Gāowēn chāodǎoguò lǜbōqì	High temperature superconductor filter	
高温氮焊	Gāowēn dàn hàn	High temperature nitrogen soldering (semiconductor mfg)	
高温高湿偏置试验	Gāowēn gāoshī piānzhì shìyàn	High temperature high humidity biased testing	HHBT
高温功率老化	Gāowēn gōnglǜ lǎohuà	High temperature power burn-in	
高温焊	Gāowēn hàn	High temperature soldering (semiconductor mfg)	
高温试验	Gāowēn shìyàn	High temperature test	
高效	Gāoxiào	Efficient	
高性能并行接口	Gāoxìngnéng bìngxíng jiēkǒu	High performance parallel interface	HIPPI
高性能服务器	Gāoxìngnéng fúwùqì	High performance server	HPS
高性能公共信道模块	Gāoxìngnéng gōnggòng xìndào mókuài	High-performance common channel signaling module	
高性能工作站	Gāoxìngnéng gōngzuòzhàn	High-performance workstation	HPW
高性能光缆连接器	Gāoxìngnéng guānglǎn liánjiēqì	High performance optical cable connector	
高性能光线单元	Gāoxìngnéng guāngxiàn dānyuán	Enhanced performance fiber unit	EPFU
高性能光纤连接器	Gāoxìngnéng guāngxiān liánjiēqì	High performance optical fiber connector	
高性能计算和通信	Gāoxìngnéng jìsuàn hé tōngxìn	High performance computing and communication	HPCC
高性能路由器操作系统	Gāoxìngnéng lùyóuqì cāozuò xìtǒng	Highly efficient router operating system	HEROS
高性能数据 GSM 环境	Gāoxìngnéng shùjù GSM huánjìng	Enhanced data GSM environment	
高性能通信适配器	Gāoxìngnéng tōngxìn shìpèiqì	High performance communications adapter	HPCA
高压电力设备	Gāoyā diànlì shèbèi	High voltage electric power equipment	
高压延时保护电路	Gāoyā yánshí bǎohù diànlù	High voltage delay-time protection circuit	
高增益放大器	Gāozēngyì fàngdàqì	High gain amplifier	HGA
高增益功放板	Gāozēngyì gōngfàng bǎn	High gain power amplifier board	HPA
高准确性	Gāozhǔnquèxìng	High resolution (semiconductor mfg)	
GARP VLAN 注册协议	GARP VLAN zhùcè xiéyì	GARP VLAN registration protocol	GVRP
GARP 协议数据单元	GARP xiéyì shùjù dānyuán	GARP protocol data unit	GARP PDU
GARP 信息发布	GARP xìnxī fābù	GARP information declaration	GID
GARP 信息广播	GARP xìnxī guǎngbō	GARP information propagation	GIP
GARP 组播注册协议	GARP zǔbō zhùcè xiéyì	GARP multicast registration protocol (IEEE 802.1P)	GMRP
Gb 以太网	Gb Yǐtàiwǎng	Gigabit ethernet	GE, GbE
Gb/s 系列发射机与接收机	Gb/s xìliè fāshèjī yǔ jiēshōujī	Gigabit/sec serial transmitter and receiver	GigSTAR
G 多边形	G-duōbiānxíng	G-polygon	
格基归约算法	Gé jī guīyuē suànfǎ	Lattice basis reduction algorithm	
隔板	Gébǎn	Baffle wall	
割边/割点连通性	Gēbiān/ gēdiǎn liántōng xìng	Edge and vertex connectivity	
个别编写的软件	Gèbié biānxiěde ruǎnjiàn	Customized software	
格斗类游戏	Gédòu-lèi yóuxì	Fighting game (computer game)	FTG
隔行	Géháng	Interlace (video term)	
给据函件	Gěijù hánjiàn	Recorded correspondence	
给据函件收据	Gěijù hánjiàn shōujù	Receipt for recorded correspondence	
割接	Gējiē	Cutover	
割接开通	Gējiē kāitōng	Cutover into operation	
戈莱码	Gē-lái mǎ	Golay code	
格雷码	Gé-léi mǎ	Golay sequential coding	
格雷戈伦反射器天线	Gé-léi-gē-lún fǎnshèqì tiānxiàn	Gregorian reflector antenna	
隔离	Gélí	Isolate	

隔离比	Gélí bǐ	Isolation	
隔离比	Gélí bǐ	Isolation ratio (of a multi-port antenna)	
隔离度	Gélí dù	Isolation	
隔离端口	Gélí duānkǒu	Isolated port	
隔离放大器	Gélí fàngdàqì	Isolation amplifier	
隔离级别	Gélí jíbié	Isolation level (for database)	
隔离区	Gélí qū	Demilitarized zone	DMZ
隔离域名服务器	Gélí yùmíng fúwùqì	Split domain name server	
格林尼治电子时间	Gé-lín-ní-zhì diànzǐ shíjiān	Greenwich electronic time	GeT
格林尼治时间	Gé-lín-ní-zhì shíjiān	Greenwich mean time	GMT
隔离器	Gélíqì	Isolator	
隔离器/分路器/滤波型波分复用器	Gélíqì/fēnlùqì/lǜbō-xíng bōfēn fùyòngqì	Isolator/tap coupler/wavelength division multiplexer	ITMX
哥伦比亚广播公司	Gē-lún-bǐ-yà guǎngbō gōngsī	Columbia Broadcasting Corp. (US)	CBS
格码调制	Gémǎ tiáozhì	Trellis coded modulation	TCM
隔膜波导	Gémó bōdǎo	Septate waveguide	
根目录	Gēn mùlù	Root directory	
根网桥	Gēn wǎngqiáo	Root bridge	
根证书	Gēn zhèngshū	Root certificate	
更改地址窃取	Gēnggǎi dìzhǐ qièqǔ	Changed address interception	
更改脚本	Gēnggǎi jiǎoběn	Change script	
更高速率的 FDDI 网络	Gènggāo sùlǜde FDDI wǎngluò	FDDI follow-on LAN	FFOL
更新	Gēngxīn	Update	
更新查询	Gēngxīn cháxún	Update query	
更新锁	Gēngxīn suǒ	Update lock	
更新统计	Gēngxīn tǒngjì	Update statistics	
更新位置	Gēngxīn wèizhì	Update location	
根基段	Gēnjī duàn	Root segment	
跟踪	Gēnzōng	Tracing	
跟踪	Gēnzōng	Trace (verb)	
跟踪保持电路	Gēnzōng bǎochí diànlù	Track and hold circuit	
跟踪程序	Gēnzōng chéngxù	Tracer	
跟踪带宽	Gēnzōng dàikuān	Tracking bandwidth	
跟踪方式	Gēnzōng fāngshì	Tracing mode	
跟踪缓冲器溢出	Gēnzōng huǎnchōngqì yìchū	Tracing buffer full	
跟踪文件	Gēnzōng wénjiàn	Trace file	
跟踪误差	Gēnzōng wùchā	Tracking error	
跟踪用户活动	Gēnzōng yònghù huódòng	Trace subscriber activity	
跟踪与数据中继卫星系统	Gēnzōng yǔ shùjù zhōngjì wèixīng xìtǒng	Tracking and data relay satellite system	TDRSS
戈帕码	Gē-pà mǎ	Goppa codes	
个人便携电话系统	Gèrén biànxié diànhuà xìtǒng	Personal handyphone system	
个人电话号码	Gèrén diànhuà hàomǎ	Personal telephone number	PTN
个人电脑	Gèrén diànnǎo	Personal computer	PC
个人电台	Gèrén diàntái	Personal (radio) station	PS
个人服务环境	Gèrén fúwù huánjìng	Personal service environment	PSE
个人股东投资计划	Gèrén gǔdōng tóuzī jìhuà	Personal equity plan	PEP

个人接入系统	Gèrén jiērù xìtǒng	Personal access system	PAS
个人计算机	Gèrén jìsuànjī	Personal computer	PC
个人计算机磁盘操作系统	Gèrén jìsuànjī cípán cāozuò xìtǒng	Personal computer-disk operating system	PC-DOS
个人计算机存储卡国际联合会	Gèrén jìsuànjī cúnchǔkǎ Guójì liánhéhuì	Personal Computer Memory Card International Association	PCMCIA
个人计算机扩充技术总线	Gèrén jìsuànjī kuòchōng jìshù zǒngxiàn	Personal computer extended technology bus	PCET
个人计算机内存卡国际标准协会	Gèrén jìsuànjī nèicúnkǎ guójì biāozhǔn xiéhuì	Personal Computer Memory Card International Association	PCMCIA
个人名	Gèrén míng	Personal name	
个人身份鉴权键	Gèrén shēnfen jiànquán jiàn	Individual subscriber authentication key	Ki
个人身份识别号	Gèrén shēnfen shíbié hào	Personal identification number	PIN
个人识别号码	Gèrén shíbié hàomǎ	Personal identification number	PIN
个人识别码	Gèrén shíbié mǎ	Personal identification number	PIN
个人识别码解锁密码	Gèrén shíbié mǎ jiěsuǒ mìmǎ	Personal identification number (PIN) unblocking key	PUK
个人手持电话系统	Gèrén shǒuchí diànhuà xìtǒng	Personal handy-phone system	PHS
个人手机系统因特网接入论坛标准	Gèrén shǒujī xìtǒng Yīntèwǎng jiērù lùntán biāozhǔn	Personal (handset system) Internet access forum standard	PIAFS
个人数字蜂窝通信系统	Gèrén shùzì fēngwō tōngxìn xìtǒng	Personal digital cellular telecommunications system (Japan)	PDC
个人数字蜂窝系统	Gèrén shùzì fēngwō xìtǒng	Personal digital cellular system (Japan)	PDC
个人数字辅助器	Gèrén shùzì fǔzhùqì	Personal digital assistant	PDA
个人数字助理	Gèrén shùzì zhùlǐ	Personal digital assistant	PDA
个人私隐安全平台	Gèrén sīyǐn ānquán píngtái	Privacy preference project	P3P
个人通信	Gèrén tōngxìn	Personal communication services	PCS
个人通信号码	Gèrén tōngxìn hàomǎ	Personal telecommunication number	PTN
个人通信系统	Gèrén tōngxìn xìtǒng	Personal communications systems	PCS
个人通信系统-移动交换中心	Gèrén tōngxìn xìtǒng—yídòng jiāohuàn zhōngxīn	Personal communication system – mobile switching center	PCS-MSC
个人通信业务	Gèrén tōngxìn yèwù	Personal communications service	PCS
个人通信网	Gèrén tōngxìnwǎng	Personal communication network	PCN
个人通讯服务	Gèrén tōngxùn fúwù	Personal communication service	PCS
个人无绳电话系统	Gèrén wúshéng diànhuà xìtǒng	Personal handy-phone system	PHS
个人携带电话	Gèrén xiédài diànhuà	Personal handy phone	PHP
个人信息管理系统	Gèrén xìnxī guǎnlǐ xìtǒng	Personal information management	PIM
个人信息助理	Gèrén xìnxī zhùlǐ	Personal information assistant	PIA
个人系统二型	Gèrén xìtǒng èr xíng	Personal system 2	PS2
个人移动无线电	Gèrén yídòng wúxiàndiàn	Personal mobile radio	PMR
个人移动性	Gèrén yídòngxìng	Personal mobility	
个人域网	Gèrén yù wǎng	Personal area network	PAN
个人化中心	Gèrénhuà zhōngxīn	Personalization center	PCS
个人间通信-消息存储	Gèrén-jiān tōngxìn- xiāoxi cúnchǔ	Interpersonal messaging - message store	IPM-MS
格式	Géshi	Format	
格式标识符	Géshi biāozhì fú	Format identifier	FI
格式控制符	Géshi kòngzhìfú	Format effector	
格式前缀	Géshi qiánzhuì	Format prefix	FP
格式转换	Géshi zhuǎnhuàn	Format conversion	
格式化	Géshihuà	Format (verb)	

格式化可处理形式	Géshihuà kěchǔlǐ xíngshì	Formatted processable form	
格式化形式	Géshihuà xíngshì	Formatted form	
铬酸银测试	Gèsuānyín cèshì	Silver chromate test (in SMT)	
个体防火	Gètǐ fánghuǒ	Autonomous fireproofing	
个体接收	Gètǐ jiēshōu	Individual reception (in satellite broadcasting)	
格网	Géwǎng	Cross hatching, grid	
格网参照	Géwǎng cānzhào	Grid reference	
格网地图	Géwǎng dìtú	Grid map	
格网格式	Géwǎng géshi	Grid format	
格网数据	Géwǎng shùjù	Grid data	
格网坐标系	Géwǎng zuòbiāo xì	Grid coordinate system	
各向同性材料	Gèxiàng tóngxìng cáiliào	Isotropic material	
各向同性辐射器	Gèxiàng tóngxìng fúshèqì	Isotropic radiator	
各向同性辐射体	Gèxiàng tóngxìng fúshètǐ	Isotropic radiator	IR
各向同性接收功率	Gèxiàng tóngxìng jiēshōu gōnglǜ	Received isotropic power	RIP
各向同性识别	Gèxiàng tóngxìng shíbié	Isotropic identification	ISOID
各向同性增益	Gèxiàng tóngxìng zēngyì	Isotropic gain (of an antenna)	
各向异性	Gèxiàng yìxìng	Anisotropic, anisotropy	
各向异性传播媒质	Gèxiàng yìxìng chuánbō méizhì	Anisotropic propagation medium	
各向异性过滤	Gèxiàngyìxìng guòlǜ	Anisotropic filtering (video)	
格形编码调制	Géxíng biānmǎ tiáozhì	Trellis coded modulation	TCM
个性化服务	Gèxìnghuà fúwù	Individuality service	
个性化控制键	Gèxìnghuà kòngzhì jiàn	Personalization control key	PCK
隔音	Géyīn	Sound insulation	SI
各异向性胶	Gèyìxiàngxìng jiāo	Anisotropic adhesive (in SMT)	
格栅编码脉冲幅度调制	Gézhà biānmǎ màichōng fúdù tiáozhì	Trellis coded pulse amplitude modulation	TCPAM
格栅编码调制	Gézhà biānmǎ tiáozhì	Trellis coded modulation	TCM
格状编码调制	Gézhuàng biānmǎ tiáozhì	Trellis coded modulation	TCM
G-环	G-huán	G-ring	
GNU 网络对象模型环境	GNU wǎngluò duìxiàng móxíng huánjìng	GNU's network object model environment	GNOME
供参考	Gōng cānkǎo	For your information	FYI
工科医	Gōng kē yī	Industrial, scientific and medical	ISM
供你参考	Gōng nǐ cānkǎo	For your reference (computer chat)	FYR
供你用的信息	Gōng nǐ yòngde xìnxī	For your information	FYI
共频道	Gòng píndào	Co-channel	C/I
公布式管理任务组	Gōngbùshì guǎnlǐ rènwuzǔ	Distributed management task force	DMTF
公布式通信体系	Gōngbùshì tōngxin tǐxì	Distributed communication architecture	DCA
工厂交货	Gōngchǎng jiāohuò	Ex-works	EXW
工程	Gōngchéng	Project; engineering	
工程安排	Gōngchéng ānpái	Job scheduling	
工程对象组	Gōngchéng duìxiàngzǔ	Engineering object group	EOG
工程仿真	Gōngchéng fǎngzhēn	Engineering simulation	
工程规划图	Gōngchéng guīhuàtú	Engineering map	
工程计算对象	Gōngchéng jìsuàn duìxiàng	Engineering computing object	ECO
工程基准面	Gōngchéng jīzhǔnmiàn	Engineering datum	
工程判定	Gōngchéng pàndìng	Engineering judgment	

工程数据管理	Gōngchéng shùjù guǎnlǐ	Engineering data management	EDM
工程修理车	Gōngchéng xiūlǐ chē	Carriage for repair equipment	
工程验收测试	Gōngchéng yànshōu cèshì	Engineering acceptance test	EAT
共道信令	Gòngdào xìnlìng	Co-channel signalling	
共道抑制	Gòngdào yìzhì	Co-channel rejection	
共道抑制	Gòngdào yìzhì	Co-channel suppression	
共电电话	Gòngdiàn diànhuà	Common battery telephone	CB
供电电源	Gōngdiàn diànyuán	Power supply	
供电连接阻抗	Gōngdiàn liánjiē zǔkàng	Service connection impedance	
供电系统阻抗	Gōngdiàn xìtǒng zǔkàng	Supply system impedance	
共轭结构-代数码激励线性预测	Gòng'è jiégòu—dàishù mǎ jīlì xiànxìng yùcè	Conjugate structure-algebraic code excited linear prediction	CS-ACELP
共轭梯度法	Gòng'è tīdù fǎ	Conjugate graduation method	CGM
公告板服务	Gōnggào bǎn fúwù	Bulletin board service	BBS
公告板业务	Gōnggào bǎn yèwù	Bulletin board service	BBS
公共安全服务	Gōnggòng ānquán fúwù	Common security service	CSS
公共被寻址节点	Gōnggòng bèi xúnzhǐ jiédiǎn	Publicly accessed node	PAN
公共边界	Gōnggòng biānjiè	Shared boundary	
公共部分	Gōnggòng bùfen	Common part	CP
公共部分会聚子层	Gōnggòng bùfen huìjù zi céng	Common part convergence sub-layer	CPCS
公共部分指示	Gōnggòng bùfen zhǐshì	Common part indicator	CPI
公共部分字层	Gōnggòng bùfen zìcéng	Common part sub-layer	CPS
公共操作环境	Gōnggòng cāozuò huánjìng	Common operating environment	COE
公共导引信道	Gōnggòng dǎoyǐn xìndào	Common pilot channel	CPICH
公共电话交换网	Gōnggòng diànhuà jiāohuàn wǎng	Public switched telephone network	PSTN
公共电信公司	Gōnggòng diànxìn gōngsī	Common carrier	
公共电源板	Gōnggòng diànyuán bǎn	Public power source board	PWC
公共顶节点	Gōnggòng dǐng jiédiǎn	Shared vertex	
公共对象服务规范	Gōnggòng duìxiàng fúwù guīfàn	Common object services specification	COSS
公共对象请求代理体系结构	Gōnggòng duìxiàng qǐngqiú dàilǐ tǐxì jiégòu	Common object request broker architecture	CORBA
公共对象请求中介器体系结构	Gōnggòng duìxiàng qǐngqiú zhōngjièqì tǐxì jiégòu	Common object request broker architecture	CORBA
公共发起节点	Gōnggòng fāqǐ jiédiǎn	Public initialization node	PIN
公共分组交换网	Gōnggòng fēnzǔ jiāohuàn wǎng	Public packet switched network	
公共工程细则	Gōnggòng gōngchéng xìzé	Common technical regulation	CTR
公共功率控制信道	Gōnggòng gōnglǜ kòngzhì xìndào	Common power control channel	CPCCH
公共广播音响系统	Gōnggòng guǎngbō yīnxiǎng xìtǒng	Public address system	PAS
公共关键字	Gōnggòng guānjiàn zì	Common key (in SQL Server)	
公共管理	Gōnggòng guǎnlǐ	Common management	COM
公共管理接口服务	Gōnggòng guǎnlǐ jiēkǒu fúwù	Common management interface service	CMIS
公共管理接口协议	Gōnggòng guǎnlǐ jiēkǒu xiéyì	Common management interface protocol	CMIP
公共管理信息服务	Gōnggòng guǎnlǐ xìnxī fúwù	Common management information service	CMIS
公共管理信息服务单元	Gōnggòng guǎnlǐ xìnxī fúwù dānyuán	Common management information service element	CMISE
公共管理信息服务要素	Gōnggòng guǎnlǐ xìnxī fúwù yàosù	Common management information service element	CMISE
公共管理信息服务元素	Gōnggòng guǎnlǐ xìnxī fúwù yuánsù	Common management information service element	CMISE
公共管理信息协议	Gōnggòng guǎnlǐ xìnxī xiéyì	Common management information protocol	CMIP

公共管理信息业务	Gōnggòng guǎnlǐ xìnxī yèwù	Common management information service	CMIS
公共管理信息业务单元	Gōnggòng guǎnlǐ xìnxī yèwù dānyuán	Common management information service element	CMISE
公共 HINA	Gōnggòng HINA	Common HINA	CH
公共环路	Gōnggòng huánlù	Public loop	
公共环路设备	Gōnggòng huánlù shèbèi	Public loop device	
公共会聚子层	Gōnggòng huìjù zicéng	Common part convergence sub-layer	CPCS
公共键构	Gōnggòng jiàn gòu	Public key infrastructure	PKI
公共交换电话网	Gōnggòng jiāohuàn diànhuà wǎng	Public switched telephone network	PSTN
公共交换电信网	Gōnggòng jiāohuàn diànxìn wǎng	Public switched telecommunication network	PSTN
公共交换分组数据网	Gōnggòng jiāohuàn fēnzǔ shùjù wǎng	Public switching packet data network	PSPDN
公共交换式电话网络	Gōnggòng jiāohuànshì diànhuà wǎngluò	Public switched telephone network	PSTN
公共机架	Gōnggòng jījià	Common rack	COMR
公共开放策略业务	Gōnggòng kāifàng cèlüè yèwù	Common open policy service	COPS
公共开放政策服务	Gōnggòng kāifàng zhèngcè fúwù	Common open policy service	COPS
公共客体请求代理体系	Gōnggòng kètǐ qǐngqiú dàilǐ tǐxì	Common object request broker architecture	CORBA
公共控制	Gōnggòng kòngzhì	Common control	
公共控制和测量平面	Gōnggòng kòngzhì hé cèliáng píngmiàn	Common control and measurement plane	CCAMP
公共控制物理信道	Gōnggòng kòngzhì wùlǐ xìndào	Common control physical channel	CCPCH
公共控制信道	Gōnggòng kòngzhì xìndào	Common control channel	CCCH
公共空中接口	Gōnggòng kōngzhōng jiēkǒu	Common air interface	CAI
公共陆地移动通信网	Gōnggòng lùdì yídòng tōngxìnwǎng	Public land mobile network	PLMN
公共陆地移动网络	Gōnggòng lùdì yídòng wǎngluò	Public land mobile network	PLMN
公共陆基移动网	Gōnggòng lùjī yídòngwǎng	Public land mobile network	PLMN
公共名	Gōnggòng míng	Common name	
公共密钥基础设施	Gōnggòng mìyào jīchǔ shèshī	Public key infrastructure	PKI
公共模式区域	Gōnggòng móshì qūyù	Common mode range	
公共目标请求掮客结构	Gōnggòng mùbiāo qǐngqiú qiánkè jiégòu	Common object request broker architecture	CORBA
公共耦合点	Gōnggòng ǒuhédiǎn	Common coupling point, point of common coupling	PCC
公共日志格式	Gōnggòng rìzhì géshi	Common log format	CLF
公共设备	Gōnggòng shèbèi	Public device	
公共数据安全架构	Gōnggòng shùjù ānquán jiàgòu	Common data security architecture	CDSA
公共通道信号控制器	Gōnggòng tōngdào xìnhào kòngzhìqì	Common channel signaling controller	CSC
公共通道信号协议	Gōnggòng tōngdào xìnhào xiéyì	Common channel signal protocol	CCSP
公共网接口	Gōnggòng wǎng jiēkǒu	Public network interface	
公共网关接口	Gōnggòng wǎngguān jiēkǒu	Common gateway interface	CGI
公共信道模块	Gōnggòng xìndào mókuài	Common channel module	CCM
公共信道网络控制器	Gōnggòng xìndào wǎngluò kòngzhìqì	Common channel network controller	CCNC
公共信道信号处理器	Gōnggòng xìndào xìnhào chǔlǐqì	Common channel signaling processor	CSP
公共信道信号后面板	Gōnggòng xìndào xìnhào hòumian bǎn	Common channel signaling back panel	CSBP
公共信道信号 MTP 处理器	Gōnggòng xìndào xìnhào MTP chǔlǐqì	Common channel signaling MTP processor	CMP
公共信道信号系统	Gōnggòng xìndào xìnhào xìtǒng	Common channel signaling system	CCSS
公共信道信令	Gōnggòng xìndào xìnlìng	Common channel signaling	CCS
公共信号控制集成板	Gōnggòng xìnhào kòngzhì jíchéngbǎn	Common signaling control board assembly	CSCA
公共信令信道	Gōnggòng xìnlìng xìndào	Common signaling channel	CSC
公共信息模型	Gōnggòng xìnxī móxíng	Common information model	CIM

公共业务信道	Gōnggòng yèwù xìndào	Common traffic channel	CTCH
公共应用服务要素	Gōnggòng yìngyòng fúwù yàosù	Common application service	CASE
公共用户数据网络	Gōnggòng yònghù shùjù wǎngluò	Common user data network	CUDN
公共用户线路	Gōnggòng yònghù xiànlù	Common user circuit	CUC
公共中介格式	Gōnggòng zhōngjiè géshi	Common intermediate format	CIF
公共资源	Gōnggòng zīyuán	Common resource	
供给	Gōngjǐ	Provisioning	
攻击	Gōngjī	Attack	
攻击事件注册及智能服务	Gōngjī shìjiàn zhùcè jí zhìnéng fúwù	Attack Registry & intelligence service	ARIS
共晶焊锡	Gòngjīng hànxī	Eutectic solders (in SMT)	
工具菜单	Gōngjù càidān	Tools menu (WP command)	
工具箱	Gōngjùxiāng	Toolbar (WP command)	
公开密钥	Gōngkāi mìyào	Public key	
公开密匙体制	Gōngkāi mìyào tǐzhì	Public key system	
公历	Gōnglì	Gregorian calendar	
功率	Gōnglǜ	Power	POW
功率步长	Gōnglǜ bùcháng	Power step	PWR_STEP
功率传输系数	Gōnglǜ chuánshū xìshù	Power transmission factor (in a transmission line)	
功率代价	Gōnglǜ dàijià	Power penalty	
功率电平	Gōnglǜ diànpíng	Power level	PL
功率放大器	Gōnglǜ fàngdàqì	Booster amplifier	BA
功率放大器	Gōnglǜ fàngdàqì	Power amplifier	
功率放大器互联面板	Gōnglǜ fàngdàqì hùlián miànbǎn	Power amplifier interconnection panel	PICP
功率反射系数	Gōnglǜ fǎnshè xìshù	Power reflection factor (in a transmission line)	
功率分配器	Gōnglǜ fēnpèiqì	Power divider	
功率光放大器	Gōnglǜ guāng fàngdàqì	Optical booster amplifier	BA
功率管理干扰机	Gōnglǜ guǎnlǐ gānrǎojī	Power-managed jammer	
功率合成	Gōnglǜ héchéng	Power synthesis	
公路交通管制系统	Gōnglù jiāotōng guǎnzhì xìtǒng	Highway traffic control system	
功率控制	Gōnglǜ kòngzhì	Power control	PC
功率控制报文	Gōnglǜ kòngzhì bàowén	Power control message	
功率控制单元	Gōnglǜ kòngzhì dānyuán	Power control unit	PCU
功率控制电平	Gōnglǜ kòngzhì diànpíng	Power control level	
功率偏移	Gōnglǜ piānyí	Power offset	
功率匹配	Gōnglǜ pǐpèi	Power matching	PM
功率谱	Gōnglǜ pǔ	Power spectrum	
功率谱密度	Gōnglǜ pǔ mìdù	Power spectrum density	PSD
功率谱密度模板	Gōnglǜ pǔ mìdù múbǎn	Power spectrum density mask	PSDMASK
功率容量	Gōnglǜ róngliàng	Power-handling capacity	
功率生成	Gōnglǜ shēngchéng	Power product	
功率生成	Gōnglǜ shēngchéng	Power product	
功率损耗	Gōnglǜ sǔnhào	Power loss	
共路信令	Gònglù xìnlìng	Common channel signaling	
共路信令网	Gònglù xìnlìng wǎng	Common channel signaling network	CCSN
共路信令系统	Gònglù xìnlìng xìtǒng	Common channel signaling system	CCSS
功率因数	Gōnglǜ yīnshù	Power factor	PF

功率因素	Gōnglǜ yīnsù	Power factor	
功率因子	Gōnglǜ yīnzǐ	Power factor	
功率驻波比	Gōnglǜ zhùbōbǐ	Power standing-wave ratio	PSWR
共模	Gòngmó	Common mode	
共模电流	Gòngmó diànliú	Common mode current	
共模电压	Gòngmó diànyā	Common mode voltage	
共模干扰	Gòngmó gānrǎo	Common code interference	
共模信号	Gòngmó xìnhào	Common mode signal	
共模抑制	Gòngmó yìzhì	Common mode rejection	
共模抑制比	Gòngmó yìzhì bǐ	Common mode rejection ratio	CMRR
共模噪声	Gòngmó zàoshēng	Common mode noise	
共模增益	Gòngmó zēngyì	Common mode gain	
共模转换	Gòngmó zhuǎnhuàn	Common mode conversion	
共模阻抗	Gòngmó zǔkàng	Common code impedance	
功能	Gōngnéng	Function	FUN
功能标准	Gōngnéng biāozhǔn	Functional standard	
功能补丁	Gōngnéng bǔdìng	Option pack	
功能测试	Gōngnéng cèshì	Capability test	
功能测试	Gōngnéng cèshì	Functional test	
功能成分	Gōngnéng chéngfèn	Functional component	
功能单元	Gōngnéng dānyuán	Function element	FE
功能单元	Gōngnéng dānyuán	Function unit	FU
功能地址	Gōngnéng dìzhǐ	Function address	FA
功能地址指示符	Gōngnéng dìzhǐ zhǐshì fú	Function address indicator	FAI
功能方式	Gōngnéng fāngshì	Functional mode	
功能分担	Gōngnéng fēndān	Function sharing	
功能分散控制	Gōngnéng fēnsàn kòngzhì	Function-divided control	
功能键	Gōngnéng jiàn	Function key	
功能检查	Gōngnéng jiǎnchá	Function check-out	
功能基线	Gōngnéng jīxiàn	Functional baseline	
功能极限状态	Gōngnéng jíxiàn zhuàngtài	Service ability limit state	
功能卡装载	Gōngnéng kǎ zhuāngzài	Function card load	fcload
功能块	Gōngnéng kuài	Function block	
功能栏	Gōngnéng lán	Palette of functions	
功能群	Gōngnéng qún	Functional group	
功能上移	Gōngnéng shàngyí	Upsizing	
功能实体	Gōngnéng shítǐ	Functional entity	FE
功能实体接入管理	Gōngnéng shítǐ jiērù guǎnlǐ	Functional entity access manager	FEAM
功能属性	Gōngnéng shǔxìng	Function attributes	
功能损失度	Gōngnéng sǔnshīdù	Functional loss	
功能体系结构	Gōngnéng tǐxì jiégòu	Functional architecture	
功能下降性维护	Gōngnéng xiàjiàngxìng wéihù	Function-degrading maintenance	
功能限制等级	Gōngnéng xiànzhì děngjí	Facility restriction level	FRL
功能信号	Gōngnéng xìnhào	Function signal	
功能运营过程	Gōngnéng yùnyíng guòchéng	Functional operations process	
功能组	Gōngnéng zǔ	Functional group	

功能型终端	Gōngnéng-xíng zhōngduān	Functional terminal	
公平接入	Gōngping jiērù	Fair access	
公平排队	Gōngping páiduì	Fair queuing	FQ
公平系数	Gōngping xìshù	Fairness index	
公平依赖关系	Gōngping yīlài guānxi	Fair dependence relation (in Petri nets)	
公平依赖体系	Gōngping yīlài tǐxì	Fair dependence hierarchy (in Petri nets)	
攻破	Gōngpò	Breach (IPsec)	
公认会计原则	Gōngrèn kuàijì yuánzé	Generally accepted accounting principles	GAAP
公式	Gōngshì	Formula	
公式翻译程序语言	Gōngshì fānyì chéngxù yǔyán	Format translator programming language	FORTRAN
公式翻译语言	Gōngshì fānyì yǔyán	Formula translator	FORTRAN
共态变量	Gòngtài biànliàng	Costate variable	
共同边界	Gòngtóng biānjiè	Conjoint boundary	
共同进化算法	Gòngtóng jìnhuà suànfǎ	Coevolutionary algorithm	CoEA
共同居住	Gòngtóng jūzhù	Doubling up	
共同的控制键	Gòngtóngde kòngzhì jiàn	Corporate control key	CCK
公务单元	Gōngwù dānyuán	Order wire unit	OWU
公务电话	Gōngwù diànhuà	Orderwire	OW
公务联络	Gōngwù liánluò	Orderwire	
公务线	Gōngwù xiàn	Orderwire	
共线电话	Gòngxiàn diànhuà	Common (party) line telephone	
贡献路线	Gòngxiàn lùxiàn	Contribution link	
共线阵	Gòngxiàn zhèn	Collinear array	
共线阵天线	Gòngxiàn zhèn tiānxiàn	Collinear array antenna	
共享保护环	Gòngxiǎng bǎohù huán	Shared protection ring	
共享保密数据	Gòngxiǎng bǎomì shùjù	Shared secret data	SSD
共享磁盘	Gòngxiǎng cípán	Share disk	SD
共享存储器	Gòngxiǎng cúnchǔqì	Shared buffer memory	SBM
共享风险链路组	Gòngxiǎng fēngxiǎn liànlù zǔ	Shared risk link group	SRLG
共享互通功能	Gòngxiǎng hùtōng gōngnéng	Shared interworking function system	SIWFS
共享密钥	Gòngxiǎng mìyào	Shared system key	
共享内存结构	Gòngxiǎng nèicún jiégòu	Shared memory architecture	SMA
共享内存映射	Gòngxiǎng nèicún yìngshè	Shared memory mapping	
共享树	Gòngxiǎng shù	Shared tree	
共享锁	Gòngxiǎng suǒ	Shared lock (for database)	
共享特征	Gòngxiǎng tèzhēng	Shared feature	
共享维度	Gòngxiǎng wéidù	Shared dimension	
共享无线访问协议	Gòngxiǎng wúxiàn fǎngwèn xiéyì	Shared wireless access protocol	SWAP
共享信道控制信道	Gòngxiǎng xìndào kòngzhì xìndào	Shared channel control channel	SHCCH
共享资源模块	Gòngxiǎng zīyuán mókuài	Shared resources module	SRM
共信道再用距离	Gòngxìndào zàiyòng jùlí	Co-channel re-use distance	
共形天线	Gòngxíng tiānxiàn	Conformal antenna	
共形涂层	Gòngxíng túcéng	Conformal coating (in SMT)	
共形阵	Gòngxíng zhèn	Conformal array	
共形阵天线	Gòngxíng zhèn tiānxiàn	Conformal array antenna	
供需链的管理	Gōngxū liànde guǎnlǐ	Supply chain management	SCM

工学键盘	Gōngxué jiànpán	Natural keyboard	
公钥分配密码体制	Gōngyào fēnpèi mìmǎ tǐzhì	Key distribution cryptosystem	
公钥基础结构	Gōngyào jīchǔ jiégòu	Public key infrastructure	PKI
公钥基础设施	Gōngyào jīchǔ shèshī	Public key infrastructure	PKI
公钥机制	Gōngyào jīzhì	Public key infrastructure	PKI
公钥密码算法	Gōngyào mìmǎ suànfǎ	Public key encryption algorithm (IPsec)	
公钥体制	Gōngyào tǐzhì	Public key system	
公钥证明	Gōngyào zhèngmíng	Public key certificate	
工业标准架构	Gōngyè biāozhǔn jiàgòu	Industry standard architecture	ISA
工业布线系统	Gōngyè bùxiàn xìtǒng	Industrial distribution system	IDS
工业干扰	Gōngyè gānrǎo	Industrial interference	
工业级电源供应器	Gōngyè jí diànyuán gōngyìngqì	Industrial power supply	
工业计算机背板	Gōngyè jìsuànjī bèibǎn	Industrial computer backplane	
工业,科学和医疗应用	Gōngyè, kēxué hé yīliáo yìngyòng	Industrial, scientific and medical applications (of radio frequency energy)	ISM
工业，科学，医疗设备	Gōngyè, kēxué, yīliáo shèbèi	Industrial, scientific and medical apparatus	ISM
工业,政府部门开放系统技术规范	Gōngyè, zhèngfǔ bùmén kāifàng xìtǒng jìshù guīfàn	Industry/Government Open System Specification	IGOSS
公益事业	Gōngyì shìyè	Public utility works	
供应链生命周期管理	Gōngyìngliàn shēngmìng zhōuqī guǎnlǐ	Supply chain lifecycle management	
供应商管理的库存	Gōngyìngshāng guǎnlǐde kùcún	Vendor managed inventory	VMI
供应商/合作伴关系管理	Gōngyìngshāng/hézuòbàn guānxi guǎnlǐ	Supplier/partner relationship management	
公用包网络接口	Gōngyòng bāo wǎngluò jiēkǒu	Public packet network interface	PPNI
共用保护环	Gòngyòng bǎohù huán	Shared protection ring	
共用保密数据	Gòngyòng bǎomì shùjù	Shared secret data	SSD
公用传真局	Gōngyòng chuánzhēnjú	Public facsimile bureau	
公用传真站	Gōngyòng chuánzhēnzhàn	Public facsimile station	
共用存储器	Gòngyòng cúnchǔqì	Global memory	
共用存取远程通信系统	Gòngyòng cúnqǔ yuǎnchéng tōngxìn xìtǒng	Common access telecommunications system	CATS
公用电话交换网	Gōngyòng diànhuà jiāohuàn wǎng	Public switched telephone network	PSTN
公用电话亭	Gōngyòng diànhuà tíng	Public telephone booth	
公用调度集群通信网	Gōngyòng diàodù jíqún tōngxìnwǎng	Public access mobile radio	PAMR
共用调度集群移动通信网	Gòngyòng diàodù jíqún yídòng tōngxìnwǎng	Public access mobile radio	
公用对象模型	Gōngyòng duìxiàng móxíng	Common object model	COM
公用分租接转网络	Gōngyòng fēnzū jiēzhuǎn wǎngluò	Public packet switched network	PPSN
公用分组数据网	Gōngyòng fēnzǔ shùjù wǎng	Public packet data network	X.25
公用分组信道	Gōngyòng fēnzǔ xìndào	Common packet channel	CPCH
公用关键基础设施	Gōngyòng guānjiàn jīchǔ shèshī	Public key infrastructure	PKI
公用管理信息服务	Gōngyòng guǎnlǐ xìnxī fúwù	Common management information service	CMIS
公用管理信息服务单元	Gōngyòng guǎnlǐ xìnxī fúwù dānyuán	Common management information service element	CMISE
公用管理信息接口	Gōngyòng guǎnlǐ xìnxī jiēkǒu	Common management information interface	
公用管理信息协议服务单元	Gōngyòng guǎnlǐ xìnxī xiéyì fúwù dānyuán	Common management information service element	CMISE
公用管理信息业务单元	Gōngyòng guǎnlǐ xìnxī yèwù dānyuán	Common management information service element	CMISE
公用管理域	Gōngyòng guǎnlǐ yù	Administration management domain	ADMD
公用号码簿管理域	Gōngyòng hàomǎbù guǎnlǐ yù	Administration directory management domain	ADDMD

公用会化期用户信息	Gōngyòng huìhuà qī yònghù xìnxī	Common session user information	CSUI
公用交换电话网	Gōngyòng jiāohuàn diànhuà wǎng	Public switched telephone network	PSTN
公用交换分组数据网	Gōngyòng jiāohuàn fēnzǔ shùjù wǎng	Public switched packet data network	PSPDN
公用交换网	Gōngyòng jiāohuàn wǎng	Public switched network	PSN
公用交换式电话网	Gōngyòng jiāohuàn-shì diànhuà wǎng	Public switched telephone network	PSTN
共用节点操作	Gòngyòng jiédiǎn cāozuò	Pooling point operation	
共用基址寄存器	Gòngyòng jīzhǐ jìcúnqì	Global base register	GBR
共用控制物理信道	Gòngyòng kòngzhì wùlǐ xìndào	Common control physical channel	CCPCH
共用领域	Gòngyòng lǐngyù	Shared area	
公用陆地蜂窝移动通信网	Gōngyòng lùdì fēngwō yídòng tōngxìnwǎng	Public land cellular mobile network	PLMN
共用陆地移动通信系统	Gòngyòng lùdì yídòng tōngxìn xìtǒng	Public land mobile telecommunications system	PLMTS
公用陆地移动通信网	Gōngyòng lùdì yídòng tōngxìnwǎng	Public land mobile communications network	PLMN
公用陆地移动网络	Gōngyòng lùdì yídòng wǎngluò	Public land mobile network	PLMN
公用密钥算法	Gōngyòng mìyào suànfǎ	Public key algorithm	PKA
共用频带	Gòngyòng píndài	Shared band	
共用区	Gòngyòng qū	Global area	
公用软件	Gōngyòng ruǎnjiàn	Public domain software	
共用入口转接设备	Gòngyòng rùkǒu zhuǎnjiē shèbèi	Common access switching equipment	CASE
公用设施网络	Gōngyòng shèshī wǎngluò	Utility network	
公用时分多址终端	Gōngyòng shífèn duōzhǐ zhōngduān	Common TDMA terminal	CTTE
公用数据	Gōngyòng shùjù	Public data	PD
公用数据安全框架	Gōngyòng shùjù ānquán kuàngjià	Common data security architecture	CDSA
公用数据传输业务	Gōngyòng shùjù chuánshū yèwù	Public data transmission service	
共用数据交换网	Gòngyòng shùjù jiāohuàn wǎng	Public switched data network	PSDN
共用数据网	Gòngyòng shùjù wǎng	Public data network	PDN
公用数据网	Gōngyòng shùjù wǎng	Public data network	PDN
共用天线电视	Gòngyòng tiānxiàn diànshì	Community antenna television	CATV
公用投币电话鉴别音	Gōngyòng tóubì diànhuà jiànbiéyīn	Coinbox discriminating tone	
公用网接口	Gōngyòng wǎng jiēkǒu	Public network interface	
共用网关接口	Gòngyòng wǎngguān jiēkǒu	Common gateway interface	CGI
共用无执照个人无线电网络	Gòngyòng wúzhízhào gèrén wúxiàndiàn wǎngluò	Shared unlicenced personal radio network	SUPERNET
公用信号通道解调器	Gōngyòng xìnhào tōngdào jiětiáoqì	Common signal channel demodulator	CSCD
公用信号信道	Gōngyòng xìnhào xìndào	Common signal channel	CSC
公用移动无线电	Gōngyòng yídòng wúxiàndiàn	Common mobile radio	CMR
共用硬件参考平台	Gòngyòng yìngjiàn cānkǎo píngtái	Common hardware reference platform	CHRP
公用域名	Gōngyòng yùmíng	Administration domain name	
公用语言	Gōngyòng yǔyán	Common language	
共用自动交换机	Gòngyòng zìdòng jiāohuànjī	Community automatic exchange	CAX
公用字段	Gōngyòng zìduàn	Common fields	
公用型会议电视系统	Gōngyòng-xíng huìyì diànshì xìtǒng	Public video conferencing system	PVCS
共有地域	Gòngyǒu dìyù	Public domain	
公证	Gōngzhèng	Notarization (IPsec)	
共振式隔离器	Gòngzhèn-shì gélíqì	Resonant isolator	
公制	Gōngzhì	Metric system	
公众安全应答服务机构	Gōngzhòng ānquán yìngdá fúwù jīgòu	Public secure answer point	PSAP

公众电话交换网	Gōngzhòng diànhuà jiāohuàn wǎng	Public switched telephone network	PSTN
公众电信运营者	Gōngzhòng diànxìn yùnyíngzhě	Public telecom operator	PTO
公众分组交换数据网	Gōngzhòng fēnzǔ jiāohuàn shùjù wǎng	Packet switched public data network	PSPDN
公众分组交换网	Gōngzhòng fēnzǔ jiāohuàn wǎng	Packet switched public data network	PSPDN
公众交换电话网	Gōngzhòng jiāohuàn diànhuà wǎng	Public switched telephone network	PSTN
工种开关	Gōngzhǒng kāiguān	Mode switch (on radio)	
公众陆地移动电话网	Gōngzhòng lùdì yídòng diànhuà wǎng	Public land mobile network	PLMN
公众目录支持	Gōngzhòng mùlù zhīchí	Public directory support	PDS
公众热点	Gōngzhòng rèdiǎn	Public hot-spot	
公众通信	Gōngzhòng tōngxìn	Public correspondence	
公众信息系统	Gōngzhòng xìnxī xìtǒng	Public information system	
公转周期	Gōngzhuàn zhōuqī	Sidereal period revolution (of a satellite)	
工字柱	Gōng-zì zhù	I column	
工作比	Gōngzuò bǐ	Duty cycle	
工作波长	Gōngzuò bōcháng	Operating wavelength	
工作波长范围	Gōngzuò bōcháng fànwéi	Bandpass (operating wavelength range)	
工作波长范围	Gōngzuò bōcháng fànwéi	Operating wavelength range	
工作参数	Gōngzuò cānshù	Operational parameter	
工作带宽	Gōngzuò dàikuān	Operating bandwidth	
工作等待时间	Gōngzuò děngdài shíjiān	Work waiting time	WWT
工作电容	Gōngzuò diànróng	Operating capacitance	
工作范围	Gōngzuò fànwéi	Working range	
工作寄存器	Gōngzuò jìcúnqì	Working register	WK
工作接地	Gōngzuò jiēdì	Working ground	
工作空间	Gōngzuò kōngjiān	Workspace	
工作类别	Gōngzuò lèibié	Operating class (of an amplifying stage)	
工作频率	Gōngzuò pínlǜ	Operating frequency	
工作频率范围	Gōngzuò pínlǜ fànwéi	Operating frequency range	
工作切换	Gōngzuò qiēhuàn	Task switch	
工作时间	Gōngzuò shíjiān	Operating time	
工作寿命	Gōngzuò shòumìng	Operating life	
工作条件	Gōngzuò tiáojiàn	Operating conditions	
工作应力设计	Gōngzuò yìnglì shèjì	Working stress design	
工作周期	Gōngzuò zhōuqī	Cycle of operation	
工作周期失真	Gōngzuò zhōuqī shīzhēn	Transmitter duty cycle distortion	TDCD
工作状态	Gōngzuò zhuàngtài	Operating state	
工作最高可用频率	Gōngzuò zuìgāo kěyòng pínlǜ	Operational maximum usable frequency	
工作流管理联盟	Gōngzuòliú guǎnlǐ liánméng	Workflow management coalition	WfMC
工作流管理系统	Gōngzuòliú guǎnlǐ xìtǒng	Workflow management system	WfMS
工作流过程定义语言	Gōngzuòliú guòchéng dìngyì yǔyán	Workflow process definition language	WPDL
工作流类型定义	Gōngzuòliú lèixíng dìngyì	Workflow type definition	
工作流模型	Gōngzuòliú móxíng	Workflow model	
工作流网	Gōngzuòliú wǎng	Workflow net	
工作流相关数据	Gōngzuòliú xiāngguān shùjù	Workflow relevant data	
工作流引擎交换	Gōngzuòliú yǐnqíng jiāohuàn	Workflow engine interchange	
工作流元模型	Gōngzuòliú yuán móxíng	Workflow meta-model	

工作区	Gōngzuòqū	Work area	WA
工作区电缆	Gōngzuòqū diànlǎn	Work area cable	
工作区光缆	Gōngzuòqū guānglǎn	Work area optical cable	
工作区软线	Gōngzuòqū ruǎnxiàn	Work area cord	
工作台炉	Gōngzuòtái lú	Bench-top oven	
工作站	Gōngzuòzhàn	Work station	WS
工作站服务器	Gōngzuòzhàn fúwùqì	Work station server	WSS
工作站功能块	Gōngzuòzhàn gōngnéng kuài	Workstation function block	WSF
工作站功能块	Gōngzuòzhàn gōngnéng kuài	Work station function block	WSF
工作站的通用连接访问	Gōngzuòzhànde tōngyòng liánjiē fǎngwèn	Common link access for workstations	CLAW
工作组	Gōngzuòzǔ	Workgroup	
工作组软件	Gōngzuòzǔ ruǎnjiàn	Workgroup software	
沟包线	Gōu-bāo xiàn	Goubau line	
构成点	Gòuchéng diǎn	Composition point	
构成体	Gòuchéngtǐ	Component	
沟道衬底平面结构	Gōudào chèndǐ píngmiàn jiégòu	Channeled substrate planar structure	CSP
构架曲线	Gòujià qūxiàn	Skeleton curve	
构件	Gòujiàn	Construct (noun)	
钩键	Gōujiàn	Switchhook	
构件库管理代理	Gòujiàn kù guǎnlǐ dàilǐ	Component library management agent (in Java)	CLMA
沟坎	Gōukǎn	Trench bank, trench ridge	
沟通更多	Gōutōng gèng duō	Do Communication More (Japanese telecom provider)	DoCoMo
构造	Gòuzào	Construct (noun; for language)	
构造函数	Gòuzào hánshù	Constructor	Ctor
构造器	Gòuzào qì	Constructor	ctor
钩子	Gōuzi	Hook	
GPRS 服务支持节点	GPRS fúwù zhīchí jiédiǎn	Serving GPRS supporting node	SGSN
GPRS 隧道协议	GPRS suìdào xiéyì	General packet radio service (GPRS) tunneling protocol	
GPRS 隧道协议用户平面	GPRS suìdào xiéyì yònghù píngmiàn	GPRS tunneling protocol for user plane	GTP-U
GPRS 网关支持节点	GPRS wǎngguān zhīchí jiédiǎn	Gateway GPRS support node	GGSN
GPRS 移动性管理	GPRS yídòngxìng guǎnlǐ	GPRS mobility management	GMM
GPRS 支持节点	GPRS zhīchí jiédiǎn	GPRS support node	GSN
GPS 接收机	GPS jiēshōujī	GPS receiver	GPSR
GSM 公共陆地移动网络	GSM gōnggòng lùdì yídòng wǎngluò	GSM public land mobile network	GSM PLMN
GSM 公用陆地移动通信网覆盖面积	GSM gōngyòng lùdì yídòng tōngxìnwǎng fùgài miànjī	GSM PLMN area	Gpa
GSM 全球漫游论坛	GSM quánqiú mànyóu lùntán	GSM global roaming forum	GGRF
GSM 认可论坛	GSM rènkě lùntán	GSM certification forum	GCF
GSM 型号认证咨询委员会	GSM xínghào rènzhèng zīxún wěiyuánhuì	GSM type approval advisory board	GSM TAAB
GSM 系统区域	GSM xìtǒng qūyù	GSM system area	GSA
GSM 演进增强数据速率	GSM yǎnjìn zēngqiáng shùjù sùlǜ	Enhanced data rates for GSM evalution	EDGE
GSM 业务区	GSM yèwù qū	GSM service area	
GSM 业务识别模块	GSM yèwù shíbié mókuài	GSM service identity module	GSIM
GSM 用户识别模块	GSM yònghù shíbié mókuài	GSM subscriber identity module	SIM
GSM 增强数据率改进	GSM zēngqiáng shùjù lǜ gǎijìn	Enhanced data rates for global evolution	EDGE

GSM/EDGE 无线接入网	GSM/EDGE wúxiàn jiērù wǎng	GSM/EDGE radio access network	GERAN
GSM 的移动智能业务	GSM-de yídòng zhìnéng yèwù	Customized applications for mobile network enhanced logic	CAMEL
gt-多边形	gt-duōbiānxíng	Gt-polygon	
gt-环	gt-huán	Gt-ring	
挂号函件	Guàhào hánjiàn	Registered correspondence	
挂号函件条码标签	Guàhào hánjiàn tiáomǎ biāoqiān	Bar code label for registered correspondence	
挂机	Guàjī	Hang up	
挂机等候	Guàjī děnghòu	On-hook waiting	
挂机信号	Guàjī xìnhào	Clear-back signal	CBK
挂机信号	Guàjī xìnhào	Hang-up signal	
挂接	Guàjiē	Attach	
关闭逻辑通道	Guānbì luóji tōngdào	Close logical channel	CLC
关闭逻辑通道拒绝	Guānbì luóji tōngdào jùjué	Close logical channel reject	CLCR
关闭逻辑通道确认	Guānbì luóji tōngdào quèrèn	Close logical channel acknowledge	CLCA
观察时间差异	Guānchá shíjiān chāyì	Observed time difference	OTD
观察数据	Guānchá shùjù	Maintainability demonstration	
贯标办	Guàn biāo bàn	Standards Adherence Section (an office responsible for assuring conformance to overall operating standards such as ISO:9001, and to QHSE (Quality, Health, Safety and Environment) standards.)	
惯导	Guàndǎo	Inertial navigation (short form)	
管道	Guǎndào	Conduit	GD
管道	Guǎndào	Duct	
管道传送	Guǎndào chuánsòng	Pipelining	
管道光缆	Guǎndào guānglǎn	Duct fiber optic cable	
管道缆	Guǎndào lǎn	Duct cable	
管道设施	Guǎndào shèshī	Pipe utilities	
管道系统	Guǎndào xìtǒng	Piping	
管吊式	Guǎndiào-shì	Conduit suspension type	DS
官方语言	Guānfāng yǔyán	Official language	
光[电]端机尾纤	Guāng [diàn] duānjī wěixiān	Opto[-electronic] terminal lead	
光包交换	Guāng bāo jiāohuàn	Optical packet switch	OPS
光被动元件	Guāng bèidòng yuánjiàn	Optical passive device	
光标记交换	Guāng biāojì jiāohuàn	Optical label switch	OLS
光波长交错器	Guāng bōcháng jiāocuòqì	Optical wavelength interleaver	
光波导形调变器	Guāng bōdǎo-xíng tiáobiànqì	Optical waveguide modulator	
光波分复用	Guāng bōfēn fùyòng	Optical wavelength division multiplexing	
光层交叉连接	Guāng céng jiāochā liánjiē	Optical layer cross connection	OLXC
光传输段	Guāng chuánshū duàn	Optical transmission stage	
光传输段层	Guāng chuánshū duàn céng	Optical transmission section layer	
光传输模块	Guāng chuánshū mókuài	Fiber transmission module	FTM
光传输设备	Guāng chuánshū shèbèi	Optical transmission equipment	
光传输网	Guāng chuánshū wǎng	Optical transmission network	OTN
光传送段	Guāng chuánsòng duàn	Optical transmission section	OTS
光传送段层	Guāng chuánsòng duàn céng	Optical transport segment layer	OTS
光传送段连续性丢失	Guāng chuánsòng duàn liánxùxìng diūshī	Loss of continuity on optical transmission section	LOC-OTS
光传送模块	Guāng chuánsòng mókuài	Optical transport module	OTM

光传送体制	Guāng chuánsòng tǐzhì	Optical transport hierarchy	OTH
光传送网管理网	Guāng chuánsòng wǎng guǎnlǐ wǎng	Optical transport management network	OMN
光传送网络	Guāng chuánsòng wǎngluò	Optical transport network	OTN
光磁碟机	Guāng cídiéjī	Magneto-optical (MO) disk drive	
光电子集成	Guāng diànzǐ jíchéng	Opto-electronic integrated circuit	OEIC
光电子集成电路	Guāng diànzǐ jíchéng diànlù	Integrated opto-electronic circuit	IOEC
光端机	Guāng duānjī	Optical terminal	
光断续器	Guāng duànxùqì	Photo interrupter	
光多业务节点设备	Guāng duō yèwù jiédiǎn shèbèi	Optical multi-service node	OMSN
光二极体	Guāng èrjítǐ	Photodiode	
光放段	Guāng fàng duàn	Optical amplifier span	OAS
光放大段	Guāng fàngdà duàn	Optical amplifier section	OAS
光放大段开销处理	Guāng fàngdà duàn kāixiao chǔlǐ	Optical amplifier section overhead handling	OASOH
光放大段适配	Guāng fàngdà duàn shìpèi	Optical amplifer section adapter	OASA
光放大段终结	Guāng fàngdà duàn zhōngjié	Optical amplifier section termination	OAST
光放大发射机	Guāng fàngdà fāshèjī	Optically amplified transmitter	OAT
光放大接收机	Guāng fàngdà jiēshōujī	Optically amplified receiver	OAR
光放大器	Guāng fàngdàqì	Optical amplifier	OA
光反射器	Guāng fǎnshèqì	Photo reflector	
光发射机	Guāng fāshèjī	Optical transmitter	Tx
光发送机	Guāng fāsòngjī	Optical transmitter	Tx
光分插复用设备	Guāng fēn/chā fùyòng shèbèi	Optical add/drop multiplexer	OADM
光分波器	Guāng fēnbōqì	Optical demultiplexer	OD
光分插复用器	Guāng fēnchā fùyòngqì	Optical add and drop multiplexer	OADM
光分路器	Guāng fēnlùqì	Optical branching device	OBD
光分配网络	Guāng fēnpèi wǎngluò	Optical distributed network	ODN
光分组交换	Guāng fēnzǔ jiāohuàn	Optical packet switching	OPS
光分组数据单元	Guāng fēnzǔ shùjù dānyuán	Optical packet data unit	OPDU
光复用	Guāng fùyòng	Optical multiplexing	OM
光复用段	Guāng fùyòng duàn	Optical multiplex stage	OMS
光复用段保护	Guāng fùyòng duàn bǎohù	Optical multiplex stage protection	OMSP
光复用段层	Guāng fùyòng duàn céng	Optical multiplex segment layer	OMS
光复用段开销处理	Guāng fùyòng duàn kāixiao chǔlǐ	Optical multiplex section overhead handling	OMSOH
光复用段适配	Guāng fùyòng duàn shì pèi	Optical multiplex section adapter	OMSA
光复用段终结	Guāng fùyòng duàn zhōngjié	Optical multiplex section termination	OMST
光复用终端	Guāng fùyòng zhōngduān	Optical multiplexing terminal	OMT
光复用器	Guāng fùyòngqì	Optical multiplexer	OM
光复用器/解复用器	Guāng fùyòngqì/jiě fùyòngqì	Optical multiplexer/demultiplexer	OM/DM
光感测元件	Guāng gǎncè yuánjiàn	Photosensing unit	
光隔离度	Guāng gélídù	Optical isolation (FOC)	
光隔离器	Guāng gélíqì	Fiber isolator, optical isolator	
光隔离器/波分复用器	Guāng gélíqì/bōfēn fùyòngqì	Fiber isolator/wavelength division multiplexer	IWDM
光攻放	Guāng gōng fàng	Optical booster amplifier	OBA
光功率放大器	Guāng gōnglǜ fàngdàqì	Booster (power) amplifier (for optical fiber)	BA
光功率控制	Guāng gōnglǜ kòngzhì	Optical power control	
光功率预算	Guāng gōnglǜ yùsuàn	Optical power budget	

光共振器	Guāng gòngzhènqì	Optical resonators	
光固化法	Guāng gùhuà fǎ	Stereolithography	SL
光孤子	Guāng gūzǐ	Soliton	
光合波器	Guāng hébōqì	Optical multiplexer	OM
光核心交换	Guāng héxīn jiāohuàn	Optical core switch	
光核心设备	Guāng héxīn shèbèi	Optical core device	OCD
光环流器	Guāng huánliúqì	Optical circulator	
光回波损耗	Guāng huíbō sǔnhào	Optical retun loss	ORL
光回呼损耗	Guāng huíhū sǔnhào	Optical return loss	ORL
光回损	Guāng huísǔn	Optical return loss	
光互联网络论坛	Guāng hùlián wǎngluò lùntán	Optical Internetworking Forum	OIF
光监控通道	Guāng jiānkòng tōngdào	Optical supervisory channel	OSC
光监控通路	Guāng jiānkòng tōnglù	Optical supervisory channel	OSC
光监控通路适配	Guāng jiānkòng tōnglù shìpèi	Optical supervisory channel adapter	OSCA
光监控信道	Guāng jiānkòng xìndào	Optical surveillance channel	OSC
光监控信道	Guāng jiānkòng xìndào	Optical supervisory channel	OSC
光交叉连接	Guāng jiāochā liánjiē	Optical cross-connection	OXC
光交叉连接节点	Guāng jiāochā liánjiē jiédiǎn	Optical cross-connect node	OXCN
光交叉连接器	Guāng jiāochā liánjiēqì	Optical cross-connect	OXC
光交换方式	Guāng jiāohuàn fāngshì	Photonic switching method	
光解复用器	Guāng jiě/fùyòngqì	Optical multiplexer/demultiplexer	OD
光截波器	Guāng jiébōqì	Optical chopper	
光节点	Guāng jiédiǎn	Fiber node	FN
光接口计数	Guāng jiēkǒu jìshù	Light interface technology	LIT
光接口适配器	Guāng jiēkǒu shìpèiqì	Optical interface adapter	OIA
光接入网	Guāng jiērù wǎng	Optical access network	OAN
光接收机	Guāng jiēshōujī	Optical receiver	Rx
光具座	Guāng jùzuò	Optical bench	
光开关	Guāng kāiguān	Optical switch	
光控可控硅开关	Guāng kòng kěkòngguī kāiguān	Light activated silicon controlled switch	LASCS
光空分多路复用	Guāng kōngfēn duōlù fùyòng	Optical space-division multiplexing	OSDM
光空分复用	Guāng kōngfēn fùyòng	Optical space-division multiplexing	OSDM
光空间传输系统	Guāng kōngjiān chuánshū xìtǒng	Spatial optical transmission system	
光控制元件	Guāng kòngzhì yuánjiàn	Optical control device	
光浪涌保护	Guāng làngyǒng bǎohù	Optical surge protection	OSP
光连接控制器	Guāng liánjiē kòngzhìqì	Optical connection controller	OCC
光连接器	Guāng liánjiēqì	Optical connector	
光链路交换接口	Guāng liànlù jiāohuàn jiēkǒu	Optic link switch interface	OLSI
光联网论坛	Guāng liánwǎng lùntán	Optical internetworking Forum	OIF
光路	Guāng lù	Optical path	
光滤波器	Guāng lǜbōqì	Optical filter	
光码分多址	Guāng mǎfēn duōzhǐ	Optical code division multiple access	
光脉冲产生设备	Guāng màichōng chǎnshēng shèbèi	Optical pulse generator	
光敏电阻	Guāng mǐndiànzǔ	Light dependent resistor	LDR
光耦合器	Guāng ǒuhéqì	Optical coupler	
光旁路开关	Guāng pánglù kāiguān	Optical bypass switch	

光配线架	Guāng pèixiànjià	Optical distribution frame	ODF
光配线网	Guāng pèixiànwǎng	Optical distribution network	ODN
光偏振	Guāng piānzhèn	Polarized light	
光频分复用	Guāng pínfēn fùyòng	Optical frequency division multiplexing	OFDM
光频谱分析单元	Guāng pínpǔ fēnxī dānyuán	Optical spectrum analyzer	OSA
光前置放大器	Guāng qiánzhì fàngdàqì	Optical pre-amplifier	
光刻机	Guāng qún jiégòu	Optical etching machine	
光区域网络系统	Guāng qūyù wǎngluò xìtǒng	Optical local area network system	
光上/下路复用器	Guāng shàng/xià lù fùyòngqì	Optical add/drop multiplexer	OADM
光时代	Guāng shídài	Optical technology for Internet with multi-wavelength environment (Chinese term based on English abbreviation)	O-TIME
光时分复用	Guāng shífèn fùyòng	Optical time-division multiplexing	OTDM
光时域反射测量法	Guāng shíyù fǎnshè cèliángfǎ	Optical time domain reflectometry	OTDR
光时域反射法	Guāng shíyù fǎnshèfǎ	Optical time domain reflectometry	OTDR
光时域反射计	Guāng shíyù fǎnshèjì	Optical time domain reflectometer	OTDR
光时域反射器	Guāng shíyù fǎnshèqì	Optical time domain reflectometer	OTDR
光时域反射仪	Guāng shíyù fǎnshèyí	Optical time domain reflectometer	OTDR
光衰减器	Guāng shuāijiǎnqì	Optical attenuator	
光数据单元	Guāng shùjù dānyuán	Optical data unit	ODU
光输入输出装置	Guāng shūrù shūchū zhuāngzhì	Optical input and output device	
光弹性调变器	Guāng tánxìng tiáobiànqì	Photoelastic modulator	
光跳	Guāng tiào	Optical frequency hopping	
光条形码阅读器	Guāng tiáoxíng mǎ yuèdúqì	Optical barcode reader	OBR
光通道	Guāng tōngdào	Optical channel	OC
光通道层	Guāng tōngdào céng	Optical channel layer	OCH
光通道代价	Guāng tōngdào dàijià	Optical channel cost	
光通道功率代价	Guāng tōngdào gōnglǜ dàijià	Optical channel power penalty	
光通道适配器	Guāng tōngdào shìpèiqì	Optical channel adapter	OCA
光通道终结	Guāng tōngdào zhōngjié	Optical channel termination	OCT
光通道转接器	Guāng tōngdào zhuǎnjiēqì	Optical channel adapter	OCA
光通路	Guāng tōnglù	Optical channel	OCh
光通路开销处理	Guāng tōnglù kāixiao chǔlǐ	Optical channel overhead handling	OCOH
光通路终结	Guāng tōnglù zhōngjié	Optical channel termination	OCT
光通讯系统	Guāng tōngxùn xìtǒng	Optical communication system	OCS
光突发交换	Guāng tūfā jiāohuàn	Optical burst switching	
光网络单元	Guāng wǎngluò dānyuán	Optical network unit	ONU
光网络终端	Guāng wǎngluò zhōngduān	Optical network termination	ONT
光无源器件	Guāng wúyuán qìjiàn	Optically passive device	OPD
光线路传输码型	Guāng xiànlù chuánshū mǎxíng	Optical line transmission coding	
光线路放大器	Guāng xiànlù fàngdàqì	Optical line amplifier	OLA
光线路后面板	Guāng xiànlù hòumian bǎn	Optic line back panel	OLBP
光线路终端	Guāng xiànlù zhōngduān	Optical line terminal	OLT
光信噪比	Guāng xìn zào bǐ	Optical signal to noise ratio	OSNR
光信道	Guāng xìndào	Optical channel	Och
光信道监控保护	Guāng xìndào jiānkòng bǎohù	Optical transmission protection	OTP
光性能监测器	Guāng xìngnéng jiāncèqì	Optical performance monitor	OPM

光性能监控	Guāng xìngnéng jiānkòng	Optical performance monitoring	OPM
光信号丢失	Guāng xìnhào diūshī	Loss of signal (optical)	LOS
光信号段	Guāng xìnhào duàn	Optical section	OS
光信号-噪声比	Guāng xìnhào-zàoshēng bǐ	Optical signal-to-noise ratio	OSNR
光信令路由协议	Guāng xìnlìng lùyóu xiéyì	Optical signaling and routing protocol	OSRP
光选址光调制器	Guāng xuǎnzhǐ guāng tiáozhìqì	Optically addressed light modulator	OALM
光虚拟专网	Guāng xūnǐ zhuān wǎng	Optical virtual private network	OVPN
光虚拟专用网	Guāng xūnǐ zhuānyòng wǎng	Optical virtual private network	OVPN
光移动通讯系统	Guāng yídòng tōngxùn xìtǒng	Mobile optical communication system	
光因特网论坛	Guāng Yīntèwǎng lùntán	Optical internetworking Forum	OIF
光移相器	Guāng yíxiàngqì	Optical phase shifter	
光用户环路载波系统	Guāng yònghù huánlù zàibō xìtǒng	Optical loop subscriber carrier system	
光有源器件	Guāng yǒuyuán qìjiàn	Optically active device	OAD
光运载第 1 级	Guāng yùnzài dì yī jí	Optical carrier level 1	OC-1
光载波	Guāng zàibō	Optical carrier	OC
光载波级 N	Guāng zàibō jí N	Optical carrier level-N	OC-N
光闸流晶体管	Guāng zháliú jīngtǐguǎn	Photothyristor	
光罩材料	Guāng zhào cáiliào	Photomask material	
光罩制造设备	Guāng zhào zhìzào shèbèi	Mask making equipment (semiconductor mfg)	
光正交码	Guāng zhèngjiāo mǎ	Optical orthogonal code	OOC
光终端复用单元	Guāng zhōngduān fùyòng dānyuán	Optical terminal multiplexer	OTM
光终端复用器	Guāng zhōngduān fùyòngqì	Optical terminal multiplexer	OTM
光转发器	Guāng zhuǎnfāqì	Optical transponder unit	OTU
光转化单元	Guāng zhuǎnhuà dānyuán	Optical transform unit	OTU
光转换单元	Guāng zhuǎnhuàn dānyuán	Optical transponder unit	OTU
光转换器	Guāng zhuǎnhuànqì	Optical transponder	OT
光转换器单元	Guāng zhuǎnhuànqì dānyuán	Optical transponder unit	OTU
光注入器	Guāng zhùrùqì	Optical injector	
光子网连接保护	Guāng zǐwǎng liánjiē bǎohù	Optical sub-network connection protection	O-SNCP
光/电转换器	Guāng/diàn zhuǎnhuànqì	Optical/electronic converter	O/E
光/电/光转换器	Guāng/diàn/guāng zhuǎnhuànqì	Optical-electrical-optical converter	OEO
光笔	Guāngbǐ	Light pen	
光笔	Guāngbǐ	Wand	
光标	Guāngbiāo	Cursor	
光标	Guāngbiāo	Optical mouse	
光标显现	Guāngbiāo xiǎnxiàn	Cursor on	CON
光标隐匿	Guāngbiāo yǐnnì	Cursor off	COF
光笔式条码扫描器	Guāngbǐ-shì tiáomǎ sǎomiáoqì	Wand bar code scanner	
广播	Guǎngbō	Broadcast	
广播传输	Guǎngbō chuánshū	Broadcast transmission	
广播电台	Guǎngbō diàntái	Broadcasting station	
光波分插复用器	Guāngbō fēn chā fùyòngqì	Optical add drop multiplexer	OADM
广播风暴	Guǎngbō fēngbào	Broadcast storm	
广播和未知地址服务器	Guǎngbō hé wèizhī dìzhǐ fúwùqì	Broadcast and unknown server	BUS
广播和未知服务器	Guǎngbō hé wèizhī fúwùqì	Broadcast and unknown server	BUS
广播交叉连接	Guǎngbō jiāochā liánjiē	Broadcast cross-connection	

广播控制功能实体	Guǎngbō kòngzhì gōngnéng shítǐ	Broadcast control functional entity	BCFE
广播控制信道	Guǎngbō kòngzhì xìndào	Broadcast control channel	BCCH
广播控制信道划分	Guǎngbō kòngzhì xìndào huàfēn	Broadcast control channel (BCCH) allocation	
广播搜索	Guǎngbō sōusuǒ	Broadcast search	
广播卫星业务	Guǎngbō wèixīng yèwù	Broadcasting satellite service	BSS
广播信道	Guǎngbō xìndào	Broadcast channel	BCH
广播寻呼系统	Guǎngbō xúnhū xìtǒng	Broadcast paging system	
广播业务	Guǎngbō yèwù	Broadcasting service	
广播与选择网	Guǎngbō yǔ xuǎnzé wǎng	Broadcast and select network	
广播/多播控制	Guǎngbō/duōbō kòngzhì	Broadcast/multicast control	BMC
广播式连接	Guǎngbōshì liánjiē	Broadcast connection type	
光程长度	Guāngchéng chángdù	Optical path length	
广带综合业务数字网	Guǎngdài zōnghé yèwù shùzì wǎng	Broadband integrated services digital network	B-ISDN
光导电池	Guāngdǎo diànchí	Photoconductive cell	
光导数据介面	Guāngdǎo shùjù jièmiàn	Fiber distributed data interface	FDDI
光导纤维	Guāngdǎo xiānwéi	Optical fiber	
光导纤维	Guāngdǎo xiānwéi	Optical fiber	
光导纤维传输系统	Guāngdǎo xiānwéi chuánshū xìtǒng	Fiber optic transmission system	FOTS
光导纤维传送功能	Guāngdǎo xiānwéi chuánsòng gōngnéng	Optical fiber transfer function	OFTF
光导板	Guāngdǎobǎn	Light-guide board	
光导波	Guāngdǎobō	Optical guided wave	OGW
光导管	Guāngdǎoguǎn	Fiber optic lightguide	
光导体	Guāngdǎotǐ	Optical conductor	
光电端机	Guāngdiàn duānjī	Opto-electronic terminal	
光电对抗	Guāngdiàn duìkàng	Electro-optical countermeasures	
光电多路复用开关	Guāngdiàn duōlù fùyòng kāiguān	Opto-electronic multiplex switch	OMS
光电二极管	Guāngdiàn èrjíguǎn	Photo-intrinsic diode	PIN
光电二极管	Guāngdiàn èrjíguǎn	Photoelectric diode	
光电感烟探测器	Guāngdiàn gǎnyān tàncèqì	Photoelectric smoke detector	PSD
光电合架	Guāngdiàn héjià	Opto-electronic combiner	
光电集成电路	Guāngdiàn jíchéng diànlù	Opto-electronic integrated circuit	OEIC
光电晶体	Guāngdiàn jīngtǐ	Phototransistor	
光电灵敏度	Guāngdiàn língmǐndù	Opto-electronic responsivity	
光电耦合器	Guāngdiàn ǒuhéqì	Photocoupler	
光电扫描仪	Guāngdiàn sǎomiáoyí	Opto-electronic scanner	
光电探测器	Guāngdiàn tàncèqì	Photo detector	PD
光电管	Guāngdiànguǎn	Phototube	
光电子增倍管	Guāngdiànzǐ zēngbèiguǎn	Photomultiplier	PMT
光碟	Guāngdié	Compact disc	CD
光碟	Guāngdié	Optical disk	
光碟基板	Guāngdié jībǎn	Optical disk substrate	
光碟基板材料	Guāngdié jībǎn cáiliào	Optical disk substrate material	
光碟录制机	Guāngdié lùzhìjī	Compact disk recorder	
光碟驱动器	Guāngdié qūdòngqì	Compact disk drive	
光碟数据记录材料	Guāngdié shùjù jìlù cáiliào	Optical disk data storage material	
光化电效应	Guānghuà diàn xiàoyìng	Actinoelectric effect	AE

光刻模拟软件	Guāngkè mónǐ ruǎnjiàn	Photolithography simulation software (semiconductor mfg)	
光刻机	Guāngkèjī	Compact disk/read-write	CD-RW
光缆	Guānglǎn	Optical fiber cable	
光缆单元	Guānglǎn dānyuán	Cable unit	
光缆分布数据接口	Guānglǎn fēnbù shùjù jiēkǒu	Fiber distributed data interface	FDDIF
光缆分配式数据接口	Guānglǎn fēnpèishì shùjù jiēkǒu	Fiber distributed data interface	FDDI
光缆固定接头	Guānglǎn gùdìng jiētóu	Optical cable splice	
光缆或光缆捆束分支	Guānglǎn huò guānglǎn kǔnshù fēnzhī	Cable or harness branch	
光缆或光缆捆束主干	Guānglǎn huò guānglǎn kǔnshù zhǔgàn	Cable or harness run	
光缆护套	Guānglǎn hùtào	Optical cable jacketing	
光缆捆束	Guānglǎn kǔnshù	Harness	
光缆捆束组件	Guānglǎn kǔnshù zǔjiàn	Harness assembly	
光缆连接器	Guānglǎn liánjiēqì	Optical cable connector	
光缆连接器界面	Guānglǎn liánjiēqì jièmiàn	Optical cable connector interface	
光缆喷射器	Guānglǎn pēnshèqì	Fiber optic cable blower	
光缆数字设备	Guānglǎn shùzì shèbèi	Fiber optic cable digital equipment	GS
光缆线	Guānglǎn xiàn	Fiber optic cable strand	FOC
光缆线路	Guānglǎn xiànlù	Fiber optic cable line	
光缆远程在线监控系统	Guānglǎn yuǎnchéng zàixiàn jiānkòng xìtǒng	Optical cable remote on-line supervision system	
光缆制造设备	Guānglǎn zhìzào shèbèi	Fiber optic cable manufacturing equipment	
光缆资源管理系统	Guānglǎn zīyuán guǎnlǐ xìtǒng	Optical cable resources management system	
光缆组件	Guānglǎn zǔjiàn	Cable assembly	
光流 ATM 交换机	Guāngliú ATM jiāohuànjī	Lightstream ATM switch	
光流交换	Guāngliú jiāohuàn	Optical flow switching	
光盘	Guāngpán	Optical disk	
光盘技术	Guāngpán jìshù	Optical disk technology	
光盘文件系统	Guāngpán wénjiàn xìtǒng	Compact disk file system	CDFS
光谱分割	Guāngpǔ fēngē	Spectrum-sliced	
光谱特性	Guāngpǔ tèxìng	Spectral characteristic	
光谱响应范围	Guāngpǔ xiǎngyìng fànwéi	Spectral response range	
光谱信号	Guāngpǔ xìnhào	Spectral signature	
光谱线宽度	Guāngpǔxiàn kuāndù	Spectral line width	
光色材料	Guāngsè cáiliào	Photochromic material	
光栅光阀	Guāngshān guāngfá	Grating light valves	GLVs
光栅耦合取样反射器	Guāngshān ǒuhé qǔyàng fǎnshèqì	Grating coupler sampled reflector	GCSR
光栅扫描	Guāngshān sǎomiáo	Raster sweep	
光栅图形元素	Guāngshān túxíng yuánsù	Raster graphics element	
光栅字体	Guāngshān zìtǐ	Raster fonts	
光束发散度	Guāngshù fāsàndù	Beam divergence	
光束宽度	Guāngshù kuāndù	Beamwidth	
光束寻址存储	Guāngshù xúnzhǐ cúnchǔ	Addressable optical storage	
光束直径	Guāngshù zhíjìng	Beam diameter	
光纤	Guāngxiān	Optical fiber	
光纤	Guāngxiān	Optical fiber	
光纤包层	Guāngxiān bāocéng	Fiber cladding	

光纤保护管	Guāngxiān bǎohù guǎn	Protective tube for fiber optic fiber	
光纤编织带涂敷机	Guāngxiān biānzhīdài túfūjī	Fiber organizer tape application	FOTA
光纤标准连接器	Guāngxiān biāozhǔn liánjiēqì	Standard optical fiber connector	
光纤标准耦合器	Guāngxiān biāozhǔn ǒuhéqì	Standard optical fiber coupler	
光纤波分复用耦合器	Guāngxiān bōfēn fùyòng ǒuhéqì	Optical fiber wave division multiplexing coupler	
光纤剥线夹	Guāngxiān bōxiàn jiā	Fiber optic stripper	
光纤布拉格光栅	Guāngxiān Bù-lā-gé guāngshān	Fiber Bragg grating	FBG
光纤材料	Guāngxiān cáiliào	Fiber optic materials	
光纤测试设备与测试方法	Guāngxiān cèshì shèbèi yǔ cèshì fāngfǎ	Fiber optic test equipment and procedures	FOTP
光纤插孔	Guāngxiān chākǒng	Fiber jack	FJ
光纤传感器	Guāngxiān chuángǎnqì	Optical fiber sensor	OFS
光纤传输系统	Guāngxiān chuánshū xìtǒng	Optical fiber transmission system	OFTS
光纤传输线	Guāngxiān chuánshūxiàn	Optical fiber transmission line	OFTL
光纤存储中心	Guāngxiān cúnchǔ zhōngxīn	Fiber storage center	FSC
光纤带	Guāngxiān dài	Optical ribbon cable	
光纤带	Guāngxiān dài	Fiber optic ribbon	
光纤带	Guāngxiān dài	Optical ribbon cable	
光线带光缆	Guāngxiàn dài guānglǎn	Optical fiber ribbon cable	
光纤带光缆	Guāngxiān dài guānglǎn	Ribbon fiber optic cable	
光纤单窗口带宽耦合器	Guāngxiān dānchuāngkǒu dàikuān ǒuhéqì	Fiber optic single window bandwidth coupler	
光纤到办公室	Guāngxiān dào bàngōngshì	Fiber to the office	FTTO
光纤到办公桌	Guāngxiān dào bàngōngzhuō	Fiber to the desk	FTTD
光纤到大楼	Guāngxiān dào dàlóu	Fiber to the building	FTTB
光纤到服务区	Guāngxiān dào fúwùqū	Fiber to the serving area	FSA
光纤到供电服务区	Guāngxiān dào gōngdiàn fúwùqū	Fiber-to-the power supply serving area	FPSA
光纤到户	Guāngxiān dào hù	Fiber to the home	FTTH
光纤到机柜	Guāngxiān dào jī guì	Fiber to the cabinet	FTTCab
光纤到家	Guāngxiān dào jiā	Fiber to the home	FTTH
光纤到家庭	Guāngxiān dào jiātíng	Fiber to the home	FTTH
光纤到节点	Guāngxiān dào jiédiǎn	Fiber to the node	FTTN
光纤到节点	Guāngxiān dào jiédiǎn	Fiber to the node	FTTN
光纤到接线柜箱	Guāngxiān dào jiēxiàn guìxiāng	Fiber to the cabinet	FTTCab
光纤到近邻	Guāngxiān dào jìnlín	Fiber to the curb	FTTC
光纤到馈线	Guāngxiān dào kuìxiàn	Fiber to feeder	FTF
光纤到楼	Guāngxiān dào lóu	Fiber to the building	FTTB
光纤到路边	Guāngxiān dào lùbiān	Fiber to the curb	FTTC
光纤到无源同轴（网络）	Guāngxiān dào wúyuán tóngzhóu (wǎngluò)	Fiber-to-the passive coaxial (network)	FTPC
光纤到小区	Guāngxiān dào xiǎoqū	Fiber to the service area	FTTSA
光纤到小区	Guāngxiān dào xiǎoqū	Fiber to the zone	FTTZ
光纤到用户	Guāngxiān dào yònghù	Fiber to the customer	FTTC
光纤到住地	Guāngxiān dào zhùdì	Fiber to the premises	FTTP
光纤到桌面	Guāngxiān dào zhuōmiàn	Fiber to the desk	FTTD
光纤到最后一个放大器	Guāngxiān dào zuìhòu yīgè fàngdàqì	Fiber to the last amplifier	FTLA
光纤电缆	Guāngxiān diànlǎn	Optical fiber cable	OFC
光纤地线	Guāngxiān dìxiàn	Fiber-optic ground	FOG

光纤段	Guāngxiān duàn	Optical section	OS
光纤端面研磨设备	Guāngxiān duānmiàn yánmó shèbèi	Fiber optic polishing machine	
光纤放大器	Guāngxiān fàngdàqì	Optical fiber amplifer	OFA
光纤纺丝设备	Guāngxiān fǎngsī shèbèi	Fiber optic spinning equipment	
光纤分布数据接口	Guāngxiān fēnbù shùjù jiēkǒu	Fiber distributed data interface	FDDI
光纤分布式数据接口	Guāngxiān Fēnbùshì shùjù jiēkǒu	Fiber distributed data interface	FDDI
光纤分配板	Guāngxiān fēnpèibǎn	Fiber optic distribution panel	
光纤分配架	Guāngxiān fēnpèijià	Optical distribution frame	ODF
光纤复合架空地线	Guāngxiān fùhé jiàkōng dìxiàn	Optical fiber pole-mounted composite ground wire	OPGW
光纤复合接地线	Guāngxiān fùhé jiēdìxiàn	Optical fiber composite ground wire	OPGW
光纤复合相导线	Guāngxiān fùhé xiāng dǎoxiàn	Optical phase conductor (FOC)	OPPC
光纤服务平台	Guāngxiān fúwù píngtái	Fiber service platform	FSP
光纤干扰测量传感器	Guāngxiān gānrǎo cèliáng chuángǎnqì	Fiber optic interferometric sensor	FOIS
光线跟踪	Guāngxiàn gēnzōng	Ray tracing	
光纤光栅外腔波长转换器	Guāngxiān guāngshān wàiqiāng bōcháng zhuǎnhuànqì	Fiber grating outer chamber wavelength transformer	
光纤光栅型增益均衡器	Guāngxiān guāngshānxíng zēngyì jūnhéngqì	Fiber grating-type gain equalizer	GEQ
光纤光源	Guāngxiān guāngyuán	Fiber optic illuminator	
光纤管理箱（碟）	Guāngxiān guǎnlǐ xiāng (dié)	Fiber management trays	FMT
光纤固定接头	Guāngxiān gùdìng jiētóu	Optical fiber splice	
光纤骨干网	Guāngxiān gǔgàn wǎng	Optical backbone network	
光纤缓冲层	Guāngxiān huǎnchōngcéng	Fiber buffer	
光纤环路系统	Guāngxiān huánlù xìtǒng	Fiber in the loop	FITL
光纤环路转换器	Guāngxiān huánlù zhuǎnhuànqì	Optical fiber loop converter	
光纤互联	Guāngxiān hùlián	Fiber connection	FICON
光纤互连网络论坛	Guāngxiān hùlián wǎngluò lùntán	Optical internetworking forum	OIF
光纤互连装置	Guāngxiān hùlián zhuāngzhì	Lightguide interconnection unit	LIU
光纤混成元件	Guāngxiān hùnchéng yuánjiàn	Fiber optic hybrid device	
光纤架空地线	Guāngxiān jiàkōng dìxiàn	Optical power grounded waveguide optical fiber	OPGW
光纤接口模块	Guāngxiān jiēkǒu mókuài	Fiber interface module	FIM
光纤接入网	Guāngxiān jiērùwǎng	Optical access network	OAN
光纤接续盒	Guāngxiān jiēxùhé	Fiber optic closure	
光纤激光器	Guāngxiān jīguāngqì	Fiber laser	FL
光纤基准面	Guāngxiān jīzhǔnmiàn	Fiber reference surface	
光纤局域网委员会	Guāngxiān júyùwǎng wěiyuánhuì	Fiber optics lan section (of TIA, US)	FOLS
光纤宽带耦合器	Guāngxiān kuāndài ǒuhéqì	Optical fiber broadband coupler	
光纤拉曼放大器	Guāngxiān lā-màn fàngdàqì	Fiber optic Raman amplifier	FRA
光纤拉伸试验	Guāngxiān lāshēn shìyàn	Fiber pulling test	
光纤连接	Guāngxiān liánjiē	Fiber connection	Ficon
光纤连接器	Guāngxiān liánjiēqì	Optical fiber connector	
光纤连接器界面	Guāngxiān liánjiēqì jièmiàn	Optical fiber connector interface	
光纤链路协商脉冲	Guāngxiān liànlù xiéshāng màichōng	Fiber link negotiation pulses	FLNPs
光纤面板	Guāngxiān miànbǎn	Fiber optic faceplate	FOFP
光纤扭力试验	Guāngxiān niǔlì shìyàn	Fiber torsion test	
光纤耦合显示器	Guāngxiān ǒuhé xiǎnshìqì	Optics coupling display unit	OCDU
光纤耦合器	Guāngxiān ǒuhéqì	Optical coupler, tap/splitter	

光纤抛光机	Guāngxiān pāoguāngjī	Fiber polisher	FPOL
光纤千米	Guāngxiān qiānmǐ	Fiber kilometers (fiber-km)	
光纤全业务网	Guāngxiān quán yèwù wǎng	Optical full service network	
光纤熔接	Guāngxiān róngjiē	Fiber fusion splice	
光纤融接设备	Guāngxiān róngjiē shèbèi	Fiber optic fusion splice equipment	
光纤熔接机	Guāngxiān róngjiējī	Optical fiber fusion splicer	
光纤软线	Guāngxiān ruǎnxiàn	Optical fiber cord	
光纤散射	Guāngxiān sǎnshè	Fiber scattering	
光纤色散	Guāngxiān sèsàn	Fiber dispersion	
光纤声传感器	Guāngxiān shēng chuángǎnqì	Acoustic fiber sensor	
光纤束	Guāngxiān shù	Optical fiber bundle	
光纤束护套	Guāngxiān shù hùtào	Bundle jacket	
光纤衰减	Guāngxiān shuāijiǎn	Fiber attenuation	
光纤双窗口带宽耦合器	Guāngxiān shuāngchuāngkǒu dàikuān ǒuhéqì	Optical fiber two-window bandwidth coupler	
光纤双芯连接器	Guāngxiān shuāngxīn liánjiēqì	Optical fiber duplex connector	
光纤双芯适配器	Guāngxiān shuāngxīn shìpèiqì	Optical fiber duplex adapter	
光纤跳接线	Guāngxiān tiàojiēxiàn	Fiber optic patchcord pigtail	
光纤跳线插头	Guāngxiān tiàoxiàn chātóu	Optical jumper	
光纤调制解调器	Guāngxiān tiáozhì jiětiáoqì	Fiber optic modem	FOM
光纤通道	Guāngxiān tōngdào	Fiber channel	
光纤通道存储网络	Guāngxiān tōngdào cúnchǔ wǎngluò	Fiber channel storage network	FCSN
光纤通道单字节	Guāngxiān tōngdào dānzì jié	Fiber channel single bytes	FC_SB
光纤通道第三代通用服务	Guāngxiān tōngdào dì sān dài tōngyòng fúwù	Fiber channel third-generation generic services	FC-GS-3
光纤通道第二代通用服务	Guāngxiān tōngdào dì' èr dài tōngyòng fúwù	Fiber channel second-generation generic services	FC-GS-2
光纤通道服务协议	Guāngxiān tōngdào fúwù xiéyì	Fiber channel service protocol	FSP
光纤通道工业协会	Guāngxiān tōngdào gōngyè xiéhuì	Fiber Channel Industry Association	FCIA
光纤通道环路接入	Guāngxiān tōngdào huánlù jiērù	Fiber channel - fabric loop attachment	FC-FLA
光纤通道环路社团	Guāngxiān tōngdào huánlù shètuán	Fiber channel loop community	FCLC
光纤通道交换架构	Guāngxiān tōngdào jiāohuàn jiàgòu	Fiber channel switch fabric	FC-SW
光纤通道通用传输	Guāngxiān tōngdào tōngyòng chuánshū	Fiber channel - common transport	FC-CT
光纤通道通用服务	Guāngxiān tōngdào tōngyòng fúwù	Fiber channel - generic services	FC-GS
光纤通道协会	Guāngxiān tōngdào xiéhuì	Fiber Channel Association	FCA
光纤通道协议	Guāngxiān tōngdào xiéyì	Fiber channel protocol	FCP
光纤通道虚拟接口	Guāngxiān tōngdào xūnǐ jiēkǒu	Fiber channel virtual interface	FC-VI
光纤通道一般要求	Guāngxiān tōngdào yībān yāoqiú	Fiber channel - fabric generic requirements	FC-FG
光纤通道仲裁环路	Guāngxiān tōngdào zhòngcái huán lù	Fiber channel - arbitrated loop	FC-AL
光纤通信	Guāngxiān tōngxìn	Optical fiber communications	OFC
光纤通信公司	Guāngxiān tōngxìn gōngsī	Fiber Optic Communication, Inc (Taiwan)	FOCI
光纤通信国际会议	Guāngxiān tōngxìn guójì huìyì	Optical fiber communication conference	OFC
光纤-同轴电缆混合系统	Guāngxiān –tóngzhóu diànlǎn hùnhé xìtǒng	Hybrid fiber coax	HFC
光纤铜轴混合网	Guāngxiān tóngzhóu hùnhé wǎng	Hybrid fiber-coaxial network	HFC
光纤陀螺	Guāngxiān tuóluó	Fiber optic gyroscope	
光纤网	Guāngxiān wǎng	Fiber optic net	FON
光纤网络	Guāngxiān wǎngluò	Fibernet inbuilding network	FIN
光纤网络承包公司	Guāngxiān wǎngluò chéngbāo gōngsī	Fiber Optic Network Solutions Corp. (US)	FONS Corp

光纤网络单元	Guāngxiān wǎngluò dānyuán	Optical network unit	ONU
光纤无线电	Guāngxiān wúxiàndiàn	Radio over fiber	ROF
光纤线路终端	Guāngxiān xiànlù zhōngduān	Optical line terminal	OLT
光纤显示器	Guāngxiān xiǎnshìqì	Optical fiber display	
光纤显微镜	Guāngxiān xiǎnwēijìng	Fiber-optic microscope	FOMS
光纤信道	Guāngxiān xìndào	Fiber channel	FC
光纤信道和光纤信道协议	Guāngxiān xìndào hé guāngxiān xìndào xiéyì	Fiber channel and fiber channel protocol (ANSI use)	FC & FCP
光纤吸收	Guāngxiān xīshōu	Fiber absorption	
光纤压力传感器	Guāngxiān yālì chuángǎnqì	Optical fiber pressure sensor	
光纤仪表销售公司	Guāngxiān yíbiǎo xiāoshòu gōngsī	Fiber Instrument Sales, Inc (US)	FIS
光纤引线炉	Guāngxiān yǐnxiàn lú	Fiber optic furnace	
光纤用户环路	Guāngxiān yònghù huánlù	Fiber to the loop	FTTL
光纤用户环路	Guāngxiān yònghù huánlù	Fiber in the loop	FTTL
光纤用户线路终端	Guāngxiān yònghù xiànlù zhōngduān	Fiber optic subscriber line terminal	FSLT
光纤余长	Guāngxiān yú cháng	Excess fiber length	EFL
光纤预型体	Guāngxiān yùxíngtǐ	Fiber optic preform	
光纤预制棒	Guāngxiān yùzhì bàng	Optical fiber preform	
光纤终端模块	Guāngxiān zhōngduān mókuài	Optical terminal module	
光纤终端箱	Guāngxiān zhōngduān xiāng	Fiber optic distribution box	
光纤中继器连接	Guāngxiān zhōngjìqì liánjiē	Fiber optic inter-repeater link	FOIRL
光纤中继站间连接	Guāngxiān zhōngjìzhàn-jiān liánjiē	Fiber optic inter-repeater link	FOIRL
光纤着色机	Guāngxiān zhuosèjī	Optical fiber coating machine	
光纤最短路径优先协议	Guāngxiān zuìduǎn lùjìng yōuxiān xiéyì	Fabric shortest path first	FSPF
光纤-公里	Guāngxiān--gōnglǐ	Fiber-kilometer	F-km
光纤缆分布式数据接口	Guāngxiānlǎn Fēnbùshì shùjù jiēkǒu	Fiber distributed data interface	FDDI
光学玻璃	Guāngxué bōli	Optical glass	
光学材料	Guāngxué cáiliào	Optical material	
光学材料机械加工	Guāngxué cáiliào jīxiè jiāgōng	Optical material machining service	
光学测距	Guāngxué cèjù	Optical distance measurement	
光学测距仪	Guāngxué cèjùyí	Optical distance measuring device	
光学砥粒研磨材料	Guāngxué dǐlì yánmó cáiliào	Optical-powder or grit abrasive	
光学定位系统	Guāngxué dìngwèi xìtǒng	Optical positioning system	OPS
光学砥石研磨材料	Guāngxué dǐshí yánmó cáiliào	Optical-wheel abrasive	
光学滑鼠	Guāngxué huáshǔ	Optical mouse	
光学馈电系统	Guāngxué kuìdiàn xìtǒng	Optical feed system	
光学连接	Guāngxué liánjiē	Optical connection	
光学录取设备	Guāngxué lùqǔ shèbèi	Light-pen extraction equipment	
光学设计顾问	Guāngxué shèjì gùwèn	Optical design consultant	
光学设计及技术服务	Guāngxué shèjì jí jìshù fúwù	Optical design and engineering services	
光学设计软件及设备	Guāngxué shèjì ruǎnjiàn jí shèbèi	Optical design software and equipment	
光学数字音频信息处理机	Guāngxué shùzì yīnpín xìnxī chǔlǐjī	Optical digital voice processor	ODVP
光学缩微光刻加密技术	Guāngxué suōwēi guāngkè jiāmì jìshù	Optical micro-photo-engraving encryption	
光学探头	Guāngxué tàntóu	Optical probe	OP
光学陶瓷	Guāngxué táocí	Photoceramic	
光学条码识读	Guāngxué tiáomǎ shídú	Optical barcode recognition	OBR

光学信号处理	Guāngxué xìnhào chǔlǐ	Optical signal processing	OSP
光学研磨材料	Guāngxué yánmó cáiliào	Optical-coated abrasive	
光学印表机	Guāngxué yìnbiǎojī	Optical printer	
光学元件订制	Guāngxué yuánjiàn dìngzhì	Optics custom fabrication	
光学元件研磨加工设备	Guāngxué yuánjiàn yánmó jiāgōng shèbèi	Optical device polishing machine	
光学元件真空蒸镀设备	Guāngxué yuánjiàn zhēnkōng zhēng dù shèbèi	Optical device vacuum evaporation equipment	
光学中继设备	Guāngxué zhōngjì shèbèi	Optical repeater equipment	ORE
光学桌平台	Guāngxué zhuō píngtái	Optical table top	
光学字符识别	Guāngxué zìfú shíbié	Optical character recognition	OCR
光学字符识读	Guāngxué zìfú shídú	Optical character recognition	OCR
光学字元阅读机	Guāngxué zìyuán yuèdújī	Optical character recognition equipment	OCR
光学用胶合剂	Guāngxué-yòng jiāohéjì	Optical cement	
光学用接著剂	Guāngxué-yòng jiēzhejì	Optical adhesive	
光学用气体	Guāngxué-yòng qìtǐ	Gases for optical applications	
光掩膜检测管理	Guāngyǎnmó jiǎncè guǎnlǐ	Reticle inspection manager (semiconductor mfg)	RIM
广义表	Guǎngyì biǎo	Generalized list	
广义处理器共享	Guǎngyì chǔlǐqì gòngxiǎng	General processor sharing	GPS
广义可靠性	Guǎngyì kěkàoxìng	Dependability	
广义逆矩阵	Guǎngyì nì jǔzhèn	Generalized inverse matrix	
广义相位控制	Guǎngyì xiàngwèi kòngzhì	Generalized phase control	
广义线性模型	Guǎngyì xiànxìng móxíng	Generalized linear model	
广域加强系统	Guǎngyù jiāqiáng xìtǒng	Wide area augmentation system	WAAS
广域信息服务系统	Guǎngyù xìnxī fúwù xìtǒng	Wide area information service	WAIS
广域信息服务系统	Guǎngyù xìnxī fúwù xìtǒng	Wide area information service	WAIS
光域业务互联	Guāngyù yèwù hùlián	Optical domain service interworking	ODSI
光域业务互连	Guāngyù yèwù hùlián	Optical domain service interconnect	ODSI
光域业务互连联盟	Guāngyù yèwù hùlián liánméng	Optical Domain Services Internetworking Federation	ODSI
光域业务内部连接	Guāngyù yèwù nèibù liánjiē	Optical domain service interconnect	ODSI
广域资讯服务	Guǎngyù zīxùn fúwù	Wide area information service	WAIS
光源	Guāngyuán	Light source	
光源耦合器	Guāngyuán ǒuhéqì	Source coupler	
光源设备	Guāngyuán shèbèi	Light source	
广域网	Guǎngyùwǎng	Wide area network	WAN
光轴	Guāngzhóu	Optical axis	
光子带隙	Guāngzǐ dàixì	Photonic band gap	PBG
光子集成电路	Guāngzǐ jíchéng diànlù	Photonic integrated circuit	PIC
光子集成多量子阱快速交换光源	Guāngzǐ jíchéng duō liàngzǐ jǐng kuàisù jiāohuàn guāngyuán	Photon integrated multi-quantum well fast switching light source	
光子禁带	Guāngzǐ jìndài	Photonic band gap	PBG
光子晶体光纤	Guāngzǐ jīngtǐ guāngxiān	Photonic crystal fiber	PCF
光子网连接保护	Guāngzǐ wǎng liánjiē bǎohù	Optical sub-network connection protection	O-SNCP
关机时间	Guānjī shíjiān	Downtime	
关键词	Guānjiàn cí	Keyword	KW
关键路径	Guānjiàn lùjìng	Critical path	
关键字	Guānjiàn zì	Keyword (IPsec)	

管脚位置	Guǎnjiǎo wèizhì	Pin location	
关口	Guānkǒu	Gateway	GW
关口服务节点	Guānkǒu fúwù jiédiǎn	Gateway service node	GSN
关口互连 MSC	Guānkǒu hùlián MSC	Gateway/interworking MSC	G/IW MSC
关口局	Guānkǒu jú	Gateway (exchange)	GW
关口 MSC	Guānkǒu MSC	Gateway MSC	GMSC
关口通信后面板	Guānkǒu tōngxìn hòumian bǎn	Gateway communication back panel	GCBP
关口通信互联网	Guānkǒu tōngxìn hùliánwǎng	Gateway communication interconnection network	GCIN
关口移动交换中心	Guānkǒu yídòng jiāohuàn zhōngxīn	Gateway mobile services switching center	GMSC
关口移动业务交换中心	Guānkǒu yídòng yèwù jiāohuàn zhōngxīn	Gateway mobile switching center	GMSC
关口局	Guānkǒujú	Gateway	GW
管缆通信	Guǎnlǎn tōngxìn	Fiber optic cable communications	
管理安全	Guǎnlǐ ānquán	Administrative security	
管理层	Guǎnlǐ céng	Management layer	
管理程序	Guǎnlǐ chéngxù	Supervisory program	
管理处理器	Guǎnlǐ chùlǐqì	Administrative processor	AP
管理耽误	Guǎnlǐ dānwù	Administrative delay (for corrective maintenance)	
管理单元	Guǎnlǐ dānyuán	Administrative unit	AU
管理单元负指针调整	Guǎnlǐ dānyuán fù zhǐzhēn tiáozhěng	Administrative unit pointer negative justification	AU-NPJE
管理单元告警指示信号	Guǎnlǐ dānyuán gàojǐng zhǐshì xìnhào	Administrative unit alarm indication signal	AU-AIS
管理单元正指针调整	Guǎnlǐ dānyuán zhèng zhǐzhēn tiáozhěng	Administrative unit pointer positive justification	AU-PPJE
管理单元指针	Guǎnlǐ dānyuán zhǐzhēn	Administrative unit pointer	AU PTR
管理单元指针	Guǎnlǐ dānyuán zhǐzhēn	Administrative unit pointer	AUP
管理单元指针丢失	Guǎnlǐ dānyuán zhǐzhēn diūshī	Administrative unit loss of pointer	AU-LOP
管理单元组	Guǎnlǐ dānyuán zǔ	Administrative unit group	AUG
管理点	Guǎnlǐ diǎn	Administrative point	AP
管理点	Guǎnlǐ diǎn	Management point	MP
管理队列	Guǎnlǐ duìliè	Administration queue	
管理对象	Guǎnlǐ duìxiàng	Managed object	MO
管理对象定义规范	Guǎnlǐ duìxiàng dìngyì guīfàn	Guidelines for the definition of managed objects	GDMO
管理对象类	Guǎnlǐ duìxiàng lèi	Managed object class	MOC
管理对象实例	Guǎnlǐ duìxiàng shílì	Managed object instance	MOI
管理方案	Guǎnlǐ fāng'àn	Managed solution	MS
管理加权	Guǎnlǐ jiāquán	Administrative weight	AW
管理结构标识符	Guǎnlǐ jiégòu biāozhì fú	Administrative structure identifier	
管理结构定义	Guǎnlǐ jiégòu dìngyì	Administrative structure definition	
管理面	Guǎnlǐ miàn	Management plane	
管理模块	Guǎnlǐ mókuài	Administration module	AM
管理目标	Guǎnlǐ mùbiāo	Managed object	MO
管理目标初始值	Guǎnlǐ mùbiāo chūshǐ zhí	Initial value managed object	IVMO
管理目标定义指南	Guǎnlǐ mùbiāo dìngyì zhǐnán	Guidelines for the definition of managed objects	GDMO
管理目标一致性句法	Guǎnlǐ mùbiāo yīzhìxìng jùfǎ	Managed object conformance statement	MOCS
管理平面	Guǎnlǐ píngmiàn	Management plane	MP
管理区域	Guǎnlǐ qūyù	Management domains	MD
管理人	Guǎnlǐ rén	Custodian	

管理实体	Guǎnlǐ shítǐ	Management entity	
管理实体 - 物理层原语	Guǎnlǐ shítǐ-wùlǐ céng yuányǔ	Management entity – physical layer (primitive)	MPH
管理数据库	Guǎnlǐ shùjùkù	Management database	
管理网关功能	Guǎnlǐ wǎngguān gōngnéng	Management gateway function	MGF
管理位距	Guǎnlǐ wèi jù	Administrative distance	
管理维护子系统	Guǎnlǐ wéihù zixìtǒng	Administration and maintenance sub-system	AMS
管理信息	Guǎnlǐ xìnxī	Management information	MI
管理信息定义	Guǎnlǐ xìnxī dìngyì	Definition of management information	DMI
管理信息定义库	Guǎnlǐ xìnxī dìngyìkù	Management information library	MIL
管理信息结构	Guǎnlǐ xìnxī jiégòu	Structure of management information	SMI
管理信息模式	Guǎnlǐ xìnxī móshì	Management information model	MIM
管理信息模型	Guǎnlǐ xìnxī móxíng	Management information model	MIM
管理信息目录	Guǎnlǐ xìnxī mùlù	Management information catalogue	MIC
管理信息系统	Guǎnlǐ xìnxī xìtǒng	Management information system	MIS
管理信息业务	Guǎnlǐ xìnxī yèwù	Management information service	MIS
管理信息基	Guǎnlǐ xìnxījī	Management information base	MIB
管理信息库	Guǎnlǐ xìnxīkù	Management information base	MIB
管理信息树	Guǎnlǐ xìnxīshù	Management information tree	MIT
管理系统	Guǎnlǐ xìtǒng	Management system	
管理业务提供者	Guǎnlǐ yèwù tígòngzhě	Management service provider	MSP
管理应用功能	Guǎnlǐ yìngyòng gōngnéng	Management application function	MAF
管理域	Guǎnlǐ yù	Administrative domain	AD
管理域	Guǎnlǐ yù	Management domain	MD
管理域名	Guǎnlǐ yùmíng	Administrative domain name	
管理域名	Guǎnlǐ yùmíng	Management domain name	
管理支持目标	Guǎnlǐ zhīchí mùbiāo	Management support object	MSO
管理支持系统	Guǎnlǐ zhīchí xìtǒng	Administrative support system	ASS
管理终端系统	Guǎnlǐ zhōngduān xìtǒng	Administrative terminal system	ATS
管理中心	Guǎnlǐ zhōngxīn	Administration center	ADC
管理子域	Guǎnlǐ ziyù	Management sub-domain	
管理/通信模块	Guǎnlǐ/Tōngxìn mókuài	Administration module/communication module	AM/CM
关联	Guānlián	Bind, binding	
关联	Guānlián	Association (IPsec)	
关联边	Guānlián biān	Incident edge	
关联电容只读存储器	Guānlián diànróng zhǐ dú cúnchǔqì	Associative capacitive read-only memory	ACROM
关联规则	Guānlián guīzé	Association rule	
关联控制服务单元	Guānlián kòngzhì fúwù dānyuán	Association control service element	ACSE
关联控制服务元素	Guānlián kòngzhì fúwù yuánsù	Association control service element (an ISO standard)	ACSE
关联失效	Guānlián shīxiào	Relevant failure	
关联数据	Guānlián shùjù	Associated data	
关联式容器	Guānlián-shì róngqì	Associative container	
关联式数据库管理系统	Guānlián-shì shùjùkù guǎnlǐ xìtǒng	Relational database management system	RDBMS
管理器	Guǎnlǐqì	Manager	
管理区	Guǎnlǐqū	Administrative area	AA
管理员帐号	Guǎnlǐyuán zhànghào	Administrator account	
管理者	Guǎnlǐzhě	Manager	M

管理者角色	Guǎnlǐzhě juésè	Manager role	
管路	Guǎnlù	Pipeline	
管路式光缆	Guǎnlù-shì guānglǎn	Ducted fiber optic cable	
关守	Guānshǒu	Gatekeeper	GK
关守标识	Guānshǒu biāozhì	Gatekeeper identifier	
关守拒绝	Guānshǒu jùjué	Gatekeeper reject	GRJ
关守请求	Guānshǒu qǐngqiú	Gatekeeper request	GRQ
关守确认	Guānshǒu quèrèn	Gatekeeper confirm (packet protocol)	GCF
关税和贸易总协定	Guānshuì hé màoyì zǒngxiédìng	General Agreement on Tariffs and Trade	GATT
管态	Guǎntài	Supervisor state	
管外气相沉积法	Guǎn-wài qìxiàng chénjī fǎ	Outside-tube vapor deposition (for FOC)	OVD
关系	Guānxi	Relationship	
关系表	Guānxi biǎo	Relationship list	
关系表达式	Guānxi biǎodá shì	Relational expression	
关系操作符	Guānxi cāozuò fú	Relational operator (in FORTRAN)	
关系代数	Guānxi dàishù	Relational algebra	
关系定义	Guānxi dìngyì	Relationship definition	
关系对象	Guānxi duìxiàng	Relationship object	
关系合并	Guānxi hébìng	Relational join	
关系类型	Guānxi lèixíng	Relationship class	
关系类型代码	Guānxi lèixíng dàimǎ	Relationship type codes	
关系联机分析处理	Guānxi liánjī fēnxī chǔlǐ	Relational online analytical processing	ROLAP
关系模型	Guānxi móxíng	Relational model (in SQL Server)	RM
关系目录	Guānxi mùlù	Relationship catalogue	
关系匹配	Guānxi pǐpèi	Relational matching	
关系数据库	Guānxi shùjùkù	Relational database	RDB
关系数据库管理系统	Guānxì shùjùkù guǎnlǐ xìtǒng	Relational database management system	RDBMS
关系算子	Guānxi suànzǐ	Relational operator	
惯性导航	Guànxìng dǎoháng	Inertial navigation	
惯性导航系统	Guànxìng dǎoháng xìtǒng	Inertial navigation system	
惯性定位系统	Guànxìng dìngwèi xìtǒng	Inertial positioning system	
惯性环节（非周期环节）	Guànxìng huánjié (fēizhōuqī huánjié)	Inertia element (aperiodic element)	
惯性矩	Guànxìngjǔ	Moment of inertia	
惯性力	Guànxìnglì	Inertia force	
关系型数据库	Guānxi-xíng shùjùkù	Relational database	
关系型数据库管理系统	Guānxi-xíng shùjùkù guǎnlǐ xìtǒng	Relational database management system	RDBMS
挂起	Guàqǐ	Suspend	
挂起拒绝	Guàqǐ jùjué	Suspend reject	
挂起认可	Guàqǐ rènkě	Suspend acknowledge	
挂起时间	Guàqǐ shíjiān	Hold off time	HO
挂起系统	Guàqǐ xìtǒng	Hung system	
挂式邮政信箱	Guàshì yóuzhèng xìnxiāng	Wall-mounted mail box	
寡行	Guǎxíng	Widow (in word processing)	
孤岛	Gūdǎo	Islanding	
固定比特率	Gùdìng bǐtèlǜ	Constant bit rate	CBR
固定比特率	Gùdìng bǐtèlǜ	Deterministic bit rate	DBR

固定比特率	Gùdìng bǐtèlǜ	Fixed bit rate	FBR
固定比特率业务	Gùdìng bǐtèlǜ yèwù	Constant bit rate service	
固定拨号	Gùdìng bōhào	Fixed dialing number	FDN
固定存储分配	Gùdìng cúnchǔ fēnpèi	Static memory allocation	
固定存储器	Gùdìng cúnchǔqì	Fixed memory	
固定电台	Gùdìng diàntái	Fixed station	
固定端系统	Gùdìng duān xìtǒng	Fixed end systems	
固定分配方式	Gùdìng fēnpèi fāngshì	Static allocation	
固定分析器	Gùdìng fēnxīqì	Fixed analyzer	FA
固定服务器角色	Gùdìng fúwùqì juésè	Fixed server role	
固定光衰减器	Gùdìng guāng shuāijiǎnqì	Fixed optical attenuator	
固定间距	Gùdìng jiānjù	Constant spacing	
固定基地电台	Gùdìng jīdì diàntái	Fixed base station	
固定基准调制	Gùdìng jīzhǔn tiáozhì	Fixed reference modulation	
固定聚合数据类型	Gùdìng jùhé shùjù lèixíng	Fixed-aggregate data type	
固定控制集	Gùdìng kòngzhì jí	Fixed control set	
固定目标检查	Gùdìng mùbiāo jiǎnchá	Fixed object check	
固定色散补偿器	Gùdìng sèsàn bǔchángqì	Fixed dispersion compensator	DCFG
固定衰减器	Gùdìng shuāijiǎnqì	Fixed pad attenuator	
固定数据库角色	Gùdìng shùjùkù juésè	Fixed database role	
固定通信与移动通信相互靠拢	Gùdìng tōngxìn yǔ yídòng tōngxìn xiānghù kàolǒng	Fixed/mobile convergence	FMC
固定网用户率	Gùdìng wǎng yònghùlǜ	Fixed network user rate	FNUR
固定网络通讯服务	Gùdìng wǎngluò tōngxùn fúwù	Fixed network services	FNS
固定卫星通讯	Gùdìng wèixīng tōngxùn	Fixed satellite communications	FSC
固定卫星业务	Gùdìng wèixīng yèwù	Fixed satellite services	FSS
固定无线接入	Gùdìng wúxiàn jiērù	Fixed radio access	FRA
固定无线接入	Gùdìng wúxiàn jiērù	Fixed wireless access	FWA
固定无线网络	Gùdìng wúxiàn wǎngluò	Fixed wireless network	FWN
固定信道分配	Gùdìng xìndào fēnpèi	Fixed channel allocation	FCA
固定信道指配	Gùdìng xìndào zhǐpèi	Fixed channel assignment	
固定业务	Gùdìng yèwù	Fixed service	
固定业务区域的支持	Gùdìng yèwù qūyùde zhīchí	Support of localized service area	SoLSA
固定用户	Gùdìng yònghù	Fixed subscriber	FS
固定用户单元	Gùdìng yònghù dānyuán	Fixed subscriber unit	FSU
固定与移动通信融合	Gùdìng yǔ yídòng tōngxìn rónghé	Fixed-mobile convergence	FMC
固定终端	Gùdìng zhōngduān	Fixed terminal	FT
固定式激光条码扫描器	Gùdìng-shì jīguāng tiáomǎ sǎomiáoqì	Fixed laser bar code scanner	
固定式偏转线圈	Gùdìng-shì piānzhuǎn xiànquān	Fixed deflection coil	
孤儿	Gū'ér	Orphan	
股份合作企业	Gǔfèn hézuò qǐyè	Joint-equity cooperative enterprise	
股份制企业	Gǔfènzhì qǐyè	Joint-equity enterprise	
骨干网络	Gǔgàn wǎngluò	Backbone network	
骨干网连接	Gǔgànwǎng liánjiē	Backbone network connection	BNC
骨干网连接链路	Gǔgànwǎng liánjiē liànlù	Backbone network connection link	BNCL
骨干网连接识别符	Gǔgànwǎng liánjiē shíbiéfú	Backbone network connection identifier	BNC-ID

骨干网载体	Gǔgànwǎng zàitǐ	Backbone bearer	BB
古河电气工业	Gǔ-hé diànqì gōngyè	Furukawa Electric Industries (Japan)	
固化炉	Gùhuà lú	Curing oven	
硅读出单元	Guī dúchū dānyuán	Silicon readout cell	
硅对称开关	Guī duìchèn kāiguān	Silicon symmetrical switch	SSS
硅交换	Guī jiāohuàn	Silicon switching	
硅交换引擎	Guī jiāohuàn yǐnqíng	Silicon switching engine	SSE
硅交换机	Guī jiāohuànjī	Silicon switch	
硅交换机处理器	Guī jiāohuànjī chǔlǐqì	Silicon switch processor	SSP
硅交换机引擎	Guī jiāohuànjī yǐnqíng	Silicon switch engine	SSE
硅片综合系统公司	Guī piàn zōnghé xìtǒng gōngsī	Silicon Integrated Systems Inc.	SiS
硅双向开关	Guī shuāngxiàng kāiguān	Silicon bi-directional switch	SBS
硅芯管	Guī xīn guǎn	Silicon core tubing	
归一最小均方	Guī yī zuìxiǎo jūn fāng	Normalized least mean square	NLMS
硅整流器	Guī zhěngliúqì	Silicon rectifier	SR
归并排序	Guībìng páixù	Merge sort	
归并/集中	Guībìng/jízhōng	Consolidation	
规程	Guīchéng	Process, procedure, (and sometimes protocol)	
规程安全	Guīchéng ānquán	Procedural security	
规程纹理	Guīchéng wénlǐ	Procedural texture (video term)	
归档文件	Guīdàng wénjiàn	Archive file	
轨道	Guǐdào	Orbit	
轨道管	Guǐdào guǎn	Orbitron (mm wave device)	
轨道平面	Guǐdào píngmiàn	Orbital plane (of a satellite)	
轨道倾角	Guǐdào qīngjiǎo	Orbital inclination (of an earth satellite)	
轨道要素	Guǐdào yàosù	Orbital elements	
轨道周期	Guǐdào zhōuqī	Orbital period (of a satellite)	
规范	Guīfàn	Specification	
规范和描述语言	Guīfàn hé miáoshù yǔyán	Specification and description language	SDL
规范描述语言	Guīfàn miáoshù yǔyán	Specification description language	SDL
规范帧标识	Guīfàn zhèng biāozhì	Authority frame identifier	AFI
规范化规则	Guīfànhuà guīzé	Normalization rules	
规格	Guīgé	Specification	
规格化	Guīgéhuà	Normalize	
硅谷留美博士企业家协会	Guīgǔ liúměi bóshì qǐyèjiā xiéhuì	Silicon Valley Chinese Overseas Business Association	SCOBA
硅谷中国工程师协会	Guīgǔ Zhōngguó gōngchéngshī xiéhuì	Silicon Valley Chinese Engineer Association	SCEA
归还	Guīhuán	Deallocate	
轨迹球	Guǐjì qiú	Trackball	
桂林光通信研究所	Guìlín guāngtōngxìn yánjiūsuǒ	Guilin Institute of Optical Communications	GIOC
归零码	Guīlíng mǎ	Return to zero coding	
归零制	Guīlíng zhì	Return to zero	RZ
硅上液晶	Guī-shàng yèjīng	Liquid crystal on silicon	LCOS
归属代理	Guīshǔ dàilǐ	Home agent	HA
归属单元	Guīshǔ dānyuán	Home unit	HU
归属地址	Guīshǔ dìzhǐ	Home address	HA
归属公用陆地移动通信网	Guīshǔ gōngyòng lùdì yídòng tōngxìnwǎng	Home public land mobile network	HPLMN

归属环境	Guīshǔ huánjìng	Home environment	HE
归属环境附加值业务提供者	Guīshǔ huánjìng fùjiāzhí yèwù tígòngzhě	Home environment value added service provider	HE-VASP
归属寄存位置寄存器	Guīshǔ jìcún wèizhì jìcúnqì	Home location register	HLR
归属 PLMN	Guīshǔ PLMN	Home PLMN	HPLMN
归属位置寄存器	Guīshǔ wèizhì jìcúnqì	Home location register	HLR
归属用户服务器	Guīshǔ yònghù fúwùqì	Home subscriber server	HSS
归属用户位置寄存器	Guīshǔ yònghù wèizhì jìcúnqì	Home location register	HLR
归属区	Guīshǔqū	Home area	
归一化差斜率	Guīyīhuà chà xiélǜ	Normalized difference slope	
归一化导纳	Guīyīhuà dǎonà	Normalized admittance	
归一化方向图	Guīyīhuà fāngxiàng tú	Normalized pattern	
归一化复数波振幅	Guīyīhuà fùshùbō zhènfú	Normalized complex wave amplitude	
归一化最小均方误差	Guīyīhuà zuìxiǎo jūnfāng wùchā	Normalized least mean squares	NLMS
归一化阻抗	Guīyīhuà zǔkàng	Normalized impedance	
归一化的偏置	Guīyīhuàde piānzhì	Normalized offset	
归约算法	Guīyuē suànfǎ	Reduction algorithm	
规则	Guīzé	Rule (IPsec)	
规则抽取	Guīzé chōuqǔ	Rule extraction	
规则集	Guīzé jí	Rule set	
规则脉冲激励编码	Guīzé màichōng jīlì biānmǎ	Regular pulse excitation	RPE
规则脉冲激励—长时预测—线性预测编码	Guīzé màichōng jīlì— chángshí yùcè—xiànxìng yùcè biānmǎ	Regular pulse excited-long term predition-linear predictive coding	RPE-LTP-LPC
规则脉冲激励线性预测编码	Guīzé màichōng jīlì xiànxìng yùcè biānmǎ	Regular pulse excitation linear predictive coding	
规则脉冲激励-长期预测-线性预测编码	Guīzé màichōng jīlì--chángqī yùcè—xiànxìng yùcè biānmǎ	Regular pulse excitation - long-term prediction - linear predictive coding	RPE-LTP-LPC
规则脉冲激励长时预测编码	Guīzé màichōng jīlì--chángshí yùcè biānmǎ	Regular pulse excitation long-term predictive coding	REP-LPC
规则信号	Guīzé xìnhào	Regular signal	
规则选项	Guīzé xuǎnxiàng	Rule option	
规章技术基础	Guīzhāng jìshù jīchǔ	Technical basis for regulation	TBR
估计零售价	Gūjì língshòujià	Estimated retail price	ERP
骨架	Gǔjià	Slotted core (optical fiber type)	
骨架结构	Gǔjià jiégòu	Framed structure	
固件	Gùjiàn	Firmware	
固件通道	Gùjiàn tōngdào	Firmware channel	FMCH
固件中心	Gùjiàn zhōngxīn	Firmware hub	FWH
骨架式光纤带	Gǔjià-shì guāngxiān dài	Slotted-core optical ribbon	
骨架式光纤带光缆	Gǔjià-shì guāngxiān dài guānglǎn	Slotted-core ribbon optical cable	
固结	Gùjié	Consolidation	
固结试验	Gùjié shìyàn	Consolidation test	
顾客	Gùkè	Customer	
孤立文件	Gūlì wénjiàn	Orphan file	
滚动	Gǔndòng	Scroll	
滚动条	Gǔndòng tiáo	Scroll bar	
滚降	Gǔnjiàng	Roll-off	
滚筒因数	Gǔntǒng yīnshù	Drum factor	

国标扩展码	Guóbiāo kuòzhǎn mǎ	GBK encoding	
国标码	Guóbiāo mǎ	GB code (computer code for Chinese characters)	
过采样技术	Guòcǎiyàng jìshù	Over-sampling	
过程	Guòchéng	Process	
过程	Guòchéng	Procedure	
过程非结构化补充服务请求	Guòchéng fēijiégòuhuà bǔchōng fúwù qǐngqiú	Process unstructured supplementary services request	PSSR
过程非结构化补充服务数据	Guòchéng fēijiégòuhuà bǔchōng fúwù shùjù	Process unstructured supplementary services data	PSSD
过程缓存	Guòchéng huǎncún	Procedure cache	
过程监督系统	Guòchéng jiāndū xìtǒng	Process monitor system	PMS
过程控制计算机	Guòchéng kòngzhì jìsuànjī	Process control computer	
过程控制语言	Guòchéng kòngzhì yǔyán	Process control language	PCL
过程蓝图	Guòchéng lántú	Process blueprint (in Visual Basic)	
过程模型模拟环境	Guòchéng móxíng mónǐ huánjìng	Process model simulating environment	PMSE
过程输入/输出装置	Guòchéng shūrù/shūchū zhuāngzhì	Process input/output device	PI/O
过程显示装置	Guòchéng xiǎnshì zhuāngzhì	Process display	
过程知识	Guòchéng zhīshi	Process knowledge	
过程化的	Guòchénghuàde	Procedural	
过程式的	Guòchéng-shìde	Procedural	
过程型语言	Guòchéng-xíng yǔyán	Procedural language	
过冲	Guòchōng	Overshoot	
过充电	Guòchōngdiàn	Overcharge (a battery)	
国道等级	Guódào děngjí	National road class	
过电流	Guòdiànliú	Overcurrent	
过电流保护	Guòdiànliú bǎohù	Over-current protection	
过电流保护装置	Guòdiànliú bǎohù zhuāngzhì	Over-current protective device	
过电压	Guòdiànyā	Over-voltage	
过电压保护	Guòdiànyā bǎohù	Over-voltage protection	
过渡	Guòdù	Transition	
过度发送	Guòdù fāsòng	Spew	
过度建设	Guòdù jiànshè	Overbuild	
过渡桥接	Guòdù qiáojiē	Transit bridging	
过渡时间	Guòdù shíjiān	Elapsed time	
过度拥挤	Guòdù yōngjǐ	Overcrowding	
过度阻尼	Guòdù zǔní	Over-damping	
过度期本地管理接口	Guòdùqī běndì guǎnlǐ jiēkǒu	Interim local management interface	ILMI
过渡型变异函数	Guòdù-xíng biànyì hánshù	Transitional variogram	
国防采办	Guófáng cǎibàn	Defense Acquisition Office (US)	DAO
国防建模和仿真办公室	Guófáng jiànmó hé fǎngzhēn bàngōngshì	Defense Modeling and Simulation Office (US)	DMSO
国防信息系统局	Guófáng xìnxī xìtǒngjú	Defense Information Systems Agency (US)	DISA
国防部通信局	Guófángbù tōngxìn jú	Defense Communication Agency (US)	DCA
国防部总体过渡策略	Guófángbù zǒngtǐ guòdù cèlüè	Department of Defense (DOD) kernel transition strategy	DDKTS
过放电	Guòfàngdiàn	Over-discharge (run down a battery)	
过负载	Guòfùzài	Overload	
过荷保护电路	Guòhè bǎohù diànlù	Overload protecting circuit	
过荷点	Guòhè diǎn	Overload point	

过荷分级控制	Guòhè fēnjí kòngzhì	Overload control category	
过荷控制	Guòhè kòngzhì	Overload control	
国际白皮书论坛	Guójì báipíshū lùntán	International forum white paper	IFWP
国际编码设计	Guójì biānmă shèjì	International code designator	ICD
国际标准规格	Guójì biāozhŭn guīgé	International standardized profile	
国际标准化组织	Guójì Biāozhŭnhuà Zŭzhī	International Standardization Organization	ISO
国际标准化组织	Guójì Biāozhŭnhuà Zŭzhī	International Organization for Standardization	ISO
国际标准化组织的活动图片专家组	Guójì Biāozhŭnhuà Zŭzhīde huódòng túpiàn zhuānjiāzŭ	International Standard Organization's Moving Picture Expert group	ISO/MPEG
国际长途自动电话	Guójì chángtú zìdòngdiànhuà	International direct distance dialing	IDDD
国际出口局	Guójì chūkŏujú	Gateway exchange	GE
国际单位制	Guójì dānwèizhì	International system of units	
国际电报电话咨询委员会	Guójì diànbào diànhuà zīxún wĕiyuánhuì	International Telegraph and Telephone Consultative Committee	CCITT
国际电磁干扰委员会	Guójì diàncí gānrăo wĕiyuánhuì	International Electromagnetic Interference Commission	CISPR
国际电工技术委员会	Guójì diàngōng jìshù wĕiyuánhuì	International Electrotechnical Commission	IEC
国际电工委员会	Guójì diàngōng wĕiyuánhuì	International Electrotechnical Commission	IEC
国际电话电报公司	Guójì diànhuà diànbào gōngsī	International Telephone and Telegraph Co. ITT (UK)	ITT
国际电话电报咨询委员会	Guójì diànhuà diànbào zīxún wĕiyuánhuì	International Telegraph and Telephone Consultative Committee	CCITT
国际电话电报咨询委员会高级语言	Guójì diànhuà diànbào zīxún wĕiyuánhuì gāojí yŭyán	International Telegraph and Telephone Consultative Committee's high-level language	CHILL
国际电话交换维护中心	Guójì diànhuà jiāohuàn wéihù zhōngxīn	International Switching Maintenance Center	ISMC
国际电话连接	Guójì diànhuà liánjiē	International telephone connection	
国际电信电话有限公司	Guójì diànxìn diànhuà yŏuxiàn gōngsī	Kokusai Denshin Denwa Co. Ltd. (Japan)	KDD
国际电信联盟	Guójì Diànxìn Liánméng	International Telecommunications Union (UN)	ITU
国际电信联盟 - 无线通讯分册	Guójì Diànxìn Liánméng - wúxiàn tōngxùn fēncè	International Telecommunication Union – Radiocommunication Sector	ITU-R
国际电信联盟-电信标准部门	Guójì Diànxìn Liánméng-- Diànxìn biāozhŭn bùmén	International Telecommunication Union-Telecommunication Standardization Sector	ITU-T
国际电信联盟-电信标准化部门	Guójì Diànxìn Liánméng—diànxìn biāozhŭnhua bùmén	International Telecommunications Union - Telecommunications Standardization Sector	ITU-T
国际电信卫星组织	Guójì diànxìn wèixīng zŭzhī	International Telecommunications satellite	INTELSAT
国际电子技术委员会	Guójì diànzĭ jìshù wĕiyuánhuì	International Electrotechnical Commission	IEC
国际段	Guójì duàn	International section	
国际多媒体电子会议协会	Guójì duōméitĭ diànzĭ huìyì xiéhuì	International Multimedia Teleconferencing Consortium	IMTC
国际二号电码	Guójì èrhào diànmă	International telegraph alphabet no.2	
国际个人计算机存储卡协会	Guójì gèrén jìsuànjī cúnchŭ qiă xiéhuì	Personal computer memory card international	PCMCIA
国际公共安全通信官方协议	Guójì gōnggòng ānquán tōngxìn guānfāng xiéyì	Association of public safety communication officials international	APCO
国际公用传真业务	Guójì gōngyòng chuánzhēn yèwù	International public facsimile service	
国际海底光缆系统	Guójì hăidĭ guānglăn xìtŏng	Fiber Link around the Globe	FLAG
国际海事卫星通信组织	Guójì hăishì wèixīng tōngxìn zŭzhī	International Maritime Satellite Telecommunications Organization	INMARSAT
国际海事卫星组织	Guójì hăishì wèixīng zŭzhī	International Maritime Satellite Organization	INMARSAT
国际会议机构	Guójì huìyì jīgòu	Institute for International Research	IIR
国际互连网	Guójì hùliánwăng	Internet	
国际互联网体系结构委员会	Guójì hùliánwăng tĭxì jiégòu wĕiyuánhuì	Internet Architecture Board	IAB

国际互联网网络体系技术委员会	Guójì hùliánwǎng wǎngluò tǐxì jìshù wěiyuánhuì	Internet Architecture Board	IAB
国际互联网网络信息中心	Guójì hùliánwǎng wǎngluò xìnxī zhōngxīn	Internet network information center	InterNIC
国际交换中心	Guójì jiāohuàn zhōngxīn	International switching center	ISC
国际接口局	Guójì jiēkǒu jú	International gateway	IG
国际晶体管电路讨论会	Guójì jīngtǐguǎn diànlù tǎolùnhuì	International Solid-State Circuits Conference	ISSCC
国际计算机安全协会	Guójì jìsuànjī ānquán xiéhuì	International Computer Security Association	ICSA
国际计算机与信息学论专题讨论会	Guójì jìsuànjī yǔ xìnxīxué lùn zhuāntí tǎolùn huì	International Symposium on Computer and Information Service	COINS
国际局	Guójì jú	International switching center	ISC
国际可视图文网关	Guójì kěshì túwén wǎngguān	International videotex gateway	
国际可选记帐业务	Guójì kěxuǎn jìzhàng yèwù	International alternative billing service	IABS
国际科学委员会	Guójì kēxué wěiyuánhuì	International Science Committee	ISC
国际连接	Guójì liánjiē	International connection	
国际链路	Guójì liànlù	International link	
国际漫游组	Guójì mànyóu zǔ	International Roaming Experts Group (GSM MoU)	IREG
国际民航组织	Guójì mínháng zǔzhī	International Civil Aviation Organization	ICAO
国际频率登记总表	Guójì pínlǜ dēngjì zǒngbiǎo	Master international frequency register	MIFR
国际软交换协会	Guójì ruǎn jiāohuàn xiéhuì	International Softswitch Consortium	ISC
国际软交换中心	Guójì ruǎnjiāohuàn zhōngxīn	International switching center	ISC
国际商业机器公司	Guójì shāngyè jīqì gōngsī	International Business Machines (US company)	IBM
国际双向中继线	Guójì shuāngxiàng zhōngjìxiàn	International both way trunk	INTBWT
国际数据传输链路	Guójì shùjù chuánshū liànlù	International data transmission link	
国际数据传输系统	Guójì shùjù chuánshū xìtǒng	International data transmission system	
国际数据加密算法	Guójì shùjù jiāmì suànfǎ	International data encryption algorithm	IDEA
国际数据机构	Guójì shùjù jīgòu	International Data Corporation	IDC
国际数据集团	Guójì shùjù jítuán	International Data Group	IDG
国际数据组织	Guójì shùjù zǔzhī	International Data Group	IDG
国际四号电码	Guójì sìhào diànmǎ	International telegraph alphabet no.4	
国际通信网络的高速分组交换	Guójì tōngxìn wǎngluòde gāosù fēnzǔ jiāohuàn	High speed international packet switching	HIPS
国际通信卫星组织	Guójì tōngxìn wèixīng zǔzhī	International communications satellite organization	INTERSAT
国际图形交换系统	Guójì túxíng jiāohuàn xìtǒng	International Graphics Exchange System (US company)	IGES
国际 USIM 标识符	Guójì USIM biāozhìfú	International user identification module identifier	IUI
国际五号电码	Guójì wǔhào diànmǎ	International alphabet no.5 (ISO 7-bit code)	IA5
国际 5 号电码表	Guójì wǔhào diànmǎ biǎo	International alphabet no. 5	IA5
国际无线电干扰委员会	Guójì wúxiàndiàn gānrǎo wěiyuánhuì	International Committee on Radio Interference	CCIR
国际无线电干扰专门委员会	Guójì wúxiàndiàn gānrǎo zhuānmén wěiyuánhuì	International Special Committee on Radio Interference	CISPR
国际无线电咨询委员会	Guójì wúxiàndiàn zīxún wěiyuánhuì	Consultative Committee on International Radio (a division of ITU)	CCIR
国际无线电咨询委员会	Guójì wúxiàndiàn zīxún wěiyuánhuì	International Radio Consultative Committee	CCIR
国际线路	Guójì xiànlù	International line	
国际线路选定计划	Guójì xiànlù xuǎndìng jìhuà	International routing plan	IRP
国际信令点	Guójì xìnlìng diǎn	International signaling point	ISP
国际信令转接点	Guójì xìnlìng zhuǎnjiē diǎn	International signal transfer point	ISTP
国际信息包交换业务	Guójì xìnxī bāojiāohuàn yèwù	International Packet Switching Service (BPO)	IPSS

国际信息处理联合会	Guójì xìnxī chǔlǐ liánhéhuì	International Federation for Information Processing	IFIP
国际虚拟专网业务	Guójì xūnǐ zhuān wǎng yèwù	International virtual private network service	IVPN
国际业务交换点	Guójì yèwù jiāohuàndiǎn	International service switching point	ISSP
国际业务控制点	Guójì yèwù kòngzhìdiǎn	International service control point	ISCP
国际移动设备标识号	Guójì yídòng shèbèi biāozhì hào	International portable equipment identifier	IPEI
国际移动设备识别号码	Guójì yídòng shèbèi shíbié hàomǎ	International mobile station equipment identity	IMEI
国际移动设备识别码	Guójì yídòng shèbèi shíbié mǎ	International mobile equipment identity	IMEI
国际移动设备识别软件版本	Guójì yídòng shèbèi shíbié ruǎnjiàn bǎnběn	International mobile equipment identity software version	IMEISV
国际移动通信	Guójì yídòng tōngxìn	International mobile telecommunications	IMT
国际移动通信 2000	Guójì yídòng tōngxìn 2000	International mobile telecommnications 2000	IMT-2000
国际移动用户标识	Guójì yídòng yònghù biāozhì	International mobile subscriber identity	IMSI
国际移动用户标识号	Guójì yídòng yònghù biāozhì hào	International portable user identity	IPUI
国际移动用户号码	Guójì yídòng yònghù hàomǎ	International mobile user number	IMUN
国际移动用户识别号码	Guójì yídòng yònghù shíbié hàomǎ	International mobile subscriber identity	IMSI
国际移动用户识别码	Guójì yídòng yònghù shíbié mǎ	International mobile subscriber ID code	IMSI
国际移动终端设备标识	Guójì yídòng zhōngduān shèbèi biāozhì	International mobile terminal equipment identity	IMEI
国际移动群识别	Guójì yídòngqún shíbié	International mobile group identity	IMGI
国际移动台标识符	Guójì yídòngtái biāozhìfú	International mobile station identity	IMSI
国际移动台识别号码	Guójì yídòngtái shíbié hàomǎ	International mobile station identity	IMSI
国际移动台识别软件版本号	Guójì yídòngtái shíbié ruǎnjiàn bǎnběn hào	International mobile equipment identity software version	IMEISV
国际一号电码	Guójì yīhào diànmǎ	International telegraph alphabet no.1	
国际用户拨号	Guójì yònghù bōhào	International subscriber dialing	ISD
国际远程通信卫星组织	Guójì yuǎnchéng tōngxìn wèixīng zǔzhī	International Telecommunications Satellite Organization	ITSO
国际原子时间	Guójì yuánzǐ shíjiān	International automatic time	TAI
国际原子时	Guójì yuánzǐshí	International atomic time	TAI
国际直拨	Guójì zhíbō	International direct dialing	IDD
国际转换中心	Guójì zhuǎnhuàn zhōngxīn	International transit switching center	ITSC
国际转接部分	Guójì zhuǎnjiē bùfen	International transit part	ITP
国际转接交换局	Guójì zhuǎnjiē jiāohuànjú	International transit switch	INTS
国际主段	Guójì zhǔduàn	International main section	
国际自动电路	Guójì zìdòng diànlù	International automatic circuit	
国际字母	Guójì zìmǔ	International alphabet set	IAS
国际租用电路	Guójì zūyòng diànlù	International leased circuit	
国家安全局	Guójiā ānquán jú	National Security Agency (US)	NSA
国家半导体	Guójiā bàndǎotǐ	National Semiconductor (US company)	
国家标准技术研究所	Guójiā biāozhǔn jìshù yánjiūsuǒ	National Institute of Standards and Technology (US)	NIST
国家标准制定部	Guójiā biāozhǔn zhìdìng bù	Gosudarstvennui Standart (Russian government standard) (used by the Chinese to indicate the agency	ГОСТ
国家标准局	Guójiā Biāozhǔnjú	National Bureau of Standards (US)	NBS
国家测量参照系	Guójiā cèliáng cānzhàoxì	National Geodetic Reference System (US)	NGRS
国家超级计算应用中心	Guójiā chāojí jìsuàn yìngyòng zhōngxīn	National Center for Supercomputing Applications (US)	NCSA
国家传输格式	Guójiā chuánshū géshi	National transfer format	NTF
国家处理中心	Guójiā chǔlǐ zhōngxīn	National processing Center	NPC
国家处理中心	Guójiā chǔlǐ zhōngxīn	National processing center (in the finance network)	NPC
国家代码	Guójiā dàimǎ	Country code	CC

国家电脑局	Guójiā diànnǎo jú	National Computer Board	NCB
国家电视标准委员会	Guójiā diànshì biāozhǔn wěiyuánhuì	National Television Standard Committee	NTSC
国家电信管理局	Guójiā diànxìn guǎnlǐjú	Agencia Nacional de Telecomunicaoes (Brazil)	ANATEL
国家地理管理局	Guójiā dìlǐ guǎnlǐjú	National Geographic Directorate	NGD
国家地理空间数据库	Guójiā dìlǐ kōngjiān shùjùkù	National Geospatial Database	NGD
国家地理信息与分析中心	Guójiā dìlǐ xìnxī yǔ fēnxī zhōngxīn	National Center for Geographic Information and Analysis	NCGIA
国家地图方里网	Guójiā dìtú fānglǐ wǎng	National map grid	
国家地图精度标准	Guójiā dìtú jīngdù biāozhǔn	National Map Accuracy Standards (US)	NMAS
国家地质图书馆	Guójiā dìzhì túshūguǎn	National Geological Library (China)	NGL
国家格网	Guójiā géwǎng	National grid	NG
国家公共交换电信网	Guójiā gōnggòng jiāohuàn diànxìn wǎng	National Public Switched Telecommunications Network	NPSIN
国家广播电影和电视总局	Guójiā guǎngbō diànyǐng hé diànshì zǒngjú	State Administration of Radio, Film and Television	SARFT
国家海洋与大气署	Guójiā hǎiyáng yǔ dàqì shǔ	National Oceanic and Atmospheric Administration (US)	NOAA
国家航空航天局	Guójiā hángkōng hángtiān jú	National Aeronautics and Space Administration (US)	NASA
国家号码	Guójiā hàomǎ	Country code	CC
国家计算机安全协会	Guójiā jìsuànjī ānquán xiéhuì	National Computer Security Association	NCSA
国家计算机安全中心	Guójiā jìsuànjī ānquán zhōngxīn	National Computer Security Center (US)	NCSC
国家科学基金会	Guójiā Kēxué Jījīnhuì	National Science Foundation (US)	NSF
国家科学基金会网络	Guójiā Kēxué Jījīnhuì wǎngluò	National Science Foundation Network (US)	NSFnet
国家科研教育网络	Guójiā kēyán jiàoyù wǎngluò	National Research and Education Network	NREN
国家码	Guójiā mǎ	Country code	CC
国家名	Guójiā míng	Country name	
国家目的码	Guójiā mùdì mǎ	National destination code	NDC
国家赔偿	Guójiā péicháng	National compensation	
国家平面坐标系	Guójiā píngmiàn zuòbiāo xì	State plane coordinate system	SPCS
国家数字制图数据库	Guójiā shùzì zhìtú shùjùkù	National Digital Cartographic Data Base	NDCDB
国家土地调查体系	Guójiā tǔdì diàochá tǐxì	Public Land Survey System (US)	PLSS
国家土地系统	Guójiā tǔdì xìtǒng	Public Land System (US)	PLS
国家信息安全测评认证中心	Guójiā xìnxī ānquán cèpíng rènzhèng zhōngxīn	National Information Security Assessment and Authentication Center	
国家信息基础结构	Guójiā xìnxī jīchǔ jiégòu	National information infrastructure	NII
国家信息基础设施	Guójiā xìnxī jīchǔ shèshī	National Information Infrastructure	NII
国家移动代码	Guójiā yídòng dàimǎ	Mobile country code	MCC
国家移动台标识符	Guójiā yídòngtái biāozhìfú	National mobile station identifier	NMSI
国家移动台识别号	Guójiā yídòngtái shíbiéhào	National mobile station identification number	NMSI
国家用户/普通用户识别模块标识符	Guójiā yònghù/pǔtōng yònghù shíbié mókuài biāozhì fú	National user/user identification module identifier	NUI
国家语言支持	Guójiā yǔyán zhīchí	National language support	NLS
国家智能计算机研究开发中心	Guójiā zhìnéng jìsuànjī yánjiū kāifā zhōngxīn	National Center for Intelligent Computing	NCIC
国家终点局代码	Guójiā zhōngdiǎnjú dàimǎ	National destination code	NDC
过量抽水	Guòliàng chōushuǐ	Excessive pumping	
过流保护	Guòliú bǎohù	Overcurrent protection	
过流保护电路	Guòliú bǎohù diànlù	Overcurrent protection circuit	
过滤标识符	Guòlǜ biāozhìfú	Filter identifier	FID
过滤带	Guòlǜ dài	Transition band	

过滤软件	Guòlǜ ruǎnjiàn	Filter software	
过密集地区	Guòmìjí dìqū	Congested district	
过模波导	Guòmó bōdǎo	Over-moded waveguide	
国内地区使用消息	Guónèi dìqū shǐyòng xiāoxi	National area message	NAM
国内干线接口	Guónèi gànxiàn jiēkǒu	Domestic trunk interface	DTI
国内号码	Guónèi hàomǎ	National number	NN
国内后向建立不成功消息	Guónèi hòuxiàng jiànlì bùchénggōng xiāoxi	National unsuccessful backward set-up message	NUB
国内后向建立成功消息	Guónèi hòuxiàng jiànlì chénggōng xiāoxi	National successful backward set-up message	NSB
国内呼叫监视消息	Guónèi hūjiào jiānshì xiāoxi	National call supervision message	NCB
国内目的地码	Guónèi mùdìdì mǎ	National destination code	NDC
国内使用	Guónèi shǐyòng	National use	NU
国内通信卫星	Guónèi tōngxìn wèixīng	Domestic communications satellite	Domsat
国内网拥塞信号	Guónèi wǎng yōngsè xìnhào	National-network-congestion signal	NNC
国内信令点	Guónèi xìnlìng diǎn	National signaling point	NSP
国内移动台识别号码	Guónèi yídòngtái shíbié hàomǎ	National mobile station identity	NMSI
国内终点号码	Guónèi zhōngdiǎn hàomǎ	National destination code	NDC
国内主段	Guónèi zhǔduàn	National main section	
过期间隔	Guòqī jiàngé	Expire interval	
过区切换	Guòqū qiēhuàn	Inter-cell hand-off (cellular telephony)	
过适	Guòshì	Overfitting	
过时错误	Guòshí cuòwù	Time-out error	TO
过调制	Guòtiáozhì	Over-modulation	
国土保护	Guótǔ bǎohù	Land conservation	
国土政策	Guótǔ zhèngcè	National land policy	
过温保护电路	Guòwēn bǎohù diànlù	Overheat protection circuit	
国信朗讯科技网络技术有限公司	Guóxìn Lǎngxùn Kējì wǎngluò jìshù yǒuxiàn gōngsī	Guoxin Lucent Network Technologies Co. Ltd. (Sino-US joint venture)	GXLU
过压保护	Guòyā bǎohù	Over-voltage protection (the O in BORSCHT)	
过压保护电路	Guòyā bǎohù diànlù	Over-voltage protection circuit	
国有土地	Guóyǒu tǔdì	State owned land	
过载	Guòzài	Overload	
过载电流	Guòzài diànliú	Overload current (of a circuit)	
过载断路器	Guòzài duànlùqì	Overload circuit breaker	OCB
过载功率	Guòzài gōnglǜ	Overload power	
过载信息	Guòzài xìnxī	Overload message	OLM
过载系数	Guòzài xìshù	Overload factor (of a receiver)	
过早释放	Guòzǎo shìfàng	Premature release	
固态发射机	Gùtài fāshèjī	Solid state transmitter	
固态激光	Gùtài jīguāng	Solid-state laser	
固态盘	Gùtài pán	Solid-state disk	
固体功率放大器	Gùtǐ gōnglǜ fàngdàqì	Solid-state power amplifier	SSPA
固体继电器	Gùtǐ jidiànqì	Solid-state relay	SSR
固体列阵式光谱辐射计	Gùtǐ lièzhèn-shì guāngpǔ fúshèjì	Solid-state array spectroradiometer	SAS
固相线	Gùxiàng xiàn	Solidus (in SMT)	
孤行	Gūxíng	Orphan (in word processing)	

固有监视	Gùyǒu jiānshì	Inherent monitoring	
固有畸变	Gùyǒu jībiàn	Inherent distortion (of a transmission channel)	
固有可靠性	Gùyǒu kěkàoxìng	Inherent reliability	
固有灵敏度	Gùyǒu língmǐndù	Intrinsic sensitivity	
固有领域	Gùyǒu lǐngyù	Proper area	
固有频差	Gùyǒu pínchà	Inherent frequency error	
固有频率	Gùyǒu pínlǜ	Natural frequency (in a cavity resonator)	
固有衰减	Gùyǒu shuāijiǎn	Intrinsic attenuation	
固有突发容限	Gùyǒu tūfā róngxiàn	Intrinsic burst tolerance	IBT
固有噪声	Gùyǒu zàoshēng	Intrinsic noise	
固有振动	Gùyǒu zhèndòng	Eigenvibration, principal vibration	
固有周期	Gùyǒu zhōuqī	Natural period	
固有值	Gùyǒuzhí	Eigenvalues	
故障	Gùzhàng	Fault, bug	
故障报告点	Gùzhàng bàogàodiǎn	Fault report point	
故障保护	Gùzhàng bǎohù	Fail safe	
故障保护	Gùzhàng bǎohù	Fault protection	
故障测试	Gùzhàng cèshì	Failure test	
故障定位	Gùzhàng dìngwèi	Fault localization	
故障定位时间	Gùzhàng dìngwèi shíjiān	Fault localization time	
故障定义程序	Gùzhàng dìngyì chéngxù	Fault definition program	
故障访问	Gùzhàng fǎngwèn	Failure access	
故障范围	Gùzhàng fànwéi	Fault coverage	
故障分析	Gùzhàng fēnxī	Fault analysis	
故障管理	Gùzhàng guǎnlǐ	Fault management	BFM
故障管理构件	Gùzhàng guǎnlǐ gòujiàn	Fault management building block	FMBB
故障管理器	Gùzhàng guǎnlǐqì	Fault manager	FM
故障回复	Gùzhàng huífù	Failback	
故障回复策略	Gùzhàng huífù cèlüè	Failback policy	
故障检测	Gùzhàng jiǎncè	Fault detection test	FDT
故障接地	Gùzhàng jiēdì	Fault grounding or earthing	
故障接口	Gùzhàng jiēkǒu	Fault interface	FI
故障解列	Gùzhàng jiělìè	Fault disconnection	
故障记录器	Gùzhàng jìlùqì	Trouble recorder	TRR
故障警报信号	Gùzhàng jǐngbào xìnhào	Alarm indicator signal	AIS
故障控制	Gùzhàng kòngzhì	Fault control	FC
故障率测试	Gùzhàng lǜ cèshì	Failure rate test	
故障模拟	Gùzhàng mónǐ	Fault simulation	
故障模式	Gùzhàng móshì	Fault mode	
故障模式和影响分析	Gùzhàng móshì hé yǐngxiǎng fēnxī	Fault modes and effects analysis	FMEA
故障模式、影响和严重性分析	Gùzhàng móshì、yǐngxiǎng hé yánzhòngxìng fēnxī	Fault modes, effects and criticality analysis	FMECA
故障耐受性	Gùzhàng nàishòuxìng	Fault tolerance	
故障弱化	Gùzhàng ruòhuà	Fail soft	
故障时触电保护	Gùzhàng shí chùdiàn bǎohù	Protection against shock in the case of a fault	
故障识别	Gùzhàng shíbié	Fault recognition	

故障树	Gùzhàng shù	Fault tree	
故障述分析	Gùzhàng shù fēnxī	Fault tree analysis	FTA
故障修复	Gùzhàng xiūfù	Fault correction	
故障修复时间	Gùzhàng xiūfù shíjiān	Fault corrective time	
故障原因	Gùzhàng yuányīn	Fault cause	
故障诊断	Gùzhàng zhěnduàn	Fault diagnostics	
故障诊断时间	Gùzhàng zhěnduàn shíjiān	Fault diagnosis time	
故障遮掩	Gùzhàng zhēyǎn	Fault masking	
故障转移	Gùzhàng zhuǎnyí	Failover	
故障转移策略	Gùzhàng zhuǎnyí cèlüè	Failover policy	
故障准则	Gùzhàng zhǔnzé	Fault criteria	
故障组成计算性能安全	Gùzhàng zǔchéng jìsuàn xìngnéng ānquán	Fault configuration accounting performance security	FCAPS
顾主网	Gùzhǔ wǎng	Client network	

H

哈尔变换	Hā-ěr biànhuàn	Haar transform	HrT
哈夫曼树	Hā-fū-màn shù	Huffman tree	
海存	Hǎi cún	Mass storage	
海岸电台	Hǎi'àn diàntái	Coast station	
海岸电台	Hǎi'àn diàntái	Coast station	
海岸地球站	Hǎi'àn dìqiú zhàn	Coast earth station	
海岸地球站	Hǎi'àn dìqiúzhàn	Coastal earth station	
海岸航空设备	Hǎi'àn hángkōng shèbèi	Coast aeronautical equipment	
海底电缆	Hǎidǐ diànlǎn	Submarine cable	HL
海底光缆	Hǎidǐ guānglǎn	Submarine optical cable	HGL
海底光缆系统	Hǎidǐ guānglǎn xìtǒng	Fiberoptic undersea systems	FUS
海尔系统	Hǎi'ěr xìtǒng	Hell system (for teleprinting)	
氦镉激光	Hài-gé jīguāng	Helium-cadmium (He-Cd) laser	
海军技术预测	Hǎijūn jìshù yùcè	Navy technological forecast	NTF
骇客	Hài-kè	Hacker	
海缆线路终端设备	Hǎilǎn xiànlù zhōngduān shèbèi	Submarine cable line termination equipment	SLTE
海明空间	Hǎi-míng kōngjiān	Hamming space	
海明码	Hǎi-míng mǎ	Hamming code	
氦氖激光	Hài-nǎi jīguāng	Helium-neon (He-Ne) laser	
海森伯格测不准原理	Hǎi-sēn-bó-gé cèbuzhǔn yuánlǐ	Heisenberg uncertainty principle (physics, math/crypto.)	
海事卫星通信	Hǎishì wèixīng tōngxìn	Maritime satellite communications	
海事卫星移动业务	Hǎishì wèixīng yídòng yèwù	Maritime mobile-satellite service	
海事无线电技术委员会	Hǎishì wúxiàndiàn jìshù wěiyuánhuì	Radio Technology Committee, Marine	RTCM
海事移动业务	Hǎishì yídòng yèwù	Maritime mobile service	
海斯调制解调器	Hǎi-sī tiáozhì jiětiáoqì	Hayes compatible modem	
海湾地区的区域性研究网络	Hǎiwān dìqūde qūyùxìng yánjiū wǎngluò	Bay Area Regional Research Network (US)	BARRNet
哈里斯公司	Hā-lǐ-sī gōngsī	Harris Corporation (US company)	
哈密尔顿环	Hā-mì-ěr-dùn huán	Hamilton circuit	
含微处理机控制式自动定位装置	Hán wēichǔlǐjī kòngzhì-shì zìdòng dìngwèi zhuāngzhì	Microprocessor-controlled automatic positioning equipment	

行	Háng	Row, line (for database or table)	
行初始位置	Háng chūshǐ wèizhì	Line home position	
航调	Háng diào	Air Traffic Control (short for 航空交通调度)	
行地址控制器	Háng dìzhǐ kòngzhìqì	Row addressable strobe	RAS
行地址选定	Háng dìzhǐ xuǎndìng	Row address selection	RAS
行过滤	Háng guòlǜ	Row filter (in SQL Server)	
行行进方向	Háng hángjìn fāngxiàng	Line progression	
行集	Háng jí	Rowset (for database)	
行间距	Háng jiānjù	Line spacing	
行聚合函数	Háng jùhé hánshù	Row aggregate function	
行控制信息	Háng kòngzhì xìnxī	File control information	FCI
行框	Háng kuàng	Line box	
航路交管中心	Háng lù jiāo guǎn zhōngxīn	Air route traffic control center (civil aviation)	ARTCC
行筛选	Háng shāixuǎn	Row filter	
行锁	Háng suǒ	Row lock (for database)	
行尾	Háng wěi	End of line	
行位置	Háng wèizhì	Row position (WP command)	
行移位	Háng yíwèi	Shift row	
行终止符	Háng zhōngzhǐfú	Line terminator	
涵盖	Hángài	Cover	
汉高化学物品公司	Hàn-gāo huàxué wùpǐn gōngsī	Henkel Chemical Products Corp. (German company)	
航海雷达	Hánghǎi léidá	Marine radar	
航空产品定型委员会	Hángkōng chǎnpǐn dìngxíng wěiyuánhuì	Aviation Product Design Finalization Commission	
航空磁通门磁力仪	Hángkōng cítōng mén cílìyí	Airborne flux gate magnetometer	
航空电台	Hángkōng diàntái	Aeronautical station	
航空地球站	Hángkōng dìqiúzhàn	Aeronautical earth station	
航空固定电台	Hángkōng gùdìng diàntái	Aeronautical fixed station	
航空固定业务	Hángkōng gùdìng yèwù	Aeronautical fixed service	
航空交通调度	Hángkōng jiāotōng diàodù	Air Traffic Control	
航空路途交通管理中心	Hángkōng lùtú jiāotōng guǎnlǐ zhōngxīn	Air route traffic control center (civil aviation)	ARTCC
航空气象服务	Hángkōng qìxiàng fúwù	Aviation weather service (civil aviation)	AWS
航空卫星移动业务	Hángkōng wèixīng yídòng yèwù	Aeronautical mobile-satellite service	
航空无线电导航业务	Hángkōng wúxiàndiàn dǎoháng yèwù	Aeronautical radio navigation service	
航空遥感	Hángkōng yáogǎn	Aerial (or airborne) remote sensing (GIS)	
航空移动卫星通信	Hángkōng yídòng wèixīng tōngxìn	Aeronautical mobile satellite service	AMSS
航空移动业务	Hángkōng yídòng yèwù	Aeronautical mobile service	
航空与宇航协调局	Hángkōng yǔ yǔháng xiétiáo jú	Aeronautics and Astronautics Coordinating Board (US, part of NASA)	AACB
航空咨询委员会	Hángkōng zīxún wěiyuánhuì	Aeronautics Advisory Committee (US, part of NASA)	AAC
航空器电台	Hángkōngqì diàntái	Aircraft station	
航空器地球站	Hángkōngqì dìqiúzhàn	Aircraft earth station	
行式打印机	Hángshì dǎyìnjī	Line printer	L/P
行式打印机程序	Hángshì dǎyìnjī chéngxù	Line printer daemon	LPD
行式打印机处理器	Hángshì dǎyìnjī chǔlǐ qì	Line printer handler	LPH
航天器	Hángtiānqì	Spacecraft	
韩国移动通信	Hánguó yídòng tōngxìn	Korea Mobile Telecom	KMT

航向标志	Hángxiàng biāozhì	Course marker	
航向相关	Hángxiàng xiāngguān	Vector correlation (radar term)	
汉化	Hànhuà	Chinese localization	
焊角	Hànjiǎo	Fillet (in SMT)	
焊接加工	Hànjiē jiāgōng	Joining (using a laser)	
焊接升离	Hànjiē shēnglí	Bond lift-off (in SMT)	
汉明间距	Hàn-míng jiānjù	Hamming distance	
汉明距离	Hàn-míng jùlí	Hamming distance	
汉明码	Hàn-míng mǎ	Hamming code	
汉明重量	Hàn-míng zhòngliàng	Hamming weight	
函数	Hánshù	Function	
函数部件	Hánshù bùjiàn	Function unit (in SPL)	
函数程序设计语言	Hánshù chéngxù shèjì yǔyán	Functional programming language	FPL
函数调用操作符	Hánshù diàoyòng cāozuò fú	Function call operator	
函数对象	Hánshù duìxiàng	Function object	
函数返回总体变异数	Hánshù fǎnhuí zǒngtǐ biànyì shù	Statistical variance for the population (in SQL Server)	VARP
函数返回总体标准差	Hánshù fǎnhuí zǒngtǐ biāozhǔn chà	Statistical standard deviation for the population (in SQL Server)	STDEVP
函数发生器	Hánshù fāshēngqì	Function generator	
函数模板	Hánshù múbǎn	Function template	
函数重载决议	Hánshù zhòngzài juéyì	Function overloaded resolution	
函数子程序	Hánshù zǐchéngxù	Function sub-program	
焊锡球	Hànxī qiú	Solder bump (in SMT)	
含锗光纤	Hánzhě guāngxiān	Germanium content fiber	GF
汉字操作系统	Hànzì cāozuò xìtǒng	Chinese character DOS	CCDOS
汉字码	Hànzì mǎ	HZ code (computer code for Chinese characters)	
汉字信息处理系统	Hànzì xìnxī chǔlǐ xìtǒng	Chinese information processing system	CHIPS
毫	Háo	Milli- (prefix meaning 10^{-3})	
号码分配模块	Hàomǎ fēnpèi mókuài	Number assignment module	NAM
号码规划	Hàomǎ guīhuà	Numbering plan	NP
号码可携带	Hàomǎ kěxiédài	Number portability	NP
号码类型	Hàomǎ lèixíng	Type of number	TON
号码流动	Hàomǎ liúdòng	Number portability	NP
号码识别附加业务	Hàomǎ shíbié fùjiā yèwù	Number identification supplementary service	
号码簿	Hàomǎbù	Directory (as the telephone book)	
号码簿登记项	Hàomǎbù dēngjì xiàng	Directory entry	
号码簿登录项	Hàomǎbù dēnglù xiàng	Directory entry	
号码簿访问控制域	Hàomǎbù fǎngwèn kòngzhì yù	Directory access control domain	DACD
号码簿访问协议	Hàomǎbù fǎngwèn xiéyì	Directory access protocol	DAP
号码簿管理域	Hàomǎbù guǎnlǐ yù	Directory management domain	DMD
号码簿号码	Hàomǎbù hàomǎ	Directory number	DN
号码簿名	Hàomǎbù míng	Directory name	
号码簿体制	Hàomǎbù tǐzhì	Directory schema	
号码簿信息树	Hàomǎbù xìnxī shù	Directory information tree	DIT
号码簿信息库	Hàomǎbù xìnxīkù	Directory information base	DIB
号码簿系统	Hàomǎbù xìtǒng	Directory system	DS
号码簿系统代理	Hàomǎbù xìtǒng dàilǐ	Directory system agent	DSA

号码簿系统协议	Hàomǎbù xìtǒng xiéyì	Directory system protocol	DSP
号码簿用户	Hàomǎbù yònghù	Directory user	
号码簿用户代理	Hàomǎbù yònghù dàilǐ	Directory user agent	DUA
毫秒	Háomiǎo	Millisecond	ms
毫米波	Háomǐbō	Millimeter wave	
毫米波单片集成电路	Háomǐbō dānpiàn jíchéng diànlù	Millimeter wave monolithic integrated circuit	MIMIC
嗥鸣器	Háomíngqì	Howler	
号盘脉冲	Hàopán màichōng	Dial pulse	DP
耗散因数	Hàosàn yīnshù	Dissipation factor	DF
耗损故障	Hàosǔn gùzhàng	Wear-out fault	
耗损失效	Hàosǔn shīxiào	Wear-out failure	
耗损失效其	Hàosǔn shīxiàoqí	Wear-out failure period	
毫微	Háowēi	Nano- (prefix meaning 10^{-9})	N
毫微秒	Háowēimiǎo	Nanosecond	NS
哈脱莱	Hā-tuō-lái	Hartley	
哈希表	Hā-xī biǎo	Hash table	
哈希消息认证代码	Hā-xī xiāoxi rènzhèng dàimǎ	Hashed message authentication code	HMAC
核函数	Hé hánshù	Kernel function	
和校验	Hé jiàoyàn	Sumcheck (telecom billing)	
核树	Hé shù	Core-based tree	CBT
合并	Hébìng	Conflation, merge	
合并	Hébìng	Merge	
合并代理	Hébìng dàilǐ	Merge agent (in SQL Server)	
合并复制	Hébìng fùzhì	Merge replication	
合并连接	Hébìng liánjiē	Merge join (in SQL Server)	
合并器	Hébìngqì	Combiner	
合成孔径雷达	Héchéng kǒngjìng léidá	Synthetic aperture radar	SAR
合成口径雷达	Héchéng kǒujìng léidá	Synthetic aperture radar	SAR
合成立体	Héchéng lìtǐ	Composite solid	
合成曲面	Héchéng qūmiàn	Composite surface	
合成曲线	Héchéng qūxiàn	Composite curve	
合成同步	Héchéng tóngbù	Synthetic synchronization	
合成音	Héchéng yīn	Composite pronunciation	
合成器	Héchéngqì	Synthesizer	
核电磁脉冲	Hédiàncí màichōng	Nuclear electromagnetic pulse	
合法用户	Héfǎ yònghù	Validated user	
合法性	Héfǎ-xìng	Legitimacy	
合法性检查	Héfǎ-xìng jiǎnchá	Validity check	
合格证书	Hégé zhèngshū	Certificate of conformity	
合格的可靠性	Hégéde kěkàoxìng	Acceptable reliability level	ARL
黑洞	Hēidòng	Black hole	
黑格巴哥码	Hēi-gé-bā-gē mǎ	Hagelbarger code	
黑客	Hēi-kè	Hacker	
黑客侵入	Hēi-kè qīnrù	Hacker intrusion	
和记	Hé-jì	Hutchison (Hong Kong company)	

和记奥普泰通信技术有限公司	Hé-jì ào-pǔ-tài tōngxìn jìshù yǒuxiàn gōngsī	Hutchison Optel Telecom Technology Co. Ltd.	
和记黄埔	Hé-jì Huángpǔ	Hutchison Whampoa (Hong Kong cellular provider)	
何勒内斯代码	Hé-lè-nèi-sī dàimǎ	Hollerith code	
何勒内四二进制代码	Hé-lè-nèi-sì èrjìnzhì dàimǎ	Binary coded Hollerith	BCH
合理化工程	Hélǐhuà gōngchéng	Rationalizing engineering (German concept)	RE
合流	Héliú	Confluence	
合理性	Hélǐxìng	Rationality	
合理性检查	Hélǐxìng jiǎnchá	Reasonableness check	
合路器	Hélùqì	Mixer	
合路器板	Hélùqì bǎn	Hybrid combiner board	HYCOM
横电磁波室	Héng diàncíbō shì	Transverse electromagnetic wave cell	
横卷动干	Héng juǎndòng gān	Horizontal scrollbar	
恒信息流控制	Héng xìnxīliú kòngzhì	Isarithmic flow control	
恒虚警接收机	Héng xūjǐng jiēshōujī	Constant false alarm receiver	CFAR
恒比码	Héngbǐ mǎ	Constant ratio code	
恒步的	Héngbùde	Homochronous	
横磁模	Héngcí mó	Transverse magnetic mode	TM
恒等同步	Héngděng tóngbù	Identical synchronization	
横堤	Héngdī	Cross levee	
恒电磁波小室	Héngdiàn cíbō xiǎoshì	Transverse electromagnetic wave cell (TEM cell)	
横电模	Héngdiàn mó	Transverse electric mode	TE
横电磁模	Héngdiàncí mó	Transverse electromagnetic mode	TEM
恒定比特率	Héngdìng bǐtè lǜ	Constant bit rate	CBR
恒定比特率业务	Héngdìng bǐtè lǜ yèwù	Constant bit rate service	CBR
恒定失效率期	Héngdìng shīxiào lǜ qī	Constant failure rate period	
恒定失效频度期	Héngdìng shīxiào píndù qī	Constant failure intensity period	
恒定线速度	Héngdìng xiànsùdù	Constant linear velocity (optical disk)	CLV
横渡太平洋的海底电缆	Héngdù Tàipíngyángde hǎidǐ diànlǎn	Transpacific cable	TPC
横断线	Héngduàn xiàn	Traverse	
横幅	Héngfú	Banner	
亨利	Hēnglì	Henry (unit of inductance)	H
横梁	Héngliáng	Cross-beam	
恒流电源	Héngliú diànyuán	Constant current power supply	
恒模算法	Héngmó suànfǎ	Constant modulus algorithm	CMA
哼声	Hēngshēng	Hum	
恒温	Héngwēn	Constant temperature	
恒温恒湿试验	Héngwēn héngshī shìyàn	Constant temperature and humidity test	
恒温热传导器机	Héngwēn rè chuándǎoqìjī	Heat exchanger (semiconductor mfg)	
横向波	Héngxiàng bō	Transverse wave	
横向错位损耗	Héngxiàng cuòwèi sǔnhào	Transverse (or lateral) offset loss	
横向抖动	Héngxiàng dǒudòng	Transverse judder	
横向偏焦	Héngxiàng piānjiāo	Lateral offset-Focus	
横向偏移	Héngxiàng piānyí	Lateral offset	
横向平铺视窗	Héngxiàng píngpū shìchuāng	Tile horizontally (Windows command)	
横向冗余检验	Héngxiàng rǒngyú jiǎnyàn	Horizontal redundancy check	HRC

横向扫描	Héngxiàng sǎomiáo	Across-track scanning	
横向制表	Héngxiàng zhìbiǎo	Horizontal tabulation	HT
恒压充电	Héngyā chōngdiàn	Constant voltage charge	
恒压电源	Héngyā diànyuán	Constant voltage power supply	
横越大西洋海底电话(电缆)	Héngyuè Dàxīyáng hǎidǐ diànhuà (diànlǎn)	Transatlantic Telephone (Cable)	TAT
恒值控制系统	Héngzhí kòngzhì xìtǒng	Constant-value control system	
衡重杂音	Héngzhòng záyīn	Weighted noise	
横坐标	Héngzuòbiāo	Abscissa	
很早分配	Hěnzǎo fēnpèi	Very early allocation	VEA
核销	Héxiāo	Cancellation after verification	
和谐安排	Héxié ānpái	Orchestration	
核心	Héxīn	Core	
核心	Héxīn	Kernel	
核心棒	Héxīn bàng	Core rod (FOC mfg)	
核心传送网络	Héxīn chuánsòng wǎngluò	Kernel transport network	KTN
核心功能	Héxīn gōngnéng	Core function	CF
核心汇接节点	Héxīn huìjiē jiédiǎn	Core tandem node	
核心交换机	Héxīn jiāohuànjī	Core switch	
核心路由器	Héxīn lùyóuqì	Core router	CR
核心网承载业务	Héxīn wǎng chéngzài yèwù	Core network bearer service	CNB
核心网服务质量管理器	Héxīn wǎng fúwù zhìliàng guǎnlǐqì	Core [Network] QoS manager	CQM
核心网络	Héxīn wǎngluò	Core network	CN
核心小组	Héxīn xiǎozǔ	Permanent nucleus (the European GSM standards setting group)	PN
核心协议	Héxīn xiéyì	Core protocol	CP
核心帧头域	Héxīn zhèng tóuyù	Core header	
盒形天线	Héxíng tiānxiàn	Cheese antenna (for centimetric radar)	
盒中脑	Hé-zhōng nǎo	Brain-state-in-a-box (neural networking term)	
盒装处理器	Hézhuāng chǔlǐqì	Processor-in-a-box	PIB
赫兹波	Hè-zī bō	Hertzian waves	
赫兹磁偶极子	Hè-zī cí'ǒujízi	Hertzian magnetic dipole	
赫兹电偶极子	Hè-zī diàn'ǒujízǐ	Hertzian electric dipole	
合作竞争	Hézuò jìngzhēng	Coopetition (buzzword formed from cooperation and competition)	
合作因数	Hézuò yīnshù	Factor of cooperation	
合作指数	Hézuò zhǐshù	Index of cooperation	
H 面扇形喇叭天线	H-miàn shànxíng lǎba tiānxiàn	H-plane sectoral horn antenna	
H 面透镜	H-miàn tòujìng	H-plane lens	
H 面 T 形环行器	H-miàn T-xíng huánxíngqì	H-plane T circulator	
H 面 T 形接头	H-miàn T-xing jiētóu	H plane T-junction	
H 面弯波导	H-miàn wān bōdǎo	H plane waveguide bend	
H-面弯头	H-miàn wāntóu	H-plane corner	
H 面 Y 形环行器	H-miàn Y-xíng huánxíngqì	H-plane Y circulator	
H-面 Y 形接头	H-miàn Y-xíng jiētóu	H-plane Y junction	
宏	Hóng	Macro, large	
宏编程	Hóng biānchéng	Macro programming	
宏病毒	Hóng bìngdú	Macro virus	

宏功能汇编语言	Hóng gōngnéng huìbiān yǔyán	Macro assembler	MAC
宏汇编程序指令	Hóng huìbiān chéngxù zhǐlìng	Macro assembler instruction	MAI
宏汇编语言	Hóng huìbiān yǔyán	Macro assembly language	
宏块	Hóng kuài	Macro-block	MB
宏流	Hóng liú	Macro-flow	
宏名字	Hóng míngzì	Macro name	
宏棋实验室	Hóng qí shíyànshì	Acer Lab (Taiwan computer company)	
宏弯损耗	Hóng wān sǔnhào	Macro-bending loss	
宏指令	Hóng zhǐlìng	Macro instruction	
宏指令处理程序	Hóng zhǐlìng chǔlǐ chéngxù	Advanced macro processor	AMP
红宝石激光	Hóngbǎoshí jīguāng	Ruby laser	
烘焙固化	Hōngbèi gùhuà	Cure (in SMT)	
洪峰流量	Hóngfēng liúliàng	Peak discharge	
宏基实验室	Hóngjī shíyànshì	Acer Lab (Taiwan computer maker)	
洪流	Hóngliú	Flooding	
洪流攻击	Hóngliú gōngjī	Flooding attack (IW)	
洪水	Hóngshuǐ	Flooding	
红外端口	Hóngwài duānkǒu	Infrared port	
红外对象交换协议	Hóngwài duìxiàng jiāohuàn xiéyì	Infrared object exchange	IrOBEX
红外反射滤光镜	Hóngwài fǎnshè lǜguāngjìng	Infrared reflecting filter	
红外跟踪试验	Hóngwài gēnzōng shìyàn	Infrared tracking test	
红外跟踪器	Hóngwài gēnzōngqì	Infrared tracker	
红外光纤	Hóngwài guāngxiān	Infrared optical fiber	
红外雷达跟踪转换试验	Hóngwài léidá gēnzōng zhuǎnhuàn shìyàn	Infrared radar tracking transfer test	
红外数据联合会	Hóngwài shùjù liánhéhuì	Infrared Data Association	IrDA
红外数据联盟	Hóngwài shùjù liánméng	Infrared Data Association	IrDA
红外数据协会	Hóngwài shùjù xiéhuì	Infrared Data Association	IrDA
红外通信	Hóngwài tōngxìn	Infrared communications	IrCOMM
红外透过滤光镜	Hóngwài tòuguò lǜguāngjìng	Infrared transmitting filter	
红外吸收射滤光镜	Hóngwài xīshōu shè lǜguāngjìng	Infrared absorbing filter	
红外移动通信	Hóngwài yídòng tōngxìn	Infrared mobile communications	IrMC
红外线	Hóngwàixiàn	Infrared	IR
红外线玻璃	Hóngwàixiàn bōli	Infrared glass	
红外线材料	Hóngwàixiàn cáiliào	Infrared material	
红外线串列接口	Hóngwàixiàn chuànliè jiēkǒu	Serial infrared port	
红外线底片	Hóngwàixiàn dǐpiàn	Infrared film	
红外线感光板	Hóngwàixiàn gǎnguāng bǎn	Infrared plate	
红外线光源	Hóngwàixiàn guāngyuán	Infrared light source	
红外线固化炉	Hóngwàixiàn gùhuà lú	Infrared curing oven	
红外线检测器	Hóngwàixiàn jiǎncèqì	Infrared detector	
红外线晶体	Hóngwàixiàn jīngtǐ	Infrared crystal	
红外线扫描仪	Hóngwàixiàn sǎomiáoyí	Infrared scanner, thermal mapper	
红外线数据标准协会	Hóngwàixiàn shùjù biāozhǔn xiéhuì	Infrared Data Association	IrDA
红外线通信系统	Hóngwàixiàn tōngxìn xìtǒng	Infrared communications system	ICS
轰炸雷达	Hōngzhà léidá	Bombing radar	
宏指令	Hóngzhǐlìng	Macro-instruction	

后奔腾	Hòu bēnténg	Pentium Pro ©	
后窗管	Hòu chuāngguǎn	Rear port	
后管理模块	Hòu guǎnlǐ mókuài	Back (or background) administrative module	BAM
后进先出表（队列）	Hòu jìn xiān chū biǎo (duìliè)	Last-in first-out list	
后瓣	Hòubàn	Back lobe	
后边缘	Hòubianyuán	Trailing edge	
后代	Hòudài	Descendant	
后端	Hòuduān	Back-end	
后端处理机	Hòuduān chǔlǐjī	Back-end processor	BEP
后端服务器	Hòuduān fúwùqì	Back-end server	
后继	Hòujì	Successor	
后继地址消息	Hòujì dìzhǐ xiāoxi	Subsequent address message	SAM
后加安全措施	Hòujiā ānquán cuòshī	Add-on security	
后馈带反射盘的振子馈电器	Hòukuì dài fǎnshè pánde zhènzǐ kuìdiànqì	Dipole-disk feed for rear-feed	
后馈双喇叭馈电器	Hòukuì shuāng lǎba kuìdiànqì	Double-horn feed for rear-feed	
后门	Hòumén	Backdoor	
后面板	Hòumian bǎn	Back board	BCBB
厚模电路	Hòumó diànlù	Thick-film circuit	
后期制作处理	Hòuqī zhìzuò chǔlǐ	Post-production processing	
后勤迟延	Hòuqín chíyán	Logistic delay	
后勤耽误	Hòuqín dānwù	Logistic delay	
后散射截面	Hòusǎnshè jiémiàn	Back-scattering cross section, back-scattering area (of an antenna)	
喉式传声器	Hóushì chuánshēngqì	Throat microphone	
后台	Hòutái	Back office, back end, background	
后台	Hòutái	Background	
后台程序	Hòutái chéngxù	Background program	
后台存储控制器	Hòutái cúnchǔ kòngzhìqì	Background memory controller	BMC
后台缓冲	Hòutái huǎnchōng	Back buffering	
后向	Hòuxiàng	Backward	
后向泵浦	Hòuxiàng bèngpǔ	Backward pump (FOC)	
后向拆线信号	Hòuxiàng chāixiàn xìnhào	Clear-back signal	
后向挂机信号	Hòuxiàng guàjī xìnhào	Clear back signal	CBK
后向互通电话事件	Hòuxiàng hùtōng diànhuà shìjiàn	Backward interworking telephone events	BITEs
后向建立不成功消息	Hòuxiàng jiànlì bùchéng gōng xiāoxi	Unsuccessful backward set-up information message	UBM
后向建立成功信息消息	Hòuxiàng jiànlì chénggōng xìnxī xiāoxi	Successful backward set-up information message	SBM
后向建立消息	Hòuxiàng jiànlì xiāoxi	Backward set-up message	BSM
后向建立信号	Hòuxiàng jiànlì xìnhào	Backward setup signal	BSM
后向兼容性	Hòuxiàng jiānróngxìng	Backward compatibility	
后向忙	Hòuxiàng máng	Backward busying	
后向散射	Hòuxiàng sǎnshè	Backscatter	
后向顺序号	Hòuxiàng shùnxù hào	Backward sequence number	BSN
后向显式拥塞通知	Hòuxiàng xiǎnshì yōngsè tōngzhī	Backward explicit congestion notification	BECN
后向显示拥塞指示	Hòuxiàng xiǎnshì yōngsè zhǐshì	Backward explicit congestion notification	BECN
后向信号	Hòuxiàng xìnhào	Backward signal	
后向信令单元	Hòuxiàng xìnlìng dānyuán	Backward signal unit	BSU

后向学习	Hòuxiàng xuéxí	Backward learning	
后向压力	Hòuxiàng yālì	Back pressure	
后向运动矢量	Hòuxiàng yùndòng shǐliàng	Backward motion vector (video term)	
后向指示比特	Hòuxiàng zhǐshì bǐtè	Backward indicator bit	BIB
后向指示位	Hòuxiàng zhǐshì wèi	Backward indicator bit	BIB
后序遍历	Hòuxù biànlì	Postorder traversal	
后续地址消息	Hòuxù dìzhǐ xiāoxi	Subsequent address message	SAM
后续流	Hòuxù liú	Subsequent flow	
后续切换程序	Hòuxù qiēhuàn chéngxù	Subsequent handover procedure	
后续切换故障	Hòuxù qiēhuàn gùzhàng	Subsequent handover failure	
后续数据	Hòuxù shùjù	More data	
后续信号单元	Hòuxù xìnhào dānyuán	Subsequent signal unit	SSU
侯选关键字	Hóuxuǎn guānjiàn zì	Candidate key (in SQL Server)	
候选键	Hòuxuǎn jiàn	Candidate key (for database)	
候选自举路由器	Hòuxuǎn zìjǔ lùyóuqì	Candidate bootstrap router	CBSR
后验概率	Hòuyàn gàilǜ	*a posteriori* probability	APP
后沿切割	Hòuyán qiēgē	Trailing edge clipping	
后沿展宽	Hòuyán zhǎnkuān	Trailing-edge broadening	
后置缓冲	Hòuzhì huǎnchōng	Back buffer	
后缀	Hòuzhuì	Suffix	
后缀数字	Hòuzhuì shùzì	Suffix digit	
弧属性表	Hú shǔxìng biǎo	Arc attribute table	AAT
呼损率	Hū sǔn lǜ	Call congestion ratio	
呼损率	Hū sǔn lǜ	Call loss rate	
呼损制	Hū sǔn zhì	Call lost system	
互耦	Hù'ou	Cross coupling	CC
划	Huà	Dash (in Morse code)	
花括号	Huā kuòhào	Brace (curly brace) { }	
华北计算技术研究所	Huáběi Jìsuàn Jìshù Yánjiūsuǒ	North China Institute of Computing Technology	NCI
画笔软件	Huàbǐ ruǎnjiàn	PrintBrush ©	
滑窗流控	Huáchuāng liú kòng	Sliding window flow control	
话单	Huàdān	Ticket	
划定范围	Huàdìng fànwéi	Scoping	
滑动	Huádòng	Slip	
滑动窗流量控制	Huádòng chuāng liúliàng kòngzhì	Sliding window flow control	
滑动窗口	Huádòng chuāngkǒu	Sliding window	
滑动阀门	Huádòng fámén	Sliding shutter	
滑动负载	Huádòng fùzài	Sliding load	
滑动控制滞后	Huádòng kòngzhì zhìhòu	Slip control hysteresis	
滑动螺钉调节器	Huádòng luódīng tiáojiéqì	Slide screw tuner	
滑动面	Huádòng miàn	Slide surface	
滑动模式	Huádòng móshì	Sliding mode	
滑动平均滤波器	Huádòng píngjūn lǜbōqì	Moving average filter	
滑动指标	Huádòng zhǐbiāo	Slip objective (SDH timing)	
划分	Huàfēn	Allocation (of a frequency band)	
划分频带外发射	Huàfēn píndài-wài fāshè	Out-of-allocated band emission	

划分生成	Huàfēn shēngchéng	Generating partitions	
划分的频带	Huàfēnde píndài	Allocated frequency band	
化合物半导体材料	Huàhéwù bàndǎotǐ cáiliào	Compound semiconductor material	
坏纪录消息	Huài jìlù xiāoxi	Bad record MAC message (IPsec TLS)	
坏证书消息	Huài zhèngshū xiāoxi	Bad certificate message (IPsec TLS)	
坏帧标志	Huàizhèng biāozhì	Bad frame indication	BFI
坏帧标识	Huàizhèng biāozhì	Bad frame identity	BFI
坏帧识别	Huàizhèng shíbié	Bad frame identity	BFI
坏帧指示	Huàizhèng zhǐshì	Bad frame indication	BFI
坏帧指示性能	Huàizhèng zhǐshì xìngnéng	Bad frame indicator function	
话机电阻	Huàjī diànzǔ	Telephone set resistance	
滑块	Huákuài	Slider	
话路	Huàlù	Speech channel	
话路	Huàlù	Voice channel	VC
话路服务接入点	Huàlù fúwù jiērù diǎn	Session service access point	SSAP
话路输入电平	Huàlù shūrù diànpíng	Voice circuit input level	
话路输入电平差异	Huàlù shūrù diànpíng chāyì	Voice circuit input level difference	
护岸	Hù'àn	Revetment	
环保护	Huán bǎohù	Ring protection	
环参数服务器	Huán cānshù fúwùqì	Ring parameter server	RPS
环差错监视器	Huán chācuò jiānshìqì	Ring error monitor	REM
换档键	Huàn dàng jiàn	Shift key	
环等待时间	Huán děngdài shíjiān	Ring latency	
环监视器	Huán jiānshìqì	Ring monitor	
换码子复	Huàn mǎzifù	Escape character	ESC
换批	Huàn pī	Alternate the batch number (radar term)	
环入/环出	Huán rù/ huán chū	Ring in, ring out	RI/RO
环室	Huán shì	Annular chamber	
环网	Huán wǎng	Ring network	
换页	Huàn yè	Form feed	FF
换义子复	Huàn yìzǐfù	Escape character	ESC
环栅阵	Huán zhàzhèn	Circular grid array	
环棒天线	Huánbàng tiānxiàn	Loop stick antenna	LSA
环测	Huáncè	Loop-back testing	
缓冲池	Huǎnchōng chí	Pooling	
缓冲存储器	Huǎnchōng cúnchǔqì	Buffer store	
缓冲地址	Huǎnchōng dìzhǐ	Buffer address	BA
缓冲放大器	Huǎnchōng fàngdàqì	Buffer amplifier	
缓冲管	Huǎnchōng guǎn	Buffer tube (FOC)	
缓冲级	Huǎnchōng jí	Buffer stage	
缓冲计数器	Huǎnchōng jìshùqì	Buffer counter reset	BCR
缓冲区	Huǎnchōng qū	Buffer zone	
缓冲区到缓冲区信用数	Huǎnchōng qū dào huǎnchōng qū xìnyòng shù	Buffer-to-buffer credit	BB_Credit
缓冲区分配容量	Huǎnchōng qū fēnpèi róngliàng	Buffer allocation size	
缓冲区溢出攻击	Huǎnchōng qū yìchū gōngjī	Buffer overflow attack (type of hacker attack)	
缓冲衰减器	Huǎnchōng shuāijiǎnqì	Pad attenuator	

缓冲器	Huǎnchōngqì	Buffer	
缓存	Huǎncún	Caching	
缓存解析程序	Huǎncún jiěxī chéngxù	Caching resolver	
缓存集群路由协议	Huǎncún jíqún lùyóu xiéyì	Cache array routing protocol	CARP
缓存目录	Huǎncún mùlù	Cache directory	
环的互连	Huánde hùlián	Ring interconnection (SDH)	
环的互通	Huánde hùtōng	Ring interworking	
黄页	Huángyè	Yellow page	
黄页服务	Huángyè fúwù	Yellow page service	YP
换行	Huànháng	Line feed	LF
环回	Huánhuí	Wrapping	
环回	Huánhuí	Loopback	
环回测试码型	Huánhuí cèshì mǎxíng	Loopback test pattern	
环回控制机制	Huánhuí kòngzhì jīzhì	Loopback control mechanism	
环回控制点	Huánhuí kòngzhìdiǎn	Loopback control point	
环回请求点	Huánhuí qǐngqiúdiǎn	Loopback requesting point	
环回应用	Huánhuí yìngyòng	Loopback application	
环回点	Huánhuídiǎn	Loopback point	
环境	Huánjìng	Context	
环境凹凸映射	Huánjìng āotū yìngshè	Environment mapped bump mapping	
环境保护局	Huánjìng bǎohù jú	Environmental Protection Agency (US)	EPA
环境变量	Huánjìng biànliàng	Environmental variable	
环境参数	Huánjìng cānshù	Environment parameters	
环境测试	Huánjìng cèshì	Environmental test	
环境电源监控(板)	Huánjìng diànyuán jiānkòng (bǎn)	Environmental [and power supply] supervision and control (board)	ESC
环境假设	Huánjìng jiǎshè	Environment assumption	
环境科学管理局	Huánjìng kēxué guǎnlǐjú	Environmental Sciences Services Administration (US)	ESSA
环境科学研究所	Huánjìng kēxué yánjiūsuǒ	Environmental Sciences Research Institute (US GIS organization)	ESRI
环境模块	Huánjìng mókuài	Environment module (in SPL)	
环境试验	Huánjìng shìyàn	Environment test	
环境试验机	Huánjìng shìyànjī	Environment chamber	
环境数据	Huánjìng shùjù	Environmental data	
环境系数	Huánjìng xìshù	Environment factor	
环境遥感	Huánjìng yáogǎn	Environmental remote sensing	
环境音效扩展技术	Huánjìng yīn xiào kuòzhǎn jìshù	Environmental audio extensions	EAX
环境应力筛选	Huánjìng yìnglì shāixuǎn	Environment stress screening	ESS
环境躁声	Huánjìng zàoshēng	Ambient noise	
环境振动	Huánjìng zhèndòng	Ambient vibration	
缓流	Huǎnliú	Sluggish stream	
环路传输	Huánlù chuánshū	Loop transmission	
环路初始化架构分配帧	Huánlù chūshǐhuà jiàgòu fēnpèi zhèng	Loop initialization fabric assigned frame	LIFA
环路初始化进程	Huánlù chūshǐhuà jìnchéng	Loop initialization primitive sequence	LIP
环路初始化软分配帧	Huánlù chūshǐhuà ruǎn fēnpèi zhèng	Loop initialization soft assigned frame	LISA
环路初始化位置报告帧	Huánlù chūshǐhuà wèizhi bàogào zhèng	Loop initialization report position frame	LIRP
环路初始化硬分配帧	Huánlù chūshǐhuà ying fēnpèi zhèng	Loop initialization hard assigned frame	LIHA

环路初始化预分配	Huánlù chūshǐhuà yùfēnpèi	Loop initialization previously assigned	LIPA
环路初始化主控制器选择帧	Huánlù chūshǐhuà zhǔ kòngzhìqì xuǎnzé zhèng	Loop initialization select master frame	LISM
环路端口旁路	Huánlù duānkǒu pánglù	Loop port bypass	LPB
环路端口启用	Huánlù duānkǒu qǐyòng	Loop port enable	LPE
环路端口状态机	Huánlù duānkǒu zhuàngtài jī	Loop port state machine	LPSM
环路环路断续信令	Huánlù duànxù xìnlìng	Loop/disconnect signaling	
环路复用器	Huánlù fùyòngqì	Loop multiplexer	LM
环路高频总增益	Huánlù gāopín zǒngzēngyì	Loop radio frequency overall gain	
环路监视器	Huánlù jiānshìqì	Ring monitor	
环路检验	Huánlù jiǎnyàn	Loop checking	
环路可锁定最底界限角频率	Huánlù kěsuǒdìng zuìdī jièxiàn jiǎopínlǜ	Loop lockable minimum margin angular frequency	
环路可锁定最高界限角频率	Huánlù kěsuǒdìng zuìgāo jièxiàn jiǎopínlǜ	Loop lockable maximum margin angular frequency	
环路滤波器比例系数	Huánlù lǜbōqì bǐlì xìshù	Loop filter proportion coefficient	
环路系统	Huánlù xìtǒng	Loop system	
环路延迟	Huánlù yánchí	Ring latency	
环路已接通	Huánlù yǐ jiētōng	Loop-back acknowledgement (ISUP message)	LPA
环路噪声带宽	Huánlù zàoshēng dàikuān	Loop noise bandwidth	
环路增益	Huánlù zēngyì	Loop gain	
环路直流总增益	Huánlù zhíliú zǒngzēngyì	Loop DC overall gain	
环路中继板	Huánlù zhōngjì bǎn	Loop trunk board	
环路自然谐振角频率	Huánlù zìrán xiézhèn jiǎopínlǜ	Loop natural resonant angular frequency	
环面反射器	Huánmiàn fǎnshèqì	Toroidal reflector	
环球光纤链路	Huánqiú guāngxiān liànlù	Fiber-optic link around the globe	FLAG
环球网	Huánqiú wǎng	Word Wide Web	www
环球网委员会	Huánqiú wǎng wěiyuánhuì	Word Wide Web Committee	W3C
环绕立体声	Huánrào lìtǐshēng	Surround sound	
换算精度	Huànsuàn jīngdù	Conversion precision	
幻线电路	Huànxiàn diànlù	Phantom circuit	
幻像	Huànxiàng	Phantom	
换向时间	Huànxiàng shíjiān	Turn-around time	
换向天线测向仪	Huànxiàng tiānxiàn cèxiàngyí	Commutated antenna direction finder	CADF
环形波	Huánxíng bō	Ring wave	
环行电桥	Huánxíng diànqiáo	Hybrid ring	
环形混频器	Huánxíng hùnpínqì	Ring mixer	
环形计数器	Huánxíng jìshùqì	Ring counter	
环形开关	Huánxíng kāiguān	Ring-switch	
环形天线	Huánxíng tiānxiàn	Loop antenna	
环形天线阵列	Huánxíng tiānxiàn zhènliè	Circular antenna array	
环形拓扑	Huánxíng tuòpū	Ring topology	
环形隙缝天线	Huánxíng xìfèng tiānxiàn	Annular slot antenna	
环行延迟	Huánxíng yánchí	Rounding relay	
环形阵	Huánxíng zhèn	Ring array	
环行器	Huánxíngqì	Circulator	
环氧树脂	Huányǎng shùzhī	Epoxy resin	
环状缝隙天线	Huánzhuàng fèngxì tiānxiàn	Annular slot antenna	ASA

环状圈	Huánzhuàng quān	Annular ring (in SMT)	
环组	Huánzǔ	Ring group	
话上数据	Huà-shàng shùjù	Data above voice	DAV
话上数据	Huà-shàng shùjù	Data over voice	DOV
华胜	Huáshèng	Sun Microsystems (US company)	
滑鼠	Huáshǔ	Mouse	
话筒插座	Huàtǒng chāzuò	Microphone socket (on radio)	MIC
话筒噪声	Huàtǒng zàoshēng	Microphone noise	
华为综合业务接入网商标	Huáwéi zōnghé yèwù jiērù wǎng shāngbiāo	Huawei Integrated Services Optical access Network (trademark)	HONET
话务量	Huàwù liáng	Telephone traffic	
话务频道	Huàwù píndào	Traffic channel	TCH
话务信道	Huàwù xìndào	Traffic channel	TCH
话务员信号	Huàwùyuán xìnhào	Operator signal	OPR
话下传输	Huà-xià chuánshū	Sub-telephone transmission	
话下数据	Huà-xià shùjù	Data under voice	DUV
话下数据传输	Huà-xià shùjù chuánshū	Data under voice transmission	DUV
化学激光器	Huàxué jīguāngqì	Chemical laser	
化学气相沉积法设备	Huàxué qìxiàng chénjī fǎ shèbèi	Chemical vapor deposition (CVD) equipment	
化学阻挡层	Huàxué zǔdǎng céng	Chemical barrier	
划一字距	Huàyī zì jù	Monospace	
划一资讯位址	Huàyī zīxùn wèizhǐ	Uniform (universal) resource locator	URL
话音编码	Huàyīn biānmǎ	Voice code	VC
话音编码器	Huàyīn biānmǎqì	Voice coder	VOCODER
话音插空	Huàyīn chā kōng	Time-assigned speech interpolation	TASI
话音电流	Huàyīn diànliú	Speech current	
话音电路	Huàyīn diànlù	Voice circuit	VC
话音广播固定类型	Huàyīn guǎngbō gùdìng lèixíng	Voice announcement fixed type	VAFX
话音广播混合类型	Huàyīn guǎngbō hùnhé lèixíng	Voice announcement mixed type	VAMX
话音广播业务	Huàyīn guǎngbō yèwù	Voice broadcast service	VBS
话音活动检测	Huàyīn huódòng jiǎncè	Voice activity detection	VAD
话音激活	Huàyīn jīhuó	Voice exciting	
话音激活检波	Huàyīn jīhuó jiǎnbō	Voice activity detection	VAD
话音激活检波器	Huàyīn jīhuó jiǎnbōqì	Voice activity detector	VAD
话音激活检测	Huàyīn jīhuó jiǎncè	Voice activity detection	VAD
话音激活率	Huàyīn jīhuólǜ	Speech activity	
话音记录	Huàyīn jìlù	Voice recording	
话音控制	Huàyīn kòngzhì	Voice control	VC
话音数位信令	Huàyīn shùwèi xìnlìng	Speech digit signaling	
话音数字信令	Huàyīn shùzì xìnlìng	Speech digit signaling	
话音数字化速率	Huàyīn shùzìhuà sùlǜ	Voice digitization rate	VDR
话音突发	Huàyīn tūfā	Speech spurt	
话音小站	Huàyīn xiǎozhàn	Telephony earth station (Hughes)	TES
话音信道	Huàyīn xìndào	Voice channel	VC
话音信道单元	Huàyīn xìndào dānyuán	Voice channel unit	VCU
话音信道控制器	Huàyīn xìndào kòngzhìqì	Voice channel controller	VCC
话音讯息交流	Huàyīn xùnxī jiāoliú	Voice messaging	

话音业务	Huàyīn yèwù	Voice feature	
话音邮件系统	Huàyīn yóujiàn xìtǒng	Voice mail system	
话音预测编码通信	Huàyīn yùcè biānmǎ tōngxìn	Speech predictive encoded communication	SPEC
话音组呼叫业务	Huàyīn zǔ hūjiào yèwù	Voice group call service	VGCS
话音/数据综合	Huàyīn/shùjù zōnghé	Voice/data integration	
话音/数据综合传输系统	Huàyīn/shùjù zōnghé chuánshū xìtǒng	Integrated voice/data transmission system	
互补	Hùbǔ	Complement	
互补晶体管逻辑电路	Hùbǔ jīngtǐguǎn luóji diànlù	Complementary transistor logic circuit	CTL
互补金属氧化物半导体	Hùbǔ jīnshǔ yǎnghuàwù bàndǎotǐ	Complementary metal oxide semiconductor	CMOS
互补金属氧化物半导体集成电路	Hùbǔ jīnshǔ yǎnghuàwù bàndǎotǐ jíchéng diànlù	Complementary metal oxide semiconductor integrated circuit	CMOS-IC
互补误差函数	Hùbǔ wùchā hánshù	Complementary error function	erfc
互补色立体影像	Hùbǔsè lìtǐ yǐngxiàng	Anaglyph	
互补色立体影象地图	Hùbǔsè lìtǐ yǐngxiàng dìtú	Anaglyphographic photomap	
互补色立体图	Hùbǔsè lìtǐtú	Anaglyph	
互操作	Hùcāozuò	Inter-operation, inter-operability	
互操作能力	Hùcāozuò nénglì	Interoperability	
互操作性	Hùcāozuòxìng	Interoperability	
互斥元	Hùchì yuán	Mutual exclusion object, mutex	
互斥元	Hùchì yuán	Mutex, mutual exclusion object	
互斥体	Hùchìtǐ	Mutual exclusion object, mutex	
互斥体	Hùchìtǐ	Mutex, mutual exclusion object	
呼出	Hūchū	Outbound	
呼出限制	Hūchū xiànzhì	Outgoing call barring	
互动电视	Hùdòng diànshì	Interactive teleVision	ITV
互动式	Hùdòngshì	Interactive	
互动式光碟	Hùdòngshì guāngdié	Compact disk-interactive	CD-I
互动式语音应答	Hùdòngshì yǔyīn yìngdá	Interactive voice response	
弧度	Húdù	Radian	
弧段	Húduàn	Arc	
弧段编码文件	Húduàn biānmǎ wénjiàn	Arc code file	
弧段数字化系统	Húduàn shùzihuà xìtǒng	Arc digitizing system	ADS
弧段-节点结构	Húduàn—jiédiǎn jiégòu	Arc-node structure	
弧段-节点拓扑	Húduàn—jiédiǎn tuòpū	Arc-node topology	
弧光灯	Húguāngdēng	Arc light source	
护航浏览	Hùháng liúlǎn	Escorted browsing	
互换	Hùhuàn	Interchange	
互换格式	Hùhuàn géshi	Interchange format	
互换格式类别	Hùhuàn géshi lèibié	Interchange format class	
互换数据元素	Hùhuàn shùjù yuánsù	Interchange data element	
汇编	Huìbiān	Assemble	
汇编程序	Huìbiān chéngxù	Assembler program	
汇编程序缓冲器	Huìbiān chéngxù huǎnchōngqì	Assembly buffer	AB
汇编语言	Huìbiān yǔyán	Assembly language	
汇编指令	Huìbiān zhǐlìng	Assembler instruction	
回波	Huíbō	Echo	

回波抵消	Huíbō dǐxiāo	Echo canceling	EC
回波抵消法	Huíbō dǐxiāo fǎ	Echo cancellation method	
回波抵消四端网络	Huíbō dǐxiāo sìduān wǎngluò	Echo cancellation hybrid	ECH
回波抵消器	Huíbō dǐxiāoqì	Echo canceller	
回波反射	Huíbō fǎnshè	Back reflection (FOC)	
回波控制器	Huíbō kòngzhìqì	Acoustic echo controller	AEC
回波散射	Huíbō sǎnshè	Back scattering (FOC)	
回波损耗	Huíbō sǔnhào	Return loss (radio term)	RL
回波损耗	Huíbō sǔnhào	Echo return loss	ERP
回波通道	Huíbō tōngdào	Acoustic echo path	AEP
回波箱	Huíbō xiāng	Echo box	
回波消除数字电路芯片	Huíbō xiāochú shùzì diànlù xìnpiàn	Digital echo-canceling chip	DECC
回波消除器	Huíbō xiāochúqì	Acoustic echo canceler	AEC
回波信道	Huíbō xìndào	Echo channel, E channel	
回波抑制	Huíbō yìzhì	Echo suppress	
回波抑制器	Huíbō yìzhìqì	Echo suppressor	
回差	Huíchà	Backlash \	
汇超	Huìchāo	Issue overrun	
回车	Huíchē	Carriage return	CR
回答到复位	Huídá dào fùwèi	Answer to reset	ATR
回到键盘	Huídào jiànpán	Back at the keyboard (computer chat)	BAK
回到 N 自动重发请求	Huídào N zìdòng chóngfā qǐngqiú	Return to N automatic repeat request	
回答式干扰	Huídá-shì gānrǎo	Repeater jamming	
汇点	Huìdiǎn	Sink	
回调	Huídiào	Callback	
辉度	Huīdù	Luminance	
汇兑单据	Huìduì dānjù	Remittance document	
汇兑中心	Huìduì zhōngxīn	Remittance service center	
汇费	Huìfèi	Remittance fee	
恢复	Huīfù	Resume	RES
恢复	Huīfù	Restore, restoration, recover	
恢复	Huīfù	Restoration; recovery	
恢复	Huīfù	Retrieval (in common channel signaling)	
回复保护运行	Huífù bǎohù yùnxíng	Revertive protection operation	
恢复单位	Huīfù dānwèi	Restoration unit	
恢复等待时间	Huīfù děngdài shíjiān	Wait to restoration	WTR
恢复规程	Huīfù guīchéng	Recovery procedure (IPsec)	
恢复规程	Huīfù guīchéng	Restorationy procedure	
恢复间歇	Huīfù jiànxiē	Recovery interval	
恢复拒绝	Huīfù jùjué	Resume reject	
恢复控制程序	Huīfù kòngzhì chéngxù	Rrestoration control program	
恢复控制点	Huīfù kòngzhì diǎn	Restoration control point	RCP
恢复控制点	Huīfù kòngzhì diǎn	Restoration control point	RCP
恢复控制中心	Huīfù kòngzhì zhōngxīn	Restoration control center	
恢复力特征	Huīfù lì tèzhēng	Restoring force characteristics	
恢复认可	Huīfù rènkě	Resume acknowledge	

恢复日志文件	Huīfù rìzhì wénjiàn	Restore log file	
恢复时间	Huīfù shíjiān	Restoration time	Tr
恢复算法	Huīfù suànfǎ	Restoration algorithm	
恢复网络	Huīfù wǎngluò	Restoration network	
恢复消息	Huīfù xiāoxi	Resume message (ISUP)	RES
恢复业务平均时间	Huīfù yèwù píngjūn shíjiān	Mean time to restore service	MTRS
恢复载波接收	Huīfù zàibō jiēshōu	Reconditioned carrier reception	
恢复载波解调	Huīfù zàibō jiětiáo	Reconditioned carrier demodulation	
恢复转移时间	Huīfù zhuǎnyí shíjiān	Restoration transfer time	T4
回归方程	Huíguī fāngchéng	Regressive equation	
回归分析	Huíguī fēnxī	Regression analysis	
回归模型	Huíguī móxíng	Regression model	
回归线	Huíguī xiàn	Regression line	
回滚	Huígǔn	Roll back	
回滚本表	Huígǔn běnbiǎo	Rollback current table	
回滚段	Huígǔn duàn	Rollback segment (in ORACLE)	
会合	Huìhé	Convergence	
会话	Huìhuà	Session (for database)	
会话	Huìhuà	Conversation (in telecommunication)	
会话层	Huìhuà céng	Session layer	
会话层协议	Huìhuà céng xiéyì	Session layer protocol (in ISO's OSI)	SP
会话测试	Huìhuà cèshì	Conversation test	
会话初始协议	Huìhuà chūshǐ xiéyì	Session initiation protocol	SIP
会话发起协议	Huìhuà fāqǐ xiéyì	Session initiation protocol	SIP
会话服务	Huìhuà fúwù	Session service	SS
会话服务层	Huìhuà fúwù céng	Presentation services layer	
会话服务访问点	Huìhuà fúwù fǎngwèn diǎn	Session service access point	SSAP
会话服务数据单元	Huìhuà fúwù shùjù dānyuán	Session service data unit	SSDU
会话管理	Huìhuà guǎnlǐ	Session manager	SM
会话脚本	Huìhuà jiǎoběn	Chat script	
会话控制协议	Huìhuà kòngzhì xiéyì	Session control protocol (in DECnet)	SCP
会话描述协议	Huìhuà miáoshù xiéyì	Session description protocol	SDP
会话启动协议	Huìhuà qǐdòng xiéyì	Session initiation protocol	SIP
会话起始协议	Huìhuà qǐshǐ xiéyì	Session initiation protocol	SIP
会话通告协议	Huìhuà tōnggào xiéyì	Session announcement protocol (IETF use)	SAP
会话通知协议	Huìhuà tōngzhī xiéyì	Session announcement protocol	SAP
会话箱	Huìhuà xiāng	Dialog box	
会话协议数据单元	Huìhuà xiéyì shùjù dānyuán	Session protocol data unit	SPDU
会话协议机	Huìhuà xiéyìjī	Session protocol machine	SPM
会话形式程序设计系统	Huìhuà xíngshì chéngxù shèjì xìtǒng	Interactive programming system	IPS
会话业务	Huìhuà yèwù	Conversation service	
会话型业务	Huìhuàxíng yèwù	Conversational service	
汇集	Huìjí	Binding	
回叫	Huíjiào	Call back	
回叫	Huíjiào	Ring-back	
回叫控制协议	Huíjiào kòngzhì xiéyì	Callback control protocol	CCP

回叫信号	Huíjiào xìnhào	Ring-back signal	
汇集点	Huìjídiǎn	Rendezvous point	RP
汇接	Huìjiē	Tandem	
汇接点	Huìjiē diǎn	Junction	
汇接交换机	Huìjiē jiāohuànjī	Tandem switch	TM
汇接局	Huìjiē jú	Tandem office	Tm, TO
汇接 MSC	Huìjiē MSC	Tandem MSC	TMSC
汇接组	Huìjiē zǔ	Transit group	
灰烬设备	Huījìn shèbèi	Ashing equipment (optical fiber mfg)	
汇集性	Huìjíxìng	Lumpability	
会聚	Huìjù	Convergence	
汇聚点	Huìjù diǎn	Rendezvous point	RP
会聚服务	Huìjù fúwù	Convergence service	CS
会聚协议	Huìjù xiéyì	Convergence protocol	
会聚协议实体	Huìjù xiéyì shítǐ	Convergence protocol entity	CPE
会聚子层	Huìjù zicéng	Convergence sub-layer	CS
会聚子层协议数据单元	Huìjù zicéng xiéyì shùjù dānyuán	Convergence sub-layer protocol data unit	CS-PDU
辉亮校正	Huīliàng jiàozhèng	Intensity correction	
辉亮控制	Huīliàng kòngzhì	Intensity control	
辉亮调制	Huīliàng tiáozhì	Intensity modulation	
回铃	Huílíng	Ring-back	
回铃信号	Huílíng xìnhào	Ring-back signal	
回铃音	Huílíng yīn	Ring-back tone	
回流焊接	Huíliú hànjiē	Reflow soldering (in SMT)	
回流户	Huíliú hù	Reflow oven (SMT)	
回流炉	Huíliú lú	Reflow oven (semiconductor mfg)	
汇流排	Huìliú pái	Bus	
汇流条母线	Huìliútiáo mǔxiàn	Bus bar	BB
回路（环）	Huílù (huán)	Cycle	
回路损耗	Huílù sǔnhào	Return loss	RL
回路延迟	Huílù yánchí	Round trip delay	
回路由波长	Huílùyóu bōcháng	Rerouting wavelength	
惠普有限公司	Huì-pǔ yǒuxiàn gōngsī	Hewlett-Packard Corp. (US company)	HP
回声参考当量	Huíshēng cānkǎo dāngliàng	Echo reference equivalent	
回声消除	Huíshēng xiāochú	Echo cancellation	EC
回声抑制单元	Huíshēng yìzhì dānyuán	Echo canceller	EC
回收站	Huíshōuzhàn	Recycle bin © (MS Windows)	
回收站	Huíshōuzhàn	Trash	
回输损耗	Huíshū sǔnhào	Return loss	RL
惠斯登自动系统	Huì-sī-dēng zìdòng xìtǒng	Wheatstone automatic system	
回送别名	Huísòng biémíng	Loopback alias	
回送方式	Huísòng fāngshì	Echoplex mode	
回送接口	Huísòng jiēkǒu	Loopback interface	
回溯跟踪	Huísù gēnzōng	Backtrace (IT term)	
回损	Huísǔn	Return loss	
回弹	Huítán	Rebound	

回填土	Huítiántǔ	Back-fill	
绘图	Huìtú	Drawing	
绘图比例尺	Huìtú bǐlìchǐ	Drafting scale	
绘图范围	Huìtú fànwéi	Drawing extent	
绘图交换格式	Huìtú jiāohuàn géshi	Drawing exchange format	
绘图区	Huìtú qū	Graphics page	
绘图实体	Huìtú shítǐ	Drawing entities	
绘图文件	Huìtú wénjiàn	Drawing file	
绘图板	Huìtúbǎn	Drawing board	
绘图仪	Huìtúyí	Plotter	
回显	Huíxiǎn	Echoplex	
回旋管	Huíxuán guǎn	Gyrotron	
回旋潘尼管	Huíxuán pān-ní-guǎn	Gyro-peniotron	
回旋佩尼管	Huíxuán pèi-ní-guǎn	Gyro-peniotron	
回旋谐振加速器	Huíxuán xiézhèn jiāsùqì	Gyroresonant accelerator	
回旋器	Huíxuánqì	Gyroscoper	
会议电话	Huìyì diànhuà	Conference call	CONF
会议电话	Huìyì diànhuà	Conference telephone	HD
会议电话呼叫混合	Huìyì diànhuà hūjiào hùnhé	Conference call mix	CCMX
会议电话总线	Huìyì diànhuà zǒngxiàn	Conference trunk	CFT
会议电视	Huìyì diànshì	Conference television	
会议电视	Huìyì diànshì	Video conference	
会议电视系统	Huìyì diànshì xìtǒng	VIdeo conference system	VCS
会议电信业务	Huìyì diànxìn yèwù	Teleconference service	
会议呼叫	Huìyì hūjiào	Conference calling	CONF
会议主持者	Huìyì zhǔchízhě	Conference conductor	
回音控制	Huíyīn kòngzhì	Acoustic echo control	
回音抑制算法	Huíyīn yìzhì suànfǎ	Echo cancellation algorithm	
绘制	Huìzhì	Rendering	
惠智	Huì-zhì	Wyse Corp.	
回转半径	Huízhuǎn bànjìng	Radius of gyration	
回转多面镜方式机械式扫描器	Huízhuǎn duō miànjìng fāngshì jīxiè-shì sǎomiáoqì	Rotating polygonal mirror mechanical optical scanner	
回转阵天线	Huízhuǎn zhèn tiānxiàn	Slewing array antenna	
回转台定位设备	Huízhuǎntái dìngwèi shèbèi	Rotation stage positioning equipment (semiconductor mfg)	
呼叫保持	Hūjiào bǎochí	Call hold	HOLD
呼叫保持补充业务	Hūjiào bǎochí bǔchōng yèwù	Call hold supplementary service	HOLD
呼叫变更	Hūjiào biàngēng	In-call modification	IM
呼叫标识符	Hūjiào biāozhì fú	Call identifier	
呼叫不可及前转	Hūjiào bùkě jí qiánzhuǎn	Call forwarding on not reachable	CFNRA
呼叫参考	Hūjiào cānkǎo	Call reference	CR
呼叫参考值	Hūjiào cānkǎo zhí	Call reference value	CRV
呼叫拆线消息	Hūjiào chāixiàn xiāoxi	Call disestablishment message	
呼叫超时	Hūjiào chāoshí	Call time-out	
呼叫重建允许	Hūjiào chóngjiàn yǔnxǔ	Call re-establishment permission	
呼叫传送补充业务	Hūjiào chuánsòng bǔchōng yèwù	Call transfer supplementary service	CT

呼叫处理	Hūjiào chǔlǐ	Call processing	
呼叫处理控制系统	Hūjiào chǔlǐ kòngzhì xìtǒng	Call processing control system	CPCS
呼叫处理语言	Hūjiào chǔlǐ yǔyán	Call processing language	CPL
呼叫初始化	Hūjiào chūshǐhuà	Call setup	
呼叫存储	Hūjiào cúnchǔ	Call store	
呼叫代理	Hūjiào dàilǐ	Call agent	
呼叫代理服务器	Hūjiào dàilǐ fúwùqì	Call agent server	
呼叫待时	Hūjiào dàishí	Call waiting	CW
呼叫单音	Hūjiào dānyīn	Calling tone	
呼叫到达	Hūjiào dàodá	Successful call	
呼叫到达信号	Hūjiào dàodá xìnhào	Call-arrival signal	
呼叫等待	Hūjiào děngdài	Call waiting	CW
呼叫等待补充业务	Hūjiào děngdài bǔchōng yèwù	Call waiting supplementary service	CW
呼叫等待音	Hūjiào děngdài yīn	Call-waiting tone	
呼叫点	Hūjiào diǎn	Point in call	
呼叫方控制	Hūjiào fāng kòngzhì	Calling party handling	CPH
呼叫放弃概率	Hūjiào fàngqì gàilǜ	Call abandonment probability	
呼叫仿真	Hūjiào fǎngzhēn	Call emulator	
呼叫分析程序	Hūjiào fēnxī chéngxù	Call analysis program	CAP
呼叫服务器控制功能	Hūjiào fúwùqì kòngzhì gōngnéng	Call server control function	CSCF
呼叫改发	Hūjiào gǎifā	Call redirection	
呼叫改发选择	Hūjiào gǎifā xuǎnzé	Call deflection selection	
呼叫改发预约	Hūjiào gǎifā yùyuē	Call deflection subscription	
呼叫改向	Hūjiào gǎixiàng	Call deflection	CD
呼叫跟踪	Hūjiào gēnzōng	Call tracing	
呼叫管理	Hūjiào guǎnlǐ	Call management	CM
呼叫管理器	Hūjiào guǎnlǐqì	Call manager	CM
呼叫挂器请求	Hūjiào guàqì qǐngqiú	Suspend request (ISUP message)	SUS
呼叫过程	Hūjiào guòchéng	Call progress (ISUP message)	CPG
呼叫故障信号	Hūjiào gùzhàng xìnhào	Call failure signal	CFL
呼叫故障循环	Hūjiào gùzhàng xúnhuán	Call-failure loop	CFL
呼叫话务员信号	Hūjiào huàwùyuán xìnhào	Operator call-in signal	
呼叫恢复请求	Hūjiào huīfù qǐngqiú	Resume request (ISUP message)	RES
呼叫建立	Hūjiào jiànlì	Call establishment	
呼叫建立差错概率	Hūjiào jiànlì chācuò gàilǜ	Call set-up error probability	
呼叫建立失败概率	Hūjiào jiànlì shībài gàilǜ	Call set-up failure probability	
呼叫建立时间	Hūjiào jiànlì shíjiān	Call set-up time	
呼叫建立消息	Hūjiào jiànlì xiāoxi	Call establishment message	
呼叫建立延迟	Hūjiào jiànlì yánchí	Call set-up delay	
呼叫监视消息	Hūjiào jiānshì xiāoxi	Call supervision message	CSM
呼叫阶段	Hūjiào jiēduàn	Call phases	
呼叫接受信号	Hūjiào jiēshòu xìnhào	Call accepted signal	
呼叫接通率	Hūjiào jiētōnglǜ	Percent of calls completed	
呼叫寄发器群	Hūjiào jìfāqì qún	Group call register	GCR
呼叫计费	Hūjiào jìfèi	Call accounting	
呼叫进程	Hūjiào jìnchéng	Call proceeding	

呼叫进程	Hūjiào jìnchéng	Call process	CALL PROC
呼叫进程消息	Hūjiào jìnchéng xiāoxi	Call progress message (ISUP)	CPG
呼叫进行	Hūjiào jìnxíng	Call proceeding	
呼叫进行信号	Hūjiào jìnxíng xìnhào	Call progress signal	
呼叫进展	Hūjiào jìnzhǎn	Call progress	
呼叫进展消息	Hūjiào jìnzhǎn xiāoxi	Call progressing (message)	CPG
呼叫控制	Hūjiào kòngzhì	Call control	CC
呼叫控制处理集成板	Hūjiào kòngzhì chǔlǐ jíchéngbǎn	Call control processor board assembly	CCPA
呼叫控制处理器	Hūjiào kòngzhì chǔlǐqì	Call control processor	CCP
呼叫控制处理器集成板	Hūjiào kòngzhì chǔlǐqì jíchéngbǎn	Call control processor board assembly	CCPA
呼叫控制代理功能	Hūjiào kòngzhì dàilǐ gōngnéng	Call control agent functioning	CCAF
呼叫控制服务器	Hūjiào kòngzhì fúwùqì	Call control server	
呼叫控制功能	Hūjiào kòngzhì gōngnéng	Call control function	CCF
呼叫控制接入功能	Hūjiào kòngzhì jiērù gōngnéng	Call control access function	CCAF
呼叫控制块	Hūjiào kòngzhì kuài	Call control block	CCB
呼叫控制信号	Hūjiào kòngzhì xìnhào	Call control signal	
呼叫连接管理业务 接入	Hūjiào liánjiē guǎnlǐ yèwù jiērù	Call connection maintenance service accept	
呼叫连接管理业务 请求	Hūjiào liánjiē guǎnlǐ yèwù qǐngqiú	Call connection maintenance service request	
呼叫流量	Hūjiào liúliàng	Call flow	
呼叫名显示	Hūjiào míng xiǎnshì	Calling name presentation	CNAP
呼叫模拟器	Hūjiào mónǐqì	Call simulator	
呼叫碰撞	Hūjiào pèngzhuàng	Call collision	
呼叫偏斜	Hūjiào piānxié	Call deflection	
呼叫前向转移	Hūjiào qiánxiàng zhuǎnyí	Call forwarding	CF
呼叫前转	Hūjiào qiánzhuǎn	Call forwarding	
呼叫清除失败概率	Hūjiào qīngchú shībài gàilǜ	Call clear failure probability	
呼叫清除消息	Hūjiào qīngchú xiāoxi	Call clearing message	
呼叫清除延时	Hūjiào qīngchú yánshí	Call clearing delay	
呼叫请求信号	Hūjiào qǐngqiú xìnhào	Call request signal	
呼叫确认	Hūjiào quèrèn	Call confirmed	
呼叫确认协议	Hūjiào quèrèn xiéyì	Call confirmation protocol	CCP
呼叫筛选	Hūjiào shāixuǎn	Call screening	
呼叫身份	Hūjiào shēnfen	Call identity	
呼叫释放	Hūjiào shìfàng	Call release	
呼叫实例码	Hūjiào shílì mǎ	Call instance code	CIC
呼叫数据包	Hūjiào shùjù bāo	Hello packet	
呼叫特性改变完毕	Hūjiào tèxìng gǎibiàn wánbì	Call modification completed (ISUP message)	CMC
呼叫提供附加业务	Hūjiào tígōng fùjiā yèwù	Call offering supplementary services	
呼叫完成附加业务	Hūjiào wánchéng fùjiā yèwù	Call completion supplementary services	
呼叫完成业务建立	Hūjiào wánchéng yèwù jiànlì	Call completion service setup	CCSS
呼叫线标识显示	Hūjiào xiàn biāozhì xiǎnshì	Calling line identification presentation	CLIP
呼叫线标识限制	Hūjiào xiàn biāozhì xiànzhì	Calling line identification restriction	CLIR
呼叫详细记录	Hūjiào xiángxì jìlù	Call detail record	CDR
呼叫详细记录计费标识（话单）	Hūjiào xiángxì jìlù jìfèi biāozhì (huà dān)	Call detail record charging identifier	CDR
呼叫消息（线）识别	Hūjiào xiāoxi (xiàn) shíbié	Calling line identity	CLI

呼叫消息（线）识别显示	Hūjiào xiāoxi (xiàn) shíbié xiǎnshì	Calling line identification presentation	CLIP
呼叫消息（线）识别限制	Hūjiào xiāoxi (xiàn) shíbié xiànzhì	Calling line identification restriction	CLIR
呼叫泄漏	Hūjiào xièlòu	Call spill-over	
呼叫协调功能	Hūjiào xiétiáo gōngnéng	Call mediation node	CMN
呼叫协调节点	Hūjiào xiétiáo jiédiǎn	Call mediation node	CMN
呼叫协议	Hūjiào xiéyì	Hello protocol	
呼叫细节记录	Hūjiào xìjié jìlù	Call detail recording	CDR
呼叫信息处理	Hūjiào xìnxī chǔlǐ	Call information processing	CIP
呼叫信息阶段消息	Hūjiào xìnxī jiēduàn xiāoxi	Call information phase message	
呼叫信息系统	Hūjiào xìnxī xìtǒng	Call information system	CIS
呼叫序列	Hūjiào xùliè	Calling sequence	
呼叫业务功能	Hūjiào yèwù gōngnéng	Call service function	CSF
呼叫业务节点功能	Hūjiào yèwù jiédiǎn gōngnéng	Call service node function	CSF-N
呼叫业务网关功能	Hūjiào yèwù wǎngguān gōngnéng	Call service gateway function	CSF-G
呼叫业务协调功能	Hūjiào yèwù xiétiáo gōngnéng	Call service mediation function	CSF-C
呼叫业务转接功能	Hūjiào yèwù zhuǎnjiē gōngnéng	Call service transit function	CSF-T
呼叫暂停	Hūjiào zàntíng	Call packing	
呼叫站响应	Hūjiào zhàn xiǎngyìng	Calling station response	
呼叫质量拨打测试	Hūjiào zhìliàng bōdǎ cèshì	Call quality test	CQT
呼叫中断	Hūjiào zhōngduàn	Call gapping	
呼叫中心	Hūjiào zhōngxīn	Call center	
呼叫中心工程	Hūjiào zhōngxīn gōngchéng	Call center engineering	
呼叫中心管理	Hūjiào zhōngxīn guǎnlǐ	Call center manager	CCM
呼叫中心软件	Hūjiào zhōngxīn ruǎnjiàn	Call center software	
呼叫状态	Hūjiào zhuàngtài	Call state	
呼叫状态控制功能	Hūjiào zhuàngtài kòngzhì gōngnéng	Call state control function	CSCF
呼叫转送	Hūjiào zhuǎnsòng	Call forwarding	CF
呼叫转送	Hūjiào zhuǎnsòng	Call transfer	CT
呼叫转向	Hūjiào zhuǎnxiàng	Call deflection	CD
呼叫转移	Hūjiào zhuǎnyí	Call transfer	CT
呼叫转移号码	Hūjiào zhuǎnyí hàomǎ	Call redirecting number	
呼叫转移信息	Hūjiào zhuǎnyí xìnxī	Call redirection information	
呼叫/承网关功能	Hūjiào/chéng wǎngguān gōngnéng	Call/bearer gateway function	C/BGF
呼叫/承载网关功能	Hūjiào/chéngzài wǎngguān gōngnéng	Call/bearer gateway function	C/B GF
呼叫/服务处理	Hūjiào/fúwù chǔlǐ	Call/service processing	
呼救	Hūjiù	Distress call	
呼救系统	Hūjiù xìtǒng	Distress system	
互控逻辑	Hùkòng luóji	Mutual control logic	
互控信令	Hùkòng xìnlìng	Compelled signaling	
互连	Hùlián	Interconnection	
互连	Hùlián	Interworking	
互联代理功能	Hùlián dàilǐ gōngnéng	Interworking agent function	IAF
互连费	Hùlián fèi	Interconnection charge	
互连功能	Hùlián gōngnéng	Interworking function	IWF
互联后面板	Hùlián hòumian bǎn	Interconnect backboard	BIBB
互联面板	Hùlián miànbǎn	Interconnect panel	XICP

互联设备	Hùlián shèbèi	Interworking equipment	IWE
互连外围设备	Hùlián wàiwéi shèbèi	Peripheral component interconnect	PCI
互连外围设备专业组	Hùlián wàiwéi shèbèi zhuānyè zǔ	Peripheral component interconnect special interest group	PCI SIG
互联网关	Hùlián wǎngguān	Interworking gateway	IWGW
互连点	Hùliándiǎn	Point of interconnection	POI
互联网	Hùliánwǎng	Internet	
互联网串行线协议	Hùliánwǎng chuànxíng xiàn xiéyì	Serial line internet protocol	SLIP
互联网短信网关	Hùliánwǎng duǎnxìn wǎngguān	Internet short message gateway	ISMG
互联网工程任务组	Hùliánwǎng gōngchéng rènwu zǔ	Internet Engineering Task Force	IETF
互联网规程	Hùliánwǎng guīchéng	Internet protocol	IP
互联网开放贸易协议	Hùliánwǎng kāifàng màoyì xiéyì	Internet open trading protocol	IOTP
互联网控制消息协议	Hùliánwǎng kòngzhì xiāoxi xiéyì	Internet control message protocol	ICMP
互联网控制子系统	Hùliánwǎng kòngzhì zixìtǒng	Interconnection network control sub-system	INCS
互联网流媒体联盟	Hùliánwǎng liú méitǐ liánméng	Internet Streaming Media Alliance (created by Apple, Cisco, Lasenna, and Philips)	
互联网内容提供商	Hùliánwǎng nèiróng tígōng shāng	Internet content provider	ICP
互联网 ORB 间通信协议	Hùliánwǎng ORB-jiān tōngxìn xiéyì	Internet inter-ORB protocol	IIOP
互联网数据中心	Hùliánwǎng shùjù zhōngxīn	Internet data center	IDC
互联网网站	Hùliánwǎng wǎngzhàn	Web server	
互联网维护子系统	Hùliánwǎng wéihù zìxìtǒng	Interconnection network maintenance sub-system	INMS
互联网消息协议	Hùliánwǎng xiāoxi xiéyì	Internet control message protocol	ICMP
互联网协议	Hùliánwǎng xiéyì	Internet protocol	IP
互联网协议数据单元	Hùliánwǎng xiéyì shùjù dānyuán	Inter-network protocol data unit	IPDU
互联网协议-第 4 版	Hùliánwǎng xiéyì--dì 4 bǎn	Internet protovol version 4	Ipv4
互联网协议-第 6 版	Hùliánwǎng xiéyì--dì 6 bǎn	Internet protocol version 6	IPv6
互联网信息服务器	Hùliánwǎng xìnxī fúwùqì	Internet information server	IIS
互联网业务提供商	Hùliánwǎng yèwù tígōng shāng	Internet service provider	ISP
互联网组管理协议	Hùliánwǎng zǔ guǎnlǐ xiéyì	Internet group management protocol	IGMP
互联网组消息协议	Hùliánwǎng zǔ xiāoxi xiéyì	Internet group message protocol	IGMP
互联网组播成员管理协议	Hùliánwǎng zǔbō chéngyuán guǎnlǐ xiéyì	Internet group message protocol	IGMP
护目镜	Hùmùjìng	Screen filter	
混叠失真	Hùndié shīzhēn	Aliasing distortion	
混沌扩频通信系统	Hùndùn kuòpín tōngxìn xìtǒng	Chaotic spread spectrum communication system	
混沌理论	Hùndùn lǐlùn	Chaos theory	
混沌密码学	Hùndùn mìmǎ xué	Chaos cryptography	
混沌调制	Hùndùn tiáozhì	Chaotic modulation	
混沌同步	Hùndùn tóngbù	Chaotic synchronization	
混合	Hùnhé	Mixing (in switching)	
混和	Hùnhé	Blend, blending	
混合（2/4 线转换电路）	Hùnhé (2/4-xiàn zhuǎnhuàn diànlù)	Hybrid (2/4-wire conversion -the H in BORSCHT)	
混合变量器	Hùnhé biànliàngqì	Hybrid transformer	
混合差错控制	Hùnhé chācuò kòngzhì	Hybrid error control	HEC
混合差动脉码调制	Hùnhé chādòng màimǎ tiáozhì	Hybrid differential pulse code modulation	HDPCM
混合单数字脉码调制	Hùnhé dānshùzì màimǎ tiáozhì	Hybrid uni-digit pulse code modulation	HU-PCM
混合电缆	Hùnhé diànlǎn	Hybrid cable	
混合地址解决方案	Hùnhé dìzhǐ jiějué fāng'àn	Coexistent addess solution	CAS

混合多路复用同步数字转换器	Hùnhé duōlù fùyòng tóngbù shùzì zhuǎnhuànqì	Hybrid multiplexed synchronous digital converter	HMSDC
混合方式	Hùnhé fāngshì	Mixed mode	
混合分集	Hùnhé fēnjí	Hybrid diversity	
混合负载均衡算法	Hùnhé fùzài jūnhéng suànfǎ	Hybrid load balancing algorithm	HLB
混合干扰	Hùnhé gānrǎo	Combinatorial jamming	
混合光集成电路	Hùnhé guāng jíchéng diànlù	Integrated optical hybrid circuit	INOHYC
混合光缆	Hùnhé guānglǎn	Hybrid optical cable	
混合光纤无线系统	Hùnhé guāngxiān wúxiàn xìtǒng	Hybrid fiber wireless system	HFW
混合光纤/同轴电缆	Hùnhé guāngxiān/tóngzhóu diànlǎn	Hybrid fiber/coaxial cable	HFC
混合关联规则	Hùnhé guānlián guīzé	Hybrid association rule	
混合环	Hùnhé huán	Hybrid ring	
混合架	Hùnhé jià	Combined rack	CMBR
混合集成电路	Hùnhé jíchéng diànlù	Hybrid integrated circuit	
混合接口结构	Hùnhé jiēkǒu jiégòu	Hybrid interface structure	
混合接收电路	Hùnhé jiēshōu diànlù	Hybrid receiver circuit	HRC
混合接头	Hùnhé jiētóu	Hybrid junction	
混合激励线性预测	Hùnhé jīlì xiànxìng yùcè	Mixed excitation linear prediction	MELP
混合激励线性预测编码器	Hùnhé jīlì xiànxìng yùcè biānmǎqì	Mixed excitation linear predictive coder	MELP
混合纠错	Hùnhé jiūcuò	Hybrid error correction	HEC
混合救错方式	Hùnhé jiùcuò fāngshì	Hybrid error-correcting method	
混合可伸缩性	Hùnhé kě shēnsuōxìng	Hybrid scalability	
混合扩频	Hùnhé kuòpín	Hybrid spread spectrum	
混合缆	Hùnhé lǎn	Hybrid cable	
混合联机分析处理	Hùnhé liánjī fēnxī chǔlǐ	Hybrid online analytical processing	HOLAP
混合路径传播	Hùnhé lùjìng chuánbō	Mixed-path propagation	
混合模	Hùnhé mó	Hybrid mode (in a waveguide)	
混合模喇叭天线	Hùnhé mó lǎba tiānxiàn	Hybrid mode horn antenna	
混合模拟和数字调制	Hùnhé mónǐ hé shùzì tiáozhì	Hybrid analog and digital modulation	HADM
混合模式	Hùnhé móshì	Mixed mode	
混合耦合器	Hùnhé ǒuhéqì	Hybrid coupler	
混合瞧型合路器	Hùnhé qiáo-xíng hélùqì	Hybrid combiner	HC/HY-COM
混合实境	Hùnhé shíjìng	Mixed reality	
混合数据结构	Hùnhé shùjù jiégòu	Hybrid data structure	
混合锁相环	Hùnhé suǒxiàng huán	Hybrid phase locked loop	HPLL
混合调相	Hùnhé tiáoxiàng	Hybrid phase modulation	HPM
混合通行路由选择	Hùnhé tōngxíng lùyóu xuǎnzé	Hybrid communication routing	HCR
混合 T 型接头	Hùnhé T-xíng jiētóu	Hybrid T-juntion	
混合网络	Hùnhé wǎngluò	Hybrid network	
混合文件	Hùnhé wénjiàn	Mixed document	
混合线圈	Hùnhé xiànquān	Hybrid coil	
混合显示	Hùnhé xiǎnshì	Mixed display	
混合信道指配	Hùnhé xìndào zhǐpèi	Hybird channel assignment	
混合信道指配方式	Hùnhé xìndào zhǐpèi fāngshì	Hybrid channel assignment	HCA
混合信号应用	Hùnhé xìnhào yìngyòng	Mixed signal applications	
混合压扩增量调制	Hùnhé yākuò zēngliàng tiáozhì	Hybrid companding delta modulation	HCDM

混合用途	Hùnhé yòngtú	Mixed use	
混合自动测试系统	Hùnhé zìdòng cèshì xìtǒng	Hybrid automatic test system	HATS
混合自动重传	Hùnhé zìdòng chóngchuán	Hybrid automatic repeat request	HARQ
混合自动请求重传	Hùnhé zìdòng qǐngqiú chóngchuán	Hybrid automatic repeat request	HARQ
混合字符串型	Hùnhé zìfú chuànxíng	Mixed character string type	MC
混合器	Hùnhéqì	Combiner, mixer	C
混合式	Hùnhé-shì	Hybrid	
混合式操作	Hùnhé-shì cāozuò	Mixed mode of operation	
混合式应用共享机制	Hùnhé-shì yìngyòng gòngxiǎng jīzhì	Composite application sharing mechanism (in CSCW)	
混合型隧道和雪崩度起时间二极管	Hùnhé-xíng suìdào hé xuěbēng dùqǐ shíjiān èrjíguǎn	Mixed tunnel and avalanche transit-time diode	MITATT
混合型文件	Hùnhé-xíng wénjiàn	Mixed document	
混乱透顶，糟极了	Hùnluàn tòudǐng, zāo jíle	Fouled up beyound all recognition	Fubar
混模器	Hùnmóqì	Mode scrambler	
混频器	Hùnpínqì	Frequency mixer	
混频器传输系数	Hùnpínqì chuánshū xìshù	Mixer transmission coefficient	
混频器的寄生响应	Hùnpínqìde jìshēng xiǎngyìng	Mixer spurious response	
混响半径	Hùnxiǎng bànjìng	Reverberation radius	RR
混响时间	Hùnxiǎng shíjiān	Reverberation time	RT
混响器	Hùnxiǎngqì	Reverberator	
混杂模式	Hùnzá móshì	Promiscuous	
“或非”	Huò fēi	Not or	NOR
“或”功能	Huò gōngnéng	OR function	OR
或逻辑电路	Huò luójídiànlù	OR logic circuit	OR
“或”门	Huò mén	OR gate	OG, OR
获得口令	Huòdé kǒulìng	Get password	
活动部分	Huódòng bùfen	Movable part	
活动 C 通路	Huódòng C tōnglù	Active comm channel	
活动槽口时分多路复用	Huódòng cáokǒu shífèn duōlù fùyòng	Movable-slot time-division multiplexing	MSTDM
活动分区	Huódòng fēnqū	Active partition	
活动服务器页面	Huódòng fúwùqì yèmiàn	Active server pages	
活动共享机制	Huódòng gòngxiǎng jīzhì	Active sharing mechanism (in CSCW)	
活动模锁定	Huódòng mó suǒdìng	Active mode lock	AML
活动模式	Huódòng móshì	Active mode	
活动目录	Huódòng mùlù	Active directory	
活动内容	Huódòng nèiróng	Active content	
活动铜缆	Huódòng tónglǎn	Active copper cable	
活动图像编码专家组	Huódòng túxiàng biānmǎ zhuānjiāzǔ	Moving Picture Coding Experts Group	MPEG
活动图象交换网	Huódòng túxiàng jiāohuàn wǎng	Video switched network	VSN
活动图像专家组	Huódòng túxiàng zhuānjiāzǔ	Motion Picture Experts Group	MPEG
活动文件	Huódòng wénjiàn	Active file	
活动语句	Huódòng yǔjù	Active statement	
活动的	Huódòngde	Active	
活动的成员地址	Huódòngde chéngyuán dìzhǐ	Active member address	AM-ADDR
“或非”门	Huòfēi mén	NOR gate	
霍夫曼编码	Huò-fū-màn biānmǎ	Huffman code	

霍夫曼行程编码	Huò-fū-màn xíngchéng biānmǎ	Huffman run-length encoding	
火花塞抑制器	Huǒhuāsāi yìzhìqì	Spark plug suppressor	
火警	Huǒjǐng	Fire alarm	
火警警铃	Huǒjǐng jǐnglíng	Fire alarm bell	FAB
火控雷达	Huǒkòng léidá	Fire control radar	
货盘	Huòpán	Pallet	
获取最近服务器	Huòqǔ zuìjìn fúwùqì	Get nearest server	GNS
活塞	Huósāi	Piston	
活塞式衰减器	Huósāi-shì shuāijiǎnqì	Piston attenuator	
火山剖面炉	Huǒshān pōumiàn lú	Volcano profile ovens (semiconductor mfg)	
活锁	Huósuǒ	Livelock (for database)	
火线	Huǒxiàn	Firewire (IEEE 1394)	
火线	Huǒxiàn	Hot wire	
活性钨	Huóxìng wū	Porous tungsten	
火焰探测器	Huǒyàn tàncèqì	Flame detector	FD
火灾报警系统	Huǒzāi bàojǐng xìtǒng	Fire alarm system	FCC
火灾事故广播	Huǒzāi shìgù guǎngbō	Fire public address	FPA
火灾自动报警控制装置	Huǒzāi zìdòng bàojǐng kòngzhì zhuāngzhì	Fire alarm automatic control unit	FACU
互配功能	Hùpèi gōngnéng	Interworking function	IWF
护坡工程	Hùpō gōngchéng	Slope works	
呼入	Hūrù	Inbound	
呼入直拨到分机用户	Hūrù zhíbō dào fēnjī yònghù	Direct inward dialing	DID
弧刷	Húshuā	Wiper (of a selector)	
互锁	Hùsuǒ	Interlock	
护套	Hùtào	Sheath, jacket	
互调	Hùtiáo	Intermodulation	IM
互调产物	Hùtiáo chǎnwù	Intermodulation product	
互调产物阶次	Hùtiáo chǎnwù jiēcì	Intermodulation product order	
互调分量	Hùtiáo fènliàng	Intermodulation component	
互调抗扰性	Hùtiáo kàngrǎoxìng	Intermodulation immunity	
互调失真	Hùtiáo shīzhēn	Intermodulation distortion	IMD
互调衰减	Hùtiáo shuāijiǎn	Intermodulation fade	
互调抑制	Hùtiáo yìzhì	Intermodulation suppression	
互调噪声	Hùtiáo zàoshēng	Intermodulation noise	
互通	Hùtōng	Interworking	
互通单元	Hùtōng dānyuán	Interworking unit	IWU
呼通概率	Hūtōng gàilǜ	Call completion probability	
互通功能	Hùtōng gōngnéng	Interworking function	IWF
互通功能单元	Hùtōng gōngnéng dānyuán	Interworking function unit	IFU
互通功能模块	Hùtōng gōngnéng mókuài	Interworking function	IWF
互通功能装备的 MSC	Hùtōng gōngnéng zhuāngbèide MSC	Interworking MSC	IWMSC
互通模块	Hùtōng mókuài	Interworking module	IWM
互通协议	Hùtōng xiéyì	Interworking protocol	IP
互同步网	Hùtóngbù wǎng	Mutually synchronized network	
互通性	Hùtōngxìng	Interoperability	
弧头	Hútóu	Head	

护腕架	Hùwàn jià	Wrist rest	
弧尾	Húwěi	Tail	
护尾雷达	Hùwěi léidá	Aircraft tail warning radar	ATWR
呼吸	Hūxī	Sniff (verb)	
互相抗	Hùxiāng kàng	Mutual impedance	
互相调制	Hùxiāng tiáozhì	Intermodulation	IM
互相关函数	Hùxiāngguān hánshù	Cross correlation function	
互相关器	Hùxiāngguānqì	Cross-correlator	
互相关性	Hùxiāngguān-xìng	Cross-correlation	
互相网控制器	Hùxiāngwǎng kòngzhìqì	Internet controller	INC
互疑	Hùyí	Mutually suspicious (IPsec)	
互易移相器	Hùyì yíxiàngqì	Reciprocal phase shifter	
互助控制信号	Hùzhù kòngzhì xìnhào	Mutual assistance control signal	
互助逻辑	Hùzhù luóji	Mutual assistance logic	
互阻抗	Hùzǔkàng	Mutual impedance (of antenna elements)	

I

I 接口用户模块	I jiēkǒu yònghù mókuài	I interface subscriber module	
ICMP 路由发现协议	ICMP lùyóu fāxiàn xiéyì	ICMP router discovery protocol	IRDP
ICMP 路由器发现协议	ICMP lùyóuqì fāxiàn xiéyì	ICMP router discovery protocol (IETF usage)	IRDP
II 类设备	II-lèi shèbèi	Class II equipment	
Intel 公司构架实验室	Intel gōngsī gòujià shíyànshì	Intel® Architecture Labs	IAL
Internet 存储名称服务	Internet cúnchǔ míngchēng fúwù	Internet storage name service (IETF usage)	iSNS
Internet 服务提供商	Internet fúwù tígōngshāng	Internet service provider	ISP
Internet 工程任务组	Internet gōngchéng rènwu zǔ	Internet Engineering Task Force	IETF
Internet 光纤信道协议	Internet guāngxiān xindào xiéyì	Internet fiber channel protocol (IETF use)	iFCP
Internet 小型计算机系统接口	Internet xiǎoxíng jìsuànjī xìtǒng jiēkǒu	Internet small computer system interface (IETF usage)	iSCSI
IP 安全协议	IP ānquán xiéyì	IP security	IPSec
IP 安全选项	IP ānquán xuǎnxiàng	IP security option	IPSO
IP 层协议安全结构	IP céng xiéyì ānquán jiégòu	Security architecture for IP network	IPsec
IP 导航器	IP dǎohángqì	Internet protocol navigator	
IP 电话	IP diànhuà	IP phone	Iphone
IP 电话路由	IP diànhuà lùyóu	Telephony routing over IP	TRIP
IP 多播	IP duōbō	IP multicast	IP-M
IP 话音	IP huàyīn	Voice over IP	VoIP
IP 活动支持协议	IP huódòng zhīchí xiéyì	Internet protocol mobility support protocol	
IP 交换	IP jiāohuàn	Internet protocol switching	
IP 控制协议	IP kòngzhì xiéyì	IP control protocol	IPCP
IP 设备控制	IP shèbèi kòngzhì	Internet protocol device control	IPDC
IP 网络安全协议	IP wǎngluò ānquán xiéyì	Internet protocol security protocol	IPSEC
IP 网络上的 SCSI 接口	IP wǎngluò-shàngde SCS jiēkǒu	SCSI over IP	SoIP
IP 网上传输话音	IP wǎngshàng chuánshū huàyīn	Voice over internet protocol	VOIP
IP 网上电话路由选择	IP wǎng-shàng diànhuà lùyóu xuǎnzé	Telephony routing over IP	TRIP
IP 组播业务	IP zǔbō yèwù	IP-multicast	IP-M
IP 上的话音	IP-shàngde huàyīn	Voice over IP	VoIP
IP 上的语音协议	IP-shàngde yǔyīn xiéyì	Voice over internet protocol (ITU-T protocol)	VOIP

IPv6 的路由信息协议	IPv6-de lùyóu xìnxī xiéyì	Routing information protocol for IPv6	RIPng
ISDN 数字用户线路	ISDN shùzì yònghù xiànlù	ISDN digital subscriber line	IDSL
ISDN 协议参考模型	ISDN xiéyì cānkǎo móxíng	ISDN protocol reference mode	ISDN-PRM
ISDN 用户部分	ISDN yònghù bùfen	ISDN user part	ISUP
ISDN 用户号码	ISDN yònghù hàomǎ	ISDN subscriber number	ISDN-SN
ISDN 用户模块	ISDN yònghù mókuài	ISDN subscriber module	ISM
ISO 国家代码	ISO guójiā dàimǎ	ISO country code	
ISO 数据和国家代码	ISO shùjù hé guójiā dàimǎ	ISO data and country code	ISO DCC
ISO 运输层协议 4 级	ISO yùnshū céng xiéyì 4 jí	ISO transport protocol class 4	TP4
IT 托管	IT tuōguǎn	IT outsourcing	
ITU-T 软件工具库 2000 年版	ITU-T ruǎnjiàn gōngjùkù 2000 nián bǎn	ITU-T Software Tools Library, release 2000	STL-2000

J

Java 安全套接字扩展	Java ānquán tàojiēzì kuòzhǎn	Java secure socket extension	JSSE
Java 电话应用程序设计接口	Java diànhuà yìngyòng chéngxù shèjì jiēkǒu	Java telephony application programming interface	JTAPI
Java 归档文件	Java guīdàng wénjiàn	Java archive file	JAR file
Java 开发包	Java kāifā bāo	Java development kit	JDK
Java 密码扩展	Java mìmǎ kuòzhǎn	Java cryptographic extension	JCE
Java 密码体系结构	Java mìmǎ tǐxì jiégòu	Java cryptographic architecture	JCA
Java 命名索引薄接口	Java mìngmíng suǒyǐn báo jiēkǒu	Java naming directory interface	JNDI
Java 芯片操作系统	Java xìnpiàn cāozuò xìtǒng	Java chip operating system	JCOS
Java 虚拟机	Java xūnǐjī	Java virtual machine	JVM
Java 自动并行化系统	Java zìdòng bìngxínghuà xìtǒng	Java automatic paralleling system	JAPS
级	Jí	Level, class	
基表	Jī biǎo	Base table	
脊波导	Jǐ bōdǎo	Ridge waveguide	RWG
极碟	Jí dié	Zip disk	
极碟驱动器	Jí dié qūdòngqì	Zip disk drive	
基地址	Jī dìzhǐ	Base address	
基地址寄存器	Jī dìzhǐ jìcúnqì	Base register	BR
基峰	Jī fēng	Base peak	
极轨道	Jí guǐdào	Polar orbit (of a satellite)	
级截断环节	Jí jiéduàn huánjié	Levels of truncation	
基类	Jī lèi	Base class	
基类库	Jī lèi kù	Base class library	BCL
基类型	Jī lèixíng	Base type	
极坐标核	Jí zuòbiāo hé	Polar coordinate kernel	
寄偶错误	Jì'ǒu cuòwù	Parity error	
寄偶校验	Jì'ǒu jiàoyàn	Parity check	PAR
价	Jià	Valency	
假变元	Jiǎ biànyuán	Dummy argument (in FORTRAN)	
假传送格式检波比率	Jiǎ chuánsòng géshi jiǎnbō bǐlǜ	False transmit format detection ratio	FDR
假负载	Jiǎ fùzài	Dummy load	
价列表	Jià lièbiǎo	Valency table	
加密钥轮	Jiā mìyào lún	Add key round	

假启动	Jiǎ qǐdòng	False start	
假天线	Jiǎ tiānxiàn	Dummy antenna	
加选比	Jiā xuǎn bǐ	Add-compare-select	ACS
甲乙双方商定	Jiǎ yǐ shuāngfāng shāngdìng	Agreed on by both parties	
加总比对法	Jiā zǒngbǐduì fǎ	Check-sum	
加插键	Jiāchā jiàn	Insert key	Ins
加成工艺	Jiāchéng gōngyì	Additive Process (in SMT)	
加电自测试	Jiādiàn zìcèshì	Power-on self test	POST
加电自检	Jiādiàn zìjiǎn	Power-on self test	POST
加法进位	Jiāfǎ jìnwèi	Add carry	AC
加法控制器	Jiāfǎ kòngzhìqì	Add control unit	ACU
加法器	Jiāfǎqì	Adder	
加法器输出缓冲器	Jiāfǎqì shūchū huǎnchōngqì	Adder output buffer	AOB
加法器输出总线	Jiāfǎqì shūchū zǒngxiàn	Adder output bus	AOB
加感线圈	Jiāgǎn xiànquān	Load coil	
价格带	Jiàgé dài	Price band	
架构	Jiàgòu	Architecture	
架构	Jiàgòu	Schema	
架构地址通知	Jiàgòu dìzhǐ tōngzhī	Fabric address notification	FAN
架构端口拒绝帧	Jiàgòu duānkǒu jùjué zhèng	Fabric port reject frame	F_RJT
架构行集	Jiàgòu hángjí	Schema rowset	
架构环路端口	Jiàgòu huánlù duānkǒu	Fabric loop port	
架构生命周期管理	Jiàgòu shēngmìng zhōuqī guǎnlǐ	Infrastructure lifecycle management	
加固工程	Jiāgù gōngchéng	Consolidation works	
夹具	Jiājù	Fixture (in SMT)	
架空插入段	Jiàkōng chārù duàn	Aerial insert	
架空光缆	Jiàkōng guānglǎn	Aerial fiber optic cable	AOFC
架空缆	Jiàkōng lǎn	Aerial cable	
伽罗华域	Jiāluóhuá yù	Galois field	GF
假冒	Jiǎmào	Masquerade, impersonation (IPsec)	
加密	Jiāmì	Encryption, encipherment	
加密保护	Jiāmì bǎohù	Encipherment protection	
加密补偿	Jiāmì bǔcháng	Ciphering offset	COF
加密触发器	Jiāmì chùfāqì	Encrypted trigger	
加密方案	Jiāmì fāng'àn	Encipherment scheme	
加密服务提供者	Jiāmì fúwù tígòngzhě	Cryptographic service provider	CSP
加密辅助单元	Jiāmì fǔzhù dānyuán	Crypto auxiliary unit	CAU
加密键序列数/号	Jiāmì jiàn xùliè shù/hào	Cipher key sequence/number	CKSN
加密机制	Jiāmì jīzhì	Encryption mechanism (IPsec)	
加密控制协议	Jiāmì kòngzhì xiéyì	Encryption control protocol	ECP
加密控制信号	Jiāmì kòngzhì xìnhào	Encryption control signal	ECS
加密令牌	Jiāmì lìngpái	Crypto token	
加密密钥	Jiāmì mìyào	Encryption key	
加密模式拒绝	Jiāmì móshì jùjué	Cipher mode reject	
加密模式命令	Jiāmì móshì mìnglìng	Cipher mode command	
加密模式设置	Jiāmì móshì shèzhì	Cipher mode setting	

加密模式完成	Jiāmì móshì wánchéng	Cipher mode complete	
加密算法	Jiāmì suànfǎ	Encryption algorithm	
加密套接字安全层	Jiāmì tàojiēzì ānquán céng	Secure socket layer	SSL
加密系统	Jiāmì xìtǒng	Cryptographic system	CS
加密/解密库	Jiāmì/jiěmì kù	Encryption/decryption library	
加密的 HTTP 协议	Jiāmìde HTTP xiéyì	Secure hypertext transfer protocol (IETF use)	S-HTTP
键	Jiàn	Key (on a keyboard, also used in databases)	
键保护	Jiàn bǎohù	Key protection	KEY
见得相一	Jiàn de xiāng yī	What you see is what you get	WYSIWYG
键范围锁	Jiàn fànwéi suǒ	Key range lock	
键列	Jiàn liè	Key column (for database)	
减载波单边带发射	Jiǎn zàibō dānbiāndài fāshè	Reduced carrier single-sideband emission	
监帧	Jiān zhèng	Supervisory frame (S-frame)	
加拿大标准联合会	Jiā-ná-dà biāozhǔn liánhéhuì	Canadian Standards Association	CSA
加拿大标准协会	Jiā-ná-dà biāozhǔn xiéhuì	Canadian Standards Association	CSA
加拿大测量工程研究所	Jiā-ná-dà cèliáng gōngchéng yánjiūsuǒ	Canadian Institute of Geomatics	CIG
加拿大地理信息系统	Jiā-ná-dà dìlǐ xìnxī xìtǒng	Canadian Geography Information System	CGIS
加拿大广播公司	Jiā-ná-dà Guǎngbō Gōngsī	Canadian Broadcasting Corp.	CBC
简报软件	Jiǎnbào ruǎnjiàn	Presentation software	
渐变波导	Jiànbiàn bōdǎo	Tapered waveguide	
渐变符号图	Jiànbiàn fúhào tú	Graduated symbol map	
渐变失效	Jiànbiàn shīxiào	Gradual failure; drift failure	
渐变梯度光纤	Jiànbiàn tīdù guāngxiān	Graded index fiber	GIF
渐变折射率	Jiànbiàn zhéshèlǜ	Graded index of refraction	
渐变折射率分布	Jiànbiàn zhéshèlǜ fēnbù	Graded index profile	
渐变折射率光纤	Jiànbiàn zhéshèlǜ guāngxiān	Graded index fiber	GI
渐变式阻抗变换器	Jiànbiàn-shì zǔkàng biànhuànqì	Graduating impedance transformer	
渐变型多模光纤	Jiànbiànxíng duōmó guāngxiān	Graded index fiber	GIF
渐变型光纤	Jiànbiànxíng guāngxiān	Graded index fiber	
鉴别	Jiànbié	Authentication	
鉴别程序	Jiànbié chéngxù	Discriminator	
鉴别程序输入客体	Jiànbié chéngxù shūrù kètǐ	Discriminator input object	
鉴别符	Jiànbié fú	Authenticator	
鉴别服务器	Jiànbié fúwùqì	Authentication server	
鉴别号码	Jiànbié hàomǎ	Identity	ID
鉴别选择器	Jiànbié xuǎnzéqì	Discriminating selector	
鉴别器群（电平 1）	Jiànbiéqì qún (diànpíng 1)	Group identifier (level 1)	GID1
鉴别器群（电平 2）	Jiànbiéqì qún (diànpíng 2)	Group identifier (level 1)	GID2
简并模	Jiǎnbìng mó	Degenerate mode (in a cavity resonator or waveguide)	
检波	Jiǎnbō	Detection	
检波失真	Jiǎnbō shīzhēn	Detection distortion	
检波效率	Jiǎnbō xiàolǜ	Detection efficiency	
检波座	Jiǎnbō zuò	Detector mount	
检波器	Jiǎnbōqì	Detector	
检波器的充电时间常数	Jiǎnbōqìde chōngdiàn shíjiān chángshù	Electrical charge time constant of a detector	
检波器的电流灵敏度	Jiǎnbōqìde diànliú língmǐndù	Detector current sensitivity	

检波器的电压灵敏度	Jiǎnbōqìde diànyā língmǐndù	Detector voltage sensitivity	
检波器的放电时间常数	Jiǎnbōqìde fàngdiàn shíjiān chángshù	Electrical discharge time constant (of a detector)	
检测重发周期	Jiǎncè chóngfā zhōuqī	Testing repetition cycle	
监测单音	Jiāncè dānyīn	Supervisory audio tone	SAT
检测点	Jiǎncè diǎn	Detection point	DP
检测耦合器	Jiǎncè ǒuhéqì	Detector coupler	
监测设备	Jiāncè shèbèi	Supervisory block	S-Block
检测时间	Jiǎncè shíjiān	Detection time	T1
监测音	Jiāncè yīn	Supervisory audio tone	SAT
监测音峰频偏	Jiāncè yīnfēng pínpiān	Supervisory audio tone peak deviation	
监测音频单音	Jiāncè yīnpín dānyīn	Supervisory audio tone	SAT
监测中心	Jiāncè zhōngxīn	Monitoring center	MC
检测准则	Jiǎncè zhǔnzé	Detection criterion	
检测器	Jiǎncèqì	Detector	
检查	Jiǎnchá	Inspection, examination	
检查比特	Jiǎnchá bǐtè	Check bit	CK
检查点	Jiǎnchá diǎn	Checkpoint (for database)	
间插分复用器	Jiānchā fēn fùyòngqì	Interleaver	
检查和错误	Jiǎnchá hé cuòwù	Check sum error	CSE
检查时间	Jiǎnchá shíjiān	Check-out time	
检查与故障隔离	Jiǎnchá yǔ gùzhàng gélí	Checkout and fault isolation	COFI
检查约束	Jiǎnchá yuēshù	Check constraint (in SQL Server)	
检出点	Jiǎnchū diǎn	Detection point	
检错	Jiǎncuò	Error detection	
检错反馈系统	Jiǎncuò fǎnkuì xìtǒng	Error-detecting and feedback system	
检错及反馈重发系统	Jiǎncuò jí fǎnkuì chóngfā xìtǒng	Error detecting and feedback system	ARQ
检错能力	Jiǎncuò nénglì	Error-detecting capacity	
检错码	Jiǎncuòmǎ	Error detection code	
简单布尔表示式	Jiǎndān Bù-ěr biǎoshì shì	Simple Boolean expression	SBE
简单对象	Jiǎndān duìxiàng	Simple object	
简单对象访问协议	Jiǎndān duìxiàng fǎngwèn xiéyì	Simple object access protocol	SOAP
简单服务器冗余协议	Jiǎndān fúwùqì rǒngyú xiéyì	Simple server redundancy protocol	SSRP
简单公共密匙 GSS - API 机制	Jiǎndān gōnggòng mìchí GSS-API jīzhì	Simple public key GSS-API mechanism	SPKM
简单和有效的 AAL	Jiǎndān hé yǒuxiàode AAL	Simple and efficient AAL	SEAL
简单回路	Jiǎndān huílù	Simple cycle	
简单鉴别	Jiǎndān jiànbié	Simple authentication	
简单校正	Jiǎndān jiàozhèng	Simple rectification	
简单可编程逻辑器件	Jiǎndān kě biānchéng luóji qìjiàn	Simple programmable logic device	
简单类型	Jiǎndān lèixíng	Simple type	
简单路径	Jiǎndān lùjing	Simple path	
简单名字服务器/服务	Jiǎndān míngzì fúwùqì/fúwù	Short name server/service	SNS
简单数据链路	Jiǎndān shùjù liànlù	Simplified data link	SDL
简单数据通路	Jiǎndān shùjù tōnglù	Simple data link	SDL
简单数字调制	Jiǎndān shùzì tiáozhì	Simple digital modulation	
简单特征	Jiǎndān tèzhēng	Simple feature	

简单网关监视协议	Jiǎndān wǎngguān jiānshì xiéyì	Simple gateway monitoring protocol	SGMP
简单网关控制协议	Jiǎndān wǎngguān kòngzhì xiéyì	Simple gateway control protocol	SGCP
简单网络定时协议	Jiǎndān wǎngluò dìngshí xiéyì	Simple network time protocol	SNTP
简单网络管理协议	Jiǎndān wǎngluò guǎnlǐ xiéyì	Simple network management protocol	SNMP
简单网络时间协议	Jiǎndān wǎngluò shíjiān xiéyì	Simple network time protocol (IETF use)	SNTP
简单文件传输协议	Jiǎndān wénjiàn chuánshū xiéyì	Trivial file transfer protocol	TFTP
简单文件传送协议	Jiǎndān wénjiàn chuánsòng xiéyì	Trivial file transfer protocol	TFTP
简单消息函数	Jiǎndān xiāoxi hánshù	Simple message function	
简单验证	Jiǎndān yànzhèng	Simple authentication	
简单引导标记规范	Jiǎndān yǐndǎo biāojì guīfàn	Simple boot flag specification	SBFS
简单因特网协议	Jiǎndān Yīntèwǎng xiéyì	Simple internet protocol	SIP
简单邮件传输协议	Jiǎndān yóujiàn chuánshū xiéyì	Simple mail transfer protocol	SMTP
简单邮件传送协议	Jiǎndān yóujiàn chuánsòng xiéyì	Simple mail transfer protocol	SMTP
简单有效的适配层	Jiǎndān yǒuxiàode shìpèi céng	Simple and efficient adaptation layer	SEAL
简单的多点电路	Jiǎndānde duōdiǎn diànlù	Simple multipoint circuit	
简单的邮件传送协议	Jiǎndānde yóujiàn chuánsòng xiéyì	Simple mail transfer protocol	SMTP
鉴定测试	Jiàndìng cèshì	Characterization test	
鉴定类型码	Jiàndìng lèixíng mǎ	Type approval code	TAC
鉴定文件头	Jiàndìng wénjiàn tóu	Authentication header	AH
溅镀设备	Jiàndù shèbèi	Sputtering equipment (semiconductor mfg)	
间断传输	Jiànduàn chuánshū	Discontinous transmission	DTX
间断线	Jiànduàn xiàn	Intermittent line	
佳能	Jiā-néng	Canon (Japanese company)	
尖峰脉冲	Jiānfēng màichōng	Spike	
尖峰信号	Jiānfēng xìnhào	Spike	
减幅载波	Jiǎnfú zàibō	Reduced carrier	
鉴幅器	Jiànfúqì	Amplitude discriminator	
降优值电路	Jiàng yōuzhí diànlù	De-Q-ing circuit	
降额	Jiàng'é	Derating	
间隔	Jiàngé	Space (between characters and words in Morse code)	
间隔刻度	Jiàngé kèdù	Interval scale	
间隔频带	Jiàngé píndài	Guard band	
间隔时间标度	Jiàngé shíjiān biāodù	Interval time scale	
间隔使用编码	Jiàngé shǐyòng biānmǎ	Interval usage coding	IUC
间隔物	Jiàngéwù	Spacer	
间隔物宽度	Jiàngéwù kuāndù	Divider width	
间隔物类型	Jiàngéwù lèixíng	Divider type	
间隔物散布装置	Jiàngéwù sànbù zhuāngzhì	Spacer dispersion equipment	
降级	Jiàngjí	Degradation	
降交点	Jiàngjiāodiǎn	Descending node (of a satellite)	
降灵	Jiànglíng	Desensitization	
降落物散射传播	Jiàngluòwù sǎnshè chuánbō	Precipitation scatter propagation	
降敏	Jiàngmǐn	Desensitizing	
检光元件	Jiǎnguāng yuánjiàn	Detector	
降雨补偿	Jiàngyǔ bǔcháng	Precipitation compensation	
降雨衰落	Jiàngyǔ shuāiluò	Precipitation degradation	

降质	Jiàngzhì	Defect	
降质管理信元	Jiàngzhì guǎnlǐ xìn yuán	Defect management cell	
降阻触点	Jiàngzǔ chùdiǎn	Wetted contact	
监护	Jiānhù	Guarding (in voice frequency signaling)	
简化	Jiǎnhuà	Simplification	
简化 CPU 双重跳线法	Jiǎnhuà CPU shuāngchóng tiàoxiànfǎ	Easy setting CPU dual jumper	ESDJ
简化双重跳线法	Jiǎnhuà shuāngchóng tiàoxiàn fǎ	Easy setting dual jumper	ESDJ
简化数据链路	Jiǎnhuà shùjù liànlù	Simplified data link	SDL
简化 TDMA 帧号	Jiǎnhuà TDMA zhènghào	Reduced TDMA frame number	RFN
键集驱动游标	Jiànjí qūdòng yóubiāo	Keyset-driven cursor	
减价费率	Jiǎnjià fèilǜ	Reduced rate	
尖叫声	Jiānjiàoshēng	Birdies (noise in telecommunications)	
间接定位	Jiànjiē dìngwèi	Indirect location	
间接地址	Jiànjiē dìzhǐ	Indirect address	
间接分配	Jiànjiē fēnpèi	Indirect distribution	
间接接触	Jiànjiē jiēchù	Indirect contact	
间接接触保护	Jiànjiē jiēchù bǎohù	Protection against indirect contact	
间接控制	Jiànjiē kòngzhì	Indirect control	
间接评估法	Jiànjiē pínggū fǎ	Indirect evaluation method	
间接调频	Jiànjiē tiáopín	Indirect frequency modulation	
间接提交	Jiànjiē tíjiāo	Indirect submission	
间接用户	Jiànjiē yònghù	Indirect user	
渐进编码增益	Jiànjìn biānmǎ zēngyì	Asymptotic coding gain	ACG
渐近不可用性	Jiànjìn bùkěyòngxìng	Asymptotic unavailability	U
渐近可用性	Jiànjìn kěyòngxìng	Asymptotic availability	A
渐近平均不可用性	Jiànjìn píngjūn bùkěyòngxìng	Asymptotic mean unavailability	
渐近平均可用性	Jiànjìn píngjūn kěyòngxìng	Asymptotic mean availability	
渐进网络音频	Jiànjìn wǎngluò yīnpín	Progressive network audio	PNA
间距比	Jiānjù bǐ	Spacing ratio	
键控	Jiànkòng	Keying	
监控	Jiānkòng	Monitoring, supervisory control	
间空	Jiānkōng	Tab (WP command)	
监控和数据采集	Jiānkòng hé shùjù cǎijí	Supervisory control and data acquisition	SCADA
监控和系统支持设施	Jiānkòng hé xìtǒng zhīchí shèshī	Monitoring and system support facilities	MSSF
监控模块	Jiānkòng mókuài	Supervision module	
监控维护盘	Jiānkòng wéihù pán	Monitoring and control panel	MCP
监控未装载	Jiānkòng wèizhuāngzài	Supervisory-unequipped	
监控信道	Jiānkòng xìndào	Supervisory channel	
监控的未装载信号	Jiānkòngde wèizhuāngzài xìnhào	Supervisory unequipped signal	
监控器	Jiānkòngqì	Adapter	
尖括号	Jiānkuòhào	Angle bracket < >	
建立	Jiànlì	Setup	
建立联系协议	Jiànlì liánxì xiéyì	Connection establishment protocol	CEP
建立临时连接	Jiànlì línshí liánjiē	Establish temporary connection	ETC
建立请求	Jiànlì qǐngqiú	Establish request (SS7)	
建立确认	Jiànlì quèrèn	Establish confirm (SS7)	

建立认可	Jiànlì rènkě	Setup acknowledge	
简码表	Jiǎnmǎ biǎo	Brevity list (IPsec)	
键帽	Jiànmào	Keycap	
简明拨号	Jiǎnmíng bōhào	Abbreviated dialing	ABD
简明的	Jiǎnmíngde	Transparent	T
建模	Jiànmó	Modelling, model building	
建模与仿真主计划	Jiànmó yǔ fǎngzhēn zhǔ jìhuà	Modeling and Simulation Master Plan (US)	MSMP
建模语言	Jiànmó yǔyán	Modeling language	
键盘	Jiànpán	Keyboard	KB
键盘布局	Jiànpán bùjú	Keyboard layout	
键盘控制器	Jiànpán kòngzhìqì	Keyboard controller	KBC
键盘设施	Jiànpán shèshī	Keypad facility	
键盘输入	Jiànpán shūrù	Key entry	
键盘性能	Jiànpán xìngnéng	Keypad facility	
鉴频系数	Jiànpín xìshù	Frequency discrimination figure	
鉴频器	Jiànpínqì	Frequency discriminator	
鉴频器幅度对称性	Jiànpínqì fúdù duìchènxìng	Frequency discriminator amplitude frequency symmetry	
鉴频器交界频率	Jiànpínqì jiāojiè pínlǜ	Frequency discriminator crossover frequency	
鉴频器频率对称性	Jiànpínqì pínlǜ duìchènxìng	Frequency discriminator frequency symmetry	
鉴频器通频带	Jiànpínqì tōngpíndài	Frequency discriminator pass band	
剑桥环	Jiànqiáo huán	Cambridge ring	CR
剪切	Jiǎnqiē	Shear	
剪切	Jiǎnqiē	Cut (WP command)	
剪切波	Jiǎnqiē bō	Shear wave	
剪切波速度	Jiǎnqiē bō sùdù	Shear wave velocity	
剪切破坏	Jiǎnqiē pòhuài	Shear failure	
剪切强度	Jiǎnqiē qiángdù	Shearing strength	
剪切实验	Jiǎnqiē shíyàn	Shearing test	
剪切像素阵列	Jiǎnqiē xiàngsù zhènliè	Clipped pixel array	
剪切应变	Jiǎnqiē yìngbiàn	Shear strain	
剪切应力	Jiǎnqiē yìnglì	Shear stress	
鉴权和密钥同意	Jiànquán hé mìyuè tóngyì	Authentication and key agreement	AKA
鉴权拒绝	Jiànquán jùjué	Authentication reject	
鉴权算法 A3	Jiànquán suànfǎ	Authentication algorithm	
鉴权响应	Jiànquán xiǎngyìng	Authentication response	
鉴权中心	Jiànquán zhōngxīn	Authentication center	AC, AUC
兼容	Jiānróng	Compatible	
兼容方式	Jiānróng fāngshì	Compatibility mode	CM
兼容频移键控	Jiānróng pínyí jiànkòng	Compatible shift keying	CSK
兼容的双工系统	Jiānróngde shuānggōng xìtǒng	Compatible duplex system	CDS
兼容性测试	Jiānróngxìng cèshì	Compatibility testing	CPT
兼容性测试法套件	Jiānróngxìng cèshìfǎ tàojiàn	Compatibility test suite	
尖锐滤光镜	Jiānruì lǜguāngjìng	Sharp cutoff filter (optical)	
监视	Jiānshì	Supervision (the S in BORSCHT)	
监视处理机	Jiānshì chǔlǐjī	Supervisory processor	
监视灯	Jiānshì dēng	Supervisory lamp	

监视接收机	Jiānshì jiēshōujī	Watch receiver	
监视时钟	Jiānshì shízhōng	Watchdog timer	WDT
监视信号	Jiānshì xìnhào	Supervisory signal	
监视信元	Jiānshì xìnyuán	Monitoring cell	
监视音	Jiānshì yīn	Supervisory tone	
监视终端	Jiānshì zhōngduān	Monitor terminal	
监视狗定时器	Jiānshìgǒu dìngshíqì	Watchdog timer	
监视狗数据包	Jiānshìgǒu shùjù bāo	Watchdog packet	
监视器	Jiānshìqì	Monitor (noun)	
监视器比特	Jiānshìqì bǐtè	Monitor bit	M
检索	Jiǎnsuǒ	Retrieval	
检索	Jiǎnsuǒ	Search	
检索(型)业务	Jiǎnsuǒ (xíng) yèwù	Retrieval service	
简缩拨号	Jiǎnsuō bōhào	Short number dialing	SND
检索词	Jiǎnsuǒ cí	Keyword	
检索数据	Jiǎnsuǒ shùjù	Retrieve data	
检索系统	Jiǎnsuǒ xìtǒng	Retrieval system	
检索业务	Jiǎnsuǒ yèwù	Retrieval service	
剪贴板	Jiǎntiē bǎn	Clipboard	
剪贴画	Jiǎntiē huà	Clipart	
剪贴纹理	Jiǎntiē wénlǐ	Clipping (video term)	
箭头	Jiàntóu	Arrowheads	
箭头操作符	Jiàntóu cāozuòfú	Arrow operator	
键位转移	Jiànwèi zhuǎnyí	Case shift	
健伍通信有限公司	Jiàn-wǔ tōngxìn yǒuxiàn gōngsī	Kenwood Communications Corp. (US company)	
间隙	Jiànxì	Gap	
间隙损耗	Jiànxì sǔnhào	Gap loss	
鉴相鉴频器	Jiànxiāng jiànpínqì	Phase detection discriminator	
鉴相灵敏度	Jiànxiāng língmǐndù	Discriminator sensitivity	
鉴相器	Jiànxiāngqì	Phase detector	
鉴相器	Jiànxiāngqì	Phase discriminator	
鉴相器输出误差电压	Jiànxiāngqì shūchū wùchā diànyā	Phase discriminator output error voltage	
渐消波	Jiànxiāo bō	Evanescent wave	
减小带宽正交相移键控	Jiǎnxiǎo dàikuān zhèngjiāo xiāngyí jiànkòng	Reduced bandwidth quadrature phase shift keying	RBQPSK
间歇故障	Jiànxiē gùzhàng	Volatile fault	
检修接地	Jiǎnxiū jiēdì	Inspection grounding	
减压阀	Jiǎnyāfá	Reducing valve	
检验比特	Jiǎnyàn bǐtè	Check bit	
检验点	Jiǎnyàn diǎn	Checkpoint	
检验机构消息	Jiǎnyàn jīgòu xiāoxi	Certificate configuration message	CCM
检验试验	Jiǎnyàn shìyàn	Verification test	
检验位	Jiǎnyàn wèi	Check bit	
检验样区	Jiǎnyàn yàngqū	Check plot	
建议	Jiànyì	RECommendation	REC
建议	Jiànyì	Recommendation	REC
简易老式电话系统	Jiǎnyì lǎoshì diànhuà xìtǒng	Plain old telephone system	POTS

建议路由	Jiànyì lùyóu	Advisory route	ADR
建议请求	Jiànyì qǐngqiú	Request for proposal	RFP
简易数据链路	Jiǎnyì shùjù liànlù	Simple data link	SDL
简易文件传输协议	Jiǎnyì wénjiàn chuánshū xiéyì	Trivial file transfer protocol	TFTP
剪音	Jiǎnyīn	Clipping	
简约指令集计算机	Jiǎnyuē zhǐlìngjí jìsuànjī	Reduced instruction-set computer	RISC
减载	Jiǎnzài	Load shedding	
舰载电子战系统	Jiànzài diànzǐzhàn xìtǒng	Naval electronic warfare system	
减载波单边带发射	Jiǎnzàibō dānbiāndài fāshè	Reduced carrier single sideband emission	
减载波发射	Jiǎnzàibō fāshè	Reduced carrier emission	
简正模	Jiǎnzhèngmó	Normal mode (in a waveguide)	
减振器	Jiǎnzhènqì	Damper	
建筑标准法	Jiànzhù biāozhǔn fǎ	Building code (standards)	
建筑法规	Jiànzhù fǎguī	Building code (regulations)	
建筑工程图	Jiànzhù gōngchéng tú	Construction drawing (CAD/CAM)	
建筑构造	Jiànzhù gòuzào	Building structure	
建筑管理系统	Jiànzhù guǎnlǐ xìtǒng	Building management system	BMS
建筑管理自动化	Jiànzhù guǎnlǐ zìdònghuà	Building management automation	
建筑结构图自动识别系统	Jiànzhù jiégòutú zìdòng shíbié xìtǒng	Automatic interpretation of structural drawings (CAD/CAM)	AISD
建筑面积	Jiànzhù miànjī	Building area	
建筑容积	Jiànzhù róngjī	Cubic contents	
建筑声学	Jiànzhù shēngxué	Architectural acoustics	AA
建筑线	Jiànzhù xiàn	Building line	
建筑限制	Jiànzhù xiànzhì	Building restrictions	
建筑与房地产网络	Jiànzhù yǔ fángdìchǎn wǎngluò	Construction and real estate network	CORENET
建筑综合布线系统	Jiànzhù zōnghé bùxiàn xìtǒng	Premises distribution system	PDS
健壮	Jiànzhuàng	Robust	
健壮性	Jiànzhuàngxìng	Robustness	
建筑群	Jiànzhùqún	Campus	
建筑群配线架	Jiànzhùqún pèixiànjià	Campus distributor	CD
建筑群主干电缆	Jiànzhùqún zhǔgàn diànlǎn	Campus backbone cable	
建筑群主干光缆	Jiànzhùqún zhǔgàn guānglǎn	Campus backbone optical cable	
建筑群主干子系统	Jiànzhùqún zhǔgàn zixìtǒng	Campus backbone sub-system	
建筑群子系统	Jiànzhùqún zixìtǒng	Campus sub-system	CS
建筑物	Jiànzhùwù	Building	
建筑物布线系统	Jiànzhùwù bùxiàn xìtǒng	Premises distribution system	PDS
建筑物穿透损耗	Jiànzhùwù chuāntòu sǔnhào	Building penetration loss	
建筑物结构化综合布线系统	Jiànzhùwù jiégòuhuà zōnghé bùxiàn xìtǒng	Premises distribution system	PDS
建筑物配线架	Jiànzhùwù pèixiànjià	Building distributor	BD
建筑物入口设施	Jiànzhùwù rùkǒu shèshī	Building entrance facility	BEF
建筑物主干电缆	Jiànzhùwù zhǔgàn diànlǎn	Building backbone cable	
建筑物主干光缆	Jiànzhùwù zhǔgàn guānglǎn	Building backbone optical cable	
建筑物自动化和控制网络	Jiànzhùwù zìdònghuà hé kòngzhì wǎngluò	Building automation and control net	BAC
建筑物综合分布网络	Jiànzhùwù zōnghé fēnbù wǎngluò	Integrated building distribution network	IBDN
建筑学	Jiànzhùxué	Architecture	

建筑业	Jiànzhùyè	Construction industry	
角编码器	Jiǎo biānmǎqì	Angular encoder	
角动量	Jiǎo dòngliàng	Angular momentum	
角反射天线	Jiǎo fǎnshè tiānxiàn	Corner reflector antenna	
叫建立失败概率	Jiào jiànlì shībài gàilǜ	Call set-up failure probability	
角灵敏度	Jiǎo língmǐndù	Angular sensitivity	
角偏差	Jiǎo piānchā	Angular misalignment	
角偏差损耗	Jiǎo piānchā sǔnhào	Angular misalignment loss	
叫人呼叫	Jiào rén hūjiào	Person-to-person call	
交钥匙项目	Jiāo yàoshi xiàngmù	Turnkey project	
角应变	Jiǎo yìngbiàn	Angle strain	
脚本	Jiǎoběn	Script	
脚本程序	Jiǎoběn chéngxù	Script program	
脚本小子	Jiǎoběn xiǎozǐ	Script kiddies	
交变负荷	Jiāobiàn fùhè	Alternating (exchange) load	
交变码	Jiāobiàn mǎ	Alternating code	
交变温热试验	Jiāobiàn wēnrè shìyàn	Alternating humidity-heat test	
教材软件	Jiàocái ruǎnjiàn	Courseware	
交叉	Jiāochā	Intersect	
交叉编译	Jiāochā biānyì	Cross compiling	
交叉编译程序	Jiāochā biānyì chéngxù	Cross compiler	
交叉表	Jiāochā biǎo	Crosstab	
交叉表查询	Jiāochā biǎo cháxún	Crosstab query (for database)	
交叉单元	Jiāochā dānyuán	Cross-connect element	XC
交叉端口亲缘性	Jiāochā duānkǒu qīnyuánxìng	Cross-port affinity	
交叉分区	Jiāochā fēnqū	Cross-tile indexing	
交叉干扰	Jiāochā gānrǎo	Crosstalk	
交叉滚子轴承	Jiāochā gǔnzi zhóuchéng	Cross roller bearing	
交叉汇编	Jiāochā huìbiān	Cross-assembling	
交叉汇编程序	Jiāochā huìbiān chéngxù	Cross assembler (computer program)	
交叉件	Jiāochā jiàn	Crossware	
交叉交织里德-所罗门编码	Jiāochā jiāozhī Lǐdé-Suǒluómén biānmǎ	Cross-interleave Reed-Solomon code	CIRC
交叉极化	Jiāochā jíhuà	Cross-polarization	
交叉极化电平	Jiāochā jíhuà diànpíng	Cross-polarization level	
交叉极化抵消器	Jiāochā jíhuà dǐxiāoqì	Cross polarization canceller	
交叉极化干扰抵消器	Jiāochā jíhuà gānrǎo dǐxiāoqì	Cross-polarization interference counteracter	XPIC
交叉极化鉴别度	Jiāochā jíhuà jiànbié dù	Cross polarization discrimination	XPD
交叉极化损失	Jiāochā jíhuà sǔnshī	Cross-polarization loss	
交叉开关	Jiāochā kāiguān	Crossbar switch	
交叉连接矩阵	Jiāochā liánjiē jǔzhèn	Cross-connect matrix	CM
交叉连接系统	Jiāochā liánjiē xìtǒng	Cross-connect system	XC
交叉耦合	Jiāochā ǒuhé	Cross coupling	CC
交叉失真	Jiāochā shīzhēn	Cross-over distortion	
交叉调制	Jiāochā tiáozhì	Cross modulation	
交叉调制因子	Jiāochā tiáozhì yīnzǐ	Cross-modulation factor	CMF
交叉相位调制	Jiāochā xiàngwèi tiáozhì	Cross-phase modulation	CPM, XPM

交叉引用对象	Jiāochā yǐnyòng duìxiàng	Cross-reference object	
交叉增益调制	Jiāochā zēngyì tiáozhì	Cross-gain modulation	CGM
交叉点	Jiāochādiǎn	Junction point	
交叉点	Jiāochādiǎn	Crosspoint	
交叉点标志	Jiāochādiǎn biāozhì	Junction flag	
交叉点特征类	Jiāochādiǎn tèzhēng lèi	Junction feature class	
交叉点元素	Jiāochādiǎn yuánsù	Junction element	
交叉点障碍	Jiāochādiǎn zhàng'ài	Junction barrier	
交错	Jiāocuò	Interleaving	
交错四相相移键控	Jiāocuò sìxiāng xiāngyí jiànkòng	Staggered quadriphase shift keying	SQPSK
交错四相移键控	Jiāocuò sìxiāngyí jiànkòng	Staggered quadriphase shift keying	SQPSK
焦点节点	Jiāodiǎn jiédiǎn	Focus node (in CSCW)	
交点周期	Jiāodiǎn zhōuqī	Nodal period	
交叠误差	Jiāodié wùchā	Aliasing error	
角度分集	Jiǎodù fēnjí	Angle diversity (in reception)	
角度截获概率	Jiǎodù jiéhuò gàilǜ	Angle intercept probability (radar term)	
角度调制	Jiǎodù tiáozhì	Angle modulation	
角度噪声	Jiǎodù zàoshēng	Angle noise	
校对多边形	Jiàoduì duōbiānxíng	Proof polygon	
焦耳	Jiāo'ěr	Joule (unit of electrical energy)	
角反射器	Jiǎofǎnshèqì	Corner reflector	
交付服务合伙人	Jiāofù fúwù héhuǒrén	Delivery service partner	DSP
交付证据	Jiāofù zhèngjù	Proof of delivery (IPsec)	
叫号呼叫	Jiàohào hūjiào	Person-to-number call	
交互	Jiāohù	Interact, interactive	
交互调式	Jiāohù diàoshì	Interactive debug	IAD
交互方式	Jiāohù fāngshì	Interactive mode	
交互仿真库	Jiāohù fǎngzhēn kù	Interactive simulation library	
交互过程	Jiāohù guòchéng	Interactive processing	
交互计算机制图	Jiāohù jìsuànjī zhìtú	Interactive computer graphics	
交互矩阵	Jiāohù jǔzhèn	Interaction matrix	
交互可视图文	Jiāohù kěshì túwén	Videotex; interactive videography	
交互可视化	Jiāohù kěshìhuà	Interactive visualization	
交互网络信息包交换	Jiāohù wǎngluò xìnxī bāo jiāohuàn	Inter-network packet exchange	IPX
交互语音响应	Jiāohù yǔyīn xiǎngyìng	Interactive voice response	IVR
交互语音应答	Jiāohù yǔyīn yìngdá	Interactive voice response	IVR
交互语音应答系统	Jiāohù yǔyīn yìngdá xìtǒng	Interactive voice response system	IVR
交互终端规约	Jiāohù zhōngduān guīyuē	Interactive terminal protocol	ITP
交互作用	Jiāohù zuòyòng	Interaction	
交换	Jiāohuàn	Switching	
交换标识	Jiāohuàn biāozhì	Exchange identification	XID
交换标识符	Jiāohuàn biāozhì fú	Exchange identifier	XID
交换处理接口电话事件	Jiāohuàn chǔlǐ jiēkǒu diànhuà shìjiàn	Switching processing interface telephone events	SPITEs
交换单元	Jiāohuàn dānyuán	Switching element	SE
交换单元	Jiāohuàn dānyuán	Switching unit	
交换点	Jiāohuàn diǎn	Switching point	SP

交换电路网	Jiāohuàn diànlù wǎng	Switched circuit network	SCN
交换端口分析器	Jiāohuàn duānkǒu fēnxīqì	Switched port analyzer	SPAN
交换多兆比特数据业务	Jiāohuàn duōzhàobǐtè shùjù yèwù	Switched muiti-megabit data service	SMDS
交换格式	Jiāohuàn géshi	Interchange format	
交换功能	Jiāohuàn gōngnéng	Switching function	SF
交换话音业务	Jiāohuàn huàyīn yèwù	Switched telephony services	
交换呼叫	Jiāohuàn hūjiào	Switched call	
交换级	Jiāohuàn jí	Switching stage	
交换集成件	Jiāohuàn jíchéng jiàn	Switch assembly	ISWA
交换节点	Jiāohuàn jiédiǎn	Switching node	
交换机构	Jiāohuàn jīgòu	Switching fabric	
交换矩阵	Jiāohuàn jǔzhèn	Switching matrix	
交换卡	Jiāohuàn kǎ	Switch card	
交换控制节点	Jiāohuàn kòngzhì jiédiǎn	Switch control node	SCN
交换连接	Jiāohuàn liánjiē	Switched connection	
交换连接单元	Jiāohuàn liánjiē dānyuán	Switched connection element	
交换模块	Jiāohuàn mókuài	Switching module	SM
交换区	Jiāohuàn qū	Switching area	
交换设备拥塞信号	Jiāohuàn shèbèi yōngsè xìnhào	Switching-equipment-congestion signal	SEC
交换通道	Jiāohuàn tōngdào	Switching path	
交换网络	Jiāohuàn wǎngluò	Switching network	SN
交换网络命令码	Jiāohuàn wǎngluò mìnglìng mǎ	Switched network order code	SNOC
交换网络子系统	Jiāohuàn wǎngluò zixìtǒng	Switch network sub-system	SNS
交换虚电路	Jiāohuàn xū diànlù	Switched virtual circuit	SVC
交换虚连接	Jiāohuàn xū liánjiē	Switched virtual connection	SVC
交换虚通路	Jiāohuàn xū tōnglù	Switched virtual channel	SVC
交换虚信道连接	Jiāohuàn xū xìndào liánjiē	Switched virtual channel connection	SVCC
交换虚拟电路	Jiāohuàn xūnǐ diànlù	Switched virtual circuit	SVC
交换虚拟网络	Jiāohuàn xūnǐ wǎngluò	Switched virtual network	SVN
交换音	Jiāohuàn yīn	Switching tone	
交换终端	Jiāohuàn zhōngduān	Exchange termination	ET
交换终接	Jiāohuàn zhōngjiē	Exchange termination	ET
交换中心	Jiāohuàn zhōngxīn	Switching center	
交换子系统	Jiāohuàn zixìtǒng	Switching sub-system	SSS
交换/信令节点	Jiāohuàn/xìnlìng jiédiǎn	Switching/signaling node	SSN
交换机	Jiāohuànjī	Switch, exchange	
交换机到交换机协议	Jiāohuànjī dào jiāohuànjī xiéyì	Switch-to-switch protocol	SSP
交换机房	Jiāohuànjī fáng	Exchange room	
交换机无线接口	Jiāohuànjī wúxiàn jiēkǒu	Exchange radio interface	
交换机终接	Jiāohuànjī zhōngjiē	Exchange termination	ET
交换机间连接	Jiāohuànjī-jiān liánjiē	Inter-switch link	ISL
交换机间临时信令系统	Jiāohuànjī-jiān línshí xìnlìng xìtǒng	Interim-interswitch signaling protocol	IISP
交换机间协议	Jiāohuànjī-jiān xiéyì	Switch-to-switch protocol	SSP
交换局	Jiāohuànjú	Exchange	
交换局连接	Jiāohuànjú liánjiē	Exchange connection	
交换局终端	Jiāohuànjú zhōngduān	Exchange termination	ET

交换式电压调节	Jiāohuàn-shì diànyā tiáojié	Switching voltage regulator	SVR
交换式多兆比特数据业务	Jiāohuàn-shì duō zhàobǐtè shùjù yèwù	Switched multimegabit data service	SMDS
交换式多兆位数据服务	Jiāohuàn-shì duō zhàowèi shùjù fúwù	Switched multimegabit data service	SMDS
交换式数字电视广播	Jiāohuàn-shì shùzì diànshì guǎngbō	Switched digital video broadcast	SDVB
交换式数字图像	Jiāohuàn-shì shùzì túxiàng	Switched digital video	SDV
交换式网络互联服务	Jiāohuàn-shì wǎngluò hùlián fúwù	Switched inter-networking services	SIS
交换式星形网络	Jiāohuàn-shì xīngxíng wǎngluò	Switched star network	SSN
交换式星形系统	Jiāohuàn-shì xīngxíng xìtǒng	Switched star system	SSS
交换式虚电路	Jiāohuàn-shì xū diànlù	Switch virtual circuit	SVC
交换式虚通路	Jiāohuàn-shì xū tōnglù	Switched virtual path	SVP
交换台座席	Jiāohuàntái zuòxí	Switchbaord position	
交换型多兆位数字式服务	Jiāohuàn-xíng duō zhàowèi shùzì-shì fúwù	Switched multimegabit digital service	SMDS
交换型连接单元	Jiāohuàn-xíng liánjiē dānyuán	Switched connection element	
交换型虚电路	Jiāohuàn-xíng xū diànlù	Switched virtual circuit	SVC
交换型永久虚电路	Jiāohuàn-xíng yǒngjiǔ xū diànlù	Switched permanent virtual circuit	SPVC
交会雷达	Jiāohuì léidá	Rendezvous radar	RVR
交互式	Jiāohù-shì	Interactive	
交互式表面模拟	Jiāohù-shì biǎomiàn mónǐ	Interactive surface modeling	
交互式 CD 盘	Jiāohùshì CD pán	Compact disk interactive	CD-I
交互式登录	Jiāohù-shì dēnglù	Interactive logon	
交互式电视	Jiāohù-shì diànshì	Interactive tevevision	ITV
交互式对话框	Jiāohù-shì duìhuà kuàng	Interactive dialog box	
交互式多媒体协议	Jiāohù-shì duōméitǐ xiéyì	Interactive Multimedia Association	IMA
交互式环绕声	Jiāohù-shì huánrào shēng	Interactive around-sound	IAS
交互式结构化查询语言	Jiāohù-shì jiégòuhuà cháxún yǔyán	Interactive structured query language	ISQL
交互式可视化	Jiāohù-shì kěshìhuà	Interactive visualization	
交互式事务	Jiāohù-shì shìwù	Interactive transaction	
交互式数字化	Jiāohù-shì shùzìhuà	Interactive digitizing	
交互式图形设计软件	Jiāohù-shì túxíng shèjì ruǎnjiàn	Interactive graphics design software	IDGS
交互式应用程序通讯	Jiāohù-shì yìngyòng chéngxù tōngxùn	Interactive application communication	IAC
交互式语音应答	Jiāohù-shì yǔyīn yìngdá	Interactive voice response	
交互型业务	Jiāohù-xíng yèwù	Interactive service	
交互型业务的基群链路	Jiāohù-xíng yèwùde jīqún liànlù	Primary link for interactive services	IPL
交集	Jiāojí	Intersection	
交接	Jiāojiē	Cross connection	
交接间	Jiāojiē jiān	Cross connections closet	
焦距	Jiāojù	Focus distance	
焦距	Jiāojù	Focal length	FL
角距离	Jiǎojùlí	Angular distance	
交流	Jiāoliú	Alternating current	AC
交流二极管充电	Jiāoliú èrjíguǎn chōngdiàn	Alternating current diode charging	
交流分量	Jiāoliú fènliàng	Alternating current component	
交流继电器	Jiāoliú jìdiànqì	Alternating current relay	ACR
交流极谱仪	Jiāoliú jípǔyí	Alternating current polarograph	
交流声和噪声抑制	Jiāoliú shēng hé zàoshēng yìzhì	Alternating current hum and noise suppression	
交流稳压器	Jiāoliú wěnyāqì	Alternating current voltage stabilizer	

交流相位跟踪法	Jiāoliú xiàngwèi gēnzōng fǎ	Alternating current phase tracking	
交流信令	Jiāoliú xìnlìng	Alternating current signaling	
交流声	Jiāoliúshēng	Supply noise	
交流声	Jiāoliúshēng	Hum	
交流式	Jiāoliú-shì	Interactive	
叫骂	Jiàomà	Flame (computer slang)	
搅模器	Jiǎomóqì	Mode scrambler	
郊区电话接续	Jiāoqū diànhuà jiēxù	Suburb connection	
交扰	Jiāorǎo	Crosstalk	
交谈	Jiāotán	Talk	
交替不归零制	Jiāotì bù guī líng zhì	Alternating non-return to zero	ANRZ
交替传号反转码	Jiāotì chuánhào fǎnzhuǎn mǎ	Alternate mark inversion code	AMI
交替代号反转码	Jiāotì dàihào fǎnzhuǎn mǎ	Alternate mark inversion code	
交替键	Jiāotì jiàn	Alt key	
交替接收者	Jiāotì jiēshōuzhě	Alternate recipient	
交替极化的	Jiāotì jíhuàde	Alternated polarization (adjective)	
交替极性翻转码	Jiāotì jíxìng fānzhuǎn mǎ	Alternate mark inversion coding	AMI
交替码	Jiāotì mǎ	Alternative code	
交替同步伙伴	Jiāotì tóngbù huǒbàn	alternate synchronization partners (in SQL Server)	
交替信号反转破坏点	Jiāotì xìnhào fǎnzhuǎn pòhuàidiǎn	Alternate mark inversion violation	
交替渲染技术	Jiāotì xuànrǎn jìshù	Alternate frame rendering (video)	AFR
交调	Jiāotiáo	Cross modulation	
交调失真	Jiāotiáo shīzhēn	Crosstalk	
角位移	Jiǎowèiyí	Angular displacement	
角位移光栅	Jiǎowèiyí guāngshān	Angular displacement grating	
角型	Jiǎo-xíng	Angle form	
角形反射器天线	Jiǎo-xíng fǎnshèqì tiānxiàn	Corner reflector antenna	
教学点	Jiàoxué diǎn	Learning station	
教学管理	Jiàoxué guǎnlǐ	Teaching management	
教学进程	Jiàoxué jìnchéng	Teaching process	
教学控制	Jiàoxué kòngzhì	Teaching control	
校验比特	Jiàoyàn bǐtè	Check bit	CK
校验和	Jiàoyàn hé	Checksum	
较验位	Jiàoyàn wèi	Check bit	CB
校验位	Jiàoyàn wèi	Check bit	
校验位发生器	Jiàoyàn wèi fāshēngqì	Check bit generator	CBG
校验字符	Jiàoyàn zìfú	Check character	
校样图	Jiàoyàng tú	Proof plot	
交易保安技术	Jiāoyì bǎo'ān jìshù	Secure transaction technology	STT
交易标识符	Jiāoyì biāozhìfú	Transaction identifier	TI
交易层	Jiāoyì céng	Transaction layer	
交易处理	Jiāoyì chǔlǐ	Transaction processing	
交义密度	Jiāoyì mìdù	Cross-spectral density	
交易能力和应用子系统	Jiāoyì nénglì hé yìngyòng zìxìtǒng	Transaction capability and application sub-system	TCAS
交越频率	Jiāoyuè pínlǜ	Crossover frequency	
校正抖动	Jiàozhèng dǒudòng	Alignment jitter	AJ

校正气球	Jiàozhèng qìqiú	Balloon for correction (radar term)	
校正网络	Jiàozhèng wǎngluò	Alignment network	AN
校正信号	Jiàozhèng xìnhào	Correction signal	
交织	Jiāozhī	Interleaving	
交至承运人	Jiāozhì chéngyùnrén	Free to carrier	
交织延时	Jiāozhī yánshí	Interleave delay	
交织语义	Jiāozhī yǔyì	Interleaving semantics	
脚注	Jiǎozhù	Footnote	
角锥形喇叭天线	Jiǎozhuī-xíng lǎba tiānxiàn	Pyramidal horn antenna	
校准	Jiàozhǔn	Alignment	AL
校准	Jiàozhǔn	Calibration	
校准传感器	Jiàozhǔn chuángǎnqì	Alignment sensor	
校准塔	Jiàozhǔn tǎ	Boresight tower	
加强绝缘	Jiāqiáng juéyuán	Reinforced insulation	
加强的链路层管理	Jiāqiángde liànlùcéng guǎnlǐ	Consolidated link layer management	CLLM
加强的数字接入通信系统	Jiāqiángde shùzì jiērù tōngxìn xìtǒng	Enhanced digital access communications system	EDACS
加权	Jiāquán	Weighting	
加权动态匹配算法	Jiāquán dòngtài pǐpèi suànfǎ	Weighted dynamic matching algorithm	
加权公平队列	Jiāquán gōngping duìliè	Weighted fair queuing	WFQ
加权公平排队	Jiāquán gōngping páiduì	Weighted fair queuing	WFQ
加权平均	Jiāquán píngjūn	Weighted average	
加权平移	Jiāquán píngyí	Weighted translation	
加权随机早期检测	Jiāquán suíjī zǎoqī jiǎncè	Weighted random early detection	WRED
加权随机早期侦测	Jiāquán suíjī zǎoqī zhēncè	Weighted random early detection	WRED
加权图	Jiāquán tú	Weighted graph	
加权往返算法	Jiāquán wǎngfǎn suànfǎ	Weighted round robin	WRR
加权噪声	Jiāquán zàoshēng	Weighted noise	
加权的公平排队算法	Jiāquánde gōngping páiduì suànfǎ	Weighted fair queuing	WFQ
加权的随机早期控测	Jiāquánde suíjī zǎoqī kòngcè	Weighted random early detection	WRED
加权的随机早期探测	Jiāquánde suíjī zǎoqī tàncè	Weighted Random Early Detection	WRED
加入模式	Jiārù móshì	Participating mode	
加入组请求消息	Jiārù zǔ qǐngqiú xiāoxi	Join group request message (in multicast)	
加色法三原色	Jiāsèfǎ sānyuánsè	Additive primary colors	
假设参考电路	Jiǎshè cānkǎo diànlù	Hypothetical reference circuit	
假设参考连接	Jiǎshè cānkǎo liánjiē	Hypothetical reference connection	HRX
假设参考数字段	Jiǎshè cānkǎo shùzì duàn	Hypothetical reference digital section	HRDS
假设参考数字链路	Jiǎshè cānkǎo shùzì liànlù	Hypothetical reference digital link	HRDL
假设参考数字通道	Jiǎshè cānkǎo shùzì tōngdào	Hypothetical reference digital path	HDRP
假设参考通道	Jiǎshè cānkǎo tōngdào	Hypothetical reference path	HRP
假设检验	Jiǎshè jiǎnyàn	Hypothesis testing	
假设数字参考连接	Jiǎshè shùzì cānkǎo liánjiē	Hypothetical digital reference connection	HDRC
加速报文处理器缓冲器	Jiāsù bàowén chǔlǐqì huǎnchōngqì	Expedited message handler buffer	EMHB
加速传送	Jiāsù chuánsòng	Expedited delivery	
加速试验	Jiāsù shìyàn	Accelerated test	
加速图形端口	Jiāsù túxíng duānkǒu	Accelerated graphics port	AGP
加速信息处理	Jiāsù xìnxī chǔlǐ	Expedited message handling	EMH

加速中心架构	Jiāsù zhōngxīn jiàgòu	Accelerated hub architecture	AHA
加速转发	Jiāsù zhuǎnfā	Expedited forwarding	EF
加速度	Jiāsùdù	Acceleration	
加速度响应谱	Jiāsùdù xiǎngyìng pǔ	Acceleration response spectrum	
加速计	Jiāsùjì	Accelerometer	
加速器	Jiāsùqì	Accelerator (chip)	
家庭单元	Jiātíng dānyuán	Home unit	HU
家庭电话线网络集团	Jiātíng diànhuà xiàn wǎngluò jítuán	Home Phoneline Networking Alliance	HPNA
家庭网络	Jiātíng wǎngluò	Homenet	HN
家庭用户服务器	Jiātíng yònghù fúwùqì	Home subscriber server	HSS
假脱机程序	Jiǎtuōjī chéngxù	Spooler program	
假脱机系统	Jiǎtuōjī xìtǒng	Spooler system	
假想参考点	Jiǎxiǎng cānkǎodiǎn	Hypothetical reference endpoint	HRE
假想滑移面	Jiǎxiǎng huáyí miàn	Assumed sliding plane	
假想经纬网	Jiǎxiǎng jīngwěiwǎng	Fictitious graticule	
加性高斯白噪声	Jiāxìng gāo-sī bái zàoshēng	Additive white Gaussian noise	AWGN
加性异常值序列	Jiāxìng yìchángzhí xùliè	Additive outlier series	
加压风机	Jiāyā fēngjī	Pressurization fan	PF
家用电话线网络联盟	Jiāyòng diànhuà xiàn wǎngluò liánméng	Home Phoneline Networking Alliance	HPNA
家用电器智能化	Jiāyòng diànqì zhìnénghuà	Home automation	HA
家用射频工作组	Jiāyòng shèpín gōngzuòzǔ	Home Radio Frequency Working Group	HRFWG
加载	Jiāzài	Load (verb)	
加载项	Jiāzài xiàng	Add-in	
加载折合偶极子	Jiāzài zhéhé ǒujízi	Loaded folded dipole	
加置卡	Jiāzhì kǎ	Add-on card	
加值网络	Jiāzhí wǎngluò	Value added network	VAN
加重对比度	Jiāzhòng duìbǐdù	Accentuated contrast	
加州教育与研究协会网	Jiāzhōu jiàoyù yǔ yánjiū xiéhuì wǎng	California Education and Research Federation Network	CERFnet
基板	Jībǎn	Substrate	
基板	Jībǎn	Baseplate	
基板栅格阵列	Jībǎn zhàgé zhènliè	Organic land grid array	OLGA
基本编码规则	Jīběn biānmǎ guīzé	Basic coding rules	
基本编码规则	Jīběn biānmǎ guīzé	Basic encoding rules	BER
基本标准	Jīběn biāozhǔn	Base standard	
基本布局客体	Jīběn bùjú kètǐ	Basic layout object	
基本参考模型	Jīběn cānkǎo móxíng	Basic reference model	
基本操作	Jīběn cāozuò	Elementary operation	EO
基本测量单位	Jīběn cèliáng dānwèi	Basic measurement unit	BMU
基本测试	Jīběn cèshì	Basic test	
基本传输标题	Jīběn chuánshū biāotí	Basic transmission header	BTH
基本传输损耗	Jīběn chuánshū sǔnhào	Basic transmission loss (of a radio link)	
基本处理装置	Jīběn chǔlǐ zhuāngzhì	Basic processing unit	BPU
基本磁偶极子	Jīběn cí'ǒujízi	Elementary magnetic dipole	
基本电偶极子	Jīběn diàn'ǒujízǐ,	Elementary electric dipole	
基本多文种平面	Jīběn duō wénzhǒng píngmiàn	Basic multilingual plane	BMP
基本分配	Jīběn fēnpèi	Elementary assignment	EA

基本服务	Jīběn fúwù	Basic service	
基本公共导频信道	Jīběn gōnggòng dǎopín xìndào	Primary common pilot channel	P-CPIH
基本公共控制物理信道	Jīběn gōnggòng kòngzhì wùlǐ xìndào	Primary common control physical channel	P-CCPCH
基本功能	Jīběn gōngnéng	Basic function	
基本构成体	Jīběn gòuchéng tǐ	Basic component	
基本会话参考	Jīběn huìhuà cānkǎo	Basic session reference	
基本呼叫不相关状态模型	Jīběn hūjiào bùxiāngguān zhuàngtài móxíng	Basic call unrelated state model	BCUSM
基本呼叫无关状态模型	Jīběn hūjiào wúguān zhuàngtài móxíng	Basic call unrelated state model	BCUSM
基本呼叫状态模型	Jīběn hūjiào zhuàngtài móxíng	Basic call status model	BCSM
基本呼叫状态模型	Jīběn hūjiào zhuàngtài móxíng	Basic call state model	BCSM
基本互连测试	Jīběn hùlián cèshì	Basic interconnection test	BIT
基本架	Jīběn jià	Base rack	BCBR
基本加密函数	Jīběn jiāmì hánshù	Basic cryptographic function	
基本交换单元	Jīběn jiāohuàn dānyuán	Basic switching element	
基本接口结构	Jīběn jiēkǒu jiégòu	Basic interface structure	
基本接入	Jīběn jiērù	Basic access	BA
基本绝缘	Jīběn juéyuán	Basic insulation	
基本空间单元	Jīběn kōngjiān dānyuán	Basic spatial unit	BSU
基本控制功能	Jīběn kòngzhì gōngnéng	Basic control function	BCF
基本控制功能	Jīběn kòngzhì gōngnéng	Basic control function	BCF
基本流量控制	Jīběn liúliàng kòngzhì	General flow control	GFC
基本逻辑客体	Jīběn luóji kètǐ	Basic logical object	
基本命令解调程序	Jīběn mìnglìng jiětiáo chéngxù	Basic command interpreter	BCI
基本密钥	Jīběn mìyào	Base key (cryptography)	
基本模式	Jīběn móshì	Fundamental mode	
基本谱减法	Jīběn pǔ jiǎnfǎ	Basic spectral subtraction	BSS
基本切换程序	Jīběn qiēhuàn chéngxù	Basic handover procedure	
基本入口	Jīběn rùkǒu	Basic access	
基本时间单元	Jīběn shíjiān dānyuán	Elementary time unit	ETU
基本时钟脉冲频率	Jīběn shízhōng màichōng pínlǜ	Basic clock pulse frequency	BCPF
基本数据管理	Jīběn shùjù guǎnlǐ	Basic data management	
基本数据类型	Jīběn shùjù lèixíng	Elementary data types	
基本数据类型	Jīběn shùjù lèixíng	Base data type	
基本数据类型	Jīběn shùjù lèixíng	Atomic data type	
基本数据型	Jīběn shùjù-xíng	Basic data type	
基本输入输出系统	Jīběn shūrù shūchū xìtǒng	Basic input/output system	BIOS
基本算术模块	Jīběn suànshù mókuài	Basic arithmetic module	BAM
基本速率接口	Jīběn sùlǜ jiēkǒu	Basic rate interface	BRI
基本速率接入	Jīběn sùlǜ jiērù	Basic rate access	BRA
基本速率的综合业务数字网	Jīběn sùlǜde zōnghé yèwù shùzì wǎng	Basic rate integrated services digital network	BRI
基本通信存取法	Jīběn tōngxìn cúnqǔ fǎ	Basic communication access method	BCAM
基本图形要素	Jīběn túxíng yàosù	Primary graphic element	
基本外部函数	Jīběn wàibù hánshù	Basic external function	
基本维护作业	Jīběn wéihù zuòyè	Elementary maintenance activity	
基本文件	Jīběn wénjiàn	Elementary file	EF
基本寻呼机标识码	Jīběn xúnhūjī biāozhìmǎ	Base radio identification code	

基本业务群	Jīběn yèwù qún	Basic service group	BSG
基本业务组	Jīběn yèwù zǔ	Basic service group	BSG
基本优先级	Jīběn yōuxiān jí	Base priority	
基本越区切换规程	Jīběn yuèqū qiēhuàn guīchéng	Basic handover procedure	
基本噪声	Jīběn zàoshēng	Basic noise	
基本值	Jīběn zhí	Basic value	
基本周期	Jīběn zhōuqī	Fundamental period	
基本最高可用频率	Jīběn zuìgāo kěyòng pínlǜ	Basic maximun usable frequency	
基本的底层功能	Jīběnde dǐcéng gōngnéng	Basic low layer function	BLLF
基本的高层功能	Jīběnde gāocéng gōngnéng	Basic high layer function	BHLF
基本的简单接口模型	Jīběnde jiǎndān jiēkǒu móxíng	Basic primitive interface model	BPIM
基本的全局功能	Jīběnde quánjú gōngnéng	Basic global function	BGF
基本的吞吐量等级协商	Jīběnde tūntǔliàng děngjí xiéshāng	Basic throughput class negotiation	
基本的用户-网络接口	Jīběnde yònghù—wǎngluò jiēkǒu	Basic user-network interface	BUNI
基本型控制规程	Jīběn-xíng kòngzhì guīchéng	Basic mode control procedure	BMCP
吉比以太网	Jíbǐ yǐtàiwǎng	Gigabit ethernet	
级别	Jíbié	Level	
级别层次结构	Jíbié céngcì jiégòu	Level hierarchy	
级别更新	Jíbié gēngxīn	Classmark update	
级别请求	Jíbié qǐngqiú	Classmark request	
吉比特	Jíbǐtè	Gigabits	Gb
吉比特级以太网	Jíbǐtè jí yǐtàiwǎng	Gigabit ethernet	GbE,Gbe
吉比特接口转换器	Jíbǐtè jiēkǒu zhuǎnhuànqì	Gigabit interface converter	GBIC
吉比特每秒	Jíbǐtè měi miǎo	Gigabits per second	Gb/s
吉比特系列产品	Jíbǐtè xìliè chǎnpǐn	Gigabit serial logic products	GSL
吉比特以太网	Jíbǐtè yǐtàiwǎng	Gigabit ethernet	GE=GbE
基波	Jībō	Fundamental (component of a sound wave)	
基波系数	Jībō xìshù	Fundamental factor	
吉波特	Jíbōtè	Gigabaud	GBd
基层直接渲染	Jīcéng zhíjiē xuànrǎn	Direct rendering infrastructure (video term)	DIR
即插即用	Jíchā jíyòng	Plug and play	PnP
集成	Jíchéng	Integration	
继承	Jìchéng	Inheritance	
集成安全性	Jíchéng ānquánxìng	Integrated security	
集成本地管理接口	Jíchéng běndì guǎnlǐ jiēkǒu	Integrated local management interface	ILMI
集成参考点	Jíchéng cānkǎo diǎn	Integrated reference point	IRP
继承等级	Jìchéng děngjí	Inheritance hierarchy	
集成电路	Jíchéng diànlù	Integrated circuit	IC
集成电路识别码	Jíchéng diànlù shíbié mǎ	Integrated circuit identity	ICCID
集成服务模型	Jíchéng fúwù móxíng	Integrated service model	IntServ
集成交换单元	Jíchéng jiāohuàn dānyuán	Integrated switching element	ISE
集成校验值	Jíchéng jiàoyàn zhí	Integrity check value	ICV
继承机制	Jìchéng jīzhì	Inheritance	
集成开发环境	Jíchéng kāifā huánjìng	Integrated development environment	IDE
集成模式	Jíchéng móshì	Integrated model	IM
继承权限过滤器	Jìchéng quánxiàn guòlǜqì	Inherited rights filter	

集成数据	Jíchéng shùjù	Integrated data	
集成数据库管理系统	Jíchéng shùjùkù guǎnlǐ xìtǒng	Integrated database management system	
集成调制解调器	Jíchéng tiáozhì jiětiáoqì	Integrated modem	
继承体系	Jìchéng tǐxì	Hierarchy	
集成通信控制器	Jíchéng tōngxìn kòngzhìqì	Integrated communications controller	
集成帧	Jíchéng zhèng	Integrated framing	
继承性	Jìchéng-xìng	Inheritance	
急充电	Jíchōngdiàn	Boost charge	
基础表	Jīchǔ biǎo	Underlying table	
基础单元业务群	Jīchǔ dānyuán yèwù qún	Elementary basic service group	EBSG
基础地图	Jīchǔ dìtú	Base map	
挤出生产线	Jǐchū shēngchǎnxiàn	Extrusion line	
基础设施	Jīchǔ shèshī	Infrastructure	
基础文件	Jīchǔ wénjiàn	Elementary file	EF
击穿	Jīchuān	Breakdown	
击穿功率	Jīchuān gōnglǜ	Breakdown power	
激磁控制	Jīcí kòngzhì	Field control (refers to magnetic field)	
计次脉冲消息	Jìcì màichōng xiāoxi	Meter pulse message	MPM
计次表	Jìcìbiǎo	Counter, meter	
寄存择码器	Jìcún zémǎqì	Register-translator	
寄存器	Jìcúnqì	Register	
寄存器不足	Jìcúnqì bùzú	Register pressure	
寄存器重命名	Jìcúnqì chóng mìngmíng	Register renaming	
寄存器冲突	Jìcúnqì chōngtū	Register contention	
寄存器文件	Jìcúnqì wénjiàn	Register file	
寄存器栈	Jìcúnqì zhàn	Register stack	
基带	Jīdài	Baseband	
基带安排	Jīdài ānpái	Baseband arragement	BBA
基带处理单元	Jīdài chǔlǐ dānyuán	Baseband processing unit	BPU
基带处理框背板	Jīdài chǔlǐ kuàng bèibǎn	Baseband processor mother board	BPB
基带带宽	Jīdài dàikuān	Baseband bandwidth	
基带和信号处理	Jīdài hé xìnhào chǔlǐ	Baseband and signal processing	BBSIG
基带滤波器	Jīdài lǜbōqì	Baseband filter	BBF
基带频率响应	Jīdài pínlǜ xiǎngyìng	Baseband response	
基带调制解调器	Jīdài tiáozhì jiětiáoqì	Baseband modem	BM
基带调制解调制器	Jīdài tiáozhì jiětiáozhìqì	Baseband modem	BM
基带协议	Jīdài xiéyì	Baseband protocol	BB
基带信号处理器	Jīdài xìnhào chǔlǐqì	Baseband signal processor	
基地航空设备	Jīdì hángkōng shèbèi	Base aeronautical equipment	
基地自动通信系统	Jīdì zìdòng tōngxìn xìtǒng	Automatic base communication system	ABCS
继电控制系统	Jìdiàn kòngzhì xìtǒng	Relay control system	
继电器接线器	Jìdiànqì jiēxiànqì	Relay switch	
继电器输出	Jìdiànqì shūchū	Relay output	
继电器组	Jìdiànqì zǔ	Relay set	
机顶盒	Jīdǐnghé	Set-top-box	STB
极低频	Jídīpín	Extremely low frequency	ELF

激动	Jīdòng	Drive	DR
激动分析	Jīdòng fēnxī	Activation analysis	AA
机动雷达	Jīdòng léidá	Movable radar	
结	Jié	Junction	
解	Jiě	Solution	
阶	Jiē	Level	
解引用	Jiě yǐnyòng	De-reference	
解闭	Jiěbì	Unblock	
解闭证实	Jiěbì zhèngshí	Unblocking acknowledge	
捷变频雷达	Jiébiànpín léidá	Agile radar, frequency agile radar	
接拨器	Jiēbōqì	Auto-dialer	
截槽障	Jiécáo zhàng	Slit-barrier	
阶层式数据	Jiēcéng-shì shùjù	Hierarchical data	
接插软线	Jiēchā ruǎnxiàn	Patch cord	
接插件	Jiēchājiàn	Socket connector	
解除闭塞请求	Jiěchú bìsè qǐngqiú	Unblocking request (ISUP message)	UBL
解除闭塞信号	Jiěchú bìsè xìnhào	Unblocking acknowledgement signal	UBA
解除闭塞信号	Jiěchú bìsèxìnhào	Unblocking signal	
解除电路群闭塞请求	Jiěchú diànlùqún bìsè qǐngqiú	Circuit group unblocking request (ISUP message)	CGU
解除电路群闭塞认可	Jiěchú diànlùqún bìsè rènkě	Circuit group unblocking acknowledgement (ISUP message)	CGUA
接触电压	Jiēchù diànyā	Contact voltage	
接触电阻	Jiēchù diànzǔ	Contact resistance	
解除激活请求	Jiěchú jīhuó qǐngqiú	Deactivate request	DR
解除激活指示	Jiěchú jīhuó zhǐshì	Deactivate indication	DI
解除阻塞程序	Jiěchú zǔsè chéngxù	Unblocking procedure	
接触不良	Jiēchùbùliáng	Poor contact	
接触式活塞	Jiēchù-shì huósāi	Contact piston	
接地	Jiēdì	Ground, earth (electrical)	
接地参考平面	Jiēdì cānkǎo píngmiàn	Ground reference plane	
接地导体	Jiēdì dǎotǐ	Grounding conductor	
接地电感器	Jiēdì diàngǎnqì	Grounding inductor	
接地电路	Jiēdì diànlù	Grounded circuit	
接地电阻	Jiēdì diànzǔ	Grounding resistance	
接地短路电流	Jiēdì duǎnlù diànliú	Ground short circuit current	
接地故障	Jiēdì gùzhàng	Ground fault, earth fault	
接地故障电流	Jiēdì gùzhàng diànliú	Ground fault current	
接地故障电路中级器	Jiēdì gùzhàng diànlù zhōngjíqì	Ground fault circuit interrupter	GFCI
接地故障因数	Jiēdì gùzhàng yīnshù	Ground fault factor	
接地环路	Jiēdì huánlù	Ground loop	
接地开关	Jiēdì kāiguān	Grounding switch	
结点	Jiédiǎn	Node	
节点	Jiédiǎn	Node	
节点 B 应用部分	Jiédiǎn B yìngyòng bùfen	Node B application part	NBAP
节点地址字节	Jiédiǎn dìzhǐ zìjié	Node address byte	NAD
节点环端口	Jiédiǎn huán duānkǒu	Node loop port	NLPort
节点互通功能	Jiédiǎn hùtōng gōngnéng	Node interworking function	NIF

节点记录	Jiédiǎn jìlù	Node record	
节点控制	Jiédiǎn kòngzhì	Node control	NC
节点匹配容差	Jiédiǎn pǐpèi róngchā	Node match tolerance	
介电强度	Jièdiàn qiángdù	Dielectric strength	
介电损耗	Jièdiàn sǔnhào	Dielectric loss	
节点吞吐	Jiédiǎn tūntǔ	Nodal throughput	
介电性能各向异性	Jièdiàn xìngnéng gèxiàng yìxìng	Dielectric anisotropy	DA
节点资源单位	Jiédiǎn zīyuán dānwèi	Node resource unit	NRU
接地线	Jiēdìxiàn	Grounding conductor	
接地线缠绕光缆	Jiēdìxiàn chánrǎo guānglǎn	Ground wire wound optical fiber cable	GWWOP
接地线复合光缆	Jiēdìxiàn fùhé guānglǎn	Optical fiber composite ground wire	OPGW
截断	Jiéduàn	Truncate	
截断差分密码分析	Jiéduàn chāfēn mìmǎ fēnxī	Truncated differential cryptanalysis	
杰尔系统有限公司	Jié-ěr xìtǒng yǒuxiàn gōngsī	Agere Systems Corp. (US company)	
解封	Jiěfēng	Decapsulate, unwrap	
界符	Jièfú	Delimiter	
解复用波长选路器	Jiěfùyòng bōcháng xuǎnlùqì	Demultiplexing wavelength router	
解复用器	Jiěfùyòngqì	Demultiplexer	DEMUX
结构	Jiégòu	Structure	
结构部件	Jiégòu bùjiàn	Structural element	
结构程序设计	Jiégòu chéngxù shèjì	Structured programming	
结构分类	Jiégòu fēnlèi	Structure category	
结构工程	Jiégòu gōngchéng	Structural engineering	
结构计算标准	Jiégòu jìsuàn biāozhǔn	Structural calculation standard	
结构类型	Jiégòu lèixíng	Structured type	
结构类型系数	Jiégòu lèixíng xìshù	Structural type factor	
结构力学	Jiégòu lìxué	Structural mechanics	
结构设计	Jiégòu shèjì	Structural planning	
结构数据传送	Jiégòu shùjù chuánsòng	Structured data transfer	SDT
结构系数	Jiégòu xìshù	Structural coefficient	
结构要素	Jiégòu yàosù	Structural factor	
结构优化	Jiégòu yōuhuà	Structure optimization	
结构元素	Jiégòu yuánsù	Structure element	
结构化布线系统	Jiégòuhuà bùxiàn xìtǒng	Structured cabling system	SCS
结构化查询语言	Jiégòuhuà cháxún yǔyán	Structured query language	SQL
结构化存储文件	Jiégòuhuà cúnchǔ wénjiàn	Structured storage file	
结构化方程模型	Jiégòuhuà fāngchéng móxíng	Structural equation modeling	SEM
结构化分析与设计技术	Jiégòuhuà fēnxī yǔ shèjì jìshù	Structured analysis and design technique	SADT
结构器波损耗	Jiégòuqì bō sǔnhào	Structural return loss	SRL
结构式询问语言	Jiégòushì xúnwèn yǔyán	Structured query language	SQL
结果集	Jiéguǒ jí	Result set (for database)	
结合输入,输出排队	Jiéhé shūrù, shūchū páiduì	Combined input/output queuing	CIOP
截获概率试验	Jiéhuò gàilǜ shìyàn	Acquisition probability test (radar term)	
截接服务	Jiéjiē fúwù	Interception of call service (by the switch, to route call to an automatic recording)	
接近多边形	Jiējìn duōbiānxíng	Proximal polygon	
接近分析工具	Jiējìn fēnxī gōngjù	Conjunction analysis tool (software)	

接近卡	Jiējìn kǎ	Proximity card	PC
接近信标探测	Jiējìn xìnbiāo tàncè	Proximity beacon detection	
捷径交换	Jiéjìng jiāohuàn	Cut-through	
结晶育成材料	Jiéjīng yùchéng cáiliào	Crystal growing material	
洁净室炉	Jiéjìngshì lú	Cleanroom oven (semiconductor mfg)	
接口	Jiēkǒu	Interface	
接口比特率	Jiēkǒu bǐtè lǜ	Interface bit rate	
接口定义语言	Jiēkǒu dìngyì yǔyán	Interface definition language	IDL
接口翻译	Jiēkǒu fānyì	Interface translation	
接口负荷	Jiēkǒu fùhè	Interface payload	
接口附加位	Jiēkǒu fùjiā wèi	Interface overhead bit	
接口服务节点	Jiēkǒu fúwù jiédiǎn	Interface service node	ISN
接口规范	Jiēkǒu guīfàn	Interface specification	
接口含义	Jiēkǒu hányì	Interface implication	
接口集成电路	Jiēkǒu jíchéng diànlù	Interface integrated circuit	
接口结构	Jiēkǒu jiégòu	Interface structure	
接口净荷	Jiēkǒu jìnghé	Interface payload	
接口开销	Jiēkǒu kāixiao	Interface overhead	
接口控制	Jiēkǒu kòngzhì	Interface control	
接口描述语言	Jiēkǒu miáoshù yǔyán	Interface description language	IDL
接口数据单元	Jiēkǒu shùjù dānyuán	Interface data unit	IDU
接口速率	Jiēkǒu sùlǜ	Interface rate	
接口网关	Jiēkǒu wǎngguān	Interface gateway	IGW
接口用户模块	Jiēkǒu yònghù mókuài	Interface subscriber module	ISM
接口有效负荷	Jiēkǒu yǒuxiào fùhè	Interface payload	
解扩	Jiěkuò	De-spreading	
节理	Jiélǐ	Joint	
接力切换	Jiēlì qiēhuàn	Baton handover	
接力站	Jiēlì zhàn	Relay station	RS
节理走向	Jiélǐ zǒuxiàng	Joint translation angle	
截铃	Jiélíng	Stop ringing	
解码	Jiěmǎ	Decode	
解码错误消息	Jiěmǎ cuòwù xiāoxi	Decode error message (IPsec TLS)	
解码状态标志	Jiěmǎ zhuàngtài biāozhì	Decode status flag	DSF
解码器	Jiěmǎqì	Decoder	
解码器保护时间	Jiěmǎqì bǎohù shíjiān	Decoder required protection time	
解码器报讯时间	Jiěmǎqì bàoxùn shíjiān	Decoder alarm time	
解码器工作电平范围	Jiěmǎqì gōngzuò diànpíng fànwéi	Decoder operating level range	
解码器恢复时间	Jiěmǎqì huīfù shíjiān	Decoder recovery time	
解码器假码虚报	Jiěmǎqì jiǎmǎ xūbào	Decoder false code falsifying	
解码器启动时间	Jiěmǎqì qǐdòng shíjiān	Decoder attack time	
解码器输入缓冲器	Jiěmǎqì shūrù huǎnchōngqì	Decoder input buffer (video term)	
解码器噪声虚报	Jiěmǎqì zàoshēng xūbào	Decoder noise falsifying	
解码器的选择性	Jiěmǎqìde xuǎnzéxìng	Decoder selectivity	
解密	Jiěmì	Decipher, decrypt, decode, decryption (IPsec)	
解密错误消息	Jiěmì cuòwù xiāoxi	Decrypt error message (IPsec TLS)	

解密失败消息	Jiěmì shībài xiāoxi	Decrypt failure message (IPsec TLS)	
界面	Jièmiàn	Interface (for GUI)	
界面凝胶法	Jièmiàn níngjiāo fǎ	Boundary state gelatinization (FOC mfg)	BSG
接纳控制	Jiēnà kòngzhì	Admission control	
接纳允许控制	Jiēnà yǔnxǔ kòngzhì	Connection admission control	CAC
截屏图	Jiépíng tú	Hard-copy	
截屏图	Jiépíng tú	Snapshot	
捷普入侵检测系统	Jiépǔ rùqīn jiǎncè xìtǒng	Joint intrusion detection system	JIDS
截取功率	Jiéqǔ gōnglǜ	Intercepted power	
解扰	Jiěrǎo	Descrambling, descramble	
解扰码器	Jiěrǎomǎqì	Descrambler	
解扰器	Jiěrǎoqì	Descrambler	
吉尔伯特码	Jí-ěr-bó-tè mǎ	Gilbert code	
接入	Jiērù	Access (telecom term)	
接入层	Jiērù céng	Access layer	
接入承载结构	Jiērù chéngzài jiégòu	Access bearer structure	
接入承载能力	Jiērù chéngzài nénglì	Access bearer capability	
接入猝发比特群	Jiērù cùfā bǐtè qún	Access burst	AB
接入单元	Jiērù dānyuán	Access unit	AU
接入单元的接入点	Jiērù dānyuánde jiērùdiǎn	Access unit's access point	AUAP
接入电路段	Jiērù diànlù duàn	Access circuit section	
接入电路段	Jiērù diànlù duàn	Access circuit section	
接入费	Jiērù fèi	Access charge	
接入分类	Jiērù fēnlèi	Access class	AC
接入服务器	Jiērù fúwùqì	Access server	AS
接入和传输层	Jiērù hé chuánshū céng	Access and transport layer	
介入监视	Jièrù jiānshì	Intrusive monitoring	
接入交换管理处理器	Jiērù jiāohuàn guǎnlǐ chùlǐqì	Access switching management processor	ASMP
接入交换控制子系统	Jiērù jiāohuàn kòngzhì zixìtǒng	Access switching control sub-system	ASCS
接入交换维护子系统	Jiērù jiāohuàn wéihù zixìtǒng	Access switching maintenance sub-system	ASMS
接入节点	Jiērù jiédiǎn	Access node	
接入接口平台	Jiērù jiēkǒu píngtái	Access interface platform	AIP
接入竞争	Jiērù jìngzhēng	Access contention	
接入竞争解决	Jiērù jìngzhēng jiějué	Access contention resolution	
接入拒绝	Jiērù jùjué	Admissions rejected	ARJ
接入拒绝信号	Jiērù jùjué xìnhào	Access barred signal	ACB
接入控制列表	Jiērù kòngzhì lièbiǎo	Access control list	ACL
接入控制信息	Jiērù kòngzhì xìnxī	Access control information	ACI
接入控制中心	Jiērù kòngzhì zhōngxīn	Access control center	ACC
接入连接单元	Jiērù liánjiē dānyuán	Access connection element	ACE
接入链路	Jiērù liànlù	Access link	AL
接入链路控制应用协议	Jiērù liànlù kòngzhì yìngyòng xiéyì	Access link control application protocol	ALCAP
接入率	Jiērù lǜ	Access rate	AR
接入能力	Jiērù nénglì	Access capability	
接入请求	Jiērù qǐngqiú	Admissions request	ARQ
接入确认	Jiērù quèrèn	Admission confirm	ACF

接入设施	Jiērù shèshī	Access facility	AF
接入适配功能	Jiērù shìpèi gōngnéng	Access adaptation function	AAF
接入受阻	Jiērù shòuzǔ	Access barred	
接入数字段	Jiērù shùzì duàn	Access digital section	
接入速率	Jiērù sùlǜ	Access rate	AR
介入损耗	Jièrù sǔnhào	Insertion loss (FOC)	IL
接入条件	Jiērù tiáojiàn	Access condition	AC
接入通路	Jiērù tōnglù	Access channel	
接入突发脉冲序列	Jiērù tūfā màichōng xùliè	Access burst	AB
接入网	Jiērù wǎng	Access network	AN
接入网关	Jiērù wǎngguān	Access gateway	AGW
接入网络	Jiērù wǎngluò	Access network	
接入网络段	Jiērù wǎngluò duàn	Access network section	
接入网守	Jiērù wǎngshǒu	Access gatekeeper	AGK
接入网用同轴电缆	Jiērù wǎng-yòng tóngzhóu diànlǎn	Access network coaxial drop cable	
接入协议	Jiērù xiéyì	Access protocol	
接入信道	Jiērù xìndào	Access channel	
接入信令	Jiērù xìnlìng	Access signaling	AS
接入信息传送	Jiērù xìnxī chuánsòng	Access transport	
接入延迟	Jiērù yánchí	Access delay	
接入业务分类	Jiērù yèwù fēnlèi	Access service class	ASC
接入引擎	Jiērù yǐnqíng	Access ramp	
接入意义	Jiērù yìyì	Access significance	
接入允许	Jiērù yǔnxǔ	Access grant	
接入允许块数	Jiērù yǔnxǔ kuài shù	Number of access permission blocks	
接入允许信道	Jiērù yǔnxǔ xìndào	Access grant channel	AGCH
介入增益	Jièrù zēngyì	Insertion gain (of two-port-network)	
接入争用	Jiērù zhēngyòng	Access contention	
接入争用裁决	Jiērù zhēngyòng cáijué	Access contention resolution	
接入质量	Jiērù zhìliàng	Quality of access	QoA
接入中继线	Jiērù zhōngjìxiàn	Access trunk	AT
接入种类	Jiērù zhǒnglèi	Categories of access	
接入准许信道	Jiērù zhǔnxǔ xìndào	Access grant channel	AGCH
接入组	Jiērù zǔ	Access group	
接入点	Jiērùdiǎn	Access point (telecom network usage)	AP
接入点标识符	Jiērùdiǎn biāozhìfú	Access point identifier	APID
接入点发送标识	Jiērùdiǎn fāsòng biāozhì	Access point identifier transmit	
接入点接收标识	Jiērùdiǎn jiēshōu biāoshí	Access point identifier accepted	
接入点名	Jiērùdiǎn míng	Access point name	APN
接入点名	Jiērùdiǎn míng	Access point name	APN
接入点识别符	Jiērùdiǎn shíbié fú	Access point identifier	APID
接入段首标记	Jiērùduàn shǒubiāoji	Access preamble	AP
接入网管理系统	Jiērùwǎng guǎnlǐ xìtǒng	Access network management system	ANMS
接入网故障管理	Jiērùwǎng gùzhàng guǎnlǐ	Access network fault manager	AFM
接入网网管系统	Jiērùwǎng wǎngguǎn xìtǒng	Access network –network management system	AN-NMS
接入网系统	Jiērùwǎng xìtǒng	Access network system	ANS

接入网系统管理功能	Jiērùwǎng xìtǒng guǎnlǐ gōngnéng	Access network system management function	AN-SMF
接入站	Jiērùzhàn	Access point	AP
结式环行器	Jiéshì huánxíngqì	Junction circulator	
解释器	Jiěshìqì	Interpreter	
接收	Jiēshōu	Receipt, receive	
接收半角	Jiēshōu bàn jiǎo	Acceptance one-half angle	
接收参考当量	Jiēshōu cānkǎo dāngliàng	Receiving reference equivalent	
接收测试	Jiēshōu cèshì	Acceptance test	
接收多路藕合器	Jiēshōu duōlù ǒuhéqì	Receiver multi-coupler	RXMUCO
接收放大/分集集成件	Jiēshōu fàngdà/ fēnjí jíchéng jiàn	Receive amplifier/divider assembly	RADA
接收分割	Jiēshōu fēngē	Splitting of the incoming line (in voice frequency signaling)	
接受光锥	Jiēshòu guāng zhuī	Acceptance cone	
接收角	Jiēshōu jiǎo	Acceptance angle	
接收角绘图器	Jiēshōu jiǎo huìtúqì	Acceptance angle plotter	
接收客观响度评定值	Jiēshōu kèguān xiǎngdù píngdìng zhí	Receive objective loudness result	ROLR
接收块	Jiēshōu kuài	Receive block	
接收前端架	Jiēshōu qiánduān jià	Receive front end shelf	RFES
接收缺陷指示	Jiēshōu quēxiàn zhǐshì	Receive defect indicator	RDI
接收特性图	Jiēshōu tèxìng tú	Acceptance characteristic pattern	
接收天线	Jiēshōu tiānxiàn	Receiving antenna	
接收天线模块	Jiēshōu tiānxiàn mókuài	Receiver antenna module	RXMOD
接收图	Jiēshōu tú	Acceptance pattern	
接收未准备好	Jiēshōu wèizhǔnbèi hǎo	Receive not ready	RNR
接收响度评定值	Jiēshōu xiǎngdù píngdìng zhí	Receiving loudness rating	RLR
接收相对当量	Jiēshōu xiāngduì dāngliàng	Relative equivalent for receiving	
接收信号等级	Jiēshōu xìnhào děngjí	Received signal level	RXLEV
接收信号电平	Jiēshōu xìnhào diànpíng	Received signal level	EXLEV
接收信号码功率	Jiēshōu xìnhào mǎ gōnglǜ	Received signal code power	RSCP
接收信号强度指示	Jiēshōu xìnhào qiángdù zhǐshì	Received signal strength indication	RSSI
接收信号质量	Jiēshōu xìnhào zhìliàng	Received signal quality	RXQUAL
接收信号质量指示	Jiēshōu xìnhào zhìliàng zhǐshì	Received signal quality indicator	RSQI
接收至发射的回波耗损	Jiēshōu zhì fāshède huíbō hàosǔn	Receive to transmit echo loss	RTEL
接收至发射的稳定耗损	Jiēshōu zhì fāshède wěndìng hàosǔn	Receive to transmit stability loss	RTSL
接收专号	Jiēshōu zhuānhào	Special number for receiving	
接收准备部件	Jiēshōu zhǔnbèi bùjiàn	Receive-ready block	R-Block
接收准备好	Jiēshōu zhǔnbèi hǎo	Receive ready	RR
接收主通道接口参考点	Jiēshōu zhǔtōngdào jiēkǒu cānkǎodiǎn	Receive main path interface reference point	MPI-R
接收机	Jiēshōujī	Receiver	Rx
接收机饱和	Jiēshōujī bǎohé	Receiver saturation	
接收机保护装置	Jiēshōujī bǎohù zhuāngzhì	Receiver protector	
接收机带宽滤波器	Jiēshōujī dàikuān lǜbōqì	Receiver band pass filter	RBPF
接收机动态范围	Jiēshōujī dòngtài fànwéi	Receiver dynamic range	
接收机分路器	Jiēshōujī fēnlùqì	Receiver multi-coupler	
接收机过载功率	Jiēshōujī guòzài gōnglǜ	Receiver overload power	
接收机空间分集	Jiēshōujī kōngjiān fēnjí	Receiver space diversity	
接收机控制域	Jiēshōujī kòngzhì yù	Receiver control field	RXCF

接收机门限电平	Jiēshōujī ménxiàn diànpíng	Receiver threshold-signal level	
接收机前端	Jiēshōujī qiánduān	Receiver front end	
接收机衰减	Jiēshōujī shuāijiǎn	Receiver attenuation	RA
接收机脱钩	Jiēshōujī tuōgōu	Receiver off-hook	ROH
接收机阻塞	Jiēshōujī zǔsè	Receiver blocking	
接收机的过载系数	Jiēshōujīde guòzài xìshù	Overload factor of receiver	
接收器	Jiēshōuqì	Receiver (in signaling)	
接收台	Jiēshōutái	Receiving station	
接收者	Jiēshōuzhě	Recipient	
结束标签	Jiéshù biāoqiān	End tag	E tag
结束定界符	Jiéshù dìngjiè fú	End delimiter	ED
结束会话命令	Jiéshù huìhuà mìnglìng	End session command	ESC
结束控制	Jiéshù kòngzhì	Termination control	
结束类别	Jiéshù lèibié	Termination class	TC
结束通告消息	Jiéshù tōnggào xiāoxi	End notice message (IPsec TLS)	
截水墙	Jiéshuǐ qiáng	Cut-off wall	
解锁密钥	Jiěsuǒ mìyào	Unblocking key	
解体	Jiětǐ	Italic (WP command)	
阶梯扭波导	Jiētī niǔ bōdǎo	Step twist	
阶梯阻抗变换器	Jiētī zǔkàng biànhuànqì	Stepped-impedance transformer	
解调	Jiětiáo	Demodulation	
解调载频控制	Jiětiáo zàipín kòngzhì	Demodulation carrier frequency control	
解调器	Jiětiáoqì	Demodulator	D
接通板（接通激励器）	Jiētōng bǎn (jiētōng jīlìqì)	On deck (switching on exciter)	
接通呼叫	Jiētōng hūjiào	Completed call	
接头	Jiētóu	Splice	
接头预失真	Jiētóu yùshīzhēn	Joint pre-distortion	JP
界外	Jièwài	Over edge	
结尾边缘	Jiéwěi biānyuán	End edge	
结尾对准	Jiéwěi duìzhǔn	End-aligned	
解析	Jiěxī	Parse	
解析	Jiěxī	Resolve	
解析测图仪	Jiěxī cètúyí	Analytical plotter	
解析过程	Jiěxī guòchéng	Resolution	
解析几何	Jiěxī jǐhé	Analytical geometry	
解析三角测量	Jiěxī sānjiǎo èliáng	Analytical triangulation	
解析信号	Jiěxī xìnhào	Analytic signal	
界限符号	Jièxiàn fúhào	Delimiter	
界限检查	Jièxiàn jiǎnchá	Bounds checking	
接线信号	Jiēxiàn xìnhào	Connect signal	
接线盒	Jiēxiànhé	Junction box	
接线器	Jiēxiànqì	Switch (in a switching network)	
接线头	Jiēxiàntóu	Wire harness	
解析度	Jiěxīdù	Resolution	
结型场效应晶体管	Jiéxíng cháng xiàoyìng jīngtǐguǎn	Junction field effect transistor	JFET
解析器	Jiěxīqì	Parser	

接续	Jiēxù	Connection	
接续管理	Jiēxù guǎnlǐ	Connection management	CM
接续网路	Jiēxù wǎnglù	Connection network	
接续信道	Jiēxù xìndào	Access channel	A-CH
接续帧号	Jiēxù zhènghào	Connection frame number	CFN
接续点	Jiēxùdiǎn	Connecting point	
解压失败消息	Jiěyā shībài xiāoxi	Decompression failure message (IPsec TLS)	
解压缩	Jiěyāsuō	Uncompress, decompress	
解译	Jiěyì	Interpretation	
阶跃型塑胶光纤	Jiēyuèxíng sùjiāo guāngxiān	Stepped index plastic optical fiber	SI-POF
介质棒天线	Jièzhì bàng tiānxiàn	Dielectric rod antenna	
截止波长	Jiézhǐ bōcháng	Cut-off wavelength	
截止波长位移光纤	Jiézhǐ bōcháng wèiyí guāngxiān	Cut-off wavelength shifted optical fiber	CSF
截止波导	Jiézhǐ bōdǎo	Waveguide below cut-off	
介质波导	Jièzhì bōdǎo	Dielectric waveguide	
介质材料	Jièzhì cáiliào	Dielectrics (semiconductor mfg)	
介质槽	Jièzhì cáo	Media bay	
介质导喇叭馈电器	Jièzhì dǎo lǎba kuìdiànqì	Conical dielectric horn-feed	
介质访问控制	Jièzhì fǎngwèn kòngzhì	Media access control	MAC
介质访问控制层	Jièzhì fǎngwèn kòngzhì céng	Medium access control layer	MAC
介质干扰杆	Jièzhì gānrǎo gǎn	Dielectric chaff rod	
介质击穿	Jièzhì jīchuān	Disruptive discharge dielectric breakdown	
介质接口连接器	Jièzhì jiēkǒu liánjiēqì	Media interface connector	MIC
介质接口适配器	Jièzhì jiēkǒu shìpèiqì	Media interface adapter	MIA
介质链接单元	Jièzhì liànjiē dānyuán	Media attachment unit	MAU
截止频率	Jiézhǐ pínlǜ	Cut-off frequency	
介质强度试验	Jièzhì qiángdù shìyàn	Dielectric strength test	
介质试验	Jièzhì shìyàn	Dielectric test	
截止衰减器	Jiézhǐ shuāijiǎnqì	Cut-off attenuator	
介质透镜	Jièzhì tòujìng	Dielectric lens	
介质透镜天线	Jièzhì tòujìng tiānxiàn	Dielectric lens antenna	
介质谐振器	Jièzhì xiézhènqì	Dielectric resonator	
介质移相器	Jièzhì yíxiàngqì	Dielectric phase shifter	
截止期	Jiézhǐqī	Deadline	
截止式衰减器	Jiézhǐ-shì shuāijiǎnqì	Cut-off attenuator	
接主确认	Jiēzhǔ quèrèn	Admissions confirmed (packet network protocol message)	ACF
激发二极管	Jīfā èrjíguǎn	Laser diode	
激发光源	Jīfā guāngyuán	Pumping light source	
激发管	Jīfāguǎn	Laser diode	
记发器功能	Jìfāqì gōngnéng	Register function	
记发器信号	Jìfāqì xìnhào	Register signal, signaling	
记发器信令	Jìfāqì xìnlìng	Register signaling	
计费	Jìfèi	Charging	
计费点	Jìfèi diǎn	Charging point (GSM term)	
计费附加业务	Jìfèi fùjiā yèwù	Charging supplementary services	
计费管理	Jìfèi guǎnlǐ	Accounting management	

计费管理平台	Jìfèi guǎnlǐ píngtái	Bill management platform	BMP
计费和管理系统	Jìfèi hé guǎnlǐ xìtǒng	Billing and management system	BMS
计费核算组	Jìfèi hésuàn zǔ	Billing and account rapporteurs group (GSM MoU)	BARG
计费汇总计数收集器	Jìfèi huìzǒng jìshù shōujíqì	Meter counts collector	MCC
计费建议信息	Jìfèi jiànyì xìnxī	Charge advice information	CAI
计费记录	Jìfèi jìlù	Charging record (telecom billing term)	
计费设备	Jìfèi shèbèi	Charging equipment	
计费收费通知	Jìfèi shōufèi tōngzhī	Advice of charge charging	AoC
计费通知	Jìfèi tōngzhī	Advice of charge	AOC
计费通知（计费）	Jìfèi tōngzhī (jìfèi)	Advice of charge for charging	AoCc
计费通知（记费）补充业务	Jìfèi tōngzhī (jìfèi) bǔchōng yèwù	Advice of charge charging supplementary service	AoCC
计费通知（信息）	Jìfèi tōngzhī (xìnxī)	Advice of charge for information	AoCi
计费通知（信息）补充业务	Jìfèi tōngzhī (xìnxī) bǔchōng yèwù	Advice of charge information supplementary service	AoCI
计费通知，计费类	Jìfèi tōngzhī, jìfèi lèi	Advice of charge, charging level	AoCC
计费通知，信息类	Jìfèi tōngzhī, xìnxī lèi	Advice of charge, information level	AoCI
计费网关	Jìfèi wǎngguān	Charging gateway	CG
计费网关功能	Jìfèi wǎngguān gōngnéng	Charging gateway function	CGF
计费网关功能性	Jìfèi wǎngguān gōngnéngxìng	Charging gateway functionality	CGF
记费完整性	Jìfèi wánzhěngxìng	Billing integrity	
计费消息	Jìfèi xiāoxi	Charging message	CHG
计费信息	Jìfèi xìnxī	Charge information (ISUP message)	CRG
计费系统	Jìfèi xìtǒng	Billing system	BS
计费中介软件	Jìfèi zhōngjiè ruǎnjiàn	Billing mediation software	
计费中心	Jìfèi zhōngxīn	Billing center	BC
计费子系统	Jìfèi zixìtǒng	Charging accounting sub-system	CAS
积分冲洗	Jīfēn chōngxǐ	Integrate-and-dump	I&D
积分环节	Jīfēn huánjié	Integral element	
积分脉冲调制	Jīfēn màichōng iáozhì	Integral pulse frequency modulation	IPFM
积分增量调制	Jīfēn zēngliàng tiáozhì	Integrating delta modulation	IDM
积分折射率仪	Jīfēn zhéshèlǜyí	Integral refractive index meter	
积分电路	Jīfēndiànlù	Integrating circuit	
积分器	Jīfēnqì	Integrator	
积分式模/数转换器	Jīfēn-shì mó/shù zhuǎnhuànqì	Integrating-type A/D converter	
吉咖波特	Jígābōtè	Gigabaud	GBd
极高大型光学计划	Jígāo dà-xíng guāngxué jìhuà	High altitude large optics	HALO
极高频	Jígāopín	Extra-high frequency	EHF
吉咖字节	Jígāzìjié,	Gigabyte	GB
激光板	Jīguāng bǎn	Laser slab	
激光棒	Jīguāng bàng	Laser rod	
激光玻璃	Jīguāng bōli	Laser glass	
激光测距仪	Jīguāng cèjùyí	Laser ranging unit	
激光传真机	Jīguāng chuánzhēnjī	Laser facsimile	
激光打印机	Jīguāng dǎyìnjī	Laser beam printer, laser printer	LBP
激光定位设备	Jīguāng dìngwèi shèbèi	Laser positioning equipment	
激光二极管	Jīguāng èrjíguǎn	Laser diode	LD
激光放大器电路	Jīguāng fàngdàqì diànlù	Laser amplifier chain	LAC

激光共振腔	Jīguāng gòngzhènqiāng	Laser resonator cavity	
激光管	Jīguāng guǎn	Laser tube or bore	
激光光绘	Jīguāng guāng huì	Laser plotting	
激光光吸收体	Jīguāng guāng xīshōu tǐ	Laser absorber	
激光光绘仪	Jīguāng guānghuìyí	Laser plotter	
激光护眼镜	Jīguāng hù yǎnjìng	Laser protective glasses	
激光互连装置	Jīguāng hùlián zhuāngzhì	Laser interconnection unit	LIU
激光加工机	Jīguāng jiāgōngjī	Laser processing equipment	
激光激发染料激光	Jīguāng jīfā rǎnliào jīguāng	Laser pumped dye laser	
激光激活媒质	Jīguāng jīhuó méizhì	Active laser medium	
激光控制设备	Jīguāng kòngzhì shèbèi	Laser control equipment	
激光雷达	Jīguāng léidá	Laser radar	
激光面镜	Jīguāng miànjìng	Laser mirror	
激光全息	Jīguāng quánxī	Laser holography	
激光衰减控制器	Jīguāng shuāijiǎn kòngzhìqì	Laser attenuator assembly	LAA
激光退火装置	Jīguāng tuìhuǒ zhuāngzhì	Laser annealing equipment	
激光显示器	Jīguāng xiǎnshìqì	Laser display	
激光选区烧结法	Jīguāng xuǎnqū shāojiéfǎ	Selective laser sintering	SLS
激光源	Jīguāng yuán	Laser source	
激光啁啾	Jīguāng zhōujiū	Laser chirp	
激光唱机	Jīguāngchàngjī	Compact disk (CD) player	
激光唱片	Jīguāngchàngpiàn	Compact disk	CD
激光器	Jīguāngqì	Laser device	LD
激光器背光功率	Jīguāngqì bèiguāng gōnglǜ	Laser backface optical power	LBOP
激光器控制域	Jīguāngqì kòngzhì yù	Laser control field	LCF
激光器偏流监视	Jīguāngqì piānliú jiānshì	Laser base current monitor	LSBCM
激光器偏置电流	Jīguāngqì piānzhì diànliú	Laser bias current	LB
激光器偏置控制	Jīguāngqì piānzhì kòngzhì	Laser offset control	
激光器温度	Jīguāngqì wēndù	Laser temperature	LT
激光器与光电系统会议	Jīguāngqì yǔ guāngdiàn xìtǒng huìyì	Conference on laser electro-optical systems	CLEOS
激光器自动关闭	Jīguāngqì zìdòng guānbì	Automatic laser shutdown	ALS
激光器组	Jīguāngqì zǔ	Laser module	
激光用盒	Jīguāng-yòng hé	Laser cell	
激光用冷却设备	Jīguāng-yòng lěngquè shèbèi	Cooling system for laser	
激光用染料	Jīguāng-yòng rǎnliào	Laser dye	
记号	Jìhào	Symbol	
集合	Jíhé	Set	
集合	Jíhé	Collection (noun)	
集合 2 通用符号	Jíhé er tōngyòng fúhào	Universal character set 2	UCS2
集合覆盖	Jíhé fùgài	Set cover	
集合关系	Jíhé guānxi	Aggregation relationship	
集合函数	Jíhé hánshù	Set function	
集合配置	Jíhé pèizhì	Set packing	
几何图形元素	Jǐhé túxíng yuánsù	Geometric graphic element	
集合信号	Jíhé xìnhào	Aggregate signal	
集合域	Jíhé yù	Aggregate domain	

集合与串的问题	Jíhé yǔ chuànde wèntí	Set and string problems	
极化	Jíhuà	Polarization (of a degenerate mode in a waveguide)	
极化比	Jíhuà bǐ	Polarization ratio (of a field vector)	
极化不灵敏移相器	Jíhuà bùlíngmǐn yíxiàngqì	Polarization-insensitive phase shifter	
极化方向	Jíhuà fāngxiàng	Direction of polarization (in a waveguide)	
极化分割多路存取	Jíhuà fēngē duōlù cúnqǔ	Polarization division multiple access	PDMA
极化分集	Jíhuà fēnjí	Polarity diversity	
极化分离器	Jíhuà fēnlíqì	Polarization resolver	
极化面	Jíhuà miàn	Plane of polarization	
极化模激光器	Jíhuà mó jīguāngqì	Polarization mode laser	
极化模色散	Jíhuà mó sèsàn	Polarization mode dispersion	PMD
极化平面	Jíhuà píngmiàn	Polarization plane	
极化匹配	Jíhuà pǐpèi	Polarization match	
极化去耦比	Jíhuà qù'ǒu bǐ	Polarization decoupling ratio (of an antenna),	
极化去相关	Jíhuà qùxiāngguān	Polarity decorrelation	
极化损耗	Jíhuà sǔnhào	Polarization loss	
极化调制脉码调制(脉冲源)	Jíhuà tiáozhì màimǎ tiáozhì (màichōng yuán)	Pulse code modulation-polarization modulation (pulse source)	PCM-PM (PS)
极化椭圆	Jíhuà tuǒyuán	Polarization ellipse	
极化选择抗干扰技术	Jíhuà xuǎnzé kàng gānrǎo jìshù	Polarization selection anti-jamming technique	
极化选择器	Jíhuà xuǎnzéqì	Polarization selector	
计划值	Jìhuà zhí	Plan value	
机会锁	Jīhuì suǒ	Oplock (in SAMBA)	
激活	Jīhuó	Activation	
激活材料	Jīhuó cáiliào	Active medium	
激活窗口	Jīhuó chuāngkǒu	Active window	
激活分析	Jīhuó fēnxī	Activation analysis	AA
激活服务器页	Jīhuó fúwùqì yè	Active server page	ASP
激活跟踪方式	Jīhuó gēnzōng fāngshì	Activate trace mode	
激活化学汽相沉积工艺	Jīhuó huàxué qìxiàng chénjī gōngyì	Activated chemical vapor deposition process	
激活媒质	Jīhuó méizhì	Active medium	
激活模式	Jīhuó móshì	Active mode	
激活请求	Jīhuó qǐngqiú	Activate request	AR
激活指示	Jīhuó zhǐshì	Activate indication	AI
级间链路	Jí-jiān liànlù	Inter-switch link	
级间损耗	Jí-jiān sǔnhào	Losses between stages	
即将操作状态	Jíjiāng cāozuò zhuàngtài	Pending operating state (IPsec)	
即将读状态	Jíjiāng dú zhuàngtài	Pending read state (IPsec)	
即将写状态	Jíjiāng xiě zhuàngtài	Pending write state (IPsec)	
机架式	Jījià-shì	Rackmount	
寂静时间	Jìjìng shíjiān	Dead time	
急剧衰落	Jíjù shuāiluò	Flutter fading	
机壳辐射	Jīké fúshè	Cabinet radiation	
击空电压	Jīkōng diànyā	Breakdown voltage	
积累平房线性误差	Jīlěi píngfáng xiànxìng wùchā	Integral square linear error	ISLE
积累损耗	Jīlěi sǔnhào	Integration loss	
级联	Jílián	Cascading, cascade connection	

级联	Jílián	Concatenation	
级联参考完整性约束	Jílián cānkǎo wánzhěng xìng yuēshù	Cascading referential integrity constraints (in SQL Server)	
级联放大发射机	Jílián fàngdà fāshèjī	Cascade amplifier transmitter	
级联放大器	Jílián fàngdàqì	Cascade amplifier	CA
级联更新	Jílián gēngxīn	Cascading update (for database)	
级联交叉矩阵	Jílián jiāochā jǔzhèn	Concatenated cross-connect matrix	
级连码	Jílián mǎ	Concatenated code	
级联删除	Jílián shānchú	Cascading delete (for database)	
级联网络	Jílián wǎngluò	Cascaded network	
级联运行	Jílián yùnxíng	Cascaded operation (in SQL Server)	
剂量	Jìliàng	Dose	
基流	Jīliú	Background current	
激励型终端	Jīlì-xíng zhōngduān	Stimulus terminal	
记录	Jìlù	Record	
纪录测井	Jìlù cèjǐng	Logging	
记录定位	Jìlù dìngwèi	Record locator	
记录定义	Jìlù dìngyì	Record definition	
记录分隔	Jìlù fēngé	Record separator	RS
记录光谱分析仪	Jìlù guāngpǔ fēnxīyí	Recording optical spectrum analyzer	ROSA
记录集	Jìlù jí	Recordset (for database)	
记录控制字段	Jìlù kòngzhì zìduàn	Record control fields	
记录密度	Jìlù mìdù	Recording density	
记录顺序	Jìlù shùnxù	Record sequence	
纪录协议	Jìlù xiéyì	Record protocol (IPsec)	
记录液出消息	Jìlù yèchū xiāoxi	Record overflow message (IPsec TLS)	
记录音	Jìlù yīn	Recording tone	
记录间间隔	Jìlù-jiān jiàngé	Inter-record gap	IRG
记录器告警音	Jìlùqì gàojǐng yīn	Recorder-warning tone	
机密性	Jīmìxìng	Confidentiality (IPsec)	
机密性保护命令	Jīmìxìng bǎohù mìnglìng	Confidentiality protected command (in FTP)	CONF
基模场强	Jīmó chǎngqiáng	Base mode field strength (FOC)	
积木块信号处理机	Jīmù kuài xìnhào chǔlǐjī	Building block signal processor	BBSP
近打字效果	Jìn dǎzì xiàoguǒ	Near letter quality	NLQ
近红外光光二极体	Jìn hóngwàiguāng guāng èrjítǐ	Near-infrared photodiode	
仅线路激活	Jǐn xiànlù jīhuó	Line-only activation	
仅用户--网络接口的去激活	Jǐn yònghù—wǎngluò jiēkǒude qùjīhuó	User-network interface only deactivation	
紧包多心式光缆	Jǐnbāo duōxīn-shì guānglǎn	Tightly buffered multifiber fiber optic cable	
近场区	Jìncháng qū	Near-field region	
近场图	Jìncháng tú	Near-field pattern	NFP
进程	Jìnchéng	Process	
进程标签	Jìnchéng biāoqiān	Process label	
进程标识	Jìnchéng biāozhì	Process ID (Unix)	pid
进程标识符	Jìnchéng biāozhìfú	Process identifier	PID
进程迁移	Jìnchéng qiānyí	Process migration	
进程间通信	Jìnchéng-jiān tōngxìn	Interprocess communication	IPC
进程间通讯	Jìnchéng-jiān tōngxùn	Interprocess communication	IPC

进尺	Jìnchǐ	Depth of embedment	
近点周期	Jìndiǎn zhōuqī	Anomalistic period	
近地点	Jìndìdiǎn	Perigee	
近地点高度	Jìndìdiǎn gāodù	Altitude of the perigee	
进动	Jìndòng	Precession	
进度指示器	Jìndù zhǐshìqì	Progress bar	
近端背景误块	Jìnduān bèijǐng wùkuài	Near-end background block error	NBBE
近端串话	Jìnduān chuànhuà	Near-end crosstalk	NEC
近端串扰	Jìnduān chuànrǎo	Near-end crosstalk	NEXT
近端串音	Jìnduān chuànyīn	Near-end cross talk	NEXT
近端串音功率和	Jìnduān chuànyīn gōnglǜ hé	Near-end crosstalk power sum	PSNEXT
近端串音衰减功率和	Jìnduān chuànyīn shuāijiǎn gōnglǜ hé	Near-end crosstalk attenuation power sum	PSNEXT
近端回波抑制器	Jìnduān huíbō yìzhìqì	Near-end echo suppressor	NES
近端缺陷秒	Jìnduān quēxiàn miǎo	Near-end defective second	NDS
近端误块计数	Jìnduān wùkuài jìshù	Near-end error block counter	NEBC
近端误块秒	Jìnduān wùkuài miǎo	Near-end errored second	NES
近端严重误块秒	Jìnduān yánzhòng wùkuài miǎo	Near-end severely errored second	NSES
近端用户接入	Jìnduān yònghù jiērù	Near-end subscriber access	SA-N
近端用户设备	Jìnduān yònghù shèbèi	Near-end subscriber installation	SI-N
机能检测	Jīnéng jiǎncè	Capability test	
静不稳定	Jìng bùwěndìng	Static instability	
经测试实现	Jīng cèshì shíxiàn	Implementation under test	IUT
经认可的运营机构	Jīng rènkěde yùnyíng jīgòu	Recognized operating authority	ROA
警报	Jǐngbào	Warning, alarm	
警报	Jǐngbào	Alert	
警报公布	Jǐngbào gōngbù	Warning statement	
警报及传递	Jǐngbào jí chuándì	Warning and its communication	
静电放电	Jìngdiàn fàngdiàn	Electrostatic discharge	ESD
静电放电防护阈值	Jìngdiàn fàngdiàn fánghù yù zhí	Electrostatic discharge protection threshold	
静电感应晶体管	Jìngdiàn gǎnyìng jīngtǐguǎn	Static induction transistor	SIT
静电感应晶闸管	Jìngdiàn gǎnyìng jīngzháguǎn	Static induction thyristor	SITH
经典格式指示符	Jīngdiǎn géshi zhǐshìfú	Canonical format indicator	CFI
静电绘图仪	Jìngdiàn huìtúyí	Electrostatic plotter	
经典进程代数	Jīngdiǎn jìnchéng dàishù	Classical process algebra	
静电聚焦	Jìngdiàn jùjiāo	Electrostatic focus	
静电偏转	Jìngdiàn piānzhuǎn	Electrostatic deflection	
静电偏转管	Jìngdiàn piānzhuǎn guǎn	Electrostatic deflection tube	
静电释放	Jìngdiàn shìfàng	Electrostatic discharge	ESD
静定结构	Jìngding jiégòu	Statically determinate structure	
精度	Jīngdù	Precision	
经度	Jīngdù	Longitude	
精度的降额	Jīngdùde jiàng'é	Dilution of precision	DOP
净负荷	Jìngfùhè	Payload (SDH term)	
景观分析	Jǐngguān fēnxī	Scene analysis	
经过资格修饰	Jīngguò zīge xiūshì	Qualified (in C++)	
净荷包头抑制	Jìnghé bāotóu yìzhì	Payload header suppression	PHS

净荷包头抑制长度	Jìnghé bāotóu yìzhì chángdù	Payload header suppression size	PHSS
净荷包头抑制规则	Jìnghé bāotóu yìzhì guīzé	Payload header suppression rule	PHS Rule
净荷包头抑制校验	Jìnghé bāotóu yìzhì jiàoyàn	Payload header suppression marker	PHSM
净荷包头抑制校验	Jìnghé bāotóu yìzhì jiàoyàn	Payload header suppression valid	PHSV
净荷包头抑制索引	Jìnghé bāotóu yìzhì suǒyǐn	Payload header suppression index	PHSI
净荷包头抑制域	Jìnghé bāotóu yìzhì yù	Payload header suppression field	PHSF
净荷长度	Jìnghé chángdù	Payload length	
净荷加密	Jìnghé jiāmì	Payload-only encryption (IPsec)	
净荷类型	Jìnghé lèixíng	Payload type	PT
净荷类型指示	Jìnghé lèixíng zhǐshì	Payload type indication	PTI
净荷模块	Jìnghé mókuài	Payload module	
净负荷起始标识符	Jìnghè qǐshǐ biāozhì fú	Payload unit start indicator	PUSI
净荷失配	Jìnghé shīpèi	Payload mismatch	PLM
经济磁盘冗余阵列	Jīngjì cípán rǒngyú zhènliè	Redundant array of inexpensive disks	RAID
静寂帧	Jìngjì zhèng	Silence descriptor	SID
精简指令集计算	Jīngjiǎn zhǐlìng jí jìsuàn	Reduced instruction set computing	RISC
精简指令集计算机	Jīngjiǎn zhǐlìng jí jìsuànjī	Reduced instruction set computing	RISC
精简指令计算机	Jīngjiǎn zhǐlìng jìsuànjī	Reduced instruction set computer	RISC
警觉	Jǐngjué	Alerting	
精良生产	Jīngliáng shēngchǎn	Lean production (Japanese concept)	LP
精灵程序	Jīnglíng chéngxù	Wizard	
精密定位服务	Jīngmì dìngwèi fúwù	Precision positioning service (in GPS)	PPS
精密定位业务	Jīngmì dìngwèi yèwù	Precision positioning service	PPS
精密光纤（缆）连接器	Jīngmì guāngxiān (lǎn) liánjiēqì	Precision optical fiber (cable) connector	
精密机械	Jīngmì jīxiè	Fine mechanics	
镜面球	Jìngmiàn qiú	Mirror ball	
近拱点	Jìngǒngdiǎn	Periapsis	
晶片	Jīngpiàn	Chip	
晶片切换	Jīngpiàn qiēhuàn	Chip swap	
晶片圆盘	Jīngpiàn yuánpán	Wafer	
晶片组	Jīngpiàn zǔ	Chipset	
镜频反射	Jìngpín fǎnshè	Image reflection	
镜频回收	Jìngpín huíshōu	Image recovery	
镜频抑制	Jìngpín yìzhì	Image rejection	
镜频抑制比	Jìngpín yìzhì bǐ	Image rejection ratio	
镜频抑制混频器	Jìngpín yìzhì hùnpínqì	Image frequency rejection mixer	
精巧机壳	Jīngqiǎo jīké	Compact casing	
精巧型	Jīngqiǎo-xíng	Compact, wallmount (when referring to chassis)	
精确串行化	Jīngquè chuànhánghuà	Precise serialization	PS
经确定轨系统	Jīngquè dìngguǐ xìtǒng	Precision orbit determination system	PODS
精确频率	Jīngquè pínlǜ	Exact frequency	
精确位置指示器	Jīngquè wèizhì zhǐshìqì	Accurate position indicator	API
精确像素插值	Jīngquè xiàngsù chāzhí	Precise pixel interpolation	
精确制导的武器	Jīngquè zhìdǎode wǔqì	Precision guided weapon	
静态存根	Jìngtài cúngēn	Static stub (CORBA term)	
静态定位	Jìngtài dìngwèi	Static positioning	

静态对话框	Jìngtài duìhuà kuàng	Static dialog box	
静态分析	Jìngtài fēnxī	Static analysis	
静态负载平衡	Jìngtài fùzài pínghéng	Static load balancing	
静态画请求	Jìngtài huà qǐngqiú	Freeze picture request	
静态结构化查询语言语句	Jìngtài jiégòuhuà cháxún yǔyán yǔjù	Static structured query language (SQL) statements (for database)	
静态库	Jìngtài kù	Static repository (in CORBA)	
静态列 RAM	Jìngtài liè RAM	Static-column RAM	
静态内核	Jìngtài nèihé	Static core	
静态疲劳	Jìngtài píláo	Static fatigue (FOC)	
静态取责分离	Jìngtài qǔzé fènlí	Static separation of duties	SSD
静态数据鉴别	Jìngtài shùjù jiànbié	Static data authentication	
静态随机存储器	Jìngtài suíjī cúnchǔqì	Static random access memory	SRAM
静态随机存取存储器	Jìngtài suíjī cúnqǔ cúnchǔqì	Static random access memory	SRAM
静态相位偏差	Jìngtài xiàngwèi piānchā	Static phase offset	
静态一致性要求	Jìngtài yīzhìxìng yāoqiú	Static conformance requirement	
静态游标	Jìngtài yóubiāo	Static cursor (for database)	
静态指定套接字	Jìngtài zhǐdìng tàojiēzì	Statically assigned socket	
晶体电极	Jīngtǐ diànjí	Crystalline electrode	
晶体光栅	Jīngtǐ guāngshān	Crystal grating	
晶体混频器	Jīngtǐ hùnpínqì	Crystal mixer	
晶体控制时钟脉冲发生器	Jīngtǐ kòngzhì shízhōng màichōng fāshēngqì	Crystal-controlled clock generator	CCCG
晶体管晶体管逻辑电路	Jīngtǐguǎn jīngtǐguǎn luójidiànlù	Transistor-transistor logic circuit	TTL
镜头设计顾问	Jìngtóu shèjì gùwèn	Lens design consultant	
经纬网	Jīngwěiwǎng	1East.com. (Shanghai Web magazine)	
经纬仪	Jīngwěiyí	Theodolite	
经纬仪	Jīngwěiyí	Transit	
精细间距	Jīngxì jiānjù	Precision fine pitch	
镜像	Jìngxiàng	Mirroring	
径向传输线	Jìngxiàng chuánshūxiàn	Radial transmission line	
镜像回收混频器	Jìngxiàng huíshōu hùnpínqì	Image recovery mixer	
镜像集	Jìngxiàng jí	Mirror set	
镜像卷	Jìngxiàng juàn	Mirrored volume	
镜像频率	Jìngxiàng pínlǜ	Image frequency (in superheterodyne reception)	
径向扫描	Jìngxiàng sǎomiáo	Radial sweep (radar term)	
镜像天线	Jìngxiàng tiānxiàn	Image antenna	
镜像抑制	Jìngxiàng yìzhì	Image rejection	
镜像抑制比	Jìngxiàng yìzhì bǐ	Image rejection ratio	
镜像站点	Jìngxiàng zhàndiǎn	Mirror site	
经销商	Jīngxiāoshāng	Commission merchant	
经验公式	Jīngyàn gōngshì	Empirical equation	
静音	Jìngyīn	Squelch	
静音描述	Jìngyīn miáoshù	Silence descriptor	SID
静音指示	Jìngyīn zhǐshì	Silence descriptor	SID
晶圆	Jīngyuán	Wafer	
静噪	Jìngzào	Squelch	

静噪开启电平和闭锁电平	Jìngzào kāiqǐ diànpíng hé bìsuǒ diànpíng	Squelch opening level and closing level	
静噪开启时延和闭锁时延	Jìngzào kāiqǐ shíyán hé bìsuǒ shíyán	Squelch opening delay and closing delay	
静噪失谐门限	Jìngzào shīxié ménxiàn	Squelch detuning threshold	
静噪调谐	Jìngzào tiáoxié	Mute tuning	
静噪阻塞门限	Jìngzào zǔsè ménxiàn	Squelch blocking threshold	
竞争条件	Jìngzhēng tiáojiàn	Race condition	
静止地球轨道	Jìngzhǐ dìqiú guǐdào	Geostationary earth orbit	GEO
静止图像电视	Jìngzhǐ túxiàng diànshì	Still-picture television	SPTV
静止图象电视电话	Jìngzhǐ túxiàng diànshì diànhuà	Still picture video-television	
静止图像会议实体	Jìngzhǐ túxiàng huìyì shítǐ	Still image conference entity	SICE
静止图象交换文件格式	Jìngzhǐ túxiàng jiāohuàn wénjiàn géshi	Still picture interchange file format	SPIFF
静止图像协商数据单元	Jìngzhǐ túxiàng xiéshāng shùjù dānyuán	Still image protocol data unit	SIPDU
静止卫星	Jìngzhǐ wèixīng	Stationary satellite	
静止卫星业务	Jìngzhǐ wèixīng yèwù	Fixed satellite service	FSS
紧急呼叫	Jǐnjí hūjiào	Emergency call	
紧急事件管理端口	Jǐnjí shìjiàn guǎnlǐ duānkǒu	Emergency incident management port	EMP
禁忌搜索算法	Jìnjì sōusuǒ suànfǎ	Tabu search algorithm	
紧急修复磁盘	Jǐnjí xiūfù cípán	Emergency repair disk	ERD
紧急度	Jǐnjídù	Criticality	
紧急指位无线信标台	Jǐnjízhǐ wèi wúxiàn xìnbiāotái	Emergency position-indicating radiobeacon station	
尽快	Jǐnkuài	As soon as possible (computer chat)	ASAP
尽力而为	Jìnlì ér wéi	Best effort	BE
尽力服务	Jìnlì fúwù	Best effort	
进料器	Jìnliàoqì	Loader (in component assembly process)	
紧密度	Jǐnmìdù	Precision	
金桥网	Jīnqiáo wǎng	Golden Bridge Network (China)	GB-Net
进气道干扰试验	Jìnqìdào gānrǎo shìyàn	Jamming test of duct	
金融服务技术联盟	Jīnróng fúwù jìshù liánméng	Financial Services Technology Consortium	FSTC
金融网络协会	Jīnróng wǎngluò xiéhuì	Financial network association (China)	FNA
金属板透镜天线	Jīnshǔ bǎn tòujìng tiānxiàn	Metal-plate lenses antenna	
金属箔对线	Jīnshǔ bó duìxiàn	Foil twisted pair	FTP
金属箔双绞电缆	Jīnshǔ bó shuāngjiǎo diànlǎn	Foil twisted pair	FTP
金属箍	Jīnshǔ gū	Metal ferrule	
金属面镜	Jīnshǔ miànjìng	Metal mirror	
金属涂层光纤	Jīnshǔ túcéng guāngxiān	Metal coated fiber	
金属线槽敷设	Jīnshǔ xiàncáo fūshè	Run in metallic raceway	
金属延迟透镜天线	Jīnshǔ yánchí tòujìng tiānxiàn	Metal delay lens antenna	
金属氧化物半导体	Jīnshǔ yǎnghuàwù bàndǎotǐ	Metal oxide semiconductor	MOS
金属氧化物半导体场效应晶体管	Jīnshǔ yǎnghuàwù bàndǎotǐ cháng xiàoyìng jīngtǐguǎn	Metal oxide semiconductor field effect transistor	MOSFET
金属氧化物变阻器	Jīnshǔ yǎnghuàwù biànzǔqì	Metal oxide varister	MOV
金属有机化学汽相沉积	Jīnshǔ yǒujī huàxué qìxiāng chénjī	Metal organic vapor phase epitaxy	MOVPE
金属有机化学汽相沉积法	Jīnshǔ yǒujī huàxué qìxiàng chénjī fǎ	Metallo-organic chemical vapor deposition	MOCVD
金属蒸气激光	Jīnshǔ zhēngqì jīguāng	Metal vapor laser	
金属自承光缆	Jīnshǔ zì chéng guānglǎn	Metallic aerial self-supporting (FOC)	MASS

近似内插	Jìnsì nèichā	Approximate interpolation	
近似曲线	Jìnsì qūxiàn	Similar curve	
近似搜索	Jìnsì sōusuǒ	Proximity search	
近似算法	Jìnsì suànfǎ	Approximation algorithm	
近似推理	Jìnsì tuīlǐ	Approximate reasoning	
紧缩	Jǐnsuō	Pack (verb)	
紧套	Jǐntào	Tight tube (FOC mfg)	
进位	Jìnwèi	Carry (mathematical term)	CAR
近误差	Jìnwùchā	Approximation error	
进行后续切换	Jìnxíng hòuxù qiēhuàn	Perform subsequent handover	
进行切换	Jìnxíng qiēhuàn	Perform handover	
进行寻呼标志	Jìnxíng xúnhū biāozhì	Paging proceed flag	PPF
金样	Jīnyàng	Golden boy (in SMT)	
进一步研究	Jìnyībù yánjiū	For further study	FFS
禁用	Jīnyòng	Disable, disabled	
禁用词	Jīnyòng cí	Stopword	
尽早类别发送控制	Jǐnzǎo lèibié fāsòng kòngzhì	Early classmark sending control	ECSC
进展请求	Jìnzhǎn qǐngqiú	Request in progress	RIP
进展指示	Jìnzhǎn zhǐshì	Progress indicator	
禁止	Jìnzhǐ	Interdiction (IPsec)	
禁止拔号	Jìnzhǐ bōhào	Barred dialling number	BDN
禁止传输	Jìnzhǐ chuánshū	Transfer prohibited	TFP
禁止对国际的呼叫	Jìnzhǐ duì guójìde hūjiào	Barring of outgoing international calls	BOIC
禁止国际出局呼叫补充业务	Jìnzhǐ guójì chūjú hūjiào bǔchōng yèwù	Barring of outgoing international calls supplementary service	BOIC
紧致汇编程序程序设计系统	Jǐnzhì huìbiānchéngxù chéngxù shèjì xìtǒng	Compact assembler programming system	CAPS
禁止所有除归属国外的国际出局呼叫补充业务	Jìnzhǐ suǒyǒu chú guīshǔ guówàide guójì chūjú hūjiào bǔchōng yèwù	Barring of outgoing international calls except those directed to the home PLMN country supplementary service	BOIC-exHC
禁止所有出局呼叫补充业务	Jìnzhǐ suǒyǒu chūjú hūjiào bǔchōng yèwù	Barring of all outgoing calls supplementary service	BAOC
禁止所有对外呼叫	Jìnzhǐ suǒyǒu duìwài hūjiào	Barring of all outgoing calls	BAOC
禁止所有呼入呼叫	Jìnzhǐ suǒyǒu hūrù hūjiào	Barring of all incoming calls	BAIC
禁止所有入局呼叫	Jìnzhǐ suǒyǒu rùjú hūjiào	Barring of all incoming calls	BAIC
禁止的数字信息	Jìnzhǐde shùzì xìnxī	Restricted digital information	RDI
奇偶检验功能	Jī'ǒu jiǎnyàn gōngnéng	Parity check function	
奇偶检验码	Jī'ǒu jiǎnyàn mǎ	Parity check code	
奇偶检验位	Jī'ǒu jiǎnyàn wèi	Parity bit	
奇偶校验	Jī'ǒu jiàoyàn	Parity check	
奇偶校验码	Jī'ǒu jiàoyàn mǎ	Parity check code	
机器编码	Jīqì biānmǎ	Machine encoding	
机器代码	Jīqì dàimǎ	Machine code	
机器地址	Jīqì dìzhǐ	Machine address	MA
机器地址控制	Jīqì dìzhǐ kòngzhì	Hardware address control	HAC
机器翻译	Jīqì fānyì	Machine translation	MT
机器码	Jīqì mǎ	Machine code	
机器视觉	Jīqì shìjué	Machine vision (in SMT)	
机器学习	Jīqì xuéxí	Machine learning	

机器语言	Jīqì yǔyán	Machine language	
机器语言程序	Jīqì yǔyán chéngxù	Machine language program	MLP
机器指令	Jīqì zhǐlìng	Machine instruction	
机器指令码	Jīqì zhǐlìng mǎ	Machine instruction code	MIC
机器中心的	Jīqì zhōngxīnde	Machine-centric	
机器周期	Jīqì zhōuqī	Machine cycle	
机器人视觉	Jīqìrén shìjué	Robotic vision	
集群	Jíqún	Trunking	
集群	Jíqún	Cluster	
集群电话互连	Jíqún diànhuà hùlián	Trunked telephone connect	
集群电话互连器	Jíqún diànhuà hùliánqì	Trunked telephone connector	
集群计算	Jíqún jìsuàn	Cluster computing	
集群基站	Jíqún jīzhàn	Trunked base station	
基群链路	Jīqún liànlù	Primary link	PLK
基群速率接口	Jīqún sùlǜ jiēkǒu	Basic rate interface	BRI
基群速率接口	Jīqún sùlǜ jiēkǒu	Primary rate interface	PRI
基群速率接入	Jīqún sùlǜ jiērù	Primary rate access	PRA
基群速率用户-网络接口	Jīqún sùlǜ yònghù—wǎngluò jiēkǒu	Primary rate user-network interface	PRUNI
集群通信系统	Jíqún tōngxìn xìtǒng	Trunking communications system	
机群文件系统	Jīqún wénjiàn xìtǒng	Cluster file system	
集群无线通信系统	Jíqún wúxiàn tōngxìn xìtǒng	Trunked radio system	
集群效率	Jíqún xiàolǜ	Trunking efficiency	
集群系统	Jíqún xìtǒng	Trunked system	
集群移动电话系统	Jíqún yídòng diànhuà xìtǒng	Trunked mobile communication system	
集群移动通信	Jíqún yídòng tōngxìn	Private mobile radio	PMR
集群移动通信	Jíqún yídòng tōngxìn	Specialized mobile radio system	SMR
集群移动通信	Jíqún yídòng tōngxìn	Trunk mobile communications	
集散型控制系统	Jísàn xíng kòngzhì xìtǒng	Distributed control system	DCS
寄生单元	Jìshēng dānyuán	Parasitic element	
寄生反馈	Jìshēng fǎnkuì	Parasitic feedback	
寄生辐射	Jìshēng fúshè	Spurious radiation	
寄生调制	Jìshēng tiáozhì	Parasitic modulation	
寄生振荡	Jìshēng zhèndàng	Parasitic oscillation	
即时	Jíshí	Real time	
即时编译	Jíshí biānyì	Just in time compilation	
及时对象激活	Jíshí duìxiàng jīhuó	Just in time (JIT) object activation	
即时更新	Jíshí gēngxīn	Immediate updating (for database)	
即时更新订阅	Jíshí gēngxīn dìngyuè	Immediate updating subscriptions	
即时更新订阅服务器	Jíshí gēngxīn dìngyuè fúwùqì	Immediate updating subscription server	
即时 I/O 扫描	Jíshí I/O sǎomiáo	Real-time input/output scan	
即时交互式视频点播	Jíshí jiāohùshì shìpín diǎnbō	Interactive voice over data with instantaneous access	IVOD-i
即时模式	Jíshí móshì	Immediate mode	
即时模型	Jíshí móxíng	Instance model	
计时票	Jìshí piào	Short-term card	
计时通道	Jìshí tōngdào	Timing channel	TC
即时维护告警	Jíshí wéihù gàojǐng	Prompt maintenance alarm	PMA

即时业务	Jíshí yèwù	Demand service	
记时器	Jìshíqì	Timer	T
寄售	Jìshòu	Sale of non-return surplus	
技术办公协议	Jìshù bàngōng xiéyì	Technical office protocol	TOP
技术报告	Jìshù bàogào	Technical report	TR
技术耽误	Jìshù dānwù	Technical delay	
技术辅助中心	Jìshù fǔzhù zhōngxīn	Technical assistance center	TAC
技术攻击	Jìshù gōngjī	Technological attack	
技术规范	Jìshù guīfàn	Technical specification	TS
技术规范小组	Jìshù guīfàn xiǎozǔ	Technical specification group	TSG
奇数奇偶校验	Jīshù jīǒu jiàoyàn	Odd-parity check	OPC
基数排序	Jīshù páixù	Radix sort	
技术数据管理	Jìshù shùjù guǎnlǐ	Technical data management	TDM
技术委员会	Jìshù wěiyuánhuì	Technical committee	TC
技术委员会技术报告	Jìshù wěiyuánhuì jìshù bàogào	Technical committee technical report	TC-TR
技术委员会特别移动通信组	Jìshù wěiyuánhuì tèbié yídòng tōngxìn zǔ	Technical Committee Special Mobile Group	TC SMG
技术文档管理	Jìshù wéndàng guǎnlǐ	Technical document management	TDM
技术信息管理	Jìshù xìnxī guǎnlǐ	Technical information management	TIM
技术支持代码	Jìshù zhīchí dàimǎ	Technical support identification number	TSID
计算传递	Jìsuàn chuándì	Calculation pass	
计算对象	Jìsuàn duìxiàng	Computing object	CO
计算公式	Jìsuàn gōngshì	Calculation formula	
计算几何学	Jìsuàn jǐhéxué	Computational geometry	
计算列	Jìsuàn liè	Computed column	
计算流体力学	Jìsuàn liútǐ lìxué	Computational fluid dynamics	CFD
计算所得成员	Jìsuàn suǒdé chéngyuán	Calculated member	
计算条件	Jìsuàn tiáojiàn	Calculation condition	
计算形势拓扑学	Jìsuàn xíngshì tuòpūxué	Computational topology	
计算语言学	Jìsuàn yǔyánxué	Computational lingustics	
计算字段	Jìsuàn zìduàn	Calculated field	
计算子多维数据集	Jìsuàn ziduōwéi shùjùjí	Calculation sub-cube	
计算组成管理	Jìsuàn zǔchéng guǎnlǐ	Computing configuration management	Com.CM
计算机安全	Jìsuànjī ānquán	Computer security	COMPUSEC
计算机病毒	Jìsuànjī bìngdú	Computer virus	CV
计算机代理分销业展览会	Jìsuànjī dàilǐ fēnxiāo yè zhǎnlǎnhuì	Computer distributors exposition	COMDEX
计算机电话集成	Jìsuànjī diànhuà jíchéng	Computer-telephony integration	CTI
计算机电话综合技术	Jìsuànjī diànhuà zōnghé jìshù	Computer-telephone integration	CTI
计算机电信集成	Jìsuànjī diànxìn jíchéng	Computer telecommunication integration	CTI
计算机地址总线	Jìsuànjī dìzhǐ zǒngxiàn	Computer address bus	CAB
计算机动画技术	Jìsuànjī dònghuà jìshù	Computer animation	
计算机辅助测试	Jìsuànjī fǔzhù cèshì	Computer-aided test	CAT
计算机辅助概念设计	Jìsuànjī fǔzhù gàiniàn shèjì	Computer-aided conceptual design	CACD
计算机辅助工程	Jìsuànjī fǔzhù gōngchéng	Computer-aided engineering	CAE
计算机辅助工艺过程设计	Jìsuànjī fǔzhù gōngyì guòchéng shèjì	Computer-aided process planning (CMM)	CAPP
计算机辅助管理	Jìsuànjī fǔzhù guǎnlǐ	Computer-aided management	CAM
计算机辅助规划	Jìsuànjī fǔzhù guīhuà	Computer-aided planning	CAP

计算机辅助规划设计程序	Jìsuànjī fǔzhù guīhuà shèjì chéngxù	Computer-aided planning and designing program	
计算机辅助建筑设计	Jìsuànjī fǔzhù jiànzhù shèjì	Computer-aided architectural design	CAAD
计算机辅助教学	Jìsuànjī fǔzhù jiàoxué	Computer-aided instruction	CAI
计算机辅助几何设计	Jìsuànjī fǔzhù jǐhé shèjì	Computer-aided geometric design	CAGD
计算机辅助会计计算	Jìsuànjī fǔzhù kuàijì jìsuàn	Computer-assisted accounting	CAA
计算机辅助群体评估	Jìsuànjī fǔzhù qúntǐ pínggū	Computer-assisted mass appraisal	CAMA
计算机辅助软件工程	Jìsuànjī fǔzhù ruǎnjiàn gōngchéng	Computer-aided software engineering	CASE
计算机辅助设计	Jìsuànjī fǔzhù shèjì	Computer-aided design	CAD
计算机辅助设计/计算机辅助制造	Jìsuànjī fǔzhù shèjì/jìsuànjī fǔzhù zhìzào	Computer-aided design/computer-aided manufacturing	CAD/CAM
计算机辅助制图	Jìsuànjī fǔzhù zhìtú	Computer-aided design drawing	CADD
计算机辅助制造	Jìsuànjī fǔzhù zhìzào	Computer-aided manufacturing	CAM
计算机兼容磁带	Jìsuànjī jiānróng cídài	Computer compatible tape	CCT
计算机集成制造系统	Jìsuànjī jíchéng zhìzào xìtǒng	Computer integrated manufacturing system	CIMS
计算机模拟	Jìsuànjī mónǐ	Computer simulation	
计算机模拟输入	Jìsuànjī mónǐ shūrù	Computer analog input	CAI
计算机软件	Jìsuànjī ruǎnjiàn	Computer software	RJ
计算机软件配置项	Jìsuànjī ruǎnjiàn pèizhì xiàng	Computer software configuration item	CSCI
计算机生成图像	Jìsuànjī shēngchéng túxiàng	Computer generated graphics	CGG
计算机事件响应小组	Jìsuànjī shìjiàn xiǎngyìng xiǎozǔ	Computer incident response team	CIRT
计算机视觉	Jìsuànjī shìjué	Computer vision	
计算机视觉综合症	Jìsuànjī shìjué zōnghézhèng	Computer vision syndrome	CVS
计算机输出缩微胶片	Jìsuànjī shūchū suōwēijiāopiàn	Computer output microfilm	COM
计算机通信技术	Jìsuànjī tōngxìn jìshù	Computer telephony integration	CTI
计算机通信技术委员会	Jìsuànjī tōngxìn jìshù wěiyuánhuì	Technical Committee on Computer Communications	TCCC
计算机图形核心系统	Jìsuànjī túxíng héxīn xìtǒng	Graphical kernel system	GKS
计算机图形元文件	Jìsuànjī túxíng yuán wénjiàn	Computer graphics metafile	CGM
计算机外设模块	Jìsuànjī wàishè mókuài	Computer peripheral module	CPM
计算机外围设备	Jìsuànjī wàiwéi shèbèi	Computer peripheral device	
计算机网络	Jìsuànjī wǎngluò	Computer network	JWL
计算机网络结构技术	Jìsuànjī wǎngluò jiégòu jìshù	Computing network architecture technology	CNAT
计算机腕管综合症	Jìsuànjī wànguǎn zōnghézhèng	Carpal tunnel sydrome	CTS
计算机协同工作支持系统	Jìsuànjī xiétóng gōngzuò zhīchí xìtǒng	Computer supported cooperative work	CSCW
计算机信息处理标准	Jìsuànjī xìnxī chǔlǐ biāozhǔn	Information processing standard for computer	IPSC
计算机信息系统	Jìsuànjī xìnxī xìtǒng	Computer-based message system	CBMS
计算机应急响应小组	Jìsuànjī yìngjí xiǎngyìng xiǎozǔ	Computer emergency response team	CERT
计算机应用开发中心	Jìsuànjī yìngyòng kāifā zhōngxīn	Center for Innovative Computer Application	CICA
计算机语言	Jìsuànjī yǔyán	Computer language	
计算机支持协同工作	Jìsuànjī zhīchí xiétóng gōngzuò	Computer supported cooperative work	CSCW
计算机支持的协同工作	Jìsuànjī zhīchíde xiétóng gōngzuò	Computer supported collaborative work	CSCW
计算机直接印刷	Jìsuànjī zhíjiē yìnshuā	Computer to print	CTP
计算机子系统控制器	Jìsuànjī zixìtǒng kòngzhìqì	Computer sub-system controller	CSC
计算机，通讯和控制	Jìsuànjī, tōngxùn hé kòngzhì	Computer, communication, control	3C
计算机，指挥和控制	Jìsuànjī, zhǐhuī hé kòngzhì	Computer, command and control	C3
计算机化国际合作中心	Jìsuànjīhuà guójì hézuò zhōngxīn	Center of International Cooperation for Computerization (Japan)	CICC
计算机化交换分机	Jìsuànjīhuà jiāohuàn fēnjī	Computerized branch exchange	CBX

计算机化数字交换系统	Jìsuànjīhuà shùzì jiāohuàn xìtǒng	Computerized digital switching system	CDSS
计算机化自动编目	Jìsuànjīhuà zìdòng biānmù	Automation of bibliography through computerization	ABC
计算机间通信链路	Jìsuànjī-jiān tōngxìn liànlù	Inter-computer communication link	ICL
基态吸收	Jītài xīshōu	Ground-state absorption	GSA
积体光元件	Jītǐ guāng yuánjiàn	Integrated optical device	
集体呼叫	Jítǐ hūjiào	Group call	
集体接收	Jítǐ jiēshōu	Community reception (in satellite broadcasting)	
即拖即用	Jítuō jíyòng	Drag and drop	
旧纳档块化技术	Jiù nà dàng kuàihuà jìshù	Cabletron Spectrum (description of this network management software)	CS
纠突发错和随机错码	Jiū tūfā cuò hé suíjī cuò mǎ	Burst and random error correction codes	
纠突发错码	Jiū tūfā cuò mǎ	Burst error correction codes	
纠错	Jiūcuò	Error correction	
纠错校正码	Jiūcuò jiàozhèng mǎ	Error correction code	ECC
纠错码	Jiūcuò mǎ	Error checking (or correcting) code	ECC
纠错能力	Jiūcuò nénglì	Error correcting capability	
纠错信号	Jiūcuò xìnhào	Error correction Signal	ECS
就近分组交换	Jiùjìn fēnzǔ jiāohuàn	On-the-fly packet switching	
救生台	Jiùshēngtái	Lifeguard station	
就绪	Jiùxù	Ready	
救助	Jiùzhù	Rescue	
吉位秒	Jíwèi miǎo	Gigabits per second	Gbit/s; Gbps
基线	Jīxiàn	Baseline	
极限承载力	Jíxiàn chéngzài lì	Ultimate bearing capacity	
基线漂移	Jīxiàn piāoyí	Baseline drift	
极限强度	Jíxiàn qiángdù	Ultimate strength	
极限强度设计	Jíxiàn qiángdù shèjì	Ultimate strength design	
极限水平耐力	Jíxiàn shuǐpíng nàilì	Ultimate lateral strength	
机箱端口	Jīxiāng duānkǒu	Enclosure port	
集线器	Jíxiànqì	Hub	HUB
集线器	Jíxiànqì	Concentrator	
机械剥离工具	Jīxiè bōlí gōngjù	Mechanical stripping tool (FOC)	
机械传动噪声	Jīxiè chuándòng zàoshēng	Machine motion noise	
机械隔离装置	Jīxiè gélí zhuāngzhì	Machine protection unit	
机械互配光纤（缆）连接器	Jīxiè hùpèi guāngxiān (lǎn) liánjiē qì	Mechanically intermateable optical fiber (cable) connector	
机械交叉点	Jīxiè jiāochādiǎn	Mechanical crosspoint	
机械挤压法	Jīxiè jǐyā fǎ	Mechanical extrusion forming (FOC mfg)	MSP
机械基准面	Jīxiè jīzhǔnmiàn	Mechanical reference surface	
机械码	Jīxiè mǎ	Machine code	
机械耐磨性	Jīxiè nàimóxìng	Mechanical abrasion resistance	
机械嵌套	Jīxiè qiàntào	Mechanical nesting	
机械时间常数	Jīxiè shíjiān chángshù	Mechanical time constant (of an indicating instrument)	
机械语言	Jīxiè yǔyán	Machine language	
机械轴	Jīxiè zhóu	Mechanical axis	
机械转换开关	Jīxiè zhuǎnhuàn kāiguān	Mechanical switch	
机械式光开关	Jīxiè-shì guāng kāiguān	Mechanical optical switch	

机械式光偏折器	Jīxiè-shì guāng piānzhéqì	Mechanical optical deflector	
机械式光扫描器	Jīxiè-shì guāng sǎomiáoqì	Mechanical optical scanner	
机械式光调变器	Jīxiè-shì guāng tiáobiànqì	Mechanical optical modulator	
机械式衰减器	Jīxiè-shì shuāijiǎnqì	Mechanical attenuator	
机械式装卸过桥	Jīxiè-shì zhuāngxiè guòqiáo	Mechanical loading and unloading foot walk	
极性	Jíxìng	Polarity	
脊形波导	Jǐxíng bōdǎo	Ridge waveguide	
极性交替反转双极性码	Jíxìng jiāotì fǎnzhuǎn shuāng jíxìng mǎ	Alternate mark inversion coding	AMI
脊形喇叭天线	Jǐxíng lǎba tiānxiàn	Ridged horn antenna	
极性调制器	Jíxìng tiáozhìqì	Polarity modulator	
记忆驻留程序	Jìyì zhùliú chéngxù	Residential program	
记忆驻留软件	Jìyì zhùliú ruǎnjiàn	Memory resident software	
基因连锁	Jīyīn liánsuǒ	Epistatic interaction	
基音同步更新码激励线性预测	Jīyīn tóngbù gēngxīn mǎ jīlì xiànxìng yùcè	Pitch synchronous innovation-code excited linear prediction	PSI-CELP
基音周期波形	Jīyīn zhōuqī bōxíng	Pitch-cycle waveform	PCW
基于案例推理	Jīyú ànlì tuīlǐ	Case-based reasoning	
基于 ATM 的无源光网络	Jīyú ATM de wúyuán guāng wǎngluò	Passive optical network based on ATM	A-PON
基于标签探测	Jīyú biāoqiān tàncè	Ticket-based probing	TBP
基于比特的符合条件的业务量失真率	Jīyú bǐtède fúhé tiáojiànde yèwù liáng shīzhēn lǜ	Bit-load condition-based traffic distortion rate	BCTDR
基于策略路由	Jīyú cèlüè lùyóu	Policy-based routing	
基于 CGI 攻击	Jīyú CGI gōngjī	Common gateway interface-based attack (IPsec)	
基于超图模型的离群点检测方法	Jīyú chāo tú móxíngde líqún diǎn jiǎncè fāngfǎ	Hypergraph-based outlier test	HOT
基于超媒体的职能计算机辅助教学	Jīyú chāoméitǐde zhínéng jìsuànjī fǔzhù jiàoxué	Hypermedia intelligent computer-based instruction	HICAI
基于代理软件服务框架	Jīyú dàilǐ ruǎnjiàn fúwù kuàngjià	Agent-based software service framework	ASF
基于单播的最小延时	Jīyú dānbōde zuìxiǎo yánshí	Minimum delay protocol for unicast	MDPU
基于电脑的小型用户交换机	Jīyú diànnǎode xiǎoxíng yònghù jiāohuànjī	Personal computer-based private branch exchange	PC-based PBX
基于对象分析合成编码	Jīyú duìxiàng fēnxī héchéng biānmǎ	Object-based analysis-synthesis coding	OBASC
基于对象的	Jīyú duìxiàngde	Object-based	
基于仿真设计	Jīyú fǎngzhēn shèjì	Simulation-based design	SBD
基于范例推理	Jīyú fànlì tuīlǐ	Case-based reasoning	CBR
基于发射天线分集的空间时间分组编码分集	Jīyú fāshè tiānxiàn fēnjíde kōngjiān shíjiān fēnzǔ biānmǎ fēnjí	Space time transmit diversity (space time block coding based on transmit antenna diversity)	STTD
基于构件的软件开发技术	Jīyú gòujiànde ruǎnjiàn kāifā jìshù	Component-based software development technology	CBSDT
基于光纤的分布数据接口	Jīyú guāngxiānde fēnbù shùjù jiēkǒu	Fiber-based distributed data interface	FDDI
基于关联性的路由算法	Jīyú guānlián xìngde lùyóu suànfǎ	Associativity-based routing	ABR
基于规则约束着色 Petri 网	Jīyú guīzé yuēshù zhuosè Petri wǎng	Rule-based colored Petri net	RCPN
基于规则的安全策略	Jīyú guīzéde ānquán cèlüè	Rule-based security policy (IPsec)	
基于滑动窗口的情景规则挖掘算法	Jīyú huádòng chuāngkǒude qíngjǐng guīzé wājué suànfǎ	Episode rule discovery by sliding windows	ERDISWIN
基于计算机的训练	Jīyú jìsuànjīde xùnliàn	Computer-based training	CBT
基于角色访问控制	Jīyú juésè fǎngwèn kòngzhì	Role-based access control	RBAC

基于角色工作流模型	Jīyú juésè gōngzuòliú móxíng	Role-based workflow model	
基于客户端设备的 VPN	Jīyú kèhù duān shèbèide VPN	Customer premises equipment-based VPN	
基于流量工程扩展的资源预留协议	Jīyú liúliàng gōngchéng kuòzhǎnde zīyuán yùliú xiéyì	Resource reservation protocol-traffic engineering (IETF usage)	RSVP-TE
基于路径的汇集	Jīyú lùjìngde huìjí	Path-based aggregation	
基于目标的 IDS	Jīyú mùbiāode IDS	Target-based IDS	
基于内容的图像检索技术	Jīyú nèiróngde túxiàng jiǎnsuǒ jìshù	Content-based image retrieval	CBIR
基于散列的消息验证代码	Jīyú sànliède xiāoxi yànzhèng dàimǎ	Hash-based message authentication code	HMAC
基于身份的安全策略	Jīyú shēnfende ānquán cèlüè	Identity-based security policy (IPsec)	
基于时分双工的以太数字用户线	Jīyú shífèn shuānggōngde yǐtài shùzì yònghùxiàn	Time division duplex-based ethernet digital subscriber line	TDD-EDSL
基于实例的机器翻译	Jīyú shílìde jīqì fānyì	Example-based machine translation	EBMT
基于网络的 VPN	Jīyú wǎngluòde VPN	Network-based VPN (virtual private network)	
基于网络的训练	Jīyú wǎngluòde xùnliàn	Web-based training	WBT
基于 Web 的企业管理	Jīyú Web de qǐyè guǎnlǐ	Web-based enterprise management	WBEM
基于线性关联技术	Jīyú xiànxìng guānlián jìshù	Linear-based correlation method	
基于消息的	Jīyú xiāoxide	Message-based	
基于心树路由算法	Jīyú xīn shù lùyóu suànfǎ	Core-based tree routing algorithm	
基于行为的汇集	Jīyú xíngwéide huìjí	Behavior-based aggregation	
基于信元	Jīyú xìnyuán	Cell-based	
基于优先级封锁-继承	Jīyú yōuxiānjí fēngsuǒ—jìchéng	Priority-based block and inheritance	PBBI
基于优先级的事务重启	Jīyú yōuxiānjíde shìwù chóngqǐ	Priority-based transaction restart	PBTS
基于约束 LSP	Jīyú yuēshù LSP	Constraint-based LSP (label switching path)	CR-LSP
基于帧和符合条件的业务量失真比	Jīyú zhèng hé fúhé tiáojiànde yèwùliàng shīzhēn bǐ	Frame-based compliant traffic distortion ratio	FCTDR
基于政策的网络管理	Jīyú zhèngcède wǎngluò guǎnlǐ	Policy-based network management	PBNM
基于帧的通用信元速率算法	Jīyú zhèngde tōngyòng xìnyuán sùlǜ suànfǎ	Frame-based generic cell rate algorithm	F-GCRA
基于主机的 IDS	Jīyú zhǔjīde IDS	Host-based IDS	
基于自集分割的零树小波编码算法	Jīyú zìjí fēngēde língshù xiǎobō biānmǎ suànfǎ	Subset-division-based zerotree wavelet coding algorithm	SDZW
基于字节的 IP 包吞吐量	Jīyú zìjiéde IP bāo tūntǔliàng	Octet-based IP packet throughput	IPOT
基于组件建模	Jīyú zǔjiàn jiànmó	Component-based modeling	
基元	Jīyuán	Primitive	
积云对流	Jīyún duìliú	Cumulus convection	
机载测距雷达	Jīzài cèjù léidá	Airborne range-finding radar	
机载电台	Jīzài diàntái	Aircraft station	
机载警戒雷达	Jīzài jǐngjiè léidá	Airborne warning radar	
机载雷达	Jīzài léidá	Airborne radar	
机载相控阵天线雷达	Jīzài xiàngkòng zhèn tiānxiàn léidá	Electronically agile radar	EAR
机载自卫电子战系统	Jīzài zìwèi diànzǐzhàn xìtǒng	Airborne self-protection electronic warfare system	
极窄脉冲雷达	Jízhǎi màichōng léidá	Extra-short-pulse radar	
极窄视频脉冲通过电路	Jízhǎi shìpín màichōng tōngguò diànlù	High-video pass circuit	HVP
基站	Jīzhàn	Base station	BS
基站	Jīzhàn	Base transmitter station	BTS
基站被叫	Jīzhàn bèi jiào	Base station terminating	BT
基站标识码	Jīzhàn biāozhì mǎ	Base station identity code	BSIC

基站测试单元	Jīzhàn cèshì dānyuán	Base station test unit	BSTU
基站测试集成件	Jīzhàn cèshì jíchéng jiàn	Base station test assembly	BSTA
基站测试模块	Jīzhàn cèshì mókuài	Base station test block	BSTB
基站测试设备	Jīzhàn cèshì shèbèi	Base station sub-system test equipment	BSSTE
基站传输子系统	Jīzhàn chuánshū zixìtǒng	Base station transmission sub-system	BTS
基站电话控制单元	Jīzhàn diànhuà kòngzhì dānyuán	Base station telephonic control element	BSTCE
基站发射器功率	Jīzhàn fāshèqì gōnglǜ	Base station transmitter power	BSTXPWR
基站管理应用部分	Jīzhàn guǎnlǐ yìngyòng bùfen	Base station management application part	BSSMAP
基站管理器	Jīzhàn guǎnlǐqì	Base station manager	BSM
基站接口	Jīzhàn jiēkǒu	Base station interface	BSI
基站接口设备	Jīzhàn jiēkǒu shèbèi	Base station interface equipment	BIE
基站控制功能（模块）	Jīzhàn kòngzhì gōngnéng (mókuài)	Base station control function (module)	BCF
基站控制切换	Jīzhàn kòngzhì qiēhuàn	Base station-controlled handoff	BCHO
基站控制器	Jīzhàn kòngzhìqì	Base station controller	BSC
基站模块	Jīzhàn mókuài	Base station module	BSM
基站区	Jīzhàn qū	Base station area	
基站色码	Jīzhàn sèmǎ	Base transceiver station color code	BCC
基站识别码	Jīzhàn shíbié mǎ	Base station identification	BSID
基站收发信机	Jīzhàn shōufā xìn jī	Base transceiver station	BTS
基站收发信机色码	Jīzhàn shōufāxìnjī sèmǎ	Base transceiver station color code	BCC
基站收发信机识别码	Jīzhàn shōufāxìnjī shíbié mǎ	Base transceiver station identity code	BSIC
基站收发信机系统	Jīzhàn shōufāxìnjī xìtǒng	Base station transceiver system	BTS
基站收发信台	Jīzhàn shōufāxìntái	Base transceiver station	BTS
基站收发信台管理	Jīzhàn shōufāxìntái guǎnlǐ	Base transceiver station management	BTSM
基站系统	Jīzhàn xìtǒng	Base station system	BSS
基站系统管理应用部分	Jīzhàn xìtǒng guǎnlǐ yìngyòng bùfen	Base station system management application part	BSSMAP
基站系统应用部分	Jīzhàn xìtǒng yìngyòng bùfen	Base station system application part	BSSAP
基站系统运营和维护应用部分	Jīzhàn xìtǒng yùnyíng hé wéihù yìngyòng bùfen	Base station system operation and maintenance application part	BSSOMAP
基站移动应用部分	Jīzhàn yídòng yìngyòng bùfen	Base station mobile application part	BSMAP
基站应用部分	Jīzhàn yìngyòng bùfen	Base station application part	BSSAP
基站应用部分加	Jīzhàn yìngyòng bùfen jiā	Base station system application part+	BSSAP+
基站主叫	Jīzhàn zhǔ jiào	Base station originating	BO
基站子系统	Jīzhàn zixìtǒng	Base station sub-system	BSS
基站子系统	Jīzhàn zixìtǒng	Base station sub-system	BSS
基站子系统操作与维护应用部分	Jīzhàn zixìtǒng cāozuò yǔ wéihù yìngyòng bùfen	Base station system operation and maintenance application part	BSSOMAP
基站子系统 GPRS 协议	Jīzhàn zixìtǒng GPRS xiéyì	Base station system GPRS protocol	BSSGP
基站子系统管理应用部分	Jīzhàn zixìtǒng guǎnlǐ yìngyòng bùfen	Base station sub-system management application part	BSSMAP
基站子系统应用部分	Jīzhàn zixìtǒng yìngyòng bùfen	Base station sub-system application part	BSSAP
记账	Jìzhàng	Mark up (in price) (verb and noun)	MU
记帐差错概率	Jìzhàng chācuò gàilǜ	Billing error probabillity	
记帐管理点	Jìzhàng guǎnlǐ diǎn	Billing management point	BMP
记帐卡呼叫	Jìzhàng kǎ hūjiào	Accounting card call	ACC
记帐信用卡	Jìzhàng xìnyòngkǎ	Account credit card	ACC
几兆比特数据交换业务	Jǐzhào bǐtè shùjù jiāohuàn yèwù	Switched multimegabit data service	SMDS

极值	Jízhí	Extreme value	
基值	Jīzhí	Benchmark	
极值分布	Jízhí fēnbù	Extreme value distribution	
极值计数	Jízhí jìshù	Extreme counting	EC
极值统计	Jízhí tǒngjì	Statistics of extremes	
基值限幅	Jīzhí xiànfú	Base limiting	
基值限幅器	Jīzhí xiànfúqì	Base limiter	
集中	Jízhōng	Concentration (in switching)	
集中电阻抑制器	Jízhōng diànzǔ yìzhìqì	Concentrated resistive suppressor	
集中叠加功能	Jízhōng diéjiā gōngnéng	Centralized overlay function	
集中监控设备	Jízhōng jiānkòng shèbèi	Centralized supervisory and control equipment	CSC
集中监视和控制设备	Jízhōng jiānshì hé kòngzhì shèbèi	Centralized supervisory and control equipment	CSC
集中交换网络控制	Jízhōng jiāohuàn wǎngluò kòngzhì	Central switching-network control	CSC
集中控制	Jízhōng kòngzhì	Centralized control	
集中模式	Jízhōng móshì	Hubbed mode	
集中业务控制	Jízhōng yèwù kòngzhì	Centralized service control	CSC
集中质量体系	Jízhōng zhìliàng tǐxì	Lumped mass system	
集中自动处理记帐	Jízhōng zìdòng chǔlǐ jìzhàng	Centralized automatic message accounting	CAMA
集中器	Jízhōngqì	Concentrator	
集中式处理	Jízhōng-shì chǔlǐ	Centralized processing	
集中式多点	Jízhōng-shì duōdiǎn	Centralized multipoint	
集中式基于路由的 IP 交换	Jízhōng-shì jīyú lùyóude IP jiāohuàn	Aggregate route-based IP switching	ARIS
集中式实时数据库	Jízhōng-shì shíshí shùjùkù	Centralized real-time database	CRTDB
集中式数据库	Jízhōng-shì shùjùkù	Centralized database	CDB
集中式帧定位信号	Jízhōngshì zhèng dìngwèi xìnhào	Bunched frame alignment signal	
集中式自动电报计费	Jízhōng-shì zìdòng diànbào jìfèi	Centralized automatic message accounting	CAMA
集中式自动通话记帐系统	Jízhōng-shì zìdòng tōnghuà jìzhàng xìtǒng	Centralized automatic message accounting system	CAMA
集中性	Jízhōngxìng	Centrality	
即装即用	Jízhuāng jíyòng	Plug-and-play	PNP
基准参考时钟	Jīzhǔn cānkǎo shízhōng	Primary reference clock	PRC
基准参考源	Jīzhǔn cānkǎoyuán	Primary reference source	PRS
基准测试	Jīzhǔn cèshì	Benchmark test	
基准测试程序数值	Jīzhǔn cèshì chéngxù shùzhí	Benchmark test program values	
基准程序	Jīzhǔn chéngxù	Benchmark	
基准电压	Jīzhǔn diànyā	Reference voltage	
基准监控概念	Jīzhǔn jiānkòng gàiniàn	Reference monitor concept	
基准面直径	Jīzhǔn miànzhíjìng	Reference surface diameter	
基准面中心	Jīzhǔn miànzhōngxīn	Reference surface center	
基准评测	Jīzhǔn píngcè	Benchmark test	
基准频率	Jīzhǔn pínlǜ	Frequency reference	
基准试验方法	Jīzhǔn shìyàn fāngfǎ	Reference test method	RTM
基准时钟	Jīzhǔn shízhōng	Primary reference clock	PRC
基准时钟	Jīzhǔn shízhōng	Reference clock	
基准数据	Jīzhǔn shùjù	Reference data	
基准条件	Jīzhǔn tiáojiàn	Reference condition	
基准钟	Jīzhǔn zhōng	Primary reference clock	PRC

基准轴	Jīzhǔn zhóu	Reference boresight (axis)	
基准主时钟	Jīzhǔn zhǔ shízhōng	Primary resource clock	PRC
基准桩	Jīzhǔn zhuāng	Reference studs	
基准阻抗	Jīzhǔn zǔkàng	Reference impedance	
基准点	Jīzhǔndiǎn	Fiducial (in SMT)	
吉字节	Jízìjié	Gigabyte	GB
集总元件隔离器	Jízǒng yuánjiàn gélíqì	Lumped-element isolator	
集总元件环行器	Jízǒng yuánjiàn huánxíngqì	Lumped-element circulator	
卷标	Juàn biāo	Volume label	
卷动	Juǎndòng	Scroll (verb)	
卷积	Juǎnjī	Convolution	
卷积码	Juànjī mǎ	Convolutional code	
卷积码的约束长度	Juànjī mǎde yuēshù chángdù	Constraint length of the convolutional code	K
卷积器	Juǎnjīqì	Convolutor	
聚苯乙烯	Jùběnyǐxī	Polystyrene	PS
句柄	Jùbǐng	Handle	
聚丙烯	Jùbǐngxī	Polypropylene	
局部变量	Júbù biànliàng	Local variable	
局部磁盘缓存	Júbù cípán huǎncún	Local caching	
局部对象	Júbù duìxiàng	Local object	
局部方位	Júbù fāngwèi	Local bearing	
局部回路	Júbù huílù	Local loop	
局部 ID 号码类型	Júbù ID hàomǎ lèixíng	Partial ID number type	PID
局部流	Júbù liú	Local flow	
局部路径索引	Júbù lùjìng suǒyǐn	Local path index (in XML)	LPI
局部路由标记分配协议	Júbù lùyóu biāojì fēnpèi xiéyì	Common route-label distribution protocol	CR-LDP
局部数字信息交换	Júbù shùzì xìnxī jiāohuàn	Local digital message exchange	LDME
局部探测器数据分组	Júbù tàncèqì shùjù fēnzǔ	Local explorer packet	
局部特化	Júbù tèhuà	Partial specialization	
局部通光检测	Júbù tōngguāng jiǎncè	Local injection and detection (FOC)	LID
局部通信网络	Júbù tōngxìn wǎngluò	Local area communications network	LACN
局部信息计费	Júbù xìnxī jìfèi	Local message metering system	LMM
局部业务区域	Júbù yèwù qūyù	Localized service area	LSA
局部业务量过滤	Júbù yèwùliàng guòlǜ	Local traffic filtering	
局部意义	Júbù yìyì	Local significance	
局部终止	Júbù zhōngzhǐ	Local termination	
局部总线	Júbù zǒngxiàn	Local bus	LB
局部坐标系	Júbù zuòbiāo xì	Parcel coordinate system	
局部的	Júbùde	Local	
局侧终端	Júcè zhōngduān	Local terminal	LT
聚簇	Jùcù	Clustering	
局地的错误	Júdìde cuòwù	Local error	
拒动	Jùdòng	Failure to operate (electrical term)	
局端	Júduān	Central office termination	COT
局端 ADSL 收发单元	Júduān ADSL shōufā dānyuán	Central office ADSL transmission unit	ATU-C
局端环路接口	Júduān huánlù jiēkǒu	Loop interface-central office end	U-C

局端 V 参考点	Júduān V cānkǎo diǎn	Central office V reference point	V-C
局端线路 U 参考点	Júduān xiànlù U cānkǎo diǎn	Central office line U reference point	U-C
局端线路 U 参考点 2	Júduān xiànlù U cānkǎo diǎn 2	Central office line U reference point 2	U-C2
局端机	Júduānjī	Central office terminal	COT
聚对苯二甲酸丁二醇酯	Jùduìběn èrjiǎsuān dīng'èrchúnzhǐ	Polybutylene terephthalate	PBT
决策和支持系统	Juécè hé zhīchí xìtǒng	Decision and support system	DSS
决策矩阵	Juécè jǔzhèn	Decision matrix	
决策树	Juécè shù	Decision tree	
决策指标体系	Juécè zhǐbiāo tǐxì	Decision index system	
决策支持	Juécè zhīchí	Decision support	
决策支持系统	Juécè zhīchí xìtǒng	Decision support system	DSS
决策智能化	Juécè zhìnénghuà	Decision intelligence	DI
绝对参考频率	Juéduì cānkǎo pínlǜ	Absolute frequency reference	AFR
绝对磁导率	Juéduì cídǎolǜ	Absolute magnetic permeability	
绝对单偏振光纤	Juéduì dānpiānzhèn guāngxiān	Absolute single polarization optical fiber	
绝对电压电平	Juéduì diànyā diànpíng	Absolute voltage level	
绝对地图精度	Juéduì dìtú jīngdù	Absolute map accuracy	
绝对地址	Juéduì dìzhǐ	Absolute address	
绝对发光率阀	Juéduì fāguāng lǜ fá	Absolute luminance threshold	
绝对发光度曲线	Juéduì fāguāngdù qūxiàn	Absolute luminosity curve	
绝对放大率	Juéduì fàngdàlǜ	Absolute magnification	
绝对功率电平	Juéduì gōnglǜ diànpíng	Absolute power level	
绝对汇编程序	Juéduì huìbiān chéngxù	Absolute assembler	AA
绝对汇编语言	Juéduì huìbiān yǔyán	Absolute assembly language	AAL
绝对精度	Juéduì jīngdù	Absolute accuracy	
绝对基准频率	Juéduì jīzhǔn pínlǜ	Absolute frequency reference	AFR
绝对亮度阀	Juéduì liàngdù fá	Absolute luminance threshold	
绝对命令	Juéduì mìnglìng	Absolute order	
绝对模式	Juéduì móshì	Absolute mode	
绝对频道号	Juéduì píndào hào	Absolute radio frequency channel number	ARFCN
绝对频率参考	Juéduì pínlǜ cānkǎo	Absolute frequency reference	AFR
绝对射频频道号	Juéduì shèpín píndào hào	Absolute radio frequency channel number	ARFCN
绝对射频信道号	Juéduì shèpín xìndàohào	Absolute RF channel number	ARFCN
绝对矢量	Juéduì shǐliàng	Absolute vector	
绝对位置	Juéduì wèizhì	Absolute position	
绝对位置	Juéduì wèizhì	Explicit position	
绝对温度	Juéduì wēndù	Absolute temperature	
绝对误差	Juéduì wùchā	Absolute error	
绝对无线载频号	Juéduì wúxiàn zàipín hào	Absolute radio frequency channel number	ARFCN
绝对相移键控	Juéduì xiāngyí jiànkòng	Absolute phase shift keying	APSK
绝对信号延时	Juéduì xìnhào yánshí	Absolute signal delay	
绝对增益	Juéduì zēngyì	Absolute gain (of an antenna)	
绝对折射率	Juéduì zhéshèlǜ	Absolute refractive index	
绝对坐标	Juéduì zuòbiāo	Absolute coordinate	
绝热变化	Juérè biànhuà	Adiabatic change	
绝热过程	Juérè guòchéng	Adiabatic process	

绝热器件	Juérè qìjiàn	Adiabatic device	
绝热图	Juérè tú	Adiabatic chart	
角色	Juésè	Role	
角色扮演游戏	Juésè bànyǎn yóuxì	Role playing game (computer game)	RPG
角色层次	Juésè céngcì	Role hierarchy	
角色集	Juésè jí	Role set	
角色任务指派	Juésè rènwu zhǐpài	Role-task assignment	
决议	Juéyì	Resolve	
绝缘	Juéyuán	Insulation	
绝缘层信移连接件	Juéyuán céng xìnyí liánjiē jiàn	Insulation displacement connection	IDC
绝缘电阻	Juéyuán diànzǔ	Insulation resistance	
绝缘故障	Juéyuán gùzhàng	Insulation fault	
绝缘监视和报警装置	Juéyuán jiānshì hé bàojǐng zhuāngzhì	Insulation monitoring and warning device	
绝缘结构	Juéyuán jiégòu	Insulation system	
绝缘试验	Juéyuán shìyàn	Dielectric test	
绝缘栅场效应晶体管	Juéyuán zhà chǎng xiàoyìng jīngtǐguǎn	Insulated gate field effect transistor	IGFET
绝缘栅双极型晶体管	Juéyuán zhà shuāngjíxíng jīngtǐguǎn	Insulated gate bipolar transistor	IGBT
绝缘体	Juéyuántǐ	Insulator	
绝缘体硅片	Juéyuántǐ guīpiàn	Silicon-on-insulator	SOI
句法结构	Jùfǎ jiégòu	Syntax	
聚光透镜	Jùguāng tòujìng	Condenser lens	
聚合	Jùhé	Aggregation	
聚合包装	Jùhé bāozhuāng	Aggregation wrapper	
聚合查询	Jùhé cháxún	Aggregate query	
聚合点	Jùhé diǎn	Rendezvous point	RP
聚合函数	Jùhé hánshù	Aggregate function	
聚合前缀	Jùhé qiánzhuì	Aggregation prefix	
聚合信道	Jùhé xìndào	Aggregate channel	
聚合体光纤	Jùhétǐ guāngxiān	Polymer optical fiber	POF
聚合物光纤	Jùhéwù guāngxiān	Polymer optical fiber	POF
聚合物光子禁带光纤	Jùhéwù guāngzǐ jìn dài guāngxiān	Polymer photonic band gap fiber	
聚合物光子晶体光纤	Jùhéwù guāngzǐ jīngtǐ guāngxiān	Polymer photonic crystal optical fiber	PPCF
聚合物微结构光纤	Jùhéwù wēi jiégòu guāngxiān	Micro-structured polymer optical fiber	MPOF
聚集	Jùjí	Clustering	
聚集服务器	Jùjí fúwùqì	Rendezvous server	
聚集索引	Jùjí suǒyǐn	Clustered index	
聚甲基丙烯酸甲酯	Jùjiǎjī bǐngxīsuān jiǎzhǐ	Polymethyl methacrylate	PMMA
局间线路	Jú-jiān xiànlù	Interoffice line	
局间中继光通讯系统	Jú-jiān zhōngjì guāng tōngxùn xìtǒng	Local interoffice optical communication system	
聚焦反射器	Jùjiāo fǎnshèqì	Focusing reflector	
拒绝	Jùjué	Reject(ion)	REJ
拒绝	Jùjué	Deny	
拒绝掉电	Jùjué diàodiàn	Reject power down	REJPDN
拒绝地址解析	Jùjué dìzhǐ jiěxī	Location reject message	LRJ
拒绝服务	Jùjué fúwù	Denial of service	
拒绝服务攻击	Jùjué fúwù gōngjī	Denial of service attack	DoS

拒绝改变呼叫特性	Jùjué gǎibiàn hūjiào tèxìng	Call modification reject (ISUP message)	CMRJ
拒绝连接	Jùjué liánjiē	Connection refused (in SS7)	CREF
拒绝原因	Jùjué yuányīn	Reject reason	
拒绝注册	Jùjué zhùcè	Registration reject message	RRJ
聚类	Jùlèi	Cluster	
聚类分析	Jùlèi fēnxī	Cluster analysis	
距离编码器	Jùlí biānmǎqì	Range encoder (radar term)	
距离标校	Jùlí biāojiào	Range calibration	
距离标志	Jùlí biāozhì	Range marker	
距离波门拖引干扰	Jùlí bōmén tuōyǐn gānrǎo	Range gate walk-off jamming	
距离度量	Jùlí dùliàng	Distance measure	
距离分辨率	Jùlí fēnbiànlǜ	Range resolution	
距离矢量路由算法	Jùlí shǐliàng lùyóu suànfǎ	Distance vector routing algorithm	
距离矢量组播路由协议	Jùlí shǐliàng zǔbō lùyóu xiéyì	Distance vector multicast routing protocol	DVMRP
距离衰减函数	Jùlí shuāijiǎn hánshù	Distance-decay function	
距离向量多点广播路由选择协议	Jùlí xiàngliàng duō diǎn guǎngbō lùyóu xuǎnzé xiéyì	Distance vector multicast routing protocol	DVMRP
距离向量路由选择算法	Jùlí xiàngliàng lùyóu xuǎnzé suànfǎ	Distance vector routing algorithm	
距离向量组播路由协议	Jùlí xiàngliàng zǔbō lùyóu xiéyì	Distance vector multicast routing protocol	DVMRP
距离噪声	Jùlí zàoshēng	Range noise	
距离振幅补偿	Jùlí zhènfú bǔcháng	Distance amplitude compensation	
距离振幅曲线	Jùlí zhènfú qūxiàn	Distance amplitude curve	
巨量平行处理架构	Jùliàng píngxíng chǔlǐ jiàgòu	Massive parallel processing	MPP
距离-方位显示器	Jùlí—fāngwèi xiǎnshìqì	Range-azimuth indicator	
聚氯乙烯	Jùlǜyǐxī	Polyvinyl chloride	PVC
巨媒体	Jùméitǐ	Megamedia	
均方信噪比	Jūn fāng xìn zào bǐ	Mean square signal-to-noise	MSSN
均方根	Jūn fānggēn	Radical mean square	Rms
均方根	Jūn fānggēn	Root mean square	RMS
均方根检波器	Jūn fānggēn jiǎnbōqì	Root-mean square detector	
均方根误差	Jūn fānggēn wùchā	Root mean square error	RMSE
均方根值	Jūn fānggēn zhí	Root mean square (rms) value	
均方根值检波器	Jūn fānggēn zhí jiǎnbōqì	Root mean square detector	RMS
均方根-波纹系数	Jūn fānggēn-bōwén xìshù	Root mean square (rms)-ripple factor	
均步的	Jūnbùde	Mesochronous	
均等系数	Jūnděng xìshù	Uniformity coefficient	
局内信令	Jú-nèi xìnlìng	Intra-exchange signaling	
局内综合定时供给系统	Jú-nèi zōnghé dìngshí gōngjǐ xìtǒng	Building integrated timing supply	BITS
军工产品定型委员会	Jūngōng chǎnpǐn dìngxíng wěiyuánhuì	Military Industrial Product Design Finalization Commission	
均衡	Jūnhéng	Equalize	EQ
均衡层次结构	Jūnhéng céngcì jiégòu	Balanced hierarchy	
均衡网络	Jūnhéng wǎngluò	Equalization network	
均衡器	Jūnhéngqì	Equalizer	
均匀编码	Jūnyún biānmǎ	Uniform encoding	
均匀波导	Jūnyún bōdǎo	Uniform waveguide	
均匀传输线	Jūnyún chuánshūxiàn	Uniform transmission line	

均匀分布	Jūnyún fēnbù	Uniform distribution	
均匀量化	Jūnyún liànghuà	Uniform quantizing	
均匀流	Jūnyún liú	Uniform flow	
均匀流公式	Jūnyún liú gōngshì	Uniform-flow equation	
均匀性	Jūnyúnxìng	Flatness	FL
聚偏二氟乙烯	Jùpiān èrfúyǐxī	Polyvinylidene fluoride	PVDF
句式	Jùshì	Phrasing	
聚四氟乙烯	Jùsìfúyǐxī	Teflon	
聚碳酸酯	Jùtànsuānzhǐ	Polycarbonate	PC
具体句法	Jùtǐ jùfǎ	Concrete syntax	
具体类	Jùtǐ lèi	Concrete class	
聚酰胺	Jùxiān'àn	Polyamide	
具现化	Jùxiànhuà	Instantiated (usually for a template)	
具现化实体	Jùxiànhuà shítǐ	Instantiation (usually for a template)	
具现体	Jùxiàntǐ	Instantiation (usually for a template)	
矩形波调制	Jǔxíng bō tiáozhì	Rectangular-wave modulation	RWM
矩形波导	Jǔxíng bōdǎo	Rectangular waveguide	
巨型磁阻	Jù-xíng cízǔ	Giant magnetoresistive	GMR
矩形密度模型	Jǔxíng mìdù móxíng	Rectangular density model	
矩形软波导	Jǔxíng ruǎn bōdǎo	Rectangular flexible waveguide	
矩形椭圆波导变换器	Jǔxíng tuǒyuán bōdǎo biànhuànqì	Rectangular-elliptical waveguide transformer	
矩形阵	Jǔxíng zhèn	Rectangular array	
聚乙烯	Jùyǐxī	Polyethylene	PE
局用数字终端	Jú-yòng shùzì zhōngduān	Host digital terminal	HDT
具有可适应比特分配的自适应预测编码	Jùyǒu kěshìyìng bǐtè fēnpèide zìshìyìng yùcè biānmǎ	Adaptive predictive coding with adaptive bit allocation	APC-AB
具有自适应比特分配的自适应预测编码	Jùyǒu zìshìyìng bǐtè fēnpèide zìshìyìng yùcè biānmǎ	Adaptive predictive coding with adaptive bit allocation	APC-AB
局域边缘总线	Júyù biānyuán zǒngxiàn	Local peripheral bus	
局域多点分布式系统	Júyù duōdiǎn Fēnbùshì xìtǒng	Local multipoint distributed system	LMDS
局域互连	Júyù hùlián	Local interconnect	
局域加强系统	Júyù jiāqiáng xìtǒng	Local area augmentation system	LAAS
局域网络	Júyù wǎngluò	Local area network	LAN
矩圆波导变换器	Jǔyuán bōdǎo biànhuànqì	Rectangular-elliptical waveguide transformer	
局域网	Júyùwǎng	Local area network	LAN
局域网仿真	Júyùwǎng fǎngzhēn	Local area network emulation	LANE
局域网仿真地址解析协议	Júyùwǎng fǎngzhēn dìzhǐ jiěxī xiéyì	LAN emulation address resolution protocol	LE-ARP
局域网仿真服务器	Júyùwǎng fǎngzhēn fúwùqì	Local area network emulation server	LES
局域网仿真客户机	Júyùwǎng fǎngzhēn kèhùjī	Local area network emulation client	LEC
局域网唤醒	Júyùwǎng huànxǐng	Wake on LAN	WOL
局域网接入点	Júyùwǎng jiērù diǎn	Local area network access point	LAP
局域网驱动	Júyùwǎng qūdòng	Local area network drivers	
局域网协议	Júyùwǎng xiéyì	Local area protocol (IEEE usage)	
矩阵	Jǔzhèn	Matrix	
矩阵乘法	Jǔzhèn chéngfǎ	Matrix multiplication	
矩阵分解	Jǔzhèn fēnjiě	Matrix decomposition	

矩阵聚类	Jǔzhèn jùlèi	Matrix clustering	
居中	Jūzhōng	Centered	
句子可懂度	Jùzi kědǒngdù	Sentence intelligibility	

K

K 桌面环境	K zhuōmiàn huánjìng	K desktop environment (in UNIX)	KDE
卡到卡交错存取	Kǎ dào kǎ jiāocuò cúnqǔ	Card-to-card interleaving	C2C
卡读写器/编码器	Kǎ dúxiěqì/biānmǎqì	Card reader/encoder	CR/E
喀声	Kā shēng	Click (in telecommunications)	
卡支持器检验信息	Kǎ zhīchíqì jiǎnyàn xìnxī	Card holder verification information	CHV
卡尔曼滤波	Kǎ-ěr-màn lǜbō	Kalman filter	
开最短路径优先组播路由协议	Kāi zuìduǎn lùjìng yōuxiān zǔbō lùyóu xiéyì	Multicast open shortest path first protocol	MOSPF
开槽同轴平衡/不平衡变换器	Kāicáo tóngzhóu pínghéng/bùpínghéng biànhuànqì	Slotted coaxial balun (balanced/unbalanced device)	
开槽盘天线	Kāicáopán tiānxiàn	Slotted panel	
开槽线	Kāicáoxiàn	Slotted line	
开槽线架	Kāicáoxiàn jià	Slotted line carriage	
开窗	Kāichuāng	Windowing (GIS)	
开发	Kāifā	Development	
开发包	Kāifā bāo	Toolkit (computer development term)	
开发促进地域	Kāifā cùjìn dìyù	Development promotion area	
开发计划	Kāifā jìhuà	Development plan	
开发权	Kāifā quán	Development rights	
开发系统	Kāifā xìtǒng	Development system	
开发组织	Kāifā zǔzhī	The Open Group	TOG
开放分布处理	Kāifàng fēnbù chǔlǐ	Open (system) distributed processing	ODP
开放分布管理体系	Kāifàng fēnbù guǎnlǐ tǐxì	Open (system) distributed management architecture	ODMA
开放分布式处理的参考模型	Kāifàng fēnbùshì chǔlǐde cānkǎo móxíng	Reference model of open distributed processing	RM-ODP
开放 JAVA 虚拟机接口	Kāifàng JAVA xūnǐ jī jiēkǒu	Open Java virtual machine interface	OJI
开放结构开发组织	Kāifàng jiégòu kāifā zǔzhī	Open Architecture Developers Group	OADG
开放期间	Kāifàng qījiān	Opening period	
开放软件基金会	Kāifàng ruǎnjiàn jījīnhuì	Open Software Foundation	OSF
开放实系统	Kāifàng shí xìtǒng	Real open system	
开放数据链路接口	Kāifàng shùjù liànlù jiēkǒu	Open data link interface	ODI
开放数据库互连	Kāifàng shùjùkù hùlián	Open database connectivity	ODBC
开放数据库连通性	Kāifàng shùjùkù liántōngxìng	Open database connectivity	ODBC
开放信息模型	Kāifàng xìnxī móxíng	Open information model	OIM
开放系统	Kāifàng xìtǒng	Open system	
开放系统环境	Kāifàng xìtǒng huánjìng	Open system environment	
开放系统互联	Kāifàng xìtǒng hùlián	Open system interchange	OSI
开放系统互连	Kāifàng xìtǒng hùlián	Open system interconnection	OSI
开放系统互连(参考模型)	Kāifàng xìtǒng hùlián (cānkǎo móxíng)	Open systems interconnection (reference model)	OSI
开放系统互连环境	Kāifàng xìtǒng hùlián huánjìng	Open system interconnection environment	
开放系统体系结构	Kāifàng xìtǒng tǐxì jiégòu	Open systems architecture	OSA
开放业务接入	Kāifàng yèwù jiērù	Open service access	OSA

开放应用体系结构	Kāifàng yìngyòng tǐxì jiégòu	Open applications architecture	OAA
开放最短路径优先	Kāifàng zuìduǎn lùjìng yōuxiān	Open shortest path first	OSPF
开放最短路经优先协议	Kāifàng zuìduǎn lùjīng yōuxiān xiéyì	Open shortest path first protocol	OSPF
开放组织	Kāifàng zǔzhī	The Open Group	
开放的业务结构	Kāifàngde yèwù jiégòu	Open service architecture	OSA
开放式 Arcade 体系论坛	Kāifàngshì Arcade tǐxì lùntán	Open Arcade Architecture Forum	OAAF
开放式地学数据互操作规范	Kāifàng-shì dìxué shùjù hùcāozuò guīfàn	Open geodata interoperability specification	OGIS
开放式 GIS 协会	Kāifàng-shì GIS xiéhuì	Open GIS consortium	OGC
开放式数据服务	Kāifàng-shì shùjù fúwù	Open data services (for database)	ODS
开放式数据库互连	Kāifàng-shì shùjùkù hùlián	Open database communication	ODBC
开放式数据库链接	Kāifàng-shì shùjùkù liànjiē	Open database connectivity	ODBC
开放式文件管理结构	Kāifàng-shì wénjiàn guǎnlǐ jiégòu	Open document management architecture	ODMA
开放式协作运算体系	Kāifàng-shì xiézuò yùnsuàn tǐxì	Open cooperative computing architecture	OCCA
开放式系统互连模型	Kāifàng-shì xìtǒng hùlián móxíng	Open system interconnection model	OSIM
开放式最短路径优先协议	Kāifàngshì zuìduǎn lùjìng yōuxiān xiéyì	Open shortest path first protocol	OSPF
开放型系统互连计划	Kāifàng-xíng xìtǒng hùlián jìhuà	Open system interconnection plan	OSIP
开发者版	Kāifāzhě bǎn	Developer edition (of software)	
开关	Kāiguān	Switch (the on-off type)	
开关电容网络	Kāiguān diànróng wǎngluò	Switched capacitor network	
开关电源	Kāiguān diànyuán	Switched power supply	
开关键控	Kāiguān jiànkòng	On-off keying	OOK
开关矩阵	Kāiguān jǔzhèn	Switching matrix	
开关整流器	Kāiguān zhěngliúqì	Switched mode rectifier	
开关组件	Kāiguān zǔjiàn	Switch assembly	SA
开户入网	Kāihù rùwǎng	Subscription	
开环电压增益	Kāihuán diànyā zēngyì	Open-loop voltage gain	
开环控制系统	Kāihuán kòngzhì xìtǒng	Open-loop control system	
开环增益	Kāihuán zēngyì	Open-loop gain	
开机自动测试	Kāijī zìdòng cèshì	Power-on self test	POST
开路	Kāilù	Open circuit	
开路电压	Kāilù diànyā	Open-circuit voltage	
开路终端	Kāilù zhōngduān	Open circuit termination	
开门告警	Kāimén gàojǐng	Door-open alarm	
开门码	Kāimén mǎ	Opening code	
开始标签	Kāishǐ biāoqiān	Beginning tag	B tag
开始移动切换	Kāishǐ yídòng qiēhuàn	Mobile originated handover	MOHO
开始用户激活	Kāishǐ yònghù jīhuó	Begin subscriber activity	
开挖	Kāiwā	Cutting	
开隙	Kāixì	Open slot, gapped	
开销	Kāixiao	Overhead (SDH term)	
开销处理	Kāixiao chǔlǐ	Overhead processing	OHP
开销处理单元	Kāixiao chǔlǐ dānyuán	Overhead processor (unit)	OHP
开销和适配路径	Kāixiao hé shìpèi lùjìng	Overhead and adaptation trail	
开销接入	Kāixiao jiērù	Overhead access	OHA
铠装电缆	Kǎizhuāng diànlǎn	Armored cable	AC

喀呖声	Kālì shēng	Click (the sound)	
喀呖声率	Kālì shēng lǜ	Click rate	
抗电网干扰系数	Kàng diànwǎng gānrǎo xìshù	Mains-interference immunity factor	
抗恶环境光纤	Kàng'èhuánjìng guāngxiān	Harsh condition-resistant fiber	
抗耦双频激电仪	Kàng'ǒu shuāngpín jīdiànyí	Anti-coupling bi-frequency induced polarization instrument	
康柏公司	Kāng-bǎi gōngsī	Compaq (US computer company)	
抗饱和	Kàngbǎohé	Anti-saturation (Radar term)	
抗拆性	Kàngchāixìng	Tamper resistance	
抗抵赖性	Kàngdǐlàixìng	Anti-repudiation (IPsec)	
抗毒软件	Kàngdú ruǎnjiàn	Antivirus software	
抗辐射光纤	Kàngfúshè guāngxiān	Radiation resistant fiber	
抗干扰	Kànggānrǎo	Anti-interference, anti-jamming	
抗干扰	Kànggānrǎo	Anti-jamming	AJ
抗干扰频率	Kànggānrǎo pínlǜ	Anti-jamming frequency	AJF
抗干扰阵	Kànggānrǎo zhèn	Anti-jamming array	
抗干扰性	Kànggānrǎoxìng	Immunity (to interference)	
抗海浪试验	Kànghǎilàng shìyàn	Anti-clutter test against the sea (radar term)	
抗毁	Kànghuǐ	Survivable, survivability	
抗拉强度	Kànglā qiángdù	Tensile strength	
抗力系数	Kànglì xìshù	Resistance factor	
康宁公司	Kāng-níng gōngsī	Corning (US company)	
康拍公司	Kāng-pāi gōngsī	Compaq (US company)	
抗扰试验电平	Kàngrǎo shìyàn diànpíng	Immunity test level	
抗扰度	Kàngrǎodù	Interference resistance or jamming resistance	
抗扰度	Kàngrǎodù	Immunity (to a disturbance)	
抗扰性	Kàngrǎoxìng	Immunity (to a disturbance)	
抗扰性电平	Kàngrǎoxìng diànpíng	Immunity level	
抗扰性限值	Kàngrǎoxìng xiànzhí	Immunity limit	
抗扰性裕量	Kàngrǎoxìng yùliàng	Immunity margin	
抗骚扰性	Kàngsāorǎoxìng	Immunity (to a disturbance)	
抗蚀	Kàngshí	Corrosion resistant	CRE
康氏外壳	Kāng-shì wàiké	Korn shell	
抗压强度	Kàngyā qiángdù	Compressive strength	
抗躁声送话器	Kàngzàoshēng sònghuàqì	Anti-noise microphone	
抗振	Kàngzhèn	Anti-vibration	
抗震保护系统	Kàngzhèn bǎohù xìtǒng	Shock protection system	SPS
拷贝	Kǎobèi	Copy (usually a noun)	
考访服务	Kǎo-fǎng fúwù	Gopher (an Internet tool)	
拷机实验	Kǎojī shíyàn	Burn-in test	
靠模性能	Kàomú xìngnéng	Profiling capability (semiconductor mfg)	
卡片穿孔机	Kǎpiàn chuānkǒngjī	Card punch	C/P
卡片适配器寄存器	Kǎpiàn shìpèiqì jìcúnqì	Card adapter register	CAR
卡片阅读机	Kǎpiàn yuèdújī	Card reader	C/R
卡塞格伦反射器天线	Kǎ-sāi-gé-lún fǎnshè qì tiānxiàn	Cassegrain reflector antenna	
卡沙米码	Kǎ-shā-mǐ mǎ	Kassmi code	
喀声率	Kāshēnglǜ	Click rate	

卡特勒馈源	Kǎ-tè-lè kuìyuán	Cutler feed	
Katmai 新指令集	Katmai xīn zhǐlìng jí	Katmai new instructions	KNI
卡西鸥	Kǎ-xī-ōu	Casio (Japanese company)	
壳	Ké	Shell, case	
可按内容寻址的文件存储	Kě àn nèiróng xúnzhǐde wénjiàn cúnchǔ	Content addressable file store	CAFS
氪灯	Kè dēng	Krypton light source	
氪离子激光	Kè lízǐ jīguāng	Krypton laser	
可研	Kě yán	Feasibility report, short for 可行性研究报告	
可预置分频器分频比	Kě yùzhì fēnpínqì fènpín bǐ	Prescalar divider division ratio	
可转换订购	Kě zhuǎnhuàn dìnggòu	Transformable subscriptions (in SQL Server)	
可安装客户端驱动程序	Kě'ānzhuāng kèhù duān qūdòng chéngxù	Installable client driver	ICD
可变比特率	Kěbiàn bǐtè lǜ	Variable bit rate	VBR
可变比特率业务	Kěbiàn bǐtè lǜ yèwù	Variable bit rate service	VBR
可变长编码	Kěbiàn cháng biānmǎ	Variable length coding	
可变长度子网掩码	Kěbiàn chángdù zìwǎng yǎnmǎ	Variable-length sub-net mask	VLSM
可编程序异步双线适配器	Kěbiān chéngxù yìbù shuāngxiàn shìpèiqì	Programmable asynchronous dual line adapter	PADLA
可编程序异步线路转换器	Kěbiān chéngxù yìbù xiànlù zhuǎnhuànqì	Programmable asynchronous line adapter	PASLA
可编程序的逻辑阵列	Kěbiān chéngxùde luóji zhènliè	Programmable logic array	PLA
可变电容器微音效应	Kěbiàn diànróngqì wēiyīn xiàoyìng	Microphone effect of variable capacitor	
可变分频器	Kěbiàn fēnpínqì	Variable division ratio divider	
可变分频器	Kěbiàn fēnpínqì	Variable division frequency divider	
可变光衰减阵列	Kěbiàn guāng shuāijiǎn zhènliè	Variable optical attenuator array	VAA
可变光衰减器	Kěbiàn guāng shuāijiǎnqì	Variable optical attenuator	VOA
可变间距	Kěbiàn jiānjù	Variable spacing	
可变间距光栅	Kěbiàn jiānjù guāngshān	Variable aperture grille pitch	VAGP
可变结构随机存取存储器	Kěbiàn jiégòu suíjī cúnqǔ cúnchǔqì	Variable topology random access memory	VTRAM
可变晶体振荡器	Kěbiàn jīngtǐ zhèndàngqì	Variable crystal oscillator	VXO
可变聚合数据类型	Kěbiàn jùhé shùjù lèixíng	Variable-aggregate data type	
可变认证码	Kěbiàn rènzhèng mǎ	Variable authentication code	VAC
可变衰减器	Kěbiàn shuāijiǎnqì	Variable attenuator	
可变速自适应多路转换	Kěbiàn sù zìshìyìng duōlù zhuǎnhuàn	Variable rate adaptive multiplexing	VRAM
可变斜率增量调制	Kěbiàn xiélǜ zēngliàng tiáozhì	Variable slope delta modulation	VSDM
可编只读存储器	Kěbiān zhǐ dú cúnchǔqì	Programmable read-only memory	PROM
可编程单结晶体管	Kěbiānchéng dānjié jīngtǐguǎn	Programmable unijunction transistor	PUT
可编程单元	Kěbiānchéng dānyuán	Programmable unit	PU
可编程逻辑控制器	Kěbiānchéng luóji kòngzhìqì	Programmable logic controller	PLC
可变程逻辑器件	Kěbiànchéng luóji qìjiàn	Programmable logic device	PLD
可编程前端处理机	Kěbiānchéng qiánduān chǔlǐjī	Programmable front end processor	PFEP
可编程输入输出模式	Kěbiānchéng shūrù shūchū móshì	Programmable input output	PIO
可编程数字无线电	Kěbiānchéng shùzì wúxiàndiàn	Programmable digital radio	PDR
可编程网	Kěbiānchéng wǎng	Programmable network	
可编程细胞自动机	Kěbiānchéng xìbāo zìdòngjī	Programmable cellular automata (crypt,)	PCA
可编程优选译码器	Kěbiānchéng yōuxuǎn yìmǎqì	Programmable priority encoder	PPE
可编程终端	Kěbiānchéng zhōngduān	Programmable terminal	
可编程中断控制器	Kěbiānchéng zhōngduàn kòngzhìqì	Programmable interrupt controller	PIC

可变的	Kĕbiànde	Mutable	
可变频频率荡器	Kĕbiànpín pínlǜ dàngqì	Variable frequency oscillator	VFO
可变速寻呼系统	Kĕbiànsù xúnhū xìtǒng	Flexible paging system	FLEX
可擦程序控制逻辑阵列	Kĕcā chéngxù kòngzhì luóji zhènliè	Erasable programmable logic array	EPLA
可擦存储器	Kĕcā cúnchǔqì	Erasable memory	
可擦可编程只读存储器	Kĕcā kĕbiānchéng zhǐdú cúnchǔqì	Erasable programmable read only memory	EPROM
可擦只读存储器	Kĕcā zhǐ dú cúnchǔqì	Erasable read only memory	EROM
可擦除的可编程只读存储器	Kĕcāchúde kĕbiānchéng zhǐdú cúnchǔqì	Erasable programmable read only memory	EPROM
可擦掉的可编程只读存储器	Kĕcādiàode kĕbiānchéng zhǐdú cúnchǔqì	Erasable programmable read only memory	EPROM
可持续信元速率	Kĕchíxù xìnyuán sùlǜ	Sustainable cell rate	SCR
可重复刻录光盘	Kĕchóngfù kèlù guāngpán	Compact disk-rewritable	CDRW
可重复性	Kĕchóngfù-xìng	Repeatability	
可重构	Kĕchónggòu	Reconfigurable	
可重写光盘	Kĕchóngxiĕ guāngpán	Rewritable optical disk	
可重用性	Kĕchóngyòng-xìng	Reusability	
可重组	Kĕchóngzǔ	Reconfigurable	
可穿戴计算	Kĕchuāndài jìsuàn	Wearable computing	
可串行	Kĕchuànháng	Serializable	
可串行性	Kĕchuànháng-xìng	Serializability	
可处理形式	Kĕchǔlǐ xíngshì	Processable form	
可达图	Kĕdá tú	Reachability graph (in stochastic process algebra)	
可到达性	Kĕdàodá-xìng	Reachability	
可达性	Kĕdá-xìng	Accessibility	
可打印区	Kĕdǎyìn qū	Printable area	
可调度分析	Kĕdiàodù fēnxī	Schedulability analysis (in CORBA)	
可定制化	Kĕdìngzhìhuà	Customizable	
可丢弃的	Kĕdiūqìde	Discard eligible	
可动线圈式变换器	Kĕdòng xiànquān-shì biànhuànqì	Moving-coil type transducer	
可懂度	Kĕdǒngdù	Intelligibility	
可读格式	Kĕdú géshi	Readable format	
可发售市场	Kĕfāshòu shìchǎng	Sales available market	SAM
可分频率展开	Kĕfēn pínlǜ zhǎnkāi	Partitionable frequency expansion	
可分配空间	Kĕfēnpèi kōngjiān	Configuration space enable	CSE
可服务性	Kĕfúwùxìng	Serviceability	
可更改维度	Kĕgēnggǎi wéidù	Changing dimension	
可购性	Kĕgòuxìng	Affordability	
客观参考当量表	Kèguān cānkǎo dāngliàng biǎo	Objective reference equivalent meter	
客观评价	Kèguān píngjià	Objective estimation or evaluation	
可观测性	Kĕguāncèxìng	Observability	
可焊性	Kĕhànxìng	Solderability	
可焊性试验	Kĕhànxìng shìyàn	Solderability test	
可核查性	Kĕhécháxìng	Verifiability	
客户	Kèhù	Client, customer	
客户端	Kèhù duān	Client	
客户端设备	Kèhù duān shèbèi	Customer premises equipment	CPE

客户端应用程序	Kèhù duān yìngyòng chéngxù	Client application	
客户端游标	Kèhù duān yóubiāo	Client cursor (for database)	
客户服务代表	Kèhù fúwù dàibiǎo	Customer service representative	CSR
客户服务和客户行销的资料探测	Kèhù fúwù hé kèhù xíngxiāode zīliào tàncè	Data mining for customer service and sales	DMCSS
客户服务中心	Kèhù fúwù zhōngxīn	Customer care center	CCC
客户管理平台	Kèhù guǎnlǐ píngtái	Costomer management plateform	CMP
客户管理系统	Kèhù guǎnlǐ xìtǒng	Customer network management	
客户关系管理	Kèhù guānxi guǎnlǐ	Customer relations manager	CRM
客户关系管理	Kèhù guānxi guǎnlǐ	Customer relationship management	
客户请求	Kèhù qǐngqiú	Client request	
客户区	Kèhù qū	Client area	
客户网	Kèhù wǎng	Client network	
客户/服务器层	Kèhù/ fúwùqì céng	Client/server layer	
客户/服务器关系	Kèhù/fúwùqì guānxi	Client/server relationship	
可换功率	Kěhuàn gōnglǜ	Exchangeable power	
可换功率增益	Kěhuàn gōnglǜ zēngyì	Exchangeable gain (of a two-port network)	
可换噪声功率	Kěhuàn zàoshēng gōnglǜ	Exchangeable noise power (of a one-port network)	
可互操作接口	Kěhùcāozuò jiēkǒu	Interoperable interface	
可互操作的对象引用	Kěhùcāozuòde duìxiàng yǐnyòng	Interoperable object reference	IOR
客户机/服务器	Kèhùjī/fúwùqì	Client/server	C/S
客户机/服务器方式	Kèhùjī/fúwùqì fāngshì	Client/server format	
客户机-服务器计算	Kèhùjī/fúwùqì jìsuàn	Client/server computing	
客户机/浏览器/服务器	Kèhùjī/liúlǎnqì/fúwùqì	Client/browser/server	C/B/S
可获得比特率	Kěhuòdé bǐtèlǜ	Available bit rate	ABR
可获性	Kěhuòxìng	Availability	
可互相配对的光纤连接器标准	Kěhùxiāng pèiduìde guāngxiān liánjiēqì biāozhǔn	Fiber optic connector intermateability standards	FOCIS
科技数据委员会	Kējì shùjù wěiyuánhuì	Committee on Data for Science and Technology	CODATA
课件	Kèjiàn	Courseware	
可见光二极体	Kějiàn guāng èrjítǐ	Visible photodiode	
可见弧	Kějiàn hú	Visible arc	
可剪裁性	Kějiǎncáixìng	Pruning (database term)	
可见度	Kějiàndù	Visibiliy	
可校正差错	Kějiàozhèng chācuò	Correctable error	
可接入性	Kějiērùxìng	Accessability	
可接受干扰	Kějiēshòu gānrǎo	Accepted interference	
可接受使用政策	Kějiēshòu shǐyòng zhèngcè	Acceptable use policy	AUP
可接收质量水平	Kějiēshōu zhìliàng shuǐpíng	Acceptable quality level (in quality standards)	AQL
可记录光盘	Kějìlù guāngpán	CD recordable	CDR
可经由浏览器访问的应用程序	Kějīng yóu liúlǎnqì fǎngwènde yìngyòng chéngxù	Browser-accessible application	
可及性	Kějíxìng	Accessibility	
可靠传输服务元素协议	Kěkào chuánshū fúwù yuánsù xiéyì	Reliable transfer service element protocol	RTSE
可靠传送	Kěkào chuánsòng	Reliable transfer	
可靠传送服务要素	Kěkào chuánsòng fúwù yàosù	Reliable transfer service element	RTSE

可靠多播协议	Kěkào duōbō xiéyì	Reliable multicast protocol	
可靠数据协议	Kěkào shùjù xiéyì	Reliable data protocol	RDP
可靠用户数据报协议	Kěkào yònghù shùjùbào xiéyì	Reliable user datagram protocol	RUDP
可靠组播传输协议	Kěkào zǔbō chuánshū xiéyì	Reliable multicast transport protocol	RMTP
可靠组播协议	Kěkào zǔbō xiéyì	Reliable multicast protocol	RMP
可靠的传送业务单元	Kěkàode chuánsòng yèwù dānyuán	Reliable transfer service element	RTSE
可靠度	Kěkàodù	Reliability	
可靠性（性能）	Kěkàoxìng (xìngnéng)	Reliability (performance)	
可靠性测试	Kěkàoxìng cèshì	Reliability testing	
可靠性分配	Kěkàoxìng fēnpèi	Reliability allocation	
可靠性改进	Kěkàoxìng gǎijìn	Reliability improvement	
可靠性和可维护性保证	Kěkàoxìng hé kěwéihùxìng bǎozhèng	Reliability and maintainability assurance	
可靠性和可维护性程序	Kěkàoxìng hé kěwéihùxìng chéngxù	Reliability and maintainability program	
可靠性和可维护性管理	Kěkàoxìng hé kěwéihùxìng guǎnlǐ	Reliability and maintainability management	
可靠性和可维护性监督	Kěkàoxìng hé kěwéihùxìng jiāndū	Reliability and maintainability surveillance	
可靠性和可维护性计划	Kěkàoxìng hé kěwéihùxìng jìhuà	Reliability and maintainability plan	
可靠性和可维护性控制	Kěkàoxìng hé kěwéihùxìng kòngzhì	Reliability and maintainability control	
可靠性和可维护性审核	Kěkàoxìng hé kěwéihùxìng shěnhé	Reliability and maintainability audit	
可靠性框图	Kěkàoxìng kuàngtú	Reliability block diagram	
可靠性模型	Kěkàoxìng móxíng	Reliability model	
可靠性设计	Kěkàoxìng shèjì	Reliability design	
可靠性试验	Kěkàoxìng shìyàn	Reliability test	
可靠性预计	Kěkàoxìng yùjì	Reliability prediction	
可靠性增长	Kěkàoxìng zēngzhǎng	Reliability growth	
可靠性、维修性和安全性	Kěkàoxìng、wéixiūxìng hé ānquánxìng	Reliability, maintainability and safety	RMS
可刻录光盘	Kěkèlù guāngpán	Compact disk recordable	CD-R
可控隔离	Kěkòng gélí	Controllable isolation (IPsec)	
可控硅开关	Kěkòng guī kāiguān	Silicon controlled switch	SCS
可控射束天线	Kěkòng shèshù tiānxiàn	Steerable-beam antenna	
可控硅整流器	Kěkòngguī zhěngliúqì	Silicon controlled rectifier	SCR
可扩充的内容定止存储器	Kěkuòchōngde nèiróng dìngzhǐ cúnchǔqì	Augmented content-addressed memory	ACAM
可扩展标记语言	Kěkuòzhǎn biāojì yǔyán	Extensible markup language	XML
可扩展标记语言模式定义语言	Kěkuòzhǎn biāojì yǔyán móshì dìngyì yǔyán	Extensible markup language schema definition	XSD
可扩展标记语言消息接口	Kěkuòzhǎn biāojì yǔyán xiāoxi jiēkǒu	Extensible markup language message interface	XMI
可扩展对象交换模型	Kěkuòzhǎn duìxiàng jiāohuàn móxíng	Extensible object exchange model	EOEM
可扩展可靠组播	Kěkuòzhǎn kěkào zǔbō	Scalable reliable multicast	SRM
可扩展平面	Kěkuòzhǎn píngmiàn	Developable surface	
可扩展权限标记语言	Kěkuòzhǎn quánxiàn biāojì yǔyán	eXtensible rights markup language	XrML
可扩展扫描椭圆孔镜头	Kěkuòzhǎn sǎomiáo tuǒyuán kǒng jìngtóu	Extended field elliptical aperture lens	EFEAL
可扩展设计语言	Kěkuòzhǎn shèjì yǔyán	Extensible stylesheet language	XSL
可扩展身份验证协议	Kěkuòzhǎn shēnfen yànzhèng xiéyì	Extensible authentication protocol	EAP
可扩展系统配置数据	Kěkuòzhǎn xìtǒng pèizhì shùjù	Extended system configuration data	ESCD
可扩展样式表语言	Kěkuòzhǎn yàngshì biǎo yǔyán	eXtensible stylesheet language	XSL

可扩展样式表语言转换	Kěkuòzhǎn yàngshì biǎo yǔyán zhuǎnhuàn	eXtensible stylesheet language transformation	XSLT
可扩展样式语言	Kěkuòzhǎn yàngshì yǔyán	Extensible style language (in SQL Server)	XSL
可扩展的	Kěkuòzhǎnde	Scalable	
可扩展性	Kěkuòzhǎnxìng	Scalability	
克雷超级电脑	Kè-léi chāojí diànnǎo	Cray supercomputer	
克里格法	Kè-lǐ-gé fǎ	Kriging	
克隆	Kèlóng	Clone	
刻录机	Kèlùjī	Compact disk burner	
可录写光碟	Kělùxiě guāngdié	Compact disk-recordable	CD-R
可录写光碟	Kělùxiě guāngdié	Recordable compact disk	
可满足性	Kěmǎnzúxìng	Satisfiability	
柯密	Kē-mì	Kermit	
肯定应答	Kěndìng yìngdá	Acknowledgement	ACK
肯定中断	Kěndìng zhōngduàn	Acknowledge interrupt	AKI
肯定字符	Kěndìng zìfú	Acknowledge	ACK
可能实行的试验项目	Kěnéng shíxíngde shìyàn xiàngmù	Executable test case	
可能实行的试验项目组	Kěnéng shíxíngde shìyàn xiàngmù zǔ	Executable test suite	
可逆天线	Kěnì tiānxiàn	Reversible antenna	
科尼卡	Kē-ní-kǎ	Konica (Japanese company)	
可配置逻辑模块	Kěpèizhì luóji mókuài	Configurable logic block	CLB
可破密的	Kěpòmìde	Breakable (i.e. cipher algorithm, etc.)	
Kerberos 应用程序库	Kerberos yìngyòng chéngxù kù	Kerberos application library	
可塞入数位时隙	Kěsāirù shùwèi shíxì	Stuffable digit time slot	
可升级性	Kěshēngjíxìng	Scalability	
可伸缩多播密钥分配	Kěshēnsuō duōbō mìyào fēnpèi	Scalable multicast key distribution	SKMD
可伸缩的	Kěshēnsuōde	Scalable	
可伸缩性	Kěshēnsuōxìng	Scalability	
可设置键	Kěshèzhì jiàn	Reconfigurable key	
可视报文	Kěshì bàowén	Videotext	
可视电话	Kěshì diànhuà	Video telephone	
可视电话会议	Kěshì diànhuà huìyì	Visual teleconference; videoconference	
可视对讲门铃	Kěshì duìjiǎng ménlíng	Video interphone	VI
可视分析	Kěshì fēnxī	Visibility analysis	
可视交互式建模	Kěshì jiāohù-shì jiànmó	Visual interactive modeling	
可视数据系统	Kěshì shùjù xìtǒng	Viewdata system	
可视图	Kěshì tú	Visibility map	
可视图文	Kěshì túwén	Videotex	
可视图文	Kěshì túwén	Teletext	
可视图文	Kěshì túwén	Videography	
可视图文闭合用户群	Kěshì túwén bìhé yònghù qún	Videotex closed user group	
可视图文和其他可恢复业务的增强人机接口	Kěshì túwén hé qítā kěhuīfù yèwùde zēngqiáng rénjī jiēkǒu	Enhanced man machine interface for videotex and other retrieval services	VEMMI
可视图文会议	Kěshì túwén huìyì	Videotex conferencing	
可视图文接口单元	Kěshì túwén jiēkǒu dānyuán	Videotex interface unit	
可视图文接入点	Kěshì túwén jiērùdiǎn	Videotex access point	VAP
可视图文软件遥装	Kěshì túwén ruǎnjiàn yáozhuāng	Videotex telesoftware	

可视图文事务处理	Kěshì túwén shìwù chǔlǐ	Videotex transaction	
可视图文数据处理	Kěshì túwén shùjù chǔlǐ	Videotex data processing	
可视图文数据库	Kěshì túwén shùjùkù	Videotex database	
可视图文通信网提供者	Kěshì túwén tōngxìnwǎng tígòngzhě	Videotex communication network provider	
可视图文外部主机	Kěshì túwén wàibù zhǔjī	External videotex host computer	
可视图文消息传递	Kěshì túwén xiāoxi chuándì	Videotex messaging	
可视图文信息检索	Kěshì túwén xìnxī jiǎnsuǒ	Videotex transaction	
可视图文系统	Kěshì túwén xìtǒng	Videotex system	
可视图文系统域	Kěshì túwén xìtǒng yù	Videotex system field	
可视图文页	Kěshì túwén yè	Videotex page	
可视图文业务	Kěshì túwén yèwù	Videotex service	
可视图文业务单元	Kěshì túwén yèwù dānyuán	Videotex service unit	
可视图文业务轮廓	Kěshì túwén yèwù lúnkuò	Videotex service profile	
可视图文业务提供者	Kěshì túwén yèwù tígòngzhě	Videotex service provider	
可视图文业务性能	Kěshì túwén yèwù xìngnéng	Videotex service facilities	
可视图文业务中心	Kěshì túwén yèwù zhōngxīn	Videotex service center	
可视图文应用	Kěshì túwén yìngyòng	Videotex application	
可视图文应用内部提供者	Kěshì túwén yìngyòng nèibù tígòngzhě	Internal videotex application provider	
可视图文应用提供者	Kěshì túwén yìngyòng tígòngzhě	Videotex application provider	
可视图文应用外部提供者	Kěshì túwén yìngyòng wàibù tígòngzhě	External videotex application provider	
可视图文用户	Kěshì túwén yònghù	Videotex user	
可视图文用户或终端标识性能	Kěshì túwén yònghù huò zhōngduān biāozhì xìngnéng	Videotex user/terminal identification facility	
可视图文帧	Kěshì túwén zhèng	Videotex frame	
可视图文证询单	Kěshì túwén zhèng xúndān	Videotex form	
可视图文终端	Kěshì túwén zhōngduān	Videotex terminal	
可视图文中心	Kěshì túwén zhōngxīn	Videotex service center	VSC
可视图文主机	Kěshì túwén zhǔjī	Videotex host computer	
可识别名	Kěshíbié míng	Distinguished name	DN
可实地替换单元	Kěshídì tìhuan dānyuán	Field replaceable unit	FRU
可视化	Kěshìhuà	Visualization	
可视化几何引擎	Kěshìhuà jǐhé yǐnqíng	Visualized geometry engine	
可适应性	Kěshìyìngxìng	Adaptability	
客体	Kètǐ	Object	
客体重用	Kètǐ chóngyòng	Object reuse (IPsec)	
客体登录项	Kètǐ dēnglù xiàng	Object entry	
客体管理组 - 通用数据表示	Kètǐ guǎnlǐ zǔ-tōng yòng shùjù biǎoshi	Object management group-common data representation	OMG-CDR
客体管理组 - 一般内部 ORB 协议	Kètǐ guǎnlǐ zǔ-yībān nèibù ORB xiéyì	Object management group-general internal object request broker (ORB) protocol	OMG-GIOP
客体类别	Kètǐ lèibié	Object class	
客体类别描述	Kètǐ lèibié miáoshù	Object class description	
客体类型	Kètǐ lèixíng	Object type	
客体描述	Kètǐ miáoshù	Object description	
可调滤波器	Kětiáo lǜbōqì	Tunable filter	
可调色散补偿器	Kětiáo sèsàn bǔchángqì	Tunable dispersion compensator	TDC
可调数位时隙	Kětiáo shùwèi shíxì	Adjustable digit time slot	

可调速率数字用户线	Kětiáo sùlǜ shùzì yònghù xiàn	Rate-adjustable digital subscriber line	RADSL
可调信道多址	Kětiáo xìndào duōzhǐ	Tunable-channel multi-access	TCMA
可调式滤光镜	Kětiáo-shì lǜguāngjìng	Tunable filter (optical)	
可听声	Kětīngshēng	Audible sound	
可通达全球因特网路连接	Kětōngdá quánqiú Yīntèwǎng lù liánjiē	Global reach internet connection	GRIC
可拓展性	Kětuòzhǎnxìng	Expansibility	
可弯波导	Kěwān bōdǎo	Bendable waveguide	
可维持信元率	Kěwéichí xìnyuán lǜ	Sustainable cell rate	SCR
可维持信元速率	Kěwéichí xìnyuán sùlǜ	Sustainable cell rate	SCR
可维护性（性能）	Kěwéihùxìng (xìngnéng)	Maintainability (performance)	
可维护性分配	Kěwéihùxìng fēnpèi	Maintainability allocation	
可维护性检验	Kěwéihùxìng jiǎnyàn	Maintainability verification	
可维护性模型	Kěwéihùxìng móxíng	Maintainability model	
可维护性预测	Kěwéihùxìng yùcè	Maintainability prediction	
可维修性	Kěwéixiūxìng	Maintainability	
可闻信号	Kěwén xìnhào	Audible signal	
可闻噪声	Kěwén zàoshēng	Audible noise	
可下载的取样音色	Kěxiàzàide qǔyàng yīnsè	Downloadable sample (Internet audio)	
可携性	Kěxiéxìng	Portability (of software)	
可信级别	Kěxìn jíbié	Assurance level	
可信接入单元	Kěxìn jiērù dānyuán	Trusted interface unit (ISO security)	TIU
可信介绍人	Kěxìn jièshàorén	Trusted introducer	
可信计算基	Kěxìn jìsuàn jī	Trusted computing base	TCB
可信计算库	Kěxìn jìsuàn kù	Trusted computing base (ISO security)	TCB
可信计算机安全评级准则	Kěxìn jìsuànjī ānquán píngjí zhǔnzé	Trusted computer security evaluation criteria	TCSEC
可信计算机系统	Kěxìn jìsuànjī xìtǒng	Trusted computer system	
可信软件	Kěxìn ruǎnjiàn	Trusted software	
可信数据库系统	Kěxìn shùjùkù xìtǒng	Trusted database system	TDBS
可信通路	Kěxìn tōnglù	Trusted path (IPsec)	
可信网络实体	Kěxìn wǎngluò shítǐ	Trusted network entity	
可信度	Kěxìndù	Certainty factor	
可行的	Kěxíngde	Viable	
可行性研究	Kěxíngxìng yánjiū	Feasibility study	
可信任的第三方	Kěxìnrènde dì sān fāng	Trusted third party (IPsec)	TTP
可选参数结束标志	Kěxuǎn cānshù jiéshù biāozhì	End of optional parameters	
可选记帐业务	Kěxuǎn jìzhàng yèwù	Alternate billing service	ABS
可选前向呼叫指示	Kěxuǎn qiánxiàng hūjiào zhǐshì	Optional forward call indicator	
可选择的别名地址	Kěxuǎnzéde biémíng dìzhǐ	Alternative alias address	
可选择的地址	Kěxuǎnzéde dìzhǐ	Alternative address	
科学技术部	Kēxué jìshù bù	Ministry of science and technology	MST
科学技术司	Kēxué jìshù sī	Department of Science and Technology (MII)	
可寻址点	Kěxúnzhǐ diǎn	Addressable point	
可寻址远程传感器高速通道	Kěxúnzhǐ yuǎnchéng chuángǎnqì gāosù tōngdào	Highway addressable remote transducer	HART
可寻址远程传感器数据公路	Kěxúnzhǐ yuǎnchéng chuángǎnqì shùjù gōnglù	Highway addressable remote transducer (used in process controls)	HART
可压缩多组分驱动	Kěyāsuō duō zǔfèn qūdòng	Compressible multi-component flow	

可移动式自动数字交换机	Kěyídòng-shì zìdòng shùzì jiāohuànjī	Transportable automatic digital switch	TADS
可移植可执行文件	Kěyízhí kě zhíxíng wénjiàn	Portable executable file	PE
可移植资料格式	Kěyízhí zīliào géshi	Portable document format (Adobe format)	.pdf
可移植性	Kěyízhíxìng	Portability	
可用比特率	Kěyòng bǐtè lǜ	Available bit rate	ABR
可用场强	Kěyòng chǎngqiáng	Usable field strength	
可用功率	Kěyòng gōnglǜ	Available power	
可用功率通量密度	Kěyòng gōnglǜ tōngliàng mìdù	Usable power flux density	Pu
可用功率增益	Kěyòng gōnglǜ zēngyì	Available power gain (of two-port network)	
可用灵敏度	Kěyòng língmǐndù	Usable sensitivity	
可用媒体池	Kěyòng méitǐ chí	Free media pool	
可用区	Kěyòng qū	Available area	
可用时间	Kěyòng shíjiān	Up time	
可用状态	Kěyòng zhuàngtài	Up state	
可用资源确认	Kěyòng zīyuán quèrèn	Resource availability confirm	RAC
可用资源指示	Kěyòng zīyuán zhǐshì	Resource availability indication	RAI
可用的信元率	Kěyòngde xìnyuán lǜ	Available cell rate	AVCR
可用性	Kěyòngxìng	Availability (IPsec)	
可再次使用的书签	Kězàicì shǐyòngde shūqiān	Reusable bookmark	
可再定位	Kězàidìngwèi	Relocatable	
可再定位地址	Kězàidìngwèi dìzhǐ	Relocatable address	
可再入程序	Kězàirù chéngxù	Reenterable program	
可再入例行程序	Kězàirù lìxíng chéngxù	Reenterable routine	
可再入子程序	Kězàirù zǐchéngxù	Reenterable sub-routine	
可再现失效	Kězàixiàn shīxiào	Reproducible failure	
可再用程序	Kězàiyòng chéngxù	Reusable program	
可再用例行程序	Kězàiyòng lìxíng chéngxù	Reusable routine	
可执行测试实例	Kězhíxíng cèshì shílì	Executable test case	
可执行测试套	Kězhíxíng cèshì tào	Executable test suite	ETS
可执行代码	Kězhíxíng dàimǎ	Executable code	
可执行文件	Kězhíxíng wénjiàn	Executable file	
可转换订阅	Kězhuǎnhuàn dìngyuè	Transformable subscription	
可追溯性	Kězhuīsùxìng	Traceability (IPsec)	
可组合键	Kězǔhé jiàn	Combinable key	
KL 变换	KL Biànhuàn	Karhunen Loeve transform	KLT
空串	Kōng chuàn	Null string	
空基类优化	Kōng jīlèi yōuhuà	Empty base class optimization	EBCO
空调制解调器	Kōng tiáozhì jiětiáoqì	Null modem	
空线信号多路存取	Kōng xiàn xìnhào duōlù cúnqǔ	Idle signal multiple access	ISMA
空白	Kòngbái	Null	NUL
空白串	Kòngbái chuàn	Blank string	
空白电位	Kòngbái diànwèi	Baseline potential	
空白汇票	Kòngbái huìpiào	Blank money order	
空白试验	Kòngbái shìyàn	Bland test	
空白值	Kòngbái zhí	Baseline value	
空白字段描述符	Kòngbái zìduàn miáoshù fú	Blank field descriptor	

空吊线	Kōngdiàoxiàn	Suspension line	
空段	Kōngduàn	Dead sector	
空对空导弹	Kōngduìkōng dǎodàn	Air-to-air missile	A/A
空对空通信	Kōngduìkōng tōngxìn	Air-to-air communication	A/A
空房	Kōngfáng	Vacancy	
空分	Kōngfēn	Space division	
空分多址	Kōngfēn duōzhǐ	Space division multiple access	SDMA
空分复用	Kōngfēn fùyòng	Space division multiplexing	SDM
空分交换	Kōngfēn jiāohuàn	Space division switching	
空分交换方式	Kōngfēn jiāohuàn fāngshì	Space division switching method	
空分交换后面板	Kōngfēn jiāohuàn hòumian bǎn	Space switch back panel	SSBP
空分交换矩阵	Kōngfēn jiāohuàn jǔzhèn	Space switch matrix	SSMX
空分交换控制和维护	Kōngfēn jiāohuàn kòngzhì hé wéihù	Space switch control and maintenance	SSCM
空分交换时钟分配集成板	Kōngfēn jiāohuàn shízhōng fēnpèi jíchéngbǎn	Space switch clock distribution board assembly	SSCA
空分交换时钟分配器	Kōngfēn jiāohuàn shízhōng fēnpèiqì	Space switch clock distributor	SSCK
空分交换输入输出	Kōngfēn jiāohuàn shūrù shūchū	Space switch input and output	SSIO
空格串	Kònggé chuàn	Blank string	
空号	Kōnghào	Unallocated-number, vacant number	UNN
空号信号	Kōnghào xìnhào	Vacant-number signal	
空号音	Kōnghàoyīn	Number-unobtainable tone	
空化	Kōnghuà	Cavitation	
空基红外监视	Kōngjī hóngwài jiānshì	Space-based infrared surveillance	SBIRS
空间逼近发	Kōngjiān bījìn fā	Spatial access methods	SAMS
空间采样	Kōngjiān cǎiyàng	Spatial sampling	
空间参照	Kōngjiān cānzhào	Spatial reference	
空间参照系（坐标）	Kōngjiān cānzhàoxì (zuòbiāo)	Spatial reference system (coordinate)	
空间操作业务	Kōngjiān cāozuò yèwù	Space operation service	
空间查询	Kōngjiān cháxún	Spatial query	
空间查询语言	Kōngjiān cháxún yǔyán	Spatial query language	
空间插值	Kōngjiān chāzhí	Spatial interpolation	
空间传播损耗	Kōngjiān chuánbō sǔnhào	Atmospheric transmission loss	
空间单元	Kōngjiān dānyuán	Spatial unit	
空间电通信	Kōngjiān diàn tōngxìn	Space radio communication	
空间叠加	Kōngjiān diéjiā	Spatial overlay	
空间对象	Kōngjiān duìxiàng	Spatial object	
空间发分集	Kōngjiān fāfēnjí	Space transmit diversity	STD
空间仿真建模	Kōngjiān fǎngzhēn jiànmó	Spatial simulation modeling	
空间飞行器	Kōngjiān fēixíngqì	Spacecraft	
空间分辨率	Kōngjiān fēnbiànlǜ	Spatial resolution	
空间分割多路存取	Kōngjiān fēngē duōlù cúnqǔ	Space division multiple access	SDMA
空间分割多种复用	Kōngjiān fēngē duōzhǒng fùyòng	Space division multiplexing	SDM
空间分集	Kōngjiān fēnjí	Space diversity	
空间分集偶极天线	Kōngjiān fēnjí ǒují tiānxiàn	Space diversity doublet	SD
空间分析	Kōngjiān fēnxī	Spatial analysis	
空间复用协议	Kōngjiān fùyòng xiéyì	Spatial reuse protocol	SRP
空间复杂型	Kōngjiān fùzáxíng	Spatial complexity	

空间概念构成	Kōngjiān gàiniàn gòuchéng	Formalization of spatial concepts	
空间跟踪	Kōngjiān gēnzōng	Space tracking	
空间关系	Kōngjiān guānxi	Spatial relationship	
空间合并	Kōngjiān hébìng	Spatial join	
空间建模	Kōngjiān jiànmó	Spatial modeling	
空间接近性	Kōngjiān jiējinxing	Spatial proximity	
空间接口	Kōngjiān jiēkǒu	Air interface	
空间激光通信	Kōngjiān jīguāng tōngxìn	Laser space communication	
空间几何分析函数	Kōngjiān jǐhé fēnxī hánshù	Generic spatial analysis function	
空间基准	Kōngjiān jīzhǔn	Spatial datum	
空间句法	Kōngjiān jùfǎ	Spatial syntax	
空间可分级编码	Kōngjiān kěfēnjí biānmǎ	Spatial scalability coding	
空间连接	Kōngjiān liánjiē	Spatial join	
空间滤波器	Kōngjiān lǜbōqì	Spatial filter	
空间码分多址	Kōngjiān mǎfēn duōzhǐ	Space-code division multiple access	SCDMA
空间模式	Kōngjiān móshì	Spatial pattern	
空间平滑	Kōngjiān pínghuá	Spatial smoothing	
空间频率调制	Kōngjiān pínlǜ tiáozhì	Space frequency modulation	SFM
空间强度分布	Kōngjiān qiángdù fēnbù	Spatial intensity distribution (FOC)	
空间实体	Kōngjiān shítǐ	Spatial entity	
空间数据	Kōngjiān shùjù	Spatial data	
空间数据操作语言	Kōngjiān shùjù cāozuò yǔyán	Spatial data manipulation language	SDML
空间数据建模	Kōngjiān shùjù jiànmó	Spatial data modeling	
空间数据交换标准/拓扑矢量产品	Kōngjiān shùjù jiāohuàn biāozhǔn/ tuòpū shǐliàng chǎnpǐn	Spatial data transfer standard / topologic vector product	SDTS/TVP
空间数据交换格式	Kōngjiān shùjù jiāohuàn géshi	Transfer format for spatial data	
空间数据基础设施	Kōngjiān shùjù jīchǔ shèshī	Spatial data infrastructure	
空间数据结构	Kōngjiān shùjù jiégòu	Spatial data structure	
空间数据记录格式	Kōngjiān shùjù jìlù géshi	Record format for spatial data	
空间数据模型	Kōngjiān shùjù móxíng	Spatial data model	
空间数据融合	Kōngjiān shùjù rónghé	Fusion technology of spatial data	
空间数据维度	Kōngjiān shùjù wéidù	Dimensionality of spatial data	
空间数据系统咨询委宴会	Kōngjiān shùjù xìtǒng zīxún wěiyànhuì	Consultative Committee on Space Data Systems	CCSDS
空间数据转换	Kōngjiān shùjù zhuǎnhuàn	Spatial data transfer	
空间数据转换标准	Kōngjiān shùjù zhuǎnhuàn biāozhǔn	Spatial data transform standard	SDTS
空间数据库管理系统	Kōngjiān shùjùkù guǎnlǐ xìtǒng	Spatial database management system	SDBMS
空间数据库引擎	Kōngjiān shùjùkù yǐnqíng	Spatial database engine	SDE
空间顺序	Kōngjiān shùnxù	Spatial order	
空间属性	Kōngjiān shǔxìng	Spatial attribute	
空间算符	Kōngjiān suànfú	Spatial operator	
空间索引	Kōngjiān suǒyǐn	Spatial indexing	
空间探测器	Kōngjiān tàncèqì	Space probe	
空间特征	Kōngjiān tèzhēng	Spatial feature	
空间调变元件	Kōngjiān tiáobiàn yuánjiàn	Spatial light modulator	
空间投影	Kōngjiān tóuyǐng	Spatial projection	
空间无线电通信	Kōngjiān wúxiàndiàn tōngxìn	Space radio communication	

空间相互作用	Kōngjiān xiānghù zuòyòng	Spatial interaction	
空间相互作用模型	Kōngjiān xiānghù zuòyòng móxíng	Spatial interaction model	
空间现象	Kōngjiān xiànxiàng	Spatial phenomena	
空间信息	Kōngjiān xìnxī	Spatial information	
空间信息查询服务	Kōngjiān xìnxī cháxún fúwù	Spatial information enquiry service	SINES
空间系统	Kōngjiān xìtǒng	Space system	
空间研究业务	Kōngjiān yánjiū yèwù	Space research service	
空间遥测技术	Kōngjiān yáocè jìshù	Space telemetry	
空间谣令	Kōngjiān yáoling	Space telecommand	
空间依赖性	Kōngjiān yīlàixìng	Spatial dependency	
空间域	Kōngjiān yù	Spatial domain	
空间元数据的内容标准	Kōngjiān yuánshùjùde nèiróng biāozhǔn	Content standard for spatial metadata	CSSM
空间原素	Kōngjiān yuánsù	Spatial primitive	
空间再利用协议	Kōngjiān zàilìyòng xiéyì	Space recycle protocol	SRP
空间再用协议	Kōngjiān zàiyòng xiéyì	Spatial reuse protocol	SRP
空间自相关	Kōngjiān zìxiāngguān	Spatial autocorrelation	
空间/光学匹配滤光镜	Kōngjiān/guāngxué pǐpèi lǜguāngjìng	Spatial/optical matched filter	
空间站	Kōngjiānzhàn	Space station	
孔径	Kǒngjìng	Aperture	
孔径比	Kǒngjìng bǐ	Aperture ratio	
孔径失真	Kǒngjìng shīzhēn	Aperture distortion	
孔径像差	Kǒngjìng xiàngchā	Aperture aberration	
孔径效应	Kǒngjìng xiàoyìng	Aperture effect	AE
空军飞行安全指导委员会	Kōngjūn fēixíng ānquán zhǐdǎo wěiyuánhuì	Air Force Flight Safety Guidance Commission	
空军学术研究委员会	Kōngjūn xuéshù yánjiū wěiyuánhuì	Air Force Science and Research Commission	
孔内测井法	Kǒng-nèi cèjǐngfǎ	Borehole logging method	
空气处理机组	Kōngqì chǔlǐjī zǔ	Air handling unit	AHU
空气动力	Kōngqì dònglì	Aerodynamic force	
空气动力导纳	Kōngqì dònglì dǎonà	Aerodynamic admittance	
空气间隙光纤	Kōngqì jiànxì guāngxiān	Air-supported fiber	
空气隙双分离透镜	Kōngqì xì shuāng fēnlí tòujìng	Air-spaced doublet	
空气隙双合透镜	Kōngqì xì shuānghé tòujìng	Air-spaced doublet	
控腔滤波器	Kòngqiāng lǜbōqì	Cavity filter	
空腔稳频本地振荡器	Kōngqiāng wěnpín běndì zhèndàngqì	Cavity-stabilized local oscillator	
空腔谐器	Kōngqiāng xiéqì	Cavity resonator	
空腔谐振器	Kōngqiāng xiézhèn	Cavity resonator	
空腔谐振器	Kōngqiāng xiézhènqì	Cavity resonator	
空腔型振荡器	Kōngqiāng-xíng zhèndàngqì	Cavity oscillator	
空深网	Kōngshēn wǎng	Deep space network	DSN
空时发射分集	Kōngshí fāshè fēnjí	Space time transmit diversity	STTD
空时发送分集	Kōngshí fāsòng fēnjí	Space-time transmission diversity	STTD
空调通风	Kōngtiáo tōngfēng	Air conditioning ducting	FK
控位卫星	Kòngwèi wèixīng	Station-keeping satellite	
孔隙比	Kǒngxì bǐ	Void ratio	
空闲	Kòngxián	Idle	

空闲模式	Kòngxián móshì	Idle mode	
空闲时间	Kòngxián shíjiān	Idle time	
空闲信道	Kòngxián xìndào	Idle channel	
空闲信道检测	Kòngxián xìndào jiǎncè	Idle channel detection	
空闲信号识别	Kòngxián xìnhào shíbié	Idle signal identification	ISID
空闲信号系统	Kòngxián xìnhào xìtǒng	Idle signal unit	IDU
空闲信元	Kòngxián xìnyuán	Idle cell	
空闲状态	Kòngxián zhuàngtài	Idle state; free state	
空心光纤	Kōngxīn guāngxiān	Hollow fiber	
空心偏转线圈	Kōngxīn piānzhuǎn xiànquān	Air core deflection coil (radar term)	
孔型定向耦合器	Kǒngxíng dìngxiàng ǒuhéq	Hole-type directional coupler	
空域	Kōngyù	Spatial domain	
空域管理	Kōngyù guǎnlǐ	Airspace management (civil aviation)	ASM
空载电路	Kōngzài diànlù	Idling circuit	IC
空占电路状态	Kōngzhàn diànlù zhuàngtài	Idle circuit condition	
空值	Kōngzhí	Null value	
控制标志	Kòngzhì biāozhì	Control flag	
控制部件	Kòngzhì bùjiàn	Control unit	
控制层	Kòngzhì céng	Control layer	
控制处理器	Kòngzhì chǔlǐqì	Control processor	BCP
控制点	Kòngzhì diǎn	Control point, reference point	
控制点配准容差	Kòngzhì diǎn pèizhǔn róngchā	Tic match tolerance	
控制点文件	Kòngzhì diǎn wénjiàn	Tic file	
控制电路	Kòngzhì diànlù	Control electronics	CE
控制功能	Kòngzhì gōngnéng	Control function	
控制观察点	Kòngzhì guānchádiǎn	Point of control and observation	PCO
控制和传输集成件	Kòngzhì hé chuánshū jíchéng jiàn	Control and transmit assembly	CATA
控制和观测点	Kòngzhì hé guāncèdiǎn	Point of control and observation	PCO
控制和观察点	Kòngzhì hé guānchá diǎn	Point of control and observation	PCO
控制和接口集成板	Kòngzhì hé jiēkǒu jíchéngbǎn	Control and interface board assembly	BCIA
控制和维护	Kòngzhì hé wéihù	Control and maintenance	BCM
控制和维护模块	Kòngzhì hé wéihù mókuài	Control and maintenance block	BCMB
控制后面板	Kòngzhì hòumian bǎn	Control back board	
控制互通后面板	Kòngzhì hùtōng hòumian bǎn	Control interworking back panel	CIBP
控制互通节点管理器	Kòngzhì hùtōng jiédiǎn guǎnlǐqì	Control interworking node manager	CINM
控制互通节点接口	Kòngzhì hùtōng jiédiǎn jiēkǒu	Control interworking node interface	CINI
控制集	Kòngzhì jí	Control set	
控制块更新设施	Kòngzhì kuài gēngxīn shèshī	Control block update facility	CBUF
控制流图	Kòngzhì liú tú	Control flow graph	CFG
控制流语言	Kòngzhì liú yǔyán	Control-of-flow language	
控制逻辑电路	Kòngzhì luóji diànlù	Control logic circuit	
控制面	Kòngzhì miàn	Control plane	
控制面板	Kòngzhì miànbǎn	Control panel	
控制命令字	Kòngzhì mìngling zì	Control command word	CCW
控制平面	Kòngzhì píngmiàn	Control plane	CP
控制区	Kòngzhì qū	Control zone	

控制设备	Kòngzhì shèbèi	Control equipment	
控制无线网络的控制器	Kòngzhì wúxiàn wǎngluòde kòngzhìqì	Controlling radio network controller	CRNC
控制信道	Kòngzhì xìndào	Control channel (ISDN usage)	CCH
控制信号	Kòngzhì xìnhào	Control signal	
控制信号传送速率	Kòngzhì xìnhào chuánsòng sùlǜ	Control signaling rate	
控制信令码	Kòngzhì xìnlìng mǎ	Control signaling code	CSC
控制系统	Kòngzhì xìtǒng	Control system	CE
控制系统误差	Kòngzhì xìtǒng wùchā	Control system error	
控制系统信息日志	Kòngzhì xìtǒng xìnxī rìzhì	Control system message log	CSML
控制系统的程序	Kòngzhì xìtǒngde chéngxù	Control system program	
控制依赖图	Kòngzhì yīlài tú	Control dependence graph	CDG
控制语句	Kòngzhì yǔjù	Control statement	
控制运算单元	Kòngzhì yùnsuàn dānyuán	Control arithmetic unit	CAU
控制栅光电培增器	Kòngzhì zhà guāngdiàn péizēngqì	Grid-gated photomultiplier	GGPM
控制栅光电培增器	Kòngzhì zhà guāngdiàn péizēngqì	Control gate photomultiplier	
控制制图	Kòngzhì zhìtú	Control mapping	
控制中断报表	Kòngzhì zhōngduàn bàobiǎo	Control-break report	
控制字	Kòngzhì zì	Control word	CW
控制字符	Kòngzhì zìfú	Control character	
控制总线寄偶校验错	Kòngzhì zǒngxiàn jì'ǒu jiàoyàn cuò	Control bus parity check error	CPAR
控制论	Kòngzhìlùn	Cybernetic	
控制台	Kòngzhìtái	Control console	CON
控制台	Kòngzhìtái	Console	
控制台打字机	Kòngzhìtái dǎzìjī	Console typewriter	
控制台接口板	Kòngzhìtái jiēkǒu bǎn	Console interface board	CIB
控制台输入输出装置	Kòngzhìtái shūrù shūchū zhuāngzhì	Console input/output	
控制站	Kòngzhìzhàn	Control station	
控制站	Kòngzhìzhàn	Control station	
空中交通服务	Kōngzhōng jiāotōng fúwù	Air traffic services (civil aviation)	ATS
空中交通管理	Kōngzhōng jiāotōng guǎnlǐ	Air traffic management (civil aviation)	ATM
空中交通管制	Kōngzhōng jiāotōng guǎnzhì	Air traffic control (civil aviation)	ATC
空中交通管制雷达	Kōngzhōng jiāotōng guǎnzhì léidá	Air traffic control radar	
空中交通量管理	Kōngzhōng jiāotōngliàng guǎnlǐ	Air traffic flow management (civil aviation)	ATFM
空中接口	Kōngzhōng jiēkǒu	Air interface	
空中接口	Kōngzhōng jiēkǒu	Space connector	UM
空中接口用户速率	Kōngzhōng jiēkǒu yònghù sùlǜ	Air interface user rate	AIUR
空中链路	Kōngzhōng liànlù	Air link	
空中下载业务准备	Kōngzhōng xiàzài yèwù zhǔnbèi	Over-the-air parameter administration	OTASP
空中下载业务准备操作	Kōngzhōng xiàzài yèwù zhǔnbèi cāozuò	Over-the-air service provisioning function	OTAF
空中信道获取时刻	Kōngzhōng xìndào huòqǔ shíkè	Air seizure time (telecom billing)	
口参考点	Kǒu cānkǎo diǎn	Mouth reference point	MRP
口令	Kǒulìng	Password	PW
口令登记故障	Kǒulìng dēngjì gùzhàng	Password registration failure	
口令对话	Kǒulìng duìhuà	Password dialog (IPsec)	
口令认证协议	Kǒulìng rènzhèng xiéyì	Password authentication protocol	PAP
口令字猜测	Kǒulìng zì cāicè	Password cracking (hacker attack)	

口面	Kǒumiàn	Aperture (of an antenna)	
口面上场的锥削分布	Kǒumiàn shàngchǎngde zhuīxiāo fēnbù	Tapered distribution of a field over an aperture	
口面天线	Kǒumiàn tiānxiàn	Aperture-type antenna	
口面相差	Kǒumiàn xiàngchà	Phase error in aperture	
口面照射函数	Kǒumiàn zhàoshè hánshù	Aperture illumination function	
口面照射效率	Kǒumiàn zhàoshè xiàolǜ	Aperture illumination efficiency	
口面阻挡	Kǒumiàn zǔdǎng	Aperture blockage	
口面阻挡损失	Kǒumiàn zǔdǎng sǔnshī	Aperture blockage loss	
口面阻挡因数	Kǒumiàn zǔdǎng yīnshù	Aperture blocking factor (in a reflector antenna)	
口头传媒	Kǒutóu chuánméi	Verbal communication	
口信	Kǒuxìn	Voicemail, voice message	
KTN 计算组成管理	KTN jìsuàn zǔchéng guǎnlǐ	KTN computing configuration management	KTN-Com.CM
KTN 连接组成管理	KTN liánjiē zǔchéng guǎnlǐ	KTN connection configuration management	KTN-Con.CM
KTN 拓扑组成管理	KTN tuòpū zǔchéng guǎnlǐ	KTN topology configuration management	KTN-TCM
KTN 协议组成管理	KTN xiéyì zǔchéng guǎnlǐ	KTN protocol configuration management	KTN-Pro.CM
KTN 组成管理	KTN zǔchéng guǎnlǐ	KTN configuration management	KTN.CM
库	Kù	Library	
跨步电压	Kuà bù diànyā	Step voltage	
跨局检验	Kuà jú jiǎnyàn	Cross-office check	
跨梁敷设	Kuà liáng fūshè	Across beam (in telecom installation)	AB
跨频带分集[接收]	Kuà píndài fēnjí (jiēshōu)	Cross band diversity (reception)	
跨区卷	Kuà qū juàn	Spanned volume	
跨珠敷设	Kuà zhū fūshè	Across column (in telecom installation)	AC
跨阻抗型	Kuà zǔkàngxíng	Transimpedance	
块	Kuài	Block (noun)	
块保护	Kuài bǎohù	Block protection	
块保护时间	Kuài bǎohù shíjiān	Block guard time	BGT
快捕带	Kuài bǔ dài	Fast pull-in range	
块差错率	Kuài chācuò lǜ	Block error rate	
块等待时间	Kuài děngdài shíjiān	Block waiting time	BWT
块浮点分布式	Kuài fúdiǎn fēnbùshì	Block floating-point distributed	BFD
块滑移	Kuài huáyí	Block glide	
块检验字符	Kuài jiǎnyàn zìfú	Block check character	BCC
块校验规程	Kuài jiàoyàn guīchéng	Block check procedure	
块结束符	Kuài jiéshùfú	End of block	EOB
块净负荷	Kuài jìng fùhè	Block payload	
块净荷	Kuài jìnghé	Block payload	
快链路脉冲	Kuài liànlù màichōng	Fast link pulse	FLP
块码	Kuài mǎ	Block code	
块密码	Kuài mìmǎ	Block cipher	
块群	Kuài qún	Group of blocks	GOB
快时间常数电路	Kuài shíjiān chángshù diànlù	Fast time constant circuit	FTC
块数据校验方式	Kuài shùjù jiàoyàn fāngshì	Block data check mode	BDCM
快跳频	Kuài tiàopín	Fast frequency hopping	FFH
块误码率	Kuài wùmǎ lǜ	Block error rate	BLER
块信元速率	Kuài xìnyuán sùlǜ	Block cell rate	BCR

块有效负荷	Kuài yǒuxiào fùhè	Block payload	
块周期	Kuài zhōuqī	Block cycle	
块字适应算法	Kuài zìshìyìng suànfǎ	Block adaptive algorithm	BAA
快剪试验	Kuàijiǎn shìyàn	Quick shear test	
快捷方式	Kuàijié fāngshì	Shortcut	
快捷键	Kuàijié jiàn	Shortcut key	
快闪存储器	Kuàishǎn cúnchǔqì	Flash memory	FM
块闪可编程只读存储器	Kuàishǎn kěbiānchéng zhǐdú cúnchǔqì	Flash programmable read only memory	FLASH-PROM
快闪要求	Kuàishǎn yāoqiú	Flash request	
快速重路由	Kuàisù chónglùyóu	Fast reroute	
快速串行接口处理器	Kuàisù chuànháng jiēkǒu chǔlǐqì	Fast serial interface processor	FSIP
快速传输协议	Kuàisù chuánshū xiéyì	Rapid transport protocol	RTP
快速传送协议	Kuàisù chuánsòng xiéyì	Rapid transport protocol	RTP
快速电路交换	Kuàisù diànlù jiāohuàn	Fast circuit switching	FCS
快速反应	Kuàisù fǎnyìng	Quick response	QR
快速分组交换	Kuàisù fēnzǔ jiāohuàn	Fast packet switching	FPS
快速傅利叶变换	Kuàisù fù-lì-yè biànhuàn	Fast Fourier transform	FFT
快速付里叶变换	Kuàisù fù-lǐ-yè biànhuàn	Fast Fourier transform	FFT
快速傅氏变换	Kuàisù fù-shì biànhuàn	Fast Fourier transform	FFT
快速更新请求	Kuàisù gēngxīn qǐngqiú	Fast update request	
快速哈达码变换	Kuàisù hǎ-dá-mǎ biànhuàn	Fast Hadamard transform	FHT
快速晶闸管	Kuàisù jīngzháguǎn	Fast switching thyristor	FST
快速进入/退出多媒体状态	Kuàisù jìnrù/tuìchū duōméitǐ zhuàngtài	Fast entry/exit multimedia state	FEMMS
快速连续传送	Kuàisù liánxù chuánsòng	Fast sequenced transport	FST
快速模式处理机	Kuàisù móshì chǔlǐjī	Fast pattern processor	FPP
快速排序	Kuàisù páixù	Quick sort	
快速频移键控	Kuàisù pínyí jiànkòng	Fast frequency-shift keying	FFSK
快速匹配	Kuàisù pǐpèi	Speed matching	
快速热欧姆转换	Kuàisù rè Oū-mǔ zhuǎnhuàn	Fast Fourier transform	FFT
快速热处理	Kuàisù rèchǔlǐ	Rapid thermal processing	RTP
快速随路控制信道	Kuàisù suílù kòngzhì xìndào	Fast associated control channel	FACCH
快速随路控制信道/半速率	Kuàisù suílù kòngzhì xìndào/bàn sùlǜ	Fast associated control channel/half rate	FACCH/H
快速随路控制信道/全速率	Kuàisù suílù kòngzhì xìndào/quánsùlǜ	Fast associated control channel/full rate	FACCH/F
快速跳频	Kuàisù tiàopín	Fast frequency hopping	FFH
快速沃尔什变换	Kuàisù wò-ěr-shí biànhuàn	Fast Walsh transform	FWT
快速相关控制信道/全速率	Kuàisù xiāngguān kòngzhì xìndào/quánsùlǜ	Fast associated control channel/full rate	FACCH/F
快速小区选择	Kuàisù xiǎoqū xuǎnzé	Fast cell selection	FCS
快速选择	Kuàisù xuǎnzé	Fast select	
快速样机平台	Kuàisù yàngjī píngtái	Rapid prototyping platform	
快速移频键控	Kuàisù yípín jiànkòng	Fast frequency shift keying	FFSK
快速以太网	Kuàisù yǐtàiwǎng	Fast ethernet (IEEE 802.3u)	
快速以太网接口处理器	Kuàisù yǐtàiwǎng jiēkǒu chǔlǐqì	Fast ethernet interface processor	FEIP
快速邮件传输协议	Kuàisù yóujiàn chuánshū xiéyì	Quick mail transfer protocol	QMTP
快速有序运输(协议)	Kuàisù yǒuxù yùnshū (xiéyì)	Fast sequenced transport (protocol)	FST
快照	Kuàizhào	Snapshot	
快照代理程序	Kuàizhào dàilǐ chéngxù	Snapshot agent	

快照代理程序实用工具	Kuàizhào dàilǐ chéngxù shíyòng gōngjù	Snapshot agent utility	
快照复制	Kuàizhào fùzhì	Snapshot replication	
快照游标	Kuàizhào yóubiāo	Snapshot cursor	
跨接损耗	Kuàjiē sǔnhào	Bridging loss	
跨接线	Kuàjiēxiàn	Jumper wire	
跨距	Kuàjù	Span	
垮客	Kuǎ-kè	Cracker (person or program that breaks passwords)	
宽动态范围	Kuān dòngtài fànwéi	Wide dynamic range	
宽孔径天线	Kuān kǒngjìng tiānxiàn	Wide aperture antenna	WAA
宽平稳	Kuān píngwěn	Wide-sense stationary	WSS
宽带	Kuāndài	Broadband, wideband	BW
宽带本地交换	Kuāndài běndì jiāohuàn	Broadband local exchange	B-LEX
宽带发射	Kuāndài fāshè	Broadband emission	
宽带干扰	Kuāndài gānrǎo	Broadband interference	
宽带光放大器	Kuāndài guāng fàngdàqì	Broadband optical fiber amplifier	BOFA
宽带光全业务接入网	Kuāndài guāng quán yèwù jiērù wǎng	Broadband optical full service network	BOFSN
宽带固定无线接入	Kuāndài gùdìng wúxiàn jiērù	Broadband fixed wireless access	BFWA
宽带 ISDN 协议参考模型	Kuāndài ISDN xiéyì cānkǎo móxíng	Protocol reference model of broadband ISDN	B-ISDN PRM
宽带 ISDN 用户部分	Kuāndài ISDN yònghù bùfen	Broadband ISDN user part	B-ISUP
宽带 ISDN 用户部分	Kuāndài ISDN yònghù bùfen	Broadband ISDN user part	BISUP
宽带交换单元	Kuāndài jiāohuàn dānyuán	Broadband switching unit	BSU
宽带交换系统	Kuāndài jiāohuàn xìtǒng	Broad band switching system	BSS
宽带交换业务	Kuāndài jiāohuàn yèwù	Broadband exchange service	BES
宽带交换终接	Kuāndài jiāohuàn zhōngjiē	Broadband exchange termination	B-ET
宽带接入	Kuāndài jiērù	Broadband access	
宽带接入单元	Kuāndài jiērù dānyuán	Broadband access unit	BAU
宽带接入服务器	Kuāndài jiērù fúwùqì	Broadband access server	BRAS
宽带接入网	Kuāndài jiērù wǎng	Broadband access network	BAN
宽带激光器	Kuāndài jīguāngqì	Wideband laser diode	
宽带拒绝	Kuāndài jùjué	Broadband rejected	BRJ
宽带码分多址	Kuāndài mǎfēn duōzhǐ	Wideband code division multiple access	WCDMA
宽带耦合器	Kuāndài ǒuhéqì	Broadband coupler	BBC
宽带器件	Kuāndài qìjiàn	Broadband device	
宽带请求	Kuāndài qǐngqiú	Broadband request	BRQ
宽带确认	Kuāndài quèrèn	Broadband confirmed	BCF
宽带设备	Kuāndài shèbèi	Broadband device	
宽带射频功率放大器	Kuāndài shèpín gōnglǜ fàngdàqì	Wideband radio frequency power amplifier	
宽带时分多路存取	Kuāndài shífēn duōlù cúnqǔ	Wideband time division multiple access	WBTDMA
宽带适配器	Kuāndài shìpèiqì	Broadband adapter	BBA
宽带数据峰值频偏	Kuāndài shùjù fēngzhí pínpiān	Wideband data peak frequency deviation	
宽带数据复用器	Kuāndài shùjù fùyòngqì	Broadband data multipexer	BDM
宽带天线	Kuāndài tiānxiàn	Broadband antenna	
宽带通信通路	Kuāndài tōngxìn tōnglù	Broadband communication channel	
宽带通信信道	Kuāndài tōngxìn xìndào	Broadband communication channel	
宽带网络	Kuāndài wǎngluò	Broadband network	
宽带网络接入服务器	Kuāndài wǎngluò jiērù fúwùqì	Broadband network access server	BNAS

宽带无线 ATM 系统	Kuāndài wúxiàn ATM xìtǒng	Broadband wireless ATM system	BWAN
宽带无线 MAN 标准	Kuāndài wúxiàn MAN biāozhǔn	Broadband wireless MAN standard (IEEE 802.16)	WiMAX
宽带无源光网络	Kuāndài wúyuán guāng wǎngluò	Wideband passive optical network	BPON
宽带无源光网络	Kuāndài wúyuán guāng wǎngluò	Broadband passive optical network	B-PON
宽带消息传递部三层	Kuāndài xiāoxi chuándì bù sāncéng	Broadband message transfer part level 3 (in SS7)	MTPL3-b
宽带信道	Kuāndài xìndào	Wideband channel	
宽带用户 - 网络接口	Kuāndài yònghù-wǎngluò jiēkǒu	Broadband user-network interface	B-UNI
宽带远程接入服务器	Kuāndài yuǎnchéng jiērù fúwùqì	Broadband remote access server	BRAS
宽带运行中心	Kuāndài yùnxíng zhōngxīn	Broadband operation center	BBOC
宽带中频放大器	Kuāndài zhōngpín fàngdàqì	Broadband intermediate frequency amplifier	
宽带综合业务数字网	Kuāndài zōnghé yèwù shùzì wǎng	Broadband integrated services digital network	B-ISDN
宽带综合业务数字网用户部分	Kuāndài zōnghé yèwù shùzìwǎng yònghù bùfen	Broadband integrated services digital network- user part	B-ISUP
框架	Kuàngjià	Framework	
框图编辑器	Kuàngtú biānjíqì	Block diagram editor	
宽频放大器	Kuānpín fàngdàqì	Broadband amplifier	
宽频段电台	Kuānpínduàn diàntái	Wideband station	
宽限名称检查	Kuānxiàn míngchēng jiǎnchá	Loose name checking	
宽域通信/电话服务	Kuānyù tōngxìn/diànhuà fúwù	Wide area telecommunications/telephone service	WATS
跨越	Kuàyuè	Span	
库存定额管理	Kùcún dìng'é guǎnlǐ	Storage quota management	
库存管理系统	Kùcún guǎnlǐ xìtǒng	Inventory control system	
库存核算价	Kùcún hésuàn jià	Storage price	
馈电	Kuìdiàn	Battery supply to subscriber line (the B in BORSCHT, q.v.)	
馈电	Kuìdiàn	Line feed	
馈电点沿轴的横向移动的偶极天线	Kuìdiàn diǎn yán zhóude héngxiàng yídòngde ǒují tiānxiàn	Dipole antenna with feed points displaced transverse to dipole axis	DAFDTA
馈电网络	Kuìdiàn wǎngluò	Feed network	
馈电器	Kuìdiànqì	Feed	
馈送链路	Kuìsòng liànlù	Feeder link	
馈线	Kuìxiàn	Feed, feeder, feed line	
馈线链路	Kuìxiàn liànlù	Feeder link	
馈线损耗	Kuìxiàn sǔnhào	Feed line loss, feeder loss	
馈线网络	Kuìxiàn wǎngluò	Feed line network	
馈源	Kuìyuán	Feed (of an antenna)	
馈纸式影像扫描器	Kuìzh-shì yǐngxiàng sǎomiáoqì	Sheet-fed color image scanner	
捆绑	Kǔnbǎng	Binding	
捆绑式服务	Kǔnbǎng-shì fúwù	Bundled services	
扩充包顺序编号	Kuòchōng bāo shùnxù biānhào	Extended packet sequence numbering	EPSN
扩充编址	Kuòchōng biānzhǐ	Extended addressing	EA
扩充标记语言	Kuòchōng biāojì yǔyán	Extensible markup language	XML
扩充槽	Kuòchōng cáo	Expansion slot	
扩充插槽	Kuòchōng chācáo	Expansion slot	
扩充存储器	Kuòchōng cúnchǔqì	Extended memory	EM
扩充工业标准体系结构	Kuòchōng gōngyè biāozhǔn tǐxì jiégòu	Extended industry standard architecture	EISA

扩充后向建立不成功消息	Kuòchōng hòuxiàng jiànlì bùchénggōng xiāoxi	Extended unsuccessful backward setup information message	EUM
扩充记忆体	Kuòchōng jìyìtǐ	eXtended memory specification	XMS
扩充内存	Kuòchōng nèicún	Expanded memory	
扩充能力端口	Kuòchōng nénglì duān kǒu	Extended capabilities port	ECP
扩充数据的嵌入	Kuòchōng shùjùde qiànrù	Augmentation data embedding	
扩充应答信息指示	Kuòchōng yìngdá xìnxī zhǐshì	Extended answer message indication	EAM
扩充运算模块	Kuòchōng yùnsuàn mókuài	Extended arithmetic module	EAM
扩充的存储器	Kuòchōngde cúnchǔqì	Extended memory unit	EMU
扩充的电话系统程序语言	Kuòchōngde diànhuà xìtǒng chéngxù yǔyán	Extended telephone systems programming language	ETSPL
扩充的二-十进制交换码	Kuòchōngde èr-shíjìnzhì jiāohuàn mǎ	Extended binary coded decimal code	EBCDIC
扩充的公共服务区	Kuòchōngde gōnggòng fúwùqū	Extended common service area	ECSA
扩充的工业标准结构	Kuòchōngde gōngyè biāozhǔn jiégòu	Extended industry standard architecture	EISA
扩充的汇编语言编码	Kuòchōngde huìbiān yǔyán biānmǎ	Extended assembler language coding	XALC
扩充的会话参考	Kuòchōngde huìhuà cānkǎo	Expanded session reference	
扩充的奇偶校验	Kuòchōngde jīǒu jiàoyàn	Augmented parity check	APC
扩充的页面表项	Kuòchōngde yèmiàn biǎoxiàng	Extended page table entry	XPTE
扩充的直接存储器存取	Kuòchōngde zhíjiē cúnchǔqì cúnqǔ	Extended direct memory access	EDMA
扩大区域服务	Kuòdà qūyù fúwù	Extended area service (telephony term)	EAS
括号	Kuòhào	Bracket [ ]	
扩频	Kuòpín	Spread spectrum (short for 扩展频谱)	
扩频多址	Kuòpín duōzhǐ	Spread spectrum multiple access	SSMA
扩频随机接入	Kuòpín suíjī jiērù	Spread spectrum random access	SSRA
扩频调制	Kuòpín tiáozhì	Spread spectrum modulation	
扩频通信	Kuòpín tōngxìn	Spread spectrum communication	SSC
扩频因子	Kuòpín yīnzǐ	Spreading factor	SF
扩频增益	Kuòpín zēngyì	Spreading gain	SG
扩谱系数	Kuòpǔ xìshù	Spread spectrum coefficient	
扩散	Kuòsàn	Diffusion	
扩散	Kuòsàn	Expansion (in switching)	
扩散电流	Kuòsàn diànliú	Diffusion current	
扩散炉	Kuòsàn lú	Diffusion furnace	
扩散修正算法	Kuòsàn xiūzhèng suànfǎ	Diffusing update algorithm	DUAL
扩散准则	Kuòsàn zhǔnzé	Propagation property	
扩声系统	Kuòshēng xìtǒng	Sound reinforcement system	SRS
扩压函数	Kuòyā hánshù	Diffusion function	
扩展标示语言支持	Kuòzhǎn biāoshì yǔyán zhīchí	Extensible markup language (in SQL Server)	XML
扩展测量	Kuòzhǎn cèliáng	Expansion measurement	EM
扩展传输时隙	Kuòzhǎn chuánshū shíxì	Expanded transmission time slots	
扩展存储过程	Kuòzhǎn cúnchǔ guòchéng	Extended stored procedure	
扩展存储器	Kuòzhǎn cúnchǔqì	Expanded memory unit	EMU
扩展带光纤放大器	Kuòzhǎn dài guāngxiān fàngdàqì	Extended band fiber amplifier	EBFA
扩展等待时间	Kuòzhǎn děngdài shíjiān	Waiting time extension	WTX
扩展地址	Kuòzhǎn dìzhǐ	Extended address	EA
扩展端口	Kuòzhǎn duānkǒu	Expansion port	
扩展短消息实体	Kuòzhǎn duǎnxiāoxi shítǐ	Expanded short message entity	ESME

扩展短消息试题代理	Kuòzhǎn duǎnxiāoxi shìtí dàilǐ	Extended short message entity agent	ESME Agent
扩展二进制编码的十进制交换格式	Kuòzhǎn èrjìnzhì biānmǎde shíjìnzhì jiāohuàn géshi	Extended binary coded decimal interchange code	EBCDIC
扩展访问控制标记语言	Kuòzhǎn fǎngwèn kòngzhì biāoji yǔyán	Extensible access control markup language	XACML
扩展分区	Kuòzhǎn fēnqū	Extended partition	
扩展耗损	Kuòzhǎn hàosǔn	Spreading loss	
扩展架	Kuòzhǎn jià	Extended rack	BCER
扩展节理	Kuòzhǎn jiélǐ	Expansion joint	
扩展卷积码	Kuòzhǎn juànjī mǎ	Diffuse convolutional codes	
扩展累加器	Kuòzhǎn lěijiāqì	Quotient register	Q
扩展马尔科夫进程代数	Kuòzhǎn mǎ-ěr-kē-fū jìnchéng dàishù	Extended Markovian process algebra	EMPA
扩展名	Kuòzhǎn míng	Extension (3-letter extension to a computer file name)	
扩展内存规范	Kuòzhǎn nèicún guīfàn	Expanded memory specification	EMS
扩展频谱	Kuòzhǎn pínpǔ	Spread spectrum	SS
扩展频谱多址	Kuòzhǎn pínpǔ duōzhǐ	Spread spectrum multiple access	SSMA
扩展频谱频率跳变	Kuòzhǎn pínpǔ pínlǜ tiàobiàn	Spread spectrum frequency hopping	SSFH
扩展频谱调制	Kuòzhǎn pínpǔ tiáozhì	Spread spectrum modulation	SSM
扩展频谱通信	Kuòzhǎn pínpǔ tōngxìn	Spread spectrum communication	
扩展认证协议	Kuòzhǎn rènzhèng xiéyì	Extensible authentication protocol (in PPP)	EAP
扩展属性邻接图	Kuòzhǎn shǔxìng línjiē tú	Extended attribute adjacency graph (CAD/CAM)	EAAG
扩展头部长度	Kuòzhǎn tóubù chángdù	Header extension length	HEL
扩展系统配置数据	Kuòzhǎn xìtǒng pèizhì shùjù	Extended system configuration data	ESCD
扩展帧头	Kuòzhǎn zhèngtóu	Extended header	EHDR
扩展字符集	Kuòzhǎn zìfú jí	Extended character set	
扩展总线	Kuòzhǎn zǒngxiàn	Expansion bus	EB
扩展的彩色图形显示适配器	Kuòzhǎnde cǎisè túxíng xiǎnshì shìpèiqì	Enhanced graphics adapter	EGA
扩展的倒换命令	Kuòzhǎnde dǎohuàn mìnglìng	Extended changeover order	XCO
扩展的倒换证实	Kuòzhǎnde dǎohuàn zhèngshí	Extended changeover acknowledgment	XCA
扩展的字符组	Kuòzhǎnde zìfú zǔ	Expanded character set	ECS
扩张速率	Kuòzhāng sùlǜ	Spreading rate	
扩展器	Kuòzhǎnqì	Expander	
扩展性标识语言	Kuòzhǎn-xìng biāozhì yǔyán	Extensible markup language	XML
扩展型简单邮件传输协议	Kuòzhǎn-xíng jiǎndān yóujiàn chuánshū xiéyì	Extended simple mail transfer protocol	ESMTP
库特公式	Kù-tè gōngshì	Kutter's formula	

L

L2R 比特定向协议	L2R bǐtè dìngxiàng xiéyì	L2R bit-oriented protocol	
L2R 性能定向协议	L2R xìngnéng dìngxiàng xiéyì	L2R function-oriented protocol	
L2TP 接入聚合器	L2TP jiērù jùhéqì	L2TP access concentrator	LAC
L2TP 网络服务器	L2TP wǎngluò fúwùqì	L2TP network server	
拉伙伴	Lā huǒbàn	Pull partner	
喇叭反射器天线	Lǎba fǎnshè qì tiānxiàn	Horn reflector antenna	
喇叭抛物反射面天线	Lǎba pāowù fǎnshèmiàn tiānxiàn	Horn parabolic reflector antenna	
喇叭天线	Lǎba tiānxiàn	Horn antenna	
喇叭型天线	Lǎba-xíng tiānxiàn	Hogg horn antenna	HA

拉丁超立方体抽样	Lā-dīng chāolìfāngtǐ chōuyàng	Latin hypercube sampling	
拉夫波	Lā-fū bō	Love wave	
拉格朗日乘积因子法	Lā-gé-lǎng-rì chéngjī yīnzǐ fǎ	Lagrange multipliers method	
来宾	Láibīn	Guest	
来宾帐户	Láibīn zhànghù	Guest account	
来访登记	Láifǎng dēngjì	Visitor register	
来访位置登记器	Láifǎng wèizhì dēngjìqì	Visitor location register	VLR
来访位置注册处	Láifǎng wèizhì zhùcèchù	Visitor location register	VLR
来访移动用户	Láifǎng yídòng yònghù	Visiting mobile subscriber	
来话	Láihuà	Incoming	
来话呼叫筛选业务	Láihuà hūjiào shāixuǎn yèwù	Incoming call screening service	ICS
来话呼叫网关	Láihuà hūjiào wǎngguān	Incoming call gateway	ICGW
来话呼叫限制	Láihuà hūjiào xiànzhì	Incoming calls barred	ICB
来话应答	Láihuà yìngdá	Incoming answer	
来往传输时间	Láiwǎng chuánshū shíjiān	Round-trip time	RTT
来自骚扰源的发射限值	Láizì sāorǎoyuánde fāshè xiànzhí	Emission limit from a disturbing source	
垃圾回收	Lājī huíshōu	Garbage collection	GC
垃圾收集	Lājī shōují	Garbage collection	GC
垃圾邮件	Lājī yóujiàn	Spam	
喇曼光纤	Lǎ-màn guāngxiān	Raman fiber	
拉曼光纤放大器	Lā-màn guāngxiān fàngdàqì	Fiber optic Raman amplifier	FRA
拉曼光学时域反射测量术	Lā-màn guāngxué shíyù fǎnshè cèliáng shù	Raman optical time-domain reflectometry	ROTDR
喇曼效应	Lǎ-màn xiàoyìng	Raman effect	
拉莫尔频率	Lā-mò-ěr pínlǜ	Larmor frequency	
LAN 仿真-网间接口	LAN fǎngzhēn- wǎngjiān jiēkǒu	LAN emulation - network to network interface	LANE-NNI
LAN 仿真-用户与网络间接口	LAN fǎngzhēn– yònghù yǔ wǎngluòjiān jiēkǒu	Local area network (LAN) emulation - user to network interface	LANE-UNI
栏分界线	Lán fēnjièxiàn	Column break (WP command)	
缆调制解调器	Lǎn tiáozhì jiětiáoqì	Cable modem	CM
缆中心管	Lǎn zhōngxīn guǎn	Central tube (FOC mfg)	
朗伯分布	Lǎng-bó fēnbù	Lambertian distribution	
朗伯辐射体	Lǎng-bó fúshètǐ	Lambertian source	
廊道	Lángdào	Corridor	
朗讯科技公司	Lǎng-xùn kējì gōngsī	Lucent Technologies Corp. (US company)	
浪涌	Làngyǒng	Surge, galloping	
浪涌保护器	Làngyǒng bǎohùqì	Surge protection device	
浪涌电流	Làngyǒng diànliú	Surge current	
浪涌抑制器	Làngyǒng yìzhìqì	Surge suppressor	
拦截飞行工具	Lánjié fēixíng gōngjù	Interceptor flight tool (software)	IFT
蓝色巨人	Lánsè jùrén	Big Blue (nickname for IBM, Inc.)	
缆式线型感温探测器	Lǎnshìxiànxíng gǎnwēn tàncèqì	Cable thermal detector	CTD
栏位	Lánwèi	Field	
蓝牙	Lányá	Bluetooth	
蓝牙接入点	Lányá jiērù diǎn	Bluetooth access point	BAP
蓝牙技术	Lányá jìshù	Bluetooth technology	
蓝牙特殊利益集团	Lányá tèshū lìyì jítuán	Bluetooth Special Interest Group (SIG)	

蓝牙质量鉴定程序	Lányá zhìliàng jiàndìng chéngxù	Bluetooth qualification program	
滥用检测	Lànyòng jiǎncè	Mis-use detection	
老化	Lǎohuà	Burn-in	
老化测试	Lǎohuà cèshì	Ageing test	
老化故障	Lǎohuà gùzhàng	Ageing fault	
老化失效	Lǎohuà shīxiào	Ageing failure	
老式普通电话业务	Lǎoshì pǔtōng diànhuà yèwù	Plain old telephone service	POTS
拉偏测试	Lāpiān cèshì	Partiality test (circuit test to determine if one component receives more voltage than another, usually within permissible range of fluctuation leading to fault on either extreme.)	
拉偏测试	Lāpiān cèshì	Bias test	
拉伸负荷	Lāshēn fùhè	Tensile load	
拉伸门	Lāshēn mén	Tainter gate (in civil engineering)	
拉伸应力	Lāshēn yìnglì	Tensile Stress	
拉手条	Lāshǒutiáo	End plate on a computer board/card	
拉丝	Lāsī	Draw (verb, FOC mfg)	
拉丝	Lāsī	Wire drawing (noun)	
拉线	Lāxiàn	Pull string	
拉下式菜单	Lāxià-shì càidān	Pull-down menu	
LCS 用户保密指南	LCS yònghù bǎomì zhǐnán	Subscriber LCS privacy profile	SLPP
类	Lèi	Class	
类标识符	Lèi biāozhìfú	Class identifier	
类层次结构	Lèi céngcì jiégòu	Class hierarchy	
类厂	Lèi chǎng	Class factory	
类定义	Lèi dìngyì	Class definition	
类继承列表	Lèi jìchéng lièbiǎo	Class derivation list	
类库	Lèi kù	Class library	
类模板	Lèi múbǎn	Class template	
类模板部分特化	Lèi múbǎn bùfen tèhuà	Class template partial specializations	
类模板特化	Lèi múbǎn tèhuà	Class template specializations	
类声明	Lèi shēngmíng	Class declaration	
类同步的	Lèi tóngbùde	Homochronous	
类装载器	Lèi zhuāngzàiqì	Class loader	
类比数位转化器	Lèibǐ shùwèi zhuǎnhuàqì	Analog-to-digital converter	
类别	Lèibié	Class	
类别分析	Lèibié fēnxī	Category analysis	
雷达	Léidá	Radar	
雷达沉默	Léidá chénmò	Radar silence	
雷达车厢	Léidá chēxiāng	Radar shelter	
雷达方舱	Léidá fāngcāng	Radar cabin	
雷达方程	Léidá fāngchéng	Radar equation	
雷达反射气球	Léidá fǎnshè qìqiú	Radar reflective balloon	
雷达分辨力	Léidá fēnbiànlì	Radar resolution	
雷达干扰弹	Léidá gānrǎo dàn	Radar jamming shell	
雷达干扰机	Léidá gānrǎojī	Radar jammer	
雷达回波	Léidá huíbō	Radar echo	

雷达警戒范围	Léidá jǐngjiè fànwéi	Radar warning coverage	
雷达目标	Léidá mùbiāo	Radar target	
雷达目标识别	Léidá mùbiāo shíbié	Radar target identification	
雷达平台运动补偿	Léidá píngtái yùndòng bǔcháng	Radar platform movement compensation	
雷达天文学	Léidá tiānwénxué	Radar astronomy	
雷达网系统	Léidá wǎng xìtǒng	Netted radar system	
雷达卫星	Léidá wèixīng	Radarsat	
雷达伪装	Léidá wěizhuāng	Radar camouflage	
雷达陷阱	Léidá xiànjǐng	Radar trap	
雷达信标	Léidá xìnbiāo	Radar beacon	Racon
雷达性能价格比	Léidá xìngnéng jiàgé bǐ	Radar performance-to-cost ratio	
雷达信管	Léidá xìnguǎn	Radar fuse	
雷达信号模拟器	Léidá xìnhào mónǐqì	Radar signals simulator	
雷达引导范围	Léidá yǐndǎo fànwéi	Radar vectoring coverage	
雷达自卫距离	Léidá zìwèi jùlí	Radar self-screening range	
雷迪有限公司	Léi-dí yǒuxiàn gōngsī	Radiodetection Corp. (US company)	
雷电冲击	Léidiàn chōngjī	Lightning surge	
类号	Lèihào	Tag	
累积不可用时间	Lěijī bùkěyòng shíjiān	Accumulated down time	
累积抖动	Lěijī dǒudòng	Accumulated jitter	
累积呼叫计量器	Lěijī hūjiào jìliàngqì	Accumulated call meter	ACM
累积呼叫计量器最大值	Lěijī hūjiào jìliàngqì zuìdàzhí	Accumulated call meter max	ACMM
累积呼叫计数	Lěijī hūjiào jìshù	Accumulated call meter	ACM
累计呼叫表	Lěijì hūjiàobiǎo	Accumulated call meter	ACM
累积时间	Lěijī shíjiān	Accumulated time	
累加器	Lěijiāqì	Accumulator	
雷诺数	Léi-nuò shù	Reynolds number	
雷声公司	Léi-shēng gōngsī	Raytheon Corp. (US company)	
类同步的	Lèitóngbùde	Homochronous	
类型	Lèixíng	Type	
类型长度值	Lèixíng chángdù zhí	Type-length-value	TLV
类型码	Lèixíng mǎ	Category code	
类型属性	Lèixíng shǔxìng	Categorical attribute	
类型-长度-取值的编码格式	Lèixíng-chángdù-qǔzhíde biānmǎ géshi	Type-length-value	TLV
类型--长度--值	Lèixíng-chángdù-zhí	Type-length-value	TLV
勒克司	Lè-kè-sī	Lux (unit of illumination)	
冷焊锡点	Lěng hànxīdiǎn	Cold solder joint (in SMT)	
冷镜	Lěng jìng	Cold mirror	
冷启动	Lěng qǐdòng	Cold boot; cold start	
冷清洗	Lěng qingxǐ	Cold cleaning (in SMT)	
冷压钳	Lěng yā qián	Cold-pressed pliers	
楞勃透镜天线	Léng-bó tòujìng tiānxiàn	Luneburg lens antenna	LLA
冷点	Lěngdiǎn	Cold point (of a radiating element)	
棱镜	Léngjìng	Prism	
冷媒	Lěngméi	Coolant	
冷却试验	Lěngquè shìyàn	Cooling test	

冷却剂	Lěngquèjì	Coolant	
锂离子电池	Lǐ lízǐ diànchí	Lithium ion battery	
链	Liàn	Chain (function calls)	
链表	Liàn biǎo	Linked list	
链代码	Liàn dàimǎ	Chain code	
连分式	Lián fēnshì	Continued fraction	
链控呼叫多频	Liàn kòng hūjiào duōpín	Touch-calling multi-frequency	TCMF
链搜索	Liàn sōusuǒ	Chaining search	
链域	Liàn yù	Link field (in software)	
联邦测量控制委员会	Liánbāng cèliáng kòngzhì wěiyuánhuì	Federal Geodetic Control Committee	FGCC
联邦调查因特网协调委员会	Liánbāng diàochá yīntèwǎng xiétiáo wěiyuánhuì	Federal Research Internet Coordinating Committee	FRICC
联邦开放市场委员会	Liánbāng kāifàng shìchǎng wěiyuánhuì	Federal Open Market Committee (US)	FOMC
联邦贸易委员会	Liánbāng màoyì wěiyuánhuì	Federal Trade Commission (US)	FTC
联邦商业委员会	Liánbāng shāngyè wěiyuánhuì	Federal Trade Commission (US)	FTC
联邦数字制图协调委员会	Liánbāng shùzì zhìtú xiétiáo wěiyuánhuì	Federal Interagency Coordinating Committee on Digital Cartography	FICCDC
联邦太平洋电缆	Liánbāng tàipíngyáng diànlǎn	Commonwealth Pacific Cable	COMPAC
联邦通信委员会	Liánbāng tōngxìn wěiyuánhuì	Federal Communications Commission (US)	FCC
联邦网络技术委员会	Liánbāng wǎngluò jìshù wěiyuánhuì	Federal Networking Council (US)	FNC
联邦网络委员会	Liánbāng wǎngluò wěiyuánhuì	Federal Networking Council (US)	FNC
联邦信息处理标准	Liánbāng xìnxī chǔlǐ biāozhǔn	Federal Information Processing Standard (US)	FIPS
联邦信息交换	Liánbāng xìnxī jiāohuàn	Federal Information Exchange (US)	FIX
联邦执行数据	Liánbāng zhíxíng shùjù	Federation execution data (in MSMP)	FED
联编	Liánbiān	Binding	
连词	Liáncí	Conjunction	
两波长光合波器	Liǎng bōcháng guāng hébōqì	Dual-wavelength optical coupler	
两阶段查找	Liǎng jiēduàn cházhǎo	Two-phase lookup (for database)	
两阶段提交	Liǎng jiēduàn tíjiāo	Two-phase commit (for database)	
两水平筛选设计	Liǎng shuǐpíng shāixuǎn shèjì	Two-level screening design	
两相提交	Liǎng xiàng tíjiāo	Two-phase commit	
两字节编码字符	Liǎng zìjié biānmǎ zìfú	Two byte code character	TBCC
两步激活	Liǎngbù jīhuó	Two-step activation	
量测	Liángcè	Measurement	
两侧声音强度差别	Liǎngcè shēngyīn qiángdù chābié	Inter-aural intensity difference	IID
亮点公司	Liàngdiǎn gōngsī	LightPointe Company (U.K. company)	
量度	Liángdù	Measure (as applied in the probabilistic treatment of reliability and related areas)	
亮度	Liàngdù	Luminance (video term)	
量刚分析	Liànggāng fēnxī	Dimensional analysis	
两个二进制一个四进制编码	Liǎnggè èrjìnzhì yīgè sìjìnzhì biānmǎ	Two binary one quaternary	2B1Q
量化	Liànghuà	Quantization, quantizing	
量化矩阵	Liànghuà jǔzhèn	Quantization matrix (video term)	
量化区间	Liànghuà qūjiān	Quantizing interval	
量化失真	Liànghuà shīzhēn	Quantizing distortion	
量化失真效率	Liànghuà shīzhēn xiàolǜ	Quantizing distortion efficiency	
量化调幅	Liànghuà tiáofú	Quantized amplitude modulation	QAM
量化噪声	Liànghuà zàoshēng	Quantizing noise	

量化增益损失	Liànghuà zēngyì sǔnshī	Quantization loss in gain	
量化振幅调制	Liànghuà zhènfú tiáozhì	Quantized amplitude modulation	QAM
量化秩值检测器	Liànghuà zhìzhí jiǎncèqì	Rank quantity detector	
量化器	Liànghuàqì	Quantizer	
量级	Liàngjí	Magnitude	
谅解备忘录	Liàngjiě bèiwànglù	Memorandum of understanding	MoU
量热计式功率计	Liángrèjì-shì gōnglǜjì	Calorimetric power meter	
连贯缓冲非统一内存寻址	Liánguàn huǎnchōng fēi tǒngyī nèicún xúnzhǐ	Cache-coherent non-uniform memory access	cc-NUMA
量子放大器	Liàngzǐ fàngdàqì	Quantum amplifier	
量子互补	Liàngzǐ hùbǔ	Quantum complementarity	
量子阱	Liàngzǐ jǐng	Quantum well	
量子阱半导体激光器	Liàngzǐ jǐng bàndǎotǐ jīguāngqì	Quantum well semiconductor laser	QWSL
量子阱分布反馈激光器	Liàngzǐ jǐng fēnbù fǎnkuì jīguāngqì	Quantum well distributed feedback laser	QW-DFB-LD
量子密码学	Liàngzǐ mìmǎxué	Quantum cryptography	
量子密钥分布	Liàngzǐ mìyào fēnbù	Quantum key distribution	QKD
量子密钥分配	Liàngzǐ mìyào fēnpèi	Quantum key distribution	QKD
量子物理学	Liàngzǐ wùlǐxué	Quantum physics	
量子效率	Liàngzǐ xiàolǜ	Quantum efficiency	
量子噪声	Liàngzǐ zàoshēng	Quantum noise	
联合查询	Liánhé cháxún	Union query (for database)	
联合电子设备工程委员会	Liánhé diànzǐ shèbèi gōngchéng wěiyuánhuì	Joint Electronic Device Engineering Council	JEDEC
联合电子支付联盟	Liánhé diànzǐ zhīfù liánméng	Joint Electronic payment initiative	JEPI
联合管理模型	Liánhé guǎnlǐ móxíng	Joint management model	
联合过滤	Liánhé guòlǜ	Joint filter (in SQL Server)	
联合海上通信系统策略	Liánhé hǎishàng tōngxìn xìtǒng cèlüè	Joint Maritime Communications Strategy	JMCOMS
联合检波	Liánhé jiǎnbō	Joint detection	JD
联合检测	Liánhé jiǎncè	Joint detection	
联合监视和目标攻击雷达系统	Liánhé jiānshì hé mùbiāo gōngjī léidá xìtǒng	Joint Surveillance and Target Attack Radar System (US military)	JSTARS
联合科研网	Liánhé kēyán wǎng	Joint academic network	JANET
联合两级图象专家组	Liánhé liǎngjí túxiàng zhuānjiāzǔ	Joint bi-level Image Experts Group	JBIG
联合码	Liánhé mǎ	Unicode	
联合摄影专家组	Liánhé shèyǐng zhuānjiāzǔ	Joint Photographic Experts Group	JPEG
联合时空处理	Liánhé shíkōng chǔlǐ	Joint space time processing	
联合双态成像组	Liánhé shuāngtài chéngxiàngzǔ	Joint bi-level Imaging Group	JBIG
联合数据库	Liánhé shùjùkù	Federated database	
联合数据库服务器	Liánhé shùjùkù fúwùqì	Federated database servers (in SQL Server)	
联合图象专家组	Liánhé túxiàng zhuānjiāzǔ	Joint Photographic Experts Group	JPEG
联合选择	Liánhé xuǎnzé	Conjugate selecting	
联合战术无线电系统	Liánhé zhànshù wúxiàndiàn xìtǒng	Joint Tactical Radio System (US military usage)	JTRS
联合战术信息分布系统	Liánhé zhànshù xìnxī fēnbù xìtǒng	Joint Tactical Information Distribution System (US)	JTIDS
联合战术信息分发系统	Liánhé zhànshù xìnxī fēnfā xìtǒng	Joint Tactical Information Distribution System (U.S.)	JTIDS
联合照相专家组	Liánhé zhàoxiàng zhuānjiāzǔ	Joint Photographic Experts Group	JPEG
联合国国际贸易法委员会	Liánhéguó guójì màoyìfǎ wěiyuánhuì	United Nations Commission on International Trade Law	UNCITRAL
联华电子公司	Liánhuá diànzǐ gōngsī	United Microelectronics Corp. (Taiwan semiconductor maker)	UMC

莲花发展集团	Liánhuā fāzhǎn jítuán	Lotus Development Corp. (US company)	
莲花智慧配套	Liánhuā zhìhuì pèitào	Lotus Smartsuite ©	
联机	Liánjī	Online	
联机重做日志	Liánjī chóngzuò rìzhì	Online redo log (for database)	
联机访问	Liánjī fǎngwèn	Online access	OA
联机分析处理	Liánjī fēnxī chǔlǐ	Online analytical processing	OLAP
联机加密操作	Liánjī jiāmì cāozuò	Online crypto-operation (IPsec)	
联机控制用先进数据处理程序	Liánjī kòngzhì-yòng xiānjìn shùjùchǔlǐ chéngxù	Advanced data handler for on-line control	ADHOC
敛集率	Liǎnjí lǜ	Packing fraction	
敛集率损耗	Liǎnjí lǜ sǔnhào	Packing fraction loss	
联机事务处理	Liánjī shìwù chǔlǐ	Online transaction processing (for database)	OLTP
廉价冗余硬磁盘阵列	Liánjià rǒngyú yìngcípán zhènliè	Redundant array of inexpensive disks	RAID
联结	Liánjié	Bond	
连结	Liánjié	Binding	
联接	Liánjiē	Join	
连接	Liánjiē	Connection	CONN
链接	Liànjiē	Chaining, join	
链接	Liànjiē	Link (in software)	
连接保持	Liánjiē bǎochí	Connection retention	
连接编辑程序	Liánjiē biānjí chéngxù	Linkage editor	LEDT
联接表	Liánjiē biǎo	Join table	
连接表	Liánjiē biǎo	Junction table	
链接表	Liànjiē biǎo	Linked table	
连接标识符	Liánjiē biāozhì fú	Connection identifier	CID
连接池	Liánjiē chí	Connection pooling	
连接单元	Liánjiē dānyuán	Connection element	CE
连接单元接口	Liánjiē dānyuán jiēkǒu	Attachment unit interface	AUI
连接到资源	Liánjiē dào zīyuán	Connect to resource	CTR
连接段	Liánjiē duàn	Connection fragment	CF
连接端点	Liánjiē duāndiǎn	Connection end point	CEP
连接端点标识符	Liánjiē duāndiǎn biāozhìfú	Connection endpoint identifier	CEI
链接多维数据集	Liànjiē duōwéi shùjùjí	Linked datacube	
连接方式网络服务	Liánjiē fāngshì wǎngluò fúwù	Connection-mode network service	CMNS
链接服务器	Liànjiē fúwùqì	Linked server	
连接功能	Liánjiē gōngnéng	Connection function	C
连接管理	Liánjiē guǎnlǐ	Connection management	CM
连接号码识别限制	Liánjiē hàomǎ shíbié xiànzhì	Connected line identification restriction	C0LR
连接键	Liánjiē jiàn	Concatenated key	
连接建立错误概率	Liánjiē jiànlì cuòwù gàilǜ	Connection establishment error probability	CEP
连接建立失败概率	Liánjiē jiànlì shībài gàilǜ	Connection establishment failure probability	CFP
连接建立原语信号	Liánjiē jiànlì yuányǔ xìnhào	Open primitive signal	OPN
连接节点	Liánjiē jiédiǎn	Connected node	
连接接纳控制	Liánjiē jiēnà kòngzhì	Connection admission control	CAC
连接机密性	Liánjiē jīmìxìng	Connection confidentiality (IPsec)	
连接矩阵	Liánjiē jǔzhèn	Connection matrix	CM

连接开销	Liánjiē kāixiao	Connection overhead	CO
连接可保持性	Liánjiē kěbǎochíxìng	Connection retainability (in telecommunication)	
连接可视	Liánjiē kěshì	Connection view	CV
连接可视状态	Liánjiē kěshì zhuàngtài	Connection view state	CVS
连接控制	Liánjiē kòngzhì	Connection control	
连接控制服务单元	Liánjiē kòngzhì fúwù dānyuán	Association control service element	ACSE
连接控制服务元素	Liánjiē kòngzhì fúwù yuánsù	Association control service element	ACSE
连接控制接口	Liánjiē kòngzhì jiēkǒu	Connection control interface	CCI
连接控制器	Liánjiē kòngzhìqì	Connection controller	CC
连接类型	Liánjiē lèixíng	Connection type	
联接列	Liánjiē liè	Join column	
联接路径	Liánjiē lùjìng	Join path	
连接请求	Liánjiē qǐngqiú	Connection request (SS7 message)	CORE, CR
连接确认	Liánjiē quèrèn	Connection acknowledged (SS7 message)	COAK, CC
连接认可	Liánjiē rènkě	Connect acknowledgement	CONNACK
联接筛选	Liánjiē shāixuǎn	Join filter	
连接识别码	Liánjiē shíbié mǎ	Linked ID	
连接属性	Liánjiē shǔxìng	Connection attribute	
连接特性	Liánjiē tèxìng	Nature of connection indicators	
联接条件	Liánjiē tiáojiàn	Join condition	
连接相关功能	Liánjiē xiāngguān gōngnéng	Connection related function	CRF
连接相同数字	Liánjiē xiāngtóng shùzì	Consecutive identical digits	CID
连接消息	Liánjiē xiāoxi	Connect message (ISUP)	CON
连接信号	Liánjiē xìnhào	Continuous signal	
链接学习	Liànjiē xuéxí	Linkage learning	
链接压扩	Liànjiē yākuò	Linked companding	
连接要求	Liánjiē yāoqiú	Connection request	
连接有关功能	Liánjiē yǒuguān gōngnéng	Connection related function	CRF
联接运算符	Liánjiē yùnsuàn fú	Join operator	
连接允许控制	Liánjiē yǔnxǔ kòngzhì	Connection admission control	CAC
连接帧号	Liánjiē zhènghào	Connection frame number	CFN
连接证实	Liánjiē zhèngshí	Connect acknowledgement	CONNACK
连接证实	Liánjiē zhèngshí	Connection confirm	CC
连接质量	Liánjiē zhìliàng	Connection quality	
连接终结点	Liánjiē zhōngjiédiǎn	Connection termination point	CTP
链接状态数据库	Liànjiē zhuàngtài shùjùkù	Link state database	
联接字段	Liánjiē zìduàn	Join field	
连接组成管理	Liánjiē zǔchéng guǎnlǐ	Connection configuration management	Con.CM
链接最小优先算法	Liànjiē zuìxiǎo yōuxiān suànfǎ	Least connection first algorithm	LCF
链接的压扩器	Liànjiēde yākuòqì	Linked compressor and expander	
连接的有关功能	Liánjiēde yǒuguān gōngnéng	Connection-related function	CRF
连接点	Liánjiēdiǎn	Connection point	CP
连接点	Liánjiēdiǎn	Articulation point	
连接号	Liánjiēhào	Connect ID	
连接器	Liánjiēqì	Connector	
连接器	Liánjiēqì	Linker (in software)	

链接器	Liànjiēqì	Linker (in software)	
连接器插入损耗	Liánjiēqì chārù sǔnhào	Connector insertion loss	
连接器光导损耗	Liánjiēqì guāngdǎo sǔnhào	Connector optical conductor loss	
连接线标识显示	Liánjiēxiàn biāozhì xiǎnshì	Connected line identification presentation	COLP
连接线标识限制	Liánjiēxiàn biāozhì xiànzhì	Connected line identification restriction	COLR
连接线识别	Liánjiēxiàn shíbié	Connected line identity	COLI
连接线识别提供	Liánjiēxiàn shíbié tígōng	Connected line identification presentation	COLP
连接线识别显示	Liánjiēxiàn shíbié xiǎnshì	Connected line identification presentation	COLP
连接线识别限制	Liánjiēxiàn shíbié xiànzhì	Connected line identification restriction	COLR
连接性	Liánjiēxìng	Connectivity, linkage	
链路	Liànlù	Link	
链路板	Liànlù bǎn	Link board (2Mb/s)	LK2M
链路标识符	Liànlù biāozhì fú	Link identification code	LIC
链路层	Liànlù céng	Link layer	LL
链路层服务单元	Liànlù céng fúwù dānyuán	Link layer service unit	LLSU
链路层协议	Liànlù céng xiéyì	Link layer protocol	
链路重启	Liànlù chóngqǐ	Link reset	LR
链路重启应答	Liànlù chóngqǐ yìngdá	Link reset response	LRR
链路到链路信令	Liànlù dào liànlù xìnlìng	Link-by-link signaling	
链路丢失	Liànlù diūshī	Loss of link	
链路断开	Liànlù duànkāi	Link disconnect	LD
链路 E1 接口集成板	Liànlù E1 jiēkǒu jíchéngbǎn	Link interface E1 board assembly	LIEA
链路访问过程平衡	Liànlù fǎngwèn guòchéng pínghéng	Link access procedure balanced (ISO usage)	LAPB
链路访问协议	Liànlù fǎngwèn xiéyì	Link access protocol	LAP
链路访问协议 D 信道	Liànlù fǎngwèn xiéyì D xìndào	Link access protocol channel D	LAP-D
链路功率预算	Liànlù gōnglǜ yùsuàn	Link power budget	
链路管理	Liànlù guǎnlǐ	Link manager	LM
链路管理协议	Liànlù guǎnlǐ xiéyì	Link management protocol	LMP
链路加密	Liànlù jiāmì	Link encryption (IPsec)	
链路建立指示	Liànlù jiànlì zhǐshì	Link establishment indication	
链路监视	Liànlù jiānshì	Link monitor	
链路接口 IPC 处理器集成件	Liànlù jiēkǒu IPC chǔlǐqì jíchéng jiàn	Link interface IPC processor assembly	LIPA
链路接入规程	Liànlù jiērù guīchéng	Link access procedure	LAP
链路接入规程 D	Liànlù jiērù guīchéng D	Link access protocol D	LAP-D
链路接入规程 – 平衡	Liànlù jiērù guīchéng –pínghéng	Link access procedure - balanced	LAPB
链路接入规程-SDH	Liànlù jiērù guīchéng-SDH	Link access procedure-SDH	LAPS
链路接入过程 D-信道	Liànlù jiērù guòchéng D-xìndào	Link access procedure D-channel	LAP-D
链路接入控制	Liànlù jiērù kòngzhì	Link access control	LAC
链路接入平衡协议	Liànlù jiērù pínghéng xiéyì	Link access protocol balanced	LAPB
链路接入协议	Liànlù jiērù xiéyì	Link access protocol	LAP
链路接入协议帧	Liànlù jiērù xiéyì zhèng	Link access protocol frame	LAPF
链路接入协议-SDH	Liànlù jiērù xiéyì-SDH	Link access protocol-SDH	LAPS
链路聚合	Liànlù jùhé	Link aggregration	
链路控制规程	Liànlù kòngzhì guīchéng	Link control procedure	
链路控制协议	Liànlù kòngzhì xiéyì	Link control protocol	LCP
链路控制器	Liànlù kòngzhìqì	Link controller	LC

链路控制器服务信令	Liànlù kòngzhìqì fúwù xìnlìng	Link controller service signaling	LCSP
链路连接	Liànlù liánjiē	Link connection	LC
链路连接的交换级	Liànlù liánjiēde jiāohuànjí	Link connected switching stage	
链路容量调节方案	Liànlù róngliàng tiáojié fāng'àn	Link capacity adjustment scheme	LCAS
链路容量调整方案	Liànlù róngliàng tiáozhěng fāng'àn	Link capacity adjusting scheme	LCAS
链路衰减值	Liànlù shuāijiǎn zhí	Link attenuation value	
链路锁定	Liànlù suǒdìng	Link lockout	
链路 T1 接口集成板	Liànlù T1 jiēkǒu jíchéngbǎn	Link interface T1 board assembly	LITA
链路误码率测试集成板	Liànlù wùmǎlǜ cèshì jíchéngbǎn	Link bit error rate test board assembly	LBTA
链路协议数据单元	Liànlù xiéyì shùjù dānyuán	Link protocol data unit	LPDU
链路选择器参数	Liànlù xuǎnzéqì cānshù	Link selector parameter	LSP
链路压扩	Liànlù yākuò	Linked compression and expansion	
链路压扩器	Liànlù yākuòqì	Lincompex, line compressor/expander	
链路质量报告	Liànlù zhìliàng bàogào	Link quality report	LQR
链路质量监视	Liànlù zhìliàng jiānshì	Link quality monitor	LQM
链路状态	Liànlù zhuàngtài	Link state	
链路状态包	Liànlù zhuàngtài bāo	Link state packet	LSP
链路状态通告	Liànlù zhuàngtài tōnggào	Link state advertisement	LSA
链路状态信号单元	Liànlù zhuàngtài xìnhào dānyuán	Link status signal unit	LSSU
链路状态信令单元	Liànlù zhuàngtài xìnlìng dānyuán	Link status Signaling unit	LSSU
链路自适应	Liànlù zìshìyìng	Link adaptation	
链路资源管理器	Liànlù zīyuán guǎnlǐqì	Link resource manager	LRM
链路租用	Liànlù zūyòng	Tenancy	
联试	Liánshì	On-line test (short for 联机测试)	
链式寻址	Liàn-shì xúnzhǐ	Chained addressing	CA
联锁机构	Liánsuǒ jīgòu	Interlocking device	
连锁码	Liánsuǒ mǎ	Interlock code (CUG SS)	IC
联通	Liántōng	China Unicom Corp.	
连通分量	Liántōng fènliàng	Connected component	
连通分支	Liántōng fēnzhī	Connected component	
连通管理器	Liántōng guǎnlǐqì	Connectivity manager	CM
连通图	Liántōng tú	Connected graph	
联网	Liánwǎng	Internet	
联网汇兑网点	Liánwǎng huìduì wǎngdiǎn	On-line remittance service counter	
联网社群	Liánwǎng shèqún	Cyber community	
联网世界	Liánwǎng shìjiè	Cyberworld	
联网协议	Liánwǎng xiéyì	Internet protocol	IP
联网寻呼系统	Liánwǎng xúnhū xìtǒng	Wide area paging system	
联网中继聊天	Liánwǎng zhōngjì liáotiān	Internet relay chat	
联系控制服务单元	Liánxì kòngzhì fúwù dānyuán	Association control service element	ACSE
联系控制服务要素	Liánxì kòngzhì fúwù yàosù	Association control service element	ACSE
联系控制协议机	Liánxì kòngzhì xiéyìjī	Association control protocol machine	ACPM
连线	Liánxiàn	Login; on-line	
联线杂志	Liánxiàn zázhì	Wired Magazine ©	
联线诊断	Liánxiàn zhěnduàn	On-line diagnostics	OLD
联想	Liánxiǎng	Legend (PRC computer company)	

连线--节点结构	Liánxiàn—jiédiǎn jiégòu	Link and node structure	
连续波	Liánxù bō	Continuous wave	CW
连续波传输	Liánxù bō chuánshū	Continuous wave transmission	CW
连续波干扰	Liánxù bō gānrǎo	Continuous wave jamming	
连续波调制信号	Liánxù bō tiáozhì xìnhào	Continuous wave modulated signal	
连续单音控制静噪制	Liánxù dānyīn kòngzhì jìngzào zhì	Connected tone-controlled squelch system	
连续单音制	Liánxù dānyīnzhì	Continuous individual tone system	
连续傅里叶变换	Liánxù fùlǐyè biànhuàn	Continuous Fourier transform	CFT
连续行	Liánxù háng	Continuation line	
连续恒等数字	Liánxù héngděng shùzì	Consecutive identical digits	CID
连续检查	Liánxù jiǎnchá	Continuous checking	
连续级联	Liánxù jílián	Continuous concatenation	
连续记录	Liánxù jìlù	Continuation record	
连续可变斜率增量方式	Liánxù kěbiàn xiélǜ zēngliàng fāngshì	Continuously variable slope delta modulation	CVSDM
连续可变斜率增量调制	Liánxù kěbiàn xiélǜ zēngliàng tiáozhì	Continuously variable slope delta modulation	CVSD
连续可变斜率△调制	Liánxù kěbiàn xiélǜ Δ tiáozhì	Continuously variable slope delta modulation	CVSD
连续可变的角变增量调制	Liánxù kěbiànde jiǎobiàn zēngliàng tiáozhì	Continuously variable slope delta modulation	CVSDM
连续库存补充计划	Liánxù kùcún bǔchōng jìhuà	Continuous replenishment program	CRP
连续平均法	Liánxù píngjūn fǎ	Continuous averaging	
连续骚扰	Liánxù sāorǎo	Continuous disturbance	
连续数据	Liánxù shùjù	Continuous data	
连续数据库	Liánxù shùjùkù	Continuous database	
连续调相	Liánxù tiáoxiàng	Continuous-phase modulation	CPM
连续无故障时间	Liánxù wúgùzhàng shíjiān	Mean time between failures	MTBF
连续相同数字	Liánxù xiāngtóng shùzì	Consecutive identical digit	CID
连续相位频移键控	Liánxù xiàngwèi pínyí jiànkòng	Continuous phase frequency shift keying	CPFSK
连续相位调制	Liánxù xiàngwèi tiáozhì	Continuous phase modulation	CPM
连续相位移频键控	Liánxù xiàngwèi yípín jiànkòng	Continuous-phase frequency shift keying	CPFSK
连续斜率△调制	Liánxù xiélǜ Δ tiáozhì	Continuous slope delta modulation	CSDM
连续寻线	Liánxù xúnxiàn	Line hunting	LH
连续严重误块秒	Liánxù yánzhòng wùkuài miǎo	Consecutive severely errored second	CSES
连续严重误码秒	Liánxù yánzhòng wùmǎ miǎo	Continuous severely errored second	CSES
连续载流量	Liánxù zàiliúliàng	Continuous current-carrying capacity (of a conductor)	
连续噪声	Liánxù zàoshēng	Continuous noise	
连续制图	Liánxù zhìtú	Continuous mapping	
连续的动态信道分配	Liánxùde dòngtài xìndào fēnpèi	Continuous dynamic channel assign	CDCA
连续谱	Liánxùpǔ	Continuous spectrum	
连续式激光	Liánxù-shì jīguāng	Continuous wave (CW) laser	
连续性重复检验输入信号	Liánxùxìng chóngfù jiǎnyàn shūrù xìnhào	Continuity-recheck incoming	CRI
连续性丢失	Liánxùxìng diūshī	Loss of continuity	LOC
连续性检测	Liánxùxìng jiǎncè	Connectivity check	CC
连续性检查	Liánxùxìng jiǎnchá	Continuity check	
连续性检验	Liánxùxìng jiǎnyàn	Continuity check	
连续性检验输入(信号)	Liánxù-xìng jiǎnyàn shūrù (xìnhào)	Continuity-check incoming (signal)	CCI
联轴器	Liánzhóuqì	Coupling	

连字符	Liánzìfú	Hyphen (-)	
聊天	Liáotiān	Chat	
聊天室	Liáotiānshì	Chat room	
力博特中国总部	Lì-bó-tè Zhōngguó zǒngbù	Liebert China Headquarters, subsidiary of Liebert Corp.	
理查森数	Lǐ-chá-sēn shù	Richardson number	
例程	Lìchéng	Routine	
里德-所罗门码	Lǐ-dé—suǒ-luó-mén mǎ	Reed-Solomon code	RSC
里德-索洛蒙码	Lǐ-dé—suǒ-luò-méng mǎ	Reed-Solomon code	RS
粒度	Lìdù	Particle size, grain size	
粒度	Lìdù	Granularity	
粒度分析	Lìdù fēnxī	Grain size analysis	
粒度累积曲线	Lìdù lěijī qūxiàn	Grain size accumulation curve	
粒度曲线	Lìdù qūxiàn	Gradation analysis curve	
利多福	Lì-duō-fú	Nidroff (Netherlands company)	
列	Liè	Column	
列地址控制器	Liè dìzhǐ kòngzhìqì	Column address strobe	CAS
列地址选定	Liè dìzhǐ xuǎndìng	Column address selection	CAS
列方式	Liè fāngshì	Column mode	COLM
列过滤	Liè guòlǜ	Column filter (in SQL Server)	
列混合	Liè hùnhé	Mix column	
列级排序规则	Liè jí páixù guīzé	Column-level collation	
列级约束	Liè jí yuēshù	Column-level constraint	
列筛选	Liè shāixuǎn	Column filter	
列约束	Liè yuēshù	Column constraint (in SQL Server)	
列表	Lièbiǎo	List	
列表框	Lièbiǎo kuàng	List box	
裂断长	Lièduàn cháng	Breaking length	
列柜	Lièguì	Cabinet	
劣化	Lièhuà	Degradation	
列集	Lièjí	Marshal	
列举	Lièjǔ	Enumeration	
裂相码	Lièxiāng mǎ	Split phase code	
列阵	Lièzhèn	Array	
列阵波导光栅	Lièzhèn bōdǎo guāngshān	Arrayed waveguide grating	AWG
立方相差	Lìfāng xiàngchà	Cube phase error	
理光	Lǐ-guāng	Ricoh (Japanese company)	
立即传输	Lìjí chuánshū	Immediate transmission	IT
立即分配	Lìjí fēnpèi	Immediate assignment	
立即事务一致性	Lìjí shìwù yīzhìxìng	Immediate transactional consistency (in SQL Server)	
立即数据	Lìjí shùjù	Immediate data	
立即指配	Lìjí zhǐpèi	Immediate assignment	
立即指配消息	Lìjí zhǐpèi xiāoxi	Immediate connection message	
立交桥	Lìjiāoqiáo	Viaduct, overpass	
理解	Lǐjiě	Perception	
粒径分布	Lìjìng fēnbù	Grain size distribution	
力矩限制器	Lìjǔ xiànzhìqì	Limiter of moment	

离开键盘	Líkāi jiànpán	Away from the keyboard (computer chat)	AFK
立康普公司	Lì-kāng-pǔ gōngsī	P-Com Inc (US company)	
力科有限公司	Lì-kē yǒuxiàn gōngsī	Lecroy Corp. (US maker of test instruments)	
力量反匮式操纵杆	Liliang fǎnkuì-shì cāozònggǎn	Force feedback joystick	FFJ
理论改正力	Lǐlùn gǎizhèng lì	Theoretical margin	
理论数值孔径	Lǐlùn shùzhí kǒngjìng	Theoretical numerical aperture	
利盟	Lì-méng	Lexmark (US company)	
瞬变电磁场辐射敏感度	Línbiàn diàncíchǎng fúshè mǐngǎndù	Transient electromagnetic field radiated susceptibility (Mil-Std-461E, RCS105)	
邻道功率	Líndào gōnglǜ	Adjacent channel power	ACP
邻道选择性	Líndào xuǎnzéxìng	Adjacent-channel selectivity	
邻道选择性	Líndào xuǎnzéxìng	Adjacent-channel selectivity	
零材料色散波长	Líng cáiliào sèsàn bōcháng	Zero material dispersion wavelength	
零插力	Líng chālì	Zero insertion force	ZIF
零插入力	Líng chārùlì	Zero insertion force	ZIF
零串	Líng chuàn	Null string	
零单元	Líng dānyuán	Zero-cell	
零等待状态	Líng děngdài zhuàngtài	Zero wait state	
零管理视窗系统	Líng guǎnlǐ shìchuāng xìtǒng	Zero administration for Windows	ZAM
铃流	Líng liú	Ringing current	
铃流源	Líng liú yuán	Source of ringing current	
零码速调整	Líng mǎsù tiáozhěng	Zero justification	
铃群组	Líng qún zǔ	Ring group	RG
零色散	Líng sèsàn	Zero dispersion	
零色散波长	Líng sèsàn bōcháng	Zero dispersion wavelength	
零色散点斜率	Líng sèsàn diǎn xiélǜ	Zero dispersion point slope	
零色散斜率	Líng sèsàn xiélǜ	Zero dispersion slope	
零时间漏洞利用	Líng shíjiān lòudòng lìyòng	Zero day exploit	
零树编码	Líng shù biānmǎ	Zerotree coding	
零树小波编码算法	Líng shù xiǎobō biānmǎ suànfǎ	Zerotree wavelet coding algorithm	
零树小波编码器	Líng shù xiǎobō biānmǎqì	Zerotree wavelet coder	
零输出	Líng shūchū	Zero output	ZO
零输入	Líng shūrù	Zero input	ZI
零调制解调器电缆	Líng tiáozhì jiětiáoqì diànlǎn	Null modem cable	
零维	Líng wéi	Zero dimension	
零相对电平点	Líng xiāngduì diànpíng diǎn	Zero relative level point	
零序	Líng xù	Zero sequence	
零知识证明	Líng zhīshi zhèngmíng	Zero knowledge proof (in cryptography)	
零中频接收机	Líng zhōngpín jiēshōujī	Zero-intermediate frequency receiver	
零状态	Líng zhuàngtài	Null state	
零转向天线	Líng zhuǎnxiàng tiānxiàn	Null-steering antenna	NSAN
零差检测	Língchà jiǎncè	Homodyne	
零差式接收	Língchàshì jiēshōu	Homodyne reception	
零点可控天线	Língdiǎn kěkòng tiānxiàn	Null-steering antenna	
零度经线	Língdù jīngxiàn	Zero meridian	
零度经线平面	Língdù jīngxiàn píngmiàn	Zero meridian plane	
灵活点	Línghuó diǎn	Flexible point	FP

灵活复接器	Línghuó fùjiēqì	Flexible multiplexer	MUX
灵活复用设备	Línghuó fùyòng shèbèi	Flexible multiplexer	FM
灵活复用器	Línghuó fùyòngqì	Flexible multiplexer	FM
灵活接入系统	Línghuó jiērù xìtǒng	Flexible access system	FA
灵活接入终端	Línghuó jiērù zhōngduān	Flexible access termination	FAT
灵活拓扑数据链路	Línghuó tuòpū shùjù liànlù	Flexible topology data link	FTDL
零控天线	Língkòng tiānxiàn	Null-steering antenna	
灵敏度	Língmǐndù	Sensitivity (of a receiver)	
灵敏度降低	Língmǐndù jiàngdī	Desensitization	
令牌	Lìngpái	Token	TK
令牌环	Lìngpái huán	Token ring	TR
令牌环传递	Lìngpái huán chuándì	Token passing	
令牌环接口处理器	Lìngpái huán jiēkǒu chǔlǐqì	Token ring interface processor	TRIP
令牌环接口耦合器	Lìngpái huán jiēkǒu ǒuhéqì	Token ring interface coupler	TIC
令牌环网	Lìngpái huán wǎng	Token ring network	
令牌环总线	Lìngpái huán zǒngxiàn	Token bus	
令牌环形网	Lìngpái huánxíng wǎng	Token ring network	
令牌提前释放	Lìngpái tíqián shìfàng	Early token release	
令牌桶标记	Lìngpái tǒng biāojì	Token bucket marking	
令牌网	Lìngpái wǎng	Token passing network	PLAN
令牌网	Lìngpái wǎng	Token ring	TR
令牌总线协议	Lìngpái zǒngxiàn xiéyì	Token bus protocol	TBP
菱形天线	Língxíng tiānxiàn	Rhombic antenna	
令信息字段	Lìngxìnxī zìduàn	Signaling information field	SIF
领域知识	Lǐngyù zhīshi	Domain knowledge	
磷化铟	Línhuàyīn	Indium phosphide	InP
历年	Lìnián	Calendar year	
李尼克斯	Lǐ-ní-kè-sī	Linux (Taiwan term)	
邻机发现协议	Línjī fāxiàn xiéyì	Neighbor discovery protocol	NDP
邻机可达性	Línjī kědáxìng	Neighbor reachability	
邻机探测	Línjī tàncè	Neighbor acquisition	
邻接	Línjiē	Adjacency	
邻接表	Línjiē biǎo	Adjacency list	
临界波长	Línjiè bōcháng	Critical wavelength (of a mode in a waveguide)	
临界电阻	Línjiè diànzǔ	Critical resistance	
邻接多重表	Línjiē duōzhòng biǎo	Adjacency multi-list	
邻接分析	Línjiē fēnxī	Adjacency analysis	
临界告警	Línjiè gàojǐng	Critical alarm	
邻接矩阵	Línjiē jǔzhèn	Adjacency matrix	
临界流速	Línjiè liúsù	Critical velocity	
临界频率	Línjiè pínlǜ	Critical frequency (of a mode in a waveguide)	
邻接区域	Línjiē qūyù	Adjacency areas	
临界闪变频率	Línjiè shǎnbiàn pínlǜ	Critical flicker frequency	
邻界效应	Línjiè xiàoyìng	Adjacency effect	
邻接性	Línjiē xìng	Contiguity	
临界压差	Línjiè yāchā	Critical pressure differential	

临界压差比	Línjiè yāchā bǐ	Critical pressure differential ratio	
临界压力比	Línjiè yālì bǐ	Critical pressure ratio	
临界阻尼	Línjiè zǔní	Critical damping	
临界点	Línjièdiǎn	Critical points	
邻近	Línjìn	Adjacency	
邻近分析	Línjìn fēnxī	Proximity analysis	
邻近路由器	Línjìn lùyóuqì	Neighboring router	
邻近 MIP 映射	Línjìn MIP yìngshè	Nearest Mipmap (video term)	
邻频干扰	Línpín gānrǎo	Adjacent channel interference	ACI
邻频干扰保护比	Línpín gānrǎo bǎohùbǐ	Neighboring channel interference protection ratio	
邻频干扰抑制	Línpín gānrǎo yìzhì	Adjacent frequency interference suppression	
邻频选择性	Línpín xuǎnzéxìng	Adjacent channel selectivity	
邻频道选择性	Línpíndào xuǎnzéxìng	Adjacent-channel selectivity	
临时按序路由算法	Línshí ànxù lùyóu suànfǎ	Temporary ordered routing algorithm	TORA
临时本地号码	Línshí běndì hàomǎ	Temporary local directory number	TLDN
临时本地号码簿号码	Línshí běndì hàomǎbù hàomǎ	Temporary local directory number	TLDN
临时表	Línshí biǎo	Temporary table (for database)	
临时存储过程	Línshí cúnchǔ guòchéng	Temporary stored procedure	
临时对象	Línshí duìxiàng	Temporary object	
临时分水道	Línshí fēnshuǐ dào	Temporary diversion channel	
临时家乡代理	Línshí jiāxiāng dàilǐ	Temporary home agent	THA
临时块流	Línshí kuàiliú	Temporary block flow	TBF
临时链路电平识别	Línshí liànlù diànpíng shíbié	Temporary link level identity	TLLI
临时流量识别	Línshí liúliàng shíbié	Temporary flow identity	TFI
临时逻辑链路标识	Línshí luóji liànlù biāozhì	Temporary logical link identity	TLLI
临时逻辑链路识别	Línshí luóji liànlù shíbié	Temporary logic link identity	TLLI
临时逻辑链路识别	Línshí luóji liànlù shíbié	Temporary logical link identity	TLLI
临时排队识别	Línshí páiduì shíbié	Temporary queuing identity	TQI
临时偏移	Línshí piānyí	Temporary offset	TO
临时设备标识符	Línshí shèbèi biāozhìfú	Temporary equipment identifier	TEI
临时数据块流	Línshí shùjùkuài liú	Temporary block flow	TBF
临时文件	Línshí wénjiàn	Temporary file, scratch file	
临时信息组流量	Línshí xìnxīzǔ liúliàng	Temporary block flow	TBF
临时移动台识别码	Línshí yídòng tái shíbié mǎ	Temporary mobile station identity	TMSI
临时移动用户标识	Línshí yídòng yònghù biāozhì	Temporary mobile subscriber identity	TMSI
临时移动用户识别号码	Línshí yídòng yònghù shíbié hàomǎ	Temporary mobile subscriber identity	TMSI
临时移动用户识别码	Línshí yídòng yònghù shíbié mǎ	Temporary mobile subscriber identity	TMSI
临时组网	Línshí zǔwǎng	Ad hoc network	
临时的局部管理接口	Línshíde júbù guǎnlǐ jiēkǒu	Interim local management interface	ILMI
邻位干扰	Línwèi gānrǎo	Adjacent bit interference	ABI
邻小区	Línxiǎoqū	Neighbor cell	
邻小区干扰	Línxiǎoqū gānrǎo	Adjacent cell interference	ACI
邻小区列表	Línxiǎoqū lièbiǎo	Neighbor cell definition table	
邻信道干扰比	Línxìndào gānrǎobǐ	Adjacent channel interference ratio	ACIR
邻信道泄漏功率比	Línxìndào xièlòu gōnglǜ bǐ	Adjacent channel leakage power ratio	ACLR
邻信道泄漏比	Línxìndào xièlòubǐ	Adjacent channel leakage ratio	ACLR

邻信道选择性	Línxìndào xuǎnzéxìng	Adjacent-channel selectivity	ACS
邻信号选择性	Línxìnhào xuǎnzéxìng	Adjacent-signal selectivity	
邻域查询	Línyù cháxún	Neighborhood query	
邻域分析	Línyù fēnxī	Neighborhood analysis	
淋雨试验	Línyǔ shìyàn	Rainfall test (radar term)	
邻站通知	Línzhàn tōngzhī	Neighbor station advice	NN
离群点	Líqúndiǎn	Outlier	
利润率	Lìrùnlǜ	Profit margin	
离散地址	Lísàn dìzhǐ	Discrete address	DA
离散地址通信系统	Lísàn dìzhǐ tōngxìn xìtǒng	Discrete address communication system	DACS
离散对数	Lísàn duìshù	Discrete logarithm	
离散对数问题	Lísàn duìshù wèntí	Discrete logarithm problem	DLP
离散多音	Lísàn duōyīn	Discrete multitone	DMT
离散多音	Lísàn duōyīn	Dispersion multitone	DMT
离散多载波	Lísàn duōzàibō	Discrete multitone	DMT
离散傅立叶变换	Lísàn fù-lì-yè biànhuàn	Discrete Fourier transform	DFT
离散付里叶变换	Lísàn fù-lǐ-yè biànhuàn	Discrete Fourier transform	
离散傅里叶反变换	Lísàn fù-lǐ-yè fǎnbiànhuàn	Inverse discrete fourier transform	IDFT
离散傅氏变换	Lísàn fù-shì biànhuàn	Discrete fourier transform	DFT
离散控制系统	Lísàn kòngzhì xìtǒng	Discrete control system	
离散时间脉冲频率调制	Lísàn shíjiān màichōng pínlǜ tiáozhì	Discrete-time-pulse-frequency modulation	DPFM
离散数据	Lísàn shùjù	Discrete data	
离散特征	Lísàn tèzhēng	Discrete feature	
离散无记忆信道	Lísàn wújìyì xìndào	Discrete memoryless channel	DMC
离散小波多音	Lísàn xiǎobō duō yīn	Discrete wavelet multiTone	DWMT
离散信号	Lísàn xìnhào	Discrete signal	
离散用户的随机接入	Lísàn yònghùde suíjī jiērù	Random access control address	RADA
离散余弦变换	Lísàn yúxián biànhuàn	Discrete cosine transform	DCT
离散化	Lísàn-huà	Discretization	
立式机箱	Lìshì jīxiāng	Tower case	
丽台	Lì-tái	Winfast (US company)	
立体	Lìtǐ	Solid	
立体地图	Lìtǐ dìtú	Relief map	
立体绘图仪	Lìtǐ huìtú yí	Stereoplotter	
立体交叉战争	Lìtǐ jiāochā zhànzhēng	Three-dimensional inter-connected warfare (air, sea, land and information technology)	
立体像素	Lìtǐ xiàngsù	Volume pixel	Voxel
立体阴影处理技术	Lìtǐ yīnyǐng chǔlǐ jìshù	Relief shading	
立体照片	Lìtǐ zhàopiàn	Anaglyph	
流	Liú	Stream	
流表	Liú biǎo	Flow table	
流标记	Liú biāojì	Stream label (in IPv6)	
六度分离	Liù dù fēnlí	"Six degrees of separation"	
六防	Liù fáng	Six protects, or six protections (in telecom construction: against salt, moisture, viruses, rats, lightning and static)	
六防	Liù fáng	Six protects (for computers: protect against self-induction, static, magnetic field, heat, dampness, vibration)	

流方式	Liú fāngshì	Streaming mode	
流分类算法	Liú fēnlèi suànfǎ	Flow classification algorithm (for IP packet classification)	
流关系	Liú guānxi	Flow relation (in Petri net)	
流汇集	Liú huìjí	Flow aggregation	
流可视化	Liú kěshihuà	Flow visualization	
流控传输协议	Liú kòng chuánshū xiéyì	Stream control transmission protocol	SCTP
流控制传输协议	Liú kòngzhì chuánshū xiéyì	Stream control transmission protocol	SCTP
流控制传送协议	Liú kòngzhì chuánsòng xiéyì	Stream control transport protocol	SCTP
流媒体服务器	Liú méitī fúwùqì	Streaming media server	
流密码	Liú mìmǎ	Stream cipher	
流密码算法	Liú mìmǎ suànfǎ	Streaming cipher algorithm	
流模式	Liú móshì	Streaming mode	
流视象	Liú shìxiàng	Streaming video	
流顺序号码	Liú shùnxù hàomǎ	Stream sequence number	SSN
流属性通知协议	Liú shǔxìng tōngzhī xiéyì	Flow attribute notification protocol (Toshiba)	FANP
流压缩	Liú yāsuō	Stream compressing	
流音频	Liú yīnpín	Streaming audio	
流变学	Liúbiànxué	Rheology (in SMT)	
流播	Liúbō	Flooding	
六叉树	Liùchā shù	Hextree	
流程控制语句	Liúchéng kòngzhì yǔjù	Flow control statements (in SQL Server)	
流程控制语言	Liúchéng kòngzhì yǔyán	Flow control language (in SQL Server)	
流程图	Liúchéngtú	Flow chart	
流程图符号	Liúchéngtú fúhào	Flow chart symbol	
流出系数	Liúchū xìshù	Discharge coefficient	
流动电文	Liúdòng diànwén	Mobitex	
硫化炉	Liúhuà lú	Curing oven (semiconductor mfg)	
硫化氢	Liúhuàqīng	Hydrogen sulfide	
流间同步	Liú-jiān tóngbù	Inter-stream synchronization	
浏览控制模块	Liúlǎn kòngzhì mókuài	Scan control block	SCB
浏览模式	Liúlǎn móshì	Browse mode	
浏览数据	Liúlǎn shùjù	Browsing data	
浏览器	Liúlǎnqì	Browser (Internet tool)	
浏览器应用	Liúlǎnqì yìngyòng	Browser applications (programs)	
流量编整	Liúliàng biānzhěng	Traffic shaping	
流量分布图	Liúliàng fēnbùtú	Distribution graph method	
流量工程	Liúliàng gōngchéng	Traffic engineering	
流量观测	Liúliàng guāncè	Discharge measurement	
流量观测站	Liúliàng guāncèzhàn	Discharge gauging	
流量管理	Liúliàng guǎnlǐ	Traffic management	
流量控保电路	Liúliàng kòng bǎo diànlù	Flow control protection circuit	
流量控制	Liúliàng kòngzhì	Flow control	
流量控制参数协商	Liúliàng kòngzhì cānshù xiéshāng	Flow control parameter negotiation	
流量控制阀	Liúliàng kòngzhì fá	Flow rate control valve	
流量系数	Liúliàng xìshù	Coefficient of discharge	
流量计	Liúliàngjì	Flow meter	

流明	Liúmíng	Lumen (unit of measure for the flow of light)	Lm
流内同步	Liú-nèi tóngbù	Intra-stream synchronization	
流入量	Liúrùliàng	Inflow	
流式	Liú-shì	Streaming	
硫屬化合物	Liúshǔhuà héwù	Chalcogenide	
流水游标	Liúshuǐ yóubiāo	Firehose cursor	
流水线计算机	Liúshuǐxiàn jìsuànjī	Pipeline computer	
流水线模式	Liúshuǐxiàn móshì	Stream mode	
流速	Liúsù	Flow velocity	
流速分布	Liúsù fēnbù	Velocity distribution	
流速计	Liúsùjì	Current meter	
流体视觉化	Liútǐ shìjuéhuà	Flow visualization	
六位字节	Liùwèi zìjié	Sextet byte	
硫系光纤	Liúxì guāngxiān	P-doped optical fiber	
流线处理	Liúxiàn chǔlǐ	Stream processor	
流线网	Liúxiàn wǎng	Flow net	
流向式绘图仪	Liúxiàng-shì huìtúyí	Drum plotter	
流向式扫描仪	Liúxiàng-shì sǎomiáoyí	Drum scanner	
流星散射通信	Liúxīng sǎnshè tōngxìn	Meteor scattering communication	
流星余迹	Liúxīng yújì	Meteor trail	
流星余迹通信	Liúxīng yújì tōngxìn	Meteor trail communications	
留作将来使用	Liúzuò jiānglái shǐyòng	Reserved for future use	RFU
例外处理器	Lìwài chǔlǐqì	Exception handler	
离线	Líxiàn	Off-line	
离线测试	Líxiàn cèshì	Off-line test	
离线原语序列	Líxiàn yuányǔ xùliè	Off-line primitive sequence	OLS
理想忙音信好多路存取	Lǐxiǎng mángyīn xìnhǎo duōlù cúnqǔ	Ideal busy tone multiple access	I-BTMA
理想瞬时	Lǐxiǎng shùnshí	Ideal instant	
例行程序	Lìxíng chéngxù	Routine	
例行或定期测试	Lìxíng huò dìngqī cèshì	Routine or periodic testing	
离子感烟探测器	Lízǐ gǎnyān tàncèqì	Ionization smoke detector	ISD
离子交换设施	Lízǐ jiāohuàn shèshī	Ion exchange works	
粒子群优化	Lìzi qún yōuhuà	Particle swarm optimization	PSO
离子植入机	Lízǐ zhírùjī	Ion implantation equipment	
离子注入机	Lízǐ zhùrùjī	Ion implanter (semiconductor mfg)	
离子束	Lízǐshù	Ion beam	
龙伯透镜天线	Lóng-bó tòujìng tiānxiàn	Luneberg lens antenna	
龙格	Lóng-gé	Runge	
笼形天线	Lóngxíng tiānxiàn	Cage antenna	
漏脉冲	Lòu màichōng	Missing pulse	
漏报	Lòubào	False negatives	
漏报概率	Lòubào gàilǜ	Probability of slip report	
漏波天线	Lòubō tiānxiàn	Leaky-wave antenna	
楼层配线架	Lóucéng pèixiànjià	Floor distributor	FD
漏电断路器	Lòudiàn duànlùqì	Residual current circuit-breaker	
漏洞	Lòudòng	Loophole (IPsec)	

漏洞	Lòudòng	Vulnerability (in IPSec)	
漏码	Lòumǎ	Drop-out	
楼内综合定时供给设备	Lóunèi zōnghé dìngshí gōngjǐ shèbèi	Building integrated time supply	BITS
漏同步	Lòutóngbù	Missed synchronization	
漏泄电缆系统	Lòuxiè diànlǎn xìtǒng	Leaky cable system	
楼宇自动化	Lóuyǔ zìdònghuà	Building automation	BA
楼宇自动化系统	Lóuyǔ zìdònghuà xìtǒng	Building automatic system	BAS
漏指令	Lòuzhǐlìng	Missing command	
乱序执行	Luànxù zhíxíng	Out of order	OoO
鲁棒性	Lǔbàngxìng	Robustness	
鲁棒型水印	Lǔbàngxíng shuǐyìn	Robust watermark	
路边改良项目	Lùbiān gǎiliáng xiàngmù	Roadside improvement project	
滤波	Lǜbō	Filtering	
滤波器	Lǜbōqì	Filter (electrical or RF)	
滤波器标识符	Lǜbōqì biāozhìfú	Filter identifer	FID
滤波器可视化工具	Lǜbōqì kěshìhuà gōngjù	Filter visualization tool	
滤波器设计和分析工具	Lǜbōqì shèjì hé fēnxī gōngjù	Filter design and analysis tool	
滤波器输出	Lǜbōqì shūchū	Filter output	
滤波型波分复用器	Lǜbō-xíng bōfēn fùyòngqì	Filter wavelength division multiplexer	FWDM
滤波型分路器	Lǜbō-xíng fēnlùqì	Filter tap coupler	FTAP
陆地测量部传输格式	Lùdì cèliángbù chuánshū géshi	Ordnance Survey Transfer Format (UK)	OSTF
陆地电台	Lùdì diàntái	Land station	
陆地卫星	Lùdì wèixīng	Landsat	
陆地移动电台	Lùdì yídòng diàntái	Land mobile station	
陆地移动无线电	Lùdì yídòng wúxiàndiàn	Land mobile radio	LMR
陆地移动业务	Lùdì yídòng yèwù	Land mobile service	
露点试验	Lùdiǎn shìyàn	Dew point test	
略位拨号	Lüèwèi bōhào	Speed dialing	
滤光镜	Lǜguāngjìng	Filter (optical)	
卤化物	Lǔhuàwù	Halides (in SMT)	
路际串扰	Lùjì chuànrǎo	Inter-channel interference	ICI
铝镓氮	Lǚjiādàn	Aluminum gallium nitride	AlGaN
路径	Lùjìng	Path (in a computer directory)	
路径	Lùjìng	Trail (ATM term)	
路径查询	Lùjìng cháxún	Pathfinding	
路径代价	Lùjìng dàijià	Path cost	
路径方向	Lùjìng fāngxiàng	Route direction	
路径分集	Lùjìng fēnjí	Path diversity	
路径控制层	Lùjìng kòngzhì céng	Path control layer	
路径控制网	Lùjìng kòngzhì wǎng	Path control network	
路径名	Lùjìng míng	Path name	
路径识别符失配	Lùjìng shíbiéfú shīpèi	Trail identification mismatch	TIM
路径宿端	Lùjìng sù duān	Trail termination sink	
路径损耗	Lùjìng sǔnhào	Pathloss	
路径损失	Lùjìng sǔnshī	Pathloss	
路径索引	Lùjìng suǒyǐn	Path index	

路径信号劣化	Lùjìng xìnhào lièhuà	Trail signal degrade (ATM term)	TSD
路径信号失效	Lùjìng xìnhào shīxiào	Trail signal fail	TSF
路径信息	Lùjìng xìnxī	Route information	
路径选择标识符	Lùjìng xuǎnzé biāozhìfú	Routing identifier	
路径选择类型	Lùjìng xuǎnzé lèixíng	Routing type	
路径选择序号	Lùjìng xuǎnzé xùhào	Routing sequence number	
路径寻找算法	Lùjìng xúnzhǎo suànfǎ	Pathfinding algorithm	
路径源端	Lùjìng yuánduān	Trail termination source	
路径终端	Lùjìng zhōngduān	Trail termination	
路径终端功能	Lùjìng zhōngduān gōngnéng	Trail termination function	TT
路径终结功能	Lùjìng zhōngjié gōngnéng	Trail termination function	TT
路径终接宿	Lùjìng zhōngjiē sù	Trail termination sink	
路径终接源	Lùjìng zhōngjiē yuán	Trail termination source	
路径踪迹标识处理	Lùjìng zōngjī biāozhì chǔlǐ	Trail trace identifier processing	TTIP
路径踪迹识别符	Lùjìng zōngjī shíbiéfú	Trail trace identifier	TTI
路径踪迹识别复帧	Lùjìng zōngjī shíbiéfù zhèng	Trail trace identifier multi-frame	TTI
陆军阿拉斯加通信系统	Lùjūn Ā-lā-sī-jiā tōngxìn xìtǒng	Army Alaska Communications System (US system built in WWII)	AACS
陆军地（区）域通讯系统	Lùjūn dì (qū) yù tōngxùn xìtǒng	Army Area Communications System	AACS
陆军战术数据链	Lùjūn zhànshù shùjù liàn	Army Tactical Data Link (US military)	ATDL
铝-聚乙烯粘结	Lǚjùyǐxī niánjié	Aluminum-polyethylene adhesive (FOC)	
轮函数	Lún hánshù	Round function (crypt.)	
论叫轮询	Lùnjiào lúnxún	Roll-call polling	
轮询	Lúnxún	Poll	
轮询间隔	Lúnxún jiàngé	Polling interval	
轮循匹配	Lúnxún pǐpèi	Round robin matching	RRM
论证阶段	Lùnzhèng jiēduàn	Concept phase (of product life cycle)	
裸光纤	Luǒ guāngxiān	Bare fiber	
裸光纤网	Luǒ guāngxiān wǎng	Bare optical fiber network	
逻辑操作符	Luójí cāozuòfú	Logical operator	
逻辑常数	Luójí chángshù	Logical constant	
逻辑查询	Luójí cháxún	Logical query	
逻辑乘积	Luójí chéngjī	Logical product	
逻辑单元	Luójí dānyuán	Logic units (ITU-T usage)	LU
逻辑单元阵列	Luójí dānyuán zhènliè	Logic cell array (FPGA term)	LCA
逻辑电路	Luójí diànlù	Logic circuit	
逻辑端口	Luójí duānkǒu	Logic port	LP
逻辑方程	Luójí fāngchéng	Boolean equation	
逻辑分析仪	Luójí fēnxīyí	Logic analyzer	
逻辑覆盖	Luójí fùgài	Logical overlay (in computers)	
逻辑赋值语句	Luójí fùzhí yǔjù	Logical assignment statement	
罗技公司	Luó-jì gongsī	Logitech (US company)	
逻辑关系	Luójí guānxi	Logical relationship	
逻辑函数	Luójí hánshù	Logical function	
逻辑和	Luójí hé	Logical sum	
逻辑环回	Luójí huánhuí	Logical loopback	
逻辑 IP 子网	Luójí IP zìwǎng	Logical IP sub-network	LIS

逻辑结构	Luójì jiégòu	Logical structure	
逻辑结构编辑处理	Luójì jiégòu biānjí chǔlǐ	Logical structure editing process	
逻辑记录	Luójì jìlù	Logical record	
逻辑抗干扰处理	Luójì kàng gānrǎo chǔlǐ	Logical anti-jamming processing	
逻辑客体	Luójì kètǐ	Logical object	
逻辑客体类别	Luójì kètǐ lèibié	Logical object class	
逻辑空间	Luójì kōngjiān	Logical space	
逻辑块寻址	Luójì kuài xúnzhǐ	Logical block addressing	LBA
逻辑联接	Luójì liánjiē	Logical_join	
逻辑连接符	Luójì liánjiēfú	Logical connector	
逻辑链路控制（子层）	Luójì liànlù kòngzhì (zǐcéng)	Logical link control (sub-layer) (IEEE 802.2)	LLC
逻辑链路控制层	Luójì liànlù kòngzhì céng	Logic link control layer	LLC
逻辑链路控制和适配协议	Luójì liànlù kòngzhì hé shìpèi xiéyì	Logical link control and adaptation protocol	L2CAP
逻辑门	Luójì mén	Logic gate, logic element	
逻辑名	Luójì míng	Logical name	LN
逻辑名称	Luójì míngchēng	Logical name	
逻辑模块	Luójì mókuài	Logic module	LM
逻辑驱动器	Luójì qūdòngqì	Logical drive	
逻辑群节点	Luójì qún jiédiǎn	Logical group node	LGN
逻辑设计	Luójì shèjì	Logic design	
逻辑式	Luójì shì	Logical expression	
逻辑数据结构	Luójì shùjù jiégòu	Logical data structures	
逻辑数据库	Luójì shùjùkù	Logical database	
逻辑条件语句	Luójì tiáojiàn yǔjù	Logical IF statement	
逻辑通道命令字	Luójì tōngdào mìnglìng zì	Logical channel command word	LCCW
逻辑通路标识符	Luójì tōnglù biāozhìfú	Logical channel identifier	LCI
逻辑线路组	Luójì xiànlù zǔ	Logical line code	LLG
逻辑信道	Luójì xìndào	Logical channel	LC
逻辑信令信道	Luójì xìnlìng xìndào	Logical signaling channel	
逻辑选择	Luójì xuǎnzé	Logical selection	
逻辑页	Luójì yè	Logical page	
逻辑因特网协议子网	Luójì Yīntèwǎng xiéyì ziwǎng	Logical Internet protocol (IP) sub-network	LIS
逻辑一致性	Luójì yīzhìxìng	Logical consistency	
逻辑用户端口	Luójì yònghù duānkǒu	Logical user port	LUP
逻辑元件	Luójì yuánjiàn	Logic element	
逻辑运算	Luójì yùnsuàn	Logical operation	
逻辑运算符	Luójì yùnsuànfú	Logical operators	
逻辑炸弹	Luójì zhàdàn	Logic bomb (hacker attack)	
逻辑炸弹病毒	Luójì zhàdàn bìngdú	Logic bomb virus	
逻辑终端轮廓	Luójì zhōngduān lúnkuò	Logical terminal profile	LTP
逻辑子光纤保护	Luójì ziguāngxiān bǎohù	Logical sub-fiber protection	LSP
逻辑组节点	Luójì zǔ jiédiǎn	Logical group node	
洛克希德马丁公司	Luò-kè-xī-dé Mǎ-dīng gōngsī	Lockheed Martin Corp. (US company)	
洛氏硬度试验	Luò-shì yìngdù shìyàn	Rockwell hardness test	
罗斯比波	Luó-sī-bǐ bō	Rossby wave	
螺线天线	Luóxiàn tiānxiàn	Helical antenna	

螺旋滤波器	Luóxuán lǜbōqì	Screw filter	
螺旋天线	Luóxuán tiānxiàn	Spiral antenna	SA
螺旋型天线	Luóxuán-xíng tiānxiàn	Helical antenna	HA
录取误差	Lùqǔ wùchā	Extraction error	
录取显示器	Lùqǔ xiǎnshìqì	Extraction display	
绿色希尔斯软件公司	Lǜsè Xī-ĕr-sī ruǎnjiàn gōngsī	Green Hills Software Co.	GHS
绿色、氧气、阳光与漫步	Lǜsè、yǎngqì、yángguāng yǔ mànbù	Green, oxygen, light and foot	GOLF
陆上集群无线电	Lùshàng jíqún wúxiàndiàn	Terrestrial trunked radio	TETRA
卤素灯	Lǔsù dēng	Halogen light source	
路线	Lùxiàn	Route	
路线编号	Lùxiàn biānhào	Route number	
路线测量	Lùxiàn cèliáng	Route measure	
路线段	Lùxiàn duàn	Section	
路线属性表	Lùxiàn shǔxing biǎo	Route attribute table	RAT
陆线调频	Lùxiàn tiáopín	Landline frequency modulation	LLFM
路线系统	Lùxiàn xìtǒng	Route system	
旅行商问题	Lǚxíng shāng wèntí	Traveling salesman problem	TSP
路由	Lùyóu	Route	
路由表	Lùyóu biǎo	Routing table	
路由表维护协议	Lùyóu biǎo wéihù xiéyì	Routing table maintenance protocol	RTMP
路由表协议	Lùyóu biǎo xiéyì	Routing table protocol	RTP
路由标签	Lùyóu biāoqiān	Routing tag	
路由查找	Lùyóu cházhǎo	Routing lookup	
路由重新分配	Lùyóu chóngxīn fēnpèi	Route redistribution	
路由处理器	Lùyóu chǔlǐqì	Route processor	RP
路由分析	Lùyóu fēnxī	Route analysis	
路由更新	Lùyóu gēngxīn	Routing update	
路由和控制处理机	Lùyóu hé kòngzhì chǔlǐjī	Routing and control processor	RCP
路由及波长分配	Lùyóu jí bōcháng fēnpèi	Routing and assignment of wavelength	RAW
路由控制	Lùyóu kòngzhì	Routing control	
路由控制器	Lùyóu kòngzhìqì	Routing controller	RC
路由扩展	Lùyóu kuòzhǎn	Route extension	
路由量度	Lùyóu liángdù	Routing metric	
路由链路	Lùyóu liànlù	Route link	
路由区	Lùyóu qū	Routing area	RA
路由区识别号	Lùyóu qū shíbiéhào	Routing area identity	RAI
路由全忙	Lùyóu quán máng	All routes busy	ARB
路由区域	Lùyóu qūyù	Routing area	RA
路由区域	Lùyóu qūyù	Routing domain	RD
路由区域码	Lùyóu qūyù mǎ	Routing area code	RAC
路由入侵检测	Lùyóu rùqīn jiǎncè	Route intrusion detection	RID
路由设置表	Lùyóu shèzhì biǎo	Route set-up packet	RSUP
路由信息协议	Lùyóu xìnxī xiéyì	Routing information protocol	RIP
路由信息域	Lùyóu xìnxī yù	Routing information field	RIF
路由选定	Lùyóu xuǎndìng	Routing	
路由选择	Lùyóu xuǎnzé	Routing	

路由选择表维护协议	Lùyóu xuǎnzé biǎo wéihù xiéyì	Routing table maintenance protocol	RTMP
路由选择表协议	Lùyóu xuǎnzé biǎo xiéyì	Routing table protocol	RTP
路由选择范围	Lùyóu xuǎnzé fànwéi	Routing area	RA
路由选择矩阵	Lùyóu xuǎnzé jǔzhèn	Routing metric	
路由选择控制功能	Lùyóu xuǎnzé kòngzhì gōngnéng	Routing control function	
路由选择类型	Lùyóu xuǎnzé lèixíng	Routing type	RT
路由选择区域更新	Lùyóu xuǎnzé qūyù gēngxīn	Routing area update	RAU
路由选择区域码	Lùyóu xuǎnzé qūyù mǎ	Routing area code	RAC
路由选择区域识别	Lùyóu xuǎnzé qūyù shíbié	Routing area identity	RAI
路由选择信息	Lùyóu xuǎnzé xìnxī	Routing information	RI
路由选择信息	Lùyóu xuǎnzé xìnxī	Routing selection information	
路由选择信息指示符	Lùyóu xuǎnzé xìnxī zhǐshìfú	Routing information indicator	RII
路由选择信息字段	Lùyóu xuǎnzé xìnxī zìduàn	Routing information field	RIF
路由选择域	Lùyóu xuǎnzé yù	Routing domain	RD
路由选择器	Lùyóu xuǎnzéqì	Route selector	
路由映射	Lùyóu yìngshè	Route map	
路由映像	Lùyóu yìngxiàng	Route mapping	
路由再选定	Lùyóu zàixuǎndìng	Re-routing	
路由摘要	Lùyóu zhāiyào	Route summarization	
路由证实测试	Lùyóu zhèngshí cèshì	Routing verification test	RVT
路由器	Lùyóuqì	Router	
路由器广播	Lùyóuqì guǎngbō	Router advertisements	
路由器和 BIN 后面板	Lùyóuqì hé BIN hòumianbǎn	Router and BIN back panel	RBBP
路由器和 GCIN 机架	Lùyóuqì hé GCIN jījià	Router and GCIN rack	RAGR
路由器请求	Lùyóuqì qǐngqiú	Router solicitations	
路由器搜索	Lùyóuqì sōusuǒ	Router discovery	
路踪误差	Lùzōng wùchā	Trace error	TE

M

码变换及子复用单元	Mǎ biànhuàn jí zifùyòng dānyuán	Transcoder and sub-multiplex unit	TCSM
码变换速率适配单元	Mǎ biànhuàn sùlǜ shìpèi dānyuán	Transcoder and rate adapter unit	TRAU
码变换子复用控制器	Mǎ biànhuàn zifùyòng kòngzhìqì	Transcoder sub-multiplexer controller	TSC
码变换器	Mǎ biànhuànqì	Transcoder	TC
码变换器和子复用设备	Mǎ biànhuànqì hé zifùyòng shèbèi	Transcoder and sub-rate channel multiplexer	TCSM
码交换	Mǎ jiāohuàn	Code conversion	
码聚焦	Mǎ jùjiāo	Aggregation	
码时分多址	Mǎ shífèn duōzhǐ	Code and time division multiple access	CTDMA
码书	Mǎ shū	Code book	
码速率	Mǎ sùlǜ	Bit rate	
码速率变换	Mǎ sùlǜ biànhuàn	Code speed-rate transformation	
码违例	Mǎ wéilì	Code violation	CV
码型	Mǎ xíng	Code pattern	
MAC 服务访问点	MAC fúwù fǎngwèn diǎn	MAC service access point	MSAP
MAC 服务数据单元	MAC fúwù shùjù dānyuán	MAC service data unit	MSDU
MAC 协议数据单元	MAC xiéyì shùjù dānyuán	MAC protocol data unit	MPDU
马达定子式偏转线圈	Mǎdá dìngzi-shì piānzhuǎn xiànquān	Motor-stator deflection coil	

马尔科夫观察一致性	Mă-ĕr-kē-fū guānchá yīzhìxìng	Markovian observational congruence	
马尔可夫过程	Mă-ĕr-kĕ-fū guòchéng	Markov process	
马尔可夫向量方法	Mă-ĕr-kĕ-fū xiàngliàng fāngfă	Markov vector method	
码分	Măfēn	Code division	
码分多路复用	Măfēn duōlù fùyòng	Code division multiplex	CDM
码分多址	Măfēn duōzhĭ	Code division multiple access	CDMA
码分多址蜂窝系统	Măfēn duōzhĭ fēngwō xìtŏng	Code division multiple access cellular system	
码分多址个人通信网	Măfēn duōzhĭ gèrén tōngxìnwăng	Code division multiple access personal communications network	CDMA PCN
码分多址个人通讯网	Măfēn duōzhĭ gèrén tōngxùnwăng	Code division multiple access personal communications network	CDMA PCN
码分多址接入	Măfēn duōzhĭ jiērù	Code division multiple access	CDMA
码分复用	Măfēn fùyòng	Code division multiplexing	CDM
码分交换	Măfēn jiāohuàn	Code division exchange	
马赫-曾德尔调制器	Mă-hè—céng-dé-ĕr tiáozhìqì	Mach-Zehnder modulator	
马赫-曾泽尔干涉仪	Mă-hè—céng-zé-ĕr gānshèyí	Mach-Zehnder interferometer	
脉伐，可变电抗混频放大	Mài fá, kĕbiàn diànkàng hùnpín fàngdà	Mixer amplification by variable reactance	MAVAR
脉宽调制	Mài kuān tiáozhì	Pulse width modulation	PWM
埋深	Mái shēn	Buried depth	
脉冲	Màichōng	Pulse	P
脉冲	Màichōng	Spike	
脉冲	Màichōng	Pulse	
脉冲编码调制	Màichōng biānmă tiáozhì	Pulse encoded modulation	PEM
脉冲编码调制	Màichōng biānmă tiáozhì	Pulse code modulation	PCM
脉冲编码调制基群	Màichōng biānmă tiáozhì jīqún	Primary pulse code modulation (PCM) group	
脉冲变压器	Màichōng biànyāqì	Pulse transformer	
脉冲拨号	Màichōng bōhào	Pulse dialing	
脉冲波形鉴别	Màichōng bōxíng jiànbié	Pulse waveform discrimination	
脉冲长度鉴别	Màichōng chángdù jiànbié	Pulse length discrimination	
脉冲持续时间	Màichōng chíxù shíjiān	Pulse duration	
脉冲持续时间调制	Màichōng chíxù shíjiān tiáozhì	Pulse duration modulation, pulse width modulation	PDM
脉冲重复频率	Màichōng chóngfù pínlǜ	Pulse repetition frequency	
脉冲重复频率调制	Màichōng chóngfù pínlǜ tiáozhì	Pulse repetition rate modulation	
脉冲重复周期	Màichōng chóngfù zhōuqī	Pulse repetition cycle	
脉冲串	Màichōng chuàn	Pulse series	
脉冲串间隔	Màichōng chuàn jiàngé	Time interval between pulse series	
脉冲单音制	Màichōng dānyīn zhì	Pulsed-individual tone system	
脉冲顶部补偿电路	Màichōng dĭngbù bŭcháng diànlù	Pulse top compensation circuit	
脉冲顶部限幅电路	Màichōng dĭngbù xiàn fú diànlù	Pulse top clipper circuit	
脉冲断续比	Màichōng duànxù bĭ	Pulse break/make ratio	
脉冲二氧化碳激光	Màichōng èryănghuàtàn jīguāng	Pulsed CO_2 laser	
脉冲发码	Màichōng fā mă	Pulse code generator	
脉冲幅度	Màichōng fúdù	Pulse amplitude modulation	PAM
脉冲幅度编码调制	Màichōng fúdù biānmă tiáozhì	Pulse-amplitude-code modulation	PACM
脉冲幅度调制	Màichōng fúdù tiáozhì	Pulse amplitude modulation	PAM
脉冲傅氏转换	Màichōng fù-shì zhuănhuàn	Pulsed Fourier transform	PFT
脉冲干扰	Màichōng gānrăo	Pulse jamming	

脉冲功率	Màichōng gōnglǜ	Pulse power	
脉冲和频率组合编码制	Màichōng hé pínlǜ zǔhé biānmǎ zhì	Combination pulse and frequency-coding system	
脉冲检波器	Màichōng jiǎnbōqì	Pulse detector	
脉冲间隔	Màichōng jiàngé	Pulse spacing	
脉冲校正器	Màichōng jiàozhèngqì	Pulse corrector	
脉冲交织	Màichōng jiāozhī	Pulse interlacing	
脉冲激励线性预测编码	Màichōng jīlì xiànxìng yùcè biānmǎ	Pulse excitation linear predictive coding	
脉冲计数制	Màichōng jìshù zhì	Pulse counting system	
脉冲开始信号	Màichōng kāishǐ xìnhào	Start-of-pulsing signal	
脉冲宽度	Màichōng kuāndù	Pulse width	
脉冲宽度鉴别	Màichōng kuāndù jiànbié	Pulse width discrimination	
脉冲宽度调制	Màichōng kuāndù tiáozhì	Pulse width modulation	PDM
脉冲宽度调制	Màichōng kuāndù tiáozhì	Pulse duration modulation	PDM
脉冲宽度制	Màichōng kuāndù zhì	Pulse duration system	
脉冲列	Màichōng liè	Pulse train	
脉冲码调制	Màichōng mǎ tiáozhì	Pulse code modulation	PCM
脉冲马达	Màichōng mǎdá	Pulse motor	
脉冲密度	Màichōng mìdù	Pulse density	
脉冲模框	Màichōng mókuàng	Pulse mask	
脉冲频率调制	Màichōng pínlǜ tiáozhì	Pulse frequency modulation	PFM
脉冲前沿抖动	Màichōng qiányán dǒudòng	Pulse front edge jitter	
脉冲区间调制	Màichōng qūjiān tiáozhì	Pulse interval modulation	PIM
脉冲塞入	Màichōng sāirù	Pulse stuffing	
脉冲骚扰	Màichōng sāorǎo	Pulse disturbance	
脉冲骚扰	Màichōng sāorǎo	Impulsive disturbance	
脉冲上升时间	Màichōng shàngshēng shíjiān	Pulse rise time	
脉冲时间调制	Màichōng shíjiān tiáozhì	Pulse time modulation	PTM
脉冲调幅调相	Màichōng tiáofú tiáoxiàng	Pulse amplitude and phase modulation	PAPM
脉冲调制	Màichōng tiáozhì	Pulse modulation	
脉冲位调制	Màichōng wèi tiáozhì	Pulse position modulation	PPM
脉冲位置调制	Màichōng wèizhì tiáozhì	Pulse position modulation	PPM
脉冲位置制	Màichōng wèizhì zhì	Pulse position system	
脉冲下降时间	Màichōng xiàjiàng shíjiān	Pulse decay time	
脉冲相位洲制	Màichōng xiàngwèi zhōuzhì	Pulse phase modulation	PPM
脉冲响应函数	Màichōng xiǎngyìng hánshù	Pulse-response function	
脉冲响应曲线	Màichōng xiǎngyìng qūxiàn	Pulse response curve	
脉冲响应特性	Màichōng xiǎngyìng tèxìng	Pulse response characteristics	
脉冲形成网络	Màichōng xíngchéng wǎngluò	Pulse forming network (radar term)	
脉冲信号	Màichōng xìnhào	Pulse signal	
脉冲信号发生器	Màichōng xìnhào fāshēngqì	Pulse signal generator	
脉冲延迟二进制调制	Màichōng yánchí èrjìnzhì tiáozhì	Pulse delay binary modulation	PDBM
脉冲压缩侦察接收机	Màichōng yāsuō zhēnchá jiēshōujī	Pulse compressive reconnaissance receiver	
脉冲与频率组合编码制	Màichōng yǔ pínlǜ zǔhé biānmǎ zhì	Combination pulse and frequency coding system	
脉冲载波	Màichōng zàibō	Pulsed carrier	
脉冲载波调制	Màichōng zàibō tiáozhì	Pulsed carrier modulation	
脉冲再生器	Màichōng zàishēngqì	Pulse regenerator	

脉冲噪声	Màichōng zàoshēng	Pulse noise	
脉冲噪声	Màichōng zàoshēng	Impulsive noise	
脉冲噪声容限	Màichōng zàoshēng róngxiàn	Impulsive noise tolerance	
脉冲增量调制	Màichōng zēngliàng tiáozhì	Pulse delta modulation	PDM
脉冲占空系数	Màichōng zhànkōng xìshù	Pulse duty factor	
脉冲振幅调制	Màichōng zhènfú tiáozhì	Pulse amplitude modulation	PAM
脉冲终了信号	Màichōng zhōngliǎo xìnhào	End-of-pulsing signal	
脉冲周期时间	Màichōng zhōuqī shíjiān	Pulse recurrent time	PRT
脉冲/秒	Màichōng/miǎo	Pulse per second	PPS
脉冲的半高宽度	Màichōngde bàngāo kuāndù	Full width half maximum (pulse)	FWHM
脉冲式激光	Màichōng-shì jīguāng	Pulsed laser	
脉动	Màidòng	Pulsating	
脉动骚扰	Màidòng sāorǎo	Impulsive disturbance	
脉动噪声	Màidòng zàoshēng	Impulsive noise	
脉间跳频	Mài-jiān tiàopín	Inter-pulse frequency shifting	
麦金塔	Mài-jīn-tǎ	Macintosh; Mac (US company)	
迈克尔逊型干涉仪	Mài-kè-ěr xùn-xíng gānshèyí	Michelson interferometer	
麦克风	Màikèfēng	Microphone	MIC
麦克斯威而模型	Mài-kè-sī-wēi-ér móxíng	Maxwell model	
脉宽鉴别	Màikuān jiànbié	Pulse width discrimination	
脉宽调制-调制	Màikuān tiáozhì—tiáozhì	Pulse-duration modulation frequency modulation	PDM-FM
脉宽制	Màikuānzhì	Pulse duration system	
麦蓝	Mài-lán	Microlab (US company)	
脉码设备	Màimǎ shèbèi	Pulse code equipment	MM
脉码调整二元码	Màimǎ tiáozhěng èryuán mǎ	Binary code	
脉码调制	Màimǎ tiáozhì	Pulse code modulation	PCM
脉码调制复用设备	Màimǎ tiáozhì fùyòng shèbèi	Pulse code modulation (PCM) multiplex equipment	
脉内跳频	Mài-nèi tiàopín	Intra-pulse frequency shifting	
埋入的通路孔	Máirùde tōnglù kǒng	Buried via (in SMT)	
埋设工	Máishè gōng	Buried works	
埋设结构	Máishè jiégòu	Buried structure	
脉数制	Màishùzhì	Pulse counting system	
迈拓公司	Mài-tuò gōngsī	Maxtor Corporation (US company)	
脉位调制	Màiwèi tiáozhì	Pulse position modulation	PPM
脉位制	Màiwèizhì	Pulse position system	
码间干扰	Mǎ-jiān gānrǎo	Inter-symbol interference	ISI
码激励	Mǎjīlì	Code-excited	
码激励线性预测	Mǎjīlì xiànxìng yùcè	Code-excited linear prediction	CELP
码激励线性预测编码	Mǎjīlì xiànxìng yùcè biānmǎ	Qualcomm code excited linear prediction	QCELP
马可尼公司	Mǎ-kě-ní gōngsī	Marconi Corp. (UK company)	
马来西亚微电子学院	Mǎ-lái-xī-yà wēidiànzǐ xuéyuàn	Malaysian Institute of Microelectronic Systems	MIMOS
码率可分级	Mǎlǜ kěfēnjí	Rate scalable	
满二叉树	Mǎn èrchā shù	Full binary tree	
满量程	Mǎn liángchéng	Full scale	FS
慢频率跳编多路存取	Màn pínlǜ tiàobiān duōlù cúnqǔ	Slow frequency hopping multiple access	SFHMA
慢波	Mànbō	Slow wave	

慢波结构	Mànbō jiégòu	Slow wave structure	
曼彻斯特编码	Màn-chè-sī-tè biānmǎ	Manchester encoding	
曼彻斯特自动带码	Màn-chè-sī-tè zìdòng dàimǎ	Manchester auto-code	MAC
慢递信息包	Màndì xìnxī bāo	Choke packet	
盲提取	Máng tíqǔ	Blind retrieval	
盲通路孔	Máng tōnglù kǒng	Blind via (in SMT)	
忙闲比特	Máng xián bǐtè	Busy/idle bit	
忙用户的呼叫完成	Máng yònghùde hūjiào wánchéng	Call completed to busy subscriber	CCBS
忙状态	Máng zhuàngtài	Busy condition	
忙状态	Máng zhuàngtài	Busy state	
忙/闲标志	Máng/xián biāozhì	Busy/Idle flag	
盲点	Mángdiǎn	Blind spot	
盲目传输格式检测	Mángmù chuánshū géshi jiǎncè	Blind transport format detection	BTFD
盲目数字化	Mángmù shùzìhuà	Blind digitizing	
盲目搜寻	Mángmù sōuxún	Jughead search (Internet tool)	
盲目着陆雷达	Mángmù zháolù léidá	Blind landing-aid radar	
盲区	Mángqū	Blind zone	
盲人读物	Mángrén dúwù	Blind literature	
忙时	Mángshí	Busy hour	
忙时负载	Mángshí fùzài	Busy hour load	BHL
忙时话务量	Mángshí huàwùliàng	Busy hour call attempts	BHCA
忙时呼叫	Mángshí hūjiào	Busy hour calls	BHC
忙时呼叫尝试	Mángshí hūjiào chángshì	Busy hour calling attempts	BHCA
忙时呼叫完成	Mángshí hūjiào wánchéng	Busy hour call completed	BHCC
忙时试呼次数	Mángshí shìhū cìshù	Busy hour calling attempts	BHCA
忙时应用	Mángshí yìngyòng	Busy hour usage	BHU
盲速	Mángsù	Blind speed	
忙闲测试	Mángxián cèshì	Busy test	
忙闲检测	Mángxián jiǎncè	Busy/idle check	
盲相	Mángxiàng	Blind phase	
忙音	Mángyīn	Busy tone	
忙音中继线	Mángyīn zhōngjìxiàn	Busy tone trunk	BTT
曼宁公式	Màn-níng gōngshì	Manning formula	
慢速辅助控制信道	Mànsù fǔzhù kòngzhì xìndào	Slow assisted control channel	SACCH
慢速辅助控制信道/半速率业务信道	Mànsù fǔzhù kòngzhì xìndào/bàn sùlǜ yèwù xìndào	Slow assisted control channel/traffic channel half rate	SACCHTH
慢速辅助控制信道/全速率业务信道	Mànsù fǔzhù kòngzhì xìndào/quánsùlǜ yèwù xìndào	Slow assisted control channel/traffic channel full rate	SACCH/TF
慢速辅助控制信道/业务信道	Mànsù fǔzhù kòngzhì xìndào/yèwù xìndào	Slow assisted control channel/traffic channel	SACCH/T
慢速随路控制信道	Mànsù suílù kòngzhì xìndào	Slow associated control channel	SACCH
慢速随路控制信道/全速率业务信道	Mànsù suílù kòngzhì xìndào/quán sùlǜ yèwù xìndào	Slow associated control channel/traffic channel full rate	SACCH/TF
慢速随路控制信道/业务信道	Mànsù suílù kòngzhì xìndào/yèwù xìndào	Slow associated control channel/traffic channel	SACCH/T
慢跳频	Màntiàopín	Slow frequency hopping	SFH

漫游	Mànyóu	Pan (video term)	
漫游	Mànyóu	Roaming (cellular telephony)	
漫游信令网关	Mànyóu xìnlìng wǎngguān	Roaming signaling gateway	R-SGW
漫游用户	Mànyóu yònghù	Roaming subscriber	
漫游用户配置文件	Mànyóu yònghù pèizhì wénjiàn	Roaming user profile	
漫游者	Mànyóuzhě	Roamer (cellular telephony)	
满载波单边带发射	Mǎnzàibō dānbiāndài fāshè	Full carrier single sideband (SSB) emission	
冒充	Màochōng	Masquerade (IPsec)	
毛刺	Máocì	Glitch, burr (PCB manufacture)	
毛刺捕获	Máocì bǔhuò	Glitch capture	
锚点	Máodiǎn	Anchor point	
冒险类游戏	Màoxiǎn lèi yóuxì	Adventure genre (computer game)	AVG
毛细管作用	Máoxìguǎn zuòyòng	Capillary action (in SMT)	
贸易服务总协定	Màoyì fúwù zǒngxiédìng	General Agreement on Trade in Services	GATS
锚子	Máozi	Anchor	
码片	Mǎpiàn	Chip	
马赛克浏览器	Mǎ-sài-kè liúlǎnqì	Mosaic browser © (Internet tool)	
码速调整	Mǎsù tiáozhěng	Justification	
码速调整比	Mǎsù tiáozhěng bǐ	Justification ratio	
码型变换器	Mǎ-xíng biànhuànqì	Transcoder	
码型转换和速率适配单元	Mǎ-xíng zhuǎnhuàn hé sùlǜ shìpèi dānyuán	Transcoder and rate adaptation unit	TRAU
码元	Mǎyuán	Coding element	
码元同步	Mǎyuán tóngbù	Element synchronization	
骂战	Màzhàn	Flame war (computer slang)	
码字	Mǎzì	Code word	
码字通道连接	Mǎzì tōngdào liánjiē	Code path connect	CPC
码字通道链路	Mǎzì tōngdào liànlù	Code path link	CPL
码字通道值	Mǎzì tōngdào zhí	Code path ID	CPI
码组	Mǎzǔ	Block (digital signal processing)	
码组差错率	Mǎzǔ chācuò lǜ	Block error rate	BLER
码组传输结束	Mazǔ chuánshū jiéshù	End of transmission block	ETB
码组检验	Mǎzǔ jiǎnyàn	Block check	
码组起始信号	Mǎzǔ qǐshǐ xìnhào	Start-of-block signal	
码组信号	Mǎzǔ xìnhào	Block signal	
美标码	Měi biāo mǎ	American standard code	ASCII
每寸多少字	Měi cùn duōshao zì	Characters per inch	CPI
每单位市场价格表	Měi dānwèi shìchǎng jiàgé biǎo	Price per unit currency table	PUCT
没电路每小时的试占次数	Méi diànlù měi xiǎoshíde shìzhàn cìshù	Bids per circuit hour	BCH
每分钟多少页	Měi fēnzhōng duōshao yè	Pages per minute	PPM
每服务器授权	Měi fúwùqì shòuquán	Per-server licensing	
每客户授权	Měi kèhù shòuquán	Per-seat licensing	
每秒百万次浮点运算	Měi miǎo bǎiwàncì fúdiǎn yùnsuàn	Million floating point operations per second	MFLOPS
每秒百万次指令	Měi miǎo bǎiwàncì zhǐlìng	Million instructions per second	MIPS
每秒百万个浮点操作	Měi miǎo bǎiwàngè fúdiǎn cāozuò	Million floating point operations per second	MFLOPS
每秒百万条指令	Měi miǎo bǎiwàntiáo zhǐlìng	Million instructions per second	MIPS
每秒处理事项数	Měi miǎo chǔlǐ shìxiàng shù	Transactions per second	TPS

每秒多少百万个指令	Měi miǎo duōshao bǎiwàngè zhǐlìng	Millions of instructions per second	MIPS
每秒多少画面	Měi miǎo duōshao huàmiàn	Frames per second (video term)	FPS
每秒多少字	Měi miǎo duōshao zì	Characters per second	CPS
每秒浮点运算次数	Měi miǎo fúdiǎn yùnsuàn cìshù	Floating point operations per second	FLOPS
每秒脉冲数	Měi miǎo màichōng shù	Pulses per second	PPS
每秒千比特	Měi miǎo qiānbǐtè	Kilobits per second	Kbps
每秒千符号（码元）	Měi miǎo qiānfúhào (mǎ yuán)	Kilo-symbols per second	Ksps
每秒试呼数	Měi miǎo shìhūshù	Call attempts per second	CAPS
每秒字符数	Měi miǎo zìfúshù	Characters per second	CPS
每跳行为	Měi tiào xíngwéi	Per-hop behavior	PHB
每调制比特的射频能量对噪声频谱密度比	Měi tiáozhì bǐtède shèpín néngliàng duì zàoshēng pínpǔ mìdùbǐ	Ratio of energy per modulating bit to noise spectral density	Ec/No
每英寸点数	Měi yīngcùn diǎnshù	Dots per inch	Dpi
每英寸的打印像素	Měi yīngcùnde dǎyìn xiàngsù	Dots per inch (printer term)	dpi
每移试呼数	Měi yíshì hūshù	Call attempts per second	CAPS
每域行为	Měi yù xíngwéi	Per domain behavior	PDB
每载波单路	Měi zàibō dānlù	Single channel per carrier	SCPC
每载波单路-脉码调制-多址联接-按申请分配	Měi zàibō dānlù-mài mǎ tiáozhì- Duō zhǐ liánjiē- Àn shēnqǐng fēnpèi	Single channel per carrier- pulse code modulation- multiple access- demand assignment	SPADE
每载波多信道	Měi zàibō duō xìndào	Multi-channel per carrier	MCPC
每载波多路	Měi zàibō duōlù	Multiple channel per carrier	MCPC
每站行为	Měi zhàn xíngwéi	Per-hop behavior	
每转发器单路	Měi zhuǎnfāqì dānlù	Single channel per transponder	SCPT
美达	Měi-dá	Maxtor (US company)	
美国标准协会	Měiguó biāozhǔn xiéhuì	American Standards Association	ASA
美国标准局	Měiguó biāozhǔnjú	American Bureau of Standards	ABS
美国测绘委员会	Měiguó cèhuì wěiyuánhuì	American Congress on Surveying and Mapping	ACSM
美国唱片工业协会	Měiguó chàngpiàn gōngyè xiéhuì	Recording Industry Association of America	RIAA
美国电报电话公司	Měiguó diànbào diànhuà gōngsī	American Telephone and Telegraph (AT&T) (US company)	ATT
美国电缆电视协会	Měiguó diànlǎn diànshì xiéhuì	National Cable Television Association (US)	NCTA
美国电气及电子工程师协会	Měiguó diànqì jí diànzǐ gōngchéngshī xiéhuì	Institute of Electrical and Electronics Engineers	IEEE
美国电信工业协会	Měiguó diànxìn gōngyè xiéhuì	Telecommunications Industry Association (US)	TIA
美国电子工业协会	Měiguó diànzǐ gōngyè xiéhuì	Electronic Industries Association (US)	EIA
美国第二级股市	Měiguó dì'èrjí gǔshì	NASDAQ	
美国地质调查所	Měiguó dìzhì diàochá suǒ	United States Geological Survey	
美国翻译协会	Měiguó fānyì xiéhuì	American Translators Association	ATA
美国工程师协会	Měiguó gōngchéngshī xiéhuì	American Association of Engineers	AAE
美国光桥网络有限公司	Měiguó guāng qiáo wǎngluò yǒuxiàn gōngsī	Photonic Bridges Inc., (US company)	
美国广播公司	Měiguó guǎngbō gōngsī	American Broadcasting Corp. (US company)	ABC
美国国家标准协会	Měiguó guójiā biāozhǔn xiéhuì	American National Standards Institute	ANSI
美国国家标准信息交换代码	Měiguó guójiā biāozhǔn xìnxī jiāohuàn dàimǎ	American Standard Code for Information Interchange	ASCII
美国国家标准研究所	Měiguó guójiā biāozhǔn yánjiūsuǒ	American National Standards Institute	ANSI
美国国家标准组织	Měiguó guójiā biāozhǔn zǔzhī	American National Standards Institute	ANSI
美国国家标准局	Měiguó guójiā biāozhǔnjú	American National Standards Institute	ANSI
美国国家地图精度标准	Měiguó guójiā dìtú jīngdù biāozhǔn	United States National Map Accuracy Standard	USNMAS

美国海军天文台	Měiguó hǎijūn tiānwéntái	United States Naval Observatory	USNO
美国科学促进协会	Měiguó kēxué cùjìn xiéhuì	American Association for the Advancement of Science	AAAS
美国科学院	Měiguó kēxuéyuàn	American Academy of Science	AAS
美国陆军数据分发系统	Měiguó lùjūn shùjù fēnfā xìtǒng	Army Data Distribution System (US)	ADDS
美国人工智能协会	Měiguó réngōng zhìnéng xiéhuì	American Association for Artificial Intelligence	AAAI
美国泰乐国际公司	Měiguó tài-lè guójì gōngsī	Tellabs International Inc. (US company)	
美国通信卫星公司	Měiguó tōngxìn wèixīng gōngsī	Comsat/RSI (US company)	
美国通信协会	Měiguó tōngxìn xiéhuì	American Communication Association	ACA
美国线规	Měiguó xiànguī	American Wire Gauge	AWG
美国线缆规格	Měiguó xiànlǎn guīgé	American Wire Gauge	AWG
美国线上	Měiguó xiànshàng	America Online	AOL
美国信息处理学会联合会	Měiguó xìnxī chǔlǐ xuéhuì liánhéhuì	American Federation of Information processing Societies	AFIPS
美国信息交换标准代码	Měiguó xìnxī jiāohuàn biāozhǔn dàimǎ	American Standard Code for Information Interchange	ASCII
美国信息交换标准码	Měiguó xìnxī jiāohuàn biāozhǔn mǎ	American Standard Code for Information Interchange	ASCII
美国信息技术协会	Měiguó xìnxī jìshù xiéhuì	Information Technology Association of America	ITAA
美国信息系统国家标准	Měiguó xìnxī xìtǒng guójiā biāozhǔn	American National Standard for Information Systems	ANSI
美国仪表协会	Měiguó yíbiǎo xiéhuì	Instrument Society of America	ISA
美国宇航学会	Měiguó yǔháng xuéhuì	American Astronautical Society	AAS
美国在线服务	Měiguó zàixiàn fúwù	America On-Line	AOL
美国智能建筑学会	Měiguó zhìnéng jiànzhù xuéhuì	American Intelligent Building Institute	AIBI
美国自动控制委员会	Měiguó zìdòng kòngzhì wěiyuánhuì	American Automatic Control Council	AACC
媒介单位	Méijiè dānwèi	Media units	
媒介访问控制	Méijiè fǎngwèn kòngzhì	Media access control	MAC
媒介接入控制	Méijiè jiērù kòngzhì	Media access control	MAC
枚举	Méijǔ	Enumeration	
枚举成员	Méijǔ chéngyuán	Enumerator	
霉菌试验	Méijùn shìyàn	Mold test	
枚举器	Méijǔqì	Enumerator	
梅利沙	Méi-lì-shā	Melissa (computer virus)	
美能达	Měi-néng-dá	Minolta (Japanese company)	
媒体	Méitǐ	Medium, media	
媒体层	Méitǐ céng	Media layer	
媒体池	Méitǐ chí	Media pool	
媒体访问控制	Méitǐ fǎngwèn kòngzhì	Media access control	MAC
媒体访问控制层	Méitǐ fǎngwèn kòngzhì céng	Media access control layer	MAC
媒体访问控制子层	Méitǐ fǎngwèn kòngzhì zicéng	Media access control sub-layer	MAC
媒体发展环境	Méitǐ fāzhǎn huánjìng	Ecosystem for Media © (by AT&T)	
媒体附加接口	Méitǐ fùjiā jiēkǒu	Media attachment unit	MAU
媒体管理	Méitǐ guǎnlǐ	Media manager	MM
媒体集	Méitǐ jí	Media set	
媒体交换模块	Méitǐ jiāohuàn mókuài	Media switching function	MSF
媒体家族	Méitǐ jiāzú	Media family	
媒体接口连接器	Méitǐ jiēkǒu liánjiēqì	Media interface connector	MIC
媒体接入控制	Méitǐ jiērù kòngzhì	Media access control	MAC
媒体接入控制子层	Méitǐ jiērù kòngzhì zicéng	Media access control sub-layer	MAC
媒体结束	Méitǐ jiéshù	End of media	EM

媒体记录	Méitǐ jìlù	Media record	
媒体记录规范	Méitǐ jìlù guīfàn	Media record specifications	
媒体控制单元	Méitǐ kòngzhì dānyuán	Media control unit	MCU
媒体控制访问	Méitǐ kòngzhì fǎngwèn	Media access control	MAC
媒体控制介面	Méitǐ kòngzhì jièmiàn	Media control interface	MCI
媒体流处理器	Méitǐ liú chǔlǐqì	Media stream processor	MSP
媒体流广播和分发	Méitǐ liú guǎngbō hé fēnfā	Media streaming broadcast and distribution	MSBD
媒体流提供程序	Méitǐ liú tígōng chéngxù	Media stream provider	MSP
媒体描述	Méitǐ miáoshù	Media description	
媒体名称	Méitǐ míngchēng	Media name	
媒体适配器	Méitǐ shìpèiqì	Media adapter	MA
媒体首部	Méitǐ shǒubù	Media header	
媒体网关	Méitǐ wǎngguān	Media gateway	MG
媒体网关单元	Méitǐ wǎngguān dānyuán	Media gateway unit	MGU
媒体网关功能	Méitǐ wǎngguān gōngnéng	Media gateway function	MGF
媒体网关控制	Méitǐ wǎngguān kòngzhì	Media gateway control	MEGACO
媒体网关控制部分	Méitǐ wǎngguān kòngzhì bùfen	Media gateway control part	MGCP
媒体网关控制单元	Méitǐ wǎngguān kòngzhì dānyuán	Media gateway control unit	MGCU
媒体网关控制功能	Méitǐ wǎngguān kòngzhì gōngnéng	Media gateway control function	MGCF
媒体网关控制协议	Méitǐ wǎngguān kòngzhì xiéyì	Media gateway control protocol	Megaco
媒体网关控制协议	Méitǐ wǎngguān kòngzhì xiéyì	Media gateway control protocol	MGCP
媒体网关控制器	Méitǐ wǎngguān kòngzhìqì	Media gateway controller	MGC
媒体网关控制器协议	Méitǐ wǎngguān kòngzhìqì xiéyì	Media gateway control protocol	MGCP
媒体无关接口	Méitǐ wúguān jiēkǒu	Media independent interface	MII
媒体相关接口	Méitǐ xiāngguān jiēkǒu	Media dependent interface	MDI
媒体依赖接口	Méitǐ yīlài jiēkǒu	Media dependent interface	MDI
媒体资源功能	Méitǐ zīyuán gōngnéng	Media resource function	MRF
媒体资源功能处理	Méitǐ zīyuán gōngnéng chǔlǐ	Media resources function processing	MRFP
媒体资源功能控制	Méitǐ zīyuán gōngnéng kòngzhì	Media resources function control	MRFC
没有可用的切换号码	Méiyǒu kěyòngde qiēhuàn hàomǎ	No handover number available	
没有可用的无线信道	Méiyǒu kěyòngde wúxiàn xìndào	No radio channel available	
没有可用的无线资源	Méiyǒu kěyòngde wúxiàn zīyuán	No radio resource available	
媒质接入控制	Méizhì jiērù kòngzhì	Media access control	MAC
媒质接入控制层	Méizhì jiērù kòngzhì céng	Medium access control	MAC
门	Mén	Gate	
门开关	Mén kāiguān	Gate switch	
门阵列	Mén zhènliè	Gate array	GA
盟军指挥信道	Méngjūn zhǐhuī xìndào	Allied Command Channel (NATO usage)	ACCHAN
蒙特卡洛模拟	Méng-tè-kǎ-luò mónǐ	Monte Carlo simulation	MCS
门户	Ménhù	Portal	
门户服务器	Ménhù fúwùqì	Portal server	
门户站点	Ménhù zhàndiǎn	Portal site	
门极可关断晶体管	Ménjí kěguānduàn jīngtǐguǎn	Gate turnoff thyristor	GTO
门禁	Ménjìn	Firewall (lit : gateway guard)	
门钮式同轴波导变换器	Ménniǔ-shì tóngzhóu bōdǎo biànhuànqì	Door-knob transformer	
门限	Ménxiàn	Threshold	

门限报告	Ménxiàn bàogào	Threshold report	TR
门限超越告警	Ménxiàn chāoyuè gàojǐng	Threshold crossing alarm	TCA
门限电平	Ménxiàn diànpíng	Threshold level	
门限复位报告	Ménxiàn fùwèi bàogào	Restore threshold report	RTR
门限跨越	Ménxiàn kuàyuè	Threshold crossing	
门限扩展解调	Ménxiàn kuòzhǎn jiětiáo	Threshold extension demodulation	
门限路	Ménxiàn lù	Gateway	
门限判定	Ménxiàn pàndìng	Thresholding	
门限通信密钥分散保管系统	Ménxiàn tōngxìn mìyào fēnsàn bǎoguǎn xìtǒng	Threshold communication secret key sharing system	TCSSS
门限译码	Ménxiàn yìmǎ	Threshold decoding	
MExE 业务环境	MexE yèwù huánjìng	MexE service environment	MSE
面	Miàn	Area, face	
免打扰服务	Miǎn dǎrǎo fúwù	Do not disturb service	
面对面	Miàn duì miàn	Face to face	FTF
面光栅	Miàn guāngshān	Concave grating	
面管理	Miàn guǎnlǐ	Plane management	
面缓冲区	Miàn huǎnchōngqū	Area buffer	
面链	Miàn liàn	Area chain	
面要素综合	Miàn yàosù zōnghé	Area generalization	
面质心	Miàn zhìxīn	Area centroid	
面板密封	Miànbǎn mìfēng	Panel seal	
免费软件	Miǎnfèi ruǎnjiàn	Freeware	
免费软件基金会	Miǎnfèi ruǎnjiàn jījīnhuì	Free Software Foundation	FSF
免费网	Miǎnfèi wǎng	Freenet	
免费业务	Miǎnfèi yèwù	Free phone	FPH
免税	Miǎnshuì	Free of tax	FOT
免维护	Miǎnwéihù	Maintenance-free (semiconductor mfg)	
面向比特的链路控制规程	Miànxiàng bǐtède liànlù kòngzhì guīchéng	Bit-oriented link control procedure	
面向操作员的语言	Miànxiàng cāozuòyuánde yǔyán	Operator-oriented language	OOL
面向对象	Miànxiàng duìxiàng	Object-oriented	
面向对象编程	Miànxiàng duìxiàng biānchéng	Object-oriented programming	OOP
面向对象编译	Miànxiàng duìxiàng biānyì	Object-oriented compiler	
面向对象程序设计	Miànxiàng duìxiàng chéngxù shèjì	Object-oriented programming	OOP
面向对象分析	Miànxiàng duìxiàng fēnxī	Object-oriented analysis	OOA
面向对象设计	Miànxiàng duìxiàng shèjì	Object-oriented design	OOD
面向对象数据库	Miànxiàng duìxiàng shùjùkù	Object-oriented database	OODB
面向对象数据库系统	Miànxiàng duìxiàng shùjùkù xìtǒng	Object-oriented database system	OODS
面向对象的	Miànxiàng duìxiàngde	Object-oriented	
面向对象的程序设计	Miànxiàng duìxiàngde chéngxù shèjì	Object-oriented programming	OOP
面向管理对象建模工具	Miànxiàng guǎnlǐ duìxiàng jiànmo gōngjù	Object management-oriented modeling tools	OOMT
面向计算机电子邮件	Miànxiàng jìsuànjī diànzi yóujiàn	Electronic computer originated mail	ECOM
面向连接	Miànxiàng liánjiē	Connection-oriented	CO
面向连接数据传送	Miànxiàng liánjiē shùjù chuánsòng	Connection-oriented data transport	CODT
面向连接数据确认	Miànxiàng liánjiē shùjù quèrèn	Connection-oriented data acknowledge	CODA
面向连接网络业务	Miànxiàng liánjiē wǎngluò yèwù	Connection oriented network service	CONS

面向连接的会议系统	Miànxiàng liánjiēde huìyì xìtǒng	Connection-oriented conference system	
面向连接的网络层服务	Miànxiàng liánjiēde wǎngluò céng fúwù	Connection-oriented network (layer) service	CONS
面向连接的网络层协议	Miànxiàng liánjiēde wǎngluò céng xiéyì	Connection-oriented network layer protocol	CONP
面向连接的网络互联	Miànxiàng liánjiēde wǎngluò hùlián	Connection-oriented internetworking	
面向连接的网络协议	Miànxiàng liánjiēde wǎngluò xiéyì	Connection-oriented network protocol (ISO use)	CONP
面向连接的运输服务	Miànxiàng liánjiēde yùnshū fúwù	Connection-oriented transport service	COTS
面向目标的设计	Miànxiàng mùbiāode shèjì	Object-oriented design	OOD
面向任务过程	Miànxiàng rènwu guòchéng	Task-oriented procedure	TOP
面向商业的通用语言	Miànxiàng shāngyède tōngyòng yǔyán	Common business-oriented language	COBOL
面向通信过程的语言	Miànxiàng tōngxìn guòchéngde yǔyán	Communications procedure-oriented language	CPOL
面向维护的群闭塞解除消息	Miànxiàng wéihùde qún bìsè jiěchú xiāoxi	Maintenance-oriented group unblocking message	MGU
面向维护的群闭塞消息	Miànxiàng wéihùde qún bìsè xiāoxi	Maintenance-oriented group blocking message	MGB
面向维护的群闭塞证实消息	Miànxiàng wéihùde qún bìsè zhèngshí xiāoxi	Maintenance-oriented group blocking acknowledgement message	MBA
面向维护的群解除闭塞证实消息	Miànxiàng wéihùde qún jiěchú bìsè zhèngshí xiāoxi	Maintenance-oriented group unblocking acknowledgement message	MUA
面向问题的语言	Miànxiàng wèntíde yǔyán	Problem-oriented language	
面向消息的中间件	Miànxiàng xiāoxide zhōngjiān jiàn	Message-oriented middleware	MOM
面向业务部分	Miànxiàng yèwù bùfen	Service-oriented part	
面向业务专用连接的协议	Miànxiàng yèwù zhuānyòng liánjiēde xiéyì	Service-specific connection-oriented protocol	SSCOP
面向硬件故障的群闭塞解除消息	Miànxiàng yìngjiàn gùzhàngde qún bìsè jiěchú xiāoxi	Hardware failure-oriented group unblocking message	HGU
面向硬件故障的群闭塞解除证实消息	Miànxiàng yìngjiàn gùzhàngde qún bìsè jiěchú zhèngshí xiāoxi	Hardware failure-oriented group unblocking-acknowledgement message	HUA
面向硬件故障的群闭塞消息	Miànxiàng yìngjiàn gùzhàngde qún bìsè xiāoxi	Hardware failure-oriented group blocking message	HGB
面向硬件故障的群闭塞证实消息	Miànxiàng yìngjiàn gùzhàngde qún bìsè zhèngshí xiāoxi	Hardware failure-oriented group blocking acknowledgement message	HBA
面向语义构件模型	Miànxiàng yǔyì gòujiàn móxíng	Semantics-oriented component model	
面向字符的通信控制器	Miànxiàng zìfúde tōngxìn kòngzhìqì	Character-oriented communications controller	COC
面型检光元件	Miàn-xíng jiǎn guāng yuánjiàn	Two dimension (i.e. planar) detector array	
绵阳凯路微电子有限公司	Miányáng kǎilù wēidiànzǐ yǒuxiàn gōngsī	Mianyang Kilopass Microelectronics Inc.	
秒脉冲	Miǎo màichōng	One pulse per second	1PPS
描绘	Miáohuì	Portrayal	
描绘服务	Miáohuì fúwù	Portrayal service	
描绘规范	Miáohuì guīfàn	Portrayal specification	
描绘规则	Miáohuì guīzé	Portrayal rule	
描绘元素	Miáohuì yuánsù	Portrayal element	
描述逻辑	Miáoshù luóji	Description logic	
描述目录	Miáoshù mùlù	Portrayal catalogue	
描述符	Miáoshùfú	Descriptor	
描述性数据	Miáoshù-xìng shùjù	Descriptive data	
描影	Miáoyǐng	Shading (video term)	
瞄准误差	Miáozhǔn wùchā	Boresight error	
密度	Mìdù	Density	
密度分割	Mìdù fēngē	Density slicing	

密度检测	Mìdù jiǎncè	Density detection	
密度流	Mìdù liú	Current density	
密度谱	Mìdù pǔ	Magnitude spectrum	
灭弧装置	Mièhú zhuāngzhì	Arc-control device	
密封窗	Mìfēng chuāng	Hermetic window	
密封接头	Mìfēng jiētóu	Hermetic seal	
密封类	Mìfēng lèi	Sealed class	
密封试验	Mìfēng shìyàn	Encapsulation test	
密封型二氧化碳激光	Mìfēng-xíng èryǎnghuàtàn jīguāng	Sealed tube CO_2 laser	
密封性试验	Mìfēngxìng shìyàn	Encapsulation test	
蜜罐	Mìguàn	Honeypot (computer security slang)	
密集波分复用	Mìjí bōfēn fùyòng	Dense wavelength division multiplexing	DWDM
密集波分复用滤波器	Mìjí bōfēn fùyòng lǜbōqì	Dense wavelength division multiplexer filter	DWFI
密集波分复用器	Mìjí bōfēn fùyòngqì	Dense wavelength division multiplexer	DWDM
密集模式	Mìjí móshì	Dense mode	DM
密件抄送	Mìjiàn chāosòng	Blind carbon copy	BCC
密脚距技术	Mìjiǎojù jìshù	Fine-pitch technology (in SMT)	FPT
密集型波分复用	Mìjíxíng bōfēn fùyòng	Dense wavelength division multiplexing	DWDM
密集型 PIM	Mìjí-xíng PIM	Dense mode PIM	
密力管	Mìlìguǎn	Millitron	
密码	Mìmǎ	Password	PS
密码	Mìmǎ	Cipher	
密码	Mìmǎ	Cryptologic, cryptographic (adj.)	
密码安全	Mìmǎ ānquán	Cryptologic security	
密码安全 TINA	Mìmǎ ānquán TINA	Cryptographically secure TINA	CrySTINA
密码本	Mìmǎ běn	Ciphering key	Kc
密码本生成算法	Mìmǎ běn shēngchéng suànfǎ	Ciphering key generating algorithm	
密码本序列号	Mìmǎ běn xùlièhào	Ciphering key sequence number	CKSN
密码变量	Mìmǎ biànliàng	Cryptologic variable, cryptovariable	
密码操作	Mìmǎ cāozuò	Crypto-operation	
密码分析	Mìmǎ fēnxī	Cryptanalysis (IPsec)	
密码分组链接	Mìmǎ fēnzǔ liàn jiē	Cipher block chaining	CPB
密码鉴权协议	Mìmǎ jiànquán xiéyì	Privacy (?) authentication protocol	PAP
密码校检值	Mìmǎ jiàojiǎn zhí	Cipher check value (IPsec)	
密码校检值	Mìmǎ jiàojiǎn zhí	Cryptographic check value (IPsec)	
密码块链	Mìmǎ kuài liàn	Cipher block chaining (IPsec)	CBC
密码链	Mìmǎ liàn	Cipher chain (IPsec)	
密码破译	Mìmǎ pòyì	Code breaking	
密码认证协议	Mìmǎ rènzhèng xiéyì	Password authentication protocol	PAP
密码说明	Mìmǎ shuōmíng	CipherSpec (IPsec)	
密码算法	Mìmǎ suànfǎ	Cryptographic algorithm	
密码索引序列号	Mìmǎ suǒyǐn xùlièhào	Ciphering key sequence number	CKSN
密码体制	Mìmǎ tǐzhì	Cryptography (IPsec)	
密码消息语法	Mìmǎ xiāoxi yǔfǎ	Cryptographic message syntax	CMS
密码协议	Mìmǎ xiéyì	Cryptographic protocol	
密码系统	Mìmǎ xìtǒng	Cryptographic system	

密码验证协议	Mìmǎ yànzhèng xiéyì	Password authentication protocol	PAP
密码注入器	Mìmǎ zhùrùqì	Key injector	
密码术	Mìmǎshù	Cryptography	
密码学	Mìmǎxué	Cryptology	
明槽浅埋	Míng cáo qiǎn mái	Open trench shallow burial	
名结合	Míng jiéhé	Name binding	
敏感器件	Mǐngǎn qìjiàn	Susceptible device	
敏感信息	Mǐngǎn xìnxī	Sensitive information	
敏感度门限	Mǐngǎndù ménxiàn	Susceptibility threshold	
敏感性分析	Mǐngǎn-xìng fēnxī	Sensitivity analysis	
名称绑定协议	Míngchēng bǎngdìng xiéyì	Name binding protocol (Apple usage)	NBP
名称句式	Míngchēng jùshì	Name phrasing	
名称数据	Míngchēng shùjù	Nominal data	
铭刻	Míngkè	Scribing (semiconductor mfg process)	
命令	Mìnglìng	Command	
命令包地区地址	Mìnglìng bāo dìqū dìzhǐ	Lower command packet address	LCPA
命令标识符	Mìnglìng biāozhìfú	Command identifier	CI
命令程序	Mìnglìng chéngxù	Command procedure	
命令处理	Mìnglìng chǔlǐ	Command handling	COH
命令管理信息业务元素	Mìnglìng guǎnlǐ xìnxī yèwù yuánsù	Command management information service element	CMISE
命令关系	Mìnglìng guānxi	Command relationship	
命令行	Mìnglìng háng	Command line	
命令行处理器	Mìnglìng háng chǔlǐqì	Command line processor	CLP
命令行界面	Mìnglìng háng jièmiàn	Command line interface	CLI
命令解释程序	Mìnglìng jiěshì chéngxù	Command interpreter	CI
命令数据缓冲器	Mìnglìng shùjù huǎnchōngqì	Command data buffer	CDB
命令输入缓冲器	Mìnglìng shūrù huǎnchōngqì	Command input buffer	CIB
命令提示符	Mìnglìng tíshìfú	Command prompt	
命令提示符窗口	Mìnglìng tíshìfú chuāngkǒu	Command prompt window	
命令与遥测数据处理	Mìnglìng yǔ yáocè shùjùchǔlǐ	Command and telemetry data handling	CTDH
命令语言	Mìnglìng yǔyán	Command language	
命令执行字节	Mìnglìng zhíxíng zìjié	Command execution byte	CEB
命令终端	Mìnglìng zhōngduān	Command terminal (in DECnet)	CTERM
命令/响应	Mìnglìng/xiǎngyìng	Command/response	C/R
命令/响应比特	Mìnglìng/xiǎngyìng bǐtè	Command/response field bit	C/R
命令/响应字段比特	Mìnglìng/xiǎngyìng zìduàn bǐtè	Command/response field bit	C/R
命名别名	Mìngmíng biémíng	Aliasing	
命名参数	Mìngmíng cānshù	Named parameter	
命名管道	Mìngmíng guǎndào	Named pipe	
命名关系	Mìngmíng guānxi	Naming relationship	
命名集	Mìngmíng jí	Named set	
命名空间	Mìngmíng kōngjiān	Namespace	
命名实例	Mìngmíng shílì	Named instance	
命名树	Mìngmíng shù	Naming tree	
命名域	Mìngmíng yù	Naming domain	
名目项	Míngmù xiàng	Whois (Internet tool)	

明渠	Míngqú	Open channel	
明确前向拥塞指示	Míngquè qiánxiàng yōngsè zhǐshì	Explicit forward congestion indicator	EFCI
明确拥塞通知	Míngquè yōngsè tōngzhī	Explicit congestion notification	ECN
明文	Míngwén	Cleartext (IPsec)	
明文	Míngwén	Plain text (IPsec)	
明线载波	Míngxiàn zàibō	Open line carrier	MZ
明细表	Míngxìbiǎo	Packing list	P/L
名义功率	Míngyì gōnglǜ	Nominal power	
名义数据	Míngyì shùjù	Nominal data	
名字绑定协议	Míngzì bǎngdìng xiéyì	Name binding protocol	NBP
名字高速缓存	Míngzì gāosù huǎncún	Name caching	
名字空间	Míngzì kōngjiān	Namespace	
敏捷制造	Mǐnjié zhìzào	Agile manufacturing (British concept)	AM
民用频带	Mínyòng píndài	Citizens band	CB
民用设备展览会	Mínyòng shèbèi zhǎnlǎnhuì	Consumer electronics show	CES
密盘只读存储器	Mìpán zhǐ dú cúnchǔqì	Compact disk read-only memory	CDROM
秘书电话机	Mìshū diànhuàjī	Secretary telephone set	
蜜网	Mìwǎng	Honeynet (computer security slang)	
密文	Mìwén	Ciphertext (IPsec)	
密文反馈	Mìwén fǎnkuì	Cipher feedback	CFB
密文流	Mìwén liú	Cipher stream	
密信码	Mìxìn mǎ	Ciphertext, message code	
密钥	Mìyào	Cipher key (IPsec) (usually only key in English)	
密钥编排	Mìyào biānpái	Cipher key scheduling	
密钥分配中心	Mìyào fēnpèi zhōngxīn	Cipher key distribution center	KDC
密钥管理	Mìyào guǎnlǐ	Cipher key management (IPsec)	
密钥管理基础设施	Mìyào guǎnlǐ jīchǔ shèshī	Cipher key management infrastructure	KMI
密钥管理机制	Mìyào guǎnlǐ jīzhì	Cipher key management mechanism (IPsec)	
密钥管理算法	Mìyào guǎnlǐ suànfǎ	Key management algorithm	K-ALG
密钥管理中心	Mìyào guǎnlǐ zhōngxīn	Cipher key management center	KMC
密钥加密密钥	Mìyào jiāmì mìyào	Key enciphering key	KK
密钥交换算法	Mìyào jiāohuàn suànfǎ	Cipher key exchange algorithm	KEA
密钥捷变	Mìyào jiébiàn	Cipher key variable	
密钥设置	Mìyào shèzhì	Cipherkey setting	
密钥树	Mìyào shù	Secret cipher key tree	
密钥托管系统	Mìyào tuōguǎn xìtǒng	Cipher key escrow system (cryptology)	KES
密钥协同方案	Mìyào xiétóng fāng'àn	Cipher key agreement scheme	
密钥序号	Mìyào xùhào	Cipher key sequence number	
密钥证书管理中心	Mìyào zhèngshū guǎnlǐ zhōngxīn	Cipher key certificate management center	KCMC
密钥注入器	Mìyào zhùrùqì	Cipher key injection device, key injector	KID
码激线性预测	M-jī xiànxìng yùcè	Code excited linear prediction	CELP
模变换	Mó biànhuàn	Mode conversion (in waveguide)	
模变换损耗	Mó biànhuàn sǔnhào	Mode conversion loss	
模变换增益	Mó biànhuàn zēngyì	Mode conversion gain	
模变换器	Mó biànhuànqì	Mode converter	
模标志	Mó biāozhì	Mode designation (in a waveguide or cavity resonator)	

模乘	Mó chéng	Modular multiplication	
模 2 加	Mó èr jiā	Modulo 2 add	
模分配噪声	Mó fēnpèi zàoshēng	Mode partition noise	MPN
模滤波器	Mó lǜbōqì	Mode filter	
模/数变换	Mó/shù biànhuàn	Analog-digital conversion	A/D
模/数变换器	Mó/shù biànhuànqì	Analog/digital converter	A/D
模/数变换器	Mó/shù biànhuànqì	Analog/digital converter	ADC
模/数转换	Mó/shù zhuǎnhuàn	Analog/digital conversion	A/D
模/数转换器	Mó/shù zhuǎnhuànqì	Analog/digital converter	A/D
模/数/模（变换）	Mó/shù/mó (biànhuàn)	Analog/digital/analog (conversion)	A/D/A
模版	Móbǎn	Template	
摩擦	Mócā	Friction	
摩擦层	Mócā céng	Friction layer	
摩擦力矩	Mócā lìjǔ	Moment of friction	
摩擦水头	Mócā shuǐtóu	Friction head	
摩擦速度	Mócā sùdù	Friction velocity	
摩擦柱	Mócā zhù	Friction pile	
模场	Mócháng	Mode field	FAT
模场同心度偏差	Mócháng tóngxīndù piānchā	Mode field concentricity deviation (FOC mfg)	
模场同心度误差	Mócháng tóngxīndù wùchā	Mode field concentricity error (FOC)	
模场直径	Mócháng zhíjìng	Mode field diameter (of FOC)	MFD
抹除	Mǒchú	Erasure	
墨带	Mòdài	Ribbon	
默冬周期	Mòdōng zhōuqī	Metonic cycle	
末端射频功率	Mòduān shèpín gōnglǜ	Terminal radio-frequency power	
末端使用设备	Mòduān shǐyòng shèbèi	End-user device	
末端系统	Mòduān xìtǒng	End system	
末端用户	Mòduān yònghù	End user	
莫顿序	Mò-dùn xù	Morton order	
摩尔定律	Mó-ěr dìnglǜ	Moore's law	
莫尔斯电报	Mò-ěr-sī diànbào	Morse telegraphy	
莫尔斯电码	Mò-ěr-sī diànmǎ	Morse code	
模仿攻击	Mófǎng gōngjī	Simulation attack (cryptography)	
墨粉	Mòfěn	Toner (for a printer)	
蘑菇数据库	Mógu shùjùkù	Mushroom database	
模糊分差	Móhu fēnchà	Fuzzy variance	
模糊分析	Móhu fēnxī	Fuzzy analysis	
模糊概念	Móhu gàiniàn	Fuzzy concept	
模糊关系数据库	Móhu guānxì shùjùkù	Fuzzy relational database	
模糊函数	Móhu hánshù	Ambiguity function (radar term)	
模糊集合	Móhu jíhé	Fuzzy set	
模糊控制	Móhu kòngzhì	Fuzzy control	
模糊逻辑	Móhu luóji	Fuzzy logic	
模糊模式分析	Móhu móshì fēnxī	Fuzzy pattern analysis	
模糊匹配	Móhu pǐpèi	Approximate string matching	
模糊容差	Móhu róngchā	Fuzzy tolerance	

模糊图	Móhu tú	Ambiguity pattern (radar term)	
模糊推理	Móhu tuīlǐ	Fuzzy reasoning	
模糊误差	Móhu wùchā	Ambiguity error	
模糊要素	Móhu yàosù	Fuzzy feature	
模糊优选	Móhu yōuxuǎn	Fuzzy optimization	
末级寄存器	Mòjí jìcúnqì	Last level register	LLR
莫吉尔 - 戴林格信号消逝	Mò-jí-ěr dài-lín-gé xìnhào xiāoshì	Mogel-Dellinger fade-out	
模块	Mókuài	Module	
模块互连语言	Mókuài hùlián yǔyán	Module interconnection language	MIL
模块试验系统	Mókuài shìyàn xìtǒng	Module test system	MTS
模块化	Mókuàihuà	Modularize	
模块化可视化环境	Mókuàihuà kěshìhuà huánjìng	Modular visualization environment	
模块间通信	Mókuài-jiān tōngxìn	Inter-module communication	
模框	Mókuàng	Mask	
模幂乘	Mómìchéng	Modular exponentiation	
模拟	Mónǐ	Analog	
模拟	Mónǐ	Simulation	
模拟测距	Mónǐ cèjù	Analog ranging	
模拟打印机	Mónǐ dǎyìnjī	Printer emulation	
模拟灯	Mónǐ dēng	Dummy lamp	
模拟电视	Mónǐ diànshì	Analog video	AV
模拟蜂窝系统	Mónǐ fēngwō xìtǒng	Analog cellular system	
模拟复用器量化器	Mónǐ fùyòngqì liànghuàqì	Analog multiplexer quantizer	AMQ
模拟公共信道处理器	Mónǐ gōnggòng xìndào chǔlǐqì	Analog common channel processor	ACCP
模拟公共信道集成板	Mónǐ gōnggòng xìndào jíchéngbǎn	Analog common channel assembly	ACCA
模拟交换	Mónǐ jiāohuàn	Analog switching	
模拟交换子系统	Mónǐ jiāohuàn zixìtǒng	Analog switching sub-system	ASS
模拟集成电路	Mónǐ jíchéng diànlù	Analog integrated circuit	
模拟集群流动通讯	Mónǐ jíqún liúdòng tōngxùn	Analog trunked mobile radio	TMR
模拟控制器	Mónǐ kòngzhìqì	Analog controller	AC
模拟扩展总线	Mónǐ kuòzhǎn zǒngxiàn	Analog expansion bus	AEB
模拟类游戏	Mónǐ lèi yóuxì	Simulation game (computer game)	SLG
模拟滤波器	Mónǐ lǜbōqì	Analog filter	
模拟屏	Mónǐ píng	Analog screen	
模拟前端	Mónǐ qiánduān	Analog front-end	AFE
模拟强度调制	Mónǐ qiángdù tiáozhì	Analog-intensity modulation	
模拟色码	Mónǐ sèmǎ	Analog color code	
模拟时分复用系统	Mónǐ shífèn fùyòng xìtǒng	Analog time division multiplexing system	ATDMS
模拟视频	Mónǐ shìpín	Simulated video	
模拟视频	Mónǐ shìpín	Analog video	AV
模拟手	Mónǐ shǒu	Artificial hand	
模拟输出	Mónǐ shūchū	Analog output	
模拟数据识别	Mónǐ shùjù shíbié	Analog data recognition	ADR
模拟输入	Mónǐ shūrù	Analog input	
模拟数字混合通路	Mónǐ shùzì hùnhé tōnglù	Mixed analog/digital channel	
模拟锁相环	Mónǐ suǒxiàng huán	Analog phase-locked loop	APLL

模拟调制	Mónǐ tiáozhì	Analog modulation	
模拟通路	Mónǐ tōnglù	Analog channel	
模拟图	Mónǐ tú	Analog map	
模拟退频	Mónǐ tuìpín	Withdrawal of analog frequencies	
模拟微波	Mónǐ wēibō	Analog microwave	WBM
模拟信令	Mónǐ xìn lìng	Analog signaling	
模拟信号	Mónǐ xìnhào	Analog signal	
模拟信号处理	Mónǐ xìnhào chǔlǐ	Analog signal processing	ASP
模拟延迟装置	Mónǐ yánchí zhuāngzhì	Analog delay unit	ADU
模拟移相器	Mónǐ yíxiàngqì	Analog phase shifter	
模拟用户电路板	Mónǐ yònghù diànlù bǎn	Analog subscriber line board	ASL
模拟用户模块	Mónǐ yònghù mókuài	Analog subscriber module	ASM
模拟用户线单元	Mónǐ yònghùxiàn dānyuán	Analog lines unit	ALU
模拟用户线电路	Mónǐ yònghùxiàn diànlù	Analog subscriber line circuit	ASLC
模拟用户线模块	Mónǐ yònghùxiàn mókuài	Subscriber line module, analog	SLMA
模拟终端适配器	Mónǐ zhōngduān shìpèiqì	Analog terminal adapter	ATA
模拟中继单元	Mónǐ zhōngjì dānyuán	Analog trunk unit	ATU
模拟中继器	Mónǐ zhōngjìqì	Analog repeater	
模拟/强度调变器	Mónǐ/qiángdù tiáobiànqì	Analog/intensity modulator	
模拟-数字记录器	Mónǐ/shùzì jìlù qì	Analog-digital recorder	ADR
模拟器	Mónǐqì	Simulator	
模拟式扫描	Mónǐ-shì sǎomiáo	Analog sweep (i.e. a continuous sweep)	
模拟式寻呼系统	Mónǐ-shì xúnhū xìtǒng	Analog paging system	
模拟-数字记录器	Mónǐ-shùzì jìlùqì	Analog-digital recorder	ADR
膜片	Mópiàn	Iris (in a waveguide)	
模切	Móqiē	Die cutting	
默认按钮	Mòrèn ànniǔ	Default button	
默认成员	Mòrèn chéngyuán	Default member	
默认打印机	Mòrèn dǎyìnjī	Default printer	
默认结果集	Mòrèn jiéguǒ jí	Default result set (for database)	
默认实例	Mòrèn shílì	Default instance (for database)	
默认数据库	Mòrèn shùjùkù	Default database	
默认属性	Mòrèn shǔxìng	Default attribute	
默认属性值	Mòrèn shǔxìng zhí	Default attribute values	
默认约束	Mòrèn yuēshù	Default constraint (for database)	
默认语言	Mòrèn yǔyán	Default language	
默认值	Mòrèn zhí	Default value	
默认主机	Mòrèn zhǔjī	Default host	
模式	Móshì	Mode	
模式	Móshì	Pattern	
模式	Móshì	Schema	
模式变换器	Móshì biànhuànqì	Mode transformer	
模式概化	Móshì gàihuà	Pattern generalization	
模式耦合	Móshì ǒuhé	Mode coupling	
模式匹配	Móshì pǐpèi	String matching	
模式色散	Móshì sèsàn	Mode dispersion	

模式识别	Móshì shíbié	Pattern recognition	
模式识别法	Móshì shíbié fǎ	Pattern recogniton method	PRM
模式探测	Móshì tàncè	Pattern detection	
模式噪声	Móshì zàoshēng	Modal noise	
模-数处理器	Mó-shù chǔlǐqì	Analog-digital processor	ADP
模数转换	Móshù zhuǎnhuàn	Modulus conversion	
模数转换器	Móshù zhuǎnhuànqì	Analog to digital converter	ADC
魔 T	Mó-T	Magic-T	
魔 T 混合网络	Mó-T hùnhé wǎngluò	Magic-T hybrid network	
摩托罗拉	Mó-tuō-luó-lā	Motorola (US company)	
模型	Móxíng	Model	
模型简化	Móxíng jiǎnhuà	Model simplification	
模型聚集技术	Móxíng jùjí jìshù	Model aggregation	
模型数据库	Móxíng shùjùkù	Model database	
模型特定寄存器	Móxíng tèdìng jìcúnqì	Model-specific register	MSR
模型相关性	Móxíng xiāngguānxìng	Model dependency	
模型验证	Móxíng yànzhèng	Model testing	
末制导雷达	Mòzhìdǎo léidá	End-guidance radar	
末制导雷达	Mòzhìdǎo léidá	Terminal guidance radar	
模组	Mózǔ	Module	
MPEG 传输流	MPEG chuánshū liú	MPEG transmission stream	MPEG TS
MPEG 传送流	MPEG chuánsòng liú	MPEG transmission stream	MPEG-TS
MPLS 论坛	MPLS lùntán	MPLS forum	MPLSF
MPLS 上的任意传输	MPLS-shàngde rènyì chuánshū	Arbitrary transmission on MPLS	AtoM
MSP 管理功能	MSP guǎnlǐ gōngnéng	MSP management function	MSP-MF
MSP 运行系统	MSP yùnxíng xìtǒng	MSP operation system	MSP-OpS
MTP 第二级用户适配层	MTP dì'èrjí yònghù shìpèi céng	MTP2-user adaptation layer	M2UA
MTP 第三级用户适配层	MTP dìsānjí yònghù shìpèi céng	MTP3-user adaptation layer	M3UA
模板	Múbǎn	Template	
母板	Mǔbǎn	Motherboard	MMB
模板参数	Múbǎn cānshù	Template parameter	
模板参数推导	Múbǎn cānshù tuīdǎo	Template argument deduction	
模板缓冲	Múbǎn huǎnchōng	Stencil buffers	
模板文件	Múbǎn wénjiàn	Template files (in SQL Server)	
模板显式特化	Múbǎn xiǎnshì tèhuà	Template explicit specialization	
目标	Mùbiāo	Object, destination, target	
目标程序	Mùbiāo chéngxù	Object program	
目标程序	Mùbiāo chéngxù	Target program	
目标程序装入器	Mùbiāo chéngxù zhuāngrùqì	Object program loader	OPL
目标代码	Mùbiāo dàimǎ	Object code	
目标对象	Mùbiāo duìxiàng	Target object	
目标分区	Mùbiāo fēnqū	Target partition	
目标检查	Mùbiāo jiǎnchá	Visual check	
目标计算机	Mùbiāo jìsuànjī	Object computer	
目标连接与嵌入	Mùbiāo liánjiē yǔ qiànrù	Object linking and embedding	OLE
目标 MAC	Mùbiāo MAC	Destination MAC	

目标模块汇编程序	Mùbiāo mókuài huìbiān chéngxù	Object module assembly program	OMAP
目标模块库	Mùbiāo mókuài kù	Object module library	OML
目标模块库修改	Mùbiāo mókuài kù xiūgǎi	Object module library update	OMLU
目标请求掮客	Mùbiāo qǐngqiú qiánkè	Object request broker	ORB
目标文件	Mùbiāo wénjiàn	Object file	
目标文件区	Mùbiāo wénjiàn qū	Object file area	OFA
目标信息	Mùbiāo xìnxī	Destination information	
目标语言	Mùbiāo yǔyán	Target language	
目标主机	Mùbiāo zhǔjī	Destination host	DST
目标自动识别	Mùbiāo zìdòng shíbié	Automatic target recognition	ATR
目的	Mùdì	Destination, objective	
目的点编码	Mùdì diǎn biānmǎ	Destination point code	DPC
目的地址	Mùdì dìzhì	Destination address	DA
目的地址编码	Mùdì dìzhǐ biānmǎ	Destination point code	DPC
目的端口	Mùdì duānkǒu	Destination port	
目的对象	Mùdì duìxiàng	Destination object	
目的类	Mùdì lèi	Destination category	DC
目的码	Mùdì mǎ	Destination code	
目的信令点编码	Mùdì xìnlìng diǎn biānmǎ	Destination point code	DPC
目的序列距离矢量	Mùdì xùliè jùlí shǐliàng	Destination-sequenced distance vector	DSDV
目的因特网协议地址	Mùdì Yīntèwǎng xiéyì dìzhǐ	Destination Internet protocol (IP) address	
目的地	Mùdìdì	Destination location	
目的地不可用	Mùdìdì bùkěyòng	Destination unavailable (SS7)	DUNA
目的地点码	Mùdìdì diǎnmǎ	Destination point code	DPC
目的地端局交换机	Mùdìdì duānjú jiāohuànjī	Destination local exchange	DLE
目的地可用	Mùdìdì kěyòng	Destination available (SS7)	DAVA
目的地信令点编码	Mùdìdì xìnlìngdiǎn biānmǎ	Destination point code	DPC
目的地用户部分不可用	Mùdìdì yònghù bùfen bùkěyòng	Destination user part unavailable (SS7)	DUPU
目的地状态查询	Mùdìdì zhuàngtài cháxún	Destination audit	DAUD
母局	Mǔjú	Host exchange	
目录	Mùlù	Directory (as a list of computer files)	
目录	Mùlù	Catalog	
目录访问协议	Mùlù fǎngwèn xiéyì	Directory access protocol	
目录服务	Mùlù fúwù	Directory service	
目录服务系统	Mùlù fúwù xìtǒng	Directory system	DS
目录复制	Mùlù fùzhì	Directory replication	
目录结构	Mùlù jiégòu	Directory structure	
目录树	Mùlù shù	Directory tree	
目录信息树	Mùlù xìnxī shù	Directory information tree	DIT
目录系统代理（程序）	Mùlù xìtǒng dàilǐ (chéngxù)	Directory system agent (program)	DSA
目录用户代理	Mùlù yònghù dàilǐ	Directory user agent	DUA
木马	Mùmǎ	Trojan horse	
木马程式	Mùmǎ chéngshì	Trojan horse program	
目视判读	Mùshì pàndú	Visual interpretation (GIS)	
母体	Mǔtǐ	Parent	
木桶理论	Mùtǒng lǐlùn	Barrel theory (the contents of a barrel can reach only to the top of the shortest stave)	

母线	Mǔxiàn	Trunk (TCOM); bus (computer use)	
MU 型连接器	MU-xíng liánjiēqì	MU-type connecter	
MU 型连接器系列	MU-xíng liánjiēqì xìliè	MU-type connector series	
幕形天线	Mùxíng tiānxiàn	Curtain antenna	
苜蓿叶形天线	Mùxu yèxíng tiānxiàn	Clover-leaf antenna	
拇指旋转开关	Mǔzhǐ xuánzhuǎn kāiguān	Thumb wheel switch	TWS
M 型器件	M-xíng qìjiàn	M-type device	
M 型显示器	M-xíng xiǎnshìqì	M-scope	

N

纳	Nà	Nano- (prefix meaning 10^{-9})	
耐电痕	Nài diànhén	Creeptrace resistance (lit. resists "electric scarring")	
耐故障能力	Nài gùzhàng nénglì	Fault withstandability	
耐环境应力开裂	Nài huánjìng yìnglì kāiliè	Environmental stress cracking resistance	ESCR
耐久性	Nàijiǔxìng	Durability	
耐久性试验	Nàijiǔxìng shìyàn	Endurance test	
奈奎斯特率	Nài-kuí-sī-tè lǜ	Nyquist rate	
耐磨性	Nàimóxìng	Abrasion resistance; wear resistance	
奈培	Nài-péi	Neper (unit of attenuation, =8.686 dB)	NP
耐燃烧试验	Nàiránshāo shìyàn	Flame resistance test	
耐热光纤	Nàirè guāngxiān	Heat resistant fiber	
耐受性	Nàishòuxìng	Resistibility	
奈特	Nàitè	Natural bit (nat)	
耐折度	Nàizhédù	Folding endurance	
纳米	Nàmǐ	Nanometer	
纳米技术	Nàmǐ jìshù	Nanotechnology	
南朝鲜京电信	Nán Cháoxiān jīng diànxìn	South Korea Telecom (GSM network operator)	SK Telecom
南方贝尔	Nánfāng bèi-ěr	Bell South	
南非自动化和计算委员会	Nánfēi zìdònghuà hé jìsuàn wěiyuánhuì	South African Council for Automation and Computation	SACAC
南京华新藤仓光通信有限公司	Nánjīng huá-xīn téngcāng guāng tōngxìn yǒuxiàn gōngsī	Nanjing Walsin Fujikura Optical Communications Co. Ltd.	
南桥芯片	Nánqiáo xìnpiàn	South Bridge chip	SBC
那诺科技	Nà-nuò kējì	Nanotechnology (Singapore usage)	
脑能	Nǎonéng	Intelligence	
闹钟服务	Nàozhōng fúwù	Alarm clock service	
那斯达克	Nà-sī-dá-kè	NASDAQ	
n 比特字节	n-bǐtè zìjié	N-bit byte	
NBMA 地址解析协议	NBMA dìzhǐ jiěxī xiéyì	NBMA address resolution protocol (IETF use)	NARP
n-层被管对象	n-céng bèiguǎn duìxiàng	N-layer managed object	
N 次谷	N-cì gǔ	N-th order valley	
n 单位代码	n-dānwèi dàimǎ	N-unit code	
n 单位电码表	n-dānwèi diànmǎ biǎo	N-unit code alphabet	
内存储器	Nèi cúnchǔqì	Internal memory	
内光点录取设备	Nèi guāng diǎn lùqǔ shèbèi	Internal spot extraction equipment	
内联接	Nèi liánjiē	Inner join (for database)	
内汽相沉积法	Nèi qìxiàng chénjī fǎ	Inside vapor phase deposition (FOC mfg)	IVPD

内波	Nèibō	Internal wave	
内波发生器	Nèibō fāshēngqì	Internal wave generator	
内部安全审计	Nèibù ānquán shěnjì	Internal security audit (IPsec)	
内部边界层	Nèibù biānjiècéng	Internal boundary layer	
内部标识符	Nèibù biāozhì fú	Internal identifier	
内部标识码	Nèibù biāozhì mǎ	Internal flag	
内部参考点	Nèibù cānkǎo diǎn	Internal reference point	IRP
内部错误消息	Nèibù cuòwù xiāoxi	Internal error (IPsec TLS)	
内部服务代理	Nèibù fúwù dàilǐ	Internal service broker (in VPN)	ISB
内部管理总线	Nèibù guǎnlǐ zǒngxiàn	Internal chassis management bus	ICMB
内部函数	Nèibù hánshù	Built-in function	
内部计息	Nèibù jìxī	Counting internal interest	
内部抗扰性	Nèibù kàngrǎo xìng	Internal immunity	
内部抗扰性	Nèibù kàngrǎoxing	Internal immunity	
内部可视性	Nèibù kěshìxìng	Intervisibility	
内部路由协议	Nèibù lùyóu xiéyì	Interior gateway protocol	IGP
内部排序	Nèibù páixù	Internal sort	
内部数据	Nèibù shùjù	Internal data	
内部数据传输率	Nèibù shùjù chuánshū lǜ	Internal data transfer rate	
内部数据结构	Nèibù shùjù jiégòu	Internal data structure	
内部网关路由协议	Nèibù wǎngguān lùyóu xiéyì	Interior gateway routing protocol (Cisco use)	IGRP
内部网关路由选择协议	Nèibù wǎngguān lùyóu xuǎnzé xiéyì	Interior gateway routing protocol	IGRP
内部网关协议	Nèibù wǎngguān xiéyì	Internal gateway protocol	IGP
内部网络	Nèibù wǎngluò	Internal network	
内部网络节点接口	Nèibù wǎngluò jiédiǎn jiēkǒu	Internal network-node interface	I-NNI
内部应用程序通讯	Nèibù yìngyòng chéngxù tōngxùn	Inter-application communication	IAC
内部噪声	Nèibù zàoshēng	Internal noise	
内部中断	Nèibù zhōngduàn	Internal interrupt	
内部主机	Nèibù zhǔjī	Internal host	
内部子层服务	Nèibù zicéng fúwù	Internal sub-layer service	ISS
内部阻尼	Nèibù zǔní	Internal damping	
内插	Nèichā	Interpolation	
内插的	Nèichāde	Interleaved (adjective)	
内插法均匀涂色	Nèichāfǎ jūnyún túsè	Gouraud shading (video)	
内存	Nèicún	Memory	
内存分配	Nèicún fēnpèi	Memory allocation	
内存和 I/O 桥控制器	Nèicún hé I/O qiáo kòngzhìqì	Memory and I/O bridge controller (chip)	MIOC
内存唤醒	Nèicún huànxǐng	Suspend to RAM	STR
内存模块	Nèicún mókuài	Memory module	
内存内部序号检测装置	Nèicún nèibù xùhào jiǎncè zhuāngzhì	Serial presence detect	SPD
内存数据处理中心	Nèicún shùjù chǔlǐ zhōngxīn	Memory repeater hub	MRH
内存泄漏	Nèicún xièlòu	Memory leak	
内存转换中心	Nèicún zhuǎnhuàn zhōngxīn	Memory transfer hub	MTH
内定设置	Nèidìng shèzhì	Default setup	
内定直	Nèidìng zhí	Default value	
内核	Nèihé	Kernel	

内建	Nèijiàn	Built-in	
内联	Nèilián	Inline	
内联表值型函数	Nèilián biǎozhíxíng hánshù	Inline table-valued functions (in SQL Server)	
内联展开	Nèilián zhǎnkāi	Inline expansion	
内联网	Nèiliánwǎng	Intranet	
内嵌对象	Nèiqiàn duìxiàng	Embedded object	
内嵌控制集	Nèiqiàn kòngzhì jí	Embedded control set	
内容	Nèiróng	Content	
内容编辑处理	Nèiróng biānjí chǔlǐ	Content editing process	
内容布局处理	Nèiróng bùjú chǔlǐ	Content layout process	
内容定址存储器	Nèiróng dìngzhǐ cúnchǔqì	Content-addressable memory	CAM
内容分发服务	Nèiróng fēnfā fúwù	Content distribution service	CDS
内容分发网络	Nèiróng fēnfā wǎngluò	Content delivery network	CDN
内容分发网络	Nèiróng fēnfā wǎngluò	Content distribution network	CDN
内容分发业务	Nèiróng fēnfā yèwù	Content delivery services	CDS
内容服务提供者	Nèiróng fúwù tígòngzhě	Content service provider	CSP
内容管理器	Nèiróng guǎnlǐqì	Content manager	
内容类型	Nèiróng lèixíng	Content type	
内容配送业务	Nèiróng pèisòng yèwù	Content delivery services	CDS
内容体系结构	Nèiróng tǐxì jiégòu	Content architecture	
内容体系结构级	Nèiróng tǐxì jiégòu jí	Content architecture level	
内容体系结构类别	Nèiróng tǐxì jiégòu lèibié	Content architecture class	
内容寻址存储器	Nèiróng xúnzhǐ cúnchǔqì	Content-addressable memory	CAM
内容元素	Nèiróng yuánsù	Content element	
内容组成部分	Nèiróng zǔchéng bùfen	Content portion	
内容组成部分描述	Nèiróng zǔchéng bùfen miáoshù	Content portion description	
内销包装	Nèixiāo bāozhuāng	Domestic package	
内因不能工作状态	Nèiyīn bùnéng gōngzuò zhuàngtài	Internal disabled state	
内置	Nèizhì	Built-in	
内置测试	Nèizhì cèshì	Built-in test	BIT
内置堆栈	Nèizhì duīzhàn	Internal stack	IS
内置函数	Nèizhì hánshù	Built-in function	
内置硬盘	Nèizhì yìngpán	Internal hard disk	
内阻	Nèizǔ	Internal impedance	
能网	Néng wǎng	Enablenet	
能直接连在 IP 网上的传真机	Néng zhíjiē liánzài IP wǎngshàngde chuánzhēnjī	Internet aware fax	IAF
能力测试	Nénglì cèshì	Capability test	
能力成熟模型	Nénglì chéngshú móxíng	Capability Maturity Model	CMM
能力集	Nénglì jí	Capability set	CS
能力集 1	Nénglì jí 1	Capability set 1	CS1
能力集 2	Nénglì jí 2	Capability set 2	CS2
能力配置参数	Nénglì pèizhì cānshù	Capability/configuration parameter	CCP
能量传播方向	Néngliàng chuánbō fāngxiàng	Direction of propagation of energy (in a transmission line)	
能量攻击	Néngliàng gōngjī	Power attack (computer hacking)	
能量扩散技术	Néngliàng kuòsàn jìshù	Energy dispersal technique	

能量密度	Néngliàng mìdù	Energy density	
能量谱密度	Néngliàng pǔ mìdù	Energy spectral density	ESD
能源科学网	Néngyuán kēxué wǎng	Energy Sciences Network	Esnet
能源之星	Néngyuán zhī xīng	Energy Star ©	
NetBIOS 扩展用户接口	NetBIOS kuòzhǎn yònghù jiēkǒu	NetBIOS extended user interface (IBM usage)	NetBEUI
NetWare 可装入模块	NetWare kězhuāngrù mókuài	NetWare loadable module	NLM
NetWare 链路服务协议	NetWare liànlù fúwù xiéyì	NetWare link state protocol (Novell usage)	NLSP
NetWare 链路服务协议	NetWare liànlù fúwù xiéyì	NetWare link services protocol	NLSP
n-服务访问点地址	n-fúwù fǎngwèn diǎn dìzhǐ	N--service-access-point-address	
逆地址解析协议	Nì dìzhǐ jiěxī xiéyì	Reverse address resolution protocol	RARP
逆后序	Nì hòuxù	Reverse post-order	
逆解析	Nì jiěxī	Inversion analysis	
逆快速傅立叶变换	Nì kuàisù fù-lì-yè biànhuàn	Inverse fast Fourier transform	IFFT
逆扩散	Nì kuòsàn	Inverse dispersion	
逆滤波器	Nì lǜbōqì	Inverse filter	
逆增益干扰	Nì zēngyì gānrǎo	Inverse gain jamming	
粘合剂	Niánhéjì	Bonding agent (in SMT)	
拟办	Nǐbàn	Draft proposal (in groupware document handling; originally a term in official circles meaning "to make a proposal for a settlement' or in legal circles meaning 'to publish a case')	
逆导晶闸管	Nìdǎo jīngzháguǎn	Reverse conducting thyristor	RCT
啮合和分离转矩	Nièhé hé fēnlí zhuànjǔ	Engagement and separation torque	
拟反应谱	Nǐfǎnyìng pǔ	Pseudo response spectrum	
尼康	Ní-kāng	Nikon (Japanese company)	
尼龙	Ní-lóng	Nylon	
匿名订阅	Nìmíng dìngyuè	Anonymous subscription	
匿名接入	Nìmíng jiērù	Anonymous access	AA
匿名文件传送协议	Nìmíng wénjiàn chuánsòng xiéyì	Anonymous file transfer protocol	AFTP
匿名用户	Nìmíng yònghù	Anonymous user	
逆时针极化波	Nìshízhēn jíhuà bō	Anti-clockwise polarized wave	
铌酸锂	Nísuānlǐ	Lithium niobate	$LiNbO_3$
扭波导	Niǔ bōdǎo	Waveguide twist	
牛顿信道	Niú-dùn xìndào	Newton channel	
扭矩	Niǔjǔ	Torsional moment	
扭振	Niǔzhèn	Torsional oscillation	
扭振波	Niǔzhèn bō	Torsional wave	
扭转变形	Niǔzhuǎn biànxíng	Torsional deflection	
逆向代理	Nìxiàng dàilǐ	Reverse proxy	
逆向地址解析协议	Nìxiàng dìzhǐ jiěxī xiéyì	Reverse address resolution protocol	RARP
逆向工程	Nìxiàng gōngchéng	Reverse engineering	
逆向路径转发	Nìxiàng lùjìng zhuǎnfā	Reverse path forwarding	RPF
逆行轨道	Nìxíng guǐdào	Retrograde orbit (of a satellite)	
匿形术	Nìxíngshù	Steganography	
拟阵结构	Nǐzhèn jiégòu	Matroid structure	
逆转层	Nìzhuǎn céng	Inversion layer	
N 阶同步传送模块	N-jiē tóngbù chuánsòng mókuài	Synchronous transmission mode-N	STM-N

n 进制数字	n-jìnzhì shùzì	N-ary digit	
n 进制数字信号	n-jìnzhì shùzì xìnhào	N-ary digital signal	
n 进制数字信令	*n*-jìnzhì shùzì xìnlìng	*n*-ary digital signaling	
n 进制位	n-jìnzhì wèi	N-ary digit	
农村电话	Nóngcūn diànhuà	Rural telephony	
农村去话电话线	Nóngcūn qùhuà diànhuà xiàn	Outgoing rural line	OGRL
n 态频移键控	n-tài pínyí jiànkòng	N-condition frequency shift keying	n-FSK
N 态正交调幅	N-tài zhèngjiāo tiáofú	N-state quadrature amplitude modulation	N-QAM
暖通空调	Nuǎn tōng kōngtiáo	Heating ventilation air conditioning	HVAC
诺顿磁盘医生	Nuò-dùn cípán yīshēng	Norton Disk Doctor ©	NDD
诺顿工具软件	Nuò-dùn gōngjù ruǎnjiàn	Norton Utilities ©	
诺基亚	Nuò-jī-yà	Nokia (Finnish company)	
诺基亚基于 X-Windows 平台的测量系统	Nuò-jī-yà jīyú X-Windows píngtáide cèliáng xìtǒng	Nokia Measurement System for X-Windows	NMS/X
诺基亚基于 X-Windows 平台的规划系统	Nuò-jī-yà jīyú X-Windows píngtáide guīhuà xìtǒng	Nokia Planning System for X-Windows	NPS/X
n 位字节	n-wèi zìjié	N-bit byte	
N 相脉冲移位链控	N-xiàng màichōng yíwèi liànkòng	N-phase pulse-shift-keying	N-PSK
n-协议控制信息	n-xiéyì kòngzhì xìnxī	N--protocol-control-information	
n-协议数据单元	n-xiéyì shùjù dānyuán	N--protocol-data-unit	
N 型显示器	N-xíng xiǎnshìqì	N scope	
N 值	N-zhí	N value	
n 状态幅度相移键控	n-zhuàngtài fúdù xiāngyí jiànkòng	N-state amplitude phase shift keying	
n 状态正交幅度调制	n-zhuàngtài zhèngjiāo fúdù tiáozhì	N-state quadrature amplitude modulation	n-QAM
N 状态正交调幅	N-zhuàngtài zhèngjiāo tiáofú	N-state quadrature amplitude modulation	N-QAM

O

哦,我明白了	Ó, wǒ míngbai le	Oh, I see (computer chat)	OIC
OADM 公共控制信道	OADM gōnggòng kòngzhì xìndào	OADM common control channel	OCCCH
OAMC 管理功能	OAMC guǎnlǐ gōngnéng	OAMC management function	OAMC-MF
OAMC 运行系统	OAMC yùnxíng xìtǒng	OAMC operation system	OAMC-OpS
ODMA 随机接入信道	ODMA suíjī jiērù xìndào	ODMA random access channel	ORACH
ODMA 专用控制信道	ODMA zhuānyòng kòngzhì xìndào	ODMA dedicated control channel	ODCCH
ODMA 专用信道	ODMA zhuānyòng xìndào	Dedicated ODMA channel	ODCH
ODMA 专用业务信道	ODMA zhuānyòng yèwù xìndào	ODMA dedicated traffic channel	ODTCH
OSI 参考模型	OSI cānkǎo móxíng	OSI reference model	OSI RM
偶检验	Ǒu jiǎnyàn	Even parity check	
偶校验	Ǒu jiàoyàn	Even parity check	
耦合	Ǒuhé	Coupling	
耦合电路	Ǒuhé diànlù	Coupled circuit	
耦合环	Ǒuhé huán	Coupling loop	
耦合口	Ǒuhé kǒu	Coupling aperture	
耦合路径	Ǒuhé lùjìng	Coupling path	
耦合腔行波管	Ǒuhé qiāng xíngbōguǎn	Coupled cavity traveling wave tube	
耦合损耗	Ǒuhé sǔnhào	Coupling loss	
耦合探针	Ǒuhé tànzhēn	Coupling probe	

耦合途径	Ǒuhé tújìng	Coupling path	
耦合效率	Ǒuhé xiàolǜ	Coupling efficiency	
耦合系数	Ǒuhé xìshù	Coupling factor	
耦合振动	Ǒuhé zhèndòng	Coupled vibration	
耦合/去耦合网络	Ǒuhé/qù'ǒuhé wǎngluò	Coupling and decoupling networks	CDN
耦合度	Ǒuhédù	Coupled factor	
耦合器	Ǒuhéqì	Coupler	
偶极天线	Ǒují tiānxiàn	Doublet antenna	
偶极天线	Ǒují tiānxiàn	Dipole antenna	
欧几里得距离	Oū-jǐ-lǐ-dé jùlí	Euclidean distance	
偶极子盘形天线	Ǒujízi pánxíng tiānxiàn	Dipole-disk antenna	DDA
偶极子平面(天线)	Ǒujízi píngmiàn (tiānxiàn)	Dipole flat plane (antenna)	DFP
偶极子天线	Ǒujízi tiānxiàn	Dipole antenna	DA
偶极子-幕形天线	Ǒujízi-mùxíng tiānxiàn	Dipole-curtain antenna	
偶联	Ǒulián	Coupling	
欧姆	Oū-mǔ	Ohm (unit of resistance)	Ω
欧姆龙	Oū-mǔ-lóng	Omron (Japan optical instrument mfr.)	
欧特克	Ōu-tè-kè	AutoCAD (engineering drawing software)	
欧洲标准化委员会	Oūzhōu biāozhǔnhuà wěiyuánhuì	Commité Européenne de Normalisation, European Committee for Standardization	CEN
欧洲大学和研究中心协会	Oūzhōu dàxué hé yánjiū zhōngxīn xiéhuì	Réseaux Associés pour la Recherche Européenne	RARE
欧洲电信标准	Oūzhōu diànxìn biāozhǔn	European Telecommunications Standard	ETS
欧洲电信标准组织/协会	Oūzhōu diànxìn biāozhǔn zǔzhī/xiéhuì	European Telecommunications Standards Institute	ETSI
欧洲电信标准化委员会	Oūzhōu diànxìn biāozhǔnhuà wěiyuánhuì	European Telecommunication Standards Institute	ETSI
欧洲地区通信计划	Oūzhōu dìqū tōngxìn jìhuà	European Area communications Plan	EACP
欧洲高级通信研究计划	Ōuzhōu gāojí tōngxìn yánjiū jìhuà	Research on Advanced Communications in Europe	RACE
欧洲高性能无线 LAN	Oūzhōu gāoxìngnéng wúxiàn LAN	High performance European radio LAN	HIPERLAN
欧洲官方地图学代表委员会	Oūzhōu guānfāng dìtúxué dàibiǎo wěiyuánhuì	European Committee of Representatives of Official Cartography	CERCO
欧洲广播联盟	Oūzhōu guǎngbō liánméng	European Broadcasting Union	EBU
欧洲航天局	Oūzhōu hángtiān jú	European Space Agency	ESA
欧洲 IP 网络	Oūzhōu IP wǎngluò	Réseaux IP Européennes	RIPE
欧洲计算机制造商协会	Oūzhōu jìsuànjī zhìzàoshāng xiéhuì	European Computer Manufacturers Association	ECMA
欧洲科学与研究网	Oūzhōu kēxué yǔ yánjiū wǎng	European Academic and Research Network	EARN
欧洲量子物理试验室	Oūzhōu liàngzǐ wùlǐ shìyànshì	European Particle Physics Laboratory	CERN
欧洲全向接入通信系统	Oūzhōu quánxiàng jiērù tōngxìn xìtǒng	European Total Access Communication System	ETACS
欧洲数字无绳电话标准密码算法	Oūzhōu shùzì wúshéng diànhuà biāozhǔn mìmǎ suànfǎ	European Digital Cordless Telephone (DECT) standard cipher algorithm	DSCA
欧洲数字无绳电信	Oūzhōu shùzì wúshéng diànxìn	Digital European Cordless Telecommunication	DECT
欧洲数字无绳通信	Oūzhōu shùzì wúshéng tōngxìn	Digital European Cordless Telecommunication	DECT
欧洲通信编号空间	Oūzhōu tōngxìn biānhào kōngjiān	European telecommunications numbering space	ETNS
欧洲通信标准	Oūzhōu tōngxìn biāozhǔn	European Telecommunications Standard	ETS
欧洲通信标准研究院	Oūzhōu tōngxìn biāozhǔn yánjiūyuàn	European Telecommunications Standards Institute	ETSI
欧洲通信临时（中间）标准	Oūzhōu tōngxìn línshí (zhōngjiān) biāozhǔn	Interim European Telecommunications Standard	I-ETS
欧洲通信事务管理委员会	Oūzhōu tōngxìn shìwù guǎnlǐ wěiyuánhuì	European Committee of Telecommunication Regulatory Affairs	ECTRA
欧洲通信卫星	Oūzhōu tōngxìn wèixīng	European communications Satellite	ECS

欧洲通信卫星组织	Oūzhōu tōngxìn wèixīng zǔzhī	European Communications Satellite Organization	ECSO
欧洲通信协调委员会	Oūzhōu tōngxìn xiétiáo wěiyuánhuì	European Communications Coordinating Committee	ECCC
欧洲无线电信息系统	Oūzhōu wúxiàndiàn xìnxī xìtǒng	European Radio Messaging System	ERMES
欧洲先进通信研究	Oūzhōu xiānjìn tōngxìn yánjiū	Research in Advanced communication for Europe	RACE
欧洲选进通信技术研究和发展规划	Oūzhōu xuǎnjìn tōngxìn jìshù yánjiū hé fāzhǎn guīhuà	Research and Development Program on Advanced communications technologies for Europe	RACE
欧洲邮电行政大会	Oūzhōu yóudiàn xíngzhèng dàhuì	Conference of European Post and Telecommunication Administrations	CEPT
欧洲邮电行政会议	Oūzhōu yóudiàn xíngzhèng huìyì	Conference of European Posts and Telecommunications Administrations	CEPT
欧洲邮政电信会议	Oūzhōu yóuzhèng diànxìn huìyì	European Conference of Posts and Telecommunications	ECPT
欧洲邮政和电信行政会议	Oūzhōu yóuzhèng hé diànxìn xíngzhèng huìyì	Conference of European Post and Telecommunication Administrations	CEPT
欧洲邮政和通信会议	Oūzhōu yóuzhèng hé tōngxìn huìyì	Conference of European Posts and Telecommunications	CEPT
欧洲邮政和远程通信会议	Oūzhōu yóuzhèng hé yuǎnchéng tōngxìn huìyì	Conference des Administrations Européennes des Postes et Telecommunications	
欧洲远程通信标准学会	Oūzhōu yuǎnchéng tōngxìn biāozhǔn xuéhuì	European Telecommunication Standards Institute	ETSI

P

p/4 相移的差分编码正交移相键控	p/4 xiàngyíde chāfēn biānmǎ zhèngjiāo yíxiàng jiànkòng	p/4 shifted, differentially encoded quadrature phase-shift keying	p/4DQPSK
爬电距离	Pádiàn jùlí	Creepage distance	
帕尔贴效应	Pà-ěr-tiē xiàoying	Peltier effect	
排版菜单	Páibǎn càidān	Format menu (WP command)	
排版工具	Páibǎn gōngjù	Format bar (WP command)	
拍比特	Pāibǐtè	Petabit (10^{15} bits)	
排除错误	Páichú cuòwù	Debugging	
排除范围	Páichú fànwéi	Exclusion range	
排出量	Páichū liàng	Amount of discharge	
排除频带滤光镜	Páichú píndài lǜguāngjìng	Rejection band filter (optical)	
排队	Páiduì	Queuing	
排队更新	Páiduì gēngxīn	Queued updating (in SQL Server)	
排队规则	Páiduì guīzé	Queuing discipline	
排队论	Páiduì lùn	Queuing theory	
排队模型	Páiduì móxíng	Queuing model	
排队时延	Páiduì shíyán	Queuing delay	
排队网络	Páiduì wǎngluò	Queuing network	QN
排队延时	Páiduì yánshí	Queuing delay	
排队指示	Páiduì zhǐshì	Queuing indication	
派发	Pàifā	Dispatch	
排列	Páiliè	Align	
排列生成	Páiliè shēngchéng	Generating permutations	
排列图标	Páiliè túbiāo	Arrange icons (Windows command)	
拍频振荡器	Pāipín zhèndàngqì	Beat-frequency oscillator	BFO
派遣路由	Pàiqiǎn lùyóu	Dispatch routing	
派生地图	Pàishēng dìtú	Derived map	
派生类	Pàishēng lèi	Derived class	
排它锁	Páitā suǒ	Exclusive lock (for database)	

排序	Páixù	Sequencing	
排序	Páixù	Sort (verb)	
排序本表	Páixù běn biǎo	Sort table	
排序次序	Páixù cìxù	Sort order	
排序关键字	Páixù guānjiàn zì	Sort key	
排序规则	Páixù guīzé	Collation	
排烟阀	Páiyān fá	Smoke damper	SD
排烟风机	Páiyān fēngjī	Smoke extractor exhaust fan	SEEF
排烟洁净系统	Páiyān jiéjìng xìtǒng	Fume extraction system (electronics mfg)	
排烟器	Páiyānqì	Smoke vent	SV
盘	Pán	Disk	
盘	Pán	Panel (of radiating element)	
判定含量	Pàndìng hánliàng	Decision content	
判定树	Pàndìng shù	Decision tree	
判定数据	Pàndìng shùjù	Decision data	
判断网络切换	Pànduàn wǎngluò qiēhuàn	Network evaluated handover	NEHO
胖客户端	Pàng kèhù duān	Fat client	
旁瓣	Pángbàn	Sidelobe	
旁瓣电平	Pángbàn diànpíng	Sidelobe level	
旁瓣消除	Pángbàn xiāochú	Sidelobe cancellation	SLC
旁瓣抑制	Pángbàn yìzhì	Sidelobe suppression	SLS
旁路电路	Pánglù diànlù	Bypass circuitry	
旁路方式	Pánglù fāngshì	Bypass mode	
旁路交换	Pánglù jiāohuàn	Bypass switching	
旁路中继	Pánglù zhōngjì	Bypass relay	
旁通	Pángtōng	Bypass	
旁通队列	Pángtōng duìliè	Bypass queue	
判决电路	Pànjué diànlù	Decision circuit	
判决值	Pànjué zhí	Decision value	
潘尼管	Pān-ní-guǎn	Peniotron	
盘式衰减器	Pánshì shuāijiǎnqì	Disc attenuator	
盘问握手认证协议	Pánwèn wòshǒu rènzhèng xiéyì	Challenge-handshake authentication protocol	CHAP
盘锥形天线	Pánzhuīxíng tiānxiàn	Discone antenna	
抛出	Pāochū	Throw	
泡沫灭火系统	Pàomò mièhuǒ xìtǒng	Foam fire extinguishing system	FFES
抛物反射面	Pāowù fǎnshè miàn	Parabolic reflector	
抛物反射面天线	Pāowù fǎnshè miàn tiānxiàn	Parabolic reflector antenna	
抛物环面天线	Pāowù huánmiàn tiānxiàn	Parabolic torus antenna	
抛物柱面天线	Pāowù zhùmiàn tiānxiàn	Parabolic cylindrical antenna	
抛物盒天线	Pāowùhé tiānxiàn	Pillbox antenna	
抛物面反射器	Pāowùmiàn fǎnshèqì	Parabolic reflector	
抛物面反射器天线	Pāowùmiàn fǎnshèqì tiānxiàn	Paraboloidal reflector antenna	
抛物面角型反射器	Pāowùmiàn jiǎo-xíng fǎnshèqì	Parabolic corner reflector	PACORE
抛物面镜	Pāowùmiàn jìng	Paraboloid mirror	
抛物面天线	Pāowùmiàn tiānxiàn	Parabolic antenna	
抛物面天线几何轴	Pāowùmiàn tiānxiàn jǐhé zhóu	Geometric axis of parabolic antenna	

P 波	P-bō	P wave	
PCI 工业计算机制造商协会	PCI gōngyè jìsuànjī zhìzàoshāng xiéhuì	PCI Industry Computer Manufacturers group	PCIMG
PCI 增强桥	PCI zēngqiáng qiáo	PCI expander bridge	PXB
配电	Pèidiàn	Wiring	PD
配对	Pèiduì	Partner	
配对表	Pèiduì biǎo	Partner list	
配合面密封	Pèihémiàn mìfēng	Mating face seal	
配件	Pèijiàn	Assembly	
配件市场	Pèijiàn shìchǎng	Aftermarket	
佩尼管	Pèi-ní-guǎn	Peniotron	
配送需求计划	Pèisòng xūqiú jìhuà	Distribution requirements planning	DRP
配送资源计划	Pèisòng zīyuán jìhuà	Distribution resource planning	DRP
配线点	Pèixiàn diǎn	Distribution point	DP
配线架	Pèixiàn jià	Distribution frame, distributor	DF
配线盘	Pèixiàn pán	Patch panel	
配线室	Pèixiàn shì	Wiring closet	
配向膜	Pèixiàng mó	Alignment film	
配向膜涂布装置	Pèixiàng mótú bù zhuāngzhì	Alignment coating equipment (semiconductor mfg)	
培训数据集	Péixùn shùjù jí	Training dataset	
配用法兰盖片	Pèiyòng fǎlán gàipiàn	Cover flange	
配置	Pèizhì	Configuration	
配置	Pèizhì	Allocate	
配置报告服务器	Pèizhì bàogào fúwùqì	Configuration report server	CRS
配置标识	Pèizhì biāozhì	Configuration identification	
配置登记码	Pèizhì dēngjì mǎ	Configuration register value	
配置管理	Pèizhì guǎnlǐ	Configuration management	
配置和资源管理	Pèizhì hé zīyuán guǎnlǐ	Configuration and resource management	CRM
配置检查	Pèizhì jiǎnchá	Configuration audit	
配置精灵	Pèizhì jīnglíng	Configuration daemon (in VPN)	CD
配置控制组	Pèizhì kòngzhì zǔ	Configuration control board	
配置生成器	Pèizhì shēngchéngqì	Configuration generator	
配置数据管理器	Pèizhì shùjù guǎnlǐqì	Configuration data manager	CDM
配置数据集	Pèizhì shùjùjí	Configuration data set	CDS
配置隧道	Pèizhì suìdào	Configured tunneling	CT
配置项	Pèizhì xiàng	Configuration item	
配置状态记录	Pèizhì zhuàngtài jìlù	Configuration status recording	
配置器	Pèizhìqì	Allocator	
配重	Pèizhòng	Counterweight	
配准	Pèizhǔn	Registration	
配准精度	Pèizhǔn jīngdù	Registration accuracy	
喷泥	Pēn ní	Mud pumping	
喷灯	Pēndēng	Blowtorch	
盆地	Péndì	Basin	
碰电源测试	Pèng diànyuán cèshì	Battery testing	
碰地气测试	Pèng dìqì cèshì	Ground testing	
膨胀	Péngzhàng	Dilation (in image coding)	

膨胀油膏	Péngzhàng yóugāo	Swelling gel	
碰撞测试	Pèngzhuàng cèshì	Colllision detection	
碰撞检波	Pèngzhuàng jiǎnbō	Collision detection	CD
碰撞检测非持续载波传感多路存取	Pèngzhuàng jiǎncè fēichíxù zàibō chuán gǎn duōlù cúnqǔ	Non-persistent carrier sensing multiple access with collision detection	NCSMA-CD
喷墨打印机	Pēnmò dǎyìnjī	Inkjet printer	
喷墨绘图仪	Pēnmò huìtúyí	Inkjet plotter	
喷墨普通纸传真机	Pēnmò pǔtōng zhǐ chuánzhēnjī	Inkjet plain paper facsimile	
喷泡式打印机	Pēnpào-shì dǎyìnjī	Bubblejet printer	
喷气推进实验室	Pēnqì tuījìn shíyànshì	Jet Propulsion Laboratory (US)	JPL
p 分位管理耽误	p-fènwèi guǎnlǐ dānwù	P-fractile administrative delay	
p 分位后勤耽误	p-fènwèi hòuqín dānwù	P-fractile logistic delay	
p 分位接入迟延	p-fènwèi jiērù chíyán	P-fractile access delay (in telecommunication)	
p 分位修理时间	p-fènwèi xiūlǐ shíjiān	P-fractile repair time	
批处理	Pī chǔlǐ	Batch processing	
批处理参数	Pī chǔlǐ cānshù	Batch parameters	
批处理队列	Pī chǔlǐ duìliè	Batch queue	
批处理文件	Pī chǔlǐ wénjiàn	Batch file	
批块操作	Pī kuài cāozuò	Batch operations	
批模式	Pī móshì	Batch model	
批日志恢复	Pī rìzhì huīfù	Bulk-logged recovery (in SQL Server)	
片	Piàn	Slice (video term)	
偏差	Piānchā	Declination	DEC
偏差	Piānchā	Offset	
片段	Piànduàn	Segment	
片段	Piànduàn	Fragment (in generic network information model)	
偏光板	Piānguāng bǎn	Polarizer layer (referring to light)	
偏光晶体	Piānguāng jīngtǐ	Polarizing crystal	
偏光滤光镜	Piānguāng lǜguāngjìng	Polarizing filter	
偏畸变	Piānjī biàn	Bias distortion	
偏畸变度	Piānjī biàndù	Degree of bias distortion	
片上存储器	Piàn-shàng cúnchǔqì	On-chip memory	OCM
片上系统	Piàn-shàng xìtǒng	System-on-a-chip	SOC
偏斜	Piānxié	Squint	
偏斜角	Piānxié jiǎo	Squint angle	
偏心光纤	Piānxīn guāngxiān	Eccentric core fiber	ECF
偏心偏转线圈	Piānxīn piānzhuǎn xiànquān	Off-centering deflection coil	
偏心数值	Piānxīn shùzhí	Off-centering	
偏压	Piānyā	Bias (of voltage)	
偏移	Piānyí	Shift, offset	
偏移键控正交相移键控	Piānyí jiànkòng zhèngjiāo xiàngyí jiànkòng	Offset-keying quadrature phase shift keying	OM-QPSK
偏移四相相移键控	Piānyí sìxiàng xiàngyí jiànkòng	Offset quadriphase phase shift keying	OQPSK
偏移四相移相键控	Piānyí sìxiāng yíxiāng jiànkòng	Offset quadrature phase shift keying	OQPSK
偏移正交幅移键控	Piānyí zhèngjiāo fúyí jiànkòng	Offset quadrature amplitude shift keying	OQASK
偏移正交相移键控	Piānyí zhèngjiāo xiàngyí jiànkòng	Offset quadrature phase shift keying	OQPSK
偏振	Piānzhèn	Polarization (referring to light, FOC)	

偏振保持光纤	Piānzhèn bǎochí guāngxiān	Polarization maintaining fiber	PMF
偏振保持和吸收衰减(纤维)	Piānzhèn bǎochí hé xīshōu shuāijiǎn (xiānwéi)	Polarization maintaining and absorption reducing (fiber)	PANDA
偏振恒持光缆	Piānzhèn héngchí guānglǎn	Polarization-maintaining fiber optic cable	
偏振恒持光纤	Piānzhèn héngchí guāngxiān	Polarization-maintaining optical fiber	
偏振模色散	Piānzhèn mó sèsàn	Polarization mode dispersion (FOC)	PMD
偏振模色散补偿器	Piānzhèn mó sèsàn bǔchángqì	Polarization mode dispersion compensator (FOC)	PMDC
偏振模色散差分群时延	Piānzhèn mó sèsàn chāfēn qún shíyán	Polarization mode dispersion (PMD) differential group delay	PMD-DGD
偏振模色散系数	Piānzhèn mó sèsàn xìshù	Polarization mode dispersion (PMD) coefficient	
偏振摸式	Piānzhèn mōshì	Polarization mode (FOC)	
偏振模式色散	Piānzhèn móshì sèsàn	Polarization mode dispersion	PMD
偏振态	Piānzhèn tài	State of polarization	SOP
偏振无关光隔离器	Piānzhèn wúguān guāng gélíqì	Polarization-insensitive fiber isolator (FOC)	PIFI
偏振相关光隔离器	Piānzhèn xiāngguān guāng gélíqì	Polarization-dependent fiber isolator (FOC)	PDFI
偏振相关损耗	Piānzhèn xiāngguān sǔnhào	Polarization-dependent loss (FOC)	PDL
偏振相关增益	Piānzhèn xiāngguān zēngyì	Polarization-dependent gain	PDG
偏振相关增益变化	Piānzhèn xiāngguān zēngyì biànhuà	Polarization-dependent gain variation	
偏振消光比	Piānzhèn xiāoguāng bǐ	Polarization extinction ratio (FOC)	
偏振度	Piānzhèndù	Degree of polarization	DOP
偏置	Piānzhì	Offset	
偏置馈源	Piānzhì kuìyuán	Offset feed	
偏置抛物面反射器天线	Piānzhì pāowùmiàn fǎnshèqì tiānxiàn	Offset paraboloidal reflector antenna	
偏置抛物面天线	Piānzhì pāowùmiàn tiānxiàn	Offset parabolic antenna	
偏置四相相移键控	Piānzhì sìxiāng xiāngyí jiànkòng	Offset quadriphase shift keying	OQPSK
偏置的	Piānzhìde	Offset (adjective)	
偏转板	Piānzhuǎn bǎn	Deflection plate	
偏转建立时间	Piānzhuǎn jiànlì shíjiān	Deflection setup time	
偏转调制	Piānzhuǎn tiáozhì	Deflection modulation	DM
偏转通道带宽	Piānzhuǎn tōngdào dàikuān	Deflection channel bandwidth	
偏转稳定时间	Piānzhuǎn wěndìng shíjiān	Deflection settling time	
偏转线圈	Piānzhuǎn xiànquān	Deflection coil	
片装电容器	Piànzhuāng diànróngqì	Chip capacitor	
片状元件	Piànzhuàng yuánjiàn	Chip component	
片状元件封装	Piànzhuàng yuánjiàn fēngzhuāng	Chip component encapsulation	
漂动	Piāodòng	Wander	
票据授予服务	Piàojù shòuyǔ fúwù	Ticket-granting service	
票面价值	Piàomiàn jiàzhí	Nominal value	
漂移	Piāoyí	Drift, wander	DR
漂移补偿	Piāoyí bǔcháng	Drift compensation	
票证许可服务器	Piàozhèng xǔkě fúwùqì	Token granting server (ISO security)	TGS
批比特	Pībǐtè	Petabyte	
批次处理	Pīcì chǔlǐ	Batch processing	
批次档案	Pīcì dàng'àn	Batch file	
皮尔逊卡方	Pí-ěr-xùn kǎ fāng	Pearson *chi*-square	
批发商	Pīfāshāng	Wholesaler	
皮可秒	Píkěmiǎo	Picosecond	

疲劳系数	Píláo xìshù	Fatigue factor	
批量更新	Pīliàng gēngxīn	Bulk update	
批量数据	Pīliàng shùjù	Batch data	
批量消息传输/处理	Pīliàng xiāoxi chuánshū/chǔlǐ	Boxcarring or batching of messages	
皮秒	Pímiǎo	Picosecond	
频标输出	Pín biāo shūchū	Frequency standard output (short for 频率标准输出)	
PIN 二极管开关	PIN erjíguǎn kāiguān	PIN diode switch	
PIN 二极管天线收发开关	PIN erjíguǎn tiānxiàn shōufā kāiguān	PIN diode antenna duplexer (lit. Rx/Tx switch)	
PIN 二极管移相器	PIN erjíguǎn yíxiàngqì	PIN diode phase shifter	
PIN 调制器	PIN tiáozhìqì	PIN modulator	
频带	Píndài	Frequency band	
频带划分	Píndài huàfēn	Band allocation	
频带扩展	Píndài kuòzhǎn	Band spread	
频带置乱	Píndài zhìluàn	Band scrambling	
频带中分	Píndài zhōngfēn	Midsplit	
频带外发射	Píndài-wài fāshè	Out-of-band emission	
频道	Píndào	Frequency channel	
频段	Pínduàn	Frequency band	
拼段	Pīnduàn	Reassembling	
频分	Pínfēn	Frequency division	
频分多路存取	Pínfēn duōlù cúnqǔ	Frequency division multiple access	FDMA
频分多路复用	Pínfēn duōlù fùyòng	Frequency division multiplexing	FDM
频分多路复用器	Pínfēn duōlù fùyòngqì	Frequency division multiplexer	FDM
频分多址	Pínfēn duōzhǐ	Frequency division multiple access	FDMA
频分复用	Pínfēn fùyòng	Frequency division multiplexing	FDM
频分复用调制	Pínfēn fùyòng tiáozhì	Frequency division multiplexing modulation	
频分和时分多址	Pínfēn hé shífēn duōzhǐ	Frequency and time division multiple access	FTDMA
频分双工	Pínfēn shuānggōng	Frequency division duplex	FDD
频分数据键	Pínfēn shùjù jiàn	Frequency division data link	FDDL
平衰落	Píng shuāiluò	Flat fading	
平衰落储备	Píng shuāiluò chǔbèi	Mean fading reserve	
平板绘图机	Píngbǎn huìtújī	Flatbed plotter	
平板激光	Píngbǎn jīguāng	Slab laser	
平板天线罩	Píngbǎn tiānxiàn zhào	Plane radome	
平板显示	Píngbǎn xiǎnshì	Flat-panel-display	FPD
平板仪	Píngbǎnyí	Planetable	
屏蔽	Píngbì	Shielding	
屏蔽	Píngbì	Squelch	SQLCH
屏蔽	Píngbì	Screen	
屏蔽电缆	Píngbì diànlǎn	Shielded cable	
屏蔽电路	Píngbì diànlù	Screened circuit	
屏蔽对绞电缆	Píngbì duìjiǎo diànlǎn	Shielded twisted pair cables	
屏蔽对线电缆	Píngbì duìxiàn diànlǎn	Shielded twisted pair cable	
屏蔽环形天线	Píngbì huánxíng tiānxiàn	Shielded-loop antenna	
屏蔽回路的转移阻抗	Píngbì huílùde zhuǎnyí zǔkàng	Transfer impedance (of a screened circuit)	
屏蔽金融箔对线	Píngbì jīnróng bó duìxiàn	Shielded foil twisted pair	SFTP

屏蔽壳体	Píngbì kétǐ	Shielded enclosure	
屏蔽路由器	Píngbì lùyóuqì	Screening router	
屏蔽墙	Píngbì qiáng	Curtain wall	
屏蔽效能	Píngbì xiàonéng	Shielding effectiveness	
屏蔽系数	Píngbì xìshù	Shielding factor	
屏蔽指示器	Píngbì zhǐshìqì	Screening indicator	SI
屏蔽子网	Píngbì zìwǎng	Screened sub-network	
屏蔽室	Píngbìshì	Shielded enclosure (radio frequency)	
屏蔽体	Píngbìtǐ	Shield	
评测	Píngcè	Profile	
平常函件	Píngcháng hánjiàn	Ordinary correspondence	
平顶天线	Píngdǐng tiānxiàn	Flat-top antenna	
平凡文件传输协议	Píngfán wénjiàn chuánshū xiéyì	Trivial file transfer protocol	TFTP
平方律检波	Píngfāng lǜ jiǎnbō	Square law detection	
平方取中法	Píngfāng qǔzhòng fǎ	Mid-square method	
平方相差	Píngfāng xiàngchà	Quadratic phase error	
平方根计算	Píngfānggēn jìsuàn	Square root calculation	SQRT
平方和平方根法	Píngfānghé píngfānggēn fǎ	Square root of the sum of the squares method	
平方和的根	Píngfānghéde gēn	Root-sum square	RSS
评估	Pínggū	Evaluate	
苹果电脑集团	Píngguǒ diànnǎo jítuán	Apple Computer Inc. (US company)	
苹果中文译写器	Píngguǒ zhōngwén yìxiěqì	Apple Chinese Dictation Kit ©	ACDK
平衡电感	Pínghéng diàngǎn	Balancing inductor	
平衡电压	Pínghéng diànyā	Symmetrical voltage	
平衡二叉树	Pínghéng èrchā shù	Balanced binary tree	
平衡归并排序	Pínghéng guībìng páixù	Balance merging sort	
平衡回损	Pínghéng huísǔn	Balanced return loss	
平衡混频器	Pínghéng hùnpínqì	Balanced mixer	
平衡集合信号	Pínghéng jíhé xìnhào	Balanced aggregate signal	
平衡链路接入规程	Pínghéng liànlù jiērù guīchéng	Link access procedure, balanced	LAPB
平衡链路接入协议	Pínghéng liànlù jiērù xiéyì	Link access protocol balanced	LAPB
平衡码	Pínghéng mǎ	Balanced code	
平衡数据链路	Pínghéng shùjù liànlù	Balanced data link	
平衡天线	Pínghéng tiānxiàn	Balanced antenna	
平衡网络	Pínghéng wǎngluò	Balancing network	
平衡/不平衡变换器	Pínghéng/bùpínghéng biànhuànqì	Balun (balanced/unbalanced devce)	
平衡 - 不平衡转换器	Pínghéng-bùpínghéng zhuǎnhuànqì	Balance-unbalance switch	Balun
平衡型参量放大器	Pínghéng-xíng cānliàng fàngdàqì	Balanced parametric amplifier	
平衡型阀芯	Pínghéng-xíng fáxīn	Balanced plug	
平衡型链路接入规程	Pínghéng-xíng liànlù jiērù guīchéng	Link access procedure-balanced	LAPB
平滑	Pínghuá	Anti-alias	
平滑	Pínghuá	Smoothing	
平滑调频	Pínghuá tiáopín	Tamed frequency modulation	TFM
平滑振荡器	Pínghuá zhèndàngqì	Tamed frequency oscillator	TFO
平滑的双向传输时间	Pínghuáde shuāngxiàng chuánshū shíjiān	Smoothed round-trip transmission time	SRTT
瓶径	Píngjìng	Bottleneck	

瓶颈	Píngjǐng	Bottleneck	
平均包延迟	Píngjūn bāo yánchí	Mean packet delay	MPD
平均保持时间	Píngjūn bǎochí shíjiān	Average holding time	AHT
平均包络检波	Píngjūn bāoluò jiǎnbō	Average envelope detection	
平均变异速度	Píngjūn biànyì sùdù	Mean slip velocity	
平均不可用时间	Píngjūn bùkěyòng shíjiān	Mean down time	MDT
平均不可用性	Píngjūn bùkěyòngxìng	Mean unavailability	
平均查找长度	Píngjūn cházhǎo chángdù	Average search length	
平均处理时间	Píngjūn chǔlǐ shíjiān	Average handling time	AHT
平均存取时间	Píngjūn cúnqǔ shíjiān	Average access time (computer disk)	AAT
平均等效噪声温度	Píngjūn děngxiào zàoshēng wēndù	Mean equivalent noise temperature (of a linear two-port network)	
平均访问时间	Píngjūn fǎngwèn shíjiān	Average access time	
平均反应谱	Píngjūn fǎnyìng pǔ	Average response spectrum	
平均发射光功率	Píngjūn fāshè guāng gōnglǜ	Mean launched power	
平均功率	Píngjūn gōnglǜ	Mean power (of a radio transmitter)	PY
平均功率	Píngjūn gōnglǜ	Average power (in a transmission line)	
平均管理耽误	Píngjūn guǎnlǐ dānwù	Mean administrative delay	MAD
平均故障间隔时间	Píngjūn gùzhàng jiàngé shíjiān	Mean time between failures	MTBF
平均故障时间	Píngjūn gùzhàng shíjiān	Mean time between failures	MTBF
平均故障数	Píngjūn gùzhàng shù	Average failure number	AFN
平均故障修理时间	Píngjūn gùzhàng xiūlǐ shíjiān	Mean time to repair	MTTR
平均后勤耽误	Píngjūn hòuqín dānwù	Mean logistic delay	MLD
平均恢复时间	Píngjūn huīfù shíjiān	Average restoration time	ART
平均恢复时间	Píngjūn huīfù shíjiān	Mean time to restoration	MTTR
平均恢复时间	Píngjūn huīfù shíjiān	Mean time to recovery	MTTR
平均恢复时间	Píngjūn huīfù shíjiān	Mean time to repair	
平均鉴定分数	Píngjūn jiàndìng fēnshù	Mean opinion score	MOS
平均减速	Píngjūn jiǎnsù	Mean slowdown	
平均接入迟延（电信中）	Píngjūn jiērù chíyán (diànxìn zhōng)	Mean access delay (in telecommunication)	
平均接收信号强度指示	Píngjūn jiēshōu xìnhào qiángdù zhǐshì	Mean received signal strength indication	
平均可用时间	Píngjūn kěyòng shíjiān	Mean up time	MUT
平均可用性	Píngjūn kěyòngxìng	Mean availability	
平均累积不可用时间	Píngjūn lěijī bùkěyòng shíjiān	Mean accumulated down time	MADT
平均名义特性	Píngjūn míngyì tèxìng	Average nominal characteristic	
平均旁瓣电平	Píngjūn pángbàn diànpíng	Average sidelobe level	ASL
平均旁瓣电平	Píngjūn pángbàn diànpíng	Mean sidelobe level	MSLL
平均偏振模色散差分群时延	Píngjūn piānzhèn mó sèsàn chāfēn qún shíyán	Mean polarization mode dispersion differential group delay	
平均平方值	Píngjūn píngfāng zhí	Mean square value	
平均评价得分	Píngjūn píngjià défēn	Mean opinion score	MOS
平均潜伏时间	Píngjūn qiánfú shíjiān	Average latency time	
平均潜伏期	Píngjūn qiánfúqī	Average latency	
平均失效间隔时间	Píngjūn shīxiào jiàngé shíjiān	Mean time between failures	MTBF
平均失效率	Píngjūn shīxiào lǜ	Mean failure rate	
平均失效频度	Píngjūn shīxiào píndù	Mean failure intensity	
平均失效前时间	Píngjūn shīxiào qián shíjiān	Mean time to failure	MTTF

平均失效间工作时间	Píngjūn shīxiào-jiān gōngzuò shíjiān	Mean operating time between failures	MTBF
平均时延	Píngjūn shíyán	Average time delay	ATD
平均使用寿命	Píngjūn shǐyòng shòumìng	Average useful life	AUL
平均首次失效前时间	Píngjūn shǒucì shīxiào qián shíjiān	Mean time to first failure	MTTFF
平均寿命预期值	Píngjūn shòumìng yùqīzhí	Average life expectancy	ALE
平均衰落时间	Píngjūn shuāiluò shíjiān	Average fade duration	AFD
平均停机时间	Píngjūn tíngjī shíjiān	Mean down time	MDT
平均图象电平	Píngjūn túxiàng diànpíng	Average picture level	APL
平均维护（间隔）时间	Píngjūn wéihù (jiàngé) shíjiān	Mean time between maintenance	MTBM
平均维护工时	Píngjūn wéihù gōngshí	Mean maintenance manhours	
平均维修间隔时间	Píngjūn wéixiū jiàngé shíjiān	Average time between maintenance	ATBM
平均无故障工作时间	Píngjūn wúgùzhàng gōngzuò shíjiān	Mean operating time between failures	MTBF
平均无故障时间	Píngjūn wúgùzhàng shíjiān	Mean time between failure	MTBF
平均无故障时间	Píngjūn wúgùzhàng shíjiān	Mean time to failure	MTTF
平均响应幅度	Píngjūn xiǎngyìng fúdù	Average response amplitude	ARA
平均信元率	Píngjūn xìnyuán lǜ	Average cell rate	ACR
平均修复率	Píngjūn xiūfù lǜ	Mean repair rate	
平均修复时间	Píngjūn xiūfù shíjiān	Mean time to repair	MTTR
平均修理时间	Píngjūn xiūlǐ shíjiān	Mean repair time	MRT
平均寻道时间	Píngjūn xúndào shíjiān	Average seek time	
平均循环误差	Píngjūn xúnhuán wùchā	Circular error average	CEA
平均业务恢复时间	Píngjūn yèwù huīfù shíjiān	Mean time to service restoration	MTTSR
平均业务接入迟延	Píngjūn yèwù jiērù chíyán	Mean service access delay	
平均业务运行中断间隔时间	Píngjūn yèwù yùnxíng zhōngduàn jiàngé shíjiān	Mean time between service outages	MTBSO
平均业务准备时间	Píngjūn yèwù zhǔnbèi shíjiān	Mean service preparation time	
平均有效修复性维护时间	Píngjūn yǒuxiào xiūfùxìng wéihù shíjiān	Mean active corrective maintenance time	
平均噪声温度	Píngjūn zàoshēng wēndù	Mean noise temperature	
平均噪声系数	Píngjūn zàoshēng xìshù	Mean noise factor (of a linear two-port net-work)	
平均占用时间	Píngjūn zhànyòng shíjiān	Average holding time	AHT
平均中断（间隔）时间	Píngjūn zhōngduàn (jiàngé) shíjiān	Mean time between interrupts	MTBI
平均中断持续时间	Píngjūn zhōngduàn chíxù shíjiān	Mean interruption duration	
平均主管得分	Píngjūn zhǔguǎn défēn	Mean opinion score	MOS
平均值	Píngjūnzhí	Average value	AV
平均值检波器	Píngjūnzhí jiǎnbōqì	Average detector	
平流层高空气艇平台	Píngliúcéng gāokōng qìtǐng píngtái	High altitude platform station	HAPS
平面波导线路	Píngmiàn bōdǎo xiànlù	Planar lightwave circuit	PLC
平面测量地图	Píngmiàn cèliáng dìtú	Planimetric map	
屏面打印键	Píngmiàn dǎyìn jiàn	PrintScreen key	
平面地图	Píngmiàn dìtú	Plat	
平面地物	Píngmiàn dìwù	Planimetric feature	
平面法兰	Píngmiàn fǎlán	Flat flange	
平面分割	Píngmiàn fēngē	Maintaining line arrangements	
平面光波导器件	Píngmiàn guāng bōdǎo qìjiàn	Planar optical waveguide device	
平面光波电路	Píngmiàn guāngbō diànlù	Planar lightwave circuit	PLC
平面接头	Píngmiàn jiētóu	Plane joint	

平面连接	Píngmiàn liánjiē	Plane connection	PC
平面连接	Píngmiàn liánjiē	Plane connection	PC
平面描影	Píngmiàn miáoyǐng	Flat shading (video term)	
平面图	Píngmiàn tú	Planar graph	
平面拓扑复合体	Píngmiàn tuòpū fùhétǐ	Planar topological complex	
平面位置显示器	Píngmiàn wèizhì xiǎnshìqì	Plane position indicator	
平面文件	Píngmiàn wénjiàn	Flat file	
平面阴极射线管	Píngmiàn yīnjí shèxiànguǎn	Flat cathode ray tube (CRT)	
平面阵	Píngmiàn zhèn	Planar array	
平面阵天线	Píngmiàn zhèn tiānxiàn	Planar array antenna	
平面阵列	Píngmiàn zhènliè	Planar array	PA
平面阵列波导光栅	Píngmiàn zhènliè bōdǎo guāngshān	Planar array waveguide grating	
平面坐标	Píngmiàn zuòbiāo	Planar coordinates	
平面坐标系统	Píngmiàn zuòbiāo xìtǒng	Planar coordinate systems	
平面内剪切模式	Píngmiàn-nèi jiǎnqiē móshì	In-plane shearing mode	
平面式发送机	Píngmiàn-shì fāsòngjī	Flat-bed transmitter	
平面外剪切模式	Píngmiàn-wài jiǎnqiē móshì	Out-of plane shear mode	
平面性检测和嵌入	Píngmiàn-xìng jiǎncè hé qiànrù	Planarity detection and embedding	
屏幕	Píngmù	Screen	
屏幕保护程序	Píngmù bǎohù chéngxù	Screen saver	
屏幕缓冲	Píngmù huǎnchōng	Screen buffer	
屏幕计事本	Píngmù jìshìběn	Screen pop	
屏幕拷贝设备	Píngmù kǎobèi shèbèi	Screen copy device	
屏幕双绞线	Píngmù shuāngjiǎoxiàn	Shielded twisted pair	STP
乒乓法	Pīngpāng fǎ	Ping-pong method	
平嵌天线	Píngqiàn tiānxiàn	Flush-mounted antenna	
平视显示器	Píngshì xiǎnshìqì	Head-up indicator	
平台	Píngtái	Platform	
平台安全部分	Píngtái ānquán bùfēn	Platform security division	PSD
平台调用服务	Píngtái diàoyòng fúwù	Platform invoke service	PInvoke
平台规范	Píngtái guīfàn	Platform specification	
平台式彩色影像扫描器	Píngtái-shì cǎisè yǐngxiàng sǎomiáoqì	Flat-bed color image scanner	
平台式上扳机	Píngtái-shì shàngbānjī	Platform loader (in component assembly process)	
平坦城市	Píngtǎn chéngshì	Terrestrial urban	TU
平坦随机噪声	Píngtǎn suíjī zàoshēng	Flat random noise	
平坦增益放大器	Píngtǎn zēngyì fàngdàqì	Flat-gain amplifier	FA
平头缝隙天线	Píngtóu fèngxì tiānxiàn	Flat headed antenna	
屏外表面	Píng-wài biǎomiàn	Off-screen surface	
平稳随机过程	Píngwěn suíjī guòchéng	Stationary random process	
平镶天线	Píngxiāng tiānxiàn	Flush-mounted antenna	
平行板透镜	Píngxíng bǎn tòujìng	Parallel-plate lens	
平行处理透视引擎	Píngxíng chǔlǐ tòushì yǐnqíng	Parallel processing perspective engine	
平行线	Píngxíng xiàn	Parallel wire	
平展行集	Píngzhǎn háng jí	Flattened rowset	
平展界面	Píngzhǎn jièmiàn	Flattened interface	
凭证	Píngzhèng	Certificate, credential (IPsec)	

平整	Píngzhěng	Grading	
凭证订阅	Píngzhèng dìngyuè	Subscription by permit	
评注	Píngzhù	Annotation	
频合器	Pínhéqì	Frequency synthesizer, short for 频率合成器	
拼接	Pīnjiē	Concatenation	
拼块	Pīnkuài	Blocking	
拼块	Pīnkuài	Clog	
频率	Pínlǜ	Frequency	F
频率变化速率	Pínlǜ biànhuà sùlǜ	Frequency variation rate	
频率变换	Pínlǜ biànhuàn	Frequency conversion	
频率变换产物	Pínlǜ biànhuàn chǎnwù	Frequency conversion product	
频率变换电路	Pínlǜ biànhuàn diànlù	Frequency-conversion circuit	
频率变换器	Pínlǜ biànhuànqì	Frequency converter	FC
频率编码脉冲压缩	Pínlǜ biānmǎ màichōng yāsuō	Frequency-coded pulse compression	
频率编码制	Pínlǜ biānmǎ zhì	Frequency-coding system	
频率标准	Pínlǜ biāozhǔn	Frequency standard	
频率标准输出	Pínlǜ biāozhǔn shūchū	Frequency standard output (may be shortened to 频标输出)	
频率步级	Pínlǜ bù jí	Frequency step size	
频率补偿	Pínlǜ bǔcháng	Frequency compensation	
频率不稳定度	Pínlǜ bùwěndìngdù	Frequency instability	
频率捕捉范围	Pínlǜ bǔzhuō fànwéi	Frequency pull-in range	
频率参数分配面板	Pínlǜ cānshù fēnpèi miànbǎn	Frequency reference divide panel	FRDP
频率带宽	Pínlǜ dàikuān	Frequency bandwidth	
频率倒置	Pínlǜ dàozhì	Frequency inversion	
频率范围	Pínlǜ fànwéi	Frequency range (of equipment)	
频率分割	Pínlǜ fēngē	Frequency division	
频率分集	Pínlǜ fēnjí	Frequency diversity	
频率分集接收	Pínlǜ fēnjí jiēshōu	Frequency diversity reception	
频率分集扩展频谱码分多址	Pínlǜ fēnjí kuòzhǎn pínpǔ mǎfēn duōzhǐ	Frequency diversity/spread spectrum multiple access	FD/SSMA
频率分集雷达	Pínlǜ fēnjí léidá	Frequency diversity radar	
频率分配	Pínlǜ fēnpèi	Frequency assignment	FA
频率改变方式	Pínlǜ gǎibiàn fāngshì	Frequency shift mode	FM
频率管理	Pínlǜ guǎnlǐ	Frequency management	
频率合成器	Pínlǜ héchéngqì	Frequency synthesizer	
频率鉴别	Pínlǜ jiànbié	Frequency discrimination	
频率鉴别号码	Pínlǜ jiànbié hàomǎ	Frequency identity	FID
频率校正短脉冲串	Pínlǜ jiàozhèng duǎnmàichōng chuàn	Frequency correction burst	FB
频率校正突发	Pínlǜ jiàozhèng tūfā	Frequency correction burst	FB
频率校正信道	Pínlǜ jiàozhèng xìndào	Frequency correction channel	FCCH
频率捷变	Pínlǜ jiébiàn	Frequency agility	
频率截获概率	Pínlǜ jiéhuò gàilǜ	Intercept probability of frequency	
频率解调	Pínlǜ jiětiáo	Frequency demodulation	
频率纠正信道	Pínlǜ jiūzhèng xìndào	Frequency correction channel	FCCH
频率控制	Pínlǜ kòngzhì	Frequency control	
频率灵敏度	Pínlǜ língmǐndù	Frequency sensitivity	

频率瞄准误差	Pínlǜ miáozhǔn wùchā	Frequency spot error	
频率偏离	Pínlǜ piānlí	Frequency departure	
频率偏移率	Pínlǜ piānyílǜ	Frequency deviation ratio	
频率偏置	Pínlǜ piānzhì	Frequency offset	
频率漂移	Pínlǜ piāoyí	Frequency drift	
频率牵引	Pínlǜ qiānyǐn	Frequency pulling	
频率起伏	Pínlǜ qǐfú	Frequency fluctuation	
频率去相关	Pínlǜ qù xiāngguān	Frequency decorrelation	
频率容差	Pínlǜ róngchā	Frequency tolerance	
频率容限	Pínlǜ róngxiàn	Frequency tolerance	
频率时间跳跃多路存取	Pínlǜ shíjiān tiàoyuè duōlù cúnqǔ	Frequency time hopping multiple access	FTHMA
频率失锁范围	Pínlǜ shīsuǒ fànwéi	Frequency lock-loss range	
频率失锁范围	Pínlǜ shīsuǒ fànwéi	Frequency pull-out range	
频率锁定环	Pínlǜ suǒdìng huán	Frequency locked loop	FLL
频率特性	Pínlǜ tèxìng	Frequency characteristic	
频率调制	Pínlǜ tiáozhì	Frequency modulation	FM
频率同步环路	Pínlǜ tóngbù huánlù	Frequency locked loop	FLL
频率微调	Pínlǜ wēitiáo	Frequency fine tuning	
频率稳定度	Pínlǜ wěndìngdù	Frequency stability	
频率稳准度	Pínlǜ wěnzhǔndù	Frequency stabilization accuracy	
频率误差	Pínlǜ wùchā	Frequency error	
频率相位同步环路	Pínlǜ xiàngwèi tóngbù huánlù	Frequency phase locked loop	FPLL
频率响应	Pínlǜ xiǎngyìng	Frequency response	FR
频率响应特性	Pínlǜ xiǎngyìng tèxìng	Frequency response characteristic	
频率响应下降	Pínlǜ xiǎngyìng xiàjiàng	Roll-off	
频率选择抗干扰技术	Pínlǜ xuǎnzé kànggānrǎo jìshù	Frequency selection anti-jamming technique	
频率选择性	Pínlǜ xuǎnzéxìng	Frequency selectivity	
频率选择性衰落	Pínlǜ xuǎnzéxìng shuāiluò	Frequency selective fading	
频率压缩解调器	Pínlǜ yāsuō jiětiáoqì	Frequency compression demodulator	FCD
频率域滤波	Pínlǜ yù lǜbō	Frequency domain filtering	
频率域滤波器	Pínlǜ yù lǜbōqì	Frequency domain filter	
频率预选	Pínlǜ yùxuǎn	Frequency pre-selection	
频率预置器	Pínlǜ yùzhìqì	Frequency presetting device	
频率再利用卫星网络	Pínlǜ zàilìyòng wèixīng wǎngluò	Frequency re-use satellite network	
频率再用	Pínlǜ zàiyòng	Frequency re-use	
频率振幅调制	Pínlǜ zhènfú tiáozhì	Frequency-amplitude modulation	FAM
频率指配	Pínlǜ zhǐpèi	Frequency allotment	
频率指配	Pínlǜ zhǐpèi	Frequency assignment	
频率重定义	Pínlǜ zhòng dìngyì	Frequency redefinition	
频率啁啾	Pínlǜ zhōujiū	Frequency chirp	FCH
频率转换效果	Pínlǜ zhuǎnhuàn xiàoguǒ	Frequency shifter effect	FSE
频率准确度	Pínlǜ zhǔnquèdù	Frequency accuracy	
频率综合器	Pínlǜ zōnghéqì	Frequency synthesizer	
频率综合仪	Pínlǜ zōnghéyí	Frequency synthesizer	
频率 / 电压转换	Pínlǜ/diànyā zhuǎnhuàn	Frequency to voltage converter	F / V
频偏	Pínpiān	Frequency deviation	

频偏校正	Pínpiān jiàozhèng	Frequency deviation correction	
频漂	Pínpiāo	Frequency drift	
频谱	Pínpǔ	Frequency spectrum	
频谱表示法	Pínpǔ biǎoshìfǎ	Spectral representation	
频谱纯度	Pínpǔ chúndù	Spectrum purity	
频谱分量	Pínpǔ fènliàng	Spectral component	
频谱分析仪	Pínpǔ fēnxīyí	Spectrum analyzer	
频谱互锁重叠的 PAM 传输	Pínpǔ hùsuǒ chóngdiéde PAM chuánshū	Overlapped PAM transmission with interlocking spectra	OPTIS
频谱节约	Pínpǔ jiéyuē	Spectrum saving	
频谱扩展	Pínpǔ kuòzhǎn	Spectral expansion	
频谱利用有效增益	Pínpǔ lìyòng yǒuxiào zēngyì	Effective gain in spectrum utilization	
频谱效率	Pínpǔ xiàolǜ	Spectrum effectiveness	
皮诺关系	Pí-nuò guānxi	Peano relation	
皮诺曲线	Pí-nuò qūxiàn	Peano curve	
皮诺元组代数	Pí-nuò yuán zǔ dàishù	Peano tuple algebra	
频响	Pínxiǎng	Frequency response	FR
频响	Pínxiǎng	Roll-off (short for 频率响应下降)	
频响平坦度	Pínxiǎng píngtǎndù	Frequency response flatness	
频移	Pínyí	Frequency shift (in keying)	
频移电报	Pínyí diànbào	Frequency-shift telegraphy	FST
频移键控	Pínyí jiànkòng	Frequency-shift keying	FSK
频移调制	Pínyí tiáozhì	Frequency-shift modulation	FSM
频域	Pínyù	Frequency domain	
频域反射计	Pínyù fǎnshèjì	Frequency domain reflectometry	
频域分析	Pínyù fēnxī	Frequency domain analysis	
品质因数	Pǐnzhì yīnshù	Figure of merit	G/T
频综器	Pínzōngqì	Frequency synthesizer	
匹配	Pǐpèi	Matching (between a load and a source)	
匹配包层单模光纤	Pǐpèi bāo céng dānmó guāngxiān	Matched coaxial single mode optical fiber	MCSM
匹配段	Pǐpèi duàn	Matching section	
匹配短线	Pǐpèi duǎnxiàn	Matching stub	
匹配负载	Pǐpèi fùzài	Matched load	
匹配负载电压	Pǐpèi fùzài diànyā	Matched-load voltage	
匹配滤波	Pǐpèi lǜbō	Matched filtering	
匹配滤波器	Pǐpèi lǜbōqì	Matched filter	
匹配滤波器接收机	Pǐpèi lǜbōqì jiēshōujī	Matched filter receiver	
匹配网络	Pǐpèi wǎngluò	Matching network	
匹配终端	Pǐpèi zhōngduān	Matched termination	
匹配项	Pǐpèixiàng	Match (noun. when searching for a term)	
批示	Pīshì	Official comment (in groupware document handling; originally a term in official circles meaning 'to write an official reply to a petition')	
批套附送软件	Pītào fùsòng ruǎnjiàn	Bundled software	
批注属性	Pīzhù shǔxìng	Annotational property	
p 进制向量表示	p-jìnzhì xiàngliàng biǎoshì	p-adic vector expression	
泊管	Póguǎn	Platinotron	
破坏标准	Pòhuài biāozhǔn	Failure criterion	

破坏承载	Pòhuài chéngzài	Breaking load	
破坏性读出	Pòhuàixìng dúchū	Destructive read-out	
破坏性试验	Pòhuàixìng shìyàn	Destructive test	
泊松比	Pó-sōng bǐ	Poisson ratio	
泊松分布	Pó-sōng fēnbù	Poisson distribution	
泊松过程	Pó-sōng guòchéng	Poisson process	
PPP 多链路协议	PPP duō liànlù xiéyì	Multilink PPP	MP
PSPDN 拨出	PSPDN bōchū	Dial-out by the PSPDN	
PTM 多播	PTM duōbō	PTM multicast	PTM-M
PTM 组呼叫	PTM zǔ hūjiào	PTM groupcall	PTM-G
谱功率密度	Pǔ gōnglǜ mìdù	Spectral power density	
普相关	Pǔ xiāngguān	Spectral coherence	
普遍服务	Pǔbiàn fúwù	Universal service	
普遍服务基金	Pǔbiàn fúwù jījīn	Universal Service Fund	USF
普遍接入	Pǔbiàn jiērù	Universal access	
普惠制	Pǔhuìzhì	Generalized system of acceptance	GSP
扑获指示信道	Pūhuò zhǐshì xìndào	Acquisition indicator channel	AICH
扑获指示器	Pūhuò zhǐshìqì	Acquisition indicator	AI
谱宽	Pǔkuān	Spectral width	
普密	Pǔmì	Common encryption (for public use)	
普特喇叭天线	Pǔ-tè lǎba tiānxiàn	Potter horn antenna	
普通操作输入	Pǔtōng cāozuò shūrù	General purpose input	GPI
普通电话交换网	Pǔtōng diànhuà jiāohuàn wǎng	General switched telephone network	GSTN
普通电话业务	Pǔtōng diànhuà yèwù	Plain old telephone service	POTS
普通光纤（缆）连接器	Pǔtōng guāngxiān (lǎn) liánjiēqì	General purpose optical fiber (cable) connector	
普通接入控制级别	Pǔtōng jiērù kòngzhì jíbié	Normal access control level	
普通老式电话业务	Pǔtōng lǎoshì diànhuà yèwù	Plain old telephone service	POTS
普通文件传送协议	Pǔtōng wénjiàn chuánsòng xiéyì	Trivial file transfer protocol	TFTP
普通信息分组	Pǔtōng xìnxī fēnzǔ	Normal burst	NB
普通用户识别模块	Pǔtōng yònghù shíbié mókuài	Universal subscriber identity module	USIM
普通邮件	Pǔtōng yóujiàn	Snail mail	
谱线	Pǔxiàn	Spectral line	
谱线宽度	Pǔxiàn kuāndù	Spectral linewidth	
谱域法	Pǔyùfǎ	Spectral domain technique	
P 型显示器(平面位置显示器)	P-xíng xiǎnshìqì (píngmiàn wèizhì xiǎnshìqì)	P scope (plane position indicator)	
P-Δ 效应	P-Δ xiàoyìng	P delta effects	

Q

奇检验	Qí jiǎnyàn	Odd parity check	
前边缘	Qián bianyuán	Leading edge	
前管理模块	Qián guǎnlǐ mókuài	Front administrative module	FAM
前函数状态	Qián hánshù zhuàngtài	Previous function state	
前一步	Qián yībù	Back (WP command)	
浅槽隔离	Qiǎncáo gélí	Shallow-trench isolation	
浅层句法分析	Qiǎncéng jùfǎ fēnxī	Shallow parsing	

前导码	Qiándǎo mǎ	Lead code	
前导字节	Qiándǎo zìjié	Preamble	
签定文件头	Qiāndìng wénjiàn tóu	Authentication header	
前端	Qiánduān	Front-end	
前端处理机	Qiánduān chǔlǐjī	Front-end processor	FEP
前端处理器	Qiánduān chǔlǐqì	Front-end processor	FEP
前端目标设备驱动	Qiánduān mùbiāo shèbèi qūdòng	Front-end target driver	FETD
前端通信处理机	Qiánduān tōngxìn chùlǐjī	Front-end communications processor	FECP
签发机构名	Qiānfā jīgòu míng	Certificate issuer	
潜伏故障	Qiánfú gùzhàng	Latent fault	
千伏安小时	Qiānfú'ān xiǎoshí	Kilovolt ampere-hour	KVAH
潜伏期	Qiánfúqī	Latency	
强鉴别	Qiáng jiànbié	Strong authentication	
强连通图	Qiáng liántōng tú	Strongly connected graph	
强马尔科夫相似	Qiáng mǎ-ěr-kē-fū xiāngsì	Strong Markovian bisimulation	
强调制的脉码调制（脉冲源）	Qiáng tiáozhìde màimǎ tiáozhì (màichōng yuán)	Pulse code modulation intensity modulated (pulse source)	PCM-IM (PS)
强验证	Qiáng yànzhèng	Strong authentication	
强插	Qiángchā	Forced insertion (call pre-emption)	
强拆	Qiángchāi	Breakdown	
强度	Qiángdù	Strength	
强力攻击	Qiánglì gōngjī	Brute force attack (cryptology)	
墙内埋设	Qiáng-nèi máishè	Burial in wall (telecom installation)	BW
强迫馈电	Qiǎngpò kuìdiàn	Constrained feed	
强迫释放	Qiǎngpò shìfàng	Forced release	
强迫通风	Qiǎngpò tōngfēng	Forced ventilation	
前滚	Qiángǔn	Roll forward (for database)	
抢先 - 恢复优先规则	Qiǎngxiān-huīfù yōuxiān guīzé	Preemptive-resume priority scheme	
强占	Qiángzhàn	Pre-emption	
抢占寄存器	Qiǎngzhàn jìcúnqì	Register contention	
强制	Qiángzhì	Mandatory	
墙纸	Qiángzhǐ	Wallpaper (computer screen background)	
强制存取控制	Qiángzhì cúnqǔ kòngzhì	Mandatory access control (Linux)	MAC
强制倒换	Qiángzhì dǎohuàn	Forced switch	FSW
强制订阅	Qiángzhì dìngyuè	Push subscription	
强制访问控制	Qiángzhì fǎngwèn kòngzhì	Mandatory access control (IPsec)	MAC
强制更新	Qiángzhì gēngxīn	Mandatory, forced updating	
强制切换	Qiángzhì qiēhuàn	Forced switchover	FSw
强制网络门户	Qiángzhì wǎngluò ménhù	Captive network portal	
强制纹理压缩	Qiángzhì wénlǐ yāsuō	Forced texture compression	
强制用户配置文件	Qiángzhì yònghù pèizhì wénjiàn	Mandatory user profile	
强制性还原	Qiángzhìxìng huányuán	Authoritative restore	
强制性的	Qiángzhìxìngde	Mandatory	M
前后比	Qiánhòu bǐ	Front-to-back ratio	
前级放大器	Qiánjí fàngdàqì	Preamplifier	
嵌块分析	Qiànkuài fēnxī	Patch analysis	
前馈	Qiánkuì	Feedforward	

前馈均衡	Qiánkuì jūnhéng	Forward feed equalizing	
钳流	Qiánliú	Clamping	
签名	Qiānmíng	Signature	
签名要素	Qiānmíng yàosù	Signature element	SIG
前趋	Qiánqū	Predecessor	
嵌入标准产品	Qiànrù biāozhǔn chǎnpǐn	Embedded standard products	ESP
嵌入操作通道	Qiànrù cāozuò tōngdào	Embedded operating channel	EOC
嵌入操作通路	Qiànrù cāozuò tōnglù	Embedded operations channel	EOC
嵌入操作信道	Qiànrù cāozuò xìndào	Embedded operations channel	EOC
嵌入测试	Qiànrù cèshì	Embedded testing	
嵌入控制通道	Qiànrù kòngzhì tōngdào	Embedded control channel	ECC
嵌入控制通路	Qiànrù kòngzhì tōnglù	Embedded control channel	ECC
嵌入模块 RAM	Qiànrù mókuài RAM	Embedded block RAM	
嵌入实时目标	Qiànrù shíshí mùbiāo	Embedded real-time target	
嵌入水印	Qiànrù shuǐyìn	Embedded watermark	
嵌入维数	Qiànrù wéishù	Embedding dimension	
嵌入移动数据库	Qiànrù yídòng shùjùkù	Embedded mobile database	EMDB
嵌入式	Qiànrù-shì	Embedded	
嵌入式	Qiànrù-shì	Recessed	
嵌入式处理器	Qiànrù-shì chǔlǐqì	Embedded processor	
嵌入式工控机	Qiànrù-shì gōngkòngjī	Embedded industrial control computer	
嵌入式控制器	Qiànrù-shì kòngzhìqì	Embedded controller	EC
嵌入式零树小波编码方法	Qiànrù-shì líng shù xiǎobō biānmǎ fāngfǎ	Embedded zerotree wavelet coding method	EZW
嵌入式 SQL 语句	Qiànrù-shì SQL yǔjù	Embedded SQL	
嵌入式语音邮件	Qiànrù-shì yǔyīn yóujiàn	Embedded voice mail	
嵌入式自适应差分脉冲编码调制	Qiànrù-shì zìshìyìng chāfēn màichōng biānmǎ tiáozhì	Embedded adaptive differential pulse code modulation	E-ADPCM
签署响应	Qiānshǔ xiǎngyìng	Signed response	SRES
前台程序	Qiántái chéngxù	Foreground program	
嵌套	Qiàntào	Nesting	
嵌套表	Qiàntào biǎo	Nested table (for database)	
嵌套测试	Qiàntào cèshì	Embedded testing	
嵌套查询	Qiàntào cháxún	Nested query (for database)	
嵌套动态容错协议	Qiàntào dòngtài róngcuò xiéyì	Nested dynamic fault-tolerant protocol	
嵌套类	Qiàntào lèi	Nested class	
欠调制	Qiàntiáozhì	Under modulation	
千瓦小时	Qiānwǎ xiǎoshí	Kilowatt hour	KWh
潜望镜天线	Qiánwàngjìng tiānxiàn	Periscope antenna	
钳位	Qiánwèi	Clamping	
钳位器	Qiánwèiqì	Clamp	
前向	Qiánxiàng	Forward	
前向泵浦	Qiánxiàng bèngpǔ	Forward pump (FOC)	
前向波管	Qiánxiàng bō guǎn	Forward wave tube	
前向差错控制	Qiánxiàng chācuò kòngzhì	Forward error control	FEC
前向拆线	Qiánxiàng chāixiàn	Clear forward	CLF
前向拆线信号	Qiánxiàng chāixiàn xìnhào	Clear forward signal	CLF

前向等效类	Qiánxiàng děngxiào lèi	Forward equivalent classification	FEC
前向地址消息	Qiánxiàng dìzhǐ xiāoxi	Forward address message	FAM
前向地址信号	Qiánxiàng dìzhǐ xìnhào	Forward address signal	
前向话音信道	Qiánxiàng huàyīn xìndào	Forward voice channel	FVC
前向呼叫指示	Qiánxiàng hūjiào zhǐshì	Forward call indicator	
前向互通电话事件	Qiánxiàng hùtōng diànhuà shìjiàn	Forward interworking telephone events	FITEs
前向建立	Qiánxiàng jiànlì	Forward set-up	
前向建立消息	Qiánxiàng jiànlì xiāoxi	Forward setup message (TUP)	FSM
前向建立信号	Qiánxiàng jiànlì xìnhào	Forward setup message	FSM
前向兼容性	Qiánxiàng jiānróngxìng	Forward compatibility	
前向接入信道	Qiánxiàng jiērù xìndào	Forward access channel	FACH
前向纠错	Qiánxiàng jiūcuò	Forward error correction	FEC
前向纠错码	Qiánxiàng jiūcuò mǎ	Forward error correction code	FEC
前向控制信道	Qiánxiàng kòngzhì xìndào	Forward control channel	FOCC
前向链	Qiánxiàng liàn	Forward chaining	
前向链路	Qiánxiàng liànlù	Forward link	
前向码分多址信道	Qiánxiàng mǎfēn duōzhǐ xìndào	Forward code division multiple access channel	
前向忙	Qiánxiàng máng	Forward busy	
前向顺序号	Qiánxiàng shùnxù hào	Forward sequence number	FSN
前向显式拥塞通知	Qiánxiàng xiǎnshì yōngsè tōngzhī	Forward explicit congestion notification	FECN
前向信道	Qiánxiàng xìndào	Forward channel	
前向信号	Qiánxiàng xìnhào	Forward signal	
前向业务信道	Qiánxiàng yèwù xìndào	Forward traffic channel	
前向运动矢量	Qiánxiàng yùndòng shǐliàng	Forward motion vector (video term)	
前向占用	Qiánxiàng zhànyòng	Forward seizure	
前向指示比特	Qiánxiàng zhǐshì bǐtè	Forward indicator bit	FIB
前向转移消息	Qiánxiàng zhuǎnyí xiāoxi	Forward transfer message (ISUP)	FOT
前向转移信号	Qiánxiàng zhuǎnyí xìnhào	Forward-transfer signal	FOT
纤芯	Qiànxīn	Fiber core	
纤芯直径	Qiànxīn zhíjìng	Core diameter	
纤芯中心	Qiànxīn zhōngxīn	Core center	
前沿切割	Qiányán qiēgē	Leading edge clipping	
前沿展宽	Qiányán zhǎnkuān	Leading-edge broadening	
前页	Qiányè	Front page	
迁移	Qiānyí	Migration	
迁移条件	Qiānyí tiáojiàn	Transition condition	
牵引	Qiānyǐn	Traction	
牵引出	Qiānyǐn chū	Pull-out	
牵引范围	Qiānyǐn fànwéi	Pull-in range	
牵引入	Qiānyǐn rù	Pull-in	
牵引力	Qiānyǐnlì	Tractive force	
签约违例	Qiānyuē wéilì	Subscription violation	
潜在接收者	Qiánzài jiēshōuzhě	Potential recipient	
潜在浏览器	Qiánzài liúlǎnqì	Potential browser	
潜在事件报告	Qiánzài shìjiàn bàogào	Potential event report	
潜在事务一致性	Qiánzài shìwù yīzhìxìng	Latent transactional consistency (in SQL Server)	

前兆	Qiánzhào	Precursor	
千兆	Qiānzhào	Giga- (prefix meaning 10^9)	G
千兆比特接口转换器	Qiānzhào bǐtè jiēkǒu zhuǎnhuànqì	Gigabit interface converter	GBIC
千兆比特链路模块	Qiānzhào bǐtè liànlù mókuài	Gigabit link module	GLM
千兆比特媒体无关接口	Qiānzhào bǐtè méitǐ wúguān jiēkǒu	Gigabit media-independent interface	GMII
千兆比特以太网	Qiānzhào bǐtè yǐtàiwǎng	Gigabit Ethernet	GE
千兆波特	Qiānzhào bōtè	Gigabaud	GBd
千兆以太网	Qiānzhào yǐtàiwǎng	Gigabit Ethernet	GE
千兆字节	Qiānzhào zìjié	Gigabyte	GB
千兆比以太网	Qiānzhàobì yǐtàiwǎng	Gigabit Ethernet	GbE
千兆比以太网交换机	Qiānzhàobǐ yǐtàiwǎng jiāohuànjī	Gigabit Ethernet switch	
千兆级交换节点	Qiānzhào-jí jiāohuàn jiédiǎn	"Gigapop"	
千兆位交换路油器	Qiānzhàowèi jiāohuàn lùyóuqì	Gigabit switch router	GSR
千兆位以太网	Qiānzhàowèi yǐtàiwǎng	Gigabit Ethernet	GbE
钳制	Qiánzhì	Suppression (e.g. output power suppression)	
牵制	Qiānzhì	Containment	
牵制等级	Qiānzhì děngjí	Containment hierarchy	
前置放大	Qiánzhì fàngdà	Preamplification	
前置放大器	Qiánzhì fàngdàqì	Pre-amplifier	PA
前置分频器	Qiánzhì fēnpínqì	Pre-scalar	
前置缓冲	Qiánzhì huǎnchōng	Front buffer	
前置声明	Qiánzhì shēngmíng	Forward declaration	
牵制树	Qiānzhì shù	Containment tree	
前置中频放大器	Qiánzhì zhōngpín fàngdàqì	Intermediate frequency preamplifier	
前置总线	Qiánzhì zǒngxiàn	Front side bus	FSB
前转号码	Qiánzhuǎn hàomǎ	Forwarded-to number	Ftn
前转检验 SS 指示	Qiánzhuǎn jiǎnyàn SS zhǐshì	Forward check SS indication	
前转接入信令	Qiánzhuǎn jiērù xìnlìng	Forward access signaling	
前转违例	Qiánzhuǎn wéilì	Forwarding violation	
钳装	Qiánzhuāng	Clamp assembly (surface mount technology)	
前缀	Qiánzhuì	Prefix	
前缀长度	Qiánzhuì chángdù	Prefix length	
前缀和算法	Qiánzhuì hé suànfǎ	Prefix sum method	
前缀搜索	Qiánzhuì sōusuǒ	Prefix search	
前缀信息可选项	Qiánzhuì xìnxī kěxuǎnxiàng	Prefix information options	
前缀字符	Qiánzhuì zìfú	Prefix characters	
签字信号	Qiānzì xìnhào	Signature signal	
千字节	Qiānzìjié	Kilobyte (1024 bytes)	KB
桥接	Qiáojiē	Bridge	
桥接抽头	Qiáojiē chōutóu	Bridge tap	
桥接抽头均衡器	Qiáojiē chōutóu jūnhéngqì	Bridged tap equalizer	BTEQ
桥接放大器	Qiáojiē fàngdàqì	Bridge amplifier	BA
桥接控制协议	Qiáojiē kòngzhì xiéyì	Bridging control protocol (in PPP)	BCP
桥接协议数据单元	Qiáojiē xiéyì shùjù dānyuán	Bridge protocol data unit	BPDU
桥接器	Qiáojiēqì	Bridge	
桥式变换器	Qiáo-shì biànhuànqì	Bridge converter	

桥式放大器	Qiáo-shì fàngdàqì	Bridging amplifier	BA
桥式控制协议	Qiáo-shì kòngzhì xiéyì	Bridge control protocol	BCP
桥式整流器	Qiáo-shì zhěngliúqì	Bridge rectifier	
奇宝高科	Qí-bǎo gāokē	Miratech (IT company)	
启闭传输	Qǐbì chuánshū	On-off transmission	
契比雪夫阵	Qì-bǐ-xuě-fū zhèn	Chebyshev array	
汽车导引系统	Qìchē dǎoyǐn xìtǒng	Vehicle navigation system	
汽车点火干扰	Qìchē diǎnhuǒ gānrǎo	Automotive ignition interference	
汽车网络交换中心	Qìchē wǎngluò jiāohuàn zhōngxīn	Automotive network eXchange	ANX
气吹光纤	Qìchuī guāngxiān	Air blown fiber	ABF
期待用户响应	Qīdài yònghù xiǎngyìng	Expected user response	XRES
启动	Qǐdòng	Start	ST
启动保护协议	Qǐdòng bǎohù xiéyì	Release guard (in CORBA)	RG
启动分区	Qǐdòng fēnqū	Boot partition	
启动检出点	Qǐdòng jiǎnchū diǎn	Initial detection point	IDP
启动记录	Qǐdòng jìlù	Boot logging	
启动卷	Qǐdòng juàn	Boot volume	
起动控制	Qǐdòng kòngzhì	Initiation control	
启动目录文件	Qǐdòng mùlù wénjiàn	Boot catalog file	BCF
启动盘	Qǐdòng pán	Boot disk	
启动区	Qǐdòng qū	Boot sector	
启动设备	Qǐdòng shèbèi	Initiator	
启动试呼	Qǐdòng shìhū	Initiate call attempt	ICA
启动文件	Qǐdòng wénjiàn	Boot file	
启动信息协商层	Qǐdòng xìnxī xiéshāng céng	Boot information negotiation layer	BINL
启动映像文件	Qǐdòng yìngxiàng wénjiàn	Boot image file	BIF
启动器	Qǐdòngqì	Starter	ST
切断	Qiēduàn	Disconnect	DISC
切断开关	Qiēduàn kāiguān	Disconnecting switch	DS
切断前向连接	Qiēduàn qiánxiàng liánjiē	Disconnect forward connection	DFC
切断性能	Qiēduàn xìngnéng	Cut-off function	
切分窗口	Qiēfēn chuāngkǒu	Splitter (in software)	
切割抛物面天线	Qiēgē pāowùmiàn tiānxiàn	Cut parabolic antenna	
切换	Qiēhuàn	Handover, handoff	HO
切换参考	Qiēhuàn cānkǎo	Handover reference	
切换故障	Qiēhuàn gùzhàng	Handover failure	
切换候选者响应	Qiēhuàn hòuxuǎnzhě xiǎngyìng	Handover candidate response	
切换候选者讯问	Qiēhuàn hòuxuǎnzhě xùnwèn	Handover candidate inquiry	
切换呼叫到达率	Qiēhuàn hūjiào dàodá lǜ	Handover call arrival rate	
切换检测到	Qiēhuàn jiǎncè dào	Handover detect	
切换接入	Qiēhuàn jiērù	Handover access	
切换控制	Qiēhuàn kòngzhì	Handover control	
切换路径开关	Qiēhuàn lùjìng kāiguān	Handover path switching	HPS
切换命令	Qiēhuàn mìnglìng	Handover command	
切换请求	Qiēhuàn qǐngqiú	Handover request	
切换请求证实	Qiēhuàn qǐngqiú zhèngshí	Handover request acknowledge	

切换完成	Qiēhuàn wánchéng	Handover complete	
切换要求	Qiēhuàn yāoqiú	Handover required	
切换噪声	Qiēhuàn zàoshēng	Switching noise	
切换资源预留	Qiēhuàn zīyuán yùliú	Handover resource reservation	HRR
切开	Qiēkāi	Cleavage (not *that* kind!)	
窃密信道	Qièmì xìndào	Wiretap channel	
切片	Qiēpiàn	Cut sheet	
切片	Qiēpiàn	Slice	
窃取	Qièqǔ	Eavesdropping (IPsec)	
窃听	Qiètīng	Eavesdropping (IPsec) (for RF communications)	
窃听	Qiètīng	Wiretapping (for wired communications), interception	
切削加工设备	Qiēxiāo jiāgōng shèbèi	Cutting machine (semiconductor mfg)	
窃用模式	Qièyòng móshì	Stealth mode	
启发	Qǐfā	Heuristics	
启发式反复的推理	Qǐfā-shì fǎnfùde tuīlǐ	Heuristic repetitive reasoning	
启发式搜索过程	Qǐfā-shì sōusuǒ guòchéng	Heuristic search procedure	
七号共用信道信令系统	Qīhào gòngyòng xìndào xìnlìng xìtǒng	Common channel signaling system no.7	SS7
七号信令系统	Qīhào xìnlìng xìtǒng	Signaling system no.7	SS7
器件带宽	Qìjiàn dàikuān	Bandwidth of a device	
其列克斯-麦斯尼天线	Qí-liè-kè-sī--mài-sī-ní tiānxiàn	Chireix-Mesny antenna	
气流型二氧化碳激光	Qìliú-xíng èryǎnghuàtàn jīguāng	Gas flow CO_2 laser	
起码元	Qǐmǎyuán	Start element	
齐明透镜	Qímíng tòujìng	Aplanatic lens	
气密式	Qìmì-shì	Air-tight	
气密性金属封垫片	Qìmìxìng jīnshǔ fēngdiànpiàn	Metal plate air seal gasket	
气囊式装卸过桥	Qìnángshì zhuāngxiè guòqiáo	Pneumatic loading and unloading foot walk	
请发码信号	Qǐng fāmǎ xìnhào	Send-digits signal	
请发送信号	Qǐng fāsòng xìnhào	Proceed-to-send signal	
清缓存	Qīng huǎncún	Clear cache	
轻铠缆	Qīng kǎi lǎn	Light armored cable	
清零和加	Qīng líng hé jiā	Zero and add	ZA
清零控制字	Qīng líng kòngzhì zì	Clear-to-zero control word	
轻便操作系统界面	Qīngbiàn cāozuò xìtǒng jièmiàn	Portable operating system interface for UNIX	POSIX
轻便文档格式	Qīngbiàn wéndàng géshi	Portable document format	PDF
清除	Qīngchú	Clear (WP command)	
清除	Qīngchú	Cleanup	
清除点	Qīngchú diǎn	Clear point	CLR
清除发送	Qīngchú fāsòng	Clear to send	CTS
请除命令	Qǐngchú mìnglìng	Clear command	
清除命令信道	Qīngchú mìnglìng xìndào	Clear command channel (in FTP)	CCC
清除请求	Qīngchú qǐngqiú	Clear request	
清除请求延迟	Qīngchú qǐngqiú yánchí	Clear request delay	
清除完成	Qīngchú wánchéng	Clear complete	
清除证实延迟	Qīngchú zhèngshí yánchí	Clear confirmation delay	
清除指示延迟	Qīngchú zhǐshì yánchí	Clear indication delay	
清单	Qīngdān	List	

清单	Qīngdān	Manifest	
轻度故障	Qīngdù gùzhàng	Minor fault	
清分	Qīngfēn	Classification	
情感符号	Qínggǎn fúhào	Emoticon	
倾角	Qīngjiǎo	Inclination (of a satellite orbit)	
清理	Qīnglǐ	Cleanup	
轻量目录访问协议	Qīngliàng mùlù fǎngwèn xiéyì	Lightweight directory access protocol	LDAP
轻量级表示协议	Qīngliàngjí biǎoshì xiéyì	Lightweight presentation protocol (IETF usage)	LPP
轻量级目录访问协议	Qīngliàngjí mùlù fǎngwèn xiéyì	Lightweight directory access protocol	LDAP
青鸟短消息平台	Qīngniǎo duǎn xiāoxi píngtái	Jade Bird short Message platform	
请求	Qǐngqiú	Request	REQ, RQ
请求（原语）	Qǐngqiú (yuányǔ)	Request (primitive)	
请求包	Qǐngqiú bāo	Request packet	RP
请求报告 BCSM 事件	Qǐngqiú bàogào BCSM shìjiàn	Request report BCSM event	RRBE
请求拨号连接	Qǐngqiú bōhào liánjiē	Demand-dial connection	
请求拨号路由选择	Qǐngqiú bōhào lùyóu xuǎnzé	Demand-dial routing	
请求参考	Qǐngqiú cānkǎo	Request reference	
请求处理中	Qǐngqiú chǔlǐ zhōng	Request in process	RIP
请求代理	Qǐngqiú dàilǐ	Request agent	RA
请求导通检验信号	Qǐngqiú dǎotōng jiǎnyàn xìnhào	Continuity-check-request signal	CCR
请求订阅	Qǐngqiú dìngyuè	Pull subscription	
请求断开	Qǐngqiú duànkāi	Request disconnect	RD
请求发送	Qǐngqiú fāsòng	Request to send	RTS
请求发送/允许发送协议	Qǐngqiú fāsòng/yǔnxǔ fāsòng xiéyì	Request to send/ clear to send	RTS/CTS
请求分配信号发送与转换子系统	Qǐngqiú fēnpèi xìnhào fāsòng yǔ zhuǎnhuàn zixìtǒng	Demand-assigned signaling and switching unit sub-system	DSSS
请求分配-数字式语音插入	Qǐngqiú fēnpèi—shùzì-shì yǔyīn chārù	Demand assignment-digital speech interpolation	DADSI
请求接入单元	Qǐngqiú jiērù dānyuán	Request acess unit	RAU
请求评论文档	Qǐngqiú pínglùn wéndàng	Request for comment	RFC
请求评议	Qǐngqiú píngyì	Request for comment	RFC
请求 SS	Qǐngqiú SS	Invoke SS	
请求信息字段随机模式	Qǐngqiú xìnxī zìduàn suíjī móshì	Random mode request information field	RA
请求序列编号	Qǐngqiú xùliè biānhào	Request sequence number	
请求帧	Qǐngqiú zhèng	Request frame	REQ
请求中断	Qǐngqiú zhōngduàn	Request interrupt	RQI
请求周期	Qǐngqiú zhōuqī	Request cycle	
轻权目录访问协议	Qīngquán mùlù fǎngwèn xiéyì	Lightweight directory access protocol	LDAP
清晰度	Qīngxīdù	Fidelity (audio)	
清晰度	Qīngxīdù	Resolution, definition (video)	
清晰度	Qīngxīdù	Articulation	
清晰度参考当量	Qīngxīdù cānkǎo dāngliàng	Articulation reference equivalent	
清晰度试验	Qīngxīdù shìyàn	Articulation test	
倾斜轨道	Qīngxié guǐdào	Inclined orbit (of a satellite)	
轻型目录存取协议	Qīngxíng mùlù cúnqǔ xiéyì	Lightweight directory access protocol	LDAP
清音	Qīngyīn	Unvoiced sounds	
亲近性	Qīnjìnxìng	Proximity	

勤务数位	Qínwù shùwèi	Service digit	
勤务通信系统	Qínwù tōngxìn xìtǒng	Service communication system	
勤务信道	Qínwù xìndào	Service channel	
穷举法	Qióngjǔfǎ	Exhaustive means	
琼斯矩阵本征分析	Qióng-sī jǔzhèn běnzhēng fēnxī	Jones matrix eigenanalysis	JME
欺骗	Qīpiàn	Spoofing	
欺骗 IP 包	Qīpiàn IP bāo	Internet protocol packet spoofing (hacker term)	
气球跟踪试验	Qìqiú gēnzōng shìyàn	Balloon tracking test (radar term)	
气溶剂	Qìróngjì	Aerosol (in SMT)	
起始边缘	Qǐshǐ biānyuán	Start edge	
起始传输	Qǐshǐ chuánshū	Start transmission	
起始点	Qǐshǐ diǎn	Origin	
起始定界符	Qǐshǐ dìngjièfú	Start delimiter	SD
起始地址信息	Qǐshǐ dìzhǐ xìnxī	Initial address information	IAI
起始对象	Qǐshǐ duìxiàng	Origin object	
起始对准	Qǐshǐ duìzhǔn	Start-aligned	
起始会话协议	Qǐshǐ huìhuà xiéyì	Session-initiated protocol	SIP
起始节点	Qǐshǐ jiédiǎn	From-node	
起始码元	Qǐshǐ mǎyuán	Start element	
启始设置	Qǐshǐ shèzhì	Default	
起始位	Qǐshǐ wèi	Start bit	
起始信号	Qǐshǐ xìnhào	Start signal	
起始信令点编码	Qǐshǐ xìnlìngdiǎn biānmǎ	Original point code	OPC
起始字段	Qǐshǐ zìduàn	Start field	SF
启始化	Qǐshǐhuà	Initialization	
其它分辨率辐射计	Qítā fēnbiànlǜ fúshèjì	Advanced very high resolution radiometer	AVHRR
其它消息	Qítā xiāoxi	Miscellaneous message	
其他智能用户电报字符总表	Qítā zhìnéng yònghù diànbào zìfú zǒng biǎo	Other teletex character repertoires	
齐套性	Qítàoxìng	Interoperability	
气体激光	Qìtǐ jīguāng	Gas laser	
气体填充设备	Qìtǐ tiánchōng shèbèi	Gas handling equipment	
气体再生设备	Qìtǐ zàishēng shèbèi	Gas recycler	
求比率法	Qiú bǐlǜ fǎ	Ratioing	
球透镜	Qiú tòujìng	Ball lens	
球栅列阵	Qiú zhà lièzhèn	Ball grid array (in SMT)	BGA
球栅阵列	Qiú zhà zhènliè	Ball grid array (electronics mfg)	BGA
求解次序	Qiújiě cìxù	Solve order	
球面凹面镜	Qiúmiàn āomiànjìng	Spherical concave mirror	
球面反射器	Qiúmiàn fǎnshèqì	Spherical reflector	
球面反射器天线	Qiúmiàn fǎnshèqì tiānxiàn	Spherical reflector antenna	
球面凸面镜	Qiúmiàn tūmiànjìng	Spherical convex mirror	
球面坐标核	Qiúmiàn zuòbiāo hé	Sphere coordinate kernel	
球心偏移度	Qiúxīn piānyídù	Spherical center deflection	
球星天线阵	Qiúxīng tiānxiàn zhèn	Spherical array (antenna)	SA
球形阵	Qiúxíng zhèn	Spherical array	
球状矩阵排列	Qiúzhuàng jǔzhèn páiliè	Ball grid array	BGA

球状网格阵列	Qiúzhuàng wǎnggé zhènliè	Ball grid array	BGA
期望接收的接入点标识	Qīwàng jiēshōude jiērù diǎn biāozhì	Access point identifier expected	
期望的测量损耗	Qīwàngde cèliáng sǔnhào	Expected measured loss	EMIL
期望值	Qīwàngzhí	Expectation	
七位字节	Qīwèi zìjié	Septet byte	
气相沉积法	Qìxiàng chénjī fǎ	Vapor deposition (for FOC)	
气象辅助业务	Qìxiàng fǔzhù yèwù	Meteorological aids service	
气象雷达	Qìxiàng léidá	Weather radar	
气象脉冲多普勒雷达	Qìxiàng màichōng duō-pǔ-lè léidá	Meteorological pulse-Doppler radar	
汽相去油器	Qìxiāng qùyóuqì	Vapor degreaser (in SMT)	
气象数据自动采集系统	Qìxiàng shùjù zìdòng cǎijí xìtǒng	Automated meteorological data acquisition system	
汽相外延	Qìxiāng wàiyán	Vapor phase epitaxy	VPE
气象卫星	Qìxiàng wèixīng	Meteorological satellite	
气相轴向沉积法	Qìxiàng zhóuxiàng chénjī fǎ	Vapor axial deposition (for FOC)	VAD
企业对企业	Qǐyè duì qǐyè	Business-to-business	B2B
企业过程模型	Qǐyè guòchéng móxíng	Business process model	
企业过程模型	Qǐyè guòchéng móxíng	Enterprise process model	
企业过程模型系统	Qǐyè guòchéng móxíng xìtǒng	Enterprise process modeling system	EPMS
企业呼叫服务器	Qǐyè hūjiào fúwùqì	Enterprise call server	
企业经营过程重组	Qǐyè jīngyíng guòchéng chóngzǔ	Business process re-engineering	
企业内部网络	Qǐyè nèibù wǎngluò	Enterprise intranet	
企业内容管理	Qǐyè nèiróng guǎnlǐ	Enterprise content management	ECM
企业外部网络	Qǐyè wàibù wǎngluò	Extranet	
企业信息管理	Qǐyè xìnxī guǎnlǐ	Enterprise information management	EIM
企业系统互联	Qǐyè xìtǒng hùlián	Enterprise systems connection	ESCON
企业需求计划	Qǐyè xūqiú jìhuà	Enterprise requirement planning	ERP
企业要害应用	Qǐyè yàohài yìngyòng	Business-critical application	
企业应用程序集成	Qǐyè yìngyòng chéngxù jíchéng	Enterprise application integration	EAI
企业应用集成	Qǐyè yìngyòng jíchéng	Enterprise application integration	EAI
企业战略管理	Qǐyè zhànlüè guǎnlǐ	Strategic enterprise management	SEM
企业资源规划	Qǐyè zīyuán guīhuà	Enterprise resource plan	ERP
企业资源规划	Qǐyè zīyuán guīhuà	Enterprise resources program	ERP
企业资源计划	Qǐyè zīyuán jìhuà	Enterprise resource planning	ERP
企业网	Qǐyèwǎng	Intranet	
企业网系统公司	Qǐyèwǎng xìtǒng gōngsī	Banyan Systems, Inc. (US company)	
启用边缘	Qǐyòng biānyuán	Edge-enabled	
起源服务器	Qǐyuán fúwùqì	Origin server	
起源点编码	Qǐyuándiǎn biānmǎ	Originating point code	OPC
契约式设计	Qìyuē-shì shèjì	Design by contract	
起止传输	Qǐzhǐ chuánshū	Start-stop transmission	
起止畸变度	Qǐzhǐ jībiàndù	Degree of start-stop distortion	
起止设备	Qǐzhǐ shèbèi	Start-stop apparatus	
起止信号	Qǐzhǐ xìnhào	Start-stop signal	
起止系统	Qǐzhǐ xìtǒng	Start-stop system	
起止式传输	Qǐ-zhǐ-shì chuánshū	Start-stop transmission	
起终点调查(测量)	Qǐ-zhōngdiǎn diàochá (cèliáng)	Origin-destination survey	

Q 适配器功能块	Q-shìpèiqì gōngnéng kuài	Q-adapter function block	QAF
取地址操作符	Qǔ dìzhǐ cāozuò fú	Address-of operator	
去反峰电路	Qù fǎnfēng diànlù	Inverse clipper circuit	
去话长途电话中心局	Qù huà chángtú diànhuà zhōngxīnjú	Originating toll center	OTC
区汇流排	Qū huìliú pái	Local bus	
去加重电路	Qù jiāzhòng diànlù	De-emphasis circuit	
去阶梯法	Qù jiētī fǎ	Anti-aliasing	
取数保护	Qǔ shù bǎohù	Fetch protection (IPsec)	
取数据时间	Qǔ shùjù shíjiān	Data acquisition time	
去中继传输系统	Qù zhōngjì chuánshū xìtǒng	Outgoing trunk transmission system	OTTS
取周期	Qǔ zhōuqī	Fetch cycle	
Qualcomm 码激励线性预测编码	Qualcomm mǎjīlì xiànxìng yùcè biānmǎ	Qualcomm code excited linear prediction	QCELP
全"1"	Quán "1"	All ones	
全闭锁入呼叫	Quán bìsuǒ rùhūjiào	Barring of all incoming calls	BI
全玻璃光纤	Quán bōli guāngxiān	All-glass fiber	
全存取通信系统	Quán cúnqǔ tōngxìn xìtǒng	Total access communications system	TACS
全光波长转换器	Quán guāng bōcháng zhuǎnhuànqì	All optical wave converter	AOWC
全光牵引阵列	Quán guāng qiānyǐn zhènliè	All-optical towed array	AOTA
全光通信	Quán guāng tōngxìn	All-optical communication	AOC
全光网络	Quán guāng wǎngluò	All optical network	AON
全光纤型光器件	Quán guāngxiānxíng guāng qìjiàn	All optical fiber and optical components	
全号码呼叫	Quán hàomǎ hūjiào	All number calling	ANC
全呼	Quán hū	General calling	
全呼叫前转业务	Quán hūjiào qiánzhuǎn yèwù	All call forwarding services	CF
全互配光纤（缆）连接器	Quán hùpèi guāngxiān (lǎn) liánjiē qì	Fully intermateable optical fiber (cable) connector	
全加法器	Quán jiāfǎqì	Full adder	FA
全架构成员	Quán jiàgòu chéngyuán	Full fabric citizenship	
全加器	Quán jiāqì	Full adder	FA
全接入通信系统	Quán jiērù tōngxìn xìtǒng	Total access communications system	TACS
全介质捆绑光缆	Quán jièzhì kǔnbǎng guānglǎn	All dielectric lashed cable (FOC)	ADL
全介质自乘式光缆	Quán jièzhì zìchéng-shì guānglǎn	All dielectric self-supporting fiber optic cable	ADSS
全空域录取	Quán kōngyù lùqǔ	All-zone extraction	
全配置	Quán pèizhì	Full allocation	FA
全频段侦察接收机	Quán pínduàn zhēnchá jiēshōujī	All-band intercept receiver	ABIR
全热风回流炉	Quán rèfēng huíliú lú	Reflow convection oven (PCB manufacture)	
全石英光纤	Quán shíyīng guāngxiān	All-silica fiber	
全数子锁相环	Quán shùzi suǒxiàng huán	All digital phase-locked loop	ADPLL
全塑料光纤	Quán sùliào guāngxiān	All-plastic fiber	
全速率	Quán sùlǜ	Full rate	
全速率	Quán sùlǜ	Full rate	FR
全通路广播可视图文	Quán tōnglù guǎngbō kěshì túwén	Full channel broadcast videography	
全网基准钟	Quán wǎng jīzhǔn zhōng	Primary reference clock	PRC
全无源光网络	Quán wúyuán guāng wǎngluò	All passive optical network	APON
全限定域名	Quán xiàndìng yùmíng	Fully qualified domain name	FQDN
全信息网络	Quán xìnxī wǎngluò	Full service network	FSN

全系统管理总线	Quán xìtǒng guǎnlǐ zǒngxiàn	System management bus	SMB
全选	Quán xuǎn	Select all (WP command)	
全选址通信系统	Quán xuǎnzhǐ tōngxìn xìtǒng	Total access communications system	TACS
全业务集	Quán yèwù jí	Full service set	FSS
全业务接入传输	Quán yèwù jiērù chuánshūde	Full-service access transmission	
全业务接入网络	Quán yèwù jiērù wǎngluò	Full service access network	FSAN
全业务台	Quán yèwù tái	Full service set (of equipment)	FSS
全业务网络	Quán yèwù wǎngluò	Full service network	
全载波	Quán zàibō	Full carrier	
全载波单边带发射	Quán zàibō dānbiāndài fāshè	Full carrier single-sideband emission	
全载波发射	Quán zàibō fāshè	Full carrier emission	
权标环	Quánbiāo huán	Token ring	TR
全波光纤	Quánbō guāngxiān	Allwave fiber (Lucent product)	
全波偶极子	Quánbō ǒujízi	Full-wave dipole	
全波天线	Quánbō tiānxiàn	All wave antenna	AWA
全部保存	Quánbù bǎocún	Save all (WP command)	
全部呼叫连接时延	Quánbù hūjiào liánjiē shíyán	Total call connection delay	TCCD
全部路径索引	Quánbù lùjìng suǒyǐn	Complete path index (in XML)	CPI
全部信道传输信令	Quánbù xìndào chuánshū xìnlìng	All channel signaling	ACS
全部中止	Quánbù zhōngzhǐ	All suspend	ASUSP
全程数据探测包	Quánchéng shùjù tàncè bāo	All-routes explorer packet	
全反射导光型	Quánfǎnshè dǎoguāng xíng	Total internal reflection (type of FOC)	TIR
全硅光纤	Quánguī guāngxiān	All-silicon fiber	
全国(移动通信)操作维护中心	Quánguó (yídòng tōngxìn) cāozuò wéihù zhōngxīn	National (Mobile Communications) Network Management Center	NNMC
全国包交换数据传输系统	Quánguó bāo jiāohuàn shùjù chuánshū xìtǒng	National Packet-Switched Data Transmission System	NPSS
全国电视系统委员会制式	Quánguó diànshì xìtǒng wěiyuánhuì zhìshì	National Television Systems Committee (US television broadcast standard)	NTSC
全国地理信息标准化技术委员会	Quánguó dìlǐ xìnxī biāozhǔnhuà jìshù wěiyuánhuì	Nation-wide Technical Standardization Committee of geographic Information	
全国基准时钟	Quánguó jīzhǔn shízhōng	Primary reference clock	PRC
全国网络管理中心	Quánguó wǎngluò guǎnlǐ zhōngxīn	National Network Management Center	NNMC
全国资讯体系	Quánguó zīxùn tǐxì	National Information Infrastructure	NII
全环探测数据分组	Quánhuán tàncè shùjù fēnzǔ	All-rings explorer packet	
全景接收机	Quánjǐng jiēshōujī	Panoramic receiver	
全景抗锯齿失真	Quánjǐng kàng jùchǐ shīzhēn	Full scene anti-aliasing (video term)	FSAA
全局变量	Quánjú biànliàng	Global variable	
全局编录	Quánjú biānlù	Global catalog	
全局布线池	Quánjú bùxiàn chí	Global routing pool	
全局存储器	Quánjú cúnchǔqì	Global memory	
全局调度多路存取	Quánjú diàodù duōlù cúnqǔ	Global scheduling multiple access	GSMA
全局订阅	Quánjú dìngyuè	Global subscriptions	
全局对象	Quánjú duìxiàng	Global object	
全局范围解析操作符	Quánjú fànwéi jiěxī cāozuò fú	Global scope resolution operator	
全局功能	Quánjú gōngnéng	Global function	GF
全局规则	Quánjú guīzé	Global rule	

全局控制	Quánjú kòngzhì	Global control	GC
全局连接 ID	Quánjú liánjiē ID	Global connection ID	GCI
全局路径索引	Quánjú lùjìng suǒyǐn	Global path index (in XML)	GPI
全局码	Quánjú mǎ	Global title	GT
全局码表示语	Quánjú mǎ biǎoshì yǔ	Global title indicator	GTI
全局描述表	Quánjú miáoshù biǎo	Global descriptor table	GDP
全局描述符表	Quánjú miáoshùfú biǎo	Global descriptor table	GDT
全局默认值	Quánjú mòrèn zhí	Global default	
全局配件缓存	Quánjú pèijiàn huǎncún	Global assembly cache	GAC
全局数据表	Quánjú shùjù biǎo	Global data table	GDP
全局属性	Quánjú shǔxìng	Global properties	
全局同步	Quánjú tóngbù	Global synchronization	
全局统一标识	Quánjú tǒngyī biāozhì	Globally uniform identifier	GUID
全局唯一标识符	Quánjú wéiyī biāozhìfú	Globally unique identifier	GUID
全局信息发布	Quánjú xìnxī fābù	Global information distribution	GID
全局信息发布后台程序	Quánjú xìnxī fābù hòutái chéngxù	Global information distribution (GID) daemon	
全局虚拟网业务	Quánjú xūnǐ wǎng yèwù	Global virtual network service	GVNS
全局帐户	Quánjú zhànghù	Global account	
全局装配件缓存	Quánjú zhuāngpèijiàn huǎncún	Global assembly cache	GAC
全局组	Quánjú zǔ	Global group (in multicast)	
全面开发	Quánmiàn kāifā	Overall development	
全面型号认证	Quánmiàn xínghào rènzhèng	Full type approval	FTA
全面硬件导向系统转移	Quánmiàn yìngjiàn dǎoxiàng xìtǒng zhuǎnyí	General hardware oriented system transfer	GHOST
全面质量管理	Quánmiàn zhìliàng guǎnlǐ	Total quality management	TQM
全屏	Quánpíng	Full screen	
全球安全性分析实验室	Quánqiú ānquánxìng fēnxī shíyànshì	Global Security Analysis Lab	GSAL
全球导航卫星系统	Quánqiú dǎoháng wèixīng xìtǒng	Global Navigation Satellite System	GLONASS
全球定轨导航卫星系统	Quánqiú dìngguǐ dǎoháng wèixīng xìtǒng	Global Orbiting Navigation Satellite System	GLONASS
全球定位系统	Quánqiú dìngwèi xìtǒng	Global positioning system	GPS
全球定位 - 惯性导航系统	Quánqiú dìngwèi-guànxìng dǎoháng xìtǒng	GPS-inertial navigation system	
全球覆盖	Quánqiú fùgài	Global area coverage	
全球服务后面板	Quánqiú fúwù hòumian bǎn	Global service back panel	GSBP
全球高容量 IPC 处理器	Quánqiú gāoróngliàng IPC chǔlǐqì	Global high capacity IPC processor	GHIP
全球个人通信系统	Quánqiú gèrén tōngxìn xìtǒng	Global personal communication system	GPCS
全球航空管制系统	Quánqiú hángkōng guǎnzhì xìtǒng	Global aviation traffic manager	GATM
全球接入有限公司	Quánqiú jiērù yǒuxiàn gōngsī	Global Access Ltd.	GAL
全球计算	Quánqiú jìsuàn	Global computing	
全球军事指挥系统控制系统	Quánqiú jūnshì zhǐhuī xìtǒng kòngzhì xìtǒng	Worldwide Military Command and Control System	WWMCCS
全球名称	Quánqiú míngchēng	Global title	GT
全球欧网络	Quánqiú ōu wǎngluò	Global European network	GEN
全球配置模式	Quánqiú pèizhì móshì	Global configuration mode	
全球视像会议网	Quánqiú shìxiàng huìyì wǎng	Worldnet	
全球数据收集 PC 机	Quánqiú shùjù shōují PC-jī	Global data collection PC	GDCP
全球数字单元	Quánqiú shùzì dānyuán	Global digital service unit	GDSU
全球随意拨号	Quánqiú suíyì bōhào	Free world dial-up	FWD

全球题目	Quánqiú tímù	Global title	GT
全球通信半导体公司	Quánqiú tōngxìn bàndǎotǐ gōngsī	Global Communication Semiconductors Inc.	GCS
全球通信卫星系统	Quánqiú tōngxìn wèixīng xìtǒng	Global Communications Satellite System	GCSS
全球网	Quánqiú wǎng	World wide web	www
全球网格论坛	Quánqiú wǎnggé lùntán	Global Grid Forum (formed by IBM, Microsoft, and Sun Microsystems)	
全球网络编地域	Quánqiú wǎngluò biāndìyù	Global network addressing domain	
全球网络编址域	Quánqiú wǎngluò biānzhǐ yù	Global network addressing domain	
全球网络服务	Quánqiú wǎngluò fúwù	Global network service	GNS
全球网络探测器	Quánqiú wǎngluò tàncèqì	Global network locator	GNL
全球网络业务	Quánqiú wǎngluò yèwù	Global network service	GNS
全球网上电子贸易市场	Quánqiú wǎngshàng diànzǐ màoyì shìcháng	Global trading web	GTW
全球卫星导航系统	Quánqiú wèixīng dǎoháng xìtǒng	Global navigation satellite system	GNSS
全球卫星定位系统	Quánqiú wèixīng dìngwèi xìtǒng	Global positioning satellite system	GPSS
全球唯一标识符	Quánqiú wéiyī biāozhì fú	Globally unique identifier	GUID
全球文本电话	Quánqiú wénběn diànhuà	Globe text telephone	GTT
全球无线通信协会	Quánqiú wúxiàn tōngxìn xiéhuì	Universal Wireless Communication Council	UWCC
全球小区识别	Quánqiú xiǎoqū shíbié	Cell global identification	CGI
全球小区识别码	Quánqiú xiǎoqū shíbiémǎ	Global cell identity	GCI
全球星	Quánqiú xīng	Globalstar (satellite system)	
全球信息交换	Quánqiú xìnxī jiāohuàn	Global information exchange	GIE
全球信息基础结构	Quánqiú xìnxī jīchǔ jiégòu	Global information infrastructure	GII
全球信息基础设施	Quánqiú xìnxī jīchǔ shèshī	Global information infrastructure	GII
全球信息网格	Quánqiú xìnxī wǎnggé	Global information grid	GIG
全球寻址码	Quánqiú xúnzhǐ mǎ	Global title	GT
全球演进增强数据速率	Quánqiú yǎnjìn zēngqiáng shùjù sùlǜ	Enhanced data rates for global evalution	EDGE
全球移动个人通信业务	Quánqiú yídòng gèrén tōngxìn yèwù	Global mobile personal communications services	GMPCS
全球移动个人卫星通信	Quánqiú yídòng gèrén wèixīng tōngxìn	Global mobile personal communications by satellite	GMPCS
全球移动通信名称	Quánqiú yídòng tōngxìn míngchēng	Mobile global title	MGT
全球移动通信图标	Quánqiú yídòng tōngxìn túbiāo	Mobile global title	MGT
全球移动通信系统	Quánqiú yídòng tōngxìn xìtǒng	Global System for Mobile Communications	GSM
全球移动通信系统(GSM)演进的增强型数据率	Quánqiú yídòng tōngxìn xìtǒng (GSM) yǎnjìnde zēngqiángxíng shùjùlǜ	Enhanced data rates for GSM evolution	EDGE
全球移动通信系统分机用专用自动小交换机接入	Quánqiú yídòng tōngxìn xìtǒng fēnjī yòng zhuānyòng zìdòng xiǎo jiāohuànjī jiērù	Private automatic branch eXchange access for GSM extension	PAGC
全球意义	Quánqiú yìyì	Global significance	
全球优化	Quánqiú yōuhuà	Global optimization	
全球有效性条件	Quánqiú yǒuxiàoxìng tiáojiàn	Global validity condition (CAD/CAM)	GVC
全球遇险与安全系统	Quánqiú yùxiǎn yǔ ānquán xìtǒng	Global maritime distress and safety system	
全球资源位置符	Quánqiú zīyuán wèizhìfú	Universal resource locator	URL
全球资源信息系统	Quánqiú zīyuán xìnxī xìtǒng	Global resource information system	
全双工	Quánshuānggōng	Full duplex	
全双工传输	Quánshuānggōng chuánshū	Full duplex transmission	
全双工数据流	Quánshuānggōng shùjùliú	Full duplex data flow	FDX
全数子锁相环	Quánshùzǐ suǒxiānghuán	All digital phase-locked loop	ADPLL
全速	Quánsù	Full rate	FR

全塑光纤	Quánsù guāngxiān	All plastic optical fiber	APOF
全速业务信道	Quánsù yèwù xìndào	Full rate traffic channel	TCH/F
全速率话音业务信道	Quánsùlǜ huàyīn yèwù xìndào	Full rate speech traffic channel (TCH)	TCH/FS
全速率数据业务信道	Quánsùlǜ shùjù yèwù xìndào	Full rate data traffic channel (2.4kbs)	TCH/F2.4
全速率业务信道	Quánsùlǜ yèwù xìndào	Full rate traffic channel	TCH/F
全速率业务信道	Quánsùlǜ yèwù xìndào	Full rate traffic channel	Bm
全文查询	Quánwén cháxún	Full-text query	
全文服务	Quánwén fúwù	Full-text service	
全文检索	Quánwén jiǎnsuǒ	Full-text search (in SQL Server)	
全文目录	Quánwén mùlù	Full-text catalog	
全文启用	Quánwén qǐyòng	Full-text enabling	
全文索引	Quánwén suǒyǐn	Full-text index	
全息	Quánxī	Holography	
全息存储	Quánxī cúnchǔ	Holographic storage	
权限关系	Quánxiàn guānxi	Authority relationship	
权限关系集	Quánxiàn guānxi jí	Authority relationship set	
权限域	Quánxiàn yù	Authority domain	
全像底片	Quánxiàng dǐpiàn	Holographic film	
全像方式机械光扫瞄器	Quánxiàng fāngshì jīxiè guāng sǎomiáoqì	Holographic mechanical optical scanner	
全向辐射天线	Quánxiàng fúshè tiānxiàn	Omni-directional antenna (in a given plane)	
全像感光板	Quánxiàng gǎnguāng bǎn	Holographic plate	
全相关	Quánxiāng guān	Full phase correlation	FPC
全像滤光镜	Quánxiàng lǜguāngjìng	Holographic filter	
全向天线	Quánxiàng tiānxiàn	Omni-directional antenna	OA, ODA
全向天线	Quánxiàng tiānxiàn	Omni-directional antenna	
全像显示器	Quánxiàng xiǎnshìqì	Holographic display	
全息图	Quánxītú	Hologram	
权重	Quánzhòng	Weight, weighted	
全自动操作	Quánzìdòng cāozuò	Fully automatic operation	
区别服务	Qūbié fúwù	Differentiated services	Diff-serv
区别业务	Qūbié yèwù	Differentiated services	DiffServ
取代	Qǔdài	Replace	
取代	Qǔdài	Substitution	SUB
取代接收者	Qǔdài jiēshōuzhě	Substitute recipient	
取定	Qǔdìng	Determined (adj), set	
驱动	Qūdòng	Drive	DR
驱动	Qūdòng	Driver (the computer program)	
驱动多接入机会	Qūdòng duō jiērù jīhuì	Opportunity driven multiple access	ODMA
驱动方法	Qūdòng fāngfǎ	Actuation method	
驱动机构	Qūdòng jīgòu	Actuator	
驱动器	Qūdòngqì	Drive, driver	
驱动器号	Qūdòngqì hào	Drive letter	
驱动器名	Qūdòngqì míng	Drive name	
区段	Qūduàn	Sector (of a digital signal)	
区段	Qūduàn	Segment (of a network)	
区段地址	Qūduàn dìzhǐ	Field address (of a computer program)	FA

区段地址	Qūduàn dìzhǐ	Sector address	SA
确保复制区	Quèbǎo fùzhì qū	Assured reproduction area	
确保工作过程	Quèbǎo gōngzuò guòchéng	Assured operations	
确保转发	Quèbǎo zhuǎnfā	Assured forwarding	AF
确定比特率	Quèdìng bǐtè lǜ	Deterministic bit rate	DBR
确定传递方式	Quèdìng chuándì fāngshì	Deterministic transfer mode	
确定方式	Quèdìng fāngshì	Deterministic method	
确定网络用户忙	Quèdìng wǎngluò yònghù máng	Network determited user busy	NDUP
确定与随机 Petri 网	Quèdìng yǔ suíjī Petri wǎng	Deterministic and stochastic Petri net	DSPN
确定的	Quèdìngde	Deterministically	
确定性	Quèdìngxìng	Deterministic	
确定性负载分担	Quèdìngxìng fùzài fēndān	Deterministic load distribution	
确定性故障	Quèdìngxìng gùzhàng	Determinate fault	
确定性流向	Quèdìngxìng liúxiàng	Determinate flow direction	
确认	Quèrèn	Acknowledge	ACK
确认	Quèrèn	Acknowledgement	ACK
确认	Quèrèn	Validation	
确认窗口	Quèrèn chuāngkǒu	Acknowledgement window	
确认投递费	Quèrèn tóudì fèi	Recorded delivery charge	
确认信号单元	Quèrèn xìnhào dānyuán	Acknowledgement signal unit	ASU
确认式信息传送服务	Quèrèn-shì xìnxī chuánsòng fúwù	Acknowledged information transfer service	AITS
缺省	Quēshěng	Default	
缺省共享	Quēshěng gòngxiǎng	Default share	
缺省路由	Quēshěng lùyóu	Default route	
缺省设置	Quēshěng shèzhì	Default setting	
缺省填	Quēshěng tián	Default entry	
缺省约束	Quēshěng yuēshù	Default constraint (in SQL Server)	
缺省值	Quēshěng zhí	Default value	
缺省的检错初始值	Quēshěngde jiǎncuò chūshǐ zhí	Default check initialization	
缺席用户	Quēxí yònghù	Absent subscriber	
缺席用户服务	Quēxí yònghù fúwù	Absent subscriber service	
缺陷	Quēxiàn	Bug	
缺陷	Quēxiàn	Defect	
缺陷	Quēxiàn	Flaw (IPsec)	
缺陷管理信元	Quēxiàn guǎnlǐ xìnyuán	Defect management cell	
缺陷管理信元	Quēxiàn guǎnlǐ xìnyuán	Defect management cell	
缺陷假设法	Quēxiàn jiǎshèfǎ	Flaw hypothesis methodology (IPsec)	
缺陷假设法	Quēxiàn jiǎshèfǎ	Flaw hypothesis methodology	
缺陷秒	Quēxiàn miǎo	Defect second	DS
区分大小写	Qūfēn dàxiǎo xiě	Case-sensitive	
区分服务	Qūfēn fúwù	Differentiated service	
区分服务模型	Qūfēn fúwù móxíng	Differentiated service model (CAD/CAM)	DiffServ
区分服务体系结构	Qūfēn fúwù tǐxì jiégòu	Differentiated service (IETF use)	DiffServ
区分业务	Qūfēn yèwù	Differentiated service	
趋肤深度	Qūfū shēndù	Skin depth	
趋肤效应	Qūfū xiàoyìng	Skin effect	

去话	Qùhuà	Outgoing call	
去活	Qùhuó	Deactivate	
去活跟踪方式	Qùhuó gēnzōng fāngshì	Deactivate trace mode	
区间	Qūjiān	Range	
去加重	Qùjiāzhòng	De-emphasis	
去极化	Qùjíhuà	Depolarization	
去激活	Qùjīhuó	Deactivation	
区块	Qūkuài	Block	
取款通知单	Qǔkuǎn tōngzhīdān	Payment notification	
曲率	Qūlǜ	Curvature; buckling	
去毛刺机	Qùmáocìjī	Deburrer	
群	Qún	Group	
群标识符	Qún biāozhì fú	Group identifier	GI
群段	Qún duàn	Group section	
群交换中心	Qún jiāohuàn zhōngxīn	Group switching center	GSC
群链路	Qún liànlù	Group link	
群路由选择和计价设备	Qún lùyóu xuǎnzé hé jìjià shèbèi	Group routing and charging equipment	GRACE
群识别	Qún shíbié	Group identification	GI
群时延	Qún shíyán	Group delay	
群时延均衡	Qún shíyán jūnhéng	Group delay equalization	
群时延频率失真	Qún shíyán pínlǜ shīzhēn	Group delay/frequency distortion	
群终接点	Qún zhōngjiēdiǎn	Group terminal point	GTP
群集	Qúnjí	Cluster	
群集地址	Qúnjí dìzhǐ	Cluster address	
群集管理器	Qúnjí guǎnlǐqì	Cluster administrator	
群集管理器扩展	Qúnjí guǎnlǐqì kuòzhǎn	Cluster administrator extension	
群集日志	Qúnjí rìzhì	Cluster log	
群集适配器	Qúnjí shìpèiqì	Cluster adapter	
群集协议	Qúnjí xiéyì	Clustering protocol	
群件	Qúnjiàn	Groupware	
群聚	Qúnjù	Herd effect	
群速	Qúnsù	Group velocity	
群速度	Qúnsùdù	Group velocity	
群速度分散	Qúnsùdù fēnsàn	Group velocity dispersion	
群速度色散	Qúnsùdù sèsàn	Group velocity dispersion	GVD
群延平坦度	Qúnyán píngtǎndù	Group delay flatness (ripple)	
去湿	Qùshī	Dewetting (in SMT)	
取水管	Qǔshuǐguǎn	Intake pipe	
去同步器	Qùtóngbùqì	Desynchronizer	
区位码	Qūwèi mǎ	Zone bit code	
曲线	Qūxiàn	Curve	
曲线部分	Qūxiàn bùfen	Curve segment	
曲线产生机	Qūxiàn chǎnshēngjī	Curve generator	
曲线光滑	Qūxiàn guānghuá	Line smoothing (GIS)	
曲线内插	Qūxiàn nèichā	Curve interpolation (GIS)	
曲线拟合	Qūxiàn nǐhé	Curve fitting	

曲线图	Qūxiàntú	Curve diagram	
取样点	Qǔyàng diǎn	Mass point	
取样分辨率	Qǔyàng fēnbiànlǜ	Sampling resolution	
取样继电器	Qǔyàng jìdiànqì	Sample relay	SR
取样数据锁相环	Qǔyàng shùjù suǒxiàng huán	Sampled data phase-locked loop	SDPLL
去映射	Qùyìngshè	Demapping	
区域	Qūyù	Region	
区域边界路由器	Qūyù biānjiè lùyóuqì	Area border router	ABR
区域分析	Qūyù fēnxī	Regional analysis	
区域管理系统	Qūyù guǎnlǐ xìtǒng	Regional management system	RMS
区域规划	Qūyù guīhuà	Regional planning	
区域号码	Qūyù hàomǎ	Band number	
区域交换中心	Qūyù jiāohuàn zhōngxīn	District switching center	DSC
区域精确度	Qūyù jīngquèdù	Zone definition (semiconductor mfg)	
区域基准时钟	Qūyù jīzhǔn shízhōng	Local primary reference	LPR
区域基准钟	Qūyù jīzhǔn zhōng	Local primary reference	LPR
区域路由协议	Qūyù lùyóu xiéyì	Zone routing protocol	ZRP
区域码	Qūyù mǎ	Region code	
区域色码	Qūyù sèmǎ	Area color code	
区域设计	Qūyù shèjì	Designation of specific areas	
区域设置	Qūyù shèzhì	Locale	
区域设置标识符	Qūyù shèzhì biāozhì fú	Locale identifier	LCID
区域使用识别码	Qūyù shǐyòng shíbié mǎ	Regional subscription zone identity	RSZI
区域网络	Qūyù wǎngluò	Local area network	LAN
区域网络系统	Qūyù wǎngluò xìtǒng	Area networking system	ANS
区域信息协议	Qūyù xìnxī xiéyì	Zone information protocol (an Apple protocol)	ZIP
区域系数	Qūyù xìshù	Regional coefficient	
区域杂波开关	Qūyù zábō kāiguān	Area clutter switch	
区域之间小区转移	Qūyù zhījiān xiǎoqū zhuǎnyí	Inter-area cell transfer	
区域化变量	Qūyù-huà biànliàng	Regionalized variable	
区域性	Qūyùxìng	Regionality	
区域性签约区域识别号码	Qūyùxìng qiānyuē qūyù shíbié hàomǎ	Regional subscription zone identity	RSZI
区域性预约区标示	Qūyùxìng yùyuēqū biāoshì	Regional subscription zone identity	RSZI
取值函数	Qǔzhí hánshù	Getter (in software)	
Qwest 企业视像业务	Qwest qǐyè shìxiàng yèwù	Qwest video services for business	QVSB
Q 因数	Q-yīnshù	Quality factor	

R

Rambus 集成电路单元	Rambus jíchéng diànlù dānyuán	Rambus application specific integrated circuit cell	RAC
RAMBUS 内嵌式内存模块	RAMBUS nèiqiàn-shì nèicún mókuài	RAMBUS in-line memory module	RIMM
染料激光	Rǎnliào jīguāng	Dye laser	
扰动法	Rǎodòng fǎ	Perturbation method	
绕杆式天线	Ràogǎnshì tiānxiàn	Turnstile antenna	
绕开	Ràokāi	Steering	
扰乱	Rǎoluàn	Disturbance	
扰码	Rǎomǎ	Scramble, scrambling	

扰码器	Rǎomǎqì	Scrambler	
绕射	Ràoshè	Refraction	
绕射极限透镜	Ràoshè jíxiàn tòujìng	Diffraction-limited lens	
RAS/CAS 发生器	RAS/CAS fāshēngqì	RAS/CAS generator	RCG
热备份	Rè bèifèn	Hot spare	
热备份路由协议	Rè bèifèn lùyóu xiéyì	Hot standby routing protocol	HSRP
热备份路由器协议	Rè bèifèn lùyóuqì xiéyì	Hot standby routing protocol	HSRP
热备用	Rè bèiyòng	Hot standby	
热剥离工具	Rè bōlí gōngjù	Heat stripping tool (FOC)	
热冲击试验	Rè chōngjī shìyàn	Thermal shock test	
热存储交换	Rè cúnchǔ jiāohuàn	Hot swapping	
热副射仪	Rè fùshèyí	Bolometer	
热互连	Rè hùlián	Hot interconnect	
热键	Rè jiàn	Hot key	
热交换	Rè jiāohuàn	Hot-swapping	
热交换器	Rè jiāohuànqì	Heat exchanger	
热镜	Rè jing	Hot mirror	
热老化	Rè lǎohuà	Heat distortion	
热连线	Rè liánxiàn	Hotwired (Web magazine)	
热敏绘图仪	Rè mǐn huìtúyí	Thermal transfer plotter	
热膨胀系数	Rè péngzhàng xìshù	Coefficient of thermal expansion	CTE
热启动	Rè qǐdòng	Warm boot; warm start	
热数据复制	Rè shùjù fùzhì	Hot data replication	
热替换	Rè tìhuan	Hot swappable	
热闻	Rè wén	Hot news	
热温度传感器	Rè wēndù chuángǎnqì	Heat temperature sensor	HTS
热噪声	Rè zàoshēng	Thermal noise, Johnson noise	
热爪哇	Rè Zhǎo-wā	HotJava © (Sun Microsystems)	
热转写传真机	Rè zhuǎnxiě chuánzhēnjī	Thermal transfer fax	
热传导液	Rèchuándǎo yè	Heat transfer fluid (semiconductor mfg)	
热电辐射控测器	Rèdiàn fúshè kòngcèqì	Pyroelectric radiation detector	PRD
热电检测器	Rèdiàn jiǎncèqì	Pyroelectric detector	
热电偶	Rèdiàn'ǒu	Thermocoupler	
热电偶检测器	Rèdiàn'ǒu jiǎncèqì	Thermocouple detector	
热堆检测器	Rèduī jiǎncèqì	Thermopile detector	
热风回流焊机	Rèfēng huíliú hànjī	Reflow oven	
热风整平机	Rèfēng zhěng píng jī	Hot air leveller (PCB manufacturing)	HAL
热感纸传真机	Règǎnzhǐ chuánzhēnjī	Thermal paper facsimile	
热管	Règuǎn	Heat pipe	
热量打印机	Rèliàng dǎyìnjī	Thermal printer	
热量转换试验	Rèliàng zhuǎnhuàn shìyàn	Thermal switch testing (semiconductor mfg)	
热流密码学	Rèliú mìmǎxué	Heat flow cryptography	
热门网站	Rèmén wǎngzhàn	Hotsite	
热敏电阻	Rèmǐn diànzǔ	Thermistor	
热敏电阻式功率计	Rèmǐn diànzǔshì gōnglǜjì	Thermistor power meter	
人机对话	Rén jī duìhuà	Human computer interaction	HCI

人机工程学	Rén jī gōngchéngxué	Ergonomics	
人机接口	Rén jī jiēkǒu	Man-machine interface	MMI
人机接口后面板	Rén jī jiēkǒu hòumian bǎn	Man-machine interface back panel	MMBP
人机接口设备	Rén jī jiēkǒu shèbèi	Human interface device	HID
人机命令	Rén jī mìnglìng	Man-machine command	MMC
人机适配	Rén jī shìpèi	Human-machine adaption	HMA
人机通信	Rén jī tōngxìn	Man-machine communication	
人机语言	Rén jī yǔyán	Man-machine language	MML
韧致辐射	Rèn zhì fúshè	Bremsstrahlung	
人防电话站	Rénfáng diànhuàzhàn	Peoples Air Defense telephone post	PAD
人工长话交换	Réngōng chánghuà jiāohuàn	Manual toll switch	CHR
人工长途局	Réngōng chángtújú	Manual-toll switch office	M-TS
人工传输再选路	Réngōng chuánshū zàixuǎnlù	Manual transmission rerouting	
人工电话	Réngōng diànhuà	Manual telephone	
人工电源网络	Réngōng diànyuán wǎngluò	Artificial mains network	AMN
人工干预	Réngōng gānyù	Manual intervention	
人工交换	Réngōng jiāohuàn	Manual switching	
人工交换台	Réngōng jiāohuàntái	Switchboard	
人工接入多信道无绳电话机	Réngōng jiērù duōxìndào wúshéng diànhuàjī	Manual access multiple channel cordless telephone	
人工接通的呼叫	Réngōng jiētōngde hūjiào	Manually routed call	
人工介质	Réngōng jièzhì	Artificial dielectric	
人工局	Réngōng jú	Manual office	
人工空间电离干扰	Réngōng kōngjiān diànlí gānrǎo	Artificial space ionization jamming	
人工录取	Réngōng lùqǔ	Manual extraction	
人工判读	Réngōng pàndú	Manual interpretation	
人工切换	Réngōng qiēhuàn	Manual switch	MSw
人工生命	Réngōng shēngmìng	Artificial life	AL
人工神经网络	Réngōng shénjīng wǎngluò	Artificial neural network	ANN
人工智能	Réngōng zhìnéng	Artificial intelligence	AI
人工坐席	Réngōng zuòxí	Manual position	
任何人，与在任何时候任何地方的任何人进行的任何形式的通信	Rènhé rén yǔ zài rènhé shíhou rènhé dìfangde rènhé rén jìnxíngde rènhé xíngshìde tōngxìn	Whoever, whenever, wherever, whomever, whatever communication	W5
人际	Rénjì	Interpersonal	IP
人际消息	Rénjì xiāoxi	Interpersonal message	IPM
人际消息传递业务	Rénjì xiāoxi chuándì yèwù	Interpersonal messaging service	IPM
人际消息通信服务	Rénjì xiāoxi tōngxìn fúwù	Interpersonal messaging service	
人际消息通信系统	Rénjì xiāoxi tōngxìn xìtǒng	Interpersonal messaging system	IPMS
认可消息	Rènkě xiāoxi	Acknowledgement message	ACK
认可的专用运行代理	Rènkěde zhuānyòng yùnxíng dàilǐ	Recognised private operating agency	RPOA
人孔	Rénkǒng	Manhole	
人力资源	Rénlì zīyuán	Liveware	
人脸识别	Rénliǎn shíbié	Face recognition	
人名查询	Rénmíng cháxún	Finger (verb)	
人声电话卡	Rénshēng diànhuà kǎ	Voice phone card	
人声识别技术	Rénshēng shíbié jìshù	Speaker recognition	SR

人事安全	Rénshì ānquán	Personnel security	
认识过程	Rènshi guòchéng	Learning process (for reliability)	
人体工学	Réntǐ gōngxué	Ergonomics	
人体总阻抗	Réntǐ zǒngzǔkàng	Total impedance of the human body	
任天堂	Rèn-tiān-táng	Nintendo	
任天堂 64 位游戏机	Rèntiāntáng 64 wèi yóuxìjī	Nintendo 64 (computer game)	N64
人为干扰	Rénwéi gānrǎo	Man-made jamming	
人为干扰	Rénwéi gānrǎo	Man-made interference	
人为因素	Rénwéi yīnsù	Human factors	HF
人为噪声	Rénwéi zàoshēng	Man-made noise	
任务	Rènwu	Task	
任务按钮	Rènwu ànniǔ	Task button	
任务板	Rènwu bǎn	Taskpad (in SQL Server)	
任务调度	Rènwu diàodù	Task scheduling	
任务定义语言	Rènwu dìngyì yǔyán	Task specification language	TSL
任务对象	Rènwu duìxiàng	Task object	
任务管理	Rènwu guǎnlǐ	Task management	
任务号	Rènwu hào	Task number	
任务号码定义块	Rènwu hàomǎ dìngyì kuài	Task number definition block	TNDB
任务空间概念模型	Rènwu kōngjiān gàiniàn móxíng	Conceptual model of the mission space	CMMS
任务控制	Rènwu kòngzhì	Task control	TC
任务控制块	Rènwu kòngzhì kuài	Task control block	TCB
任务栏	Rènwu lán	Taskbar	
任务栏按钮	Rènwu lán ànniǔ	Taskbar button	
任务条	Rènwu tiáo	Taskbar	
韧性	Rènxìng	Ductility	
韧性估计	Rènxìng gūjì	Robust estimation	
人行道	Rénxíngdào	Pedestrian way	
任选参数	Rènxuǎn cānshù	Optional parameter	
任选服务子系统	Rènxuǎn fúwù zixìtǒng	Optional service sub-system	OSS
任选响应轮询(位协议控制)	Rènxuǎn xiǎngyìng lúnxún (wèi xiéyì kòngzhì)	Optional response poll (bit protocol control)	ORP
任选用户设施	Rènxuǎn yònghù shèshī	Optional user facility	OUF
任意访问控制列表	Rènyì fǎngwèn kòngzhì lièbiǎo	Discretionary access control list	DACL
任意广播地址	Rènyì guǎngbō dìzhǐ	Anycast addressing	AA
任意设备处理程序	Rènyì shèbèi chǔlǐ chéngxù	Arbitrary device handler	ADH
任意投影	Rènyì tóuyǐng	Arbitrary projection (GIS)	
任意图素	Rènyì tú sù	Variable picture element	
人员,价格和产品	Rényuán, jiàgé hé chǎnpǐn	People, price and product	P3
人造介质	Rénzào jièzhì	Artificial dielectric	
人造卫星激光测距	Rénzào wèixīng jīguāng cèjù	Satellite laser ranging	
人造卫星直接广播式 PC	Rénzào wèixīng zhíjiē guǎngbō shì PC	Direct broadcast satellite PC	DBS-PC
认证	Rènzhèng	Authentication; certification	
认证标记	Rènzhèng biāojì	Authentication token	AUTN
认证当局	Rènzhèng dāngjú	Certification authority	CA
认证服务器	Rènzhèng fúwùqì	Authentication server	
认证服务器	Rènzhèng fúwùqì	Radius server	RS

认证管理部门	Rènzhèng guǎnlǐ bùmén	Certification authority	CA
认证管理范围	Rènzhèng guǎnlǐ fànwéi	Authentication management field	AMF
认证管理机构	Rènzhèng guǎnlǐ jīgòu	Certificate authority	CA
认证交换机制	Rènzhèng jiāohuàn jīzhì	Authentication exchange mechanism (IPsec)	
认证机构消息	Rènzhèng jīgòu xiāoxi	Certificate configuration message	CCM
认证码	Rènzhèng mǎ	Authentication code	
认证密钥	Rènzhèng mìyào	Authorization key (cipher key)	
认证算法 A3	Rènzhèng suànfǎ A3	Authentication algorithm A3	A3
认证头	Rènzhèng tóu	Authentication header (in IPsec)	AH
认证头	Rènzhèng tóu	Authentication header (in IPSec)	
认证消息码	Rènzhèng xiāoxi mǎ	Message authentication code	MAC
认证协议	Rènzhèng xiéyì	Authentication protocol	
认证信息	Rènzhèng xìnxī	Authentication information (IPsec)	
认证职权	Rènzhèng zhíquán	Certification authority	CA
认证中心	Rènzhèng zhōngxīn	Certification authority	CA
认证、授权、计费	Rènzhèng、shòuquán、jì fèi	Authentication, authorization, accounting	AAA
认证/安全机制	Rènzhèng/ānquán jīzhì	Authentication/security mechanism (in FTP)	AUTH
认证/安全数据	Rènzhèng/ānquán shùjù	Authentication/security data (in FTP)	ADAT
认证式网络文件系统	Rènzhèng-shì wǎngluò wénjiàn xìtǒng	Authenticated network file system	
认知科学	Rènzhī kēxué	Cognitive science	
热色材料	Rèsè cáiliào	Thermochromic material	
热水供应系统	Rèshuǐ gōngyìng xìtǒng	Hot water supply	HWS
热塑性聚酯弹性体	Rèsùxìng jùzhǐ tánxìngtǐ	Thermoplastic polyester elastomer (FOC)	TPE
热线服务	Rèxiàn fúwù	Hot line service	
热线检流计	Rèxiàn jiǎnliújì	Barretter	
RF 保护比	RF bǎohù bǐ	RF protection ratio	
RF 信号干扰比	RF xìnhào gānrǎo bǐ	RF signal-to-interference ratio	
日电	Rì diàn	Nippon Electronics Corporation	NEC
日切时间	Rì qiē shíjiān	Time of switching of date	
日本电报电话	Rìběn Diànbào Diànhuà	Nippon Telegraph & Telephone	NTT
日本电报电话多科莫	Rìběn Diànbào Diànhuà duō-kē-mò	NTT DoCoMo	
日本电气公司先进移动电话系统	Rìběn Diànqì Gōngsī xiānjìn yídòng diànhuà xìtǒng	Nippon Electric Company Advanced Mobile Telephone System	NAMTS
日本地球资源卫星	Rìběn dìqiú zīyuán wèixīng	Japanese earth resources satellite	JERS
日本数字蜂窝系统	Rìběn shùzì fēngwō xìtǒng	Japan digital cellular system	JDC
日本 UNIX 网络	Rìběn UNIX wǎngluò	Japan Unix Network	JUNET
日出日落过渡期	Rìchū rìluò guòdùqī	Sunrise and sunset transition	
日光滤光镜	Rìguāng lǜguāngjìng	Daylight filter	
日立	Rìlì	Hitachi (Japanese company)	
日晒试验	Rìshài shìyàn	Solarizing test	
日志	Rìzhì	Logging	
日志	Rìzhì	Log	
日志文件	Rìzhì wénjiàn	Log file	
日志页	Rìzhì yè	Log page (in Sybase)	
日志阅读代理	Rìzhì yuèdú dàilǐ	Log reader agent (in SQL Server)	
RNS 漂移	RNS piāoyí	Drift RNS [radio network sub-system]	DRNS

冗余 n进制信号	Rǒng yú n-jìnzhì xìnhào	Redundant n-ary signal	
容差分析	Róngchā fēnxī	Fault-tolerant analysis	
容差文件	Róngchā wénjiàn	Tolerance file	
容错	Róngcuò	Error acceptance; error handling	
容错	Róngcuò	Fault tolerance	
容错技术	Róngcuò jìshù	Fault-tolerant technique	
熔断器	Róngduànqì	Fuse	
容积法	Róngjī fǎ	Volume method	
容积率	Róngjī lǜ	Capacity volume ratio	
容积应变仪	Róngjī yìngbiànyí	Volumetric strain-meter	
溶胶-凝胶法	Róngjiāo—níngjiāo fǎ	Sol-gel method (FOC mfg)	SOL-GEL
熔接点	Róngjiē diǎn	Splice point	
熔接配线单元	Róngjiē pèixiàn dānyuán	Splice and distribution unit	
融接箱	Róngjiē xiāng	Closure (FOC)	
熔接机	Róngjiējī	Fusion splicer (FOC)	
容量	Róngliàng	Capacity	
容量比全速率业务信道低的业务信道	Róngliàng bǐ quánsùlǜ yèwù xìndào dīde yèwù xìndào	Traffic channel with capacity lower than a full rate channel	Lm
容量重新分配	Róngliàng chóngxīn fēnpèi	Capacity deallocation	CD
容量重新分配认可	Róngliàng chóngxīn fēnpèi rènkě	Capacity deallocation acknowledgement	CDA
容量配置	Róngliàng pèizhì	Capacity allocation	CA
容量配置认可	Róngliàng pèizhì rènkě	Capacity allocation acknowledgement	CAA
容器	Róngqì	Container (SDH term)	C
熔融沉积法	Róngróng chénjī fǎ	Fused deposition modeling	FDM
熔融拉锥式	Róngróng lāzhuī-shì	Fused biconic taper (FOC)	FBT
冗余存贮器	Rǒngshé cúnzhùqì	Redundancy memory unit	RMU
熔丝集成板	Róngsī jíchéngbǎn	Fuse assembly board	FAB
融通性	Róngtōngxìng	Scalability	
容许标准	Róngxǔ biāozhǔn	Allowable criterion	
容许沉积量	Róngxǔ chénjī liàng	Allowable settlement	
容许应力	Róngxǔ yìnglì	Allowable stress	
容许应力设计法	Róngxǔ yìnglì shèjì fǎ	Allowable stress design method	
容易使用	Róngyì shǐyòng	User-friendly	
冗余	Rǒngyú	Redundancy	
冗余备分	Rǒngyú bèifēn	Redundant backup	
冗余廉价磁盘阵列	Rǒngyú liánjià cípán zhènliè	Redundant arrays of inexpensive disks	RAID
冗余码	Rǒngyú mǎ	Redundant code	
冗余数字信号	Rǒngyú shùzì xìnhào	Redundant digital signal	
冗余线路码	Rǒngyú xiànlù mǎ	Redundant line code	
冗余循环校验	Rǒngyú xúnhuán jiàoyàn	Cyclic redundancy check	
冗余的空间和频率树	Rǒngyúde kōngjiān hé pínlǜ shù	Redundant space and frequency tree	RSFT
柔和反射	Róuhe fǎnshè	Soft reflections (video term)	
柔和阴影	Róuhe yīnyǐng	Soft shadows (video term)	
R-树	R-shù	R-tree	
入标记映射	Rù biāojì yìngshè	Incoming label map	ILM
入呼叫变更	Rù hūjiào biàngēng	Incoming call modification	ICM

入呼叫，出呼叫交换虚电路请求	Rù hūjiào, chū hūjiào jiāohuàn xū diànlù qǐngqiú	Incoming/outgoing switched virtual circuit setup request	
入接口	Rù jiēkǒu	Incoming interface	iif
入帧	Rù zhèng	Incoming frame	ICF
入中继业务类别	Rù zhōngjì yèwù lèibié	Service class of incoming trunk	
软波导	Ruǎn bōdǎo	Flexible waveguide	
软磁盘	Ruǎn cípán	Floppy disk	
软反馈	Ruǎn fǎnkuì	Flexible feedback	
软光缆	Ruǎn guānglǎn	Optical fiber cord	
软行终止符	Ruǎn háng zhōngzhǐ fú	Soft line terminator	
软交换	Ruǎn jiāohuàn	SoftSwitch	
软交换控制设备	Ruǎn jiāohuàn kòngzhì shèbèi	Softswitch control device	SCD
软交换机	Ruǎn jiāohuànjī	Softswitch	
软拷贝	Ruǎn kǎobèi	Softcopy	
软连接查找表	Ruǎn liánjiē cházhǎo biǎo	Soft-wired lookup table	
软判决解码	Ruǎn pànjué jiěmǎ	Soft decision decoding	
软判决译码	Ruǎn pànjué yìmǎ	Soft decision decoding	
软切换	Ruǎn qiēhuàn	Soft handoff	
软设备	Ruǎn shèbèi	Soft device	
软输出维特比算法	Ruǎn shūchū wéi-tè-bǐ suànfǎ	Soft output Viterbi algorithm	SOVA
软输入软输出（算法）	Ruǎn shūrù ruǎn shūchū (suànfǎ)	Soft input soft output (algorithm)	SISO
软同轴线	Ruǎn tóngzhóu xiàn	Flexible coaxial line	
软新闻	Ruǎn xīnwén	Trivial entertainment news	
软永久电路模式	Ruǎn yǒngjiǔ diànlù móshì	Soft permanent circuit mode	SPC
软永久电路模型	Ruǎn yǒngjiǔ diànlù móxíng	Soft permanent circuit model	SPC Model
软永久虚电路	Ruǎn yǒngjiǔ xū diànlù	Soft permanent virtual path	SPVP
软永久虚信道	Ruǎn yǒngjiǔ xū xìndào	Soft permanent virtual channel	SPVC
软圆铜线	Ruǎn yuán tóngxiàn	Soft copper wire	
软质地基	Ruǎn zhìdì jī	Soft ground	
软质量	Ruǎn zhìliàng	Quality of technical service	
软硬盘监控卡	Ruǎn/yìngpán jiānkòng qiǎ	Hard disk – floppy disk controller card	
软件	Ruǎnjiàn	Software	
软件版号	Ruǎnjiàn bǎn hào	Software version number	SVN
软件包	Ruǎnjiàn bāo	Software package	
软件产品库	Ruǎnjiàn chǎnpǐn kù	Software product library	
软件出版商协会	Ruǎnjiàn chūbǎnshāng xiéhuì	Software Publishers Association	SPA
软件盗版	Ruǎnjiàn dàobǎn	Software piracy	
软件电台	Ruǎnjiàn diàntái	Software radio, software station	
软件定义的无线电	Ruǎnjiàn dìngyìde wúxiàndiàn	Software defined radio	SDR
软件工程	Ruǎnjiàn gōngchéng	Software engineering	
软件工程组	Ruǎnjiàn gōngchéng zǔ	Software Engineering Group (CMM)	SWEG
软件狗	Ruǎnjiàn gǒu	Dongle	
软件构架描述语言	Ruǎnjiàn gòujià miáoshù yǔyán	Software architectural description language	SADL
软件环境	Ruǎnjiàn huánjìng	Software environment	
软件兼容性测试	Ruǎnjiàn jiānróngxìng cèshì	Software compatibility test	SCT
软件解码器	Ruǎnjiàn jiěmǎqì	Software decoder	

软件开发包	Ruǎnjiàn kāifā bāo	Software development kit	SDK
软件开发单位	Ruǎnjiàn kāifā dānwèi	Software development organization	
软件开发工具	Ruǎnjiàn kāifā gōngjù	Software development tool	
软件开发工具包	Ruǎnjiàn kāifā gōngjù bāo	Software development kit	SDK
软件开发库	Ruǎnjiàn kāifā kù	Software development library	
软件开发套件	Ruǎnjiàn kāifā tàojiàn	Software development toolkit	SDK
软件配置	Ruǎnjiàn pèizhì	Software configuration	
软件生产语言	Ruǎnjiàn shēngchǎn yǔyán	Software production language	SPL
软件生存周期	Ruǎnjiàn shēngcún zhōuqī	Software life cycle	
软件使用权	Ruǎnjiàn shǐyòngquán	Software license	
软件时钟	Ruǎnjiàn shízhōng	Software timer	
软件受控库	Ruǎnjiàn shòukòng kù	Software controlled library (configuration management)	
软件无线电	Ruǎnjiàn wúxiàndiàn	Software radio	
软件相关组	Ruǎnjiàn xiāngguān zǔ	Software Relational Group (CMM)	SRG
软件项目跟踪和监控	Ruǎnjiàn xiàngmù gēnzōng hé jiānkòng	Software project tracking and oversight (CMM term)	SPTO
软件项目计划	Ruǎnjiàn xiàngmù jìhuà	Software project plan (CMM)	SPP
软件研究所	Ruǎnjiàn yánjiūsuǒ	Institute of Software (under the China Academy of Sciences)	
软件优选段	Ruǎnjiàn yōuxuǎn duàn	Software priority level	
软件运行支口	Ruǎnjiàn yùnxíng zhīkǒu	Software call-up hook (to invoke a sub-routine)	
软件中断请求寄存器	Ruǎnjiàn zhōngduàn qǐngqiú jìcúnqì	Software interrupt request register	SIRR
软件中心	Ruǎnjiàn zhōngxīn	Software center	SC
软件自动化	Ruǎnjiàn zìdònghuà	Software automation (semiconductor mfg)	
软盘驱动器	Ruǎnpán qūdòngqì	Floppy disk driver	FDD
软盘驱动器控制装置	Ruǎnpán qūdòngqì kòngzhì zhuāngzhì	Floppy disk controller	FDC
软盘外套	Ruǎnpán wàitào	Disk jacket, disk sleeve	
入厂校验	Rùchǎng jiàoyàn	Incoming inspection test	
入度	Rùdù	Indegree	
瑞典国立工业和技术发展委员会制订	Ruìdiǎn guólì gōngyè hé jìshù fāzhǎn wěiyuánhuì zhìdìng	National Board for Industrial and Technical Development (Sweden)	NBITD
瑞典空间公司	Ruìdiǎn kōngjiān gōngsī	Swedish Aerospace Corp.	
瑞侃公司	Ruì-kǎn gōngsī	Raychem (US company)	
瑞利波	Ruì-lì bō	Rayleigh wave	
瑞利散射	Ruì-lì sǎnshè	Rayleigh scattering	
瑞利衰减	Ruì-lì shuāijiǎn	Rayleigh fading	
瑞利衰落	Ruì-lì shuāiluò	Rayleigh fading	
瑞士联邦技术研究所	Ruìshì liánbāng jìshù yánjiūsuǒ	Swiss Federal Institute of Technology	
瑞通公司	Ruì-tōng gōngsī	Riverstone Networks Inc. (US company)	
入界包处理	Rùjiè bāo chǔlǐ	Inbound packet processing (IPsec)	
入境控制信道	Rùjìng kòngzhì xìndào	Inbound control channel	ICC
入局	Rùjú	Incoming	
入局呼叫禁止（限于闭合用户群）	Rùjú hūjiào jìnzhǐ (xiànyú bìhé yònghù qún)	Incoming calls barred (within the CUG)	ICB
入局呼叫选项	Rùjú hūjiào xuǎnxiàng	Incoming call option	IOPT
入局记发链路	Rùjú jìfā liànlù	Incoming register link	IRL
入局业务量	Rùjú yèwùliàng	Incoming traffic	

入局中继	Rùjú zhōngjì	Incoming trunk	ICT
入口	Rùkǒu	Portal	
入口	Rùkǒu	Inlet	
入口单元	Rùkǒu dānyuán	Access unit	AU
入口 MSC	Rùkǒu MSC	Gateway mobile switching center (MSC)	GMSA
入口移动交换中心	Rùkǒu yídòng jiāohuàn zhōngxīn	Gateway mobile switch center	GMSC
入口移动无线局	Rùkǒu yídòng wúxiànjú	Gateway mobile switching center	GMSC
弱公平依赖关系	Ruò gōngping yīlài guānxi	Weak fair dependence relation (in Petri nets)	
弱口令	Ruò kǒulìng	Weak password	
弱连通图	Ruò liántōng tú	Weakly connected graph	
弱马尔科夫相似	Ruò mǎ-ěr-kē-fū xiāngsì	Weak Markovian bisimulation	
弱点故障	Ruòdiǎn gùzhàng	Weakness fault	
弱点失效	Ruòdiǎn shīxiào	Weakness failure	
弱电系统	Ruòdiàn xìtǒng	Weak current system	RD
入侵监测	Rùqīn jiāncè	Intrusion detection	
入侵检测工作组	Rùqīn jiǎncè gōngzuòzǔ	Intrusion detection working group	IDWG
入侵检测任务组	Rùqīn jiǎncè rènwuzǔ	Intrusion detection working group	IDWG
入侵监测系统	Rùqīn jiāncè xìtǒng	Intrusion detection system	IDS
入侵检测系统交换格式	Rùqīn jiǎncè xìtǒng jiāohuàn géshi	Intrusion detection system exchange format	IDEF
入侵容忍	Rùqīn róngrěn	Intrusion tolerance	
入侵事件产生器	Rùqīn shìjiàn chǎnshēngqì	Intrusion event generator	
入射波	Rùshè bō	Incident wave	
入射电流	Rùshè diànliú	Incident current	
入射方向	Rùshè fāngxiàng	Direction of arrival	DOA
入射角	Rùshèjiǎo	Angle of arrival	
入射角	Rùshèjiǎo	Angle of incidence	
入网信道	Rùwǎng xìndào	Access channel	

S

S3 多边形转换和光源处理	S3 duōbiānxíng zhuǎnhuàn hé guāngyuán chǔlǐ	S3 transformation and lighting (video term)	S3TL
S3 纹理压缩	S3 wénlǐ yāsuō	S3 texture compression (video term)	S3TC
赛车类游戏	Sàichē lèi yóuxì	Racing game (computer game)	RAC
塞孔	Sāikǒng	Jack	
塞曼效应	Sāi-màn xiàoyìng	Zeeman effect	
塞入比	Sāirù bǐ	Stuffing ratio	
塞入码位	Sāirù mǎ wèi	Stuffing digit	
塞绳	Sāishéng	Cord	
塞绳电路	Sāishéng diànlù	Cord circuit	
萨基姆有限公司	Sà-jī-mǔ yǒuxiàn gōngsī	Sagem Ltd. (French company)	
三防	Sān fáng	Three protects (protect against interference, emissions and static)	
三分贝耦合器	Sān fēnbèi ǒuhéqì	Three decibel coupler	
三化	Sān huà	Three "-izations" (in electronics, 数字化 digitization, 网络化 networked and 知识化 made intelligent)	
三化	Sān huà	Three "-izations" (in telecom, 通用化 or 标准化 standardization, 系列化 serialization and 模块化 modularization)	

三连码	Sān lián mǎ	Triple code [tentative definition]	
三零取代双极性码	Sān líng qǔdài shuāng jíxìng mǎ	Bipolar with three-zero substitution	B3ZS
三重按内容寻址存储器	Sānchóng àn nèiróng xúnzhǐ cúnchǔqì	Ternary content-addressable memory	TCAM
三重数字加密标准	Sānchóng shùzì jiāmì biāozhǔn	Triple data encryption standard	Triple-DES
三次群	Sāncì qún	Digital standard 3 (3rd level digital standard transmission rate = 34Mbps)	DS-3
三次数字复用器	Sāncì shùzì fùyòngqì	Tertiary digital multiplexer	
三次线性 MIP 材质贴图	Sāncì xiànxìng MIP cáizhì tiē tú	Trilinear MIP mapping	TMIPM
三次谐波序列	Sāncì xiébō xùliè	Triplet harmonics	
三次样条插值	Sāncì yàngtiáo chāzhí	Cubic spline interpolation	CSI
散弹噪声	Sàndàn zàoshēng	Shot noise	
散点图	Sàndiǎntú	Scatter graph	
三端稳压器	Sānduān wěnyāqì	Three terminal regulator	
三防	Sānfáng	Three proofings (防潮moisture-proof, 防霉mildew proof, 防烟雾smog-proof)	
三方接续	Sānfāng jiēxù	Three-way connection	
三方通话	Sānfāng tōnghuà	Three-way conversation	
三方通信	Sānfāng tōngxìn	Three party communications	3PTY
三方业务	Sānfāng yèwù	Three party service	3PTY
三级互调	Sānjí hùtiáo	Third order intermodulation	
三级体系	Sānjí tǐxì	Three-tier architecture	
三鉴传感器	Sānjiàn chuángǎnqì	Tri-technology sensor	TTS
散焦	Sànjiāo	Focus-out	
散焦保护电路	Sànjiāo bǎohù diànlù	Defocusing protection circuit	
三角侧面化	Sānjiǎo cèmiànhuà	Trilateration	
三角点	Sānjiǎo diǎn	Triangulation station	
三角矩阵	Sānjiǎo jǔzhèn	Triangular matrix	
三角路由	Sānjiǎo lùyóu	Triangular routing	
三角剖分	Sānjiǎo pōufēn	Triangulation	
三角网格化	Sānjiǎo wǎnggéhuà	Triangulation	
三角噪声	Sānjiǎo zàoshēng	Triangular noise	
三角形槽	Sānjiǎoxíng cáo	V-slot	
三角洲	Sānjiǎozhōu	Delta	
三阶高密度双极性码	Sānjiē gāomìdù shuāng jíxìng mǎ	Third order high density bipolar code	HDB3
三阶互调干扰	Sānjiē hùtiáo gànrǎo	Third order intermodulation interference	
三阶失真	Sānjiē shīzhēn	Third order distortion	
三极管交流开关	Sānjíguǎn jiāoliú kāiguān	Triode AC switch	TRIAC
三军联合战术通信系统	Sānjūn liánhé zhànshù tōngxìn xìtǒng	Tri-service Joint Tactical Communications System	TRI-TAC
三类传真	Sānlèi chuánzhēn	Group 3 facsimile	G3 FAX
散列	Sànliè	Hashing (in cryptography)	
散列表	Sànliè biǎo	Hash table	
散列查找	Sànliè cházhǎo	Hash search	
散列法	Sànliè fǎ	Hashing	
散列函数	Sànliè hánshù	Hash function (cryptography)	
散列连接	Sànliè liánjiē	Hash join (in SQL Server)	
散列算法	Sànliè suànfǎ	Hash algorithm (IPsec)	
三菱	Sān-líng	Mitsubishi (Japanese company)	

三菱重工	Sān-líng zhònggōng	Mitsubishi Heavy Industries (Japan)	MHI
三氯化铝	Sānlǜhuàlǚ	Aluminum trichloride	$AlCl_3$
三氯化硼	Sānlǜhuàpéng	Boron trichloride	BCl_3
三氯化氧磷	Sānlǜhuàyǎnglín	Phosphorous oxychloride	$POCl_3$
三氯氢硅	Sānlǜqīngguī	Silicon hydrochloride (used in FOC manufacture)	$SiHCl_3$
三面角形反射器	Sānmiànjiǎoxíng fǎnshèqì	Trihedral corner reflector	
散热	Sànrè	Heat dissipation	
散热器	Sànrèqì	Heat sink	
散射	Sǎnshè	Diffuse reflection; scattering	
散射参数	Sǎnshè cānshù	Scattering parameter	Sij
散射截面	Sǎnshè jiémiàn	Scattering cross section, scattering area (of an antenna)	
散射剂量	Sǎnshè jìliàng	Dispersion dose	
散射矩阵	Sǎnshè jǔzhèn	Scattering matrix	
散射通信	Sǎnshè tōngxìn	Scatter communication	
三态	Sāntài	Three condition	
三网合一	Sānwǎng héyī	Three-in-one network (see above)	
三网融合 （通信网，计算机网，有线电视网）	Sānwǎng rónghé (tōngxìnwǎng, jìsuànjī wǎng, yǒuxiàn diànshì wǎng)	Three-network convergence (telecommunications networks, computer networks, cable TV networks)	
三维	Sānwéi	Three dimensional	3D
三位差错	Sānwèi chācuò	Triple error	
三维定位音频	Sānwéi dìngwèi yīnpín	Three dimensional (3D) positional audio	3DPA
三维多边形	Sānwéi duōbiānxíng	Volygon (in 3D modelling, a three-dimensional polygon)	
三维基准面	Sānwéi jīzhǔnmiàn	Tridimensional datum	
三维流水线	Sānwéi liúshuǐxiàn	Three-dimensional pipeline	
三维试算表	Sānwéi shìsuànbiǎo	Three-dimensional spreadsheet	
三维实体约束图	Sānwéi shítǐ yuēshù tú	Three-dimensional entity-constraint graph (CAD/CAM)	
三维数据	Sānwéi shùjù	Three-dimensional data	
三维像素	Sānwéi xiàngsù	Voxel (volume element) (in 3D modelling)	
三维振动	Sānwéi zhèndòng	Three-dimensional vibration	
三位字节	Sānwèi zìjié	Triplet byte	
三维子系统	Sānwéi zixìtǒng	Three dimensional sub-system (video)	3DS
三相	Sānxiàng	Three-phase	
三线性过滤	Sānxiànxìng guòlǜ	Trilinear filtering (video term)	
三芯光纤结构	Sānxīn guāngxiān jiégòu	Triple coated fiber structure	TCFS
三星电子株式会社	Sān-xīng diànzǐ zhūshì huìshè	Samsung Electronics Ltd (Korean company)	
伞形反射器天线	Sǎnxíng fǎnshèqì tiānxiàn	Umbrella reflector antenna	
伞形天线	Sǎnxíng tiānxiàn	Umbrella antenna	
三洋	Sān-yáng	Sanyo (Japanese company)	
三元按内容寻址存储器	Sānyuán àn nèiróng xúnzhǐ cúnchǔqì	Ternary content-addressable memory	TCAM
三元内容寻址存储器	Sānyuán nèiróng xúnzhǐ cúnchǔqì	Ternary content-addressable memory	TCAM
三原色	Sānyuánsè	Three primary colors (red, green, blue; refers to system for representing colors on a computer display)	RGB
伞状天线	Sǎnzhuàng tiānxiàn	Umbrella antenna	
扫描	Sǎomiáo	Scan, sweep	
扫描行距	Sǎomiáo hángjù	Scanning pitch	
扫描及信号单元	Sǎomiáo jí xìnhào dānyuán	Scan and signal unit	SSU
扫描接收机	Sǎomiáo jiēshōujī	Panoramic receiver	

扫描密度	Sǎomiáo mìdù	Scanning density	
扫描频率调制	Sǎomiáo pínlǜ tiáozhì	Swept frequency modulation	SFM
扫描驱动器	Sǎomiáo qūdòngqì	Sweep driver	SD
扫描天线	Sǎomiáo tiānxiàn	Scanning antenna	
扫描线	Sǎomiáo xiàn	Scanning line	
扫描线间插	Sǎomiáo xiànjiān chā	Scanline interleave	SLI
扫描转换	Sǎomiáo zhuǎnhuàn	Scan conversion	
扫描器	Sǎomiáoqì	Scanner	SCN
扫描器控制部件	Sǎomiáoqì kòngzhì bùjiàn	Scanner control unit	SCU
扫描仪	Sǎomiáoyí	Scanner	
扫频	Sǎopín	Frequency sweep	
骚扰场强	Sāorǎo chǎngqiáng	Disturbance field strength	
骚扰电流	Sāorǎo diànliú	Disturbance current	
骚扰电压	Sāorǎo diànyā	Disturbance voltage	
骚扰功率	Sāorǎo gōnglǜ	Disturbance power	
骚扰限值	Sāorǎo xiànzhí	Limit of disturbance	
骚扰抑制	Sāorǎo yìzhì	Disturbance suppression	
骚扰源的发射电平	Sāorǎo yuánde fāshè diànpíng	Emission level of a disturbance source	
骚扰源的发射限量	Sāorǎo yuánde fāshè xiànliàng	Emission limit of a disturbance source	
S 波速度	S-bō sùdù	S wave velocity	
SCCP 路由证实测试	SCCP lùyóu zhèngshí cèshì	SCCP routing verification test	SRVT
SCCP 用户适配层	SCCP yònghù shìpèi céng	SCCP user adaptation layer	SUA
SCSI 同业公会	SCSI tóngyè gōnghuì	SCSI Trade Association	STA
SDH 管理网	SDH guǎnlǐ wǎng	SDH management network	SMN
SDH 管理子网	SDH guǎnlǐ ziwǎng	SDH management sub-network	SMS
SDH 交叉连接	SDH jiāochā liánjiē	SDH cross-connection	SDXC
SDH 链路终端板	SDH liànlù zhōngduān bǎn	SDH link termination board	SLK
SDH 设备时钟	SDH shèbèi shízhōng	SDH equipment clock	SEC
SDH 物理接口	SDH wùlǐ jiēkǒu	SDH physical interface	SPI
SDH 映射	SDH yìngshè	SDH mapping	
SDH 上传送 IP	SDH-shàng chuansòng IP	Internet protocol (IP) over synchronous digital hierarchy (SDH)	POS
SDL 开发工具	SDL kāifā gōngjù	SDL development tool	SDT
色阶	Sè jiē	Color gamut	
色心	Sè xīn	Color center	
色吸收滤光镜	Sè xīshōu lǜguāngjìng	Absorption filter (optical)	
色噪声	Sè zàoshēng	Colored noise	
色调	Sèdiào	Hue	
色度	Sèdù	Chrominance	C, CHR
色度格式	Sèdù géshi	Chromination format (video term)	
色度色散	Sèdù sèsàn	Chromatic dispersion	
色码	Sèmǎ	Color code	
色散	Sèsàn	Dispersion	
色散本领	Sèsàn běnlǐng	Dispersion power	
色散补偿单模光纤	Sèsàn bǔcháng dānmó guāngxiān	Dispersion compensation single mode optical fiber	DCSM
色散补偿光纤	Sèsàn bǔcháng guāngxiān	Dispersion compensation fiber	DCF
色散补偿模块	Sèsàn bǔcháng mókuài	Dispersion compensation module	DCM

色散管理光纤	Sèsàn guǎnlǐ guāngxiān	Dispersion managed fiber	DMF
色散滤波器	Sèsàn lǜbōqì	Dispersion filter	
色散漂移光纤	Sèsàn piāoyí guāngxiān	Dispersion-shifted optical fiber	DSF
色散平坦单模光纤	Sèsàn píngtǎn dānmó guāngxiān	Dispersion flattened single mode optical fiber	DFSM
色散平坦光纤	Sèsàn píngtǎn guāngxiān	Dispersion flattened optical fiber	DFF
色散容纳	Sèsàn róngnà	Dispersion accommodation	DA
色散容纳技术	Sèsàn róngnà jìshù	Dispersion accommodation	DA
色散调节	Sèsàn tiáojié	Dispersion accommodation	DA
色散位移单模光纤	Sèsàn wèiyí dānmó guāngxiān	Dispersion-shifted single mode optical fiber	DSSM
色散位移光缆	Sèsàn wèiyí guānglǎn	Dispersion-shifted fiber optic cable	
色散位移光纤	Sèsàn wèiyí guāngxiān	Dispersion-shifted optical fiber	DSF
色散斜率补偿光纤	Sèsàn xiélǜ bǔcháng guāngxiān	Dispersion slope compensating fiber	DSCF
色散系数	Sèsàn xìshù	Chromatic dispersion coefficient (FOC)	
色散系数	Sèsàn xìshù	Dispersion coefficient	
色散移位光纤	Sèsàn yíwèi guāngxiān	Dispersion-shift fiber	DSF
色散支持传输	Sèsàn zhīchí chuánshū	Dispersion supported transmission	DST
色温变换滤光镜	Sèwēn biànhuàn lǜguāngjìng	Color conversion filter	
沙尘试验	Shāchén shìyàn	Sand-and-dust test	
筛选	Shāixuǎn	Screening	
筛选	Shāixuǎn	Filter (for database)	
筛选路由器	Shāixuǎn lùyóuqì	Screening router	
筛选试验	Shāixuǎn shìyàn	Screening test	
筛选张力	Shāixuǎn zhānglì	Screening tensile strength (FOC)	
筛选机	Shāixuǎnjī	Jig	
闪存	Shǎn cún	Flash memory	Flash
闪存技术	Shǎn cún jìshù	Flash technology	
闪变	Shǎnbiàn	Flicker	
闪变觉察门限	Shǎnbiàn juéchá ménxiàn	Threshold of flicker perceptibility	
闪变应激性门限	Shǎnbiàn yìngjīxìng ménxiàn	Threshold of flicker irritability	
闪变计	Shǎnbiànjì	Flickermeter	
扇出	Shànchū	Fan-out	
删除	Shānchú	Delete, erase, cancel	
删除标记	Shānchú biāojì	Deletion flag	
删除查询	Shānchú cháxún	Delete query	
扇出单元	Shànchū dānyuán	Fan-out unit	
删除方格	Shānchú fānggé	Delete cells (WP command)	
删除位置	Shānchú wèizhì	Cancel location	
删除线	Shānchú xiàn	Strikethrough (WP command)	
删除用户数据	Shānchú yònghù shùjù	Delete subscriber data	
删除字符	Shānchú zìfú	Delete character	DEL
闪电电磁脉冲	Shǎndiàn diàncí màichōng	Lightning electromagnetic pulse	LEMP
闪电数据传输总线	Shǎndiàn shùjù chuánshū zǒngxiàn	Lightning data transport	LDT
上变频器	Shàng biànpínqì	Up converter	
上变频器	Shàng biànpínqì	Up-converter	
上电视	Shàng diànshì	Go on TV	GOTV,G.O.T.V.
上阀盖	Shàng fágài	Bonnet	

熵漏	Shāng lòu	Entropy leakage	
商密	Shāng mì	Commercial encryption	
上衔	Shàng xián	Uplink	
上页	Shàng yè	Page up key	
上溢	Shàng yì	Overflow	OVF
上/下复用器	Shàng/xià fùyòngqì	Add/drop multiplexer	ADM
上/下路复用器	Shàng/xià lù fùyòngqì	Add/drop multiplexer	ADM
上/下路光模块	Shàng/xià lù guāng mókuài	Add/drop optical module	ADOM
上班	Shàngbān	Commutation	
上班人	Shàngbān rén	Commuter	
上边带	Shàngbiandài	Upper sideband	USB
上边缘	Shàngbianyuán	Coboundary	
上边缘	Shàngbianyuán	Top edge	
上边缘函数	Shàngbianyuán hánshù	Coboundary function	
上标	Shàngbiāo	Superscript (WP command)	
上部结构	Shàngbù jiégòu	Superstructure	
上传消息	Shàngchuán xiāoxi	Message origination	MO
上次已知的正确配置	Shàngcì yǐzhīde zhèngquè pèizhì	Last known good configuration	
上电修复	Shàngdiàn xiūfù	Power-on restore	
上电自检	Shàngdiàn zì jiǎn	Power-on self test	POST
删格大小	Shāngé dàxiǎo	Cell size	
上海贝尔	Shànghǎi bèi-ěr	Shanghai Bell Corp.	
上海光学精密机械研究所	Shànghǎi guāngxué jīngmìjīxiè yánjiūsuǒ	Shanghai Research Institute of Optics and Fine Mechanics	
上海瑞侃电缆附件有限公司	Shànghǎi ruì-kǎn diànlǎn fùjiàn yǒuxiàn gōngsī	Shanghai Raychem (China subsidiary of Raychem US)	
上级	Shàngjí	Superior	
上机	Shàngjī	Login	
上级类别	Shàngjí lèibié	Superclass	
上拉电阻	Shànglā diànzǔ	Pull-up resistance	
上流标志交换路由器	Shàngliú biāozhì jiāohuàn lùyóuqì	Upstream label switching router	
上路波长转换器	Shànglù bōcháng zhuǎnhuànqì	Optical transponder unit-add	OTU-A
上盘	Shàngpán	Hanging wall	
商品防伪认证解决方案	Shāngpǐn fángwěi rènzhèng jiějué fāng'àn	Merchandise counterfeit authentication solution	MCAS
上升率	Shàngshēng lǜ	Rise rate	
上升气流	Shàngshēng qìliú	Upstream current	
上升时向	Shàngshēng shí xiàng	Rise time	
上升时间	Shàngshēng shíjiān	Rise time (of a pulse)	
上升时间展宽	Shàngshēng shíjiān zhǎnkuān	Rise-time broadening	
上市	Shàngshì	Initial public offering	IPO
上视最大探测距离	Shàngshì zuìdà tàncè jùlí	Maximum uplook detection range (of radar)	
闪光光纤	Shǎnguāng guāngxiān	Scintillation fiber	
闪光光源	Shǎnguāng guāngyuán	Stroboscopic light source	
闪光灯激发染料激光	Shǎnguāngdēng jīfā rǎnliào jīguāng	Flashlamp pumped dye laser	
商务处理流程定义	Shāngwù chùlǐ liúchéng dìngyì	Business process definition	
上下标志	Shàngxià biāozhì	Up-down marker	
上限溢位	Shàngxiàn yìwèi	Overflow	

上下文	Shàngxiàwén	Context	
上行	Shàngxíng	Uplink	
上行波束成形矩阵	Shàngxíng bōshù chéngxíng jǔzhèn	Uplink beam shaping matrix	
上行测量	Shàngxíng cèliáng	Uplink measurement	
上行传输方向	Shàngxíng chuánshū fāngxiàng	Upstream	
上行带宽分配消息	Shàngxíng dàikuān fēnpèi xiāoxi	Uplink bandwidth allocation message	
上行导引时隙	Shàngxíng dǎoyǐn shíxì	Uplink pilot time slot	UpPTS
上行方向	Shàngxíng fāngxiàng	Upstream	
上行共用物理信道	Shàngxíng gòngyòng wùlǐ xìndào	Physical uplink shared channel	PUSCH
上行共用信道	Shàngxíng gòngyòng xìndào	Uplink shared channel	USCH
上行链路	Shàngxíng liànlù	Uplink	UL
上行链路共享物理信道	Shàngxíng liànlù gòngxiǎng wùlǐ xìndào	Physical uplink shared channel	PUSCH
上行链路共享信道	Shàngxíng liànlù gòngxiǎng xìndào	Uplink shared channel	USCH
上行链路快速信令信道	Shàngxíng liànlù kuàisù xìnlìng xìndào	Fast uplink signaling channel	FAUSCH
上行链路状态标记	Shàngxíng liànlù zhuàngtài biāojì	Uplink state flag	USF
上行链路状态标志	Shàngxíng liànlù zhuàngtài biāozhì	Uplink state flag	USF
上行数据信道	Shàngxíng shùjù xìndào	Uplink data channel	
上行同步	Shàngxíng tóngbù	Uplink synchronization	
上行同步传输计划	Shàngxíng tóngbù chuánshū jìhuà	Uplink synchronous transmission scheme	USTS
上行伪随机数据	Shàngxíng wěisuíjī shùjù	Uplink pseudo-random data	UPRD
上行伪随机序列	Shàngxíng wěisuíjī xùliè	Uplink pseudo-random sequence	PRU
上行信道改变请求消息	Shàngxíng xìndào gǎibiàn qǐngqiú xiāoxi	Uplink channel change request message	UCC-REQ
上行信道改变响应消息	Shàngxíng xìndào gǎibiàn xiǎngyìng xiāoxi	Uplink channel change response message	UCC-RSP
上行信道描述符消息	Shàngxíng xìndào miáoshùfú xiāoxi	Uplink channel descriptor message	UCD
上行状态标记	Shàngxíng zhuàngtài biāojì	Uplink state flag	USF
上行状态标志	Shàngxíng zhuàngtài biāozhì	Uplink state flag	USF
商业成品	Shāngyè chéngpǐn	Commercial off-the-shelf products	COTS
商业访问提供者	Shāngyè fǎngwèn tígòngzhě	Commercial access provider	
商业管理	Shāngyè guǎnlǐ	Business management	BM
商业管理层	Shāngyè guǎnlǐ céng	Business management layer	BML
商业软件联盟	Shāngyè ruǎnjiàn liánméng	Business Software Alliance	BSA
商业因特网交换中心	Shāngyè Yīntèwǎng jiāohuàn zhōngxīn	Commercial Internet exchange	CIX
商业因特网交易协会	Shāngyè Yīntèwǎng jiāoyì xiéhuì	Commercial Internet Exchange Association	CIEA
商业智能化	Shāngyè zhìnénghuà	Business intelligence	BI
商业组群	Shāngyè zǔqún	Business group	BG
商业区图	Shāngyèqū tú	Trade-area map	
商用因特网交换中心	Shāngyòng Yīntèwǎng jiāohuàn zhōngxīn	Commercial Internet exchange	CIX
上游故障指示	Shàngyóu gùzhàng zhǐshì	Upstream failure indication	
上游邻站地址	Shàngyóu línzhàn dìzhǐ	Upstream neighbor's address	UNA
上游路由器	Shàngyóu lùyóuqì	Upstream router	Ru
上游失效指示	Shàngyóu shīxiào zhǐshì	Upstream failure indication	UFI
上载	Shàngzài	Upload	
栅极	Shānjí	Grid (as a grating)	G
山农	Shān-nóng	Shannon, Claude	

扇区	Shànqū	Sector (of a hard drive or mobile telephone cell)	
山区	Shānqū	High terrain	HT
扇区共享	Shànqū gòngxiǎng	Sector sharing	
扇区接口处理器	Shànqū jiēkǒu chǔlǐqì	Sector interface processor	SIP
扇区接口卡处理器	Shànqū jiēkǒu kǎ chǔlǐqì	Sector interface card processor	SICP
扇区接口卡集成件	Shànqū jiēkǒu kǎ jíchéng jiàn	Sector interface card assembly	SICA
扇区接口模块	Shànqū jiēkǒu mókuài	Sector interface block	SIB
扇区天线	Shànqū tiānxiàn	Fan antenna	
扇入	Shànrù	Fan-in	
闪烁	Shǎnshuò	Flicker	
闪烁感觉阈值	Shǎnshuò gǎnjué yùzhí	Threshold of flicker perceptibility	
闪烁应激性阈值	Shǎnshuò yìngjīxìng yùzhí	Threshold of flicker irritability	
闪烁噪声	Shǎnshuò zàoshēng	Flicker noise	
闪烁计	Shǎnshuòjì	Flickermeter	
闪速存储器	Shǎnsù cúnchǔqì	Flash memory	
扇尾	Shànwěi	Fantail	
扇形波束天线	Shànxíng bōshù tiānxiàn	Fan-beam antenna	
扇形地	Shànxíng dì	Alluvial fan	
扇形地址类型	Shànxíng dìzhǐ lèixíng	Sector address type	SA
扇形喇叭天线	Shànxíng lǎba tiānxiàn	Sectoral horn antenna	
扇形射束天线	Shànxíng shèshù tiānxiàn	Fan-beam antenna	
扇型小区	Shàn-xíng xiǎoqū	Sectored cell	
烧穿	Shāo chuān	Burn through	
捎带确认	Shāodài quèrèn	Piggybacked acknowledge	
烧结	Shāojié	Sintering (FOC manufacture)	
射极耦合逻辑	Shè jí ǒuhé luóji	Emitter coupled logic	ECL
设备编码容量	Shèbèi biānmǎ róngliàng	Equipment coding capacity	
设备标示寄存器	Shèbèi biāoshì jìcúnqì	Equipment identity register	EIR
设备标识符	Shèbèi biāozhìfú	Equipment identifier	EID
设备不支持	Shèbèi bùzhīchí	Facility not supported	
设备插架	Shèbèi chājià	Device bay	DB
设备等待	Shèbèi děngdài	Device wait	DW
设备电缆	Shèbèi diànlǎn	Equipment cable	
设备额定电压	Shèbèi édìng diànyā	Rated voltage for equipment	
设备访问码	Shèbèi fǎngwèn mǎ	Device access code	DCE
设备服务器	Shèbèi fúwùqì	Device server	
设备光缆	Shèbèi guānglǎn	Equipment optical cable	
设备管理功能	Shèbèi guǎnlǐ gōngnéng	Equipment management function	EMF
设备间	Shèbèi jiān	Equipment room	ER
设备接线阻抗	Shèbèi jiēxiàn zǔkàng	Installation wiring impedance	
设备空间	Shèbèi kōngjiān	Device space	
设备控制	Shèbèi kòngzhì	Device control	DC
设备描述符表	Shèbèi miáoshùfú biǎo	Device descriptor table	DDT
设备能力底线	Shèbèi nénglì dǐxiàn	Baseline implementation capabilities	BIC
设备能力基线	Shèbèi nénglì jīxiàn	Baseline implementation capabilities	BIC
设备启动	Shèbèi qǐdòng	Device start	DST

设备驱动	Shèbèi qūdòng	Device driver	
设备身份寄存器	Shèbèi shēnfen jìcúnqì	Equipment identity register	EIR
设备识别登记器	Shèbèi shíbié dēngjìqì	Equipment identification register	EIR
设备识别寄存器	Shèbèi shíbié jìcúnqì	Equipment identity register	EIR
设备识别中心	Shèbèi shíbié zhōngxīn	Equipment identity center	EIR
设备识别注册处	Shèbèi shíbié zhùcèchù	Equipment identity register	EIR
设备停止	Shèbèi tíngzhǐ	Device stop	DSP
设备无关性位图	Shèbèi wúguānxìng wèi tú	Device-independent bitmap	DIB
设备状态位	Shèbèi zhuàngtài wèi	Device status bit	DSB
设备状态字	Shèbèi zhuàngtài zì	Device status word	DSW
设备最高电压	Shèbèi zuìgāo diànyā	Highest voltage for equipment	
设备阻抗	Shèbèi zǔkàng	Appliance impedance	
设备坐标	Shèbèi zuòbiāo	Device coordinate	
射出成形机	Shèchū chéngxíngjī	Injection molding equipment	
射出角	Shèchū jiǎo	Take-off angle	
射电天文	Shèdiàn tiānwén	Radio astronomy	
射电天文电台	Shèdiàn tiānwén diàntái	Radio astronomy station	
射电天文业务	Shèdiàn tiānwén yèwù	Radio astronomy service	
射电天文学	Shèdiàn tiānwénxué	Radio astronomy	
设定记录	Shèdìng jìlù	Setup record	
设定整表	Shèdìng zhěngbiǎo	Setup entire table	
设计	Shèjì	Design	
设计标准	Shèjì biāozhǔn	Design standard	
设计故障	Shèjì gùzhàng	Design fault	
射击类游戏	Shèjī lèi yóuxì	Shooting game (computer game)	STG
设计模式	Shèjì móshì	Design pattern	
设计评审	Shèjì píngshěn	Design review	
设计失效	Shèjì shīxiào	Design failure	
设计算法	Shèjì suànfǎ	Design algorithm	DA
设计速度	Shèjì sùdù	Designed speed	
设计形式	Shèjì xíngshì	Design formula	
设计再现期间	Shèjì zàixiàn qījiān	Designed return period	
设计阻抗	Shèjì zǔkàng	Design impedance	
设立异步均衡模式	Shèlì yìbù jūnhéng móshì	Set asynchronous balanced mode	SABM
伸臂范围	Shēnbì fànwéi	Arm's reach	
甚低频	Shèndīpín	Very low frequency	VLF
甚低频无线电波传输	Shèndīpín wúxiàndiànbō chuánshū	Very low frequency (VLF) radio wave propagation	
深度暗示	Shēndù ànshì	Depth cueing	
深度缓冲	Shēndù huǎnchōng	Deep buffer (in RAM or ROM)	DB
深度基准	Shēndù jīzhǔn	Sounding datum	
深度空间	Shēndù kōngjiān	Deep space	
深度空间探测器	Shēndù kōngjiān tàncèqì	Deep space probe	
深度曲线	Shēndù qūxiàn	Depth curve	
身份标识	Shēnfen biāozhì	Identification/Identity	ID
身分窃取	Shēnfen qièqǔ	Identity interception	
身份识别码	Shēnfen shíbié mǎ	Personal identification number	PIN

身份验证	Shēnfen yànzhèng	Authentication	
身份验证随机号	Shēnfen yànzhèng suíjī hào	Authentication random number	ARN
身份验证序列号	Shēnfen yànzhèng xùlièhào	Authentication sequence number	ASN
声表面滤波器	Shēng biǎomiàn lǜbōqì	Surface acoustic wave filter	
声表面波	Shēng biǎomiànbō	Surface acoustic wave	SAW
声表面波器件	Shēng biǎomiànbō qìjiàn	Surface acoustic wave (SAW) device	
声反馈	Shēng fǎnkuì	Acoustic feedback	AF
声发射	Shēng fāshè	Acoustic emission	
声换能器	Shēng huànnéngqì	Acoustic transducer	
省监测中心	Shěng jiāncè zhōngxīn	Provincial monitoring center	PMC
声雷达	Shēng léidá	Sound detection and ranging	SODAR
绳路	Shéng lù	Cord circuit	
声耦合器	Shēng ǒuhéqì	Acoustic coupler	AC
声疲劳	Shēng píláo	Acoustic fatigue	
声匹配层	Shēng pǐpèi céng	Acoustic matching layer	
声全息图	Shēng quánxī tú	Acoustic hologram	
声视	Shēng shì	Audio-visual	AV
声释放器	Shēng shìfàngqì	Acoustic releaser	
声吸收系数	Shēng xīshōu xìshù	Acoustical absorption coefficient	AAC
声延迟线	Shēng yánchíxiàn	Acoustical delay line	ADL
省移动通信网网络管理中心	Shěng yídòng tōngxìnwǎng wǎngluò guǎnlǐ zhōngxīn	Provincial (mobile communications net) network management center	PNMC
升余弦	Shēng yúxián	Root raised cosine	
声阻抗	Shēng zǔkàng	Acoustic impedance	
甚高频	Shèngāopín	Very high frequency	VHF
甚高频传播	Shèngāopín chuánbō	Very high frequency (VHF) radio wave propagation	
甚高速数字用户线	Shèngāosù shùzì yònghù xiàn	Very high speed digital subscriber line (downlink 12.9Mb/s to 52.8Mb/s, uplink 1.6Mb/s to 2.3Mb/s)	VDSL
胜宝旺通讯私人有限公司	Shèng-bǎo-wàng tōngxùn sīrén yǒuxiàn gōngsī	Sembawang Telecommunications Pvt.Ltd. (Singapore company)	
声比	Shēngbǐ	Acoustic ratio	
声波	Shēngbō	Sonic wave	
声波幅度测井仪	Shēngbō fúdù cèjǐngyí	Acoustic amplitude logger	
生产后处理	Shēngchǎn hòuchǔlǐ	Post-production processing	
生产阶段	Shēngchǎn jiēduàn	Production phase (of product life cycle)	
生产自动化协议	Shēngchǎn zìdònghuà xiéyì	Manufacturing automation protocol	MAP
声场不均匀度	Shēngchǎng bùjūnyún dù	Sound field non-uniformity	SFN
声场处进器	Shēngchǎng chùjìnqì	Sound field processor	SFP
生产线确认	Shēngchǎnxiàn quèrèn	Line certification	
生成表查询	Shēngchéng biǎo cháxún	Make table query	
生成森林	Shēngchéng sēnlín	Spanning forest	
生成树	Shēngchéng shù	Spanning tree	
生成树算法	Shēngchéng shù suànfǎ	Spanning tree algorithm	STA
生成树协议	Shēngchéng shù xiéyì	Spanning tree protocol (IEEE 802.1D)	STP
生成探测包	Shēngchéng tàncè bāo	Spanning explorer packet	
生存空间	Shēngcún kōngjiān	Scope	
生存空间操作符	Shēngcún kōngjiān cāozuò fú	Scope operator	
生存空间解析操作符	Shēngcún kōngjiān jiěxī cāozuò fú	Scope resolution operator	

生存期	Shēngcún qī	Time to live (SDH term)	TTL
生存时间	Shēngcún shíjiān	Time to live	TTL
生存性	Shēngcún-xìng	Survivability	
声导	Shēngdǎo	Acoustical conduction	
声道分离	Shēngdào fēnlí	Channel separation	CS
声调译码器	Shēngdiào yìmǎqì	Audio tone decoder	ATD
声光	Shēngguāng	Acousto-optical	
声光玻璃	Shēngguāng bōli	Acousto-optic glass	
声光光学晶体	Shēngguāng guāngxué jīngtǐ	Acousto-optic crystal	
声光开关	Shēngguāng kāiguān	Acousto-optic switch	AOS
声光可调滤波器	Shēngguāng kětiáo lǜbōqì	Acoustic-optic tunable filter	AOTF
声光率波器	Shēngguāng lǜbōqì	Acousto-optic filter	AOF
声光偏折器	Shēngguāng piānzhéqì	Acousto-optic deflector	
声光扫描器	Shēngguāng sǎomiáoqì	Acousto-optic scanner	
声光调变器	Shēngguāng tiáobiànqì	Acousto-optic modulator	
声光调制器	Shēngguāng tiáozhìqì	Acousto-optic modulator	AOM
省级管理中心	Shěngjí guǎnlǐ zhōngxīn	Provincial management center	P-PMS
省际汇兑交易	Shěngjì huìduì jiāoyì	Transaction between provinces	
升级向导	Shēngjí xiàngdǎo	Upgrade wizard (in SQL Server)	
升交点	Shēngjiāodiǎn	Ascending node (of a satellite)	
声控	Shēngkòng	Voice control	
声控和遥测系统	Shēngkòng hé yáocè xìtǒng	Acoustical control and telemetry system	ACTS
声控灵敏度	Shēngkòng língmǐndù	Voice control sensitivity	
声码器	Shēngmǎqì	Vocoder	
声明	Shēngmíng	Declaration	
声明	Shēngmíng	Statement	
生命期	Shēngmìng qī	Lifetime	
声明引用完整性	Shēngmíng yǐnyòng wánzhěng xìng	Declarative referential integrity (for database)	DRI
生命周期	Shēngmìng zhōuqī	Lifecycle	
声纳	Shēngnà	Sound navigation and ranging	SONAR
省内异地汇兑交易	Shěngnèi yìdì huìduì jiāoyì	Transaction between cities within a province	
声能	Shēngnéng	Sound energy	SE
声能密度	Shēngnéng mìdù	Sound energy density	SED
声频	Shēngpín	Audio frequency	AF
声频信号	Shēngpín xìnhào	Audio signal	
生物特性认证	Shēngwù tèxìng rènzhèng	Biometric authentication	BA
生物医药网络	Shēngwù yīyào wǎngluò	BioMed net	
声讯	Shēngxùn	Audio signal	
升压电池组	Shēngyā diànchízǔ	Booster battery	
声压级	Shēngyājí	Sound pressure level	SPL
升压器-分布放大器	Shēngyāqì—fēnbù fàngdàqì	Booster-distribution amplifier	BDA
升压式变换器	Shēngyā-shì biànhuànqì	Booster converter	
声音	Shēngyīn	Sonic	
声音广播	Shēngyīn guǎngbō	Sound broadcasting (by radio)	
声音和数据同时传输协议	Shēngyīn hé shùjù tóngshí chuánshū xiéyì	Digital simultaneous voice and data (ITU-T Recommendation H.320)	DSVD
声音检索业务	Shēngyīn jiǎnsuǒ yèwù	Sound retrieval service	

声音图像会议业务	Shēngyīn túxiàng huìyì yèwù	Audiographic conference service	
声音信息检索系统	Shēngyīn xìnxī jiǎnsuǒ xìtǒng	Voice message retrieval system	VMRS
声音信息交换	Shēngyīn xìnxī jiāohuàn	Voice message exchange	VME
声音修复系统	Shēngyīn xiūfù xìtǒng	Sound retrieval system	SRS
声音寻呼	Shēngyīn xúnhū	Tone paging	
剩余差错率	Shèngyú chācuòlǜ	Residual error-rate	
剩余段	Shèngyú duàn	Segments left	SL
剩余可懂度	Shèngyú kědǒngdù	Residual intelligibility	
剩余频偏	Shèngyú pínpiān	Residual frequency deviation	
剩余生存时间为 0	Shèngyú shēngcún shíjiān wéi 0	Zero remaining lifetime	ZRLT
剩余时间标志法	Shèngyú shíjiān biāozhì fǎ	Residual time stamp	RTS
剩余调幅	Shèngyú tiáofú	Residual amplitude modulation	
剩余调频	Shèngyú tiáopín	Residual frequency modulation	
审核	Shěnhé	Auditing	
审核记录	Shěnhé jìlù	Audit logging	
深化/浅化	Shēnhuà/qiǎnhuà	Drill down/drill up	
砷化镓	Shēnhuàjiā	Gallium arsenide	GaAs
砷化镓集成电路	Shēnhuàjiā jíchéng diànlù	Gallium arsenide integrated circuit	
审计跟踪	Shěnjì gēnzōng	Audit trail	
神经网络	Shénjīng wǎngluò	Neural network	
深空	Shēnkōng	Deep space	
深空探测器	Shēnkōng tàncèqì	Deep space probe	
深空通信	Shēnkōng tōngxìn	Deep space communication	
审批	Shěnpī	Accreditation (computer systems)	
申请计费	Shēnqǐng jìfèi	Apply charging	AC
申请计费报告	Shēnqǐng jìfèi bàogào	Apply charging report	ACR
深水散射层	Shēnshuǐ sǎnshè céng	Deep scattering layer	DSL
伸缩天线	Shēnsuō tiānxiàn	Telescopic antenna	
伸缩计	Shēnsuōjì	Extensometer	
身体电容	Shēntǐ diànróng	Body capacitance	
渗透	Shèntòu	Penetration (IPsec)	
渗透测试	Shèntòu cèshì	Penetration testing (IPsec)	
渗透概述	Shèntòu gàishù	Penetration profile (IPsec)	
渗透率	Shèntòu lǜ	Penetration rate	
渗透印迹	Shèntòu yìnjī	Penetration signature (IPsec)	
甚小口径天线地球站	Shènxiǎo kǒujìng tiānxiàn dìqiú zhàn	Very small aperture terminal	VSAT
甚小口径终端	Shènxiǎo kǒujìng zhōngduān	Very small aperture terminal	VSAT
射频	Shèpín	Radio frequency	RF
射频保护比	Shèpín bǎohù bǐ	Radio frequency protection ratio	
射频测试设备	Shèpín cèshì shèbèi	Radio-frequency test equipment	RFTE
射频放大器	Shèpín fàngdàqì	Radio frequency amplifier	
射频辐射	Shèpín fúshè	Radio-frequency radiation	
射频干扰	Shèpín gānrǎo	Radio frequency interference	RFI
射频功率放大器	Shèpín gōnglǜ fàngdàqì	Radio-frequency power amplifier	
射频加热装置	Shèpín jiārè zhuāngzhì	Radio frequency heating apparatus	
射频滤波器	Shèpín lǜbōqì	Radio frequency filter	

射频脉冲频谱	Shèpín màichōng pínpǔ	Radio frequency pulse spectrum	
射频骚扰	Shèpín sāorǎo	Radio-frequency disturbance	
射频天文电台	Shèpín tiānwén diàntái	Radio astronomy station	
射频天文业务	Shèpín tiānwén yèwù	Radio astronomy service	
射频泄漏	Shèpín xièlòu	Radio frequency leakage	
射频信道	Shèpín xìndào	Radio-frequency channel	
射频信号干扰比	Shèpín xìnhào gānrǎo bǐ	Radio-frequency signal-to-interference ratio	
射频源	Shèpín yuán	Radio source	
射频噪声	Shèpín zàoshēng	Radio (frequency) noise	
射频占有带宽	Shèpín zhànyǒu dàikuān	Occupied bandwidth	OBW
射频终端	Shèpín zhōngduān	Radio frequency terminal	RFT
舍弃	Shěqì	Abandon	
舍弃	Shěqì	Purge	
社区	Shèqū	Community	
社区宽带网络	Shèqū kuāndài wǎngluò	Residential broadband network	RBB
社区网关	Shèqū wǎngguān	Residential gateway	RG
设施	Shèshī	Facility	
设施管理	Shèshī guǎnlǐ	Facility management	
设施管理	Shèshī guǎnlǐ	Utility management	
设施制图	Shèshī zhìtú	Utilities mapping	
设施制图系统	Shèshī zhìtú xìtǒng	Facility mapping systems	
射手系统射线路径传输损耗	Shèshǒu xìtǒng shèxiàn lùjìng chuánshū sǔnhào	Ray path transmission loss	
射束波导	Shèshù bōdǎo	Beam waveguide	
射束传输线	Shèshù chuánshūxiàn	Beam transmission line	
射束宽度	Shèshù kuāndù	Beam width	
射束立体角	Shèshù lìtǐjiǎo	Beam solid angle	BSA
射束轴	Shèshù zhóu	Beam axis (of an antenna)	BA
射束准直误差	Shèshù zhǔnzhí wùchā	Beam collimation error	BCE
社团性附加业务	Shètuánxìng fùjiā yèwù	Community of interest supplementary services	
舍位	Shèwèi	Truncation	
摄像管	Shèxiàng guǎn	Camera tube	
摄像机	Shèxiàngjī	Camera	
摄像机镜头	Shèxiàngjī jìngtóu	Camera lens	
摄影测度定标	Shèyǐng cèdù dìngbiāo	Photogrammetric calibration	
摄影测量数字化	Shèyǐng cèliáng shùzìhuà	Photogrammetric digitizing	
摄影测量制图	Shèyǐng cèliáng zhìtú	Photogrammetric mapping	
摄影测量学	Shèyǐng cèliángxué	Photogrammetry	
设置	Shèzhì	Reset	RST
设置初始化模式	Shèzhì chūshǐhuà móshì	Set initialization mode	SIM
设值函数	Shèzhí hánshù	Setter (in software)	
设置时间	Shèzhì shíjiān	Settling time	
设置异步平衡模式	Shèzhì yìbù pínghéng móshì	Set asynchronous balanced mode	SABM
设置正常应答	Shèzhì zhèngcháng yìngdá	Set normal response	SNR
时变量	Shí biànliáng	Time-varying quantity	
史端乔选择器	Shǐ duānqiáo xuǎnzéqì	Strowger selector	
拾放机	Shí fàng jī	Pick and place machine (semiconductor mfg)	

使非规范化	Shǐ fēiguīfànhuà	Denormalize	
是或否测试	Shì huò fǒu cèshì	Yes or no test	
势轮转算法	Shì lúnzhuàn suànfǎ	Potential round robin	PRR
实媒体架构	Shí méitǐ jiàgòu	RealMedia architecture ©	RMA
实系统	Shí xìtǒng	Real system	
实自变量	Shí zìbiànliàng	Actual argument (in FORTRAN)	
实子网	Shí zìwǎng	Real sub-network	
十倍频程	Shíbèi pínchéng	Decade (10 Hertz interval)	
时标	Shíbiāo	Timestamp	TS
时标	Shíbiāo	Time-scale	
时标段	Shíbiāo duàn	Timestamp interval	TI
时标中断请求块	Shíbiāo zhōngduàn qǐngqiú kuài	Timer interrupt request block	TIRB
识别	Shíbié	Identification/identity, recognition	ID
识别码	Shíbié mǎ	Identification code	
识别名	Shíbié míng	Distinguished name	DN
识别请求	Shíbié qǐngqiú	Identity request	
识别时间	Shíbié shíjiān	Recognition time	
识别序列字段	Shíbié xùliè zìduàn	Identification sequence field	ID SEQ
识别器	Shíbiéqì	Identifier	ID
失步系数	Shībù xìshù	Lost synchronization coefficient	
实参	Shícān	Actual parameter	
时槽	Shícáo	Time-slot	
视差	Shìchā	Parallax	
市场规划组	Shìchǎng guīhuà zǔ	Marketing Planning group (GSM MoU)	MP
市场普及率	Shìchǎng pǔjílǜ	Market penetration	PM
时程反应分析法	Shíchéng fǎnyìng fēnxīfǎ	Time history response analysis method	
视窗	Shìchuāng	Window	
视窗菜单	Shìchuāng càidān	Windows menu (WP command)	
视窗脚本程序	Shìchuāng jiǎoběn chéngxù	Windows scripting host	WSH
视窗加速器	Shìchuāng jiāsùqì	Windows accelerator	
视窗驱动程序模块	Shìchuāng qūdòng chéngxù mókuài	Windows driver model	WDM
视窗套接口	Shìchuāng tào jiēkǒu	Windows socket	Winsock
视窗套接	Shìchuāng tàojiē	Windows socket; Winsock	
视窗新技	Shìchuāng xīn jì	Windows NT (operating system)	
视窗硬件工程会议	Shìchuāng yìngjiàn gōngchéng huìyì	Windows hardware Engineering conference	WinHEC
时戳	Shíchuō	Time stamp (IPsec)	
实地调查	Shídì diàochá	Field survey	
实地观测	Shídì guāncè	Field observations	
实地勘查	Shídì kānchá	Field reconnaissance	
视点	Shìdiǎn	Viewpoint	
视点	Shìdiǎn	Vista point	
始点	Shǐdiǎn	Start point	
市电电源	Shìdiàn diànyuán	Mains supply	
始点端口地址	Shǐdiǎn duānkǒu dìzhǐ	Origin port address	OPA
始点码	Shǐdiǎn mǎ	Start code	
始点码	Shǐdiǎn mǎ	Originating point code	OPC

湿度试验	Shīdù shìyàn	Humidty test	
实端系统	Shíduān xìtǒng	Real end system	
始发 CAMEL 签约信息	Shǐfā CAMEL qiānyuē xìnxī	Originating camel subscription information	O-CSI
始发基本呼叫状态模型	Shǐfā jīběn hūjiào zhuàngtài móxíng	Originating basic call state model	O-BCSM
始发用户	Shǐfā yònghù	Originating subscriber	OS
始发 / 终接 CAMEL 用户签约信息	Shǐfā/zhōngjiē CAMEL yònghù qiānyuē xìnxī	Origination/termination-CAMEL subscription information	O/T-CSI
示范工程	Shìfàn gōngchéng	Model project	
释放	Shìfàng	Release	REL
释放保护信号	Shìfàng bǎohù xìnhào	Release-guard signal	
释放查询	Shìfàng cháxún	Release query	QoR
拾放工作站	Shífàng gōngzuòzhàn	Pick and place workstation (semiconductor mfg)	
释放呼叫	Shìfàng hūjiào	Release call	RC
释放监护	Shìfàng jiānhù	Release guard	
释放监护信号	Shìfàng jiānhù xìnhào	Release guard signal	RLG
释放连接	Shìfàng liánjiē	Connection released (in SS7)	RLSD
释放请求	Shìfàng qǐngqiú	Release request (SS7, SCCP message)	RELRE
释放确认	Shìfàng quèrèn	Release acknowledged (SCCP message)	RELAK
释放确认	Shìfàng quèrèn	Release confirm (SS7)	
释放时间	Shìfàng shíjiān	Release time	
释放完成	Shìfàng wánchéng	Release complete (ISUP message)	RLC
释放完成消息	Shìfàng wánchéng xiāoxi	Release complete message (ISUP)	RLC
释放消息	Shìfàng xiāoxi	Release message (ISUP)	REL(ISUP)
释放指示	Shìfàng zhǐshì	Release indication (SS7)	
始发者	Shǐfāzhě	Originator	
始发者/接收者	Shǐfāzhě/jiēshōuzhě	Originator/recipient	O/R
时分	Shífēn	Time division	
时分电路交换	Shífēn diànlù jiāohuàn	Time division circuit switching	TDCS
时分多路复用	Shífēn duōlù fùyòng	Time division multiplex	TDM
时分多路复用器	Shífēn duōlù fùyòngqì	Time division multiplexer	TDM
时分多路脉冲调幅	Shífēn duōlù màichōng tiáofú	Time division multiplexed-pulse amplitude modulation	TDM-PAM
时分多路脉码调制	Shífēn duōlù màimǎ tiáozhì	Time division multiplexed-pulse code modulation	TDM-PCM
时分多址	Shífēn duōzhǐ	Time division multiple access	TDMA
时分多址访问	Shífēn duōzhǐ fǎngwèn	Time division multiple access	TDMA
时分多址接入	Shífēn duōzhǐ jiērù	Time division multiple access	TDMA
时分复用	Shífēn fùyòng	Time division multiplex	TDM
时分复用变址多路存取	Shífēn fùyòng biànzhǐ duōlù cúnqǔ	Time division multiplexed-variable destination multiple access	TDM-VDMA
时分复用传输	Shífēn fùyòng chuánshū	Time division multiplex transmission	
时分复用信道	Shífēn fùyòng xìndào	Time division multiplexed channel	TDMC
时分复用系统	Shífēn fùyòng xìtǒng	Time division multiplexing system	TDMS
时分话音插空	Shífēn huàyīn chākōng	Time assigned speech interpolation	TAST
时分交换	Shífēn jiāohuàn	Time division switching	
时分交换后面板	Shífēn jiāohuàn hòumian bǎn	Time switch back panel	TSBP
时分交换结构	Shífēn jiāohuàn jiégòu	Time division switching	TDS
时分交换控制和维护	Shífēn jiāohuàn kòngzhì hé wéihù	Time switch control and maintenance	TSCM
时分控制	Shífēn kòngzhì	Time-divided control	

时分码分多址接入	Shífèn mǎfēn duōzhǐ jiērù	Time division – code division multiple access	TD-CDMA
时分时隙交换器	Shífèn shíxì jiāohuànqì	Time division-time slot interchanger	TDTSI
时分双工	Shífèn shuānggōng	Time division duplex	TDD
时分数据链	Shífèn shùjù liàn	Time division data link	TDDL
时分数字网络	Shífèn shùzì wǎngluò	Time division digital network	TDDN
时分调制	Shífèn tiáozhì	Time division modulation	TDM
时分同步码分多址	Shífèn tóngbù mafēn duōzhǐ	Time division synchronous code division multiple access	TD-SCDMA
时分信道	Shífèn xindào	Time-division channel	
时分-码分多址	Shífèn-mǎfēn duōzhǐ	Time division-code division multiple access	TD-CDMA
施工监测	Shīgōng jiāncè	Observation during and after construction	
事故	Shìgù	Accident	
事故标识符	Shìgù biāozhìfú	Accident identifier	
事故电流	Shìgù diànliú	Fault current	
事故日期	Shìgù rìqī	Accident date	
适合性检验	Shìhéxìng jiǎnyàn	Conformance testing	
适合性检验报告	Shìhéxìng jiǎnyàn bàogào	Conformance test report	
适合性评价过程	Shìhéxìng píngjià guòchéng	Conformance assessment process	
适合性品质水平	Shìhéxìng pǐnzhì shuǐpíng	Conformance quality level	
适合性的条款	Shìhéxìngde tiáokuǎn	Conformance clause	
事后检查	Shìhòu jiǎnchá	Inspecting afterwards	
试呼	Shìhū	Call attempt (by a user)	
试呼上界	Shìhū shàngjiè	Upper call attempt threshold	
试呼下界	Shìhū xiàjiè	Lower call attempt threshold	
市话	Shìhuà	Urban call	
市话电缆	Shìhuà diànlǎn	Local cable	
市话电缆线路	Shìhuà diànlǎn xiànlù	City telephone cable lines	SXD
市话端局	Shìhuà duān jú	End office	EO
市话光缆线路	Shìhuà guānglǎn xiànlù	City telephone optical cable lines	SXG
市话/中继混合交换局	Shìhuà/zhōngjì hùnhé jiāohuànjú	Combined local/transit exchange	
视话机	Shìhuàjī	Videophone	
时基	Shíjī	Time base	
实际变元	Shíjì biànyuán	Actual argument (in FORTRAN)	
实际传送速率	Shíjì chuánsòng sùlǜ	Actual transfer rate	
实际接收者	Shíjì jiēshōuzhě	Actual recipient	
实际晶体	Shíjì jīngtǐ	Actual crystal	
时基计数器	Shíjī jìshùqì	Timebase counters	
实际时钟差异	Shíjì shízhōng chāyì	Real-time difference	RTD
实际占用时间	Shíjì zhànyòng shíjiān	Actual work time	AWT
世嘉	Shì-jiā	Sega (Japanese company)	
世嘉土星 32 位游戏机	Shì-jiā tǔxīng 32- wèi yóuxìjī	Sega Saturn (computer game)	
事件	Shìjiàn	Event	
事件报告	Shìjiàn bàogào	Event report	
事件报告管理功能	Shìjiàn bàogào guǎnlǐ gōngnéng	Event report management function	
时间编差	Shíjiān biānchà	Time deviation	TDEV
时间变量电平	Shíjiān biànliàng diànpíng	Level of a time variable	
时间参考波束成型	Shíjiān cānkǎo bōshù chéngxíng	Time reference beamforming	TRB

时间参照系	Shíjiān cānzhàoxì	Temporal reference system	
事件处理	Shìjiàn chǔlǐ	Incident handling	
事件处理器	Shìjiàn chǔlǐqì	Event handler	
时间戳	Shíjiān chuō	Time stamp	
时间等级	Shíjiān děngjí	Timing stratum	
时间电路	Shíjiān diànlù	Timing circuit	TIM
时间方差	Shíjiān fāngchà	Timing deviation	TDEV
时间范围	Shíjiān fànwéi	Temporal extent	
事件发生器	Shìjiàn fāshēngqì	Event generator	
时间分辨力	Shíjiān fēnbiàn lì	Temporal resolution	
时间分割数据传输器	Shíjiān fēngē shùjù chuánshūqì	Time-division data link	TDDL
时间分集	Shíjiān fēnjí	Time diversity	
时间分配数字插入	Shíjiān fēnpèi shùzì chārù	Time assignment digit	
时间分片	Shíjiān fēnpiàn	Time slicing	
事件分析器	Shìjiàn fēnxīqì	Event analyzer	
时间服务器	Shíjiān fúwùqì	Time server	
时间复杂度	Shíjiān fùzádù	Time complexity	
事件广播	Shìjiàn guǎngbō	Event dissemination	
事件黑心发鉴别器	Shìjiàn hēixīnfā jiànbiéqì	Event forwarding discriminator	EFD
事件检测点 - 请求	Shìjiàn jiǎncè diǎn-qǐngqiú	Event detection point-request	EDP-R
事件检测点 - 通知	Shìjiàn jiǎncè diǎn-tōngzhī	Event detection point-notification	EDP-N
事件检出点	Shìjiàn jiǎnchū diǎn	Event detection point	EDP
事件检出点-通知	Shìjiàn jiǎnchū diǎn - tōngzhī	Event detection point-notification	EDP-N
事件检出点-请求	Shìjiàn jiǎnchū diǎn -qǐngqiú	Event detection point-request	EDP-R
时间间隔	Shíjiān jiàngé	Time interval	
时间间隔误差	Shíjiān jiàngé wùchā	Time interval error	TIE
时间监视	Shíjiān jiānshì	Time supervision	
时间加速系数	Shíjiān jiāsù xìshù	Time acceleration factor	
时间畸变	Shíjiān jībiàn	Time distortion	
时间进程代数	Shíjiān jìnchéng dàishù	Timed process algebra	
时间基准	Shíjiān jīzhǔn	Primary reference source (timing)	PRS
时间决定星座	Shíjiān juéding xīngzuò	Time dependent constellation	TDC
事件控制块	Shìjiàn kòngzhì kuài	Event control block	ECB
事件控制字组	Shìjiàn kòngzhì zìzǔ	Event control block	ECB
时间离散信号	Shíjiān lísàn xìnhào	Discretely timed signal	
时间轮循方式	Shíjiān lúnxún fāngshì	Round robin method	
时间片	Shíjiān piàn	Time slice	
时间片分配电路	Shíjiān piàn fēnpèi diànlù	Time slot assignment circuit	TSAC
时间偏差	Shíjiān piānchā	Time deviation, timing deviation	TDEV
时间频率编码多路存取	Shíjiān pínlǜ biānmǎ duōlù cúnqǔ	Time-frequency coded multiple access	TFCMA
时间频率跳变	Shíjiān pínlǜ tiàobiàn	Time-frequency hopping	TFH
事件前向判别	Shìjiàn qiánxiàng pànbié	Event forwarding discrimination	EFD
时间切换发送分集	Shíjiān qiēhuàn fāsòng fēnjí	Time switched transmission diversity	TSTD
事件驱动的	Shìjiàn qūdòngde	Event driven	
事件时间	Shìjiàn shíjiān	Event time	
时间失真	Shíjiān shīzhēn	Time distortion	

事件数据库	Shìjiàn shùjùkù	Event database	
时间数量级分解	Shíjiān shùliàngjí fēnjiě	Time scale decomposition	TSD
时间特征操作	Shíjiān tèzhēng cāozuò	Temporal feature operation	
时间特征关系	Shíjiān tèzhēng guānxi	Temporal feature relationship	
时间特征属性	Shíjiān tèzhēng shǔxìng	Temporal feature attribute	
时间提前	Shíjiān tíqián	Timing advance	TA
时间提前量	Shíjiān tíqiánliàng	Timing advance	TA
时间通知	Shíjiān tōngzhī	Time notify	Tnotify
时间透明	Shíjiān tòumíng	Time transparency	
时间维度	Shíjiān wéidù	Time dimension	
时间微分相移键控	Shíjiān wēifēn xiàngyí jiànkòng	Time differential phase-shift keying	TDPSK
时间位置	Shíjiān wèizhì	Temporal position	
时间相关口令	Shíjiān xiāngguān kǒulìng	Time-dependent password	
时间项图	Shíjiān xiàngtú	Travel-time	
事件响应	Shìjiàn xiǎngyìng	Incident response	
事件响应和安全团队论坛	Shìjiàn xiǎngyìng hé ānquán tuánduì lùntán	Forum of Incident Response and Security Teams	FIRST
时间效率系数	Shíjiān xiàolǜ xìshù	Time efficiency factor	
时间信息	Shíjiān xìnxī	Temporal information	
时间系数	Shíjiān xìshù	Time factor	
时间序列预测	Shíjiān xùliè yùcè	Time series forecasting	TSF
时间延迟	Shíjiān yánchí	Time delay	
时间压缩多路复用	Shíjiān yāsuō duōlù fùyòng	Time compression multiplex	TCM
时间压缩法	Shíjiān yāsuō fǎ	Time compression	
时间压缩复用器	Shíjiān yāsuō fù yòngqì	Time compression multiplexer	TCM
时间压缩复用	Shíjiān yāsuō fùyòng	Time compression multiplexing	TCM
时间已过	Shíjiān yǐguò	Time-out	TMO
时间印章	Shíjiān yìnzhāng	Time stamp	
事件源	Shìjiàn yuán	Event source	
时间原素	Shíjiān yuánsù	Temporal primitive	
时间预分配多址	Shíjiān yùfēnpèi duōzhǐ	Time-preassigned multiple access	
事件转发鉴别程序	Shìjiàn zhuǎnfā jiànbié chéngxù	Event forwarding discriminator	
事件转发判定程度	Shìjiàn zhuǎnfā pàndìng chéngdù	Event forwarding discriminator	
时间自动机	Shíjiān zìdòngjī	Timed automaton	
时间/事件处理软件	Shíjiān/shìjiàn chǔlǐ ruǎnjiàn	Time/event processing software	TEP
时间表问题	Shíjiānbiǎo wèntí	Timetabling problem	
世界工业与技术研究组织协会	Shìjiè gōngyè yǔ jìshù yánjiū zǔzhī xiéhuì	World Association of Industrial and Technological Research Organizations	WAITRO
世界科学信息中心	Shìjiè kēxué xìnxī zhōngxīn	World Center for Scientific Information	WCSI
世界时	Shìjiè shí	Universal Time	UT
世界数字化图	Shìjiè shùzìhuà tú	Digital chart of the world	DCW
世界随意拨号	Shìjiè suíyì bōhào	Free world dial-up	FWD
世界无线电管理大会	Shìjiè wúxiàndiàn guǎnlǐ dàhuì	World Administrative Radio Conference	WARC
世界无线电通信大会	Shìjiè wúxiàndiàn tōngxìn dàhuì	World Radio-communication Conference	WRC
世界无线电行政大会	Shìjiè wúxiàndiàn xíngzhèng dàhuì	World Administrative Radio Conference	WARC
世界协调时	Shìjiè xiétiáo shí	Universal coordinated time	UTC

世界银行间金融电信协会	Shìjiè yínháng-jiān jīnróng diànxìn xiéhuì	Society for Worldwide Interbank Financial Telecommunications	SWIFT
实境	Shíjìng	Reality	
拭镜纸	Shìjìng zhǐ	Lens tissue	
十进制点格式	Shíjìnzhì diǎn géshi	Dotted decimal notation	
十进制加法器	Shíjìnzhì jiāfǎqì	Decimal adder	DA
十进制经纬度	Shíjìnzhì jīngwěi dù	Decimal degrees	
十进制记数法	Shíjìnzhì jìshù fǎ	Decimal notation	
十进制数的二进制编码	Shíjìnzhì shùde èrjìnzhì biānmǎ	Binary coded decimal	BCD
十进制信号	Shíjìnzhì xìnhào	Decadic signal	
视距	Shìjù	Line of sight	LoS
视距传播	Shìjù chuánbō	Line-of-sight propagation	
视距无线电中继链路	Shìjù wúxiàndiàn zhōngjì liànlù	Line-of-sight radio-relay link	LOSRRL
视距无线电中继系统	Shìjù wúxiàndiàn zhōngjì xìtǒng	Line-of-sight radio-relay system	LOSRRL
视觉感知	Shìjué gǎnzhī	Visual perception	
视觉理解	Shìjué lǐjiě	Visual perception	
视觉停闪频率	Shìjué tíngshǎn pínlǜ	Fusion frequency (when flashes seem like a steady light)	
视觉显示器	Shìjué xiǎnshìqì	Visual display unit	
视觉掩模	Shìjué yǎnmó	Visual mask	
时刻	Shíkè	Instant	
时刻	Shíkè	Time of day	TOD
蚀刻服务	Shíkè fúwù	Etching services	
蚀刻光栅	Shíkè guāngshān	Etched grating	
蚀刻设备	Shíkè shèbèi	Etching machine (semiconductor mfg)	
时空对象关系模型	Shíkōng duìxiàng guānxi móxíng	Spatio-temporal object relationship model	STORM
时空数据库	Shíkōng shùjùkù	Spatio-temporal database	
时空索引	Shíkōng suǒyǐn	Spatio-temporal key	
时控调频	Shíkòng tiáopín	Timed frequency modulation	TFM
时空拓扑	Shíkōng tuòpū	Spatio-temporal topology	
时空资源	Shíkōng zīyuán	Space and time resource	STR
施乐	Shī-lè	Xerox (US corp.)	
实例	Shílì	Instance	
实例级	Shílì jí	Instance level	
事例集	Shìlì jí	Case set	
事例键	Shìlì jiàn	Case key	
示例数据	Shìlì shùjù	Sample data	
矢量	Shǐliàng	Vector	
矢量产品格式	Shǐliàng chǎnpǐn géshi	Vector product format	VPF
矢量地图	Shǐliàng dìtú	Vector map	
矢量对消器	Shǐliàng duìxiāoqì	Vector canceller	
矢量关系格式	Shǐliàng guānxi géshi	Vector relational format	VRF
矢量和激励线性预测编码	Shǐliàng hé jīlì xiànxìng yùcè biānmǎ	Vector sum excited linear predictive coding	VSELP
矢量和量化	Shǐliàng hé liànghuà	Vector quantization	
矢量化	Shǐliàng huà	Vectorization	
矢量控制	Shǐliàng kòngzhì	Vector control	VC
矢量量化	Shǐliàng liànghuà	Vector quantization	VQ

矢量数据	Shǐliàng shùjù	Vector data	
矢量数据模型	Shǐliàng shùjù móxíng	Vector data model	
矢量数据栅格化	Shǐliàng shùjù zhàgéhuà	Rasterization	
矢量算法	Shǐliàng suànfǎ	Vector algorithms	
矢量中断机构	Shǐliàng zhōngduàn jīgòu	Vector interrupt mechanism	VIM
矢量字库	Shīliáng zìkù	Vector font	
矢量-栅格转换	Shǐliàng—zhàgé zhuǎnhuàn	Vector-to-raster conversion	
十六进制	Shíliùjìnzhì	Hexadecimal	
十六进制符号装入程序	Shíliùjìnzhì fúhào zhuāngrù chéngxù	Hexadecimal symbolic loader	HDLR
十六进制记数法	Shíliùjìnzhì jìshù fǎ	Hexadecimal notation	
十六进制的	Shíliùjìnzhìde	Hexadecimal	H
施密德公司	Shī-mì-dé gōngsī	Schmid Corp. (Swiss company)	
史密斯圆图	Shǐ-mì-sī yuántú	Smith chart	
施密特触发器	Shī-mì-tè chùfāqì	Schmitt trigger	
室内单元	Shìnèi dānyuán	Indoor unit	IDU
市内电话交换机	Shìnèi diànhuà jiāohuànjī	Urban telephone switch	
市内电话网	Shìnèi diànhuà wǎng	Urban telephone network	
市内电话局	Shìnèi diànhuàjú	Urban telephone exchange	
室内动力实验	Shìnèi dònglì shíyàn	Dynamic laboratory test	
室内光缆	Shìnèi guānglǎn	Indoor optical cable	
市内局间中继线	Shìnèi jú-jiān zhōngjìxiàn	Local inter-office trunking	LIT
室内水平俯仰云台	Shìnèi shuǐpíng fǔyǎng yúntái	Indoor pan and tilt unit	IPTU
室内通信	Shìnèi tōngxìn	Inter-office communication	IOC
市内自动线路交换机	Shìnèi zìdòng xiànlù jiāohuànjī	Local automatic circuit exchange	LACE
使能和止能	Shǐnéng hé zhǐnéng	Able and disable	
适配层	Shìpèi céng	Adaptation layer (for ATM)	
适配单元	Shìpèi dānyuán	Adaptation unit	AU
适配功能	Shìpèi gōngnéng	Adaptation function	AF
适配信息	Shìpèi xìnxī	Adaptation information	AI
失配终端	Shīpèi zhōngduān	Mismatched termination	
适配器	Shìpèiqì	Adapter	
适配器卡	Shìpèiqì kǎ	Adapter card	
适配器信号处理	Shìpèiqì xìnhào chǔlǐ	Adapter signal processing	ASP
视频	Shìpín	Video frequency (VF)	
视频保护比	Shìpín bǎohù bǐ	Video-frequency protection ratio	
视频编解码	Shìpín biānjiěmǎ	Video codec	
视频编码	Shìpín biānmǎ	Video encoding	
视频 CD	Shìpín CD	Video CD	VCD
视频传输单元	Shìpín chuánshū dānyuán	Video transmission unit	VTU
视频点播	Shìpín diǎnbō	Video on demand	VoD
视频电子信函	Shìpín diànzi xìnhán	Video messaging	
视频对消器	Shìpín duìxiāoqì	Video canceller	
视频放大器	Shìpín fàngdàqì	Video amplifier	
视频分割	Shìpín fēngē	Video segmentation	
视频光传输系统	Shìpín guāng chuánshū xìtǒng	Video optical transmission system	
视频光盘	Shìpín guāngpán	Video compact disc	VCD

视频会议	Shìpín huìyì	Video conference	VC
视频接口	Shìpín jiēkǒu	Video interface port	VIP
视频描写图形引擎	Shìpín miáoxiě túxíng yǐnqíng	Video and rendering graphics engine	ViRGE
视频命令	Shìpín mìnglìng	Video command	
视频命令 〝快速更新请求〞	Shìpín mìnglìng "kuàisù gēngxīn qǐngqiú"	Video command "Fast update request"	VCU
视频命令 〝静态画请求〞	Shìpín mìnglìng "jìngtài huà qǐngqiú"	Video command "Freeze picture request"	VCF
时频偏移键控	Shípín piānyí jiànkòng	Time-frequency-shift keying	TFSK
实频特性	Shípín tèxìng	Real frequency characteristic	
视频通道带宽	Shìpín tōngdào dàikuān	Video channel bandwidth	
视频图象冻结	Shìpín túxiàng dòngjié	Video image freezing	
视频图象解结	Shìpín túxiàng jiě jié	Video image unfreezing	
视频图形显示适配器	Shìpín túxíng xiǎnshì shìpèiqì	Video graphic adapter	VGA
视频显示单元	Shìpín xiǎnshì dānyuán	Video display unit	VDU
视频显示终端	Shìpín xiǎnshì zhōngduān	Video display terminal	VDT
视频显示器	Shìpín xiǎnshìqì	Video display unit	VDU
视频消息处理业务	Shìpín xiāoxi chǔlǐ yèwù	Video messaging service	
视频消息业务	Shìpín xiāoxi yèwù	Video messaging	
视频信号标准	Shìpín xìnhào biāozhǔn	Video signal standard	VSIS
视频信号干扰比	Shìpín xìnhào gānrǎo bǐ	Video-frequency signal-to-interference ratio	
视频译码器	Shìpín yìmǎqì	Video decoder	VD
视频终端	Shìpín zhōngduān	Video terminal	VT
视频、音频、速度	Shìpín、yīnpín、sùdù	Sight, sound, speed	S3
时区	Shíqū	Time zone	
失去定时信息	Shīqù dìngshí xìnxī	Loss of timing information	LTI
失去信号	Shīqù xìnhào	Loss of signal	LOS
拾取-贴装设备	Shíqǔ-tiēzhuāng shèbèi	Pick-and-place (in SMT)	
湿热试验	Shīrè shìyàn	Humid heat test	
实时	Shíshí	Real time	
事实	Shìshí	Fact	
实时安全管理	Shíshí ānquán guǎnlǐ	Real-time security management	RTSec.M
实时安全管理段	Shíshí ānquán guǎnlǐ duàn	Real-time security management fragment	RSMF
实时操作系统	Shíshí cāozuò xìtǒng	Real-time operating system	RTOS
实时查询业务	Shíshí cháxún yèwù	Real-time polling service	rtPS
实时传输控制协议	Shíshí chuánshū kòngzhì xiéyì	Real-time transmission control protocol	RTCP
实时传输协议	Shíshí chuánshū xiéyì	Real-time transport protocol	RTP
实时传送流	Shíshí chuánsòng liú	Real-time transport production	RTP
实时传送协议	Shíshí chuánsòng xiéyì	Real-time transport protocol	RTP
实时动态管控支持	Shíshí dòngtài guǎnkòng zhīchí	Real-time and dynamic management and control support	RDMCS
实时多任务操作系统	Shíshí duō rènwu cāozuò xìtǒng	Real-time multi-tasking operating system	RMOS
实时高级应用	Shíshí gāojí yìngyòng	Realtime exclusive mode applications	REMA
实时管控支持段	Shíshí guǎnkòng zhīchí duàn	Real-time management and control support fragment	RMCSF
实时管理协调功能	Shíshí guǎnlǐ xiétiáo gōngnéng	Real-time management control function	RTMC
实时会议	Shíshí huìyì	Real-time conferencing	
实时计费	Shíshí jìfèi	Real-time billing	RTB
实时可变比特率	Shíshí kěbiàn bǐtè lǜ	Real-time variable bit rate	RT-VBR

实时控制协议	Shíshí kòngzhì xiéyì	Real-time control protocol	RTCP
实时流协议	Shíshí liú xiéyì	Real-time streaming protocol	RTSP
实时流媒体协议	Shíshí liúméitǐ xiéyì	Real-time streaming media protocol	RTSP
实时流式传输	Shíshí liú-shì chuánshū	Real-time streaming	
实时时钟	Shíshí shízhōng	Real-time clock	RTC
事实数据表	Shìshí shùjù biǎo	Fact table	
实时数据库管理系统	Shíshí shùjùkù guǎnlǐ xìtǒng	Real-time database management system	RTDMS
实时通信	Shíshí tōngxìn	Real-time communication	RTC
实时协议	Shíshí xiéyì	Real-time protocol	RTP
实时信道估算	Shíshí xìndào gūsuàn	Real-time channel estimation	
实时战略	Shíshí zhànlüè	Real time strategy (computer game)	RTS
实时执行	Shíshí zhíxíng	Real-time executive	RTE
实时自适应控制	Shíshí zìshìyìng kòngzhì	Real-time adaptive control	RTAC
事实上标准	Shìshíshang biāozhǔn	De facto standard	
失锁频率	Shīsuǒ pínlǜ	Unlocked frequency	
时态精度	Shítài jīngdù	Temporal accuracy	
时态数据库	Shítài shùjùkù	Temporal database	
时态属性	Shítài shǔxìng	Temporal attribute	
时态特征	Shítài tèzhēng	Temporal characteristic	
时态坐标	Shítài zuòbiāo	Temporal coordinate	
时态坐标系	Shítài zuòbiāo xì	Temporal coordinate system	
实体	Shítǐ	Entity	
实体波	Shítǐ bō	Body wave	
实体点	Shítǐ diǎn	Entity point	
实体关系建模	Shítǐ guānxi jiànmó	Entity-relationship modeling; ER modeling	
实体关系模型	Shítǐ guānxi móxíng	Entity-relationship model; ER model	
实体关系图表	Shítǐ guānxi túbiǎo	Entity-relationship diagram; ER diagram	
实体集	Shítǐ jí	Entity set	
实体类	Shítǐ lèi	Entity class	
实体类型	Shítǐ lèixíng	Entity type	
实体认证	Shítǐ rènzhèng	Entity authentication (IPsec)	
实体实例	Shítǐ shílì	Entity instance	
实体属性	Shítǐ shǔxìng	Entity attribute	
实体完整性	Shítǐ wánzhěngxìng	Entity integrity	
失调	Shītiáo	Detuning	
事条能力应用部分	Shìtiáo nénglì yìngyòng bùfen	Transaction capabilities application part	TCAP
实体化	Shítǐhuà	Instantiated (usually for a template)	
视听	Shìtīng	Audio-visual	AV
视图	Shìtú	View	
视图生成	Shìtú shēngchéng	View generation	
室外单元	Shìwài dānyuán	Outdoor unit	ODU
事务	Shìwù	Transaction	
事务标识	Shìwù biāozhì	Transaction identifier	TI
事务触发	Shìwù chùfā	Transaction triggering	
事务处理标识符	Shìwù chǔlǐ biāozhìfú	Transaction identifier	TI
事务处理部分	Shìwù chǔlǐ bùfen	Transaction capabilities application part	TCAP

事务处理功能应用部	Shìwù chǔlǐ gōngnéng yìngyòng bù	Transaction capabilities application part	TCAP
事务处理能力	Shìwù chǔlǐ nénglì	Transaction capabilities	TC
事务处理能力部分	Shìwù chǔlǐ nénglì bùfen	Transaction capabilities part	
事务处理能力应用部分	Shìwù chǔlǐ nénglì yìngyòng bùfen	Transaction capability application part	TCAP
事务处理系统	Shìwù chǔlǐ xìtǒng	Transaction processing system	
事务处理应用部分	Shìwù chǔlǐ yìngyòng bùfen	Transaction capabilities application part	TCAP
事务处理状态	Shìwù chǔlǐ zhuàngtài	Transaction state	
事务复制	Shìwù fùzhì	Transactional replication (for database)	
事务管理层	Shìwù guǎnlǐ céng	Business management layer	BML
事务管理器	Shìwù guǎnlǐqì	Transaction manager	TM
事务回滚	Shìwù huígǔn	Transaction rollback (for database)	
事务记录器	Shìwù jìlùqì	Transaction logger	
事务控制	Shìwù kòngzhì	Transaction control	
实物模型	Shíwù móxíng	Mock-up	
事务能力应用部分	Shìwù nénglì yìngyòng bùfen	Transaction capability application part	TCAP
事务日志	Shìwù rìzhì	Transaction log (for database)	
事务日志文件	Shìwù rìzhì wénjiàn	Transaction log file (in SQL Server)	
事务依赖	Shìwù yīlài	Transaction dependency	
事务的一致性	Shìwùde yīzhìxìng	Transactional consistency (in SQL Server)	
时隙	Shíxì	Time slot	TS
时隙 ALOHA 系统	Shíxì ALOHA xìtǒng	Slotted ALOHA system	
时隙变换	Shíxì biànhuàn	Time slot interchange	
时隙访问	Shíxì fǎngwèn	Time slot access	TSA
时隙号	Shíxì hào	Time slot number	TN
时隙号码	Shíxì hàomǎ	Timeslot number	TN
时隙环	Shíxì huán	Slotted ring	
时隙互换	Shíxì hùhuàn	Time slot interchanging	TSI
时隙交换	Shíxì jiāohuàn	Time slot interchange	TSI
时隙交换单元	Shíxì jiāohuàn dānyuán	Time slot switching unit	TSU
时隙振铃	Shíxì zhènlíng	Slotted ring	
实现	Shíxiàn	Implementation	
实线传输	Shíxiàn chuánshū	Physical line transmission	
实线电路	Shíxiàn diànlù	Physical line	
时限服务	Shíxiàn fúwù	Time limited service	TLS
实现业务容量	Shíxiàn yèwù róngliàng	Service implementation capabilities	SIC
实现一致性声明	Shíxiàn yīzhìxìng shēngmíng	Implementation conformance statement	ICS
视线转率	Shìxiàn zhuǎn lǜ	Turn rate of sight line	
失效	Shīxiào	Failure	
失效保护	Shīxiào bǎohù	Fail-safe	
失效保险	Shīxiào bǎoxiǎn	Fail-safe	
失效次数	Shīxiào cìshù	Failure count	FC
失效分析	Shīxiào fēnxī	Failure analysis	
失效管理	Shīxiào guǎnlǐ	Fault management	FM
失效恢复	Shīxiào huīfù	Failure recovery	
失效间隔时间	Shīxiào jiàngé shíjiān	Time between failures	
失效机理	Shīxiào jīlǐ	Failure mechanism	

失效率加速因子	Shīxiào lǜ jiāsù yīnzǐ	Failure rate acceleration factor	
失效模式	Shīxiào móshì	Failure mode	
失效频度加速因子	Shīxiào píndù jiāsù yīnzǐ	Failure intensity acceleration factor	
失效区域	Shīxiào qūyù	Failure domain	
失效原因	Shīxiào yuányīn	Failure cause	
失效预测	Shīxiào yùcè	Failure prediction	
失效间工作时间	Shīxiào-jiān gōngzuò shíjiān	Operating time between failures	
失效率	Shīxiàolǜ	Failure rate	
失效前时间	Shīxiào-qián shí jiān	Time to failure	
时隙的非活动部分	Shíxìde fēihuódòng bùfen	Inactive part of timeslot	
时隙的活动部分	Shíxìde huódòng bùfen	Active part of timeslot	
时隙的有用部分	Shíxìde yǒuyòng bùfen	Useful part of timeslot	
实型数据	Shíxíng shùjù	Real numbers	
时序电路	Shíxù diànlù	Series circuit, sequential circuit	
时序描述语言	Shíxù miáoshù yǔyán	Language of temporal ordering specification	LOTOS
时序模糊语言	Shíxù móhu yǔyán	Sequential fuzzy language	SFL
时序状态转换系统	Shíxù zhuàngtài zhuǎnhuàn xìtǒng	Temporal status transition system	TSTS
视讯电话	Shìxùn diànhuà	Video phone	
视讯會议	Shìxùn hùiyi	Video conferencing	
视讯會议系统	Shìxùn hùiyì xìtǒng	Video conference system	VCS
时延	Shíyán	Delay	
时延	Shíyán	Latency	
试验	Shìyàn	Test	
实验包交换系统	Shíyàn bāo jiāohuàn xìtǒng	Experimental packet switching network	EPSN
时延差	Shíyán chà	Delay inequality	
试验场地	Shìyàn chǎngdì	Test site	
试验程序语言	Shìyàn chéngxù yǔyán	Test program language	TPL
试验床	Shìyàn chuáng	Test bed	
实验电台	Shíyàn diàntái	Experimental station	
时延抖动	Shíyán dǒudòng	Delay jitter	
实验分组交换系统	Shíyàn fēnzǔ jiāohuàn xìtǒng	Experimental packet switched system	EPSS
试验负载	Shìyàn fùzài	Test load	
时延集成板	Shíyán jíchéngbǎn	Clock relay board assembly	BCRA
试验耦合转矩	Shìyàn ǒuhé zhuànjǔ	Proof coupling torque	
时延频率特性	Shíyán pínlǜ tèxìng	Delay frequency characteristic	
时延散布	Shíyán sànbù	Time delay spread	
试验设计法	Shìyàn shèjì fǎ	Experimental programming method	
试验实施过程	Shìyàn shíshī guòchéng	Test campaign	
试验数据	Shìyàn shùjù	Test data	
实验无线电台	Shíyàn wúxiàndiàntái	Experimental radio station	
实验室试验	Shíyànshì shìyàn	Laboratory test	
试验用辅助信息	Shìyànyòng fǔzhù xìnxī	Extra information for testing	
事业	Shìyè	Project	
适宜操作	Shìyí cāozuò	Conforming implementation	
十亿次运算/秒	Shíyì cì yùnsuàn/miǎo	Billion operations per second	BOPS
时移键控	Shíyí jiànkòng	Time shift keying	TSK

试音音节清晰度	Shìyīn yīnjié qīngxīdù	Logatom articulation	
适应层	Shìyìng céng	Adaption layer	
石英光纤	Shíyīng guāngxiān	Silica optical fiber	
石英镜片	Shíyīng jìngpiàn	Fused silica glass	
石英晶体振荡器	Shíyīng jīngtǐ zhèndàngqì	Quartz crystal oscillator	
石英系多模态步阶式折射率型光纤	Shíyīng xì duōmótài bùjiēshì zhéshèlǜ-xíng guāngxiān	Silica multimode stepped index [of refraction] optical fiber	
石英系多模态渐近式折射率型光纤	Shíyīng xì duōmótài jiànjìn-shì zhéshèlǜ-xíng guāngxiān	Silica multimode graded index [of refraction] optical fiber	
石英系塑胶包覆光缆	Shíyīng xì sùjiāo bāofù guānglǎn	Plastic-clad silica fiber optic cable	
石英系塑胶包覆光纤	Shíyīng xì sùjiāo bāofù guāngxiān	Plastic-clad silica optical fiber	
石英系影像光纤	Shíyīng xì yǐngxiàng guāngxiān	Silica imaging fiber optic bundle	
拾音器	Shíyīnqì	Pickup (audio)	PU
适宜性分级	Shìyíxìng fenjí	Suitability ranking	
适宜性模型	Shìyíxìng móxíng	Suitability model	
使用参数控制	Shǐyòng cānshù kòngzhì	Usage parameter control	UPC
实用程序	Shíyòng chéngxù	Utility	
使用程序	Shǐyòng chéngxù	Utility program	
使用电子数据交换/消息处理系统的用户网络管理接口	Shǐyòng diànzi shùjù jiāohuàn/Xiāoxi chǔlǐ xìtǒngde yònghù wǎngluò guǎnlǐ jiēkǒu	Customer network management interface using EDI/MHS	CNMe
实用工具	Shíyòng gōngjù	Utility	
使用价格	Shǐyòng jiàgé	Cost of use	
使用阶段	Shǐyòng jiēduàn	Operational phase (of product life cycle)	
使用寿命	Shǐyòng shòumìng	Lifetime; service life	
使用鼠标拷贝对象	Shǐyòng shǔbiāo kǎobèi duìxiàng	Click and copy [copy using a computer mouse]	
使用鼠标移动对象	Shǐyòng shǔbiāo yídòng duìxiàng	Drag-and-drop [move using a computer mouse]	
使用通用管理信息协议的用户网络管理接口	Shǐyòng tōngyòng guǎnlǐ xìnxī xiéyìde yònghù wǎngluò guǎnlǐ jiēkǒu	Customer network management interface using common management information protocol	CNMc
实用通用组播协议	Shíyòng tōngyòng zǔbō xiéyì	Pragmatic general multicast protocol (IETF usage)	PGM
使用要求	Shǐyòng yāoqiú	Service requirement	
实用摘录与报告语言	Shíyòng zhāilù yǔ bàogào yǔyán	Practical extraction and report language	PERL
使用证明书	Shǐyòng zhèngmíngshū	Certification practice statement	CPS
适用度	Shìyòngdù	Fitness for use	
使用者通路	Shǐyòngzhě tōnglù	User channels	USR
时域	Shíyù	Time domain	
时域编码	Shíyù biānmǎ	Time domain coding	TDC
时域反射计量	Shíyù fǎnshèjì liáng	Time domain reflectometry	
时域反射仪	Shíyù fǎnshèyí	Time domain reflector	TDR
试运行阶段	Shìyùnxíng jiēduàn	Trial run period	
视在功率	Shìzài gōnglǜ	Apparent power	
视在亮度	Shìzài liàngdù	Apparent luminance	
视在线路误差码率	Shìzài xiànlù wùchā mǎ lǜ	Apparent line error ratio	
失真	Shīzhēn	Distortion (of a signal)	
失真检测环路	Shīzhēn jiǎncè huánlù	Distortion detection loop	DDL
失真时延	Shīzhēn shíyán	Distortion delay	
失真因数	Shīzhēn yīnshù	Distortion factor	DF

失真指示器	Shīzhēn zhǐshìqì	Distortion detection loop	DDL
失真度	Shīzhēndù	Distortion	
时帧	Shízhèng	Time-frame	
时钟	Shízhōng	Clock, timer	
始终保持	Shǐzhōng bǎochí	Always on	AO
始终保持服务器	Shǐzhōng bǎochí fúwùqì	Always on server	AOS
时钟表	Shízhōng biǎo	Timer table	
时钟产生集成板	Shízhōng chǎnshēng jíchéngbǎn	Clock generation board assembly	
时钟存取时间	Shízhōng cúnqǔshíjiān	Access time from clock (in RAM or ROM)	ATC
时钟发生器	Shízhōng fāshēngqì	Clock generator	CG
时钟分配后面板	Shízhōng fēnpèi hòumian bǎn	Clock distribution back panel	
时钟分配集成板	Shízhōng fēnpèi jíchéngbǎn	Clock distribution board assembly	BCDA
时钟分频电路	Shízhōng fēnpín diànlù	Clock frequency dividing circuit	
时钟合成器	Shízhōng héchéngqì	Clock synthesizer	
时钟监测和分配/AGC 集成板	Shízhōng jiāncè hé fēnpèi/AGC jíchéngbǎn	Clock monitoring and distribution /AGC bank assembly	CABA
时钟接收机	Shízhōng jiēshōujī	Clock receiver	
时钟机架面板	Shízhōng jījià miànbǎn	Clock rack panel	BCBP
时钟控制信号	Shízhōng kòngzhì xìnhào	Clock control signal	
时钟脉冲	Shízhōng màichōng	Clock pulse	
时钟脉冲发生器	Shízhōng màichōng fāshēngqì	Clock pulse generator	CPG
时钟起动命令	Shízhōng qǐdòng mìnglìng	Clock start command	CSC
时钟设备	Shízhōng shèbèi	Clock device	CKD
时钟信号	Shízhōng xìnhào	Clock signal (timing information)	CK
时钟移位寄存器	Shízhōng yíwèi jìcúnqì	Clock shift register	CSR
时钟与信号音模块	Shízhōng yǔ xìnhào yīn mókuài	Clock tone module	CTM
时钟源	Shízhōng yuán	Clock source (timing information)	CS
时钟源质量等级	Shízhōng yuán zhìliàng děngjí	Clock source quality level	
时钟源指示器	Shízhōng yuán zhǐshìqì	Clock source identifier	Csid
时钟周期	Shízhōng zhōuqī	Clock cycle time	CCT
视轴误差	Shìzhóu wùchā	Boresight error (of an antenna)	
实转	Shízhuǎn	Put a project into practice	
实装测试	Shízhuāng cèshì	Installation test	
十字缝隙天线	Shízì fèngxì tiānxiàn	Crossed slot antenna	
十字链表	Shízì liàn biǎo	Orthogonal list	
收缓存	Shōu huǎncún	Receive buffer	
受检测器噪声限制的工作状态	Shòu jiǎncèqì zàoshēng xiànzhìde gōngzuò zhuàngtài	Detector noise limited operation	
瘦客户端	Shòu kèhù duān	Thin client	
瘦客户机	Shòu kèhùjī	Thin client	
手孔	Shǒu kǒng	Hand hole (for access to buried cable)	
受保护网洛	Shòubǎohù wǎngluò	Protected network	
手柄	Shǒubǐng	Handset	
手持机	Shǒuchíjī	Handset, handheld device	
手持式电脑	Shǒuchí-shì diànnǎo	Hand-held PC	HPC
手持式激光条码扫描器	Shǒuchí-shì jīguāng tiáomǎ sǎomiáoqì	Hand-held laser bar code scanner	
手持式影像扫描器	Shǒuchí-shì yǐngxiàng sǎomiáoqì	Hand-held color image scanner	

首次定位时长	Shǒucì dìngwèi shícháng	Time to first fix (in position location)	TTFF
首次失效前时间	Shǒucì shīxiào-qián shíjiān	Time to first failure	
收到的上游邻站地址	Shōudàode shàngyóu línzhàn dìzhǐ	Received upstream neighbor station address	RUA
手动屏印制机	Shǒudòng píng yìnzhìjī	Manual screen printer (semiconductor mfg)	
手动频率控制	Shǒudòng pínlǜ kòngzhì	Manual frequency control	
手动拾放工作站	Shǒudòng shífàng gōngzuòzhàn	Manual pick and place workstation (semiconductor mfg)	
手动拾放机	Shǒudòng shífàngjī	Manual pick and place workstation (semiconductor mfg)	
手动丝网印刷机	Shǒudòng sīwǎng yìnshuājī	Manual screen printer (semiconductor mfg)	
手动增益控制	Shǒudòng zēngyì kòngzhì	Manual gain control	
收端	Shōuduān	Terminating	
收发报机	Shōufābàojī	Transceiver	XCVR
受访公众陆地移动网	Shòufǎng gōngzhòng lùdì yídòng wǎng	Visited public land mobile network (PLMN)	VPLMN
受访移动无线局	Shòufǎng yídòng wúxiàn jú	Visited mobile services switching centre	VMSC
收发信机（板）	Shōufāxìnjī (bǎn)	Transceiver (board)	TRX
收发信机从属控制单元	Shōufāxìnjī cóngshǔ kòngzhì dānyuán	Transceiver slave controller unit	XSCB
收发信机单元	Shōufāxìnjī dānyuán	Transceiver unit	XCVU
收发信机单元处理器	Shōufāxìnjī dānyuán chǔlǐqì	Transceiver unit processor	TRUP
收发信机功率供给单元	Shōufāxìnjī gōnglǜ gōngjǐ dānyuán	Transceiver power supply unit	TPSU
收发信机功率供给集成件	Shōufāxìnjī gōnglǜ gōngjǐ jíchéng jiàn	Transceiver power supply assembly	XPSA
收发信机后面板	Shōufāxìnjī hòumian bǎn	Transceiver back plane board	XBPB
收发信机话音和数据接口	Shōufāxìnjī huàyīn hé shùjù jiēkǒu	Transceiver speech and data interface	TSDI
收发信机架	Shōufāxìnjī jià	Transceiver shelf	XCVS
收发信机集成板	Shōufāxìnjī jíchéngbǎn	Transceiver assembly	XCVA
收发信机接口处理器	Shōufāxìnjī jiēkǒu chǔlǐqì	Transceiver interface processor	TIP
收发信机机架	Shōufāxìnjī jījià	Transceiver rack	XCVR
收发信机控制接口	Shōufāxìnjī kòngzhì jiēkǒu	Transceiver control interface	TCI
收发信机模块	Shōufāxìnjī mókuài	Transceiver block	XCVB
收发信机频率同步面板	Shōufāxìnjī pínlǜ tóngbù miànbǎn	Transceiver frequency synthesizer board	XFSB
收发信机主机控制单元	Shōufāxìnjī zhǔjī kòngzhì dānyuán	Transceiver master control unit	XMCU
收费点	Shōufèi diǎn	Charging point	CHP
收费点的末端	Shōufèi diǎnde mòduān	End of charge point	CEND
收费通知	Shōufèi tōngzhī	Advice of charge	AOC
收费通知信息	Shōufèi tōngzhī xìnxī	Charge advice information	CAI
收费站类型	Shōufèizhàn lèixíng	Toll point type	
手工数字化	Shǒugōng shùzìhuà	Manual digitizing	
受管节点	Shòuguǎn jiédiǎn	Managed node	
受管网络服务	Shòuguǎn wǎngluò fúwù	Managed network service	
守护程序	Shǒuhù chéngxù	Daemon	
守护进程	Shǒuhù jìnchéng	Daemon	
受话器	Shòuhuàqì	Telephone receiver	
收汇	Shōuhuì	Issue	
收汇局	Shōuhuì jú	Office of issue	
收集	Shōují	Collection	
受激布里渊散射	Shòujī bù-lǐ-yuān sǎnshè	Stimulated Brillouin scattering	SBS
受激单元	Shòujī dānyuán	Driven element	
收集和截获	Shōují hé jiéhuò	Attract and intercept	

受激拉曼散射	Shòujī lā-màn sǎnshè	Stimulated Raman scattering	SRS
手键	Shǒujiàn	Telegraph key	
受监视参数	Shòujiānshì cānshù	Monitored parameter	
受控代码	Shòukòng dàimǎ	Managed code	
受控 DTE 未装备好	Shòukòng DTE wèi zhuāngbèi hǎo	Controlled data transfer element (DTE) not installed	
受控对象	Shòukòng duìxiàng	Managed object	
受控访问	Shòukòng fǎngwèn	Controlled access	
受控访问性	Shòukòng fǎngwènxìng	Controlled accessability	
受控负载业务	Shòukòng fùzài yèwù	Controlled load service	CLS
受控共享	Shòukòng gòngxiǎng	Controlled sharing (IPsec)	
受控滑动	Shòukòng huádòng	Controlled slip	
受控会议	Shòukòng huìyì	Conducted conference	
受控扩充件	Shòukòng kuòchōng jiàn	Managed extensions	
手控频率位置调制	Shǒukòng pínlǜ wèizhì tiáozhì	Gated frequency position modulation	GFPM
受控维护	Shòukòng wéihù	Controlled maintenance	
受控站	Shòukòng zhàn	Controlled station	
收款人	Shōukuǎnrén	Payee	
收敛	Shōuliǎn	Convergence	C
收敛比	Shōuliǎn bǐ	Convergence ratio	
收敛速度	Shōuliǎn sùdù	Convergence rate	
收码器	Shōumǎqì	Code receiver	
寿命	Shòumìng	Lifetime	
寿命长的陶瓷发射器	Shòumìng chángde táocí fāshèqì	Long life ceramic emitters (semiconductor mfg)	
寿命试验	Shòumìng shìyàn	Life test	
寿命周期	Shòumìng zhōuqī	Life cycle	
授权	Shòuquán	Authorization	
授权	Shòuquán	Grant (for database)	
授权掉电	Shòuquán diàodiàn	Grant power down	GNTPDN
授权管理消息	Shòuquán guǎnlǐ xiāoxi	Empowering management message	EMM
授权和格式标识符	Shòuquán hé géshi biāozhìfú	Authority and format identifier	AFI
授权控制消息	Shòuquán kòngzhì xiāoxi	Empowering control message	ECM
授权状态	Shòuquán zhuàngtài	Authorization state (status)	
受热噪声限制的工作状态	Shòurè zàoshēng xiànzhìde gōngzuò zhuàngtài	Thermal noise limited operation	
收入模式	Shōurù móshì	Revenue model	
受试设备	Shòushì shèbèi	Equipment under test	EUT
收缩流	Shōusuō liú	Contraction	
手提单元	Shǒutí dānyuán	Hand portable unit	HPU
手提电脑	Shǒutí diànnǎo	Portable computer	
受托第三方	Shòutuō dìsānfāng	Trusted third party	TTP
首席财务官	Shǒuxí cáiwù guān	Chief financial officer	CFO
首席管理官	Shǒuxí guǎnlǐ guān	Chief organizing officer	COO
首席技术官	Shǒuxí jìshù guān	Chief technical officer	CTO
首席技术官	Shǒuxí jìshù guān	Chief technology officer	CTO
首席信息官	Shǒuxí xìnxī guān	Chief information officer	CIO
首席运营官	Shǒuxí yùnyíng guān	Chief operating officer	COO
首席执行官	Shǒuxí zhíxíng guān	Chief executive officer	CEO

受限标签分配协议	Shòuxiàn biāoqiān fēnpèi xiéyì	Constraint-based label distribution protocol	CR-LDP
受限访问	Shòuxiàn fǎngwèn	Limited access (IPsec)	
受限路由	Shòuxiàn lùyóu	Constraint-based routing	
手写辨识	Shǒuxiě biànshí	Handwriting recognition	
手写识别	Shǒuxiě shíbié	Handwriting recognition	
手写输入	Shǒuxiě shūrù	Hand input	
收信电平值	Shōuxìn diànpíng zhí	Receive level	RXLE
收信质量级	Shōuxìn zhìliàng jí	Receive quality	RXQUA
收信机的连续骚扰	Shōuxìnjīde liánxù sāorǎo	Receiver continuous disturbance	CR
收信机的瞬态骚扰	Shōuxìnjīde shùntài sāorǎo	Receiver transient disturbance	TR
首选电路组	Shǒuxuǎn diànlù zǔ	First choice set of circuits	
首选漫游的系统选择	Shǒuxuǎn mànyóude xìtǒng xuǎnzé	System selection for preferred roaming	SSPR
首页标	Shǒuyè biāo	Header (WP command)	
收音机/接收	Shōuyīnjī/ jiēshōu	Receiver/reception	
受约束非线性回归	Shòuyuēshù fēixiànxìng huíguī	Constrained non-linear regression	
受主	Shòuzhǔ	Acceptor	
树	Shù	Tree	
树遍历	Shù biànlì	Tree traversal	
树表结合表示	Shù biǎo jiéhé biǎoshì	Tree and tabular combined notation	TTCN
数传台	Shù chuán tái	Data transmission radio	
输电线	Shū diànxiàn	Transmission line	
数模变换	Shù mó biànhuàn	Digital to analog (D/A) conversion	
数模传换器	Shù mó chuánhuànqì	Digital to analog converter	DAC
数模电路	Shù mó diànlù	Digital-analog (digilog) circuit	
数模信道	Shù mó xìndào	Digital-analog (digilog) channel	
数模转换子集成板	Shù mó zhuǎnhuàn zǐjíchéng bǎn	Digital to analog conversion daughter board assembly	DACD
数模转换器	Shù mó zhuǎnhuànqì	Digital to analog converter	DAC
数/模转换器	Shù/mó zhuǎnhuànqì	Digital/analog converter	D/A
衰耗	Shuāihào	Attenuation	
衰减	Shuāijiǎn	Attenuation	
衰减常数	Shuāijiǎn chángshù	Attenuation coefficient (FOC)	
衰减串扰	Shuāijiǎn chuànrǎo	Attenuation crosstalk	
衰减串扰比	Shuāijiǎn chuànrǎo bǐ	Attenuation crosstalk ratio	ACR
衰减串音比	Shuāijiǎn chuànyīn bǐ	Attenuation crosstalk ratio	ACR
衰减串音功率和	Shuāijiǎn chuànyīn gōnglǜ hé	Attenuation crosstalk ratio power sum	PSACR
衰减分瓣率	Shuāijiǎn fēnbàn lǜ	Attenuation resolution	
衰减光谱特性	Shuāijiǎn guāngpǔ tèxìng	Attenuation spectral dependency	
衰减均衡	Shuāijiǎn jūnhéng	Attenuation equalization	
衰减频率失真	Shuāijiǎn pínlǜ shīzhēn	Attenuation/frequency distortion	
衰减曲线	Shuāijiǎn qūxiàn	Attenuation curve	
衰减系数	Shuāijiǎn xìshù	Damping factor	
衰减系数	Shuāijiǎn xìshù	Attenuation coefficient	
衰减与串扰比	Shuāijiǎn yǔ chuànrǎo bǐ	Attenuation to crosstalk ratio	ACR
衰减-串音比率	Shuāijiǎn—chuànyīn bǐlǜ	Attenuation to crosstalk ratio	ACR
衰减器	Shuāijiǎnqì	Attenuator	
衰落	Shuāiluò	Fading	

衰落包络	Shuāiluò bāoluò	Fading envelope	
衰落带宽	Shuāiluò dàikuān	Fading bandwidth	
衰落幅度	Shuāiluò fúdù	Amplitude of fading	
衰落深度	Shuāiluò shēndù	Fading depth	
衰落信道	Shuāiluò xìndào	Fading channel	
衰落周期	Shuāiluò zhōuqī	Fading duration	
衰落率	Shuāiluòlǜ	Fading rate	
双边带	Shuāng biāndài	Double sideband	DSB
双边带幅度调制	Shuāng biāndài fúdù tiáozhì	Double sideband amplitude modulation	DSBAM
双波段电台	Shuāng bōduàn diàntái	Two-waveband radio telephone	
双波段光纤放大器	Shuāng bōduàn guāngxiān fàngdàqì	Dual band fiber amplifier	DBFA
双窗孔纤维	Shuāng chuāngkǒng xiānwéi	Double window fiber	DWF
双电平脉冲	Shuāng diànpíng màichōng	Bi-level pulse	
双抖动环	Shuāng dǒudòng huán	Double dither loop	DDL
双端对网络	Shuāng duānduì wǎngluò	Two-terminal-pair network	
双端口	Shuāng duānkǒu	Two-port	
双端口存储器	Shuāng duānkǒu cúnchǔqì	Dual port memory	DPM
双端口 RAM	Shuāng duānkǒu RAM	Dual port RAM	DPRAM
双端口网络	Shuāng duānkǒu wǎngluò	Two-port network	
双堆叠	Shuāng duīdié	Dual stack	
双独立总线	Shuāng dúlì zǒngxiàn	Dual independent bus	DIB
双反向旋转环	Shuāng fǎnxiàng xuánzhuǎn huán	Dual counter-rotating ring	
双分（复用）器	Shuāng fēn (fù yòng) qì	Bisector	
双归属	Shuāng guīshǔ	Dual-homing	
双滑动梁型贴片机	Shuāng huádòng liáng xíng tiēpiànjī	Dual sliding beam pick and placer (in SMT)	
双缓冲区	Shuāng huǎnchōngqū	Double buffering	
双缓存结构	Shuāng huǎncún jiégòu	Twin cache architecture	TCA
双幻线电路	Shuāng huànxiàn diànlù	Double phantom circuit	
双汇接业务	Shuāng huìjiē yèwù	Dual hubbed service (SDH)	
双击	Shuāng jī	Double click (WP command)	
双机	Shuāng jī	Dual processor	
双极 3 零替代	Shuāng jí san líng tìdài	Bipolar 3-zero substitution	
双鉴传感器	Shuāng jiàn chuángǎnqì	Dual -technology sensor	DTS
双绞线分布式数据接口	Shuāng jiàoxiàn Fēnbùshì shùjù jiēkǒu	Twisted pair distributed data interface	TPDDI
双基地雷达	Shuāng jīdì léidá	Bistatic radar	
双极点	Shuāng jídiǎn	Double pole	
双极点滤波器	Shuāng jídiǎn lǜbōqì	Double pole filter	
双节点互连	Shuāng jiédiǎn hùlián	Dual node interconnection (SDH)	
双极化接收	Shuāng jíhuà jiēshōu	Double polarization receive	
双极化天线	Shuāng jíhuà tiānxiàn	Dual-polarity antenna	
双精度	Shuāng jīngdù	Double precision	
双金属	Shuāng jīnshǔ	Bi-metallic	
双极性破坏	Shuāng jíxìng pòhuài	Bipolar violation	BPV
双棱镜	Shuāng léngjìng	Biprism	
双连接工作站	Shuāng liánjiē gōngzuòzhàn	Dual-attachment station	DAS
双连接集中器	Shuāng liánjiē jízhōngqì	Dual-attached concentrator	DAC

双列直插式封装	Shuāng liè zhíchā-shì fēngzhuāng	Dual in-line package	DIP
双路径多播	Shuāng lùjìng duōbō	Dual-path multicast	
双码流	Shuāng mǎliú	Dual stream	
双门限检测	Shuāng ménxiàn jiǎncè	Double threshold detection	
双门限检测器	Shuāng ménxiàn jiǎncèqì	Double threshold detector	
双密度	Shuāng mìdù	Double density	DD
双模式干扰机	Shuāng móshì gānrǎojī	Dual-mode jammer	
双扭线对	Shuāng niǔxiànduì	Twisted wire pair	TWP
双偏管	Shuāng piān guǎn	Double deflection CRT	
双偏转	Shuāng piānzhuǎn	Double-deflection	
双频段	Shuāng pínduàn	Dual band	
双曲线无线电导航	Shuāng qūxiàn wúxiàndiàn dǎoháng	Hyperbolic radionavigation	
双色向滤光镜	Shuāng sèxiàng lǜguāngjìng	Dichromic filter	
双色向面镜	Shuāng sèxiàng miànjìng	Dichromic mirror	
双声道	Shuāng shēngdào	Stereo	
双时间印的事各级同步	Shuāng shíjiān yìnde shì gèjí tóngbù	Double time-stamp transaction-level synchronization	DTSTLS
双数据率 SDRAM	Shuāng shùjù lǜ SDRAM	Double data rate SDRAM	DDR-SDRAM
双四相调制	Shuāng sìxiāng tiáozhì	Double quaternary modulation	DQM
双 T 接头	Shuāng T jiētóu	Double T junction	
双弹性散射峰	Shuāng tánxìng sǎnshè fēng	Binary elastic scattering peak	
双弹性散射过程	Shuāng tánxìng sǎnshè guòchéng	Binary elastic scattering event	
双同步通信转接器	Shuāng tóngbù tōngxìn zhuǎnjiēqì	Bisynchronous communications adapter	BCA
双位	Shuāng wèi	Double bit	
双稳态触发电路	Shuāng wěntài chùfā diànlù	Bistable trigger circuit	
双线性过滤	Shuāng xiànxìng guòlǜ	Bilinear filtering (video)	
双线型模型	Shuāng xiànxíng móxíng	Bilinear model	
双线性内插法	Shuāng xiànxìng nèichāfǎ	Bilinear interpolation	
双削波	Shuāng xiāo bō	Slicing	
双削波器	Shuāng xiāo bōqì	Slicer	
双信道异步接受器/发射器	Shuāng xìndào yìbù jiēshòuqì/ fāshèqì	Dual-channel asynchronous receiver/transmitter	DART
双行程选择器	Shuāng xíngchéng xuǎnzéqì	Two-motion selector	
双信号法	Shuāng xìnhào fǎ	Two-signal method	
双悬浮动态减震系统	Shuāng xuánfú dòngtài jiǎnzhèn xìtǒng	Double dynamic suspension system	DDSS
双循环计数环	Shuāng xúnhuán jìshù huán	Dual rotating counter ring	
双移频键控	Shuāng yípín jiànkòng	Double frequency shift keying	DFSK
双异质结	Shuāng yìzhì jié	Double heterogeneous	
双增益级对数放大器	Shuāng zēngyì jí duìshù fàngdàqì	Double gain stage logarithmic amplifier	
双栈过渡机制	Shuāng zhàn guòdù jīzhì	Dual stack transition mechanism (in IPv6)	DSTM
双折射光晶体	Shuāng zhéshè guāng jīngtǐ	Birefringent crystal	
双锥形连接器	Shuāng zhuīxíng liánjiēqì	Biconic connector	
双锥形天线	Shuāng zhuīxíng tiānxiàn	Biconical antenna	
双字节字符集	Shuāng zìjié zìfú jí	Double-byte character set	DBCS
双总线	Shuāng zǒngxiàn	Dual bus	
双倍数据速率	Shuāngbèi shùjù sùlǜ	Double data rate	DDR
双倍字长	Shuāngbèi zìcháng	Double-length word	
双边闭合用户群	Shuāngbiān bìhé yònghù qún	Bilateral closed user group	BCUG

双边接触内存模组	Shuāngbiān jiēchù nèicún mózǔ	Dual inline memory module	DIMM
双边带	Shuāngbiāndài	Double sideband	DSB
双边带调制	Shuāngbiāndài tiáozhì	Double sideband modulation	
双变频接收机	Shuāngbiànpín jiēshōujī	Double conversion receiver	
双参函数	Shuāngcān hánshù	Binary function	
双重地址周期	Shuāngchóng dìzhǐ zhōuqī	Dual address cycle	DAC
双重独立地图编码文件	Shuāngchóng dúlì dìtú biānmǎ wénjiàn	Dual independent map encoding	DIME
双重分集接收	Shuāngchóng fēnjí jiēshōu	Double diversity reception	
双重绝缘	Shuāngchóng juéyuán	Double insulation	
双重内嵌式内存模块	Shuāngchóng nèiqiàn-shì nèicún mókuài	Dual in-line memory module	DIMM
双重平衡混频器	Shuāngchóng pínghéng hùnpínqì	Double balanced mixer	
双重启动	Shuāngchóng qǐdòng	Dual boot	
双重调制	Shuāngchóng tiáozhì	Double modulation	
双重通信控制集成板	Shuāngchóng tōngxìn kòngzhì jíchéngbǎn	Duplication communication control board assembly	DCCA
双重文件	Shuāngchóng wénjiàn	Dualized file	
双重系统	Shuāngchóng xìtǒng	Duplex system	
双重修改方式	Shuāngchóng xiūgǎi fāngshì	Double modification	
双重意义	Shuāngchóng yìyì	Dual significance	
双重自适应文卷压缩	Shuāngchóng zìshìyìng wénjuàn yāsuō	Double-adaptive file compression	DAFC
双带光纤放大器	Shuāngdài guāngxiān fàngdàqì	Dual band fiber amplifier	DBFA
双刀单掷开关	Shuāngdāo dānzhì kāiguān	Double-pole, single-throw switch	DPST
双端列表	Shuāngduān lièbiǎo	Double-ended queue	
双端同步	Shuāngduān tóngbù	Double-ended synchronization	
双方控制释放	Shuāngfāng kòngzhì shìfàng	First-party release	
双方中继	Shuāngfāng zhōngjì	Both-ways trunk	BWT
双工	Shuānggōng	Duplex	
双工操作	Shuānggōng cāozuò	Duplex operation	
双工传输	Shuānggōng chuánshū	Duplex transmission	
双工频率间隔	Shuānggōng pínlǜ jiàngé	Duplex frequency separation	
双工无线电话机	Shuānggōng wúxiàn diànhuà jī	Duplex radiotelephone	
双工器	Shuānggōngqì	Diplexer	DPX
双工器	Shuānggōngqì	Duplexer, diplexer (for antennas)	
双机系统	Shuāngjī xìtǒng	Dual system	
双极型晶体管	Shuāngjíxíng jīngtǐguǎn	Bipolar transistor	
双极性破坏点	Shuāngjíxìng pòhuài diǎn	Bipolar violation	
双链传动装置	Shuāngliàn chuándòng zhuāngzhì	Dual-train drive device	
双链树	Shuāngliàn shù	Doubly linked tree	
双列直插	Shuāngliè zhíchā	Dual in-line package	DIP
双列直插式封装	Shuānglièzhí chāshì fēngzhuāng	Dual-in-line package	DIP
双流传输	Shuāngliú chuánshū	Double current transmission	
双流归零制	Shuāngliú guīlíng zhì	Double current return to zero system	
双路复用器	Shuānglù fùyòngqì	Diplexer (of an antenna)	
双面角形反射器	Shuāngmiàn jiǎoxíng fǎnshè qì	Dihedral corner reflector	
双面双密度（磁盘）	Shuāngmiàn shuāng mìdù (cípán)	Double side/double density (disk)	DS/DD
双栅极MOS四极管	Shuāngshānjí MOS sìjíguǎn	Double gate MOS four terminal device	

双位差错	Shuāngwèi chācuò	Double error	
双线制高比特率数字用户线	Shuāngxiàn zhìgāo bǐtèlǜ shùzì yònghù xiàn	Pair high bit-rate digital subscriber line	PHDSL
双向	Shuāngxiàng	Two-way, bilateral, both-ways	
双向保护倒换	Shuāngxiàng bǎohù dǎohuàn	Bidirectional protection switching	
双相编码	Shuāngxiàng biānmǎ	Biphase coding	
双向传播时间	Shuāngxiàng chuánbō shíjiān	Round-trip transmission time	RTT
双向传播时间变化	Shuāngxiàng chuánbō shíjiān biànhuà	Round-trip transmission time variation	RTTVAR
双向传输	Shuāngxiàng chuánshū	Bidirectional transmission	
双向等离子体沉积（工艺）	Shuāngxiàng děnglí zǐtǐ chénjī (gōngyì)	Axial and lateral plasma deposition (process)	
双向对称通信	Shuāngxiàng duìchèn tōngxin	Symmetrical communications	SC
双向封闭用户集团	Shuāngxiàng fēngbì yònghù jítuán	Bilateral closed user group	BCUG
双向硅开关	Shuāngxiàng guī kāiguān	Silicon bi-directional switch	SBS
双向建立呼叫	Shuāngxiàng jiànlì hūjiào	Both way call setup	
双向交替	Shuāngxiàng jiāotì	Two way alternate	TWA
双向交替	Shuāngxiàng jiāotì	Two-way alternate	TWA
双向近似推力	Shuāngxiàng jìnsì tuīlì	Bidirectional approximate reasoning	
双向可控硅	Shuāngxiàng kěkòng guī	Silicon symmetrical switch	SSS
双向控制	Shuāngxiàng kòngzhì	Bilateral control	
双向链表	Shuāngxiàng liàn biǎo	Doubly linked list	
双向连接站	Shuāngxiàng liánjiē zhàn	Dual attachment station	DAS
双向路径/连接类型	Shuāngxiàng lùjìng/liánjiē lèixíng	Bidirectional trail/connection type	
双向入力	Shuāngxiàng rùlì	Two-directional input	
双向数据传送	Shuāngxiàng shùjù chuánsòng	Bidirectional data transfer	BDT
双向数据总线	Shuāngxiàng shùjù zǒngxiàn	Bidirectional data bus	BDB
双向通道保护环	Shuāngxiàng tōngdào bǎohù huán	Bidirectional path protection ring	
双向同时	Shuāngxiàng tóngshí	Two way simultaneous	TWS
双向图文视传	Shuāngxiàng túwén shìchuán	Interactive videography	
双向稳流器	Shuāngxiàng wěnliúqì	Bilateral current stabilizer	
双向线路倒换环	Shuāngxiàng xiànlù dǎohuàn huán	Bidirectional line switching ring	BLSR
双向信任	Shuāngxiàng xìnrèn	Two-way trust	
双向寻呼	Shuāngxiàng xúnhū	Two-way paging	
双向映射	Shuāngxiàng yìngshè	Bi-directional mapping (in Visual Basic)	
双向预测编码图像	Shuāngxiàng yùcè biānmǎ túxiàng	Bidirectionally-predictive coded picture (video term)	
双信号方法	Shuāngxìnhào fāngfǎ	Two-signal method	
双音多频	Shuāngyīn duōpín	Dual tone multi-frequency	DTMF
刷新	Shuāxīn	Flush	
刷新率	Shuāxīn lǜ	Update rate	
刷新频率	Shuāxīn pínlǜ	Refresh rate	
刷新数据	Shuāxīn shùjù	Refresh data (for database)	
鼠标垫	Shǔbiāo diàn	Mouse pad	
数表结合的表示法	Shùbiǎo jiéhéde biǎoshì fǎ	Tree tabular combined notation	TTCN
鼠标器	Shǔbiāoqì	Mouse	
输出	Shūchū	Output	
输出波形幅度	Shūchū bōxíng fúdù	Transmitted waveform amplitude	TLA
输出布线池	Shūchū bùxiàn chí	Output routing pool	

输出参考面	Shūchū cānkǎo miàn	Output reference plane	
输出处理器	Shūchū chǔlǐqì	Output handler	OPH
输出打印机	Shūchū dǎyìnjī	Output printer	OP
输出电平	Shūchū diànpíng	Power output	
输出电平	Shūchū diànpíng	Output level	
输出电源控制	Shūchū diànyuán kòngzhì	Output power control	
输出抖动	Shūchū dǒudòng	Output jitter	
输出多路复用同步装置	Shūchū duōlù fùyòng tóngbù zhuāngzhì	Output multiplex synchronizer	OMS
输出反馈	Shūchū fǎnkuì	Output feedback	OFB
输出格式处理器	Shūchū géshi chǔlǐqì	Output format handler	OFH
输出光功率	Shūchū guāng gōnglǜ	Output optical power	
输出缓冲寄存器	Shūchū huǎnchōng jìcúnqì	Output buffer register	OBR
输出绞波电压	Shūchū jiǎobō diànyā	Output ripple voltage	
输出寄存器	Shūchū jìcúnqì	Output register	OR
输出接口列表	Shūchū jiēkǒu lièbiǎo	Outgoing interface list	OIL
输出控制移位寄存器	Shūchū kòngzhì yíwèi jìcúnqì	Output control shift register	OCSR
输出滤波器	Shūchū lǜbōqì	Output filter	
输出逻辑宏单元	Shūchū luóji hóngdānyuán	Output logic macrocell	
输出缺陷指示	Shūchū quēxiàn zhǐshì	Outgoing defect indication	ODI
输出认可	Shūchū rènkě	Output acknowledged	OA
输出数据缓冲器	Shūchū shùjù huǎnchōngqì	Output data buffer	ODBR
输出输入模块	Shūchū shūrù mókuài	Input-output block	IOB
输出特性	Shūchū tèxìng	Output characteristics	
输出误码指示	Shūchū wùmǎ zhǐshì	Outgoing error indication	OEI
输出限制消息	Shūchū xiànzhì xiāoxi	Output limited message (IPsec TLS)	
输出指令数据装置	Shūchū zhǐlìng shùjù zhuāngzhì	Output command data set	OCDS
输出中继器	Shūchū zhōngjìqì	Outgoing repeater or relay	OGR
输出转换器	Shūchū zhuǎnhuànqì	Outgoing repeater	OGR
输出转矩	Shūchū zhuànjǔ	Output torque	
输出总线驱动器	Shūchū zǒngxiàn qūdòngqì	Output bus driver	OBD
输出阻抗	Shūchū zǔkàng	Output impedance	
数传机	Shùchuánjī	Data transmitter	
数传台	Shùchuántái	Data transmission radio	
输出口信号平衡	Shūchūkǒu xìnhào pínghéng	Output signal balance	OSB
疏导	Shūdǎo	Grooming (of a digital signal)	
疏导和合并	Shūdǎo hé hébìng	Grooming and consolidation	
树的遍历	Shùde biànlì	Tree traversal	
树的描绘	Shùde miáohuì	Drawing trees	
数管日志	Shùguǎn rìzhì	Daily data manager record	
曙光	Shǔguāng	Dawning (Chinese supercomputer maker)	
数管台	Shùguǎntái	Data management terminal	
水负载	Shuǐ fùzài	Water load	
水底电缆	Shuǐdǐ diànlǎn	Submerged cable	SL
水底光缆	Shuǐdǐ guānglǎn	Submerged optical cable	SG
睡眠方式	Shuìmián fāngshì	Sleep mode	
水平拆分	Shuǐpíng chāifēn	Split horizon	

水平长度	Shuǐpíng chángdù	Horizontal length	HL
水平磁偶极子	Shuǐpíng cí ǒujízi	Horizontal magnetic dipole	HMD
水平电缆	Shuǐpíng diànlǎn	Horizontal cabling	
水平方向性图	Shuǐpíng fāngxiàngxìng tú	Horizontal directivity pattern	
水平分割更新	Shuǐpíng fēngē gēngxīn	Split-horizon updates	
水平分区	Shuǐpíng fēnqū	Horizontal partitioning	
水平光缆	Shuǐpíng guānglǎn	Horizontal optical cabling	
水平交叉连接	Shuǐpíng jiāochā liánjiē	Horizontal cross connect	HCC
水平极化场矢量	Shuǐpíng jíhuà cháng shǐliàng	Horizontally polarized field vector	
水平控制网	Shuǐpíng kòngzhì wǎng	Horizontal control network	
水平偏转	Shuǐpíng piānzhuǎn	Horizontal deflection	HD
水平扫描频率	Shuǐpíng sǎomiáo pínlǜ	Horizontal scan frequency	
水平面	Shuǐpíngmiàn	Horizontal plane	
水平面波束宽度	Shuǐpíngmiàn bōshù kuāndù	Horizontal plane bandWidth	HPBW
水上数字选呼系统	Shuǐshàng shùzì xuǎnhū xìtǒng	Maritime digital selective-calling system	
水上无线电导航业务	Shuǐshàng wúxiàndiàn dǎoháng yèwù	Maritime radio navigation service	
水上移动业务	Shuǐshàng yídòng yèwù	Maritime mobile service	
水声通信系统	Shuǐshēng tōngxìn xìtǒng	Hydro-acoustic communication system	
水下电话	Shuǐxià diànhuà	Underwater telephone	
水下光缆	Shuǐxià guānglǎn	Submarine optical fiber cable	SOFC
水下激光通信	Shuǐxià jīguāng tōngxìn	Underwater laser communication	
水胀热融	Shuǐzhàng rèróng	Water swelling heat melting (FOC)	WSHM
水准变动	Shuǐzhǔn biàndòng	Level change	
水准测量	Shuǐzhǔn cèliáng	Leveling	
水准路线	Shuǐzhǔn lùxiàn	Leveling route	
水准面	Shuǐzhǔn miàn	Level surface	
水准原点	Shuǐzhǔn yuándiǎn	Leveling origin	
水准点	Shuǐzhǔndiǎn	Benchmark	
水准仪	Shuǐzhǔnyí	Level (the instrument)	
竖井	Shùjǐng	Riser (FOC)	
数据	Shùjù	Data	D
数据安全	Shùjù ānquán	Data security	
数据安全性	Shùjù ānquánxìng	Data security	
数据绑定	Shùjù bǎngdìng	Data-bound (for database)	
数据报	Shùjù bào	Datagram	
数据包调度算法	Shùjù bāo diàodù suànfǎ	Packet scheduling algorithm	
数据包分组/重组功能	Shùjù bāo fēnzǔ/chóngzǔ gōngnéng	Data packet assembly/disassembly function	PAD
数据保安	Shùjù bǎo'ān	Data security	
数据保护工程	Shùjù bǎohù gōngchéng	Data protection engineering (IPsec)	
数据保密算法	Shùjù bǎomì suànfǎ	Data confidentiality algorithm	C-ALG
数据报文	Shùjù bàowén	Datagram	
数据爆炸	Shùjù bàozhà	Data explosion	
数据备份	Shùjù bèifèn	Data backup	
数据泵	Shùjù bèng	Data pump	
数据编辑	Shùjù biānjí	Data edit	
数据编码	Shùjù biānmǎ	Data encoding	

数据编码方案	Shùjù biānmǎ fāng'àn	Data coding scheme	DCS
数据表	Shùjù biǎo	Data table (for database)	
数据表达	Shùjù biǎodá	Data presentation	
数据标准化	Shùjù biāozhǔnhuà	Data standardization	
数据不确定性	Shùjù bùquèdìngxìng	Data uncertainty	
数据采集	Shùjù cǎijí	Data collection	
数据采集电路	Shùjù cǎijí diànlù	Data acquisition circuit	
数据采集器	Shùjù cǎijíqì	Data accumulation unit	DQU
数据仓库	Shùjù cāngkù	Data clearinghouse	
数据仓库	Shùjù cāngkù	Data warehouse	DW
数据槽	Shùjù cáo	Data sink	
数据操纵语言	Shùjù cāozòng yǔyán	Data manipulation language	DML
数据操作语言	Shùjù cāozuò yǔyán	Data manipulation language	DML
数据层	Shùjù céng	Data layer	DL
数据产品	Shùjù chǎnpǐn	Data product	
数据成员	Shùjù chéngyuán	Data member	
数据重放	Shùjù chóngfàng	Data replay (IPsec)	
数据抽取	Shùjù chōuqǔ	Data extraction	
数据抽取	Shùjù chōuqǔ	Data pump (for database)	
数据抽象	Shùjù chōuxiàng	Data abstraction	
数据串行接口	Shùjù chuànháng jiēkǒu	Data serial interface	DSI
数据传接交换台	Shùjù chuánjiē jiāohuàntái	Data switching exchange	DSE
数据传输	Shùjù chuánshū	Data transmission	
数据传输函数	Shùjù chuánshū hánshù	Data transmission function	DTF
数据传输设备	Shùjù chuánshū shèbèi	Data transmission equipment	DTE
数据传输速度	Shùjù chuánshū sùdù	Data transmission speed	
数据传输通信	Shùjù chuánshū tōngxìn	Data transmission telecommunication	SC
数据传输线路	Shùjù chuánshū xiànlù	Data transmission line	
数据传输协议	Shùjù chuánshū xiéyì	Data transmission protocol	DTP
数据传输系统	Shùjù chuánshū xìtǒng	Data transmission system	
数据传送	Shùjù chuánsòng	Data transfer	
数据传送速率	Shùjù chuánsòng sùlǜ	Data transmission rate	DTR
数据传送速率	Shùjù chuánsòng sùlǜ	Data transfer rate	
数据传送协议	Shùjù chuánsòng xiéyì	Data transfer protocol	DTP
数据储库	Shùjù chǔkù	Data warehousing	
数据处理	Shùjù chǔlǐ	Data processing	
数据处理子系统	Shùjù chǔlǐ zixìtǒng	Data handling sub-system	DHS
数据初值语句	Shùjù chūzhí yǔjù	Data initialization (in FORTRAN)	DATA
数据词典	Shùjù cídiǎn	Data dictionary	
数据存储单元	Shùjù cúnchǔ dānyuán	Data cache	
数据存储库	Shùjù cúnchǔkù	Data storage library	DL
数据存储器	Shùjù cúnchǔqì	Data storage device	DSD
数据存取	Shùjù cúnqǔ	Data access	DA
数据存贮	Shùjù cúnzhù	Data storage	
数据代码	Shùjù dàimǎ	Data code	
数据档案	Shùjù dàng'àn	Data archive	

数据单元	Shùjù dānyuán	Data cell	
数据单元的长度	Shùjù dānyuánde chángdù	Data cell length	LGTH
数据电话编制器	Shùjù diànhuà biānzhìqì	Dataphone line formatter	DPLF
数据电话交换数字业务	Shùjù diànhuà jiāohuàn shùzì yèwù	Dataphone switched digital service	DSDS
数据电话机	Shùjù diànhuàjī	Data phone	
数据电路	Shùjù diànlù	Data circuit	
数据电路端接设备	Shùjù diànlù duānjiē shèbèi	Data circuit terminating equipment	DCI
数据电路集中器	Shùjù diànlù jízhōngqì	Data circuit concentrator	DCC
数据电路设备	Shùjù diànlù shèbèi	Data circuit equipment	DCE
数据电路设备	Shùjù diànlù shèbèi	Data circuit equipment	DCE
数据电路透明性	Shùjù diànlù tòumíngxìng	Data circuit transparency	
数据电路终端设备	Shùjù diànlù zhōngduān shèbèi	Data circuit terminating equipment	DCE
数据电路终接设备	Shùjù diànlù zhōngjiē shèbèi	Data circuit (terminating) equipment	DCE
数据定界符	Shùjù dìngjièfú	Data delimiter	
数据定义	Shùjù dìngyì	Data definition	
数据定义查询	Shùjù dìngyì cháxún	Data definition query	
数据定义语言	Shùjù dìngyì yǔyán	Data definition language	DDL
数据丢失	Shùjù diūshī	Data missing	
数据地址	Shùjù dìzhǐ	Data address	DA
数据地址寄存器	Shùjù dìzhǐ jìcúnqì	Data address register	DAR
数据对传	Shùjù duìchuán	Data transfer	
数据对象	Shùjù duìxiàng	Data object	
数据发布	Shùjù fābù	Data dissemination	
数据访问安全性	Shùjù fǎngwèn ānquánxìng	Data access security	
数据访问对象	Shùjù fǎngwèn duìxiàng	Data access object	DAO
数据访问协议	Shùjù fǎngwèn xiéyì	Data access protocol (in DECnet)	DAP
数据访问语言	Shùjù fǎngwèn yǔyán	Data access language	DAL
数据分析	Shùjù fēnxī	Data analysis	
数据分组传送延迟	Shùjù fēnzǔ chuánsòng yánchí	Data packet transfer delay	
数据分组通信	Shùjù fēnzǔ tōngxìn	Data packet communications	DPC
数据符号	Shùjù fúhào	Data symbol	
数据服务部门	Shùjù fúwù bùmén	Data service division	DSD
数据服务单元	Shùjù fúwù dānyuán	Data service unit	DSU
数据服务器	Shùjù fúwùqì	Data server	
数据感知控件	Shùjù gǎnzhī kòngjiàn	Data-aware control (for database)	
数据高速通路	Shùjù gāosù tōnglù	Information superhighway; data highway	
数据更新	Shùjù gēngxīn	Data updating	
数据格式	Shùjù géshi	Data format	
数据共享	Shùjù gòngxiǎng	Data sharing	
数据广播	Shùjù guǎngbō	Intercast	
数据管理	Shùjù guǎnlǐ	Data administrator	
数据管理	Shùjù guǎnlǐ	Data management	
数据管理台	Shùjù guǎnlǐtái	Data management terminal	
数据关系图	Shùjù guānxi tú	Database diagram	
数据规范化	Shùjù guīfànhuà	Data normalization	
数据国家代码	Shùjù guójiā dàimǎ	Data country code	DCC

数据后处理系统	Shùjù hòuchǔlǐ xìtǒng	Data post-processing system	DPPS
数据缓冲器	Shùjù huǎnchōngqì	Data buffer cache (in SQL Server)	
数据汇	Shùjù huì	Data sink	
数据恢复请求	Shùjù huīfù qǐngqiú	Data retrieval request (SS7)	
数据恢复确认	Shùjù huīfù quèrèn	Data retrieval confirm (SS7)	
数据恢复完成指示	Shùjù huīfù wánchéng zhǐshì	Data retrieval complete indication (SS7)	
数据恢复指示	Shùjù huīfù zhǐshì	Data retrieval indication (SS7)	
数据会议	Shùjù huìyì	Data conferencing	
数据获取	Shùjù huòqǔ	Data acquisition	
数据获取	Shùjù huòqǔ	Data capture	
数据集	Shùjù jí	Data set	
数据集就绪	Shùjù jí jiùxù	Data set ready	DSR
数据加密	Shùjù jiāmì	Data encryption	
数据加密标准	Shùjù jiāmì biāozhǔn	Data encryption standard	DES
数据加密键	Shùjù jiāmì jiàn	Data encryption key	DEK
数据加密算法	Shùjù jiāmì suànfǎ	Data encryption algorithm	DEA
数据检验	Shùjù jiǎnyàn	Data verification	
数据交叉连接系统	Shùjù jiāochā liánjiē xìtǒng	Digital cross-connect system	DCS
数据交换	Shùjù jiāohuàn	Data exchange, data interchange	
数据交换标准	Shùjù jiāohuàn biāozhǔn	Data exchange standard	
数据交换标准协会	Shùjù jiāohuàn biāozhǔn xiéhuì	Data Interchange Standard Association	DISA
数据交换格式	Shùjù jiāohuàn géshi	Data exchange format	DXF
数据交换接口	Shùjù jiāohuàn jiēkǒu	Data exchange interface	DXI
数据交换设备	Shùjù jiāohuàn shèbèi	Data switching equipment	DSE
数据交换输入输出设备	Shùjù jiāohuàn shūrù shūchū shèbèi	Data exchange input-output device	DXIO
数据交换组	Shùjù jiāohuàn zǔ	Transferred account data interchange group (GSM MoU)	TADIG
数据交换机	Shùjù jiāohuànjī	Data switch exchange	DSE
数据交织	Shùjù jiāozhī	Data interleaving	
数据集成	Shùjù jíchéng	Data integration	
数据结构	Shùjù jiégòu	Data structure	
数据接口板	Shùjù jiēkǒu bǎn	Data interface board	DDU
数据记录光盘	Shùjù jìlù guāngpán	Optical data disk	ODD
数据记录器	Shùjù jìlùqì	Data recorder	
数据机密性	Shùjù jīmìxìng	Data confidentiality (IPsec)	
数据集市	Shùjù jíshì	Data mart (for database)	
数据记事	Shùjù jìshì	Data logging	
数据集中器	Shùjù jízhōngqì	Data concentrator	
数据聚合	Shùjù jùhé	Data aggregation	
数据可访问性	Shùjù kěfǎngwènxìng	Data accessibility	
数据可靠性	Shùjù kěkàoxìng	Data reliability	
数据可视化	Shùjù kěshìhuà	Data visualization	
数据可用性	Shùjù kěyòngxìng	Data availability	
数据控制	Shùjù kòngzhì	Data control	
数据控制语言	Shùjù kòngzhì yǔyán	Data control language (for database)	DCL
数据块	Shùjù kuài	Data block	
数据块地址	Shùjù kuài dìzhǐ	Data block address (in ORACLE)	DBAD

数据块检查序列	Shùjù kuài jiǎnchá xùliè	Block check sequence	BCS
数据类型	Shùjù lèixíng	Data type	
数据链转义	Shùjù liàn zhuǎnyì	Data link escape	DLE
数据量	Shùjù liàng	Volume of data	
数据连接	Shùjù liánjiē	Data connection (for database)	
数据链路	Shùjù liànlù	Data link	DL
数据链路层	Shùjù liànlù céng	Data link layer	DLL
数据链路服务	Shùjù liànlù fúwù	Data link service	DLS
数据链路服务访问点	Shùjù liànlù fúwù fǎngwèndiǎn	Data link service access point	DLSAP
数据链路服务数据单元	Shùjù liànlù fúwù shùjù dānyuán	Data link service data unit	DLSDU
数据链路核心层	Shùjù liànlù héxīn céng	Data link core	DL-CORE
数据链路后面板	Shùjù liànlù hòumian bǎn	Data link back panel	DLBP
数据链路鉴别器	Shùjù liànlù jiànbiéqì	Data link discriminator	DLD
数据链路交换	Shùjù liànlù jiāohuàn	Data-link switching	DLSw
数据链路交换协议	Shùjù liànlù jiāohuàn xiéyì	Data link switching protocol	DLSw
数据链路控制	Shùjù liànlù kòngzhì	Data link control	DL-Control
数据链路连接	Shùjù liànlù liánjiē	Data link connection	DLC
数据链路连接标志	Shùjù liànlù liánjiē biāozhì	Data link connection identifier	DLCI
数据链路连接标识	Shùjù liànlù liánjiē biāozhì	Data link connection identifier	DLCI
数据链路连接标识符	Shùjù liànlù liánjiē biāozhìfú	Data link connection identifier	DLCI
数据链路连接识别	Shùjù liànlù liánjiē shíbié	Data link connection identity	DLCI
数据链路连接证实	Shùjù liànlù liánjiē zhèngshí	Data link connection identity	DLCI
数据链路连接型数据传输	Shùjù liànlù liánjiēxíng shùjù chuánshū	Data-link-connection-mode data transmission	
数据链路无连接型数据传输	Shùjù liànlù wúliánjiēxíng shùjù chuánshū	Data-link-connectionless-mode data transmission	
数据链路协议	Shùjù liànlù xiéyì	Data link protocol	
数据链路转义字符	Shùjù liànlù zhuǎnyì zìfú	Data link escape character	DLE
数据立方	Shùjù lìfāng	Data cube	
数据立方体	Shùjù lìfāngtǐ	Datacube	
数据流	Shùjù liú	Data-flow, data stream	
数据流分析	Shùjù liú fēnxī	Traffic analysis	
数据流控制层	Shùjù liú kòngzhì céng	Data-flow control layer	
数据描述语言	Shùjù miáoshù yǔyán	Data description language	DDL
数据描述字	Shùjù miáoshù zì	Data descripition word	DDW
数据敏感性故障	Shùjù mǐngǎnxìng gùzhàng	Data-sensitive fault	
数据密钥	Shùjù mìyào	Data key	DK
数据模块	Shùjù mókuài	Datem	
数据模式	Shùjù móshì	Schema	
数据模式模型	Shùjù móshì móxíng	Schema model	
数据模型	Shùjù móxíng	Data model	
数据目标	Shùjù mùbiāo	Data object	DO
数据目录	Shùjù mùlù	Data catalog	
数据内插	Shùjù nèichā	Data interpolation	
数据平滑	Shùjù pínghuá	Data smoothing	
数据品质测定	Shùjù pǐnzhì cèdìng	Data quality measure	
数据品质评价值程序	Shùjù pǐnzhì ping jiàzhí chéngxù	Data quality evaluation procedure	

数据品质评价值的类型	Shùjù pǐnzhì ping jiàzhíde lèixíng	Data quality value type	
数据品质评价结果	Shùjù pǐnzhì píngjià jiéguǒ	Data quality result	
数据品质日期	Shùjù pǐnzhì rìqī	Data quality date	
数据品质要素	Shùjù pǐnzhì yàosù	Data quality element	
数据品质的次生要素	Shùjù pǐnzhìde cìshēng yàosù	Data quality sub-element	
数据品质的浏览要素	Shùjù pǐnzhìde liúlǎn yàosù	Data quality overview element	
数据品质的使用范围	Shùjù pǐnzhìde shǐyòng fànwéi	Data quality scope	
数据前送	Shùjù qiánsòng	Data forwarding	
数据窃取	Shùjù qièqǔ	Data interception	
数据清理	Shùjù qīnglǐ	Data scrubbing (for database)	
数据权限	Shùjù quánxiàn	Data rights	
数据驱动攻击	Shùjù qūdòng gōngjī	Data-driven attack (IPsec)	
数据确认	Shùjù quèrèn	Data validation	
数据融合	Shùjù rónghé	Data fusion	
数据冗余度	Shùjù rǒngyúdù	Data redundancy	
数据商场	Shùjù shāngchǎng	Data mart	
数据视图	Shùjù shìtú	Data view	
数据时隙分配板	Shùjù shíxì fēnpèi bǎn	Data time-slot distribution (board)	DTD
数据收集处理器	Shùjù shōují chǔlǐqì	Data collection processor	
数据收集 PC 机	Shùjù shōují PC-jī	Data collection PC	DCP
数据手套	Shùjù shǒutào	Data glove (robotics)	
数据输出	Shùjù shūchū	Data export; data output	
数据说明	Shùjù shuōmíng	Data specification	
数据输入	Shùjù shūrù	Data entry; data input	
数据输入话音输出电话系统	Shùjù shūrù huàyīn shūchū diànhuà xìtǒng	Data input voice output telephone system	DIVOTS
数据属性	Shùjù shǔxing	Data attribute	
数据宿	Shùjù sù	Data sink	
数据损害	Shùjù sǔnhài	Data contamination (IPsec)	
数据索引	Shùjù suǒyǐn	Data indexing	
数据探索	Shùjù tànsuǒ	Data exploration	
数据通信	Shùjù tōngxìn	Data communication	
数据通信多路复用器	Shùjù tōngxìn duōlù fùyòngqì	Data communication multiplexer	DCM
数据通信功能	Shùjù tōngxìn gōngnéng	Data communication function	DCF
数据通信接口	Shùjù tōngxìn jiēkǒu	Data communication interface	DCI
数据通信控制规程	Shùjù tōngxìn kòngzhì guīchéng	Data communication control procedure	DCCP
数据通信设备	Shùjù tōngxìn shèbèi	Data communication equipment	DCE
数据通信设备监控与转换	Shùjù tōngxìn shèbèi jiānkòng yǔ zhuǎnhuàn	Data communication equipment monitoring and switching	DACEMS
数据通信通道	Shùjù tōngxìn tōngdào	Data communications channel	DCC
数据通信通路	Shùjù tōngxìn tōnglù	Data communication channel	DCC
数据通信信道	Shùjù tōngxìn xìndào	Data communication channel	DCC
数据通信网	Shùjù tōngxìnwǎng	Data communication network	DCN
数据透视	Shùjù tòushì	Pivot	
数据挖掘	Shùjù wājué	Data mining	
数据挖掘工具	Shùjù wājué gōngjù	Data mining tool	
数据网标别码	Shùjù wǎng biāobiémǎ	Data network identification code	DNIC

数据网标识码	Shùjù wǎng biāozhìmǎ	Data network identification code	DNIC
数据网格	Shùjù wǎnggé	Data grid	
数据网络标识符	Shùjù wǎngluò biāozhìfú	Data network identifier	DNID
数据网络识别码	Shùjù wǎngluò shíbiéma	Data network identification code	DNIC
数据完全性	Shùjù wánquánxìng	Data completeness	
数据完整性	Shùjù wánzhěngxìng	Data integrity (IPsec)	
数据完整性算法	Shùjù wánzhěngxìng suànfǎ	Data integrity algorithm	I-ALG
数据位	Shùjù wèi	Data bit	
数据文件	Shùjù wénjiàn	Data file (for database)	
数据误差	Shùjù wùchā	Data error	
数据项	Shùjù xiàng	Data item	
数据项标签	Shùjù xiàng biāoqiān	Data item label	
数据相关性	Shùjù xiāngguānxìng	Data relativity	
数据线路复用器	Shùjù xiànlù fùyòngqì	Data line multiplexer	DLM
数据消息传送	Shùjù xiāoxi chuánsòng	Data message transmission	DMT
数据消息处理	Shùjù xiāoxi chǔlǐ	Data message handling	DMH
数据消息处理器	Shùjù xiāoxi chǔlǐqì	Data message handler	DMH
数据信道	Shùjù xìndào	Data channel (D channel)	
数据信道保护级别	Shùjù xìndào bǎohù jíbié	Data channel protection level (in FTP)	PROT
数据信道单元	Shùjù xìndào dānyuán	Data channel unit	DCU
数据形式 1	Shùjù xíngshì 1	Data form1	DT1
数据信号	Shùjù xìnhào	Data signal	
数据信号处理器	Shùjù xìnhào chǔlǐqì	Data signal processor	DSP
数据信号率选择 (信号)	Shùjù xìnhào lǜ xuǎnzé (xìnhào)	Data signal rate selection (signal)	DSRS
数据信号速率	Shùjù xìnhào sùlǜ	Data signal rate	
数据信令速率	Shùjù xìnlìng sùlǜ	Data signaling rate	
数据修改	Shùjù xiūgǎi	Data modification	
数据选通连接	Shùjù xuǎntōng liánjiē	Data strobe link	DSL
数据沿袭	Shùjù yánxí	Data lineage	
数据压缩	Shùjù yāsuō	Data compression	
数据页	Shùjù yè	Data page (in Sybase)	
数据业务单元	Shùjù yèwù dānyuán	Data services unit	DSU
数据溢出错误	Shùjù yìchū cuòwù	Data overrun error	
数据依赖图	Shùjù yīlài tú	Data dependence graph	DDG
数据隐藏	Shùjù yǐncáng	Data hiding	
数据用户部分	Shùjù yònghù bùfen	Data user part	DUP
数据用户终端设备	Shùjù yònghù zhōngduān shèbèi	Data subscriber terminal equipment	DSTE
数据与信息责任	Shùjù yǔ xìnxī zérèn	Liability for data and information	
数据元	Shùjù yuán	Data element	
数据源	Shùjù yuán	Data source	
数据源名称	Shùjù yuán míngchēng	Data source name (for database)	DSN
数据源认证	Shùjù yuán rènzhèng	Data source authentication (IPsec)	
数据元素	Shùjù yuánsù	Data element	
数据载波故障检测器	Shùjù zàibō gùzhàng jiǎncèqì	Data carrier failure detector	DCF
数据载体监测	Shùjù zàitǐ jiāncè	Data carrier detect	DCD
数据站	Shùjù zhàn	Data station	

数据帧	Shùjù zhèng	Data frame	DF
数据志	Shùjù zhì	Lineage	
数据质量	Shùjù zhìliàng	Data quality	
数据终端就绪	Shùjù zhōngduān jiùxù	Data terminal ready	
数据终端设备	Shùjù zhōngduān shèbèi	Data terminal (or termination) equipment	DTE
数据终端设备与数据电路设备接口	Shùjù zhōngduān shèbèi yǔ shùjù diànlù shèbèi jiēkǒu	Data terminal equipment/data circuit equipment (DTE/DCE) interface	
数据中心	Shùjù zhōngxīn	Data center	
数据中心标记语言	Shùjù zhōngxīn biāojì yǔyán	Data center markup language	DCML
数据转化	Shùjù zhuǎnhuà	Data conversion	
数据转换服务	Shùjù zhuǎnhuàn fúwù	Data transformation services (in SQL Server)	DTS
数据转换交换机	Shùjù zhuǎnhuàn jiāohuànjī	Data switching exchange	DSE
数据转换模块	Shùjù zhuǎnhuàn mókuài	Data conversion module	DCM
数据转接客户访问协议	Shùjù zhuǎnjiē kèhù fǎngwèn xiéyì	Data link switching client access protocol (IETF use)	DCAP
数据转移	Shùjù zhuǎnyí	Data transfer	
数据字典	Shùjù zìdiǎn	Data dictionary (for database)	
数据字典视图	Shùjù zìdiǎn shìtú	Data dictionary view (for database)	
数据自适应鉴别器与监视器	Shùjù zìshìyìng jiànbiéqì yǔ jiānshìqì	Data adaptive evaluator and monitor	DAEMON
数据自由路	Shùjù zìyóu lù	Data freeway	DFW
数据自由通道	Shùjù zìyóu tōngdào	Data freeway	DFW
数据总线	Shùjù zǒngxiàn	Data bus	D-BUS
数据总线连接器	Shùjù zǒngxiàn liánjiēqì	Data bus connector	
数据报传送协议	Shùjùbào chuánsòng xiéyì	Datagram delivery protocol (Apple use)	DDP
数据的集中性	Shùjùde jízhōngxìng	Data convergence (in SQL Server)	
数据集	Shùjùjí	Dataset (for database)	
数据库	Shùjùkù	Database	DB
数据库安全系统	Shùjùkù ānquán xìtǒng	Database security system	DBSS
数据库表述类型	Shùjùkù biǎoshù lèixíng	Database portrayal catalog	
数据库处理	Shùjùkù chǔlǐ	Database handling	DBH
数据库对象	Shùjùkù duìxiàng	Database object	
数据库复制软件	Shùjùkù fùzhì ruǎnjiàn	Database propagation software	
数据库工程	Shùjùkù gōngchéng	Database project	
数据库管理系统	Shùjùkù guǎnlǐ xìtǒng	Database management system	DBMS
数据库管理者	Shùjùkù guǎnlǐzhě	Database administrator	DBA
数据库故障管理	Shùjùkù gùzhàng guǎnlǐ	Database fault management	DB-FM
数据库架构	Shùjùkù jiàgòu	Database schema	
数据库脚本	Shùjùkù jiǎoběn	Database script	
数据库集成器	Shùjùkù jíchéngqì	Database integrator	
数据库角色	Shùjùkù juésè	Database role	
数据库控制系统核心	Shùjùkù kòngzhì xìtǒng héxīn	Database control system nucleus	DCSN
数据库逻辑设计	Shùjùkù luójì shèjì	Logical database design	
数据库模式	Shùjùkù móshì	Database schema	
数据库目录	Shùjùkù mùlù	Database directory	
数据库目录	Shùjùkù mùlù	Database catalog	
数据库设计	Shùjùkù shèjì	Database design	
数据库寿命	Shùjùkù shòumìng	Database longevity	

数据库锁定	Shùjùkù suǒdìng	Database lock	
数据库所有者	Shùjùkù suǒyǒuzhě	Database owner	
数据库完整性	Shùjùkù wánzhěngxìng	Database integrity	
数据库文件	Shùjùkù wénjiàn	Database file	
数据库物理设计	Shùjùkù wùlǐ shèjì	Physical database design	
数据库系列	Shùjùkù xìliè	Dataset series	
数据库溢出	Shùjùkù yìchū	Database overload	DBOL
数据库引擎	Shùjùkù yǐnqíng	Database engine	
数据库一致性检查程序	Shùjùkù yīzhìxìng jiǎnchá chéngxù	Database consistency checker (in SQL Server)	DBCC
数据库语言	Shùjùkù yǔyán	Database language	
数据库组织系统	Shùjùkù zǔzhī xìtǒng	Database organizing system	DBOS
数据库中的知识发现	Shùjùkù-zhōngde zhīshi fāxiàn	Knowledge discovery in databases	KDD
数控振荡器	Shùkòng zhèndàngqì	Numerically controlled oscillator	NCO
束流	Shùliú	Beam	
束流天线	Shùliú tiānxiàn	Beam antenna	
鼠笼型	Shǔlóng xíng	Squirrel-cage	
数码管	Shùmǎ guǎn	Nixie light	
数码集群流动通讯	Shùmǎ jíqún liúdòng tōngxùn	Terrestrial trunked radio	TETRA
数码相机	Shùmǎ xiàngjī	Digital camera	
疏密波	Shūmìbō	Dilatational wave	
瞬变电磁脉冲发射标准	Shùnbiàn diàncí màichōng fāshè biāozhǔn	Transient electromagnetic pulse emanation standard	TEMPEST
瞬变过程	Shùnbiàn guòchéng	Transient process	
顺从流	Shùncóng liú	Conformant traffic	
顺从周期	Shùncóng zhōuqī	Compliance period	
瞬断	Shùnduàn	Interruption	
瞬间电压抑制器	Shùnjiān diànyā yìzhìqì	Transient voltage suppressor	
瞬间过冲	Shùnjiān guòchōng	Transient overshoot	
瞬间故障	Shùnjiān gùzhàng	Transient fault	
瞬间特性	Shùnjiān tèxìng	Transient characteristic	TC
瞬时	Shùnshí	Moment	
瞬时不可用性	Shùnshí bùkěyòngxìng	Instantaneous unavailability	U(t)
瞬时测频接收机	Shùnshí cèpín jiēshōujī	Instantaneous frequency measurement receiver	
瞬时峰值功率	Shùnshí fēngzhí gōnglǜ	Instantaneous peak power (in a transmission line)	
瞬时故障	Shùnshí gùzhàng	Transient fault	
瞬时可用性	Shùnshí kěyòngxìng	Instantaneous availability	A(t)
瞬时频率	Shùnshí pínlǜ	Instantaneous frequency (of a signal)	
瞬时频率偏移	Shùnshí pínlǜ piānyí	Instantaneous frequency deviation	
瞬时频偏控制	Shùnshí pínpiān kòngzhì	Instantaneous deviation control	IDC
瞬时频偏控制器	Shùnshí pínpiān kòngzhìqì	Instantaneous deviation controller	IDC
瞬时失效率	Shùnshí shīxiào lǜ	Instantaneous failure rate	
瞬时失效频度	Shùnshí shīxiào píndù	Instantaneous failure intensity	Z(t)
瞬时通信	Shùnshí tōngxìn	Transient communication	
瞬时相位偏移	Shùnshí xiàngwèi piānyí	Instantaneous phase deviation	
瞬时响应时间常数	Shùnshí xiǎngyìng shíjiān chángshù	Transient response time constant	
瞬时修复率	Shùnshí xiūfù lǜ	Instantaneous repair rate	
瞬时增益响应	Shùnshí zēngyì xiǎngyìng	Transient gain response	

瞬时自动增益控制	Shùnshí zìdòng zēngyì kòngzhì	Instantaneous automatic gain control	IAGC
顺时针极化波	Shùnshízhēn jíhuà bō	Clockwise polarized wave	
瞬态	Shùntài	Instantaneous state	
瞬态	Shùntài	Transient (adjective and noun)	
瞬态交扰饱和	Shùntài jiāorǎo bǎohé	Transient cross saturation	
瞬态失真	Shùntài shīzhēn	Transient distortion	
瞬态响应	Shùntài xiǎngyìng	Transient response	
瞬态信号的上升时间	Shùntài xìnhàode shàngshēng shíjiān	Transient signal rise time	Tr/Th
顺行轨道	Shùnxíng guǐdào	Direct orbit (of a satellite)	
顺序布局次序	Shùnxù bùjú cìxù	Sequential layout order	
顺序彩色和存储视频制式	Shùnxù cǎisè hé cúnchǔ shìpín zhìshì	Sequential Couleur avec Memoire (Middle East television standard)	SECAM
顺序查找	Shùnxù cházhǎo	Sequential search	
顺序磁盘处理机	Shùnxù cípán chǔlǐjī	Sequential disk processor	SDP
顺序次序	Shùnxù cìxù	Sequential order	
顺序单音制	Shùnxù dānyīn zhì	Individual tone sequential system	
顺序分配多路存取	Shùnxù fēnpèi duōlù cúnqǔ	Sequence division multiple access	SDMA
顺序分组交换	Shùnxù fēnzǔ jiāohuàn	Sequenced packet exchange	SPX
顺序分组协议	Shùnxù fēnzǔ xiéyì	Sequenced packet protocol	SPP
顺序关系	Shùnxù guānxi	Sequenced relationship	
顺序号	Shùnxù hào	Sequence number	SN
顺序号码保护	Shùnxù hàomǎ bǎohù	Sequence number protection	SNP
顺序集合	Shùnxù jíhé	Sequenced collection	
顺序刻度	Shùnxù kèdù	Ordinal scale	
顺序控制逻辑	Shùnxù kòngzhì luóji	Sequential control logic	SCL
顺序流式传输	Shùnxù liú-shì chuánshū	Progressive streaming	
顺序逻辑次序	Shùnxù luóji cìxù	Sequential logical order	
顺序路由更新协议	Shùnxù lùyóu gēngxīn xiéyì	Sequenced routing update protocol	SRTP
顺序脉冲单音制	Shùnxù màichōng dānyīn zhì	Pulsed individual tone sequential system	
顺序脉冲单音制	Shùnxù màichōng dānyīn zhì	Pulsed individual tone sequential system	
顺序搜寻	Shùnxù sōuxún	Sequential hunting	
顺序位移键控-直接序列扩展频谱	Shùnxù wèiyí jiànkòng—zhíjiē xùliè kuòzhǎn pínpǔ	Sequence shift keying-direct sequence spread spectrum	SSK-DS-SS
顺序文件	Shùnxù wénjiàn	Sequential file	
顺序信息包协议	Shùnxù xìnxī bāo xiéyì	Sequenced packet protocol	SPP
顺序与存储彩色电视系统	Shùnxù yǔ cúnchǔ cǎisè diànshì xìtǒng	SEquential Couleur avec memoire (French television broadcast standard)	SECAM
顺序列单音制	Shùnxùliè dānyīn zhì	Individual tone sequential system	
说明部件	Shuōmíng bùjiàn	Declaration unit	
说明与描述语言	Shuōmíng yǔ miáoshù yǔyán	Specification description language	SDL
书签	Shūqiān	Bookmark (for Web browser)	
输入	Shūrù	Input; import	
输入补偿电流	Shūrù bǔcháng diànliú	Input offset current	
输入参考面	Shūrù cānkǎo miàn	Input reference plane	
输入成员	Shūrù chéngyuán	Input member	
输入电平	Shūrù diànpíng	Input level	
输入电压范围	Shūrù diànyā fànwéi	Input voltage range	

输入电源控制	Shūrù diànyuán kòngzhì	Input power control	
输入抖动	Shūrù dǒudòng	Input jitter	
输入抖动容限	Shūrù dǒudòng róngxiàn	Input jitter tolerance	
输入法编辑器	Shūrù fǎ biānjíqì	Input method editor	IME
输入法窗口	Shūrù fǎ chuāngkǒu	Input method window (WP command)	
输入访问控制寄存器	Shūrù fǎngwèn kòngzhì jìcúnqì	Input access control register	IACR
输入功率	Shūrù gōnglǜ	Input power	
输入功率控制	Shūrù gōnglǜ kòngzhì	Input power control	
输入光功率	Shūrù guāng gōnglǜ	Input optical power	IOP
输入回波抑制器	Shūrù huíbō yìzhìqì	Incoming echo suppressor	IES
输入集	Shūrù jí	Input set	
输入模拟网络	Shūrù mónǐ wǎngluò	Input simulation network	
输入漂移容限	Shūrù piāoyí róngxiàn	Input wander tolerance	
输入认可	Shūrù rènkě	Input acknowledge	IA
输入输出结合排队	Shūrù shūchū jiéhé páiduì	Combined input/output queuing	CIOQ
输入特性	Shūrù tèxìng	Input characteristics	
输入误码计数	Shūrù wùma jìshù	Incoming error count	IEC
输入信号电压	Shūrù xìnhào diànyā	Input-signal voltage	
输入信号失效	Shūrù xìnhào shīxiào	Incoming signal failure	ISF
输入信号源	Shūrù xìnhào yuán	Input-signal source	
输入源	Shūrù yuán	Input source	
输入语音域	Shūrù yǔyīn yù	Input speech domain	
输入阻抗	Shūrù zǔkàng	Input impedance	
输入/输出	Shūrù/shūchū	Input/output	I/O
输入/输出表	Shūrù/shūchū biǎo	Input/output list	
输入/输出处理机	Shūrù/shūchū chǔlǐjī	Input/output processor	IOP
输入/输出单元	Shūrù/shūchū dānyuán	Input/output cell	
输入/输出控制中心	Shūrù/shūchū kòngzhì zhōngxīn	Input/output controller hub	ICH
输入/输出设备	Shūrù/shūchū shèbèi	Input/output device	I/O
输入/输出通道	Shūrù/shūchū tōngdào	Input/output channel	
输入/输出语句	Shūrù/shūchū yǔjù	Input/output statement	
输入/输出指令	Shūrù/shūchū zhǐlìng	Input/output instruction	
输送区	Shūsòng qū	Transporting zone	
输送带	Shūsòngdài	Conveyer (in component assembly process)	
数位	Shùwèi	Digit (in telecommunication signaling)	
数位拨号	Shùwèi bōhào	Abbreviated dialling numbers	ADN
数位删除	Shùwèi shānchú	Digit deletion	
数位时隙	Shùwèi shíxì	Digit time slot	
数位调变器	Shùwèi tiáobiànqì	Digital modulator	
数位吸收	Shùwèi xīshōu	Digit absorption	
数位式欧洲无绳电话	Shùwèi-shì Oūzhōu wúshéng diànhuà	Digital European Cordless Telephone	DECT
书写电报	Shūxiě diànbào	Telewriting telescript	
属性	Shǔxìng	Attribute	
属性	Shǔxìng	Property	
属性编码	Shǔxìng biānmǎ	Attribute code	
属性表	Shǔxìng biǎo	Attribute list	

属性表	Shǔxìng biǎo	Attribute table	
属性标题	Shǔxìng biāotí	Attribute header	
属性标识符	Shǔxìng biāozhìfú	Attribute identifier	
属性查询	Shǔxìng cháxún	Attribute query	
属性抽样	Shǔxìng chōuyàng	Attribute sampling	
属性错误	Shǔxìng cuòwù	Attribute error	
属性定义	Shǔxìng dìngyì	Attribute definition	
属性关联	Shǔxìng guānlián	Attribute association	
树形和板状的组合标志	Shùxíng hé bǎnzhuàngde zǔhé biāozhì	Tree and tabular combined notation	TTCN
属性检验规则	Shǔxìng jiǎnyàn guīzé	Attribute validation rule	
属性记录	Shǔxìng jìlù	Attribute record	
属性精度	Shǔxìng jīngdù	Attribute accuracy	
属性类型	Shǔxìng lèixíng	Attribute class	
属性类型	Shǔxìng lèixíng	Attribute type	
属性类型码	Shǔxìng lèixíng mǎ	Attribute type codes	
属性类型名称	Shǔxìng lèixíng míngchēng	Attribute type name	
属性连接	Shǔxìng liánjiē	Attribute linkage	
属性邻接图	Shǔxìng línjiē tú	Attributed adjacency graph (CAD/CAM)	AAG
属性目录	Shǔxìng mùlù	Attribute catalogue	
树型耦合器	Shù-xíng ǒuhéqì	Tree coupler	
属性匹配	Shǔxìng pǐpèi	Attribute matching	
属性数据	Shǔxìng shùjù	Attribute data	
树型索引	Shù-xíng suǒyǐn	Tree index	
属性文件	Shǔxìng wénjiàn	Attribute file	
属性相似性	Shǔxìng xiāngsìxìng	Attribute similarity	
属性页	Shǔxìng yè	Property pages	
属性一致性检验	Shǔxìng yīzhìxìng jiǎnyàn	Attribute consistency checking	
属性域	Shǔxìng yù	Attribute domain	
属性约简	Shǔxìng yuējiǎn	Attribute reduction	
属性证书	Shǔxìng zhèngshū	Attribute certificate	
属性值	Shǔxìng zhí	Attribute value	
属性值代码	Shǔxìng zhí dàimǎ	Attribute value codes	
属性值定义	Shǔxìng zhí dìngyì	Attribute value definition	
属性值断言	Shǔxìng zhí duànyán	Attribute value assertion	
属性值判断语	Shǔxìng zhí pànduàn yǔ	Attribute value assertion	AVA
属性准确度	Shǔxìng zhǔnquèdù	Attribute accuracy	
树型-分支结构	Shù-xíng—fēnzhī jiégòu	Tree and branch architecture	
数学附处理器	Shùxué fùchǔlǐqì	Math coprocessor	
数学形态学	Shùxué xíngtàixué	Mathematical morphology (in GIS)	
数值表达式	Shùzhí biǎodá shì	Numeric expression	
数值分类	Shùzhí fēnlèi	Numerical classification	
数值解析	Shùzhí jiěxī	Numerical analysis	
数值孔径	Shùzhí kǒngjìng	Numerical aperture (of FOC)	NA
数值模拟	Shùzhí mónǐ	Numerical simulation	
数值模型	Shùzhí móxíng	Numerical model	
数值实验	Shùzhí shíyàn	Numerical experiments	

数值问题	Shùzhí wèntí	Numerical problem	
输纸装置	Shūzhǐ zhuāngzhì	Cut-sheet feeder	
树状多播	Shù-zhuàng duōbō	Tree-based multicast	
树状分支光纤耦合器	Shù-zhuàng fēnzhī guāngxiān ǒuhéqì	Tree optical coupler	
数字	Shùzì	Digit, digital	
数字安全	Shùzì ānquán	Data safety	
数字包统计多路复用	Shùzì bāo tǒngjì duōlù fùyòng	Packet statistical multiplexing	
数字包封	Shùzì bāofēng	Digital wrapper	
数字本地交换运营	Shùzì běndì jiāohuàn yùnyíng	Building local exchange carrier	BLEC
数字编码	Shùzì biānmǎ	Numeric coding	
数字编码将净躁制	Shùzì biānmǎ jiāngjìngzào zhì	Digital code squelch	DCS
数字编码语音	Shùzì biānmǎ yǔyīn	Digitally coded voice	DCV
数字比例尺	Shùzì bǐlìchǐ	Digitial scale	
数字波束行成	Shùzì bōshù xíngchéng	Digital beam forming	
数字参考序列	Shùzì cānkǎo xùliè	Digital reference sequence	DRS
数字测距	Shùzì cèjù	Digital ranging	
数字参差调制	Shùzì cēncī tiáozhì	Digital offset modulation	
数字参差调制	Shùzì cēncī tiáozhì	Digital staggered modulation	
数字差错	Shùzì chācuò	Digital error	
数字差错率	Shùzì chācuò lǜ	Digit error ratio	
数字插入装置	Shùzì chārù zhuāngzhì	Digital patch unit	DPU
数字查找树	Shùzì cházhǎo shù	Digital search tree	
数字成图组织	Shùzì chéngtú zǔzhī	Digital imaging group	DIG
数字传感器	Shùzì chuángǎnqì	Digital sensor	
数字传声器	Shùzì chuánshēngqì	Digital microphone	
数字传输	Shùzì chuánshū	Digital transmission	
数字传输链路	Shùzì chuánshū liànlù	Digital transmission link	
数字传输通路	Shùzì chuánshū tōnglù	Digital transmission channel	
数字传输信道	Shùzì chuánshū xìndào	Digital transmission channel	
数字传真接口系统	Shùzì chuánzhēn jiēkǒu xìtǒng	Digital facsimile interface system	DFIS
数字存储媒体-控制命令	Shùzì cúnchǔ méitǐ—kòngzhì mìngling	Digital storage media-control command	DSM-CC
数字存储媒体 - 控制命令	Shùzì cúnchǔ méitǐ-kòngzhì mìnglìng	Digital storage media - control command	DSM - CC
数字存储媒体 - 控制命令用户至用户	Shùzì cúnchǔ méitǐ-kòngzhì mìnglìng yònghù zhì yònghù	Digital storage media - control command, user-to-user	DSM-CC U-U
数字存取和交叉连接系统	Shùzì cúnqǔ hé jiāochā liánjiē xìtǒng	Digital access and cross-connect system	DACS
数字单元	Shùzì dānyuán	Digital unit	DU
数字单元	Shùzì dānyuán	Digital block	
数字单元底版	Shùzì dānyuán dǐbǎn	Digital unit backplane board	DUBB-A
数字单元后面板	Shùzì dānyuán hòumian bǎn	Digital unit back board	DUBB
数字电流表	Shùzì diànliúbiǎo	Digital ammeter	
数字电路	Shùzì diànlù	Digital circuit	
数字电路倍增设备	Shùzì diànlù bèizēng shèbèi	Digital circuit multiplication equipment	DCME
数字电路倍增设备–自适应差分脉冲编码调制	Shùzì diànlù bèizēng shèbèi—zìshìyìng chāfēn màichōng biānmǎ tiáozhì	Digital circuit multiplication equipment- adaptive differential pulse code modulation	DCME-ADPCM
数字电路网	Shùzì diànlù wǎng	Digital circuit network	DCN
数字电路终接设备	Shùzì diànlù zhōngjiē shèbèi	Data circuit terminating equipment	DCE

数字电视广播	Shùzì diànshì guǎngbō	Digital video broadcast	DVB
数子电视显示系统	Shùzi diànshì xiǎnshì xìtǒng	Digital television display system	DTDS
数字电信电路	Shùzì diànxìn diànlù	Digital telecommunication circuit	
数字电子报文业务	Shùzì diànzǐ bàowén yèwù	Digital electronic message service	DEMS
数字地理空间元数据	Shùzì dìlǐ kōngjiān yuán shùjù	Digital geospatial metadata	DGM
数字地球	Shùzì dìqiú	Digital earth	
数字地图	Shùzì dìtú	Digital map	
数字地图数据	Shùzì dìtú shùjù	Digital map data	
数字地形模型	Shùzì dìxíng móxíng	Digital terrain model	DTM
数字地址	Shùzì dìzhǐ	Internet protocol address	
数字地址接收器	Shùzì dìzhǐ jiēshōuqì	Address digital receiver	ADR
数字段	Shùzì duàn	Digital section or segment	DS
数字段拉远	Shùzì duàn lāyuǎn	Digital segment extension	
数字段的级	Shùzì duànde jí	Digital section level	
数字多波段传输系统	Shùzì duōbōduàn chuánshū xìtǒng	Digital multi-wavelength transmission system	DWTS
数字耳机	Shùzì ěrjī	Digital earphone	
数字访问协议	Shùzì fǎngwèn xiéyì	Digital access protocol	DAMPS
数字反馈调频系统	Shùzì fǎnkuì tiáopín xìtǒng	Digital feedback frequency modulation system	DFFMS
数字发送保密监控系统	Shùzì fāsòng bǎomì jiānkòng xìtǒng	Digital dispatch security monitoring system	DDSMS
数字蜂窝分组数据	Shùzì fēngwō fēnzǔ shùjù	Cellular digital packet data	CDPD
数字蜂窝陆地移动通信系统	Shùzì fēngwō lùdì yídòng tōngxìn xìtǒng	Digital cellular land mobile telecommunication system	DCLMTS
数字蜂窝无线频率子系统	Shùzì fēngwō wúxiàn pínlǜ zixìtǒng	Digital cellular radio frequency sub-system	DRFS
数字蜂窝系统	Shùzì fēngwō xìtǒng	Digital cellular system	DCS
数字蜂窝移动	Shùzì fēngwō yídòng	Digital cellular mobile	
数字封装器	Shùzì fēngzhuāngqì	Digital wrapper	
数字分接	Shùzì fēnjiē	Digital demultiplexing	
数字分接器	Shùzì fēnjiēqì	Digital demultiplexer	
数字分配架	Shùzì fēnpèijià	Digital distribution frame	DDF
数字分频	Shùzì fēnpín	Digital frequency division	
数字分析法	Shùzì fēnxīfǎ	Digital analysis method	
数字分析器	Shùzì fēnxīqì	Digital analyzer	
数字分支板	Shùzì fēnzhī bǎn	Digital branching board (2Mb/s)	DB2M
数字分组网	Shùzì fēnzǔ wǎng	Digital packet network	DPN
数字复接	Shùzì fù jiē	Digital multiplexing	
数字附处理器	Shùzì fùchǔlǐqì	Numeric coprocessor	
数字复接体系	Shùzì fùjiē tǐxì	Digital multiplex hierarchy	
数字复接器	Shùzì fùjiēqì	Digital multiplexer	
数字复用	Shùzì fùyòng	Digital multiplexing	
数字复用分级系统	Shùzì fùyòng fēnjí xìtǒng	Digital multiplex hierarchy	
数字复用设备	Shùzì fùyòng shèbèi	Digital multiplex equipment	
数字复用系列	Shùzì fùyòng xìliè	Digital multiplex hierarchy	
数字复用器	Shùzì fùyòngqì	Digital multiplexer	
数字高程模型	Shùzì gāochéng móxíng	Digital elevation model	DEM
数字公务通道	Shùzì gōngwù tōngdào	Digital service channel	DSC
数字光处理	Shùzì guāng chǔlǐ	Digital light processing (video term)	DLP
数字广播卫星	Shùzì guǎngbō wèixīng	Digital broadcast satellite	DBS

数字和	Shùzì hé	Digital sum	
数字和之差	Shùzì hé zhīchà	Digital sum variation	
数字话路扩容系统	Shùzì huàlù kuòróng xìtǒng	Digital circuit multiplication system	
数字环回	Shùzì huánhuí	Digital loopback	
数字环路载波	Shùzì huánlù zàibō	Digital loop carrier	DLC
数字话音插空	Shùzì huàyīn chākōng	Digital speech interpolation	DSI
数字话音插入	Shùzì huàyīn chārù	Digital speech interpolation	DSI
数字话音信号	Shùzì huàyīn xìnhào	Digital speech signal	DSS
数字回波抑制器 A	Shùzì huíbō yìzhìqì A	Digital echo canceler board (A)	DECA
数字汇接局	Shùzì huìjiējú	Digital tandem	DTm
数字回声消除器	Shùzì huíshēng xiāochúqì	Digital echo canceler	
数字键位	Shùzì jiàn wèi	Number lock key	NumLock
数字交叉校正	Shùzì jiāochā jiàozhèng	Digital cross-correct	DCC
数字交叉连接	Shùzì jiāochā liánjiē	Digital cross-connect	DXC
数字交叉连接设备	Shùzì jiāochā liánjiē shèbèi	Digital cross-connect equipment	DXC
数字交叉连接系统	Shùzì jiāochā liánjiē xìtǒng	Digital cross-connect system	DCS
数字交叉连接器	Shùzì jiāochā liánjiēqì	Digital cross-connect equipment	DXC
数字交换	Shùzì jiāohuàn	Digital switching	
数字交换板	Shùzì jiāohuàn bǎn	Digital cross-connect board (2Mb/s)	DX2M
数字交换标准	Shùzì jiāohuàn biāozhǔn	Digital exchange format	
数字交换节点	Shùzì jiāohuàn jiédiǎn	Digital switching node	
数字交换时延	Shùzì jiāohuàn shíyán	Digital switching delay	
数字交换网络	Shùzì jiāohuàn wǎngluò	Digital switch network	DSN
数字交换系统	Shùzì jiāohuàn xìtǒng	Digital switching system	DSS
数字交换机	Shùzì jiāohuànjī	Digital exchange	
数字交换局	Shùzì jiāohuànjú	Digital exchange	
数字交替反转码	Shùzì jiāotì fǎnzhuǎn mǎ	Alternate digital inversion coding	ADI
数字集成电路	Shùzì jíchéng diànlù	Digital integrated circuit	
数字积累器	Shùzì jīlěiqì	Digital accumulator	
数字景观模型	Shùzì jǐngguān móxíng	Digital landscape model	DLM
数字基群	Shùzì jīqún	Primary digital group	PDG
数字集群调度专网	Shùzì jíqún diàodù zhuānwǎng	Integrated digital enhanced network	iDEN
数字集群通信系统	Shùzì jíqún tōngxìn xìtǒng	Digital trunked radio	
数字均方误差 (标准)	Shùzì jūn fāng wùchā (biāozhǔn)	Digital mean square error (criteria)	DMSE
数字矩阵	Shùzì jǔzhèn	Digital array	
数字控制信道	Shùzì kòngzhì xìndào	Digital control channel	DBR
数字控制增量调制	Shùzì kòngzhì zēngliàng tiáozhì	Digitally controlled delta modulation	DCDM
数字连接	Shùzì liánjiē	Digital connection	
数字链路	Shùzì liànlù	Digital link	
数字率	Shùzì lǜ	Digit rate	
数字滤波器	Shùzì lǜbōqì	Digital filter	
数字录像机	Shùzì lùxiàngjī	Digital video recorder	DVR
数字码值	Shùzì mǎ zhí	Data number value	DNV
数字模块化无线电	Shùzì mókuàihuà wúxiàndiàn	Digital modularized radio	DMR
数字模拟计算机系统	Shùzì mónǐ jìsuànjī xìtǒng	Digital simulator computer system	DSCS
数字模拟转换	Shùzì mónǐ zhuǎnhuàn	Digital/analog conversion	D/A

数字拇印	Shùzì mǔyìn	Digital fingerprint	
数字 n 次群	Shùzì *n*-cì qún	*n*-ary digital group	
数字配线架	Shùzì pèixiàn jià	Digital distribution frame	DDF
数字朋客	Shùzì péngkè	Cyberpunk	
数字频率合成器	Shùzì pínlǜ héchéngqì	Digital frequency synthesizer	
数字匹配滤波器	Shùzì pǐpèi lǜbōqì	Digital matched filter	
数字签名	Shùzì qiānmíng	Digital signature (IPsec)	
数字签名算法	Shùzì qiānmíng suànfǎ	Digital signature algorithm	DSA
数字企业	Shùzì qǐyè	Digital business	
数字权限管理	Shùzì quánxiàn guǎnlǐ	Digital rights management	DRM
数字区段	Shùzì qūduàn	Digital block	
数字色码	Shùzì sèmǎ	Digital color code	DCC
数字上变频	Shùzì shàngbiànpín	Digital up-converter	DUC
数字伸缩扫描	Shùzì shēnsuō sǎomiáo	Digital flex scan (video term)	DFS
数字 10 年	Shùzì shí nián	Digital decade	
数字时间分配语言内插入	Shùzì shíjiān fēnpèi yǔyán nèichārù	Digital time assignment speech interpolation	DTASI
数字视频	Shùzì shìpín	Digital video	DV
数字视频广播	Shùzì shìpín guǎngbō	Digital video broadcast	DVB
数字视频光盘	Shùzì shìpín guāngpán	Digital video disk	DVD
数字视频接口	Shùzì shìpín jiēkǒu	Digital video interface	DVI
数字视频业务	Shùzì shìpín yèwù	Digital video services	
数字时隙	Shùzì shíxì	Digit time slot	
数字输出	Shùzì shūchū	Digital output	DO
数字水印	Shùzì shuǐyìn	Digital watermarking	
数字数据	Shùzì shùjù	Digital data	
数字数据采集系统	Shùzì shùjù cǎijí xìtǒng	Digital data acquisition system	
数字数据测量系统	Shùzì shùjù cèliáng xìtǒng	Digital data measuring system	DDMS
数字数据多路复用器	Shùzì shùjù duōlù fùyòngqì	Digital data multiplexer	DDM
数字数据分组交换网络	Shùzì shùjù fēnzǔ jiāohuàn wǎngluò	Digital data packet switching network	DDX
数字数据交换业务	Shùzì shùjù jiāohuàn yèwù	Digital data switching service	DDXS
数字数据交换局	Shùzì shùjù jiāohuànjú	Digital data exchange	DDX
数字数据交换局	Shùzì shùjù jiāohuànjú	Digital data switching exchange	DDSE
数字数据开关矩阵	Shùzì shùjù kāiguān jǔzhèn	Digital data switching matrix	DDSM
数字数据通信报文协议	Shùzì shùjù tōngxìn bàowén xiéyì	Digital data communications message protocol (in DECnet)	DDCMP
数字数据网	Shùzì shùjù wǎng	Digital data network	SSW
数字数据网	Shùzì shùjù wǎng	Digital data network	DDN
数字数据信包交换网络	Shùzì shùjù xìnbāo jiāohuàn wǎngluò	Digital data packet switching network	DDX
数字数据业务	Shùzì shùjù yèwù	Digital data service	DDS
数字数据终端设备	Shùzì shùjù zhōngduān shèbèi	Digital data terminal equipment	DDTE
数字数据终端设备服务模块	Shùzì shùjù zhōngduān shèbèi fúwù mókuài	Digital data terminal equipment service module	DDTESM
数字数据转输系统	Shùzì shùjù zhuǎnshū xìtǒng	Digital data transmission system	DDTS
数字输入	Shùzì shūrù	Digital input	DI
数字输入声音应答部件	Shùzì shūrù shēngyīn yìngdá bùjiàn	Digital input voice answer block	DIVA
数字速率	Shùzì sùlǜ	Digital rate	
数字锁定键	Shùzì suǒdìng jiàn	NumLock key	

数字锁相环	Shùzì suǒxiāng huán	Digital phase-locked loop	
数字填充	Shùzì tiánchōng	Digital filling	
数字调制	Shùzì tiáozhì	Digital modulation	
数字同步	Shùzì tóngbù	Digital synchronization	DS
数字通道	Shùzì tōngdào	Digital path	
数字通路	Shùzì tōnglù	Digital channel	
数字通信通路	Shùzì tōngxìn tōnglù	Digital communication channel	DCC
数字通信协议	Shùzì tōngxìn xiéyì	Digital communication protocol	DCP
数字通信用户音频终端	Shùzì tōngxìn yònghù yīnpín zhōngduān	Digital subscriber voice terminal	DSVT
数字通信终端设备	Shùzì tōngxìn zhōngduān shèbèi	Digital communication terminal equipment	DCTE
数字透明性	Shùzì tòumíngxìng	Digital transparency	
数字图像	Shùzì túxiàng	Digital image	
数字图象处理	Shùzì túxiàng chǔlǐ	Digital image processing	DIP
数字图像控制	Shùzì túxiàng kòngzhì	Digital image control (video term)	DIC
数字图像水印	Shùzì túxiàng shuǐyìn	Digital image watermark	
数字网	Shùzì wǎng	Digital network	
数字网标识码	Shùzì wǎng biāozhì mǎ	Digital network identification code	DNIC
数字网络体系结构	Shùzì wǎngluò tǐxì jiégòu	Digital network architecture	DNA
数字微波	Shùzì wēibō	Digital microwave	WBS
数字微波传输设备	Shùzì wēibō chuánshū shèbèi	Digital microwave radio	DMR
数字微波接力系统	Shùzì wēibō jiēlì xìtǒng	Digital [Microwave] radio relay system	DRRS
数字微波系统	Shùzì wēibō xìtǒng	Digital microwave system	DMS
数字卫星标准	Shùzì wèixīng biāozhǔn	Digital satellite standard	DSS
数字卫星中心	Shùzì wèixīng zhōngxīn	Digital satellite center	DSC
数字位置	Shùzì wèizhì	Digital position	
数字无线段	Shùzì wúxiàn duàn	Digital radio section	
数字无线通道	Shùzì wúxiàn tōngdào	Digital radio path	
数字无线移动	Shùzì wúxiàn yídòng	Digital mobile radio	DMR
数字无线电	Shùzì wúxiàndiàn	Digital radio	DR
数字无线电集中器	Shùzì wúxiàndiàn jízhōngqì	Digital radio concentrator	
数字下变频	Shùzì xiàbiànpín	Digital down converter	DDC
数字线单元	Shùzì xiàn dānyuán	Digital line unit	DLU
数字线划图	Shùzì xiàn huàtú	Digital line graph	DLG
数字相位斜波反馈	Shùzì xiàngwèi xiébō fǎnkuì	Digital phase ramp feedback	
数字先进移动电话系统	Shùzì xiānjìn yídòng diànhuà xìtǒng	Digital advanced mobile phone system	DAVID
数字先进移动电话业务	Shùzì xiānjìn yídòng diànhuà yèwù	Digital advanced mobile phone service	D-AMPS
数字小键盘	Shùzì xiǎojiànpán	Numeric keypad	
数字小型交换机	Shùzì xiǎoxíng jiāohuànjī	Digital branch exchange	DBX
数字系列完整性	Shùzì xìliè wánzhěngxìng	Digital sequence integrity	
数字信道集成件	Shùzì xìndào jíchéng jiàn	Digital channel element assembly	DCEA
数字信道连接	Shùzì xìndào liánjiē	Digital channel link	DCL
数字信道模块	Shùzì xìndào mókuài	Digital channel block	DCB
数字信道子系统	Shùzì xìndào zixìtǒng	Digital channel sub-system	
数字形式的	Shùzì xíngshìde	Digital	
数字信号	Shùzì xìnhào	Digital signal	
数字信号处理	Shùzì xìnhào chǔlǐ	Digital signal processing	DSP

数字信号处理器	Shùzì xìnhào chǔlǐqì	Digital signal processor	DSP
数字信号发生器	Shùzì xìnhào fāshēngqì	Digital signal generater	
数字信号接收器	Shùzì xìnhào jiēshōuqì	Digital signal receiver	
数字信号的判决瞬时	Shùzì xìnhàode pànjué shùnshí	Decision instant of digital signal	
数字信号的有效瞬时	Shùzì xìnhàode yǒuxiào shùnshí	Significant instants of a digital signal	
数字信令	Shùzì xìnlìng	Digital signaling	
数字信息传输系统	Shùzì xìnxī chuánshū xìtǒng	Digital information transmission system	DITS
数字选呼系统	Shùzì xuǎnhū xìtǒng	Digital selective calling system	
数字序列完整性	Shùzì xùliè wánzhěngxìng	Digit sequence integrity	DSI
数字延时器	Shùzì yánshíqì	Digital time delayer	
数字压缩卫星直播	Shùzì yāsuō wèixīng zhíbō	Digitally compressed direct satellite broadcast	DTH
数字业务单元	Shùzì yèwù dānyuán	Digital service unit	DSU
数字业务电路	Shùzì yèwù diànlù	Digital service circuit	DSC
数字业务信道	Shùzì yèwù xìndào	Digital service channels	DSC
数字一次群	Shùzì yīcì qún	Primary digital group	
数字影院系统	Shùzì yǐngyuàn xìtǒng	Digital theater system	DTS
数字音频广播	Shùzì yīnpín guǎngbō	Digital audio broadcast	DAB
数字音频视频委员会	Shùzì yīnpín shìpín wěiyuánhuì	Digital Audio Video committee	DAVIC
数子音频抓取	Shùzì yīnpín zhuāqǔ	Digital audio extraction	DAE
数字音频/视频交互式译码器	Shùzì yīnpín/shìpín jiāohùshì yìmǎqì	Digital audio/video interactive decoder	DBF
数字音像委员会	Shùzì yīnxiàng wěiyuánhuì	Digital Audio Video committee	DAVIC
数字以太网接入系统	Shùzì yǐtàiwǎng jiērù xìtǒng	Building Ethernet access system	BEAS
数字移相器	Shùzì yíxiàngqì	Digital phase shifter	
数字用户电路板	Shùzì yònghù diànlù bǎn	Digital subscriber line board	DSL
数字用户环路	Shùzì yònghù huánlù	Digital subscriber loop	DSL
数字用户环路载波	Shùzì yònghù huánlù zàibō	Digital subscriber loop carrier	SHZ
数字用户控制器	Shùzì yònghù kòngzhìqì	Digital subscriber controller	DSC
数字用户线	Shùzì yònghù xiàn	Digital subscriber line	DSL
数字用户线接入复用器	Shùzì yònghù xiàn jiērù fùyòngqì	Digital subscriber line access multiplexer	DSLAM
数字用户线模块	Shùzì yònghù xiàn mókuài	Subscriber line module, digital	SLMD
数字用户信令系统 1	Shùzì yònghù xìnlìng xìtǒng 1	Digital subscriber signaling system no. one	DSS1
数字有线段	Shùzì yǒuxiàn duàn	Digital line section	
数字有线通道	Shùzì yǒuxiàn tōngdào	Digital line path	
数字运算	Shùzì yùnsuàn	"Number crunching"	
数字语音编码	Shùzì yǔyīn biānmǎ	Digital speech code	
数字语音插空	Shùzì yǔyīn chākōng	Digital speech interpolation	DSI
数字语音插值	Shùzì yǔyīn chāzhí	Digital speech interpolation	
数字增强无绳电话	Shùzì zēngqiáng wúshéng diànhuà	Digital enhanced cordless telephone	DECT
数字增强型无绳通信	Shùzì zēngqiáng-xíng wúshéng tōngxìn	Digital enhanced cordless telecommunications	DECT
数字证书	Shùzì zhèngshū	Digital certificate	
数字制图	Shùzì zhìtú	Digital mapping	
数字制图数据标准国家委员会	Shùzì zhìtú shùjù biāozhǔn guójiā wěiyuánhuì	National Committee for Digital Cartographic Data Standards	NCDCDS
数字指纹	Shùzì zhǐwén	Digital fingerprint	
数字终端	Shùzì zhōngduān	Digital terminal	SZ

数字终端多路复用装置	Shùzì zhōngduān duōlù fùyòng zhuāngzhì	Digital termination multiplex unit	DTMU
数字终端设备	Shùzì zhōngduān shèbèi	Data terminal equipment	DTE
数字中继板	Shùzì zhōngjì bǎn	Digital trunk module	DTM
数字中继板(块)	Shùzì zhōngjì bǎn (kuài)	Digital trunk board (module)	DTM
数字中继后面板	Shùzì zhōngjì hòumian bǎn	Digital trunk back panel	DTBP
数字中继接口	Shùzì zhōngjì jiēkǒu	Digital trunk interface	DTI
数字中继/回波抑制模块	Shùzì zhōngji/huíbō yìzhì mókuài	Digital trunk/echo canceler module	DT/ECM
数字中心	Shùzì zhōngxīn	Digital center	DC
数字转换器的语言模拟输入	Shùzì zhuǎnhuànqìde yǔyán mónǐ shūrù	Speech analog input to digitizer	SAID
数字综合网	Shùzì zōnghé wǎng	Integrated digital network	IDN
数字租用线业务	Shùzì zūyòng xiàn yèwù	Digital leased line service	DLL
数字的	Shùzìde	Digital	
数字化	Shùzìhuà	Digitize	
数字化采集设备	Shùzìhuà cǎijí shèbèi	Digitizing capture device	
数字化地理信息交换标准	Shùzìhuà dìlǐ xìnxī jiāohuàn biāozhǔn	Digital Geographic Information exchange Standard	DIGEST
数字化高级移动电话系统	Shùzìhuà gāojí yídòng diànhuà xìtǒng	Digital advanced mobile phone service	DAMPS
数字化精确谱 Buffalo 实验室应用(系统)	Shùzìhuà jīngquè pǔ Buffalo shíyànshì yìngyòng (xìtǒng)	Buffalo Laboratories application of digitally exact spectra	BLADES
数字化逻辑单元	Shùzìhuà luóji dānyuán	Digitizer logic unit	DLU
数字化仪	Shùzìhuàyí	Digitizer; tablet	
数字化仪菜单	Shùzìhuàyí càidān	Tablet menu	
数字化仪坐标	Shùzìhuàyí zuòbiāo	Tablet coordinate	
数字式电动执行机构	Shùzì-shì diàndòng zhíxíng jīgòu	Digital electric actuator	
数字式电子交换系统	Shùzì-shì diànzǐ jiāohuàn xìtǒng	Digital electronic switching system	DESS
数字式分解	Shùzì-shì fēnjiě	Digital resolving	
数字式景象匹配区域相关制导	Shùzì-shì jǐngxiàng pǐpèi qūyù xiāngguān zhìdǎo	Digital scene matching area correlation	
数字式 O/R 地址	Shùzì-shì O/R dìzhǐ	Numeric O/R address	
数字式 O/R 地址	Shùzì-shì O/R dìzhǐ	Numeric O/R address	
数字式平面显示器	Shùzì-shì píngmiàn xiǎnshìqì	Digital flat panel	DFP
数字式扫描	Shùzì-shì sǎomiáo	Digital sweep	
数字式市内主交换机	Shùzì-shì shìnèi zhǔ jiāohuànjī	Digital principal local exchange	DPLE
数字式锁相环	Shùzì-shì suǒxiàng huán	Digital phase lock loop	DPLL
数字式铁氧体移相器	Shùzì-shì tiěyǎngtǐ yíxiàngqì	Digital ferrite phase shifter	DFPS
数字式误差监控子系统	Shùzì-shì wùchā jiānkòng zìxìtǒng	Digital error monitor sub-system	DEMS
数字式现代移动电话系统	Shùzì-shì xiàndài yídòng diànhuà xìtǒng	Digital-advanced mobile phone system	D-AMPS
数字式寻呼系统	Shùzì-shì xúnhū xìtǒng	Digital paging system	
数字式影视光盘	Shùzì-shì yǐngshì guāngpán	Digital video disk	DVD
数字式智能多频追踪	Shùzì-shì zhìnéng duōpín zhuīzōng	Digital multiscan II (video term)	
数字式专用小交换机	Shùzì-shì zhuānyòng xiǎo jiāohuànjī	Digital private branch exchange	DPBX
数组	Shùzǔ	Array (mathematical)	
数组变换处理机	Shùzǔ biànhuàn chǔlǐjī	Array transform processor	ATP
数组处理指令系统	Shùzǔ chǔlǐ zhǐlìng xìtǒng	Array processing instruction set	APIS
数组结构体	Shùzǔ jiégòu tǐ	Array structure	
数组说明符	Shùzǔ shuōmíng fú	Array declarator	

数组元件	Shùzǔ yuánjiàn	Array element	
四电平调频	Sì diànpíng tiáopín	Four-level frequency modulation	4-level FM
四分之一公共中介格式	Sì fēn zhī yī gōnggòng zhōngjiè géshi	Quarter-common intermediate format	QCIF
四分支	Sì fēnzhī	Four-tap	
四接口加速	Sì jiēkǒu jiāsù	Quad-port acceleration	QPA
死库容	Sǐ kùróng	Dead storage	
四喇叭馈电器	Sì lǎba kuìdiànqì	Four-horn feed	
四通道附加序列控制	Sì tōngdào fùjiā xùliè kòngzhì	Four-channel additional sequence control	FASC
四倍边带内存	Sìbèi biāndài nèicún	Quad-band memory	QBM
四边形	Sìbiānxíng	Quadrangle	
四波混频	Sìbō hùnpín	Four wave mixing	FWM
四叉树	Sìchā shù	Quadtree	
四川省优立微波通讯设备工程公司	Sìchuān-shěng yōulì wēibō tōngxùn shèbèi gōngchéng gōngsī	Sichuan Unilink Microwave Communications Equipment and Engineering Co. Ltd.	
四次群	Sìcì qún	Digital standard 4 (4th digital standard rate =140Mbps)	DS-4
四电平调频	Sìdiànpíng tiáopín	Four-level frequency modulation	4-level FM
四分圆	Sìfēn yuán	Quarter circle	
四分之一波长板	Sìfēnzhīyī bōcháng bǎn	Quarter-wave plate (in a waveguide)	
四分之一波长变换器	Sìfēnzhīyī bōcháng biànhuànqì	Quarter-wave transformer	
四分之一波长接触式活塞	Sìfēnzhīyī bōcháng jiēchù-shì huósāi	Quarter-wave contact piston	
四分之一波长阻塞滤波器	Sìfēnzhīyī bōcháng zǔsè lǜbōqì	Quarter-wave stop filter	
伺服驱动系统	Sì-fú qūdòng xìtǒng	Servo drive system	SDS
四氟丙基丙烯酸甲酸	Sìfúbǐngjī bǐngxīsuān jiǎsuān	Tetrafluoro propyl methyl acrylate (FOC mfg)	TFPMA
死机	Sǐjī	Crash, hang (computer slang)	
四阶累积量	Sìjiē lěijī liàng	Fourth order cumulant (in digital signal processing)	
思科动态中继协议	Sī-kē dòngtài zhōngjì xiéyì	Dynamic trunk protocol	DTP
思科发现协议	Sī-kē fāxiàn xiéyì	Cisco discovery protocol	CDP
思科交换链路内协议	Sī-kē jiāohuàn liànlù-nèi xiéyì	Cisco inter-switch link protocol	ISL
思科路由器端口组管理协议	Sī-kē lùyóuqì duānkǒuzǔ guǎnlǐ xiéyì	Cisco router port group management protocol	RGMP
思科网络操作系统	Sī-kē wǎngluò cāozuò xìtǒng	Cisco internetwork operating system	
思科系统公司	Sī-kē xìtǒng gōngsī	Cisco Systems (US company)	
思科组管理协议	Sī-kē zǔ guǎnlǐ xiéyì	Cisco group management protocol	CGMP
四类传真	Sìlèi chuánzhēn	Group 4 facsimile	
四列扁平封装	Sìliè biǎnpíng fēngzhuāng	Quad flat package	QFP
四路功率分配器	Sìlù gōnglǜ fēnpèiqì	Four-way power divider	4WPD
四氯化硅	Sìlǜhuàguī	Silicon chlorate (used in FOC manufacture)	$SiCl_4$
四氯化锗	Sìlǜhuàzhě	Germanium chlorate or tetrachloride	$GeCl_4$
私密性	Sīmìxìng	Privacy, confidentiality	
斯普林特	Sī-pǔ-lín-tè	Sprint (US company)	
似然比	Sìrán bǐ	Likelihood ratio	
私人通话（选呼）	Sīrén tōnghuà (xuǎn hū)	Private conversation	
私人网路接入节点	Sīrén wǎnglù jiērù jiédiǎn	Private network access point	PNAP
私人运营机构	Sīrén yùnyíng jīgòu	Private operating agencies	
死锁	Sǐsuǒ	Dead lock (for database)	
四态	Sìtài	Four-state, four condition	
斯坦富电信公司	Sī-tǎn-fù diànxìn gōngsī	Stanford Telecom (US company)	

斯托克斯参数测定	Sī-tuō-kè-sī cānshù cèdìng	Stokes parameter evaluation	SPE
斯托克斯参数测定法	Sī-tuō-kè-sī cānshù cèdìng fǎ	Stokes parameter evaluation technique	
斯托克斯线	Sī-tuō-kè-sī xiàn	Stokes line	
丝网印刷及	Sīwǎng yìnshuājí	Screen printer (in printed circuit board manufacture)	
四位元	Sìwèi yuán	Nibble (half of a byte)	
四位字节	Sìwèi zìjié	Quartet byte	
四线交换	Sìxiàn jiāohuàn	Four-wire switching	
四纤双向服用段共享保护环	Sìxiān shuāngxiàng fúyòng duàn gòngxiǎng bǎohù huán	Four-fiber multiplex section shared protection ring	
四相差分相移键控	Sìxiāng chàfēn xiàngyí jiànkòng	Quadrature differential phase shift keying	QDPSK
四相相移键控	Sìxiāng xiāngyí jiànkòng	Quadriphase shift keying	QPSK
四相相移键控	Sìxiāng xiāngyí jiànkòng	Quadrature phase-shift keying	QPSK
四相移相键控	Sìxiàng yíxiàng jiànkòng	Quaternary phase-shift keying	QPSK
死信队列	Sǐxìn duìliè	Dead-letter queue	
死循环	Sǐxúnhuán	Endless loop, infinite loop, deadloop	
私有环路直接连接	Sīyǒu huánlù zhíjiē liánjiē	Private loop direct attached	PLDA
私有加强邮件	Sīyǒu jiāqiáng yóujiàn	Privacy enhanced mail	PEM
私有密钥	Sīyǒu mìyào	Private key	
四元点分符号	Sìyuán diǎnfēn fúhào	Four-part dotted notation	
四元数	Sìyuánshù	Quarterion	
四轴稳定系统	Sìzhóu wěndìng xìtǒng	Four-axial stable system	
SNAP 编码标记协议标识符	SNAP biānmǎ biāojì xiéyì biāozhìfú	SNAP-encoded tag protocol identifier	STPID
SNI 承载能力	SNI chéngzài nénglì	SNI bearer capability	
松套	Sōng tào	Loose tube (of fiber optic cable)	
松套层	Sōng tàocéng	Loose jacket (of fiber optic cable)	
松套层绞光缆	Sōng tàocéng jiǎo guānglǎn	Loose-tube stranded optical cable	
松套层绞式光纤带光缆	Sōng tàocéng jiǎo-shì guāngxiāndài guānglǎn	Loose-tube layer stranded optical fiber ribbon cable	
松包式光缆	Sōngbāo-shì guānglǎn	Loosely buffered fiber optic cable	
松弛时间	Sōngchí shíjiān	Relaxation time	
送话器	Sònghuàqì	Telephone transmitter	
松散耦合	Sōngsǎn ǒuhé	Loose coupling	
松散网	Sōngsǎn wǎng	Scatternet	
松下	Sōngxià	Matsushita (sometimes used for Panasonic, a trade name of Matsushita, Japanese electronics company)	
松下电器研究发展（中国）有限公司	Sōngxià diànqì yánjiū fāzhǎn (Zhōngguó) yǒuxiàn gōngsī	Matsushita Electric Research and Development (China) Corp. (subsidiary of Matsushita Japan)	CMRD
送者初始	Sòngzhě chūshǐ	Sender-initiated	
搜狐	Sōuhú	Sohu.com (Web magazine)	
搜狐网站	Sōuhú wǎngzhàn	Sohu.com	
搜集	Sōují	Gleaning	
搜索代理	Sōusuǒ dàilǐ	Search agent (in Java)	
搜索工具	Sōusuǒ gōngjù	Search tool	
搜索救援	Sōusuǒ jiùyuán	Search and rescue	SAR
搜索区	Sōusuǒ qū	Search region	
搜索条件	Sōusuǒ tiáojiàn	Search condition	
搜索引警	Sōusuǒ yǐnjǐng	Search engine	
搜索引擎	Sōusuǒ yǐnqíng	Search engine	

搜索载波	Sōusuǒ zàibō	Searching carrier	
搜寻	Sōuxún	Scavenging (IPsec)	
搜寻	Sōuxún	Search	
搜寻取代	Sōuxún qǔdài	Search and replace	
搜寻引擎	Sōuxún yǐnqíng	Search engine	
搜寻组	Sōuxún zǔ	Hunt group	HG
SRNC 无线网络临时识别	SRNC wúxiàn wǎngluò línshí shíbié	SRNC radio network temporary identity	S-RNTI
宿	Sù	Sink	
算法	Suànfǎ	Algorithm	
算法分析	Suànfǎ fēnxī	Algorithm analysis	
算法语言	Suànfǎ yǔyán	Algorithmic language	ALGOL
算法状态机	Suànfǎ zhuàngtài jī	Algorithm state machine	ASM
算术标志	Suànshù biāozhì	Arithmetic flag	AF
算术及逻辑运算部件	Suànshù jí luóji yùnsuàn bùjiàn	Arithmetic and logic unit	ALU
算术逻辑单元	Suànshù luóji dānyuán	Arithmetic logic unit	ALU
算术平均	Suànshù píngjūn	Arithmetic average	AA
算信	Suànxìn	Computer communication, compunication	
塑包光纤	Sùbāo guāngxiān	Plastic clad fiber	
塑包石英光纤	Sùbāo shíyīng guāngxiān	Plastic clad silica fiber	PCS
素材	Sùcái	Contribution	
素材应用	Sùcái yìngyòng	Contribution application	
速度	Sùdù	Velocity	
速度反应谱	Sùdù fǎnyìng pǔ	Velocity response spectrum	
速度鉴别	Sùdù jiànbié	Velocity discrimination	
速度控制系统	Sùdù kòngzhì xìtǒng	Speed control system	SCS
速度匹配	Sùdù pǐpèi	Speed matching	
速度相关	Sùdù xiāngguān	Velocity correlation	
速度压	Sùdù yā	Dynamic pressure	
速端曲线	Sùduān qūxiàn	Hodograph curve	
碎多边形	Suì duōbiānxíng	Sliver polygon (GIS)	
随拨服务	Suíbō fúwù	Dial-on-demand	
隧道	Suìdào	Tunnel; tunneling	
隧道标识符	Suìdào biāozhìfú	Tunnel identifier	TID
隧道代理	Suìdào dàilǐ	Tunnel broker (in IPv6)	
隧道端点标识符	Suìdào duāndiǎn biāozhìfú	Tunnel end point identifier	TEID
隧道渡越时间二极管	Suìdào dùyuè shíjiān èrjíguǎn	Tunnel transit time diode	TUNNETT
隧道技术	Suìdào jìshù	Tunneling	
隧道模式	Suìdào móshì	Tunneling mode (IPsec)	
隧道排水工程	Suìdào páishuǐ gōngchéng	Tunnel drainage works	
隧道协议	Suìdào xiéyì	Tunneling protocol (in GPRS)	GTP
随机	Suíjī	Random	
随机	Suíjī	Stochastic	
随机不归零制	Suíjī bù guī líng zhì	Randomized non-return to zero	RNZR
随机不确定性	Suíjī bùquèdìngxìng	Stochastic uncertainty	
随机差错	Suíjī chācuò	Random error	
随机存储器数/模转换器	Suíjī cúnchǔqì shù/mó zhuǎnhuànqì	Random access memory digital to analog converter	RAMDAC

随机存取存储器	Suíjī cúnqǔ cúnchǔqì	Random access memory	RAM
随机存取记存器	Suíjī cúnqǔ jìcúnqì	Random access memory	RAM
随机点	Suíjī diǎn	Random dot	
随机访问	Suíjī fǎngwèn	Random access	
随机分配多址	Suíjī fēnpèi duōzhǐ	Random assignment multiple access	
随机分时多路存取	Suíjī fēnshí duōlù cúnqǔ	Random time division multiple access	RTDMA
随机服务	Suíjī fúwù	Service in random order	
随机公平共享	Suíjī gōngping gòngxiǎng	Stochastic fair sharing	SFS
随机共振理论	Suíjī gòngzhèn lǐlùn	Stochastic resonance theory	
随机号码	Suíjī hàomǎ	Random number	RAND
随机缓慢跳频变多路存取	Suíjī huǎnmàn tiàopín biàn duōlù cúnqǔ	Random slow frequency hopping multiple access	RSFHMA
随机接入分组	Suíjī jiērù fēnzǔ	Random access burst	RAB
随机接入立即分配	Suíjī jiērù lìjí fēnpèi	Random access instant assignment	
随机接入物理信道	Suíjī jiērù wùlǐ xìndào	Physical random access channel	PRACH
随机接入信道	Suíjī jiērù xìndào	Random access channel	RACH
随机进程代数	Suíjī jìnchéng dàishù	Stochastic process algebra	SPA
随机馈相	Suíjī kuìxiàng	Random phase feed	
随机频移键控/频率跳变	Suíjī pínyí jiànkòng/pínlǜ tiàobiàn	Random frequency shift keying/frequency hopping	RFSK/FH
随机扫描	Suíjī sǎomiáo	Random sweep	
随机骚扰	Suíjī sāorǎo	Random disturbance	
随机失效率	Suíjī shīxiào lǜ	Random failure rate	
随机数	Suíjī shù	Random number (used for authentication)	RAND
随机数	Suíjī shù	Nonce (in IP)	
随机数生成	Suíjī shù shēngchéng	Random number generation	
随机数法	Suíjī shùfǎ	Random number method	
随机数字发生器	Suíjī shùzì fāshēngqì	Random number generator	RNG
随机搜寻	Suíjī sōuxún	Random search	
随机跳频	Suíjī tiàopín	Random frequency hopping	
随机图刑模型	Suíjī túxíng móxíng	Stochastic graph model	
随机误差	Suíjī wùchā	Random error	
随机误差	Suíjī wùchā	Stochastic uncertainty	
随机相位调制	Suíjī xiàngwèi tiáozhì	Random phase modulation	RPM
随机现象	Suíjī xiànxiàng	Stochastic phenomena	
随机早期检测	Suíjī zǎoqī jiǎncè	Random early detection	RED
随机早期侦测	Suíjī zǎoqī zhēncè	Random early detection	RED
随机噪声	Suíjī zàoshēng	Random noise	
随机振动	Suíjī zhèndòng	Random vibration	
随机自动机网络	Suíjī zìdòngjī wǎngluò	Stochastic automata network	
碎裂图型	Suìliè túxíng	Cracking pattern	
随路控制信道	Suílù kòngzhì xìndào	Associated control channel	ACCH
随路信令	Suílù xìnlìng	Channel associated signaling	CAS
碎片	Suìpiàn	Fragment, sliver	
碎片	Suìpiàn	Fragmentation (for database)	
碎片整理	Suìpiàn zhěnglǐ	Degragment, defrag	
随小增量排序	Suíxiǎo zēngliàng páixù	Diminishing increment sort	
随选伴唱服务	Suíxuǎn bànchàng fúwù	Karaoke on demand	

随选传真	Suíxuǎn chuánzhēn	Fax on demand	FOD
随选多媒体服务	Suíxuǎn duōméitǐ fúwù	Multimedia on demand	
塑胶箍	Sùjiāo gū	Plastic ferrule	
塑胶光缆	Sùjiāo guānglǎn	Plastic fiber optic cable	
塑胶光纤	Sùjiāo guāngxiān	Plastic optical fiber	
塑胶滤光镜	Sùjiāo lǜguāngjìng	Plastic filter	
塑胶针状矩阵封装	Sùjiāo zhēnzhuàng jǔzhèn fēngzhuāng	Plastic pin grid array	PPGA
塑料方块平面封装	Sùliào fāngkuài píngmiàn fēngzhuāng	Plastic quad flat package	PQFP
塑料光纤	Sùliào guāngxiān	Plastic optical fiber	
塑料光纤	Sùliào guāngxiān	Polymer optical fiber	
塑料夹敷设	Sùliào jiā fūshè	Secured by PVC clip	PCL
塑料线槽敷设	Sùliào xiàncáo fūshè	Run in PVC raceway (telecom installation)	
速率变换	Sùlǜ biànhuàn	Speedrate conversion	
速率电桥	Sùlǜ diànqiáo	Rate bridge	
速率队列	Sùlǜ duìliè	Rate queue	
速率改变	Sùlǜ gǎibiàn	Rate change	
速率控制	Sùlǜ kòngzhì	Rate enforcement	
速率适配	Sùlǜ shìpèi	Rate adaptation	RA
速率适配凿孔 Turbo 码	Sùlǜ shìpèi záokǒng Turbo mǎ	Rate compatible puncturing Turbo code	RCPT
速率适配器	Sùlǜ shìpèiqì	Rate adapter	RA
速率失真编码代价函数	Sùlǜ shīzhēn biānmǎ dàijià hánshù	Rate-distortion coding cost function	
速率自适应数字订阅线路	Sùlǜ zìshìyìng shùzì dìngyuè xiànlù	Rate adaptive digital subscriber line	RADSL
速率自适应数字用户线	Sùlǜ zìshìyìng shùzì yònghù xiàn	Rate adaptive digital subscriber line	RADSL
损耗比	Sǔnhào bǐ	Loss ratio	
损耗角	Sǔnhào jiǎo	Loss angle	
损坏率	Sǔnhuài lǜ	Damage factor	
损伤	Sǔnshāng	Damage	
损伤	Sǔnshāng	Mutilation	
损失时间	Sǔnshī shíjiān	Lost time	
锁	Suǒ	Lock	
缩放格	Suō fàng gé	Zoom	
锁和密钥保护系统	Suǒ hé mìyào bǎohù xìtǒng	Lock-and-key protection system (IPsec)	
索材	Suǒcái	Contribution	
索材应用	Suǒcái yìngyòng	Contribution application	
锁定放大器	Suǒdìng fàngdàqì	Lock-in amplifier	
锁定建立时间	Suǒdìng jiànlì shíjiān	Locked set-up time	
锁定时间	Suǒdìng shíjiān	Locking time	
锁定稳定性	Suǒdìng wěndìngxìng	Latching stability	
锁定状态	Suǒdìng zhuàngtài	Locked mode	Lo
缩短循环码	Suōduǎn xúnhuán mǎ	Shortened cyclic codes	
所见即所得	Suǒjiàn jí suǒdé	What you see is what you get	WYSIWYG
缩进	Suōjìn	Indentation	
缩略	Suōlüè	Abbreviation	
缩略图	Suōlüè tú	Thumbnail	
锁码	Suǒmǎ	Encode	
索尼	Suǒ-ní	Sony (Japan company)	

索尼 32 位游戏机	Suǒní 32 wèi yóuxìjī	Sony Play Station (computer game)	PS
索尼计算机娱乐部	Suǒní jìsuànjī yúlè bù	Sony Computer Entertainment (company)	SCE
索尼手提游戏机	Suǒní shǒutí yóuxìjī	Sony Pocket Station (computer game)	PS
索尼/飞利普数字接口	Suǒ-ní—fēi-lì-pǔ shùzì jiēkǒu	Sony/Phillips digital interface	S/PDIF
缩位拨号	Suōwèi bōhào	Abbreviated dialing	AD
缩位拨号	Suōwèi bōhào	Short number dialing	SND
缩微胶片	Suōwēi jiāopiàn	Microfiche	
缩微视图	Suōwēi shìtú	Thumbnail view	
锁相捕获	Suǒxiāng bǔhuò	Phase-lock acquisition	
锁相电路	Suǒxiàng diànlù	Phase locking circuit	
锁相环	Suǒxiàng huán	Phase locked loop	PLL
锁相环四相相移键控	Suǒxiāng huán sìxiāng xiāngyí jiànkòng	Phase-locked loop quadrature phase shift keying	PLL-QPSK
锁相环路	Suǒxiàng huánlù	Phase locked loop	PLL
锁相接收机	Suǒxiàng jiēshōujī	Phase-locked receiver	
锁相环四相相移键控	Suǒxiānghuán sìxiāng xiāngyí jiànkòng	Phased-locked loop quadrature phase shift keying	PLL-QPSK
缩小投影曝光设备	Suōxiǎo tóuyǐng bàoguāng shèbèi	Wafer stepper (semiconductor mfg)	
缩写	Suōxiě	Abbreviations	
缩写记录	Suōxiě jìlù	Abbreviation record	
缩写词	Suōxiěcí	Abbreviation	
所需功能	Suǒxū gōngnéng	Required function	
所需最小辐射功率	Suǒxū zuìxiǎo fúshè gōnglǜ	Lowest required radiated power	LRRP
索引	Suǒyǐn	Index	
索引非顺序文件	Suǒyǐn fēishùnxù wénjiàn	Indexed non-sequential file	
索引服务器	Suǒyǐn fúwùqì	Index server	
索引或运算	Suǒyǐn huò yùnsuàn	Index OR operation	
索引顺序访问方法	Suǒyǐn shùnxù fǎngwèn fāngfǎ	Indexed sequential access method	ISAM
索引顺序文件	Suǒyǐn shùnxù wénjiàn	Indexed sequential file	
索引调整向导	Suǒyǐn tiáozhěng xiàngdǎo	Index tuning wizard (in SQL Server)	
索引图层	Suǒyǐn tú céng	Index coverage	
索引文件	Suǒyǐn wénjiàn	Indexed file	
索引页	Suǒyǐn yè	Index page	
索引化视图	Suǒyǐnhuà shìtú	Indexed views (in SQL Server)	
所有出局禁止补充业务	Suǒyǒu chūjú jìnzhǐ bǔchōng yèwù	Barring of all outgoing calls supplementary service	BO
所有入局禁止补充业务	Suǒyǒu rùjú jìnzhǐ bǔchōng yèwù	Barring of all incoming calls supplementary service	BI
所有的呼叫前转业务	Suǒyǒude hūjiào qiánzhuǎn yèwù	All call forwarding services	CF
所有权	Suǒyǒuquán	Ownership	
所有者对象	Suǒyǒuzhě duìxiàng	Container object	
素数码	Sùshù mǎ	Prime code	
速调管	Sùtiáoguǎn	Klystron	
速调管放大器	Sùtiáoguǎn fàngdàqì	Klystron amplifier	KLA
塑性	Sùxìng	Plasticity	
塑性解析	Sùxìng jiěxī	Plastic analysis	
塑性界限	Sùxìng jièxiàn	Plastic limit	
塑性调节	Sùxìng tiáojié	Plastic conditioning (semiconductor mfg)	
塑性图	Sùxìng tú	Plasticity chart	

塑性指数	Sùxìng zhǐshù	Plastic index	
宿主（应用程序）	Sùzhǔ (yìngyòng chéngxù)	Host (application program)	
宿主单元	Sùzhǔ dānyuán	Host element	
宿主机	Sùzhǔ jī	Host machine	
宿主机监视协议	Sùzhǔ jī jiānshì xiéyì	Host monitoring protocol	HMP
宿主目录	Sùzhǔ mùlù	Home directory	
宿主业务提供商	Sùzhǔ yèwù tígōng shāng	Host service provider	HSP
Sybase 开发者网络	Sybase kāifāzhě wǎngluò	Sybase developer network	SDN

T

T 接口	T jiēkǒu	T interface (user interface)	
态	Tài	State	
太比特	Tài bǐtè	Terabit (10^{12} bits)	
太比特核心路由器	Tài bǐtè héxīn lùyóuqì	Terabit core router	
太比特交换路由器	Tài bǐtè jiāohuàn lùyóuqì	Terabit switch router	TSR
太比特网络路由器	Tài bǐtè wǎngluò lùyóuqì	Terabit network router	TNR
台间静噪	Tái-jiān jìngzào	Inter-station muting	
台间噪声抑制	Tái-jiān zàoshēng yìzhì	Inter-station noise suppression	
泰克电子（中国）有限公司	Tài-kè diànzǐ (Zhōngguó) yǒuxiàn gōngsī	Tektronix Electronics (China) Co. Ltd.	
太拉	Tài-lā	Tera (prefix meaning 10^{12})	
泰勒图表	Tài-lè túbiǎo	Taylor's chart	
太平洋网际网络	Tàipíngyáng wǎngjì wǎngluò	Pacific Internet	
泰森多边形	Tài-sēn duōbiānxíng	Thiessen polygon	
抬升	Táishēng	Lift	
台式电脑	Tái-shì diànnǎo	Desktop computer	
台式文氏强制对流红外回流炉	Táishì wén-shì qiángzhì duìliú hóngwài huíliú lú	Benchtop Venturi forced convection infrared reflow oven (semiconductor mfg)	
钛酸锆酸铅晶圆	Tàisuān gàosuān qiān jīngyuán	Lead-zirconium titanate wafer	PLZT
抬头显示器	Táitóu xiǎnshìqì	Head-up display	HUD
泰晤士金融股票交易 100 家顶级公司	Tàiwùshì jīnróng gǔpiào jiāoyì 100 jiā dǐngjí gōngsī	Financial Times Stock Exchange top 100 companies	FTSE100
太阳电池	Tàiyáng diànchí	Solar cell	
太阳微系统公司	Tàiyáng wēi xìtǒng gōngsī	Sun Microsystems, Inc. (US company)	
太阳系	Tàiyángxì	Solaris © (Sun Microsystems software)	
探测	Tàncè	Sniffer (computer web application)	
探测	Tàncè	Sounding	
探测率	Tàncè lǜ	Detectivity	
探测数据分组	Tàncè shùjù fēnzǔ	Explorer packet	
探测帧	Tàncè zhèng	Explorer frame	
探查	Tànchá	Probe	
弹出式	Tánchū-shì	Pop up	
弹出式窗口	Tánchū-shì chuāngkǒu	Pop-up window	
汤姆逊公司	Tāng-mǔ-xùn gōngsī	Thomson Corp (French company)	
探路	Tànlù	Pathfinding	
探路算法	Tànlù suànfǎ	Pathfinding algorithm	
坍落	Tānluò	Slump (in SMT)	

探索数据分析	Tànsuǒ shùjù fēnxī	Exploratory data analysis	
弹塑性	Tánsùxìng	Elasto-plasticity	
弹塑性反应谱	Tánsùxìng fǎnyìng pǔ	Elasto-plastic response spectrum	
弹塑性连接	Tánsùxìng liánjiē	Elasto-plastic joint	
碳涂层光纤	Tàntúcéng guāngxiān	Carbon coated fiber	CCF
弹性	Tánxìng	Elasticity	
弹性波	Tánxìng bō	Elastic wave	
弹性带宽运用	Tánxìng dàikuān yùnyòng	Bandwidth on demand	BOD
弹性反应	Tánxìng fǎnyìng	Elastic rebound	
弹性分组环	Tánxìng fēnzǔ huán	Resilient packet ring	RPR
弹性干扰物	Tánxìng gānrǎowù	Resilient chaff	
弹性类	Tánxìng lèi	Spring jig	
弹性模量	Tánxìng mólìàng	Elastic modulus (measured in Gpa)	
弹性限度	Tánxìng xiàndù	Elastic limit	
弹性异步-同步接口	Tánxìng yìbù—tóngbù jiēkǒu	Elastic asynchronous-to-synchronous interface	EASI
弹性体	Tánxìngtǐ	Elastic body	
探询系统	Tànxún xìtǒng	Polling system	
探询，终止	Tànxún, zhōngzhǐ	Poll/final	P/F
套打	Tào dǎ	Register dump	
陶瓷单层电容器	Táocí dāncéng diànróngqì	Single layer ceramic capacitor	SLC
陶瓷多层电容器	Táocí duōcéng diànróngqì	Multi-layer ceramic capacitor	MLC
陶瓷箍	Táocí gū	Ceramic ferrule (ring)	
陶瓷套管	Táocí tàoguǎn	Ceramic ferrule (pipe)	
陶瓷针型栅格阵列	Táocí zhēn-xíng zhàgé zhènliè	Ceramic pin grid array	CPGA
套管	Tàoguǎn	Casing	
套管	Tàoguǎn	Ferrule	
套管型抑制器	Tàoguǎn-xíng yìzhìqì	Sleeve type suppressor	
套接字	Tàojiēzì	Socket	
套刻	Tàokè	Alignment	
讨论组	Tǎolùn zǔ	Discussion group	
套筒	Tàotǒng	Sleeve	
套筒单极子	Tàotǒng dānjízi	Sleeve monopole, sleeve stub (antenna)	
套筒偶极子	Tàotǒng ǒujízi	Sleeve dipole (antenna)	
塔式机箱	Tǎ-shì jīxiāng	Tower case	
獭尾形射束天线	Tǎwěixíng shèshù tiānxiàn	Beaver-tail beam antenna	
TCP/IP 数据包分析	TCP/IP shùjùbāo fēnxī	TCP/IP packet analysis utility	TCPDUMP
TCP/IP 数据包路由追踪工具	TCP/IP shùjùbāo lùyóu zhuīzōng gōngjù	TCP/IP packet route tracing tool (Traceroute)	
特别兴趣小组	Tèbié xìngqu xiǎozǔ	Special interest group	SIG
特别业务	Tèbié yèwù	Special service	
特别移动通信组	Tèbié yídòng tōngxìn zǔ	Special mobile group	SMG
特定布局结构	Tèdìng bùjú jiégòu	Specific layout structure	
特定服务的汇聚子层	Tèdìng fúwùde huìjù zicéng	Service-specific convergence sub-layer	SSCS
特定服务的面向连接协议	Tèdìng fúwùde miànxiàng liánjiē xiéyì	Service-specific connection-oriented protocol	SSCOP
特定管理应用元素	Tèdìng guǎnlǐ yìngyòng yuánsù	Special management application element	SMASE
特定接入功能	Tèdìng jiērù gōngnéng	Specific access function	SAF

特定逻辑结构	Tèdìng luóji jiégòu	Specific logical structure	
特定应用服务要素	Tèdìng yìngyòng fúwù yàosù	Specialized application service	SASE
特定应用模式	Tèdìng yìngyòng móshì	Application-specific schema	
特定的场强-距离乘积	Tèdìngde chǎngqiáng-jùlí chéngjī	Specific cymomotive force	
特定的场强-距离乘积	Tèdìngde chǎngqiáng-jùlí chéngjī	Specific field strength-distance product	SCMF
特定的通用分组无线电业务节点	Tèdìngde tōngyòng fēnzǔ wúxiàndiàn yèwù jiédiǎn	Specific general packet radio service node	SGSN
特发报刊	Tèfā bàokān	Newspapers and periodicals of special distribution	
特服号	Tèfúhào	Special service number (such as 411 for information, 117 for fire)	
特高频	Tègāopín	Ultra-high frequency	UHF
特化	Tèhuà	Specialization	
特价报刊	Tèjià bàokān	Newspapers and periodicals of special price	
特洛伊木马	Tè-luò-yī mùmǎ	Trojan horse	
特权存取控制	Tèquán cúnqǔ kòngzhì	Privileged access control (in Linux)	PAC
特权管理基础设施	Tèquán guǎnlǐ jīchǔ shèshī	Privilege management infrastructure	PMI
特权模式	Tèquán móshì	Privileged mode	
特权指令	Tèquán zhǐlìng	Privileged instruction	
特锐光纤	Tè-ruì guāngxiān	Teralight®, an Alcatel optical fiber	
特殊拨号音	Tèshū bōhàoyīn	Special dial tone	
特殊功能	Tèshū gōngnéng	Special function (WP command)	
特殊检查水平	Tèshū jiǎnchá shuǐpíng	Specific inspection level (in quality standards)	
特殊接入控制级别	Tèshū jiērù kòngzhì jíbié	Special access control level	
特殊连接器名称	Tèshū liánjiēqì míngchēng	ad hoc connector name	
特殊利益集团	Tèshū lìyì jítuán	Special interest group	SIG
特殊路由选择	Tèshū lùyóu xuǎnzé	Special routing	
特殊限制	Tèshū xiànzhì	Special restrictions	
特殊业务分段和重新装配子层	Tèshū yèwù fēnduàn hé chóngxīn zhuāngpèi zicéng	Service-specific segmentation and re-assembly sub-layer	SSSAR
特殊业务会聚子层	Tèshū yèwù huìjù zicéng	Service-specific convergence sub-layer	SSCS
特殊业务协调功能	Tèshū yèwù xiétiáo gōngnéng	Service-specific coordination function	SSCF
特殊业务协调功能-网络节点接口	Tèshū yèwù xiétiáo gōngnéng-wǎngluò jiédiǎn jiēkǒu	Service-specific coordination function-network node interface	SSCF-NNI
特殊应用集成电路	Tèshū yìngyòng jíchéng diànlù	Application specific integrated circuit	ASIC
特殊资源功能	Tèshū zīyuán gōngnéng	Special resources function	SRF
特性	Tèxìng	Attribute	
特性波阻抗	Tèxìng bō zǔkàng	Characteristic wave impedance (of a transmission line)	
特性畸变	Tèxìng jībiàn	Characteristic distortion	
特性激活	Tèxìng jīhuó	Feature activation	
特性指示	Tèxìng zhǐshì	Feature indication	
特性阻抗	Tèxìng zǔkàng	Characteristic impedance	
特业台	Tèyètái	Special service device	SSD
特征	Tèzhēng	Attribute; tag; feature; trait	
特征包	Tèzhēng bāo	Packages (in generic network information model)	
特征编码	Tèzhēng biānmǎ	Feature code	
特征标识码	Tèzhēng biāozhì mǎ	Feature identifer	
特征波形内插	Tèzhēng bōxíng nèichā	Characteristic waveform interpolation	CWI

特征操作	Tèzhēng cāozuò	Feature operation	
特征操作类型	Tèzhēng cāozuò lèixíng	Feature operation type	
特征测试	Tèzhēng cèshì	Behavior test	
特征多项式	Tèzhēng duōxiàngshì	Characteristic polynomial	
特征分割	Tèzhēng fēngē	Feature division	
特征功能	Tèzhēng gōngnéng	Feature function	
特征关联	Tèzhēng guānlián	Feature association	
特征关系	Tèzhēng guānxi	Feature relationship	
特征关系类型	Tèzhēng guānxi lèixíng	Feature relationship type	
特征合并检查	Tèzhēng hébìng jiǎnchá	Feature mergence check (CAD/CAM)	
特征间隔	Tèzhēng jiàngé	Significant interval	
特征间隔的理论持续时间	Tèzhēng jiàngéde lǐlùn chíxù shíjiān	Theoretical duration of a significant interval	
特征句式	Tèzhēng jùshì	Trait phrasing	
特征类	Tèzhēng lèi	Feature class	
特征类型	Tèzhēng lèixíng	Feature catalogue	
特征类型	Tèzhēng lèixíng	Feature type	
特征类型实体	Tèzhēng lèixíng shítǐ	Feature catalogue entity	
特征类型要素	Tèzhēng lèixíng yàosù	Feature catalogue element	
特征描述法	Tèzhēng miáoshù fǎ	Feature portrayal	
特征频率	Tèzhēng pínlǜ	Characteristic frequency	
特征取代	Tèzhēng qǔdài	Feature substitution	
特征融合	Tèzhēng rónghé	Feature fusion	
特征瞬时	Tèzhēng shùnshí	Significant instant	
特征属性	Tèzhēng shǔxìng	Feature attribute	
特征属性表	Tèzhēng shǔxìng biǎo	Feature attribute table	
特征提取	Tèzhēng tíqǔ	Feature extraction	
特征拓扑	Tèzhēng tuòpū	Feature topology	
特征线	Tèzhēng xiàn	Feature line (CAD/CAM)	
特征信息	Tèzhēng xìnxī	Characteristic information	CI
特征选取	Tèzhēng xuǎnqǔ	Feature selection	
特征序列号	Tèzhēng xùlièhào	Feature serial number	
特征延续	Tèzhēng yánxù	Feature succession	
特征元素	Tèzhēng yuánsù	Feature element	
特征造型	Tèzhēng zàoxíng	Feature modeling	
特征状态	Tèzhēng zhuàngtài	Significant condition	
特征状态数	Tèzhēng zhuàngtài shù	Number of significant conditions	
特种电台	Tèzhǒng diàntái	Special radio station	
特种接续	Tèzhǒng jiēxù	Special connection	
特种移动通信系统	Tèzhǒng yídòng tōngxìn xitǒng	Particular mobile communication system	
体分布目标	Tǐ fēnbù mùbiāo	Volume distributive target	
体声波	Tǐ shēngbō	Bulk acoustic wave	BAW
体实体	Tǐ shítǐ	Body entity	
体效应二极管本地振荡器	Tǐ xiàoyìng èrjíguǎn běndì zhèndàngqì	Bulk effect diode local oscillator	
天波	Tiānbō	Sky wave	
天波路径损耗	Tiānbō lùjìng sǔnhào	Sky-wave path loss	
天波时延	Tiānbō shíyán	Sky-wave delay	

天才	Tiāncái	Prodigy (ISP)	
填充	Tiánchōng	Fill, pad (verb)	
填充	Tiánchōng	Stuffing (video term)	
填充电缆	Tiánchōng diànlǎn	Filled cable	
填充率	Tiánchōng lǜ	Fill rate	
填充信号单元	Tiánchōng xìnhào dānyuán	Fill-in signal unit	FISU
填充系数	Tiánchōng xìshù	Fill factor (SDH structure)	
填充因子	Tiánchōng yīnzǐ	Fill factor	
填充式	Tiánchōng-shì	Filled (FOC type, usually jelly-filled)	
天电	Tiāndiàn	Atmospherics	
天电干扰	Tiāndiàn gānrǎo	Atmospheric interference	
天花板	Tiānhuābǎn	Plenum	
天花板隔层电缆	Tiānhuābǎn gécéng diànlǎn	Plenum cable	
添加标题	Tiānjiā biāotí	Add-on header	AOH
天馈线	Tiānkuìxiàn	Antenna feed line	
天然气候试验	Tiānrán qìhòu shìyàn	Natural climate test	
天网	Tiānwǎng	Skynet	
天文雷达	Tiānwén léidá	Astronomical radar	
天文用面镜	Tiānwén-yòng miànjìng	Astronomical mirror	
天线	Tiānxiàn	Antenna	
天线波长	Tiānxiàn bōcháng	Antenna wavelength	
天线波束	Tiānxiàn bōshù	Antenna beam	
天线带宽	Tiānxiàn dàikuān	Antenna bandwidth	
天线导纳	Tiānxiàn dǎonà	Antenna admittance	
天线电流	Tiānxiàn diànliú	Antenna current	
天线电轴	Tiānxiàn diànzhóu	Antenna electrical boresight	
天线动态特性	Tiānxiàn dòngtài tèxìng	Antenna dynamics	
天线端子传导发射	Tiānxiàn duānzi chuándǎo fāshè	Antenna terminal conducted emissions (Mil-Std-461E, CE106)	
天线端子互调传导敏感度	Tiānxiàn duānzi hùtiáo chuándǎo mǐngǎndù	Antenna terminal intermodulation conducted susceptibility (Mil-Std-461E, CS103)	
天线端子交调传导敏感度	Tiānxiàn duānzi jiāotiáo chuándǎo mǐngǎndù	Antenna terminal cross-modulation conducted susceptibility (Mil-Std-461E, CS105)	
天线端子无用信号抑制传导传敏感	Tiānxiàn duānzi wúyòng xìnhào yìzhì chuándǎo chuán mǐngǎn	Antenna port signal rejection conducted susceptibility (Mil-Std-461E, CS104)	
天线额定电压	Tiānxiàn édìng diànyā	Antenna voltage rating	
天线额定功率	Tiānxiàn édìng gōnglǜ	Antenna power rating	
天线放大器	Tiānxiàn fàngdàqì	Antenna amplifier	AA
天线方位处理机	Tiānxiàn fāngwèi chǔlǐjī	Antenna aspect processor	AAP
天线方向性图	Tiānxiàn fāngxiàngxìng tú	Antenna directivity diagram	
天线光轴	Tiānxiàn guāngzhóu	Antenna optical boresight	
天线合成单元	Tiānxiàn héchéng dānyuán	Antenna combining unit	
天线合路器	Tiānxiàn hélùqì	Antenna combiner	ACOM
天线极化	Tiānxiàn jíhuà	Antenna polarization	
天线控制部件	Tiānxiàn kòngzhì bùjiàn	Antenna control unit	ACU
天线控制器	Tiānxiàn kòngzhìqì	Antenna control unit	ACU
天线耦合器单元	Tiānxiàn ǒuhéqì dānyuán	Antenna coupler unit	ACU

天线匹配装置	Tiānxiàn pǐpèi zhuāngzhì	Antenna matching device	
天线前端单元	Tiānxiàn qiánduān dānyuán	Antenna front end unit	AFEU
天线前端模块	Tiānxiàn qiánduān mókuài	Antenna front end block	AFEB
天线升降机构	Tiānxiàn shēngjiàng jīgòu	Antenna elevating/subsiding machine	
天线实际增益	Tiānxiàn shíjì zēngyì	Antenna realized gain	
天线收发开关	Tiānxiàn shōufā kāiguān	Antenna transmit-receive (T-R) switch	
天线收集面	Tiānxiàn shōují miàn	Antenna capture area	
天线输入导纳	Tiānxiàn shūrù dǎonà	Antenna input admittance	
天线输入阻抗	Tiānxiàn shūrù zǔkàng	Antenna input impedance	
天线锁定装置	Tiānxiàn suǒdìng zhuāngzhì	Antenna locking device	
天线调谐室	Tiānxiàn tiáoxié shì	Antenna tuning housing	
天线效率	Tiānxiàn xiàolǜ	Antenna efficiency (for an aperture-type antenna)	
天线谐波和乱真输出辐射发射	Tiānxiàn xiébō hé luànzhēn shūchū fúshè fāshè	Antenna harmonic and spurious output radiated emissions (Mil-Std-461E, RE103)	
天线谐振频率	Tiānxiàn xiézhèn pínlǜ	Antenna resonance frequency	
天线系统	Tiānxiàn xìtǒng	Antenna system	
天线噪声温度	Tiānxiàn zàoshēng wēndù	Antenna noise temperature	
天线噪声温度	Tiānxiàn zàoshēng wēndù	Noise temperature of antenna	NTA
天线增益	Tiānxiàn zēngyì	Antenna gain	
天线罩	Tiānxiàn zhào	Radome	
天线罩波束指向误差	Tiānxiàn zhào bōshù zhǐxiàng wùchā	Radome beam pointing error	
天线罩插入相移	Tiānxiàn zhào chārù xiāngyí	Radome insertion	
天线照射效率	Tiānxiàn zhàoshè xiàolǜ	Antenna illumination efficiency	AIE
天线指向误差	Tiānxiàn zhǐxiàng wùchā	Antenna pointing (boresight) error	
天线转换矩阵	Tiānxiàn zhuǎnhuàn jǔzhèn	Antenna switching matrix	
天线自动调谐	Tiānxiàn zìdòng tiáoxié	Antenna automatic tuning	
天线子阵	Tiānxiàn zizhèn	Antenna bay	
天线组合单元	Tiānxiàn zǔhé dānyuán	Antenna combining unit	ACU
天线阻抗	Tiānxiàn zǔkàng	Antenna impedance	
天线座	Tiānxiàn zuò	Antenna pedestal	
天线间的隔离度	Tiānxiàn-jiānde gélídù	Isolation between antennae	
跳计数	Tiào jìshù	Hop count	
跳计数器	Tiào jìshùqì	Hop counter (in SS7)	
跳数	Tiào shù	Hop count	
跳信道	Tiào xìndào	Channel hop	
跳周	Tiào zhōu	Cycle-skipping	
调步	Tiáobù	Pacing	
跳出式菜单	Tiàochū-shì càidān	Pop-up menu	
条带效应	Tiáodài xiàoyìng	Banding	
跳动	Tiàodòng	Jitter	
调幅	Tiáofú	Amplitude modulation	AM
调幅电报	Tiáofú diànbào	Amplitude modulation (AM) telegraph	
调幅电台	Tiáofú diàntái	Amplitude modulation (AM) station	
调幅发射机	Tiáofú fāshèjī	Amplitude modulation (AM) transmitter	
调幅干扰	Tiáofú gānrǎo	Amplitude modulation jamming (radar term)	
调幅躁声	Tiáofú zàoshēng	Amplitude modulation (AM) noise	

调幅度不对称性	Tiáofúdù bùduìchènxìng	Asymmetry of AM envelope	
条件不稳定性	Tiáojiàn bùwěndìngxìng	Conditional instability	
条件操作符	Tiáojiàn cāozuò fú	Conditional operator	
条件二相码	Tiáojiàn èr xiàng mǎ	Conditional dual phase coding	CDP
条件呼叫前转	Tiáojiàn hūjiào qiánzhuǎn	Conditional call forwarding	CCF
条件呼叫转移	Tiáojiàn hūjiào zhuǎnyí	Conditional call forwarding	CCF
条件接入	Tiáojiàn jiērù	Conditional access	CA
条件接收系统	Tiáojiàn jiēshōu xìtǒng	Conditional access system	CAS
条件特征包	Tiáojiàn tèzhēng bāo	Conditional package	
条件位	Tiáojiàn wèi	Condition bit	CB
条件稳定系统	Tiáojiàn wěndìng xìtǒng	Conditionally stable system	
条件转移地址	Tiáojiàn zhuǎnyí dìzhǐ	Conditionality branch address	CBRA
调节	Tiáojié	Accomodation	
调节变压器	Tiáojié biànyāqì	Regulating transformer	
调节短线	Tiáojié duǎnxiàn	Stub tuner	
调节螺钉	Tiáojié luódīng	Tuning screw	
调节水库	Tiáojié shuǐkù	Detention reservoir; regulating reservoir	
调节条	Tiáojié tiáo	Tuning slug	
调节线路段	Tiáojié xiànlù duàn	Regulated line section	
跳距	Tiàojù	Hop distance	
条码	Tiáomǎ	Bar code	
条码扫描器	Tiáomǎ sǎomiáoqì	Bar code scanner	
条码扫描器镜头	Tiáomǎ sǎomiáoqì jìngtóu	Bar code scanning lens	
条码阅读器	Tiáomǎ yuèdúqì	Bar code reader	
跳模	Tiàomó	Mode hopping	
调频	Tiáopín	Frequency modulation	FM
跳频	Tiàopín	Frequency hopping	FH
调频差动相干相移键控	Tiáopín chādòng xiānggān xiàngyí jiànkòng	Frequency modulation and differentially coherent PSK	FM-DCPSK
跳频多重存取	Tiàopín duōzhòng cúnqǔ	Frequency hopping multiple access	FHMA
调频发射机	Tiáopín fāshèjī	Frequency modulated transmitter	FMX
调频干扰	Tiáopín gānrǎo	Frequency modulated jamming	
跳频扩频	Tiàopín kuòpín	Frequency hopping spread spectrum	FHSS
跳频扩频调制	Tiàopín kuòpín tiáozhì	Frequency hopping spread spectrum modulation	
调频雷达发射机	Tiáopín léidá fāshèjī	Frequency modulation radar transmitter	
调频连续波	Tiáopín liánxù bō	Frequency modulated continuous wave	FMCW
调频连续波	Tiáopín liánxù bō	Frequency modulated continuous wave	FMCW
跳频码分多址	Tiàopín mǎfēn duōzhǐ	Frequency hopping code division multiple access	FH-CDMA
跳频同步	Tiàopín tóngbù	Frequency hop synchronization	FHS
调频无线电话机	Tiáopín wúxiàn diànhuàjī	Frequency modulation radio telephone	
跳频序列号码	Tiàopín xùliè hàomǎ	Hopping sequence number	HSN
跳频序列号	Tiàopín xùlièhào	Frequency hopping sequence number	HSN
调频躁声	Tiáopín zàoshēng	Frequency-modulation (FM) noise	
跳频/差分四相移相键控	Tiàopín/chāfēn sìxiāng yíxiāng jiànkòng	Frequency hopping/differential quadriphase shift keying	FH/DQPSK
调频/频分多路存取	Tiáopín/pínfēn duōlù cúnqǔ	Frequency modulation/frequency division multiple access	FM/FDMA
调前高斯滤波的 MSK	Tiáoqián gāo-sī lǜbōde MSK	Premodulation Gaussian filtered MSK	GMSK

调色板	Tiáosèbǎn	Palette	
调试	Tiáoshì	Debugging	
跳时	Tiàoshí	Time hopping	TH
调试帮助程序	Tiáoshì bāngzhù chéngxù	Debugging helper	DHP
调试工具	Tiáoshì gōngjù	Debugging aids	DA
调试架	Tiáoshì jià	Regulating stand	
调试计算机程序	Tiáoshì jìsuànjī chéngxù	Debugging computer program	DCP
调试器	Tiáoshìqì	Debugger	
调停手段	Tiáoting shǒuduàn	Mediation device	MD
跳线	Tiàoxiàn	Jumper wire	
跳线尾纤	Tiàoxiàn wěixiān	Patch cord, jumper	
调相	Tiáoxiàng	Phase modulation	PM
调谐	Tiáoxié	Tuning	
调谐放大器	Tiáoxié fàngdàqì	Tuned amplifier	
调谐线性	Tiáoxié xiànxìng	Linearity of tuning	
调谐旋钮	Tiáoxié xuánniǔ	Tuning knob	
调谐指示器	Tiáoxié zhǐshìqì	Tuning indicator	
条形图	Tiáoxíng tú	Bar chart	
跳跃转换	Tiàoyuè zhuǎnhuàn	Jump transition	
挑战握手认证协议	Tiǎozhàn wòshǒu rènzhèng xiéyì	Challenge handshake authentication protocol (IPsec)	CHAP
挑战应答机制	Tiǎozhàn yìngdá jīzhì	Challenge response mechanism (IPsec)	
调整错误	Tiáozhěng cuòwù	Alignment error	
调整码位	Tiáozhěng mǎwèi	Justifying digit	
调整指示码位	Tiáozhěng zhǐshì mǎwèi	Justification service digits	
调制	Tiáozhì	Modulation	
调制编码	Tiáozhì biānmǎ	Modulation code	
调制波	Tiáozhì bō	Modulating wave	
调制不稳定性	Tiáozhì bùwěndìngxìng	Modulation instability	MI
调制交流声	Tiáozhì jiāoliúshēng	Modulation hum	
调制解调器	Tiáozhì jiětiáoqì	Modulator demodulator	MODEM
调制解调器的链路接入规程	Tiáozhì jiětiáoqìde liànlù jiērù guīchéng	Link access procedure for modem	LAPM
调制灵敏度	Tiáozhì língmǐndù	Modulation sensitivity	
调制脉冲顶部不平度	Tiáozhì màichōng dǐngbù bùpíngdù	Modulating pulse top unevenness	
调制脉冲幅度	Tiáozhì màichōng fúdù	Modulating pulse amplitude	
调制脉冲幅度稳定度	Tiáozhì màichōng fúdù wěndìngdù	Modulating pulse amplitude stability	
调制脉冲后沿	Tiáozhì màichōng hòuyán	Modulating pulse lagging edge	
调制脉冲宽度	Tiáozhì màichōng kuāndù	Modulating pulse length	
调制脉冲前沿	Tiáozhì màichōng qiányán	Modulating pulse front edge	
调制脉冲上冲（波尖）	Tiáozhì màichōng shàngchōng (bōjiān)	Modulating pulse overshoot (spike)	
调制脉冲下冲（反峰）	Tiáozhì màichōng xiàchōng (fǎn fēng)	Modulating pulse undershoot (negative spike)	
调制深度	Tiáozhì shēndù	Modulation depth	
调制速率	Tiáozhì sùlǜ	Modulation rate	
调制特性	Tiáozhì tèxìng	Modulation characteristic	
调制限制	Tiáozhì xiànzhì	Modulation limiting	
调制信号	Tiáozhì xìnhào	Modulating signal	

调制系数	Tiáozhì xìshù	Modulation factor	
调制增益	Tiáozhì zēngyì	Modulation gain	
调制指数	Tiáozhì zhǐshù	Modulation index	
调制/解调器	Tiáozhì/jiětiáoqì	Modem, modulator/demodulator	MODEM
调制器	Tiáozhìqì	Modulator	
跳周	Tiàozhōu	Cycle-skipping	
跳周平均时间	Tiàozhōu píngjūn shíjiān	Cycle-skipping average time	
条状分布数据	Tiáozhuàng fēnbù shùjù	Data striping	
条状调节器	Tiáozhuàng tiáojiéqì	Slug tuner	
调准分贝	Tiáozhǔn fēnbèi	Adjusted decibels	dBA
体波大小	Tǐbō dàxiǎo	Body-wave magnitude (Mb)	
替代测试法	Tìdài cèshì fǎ	Alternative test method	ATM
替代地址	Tìdài dìzhǐ	Alternate address	AADR
替代地址使用预约	Tìdài dìzhǐ shǐyòng yùyuē	Alternative address usage subscription	
替代试验方法	Tìdài shìyàn fāngfǎ	Alternative test method	ATM
替代数据	Tìdài shùjù	Surrogate data	
提单	Tídān	Bill of lading	B/L
梯度	Tīdù	Gradient	
梯度折射率	Tīdù zhéshèlǜ	Graded index (FOC)	
梯度折射率塑料光纤	Tīdù zhéshèlǜ sùliào guāngxiān	Graded index polymer optical fiber	GI-POF
铁离子中心激光	Tiě lízǐ zhōngxīn jīguāng	Ferrous-center laser	
铁通公司（铁路通信有限公司）	Tiě tōng gōngsī (tiělù tōngxìn yǒuxiàn gōngsī)	Railcom (Railway Telecommunications Information Co. Ltd.)	
贴报	Tiēbào	Newspapers pasted on public bulletin boards	
铁路编组站自动化	Tiělù biānzǔzhàn zìdònghuà	Railway yard automation	
铁路列车调度系统	Tiělù lièchē diàodù xìtǒng	Railway train dispatch system	
铁路通信有限公司（铁通公司）	Tiělù tōngxìn yǒuxiàn gōngsī (tiě tōng gōngsī)	Railway Telecommunications Information Co. Ltd. (Railcom) (China company)	
铁路行车指挥自动化系统	Tiělù xíngchē zhǐhuī zìdònghuà xìtǒng	Railway traffic control automation	
贴片机	Tiēpiànjī	Chip mounter	
贴片机	Tiēpiànjī	Parts mounter (SMT)	
贴片机	Tiēpiànjī	Chip paster (in component assembly process)	
铁塔	Tiětǎ	Tower	
铁芯偏转线圈	Tiěxīn piānzhuǎn xiànquān	Iron-core deflection coil	
铁氧体	Tiěyǎngtǐ	Ferrite	
铁氧体棒天线	Tiěyǎngtǐ bàng tiānxiàn	Ferrite rod antenna	
铁氧体开关	Tiěyǎngtǐ kāiguān	Ferrite switch	
铁氧体天线	Tiěyǎngtǐ tiānxiàn	Ferrite antenna	
铁氧体天线收发开关	Tiěyǎngtǐ tiānxiàn shōufā kāiguān	Ferrite duplexer	
铁氧体移相器	Tiěyǎngtǐ yíxiàngqì	Ferrite phase shifter	
贴装设备	Tiēzhuāng shèbèi	Placement equipment (in SMT)	
提供程序	Tígōng chéngxù	Provider program	
提供计费信息	Tígōng jìfèi xìnxī	Furnish charging information	FCI
提供漫游号码	Tígōng mànyóu hàomǎ	Provide roaming number	
提供商边缘	Tígōng shāng biānyuán	Provider edge	PE
提供者发起型业务	Tígòngzhě fāqǐ-xíng yèwù	Provider-initiated-service	

提供者起始型服务	Tígòngzhě qǐshǐxíng fúwù	Provider-initiated service	
替换	Tìhuan	Replace (WP command)	
替换	Tìhuan	Supersede	
替换关系	Tìhuan guānxi	Fallback relationships	
替换接收者	Tìhuan jiēshōuzhě	Alternate recipient	
替换名字	Tìhuan míngzì	Alternate name	
替换名字体	Tìhuan míngzì tǐ	Alternate name body	
替换名字文本	Tìhuan míngzì wénběn	Alternate name text	
替换模	Tìhuan mó	Mode switching	
替换通路名	Tìhuan tōnglù míng	Alternate street name	
体积测定空间函数	Tǐjī cèdìng kōngjiān hánshù	Volumetric spatial function	
体积收缩率	Tǐjī shōusuō lǜ	Volume shrinkage	
体积弹性模量	Tǐjī tánxìng móliàng	Bulk modulus	
体积纹理压缩	Tǐjī wénlǐ yāsuō	Volume texture compression	
提交	Tíjiāo	Commit	
提交本表	Tíjiāo běn biǎo	Submit current table	
提交阶段	Tíjiāo jiēduàn	Validation phase	
提交信息率	Tíjiāo xìnxī lǜ	Submission information rate	SIR
提领运算子	Tílǐng yùnsuànzǐ	De-reference operator	
TINA 开放业务生产结构	TINA kāifàng yèwù shēngchǎn jiégòu	TINA open service creation architecture	TOSCA
TINA 试验	TINA shìyàn	The TINA trial	TTT
TINA 业务结构和或智能网业务	TINA yèwù jiégòu hé zhìnéng wǎng yèwù	TINA service architecture and intelligent network services	SATIN
停播建立呼叫	Tíngbō jiànlì hūjiào	Off-air call set up	
停顿	Tíngdùn	Quiesce	
停顿	Tíngdùn	Stall; stalled	
停顿时间	Tíngdùn shíjiān	Dwell time	
停机时间	Tíngjī shíjiān	Downtime	
听觉和视觉信号编码	Tīngjué hé shìjué xìnhào biānmǎ	Aural and visual code	AVC
听觉距离	Tīngjué jùlí	Auditory distance	
听力参考点	Tīnglì cānkǎo diǎn	Ear reference point	
停闪频率	Tíngshǎn pínlǜ	Flashing frequency	
停止定时器	Tíngzhǐ dìngshíqì	Stop timer	
停止键	Tíngzhǐ jiàn	Pause key	
停止卷动键	Tíngzhǐ juǎndòng jiàn	Scroll lock key	
停止码元	Tíngzhǐ mǎyuán	Stop element	
停止位	Tíngzhǐ wèi	Stop bit	
停止信号	Tíngzhǐ xìnhào	Stop signal	
提前释放	Tíqián shìfàng	Premature disconnection	
提前时间	Tíqián shíjiān	Time advance	TA
提取	Tíqǔ	Fetch	
提示并收集用户信息	Tíshì bìng shōují yònghù xìnxī	Prompt and collect user information	P&C
提示并收集用户信息的返回结果	Tíshì bìng shōují yònghù xìnxīde fǎnhuí jiéguǒ	Return result of prompt and collect user information	RR-P&C
提示符	Tíshì fú	Prompt (noun)	
提示音增益	Tíshì yīn zēngyì	Cueing tone gain	

梯调	Tītiáo	Trapezoidal modulation	
提醒	Tíxǐng	Alerting	
梯型硅氧烷聚合物	Tī-xíng guīyǎng wán jùhéwù	Laddered siloxane polymer (FOC mfg)	LSP
梯型滤波器	Tī-xíng lǜbōqì	Ladder filter	
梯形调制	Tīxíng tiáozhì	Trapezoidal modulation	
替续透镜	Tìxù tòujìng	Relay lens	
通断键控	Tōng duàn jiànkòng	On-off keying	OOK
铜芯	Tóng xīn	Copper conductor	
同型号光纤（缆）连接器转接座	Tóng xínghào guāngxiān (lǎn) liánjiēqì zhuǎnjiēzuò	Within-type optical fiber (cable) connector adapter	
同伴芯片	Tóngbàn xìnpiàn	Companion chip	
同边聚合	Tóngbiān jùhé	Same-edge aggregation (CAD/CAM)	
铜箔	Tóngbó	Copper foil (in SMT)	
通播	Tōngbō	Announcement call	
同波长双工	Tóngbōcháng shuānggōng	Duplex working	
同波道干扰	Tóngbōdào gānrǎo	Co-channel interference	CCI
同步	Tóngbù	Synchronization, synchronous	
同步保持时间	Tóngbù bǎochí shíjiān	Synchronization hold-in time	
同步比特	Tóngbù bǐtè	Synchronization bit	
同步传递方式	Tóngbù chuándì fāngshì	Synchronous transfer mode	STM
同步传递模式	Tóngbù chuándì móshì	Synchronous transfer mode	STM
同步串行数据转换器	Tóngbù chuànháng shùjù zhuǎnhuànqì	Synchronous serial data adapter	SSDA
同步传输	Tóngbù chuánshū	Synchronous transmission	
同步传输模块	Tóngbù chuánshū mókuài	Synchronous transport module	STM
同步传输模式	Tóngbù chuánshū móshì	Synchronous transfer mode	STM
同步传送模块	Tóngbù chuánsòng mókuài	Synchronous transport module	STM
同步传送模块等级 N	Tóngbù chuánsòng mókuài děngjí N	Synchronous transport module level-N	STM-N
同步传送模式	Tóngbù chuánsòng móshì	Synchronous transfer mode	STM
同步带	Tóngbù dài	Hold-in range	
同步电报	Tóngbù diànbào	Synchronous telegraphy	
同步定时产生器	Tóngbù dìngshí chǎnshēngqì	Synchronous timing generator	STG
同步定时发生器	Tóngbù dìngshí fāshēngqì	Synchronous timing generator	STG
同步地球轨道	Tóngbù dìqiú guǐdào	Geosynchronous earth orbit	GEO
同步地球轨道卫星	Tóngbù dìqiú guǐdào wèixīng	Geosynchronous earth orbit satellite	GEOS
同步动态随机存储器	Tóngbù dòngtài suíjī cúnchǔqì	Synchronous dynamic random access memory	SDRAM
同步多路控制器	Tóngbù duōlù kòngzhìqì	Synchronous multi-line controller	SMLC
同步多媒体集成语言	Tóngbù duōméitǐ jíchéng yǔyán	Synchronous multimedia integrated language	SMIL
同步多周控制	Tóngbù duōzhōu kòngzhì	Synchronous multi-cycle control	
同步分配	Tóngbù fēnpèi	Synchronization distribution	SD
同步复用器	Tóngbù fùyòngqì	Synchronous multiplexer	SM
同步供给单元	Tóngbù gōngjǐ dānyuán	Synchronous supply unit	SSU
同步光网络	Tóngbù guāng wǎngluò	Synchronous optical network	SONET
同步光缆网络	Tóngbù guānglǎn wǎngluò	Synchronous optical network	SONET
同步光纤网络和同步数字系列	Tóngbù guāngxiān wǎngluò hé tóngbù shùzì xìliè	Synchronous optical network (ANSI/ITU-T)	SONET/SDH
同步和会聚功能	Tóngbù hé huìjù gōngnéng	Synchronization and convergence function	SCF

同步监控模块	Tóngbù jiānkòng mókuài	Synchronization supervisor module	SSM
同步校正	Tóngbù jiàozhèng	Synchronous correction	
同步节点	Tóngbù jiédiǎn	Synchronization node	
同步解调	Tóngbù jiětiáo	Synchronous demodulation	
同步计算机	Tóngbù jìsuànjī	Synchronous computer	
同步空闲	Tóngbù kòngxián	Synchronous idle	SYN
同步空闲字符	Tóngbù kòngxián zìfú	Synchronous idle character	SYN
同步控制信道	Tóngbù kòngzhì xìn dào	Synchronization control channel	SCCH
同步宽带控制器	Tóngbù kuāndài kòngzhìqì	Synchronous broadband control element	SBCE
同步连接链路	Tóngbù liánjiē liànlù	Synchronous connecting link	SCO
同步链路	Tóngbù liànlù	Synchronization link	
同步链路选择	Tóngbù liànlù xuǎnzé	Synchronization link selection	
同步码	Tóngbù mǎ	Synchronization code	SC
同步脉冲串	Tóngbù màichōng chuàn	Synchronization burst	SB
同步面向连接	Tóngbù miànxiàng liánjiē	Synchronous connection-oriented	SCO
同步频率编号技术	Tóngbù pínlǜ biānhào jìshù	Synchronous frequency encoding technique	SFET
同步起止改正力	Tóngbù qǐzhǐ gǎizhèng lì	Synchronous start-stop margin	
同步起止畸变度	Tóngbù qǐzhǐ jībiàn dù	Degree of synchronous start-stop distortion	
同步设备定时发生器	Tóngbù shèbèi dìngshí fāshēngqì	Synchronous equipment timing generator	SETG
同步设备定时物理接口	Tóngbù shèbèi dìngshí wùlǐ jiēkǒu	Synchronous equipment timing physical interface	SETPI
同步设备定时源	Tóngbù shèbèi dìngshí yuán	Synchronous equipment timing source	SETS
同步设备管理功能	Tóngbù shèbèi guǎnlǐ gōngnéng	Synchronous equipment management function	SEMF
同步剩余时间标志法	Tóngbù shèngyú shíjiān biāozhì fǎ	Synchronous residual time stamp	SRTS
同步时分多路存取	Tóngbù shífèn duōlù cúnqǔ	Synchronous time division multiple access	STDMA
同步时分复用	Tóngbù shífèn fùyòng	Synchronous time division multiplexing	STDM
同步失效	Tóngbù shīxiào	Desynchronization	
同步时钟	Tóngbù shízhōng	Synchronization clock	
同步收报机的改正力	Tóngbù shōubàojīde gǎizhèng lì	Margin of a synchronous receiver	
同步数据传输	Tóngbù shùjù chuánshū	Synchronous (data) transmission	
同步数据电路	Tóngbù shùjù diànlù	Synchronous data circuit	CDS
同步数据链路控制	Tóngbù shùjù liànlù kòngzhì	Synchronous data link control	SDLC
同步数据链路控制协议	Tóngbù shùjù liànlù kòngzhì xiéyì	Synchronous data link control protocol (IBM use)	SDLC
同步数据通信控制器	Tóngbù shùjù tōngxìn kòngzhìqì	Synchronous data communication control unit	SDCCU
同步数据通讯适配器	Tóngbù shùjù tōngxùn shìpèiqì	Synchronization data communications adapter	SDCA
同步数据网	Tóngbù shùjù wǎng	Synchronous data network	
同步数据转接器	Tóngbù shùjù zhuǎnjiēqì	Synchronous data adapter	SDA
同步数字传输体系	Tóngbù shùzì chuánshū tǐxì	Synchronous digital hierarchy	SDH
同步数字交叉连接设备	Tóngbù shùzì jiāochā liánjiē shèbèi	Synchronous digital cross connect equipment	SDXC
同步数字交叉连接器	Tóngbù shùzì jiāochā liánjiēqì	Synchronous digital cross-connector	SDXC
同步数字体系	Tóngbù shùzì tǐxì	Synchronous digital hierarchy	SDH
同步数字体系管理网络	Tóngbù shùzì tǐxì guǎnlǐ wǎngluò	Synchronous digital hierarchy management network	SMN
同步数字体系管理子网	Tóngbù shùzì tǐxì guǎnlǐ ziwǎng	Synchronous digital hierarchy management sub-network	SMS
同步数字体系设备时钟	Tóngbù shùzì tǐxì shèbèi shízhōng	Synchronous digital hierarchy equipment clock	SEC
同步数字体系物理接口	Tóngbù shùzì tǐxì wùlǐ jiēkǒu	Synchronous digital hierarchy physical interface	SPI
同步数字系列	Tóngbù shùzì xìliè	Synchronous digital hierarchy	SDH

同步数字系列上的因特网协议	Tóngbù shùzì xìliè shàngde Yīntèwǎng xiéyì	Internet protocol over synchronous digital hierarchy	IP over SDH
同步数字序列	Tóngbù shùzì xùliè	Synchronous digital hierarchy	SDH
同步通信	Tóngbù tōngxìn	Synchronous communications	
同步通信卫星	Tóngbù tōngxìn wèixīng	Synchronous communication satellite	
同步突发	Tóngbù tūfā	Synchronous burst	SB
同步突发脉冲序列	Tóngbù tūfā màichōng xùliè	Synchronization burst	SB
同步图形随机储存器	Tóngbù túxíng suíjī chǔcúnqì	Synchronous graphics random access memory	SGRAM
同步网	Tóngbù wǎng	Synchronous network	TBW
同步网本地管理中心	Tóngbù wǎng běndì guǎnlǐ zhōngxīn	Synchronization network local manager	SLM
同步网全网管理中心	Tóngbù wǎng quánwǎng guǎnlǐ zhōngxīn	Synchronization network manager	SNM
同步网区域管理中心	Tóngbù wǎng qūyù guǎnlǐ zhōngxīn	Synchronization network regional manager	SRM
同步卫星	Tóngbù wèixīng	Geostationary satellite	Geos
同步卫星	Tóngbù wèixīng	Synchronous satellite	
同步物理接口	Tóngbù wùlǐ jiēkǒu	Synchronous physical interface	SPI
同步线转换器	Tóngbù xiàn zhuǎnhuànqì	Synchronous line adapter	SLA
同步线路光口板	Tóngbù xiànlù guāng kǒu bǎn	Synchronous line optical interface	SLI
同步信道	Tóngbù xìndào	Synchronization channel	SCH
同步信道信息	Tóngbù xìndào xìnxī	Synchronization channel information	
同步信号产生	Tóngbù xìnhào chǎnshēng	Synchronizing signal generation	SSG
同步信号单元	Tóngbù xìnhào dānyuán	Synchronization signal unit	SYU
同步信令方式	Tóngbù xìnlìng fāngshì	Sychronous signaling (in common channel signaling)	
同步信息	Tóngbù xìnxī	Synchronization information	
同步信息骨干系统	Tóngbù xìnxī gǔgàn xìtǒng	Synchronous backbone system	SBS
同步信息未知	Tóngbù xìnxī wèizhī	Synchronization traceability unknown	STU
同步压扩	Tóngbù yākuò	Synchronized compression and expansion	Syncompex
同步压扩	Tóngbù yākuò	Syncompex	
同步与会聚功能	Tóngbù yǔ huìjù gōngnéng	Synchronization and convergence function	SCF
同步运输模块	Tóngbù yùnshū mókuài	Synchronous transport module	STM
同步运输信号第 1 层	Tóngbù yùnshū xìnhào dìyīcéng	Synchronous transport signal level-1	STS-1
同步指示	Tóngbù zhǐshì	Synchronization indication	
同步状态消息字节	Tóngbù zhuàngtài xiāoxi zìjié	Synchronization status message byte	SSMB
同步状态信息	Tóngbù zhuàngtài xìnxī	Synchronization status message	SSM
同步转移模块	Tóngbù zhuǎnyí mókuài	Synchronous transfer module	STM
同步转移模式	Tóngbù zhuǎnyí móshì	Synchronous transfer mode	STM
同步字丢失	Tóngbù zì diūshī	Loss of sync word	LOSW
同步子层	Tóngbù zicéng	Synchronization sub-layer	SSL
同步字节	Tóngbù zìjié	Synchronization byte	SB
同步的	Tóngbùde	Mesochronous	
同步化卫星	Tóngbùhuà wèixīng	Synchronized satellite	
同城汇兑交易	Tóngchéng huìduì jiāoyì	Transaction within a city	
通带	Tōngdài	Passband	
通带平坦度	Tōngdài píngtǎndù	Passband flatness	
通道	Tōngdào	Channel	
通道	Tōngdào	Path (in communications networks and SDH)	
通道保护环	Tōngdào bǎohù huán	Path protection ring	

通道层网络	Tōngdào céng wǎngluò	Path layer network	
通道重配置硬件	Tōngdào chóng pèizhì yìngjiàn	Channel reconfiguration hardware	CRH
通道存取协议	Tōngdào cúnqǔ xiéyì	Channel access protocol	CAP
通道倒换环	Tōngdào dǎohuàn huán	Path-switched ring	
通道地址翻译器	Tōngdào dìzhǐ fānyìqì	Channel address translator	CAT
通道地址寄存器	Tōngdào dìzhǐ jìcúnqì	Channel address register	CAR
通道端点	Tōngdào duāndiǎn	Path end point	PEP
通道分配	Tōngdào fēnpèi	Path allocation	
通道分配命令	Tōngdào fēnpèi mìnglìng	Channel assignment order	CAO
通道分组多路器	Tōngdào fēnzǔ duōlùqì	Channel division multiplexer	CDM
通道附加值	Tōngdào fùjiā zhí	Path overhead	
通道缓冲存储器	Tōngdào huǎnchōng cúnchǔqì	Channel buffer storage	CBS
通道缓冲器指针	Tōngdào huǎnchōngqì zhǐzhēn	Channel buffer pointer	CBP
通道缓冲区表	Tōngdào huǎnchōngqū biǎo	Channel buffer table	CBT
通道检测	Tōngdào jiǎncè	Channel check test	CCT
通道坚定和呼叫	Tōngdào jiāndìng hé hūjiào	Channel evaluation and call	CHEC
通道开销	Tōngdào kāixiao	Path overhead	POH
通道可用性表	Tōngdào kěyòngxing biǎo	Channel availability table	CAT
通道命令字	Tōngdào mìnglìng zì	Channel command word	CCW
通道请求优先	Tōngdào qǐngqiú yōuxiān	Channel request priority	CRP
通道设定	Tōngdào shèdìng	Path setting	
通道适配器方式寄存器	Tōngdào shìpèiqì fāngshì jìcúnqì	Channel adapter mode register	CAMR
通道信息流控制	Tōngdào xìnxī liú kòngzhì	Channel flow control	CFC
通道选择器	Tōngdào xuǎnzéqì	Path selector (SDH)	
通道许可	Tōngdào xǔkě	Channel grant	CG
通道音码器	Tōngdào yīnmǎqì	Channel vocoder	CV
通道终端	Tōngdào zhōngduān	Path termination	PT
通道终端设备	Tōngdào zhōngduān shèbèi	Path terminating element	PTE
通道终结	Tōngdào zhōngjié	Path termination	PT
通道状态指示器	Tōngdào zhuàngtài zhǐshìqì	Channel status indicator	CSI
通道状态字节	Tōngdào zhuàngtài zìjié	Channel status byte	CSB
通道资源管理	Tōngdào zīyuán guǎnlǐ	Supply chain management	
通道踪迹标识	Tōngdào zōngjī biāozhì	Path trace identifier	
通道间时基误差	Tōngdào-jiān shíjī wùchā	Inter-channel time base error	ITBE
同等的错误保护	Tóngděngde cuòwù bǎohù	Equal error protection	EEP
通电自检	Tōngdiàn zì jiǎn	Power-on self-test	POST
通断键控	Tōngduàn jiànkòng	On-off keying	OOK
通兑	Tōngduì	On-line payment	
通风车	Tōngfēng chē	Ventilating carriage	
同构	Tónggòu	Homogeneous	
同构图	Tónggòu tú	Isomorphic mapping	
通广北方公司	Tōngguǎng běifāng gōngsī	Tongguang Nortel Corp. (China-Canada joint venture)	
通过端口接入的互通	Tōngguò duānkǒu jiērùde hùtōng	Interworking by port access	
通过呼叫控制映射的互通	Tōngguò hūjiào kòngzhì yìngshède hùtōng	Interworking by call control mapping	
通过判定	Tōngguò pàndìng	Pass verdict	
通过延迟	Tōngguò yánchí	Transit delay	

通过字	Tōngguò zì	Password	PW
通过式频率计	Tōngguò-shì pínlǜjì	Transmission frequency meter	
同化	Tónghuà	Assimilation	
通话	Tōnghuà	Conversation (in telecommunication)	
通话播放	Tōnghuà bōfàng	Call screening	
通话鉴定的响应分析	Tōnghuà jiàndìngde xiǎngyìng fēnxī	Response analysis for call evaluation	RACE
通话明细记录	Tōnghuà míngxì jìlù	Call detail recording	CDR
通话线	Tōnghuà xiàn	Speech wire	
通汇国（地区）	Tōnghuì guó (dìqū)	Countries (regions) exchanging international remittances	
通汇局	Tōnghuì jú	Offices exchanging international remittances	
同级	Tóngjí	Sibling	
统计	Tǒngjì	Statistics	
统计变异数	Tǒngjì biànyì shù	Statistical variance (in SQL Server)	
统计比特率	Tǒngjì bǐtè lǜ	Statistical bit rate	SBR
统计方法	Tǒngjì fāngfǎ	Statistical method	
统计分析	Tǒngjì fēnxī	Statistical analysis	
统计复用	Tǒngjì fùyòng	Statistical multiplex	
统计过程控制	Tǒngjì guòchéng kòngzhì	Statistical process control	SPC
统计量	Tǒngjì liàng	Statistic	
统计面	Tǒngjì miàn	Statistical surface	
统计模式识别	Tǒngjì móshì shíbié	Statistical pattern recognition	
统计时分复用	Tǒngjì shífēn fùyòng	Statistical time-division multiplexing	STDM
统计时分复用器	Tǒngjì shífēn fùyòngqì	Statistical time-division multiplexer	STMPX
统计通信理论	Tǒngjì tōngxìn lǐlùn	Statistical communication	
统计维护管理器	Tǒngjì wéihù guǎnlǐqì	Statistics maintenance manager	SMM
统计相关	Tǒngjì xiāngguān	Statistical correlation	
同极化方向图	Tóngjíhuà fāngxiàngtú	Co-polar pattern (of an antenna)	
铜镜测试	Tóngjìng cèshì	Copper mirror test (in SMT)	
统计性	Tǒngjìxìng	Statistical	
统计型传递方式	Tǒngjìxíng chuándì fāngshì	Statistical transfer mode	
同类复用	Tónglèi fùyòng	Homogeneous multiplex	
同类数据	Tónglèi shùjù	Homogeneous data	
通路	Tōnglù	Channel (preferred), path	
通路开销	Tōnglù kāixiao	Path overhead	POH
通路耦合器	Tōnglù ǒuhéqì	Access coupler	
通路全忙	Tōnglù quánmáng	All-path-busy	APB
通路确认	Tōnglù quèrèn	Channel identification	
通配符	Tōngpèifú	Wildcard	
通配符搜索	Tōngpèifú sōusuǒ	Wildcard search (for database)	
通配符掩码	Tōngpèifú yǎnmǎ	Wildcard mask	
通配符字符	Tōngpèifú zìfú	Wildcard characters (for database)	
同频干扰	Tóngpín gānrǎo	Co-channel interference	
同频干扰保护比	Tóngpín gānrǎo bǎohù bǐ	Co-channel interference protection ratio	
同频信道电台	Tóngpín xìndào diàntái	Co-channel station	
通频带	Tōngpíndài	Passband	
同频道的	Tóngpíndàode	Co-channel (adjective)	

同屏数字化显示	Tóngpíng shùzìhuà xiǎnshì	Digital on-screen display	DOSD
同抢	Tóngqiǎng	Double seizure	
同齐性分析	Tóngqíxìng fēnxī	Homogeneity analysis	
同声传译系统	Tóngshēng chuányì xìtǒng	Simultaneous interpretation conference system	SICS
同时单音顺序制	Tóngshí dānyīn shùnxù zhì	Simultaneous tone sequential system	
同时单音制	Tóngshí dānyīn zhì	Simultaneous tone system	
同时纠随机与突发错误码	Tóngshí jiū suíjī yǔ tūfā cuòwù mǎ	Random and burst error correcting code	
同时可触及部分	Tóngshí kěchùjí bùfen	Simultaneously accessible parts	
同时双向互发	Tóngshí shuāngxiàng hùfā	Two-way simultaneous call	TWS
同时用户中断	Tóngshí yònghù zhōngduàn	Simultaneous line downtime	
同时中继中断	Tóngshí zhōngjì zhōngduàn	Simultaneous trunk downtime	
同态信号处理	Tóngtài xìnhào chǔlǐ	Homomorphic signal processing	
铜酞菁	Tóngtàijīng	Copper phthalo-cyanine	CuPc
铜线电缆	Tóngxiàn diànlǎn	Copper cable	CC
铜线分布式数据接口	Tóngxiàn Fēnbùshì shùjù jiēkǒu	Copper distributed data interface	CDDI
同向	Tóngxiàng	Co-directional	
同相检波	Tóngxiāng jiǎnbō	Phase-locked detector	PLD
同向接口	Tóngxiàng jiēkǒu	Co-directional interface	
同相+正交	Tóngxiàng+zhèngjiāo	In-phase + quadrature	IQ
同相+正交信道环路	Tóngxiàng+zhèngjiāo xìndào huánlù	In-phase + quadrature channel loop	IQL
同相+正交直接序列扩展频谱	Tóngxiàng+zhèngjiāo zhíjiē xùliè kuòzhǎn pínpǔ	In-phase + quadrature direct sequence spread spectrum	IQ-DS-SS
通信	Tōngxìn	Communication, telecommmuncation	
通信安全	Tōngxìn ānquán	Communications security	COMSEC
通信保密	Tōngxìn bǎomì	Communications secrecy	COMSEC
通信保密	Tōngxìn bǎomì	Communications privacy	
通信产品认证机构	Tōngxìn chǎnpǐn rènzhèng jīgòu	Telecommunication certification body	TBC
通信插座	Tōngxìn chāzuò	Telecommunication socket	
通信插座	Tōngxìn chāzuò	Telecommunications outlet	TO
通信程序	Tōngxìn chéngxù	Communications program	
通信导航识别	Tōngxìn dǎoháng shíbié	Communications, navigation and identification (avionics)	CNI
通信电缆交接箱	Tōngxìn diànlǎn jiāojiē xiāng	Telecommunications cable junction box	
通信调查	Tōngxìn diàochá	Questionnaire by mail	
通信地球站	Tōngxìn dìqiú zhàn	Telecommunication earth station	TES
通信服务器	Tōngxìn fúwùqì	Communications server	CS
通信工业协会	Tōngxìn gōngyè xiéhuì	Telecommunications Industry Association	TIA
通信管理	Tōngxìn guǎnlǐ	Communication management	CM
通信管理网络	Tōngxìn guǎnlǐ wǎngluò	Telecommunication management network	TMN
通信规约	Tōngxìn guīyuē	Communication protocol (computer term)	
通信缓冲存储器	Tōngxìn huǎnchōng cúnchǔqì	Communications buffer memory	CBM
通信缓冲器	Tōngxìn huǎnchōngqì	Communications buffer	CB
通信互联网络	Tōngxìn hùlián wǎngluò	Communication interconnect network	BCIN
通信互联子系统	Tōngxìn hùlián zixìtǒng	Communication interconnection sub-system	CIS
通信互联子系统机架	Tōngxìn hùlián zixìtǒng jījià	Communication interconnection sub-system rack	CISR
通信互联网	Tōngxìn hùliánwǎng	Communication interconnection network	CIN
通信交换机台	Tōngxìn jiāohuànjī tái	Communication switch-board	CSB

同心孔板	Tóngxīn kǒngbǎn	Concentric orifice plate	
通信控制单元	Tōngxìn kòngzhì dānyuán	Communication control unit	CCU
通信控制中心	Tōngxìn kòngzhì zhōngxīn	Communications control center	CCC
通信控制器	Tōngxìn kòngzhìqì	Communication control unit	CCU
通信联机测试系统	Tōngxìn liánjī cèshì xìtǒng	Communication on-line testing system	COLTS
通信连接控制器	Tōngxìn liánjiē kòngzhìqì	Communication linkage controller	CLC
通信链路分析系统	Tōngxìn liànlù fēnxī xìtǒng	Communication link analysis system	CLAS
通信流安全	Tōngxìn liú ānquán	Traffic flow security	
通信楼综合定时供给系统	Tōngxìn lóu zōnghé dìngshí gōngjǐ xìtǒng	Building integrated timing system	BITS
通信路径	Tōngxìn lùjìng	Communications path	
通信模块	Tōngxìn mókuài	Connection module	CM
通信模块	Tōngxìn mókuài	Communication module	CM
通信能力	Tōngxìn nénglì	Communication capability	
通信区主控站	Tōngxìn qū zhǔkòngzhàn	Communication area master station	CAMS
通信软件	Tōngxìn ruǎnjiàn	Telecommunications software	
通信设备制造商协会	Tōngxìn shèbèi zhìzàoshāng xiéhuì	Communication Equipment Manufacturers Association	CEMA
通信输出中断(信息)处理机	Tōngxìn shūchū zhōngduàn (xìnxī) chǔlǐjī	Communication output interrupt handler	COIH
通信输入/输出多路复用期	Tōngxìn shūrù/shūchū duōlù fùyòngqī	Communications input/output multiplexer	CIOM
通信统计网络分析过程	Tōngxìn tǒngjì wǎngluò fēnxī guòchéng	Communications statistical network analysis procedure	CSNAP
通信通路	Tōngxìn tōnglù	Communications channel	
通信网络分析程序	Tōngxìn wǎngluò fēnxī chéngxù	Communication network analysis program	CNAP
通信网络管理程序	Tōngxìn wǎngluò guǎnlǐ chéngxù	Communication network manager	CNM
通信网络管理应用	Tōngxìn wǎngluò guǎnlǐ yìngyòng	Communication network management application	CNMA
通信网络结构	Tōngxìn wǎngluò jiégòu	Communication network architecture	CNA
通信卫星	Tōngxìn wèixīng	Communication satellite	CS
通信卫星覆盖范围	Tōngxìn wèixīng fùgài fànwéi	Communication satellite coverage area	
通信卫星公司	Tōngxìn wèixīng gōngsī	Communications Satellite Corp.	COMSAT
通信卫星计划	Tōngxìn wèixīng jìhuà	Communication satellite program	CSP
通信卫星转发器	Tōngxìn wèixīng zhuǎnfāqì	Communication satellite transponder	
通信文本区	Tōngxìn wénběn qū	Communicated text area	
通信文件控制块	Tōngxìn wénjiàn kòngzhì kuài	Communications file control block	CFCB
通信线路品质评分	Tōngxìn xiànlù pǐnzhì píngfēn	Circuit merit rating	
通信信号分配系统	Tōngxìn xìnhào fēnpèi xìtǒng	Communication signal distribution system	CSDS
通信系统	Tōngxìn xìtǒng	Telecommunication system	TCS
通信系统管理程序	Tōngxìn xìtǒng guǎnlǐ chéngxù	Communication system manager	CSM
通信系统管理程序接口	Tōngxìn xìtǒng guǎnlǐ chéngxù jiēkǒu	Communication system manager interface	CSMI
通信系统监视	Tōngxìn xìtǒng jiānshì	Communication system monitoring	CSM
通信系统计划环节	Tōngxìn xìtǒng jìhuà huánjié	Communication system planning element	CSPE
通信系统模型	Tōngxìn xìtǒng móxíng	Communication system model	
通信业务	Tōngxìn yèwù	Communication service	
通信业务分析	Tōngxìn yèwù fēnxī	Traffic analysis (IPsec)	
通信业务填充	Tōngxìn yèwù tiánchōng	Traffic padding (IPsec)	
通信业务中心	Tōngxìn yèwù zhōngxīn	Communication service center	CSC
通信引出端	Tōngxìn yǐnchū duān	Telecommunication outlet	TO
通信与跟踪子系统	Tōngxìn yǔ gēnzōng zixìtǒng	Communications and tracking sub-system	CTS

通信运行地址变换	Tōngxìn yùnxíng dìzhǐ biànhuàn	Telecommunications operations map	TO
通信整形	Tōngxìn zhěngxíng	Traffic shaping	
通信中断程序	Tōngxìn zhōngduàn chéngxù	Communications interrupt program	CIP
通信状态寄存器	Tōngxìn zhuàngtài jìcúnqì	Communications status register	CSR
通信自动处理设备	Tōngxìn zìdòng chǔlǐ shèbèi	Communications automatic processing equipment	CAPE
通信自动化	Tōngxìn zìdònghuà	Communication automation	CA
通信自动化,办公自动化,建筑管理自动化,消防自动化和安全自动化	Tōngxìn zìdònghuà, Bàngōng zìdònghuà, jiànzhù guǎnlǐ zìdònghuà, xiāofáng zìdònghuà hé ānquán zìdònghuà	Communication automation, office automation, building management automation, fire automation and safety automation	A5
通信总线	Tōngxìn zǒngxiàn	Communication bus	CB
通信总线转换器	Tōngxìn zǒngxiàn zhuǎnhuànqì	Communication bus translator	CBT
通信组地址	Tōngxìn zǔ dìzhǐ	Field address (telecom term)	FA
同心、导航、监视	Tóngxīn、dǎoháng、jiānshì	Communications, navigation and surveillance (GPS)	CNS
同信道干扰	Tóngxìndào gānrǎo	Co-channel interference	
同心度	Tóngxīndù	Concentricity	
同心度误差	Tóngxīndù wùchā	Concentricity error	
通行费	Tōngxíng fèi	Toll	
通行码	Tōngxíng mǎ	Passphrase	
通行权	Tōngxíng quán	Right-of-way	
通行字	Tōngxíng zì	Password	
同型性	Tóngxíngxìng	Isomorphism	
通信线路终端	Tōngxìniànlù zhōngduān	Communication line terminal	CLT
通信量矩阵	Tōngxìnliàng jǔzhèn	Traffic matrix	
通信用长波长检光元件	Tōngxìn-yòng cháng bōcháng jiǎn guāng yuánjiàn	Long-wavelength detector for communication	
通信用邮资票品	Tōngxìn-yòng yóuzī piàopǐn	Postage item for communication	
通讯端口	Tōngxùn duānkǒu	Communications port (computers)	COM
通讯社群	Tōngxùn shèqún	Communicopia	
通讯系统	Tōngxùn xìtǒng	Telecommunication system	TCS
同一标准的 PCM 接口	Tóngyī biāozhǔnde PCM jiēkǒu	Uniform PCM interface	UPCMI
统一建模语言	Tǒngyī jiànmó yǔyán	Unified modeling language	UML
统一联络中心	Tǒngyī liánluò zhōngxīn	Unified contact center	UCC
统一码	Tǒngyī mǎ	Unicode	
统一模型语言	Tǒngyī móxíng yǔyán	Unified modelling language	UML
统一内存架构	Tǒngyī nèicún jiàgòu	Unified memory architecture	UMA
统一权限	Tǒngyī quánxiàn	Single sign-on	
统一 TMN 需求、分析和设计	Tǒngyī TMN xūqiú、fēnxī hé shèjì	Unified TMN requirement, analysis and design	UTRAD
统一通信	Tǒngyī tōngxìn	Unified communications	
统一消息	Tǒngyī xiāoxi	Unified message service	UMS
统一系统监测管理器	Tǒngyī xìtǒng jiāncè guǎnlǐqì	Unified system diagnostic manager	USDM
统一业务	Tǒngyī yèwù	Unitary service	US
统一资源标识符	Tǒngyī zīyuán biāozhìfú	Uniform resource identifier	URI
统一资源定位地址	Tǒngyī zīyuán dìngwèi dìzhǐ	Uniform resource locator	URL
统一资源定位器(符)	Tǒngyī zīyuán dìngwèiqì (fú)	Uniform resource locator	URL
通用 ADSL 工作组	Tōngyòng ADSL gōngzuòzǔ	Universal ADSL Working Group	UAWG
通用安全服务应用程序接口	Tōngyòng ānquán fúwù yìngyòng chéngxù jiēkǒu	Generic security service application program interface	GSS-API

通用不对称数字用户线路	Tōngyòng bùduìchèn shùzì yònghù xiànlù	Usual asymmetric digital subscriber line	UADSL
通用部分会聚子层	Tōngyòng bùfen huìjù zicéng	Common part convergence sub-layer	CPCS
通用产品代码	Tōngyòng chǎnpǐn dàimǎ	Universal product code	UPC
通用查询访问码	Tōngyòng cháxún fǎngwèn mǎ	General inquiry access code	GIAC
通用成帧协议	Tōngyòng chéng zhèng xiéyì	Generic framing protocol	GFP
通用成帧规程	Tōngyòng chéngzhèng guīchéng	Generic framing procedure	GFP
通用串行总线	Tōngyòng chuànháng zǒngxiàn	Universal serial bus	USB
通用串联总线	Tōngyòng chuànlián zǒngxiàn	Universal serial bus	USB
通用传输语义	Tōngyòng chuánshū yǔyì	Common transport semantic	CTS
通用存储器系统	Tōngyòng cúnchǔqì xìtǒng	Universal Memory System (Intel Corp.)	UMS
通用存取监控程序	Tōngyòng cúnqǔ jiānkòng chéngxù	Common access monitor program	CAMP
同用电话交换网	Tóngyòng diànhuà jiāohuàn wǎng	General switch telephone network	GSTN
通用地面无线接入	Tōngyòng dìmiàn wúxiàn jiērù	Universal terrestrial radio access	UTRA
通用定义	Tōngyòng dìngyì	Generic definition	
通用对象交换应用	Tōngyòng duìxiàng jiāohuàn yìngyòng	Generic object exchange profile	GOEP
通用对象命名	Tōngyòng duìxiàng mìngmíng	Universal object naming	UON
通用对象模型	Tōngyòng duìxiàng móxíng	Common object modeling	COM
通用对象请求代理结构	Tōngyòng duìxiàng qǐngqiú dàilǐ jiégòu	Common object request broker architecture	CORBA
通用对象请求代理体系结构	Tōngyòng duìxiàng qǐngqiú dàilǐ tǐxì jiégòu	Common object request broker architecture	CORBA
通用对象请求中间件	Tōngyòng duìxiàng qǐngqiú zhōngjiān jiàn	Common object request broker	CORBA
通用对象请求中介架构	Tōngyòng duìxiàng qǐngqiú zhōngjiè jiàgòu	Common object request broker architecture	CORBA
通用对象申请代理结构	Tōngyòng duìxiàng shēnqǐng dàilǐ jiégòu	Common object request broker architecture	CORBA
通用对象文件格式	Tōngyòng duìxiàng wénjiàn géshi	Common object file format	COFF
通用多 8 位编码字符集	Tōngyòng duō bāwèi biānmǎ zìfú jí	Universal multiple-octet coded character set	UCS
通用多协议标志交换协议	Tōngyòng duōxiéyì biāozhì jiāohuàn xiéyì	Generalized multi-protocol label switching	GMPLS
通用访问应用	Tōngyòng fǎngwèn yìngyòng	Generic access profile	GAP
通用非对称数字用户线	Tōngyòng fēiduìchèn shùzì yònghù xiàn	Universal asynchronous digital subscriber line	UADSL
通用分组无线业务	Tōngyòng fēnzǔ wúxiàn yèwù	General packet radio service	GPRS
通用分组无线业务交换功能	Tōngyòng fēnzǔ wúxiàn yèwù jiāohuàn gōngnéng	General packet radio service- service switch function	GPRSSSF
通用个人电信号码	Tōngyòng gèrén diànxìn hàomǎ	Universal personal telecommunication number	UPTN
通用个人通信	Tōngyòng gèrén tōngxìn	Universal personal telecommunications	UPT
通用格式标识符	Tōngyòng géshi biāozhìfú	General format identifier	GFI
通用功率电源单元	Tōngyòng gōnglǜ diànyuán dānyuán	General power supply unit	GPSU
通用广播信令信元	Tōngyòng guǎngbō xìnlìng xìnyuán	General broadcast signaling cell	
通用广播信令虚通路	Tōngyòng guǎngbō xìnlìng xū tōnglù	General broadcast signaling virtual channel	
通用广播信令虚信道	Tōngyòng guǎngbō xìnlìng xū xìndào	General broadcast signaling virtual channel	GBSVC
通用关键子密码方法	Tōngyòng guānjiàn zi mìmǎ fāngfǎ	Rivest-Shamir-Adelman coding	RSA
通用管理信息服务	Tōngyòng guǎnlǐ xìnxī fúwù	Common management information service (IETF standard)	CMIS
通用管理信息协议	Tōngyòng guǎnlǐ xìnxī xiéyì	Common management information protocol	CMIP
通用规范	Tōngyòng guīfàn	Generic specification	
通用横轴墨卡托	Tōngyòng héngzhóu mò-kǎ-tuō	Universal Transverse Mercator	UTM
通用横轴墨卡托投影栅格	Tōngyòng héngzhóu Mò-kǎ-tuō tóuyǐng zhàgé	Universal Transverse Mercator grid projection	

通用话音服务器	Tōngyòng huàyīn fúwùqì	Universal audio server	UAS
通用会议控制	Tōngyòng huìyì kòngzhì	General conference control	Gcc
通用会议控制服务接入点	Tōngyòng huìyì kòngzhì fúwù jiērù diǎn	General conference control- service access point	GccSAP
通用 Internet 文件系统	Tōngyòng Internet wénjiàn xìtǒng	Common Internet file system	CIFS
通用即插即用	Tōngyòng jí chā jíyòng	Universal plug and play	UpnP
同用交换电话网	Tóngyòng jiāohuàn diànhuà wǎng	General switched telephone network	GSTN
通用交换管理协议	Tōngyòng jiāohuàn guǎnlǐ xiéyì	General switch management protocol	GSMP
通用集成电路卡	Tōngyòng jíchéng diànlù kǎ	Universal integrated circuit card	UICC
通用寄存器堆栈	Tōngyòng jìcúnqì duīzhàn	General register stack	GRS
通用接口处理器	Tōngyòng jiēkǒu chǔlǐqì	Versatile interface processor	VIP
通用接口配置	Tōngyòng jiēkǒu pèizhì	Generic access profile	GAP
通用接入号码	Tōngyòng jiērù hàomǎ	Universal access number	UAN
通用接入图	Tōngyòng jiērù tú	Generic access profile	GAP
通用技术规定	Tōngyòng jìshù guīdìng	Common technical regulation	CTR
通用计算机	Tōngyòng jìsuànjī	General purpose computer	
通用开放策略服务	Tōngyòng kāifàng cèlüè fúwù	Common open policy service	COPS
通用客体请求代理体系结构	Tōngyòng kètǐ qǐngqiú dàilǐ tǐxì jiégòu	Common object request broker architecture	CORBA
通用控制	Tōngyòng kòngzhì	General control	GC
通用空中接口	Tōngyòng kōngzhōng jiēkǒu	Common air interface (CDMA)	CAI
通用宽带无线接入网络	Tōngyòng kuāndài wúxiàn jiērù wǎngluò	Broadband generalized radio access network	BGRAN
通用类型系统	Tōngyòng lèixíng xìtǒng	Common type system	CTS
通用链接定位	Tōngyòng liànjiē dìngwèi	Uniform resource locator	URL
通用连接接纳控制	Tōngyòng liánjiē jiēnà kòngzhì	Generic connection acceptance control	GCAC
通用流量控制	Tōngyòng liúliàng kòngzhì	Generic flow control	GFC
通用漏洞披露	Tōngyòng lòudòng pīlù	Common vulnerabilities and exposures	CVE
通用陆地无线接入网络	Tōngyòng lùdì wúxiàn jiērù wǎngluò	Universal terrestrial radio access network	UTRAN
通用路由封装	Tōngyòng lùyóu fēngzhuāng	Generic routing encapsulation	GRE
通用路由选择封装	Tōngyòng lùyóu xuǎnzé fēngzhuāng	Generic routing encapsulation	GRE
通用描述发现和集成协议	Tōngyòng miáoshù fāxiàn hé jíchéng xiéyì	Universal description, discovery and integration protocol	UDDI
通用命名规则名称	Tōngyòng mìngmíng guīzé míngchēng	Universal naming convention (UNC) name	
通用内部多路转换系统	Tōngyòng nèibù duōlù zhuǎnhuàn xìtǒng	Versatile interior multiplex system	VIMS
通用 ORB 间协议	Tōngyòng ORB-jiān xiéyì	General inter-ORB protocol (CORBA term)	GIOP
通用平滑调频	Tōngyòng pínghuá tiáopín	Generalized tamed frequency modulation	GTFM
通用汽车公司	Tōngyòng qìchē gōngsī	General Motors Corporation (US company)	GM
通用入侵规范语言	Tōngyòng rùqīn guīfàn yǔyán	Common intrusion specification language	CISL
通用入侵检测对象	Tōngyòng rùqīn jiǎncè duìxiàng	Generalized intrusion detection objects	GIDO
通用入侵检测框架	Tōngyòng rùqīn jiǎncè kuàngjià	Common intrusion detection framework	CIDF
通用上层安全性	Tōngyòng shàngcéng ānquánxìng	Generic upper layer security	GULS
通用商业语言	Tōngyòng shāngyè yǔyán	Common business-oriented language	COBOL
通用时间	Tōngyòng shíjiān	Universal time	UT
通用时间坐标	Tōngyòng shíjiān zuòbiāo	Universal time coordinate	UTC
通用世界时	Tōngyòng shìjièshí	Universal time constant	UTC
通用时钟	Tōngyòng shízhōng	Universal time clock	UTC
通用属性注册协议	Tōngyòng shǔxìng zhùcè xiéyì	Generic attribute registration protocol	GARP
通用算法	Tōngyòng suànfǎ	Generic algorithm	

通用网关接口	Tōngyòng wǎngguān jiēkǒu	Common gateway interface	CGI
通用网络信息模型	Tōngyòng wǎngluò xìnxī móxíng	Generic network information model	GNM
通用微波系统公司	Tōngyòng wēibō xìtǒng gōngsī	General MicroSystems Corp.	GMS
通用唯一标识	Tōngyòng wéiyī biāozhì	Universal unique identifier	UUID
通用无线分组业务	Tōngyòng wúxiàn fēnzǔ yèwù	General packet radio service	GPRS
通用无线通信	Tōngyòng wúxiàn tōngxìn	Universal wireless communications	UWC
通用无线通信协议	Tōngyòng wúxiàn tōngxìn xiéyì	Universal wireless communications consortium	UWCC
通用线性模型	Tōngyòng xiànxìng móxíng	General linear model	
通用消息事务处理协议	Tōngyòng xiāoxi shìwù chǔlǐ xiéyì	Versatile message transaction protocol	VMTP
通用信号后面板	Tōngyòng xìnhào hòumian bǎn	Universal signaling back panel	USBP
通用信息传送服务	Tōngyòng xìnxī chuánsòng fúwù	Universal messaging service	UMS
通用信息模块	Tōngyòng xìnxī mókuài	Generic information block	GIB
通用信息模型	Tōngyòng xìnxī móxíng	Common information model	CIM
通用信息帧	Tōngyòng xìnxī zhèng	Unnumbered information frame	UI
通用信元速率算法	Tōngyòng xìnyuán sùlǜ suànfǎ	Generic cell rate algorithm	GCRA
通用信元率算法	Tōngyòng xìnyuánlǜ suànfǎ	Generic cell rate algorithm	GCRA
通用选路封装	Tōngyòng xuǎnlù fēngzhuāng	Generic routing encapsulation	GRE
通用验收测试软件	Tōngyòng yànshōu cèshì ruǎnjiàn	General acceptance test software	GATS
通用异步接收/发送装置	Tōngyòng yìbù jiēshōu/fāsòng zhuāngzhì	Universal asynchronous receiver/transmitter	UART
通用异步收/发器	Tōngyòng yìbù shōu/fāqì	Universal asynchronous receiver/transmitter	UART
通用移动电信系统	Tōngyòng yídòng diànxìn xìtǒng	Universal mobile telecommunications system	UMTS
通用移动通信系统	Tōngyòng yídòng tōngxìn xìtǒng	Universal mobile telecommunication system	UMTS
通用移动通信系统地面无线接入	Tōngyòng yídòng tōngxìn xìtǒng dìmiàn wúxiàn jiērù	Universal mobile telecommunications system- terrestrial radio access	UTRA
通用移动通信系统用户识别模块	Tōngyòng yídòng tōngxìn xìtǒng yònghù shíbié mókuài	Universal mobile telecommunications system subscriber identity module	USIM
通用于滑调频	Tōngyòng yúhuá tiáopín	Generalized tamed frequency modulation	GTFM
通用语言规范	Tōngyòng yǔyán guīfàn	Common language specification	CLS
通用语言基础设施	Tōngyòng yǔyán jīchǔ shèshī	Common language infrastructure	CLI
通用指令集	Tōngyòng zhǐlìng jí	Common command set	CCS
通用中间语言	Tōngyòng zhōngjiān yǔyán	Common intermediate language	CIL
通用中介语言	Tōngyòng zhōngjiè yǔyán	Common intermediate language	CIL
通用专线通信	Tōngyòng zhuānxiàn tōngxìn	Universal private telecommunication	UPT
通用字元	Tōngyòng zìyuán	Wild card	
通用资源定位符	Tōngyòng zīyuán dìngwèifú	Universal resource locator	URL
通用资源定位器	Tōngyòng zīyuán dìngwèiqì	Universal resource locator	URL
通用总线分支适配器	Tōngyòng zǒngxiàn fēnzhī shìpèiqì	Common bus branch adapter	CBBA
通用的	Tōngyòngde	Generic	
通用的呼叫表	Tōngyòngde hūjiào biǎo	Current call meter	CCM
同质	Tóngzhì	Homomorphism	
通知	Tōngzhī	Notify	
通知信道	Tōngzhī xìndào	Notification channel	NCH
通知指示	Tōngzhī zhǐshì	Notification indicator	
同轴波导变换器	Tóngzhóu bōdǎo biànhuànqì	Coaxial-waveguide transformer	
同轴带线变换器	Tóngzhóu dàixiàn biànhuànqì	Coaxial-stripline transformer	
同轴电缆	Tóngzhóu diànlǎn	Coaxial cable	CC

同轴电缆载波电话	Tóngzhóu diànlǎn zàibō diànhuà	Coaxial cable carrier telephone	
同轴定向耦合器	Tóngzhóu dìngxiàng ǒuhéqì	Coaxial directional coupler	
同轴度	Tóngzhóu dù	Coaxiality	
同轴环行电桥	Tóngzhóu huánxíng diànqiáo	Coaxial hybrid ring	
同轴接头	Tóngzhóu jiētóu	Coaxial connector	
同轴滤波器	Tóngzhóu lǜbōqì	Coaxial filter	
同轴天线	Tóngzhóu tiānxiàn	Coaxial antenna	
同轴线	Tóngzhóu xiàn	Coaxial line	
同轴线表面转移阻抗	Tóngzhóu xiàn biǎomiàn zhuǎnyí zǔkàng	Surface transfer impedance of a coaxial line	
通轴线铠装电缆	Tōngzhóu xiàn kǎizhuāng diànlǎn	Coaxial wire armored cable	WA
同轴谐振腔	Tóngzhóu xiézhènqiāng	Coaxial cavity	
同轴旋转关节	Tóngzhóu xuánzhuǎn guānjié	Coaxial rotary joint	
同轴转换开关	Tóngzhóu zhuǎnhuàn kāiguān	Coaxial switch	
同轴的	Tóngzhóude	Coaxial	CA
头校验码	Tóu jiàoyàn mǎ	Header error check	HEC
头结点	Tóu jiédiǎn	Head node	
头记录	Tóu jìlù	Header record	
头盘部件	Tóu pán bùjiàn	Head disk assembly	I
头文件	Tóu wénjiàn	Header file	
头指针	Tóu zhǐzhēn	Head pointer	
投币电话识别廛	Tóubì diànhuà shíbié chán	Coinbox identification tone	
头标垂向冗余校验错	Tóubiāo chuíxiàng rǒngyú jiàoyàn cuò	Header vertical redundancy check error	HRC
头部差错控制	Tóubù chācuò kòngzhì	Header error control	HEC
头部关联传输功能	Tóubù guānlián chuánshū gōngnéng	Head related transfer function	HRTF
透传	Tòuchuán	Bypass	
头戴式显示器	Tóudài-shì xiǎnshìqì	Head mounted display	HMD
投递	Tóudì	Delivery	
投递报告	Tóudì bàogào	Delivery report	
头端	Tóuduān	Head end	
透镜校正的喇叭天线	Tòujìng jiàozhèngde lǎba tiānxiàn	Lens-corrected horn antenna	
透镜天线	Tòujìng tiānxiàn	Lens antenna	LA
透明带内导频单边带	Tòumíng dàinèi dǎopín dānbiāndài	Transparent tone-in-band single sideband	TTIB
透明复用设备	Tòumíng fùyòng shèbèi	Transparent multiplexing equipment	TMUX
透明桥接	Tòumíng qiáojiē	Transparent bridging	
透明位块传输	Tòumíng wèikuài chuánshū	Transparent blitting	
透明中继器	Tòumíng zhōngjìqì	Transparent repeater	
透明转发器	Tòumíng zhuǎnfāqì	Transparent transponder	
透明状效果	Tòumíng zhuàng xiàoguǒ	Transparency (video term)	
透明字段描述符	Tòumíng zìduàn miáoshù fú	Transparent field descriptor	
透明的数据传送阶段	Tòumíngde shùjù chuánsòng jiēduàn	Transparent data transfer phase	
透明度	Tòumíngdù	Transparency	
偷窃提货不着险	Tōuqiè tíhuò bùzháo xiǎn	Theft, pilferage and non-delivery	t.p.n.d
投入业务性能指标	Tóurù yèwù xìngnéng zhǐbiāo	Bring into service performance objective	BISPO
透射端口	Tòushè duānkǒu	Pass port (FOC)	
投市	Tóushì	Appear on the market (verb phrase)	
透视纠正	Tòushì jiūzhèng	Perspective correction	PC

投送	Tóusòng	Contribution	
投送应用	Tóusòng yìngyòng	Contribution application	
投影	Tóuyǐng	Projection	
投影变换	Tóuyǐng biànhuàn	Projection transformation	
投影法	Tóuyǐng fǎ	Projection method	
投影文件	Tóuyǐng wénjiàn	Projection file	
投影坐标系统	Tóuyǐng zuòbiāo xìtǒng	Projected coordinate system	
透支	Tòuzhī	Overdraw (video term)	
投资成本	Tóuzī chéngběn	Capital expenses	CAPEX
投资回报	Tóuzī huíbào	Return on investment	ROI
TPDU 命令	TPDU mìnglìng	Command TPDU	C-TPDU
T-R 盒	T-R hé	T-R cell	
T-R 开关	T-R kāiguān	T-R switch	
TSB E1 接口集成板	TSB E1 jiēkǒu jíchéngbǎn	TSB interface E1 board assembly	TIEA
TSB 控制	TSB kòngzhì	TSB control	TCO
TSB T1 接口集成板	TSB T1 jiēkǒu jíchéngbǎn	TSB interface T1 board assembly	TITA
凸包	Tū bāo	Convex hull	
团体	Tuántǐ	Community	
突变折射率分布	Tūbiàn zhéshèlǜ fēnbù	Step index profile	
突变型多模光纤	Tūbiànxíng duōmó guāngxiān	Step index fiber	SIF
突变型光纤	Tūbiànxíng guāngxiān	Step index fiber	
图表	Túbiǎo	Graphics table	
图标	Túbiāo	Icon	
图层	Túcéng	Cover; coverage; layer; coverage extent	
涂层	Túcéng	Coating (FOC mfg)	
图层单位	Túcéng dānwèi	Cover ID	
图层范围	Túcéng fànwéi	Coverage units	
涂层黏附力测定仪	Túcéng niánfùlì cèdìngyí	Coating adhesion tester (semiconductor mfg)	
涂层直径	Túcéng zhíjìng	Coating diameter (FOC mfg)	
突出显示	Tūchū xiǎnshì	Highlight	
图的划分	Túde huàfēn	Graph partition	
图的描绘	Túde miáohuì	Drawing graphs nicely	
图的生成	Túde shēngchéng	Generating graphs	
图的同构	Túde tóng gòu	Graph isomorphism	
土地分类系统	Tǔdì fēnlèi xìtǒng	Land classification system	
土地信息系统	Tǔdì xìnxī xìtǒng	Land information system	LIS
突发	Tūfā	Burst	
突发包特征	Tūfā bāo tèzhēng	Burst packet attribute	BPA
突发差错	Tūfā chācuò	Burst error	
突发长度	Tūfā chángdù	Burst length	
突发错误处理程序	Tūfā cuòwù chǔlǐ chéngxù	Burst-error processor	BEP
突发电离层骚扰	Tūfā diànlícéng sāorǎo	Sudden ionospheric disturbance	SID
突发方法	Tūfā fāngfǎ	Burst method	
突发访问	Tūfā fǎngwèn	Access burst (GSM term)	
突发脉冲	Tūfā màichōng	Burst	
突发脉冲序列周期	Tūfā màichōng xùliè zhōuqī	Burst period	BP

突发模式光接收机	Tūfā móshì guāng jiēshōujī	Burst-mode optical receiver	
突发模式控制器	Tūfā móshì kòngzhìqì	Burst-mode controller	BMC
突发频率校正	Tūfā pínlǜ jiàozhèng	Frequency correction burst	FB
突发容限	Tūfā róngxiàn	Burst tolerance	BT
突发数据传输率	Tūfā shùjù chuánshū lǜ	Burst data transfer rate	
突发数据业务	Tūfā shùjù yèwù	Bursty data services	
突发业务	Tūfā yèwù	Burst traffic	
突发宇宙噪声吸收	Tūfā yǔzhòu zàoshēng xīshōu	Sudden cosmic noise absorption	SCNA
突发式传输	Tūfā-shì chuánshū	Burst transmission	
突发式管道同步静态存储器	Tūfā-shì guǎndào tóngbù jìngtài cúnchǔqì	Burst pipelined synchronous static RAM	BSRAM
突发式调制解调器	Tūfā-shì tiáozhì jiětiáoqì	Burst modem	
突发性	Tūfāxìng	Burstiness	
图幅	Túfú	Map extent	
图幅范围	Túfú fànwéi	Map limits	
图幅拼接	Túfú pīnjiē	Adjoining sheets	
推换式	Tuī huàn shì	Push-pull type	
推伙伴	Tuī huǒbàn	Push partner	
退N步ARQ	Tuì N-bù ARQ	Go-back-N ARQ	
推推型	Tuī tuī xíng	Push-push type (switch or smart card reader)	
推信息	Tuī xìnxī	Message push	MP
退避	Tuìbì	Back off	
推迟	Tuīchí	Defer	
退出	Tuìchū	Exit (WP command)	
退出拒绝	Tuìchū jùjué	Disengage rejected	DRJ
退出连线	Tuìchū liánxiàn	Logout	
退出请求	Tuìchū qǐngqiú	Disengage request	DRQ
退出确认	Tuìchū quèrèn	Disengage confirmed	DCF
退出组请求消息	Tuìchū zǔ qǐngqiú xiāoxi	Leave group request message (in multicast)	
推导	Tuīdǎo	Deduction	
退格	Tuìgé	Backspace	BS
退化	Tuìhuà	Decay	
退化失效	Tuìhuà shīxiào	Degradation failure	
退汇	Tuìhuì	Return of remittance	
推荐	Tuījiàn	Recommendation	REC
推荐系统	Tuījiàn xìtǒng	Recommendation system	
退缴	Tuìjiǎo	Refund	
退款手续费	Tuìkuǎn shǒuxùfèi	Procedures fee for return payments	
推送和拉取方式	Tuīsòng hé lāqǔ fāngshì	Push and pull media	
推送技术	Tuīsòng jìshù	Push technology	
退缩	Tuìsuō	Degeneration	
推挽放大器	Tuīwǎn fàngdàqì	Push-pull amplifier	
退位键	Tuìwèi jiàn	Backslash key (\ )	
退役阶段	Tuìyì jiēduàn	Retirement phase (of product life cycle)	
图库	Túkù	Library (for imagery)	
图库管理系统	Túkù guǎnlǐ xìtǒng	Librarian	
图廓	Túkuò	Map border	

图廓	Túkuò	Margin	
图廓注记	Túkuò zhùjì	Border information	
图廓线	Túkuòxiàn	Border line	
图例	Túlì	Legend	
图论	Túlùn	Graph theory	
图论-多项式算法	Túlùn- duōxiàngshì suànfǎ	Graph problems -- polynomial	
图面配置视图	Túmiàn pèizhì shìtú	Layout view	
图面天底点	Túmiàn tiāndǐ diǎn	Map nadir	
图名	Túmíng	Map name	
吞吐量	Tūntǔliàng	Throughput (quantity)	
吞吐率	Tūntǔlǜ	Throughput (rate)	
拖放	Tuō fàng	Drag and drop	
拖动	Tuōdòng	Drag	
托管	Tuōguǎn	Hosting	
托管代码	Tuōguǎn dàimǎ	Managed code	
托管对象	Tuōguǎn duìxiàng	Managed object	
托管扩展	Tuōguǎn kuòzhǎn	Managed extensions	
托管组	Tuōguǎn zǔ	Managed group (in multicast)	
脱机	Tuōjī	Off-line	
脱机测试	Tuōjī cèshì	Off-line test	
脱机加密操作	Tuōjī jiāmì cāozuò	Off-line crypto operation	
脱节	Tuōjié	Underlap	
脱扣器	Tuōkòuqì	Release (of a mechanical switching device)	
脱离拒绝	Tuōlí jùjué	Disengage reject	DRJ
脱离瞄视角	Tuōlí miáo shìjiǎo	Off-boresight angle	OBA
脱离请求	Tuōlí qǐngqiú	Disengage request	DRQ
脱离确认	Tuōlí quèrèn	Disengage confirm	DCF
椭偏仪	Tuǒpiānyí	Ellipsometry (semiconductor mfg)	
拓扑	Tuòpū	Topology	
拓扑边界	Tuòpū biānjiè	Topological boundary	
拓扑表述	Tuòpū biǎoshù	Topological expression	
拓扑错误	Tuòpū cuòwù	Topological error	
拓扑叠加	Tuòpū diéjiā	Topological overlay	
拓扑对象	Tuòpū duìxiàng	Topological object	
拓扑复合物	Tuòpū fùhéwù	Topological complex	
拓扑关系	Tuòpū guānxi	Topological relationship	
拓扑函数	Tuòpū hánshù	Topological function	
拓扑结构	Tuòpū jiégòu	Topological structure	
拓扑结构数据	Tuòpū jiégòu shùjù	Topologically structured data	
拓扑排序	Tuòpū páixù	Topological sorting	
拓扑有序	Tuòpū yǒu xù	Topological order	
拓扑优化	Tuòpū yōuhuà	Topological optimization	
拓扑有效性条件	Tuòpū yǒuxiàoxìng tiáojiàn	Topologic validity condition (CAD/CAM)	TVC
拓扑元件	Tuòpū yuánjiàn	Topological component	
拓扑原素	Tuòpū yuánsù	Topological primitive	
椭球变异函数	Tuǒqiú biànyì hánshù	Elliptical variogram	

脱网工作	Tuōwǎng gōngzuò	Talkaround	
拖延时间	Tuōyán shíjiān	Hold off time	
椭圆	Tuǒyuán	Ellipse; elliptic	
椭圆波导管	Tuǒyuán bōdǎoguǎn	Elliptical waveguide	
椭圆轨道	Tuǒyuán guǐdào	Highly elliptical orbit	HEO
椭圆轨道	Tuǒyuán guǐdào	Elliptical orbit (of a satellite)	
椭圆极化	Tuǒyuán jíhuà	Elliptical polarization	
椭圆极化波	Tuǒyuán jíhuà bō	Elliptically polarized wave	
椭圆面镜	Tuǒyuán miànjìng	Ellipsoid mirror	
椭圆曲线加密	Tuǒyuán qūxiàn jiāmì	Elliptic curve crypto	ECC
椭圆曲线离散对数问题	Tuǒyuán qūxiàn lísàn duìshù wèntí	Elliptical curve discrete logarithm problem	ECDLP
椭圆曲线密码体制	Tuǒyuán qūxiàn mìmǎ tǐzhì	Elliptic curve cryptosystem	
椭圆软波导	Tuǒyuán ruǎn bōdǎo	Elliptical flexible waveguide	
椭圆振荡	Tuǒyuán zhèndàng	Oval oscillation	
椭圆体	Tuǒyuántǐ	Ellipsoid	
椭圆体高度	Tuǒyuántǐ gāodù	Ellipsoidal height	
椭圆形波导	Tuǒyuánxíng bōdǎo	Elliptical waveguide	
图片	Túpiàn	Picture (WP command)	
图片传真	Túpiàn chuánzhēn	Picture facsimile	
图奇系统	Túqí xìtǒng	Turnkey system	
图签	Túqiān	Icon	
突然失效	Tūrán shīxiào	Sudden failure	
涂色描绘	Túsè miáohuì	Rendering	
图书馆资讯门	Túshūguǎn zīxùn mén	Library InfoGate	
图文电视	Túwén diànshì	Teletext; broadcast videography; videocast	
图文广播	Túwén guǎngbō	Broadcast videography	
图文界面	Túwén jièmiàn	Graphical interface	
图文区	Túwén qū	Image area	
图文视传	Túwén shìchuán	Videography	
图像	Túxiàng	Image, graphic	
图像	Túxiàng	Imagery	
图像编码	Túxiàng biānmǎ	Image coding	
图像处理	Túxiàng chǔlǐ	Image processing	
图像处理和模式识别	Túxiàng chǔlǐ hé móshì shíbié	Image processing and pattern recognition	IPPR
图像短信息传送服务	Túxiàng duǎn xìnxī chuánsòng fúwù	Picture messaging service	PMS
图像分割	Túxiàng fēngē	Image segmentation	
图像分析	Túxiàng fēnxī	Image analysis	
图像复原	Túxiàng fùyuán	Image restoration (GIS)	
图像管理	Túxiàng guǎnlǐ	Image management	
图像恢复	Túxiàng huīfù	Image restoration	
图像检索	Túxiàng jiǎnsuǒ	Image search	
图像接入单元	Túxiàng jiērù dānyuán	Picture access unit	PAU
图像目录	Túxiàng mùlù	Image catalog	
图像平滑	Túxiàng pínghuá	Image smoothing	
图象切换控制器	Túxiàng qiēhuàn kòngzhìqì	Video handoff controller	
图像区	Túxiàng qū	Image area	

图像锐化	Túxiàng ruìhuà	Image sharpening	
图象使用者介面	Túxiàng shǐyòngzhě jièmiàn	Graphical user interface	GUI
图象刷新	Túxiàng shuāxīn	Refresh graphics	
图像水印	Túxiàng shuǐyìn	Image watermarking	
图像搜索引擎	Túxiàng sōusuǒ yǐnqíng	Image search engine	
图象微调	Túxiàng wēitiáo	Differential rectification	
图象稳定度	Túxiàng wěndìngdù	Graphic stability	
图像显示终端	Túxiàng xiǎnshì zhōngduān	Video display terminal	VDT
图像形态学	Túxiàng xíngtàixué	Image morphology	
图象要素	Túxiàng yàosù	Picture element	
图像压缩	Túxiàng yāsuō	Image compression	
图像压缩编码	Túxiàng yāsuō biānmǎ	Image compression encoding	
图象用户介面	Túxiàng yònghù jièmiàn	Graphical user interface	GUI
图形	Túxíng	Graph, graphic	
图形操作	Túxíng cāozuò	Graphic manipulation	
图形插印	Túxíng chāyìn	Graphic fudging	
图形处理器	Túxíng chǔlǐqì	Graphic handler	GPH
图形处理器	Túxíng chǔlǐqì	Graphics processing unit	GPU
图形代码扩充	Túxíng dàimǎ kuòchōng	Graphic code extension	
图形叠加	Túxíng diéjiā	Graphic overlay	
图形地址重绘表	Túxíng dìzhǐ chónghuì biǎo	Graphic address remapping table	GART
图形符号	Túxíng fúhào	Graphic symbol	
图形和内存控制中心	Túxíng hé nèicún kòngzhì zhōngxīn	Graphics and memory controller hub	GMCH
图形交换格式	Túxíng jiāohuàn géshi	Graphic interchange format	GIF
图形加速接口	Túxíng jiāsù jiēkǒu	Accelerated graphics port	AGP
图形界面	Túxíng jièmiàn	Graphical user interface	GUI
图形设备接口	Túxíng shèbèi jiēkǒu	Graphics device interface	GDI
图形实体	Túxíng shítǐ	Graphic entity	
图形失真	Túxíng shīzhēn	Graphic distortion	
图形失真校正	Túxíng shīzhēn jiàozhèng	Graphic distortion correction	
图形输出电路分析程序	Túxíng shūchū diànlù fēnxī chéngxù	Graphic output circuit analysis program	GOCAP
图形数据	Túxíng shùjù	Graphic data	
图形数据互换说明	Túxíng shùjù hùhuàn shuōmíng	Graphics exchange specification	GES
图形数据库	Túxíng shùjùkù	Graphic database	
图形通信终端	Túxíng tōngxìn zhōngduān	Graphics communications terminal	GCT
图形通讯	Túxíng tōngxùn	Graphic communication	
图形网编辑	Túxíng wǎng biānjí	Graphic network editor	GNE
图形网浏览	Túxíng wǎng liúlǎn	Graphic network browser	GNB
图形文件	Túxíng wénjiàn	Graphic file	
图形显示终端	Túxíng xiǎnshì zhōngduān	Graphics display terminal	
图形信息	Tú-xíng xìnxī	Graphic information	
图形信息系统	Túxíng xìnxī xìtǒng	Graphical information system	GIS
图形要素	Túxíng yàosù	Graphic primitive	
图形用户接口	Túxíng yònghù jiēkǒu	Graphical user interface	GUI
图形用户界面	Túxíng yònghù jièmiàn	Graphical user interface	GUI
图形用户终端	Túxíng yònghù zhōngduān	Graphical user terminal	

图形元素	Túxíng yuánsù	Graphic element	
图形语言	Túxíng yǔyán	Graphical language	
图形终端	Túxíng zhōngduān	Graphic terminal	
图形字符	Túxíng zìfú	Graphic character	

U

UE 业务容量	UE yèwù róngliàng	UE service capabilities	USC
UICC 信息字段大小	UICC xìnxī zìduàn dàxiǎo	Information field sizes for the UICC	IFSC
UMTS 无线接入网	UMTS wúxiàn jiērù wǎng	UMTS radio access network	URAN
UMTS 移动业务交换中心	UMTS yídòng yèwù jiāohuàn zhōngxīn	UMTS mobile services switching center	UMSC
UNI 承载能力	UNI chéngzài nénglì	UNI bearer capability	
UT 斯达康	UT sī-dá-kāng	UTSTARCOM (US company)	
UTRA 绝对无线电频率号码	UTRA juéduì wúxiàndiàn pínlǜ hàomǎ	Utra absolute radio frequency number	UARFN
UTRA 绝对无线电频率信道号码	UTRA juéduì wúxiàndiàn pínlǜ xìndào hàomǎ	Utra absolute radio frequency channel number	UARFCN
UTRAN 无线电网络临时识别	UTRAN wúxiàndiàn wǎngluò línshí shíbié	UTRAN radio network temporary identity	U-RNTI
UTRAN 注册区域	UTRAN zhùcè qūyù	UTRAN registration area	URA

V

V 端子电压	V duānzi diànyā	V-terminal voltage	
VC 交叉连接	VC jiāochā liánjiē	VC cross connect	
VP-VC 交换机	VP-VC jiāohuànjī	VP-VC switch	
V 形波束雷达	V-xíng bōshù léidá	V-beam radar	

W

挖方坡面	Wāfāng pōmiàn	Cut slope	
挖沟	Wāgōu	Trenching	
外关键字	Wài guānjiàn zì	Foreign key	
外关键字约束	Wài guānjiàn zì yuēshù	Foreign key constraint (in SQL Server)	
外联接	Wài liánjiē	Outer join (for database)	
外汽相沉积法	Wài qìxiàng chénjī fǎ	Outside vapor phase deposition (FOC mfg)	OVPD
外包	Wàibāo	Outsourcing	
外包研究所	Wàibāo yánjiūsuǒ	Outsourcing institute	
外表	Wàibiǎo	Foreign table	
外部安全审计	Wàibù ānquán shěnjì	External security audit (IPsec)	
外部报警	Wàibù bàojǐng	External alarms	EA
外部标识符	Wàibù biāozhì fú	External identifier	
外部部件互连	Wàibù bùjiàn hùlián	Peripheral component interconnect	PCI
外部仓库	Wàibù cāngkù	External repository	ER
外部存储器	Wàibù cúnchǔqì	External memory	
外部代理	Wàibù dàilǐ	Foreign agent	FA
外部导电部分	Wàibù dǎodiàn bùfen	Extraneous conductive part	
外部调用	Wàibù diàoyòng	External reference	
外部董事	Wàibù dǒngshì	Outside director	
外部端口	Wàibù duānkǒu	Enclosure port	

外部服务代理	Wàibù fúwù dàilǐ	External service broker (in VPN)	ESB
外部干扰	Wàibù gānrǎo	External interference	
外部工厂设备	Wàibù gōngchǎng shèbèi	Outside plant equipment	
外部函数	Wàibù hánshù	External function	
外部化学气相沉积法	Wàibù huàxué qìxiàng chénjī fǎ	Outside-tube [chemical] vapor deposition (for FOC)	OVD
外部交换站	Wàibù jiāohuàn zhàn	Foreign exchange station	FXS
外部交换局	Wàibù jiāohuànjú	Foreign exchange office	FXO
外部接口	Wàibù jiēkǒu	External interface	
外部接入设备	Wàibù jiērù shèbèi	External access equipment	EA
外部抗扰性	Wàibù kàngrǎoxìng	External immunity	
外部控制集	Wàibù kòngzhì jí	External control set	
外部路由协议	Wàibù lùyóu xiéyì	Exterior gateway protocol	EGB
外部命令	Wàibù mìnglìng	External command	EXTCMD
外部排序	Wàibù páixù	External sort	
外部汽相沉积法	Wàibù qìxiàng chénjī fǎ	Outside vapor deposition (FOC mfg)	OVD
外部数据表示	Wàibù shùjù biǎoshì	External data representation	XDR
外部数据传输率	Wàibù shùjù chuánshū lǜ	External data transfer rate	
外部属性数据库	Wàibù shǔxìng shùjùkù	External attribute database	
外部网点协议	Wàibù wǎngdiǎn xiéyì	Exterior gateway protocol	EGP
外部网关协议	Wàibù wǎngguān xiéyì	Exterior gateway protocol	EGP
外部网络	Wàibù wǎngluò	External network	
外部网络节点接口	Wàibù wǎngluò jiédiǎn jiēkǒu	External network-node interface	E-NNI
外部文件	Wàibù wénjiàn	External file	
外部文件类别	Wàibù wénjiàn lèibié	External document class	
外部系统	Wàibù xìtǒng	External system (outside the purview of official PTT networks)	
外部引用	Wàibù yǐnyòng	External reference	
外部主机	Wàibù zhǔjī	External host	
外差放大器	Wàichāi fàngdàqì	Heterodyne amplifier	HA
外差跟踪	Wàichāi gēnzōng	Heterodyne tracking	
外差式接收	Wàichāishì jiēshōu	Heterodyne reception	
外存	Wàicún	External storage	
外地代理	Wàidì dàilǐ	Foreign agent	FA
外地代理转交地址	Wàidì dàilǐ zhuǎnjiāo dìzhǐ	Foreign agent care-of address	
外观	Wàiguān	Appearance	
外加信息转送附加业务	Wàijiā xìnxī zhuǎnsòng fùjiā yèwù	Additional information transfer supplementary service	
外键	Wàijiàn	Foreign key (for database)	FK
外界噪声	Wàijiè zàoshēng	External noise	
外径	Wàijìng	Outside diameter; exradius; outer diameter; external diameter; major diameter	
外壳	Wàiké	Case; casing; shell; housing	
外壳	Wàiké	Enclosure	
外联网	Wàiliánwǎng	Extranet	
外露导电部分	Wàilù dǎodiàn bùfen	Exposed conductive part	
外区代理	Wàiqū dàilǐ	Foreign agent	FA
外设板控制器	Wàishèbǎn kòngzhìqì	Peripheral board controller	PBC
外推(预测)	Wàituī (yùcè)	Extrapolation (prediction)	

外围交换同步化	Wàiwéi jiāohuàn tóngbùhuà	Peripheral exchange synchronization	PESY
外围类别	Wàiwéi lèibié	Enclosing class	
外围设备互联	Wàiwéi shèbèi hùlián	Peripheral component interconnect	PCI
外围设备接口	Wàiwéi shèbèi jiēkǒu	Peripheral component interface	PCI
歪斜	Wāixié	Skew	
外形规格	Wàixíng guīgé	Exterior size	
外形线	Wàixíng xiàn	Outline	
外延点	Wàiyán diǎn	Extension joint	
外延数据	Wàiyán shùjù	Extended data	
外延网	Wàiyán wǎng	Extranet	
外延的企业	Wàiyánde qǐyè	Extended enterprise	
外因	Wàiyīn	Exogenous factors	
外因不能工作时间	Wàiyīn bùnéng gōngzuò shíjiān	External disabled time; external loss time	
外因不能工作状态	Wàiyīn bùnéng gōngzuò zhuàngtài	External disabled state	
外置磁盘驱动器	Wàizhì cípán qūdòngqì	External drive	
外置硬盘	Wàizhì yìngpán	External hard drive	
外资企业	Wàizī qǐyè	Foreign-funded enterprise	
挖掘模型	Wājué móxíng	Mining model	
挖掘模型培训	Wājué móxíng péixùn	Mining model training	
弯波导	Wān bōdǎo	Waveguide bend	
完备线性复杂度序列	Wánbèi xiànxìng fùzádù xùliè	Perfect linear complexity sequence	
完成到示忙用户呼叫	Wánchéng dào shìmáng yònghù hūjiào	Completion of calls to busy subscribers	CCBS
完成到遇忙用户的呼叫	Wánchéng dào yùmáng yònghùde hūjiào	Completion of calls to busy subscriber	CCBS
完成对状态忙用户的呼叫补充业务	Wánchéng duì zhuàngtài máng yònghùde hūjiào bǔchōng yèwù	Completion of calls to busy subscriber supplementary service	CCBS
完成接续	Wánchéng jiēxù	Complete connection	
顽存性	Wáncúnxing	Survivability	
王安电脑	Wáng ān diànnǎo	Wang Computers (US company)	
网同步	Wǎng tóngbù	Network synchronization	NS
网同步连接功能模块	Wǎng tóngbù liánjiē gōngnéng mókuài	Network synchronization connection function module	NS-C
网吧	Wǎngbā	Internet café	
网播	Wǎngbō	Webcasting	
网虫	Wǎngchóng	Webaholic	
网段	Wǎngduàn	Segment	
往返时间	Wǎngfǎn shíjiān	Round-trip time	RTT
往返行程时延	Wǎngfǎn xíngchéng shíyán	Round trip delay	
网格	Wǎnggé	Grid (as network); lattice; mesh	G
网格安全基础设施	Wǎnggé ānquán jīchǔ shèshī	Grid security infrastructure	GSI
网格编码	Wǎnggé biānmǎ	Trellis encoding	TE
网格编码调制	Wǎnggé biānmǎ tiáozhì	Trellis coded modulation	TCM
网格单元	Wǎnggé dānyuán	Grid cell	
网格点	Wǎnggé diǎn	Mesh point	
网格互连	Wǎnggé hùlián	Mesh-connected	
网格简化	Wǎnggé jiǎnhuà	Mesh simplification	
网格结构	Wǎnggé jiégòu	Grid structure	
网格计算	Wǎnggé jìsuàn	Grid computing	

网格中间件	Wǎnggé zhōngjiān jiàn	Grid middleware	
网管	Wǎngguǎn	Network management	NM
网关	Wǎngguān	Gateway (on a network)	GW
网关查找协议	Wǎngguān cházhǎo xiéyì	Gateway discovery protocol	GDP
网关到网关连接协议	Wǎngguān dào wǎngguān liánjiē xiéyì	Gateway-to-gateway protocol	GGP
网关地球站	Wǎngguān dìqiúzhàn	Gateway earth station	GES
网关发现协议	Wǎngguān fāxiàn xiéyì	Gateway discovery protocol	GDP
网关服务节点	Wǎngguān fúwù jiédiǎn	Gateway services node	GSN
网管工作站	Wǎngguǎn gōngzuòzhàn	Network management work station	NAWS
网关 GPRS 支持节点	Wǎngguān GPRS zhīchí jiédiǎn	Gateway GPRS support node	GGSN
网管接口	Wǎngguǎn jiēkǒu	Network management interface	NMI
网关路由器	Wǎngguān lùyóuqì	Gateway router	GW
网关网元	Wǎngguān wǎngyuán	Gateway network element	GNE
网管系统	Wǎngguǎn xìtǒng	Network management system	NMS
网关移动交换中心	Wǎngguān yídòng jiāohuàn zhōngxīn	Gateway mobile switching center	GMSC
网关移动业务交换中心	Wǎngguān yídòng yèwù jiāohuàn zhōngxīn	Gateway mobile services switching center	GMSC
网关帐户	Wǎngguān zhànghù	Gateway account	
网管终端	Wǎngguǎn zhōngduān	Network management terminal	NMT
网管中心	Wǎngguǎn zhōngxīn	Network management center	NMC
网关主机	Wǎngguān zhǔjī	Gateway host	
网规	Wǎngguī	Netiquette	
往猴	Wǎnghóu	NetMonkey (website software)	
网际包探测器	Wǎngjì bāo tàncèqì	Packet Internet groper	PING
网际电话	Wǎngjì diànhuà	Internet phone	
网际公民	Wǎngjì gōngmín	Cyber citizen; netizen	
网际广播	Wǎngjì guǎngbō	Internet talk radio	ITR
网际互联协议	Wǎngjì hùlián xiéyì	Internet protocol	IP
网际咖啡屋	Wǎngjì kāfēiwū	Cyber café	
网际控制消息协议	Wǎngjì kòngzhì xiāoxi xiéyì	Internet control message protocol	ICMP
网际漫游者	Wǎngjì mànyóuzhě	Cyber surfer	
网际清淡	Wǎngjì qīngdàn	Internet relay chat	IRC
网际群组管理协议	Wǎngjì qúnzǔ guǎnlǐ xiéyì	Internet group management protocol (IPsec)	IGMP
网际色情	Wǎngjì sèqíng	Cybersex; cyberporn; cybersmut	
网际数据包(分组)交换	Wǎngjì shùjù bāo (fēnzǔ) jiāohuàn	Inter-network packet exchange	IPX
网际网络信息中心	Wǎngjì wǎngluò xìnxī zhōngxīn	Internet network information center	InterNIC
网际协议	Wǎngjì xiéyì	Internet protocol	IP
网际协议安全	Wǎngjì xiéyì ānquán	Internet protocol security	IPSec
网际行销	Wǎngjì xíngxiāo	Cyber sales	
网际转发闲聊协议	Wǎngjì zhuǎnfā xiánliáo xiéyì	Internet relay chat protocol (IETF usage)	IRCP
网件	Wǎngjiàn	Netware	
网间电路段	Wǎngjiān diànlù duàn	Inter-network circuit section	ICS
网间互通	Wǎng-jiān hùtōng	Interworking between networks	
网间互通数据报协议	Wǎngjiān hùtōng shùjùbào xiéyì	Inter-network datagram protocol	IDP
网间接口单元	Wǎngjiàn jiēkǒu dānyuán	Gateway network element	GNE
网间数据包交换控制协议	Wǎngjiān shùjù bāo jiāohuàn kòngzhì xiéyì	Inter-network packet exchange control protocol	IPXCP

网捷网络公司	Wǎngjié wǎngluò gōngsī	Foundry Networks Inc.	
网景导览器	Wǎngjǐng dǎolǎnqì	Netscape Navigator ©	
网景公司	Wǎngjǐng gōngsī	Netscape Corporation	
网景浏览器	Wǎngjǐng liúlǎnqì	Netscape ® browser	
网卡	Wǎngkǎ	Network card	
网客	Wǎngkè	Cybernaut	
网孔分裂	Wǎngkǒng fēnliè	Cell split	
网孔裂向	Wǎngkǒng lièxiàng	Cell sectorize	
网路	Wǎnglù	Network (mainly Taiwan usage)	
网路节点接口	Wǎnglù jiédiǎn jiēkǒu	Network node interface	NNI
网络	Wǎngluò	Network	
网络安全分析器	Wǎngluò ānquán fēnxīqì	Security administrator tool for analyzing networks	SATAN
网络安全管理和访问控制	Wǎngluò ānquán guǎnlǐ hé fǎngwèn kòngzhì	Network security management and access control	
网络保安	Wǎngluò bǎo'ān	Network security	
网络保护设备	Wǎngluò bǎohù shèbèi	Network protection equipment	NPE
网络保密	Wǎngluò bǎomì	Network security	
网络编译程序的仿真程序	Wǎngluò biānyì chéngxùde fǎngzhēn chéngxù	Network compiler simulation program	NCSP
网络编址域	Wǎngluò biānzhǐ yù	Network addressing domain	
网络表示语	Wǎngluò biǎoshì yǔ	Network indicator	NI
网络标识	Wǎngluò biāozhì	Network identification	NID
网络参数控制	Wǎngluò cānshù kòngzhì	Network parameter control	NPC
网络操作和维护中心	Wǎngluò cāozuò hé wéihù zhōngxīn	Network operation and maintenance center	NOMC
网络操作系统	Wǎngluò cāozuò xìtǒng	Network operation system	NOS
网络操作中心	Wǎngluò cāozuò zhōngxīn	Network operations center	NOC
网络测量结果	Wǎngluò cèliáng jiéguǒ	Network measurement results	NMR
网络层	Wǎngluò céng	Network layer	
网络层控制协议	Wǎngluò céng kòngzhì xiéyì	Network layer control protocol	NCP
网络层拓扑结构	Wǎngluò céng tuòpū jiégòu	Network layer topology configurator	NLTC
网络层协议标识符	Wǎngluò céng xiéyì biāozhì fú	Network layer protocol identifier	NLPI
网络层业务接入点标识符	Wǎngluò céng yèwù jiērùdiǎn biāozhìfú	Network layer service access point identifier	NSAPI
网络测试设备	Wǎngluò cèshì shèbèi	Network test equipment	
网络传输时延	Wǎngluò chuánshū shíyán	Network transfer delay	
网络传送延迟	Wǎngluò chuánsòng yánchí	Network transfer delay	
网络存储	Wǎngluò cúnchǔ	Network storage	
网络存储设备	Wǎngluò cúnchǔ shèbèi	Network attached storage	NAS
网络错误管理设施	Wǎngluò cuòwù guǎnlǐ shèshī	Network error management facilities	NEMF
网络单元	Wǎngluò dānyuán	Network element	NE
网络单元登录	Wǎngluò dānyuán dēnglù	Network element log	
网络单元功能	Wǎngluò dānyuán gōngnéng	Network element function	NEF
网络单元功能块	Wǎngluò dānyuán gōngnéng kuài	Network element function block	NEF
网络单元资源控制	Wǎngluò dānyuán zīyuán kòngzhì	Network element resources control	RCne
网络电话	Wǎngluò diànhuà	Voice over Internet protocol	VOIP
网络定时协议	Wǎngluò dìngshí xiéyì	Network timing protocol	NTP
网络地址	Wǎngluò dìzhǐ	Network address	
网络地址端口转换	Wǎngluò dìzhǐ duānkǒu zhuǎnhuàn	Network address port translation	NAPT

网络地址翻译器	Wǎngluò dìzhǐ fānyìqì	Network address translator	NAT
网络地址及端口转换	Wǎngluò dìzhǐ jí duānkǒu zhuǎnhuàn	Network address port translation	NAPT
网络地址解析	Wǎngluò dìzhǐ jiěxī	Network address translation	NAT
网络地址块	Wǎngluò dìzhǐ kuài	Network address block	NAB
网络地址转换	Wǎngluò dìzhǐ zhuǎnhuàn	Network address translation	NAT
网络地址转换/协议转换技术	Wǎngluò dìzhǐ zhuǎnhuàn/ xiéyì zhuǎnhuàn jìshù	Network address translation/protocol translation (in IPv6)	NAT-PT
网络地址转换器	Wǎngluò dìzhǐ zhuǎnhuànqì	Network address translator	NAT
网络动态数据交换	Wǎngluò dòngtài shùjù jiāohuàn	Network dynamic data exchange	NetDDE
网络段	Wǎngluò duàn	Network section	
网络段集合	Wǎngluò duàn jíhé	Network section ensemble	NSE
网络独立同步	Wǎngluò dúlì tóngbù	Network independent clocking	NIC
网络防卫	Wǎngluò fángwèi	Network defense	ND
网络访问点	Wǎngluò fǎngwèn diǎn	Network access point	NAP
网络访问服务器	Wǎngluò fǎngwèn fúwùqì	Network access server	NAS
网络分区	Wǎngluò fēnqū	Network partition	
网络分析	Wǎngluò fēnxī	Network analysis	
网络分析点	Wǎngluò fēnxī diǎn	Network analysis point	
网络分析系统	Wǎngluò fēnxī xìtǒng	Network analysis system	
网络分组交换协议	Wǎngluò fēnzǔ jiāohuàn xiéyì	Internetwork packet exchange protocol (Novell usage)	IPX
网络附加存储	Wǎngluò fùjiā cúnchǔ	Network attached storage	NAS
网络服务	Wǎngluò fúwù	Network service	NS
网络服务部分	Wǎngluò fúwù bùfen	Network service part	NSP
网络服务访问点	Wǎngluò fúwù fǎngwèn diǎn	Network service access point	NSAP
网络服务接入点	Wǎngluò fúwù jiērù diǎn	Network service access point	NSAP
网络服务描述语言	Wǎngluò fúwù miáoshù yǔyán	Web services description language	WSDL
网络服务数据单元	Wǎngluò fúwù shùjù dānyuán	Network service data unit	NSDU
网络服务提供商	Wǎngluò fúwù tígōngshāng	Network service provider	NSP
网络服务协议	Wǎngluò fúwù xiéyì	Network service protocol (in DECnet)	NSP
网络服务中心	Wǎngluò fúwù zhōngxīn	Network service center	NSC
网络服务器	Wǎngluò fúwùqì	Network server	
网络复杂性系数	Wǎngluò fùzáxìng xìshù	Coefficient of network complexity	CNC
网络功能	Wǎngluò gōngnéng	Network function	NF
网络管理	Wǎngluò guǎnlǐ	Network management	NM
网络管理层	Wǎngluò guǎnlǐ céng	Network management layer	NML
网络管理层拓扑结构	Wǎngluò guǎnlǐ céng tuò pū jiégòu	Network management layer topology configurator	NMLTC
网络管理论坛	Wǎngluò guǎnlǐ lùntán	Network management forum	NMF
网络管理相量传输	Wǎngluò guǎnlǐ xiāngliáng chuánshū	Network management vector transport	NMVT
网络管理系统	Wǎngluò guǎnlǐ xìtǒng	Network management system	NMS
网络管理中心	Wǎngluò guǎnlǐ zhōngxīn	Network management center	NMC
网络管理子系统	Wǎngluò guǎnlǐ zixìtǒng	Network management sub-system	NMS
网络管理者	Wǎngluò guǎnlǐzhě	Network manager	NM
网络规范	Wǎngluò guīfàn	Network specification	
网络规划	Wǎngluò guīhuà	Network planning	
网络故障管理	Wǎngluò gùzhàng guǎnlǐ	Network fault management	
网络核心协议	Wǎngluò héxīn xiéyì	Network core protocol (Novell usage)	NCP

网络话务管理系统	Wǎngluò huàwù guǎnlǐ xìtǒng	Network traffic management system	NTMS
网络互操作联盟	Wǎngluò hùcāozuò liánméng	Networking Interoperability Alliance	NIA
网络回音消除	Wǎngluò huíyīn xiāochú	Network echo cancellation	ECAN
网络呼叫控制器	Wǎngluò hūjiào kòngzhìqì	Network call controller	NCC
网络呼叫器	Wǎngluò hūjiàoqì	I seek you	ICQ
网络互连	Wǎngluò hùlián	Network interworking	
网络互连功能	Wǎngluò hùlián gōngnéng	Network interconnect function	NIF
网络互连数据交换机	Wǎngluò hùlián shùjù jiāohuànjī	Internetworking data switching exchange	IDSE
网络互通	Wǎngluò hùtōng	Network interworking	
网络级聚集标识符	Wǎngluò jí jùjí biāozhìfú	Network level aggregation identifer	NLAID
网络及总线控制	Wǎngluò jí zǒngxiàn kòngzhì	Network and trunk control	NTC
网络监控	Wǎngluò jiānkòng	Network monitor and control	NMAC
网络交换子系统	Wǎngluò jiāohuàn zixìtǒng	Network switching sub-system	NSS
网络基本输入输出系统	Wǎngluò jīběn shūrù shūchū xìtǒng	Network basic input output system (IBM usage)	NetBIOS
网络基本输入/输出系统	Wǎngluò jīběn shūrù/shūchū xìtǒng	Network basic input/output system	NetBIOS
网络基本输入/输出系统扩展用户接口	Wǎngluò jīběn shūrù/shūchū xìtǒng kuòzhǎn yònghù jiēkǒu	NetBIOS extended user interface	NetBEUI
网络集成	Wǎngluò jíchéng	Network integration	
网络节点	Wǎngluò jiédiǎn	Network node	
网络节点接口	Wǎngluò jiédiǎn jiēkǒu	Network node interface	NNI
网络结构的七层模型	Wǎngluò jiégòude qī céng móxíng	Network architecture 7-layer model (the OSI reference model)	
网络接口	Wǎngluò jiēkǒu	Network interface	NI
网络接口传接器	Wǎngluò jiēkǒu chuánjiēqì	Network interface adapter	NIA
网络接口单元	Wǎngluò jiēkǒu dānyuán	Network interface element	NIE
网络接口单元	Wǎngluò jiēkǒu dānyuán	Network interface unit	NIU
网络接口卡	Wǎngluò jiēkǒu kǎ	Network interface card	NIC
网络接口控制器	Wǎngluò jiēkǒu kòngzhìqì	Network interface controller	NIC
网络接入标识符	Wǎngluò jiērù biāozhì fú	Network access identifier	NAI
网络接入点	Wǎngluò jiērù diǎn	Network access point	
网络接入服务器	Wǎngluò jiērù fúwùqì	Network access server	NAS
网络接入控制器	Wǎngluò jiērù kòngzhìqì	Network access controller	NAC
网络计算	Wǎngluò jìsuàn	Network computing	
网络计算机	Wǎngluò jìsuànjī	Network computer	NC
网络决定用户忙	Wǎngluò juédìng yònghù máng	Network determined user busy	NDUB
网络可达性	Wǎngluò kědáxìng	Network reachability	
网络可寻址单元	Wǎngluò kěxúnzhǐ dānyuán	Network addressable unit (IBM usage)	NAU
网络空间	Wǎngluò kōngjiān	Cyberspace	
网络空间运营商	Wǎngluò kōngjiān yùnyíng shāng	Cyber carrier	CC
网络控制单元	Wǎngluò kòngzhì dānyuán	Network control unit	NCU
网络控制键	Wǎngluò kòngzhì jiàn	Network control key	NCK
网络控制切换	Wǎngluò kòngzhì qiēhuàn	Network control hand-off	NCHO
网络控制协议	Wǎngluò kòngzhì xiéyì	Network control protocol	NCP
网络控制中心	Wǎngluò kòngzhì zhōngxīn	Network control center	NCC
网络口	Wǎngluò kǒu	Network port	
网络库	Wǎngluò kù	Net-library (in SQL Server)	
网络链	Wǎngluò liàn	Network chain; network link	

网络连接	Wǎngluò liánjiē	Network connection	NC
网络连接存储	Wǎngluò liánjiē cúnchǔ	Network attached storage	NAS
网络连接块	Wǎngluò liánjiē kuài	Network connect block	NCB
网络联盟	Wǎngluò liánméng	Network Associates (US company)	
网络聊天	Wǎngluò liáotiān	Internet relay chat	IRC
网络流	Wǎngluò liú	Network flow	
网络礼仪	Wǎngluò lǐyí	Net etiquette; netiquette	
网络漏洞扫描器	Wǎngluò lòudòng sǎomiáoqì	Network vulnerability scanner	
网络默认值	Wǎngluò mòrèn zhí	Network default	ND
网络内存储	Wǎngluò nèicúnchǔ	Storage within the network	
网络能力网关	Wǎngluò nénglì wǎngguān	Network capability gateway	
网络配置管理	Wǎngluò pèizhì guǎnlǐ	Network configuration management	
网络驱动程序接口规范	Wǎngluò qūdòng chéngxù jiēkǒu guīfàn	Network driver interface specification	NDIS
网络驱动器接口规范	Wǎngluò qūdòngqì jiēkǒu guīfàn	Network driver interface specification	NDIS
网络确定用户忙	Wǎngluò quèdìng yònghù máng	Network determined user busy	NDUB
网络软件	Wǎngluò ruǎnjiàn	Networking software	
网络入侵检测系统	Wǎngluò rùqīn jiǎncè xìtǒng	Network intrusion detection system	
网络扫描器	Wǎngluò sǎomiáoqì	Network scanner	
网络色码	Wǎngluò sèmǎ	Network color code	NCC
网络设备	Wǎngluò shèbèi	Network equipment	NE
网络设计和管理系统	Wǎngluò shèjì hé guǎnlǐ xìtǒng	Network design and management system	NDMS
网络设施扩展	Wǎngluò shèshī kuòzhǎn	Network facility extensions	NFE
网络识别和时域	Wǎngluò shíbié hé shíyù	Network identity and time zone	NITZ
网络识别码	Wǎngluò shíbié mǎ	Network identity	NID
网络时间同步协议	Wǎngluò shíjiān tóngbù xiéyì	Network time protocol	NTP
网络时间协议	Wǎngluò shíjiān xiéyì	Network time protocol	NTP
网络适配器	Wǎngluò shìpèiqì	Network adapter	NA
网络实体标识符	Wǎngluò shítǐ biāozhìfú	Network entity identifier	NEI
网络实体名称	Wǎngluò shítǐ míngchēng	Network entity title	NET
网络时钟参考	Wǎngluò shízhōng cānkǎo	Network time reference	NTR
网络数据管理协议	Wǎngluò shùjù guǎnlǐ xiéyì	Network data management protocol	NDMP
网络数据链控制	Wǎngluò shùjù liàn kòngzhì	Network data link control	NDLC
网络数据嗅探器软件	Wǎngluò shùjù xiùtànqì ruǎnjiàn	Network packet sniffing software	
网络数字	Wǎngluò shùzì	Network digit	ND
网络搜索器	Wǎngluò sōusuǒqì	Web crawler	
网络特有性能	Wǎngluò tèyǒu xìngnéng	Network-specific facilities	
网络提供商	Wǎngluò tígōngshāng	Network provider	NP
网络体系结构	Wǎngluò tǐxì jiégòu	Network architecture	
网络同步分配器后面板	Wǎngluò tóngbù fēnpèiqì hòumianbǎn	Network synchronization distributor back panel	NDBP
网络同步后面板	Wǎngluò tóngbù hòumianbǎn	Network synchronization back panel	NSBP
网络同步控制处理器集成板	Wǎngluò tóngbù kòngzhì chǔlǐqì jíchéngbǎn	Network synchronization control processor board assembly	NCPA
网络同步时钟发生器	Wǎngluò tóngbù shízhōng fāshēngqì	Network synchronization clock generation	NSCG
网络同步时钟维护	Wǎngluò tóngbù shízhōng wéihù	Network synchronization clock maintenance	NSCM
网络同步时钟中继器	Wǎngluò tóngbù shízhōng zhōngjìqì	Network synchronization clock repeater	NSCR
网络通路	Wǎngluò tōnglù	Network path	

网络通信访问法	Wǎngluò tōngxìn fǎngwèn fǎ	Network communication access method	NCAM
网络统一控制系统	Wǎngluò tǒngyī kòngzhì xìtǒng	Network integrity control system	NICS
网络图层	Wǎngluò túcéng	Network coverage	
网络图解协议	Wǎngluò tújiě xiéyì	Network graphics protocol	NGP
网络托管	Wǎngluò tuōguǎn	Network hosting	
网络拓扑	Wǎngluò tuòpū	Network topology	
网络拓扑管理	Wǎngluò tuòpū guǎnlǐ	Network topology management	
网络拓扑结构	Wǎngluò tuòpū jiégòu	Network topology	
网络拓扑组成管理	Wǎngluò tuòpū zǔchéng guǎnlǐ	Network topology configuration management	NTCM
网络图	Wǎngluò túxiàng	Network image	
网络外貌	Wǎngluò wàimào	Network appearance	
网络文件访问存取协议	Wǎngluò wénjiàn fǎngwèn cúnqǔ xiéyì	Network file access protocol	NFAP
网络文件系统	Wǎngluò wénjiàn xìtǒng	Network file system	NFS
网络协议	Wǎngluò xiéyì	Network protocol	
网络协议地址信息	Wǎngluò xiéyì dìzhǐ xìnxī	Network protocol address information	NPAI
网络协议数据单元	Wǎngluò xiéyì shùjù dānyuán	Network protocol data unit	NPDU
网络性能	Wǎngluò xìngnéng	Network performance	NP
网络性能分析程序	Wǎngluò xìngnéng fēnxī chéngxù	Network performance analyzer	NPA
网络性能管理	Wǎngluò xìngnéng guǎnlǐ	Network performance management	
网络性能请求	Wǎngluò xìngnéng qǐngqiú	Facility request (ISUP message)	FAR
网络性能请求拒绝	Wǎngluò xìngnéng qǐngqiú jùjué	Facility reject (ISUP message)	FRJ
网络性能请求许可	Wǎngluò xìngnéng qǐngqiú xǔkě	Facility accepted (ISUP message)	FAA
网络行政管理	Wǎngluò xíngzhèng guǎnlǐ	Network administration	
网络新闻传输协议	Wǎngluò xīnwén chuánshū xiéyì	Network news transfer protocol	NNTP
网络新闻传送协议	Wǎngluò xīnwén chuánsòng xiéyì	Network news transfer protocol	NNTP
网络信息服务	Wǎngluò xìnxī fúwù	Network information system	NIS
网络信息和控制交换协议	Wǎngluò xìnxī hé kòngzhì jiāohuàn xiéyì	Network information and control exchange protocol (in DECnet)	NICE
网络信息文件	Wǎngluò xìnxī wénjiàn	Network information files	NIF
网络信息中心	Wǎngluò xìnxī zhōngxīn	Network information center	NIC
网络嗅探器	Wǎngluò xiùtànqì	Network sniffer	
网络钥匙交换	Wǎngluò yàoshi jiāohuàn	Internet key exchange	IKE
网络业务	Wǎngluò yèwù	Network service	NS
网络业务层	Wǎngluò yèwù céng	Network service layer	
网络业务接入点	Wǎngluò yèwù jiērù diǎn	Network service access point	NSAP
网络业务接入点标识符	Wǎngluò yèwù jiērù diǎn biāozhìfú	Network service access point identifier	NSAPI
网络业务实体	Wǎngluò yèwù shítǐ	Network service entity	NSE
网络业务实体标识符	Wǎngluò yèwù shítǐ biāozhìfú	Network service entity identifier	NSEI
网络业务数据单元	Wǎngluò yèwù shùjù dānyuán	Network service data unit	NSDU
网络业务提供者	Wǎngluò yèwù tígòngzhě	Network service provider	NSP
网络业务虚连接	Wǎngluò yèwù xū liánjiē	Network service virtual connection	NS-VC
网络业务虚连接标识符	Wǎngluò yèwù xū liánjiē biāozhìfú	Network service virtual connection identifier	NS-VCI
网络业务虚链路	Wǎngluò yèwù xū liànlù	Network service virtual link	NS-VL
网络业务虚链路标识符	Wǎngluò yèwù xū liànlù biāozhìfú	Network service virtual link identifier	NS-VLI
网络映射器	Wǎngluò yìngshèqì	Network mapper	
网络映像	Wǎngluò yìngxiàng	Network mapping	
网络应用软件	Wǎngluò yìngyòng ruǎnjiàn	Network application software	

网络应用业务	Wǎngluò yìngyòng yèwù	Network application service	
网络用户标示	Wǎngluò yònghù biāoshì	Network user identification	NUI
网络用户部分	Wǎngluò yònghù bùfen	Network user part	NUP
网络用户电话机控制键	Wǎngluò yònghù diànhuàjī kòngzhì jiàn	Network subset control key	NSCK
网络用户地址	Wǎngluò yònghù dìzhǐ	Network user access	NUA
网络用户识别	Wǎngluò yònghù shíbié	Network user identification	NUI
网络拥挤	Wǎngluò yōngjǐ	Network congestion	
网络优化	Wǎngluò yōuhuà	Network optimization	
网络与交换管理	Wǎngluò yǔ jiāohuàn guǎnlǐ	Network and switch management	NSM
网络元素	Wǎngluò yuánsù	Network element	
网络运行中心	Wǎngluò yùnxíng zhōngxīn	Network operating center	NOC
网络运营商	Wǎngluò yùnyíngshāng	Network operator	NO
网络指定判据	Wǎngluò zhǐdìng pànjù	Network directed criteria	
网络指示的系统选择	Wǎngluò zhǐshìde xìtǒng xuǎnzé	Network directed system selection	NDSS
网络终端	Wǎngluò zhōngduān	Network terminal, termination	NT
网络终端单元	Wǎngluò zhōngduān dānyuán	Network terminal unit	NTU
网络终端端点	Wǎngluò zhōngduān duāndiǎn	Network termination point	NTP
网络终端号码	Wǎngluò zhōngduān hàomǎ	Network terminal number	NTN
网络终端设备 1	Wǎngluò zhōngduān shèbèi 1	Network termination 1	NT-1
网络中继聊天	Wǎngluò zhōngjì liáotiān	Internet relay chat	IRC
网络终接	Wǎngluò zhōngjiē	Network termination	NT
网络中心计算	Wǎngluò zhōngxīn jìsuàn	Network centric computing	
网络子系统	Wǎngluò zixìtǒng	Network sub-system	NSS
网络资源	Wǎngluò zīyuán	Network resource	NR
网络资源管理	Wǎngluò zīyuán guǎnlǐ	Network resource management	NRM
网络资源结构	Wǎngluò zīyuán jiégòu	Network resource architecture	NRA
网络资源控制	Wǎngluò zīyuán kòngzhì	Network resources control	NRC
网络资源模型	Wǎngluò zīyuán móxíng	Network resource model	NRM
网络资源信息模型	Wǎngluò zīyuán xìnxī móxíng	Network resource information model	NRIM
网络综合器	Wǎngluò zōnghéqì	Network integrator	NI
网络组成管理	Wǎngluò zǔchéng guǎnlǐ	Network configuration management	NCM
网络最大段长度	Wǎngluò zuìdà duàn chángdù	Network maximum segment size	NMSS
网络化多媒体对象技术	Wǎngluòhuà duōméitǐ duìxiàng jìshù	ActiveX	
网络间接口	Wǎngluò-jiān jiēkǒu	Network to network interface	NNI
网络-网络接口	Wǎngluò—wǎngluò jiēkǒu	Network-to-network interface	NNI
网桥	Wǎngqiáo	Bridge	
网桥号	Wǎngqiáo hào	Bridge number	
网桥静态过滤	Wǎngqiáo jìngtài guòlǜ	Bridge static filtering	
网桥路由器	Wǎngqiáo lùyóuqì	Bridge-router (brouter)	
网桥协议数据单元	Wǎngqiáo xiéyì shùjù dānyuán	Bridge protocol data unit	BPDU
网桥转发	Wǎngqiáo zhuǎnfā	Bridge forwarding	
网桥组	Wǎngqiáo zǔ	Bridge group	
网上	Wǎngshàng	On-line	
网上传输话音	Wǎngshàng chuánshū huàyīn	Voice over Internet protocol	VOIP
网上出版	Wǎngshàng chūbǎn	Webtop publishing	
网上汇款	Wǎngshàng huìkuǎn	On-line remittance	

网上集邮业务	Wǎngshàng jíyóu yèwù	On-line philatelic service	
网上女杰	Wǎngshàng nǚjié	Web mistress	
网守	Wǎngshǒu	Gatekeeper	
网守发现拒绝	Wǎngshǒu fāxiàn jùjué	Gatekeeper reject	GRJ
网守发现请求	Wǎngshǒu fāxiàn qǐngqiú	Gatekeeper request	GRQ
网守发现确认	Wǎngshǒu fāxiàn quèrèn	Gatekeeper confirm	GCF
网守功能	Wǎngshǒu gōngnéng	Gatekeeper function	GKF
网通	Wǎngtōng	China Netcom	CNC
万国商业机器	Wànguó shāngyè jīqì	IBM Corporation	
网页	Wǎngyè	Web page	WEB
网页标识	Wǎngyè biāozhì	Banner	
网友	Wǎngyǒu	Cybernaut	
网域地址	Wǎngyù dìzhǐ	Domain name	
网元	Wǎngyuán	Network element	NE
网元层	Wǎngyuán céng	Network element level	NEL
网元层	Wǎngyuán céng	Network element layer	NEL
网元功能	Wǎngyuán gōngnéng	Network element function	NEF
网元管理	Wǎngyuán guǎnlǐ	Element management	EM
网元管理层	Wǎngyuán guǎnlǐ céng	Element management layer	EML
网元管理系统	Wǎngyuán guǎnlǐ xìtǒng	Network element management system	NEMS
网元管理系统	Wǎngyuán guǎnlǐ xìtǒng	Element management system	EMS
网元转接延时	Wǎngyuán zhuǎnjiē yánshí	Network element transit delay	
网闸	Wǎngzhá	Gatekeeper	GK
网站	Wǎngzhàn	Website	
网址变换	Wǎngzhǐ biànhuàn	Network addess transform	NAT
网中人	Wǎng-zhōng rén	Cybernaut	
网状反射面	Wǎngzhuàng fǎnshè miàn	Net-shaped reflecting surface	
网状数据模型	Wǎngzhuàng shùjù móxíng	Network data model	
完好信号	Wánhǎo xìnhào	Perfect signal	
挽救切换	Wǎnjiù qiēhuàn	Rescue handoff	
万利达电子有限公司	Wàn-lì-dá diànzǐ yǒuxiàn gōngsī	Malata Electronics Co. Ltd., Fujian	
完美文书	Wánměi wénshū	WordPerfect ©	
万能数据访问	Wànnéng shùjù fǎngwèn	Universal data access	UDA
弯曲	Wānqū	Bending	
弯曲半径	Wānqū bànjìng	Bend radius	
弯曲剪切模型	Wānqū jiǎnqiē móxíng	Flexural shear model	
弯曲率	Wānqū lǜ	Bending moment	
弯曲强度	Wānqū qiángdù	Bending strength	
弯曲衰耗	Wānqū shuāihào	Bend attenuation	
弯曲损耗	Wānqū sǔnhào	Bending loss (FOC)	
弯曲振动	Wānqū zhèndòng	Bending vibration	
完全安装	Wánquán ānzhuāng	Full installation (of software)	
完全第三层信息	Wánquán dìsāncéng xìnxī	Complete layer 3 information	
完全多项式时间近似	Wánquán duōxiàngshì shíjiān jìnsì	Fully polynomial time approximation	FPTA
完全二叉树	Wánquán èrchā shù	Complete binary tree	
完全非直联信令方式	Wánquán fēizhílián xìnlìng fāngshì	Fully dissociated signaling	

完全共享	Wánquán gòngxiǎng	Share everything	SE
完全	Wánquán gùzhàng	Complete fault	
完全故障	Wánquán gùzhàng	Complete failure	
完全合格域名	Wánquán hégé yùmíng	Fully qualified domain name	FQDN
完全环回	Wánquán huán huí	Complete loopback	
完全空间随机性	Wánquán kōngjiān suíjīxìng	Complete spatial randomness	CSR
完全链	Wánquán liàn	Complete chain	
完全生成符集	Wánquán shēngchéngfú jí	Complete generator set	
完全失效	Wánquán shīxiào	Complete failure	
完全特化	Wánquán tèhuà	Full specialization	
完全图	Wánquán tú	Complete graph	
完全握手证实	Wánquán wòshǒu zhèngshí	Full handshake authentication	
完全序列号协议数据单元	Wánquán xùlièhào xiéyì shùjù dānyuán	Complete sequence numbers protocol data unit	CSNP
完全液化温度	Wánquán yèhuà wēndù	Full liquidus temperature (in SMT)	
完全的无线频率信道号码	Wánquánde wúxiàn pínlǜ xìndào hàomǎ	Absolute radio frequency channel number	ARFCN
万事达公司	Wàn-shì-dá gōngsī	MasterCard International Inc.	
完税后交货	Wánshuì-hòu jiāohuò	Delivered duty paid	
完税前交货	Wánshuì-qián jiāohuò	Delivered duty unpaid	DDU
万维网	Wànwéiwǎng	World Wide Web	WWW
万维网 GIS	Wànwéiwǎng GIS	WebGIS	
万维网协会	Wànwéiwǎng xiéhuì	World Wide Web Consortium	W3C
万用字元	Wànyòng zìyuán	Wild card	
完整接续	Wánzhěng jiēxù	Complete connection	
完整面	Wánzhěng miàn	Universal face	
完整区域传送	Wánzhěng qūyù chuánsòng	Full zone transfer	AXFR
完整外部联接	Wánzhěng wàibù liánjiē	Full outer join	
完整性	Wánzhěngxìng	Integrity (IPsec) ; completeness	
完整性保护命令	Wánzhěngxìng bǎohù mìnglìng	Integrity protected command (in FTP)	MIC
完整性检测向量	Wánzhěngxìng jiǎncè xiàngliàng	Integrity check vector	ICV
完整性检测值	Wánzhěngxìng jiǎncè zhí	Integrity check value	ICV
完整性检查值	Wánzhěngxìng jiǎnchá zhí	Integrity check value	ICV
完整性鉴定	Wánzhěngxìng jiàndìng	Integrity authentication	
完整性效验值	Wánzhěngxìng xiàoyàn zhí	Integrity check value	
完整性约束	Wánzhěngxìng yuēshù	Integrity constraint (for database)	
瓦片	Wǎpiàn	Tile	
挖土	Wātǔ	Cut (in GIS or telecom construction)	
Web 分布式数据交换	Web Fēnbùshì shùjù jiāohuàn	Web distributed data exchange	WDDX
Web 服务描述语言	Web fúwù miáoshù yǔyán	Web services description language	WSDL
Weed 容差	Weed róngchā	Weed tolerance	
位	Wèi	Bit	
微	Wēi	Micro- (prefix meaning 10^{-6})	
位操作	Wèi cāozuò	Position manipulation	
位串行	Wèi chuànháng	Bit serial	
为单元进行复制	Wéi dānyuán jìnxíng fùzhì	Bitwise copy	
未恢复时间	Wèi huīfù shíjiān	Time to restoration; time to recovery	
未检出故障时间	Wèi jiǎnchū gùzhàng shíjiān	Undetected fault time	

为空性	Wéi kōngxìng	Nullability	
位控制序块	Wèi kòngzhì xùkuài	Bit control block	BCB
位每秒	Wèi měi miǎo	Bits per second	bps
惟密文攻击	Wéi mìwén gōngjī	Ciphertext-only attack	
位模式	Wèi móshì	Bit pattern	
为您提供信息	Wéi nín tígōng xìnxī	For your information	FYI
位屏蔽	Wèi píngbì	Bit mask	
位速率乘法器	Wèi sùlǜ chéngfǎqì	Bit rate multiplier	BRM
位损耗概率	Wèi sǔnhào gàilǜ	Bit loss probability	BLP
位协议控制	Wèi xiéyì kòngzhì	Bit protocol control	
为以后研究	Wéi yǐhòu yánjiū	For further study	FFS
位映射协议	Wèi yìngshè xiéyì	Bit mapping protocol	BMP
为制造着想的设计	Wéi zhìzàozhe xiǎngde shèjì	Designed for the manufacturer (in SMT)	DFM
尾指针	Wěi zhǐzhēn	Tail pointer	
位总线网	Wèi zǒngxiàn wǎng	BITBUS © (Intel product)	
位组	Wèi zǔ	Bit combination	
位/秒	Wèi/miǎo	Bits per second	Bps
微安	Wēi'ān	Microampere	μ A
微巴	Wēibā	Microbar	
未保护网洛	Wèibǎohù wǎngluò	Unprotected network	
伪变量	Wěibiànliàng	Pseudo variable	
未标识用户	Wèibiāozhì yònghù	Unidentified subscriber	
伪比特	Wěibǐtè	Dummy bits	
尾波	Wěibō	Coda wave	
微波	Wēibō	Microwave	
微波暗室	Wēibō ànshì	Microwave unreflected chamber	
微波暗室	Wēibō ànshì	Microwave unreflected chamber	
微波场效应晶体管放大器	Wēibō cháng xiàoying jīngtǐguǎn fàngdàqì	Microwave field effect transistor amplifier	
微波传输设备	Wēibō chuánshū shèbèi	Microwave transport equipment	MTE
微波带阻滤波器	Wēibō dàizǔ lǜbōqì	Microwave band-stop filter	
微波单片集成电路	Wēibō dānpiàn jíchéng diànlù	Microwave monolithic integrated circuit	MMIC
微波电路	Wēibō diànlù	Microwave circuit	
微波低通滤波器	Wēibō dītōng lǜbōqì	Microwave low-pass filter	
微波低躁声放大器	Wēibō dīzàoshēng fàngdàqì	Microwave low noise amplifier	
微波低噪声晶体管放大器	Wēibō dīzàoshēng jīngtǐguǎn fàngdàqì	Microwave low noise transistor amplifier	
微波多点分配系统	Wēibō duōdiǎn fēnpèi xìtǒng	Microwave multipoint distribution system	MMDS
微波多工器	Wēibō duōgōngqì	Microwave multiplexer	
韦伯分布	Wéibó fēnbù	Weibull distribution	
微波干扰防护	Wēibō gānrǎo fánghù	Microwave interference protection	MIP
微波高通滤波器	Wēibō gāotōng lǜbōqì	Microwave high-pass filter	
微波功率放大器	Wēibō gōnglǜ fàngdàqì	Microwave power amplifier	
微波功率计	Wēibō gōnglǜjì	Microwave power meter	
微波混合集成电路	Wēibō hùnhé jíchéng diànlù	Microwave hybrid integrated circuit	
微波检波器	Wēibō jiǎnbōqì	Microwave detector	
微波集成电路	Wēibō jíchéng diànlù	Microwave integrated circuit	
微波集成高频放大器	Wēibō jíchéng gāopín fàngdàqì	Microwave integrated high frequency amplifier	

微波接力设备接口	Wēibō jiēlì shèbèi jiēkǒu	Radio relay equipment interface (microwave)	RR-EI
微波接力系统的参考点	Wēibō jiēlì xìtǒngde cānkǎo diǎn	Radio relay system reference point	RR-RP
微波链路	Wēibō liànlù	Microwave link	
微波脉冲整形网络	Wēibō màichōng zhěngxíng wǎngluò	Microwave pulse shaping network	MPSN
微波全息雷达	Wēibō quánxī léidá	Microwave hologram radar	
微波视像分配系统	Wēibō shìxiàng fēnpèi xìtǒng	Microwave video distribution system (European term for LMDS)	MVDS
微波双工器	Wēibō shuānggōngqì	Microwave duplexer	
微波铁塔	Wēibō tiětǎ	Microwave tower	WT
微波通信	Wēibō tōngxìn	Microwave communications	
微波无线电链接	Wēibō wúxiàndiàn liànjiē	Microwave radio link	
微波载波	Wēibō zàibō	Microwave carrier	WZ
微波终端站	Wēibō zhōngduān zhàn	Microwave terminal station	
微波中继装置	Wēibō zhōngjì zhuāngzhì	Microwave relay unit	MRU
微波中继站	Wēibō zhōngjìzhàn	Microwave relay station	
微波着陆系统	Wēibō zhuólù xìtǒng	Microwave landing system	MLS
微波/毫米波单片集成电路	Wēibō/háomībō dānpiàn jíchéng diànlù	Microwave/millimeter wave monolithic integrated circuit	
微步闭环回路控制	Wēibù bìhuán huílù kòngzhì	Micro stepping closed loop control	
尾部比特	Wěibù bǐtè	Tail bits	
威布分布	Wēi-bù fēnbù	Weibull distribution	
维测台	Wéicè tái	Maintenance and test console	
微程序	Wēichéngxù	Microprogram	
维持图	Wéi-chí tú	Veitch diagram	
微处理机	Wēichǔlǐjī	Microprocessor	
微处理机开发系统	Wēichǔlǐjī kāifā xìtǒng	Microprocessor development system	
微处理器	Wēichǔlǐqì	Microprocessor	
位错	Wèicuò	Dislocation	
微带	Wēidài	Microstrip	
微带天线	Wēidài tiānxiàn	Microstrip antenna	MA, MSA
微带线性天线	Wēidài xiànxìng tiānxiàn	Microstrip linear antenna	MLA
微带阵列	Wēidài zhènliè	Microstrip array	MA
伪代理	Wěidàilǐ	Rogue agent	
微代码	Wēidàimǎ	Microcode	
伪代码算法	Wěidàimǎ suànfǎ	Pseudocode algorithm	
微带线	Wēidàixiàn	Microstrip	
微道板	Wēidàobǎn	Microchannel plate	
未登记的访问	Wèidēngjìde fǎngwèn	Non-registered access	
微电机镜阵列	Wēidiànjī jìng zhènliè	Microelectromechanical mirror arrays	MEMMA
微电 - 机系统	Wēidiànjī xìtǒng	Micro electronic mechanical system	MEMS
微电子机械开关	Wēidiànzǐ jīxiè kāiguān	MicroElectroMechanical switch	MEMS
微电子机械系统	Wēidiànzǐ jīxiè xìtǒng	Microelectronic mechanical system	MEMS
微电子组装	Wēidiànzǐ zǔzhuāng	Microelectronic packaging	
未定义	Wèidìngyì	To be defined	TBD
未定义比特	Wèidìngyì bǐtè	Undefined bit	
未定义字节	Wèidìngyì zìjié	Undefined byte	
微地形	Wēidìxíng	Small topographies	
维度	Wéidù	Dimension	

维度表	Wéidù biǎo	Dimension table	
维度层次结构	Wéidù céngcì jiégòu	Dimension hierarchy	
唯读光碟	Wéidú guāngdié	Compact disk-read only memory	CD-ROM
唯读光盘增强形架构	Wéidú guāngpán zēngqiáng-xíng jiàgòu	Compact disk-read only memory eXtended architecture	CD-ROM/XA
唯读记忆体	Wéidú jìyìtǐ	Read-only memory	ROM
维度约简技术	Wéidù yuējiǎn jìshù	Dimensionality reduction	
纬度/经度	Wěidù/jīngdù	Latitude / longitude	LL
伪多边形	Wěiduōbiānxíng	Spurious polygon	
微分编码相干移相键控	Wēifēn biānmǎ xiānggān yíxiàng jiànkòng	Differential encoded coherent phase shift keying	DECPSK
微分电路	Wēifēn diànlù	Differentiating circuit	
微分反模调制	Wēifēn fǎnmó tiáozhì	Differential mode inversion (modulation)	DMI
微分群时延	Wēifēn qún shíyán	Differential group delay	DGD
微分相位脉冲调制	Wēifēn xiàngwèi màichōng tiáozhì	Differential phase pulse modulation	DPPM
微分相位失真	Wēifēn xiàngwèi shīzhēn	Differential phase distortion	
微分增益	Wēifēn zēngyì	Differential gain	DG
微分增益失真	Wēifēn zēngyì shīzhēn	Differential gain distortion	
微分段	Wēifēnduàn	Micro-segmentation	
微蜂窝系统	Wēifēngwō xìtǒng	Microcellular system	MCS
微封装	Wēifēngzhuāng	Micro-packaging (electronics mfg)	
未分配信元	Wèifēnpèi xìnyuán	Unassigned cell	
微分器	Wēifēnqì	Differentiator	
微光子学	Wēiguāngzixué	Micro-optics	
未规定比特率	Wèiguīdìng bǐtèlǜ	Unspecified bit rate	UBR
维护	Wéihù	Maintain	
维护操作协议	Wéihù cāozuò xiéyì	Maintenance operation protocol	MOP
维护策略	Wéihù cèlüè	Maintenance policy	
维护程度	Wéihù chéngdù	Level of maintenance	
维护等级	Wéihù děngjí	Maintenance echelon; line of maintenance	
维护方针	Wéihù fāngzhēn	Maintenance policy	
维护服务合同等级	Wéihù fúwù hétong děngjí	Contract level maintenance	
维护工时	Wéihù gōngshí	Maintenance man-hours	MMH
维护工作	Wéihù gōngzuò	Maintenance action; maintenance task	
维护管理	Wéihù guǎnlǐ	Maintenance management	
维护和供应中心	Wéihù hé gōngyìng zhōngxīn	Maintenance and supply center	MSC
维护和管理 PC 机	Wéihù hé guǎnlǐ PC-jī	Maintenance and administration personal computer	MAP
维护和故障后面板	Wéihù hé gùzhàng hòumianbǎn	Maintenance and fault back panel	MFBP
维护和适配	Wéihù hé shìpèi	Maintenance and adaptation	MA
维护控制子系统	Wéihù kòngzhì zixìtǒng	Maintenance control sub-system	MCS
维护流丢失	Wéihù liú diūshī	Loss of maintenance flow	LMF
维护日志	Wéihù rìzhì	Daily maintenance record	
维护事件	Wéihù shìjiàn	Maintenance event	
维护事件信息	Wéihù shìjiàn xìnxī	Maintenance event information	MEI
维护实体	Wéihù shítǐ	Maintenance entity	ME
维护实体功能	Wéihù shítǐ gōngnéng	Maintenance entity function	MEF
维护实体组	Wéihù shítǐ zǔ	Maintenance entity assembly	MEA

维护树	Wéihù shù	Maintenance tree	
维护通道缓冲寄存器	Wéihù tōngdào huǎnchōng jìcúnqì	Maintenance channel buffer register	MCHB
维护通道指令寄存器	Wéihù tōngdào zhǐlìng jìcúnqì	Maintenance channel command register	MCHC
维护信元描述	Wéihù xìnyuán miáoshù	Maintenance cell description	MCD
维护业务提供者	Wéihù yèwù tígòngzhě	Maintenance service provider	MSP
维护支持性能	Wéihù zhīchí xìngnéng	Maintenance support performance	
维护中心	Wéihù zhōngxīn	Maintenance center	
维护准则	Wéihù zhǔnzé	Maintenance philosophy	
维护子实体	Wéihù zǐshítǐ	Maintenance sub-entity	MSE
维护总线	Wéihù zǒngxiàn	Maintenance bus	M-BUS
微化空间	Wēihuà kōngjiān	Microcosm	
微机电技术	Wēijī diàn jìshù	Micro-machining	
微机电系统	Wēijī diàn xìtǒng	Micro-electromechanical system	MEMS
微机通信	Wēijī tōngxìn	Microcomputer communications	
伪节点	Wěijiédiǎn	Pseudo node	
未解释	Wèijiěshì	Uninterpreted (IPsec)	
未经处理的	Wèijīng chǔlǐde	Raw	
未经限定的	Wèijīng xiàndìngde	Unqualified	
未经修饰的	Wèijīng xiūshìde	Unqualified	
微晶片	Wēijīngpiàn	Microchip	
微计算机	Wēijìsuànjī	Microcomputer	
伪距	Wěijù	Pseudo range (GPS term)	
位块传输	Wèikuài chuánshū	Bit block transfer	Blit
微块天线	Wēikuài tiānxiàn	Patch antenna	
未来公用陆地移动通信系统	Wèilái gōngyòng lùdì yídòng tōngxìn xìtǒng	Future public land mobile telecommunication system	FPLMTS
未来公众移动通信系统	Wèilái gōngzhòng yídòng tōngxìn xìtǒng	Future public land mobile telecommunication system	FPLMTS
威力电脑	Wēilì diànnǎo	Power PC	
威力麦金塔	Wēilì mài-jīn-tǎ	Power Mac ©	
未连接	Wèiliánjiē	Unconnected	UNC
未连接信号	Wèiliánjiē xìnhào	Unconnected signal	
位流	Wèiliú	Bit stream	
尾流	Wěiliú	Wake	
维洛尼卡检索	Wéi-luò-ní-kǎ jiǎnsuǒ	Veronica search	
伪码	Wěimǎ	Pseudo code	
微码	Wēimǎ	Microcode	
微米	Wēimǐ	Micron	
微妙	Wēimiào	Microsecond	μs
维纳滤波器	Wéi-nà lǜbōqì	Wiener filter	
微内核	Wēinèihé	Micro-kernel	
未强制关系	Wèiqiángzhì guānxi	Unenforced relationship	
微区	Wēiqū	Microcell	
微渠道架构	Wēiqúdào jiàgòu	Micro channel architecture	MCA
伪缺陷	Wěiquēxiàn	Pseudo-flaw (IPsec)	
未扰轨道	Wèirǎo guǐdào	Unperturbed orbit (of a satellite)	
微软百科全书	Wēiruǎn bǎikē quánshū	Microsoft Encarta ©	

微软办公前 / 后室	Wēiruǎn bàngōng qián/hòushì	Microsoft Front/Backoffice ©	
微软办公室配套软件	Wēiruǎn bàngōngshì pèitào ruǎnjiàn	Microsoft Office ©	
微软电力站简报软件	Wēiruǎn diànlìzhàn jiǎnbào ruǎnjiàn	Microsoft PowerPoint ©	
微软富豪	Wēiruǎn fùháo	Microsoft Millionaire ©	
微软公司	Wēiruǎn gōngsī	Microsoft (US company)	MS
微软公司视窗硬件质量实验室	Wēiruǎn gōngsī shìchuāng yìngjiàn zhìliàng shíyànshì	Microsoft Windows Hardware Quality lab	WHQL
微软工作软件	Wēiruǎn gōngzuò ruǎnjiàn	Microsoft Works ©	
微软交流群组软件	Wēiruǎn jiāoliú qúnzǔ ruǎnjiàn	Microsoft Exchange ©	
微软教学与娱乐公司	Wēiruǎn jiàoxué yǔ yúlè gōngsī	Microsoft Learning and Entertainment	MLE
微软家用软件	Wēiruǎn jiāyòng ruǎnjiàn	Microsoft Home ©	
微软基础类库	Wēiruǎn jīchǔ lèi kù	Microsoft foundation classes	MFC
微软集团	Wēiruǎn jítuán	Microsoft Corporation; MS ©	
微软媒体服务器	Wēiruǎn méitǐ fúwùqì	Microsoft® media server	MMS
微软认证解决方案供应商	Wēiruǎn rènzhèng jiějué fāng'àn gōngyìngshāng	Microsoft Certified Solution Providers	MCSP
微软 TV 平台适配套件	Wēiruǎn TV píngtái-shì pèitào jiàn	Microsoft TV Platform adaptation kit	MTVPAK
微软网络	Wēiruǎn wǎngluò	Microsoft Network ©	MSN
微软文书软件	Wēiruǎn wénshū ruǎnjiàn	Microsoft Word ©	
微软优越试算表	Wēiruǎn yōuyuè shìsuànbiǎo	Microsoft Excel ©	
微软诊断程序	Wēiruǎn zhěnduàn chéngxù	Microsoft diagnostics	MSD
伪三进制码	Wěisān jìnzhì mǎ	Pseudo-ternary code	
伪三进制信号	Wěisānjìnzhì xìnhào	Pseudo-ternary signal	
未授权的访问	Wèishòuquánde fǎngwèn	Unauthorized access	
尾数	Wěishù	Mantissa	
伪速度反应谱	Wěisùdù fǎnyìng pǔ	Pseudo velocity response spectrum	
伪随机比特序列	Wěisuíjī bǐtè xùliè	Pseudo-random bit sequence	PRBS
伪随机二进制序列	Wěisuíjī èrjìnzhì xùliè	Pseudo-random binary sequence	PRBS
伪随机二元序列	Wěisuíjī èryuán xùliè	Pseudo-random binary sequence	PRBS
伪随机码	Wěisuíjī mǎ	Pseudo-random code	
伪随机码序列	Wěisuíjī mǎ xùliè	Pseudo-random binary sequence	PRBS
伪随机序列	Wěisuíjī xùliè	Pseudo-random sequence	
伪随机噪声	Wěisuíjī zàoshēng	Pseudo-random noise	PN
伪随机噪声生成	Wěisuíjī zàoshēng shēngchéng	Pseudo-random noise generation	PRNG
伪随机数	Wěisuíjīshù	Pseudo-random number	RAND
维特比算法	Wéi-tè-bǐ suànfǎ	Viterbi algorithm	VA
伪同步数字网	Wěitóngbù shùzì wǎng	Pseudo-synchronous digital hierarchy	PDH
微通道体系结构	Wēitōngdào tǐxì jiégòu	Micro channel architecture	MCA
位图	Wèitú	Bit mapping	
位图文件	Wèitú wénjiàn	Bitmap file	.bmp
伪突发	Wěitūfā	Dummy burst	DB
委托	Wěituō	Delegate (verb)	
微弯损耗	Wēiwān sǔnhào	Microbending loss	
未完成呼叫	Wèiwánchéng hūjiào	Unsuccessful call	
未完税交货	Wèiwánshuì jiāohuò	Delivered duty unpaid	
微微	Wēiwēi	Pico- (prefix meaning 10^{-12})	P
微微蜂窝	Wēiwēi fēngwō	Picocell	

微微秒	Wēiwēi miǎo	Picosecond	
微微区	Wēiwēi qū	Picocell	
微微网	Wēiwēi wǎng	Pico-net	
尾纤	Wěixiān	Lead, Pigtail	
伪线仿真边缘到边缘	Wěixiàn fǎngzhēn biānyuán dào biānyuán	Pseudo wire emulation edge to edge	PWE3
危险故障	Wēixiǎn gùzhàng	Critical fault	
危险失效	Wēixiǎn shīxiào	Critical failure	
尾纤弯曲半径	Wěixiān wānqū bànjìng	Fiber bend radius	
危险状态	Wēixiǎn zhuàngtài	Critical state	
微小干涉滤光镜	Wēixiǎo gānshè lǜguāngjìng	Micro interference filter (optical)	
微小棱镜	Wēixiǎo léngjìng	Micro prism	
微小区	Wēixiǎo qū	Microcell (cellular telephony)	
微小组	Wēixiǎo zǔ	Microcell	MC
微小组控制器	Wēixiǎo zǔ kòngzhìqì	Microcell controller	MCC
威胁监控	Wēixié jiānkòng	Threat monitoring	
威胁模型	Wēixié móxíng	Threat model	
维信电脑	Wéi-xìn diànnǎo	Wearnes Computers (Singapore company)	
微信道结构	Wēixìndào jiégòu	Micro channel architecture	MCA
卫星	Wèixīng	Satellite	
卫星标准频率和时间信号业务	Wèixīng biāozhǔn pínlǜ hé shíjiān xìnhào yèwù	Standard frequency and time signal-satellite service	
卫星测地学	Wèixīng cèdìxué	Satellite geodesy	
微型唱盘	Wēixíng chàngpán	Mini disk	
卫星城市	Wèixīng chéngshì	Satellite city	
卫星电话	Wèixīng diànhuà	Satellite telephony	
卫星电话交换中心	Wèixīng diànhuà jiāohuàn zhōngxīn	Satellite telephone switching center	STC
微型电脑	Wēixíng diànnǎo	Minicomputer	
卫星电视	Wèixīng diànshì	Satellite television	SATV
卫星电视接收地面站	Wèixīng diànshì jiēshōu dìmiànzhàn	Television receive only satellite ground station	
卫星定位系统	Wèixīng dìngwèi xìtǒng	Satellite positioning systems	
卫星地球探测业务	Wèixīng dìqiú tàncè yèwù	Earth exploration-satellite service	
卫星地球站	Wèixīng dìqiúzhàn	Satellite earth station	WD
卫星多业务系统	Wèixīng duō yèwù xìtǒng	Satellite multi-service system	SMS
卫星共用天线电视/共用天线电视	Wèixīng gòngyòng tiānxiàn diànshì/Gòngyòng tiānxiàn diànshì	Satellite master antenna television /master antenna television	SMATV/MATV
卫星观测点	Wèixīng guāncèdiǎn	Satellite station	
卫星广播	Wèixīng guǎngbō	Satellite broadcasting	
卫星广播业务	Wèixīng guǎngbō yèwù	Broadcasting-satellite service	
卫星固定无线接入	Wèixīng gùdìng wúxiàn jiērù	Satellite fixed wireless access	SFWA
卫星固定业务	Wèixīng gùdìng yèwù	Fixed-satellite service	
卫星航空无线电导航业务	Wèixīng hángkōng wúxiàndiàn dǎoháng yèwù	Aeronautical radio navigation satellite service	
卫星航空移动业务	Wèixīng hángkōng yídòng yèwù	Aeronautical mobile-satellite service	
卫星交换多址	Wèixīng jiāohuàn duōzhǐ	Satellite switched multiple access	SSMA
卫星接入	Wèixīng jiērù	Satellite access	SA
微型开关	Wēixíng kāiguān	Micro-switch	MSW

微型控制器	Wēixíng kòngzhìqì	Embedded controller	EC
卫星控制网	Wèixīng kòngzhìwǎng	Satellite control network	SCN
卫星链路	Wèixīng liànlù	Satellite link	
卫星陆地移动业务	Wèixīng lùdì yídòng yèwù	Land mobile-satellite service	
卫星抛物反射面焦距对天线口径之比	Wèixīng pāowù fǎnshè miàn jiāojù duì tiānxiàn kǒujìng zhī bǐ	Focal-length-to–diameter ratio of a satellite parabolic reflector	f/D
卫星气象业务	Wèixīng qìxiàng yèwù	Meteorological satellite service	
卫星容量	Wèixīng róngliàng	Satellite capacity	
卫星上链服务	Wèixīng shàngliàn fúwù	Uplink services	ULS
卫星水上无线电导航业务	Wèixīng shuǐshàng wúxiàndiàn dǎoháng yèwù	Maritime radio navigation satellite service	
卫星水上移动业务	Wèixīng shuǐshàng yídòng yèwù	Maritime mobile satellite service	
卫星数据传输	Wèixīng shùjù chuánshū	Satellite data transmission	
卫星数字通信系统	Wèixīng shùzì tōngxìn xìtǒng	Satellite digital communications system	SDCS
卫星天碟	Wèixīng tiāndié	Satellite disk	
卫星通信	Wèixīng tōngxìn	Satellite communications	
卫星网络	Wèixīng wǎngluò	Satellite network	
卫星无线电测定	Wèixīng wúxiàndiàn cèdìng	Satellite radio-determination	
卫星无线电测定业务	Wèixīng wúxiàndiàn cèdìng yèwù	Radio-determination satellite service	
卫星无线电导航	Wèixīng wúxiàndiàn dǎoháng	Satellite radio-navigation	
卫星无线电导航业务	Wèixīng wúxiàndiàn dǎoháng yèwù	Radio-navigation satellite service	
卫星无线电定位系统	Wèixīng wúxiàndiàn dìngwèi xìtǒng	Satellite radio location systems	
卫星像片	Wèixīng xiàngpiàn	Satellite image	
卫星线路	Wèixīng xiànlù	Satellite link	
卫星信号网络	Wèixīng xìnhào wǎngluò	Signal-satellite network	SSN
卫星系统	Wèixīng xìtǒng	Satellite system	
卫星延迟补偿器	Wèixīng yánchí bǔchángqì	Satellite delay compensation unit	SDCU
卫星业余业务	Wèixīng yèyú yèwù	Amateur satellite service	
卫星移动接入	Wèixīng yídòng jiērù	Satellite mobile access	SMA
卫星移动通信系统	Wèixīng yídòng tōngxìn xìtǒng	Satellite mobile communication system	
卫星移动业务	Wèixīng yídòng yèwù	Mobile satellite service	
卫星移动业务交换中心	Wèixīng yídòng yèwù jiāohuàn zhōngxīn	Satellite mobile service switching center	SMSC
卫星战术数据信息链	Wèixīng zhànshù shùjù xìnxī liàn	Satellite Tactical Data Information Link (US military)	STADIL
卫星直播	Wèixīng zhíbō	Direct broadcasting by satellite	DBS
卫星周期	Wèixīng zhōuqī	Period (of a satellite)	
卫星转发器	Wèixīng zhuǎnfāqì	Satellite transponder	
卫星转接十分多路存取	Wèixīng zhuǎnjiē shífēn duōlù cúnqǔ	Satellite switched time-division multiple access	SSTDMA
微型自由空间光隔离器	Wēixíng zìyóu kōngjiān guāng gélíqì	Miniature free space optical isolator	MOFI
卫星间链路	Wèixīng-jiān liànlù	Inter-satellite link	
卫星间业务	Wèixīng-jiān yèwù	Inter-satellite service	
维修	Wéixiū	Maintenance	
维修性	Wéixiūxìng	Maintainability	
围压	Wéiyā	Confining pressure	
尾页标	Wěiyè biāo	Footer (WP command)	
位移	Wèiyí	Displacement	DISP
唯一编码规则	Wéiyī biānmǎ guīzé	Distinguished encoding rules	DER

位移反应谱	Wèiyí fǎnyìng pǔ	Displacement response spectrum	
位移码	Wèiyí mǎ	Displacement code	
唯一索引	Wéiyī suǒyǐn	Unique index (for database)	
位移向量	Wèiyí xiàngliàng	Displacement vector	
未应答的呼叫完成	Wèiyìngdáde hūjiào wánchéng	Completion of calls on no reply	CCNR
微音器	Wēiyīnqì	Microphone	MIC
位移式操作	Wèiyí-shì cāozuò	Deviation operation	
惟一性约束	Wéiyīxing yuēshù	Unique constraint (in SQL Server)	
位元逐一复制	Wèiyuán zhúyī fùzhì	Bitwise copy	
位元组	Wèiyuánzǔ	Byte	
伪造	Wěizào	Falsification (IW attack)	
伪造	Wěizào	Forgery (IPsec)	
伪噪声	Wěizàoshēng	Pseudo-noise	PN
位置	Wèizhì	Place (in Petri net)	
位置	Wèizhì	Position	
位置保持卫星	Wèizhì bǎochí wèixīng	Station-keeping satellite	
位置参考框架	Wèizhì cānkǎo kuàngjià	Positional reference frame	
位置参照	Wèizhì cānzhào	Location reference	
位置参照代码	Wèizhì cānzhào dàimǎ	Location reference code	
位置参照类型	Wèizhì cānzhào lèixíng	Location reference type	
位置查询	Wèizhì cháxún	Point location query	
位置撤消登记	Wèizhì chèxiāo dēngjì	Location deregistration	
位置登记	Wèizhì dēngjì	Location registration	
位置登记子系统	Wèizhì dēngjì zìxìtǒng	Location registration sub-system	LRS
位置登记器	Wèizhì dēngjìqì	Location register	LR
位置分辨率	Wèizhì fēnbiànlǜ	Position resolution	
位置分集接收	Wèizhì fēnjí jiēshōu	Site diversity reception	
位置服务器	Wèizhì fúwùqì	Location server	
位置告警模块	Wèizhì gàojǐng mókuài	Site alarm block	SAB
位置更新	Wèizhì gēngxīn	Location update	LU
位置更新程序	Wèizhì gēngxīn chéngxù	Location updating procedure	
位置更新规程	Wèizhì gēngxīn guīchéng	Location updating procedure	
位置更新接受	Wèizhì gēngxīn jiēshòu	Location update accept	
位置更新类型	Wèizhì gēngxīn lèixíng	Location updating type	
位置跟踪	Wèizhì gēnzōng	Location tracking	
位置划分多路存取	Wèizhì huàfēn duōlù cúnqǔ	Location division multiple access	LDMA
位置寄存器	Wèizhì jìcúnqì	Location register	LR
位置寄存器系统 ACE	Wèizhì jìcúnqì xìtǒng ACE	Location register system ACE	LRSACE
位置精度	Wèizhì jīngdù	Positional precision	
位置目録	Wèizhì mùlù	Location directory	LD
位置区	Wèizhì qū	Location area	LA
位置区服务	Wèizhì qū fúwù	Support of local service area	SOLSA
位置区号	Wèizhì qū hào	Location area identity	LAI
位置区码	Wèizhì qū mǎ	Location area code	LAC
位置区识别	Wèizhì qū shíbié	Location area identification	LAI
位置区信息	Wèizhì qū xìnxī	Location area information	LAI

位置确定实体	Wèizhì quèdìng shítǐ	Position determining entity	PDE
位置取消规程	Wèizhì qǔxiāo guīchéng	Location cancellation procedure	
位置区域	Wèizhì qūyù	Location area	LA
位置区域更新	Wèizhì qūyù gēngxīn	Location area update	LAU
位置区域码	Wèizhì qūyù mǎ	Location area code	LAC
位置区域识别	Wèizhì qūyù shíbié	Location area identification	LAI
位置删除程序	Wèizhì shānchú chéngxù	Location cancellation procedure	
位置相关	Wèizhì xiāngguān	Location correlation	
位置信息	Wèizhì xìnxī	Location information	
位置信息恢复规程	Wèizhì xìnxī huīfù guīchéng	Location information retrieval procedure	
位置信息请求规程	Wèizhì xìnxī qǐngqiú guīchéng	Location information requested procedure	
位置准确性	Wèizhì zhǔnquèxìng	Positional accuracy	
位置字段描述符	Wèizhì zìduàn miáoshù fú	Position field descriptor	
未指定比特率	Wèizhǐdìng bǐtèlǜ	Undefined bit rate	UBR
未指定比特率	Wèizhǐdìng bǐtèlǜ	Unspecified bit rate	UBR
微支付	Wēizhīfù	Micro-payment	
微支付传输协议	Wēizhīfù chuánshū xiéyì	Micro-payment transport protocol	MPTP
伪指令	Wěizhǐlìng	Pseudo instruction	PSEUDO
微指令	Wēizhǐlìng	Micro instruction	
伪装	Wěizhuāng	Masquerade (IPsec)	
伪装成目的用户入侵	Wěizhuāng chéng mùdì yònghù rùqīn	Target-concealed user intrusion	
伪装成源的用户入侵	Wěizhuāng chéng yuánde yònghù rùqīn	Source-concealed user intrusion	
未装电路标志码	Wèizhuāng diànlù biāozhìmǎ	Unequipped circuit identification code (ISUP message)	UCIC
伪装攻击	Wěizhuāng gōngjī	Impersonation attack (IPsec)	
伪装媒体	Wěizhuāng méitǐ	Stegano-media	
未装备电路	Wèizhuāngbèi diànlù	Unequipped circuit	
未装载	Wèizhuāngzài	Unequipped	UNEQ
未装载	Wèizhuāngzài	Unequal	UNEQ
温备用	Wēn bèiyòng	Warm-standby	
温补晶振	Wēn bǔ jīng zhèn	Temperature compensation crystal oscillator	TCXO
温盘	Wēn pán	Winchester disk	
文实相符	Wén shí xiàngfú	Implementation corresponds to the documentation; done as written	
文语转换	Wén yǔ zhuǎnhuàn	Text-to-speech	TTS
文本	Wénběn	Text	
文本保真度	Wénběn bǎozhēndù	Textual fidelity	
文本窗口	Wénběn chuāngkǒu	Text window	
文本单元	Wénběn dānyuán	Text unit	
文本符号	Wénběn fúhào	Text symbol	
文本区	Wénběn qū	Text area	
文本数据库	Wénběn shùjùkù	Textual database	
文本属性	Wénběn shǔxìng	Text attribute	
文本属性表	Wénběn shǔxìng biǎo	Text attribute table	
文本文件	Wénběn wénjiàn	Text file	
文本样式	Wénběn yàngshì	Text style	
文本语	Wénběn yǔ	Text-to-speech	
文本增强技术	Wénběn zēngqiáng jìshù	Text enhanced technology	TET

文本至语音的转换	Wénběn zhì yǔyīnde zhuǎnhuàn	Text-to-speech conversion	TTS
纹波	Wénbō	Ripple	
纹波峰值系数	Wénbō fēngzhí xìshù	Peak ripple factor	
纹波均方根系数	Wénbō jūnfānggēn xìshù	Root mean square ripple factor	
温彻斯特磁盘机	Wēn-chè-sī-tè cípánjī	Winchester disk drive	
文档	Wéndàng	Document	
文档窗口	Wéndàng chuāngkǒu	Document window	
文档对象模型	Wéndàng duìxiàng móxíng	Document object model	DOM
文档解析代理	Wéndàng jiěxī dàilǐ	Archive parser agent (in Java)	APA
文档类型定义	Wéndàng lèixíng dìngyì	Document type definition	DTD
文档文件	Wéndàng wénjiàn	Document file	
文档支持组	Wéndàng zhīchí zǔ	Document maintenance Group (in CMM)	DMG
文电传递代理	Wéndiàn chuándì dàilǐ	Message transfer agent	MTA
稳定点	Wěndìng diǎn	Steady point	
稳定分析	Wěndìng fēnxī	Stability analysis	
稳定河道	Wěndìng hédào	Stable channel	
稳定斜面	Wěndìng xiémiàn	Equilibrium slope	
稳定系数	Wěndìng xìshù	Stability coefficient	
稳定度	Wěndìngdù	Stability	
温度补偿瓷介电容器	Wēndù bǔcháng cíjiè diànróngqì	Temperature compensated ceramic capacitor	
温度补偿晶体振荡器	Wēndù bǔcháng jīngtǐ zhèndàngqì	Temperature compensation crystal oscillator	TCXO
温度补偿式功率计	Wēndù bǔchángshì gōnglǜjì	Temperature compensated power bridge	
温度传感器	Wēndù chuángǎnqì	Temperature probe	TP
温度膨胀系数	Wēndù péngzhàng xìshù	Coefficient of the thermal expansion	
温度相关损耗	Wēndù xiāngguān sǔnhào	Temperature-dependent loss	TDL
温度循环试验	Wēndù xúnhuán shìyàn	Temperature cycling test	
问号	Wènhào	Question mark (?)	
文件	Wénjiàn	File	
文件	Wénjiàn	Document	
文件保护	Wénjiàn bǎohù	File protection (IPsec)	
文件编号	Wénjiàn biānhào	File number	
文件编制	Wénjiàn biānzhì	Documentation	
文件布局处理	Wénjiàn bùjú chǔlǐ	Document layout process	
文件布局根	Wénjiàn bùjú gēn	Document layout root	
文件菜单	Wénjiàn càidān	File menu (WP command)	
文件成批传送	Wénjiàn chéngpī chuánsòng	Document bulk transfer	
文件成批传送和管理操作	Wénjiàn chéngpī chuánsòng hé guǎnlǐ cāozuò	Document bulk transfer and manipulation	
文件传输访问管理	Wénjiàn chuánshū fǎngwèn guǎnlǐ	File transmission, access and management	FTAM
文件传输访问和管理	Wénjiàn chuánshū fǎngwèn hé guǎnlǐ	File transfer access and management (ISO use)	FTAM
文件传输协议	Wénjiàn chuánshū xiéyì	File transfer protocol	FTP
文件传输，接入和使用	Wénjiàn chuánshū, jiērù hé shǐyòng	File transfer, access and manipulation	FTAM
文件传输、存取和管理	Wénjiàn chuánshū、cúnqǔ hé guǎnlǐ	File transfer, access and management	FTAM
文件传送存放与管理	Wénjiàn chuánsòng cúnfàng yǔ guǎnlǐ	File transfer access management	FTAM
文件传送点	Wénjiàn chuánsòng diǎn	File transfer protocol site (Internet location for downloading files using FTP)	FTP site
文件传送地址和管理	Wénjiàn chuánsòng dìzhǐ hé guǎnlǐ	File transfer addressing and management	FTAM

文件传送方式	Wénjiàn chuánsòng fāngshì	Document transfer mode	
文件传送和管理操作用户	Wénjiàn chuánsòng hé guǎnlǐ cāozuò yònghù	Document transfer and manipulation user	DTAM
文件传送及交互方式	Wénjiàn chuánsòng jí jiāohù fāngshì	Document transfer and interactive mode	
文件传送接入及管理协议	Wénjiàn chuánsòng jiērù jí guǎnlǐ xiéyì	File transfer, access and management protocol	FTAM
文件传送协议	Wénjiàn chuánsòng xiéyì	File transfer protocol	FTP
文件传真	Wénjiàn chuánzhēn	Document facsimile	
文件存储类型	Wénjiàn cúnchǔ lèixíng	File storage type	
文件存取块	Wénjiàn cúnqǔ kuài	File access block	FAB
文件地址寄存器	Wénjiàn dìzhǐ jìcúnqì	File address register	FAR
文件分隔	Wénjiàn fēngé	File separator	FS
文件分配表	Wénjiàn fēnpèi biǎo	File allocation table	FAT
文件服务器	Wénjiàn fúwùqì	File server	
文件复制服务	Wénjiàn fùzhì fúwù	File replication service	
文件管理	Wénjiàn guǎnlǐ	Document management	
文件管理操作	Wénjiàn guǎnlǐ cāozuò	Document manipulation	
文件管理系统	Wénjiàn guǎnlǐ xìtǒng	File management system	FMS
文件后缀	Wénjiàn hòuzhuì	File extension	
文件夹	Wénjiàn jiā	Folder	
文件交换体系结构	Wénjiàn jiāohuàn tǐxì jiégòu	Document interchange architecture	DIA
文件结构	Wénjiàn jiégòu	File structure	
文件结束标志	Wénjiàn jiéshù biāozhì	End-of-file mark	EOF
文件控制块	Wénjiàn kòngzhì kuài	File control block	FCB
文件类别	Wénjiàn lèibié	Document class	
文件类别描述	Wénjiàn lèibié miáoshù	Document class description	
文件类型	Wénjiàn lèixíng	File type	
文件类型定义	Wénjiàn lèixíng dìngyì	Document type definition (in XML)	DTD
文件轮廓	Wénjiàn lúnkuò	Document profile	
文件轮廓级	Wénjiàn lúnkuò jí	Document profile level	
文件逻辑根	Wénjiàn luóji gēn	Document logical root	
文件名	Wénjiàn míng	File name	
文件内布寻找时间	Wénjiàn nèibù xúnzhǎo shíjiān	Intra-file seek time	
文件内容描述	Wénjiàn nèiróng miáoshù	Document content description (in XML)	DCD
文件派生	Wénjiàn pàishēng	File fork	
文件数据误操作	Wénjiàn shùjù wùcāozuò	Clobbering	
文件属性	Wénjiàn shǔxìng	File attribute	
文件搜寻站	Wénjiàn sōuxúnzhàn	Archie (Internet tool)	
文件锁定	Wénjiàn suǒdìng	File locking	
文件索引	Wénjiàn suǒyǐn	File indexing	
文件体系结构	Wénjiàn tǐxì jiégòu	Document architecture	
文件体系结构级	Wénjiàn tǐxì jiégòu jí	Document architecture level	
文件体系结构类别	Wénjiàn tǐxì jiégòu lèibié	Document architecture class	
文件图像业务	Wénjiàn túxiàng yèwù	Telematics service	
文件完整性检查器	Wénjiàn wánzhěngxìng jiǎncháqì	File integrity checker	
文件尾	Wénjiàn wěi	End of file	
文件压缩	Wénjiàn yāsuō	File compression	
文件应用轮廓	Wénjiàn yìngyòng lúnkuò	Document application profile	

文件用户电报	Wénjiàn yònghù diànbào	Teletex	
文件主体	Wénjiàn zhǔtǐ	Document subject, document body	
文件组	Wénjiàn zǔ	File group	
问卷调查	Wènjuàn diàochá	Questionnaire	
纹理分析	Wénlǐ fēnxī	Grained analysis	
纹理交换	Wénlǐ jiāohuàn	Texture swapping	
纹理模式	Wénlǐ móshì	Texture mode	
纹理内存	Wénlǐ nèicún	Texture memory	
纹理像素	Wénlǐ xiàngsù	Texture pixels	
纹理像素	Wénlǐ xiàngsù	Texture element	Texel
纹理压缩	Wénlǐ yāsuō	Texture compression (video term)	
纹理真实性	Wénlǐ zhēnshíxìng	Texture fidelity (video term)	
稳频激光	Wěnpín jīguāng	Frequency stabilized laser	
温热试验	Wēnrè shìyàn	Damp heat test	
文氏强制对流	Wén-shì qiángzhì duìliú	Venturi forced convection (semiconductor mfg)	
文式图	Wén-shì tú	Venn diagram	
稳态	Wěntài	Equilibrium condition	
稳态不可用性	Wěntài bùkěyòngxìng	Steady-state unavailability	
稳态可用性	Wěntài kěyòngxìng	Steady-state availability	
稳态数值孔径	Wěntài shùzhí kǒngjìng	Equilibrium numerical aperture	
稳态增益响应	Wěntài zēngyì xiǎngyìng	Steady state gain response	
稳态的	Wěntàide	Steady state	
问题模板	Wèntí múbǎn	Question template	
问题生成器	Wèntí shēngchéng qì	Question builder	
问题文件	Wèntí wénjiàn	Question file (.eqq)	
文通笔	Wéntōng bǐ	Wintone pen (product of a Qinghua University subsidiary company, used as input device for an electronic tablet)	
文献资料	Wénxiàn zīliào	Documentary records	
稳压电源	Wěnyā diànyuán	Regulated voltage supply	
稳压系数	Wěnyā xìshù	Regulation factor	
稳压器	Wěnyāqì	Voltage regulator	VR
稳压器的基准电压	Wěnyāqìde jīzhǔn diànyā	Regulator reference voltage	
稳压器的性能参数	Wěnyāqìde xìngnéng cānshù	Regulator performance parameter	
文字连接光标	Wénzì liánjiē guāngbiāo	Hypertext cursor (WP command)	
Windows 多媒体扩充板	Windows duōméitǐ kuòchōng bǎn	Windows multimedia extensions	WME
Windows 开放服务结构	Windows kāifàng fúwù jiégòu	Windows open service architecture	WOSA
我的浅见	Wǒde qiǎnjiàn	In my humble opinion (computer chat)	IMHO
沃尔什函数	Wò-ěr-shí hánshù	Walsh function	
沃尔什-哈达码变换	Wò-ěr-shí—Hǎ-dá-mǎ biànhuàn	Walsh-Hadamard transform	WHT
沃格特模型	Wò-gé-tè móxíng	Voigt model	
握奇数据系统有限公司	Wòjī shùjù xìtǒng yǒuxiàn gōngsī	Watchdata System Corp (Beijing)	
握手	Wòshǒu	Handshake	
握手规程	Wòshǒu guīchéng	Handshaking procedure (IPsec)	
握手认证协议	Wòshǒu rènzhèng xiéyì	Challenge-handshake authentication protocol	CHAP
握手失败消息	Wòshǒu shībài xiāoxi	Handshake failure message (IPsec TLS)	
握手协议	Wòshǒu xiéyì	Handshake protocol (IPsec)	

误比特率	Wù bǐtè lǜ	Bit error rate	BER
钨传输阴级射线枪	Wū chuánshū yīnjí shèxiàn qiāng	Tungsten impregnated cathode ray gun (video)	TICRG
五大码	Wǔ dà mǎ	Big 5 code (computer coding of Chinese characters)	
无光告警光功率	Wú guāng gàojǐng guāng gōnglǜ	Optical power without optical alarm	
五阶段预留协议	Wǔ jiēduàn yùliú xiéyì	Five-phase reservation protocol	FPRP
五喇叭馈电器	Wǔ lǎba kuìdiànqì	Five-horn feed	
五类线	Wǔ lèi xiàn	Category 5 wiring	
无二次编解码操作	Wú'èrcì biānjiěmǎ cāozuò	Tandem free operation	TFO
无二次编解码操作	Wú'èrcì biānjiěmǎ cāozuò	Tandem free operation	TFO
误报	Wùbào	False positives	
无保障的通信	Wúbǎozhàngde tōngxìn	Uninsured traffic	
无编号确认	Wúbiānhào quèrèn	Unnumbered acknowledge	UA
无编号信息	Wúbiānhào xìnxī	Unnumbered information	UI
无编号信息帧	Wúbiānhào xìnxī zhèng	Unnumbered information frame	UI
无编号帧	Wúbiānhào zhèng	Unnumbered frames	UF
无编号证实	Wúbiānhào zhèngshí	Unnumbered acknowledge	UA
无变压器电源	Wúbiànyāqì diànyuán	Non-transformer power supply	
误操作故障	Wùcāozuò gùzhàng	Mishandling fault	
误操作失效	Wùcāozuò shīxiào	Mishandling failure	
误差	Wùchā	Error	
误差传播	Wùchā chuánbō	Error propagation	
误差处理	Wùchā chǔlǐ	Error handling	
误差概率	Wùchā gàilǜ	Word error probability	
误差函数	Wùchā hánshù	Error function	erf
误差检测和纠正	Wùchā jiǎncè hé jiūzhèng	Error detection and correction	
误差模型	Wùchā móxíng	Error modeling	
误差信号	Wùchā xìnhào	Error signal	
误差信号分解器	Wùchā xìnhào fēnjiěqì	Error signal resolver	
无差错秒	Wúchācuò miǎo	Error free seconds	EFS
无尘室	Wúchénshì	Clean room	
无尘室用机具	Wúchénshì-yòng jījù	Clean room supplies	
无冲突多路存取	Wúchōngtū duōlù cúnqǔ	Collision-free multiple access	CFMA
无冲突哈希查找算法	Wúchōngtū hāxī cházhǎo suànfǎ	Collision-free Hash search (for IP packet classification)	
误传	Wùchuán	Mis-routing	
误传帧	Wùchuán zhèng	Mis-routed frames	
无触发保护电路	Wúchùfā bǎohù diànlù	Non-trigger protection circuit	
无错数据	Wúcuò shùjù	Clean data	
无导体竖井光缆	Wúdǎotǐ shùjǐng guānglǎn	Optical fiber cable with no riser	OFNR
无导体天花板隔层光缆	Wúdǎotǐ tiānhuābǎn gécéng guānglǎn	Optical fiber with no plenum layer	OFNP
无答应	Wúdáying	No answer	NA
误动	Wùdòng	Malfunction (electric power term)	
无堵塞交叉连接	Wúdǔsè jiāochā liánjiē	Non-blocking cross-connect connection	
无法兑付汇款	Wúfǎ duìfù huìkuǎn	Non-delivery remittance	
无法退还汇款	Wúfǎ tuìhuán huìkuǎn	Undeliverable remittance	
无法退还汇款撤回	Wúfǎ tuìhuán huìkuǎn chèhuí	Withdrawal of undeliverable remittance	
无法遵循	Wúfǎ zūnxún	Unable to comply	UTC

无方向性辐射器	Wúfāng xiàngxìng fúshèqì	Omni-directional radiator	
无防备攻击	Wúfángbèi gōngjī	Nak attack (Ipsec, attack based on 'negative acknowledge' or NAK message)	
无缝钢管	Wúfèng gāngguǎn	Seamless steel pipe	
无缝数据库	Wúfèng shùjùkù	Seamless database	
无缝越区切换	Wúfèng yuèqū qiēhuàn	Seamless handover	
无功近场区	Wúgōng jìncháng qū	Reactive near field (region)	
武汉邮电科学研究院	Wǔhàn yóudiàn kēxué yánjiūyuàn	Wuhan Research Institute of Posts & telecommunications	WRI
雾化表画质	Wùhuà biǎohuà zhì	Fog table quality (video)	
雾化效果	Wùhuà xiàoguǒ	Atmospheric effects	AE
雾化效果	Wùhuà xiàoguǒ	Fog (video term)	
无缓冲思索联合写操作	Wúhuǎnchōng sīsuǒ liánhé xiě cāozuò	Uncached speculative write combining	USWC
无话音分离器的低速不对称数字用户线	Wúhuàyīn fēnlíqìde dīsù bùduìchèn shùzì yònghù xiàn	Low speed-rate asynchronous digital subscriber line without voice splitter	ADSL.lite
无恢复连接完整性	Wúhuīfù liánjiē wánzhěngxìng	Connection integrity without recovery (IPsec)	
无级调速	Wújí tiáosù	Classless speed-rate adjustment	
无监护间隔	Wújiānhù jiàngé	Unguarded interval	
无结论判定	Wújiélùn pàndìng	Inconclusive verdict	
无记名文件存取	Wújìmíng wénjiàn cúnqǔ	Anonymous FTP	
无计数帧	Wújìshù zhèng	Unnumbered frames	
无机物绝缘电缆	Wújīwù juéyuán diànlǎn	Mineral-insulated cable	MIC
无聚焦结的光纤（缆）连接器	Wújù jiāojiéde guāngxiān (lǎn) liánjiē qì	Optical fiber (cable) connector without focusing junction	
无可用漫游号码	Wúkěyòng mànyóu hàomǎ	No roaming number available	
误块	Wùkuài	Errored block	EB
误块计数	Wùkuài jìshù	Errored block count	EBC
误块秒	Wùkuài miǎo	Errored second	ES
误块秒比	Wùkuài miǎo bǐ	Errored second ratio	ESR
误块秒率	Wùkuài miǎo lǜ	Errored second rate	
无类地址分配	Wúlèi dìzhǐ fēnpèi	Classless addressing (IPsec)	
无类域间路由选择	Wúlèi yùjiān lùyóu xuǎnzé	Classless inter-domain routing	CIDR
无类别域际路由选择	Wúlèibié yùjì lùyóu xuǎnzé	Classless inter-domain routing	CIDR
无类别域间选路	Wúlèibié yùjiān xuǎnlù	Classless inter-domain routing	CIDR
物理安全	Wùlǐ ānquán	Physical security (IPsec)	
物理编码子层	Wùlǐ biānmǎ zicéng	Physical coding sub-layer	PCS
物理层	Wùlǐ céng	Physical layer	PH, PHY
物理层设备	Wùlǐ céng shèbèi	Physical layer device	PHY
物理层信令	Wùlǐ céng xìnlìng	Physical layer signaling	PLS
物理层-操作和维护(信元)	Wùlǐ céng—cāozuò hé wéihù (xìnyuán)	Physical layer-operation and maintenance (cell)	PL-OAM
物理读取	Wùlǐ dúqǔ	Physical reads	
物理发泡	Wùlǐ fāpāo	Physically foaming	
物理服务	Wùlǐ fúwù	Physical service	PhS
物理服务数据单元	Wùlǐ fúwù shùjù dānyuán	Physical service data unit	PhSDU
物理复现	Wùlǐ fùxiàn	Physical rendition	
物理公共分组信道	Wùlǐ gōnggòng fēnzǔ xìndào	Physical common packet channel	PCPCH
物理共享信道	Wùlǐ gòngxiǎng xìndào	Physical shared channel	PSCH

物理结构	Wùlǐ jiégòu	Physical structure	
物理接口	Wùlǐ jiēkǒu	Physical interface	
物理接口规范	Wùlǐ jiēkǒu guīfàn	Physical interface specification	
物理介质接入	Wùlǐ jièzhì jiērù	Physical media access	PMA
物理介质相关	Wùlǐ jièzhì xiāngguān	Physical medium dependent	PMD
物理介质相关子层	Wùlǐ jièzhì xiāngguān zicéng	Physical medium dependent sub-layer	PMD
物理空间	Wùlǐ kōngjiān	Physical space	
物理连接	Wùlǐ liánjiē	Physical connection	PHC
物理媒介子层	Wùlǐ méijiè zicéng	Physical media sub-layer	
物理媒体	Wùlǐ méitǐ	Physical media	PM
物理媒体无关	Wùlǐ méitǐ wúguān	Physical media independent	PMI
物理媒体相关	Wùlǐ méitǐ xiāngguān	Physical media dependent	PMD
物理媒体相关/传输会聚	Wùlǐ méitǐ xiāngguān/chuánshū huìjù	Physical medium dependent/transmission channel	PMD/TC
物理媒体有关	Wùlǐ méitǐ yǒuguān	Physical media dependent	PMC
物理媒体子层	Wùlǐ méitǐ zicéng	Physical medium sub-layer	PM
物理媒质特定传输汇聚层	Wùlǐ méizhì tèdìng chuánshū huìjù céng	Physical media-specific transmission channel layer	PMS-TC
物理媒质相关	Wùlǐ méizhì xiāngguān	Physical media dependent	PMD
物理媒质子层	Wùlǐ méizhì zicéng	Physical media sub-layer	
物理名称	Wùlǐ míngchēng	Physical name	
物理模型	Wùlǐ móxíng	Physical model	
物理配置	Wùlǐ pèizhì	Physical configuration	
物理设计交换格式	Wùlǐ shèjì jiāohuàn géshi	Physical design exchange format	PDEF
物理实体	Wùlǐ shítǐ	Physical entity	PE
物理随机接入信道	Wùlǐ suíjī jiērù xìndào	Physical random access channels	PRACH
物理体系结构	Wùlǐ tǐxì jiégòu	Physical architecture	
物理投递	Wùlǐ tóudì	Physical delivery	PD
物理投递地址的组成成份	Wùlǐ tóudì dìzhǐde zǔchéng chéngfèn	Physical delivery address components	
物理投递访问单元	Wùlǐ tóudì fǎngwèn dānyuán	Physical delivery access unit	PDAU
物理投递服务	Wùlǐ tóudì fúwù	Physical delivery service	
物理投递服务名	Wùlǐ tóudì fúwù míng	Physical delivery service name	
物理投递个人名	Wùlǐ tóudì gèrén míng	Physical delivery personal name	
物理投递国家名	Wùlǐ tóudì guójiā míng	Physical delivery country name	
物理投递消息	Wùlǐ tóudì xiāoxi	Physical delivery message	PDM
物理投递系统	Wùlǐ tóudì xìtǒng	Physical delivery system	PDS
物理投递组织名	Wùlǐ tóudì zǔzhī míng	Physical delivery organization name	
物理投递局地址组成成份	Wùlǐ tóudìjú dìzhǐ zǔchéng chéngfèn	Physical delivery office address components	
物理投递局号	Wùlǐ tóudìjú hào	Physical delivery office number	
物理投递局名	Wùlǐ tóudìjú míng	Physical delivery office name	
物理线路	Wùlǐ xiànlù	Physical circuit	
物理消息	Wùlǐ xiāoxi	Physical message	
物理下行共享信道	Wùlǐ xiàxíng gòngxiǎng xìndào	Physical downlink shared channel	PDSCH
物理协议数据单元	Wùlǐ xiéyì shùjù dānyuán	Physical protocol data unit	PHPDU
物理信道	Wùlǐ xìndào	Physical channel	
物理信令通路	Wùlǐ xìnlìng tōnglù	Physical signaling channel	
物理信令信道	Wùlǐ xìnlìng xìndào	Physical signaling channel	
物理信息	Wùlǐ xìnxī	Physical information	

物理页	Wùlǐ yè	Physical page	
物理业务端口	Wùlǐ yèwù duānkǒu	Physical service port	PSP
物理业务访问点	Wùlǐ yèwù fǎngwèn diǎn	Physical service access point	PhSAP
物理用户端口	Wùlǐ yònghù duān kǒu	Physical user port	PUP
物理帧	Wùlǐ zhèng	Physical frame	
无连接	Wúliánjiē	Connectionless	CL
无连接承载控制	Wúliánjiē chéngzài kòngzhì	Connectionless bearer control	CBC
无连接服务器	Wúliánjiē fúwùqì	Connectionless server	CLS
无连接机密性	Wúliánjiē jīmìxìng	Connectionless confidentiality (IPsec)	
无连接宽带数据服务	Wúliánjiē kuāndài shùjù fúwù	Connectionless broadband data service	CBDS
无连接模式网络层协议	Wúliánjiē móshì wǎngluò céng xiéyì	Connectionless network protocol	CLNP
无连接数据传送	Wúliánjiē shùjù chuánsòng	Connectionless data transfer (SS7 message)	CLDT
无连接数据确认	Wúliánjiē shùjù quèrèn	Connectionless data acknowledged (SS7 message)	CLDA
五连接网络服务	Wǔliánjiē wǎngluò fúwù	Connectionless network service	CLNS
无连接网络协议	Wúliánjiē wǎngluò xiéyì	Connectionless network protocol	CLNP
无连接完整性	Wúliánjiē wánzhěngxìng	Connectionless integrity (IPsec)	
无连接业务	Wúliánjiē yèwù	Connectionless service	
无连接业务功能	Wúliánjiē yèwù gōngnéng	Connectionless service function	CLSF
无连接的网络层服务	Wúliánjiēde wǎngluò céng fúwù	Connectionless network layer service	CLNS
无连接的网络层协议	Wúliánjiēde wǎngluò céng xiéyì	Connectionless network layer protocol	CLNP
无连接型宽带数据业务	Wúliánjiēxíng kuāndài shùjù yèwù	Connectionless broadband data service	CBDS
无连接型业务	Wúliánjiēxíng yèwù	Connectionless service	
物料需求计划	Wùliào xūqiú jìhuà	Material requirement planning	MRP
物流管理	Wùliú guǎnlǐ	Logistics management	
物流资源计划	Wùliú zīyuán jìhuà	Logistics resource planning	LRP
无卤阻燃护套	Wúlǔ zǔrán hùtào	Halogen-free, flame retardant jacket (FOC)	HFFR
误码	Wùmǎ	Error code	
误码扩散	Wùmǎ kuòsàn	Error spread	
误码秒	Wùmǎ miǎo	Errored second	ES
误码秒比	Wùmǎ miǎo bǐ	Errored second ratio	ESR
误码秒比率	Wùmǎ miǎo bǐlǜ	Errored second ratio	ESR
误码秒类型A	Wùmǎ miǎo lèixíng A	Error second A	ESA
误码秒类型B	Wùmǎ miǎo lèixíng B	Error second B	ESB
误码增殖	Wùmǎ zēngzhí	Error multiplication	
误码增殖因子	Wùmǎ zēngzhí yīnzǐ	Error multiplication factor	
误码率	Wùmǎlǜ	Bit error rate	BER
误码率测试仪	Wùmǎlǜ cèshìyí	Bit error rate tester	BERT
五面棱镜	Wǔmiàn léngjìng	Pentagonal prism	
无名键	Wúmíng jiàn	Anonymity key	AK
无碰头多路存取	Wúpèngtóu duōlù cúnqǔ	Collision-free multiple access	CFMA
无屏蔽双绞线	Wúpíngbì shuāngjiǎoxiàn	Unshielded twisted pair	UTP
无穷计数	Wúqióng jìshù	Count to infinity	
无人管理应答辅助设备	Wúrén guǎnlǐ yìngdá fǔzhù shèbèi	Unattended answering accessory	UNA
无绳电话模型	Wúshéng diànhuà móxíng	Cordless telephony profile	
无绳电话系统	Wúshéng diànhuà xìtǒng	Cordless telephone system	
无绳电话站	Wúshéng diànhuà zhàn	Telepoint	

无绳电话机	Wúshéng diànhuàjī	Cordless telephone set	
无绳交换台	Wúshéng jiāohuàntái	Cordless switchboard	
无声阶段	Wúshēng jiēduàn	Silent period (in signaling)	
无绳局域网	Wúshéng júyùwǎng	Cordless local area network	CLAN
无绳手机	Wúshéng shǒujī	Cordless portable part (telephone)	CPP
无绳座机	Wúshéng zuòjī	Cordless fixed part (telephone)	CFP
无损只读	Wúsǔn zhǐdú	Non-destructive read-only	NDRO
无条件呼叫前向转移	Wútiáojiàn hūjiào qiánxiàng zhuǎnyí	Call forwarding unconditional	CFU
无条件呼叫前转	Wútiáojiàn hūjiào qiánzhuǎn	Call forwarding unconditional	CFU
无条件呼叫前转补充业务	Wútiáojiàn hūjiào qiánzhuǎn bǔchōng yèwù	Call forwarding unconditional supplementary service	CFU
无条件呼叫转发	Wútiáojiàn hūjiào zhuǎnfā	Call forwarding unconditional	CFU
无条件呼叫转送	Wútiáojiàn hūjiào zhuǎnsòng	Call forwarding unconditional	CFU
无条件呼叫转移	Wútiáojiàn hūjiào zhuǎnyí	Call forward unconditional	
无条件前转	Wútiáojiàn qiánzhuǎn	Call forwarding unconditional	CFU
五位字节	Wǔwèi zìjié	Quintet byte	
无误通信线路	Wúwù tōngxìn xiànlù	Error-free communication link	EFCL
无误码秒	Wúwùmǎ miǎo	Error-free seconds	EFS
无线保真	Wúxiàn bǎozhēn	Wireless fidelity	Wi-Fi
无线本地环路	Wúxiàn běndì huánlù	Wireless local loop	WLL
无线本地网	Wúxiàn běndì wǎng	Wireless local area network	WLAN
无线标记语言	Wúxiàn biāojì yǔyán	Wireless markup language	WML
无线标志语言	Wúxiàn biāozhì yǔyán	Wireless markup language	WML
无线测试设备(板)	Wúxiàn cèshì shèbèi (bǎn)	Radio test equipment (board)	RTE
无线承载电路	Wúxiàn chéngzài diànlù	Radio bearer	RB
无线承载共用功能	Wúxiàn chéngzài gòngyòng gōngnéng	Radio bearer common functionality	RBCF
无线传声器	Wúxiàn chuánshēngqì	Wireless microphone	
无线传输层安全	Wúxiàn chuánshū céng ānquán	Wireless transmission level security	WTLS
无线传输特定功能	Wúxiàn chuánshū tèdìng gōngnéng	Radio transmission specific functionality	RTSF
无线传送层安全性	Wúxiàn chuánsòng céng ānquánxìng	Wireless transport layer security	WTLS
无线传讯	Wúxiàn chuánxùn	Data roam	
无线电测向电台	Wúxiàn diàncè xiàng diàntái	Radio direction-finding station	
无线电话	Wúxiàn diànhuà	Radio telephone	
无线电话呼叫	Wúxiàn diànhuà hūjiào	Radiotelephone call	
无线电话交换机	Wúxiàn diànhuà jiāohuànjī	Wireless telephone exchange	WTX
无线电话技术	Wúxiàn diànhuà jìshù	Radio telephony	
无线电话应用	Wúxiàn diànhuà yìngyòng	Wireless telephony application	WTA
无线电话应用接口	Wúxiàn diànhuà yìngyòng jiēkǒu	Wireless telephony applications interface	WTAI
无限递归	Wúxiàn dìguī	Infinite recursive	
无线二进制运行环境	Wúxiàn èrjìnzhì yùnxíng huánjìng	Binary running environment for wireless	BREW
无线发射设备	Wúxiàn fāshè shèbèi	Wireless transmission equipment	WF
无线非对称传输模式	Wúxiàn fēiduìchèn chuánshū móshì	Wireless asymmetrical transmission system	WATS
无线蜂窝网络临时识别	Wúxiàn fēngwō wǎngluò línshí shíbié	Cell radio network temporary identity	C-RNTI
无线分系统指定越区切换	Wúxiàn fēnxìtǒng zhǐdìng yuèqū qiēhuàn	Radio sub-system directed handover	
无线分系统准则	Wúxiàn fēnxìtǒng zhǔnzé	Radio sub-system criteria	
无线分组业务	Wúxiàn fēnzǔ yèwù	General packet radio service	GPRS

无线覆盖域网络	Wúxiàn fùgài yù wǎngluò	Wireless coverage area network	WCAN
无线干扰误码	Wúxiàn gānrǎo wùmǎ	Radio interference error code	
无线革命	Wúxiàn gémìng	Wireless revolution	
无线个人通信	Wúxiàn gèrén tōngxìn	Wireless personal communication	WPC
无线个人域网	Wúxiàn gèrén yù wǎng	Wireless personal area network	WPAN
无线广告业务	Wúxiàn guǎnggào yèwù	Wireless advertisement	WAD
无线行业企业协会	Wúxiàn hángyè qǐyè xiéhuì	Association of Radio Industry Businesses (Japan)	ARIB
无线会话协议	Wúxiàn huìhuà xiéyì	Wireless speech protocol	WSP
无线会话协议	Wúxiàn huìhuà xiéyì	Wireless session protocol	WSP
无线家庭网	Wúxiàn jiātíng wǎng	Wireless home network	
无线接口层	Wúxiàn jiēkǒu céng	Radio interface layer	RIL
无线接入	Wúxiàn jiērù	Wireless access	WA
无线接入承载	Wúxiàn jiērù chéngzài	Radio access bearer	RAB
无线接入承载业务	Wúxiàn jiērù chéngzài yèwù	Radio access bearer service	RAB
无线接入服务器	Wúxiàn jiērù fúwùqì	Wireless access server	WAS
无线接入技术	Wúxiàn jiērù jìshù	Wireless access technology	
无线接入网	Wúxiàn jiērù wǎng	Radio access network	RAN
无线接入网系统	Wúxiàn jiērù wǎng xìtǒng	Radio access network system	RNS
无线接入网应用部分	Wúxiàn jiērù wǎng yìngyòng bùfen	Radio access network application part	RANAP
无线接入网关	Wúxiàn jiērù wǎngguān	Wireless access gateway	WAG
无线接入网络	Wúxiàn jiērù wǎngluò	Radio access network	RAN
无线接入网络应用部分	Wúxiàn jiērù wǎngluò yìngyòng bùfen	Radio access network application part	RANAP
无线接入站	Wúxiàn jiērùzhàn	Wireless access point	
无线接收设备	Wúxiàn jiēshōu shèbèi	Wireless receiver equipment	WS
无线集群系统	Wúxiàn jíqún xìtǒng	Wireless trunking system	
无线基站	Wúxiàn jīzhàn	Radio base station	RBS
无线局域网	Wúxiàn júyùwǎng	Wireless local area network	WLAN
无线控制消息协议	Wúxiàn kòngzhì xiāoxi xiéyì	Wireless control message protocol	WCMP
无线链路管理	Wúxiàn liànlù guǎnlǐ	Radio link management	RLM
无线链路规约	Wúxiàn liànlù guīyuē	Radio link protocol	RLP
无线链路建立	Wúxiàn liànlù jiànlì	Radio link setup	RLS
无线链路控制	Wúxiàn liànlù kòngzhì	Radio link control	RLC
无线链路控制协议	Wúxiàn liànlù kòngzhì xiéyì	Radio link control protocol	RLCP
无线链路控制子层	Wúxiàn liànlù kòngzhì zicéng	Radio link control sub-layer	RLC
无线链路连接定时器	Wúxiàn liànlù liánjiē dìngshíqì	Wireless link connection timer	
无线链路协议	Wúxiàn liànlù xiéyì	Radio link protocol	RLP
无线漂移网络控制器	Wúxiàn piāoyí wǎngluò kòngzhìqì	Drift radio network controller	DRNC
无线平台二进制运行环境	Wúxiàn píngtái èrjìnzhì yùnxíng huánjìng	Binary running environment for wireless platforms	BREW
无线频率测试设备	Wúxiàn pínlǜ cèshì shèbèi	Radio frequency test equipment	RFTE
无线频率单元	Wúxiàn pínlǜ dānyuán	Radio frequency unit	RFU
无线频率单元机架	Wúxiàn pínlǜ dānyuán jījià	Radio frequency unit rack	RFUR
无限区间脉冲响应	Wúxiàn qūjiān màichōng xiǎngyìng	Infinite duration impulse response	IIR
无线区域网路	Wúxiàn qūyù wǎnglù	Wireless local area network	WLAN
无线设备	Wúxiàn shèbèi	Radio equipment	REP
无线事务处理协议	Wúxiàn shìwù chǔlǐ xiéyì	Wireless transaction protocol	WTP
无线事务协议	Wúxiàn shìwù xiéyì	Wireless transaction protocol	WTP

无线双向中继	Wúxiàn shuāngxiàng zhōngjì	Wireless both-way trunk	WBWT
无线数据报文协议	Wúxiàn shùjù bàowén xiéyì	Wireless datagram protocol	WDP
无线数据传输链路	Wúxiàn shùjù chuánshū liànlù	Wireless data link	WDL
无线数据广播	Wúxiàn shùjù guǎngbō	Radio data system transmission	RDS
无线数据协议	Wúxiàn shùjù xiéyì	Wireless data protocol	WDP
无线数据报协议	Wúxiàn shùjùbào xiéyì	Wireless datagram protocol	WDP
无线数字段	Wúxiàn shùzì duàn	Digital radio section	
无线数字通道	Wúxiàn shùzì tōngdào	Digital radio path	
无线数字系统	Wúxiàn shùzì xìtǒng	Digital radio system	
无线通信业务	Wúxiàn tōngxìn yèwù	Radio communication service	
无线网络子系统	Wúxiàn wǎngluò zixìtǒng	Radio network sub-system	RNS
无线网络子系统应用部分	Wúxiàn wǎngluò zixìtǒng yìngyòng bùfen	Radio network sub-system application part	RNSAP
无线线路	Wúxiàn xiànlù	Radio link	
无线小区	Wúxiàn xiǎoqū	Radio cell	RC
无线信道	Wúxiàn xìndào	Wireless channel	
无线信道群	Wúxiàn xìndào qún	Radio channel group	RCG
无线信令链路	Wúxiàn xìnlìng liànlù	Radio signaling link	RSL
无线系统管理	Wúxiàn xìtǒng guǎnlǐ	Radio system management	RSM
无线系统研究开发中心	Wúxiàn xìtǒng yánjiū kāifā zhōngxīn	Research and Development Center for Radio System (Japan)	RCR
无线寻呼系统	Wúxiàn xúnhū xìtǒng	Radio paging system	
无线寻呼 1 号码	Wúxiàn xúnhū yihàomǎ	Radio-paging code no.1	
无限循环	Wúxiàn xúnhuán	Infinite loop	
无线虚拟专用网络	Wúxiàn xūnǐ zhuānyòng wǎngluò	Wireless virtual private network	WVPN
无线演示文稿机	Wúxiàn yǎnshì wéngǎojī	Wireless presentation gateway	
无线应用环境	Wúxiàn yìngyòng huánjìng	Wireless application environment	WAE
无线应用协议	Wúxiàn yìngyòng xiéyì	Wireless application protocol	WAP
无线以太网兼容联盟	Wúxiàn yǐtàiwǎng jiānróng liánméng	Wireless Ethernet Compatibility Alliance	WECA
无线用户	Wúxiàn yònghù	Radio subscriber	RS
无线用户接入	Wúxiàn yònghù jiērù	Wireless subscriber access	WSA
无线用户组	Wúxiàn yònghù zǔ	Wireless user group	WUG
无线智能网络	Wúxiàn zhìnéng wǎngluò	Wireless intelligent network	WIN
无线终端	Wúxiàn zhōngduān	Wireless terminal	WT
无线专用交换机	Wúxiàn zhuānyòng jiāohuànjī	Wireless private branch exchange	WPBX
无线助听系统	Wúxiàn zhùtīng xìtǒng	Wireless hearing aid system	
无线子系统管理	Wúxiàn zixìtǒng guǎnlǐ	Radio sub-system management	RSM
无线资源	Wúxiàn zīyuán	Radio resource	RR
无线资源管理	Wúxiàn zīyuán guǎnlǐ	Radio resource management	RRM
无线资源管理实体	Wúxiàn zīyuán guǎnlǐ shítǐ	Radio resource management entity	RRME
无线资源管理协议	Wúxiàn zīyuán guǎnlǐ xiéyì	Radio resource management protocol	RRMP
无线资源控制	Wúxiàn zīyuán kòngzhì	Radio resource control	RRC
无线资源控制层	Wúxiàn zīyuán kòngzhì céng	Radio resource control layer	RRC
无线波调幅与调相	Wúxiànbō tiáofú yǔ tiáoxiàng	Carrierless amplitude and phase modulation	CAP
无线电	Wúxiàndiàn	Radio	
无线电报	Wúxiàndiàn bào	Radio telegram	
无线电波	Wúxiàndiàn bō	Radio waves	

无线电波透镜	Wúxiàndiàn bō tòujìng	Radio-wave lens	
无线电波道	Wúxiàndiàn bōdào	Radio channel	RC
无线电测定	Wúxiàndiàn cèdìng	Radio determination	
无线电测定电台	Wúxiàndiàn cèdìng diàntái	Radio determination station	
无线电测定业务	Wúxiàndiàn cèdìng yèwù	Radio determination service	
无线电测向	Wúxiàndiàn cèxiàng	Radio direction-finding	
无线电测向电台	Wúxiàndiàn cèxiàng diàntái	Radio direction-finding station	
无线电传打字电报	Wúxiàndiàn chuándǎzì diànbào	Radio teletype	RTTY
无线电传输技术	Wúxiàndiàn chuánshū jìshù	Radio transmission technology	RTT
无线电导航	Wúxiàndiàn dǎoháng	Radio navigation	
无线电导航陆地电台	Wúxiàndiàn dǎoháng lùdì diàntái	Radio navigation land station	
无线电导航业务	Wúxiàndiàn dǎoháng yèwù	Radio navigation service	
无线电导航移动电台	Wúxiàndiàn dǎoháng yídòng diàntái	Radio navigation mobile station	
无线电定位	Wúxiàndiàn dìngwèi	Radio location	
无线电定位陆地电台	Wúxiàndiàn dìngwèi lùdì diàntái	Radio location land station	
无线电定位业务	Wúxiàndiàn dìngwèi yèwù	Radio location service	
无线电定位移动电台	Wúxiàndiàn dìngwèi yídòng diàntái	Radio location mobile station	
无线电定向	Wúxiàndiàn dìngxiàng	Radio direction-finding	
无线电地平线	Wúxiàndiàn dìpíngxiàn	Radio horizon	
无线电发射机	Wúxiàndiàn fāshèjī	Radio transmitter	
无线电干扰	Wúxiàndiàn gānrǎo	Radio interference	
无线电干扰	Wúxiàndiàn gānrǎo	Radio jamming	
无线电干扰测量仪	Wúxiàndiàn gānrǎo cèliángyí	Radio interference meter	
无线电高度表	Wúxiàndiàn gāodùbiǎo	Radio altimeter	
无线电高空测候器	Wúxiàndiàn gāokōng cèhòuqì	Radiosonde	
无线电广播	Wúxiàndiàn guǎngbō	Radio broadcasting	
无线电管理局	Wúxiàndiàn guǎnlǐjú	Bureau of Radio Regulation (MII)	
无线电规范	Wúxiàndiàn guīfàn	Radio standard	RS
无线电环境	Wúxiàndiàn huánjìng	Radio environment	
无线电环境	Wúxiàndiàn huánjìng	Radio environment	
无线电接力通信	Wúxiàndiàn jiēlì tōngxìn	Radio relay communication	
无线电接入点	Wúxiàndiàn jiērù diǎn	Radio access point	RAP
无线电接收	Wúxiàndiàn jiēshōu	Radio reception	
无线电接收机	Wúxiàndiàn jiēshōujī	Radio receiver	
无线电寂静	Wúxiàndiàn jìjìng	Radio silence	
无线电控制终端	Wúxiàndiàn kòngzhì zhōngduān	Radio control terminal	RCT
无线电空中接口	Wúxiàndiàn kōngzhōng jiēkǒu	Radio air interface	
无线电链路	Wúxiàndiàn liànlù	Radio link	
无线电频道	Wúxiàndiàn píndào	Radio frequency channel	
无线电频率	Wúxiàndiàn pínlǜ	Radio frequency	RF
无线电频率干扰	Wúxiàndiàn pínlǜ gānrǎo	Radio-frequency interference	RFI
无线电频率加热装置	Wúxiàndiàn pínlǜ jiārè zhuāngzhì	Radio-frequency heating apparatus	
无线电频率骚扰	Wúxiàndiàn pínlǜ sāorǎo	Radio-frequency disturbance	
无线电频率信道	Wúxiàndiàn pínlǜ xìndào	Radio-frequency channel	RFC
无线电频率噪声	Wúxiàndiàn pínlǜ zàoshēng	Radio-frequency noise	
无线电骚扰	Wúxiàndiàn sāorǎo	Radio disturbance	

无线电射频	Wúxiàndiàn shèpín	Radio frequency	
无线电通信	Wúxiàndiàn tōngxìn	Radio communication	
无线电网络控制器	Wúxiàndiàn wǎngluò kòngzhìqì	Radio network controller	RNC
无线电网络临时识别	Wúxiàndiàn wǎngluò línshí shíbié	Radio network temporary identity	RNTI
无线电网络子系统	Wúxiàndiàn wǎngluò zixìtǒng	Radio network sub-system	RNS
无线电网络子系统应用部分	Wúxiàndiàn wǎngluò zixìtǒng yìngyòng bùfen	Radio network sub-system application part	RNSAP
无线电微波线路	Wúxiàndiàn wēibō xiànlù	Radio microwave link	RML
无线电线路规约	Wúxiàndiàn xiànlù guīyuē	Radio line protocol	RLP
无线电显示寻呼	Wúxiàndiàn xiǎnshì xúnhū	Radio display paging	
无线电信标	Wúxiàndiàn xìnbiāo	Radio beacon	
无线电信标电台	Wúxiàndiàn xìnbiāo diàntái	Radio beacon station	
无线电信道	Wúxiàndiàn xìndào	Radio channel	RC
无线电信令链路	Wúxiàndiàn xìnlìng liànlù	Radio signaling link	RSL
无线电系统实体	Wúxiàndiàn xìtǒng shítǐ	Radio system entity	RSE
无线电寻的	Wúxiàndiàn xúndì	Radio homing	
无线电寻呼	Wúxiàndiàn xúnhū	Radio paging	
无线电寻呼机	Wúxiàndiàn xúnhūjī	Radio pager	
无线电遥测技术	Wúxiàndiàn yáocè jìshù	Radio telemetry	
无线电业余爱好者	Wúxiàndiàn yèyú àihàozhě	Radio amateur, ham	
无线电用户电报呼叫	Wúxiàndiàn yònghù diànbào hūjiào	Radiotelex call	
无线电噪声	Wúxiàndiàn zàoshēng	Radio noise	
无线电制导	Wúxiàndiàn zhìdǎo	Radio guidance	
无线电终端功能	Wúxiàndiàn zhōngduān gōngnéng	Radio terminal function	RTF
无线电中继链路	Wúxiàndiàn zhōngjì liànlù	Radio relay link	RRL
无线电中继系统	Wúxiàndiàn zhōngjì xìtǒng	Radio relay system	RRL
无线电中继器	Wúxiàndiàn zhōngjìqì	Radio repeater	
无线电转发器	Wúxiàndiàn zhuǎnfāqì	Radio transponder	
无线电资源	Wúxiàndiàn zīyuán	Radio resources	RR
无线电资源管理	Wúxiàndiàn zīyuán guǎnlǐ	Radio resources management	RRM
无线电资源控制	Wúxiàndiàn zīyuán kòngzhì	Radio resources control	RRC
无线电报	Wúxiàndiànbào	Radiotelegram	
无线电报技术	Wúxiàndiànbào jìshù	Radio telegraphy	
无线电波	Wúxiàndiànbō	Radio wave	
无线电波传播	Wúxiàndiànbō chuánbō	Radio wave propagation	
无线电台	Wúxiàndiàntái	Radio station	
无向图	Wúxiàng tú	Undirected graph	
无限制的数字信息	Wúxiànzhìde shùzì xìnxī	Unrestricted digital information	UDI
无效超频	Wúxiào chāopín	No-account overclock	NAOC
无效多边形	Wúxiào duōbiānxíng	Void polygon	
无效信元	Wúxiào xìnyuán	Invalid cell	
无效指令	Wúxiào zhǐlìng	Invalid instruction	
无效指针指示	Wúxiào zhǐzhēn zhǐshì	Null point identification	NPI
无效中断	Wúxiào zhōngduàn	Invalid interrupt	
无效字符	Wúxiào zìfú	Inactive character	
无信元定界	Wúxìnyuán dìngjiè	No cell defined	NCD
误信元率	Wùxìnyuán lǜ	Cell error rate	CER

无序对	Wúxù duì	Unordered pair	
无序数	Wúxù shù	Unordered tree	
无序信息（帧）	Wúxù xìnxī (zhèng)	Unnumbered information (frame)	UI
无选网络控制器	Wúxuǎn wǎngluò kòngzhìqì	Radio network controller	RNC
无氧高电导铜	Wúyǎng gāodiàndǎo tóng	Oxygen-free high conductivity copper	OFHC
无要求的时间	Wúyāoqiúde shíjiān	Non-required time	
五音顺序制	Wǔyīn shùnxù zhì	Five tone sequential system	
无应答呼叫前向转移	Wúyìngdá hūjiào qiánxiàng zhuǎnyí	Call forwarding on no reply	CFNRy, CFNREP
无应答呼叫前转	Wúyìngdá hūjiào qiánzhuǎn	Call forwarding on no reply	CFNR
无应答呼叫转发	Wúyìngdá hūjiào zhuǎnfā	Call forwarding on no reply	CFNR
无应答呼叫转送	Wúyìngdá hūjiào zhuǎnsòng	Call forwarding on no reply	CFNR
无应答模式	Wúyìngdá móshì	Unacknowledged mode	UM
无应答前转	Wúyìngdá qiánzhuǎn	Call forwarding on no reply	CFNRP
无应答前转补充业务	Wúyìngdá qiánzhuǎn bǔchōng yèwù	Call forwarding on no reply supplementary service	CFU
无用发射	Wúyòng fāshè	Unwanted emission	
误用故障	Wùyòng gùzhàng	Misuse fault	
误用检测	Wùyòng jiǎncè	Misuse detection	
误用失效	Wùyòng shīxiào	Misuse failure	
无用输入无用输出	Wúyòng shūrù wúyòng shūchū	Garbage in, garbage out	GIGO
无用信号	Wúyòng xìnhào	Unwanted signal	
无用户各自控制的分配性业务	Wúyònghù gèzì kòngzhìde fēnpèi-xìng yèwù	Distribution service without user individual presentation control	
无源定位	Wúyuán dìngwèi	Passive location	
无源反射器	Wúyuán fǎnshèqì	Passive reflector	
无源干扰	Wúyuán gānrǎo	Passive jamming	
无源跟踪	Wúyuán gēnzōng	Passive tracking	
无源光网络	Wúyuán guāng wǎngluò	Passive optical network	PON
无源光纤网	Wúyuán guāngxiān wǎng	Passive optical network	PON
无源校正网络	Wúyuán jiàozhèng wǎngluò	Passive corrective network	
无源滤波器	Wúyuán lǜbōqì	Passive filter	
无源色散补偿器	Wúyuán sèsàn bǔchángqì	Passive dispersion compensator	PDC
无源探测	Wúyuán tàncè	Passive detection	
无源网络	Wúyuán wǎngluò	Passive network	
无源遥感器	Wúyuán yáogǎnqì	Passive sensor	
无源元件	Wúyuán yuánjiàn	Passive component	
无源中继站	Wúyuán zhōngjìzhàn	Passive relay station	
无约束非线性回归	Wúyuēshù fēixiànxìng huíguī	Unconstrained non-linear regression	
无约束时延的数据	Wúyuēshù shíyánde shùjù	Unconstrained delay data	UDD
无载波幅相调制	Wúzàibō fú xiāng tiáozhì	Carrierless amplitude and phase modulation	CAP
无载波调幅/调相	Wúzàibō tiáofú/tiáoxiàng	Carrierless amplitude/phase modulation	CAP
无再生中继器	Wúzàishēng zhōngjìqì	Non-regenerative repeater	NrREP
误帧率	Wùzhèng lǜ	Frame error rate	FER
无证实操作	Wúzhèngshí cāozuò	Unacknowledged operation	
无中心多信道选址系统	Wúzhōngxīn duōxìndào xuǎnzhǐ xìtǒng	Multi-channel access system without central control	
无状态的	Wúzhuàngtàide	Stateless	
无主题	Wúzhǔtí	Un-themed	

X

X 显示管理器控制协议	X xiǎnshì guǎnlǐqì kòngzhì xiéyì	X display manager control protocol	XDMCP
X.400 消息处理系统	X.400 xiāoxi chǔlǐ xìtǒng	X.400 message handling system	
X^2 分布	X^2 fēnbù	Chi-squared distribution	
X 窗口	X-chuāngkǒu	X-Windows	
X 窗口图形用户接口	X-chuāngkǒu túxíng yònghù jiēkǒu	X-Windows graphical user interface	
矽半导体材料	Xī bàndǎotǐ cáiliào	Silicon semiconductor material	
细电缆网	Xì diànlǎn wǎng	Thinnet	
矽谷	Xī gǔ	Silicon Valley	
西古	Xī gǔ	Shianfu (abbreviation for the Shianfu Optical Fiber and Cables Co. Ltd.)	
细间距	Xì jiānjù	Fine pitch	
矽图	Xī tú	Silicon Graphics (US company)	
细以太网	Xì yǐtàiwǎng	ThinNet; cheaperNet	
下凹	Xià'āo	Notch	
下扳机	Xiàbānjī	Magazine (in component assembly)	
夏比缺口冲击试验	Xià-bǐ quēkǒu chōngjī shìyàn	Charpy notch impact test	
下边带	Xiàbiandài	Lower sideband	LSB
下变频器	Xiàbiànpínqì	Down converter	
下边缘	Xiàbianyuán	Bottom edge	
下标	Xiàbiāo	Subscript (WP command)	
下标操作符	Xiàbiāo cāozuò fú	Subscript operator	
下传消息	Xiàchuán xiāoxi	Message termination	MT
下垂天线	Xiàchuí tiānxiàn	Trailing wire antenna	TWA
下划双线	Xiàhuà shuāngxiàn	Double underline (WP command)	
下划线	Xiàhuàxiàn	Underline (WP command)	
下级	Xiàjí	Subordinate, inferior	
下级被管理对象	Xiàjí bèiguǎnlǐ duìxiàng	Subordinate managed object	
下降时间展宽	Xiàjiàng shíjiān zhǎnkuān	Decay-time broadening	
下降特性	Xiàjiàng tèxìng	Drooping characteristic	
下井仪器	Xiàjǐng yíqì	Downhole instrument	
下拉	Xiàlā	Pull-down	
下拉电阻	Xiàlā diànzǔ	Pull-down resistance	
下拉式选单	Xiàlā-shì xuǎndān	Pull-down menu	
下流标志交换路由器	Xiàliú biāozhì jiāohuàn lùyóuqì	Downstream label switching router	
下路波长转换器	Xiàlù bōcháng zhuǎnhuànqì	Optical transponder unit-drop	OTU-D
下路和继续传送	Xiàlù hé jìxù chuánsòng	Drop-and-continue (SDH)	
线	Xiàn	Line, wire	
先到先服务	Xiān dào xiān fúwù	First come first service	FCFS
显呼叫传送附加业务	Xiǎn hūjiào chuánsòng fùjiā yèwù	Explicit call transfer supplementary service	ECT
西安交通大学	Xī'ān Jiāotōng Dàxué	Xi'an Jiaotong University	
线极化	Xiàn jíhuà	Linear polarization	
线极化波	Xiàn jíhuà bō	Linearly polarized wave	
线极化场平面波	Xiàn jíhuàcháng píngmiànbō	Linearly polarized plane wave	
线极化场矢量	Xiàn jíhuàcháng shǐliàng	Linearly polarized field vector	
先进先出	Xiān jìn xiān chū	First in, first out	FIFO

先进先出表（队列）	Xiān jìn xiān chū biǎo (duìliè)	First-in first-out list	
线拷贝	Xiàn kǎobèi	Line drawing	
先来先服务	Xiān lái xiān fúwù	First-come first service	
线连续性	Xiàn liánxùxìng	Line continuity	
西安理工大学	Xī'ān lǐgōng dàxué	Xi'an University of Science and Engineering	
线谱对	Xiàn pǔ duì	Line-spectrum pair	
西安全产业分会	Xī'ān quán chǎnyè fēnhuì	Information Security Sub-Committee (of CIITA)	ISSC
显热	Xiǎn rè	Sensed heat	
先入先出队列	Xiān rù xiān chū duìliè	First input first output	FIFO
线实体	Xiàn shítǐ	Line entity	
线属性	Xiàn shǔxìng	Line attribute	
线型	Xiàn xíng	Line type	
线要素	Xiàn yàosù	Line feature	
线要素	Xiàn yàosù	Linear feature	
线综合	Xiàn zōnghé	Line generalization	
陷波模式对流层传播	Xiànbō móshì duìliúcéng chuánbō	Trapped mode tropospheric propagation	
陷波器	Xiànbōqì	Wave-trap	
现场激活	Xiànchǎng jīhuó	In-place active	
现场可编程序门阵列	Xiànchǎng kěbiān chéngxù mén zhènliè	Field-programmable gate arrays	FPGAs
现场可编程序系统芯片	Xiànchǎng kěbiān chéngxù xìtǒng xìnpiàn	Field programmable systems chip	FPSC
现场可编程逻辑阵列	Xiànchǎng kěbiānchéng luóji zhènliè	Field programmable logic array	FPLA
现场可编程门阵列	Xiànchǎng kěbiānchéng mén zhènliè	Field programmable gate array	FPGA
现场可换件	Xiànchǎng kěhuàn jiàn	Field replaceable unit	FRU
现场可替换部件	Xiànchǎng kětìhuan bùjiàn	Field replaceable unit	FRU
现场试验	Xiànchǎng shìyàn	On-site test, in-situ test	
现场试验	Xiànchǎng shìyàn	Field test	
现场数据	Xiànchǎng shùjù	Field data	
现场数据处理	Xiànchǎng shùjù chǔlǐ	On-site data processing	OSDP
现场数据库	Xiànchǎng shùjùkù	Site database	SDB
现场同步	Xiànchǎng tóngbù	Live synchronization	
现场维护	Xiàncháng wéihù	Field maintenance	
现场维护	Xiàncháng wéihù	On-site maintenance; in situ maintenance	
现场应用工程师	Xiànchǎng yìngyòng gōngchéngshī	Field application engineer	
现场总线	Xiànchǎng zǒngxiàn	Field bus	
现场总线控制系统	Xiànchǎng zǒngxiàn kòngzhì xìtǒng	Fieldbus control system	FCS
现场总线数据链路	Xiànchǎng zǒngxiàn shùjù liànlù	Field bus datalink	FDL
线程	Xiànchéng	Thread	
线程安全的	Xiànchéng ānquánde	Thread-safe	
现存帧总量计数	Xiàncún zhèng zǒngliàng jìshù	Existing-frame capacity count	EFCC
现代通信技术和业务	Xiàndài tōngxìn jìshù hé yèwù	Advanced communication technologies and services	ACTS
氙灯	Xiāndēng	Xenon flashlamp	
限定式逻辑链路控制	Xiàndìngshì luóji liànlù kòngzhì	Qualified logic link control (for SNA over X.25)	QLLC
线段	Xiànduàn	Line segment	
线对增容	Xiànduì zēngróng	Pair gain	
先锋	Xiānfēng	Pioneer (US company)	

氙分子激光	Xiānfènzi jīguāng	Xenon laser	
限幅	Xiànfú	Limiting	
限幅电路	Xiànfú diànlù	Amplitude limiting circuit	
限幅灵敏度	Xiànfú língmǐndù	Amplitude limiting sensitivity	
限幅中频放大器	Xiànfú zhōngpín fàngdàqì	Intermediate frequency limiting amplifier	
限幅器	Xiànfúqì	Amplitude limiter	AL
限幅式中频放大器	Xiànfú-shì zhōngpín fàngdàqì	Limiting intermediate frequency amplifier	
项	Xiàng	Item, subject	
项标识符	Xiàng biāozhìfú	Item identifier	
相频特性	Xiāng/pín tèxìng	Phase/frequency characteristic	
相变	Xiàngbiàn	Phase transition	
向导	Xiàngdǎo	Wizard, guide	
相等	Xiāngděng	Equal	
相等性	Xiāngděngxìng	Equality	
响度评定值	Xiǎngdù píngdìngzhí	Loudness rating	LR
相对辨别名	Xiāngduì biàn biémíng	Relative distinguished name	RDN
相对当量	Xiāngduì dāngliàng	Relative equivalent	
相对电平	Xiāngduì diànpíng	Relative level	
相对电压变化	Xiāngduì diànyā biànhuà	Relative voltage change	
相对地址	Xiāngduì dìzhǐ	Relative address	
相对功率电平	Xiāngduì gōnglǜ diànpíng	Relative power level	
相对互调产物电平	Xiāngduì hùtiáo chǎnwù diànpíng	Relative intermodulation product level	
相对交叉熵	Xiāngduì jiāochā shāng	Relative cross entropy	
相对可识别名	Xiāngduì kěshíbié míng	Relative distinguished name	RDN
相对密度	Xiāngduì mìdù	Relative density	
相对识别名	Xiāngduì shíbié míng	Relative distinguished name	RDN
相对位置	Xiāngduì wèizhì	Relative position	
相对位置精度	Xiāngduì wèizhì jīngdù	Relative positional accuracy	
相对误差	Xiāngduì wùchā	Relative error	
相对线路号	Xiāngduì xiànlù hào	Relative line number	
相对音频互调产物电平	Xiāngduì yīnpín hùtiáo chǎnwù diànpíng	Relative audio frequency intermodulation product level	
相对音频互调失真	Xiāngduì yīnpín hùtiáo shīzhēn	Relative audio frequency intermodulation distortion	
相对于半波偶极振子的增益	Xiāngduì yú bànbō ǒují zhènzǐde zēngyì	Gain relative to a half-wave dipole	
相对于短垂直天线的增益	Xiāngduì yú duǎn chuízhí tiānxiànde zēngyì	Gain relative to a short vertical antenna	
相对元素位置指示编码	Xiāngduì yuánsù wèizhì zhǐshì biānmǎ	Relative element address designator code	
相对运动显示器	Xiāngduì yùndòng xiǎnshìqì	Relative-motion indicator	
相对增益	Xiāngduì zēngyì	Relative gain (of an antenna with respect to that of a reference antenna)	
相对准确性	Xiāngduì zhǔnquèxìng	Relative accuracy	
相对坐标	Xiāngduì zuòbiāo	Relative coordinate	
相对于自由空间的损耗	Xiāngduìyú zìyóu kōngjiānde sǔnhào	Loss relative to free space	
相反缓存	Xiāngfǎn huǎncún	Negative caching	
相分多路复用	Xiàngfēn duōlù fùyòng	Phase division multiplexing	PDM
相干动目标显示	Xiānggān dòngmùbiāo xiǎnshì	Coherent mobile target indicator	Coherent MTI
相干光通信	Xiānggān guāng tōngxìn	Coherent optical communication	
相干解调	Xiānggān jiětiáo	Coherent demodulation	

相干旁瓣消除法	Xiānggān pángbàn xiāochú fǎ	Coherent sidelobe cancellation	CSLC
相干数字相控阵列系统	Xiānggān shùzì xiàng kòng zhènliè xìtǒng	Coherent digital phased array system	CODIPHASE
相干调制	Xiānggān tiáozhì	Coherent modulation	
相干相移键控调制	Xiānggān xiàngyí jiànkòng tiáozhì	Coherent phase shift keying modulation	CPSK
相干线性调频	Xiānggān xiànxing tiáopín	Coherent linear frequency modulation	CLFM
相干信号处理系统	Xiānggān xìnhào chǔlǐ xìtǒng	Coherent signal processing system	CSPS
相干信号处理机	Xiānggān xìnhào chǔlǐjī	Coherent signal processor	CSP
相干载波键控	Xiānggān zàibō jiànkòng	Coherent carrier keying	CCK
相干振荡器	Xiānggān zhèndàngqì	Coherent oscillator	
香港和记电讯	Xiānggǎng hé-ji diànxùn	Hutchison Telecom (Hong Kong GSM network operator)	
香港星光国际网络服务公司	Xiānggǎng xīngguāng guójì wǎngluò fúwù gōngsī	Hong Kong Star Internet Service	
香港移动通信	Xiānggǎng yídòng tōngxìn	CSL Hong Kong (GSM network operator)	
香港因特网交换中心	Xiānggǎng Yīntèwǎng jiāohuàn zhōngxīn	Hong Kong Internet Exchange	HKIX
相干性	Xiānggānxìng	Coherence	
相馆	Xiàngguǎn	PhotoShop ©	
相关	Xiāngguān	Correlation	
相关编码	Xiāngguān biānmǎ	Correlative coding	
相关点	Xiāngguān diǎn	Point in association	PIA
相关抖动	Xiāngguān dǒudòng	Correlated jjitter	
相关分析	Xiāngguān fēnxī	Correlative analysis	
相关干扰	Xiāngguān gānrǎo	Coherent jamming; coherent interference	
相关攻击	Xiāngguān gōngjī	Correlation attack	
相关控制信道	Xiāngguān kòngzhì xìndào	Associated control channel	ACCH
相关免疫	Xiāngguān miǎnyì	Correlation immunity	
相关目标	Xiāngguān mùbiāo	Associated object	AO
相关内容可寻止存储器	Xiāngguān nèiróng kěxúnzhǐ cúnchǔqì	Associative content addressable memory	ACAM
相关数据处理	Xiāngguān shùjù chǔlǐ	Associative data processing	ADP
相关跳频	Xiāngguān tiàopín	Correlated frequency hopping	
相关文章	Xiāngguān wénzhāng	Thread (computer documents or e-mail messages on one subject)	
相关相移键控	Xiāngguān xiàngyí jiànkòng	Correlative phase shift keying	CORPSK
相关系数	Xiāngguān xìshù	Correlation coefficient	
相关移相键控	Xiāngguān yíxiàng jiànkòng	Correlative phase shift keying	CORPSK
相关预警	Xiāngguān yùjǐng	Correlation alert	
相关运算	Xiāngguān yùnsuàn	Cyclic correlation	
相关子查询	Xiāngguān zicháxún	Correlated subquery	
相关器	Xiāngguānqì	Correlator (in GPS system)	
相关性	Xiāngguānxing	Dependencies	
向后散射法	Xiànghòu sǎnshè fǎ	Back scattering technique	
向后显式拥挤通告	Xiànghòu xiǎn-shì yōngjǐ tōnggào	Backward explicit congestion notification	BECN
相互波道间增益变化差	Xiānghù bōdào-jiān zēngyì biànhuà chà	Inter-channel gain-change difference	
相互波道间增益变化率	Xiānghù bōdào-jiān zēngyì biànhuà lǜ	Inter-channel gain-change ratio	
相互波道间增益差	Xiānghù bōdào-jiān zēngyì chà	Inter-channel gain difference	
相互认可协议	Xiānghù rènkě xiéyì	Mutual recognition agreements	MRA
相互通信	Xiānghù tōngxìn	Inter-communication	
相加-比较-选择，加选比	Xiāngjiā-bǐjiào-xuǎnzé, jiā xuǎn bǐ	Add-compare-select	ACS

相交区	Xiāngjiāoqū	Intersection	
相控阵	Xiàngkòng zhèn	Phase-controlled array	
相控阵干扰机	Xiàngkòng zhèn gānrǎojī	Phased array jammer	
相控阵馈电网络	Xiàngkòng zhèn kuìdiàn wǎngluò	Feed network for phase controlled array	
相控阵雷达	Xiàngkòng zhèn léidá	Phased array radar	
相控阵天线	Xiàngkòng zhèn tiānxiàn	Phased array antenna	
相控阵天线	Xiàngkòng zhèn tiānxiàn	Phase-controlled array antenna	
相联处理机计算系统	Xiānglián chǔlǐjī jìsuàn xìtǒng	Associative processor computer system	APCS
相联通道信号传输	Xiānglián tōngdào xìnhào chuánshū	Channel associated signaling	CAS
相连阵列处理机	Xiānglián zhènliè chǔlǐjī	Associative array processor	AAP
向量	Xiàngliàng	Vector (in Java)	
向量标识符	Xiàngliàng biāozhì fú	Vector identifier	VI
向量长度	Xiàngliàng chángdù	Vector length	VL
向量处理单元	Xiàngliàng chǔlǐ dānyuán	Vector processing element	VPE
向量处理单元	Xiàngliàng chǔlǐ dānyuán	Vector processing unit	VPU
向量符号集	Xiàngliàng fúhào jí	Vector symbol set	VSS
向量几何特征	Xiàngliàng jǐhé tèzhēng	Vector geometry	
向量排列单元	Xiàngliàng páiliè dānyuán	Vector permutate unit	VPU
向量算术逻辑单元	Xiàngliàng suànshù luóji dānyuán	Vector arithmetic logic unit	VALU
向量纹理压缩	Xiàngliàng wénlǐ yāsuō	Vector-quantization texture compression	VQTC
向量中断机构	Xiàngliàng zhōngduàn jīgòu	Vector interrupt mechanism	VIM
向量字库	Xiàngliàng zìkù	Vector font	
向量最优化问题	Xiàngliàng zuìyōuhuà wèntí	Vector optimization problem	VOP
相邻边	Xiānglín biān	Adjacent edge	
相邻顶点	Xiānglín dǐngdiǎn	Adjacent vertex	
相邻节点	Xiānglín jiédiǎn	Adjacent nodes	
相邻频道	Xiānglín píndào	Adjacent channel	C/A, AC
相邻小区	Xiānglín xiǎoqū	Neighboring cell	NCELL
相临小区干扰	Xiānglín xiǎoqū gānrǎo	Adjacent cell interference	ACI
相邻信道	Xiānglín xìndào	Adjacent channel	
相邻信道衰减	Xiānglín xìndào shuāijiǎn	Adjacent channel attenuation	ACA
相邻业务区	Xiānglín yèwù qū	Neighboring service area	
相邻移动接入点	Xiānglín yídòng jiērù diǎn	Neighboring mobile access point	NMAP
相邻站点信息帧	Xiānglín zhàndiǎn xìnxī zhèng	Neighbor information frame	NIF
响铃	Xiǎnglíng	Beep	
项目	Xiàngmù	Project	
项目承办单位	Xiàngmù chéngbàn dānwèi	Project undertaking organization	
项目交付	Xiàngmù jiāofù	Project delivery (CMM term)	PD
项目启动申请	Xiàngmù qǐdòng shēnqǐng	Project initiation request (CMM)	PIR
项目协调组	Xiàngmù xiétiáo zǔ	Project coordination group	PCG
项目主管	Xiàngmù zhǔguǎn	Project authority (CMM)	PA
香农	Xiāng-nóng	Shannon (Claude Shannon, a pioneer of digital communications)	
橡皮	Xiàngpí	Rubber	
橡皮拉伸	Xiàngpí lāshēn	Rubber sheeting	
相片传真	Xiàngpiàn chuánzhēn	Photo facsimile	
相片光碟	Xiàngpiàn guāngdié	Photo compact disk	

相片绘图仪	Xiàngpiàn huìtúyí	Photoplotter (in SMT)	
相片用化学药品	Xiàngpiàn-yòng huàxué yàopǐn	Photographic chemical	
相频特性	Xiàngpín tèxìng	Phase-frequency characteristic	
像频抑制比	Xiàngpín yìzhì bǐ	Image frequency rejection ratio	
相频一致性	Xiàngpín yīzhìxìng	Phase-frequency equalization	
镶嵌电报	Xiāngqiàn diànbào	Mosaic telegraphy	
向前读	Xiàngqián dú	Read-ahead (in SAMBA)	
向前验证	Xiàngqián yànzhèng	Forward validation	FV
相容方式	Xiāngróng fāngshì	Compatibility mode	CM
相扫	Xiàngsǎo	Phase-sweep	
相似性	Xiāngsìxìng	Affinity	
相似性变换	Xiāngsìxìng biànhuàn	Similarity transformation	
相似形法则	Xiāngsìxíng fǎzé	Scaling law	
相似性分析	Xiāngsìxìng fenxī	Similarity analysis	
相似性检索	Xiāngsìxìng jiǎnsuǒ	Similarity retrieval	
像素	Xiàngsù	Pixel	
相速	Xiàngsù	Phase velocity	
象素地址	Xiàngsù dìzhǐ	Pixel address	PA
像素间距	Xiàngsù jiānjù	Pixel spacing	
像素填充率	Xiàngsù tiánchōng lǜ	Pixel fill rate (measured in Mpix/sec)	
像素阵列	Xiàngsù zhènliè	Pixel array	
像素走向	Xiàngsù zǒuxiàng	Pixel path	
相同寻呼间帧数	Xiāngtóng xúnhū-jiān zhèng shù	Number of frames between Similar pages	
向外访问	Xiàngwài fǎngwèn	Outgoing access	OA
相位	Xiàngwèi	Phase (of a signal)	γ, φ
相位变换器	Xiàngwèi biànhuànqì	Phase changer (in a transmission line)	
相位编码	Xiàngwèi biānmǎ	Phase encoding	PE
相位编码扩展频谱调制	Xiàngwèi biānmǎ kuòzhǎn pínpǔ tiáozhì	Phase-coded spread-spectrum modulation	PCSSM
相位编码扩展频谱信号	Xiàngwèi biānmǎ kuòzhǎn pínpǔ xìnhào	Phase-coded spread-spectrum signal	PCSS
相位编码脉冲压缩	Xiàngwèi biānmǎ màichōng yāsuō	Phase-coded pulse compression	
相位比较正弦移频键控	Xiàngwèi bǐjiào zhèngxián yípín jiànkòng	Phase comparison sinusoidal frequency shift keying	PCSFSK
相位不连续性	Xiàngwèi bùliánxùxìng	Phase discontinuity	
相位差板	Xiàngwèi chà bǎn	Phase shift layer	
相位抖动	Xiàngwèi dǒudòng	Phase jitter	
相位对消器	Xiàngwèi duìxiāoqì	Phase canceller	
相位方向图	Xiāngwèi fāngxiàng tú	Phase pattern	
相位方向图的数学表达式	Xiàngwèi fāngxiàng túde shùxué biǎodá shì	Phase pattern (mathematical representation)	
相位方向图的图示法	Xiàngwèi fāngxiàng túde túshìfǎ	Phase pattern (graphical representation)	
相位幅度失真	Xiāngwèi fúdù shīzhēn	Phase/amplitude distortion	
相位干涉	Xiàngwèi gānshè	Phase interference	
相位关系	Xiàngwèi guānxi	Phase relationship	
相位鉴别	Xiàngwèi jiànbié	Phase discrimination	
相位检波器	Xiàngwèi jiǎnbōqì	Phase detector	
相位解调	Xiàngwèi jiětiáo	Phase demodulation	
相位均衡	Xiàngwèi jūnhéng	Phase equalization	

相位控制	Xiàngwèi kòngzhì	Phase control	
相位量化	Xiàngwèi liànghuà	Phase quantization	
相位连续载波带	Xiàngwèi liánxù zàibō dài	Phase continuous carrier band	
相位偏移	Xiàngwèi piānyí	Phase deviation	
相位频率失真	Xiàngwèi pínlǜ shīzhēn	Phase/frequency distortion	
相位频率特性	Xiāngwèi pínlǜ tèxìng	Phase/frequency characteristic	
相位谱	Xiàngwèi pǔ	Phase spectrum	
相位扫描雷达	Xiàngwèi sǎomiáo léidá	Phase-scanned radar	
相位舍位	Xiàngwèi shèwèi	Phase truncation	
相位舍位误差信号	Xiàngwèi shèwèi wùchā xìnhào	Phase truncation error signal	
相位失真	Xiàngwèi shīzhēn	Phase distortion	
相位失真校正	Xiàngwèi shīzhēn jiàozhèng	Phase distortion correction	
相位瞬变响应	Xiàngwèi shùnbiàn xiǎngyìng	Phase transient response	
相位速度	Xiàngwèi sùdù	Phase velocity	
相位锁定本地振荡器	Xiàngwèi suǒdìng běndì zhèndàngqì	Phase-locked local oscillator	
相位态低电子驱动存储器	Xiàngwèi tài dīdiànzǐ qūdòng cúnchǔqì	Phase-state low electron (hole)-number drive memory	PLEDM
相位特征	Xiàngwèi tèzhēng	Phase characteristics	
相位调制	Xiàngwèi tiáozhì	Phase modulation	PM
相位调制灵敏度	Xiàngwèi tiáozhì língmǐndù	Phase modulated sensitivity	
相位相干	Xiàngwèi xiānggān	Phase coherence	PC
相位相干载波带	Xiàngwèi xiānggān zàibō dài	Phase coherent carrier band	
相位系数	Xiàngwèi xìshù	Phase coefficient	
相位修改同步协议	Xiàngwèi xiūgǎi tóngbù xiéyì	Phase modification synchronization (in CORBA)	PM
相位一致性	Xiàngwèi yīzhìxìng	Phase equalization	
相位噪声	Xiàngwèi zàoshēng	Phase noise	
相位噪声功率谱密度	Xiàngwèi zàoshēng gōnglǜ pǔ mìdù	Phase noise power spectrum density	
相位阵控制电子设备	Xiàngwèi zhèn kòngzhì diànzǐ shèbèi	Phased array control electronics	PACE
相位阵列雷达	Xiàngwèi zhènliè léidá	Phased array radar	
相位中心	Xiàngwèi zhōngxīn	Phase center	
详细流程图	Xiángxì liúchéngtú	Detail flowchart	DFC
详细视图	Xiángxì shìtú	Details view	
向下辐射	Xiàngxià fúshè	Downward radiation	
向下规模化	Xiàngxià guīmóhuà	Downsizing	
向下兼容	Xiàngxià jiānróng	Downward compatible	
向下兼容	Xiàngxià jiānróng	Backward compatible	
向下调整	Xiàngxià tiáozhěng	Downward regulation	
相移	Xiāngyí	Phase shift	
相移常数	Xiāngyí chángshù	Phase-shift constant	
相移键控	Xiàngyí jiànkòng	Phase-shift keying	PSK
相移相干振荡器	Xiàngyí xiānggān zhèndàngqì	Phase-shift coherent oscillator	
相移中心天线	Xiàngyí zhōngxīn tiānxiàn	Displaced phase center antenna	DPCA
响应(原语)	Xiǎngyìng (yuányǔ)	Response (primitive)	
响应标识符	Xiǎngyìng biāozhìfú	Response identifier	RI
响应单元	Xiǎngyìng dānyuán	Response unit (in IDS)	
响应分析	Xiǎngyìng fēnxī	Response analysis	
响应频谱	Xiǎngyìng pínpǔ	Response spectrum	

响应请求	Xiǎngyìng qǐngqiú	Response request	
响应时间近似变换	Xiǎngyìng shíjiān jìnsì biànhuàn	Response time approximation	RTA
响应修正系数	Xiǎngyìng xiūzhèng xìshù	Response modification factor	
响应中心	Xiǎngyìng zhōngxīn	Response center	
响应周期	Xiǎngyìng zhōuqī	Request cycle	
像元分辨率	Xiàngyuán fēnbiànlǜ	Cell resolution	
像元码	Xiàngyuán mǎ	Cell code (video term)	
线弧	Xiànhú	Bank (of a selector)	
线划平滑	Xiànhuà pínghuá	Line smoothing	
线划拼接	Xiànhuà pīnjiē	Line snapping	
线划细划	Xiànhuà xìhuà	Line thinning	
线划增强	Xiànhuà zēngqiáng	Line enhancement	
县级处理中心	Xiànjí chǔlǐ zhōngxīn	County level branch (of the financial network)	CLB
线间侵入	Xiàn-jiān qīnrù	Between-the-lines entry (IPsec)	
先进	Xiānjìn	Advanced, modern	
现金到财户	Xiànjīn dào cáihù	Cash to account	
现金到现金	Xiànjīn dào xiànjīn	Cash to cash	
现金汇款	Xiànjīn huìkuǎn	Remitting in cash	
先进加密标准	Xiānjìn jiāmì biāozhǔn	Advanced encryption standard	AES
先进技术存储	Xiānjìn jìshù cúnchǔ	Advanced technology storage	ADTX
先进流媒体格式	Xiānjìn liúméitǐ géshi	Advanced streaming (media) format	ASF
先进声信号处理器	Xiānjìn shēng xìnhào chǔlǐqì	Advanced acoustic signal processor	AASP
先进设置和电源管理	Xiānjìn shèzhì hé diànyuán guǎnlǐ	Advanced configuration and power interface	ACPI
先进数据通信规程	Xiānjìn shùjù tōngxìn guīchéng	Advanced data communications procedure	ADCCP
先进通信功能	Xiānjìn tōngxìn gōngnéng	Advanced communications function	ACF
先进寻呼操作码	Xiānjìn xúnhū cāozuòmǎ	Advanced paging operator code	APOC
先进研究计划局	Xiānjìn yánjiū jìhuàjú	Advanced Research Project Agency	ARPA
先进移动安全体系结构	Xiānjìn yídòng ānquán tǐxì jiégòu	Advanced mobile security architecture	AMSA
先进移动电话业务	Xiānjìn yídòng diànhuà yèwù	Advanced mobile phone service	AMPS
先进音频编码	Xiānjìn yīnpín biānmǎ	Advanced audio coding	AAC
先进的电子商务通信平台	Xiānjìnde diànzǐ shāngwù tōngxìn píngtái	E-business advanced communication platform	EACP
先进的加密系统	Xiānjìnde jiāmì xìtǒng	Advanced encryption system	AES
先进的同层互联网	Xiānjìnde tóngcéng hùliánwǎng	Advanced peer-to-peer internetworking	APPI
先进的同层通信	Xiānjìnde tóngcéng tōngxìn	Advanced peer-to-peer communications	APPC
先进的通信技术业务	Xiānjìnde tōngxìn jìshù yèwù	Advanced communication technologies and services	ATCS
先进的移动电话系统	Xiānjìnde yídòng diànhuà xìtǒng	Advanced mobile phone system	AMPS
先进的移动宽带应用系统	Xiānjìnde yídòng kuāndài yìngyòng xìtǒng	System for advanced mobile broadband applications	SAMBA
先进的语音呼叫项目	Xiānjìnde yǔyīn hūjiào xiàngmù	Advanced speech call items	ASCI
陷阱	Xiànjǐng	Trap	
线卡到交换机	Xiànkǎ dào jiāohuànjī	Line card to switch	LCS
线缆服务接口数据规格	Xiànlǎn fúwù jiēkǒu shùjù guīgé	Data over cable service interface specifications	DOCSIS
线缆调制解调器终端系统	Xiànlǎn tiáozhì jiětiáoqì zhōngduān xìtǒng	Cable MODEM termination system	CMTS
限流保护	Xiànliú bǎohù	Current-limiting protection	
限流电路	Xiànliú diànlù	Limited current circuit	
限流装置	Xiànliú zhuāngzhì	Current limiting device	

线路	Xiànlù	Circuit, line, route	
线路保持	Xiànlù bǎochí	Short-hold (ISDN term)	
线路编码类型	Xiànlù biānmǎ lèixíng	Line code type	
线路不工作信号	Xiànlù bùgōngzuò xìnhào	Line-out-of-service signal	LOS
线路测试模块	Xiànlù cèshì mókuài	Line test block	LTB
线路代理	Xiànlù dàilǐ	Circuit proxy	
线路单元	Xiànlù dānyuán	Line unit	LU
线路打印机监控	Xiànlù dǎyìnjī jiānkòng	Line printer daemon	
线路电长度变换器	Xiànlù diànchángdù biànhuànqì	Line lengthener	
线路 E1 接口链路集成件	Xiànlù E1 jiēkǒu liànlù jíchéngjiàn	Line interface E1 link assembly	LIEA
线路放大器	Xiànlù fàngdàqì	Line amplifier	LA
线路分配命令	Xiànlù fēnpèi mìnglìng	Circuit allocation order	CAO
线路符号速率	Xiànlù fúhào sùlǜ	Line symbol rate	
线路负荷控制	Xiànlù fùhè kòngzhì	Line-load control	
线路光放大器	Xiànlù guāng fàngdàqì	Optical line amplifier	OLA
线路故障	Xiànlù gùzhàng	Line fault	
线路和中继通路	Xiànlù hé zhōngjì tōnglù	Line and trunk access	LTA
线路和中继通路子系统	Xiànlù hé zhōngjì tōnglù zixìtǒng	Line and trunk access sub-system	LTAS
线路交换声	Xiànlù jiāohuàn shēng	Circuit switched voice	CSV
线路交换数字电路	Xiànlù jiāohuàn shùzì diànlù	Circuit switched digital circuitry	CSDC
线路接口电路	Xiànlù jiēkǒu diànlù	Line interface circuit	LIC
线路接口模块	Xiànlù jiēkǒu mókuài	Line interface module	LIM
线路接口耦合器	Xiànlù jiēkǒu ǒuhéqì	Line interface coupler	LIC
线路接入点	Xiànlù jiērùdiǎn	Line access point	
线路激活	Xiànlù jīhuó	Line activation	
线路集线器模块	Xiànlù jíxiànqì mókuài	Line concentrator module	LCM
线路集中器	Xiànlù jízhōngqì	Line concentrator	
线路卡控制	Xiànlù kǎ kòngzhì	Line card control	LCC
线路扩展模块	Xiànlù kuòzhǎn mókuài	Line expansion module	LEM
线路拉伸器	Xiànlù lāshēnqì	Line stretcher	
线路链路	Xiànlù liànlù	Line link	
线路码	Xiànlù mǎ	Line code	
线路启用命令	Xiànlù qǐyòng mìnglìng	Circuit activation order	CAO
线路驱动器	Xiànlù qūdòngqì	Line driver	
线路识别	Xiànlù shíbié	Line identity	LI
线路释放完成	Xiànlù shìfàng wánchéng	Release complete	RLC
线路释放消息	Xiànlù shìfàng xiāoxi	Line release message	REL
线路时钟	Xiànlù shízhōng	Route clock	RCLK
线路衰减	Xiànlù shuāijiǎn	Line attenuation	
线路瞬时抑制	Xiànlù shùnshí yìzhì	Line transient suppression	LTS
线路数字速率	Xiànlù shùzì sùlǜ	Line digital rate	
线路 T1 接口链路集成件	Xiànlù T1 jiēkǒu liànlù jíchéngjiàn	Line interface T1 link assembly	LITA-A/D
线路调整	Xiànlù tiáozhěng	Line conditioning	
线路信号	Xiànlù xìnhào	Line signal	
线路信令	Xiànlù xìnlìng	Line signaling	
线路映射	Xiànlù yìngshè	Wire map	

线路终端	Xiànlù zhōngduān	Line termination	LT
线路终端	Xiànlù zhōngduān	Line terminal	LT
线路终端设备	Xiànlù zhōngduān shèbèi	Line termination equipment	LT
线路终接	Xiànlù zhōngjiē	Line termination	LT
线路状态信号	Xiànlù zhuàngtài xìnhào	Line status signaling	
线路转接数据网络	Xiànlù zhuǎnjiē shùjù wǎngluò	Circuit-switched data network	CSDN
线路阻抗稳定网络	Xiànlù zǔkàng wěndìng wǎngluò	Line impedance stability network	LISN
陷门	Xiànmén	Trapdoor (computer hacking)	
线谱	Xiànpǔ	Line spectrum	
先前速率	Xiānqián sùlǜ	Previous rate	
线圈骨架	Xiànquān gǔjià	Coil rack, bobbin	
线圈炮	Xiànquān páo	Coil gun	
线上	Xiànshàng	On-line	
线上美国	Xiànshàng Měiguó	America Online ® (US company)	AOL
线上实时控制	Xiànshàng shíshí kòngzhì	On-line real-time control	
显示	Xiǎnshì	Display, (computer) monitor	
显示表格线	Xiǎnshì biǎogé xiàn	Show table grid (WP command)	
显示并行指令代码	Xiǎnshì bìngxíng zhǐlìng dàimǎ	Explicitly parallel instruction code	EPIC
显示菜单	Xiǎnshì càidān	View menu (WP command)	
显示地址	Xiǎnshì dìzhǐ	Explicit addressing	
显示发生软件	Xiǎnshì fāshēng ruǎnjiàn	Display generating software	DGS
显式呼叫转接	Xiǎnshì hūjiào zhuǎnjiē	Explict call transfer	ECT
显示计划	Xiǎnshì jìhuà	Show plan	
显示技术	Xiǎnshì jìshù	Display technology	
显示控制功能	Xiǎnshì kòngzhì gōngnéng	Presentation control functions	
显示控制台	Xiǎnshì kòngzhìtái	Display console	DC
显式率	Xiǎnshì lǜ	Explicit rate	ER
显示路由	Xiǎnshì lùyóu	Explicit routing	
显示面板	Xiǎnshì miànbǎn	Display panel	
显示能源管理信号	Xiǎnshì néngyuán guǎnlǐ xìnhào	Display power management signalling	DPMS
显示前向拥塞指示	Xiǎnshì qiánxiàng yōngsè zhǐshì	Explicit forward congestion indication	EFCI
显式前向拥塞指示符	Xiǎnshì qiánxiàng yōngsè zhǐshìfú	Explicit forward congestion indicator	EFCI
显式前向阻塞指示	Xiǎnshì qiánxiàng zǔsè zhǐshì	Explicit forward congestion indication	EFCI
显式事务	Xiǎnshì shìwù	Explicit transaction (for database)	
显示数据通道	Xiǎnshì shùjù tōngdào	Display data channel (video term)	DDC
显式特化	Xiǎnshì tèhuà	Explicit specialization	
显式拓扑记述	Xiǎnshì tuòpū jìshù	Explicit topological description	
限时消息	Xiànshí xiāoxi	Limited time message	
显示拥塞指标	Xiǎnshì yōngsè zhībiāo	Explicit congestion notification	ECN
显式正向阻塞通知	Xiǎnshì zhèngxiàng zǔsè tōngzhī	Forward explicit congestion notification	FECN
显示支援软件	Xiǎnshì zhīyuán ruǎnjiàn	Display support software	DSS
显示转换	Xiǎnshì zhuǎnhuàn	Explicit conversion	
显示器	Xiǎnshìqì	Graphic display	
显示器电磁屏蔽	Xiǎnshìqì diàncí píngbì	Monitor electromagnetic screening	
线速	Xiànsù	Wire speed	
限速	Xiànsù	Speed restrictions	

线速交换路由器	Xiànsù jiāohuàn lùyóuqì	Line-speed switch router	
线索	Xiànsuǒ	Line searching	
线索二叉树	Xiànsuǒ èrchā shù	Threaded binary tree	
闲谈频道	Xiántán píndào	Chat channel	
线条图	Xiàntiáo tú	Bar graph	
纤维缠线	Xiānwéi chánxiàn	Filament winding	
纤维光缆	Xiānwéi guānglǎn	Fiber optic cable	FOC
纤维光学	Xiānwéi guāngxué	Fiber optics	
纤维光学环行器	Xiānwéi guāngxué huánxíngqì	Fiber optic circulator	
纤维光学连接器	Xiānwéi guāngxué liánjiēqì	Fiber optics connector	
纤维光学连接器分类	Xiānwéi guāngxué liánjiēqì fènlèi	Fiber optics connector classification	
纤维光学每周新闻简报服务	Xiānwéi guāngxué měizhōu xīnwén jiǎnbào fúwù	Weekly Fiberoptics Newsbrief Service (from KMI - Kinder Morgan Inc.)	FNB
纤维光学市场情报	Xiānwéi guāngxué shìchǎng qíngbào	Fiberoptics Marketing Intelligence (from KMI - Kinder Morgan Inc.)	FMI
纤维光学市场研究服务	Xiānwéi guāngxué shìchǎng yánjiū fúwù	Fiberoptics Market Research Service (from KMI - Kinder Morgan Inc.)	FMRS
显微镜浸液	Xiǎnwēijìng jìnyè	Microscope immersion liquid	
显微镜埋置用材料	Xiǎnwēijìng máizhìyòng cáiliào	Microscope imbedding media	
显现	Xiǎnxiàn	Presentation	
显现媒体	Xiǎnxiàn méitǐ	Presentation medium	
显现面	Xiǎnxiàn miàn	Presentation surface	
显现式样	Xiǎnxiàn shìyàng	Presentation style	
显现元素	Xiǎnxiàn yuánsù	Presentation element	
现象波动	Xiànxiàng bōdòng	Phenomenon fluctuation	
现象综合	Xiànxiàng zōnghé	Phenomenon generalization	
纤芯	Xiānxīn	Fiber core	
线心矩阵	Xiànxīn jǔzhèn	Wire-core matrix	WCM
线性变换	Xiànxìng biànhuàn	Linear transform	
线性表	Xiànxìng biǎo	Linear list	
线性参照系统	Xiànxìng cānzhào xìtǒng	Linear referencing system	
线性查找	Xiànxìng cházhǎo	Linear search	
线性插值	Xiànxìng chāzhí	Linear interpolation	
线性充电	Xiànxìng chōngdiàn	Linear charging	
线性电路	Xiànxìng diànlù	Linear circuit	
线性电路测试接口	Xiànxìng diànlù cèshì jiēkǒu	Line and circuit test interface	LCTI
线性低密聚乙烯	Xiànxìng dīmì jùyǐxī	Linear low density polyethylene	LLDPE
线形定位系统	Xiànxíng dìngwèi xìtǒng	Linear positioning system	
线性方程组	Xiànxìng fāngchéngzǔ	Linear equation	
线性放大器	Xiànxìng fàngdàqì	Linear amplifier	
现行反馈移位寄存器	Xiànxíng fǎnkuì yíwèi jìcúnqì	Linear feedback shift register	LFSR
线性分叉复用器	Xiànxìng fēnchā fùyòngqì	Linear add/drop multiplexer	LADM
线性分组码	Xiànxìng fēnzǔ mǎ	Linear block code	
线性复杂度曲线	Xiànxìng fùzádù qǔxiàn	Linear complexity profile	
线性功率放大器架子	Xiànxìng gōnglǜ fàngdàqì jiàzi	Linear power amplifier shelf	LPAS
线性功率放大器机架	Xiànxìng gōnglǜ fàngdàqì jījià	Linear power amplifier rack	LPAR
线型光速火焰探测器	Xiànxíng guāngsù huǒyàn tàncèqì	Optical beam flame detector	OBFD
线性规划	Xiànxìng guīhuà	Linear programming	

线性过滤	Xiànxìng guòlǜ	Linear filtering	LF
线性回归	Xiànxìng huíguī	Linear regression	
线性检波	Xiànxìng jiǎnbō	Linear detection	
线型检光元件	Xiànxíng jiǎnguāng yuánjiàn	Linear detector array	
线性集成电路	Xiànxìng jíchéng diànlù	Linear integrated circuit	
线性激动器	Xiànxìng jīdòngqì	Linear actuator	
线性结构	Xiànxìng jiégòu	Linear structure	
线性解调	Xiànxìng jiětiáo	Linear demodulation	
线性近似	Xiànxìng jìnsì	Linear approximation	
线形控制系统	Xiànxíng kòngzhì xìtǒng	Linear control system	
线性链表	Xiànxìng liàn biǎo	Linear linked list	
线性滤波器	Xiànxìng lǜbōqì	Linear filter	
线型码	Xiànxíng mǎ	Line coding	
线性脉码调制	Xiànxìng màimǎ tiáozhì	Pulse code modulation-linear	PCM-LIN
线性密码分析	Xiànxìng mìmǎ fēnxī	Linear cryptanalysis	
线性模拟控制	Xiànxìng mónǐ kòngzhì	Linear analog control	
线形偏转速度	Xiànxíng piānzhuǎn sùdù	Linear deflection speed	
线性频率调制	Xiànxìng pínlǜ tiáozhì	Linear frequency modulation	LFM
先行取指令	Xiānxíng qǔ zhǐlìng	Advanced fetch	
线性时序逻辑	Xiànxìng shíxù luóji	Linear temporal logic	LTL
线性失真	Xiànxìng shīzhēn	Linear distortion	
线性失真校正	Xiànxìng shīzhēn jiàozhèng	Linear distortion correction	
现行数据位	Xiànxíng shùjù wèi	Current data bit	CDB
线性数字调制	Xiànxìng shùzì tiáozhì	Linear digital modulation	
线性天线阵	Xiànxìng tiānxiàn zhèn	Linear array antenna	LAA
线性调频	Xiànxìng tiáopín	Linear frequency modulation (FM)	
线性调频	Xiànxìng tiáopín	Linear frequency modulation	
线性调频脉冲压缩	Xiànxìng tiáopín màichōng yāsuō	Linear frequency modulation (FM) pulse compression	
线性调制	Xiànxìng tiáozhì	Linear modulation	
线性调制信号	Xiànxìng tiáozhì xìnhào	Linear modulated signal	
线型调制器	Xiànxíng tiáozhìqì	Line modulator	
线性突发	Xiànxìng tūfā	Linear burst	
线性网络	Xiànxìng wǎngluò	Linear network	
线性稳压器	Xiànxìng wěnyāqì	Linear voltage regulator	
线性误差校正码	Xiànxìng wùchā jiàozhèng mǎ	Linear error correcting code	LECC
线性相码调制	Xiànxìng xiàngmǎ tiáozhì	Linear phase code modulation	LPCM
线性预测	Xiànxìng yùcè	Linear prediction	
线性预测编码	Xiànxìng yùcè biānmǎ	Linear predictive coding	LPC
线性预测编码	Xiànxìng yùcè biānmǎ	Linear predictive code	LPC
线性预测残差-基音周期波形	Xiànxìng yùcè cánchā—jīyīn zhōuqī bōxíng	Linear predictive residual - pitch-cycle waveform	LPR-PCW
线性预测声码器	Xiànxìng yùcè shēngmǎqì	Linear prediction vocoder	
线性预测系数	Xiànxìng yùcè xìshù	Linear prediction coefficient	LP
线性增量调制	Xiànxìng zēngliàng tiáozhì	Linear delta modulation	LDM
线性振动	Xiànxìng zhèndòng	Linear vibration	
线性阵列天线	Xiànxìng zhènliè tiānxiàn	Linear array antenna	LAA
线性致动器	Xiànxìng zhìdòngqì	Linear actuator	

线性转发器	Xiànxìng zhuǎnfāqì	Linear transponder	
线性最小方差估计	Xiànxìng zuìxiǎo fāngchà gūjì	Linear minimum variance estimation	
先序遍历	Xiānxù biànlì	Preorder traversal	
现役	Xiànyì	Active, ad hoc	
现有质量的电视	Xiànyǒu zhìliàngde diànshì	Existing-quality television	
显著周期	Xiǎnzhe zhōuqī	Predominant period	
线阵试验	Xiànzhèn shìyàn	Linear array test	
线阵天线	Xiànzhèn tiānxiàn	Linear array antenna	
闲置	Xiánzhì	Idle	
限值	Xiànzhí	Limit value	
限制	Xiànzhì	Constraints	
限值测试	Xiànzhí cèshì	Limit test	
限制等级	Xiànzhì děngjí	Restriction level (in SS7)	RL
限制区	Xiànzhì qū	Restricted area	
限制通行	Xiànzhì tōngxíng	Passing restrictions	
闲置信号单元	Xiánzhì xìnhào dānyuán	Idle signal unit	IDU
限制子等级	Xiànzhì ziděngjí	Restriction sub-level (in SS7)	RSL
限制的数字信息	Xiànzhìde shùzì xìnxī	Restricted digital information	RDI
线状比例尺	Xiànzhuàng bǐlìchǐ	Scale bar	
线状符号	Xiànzhuàng fúhào	Line symbol	
线状解译	Xiànzhuàng jiěyì	Linear interpretation	
线状图	Xiànzhuàng tú	Line map	
小办公室/家庭办公室	Xiǎo bàngōngshì/Jiātíng bàngōngshì	Small office/home office	SOHO
小插接力	Xiǎo chājiēlì	Low insertion force	LIF
小幅度摆动差动信号	Xiǎo fúdù bǎidòng chādòng xìnhào	Reduced swing differential signal	RSDS
小服务程序	Xiǎo fúwù chéngxù	Servlet	
小环路	Xiǎo huánlù	Looplet	
小世界网络	Xiǎo shìjiè wǎngluò	Small World Networks	
小甜饼	Xiǎo tiánbǐng	Cookie	
小卫星地球站	Xiǎo wèixīng dìqiúzhàn	Mini-satellite earth station	XWD
小信号增益	Xiǎo xìnhào zēngyì	Small-signal gain	
小信号增益波长变化	Xiǎo xìnhào zēngyì bōcháng biànhuà	Small-signal gain wavelength variation	
小信号增益波长带宽	Xiǎo xìnhào zēngyì bōcháng dàikuān	Small-signal gain wavelength bandwidth	
小信号增益稳定性	Xiǎo xìnhào zēngyì wěndìngxìng	Small-signal gain stability	
小应用程序	Xiǎo yìngyòng chéngxù	Applet (computer mini-program)	
消边聚合	Xiāobiān jùhé	Eliminating-edge aggregation (CAD/CAM)	
小波	Xiǎobō	Wavelet	
削波	Xiāobō	Clipping	
小波包	Xiǎobō bāo	Wavelet packet	WP
小波变换	Xiǎobō biànhuàn	Wavelet transform	
小波分解	Xiǎobō fēnjiě	Wavelet decomposition	
小波数据的形态学表示	Xiǎobo shùjùde xíngtàixué biǎoshì	Morphological representation of wavelet data	MRWD
削波器	Xiāobōqì	Clipper	
消侧音电路	Xiāocèyīn diànlù	Anti-sidetone circuit	
消除	Xiāochú	Purge (IPsec), erasure	
消除迂回路由	Xiāochú yūhuí lùyóu	Alternative route cancel	ARC

消磁电压敏电阻器	Xiāocí diànyā mǐn diànzǔqì	Anti-magnetized varistor	
小额支付传输协议	Xiǎo'é zhīfù chuánshū xiéyì	Micro payment transfer protocol	MPTP
消防自动化	Xiāofáng zìdònghuà	Fire automation	
消费电子	Xiāofèi diànzǐ	Consumer electronics	
消费者电子制造业协会	Xiāofèizhě diànzǐ zhìzàoyè xiéhuì	Consumer Electronics Manufacturing Association	CEMA
消费者数字订阅线路	Xiāofèizhě shùzì dìngyuè xiànlù	Consumer digital subscriber line	CDSL
消光比	Xiāoguāng bǐ	Extinction ratio	
小规模集成	Xiǎoguīmó jíchéng	Small scale integrated circuit	SSIC
效果	Xiàoguǒ	Effect	
销毁	Xiāohuǐ	Destroy	
消火栓	Xiāohuǒshuān	Fire hydrant	FH
消极确认	Xiāojí quèrèn	Negative acknowledge	NAK
消喀呖音电路	Xiāokā-lìyīn diànlù	Anti-click circuit	
小客户控制协议	Xiǎokèhù kòngzhì xiéyì	Skinny client control protocol (Cisco use)	SCCP
笑脸符号	Xiàoliǎn fúhào	Smiley ☺, :-)	
效率	Xiàolǜ	Efficiency	
小面阵试验	Xiǎomiàn zhèn shìyàn	Partial array test	
效能评测器	Xiàonéng píngcè qì	Profiler	
消球差透镜	Xiāoqiúchā tòujing	Aplanatic lens	
小区	Xiǎoqū	Cell (mobile telephone coverage area)	
小区（频率）分配	Xiǎoqū (pínlǜ) fēnpèi	Cell (frequency) allocation	CA
小区标识号	Xiǎoqū biāozhì hào	Cell identity	CI
小区重先偏置	Xiǎoqū chóngxiān piānzhì	Cell reselection offset	CRO
小区重选偏移量	Xiǎoqū chóngxuǎn piānyí liáng	Cell re-select offset	CRO
小区重选滞后	Xiǎoqū chóngxuǎn zhìhòu	Cell re-selection blocking	
小区重选滞后参数	Xiǎoqū chóngxuǎn zhìhòu cānshù	Cell re-selection hysteresis parameter	
小区存取允许	Xiǎoqū cúnqǔ yǔnxǔ	Cell access permission	
小区短消息广播	Xiǎoqū duǎnxiāoxi guǎngbō	Cell short message broadcasting	
小区分配	Xiǎoqū fēnpèi	Cell allocation (GSM term)	
小区覆盖范围	Xiǎoqū fùgài fànwéi	Cell coverage area	
小区告警集成件	Xiǎoqū gàojǐng jíchéng jiàn	Cell site alarm assembly	CSAA
小区广播	Xiǎoqū guǎngbō	Cell broadcast	CB
小区广播短消息	Xiǎoqū guǎngbō duǎnxiāoxi	Cell broadcast short message	CBSM
小区广播短消息业务	Xiǎoqū guǎngbō duǎnxiāoxi yèwù	Cell broadcast short message service	CBSMS
小区广播短消息中心	Xiǎoqū guǎngbō duǎnxiāoxi zhōngxīn	Cell broadcast center	CBC
小区广播控制信道	Xiǎoqū guǎngbō kòngzhì xìndào	Cell broadcast control channel	CBCH
小区广播实体	Xiǎoqū guǎngbō shítǐ	Cell broadcast entity	CBE
小区广播消息识别符	Xiǎoqū guǎngbō xiāoxi shíbiéfú	Cell broadcast message identifier	CBMI
小区广播信道	Xiǎoqū guǎngbō xìndào	Cell broadcast channel	
小区广播业务	Xiǎoqū guǎngbō yèwù	Cell broadcast service	CBS
小区广播中心	Xiǎoqū guǎngbō zhōngxīn	Cell broadcast center	CBC
小区划	Xiǎoqū huà	Micro-zoning	
小区间的越区切换	Xiǎoqū jiānde yuèqū qiēhuàn	Inter-cell handover	
小区接入节点	Xiǎoqū jiērù jiédiǎn	Zone access node	ZAN
小区禁止限制	Xiǎoqū jìnzhǐ xiànzhì	Cell bar qualify	CBQ
小区控制器	Xiǎoqū kòngzhìqì	Cell site controller	CSC

小区描述	Xiǎoqū miáoshù	Cell description	
小区配置	Xiǎoqū pèizhì	Cell allocation	CA
小区全球识别	Xiǎoqū quánqiú shíbié	Cell global identification	CGI
小区身份	Xiǎoqū shēnfen	Cell identity	
小区识别	Xiǎoqū shíbié	Cell identity	CI
小区天线单元	Xiǎoqū tiānxiàn dānyuán	Cell antenna unit	CAU
小区调制解调软件	Xiǎoqū tiáozhì jiětiáo ruǎnjiàn	Cell site modem software	CSMS
小区信道描述	Xiǎoqū xìndào miáoshù	Cell channel description	
小区间切换	Xiǎoqū-jiān qiēhuàn	Inter-cell handover; intercell hand-off	
小区内切换	Xiǎoqū-nèi qiēhuàn	Intra-cell handover ; intra-cell hand-off	
消色差	Xiāosèchā	Achromatic	
啸声	Xiàoshēng	Whistler	
啸声	Xiàoshēng	Whistling (in telecommunications)	
消声室	Xiāoshēng shì	Anechoic chamber	
消声水池	Xiāoshēng shuǐchí	Anechoic tank	
消失距	Xiāoshī jù	Vanishing moment	
小时率	Xiǎoshí lǜ	Hourly rate	
消售包装	Xiāoshòu bāozhuāng	Consumer package	
销售点	Xiāoshòu diǎn	Point of sale	POS
销售点系统	Xiāoshòu diǎn xìtǒng	Point of sale system	POS
销售点终端	Xiāoshòu diǎn zhōngduān	Point of sales	POS
销售确认书	Xiāoshòu quèrènshū	Sales contract	S/C
销售终端机	Xiāoshòu zhōngduānjī	Point of sale machine	
销售自动化	Xiāoshòu zìdònghuà	Sales automation	
消息	Xiāoxi	Message	
消息报头	Xiāoxi bàotóu	Message header	HEADER
消息编号	Xiāoxi biānhào	Message number	
消息标识符	Xiāoxi biāozhìfú	Message identifier	MID
消息差错率	Xiāoxi chācuò lǜ	Message error rate	MER
消息传递部分	Xiāoxi chuándì bùfen	Message transfer part	MTP
消息传递部分第二级对等适配层	Xiāoxi chuándì bùfen dì'èrjí duìděng shìpèi céng	Message transfer protocol 2 (MTP2) peer-to-peer adaptation layer	M2PA
消息传递部分第三级用户适配层	Xiāoxi chuándì bùfen dìsānjí yònghù shìpèi céng	Message transport protocol 3 (MTP3) user adaptation layer	M3UA
消息传递接口	Xiāoxi chuándì jiēkǒu	Message passage interface	
消息传递系统	Xiāoxi chuándì xìtǒng	Messaging system	
消息传递部二层	Xiāoxi chuándìbù èrcéng	Message transfer part level 2 (in SS7)	MTPL2
消息传输部分	Xiāoxi chuánshū bùfen	Message transfer part	MTP
消息传送	Xiāoxi chuánsòng	Message transfer	MT
消息传送部分	Xiāoxi chuánsòng bùfen	Message transfer part	MTP
消息传送代理	Xiāoxi chuánsòng dàilǐ	Message transfer agent	MTA
消息传送服务	Xiāoxi chuánsòng fúwù	Message transfer service	
消息传送服务要素	Xiāoxi chuánsòng fúwù yàosù	Message transfer service element	MTSE
消息传送系统	Xiāoxi chuánsòng xìtǒng	Message transfer system	MTS
消息传送业务	Xiāoxi chuánsòng yèwù	Message transfer service	
消息处理	Xiāoxi chǔlǐ	Message handling	

消息处理服务	Xiāoxi chǔlǐ fúwù	Message handling service	
消息处理环境	Xiāoxi chǔlǐ huánjìng	Message handling environment	
消息处理系统	Xiāoxi chǔlǐ xìtǒng	Message handling system	MHS
消息处理业务	Xiāoxi chǔlǐ yèwù	Message handling service	
消息存储	Xiāoxi cúnchǔ	Message store	MS
消息等待数据	Xiāoxi děngdài shùjù	Message waiting data	MWD
消息等待指示	Xiāoxi děngdài zhǐshì	Message waiting indication	MWI
消息定位表示语	Xiāoxi dìngwèi biǎoshìyǔ	Message alignment indicator	
消息队列	Xiāoxi duìliè	Message queuing	
消息方式	Xiāoxi fāngshì	Message mode	
消息分配	Xiāoxi fēnpèi	Message distribution	
消息格式	Xiāoxi géshi	Message format	
消息管理服务要素	Xiāoxi guǎnlǐ fúwù yàosù	Message administration service element	MASE
消息环	Xiāoxi huán	Message loop	
消息恢复	Xiāoxi huīfù	Message recovery	
消息鉴别	Xiāoxi jiànbié	Message discrimination	
消息鉴权码	Xiāoxi jiànquán mǎ	Message authentication code	MAC
消息检索服务要素	Xiāoxi jiǎnsuǒ fúwù yàosù	Message retrieval service element	MRSE
消息交换	Xiāoxi jiāohuàn	Message switching	
消息校验码	Xiāoxi jiàoyàn mǎ	Message authentication code	MAC
消息结束	Xiāoxi jiéshù	End of message	EOM
消息集群	Xiāoxi jíqún	Message trunking	
消息继续	Xiāoxi jìxù	Continuation of message	COM
消息句法	Xiāoxi jùfǎ	Message syntax	
消息开始	Xiāoxi kāishǐ	Beginning of message	BOM
消息类型	Xiāoxi lèixíng	Message type	
消息路由控制	Xiāoxi lùyóu kòngzhì	Message routing control	
消息路由器	Xiāoxi lùyóuqì	Message router	BMR
消息模式	Xiāoxi móshì	Message mode	
消息认证码	Xiāoxi rènzhèng mǎ	Message authentication code	MAC
消息识别码	Xiāoxi shíbié mǎ	Message identifier	MID
消息顺序表	Xiāoxi shùnxù biǎo	Message sequence chart	MSC
消息输入设备	Xiāoxi shūrù shèbèi	Message entry device	MED
消息提文服务要素	Xiāoxi tíwén fúwù yàosù	Message submission service element	MSSE
消息通信功能	Xiāoxi tōngxìn gōngnéng	Message communications function	MCF
消息通信系统	Xiāoxi tōngxìn xìtǒng	Messaging system	
消息通信系统	Xiāoxi tōngxìn xìtǒng	Messaging system	
消息投递服务要素	Xiāoxi tóudì fúwù yàosù	Message delivery service element	MDSE
消息完整性编码	Xiāoxi wánzhěngxìng biānmǎ	Message integrity code	MIC
消息信号单元	Xiāoxi xìnhào dānyuán	Message signal unit	MSU
消息信令单元	Xiāoxi xìnlìng dānyuán	Message signaling unit	MSU
消息序列表	Xiāoxi xùliè biǎo	Message sequence chart	MSC
消息验证码	Xiāoxi yànzhèng mǎ	Message authentication code	MAC
消息应用程序接口	Xiāoxi yìngyòng chéngxù jiēkǒu	Messaging application programming interface	MAPI
消息摘要	Xiāoxi zhāiyào	Message digest	
消息摘要版本 5	Xiāoxi zhāiyào bǎnběn 5	Message digest version 5	MD5

消息中心	Xiāoxi zhōngxīn	Message center	MC
消息资源保护模式	Xiāoxi zīyuán bǎohù móshì	Message security mode	
小写转换	Xiǎoxiě zhuǎnhuàn	Down-casing	
小写字母	Xiǎoxiě zìmǔ	Lower case	
小型单元耦合型	Xiǎoxíng dānyuán ǒuhéxíng	Miniature unit-coupling (FOC term)	MU
小型点光源	Xiǎoxíng diǎn guāngyuán	Spotlight	
小型电脑系统介面	Xiǎoxíng diànnǎo xìtǒng jièmiàn	Small computer system interface	SCSI
小型光源	Xiǎoxíng guāngyuán	Miniature light source	
小型家庭办公室	Xiǎoxíng jiātíng bàngōngshì	Small office home office	SOHO
小型计算机	Xiǎoxíng jìsuànjī	Minicomputer	
小型计算机系统接口	Xiǎoxíng jìsuànjī xìtǒng jiēkǒu	Small computer system interface	SCSI
小型模拟用户线接口	Xiǎoxíng mónǐ yònghù xiàn jiēkǒu	Compact analog line interface	CALI
小型桥接器	Xiǎoxíng qiáojiēqì	Flamethrower mini-bridger	FTMB
小型双重内嵌式内存模块	Xiǎoxíng shuāngchóng nèiqiàn-shì nèicún mókuài	Small outline dual-inline memory module	SO-DIMM
小型塑封集成电路	Xiǎoxíng sùfēng jíchéng diànlù	Small outline integrated circuit	SOIC
小型塑封晶体管	Xiǎoxíng sùfēng jīngtǐguǎn	Small outline transistor	SOT
小型通信终端设备	Xiǎoxíng tōngxìn zhōngduān shèbèi	Small communication terminal	SCOT
消息型业务	Xiāoxixíng yèwù	Messaging service	
小组签名方案	Xiǎozǔ qiānmíng fāng'àn	Group signature scheme	
下盘	Xiàpán	Foot wall	
夏普	Xià-pǔ	Sharp (Japanese company)	
下视显示器	Xiàshì xiǎnshìqì	Head-down indicator	
下视最大探测距离	Xiàshì zuìdà tàncè jùlí	Maximum downlook detection range (of radar)	
下午效应	Xiàwǔ xiàoyìng	Afternoon effect	
下限溢位	Xiàxiàn yì wèi	Underflow	
下行	Xiàxíng	Downlink	
下行传输方向	Xiàxíng chuánshū fāngxiàng	Downstream transmission	
下行导引时隙	Xiàxíng dǎoyǐn shíxì	Downlink pilot time slot	DwPTS
下行方向	Xiàxíng fāngxiàng	Downstream	
下行共用信道	Xiàxíng gòngyòng xìndào	Downlink shared channel	DSCH
下行链路	Xiàxíng liànlù	Downlink	
下行链路共享物理信道	Xiàxíng liànlù gòngxiǎng wùlǐ xìndào	Physical downlink shared channel	PDSCH
下行链路共享信道	Xiàxíng liànlù gòngxiǎng xìndào	Downlink shared channel	DSCH
下行数据信道	Xiàxíng shùjù xìndào	Downlink data channel	
下行伪随机序列	Xiàxíng wěi suíjī xùliè	Pseudo-random downlink sequence	PRD
下行伪随机数据	Xiàxíng wěisuíjī shùjù	Downlink pseudo-random data	DPRD
下行线路	Xiàxíng xiànlù	Downlink	DL
下行线路	Xiàxíng xiànlù	Downward link	DLINK
下行专用物理控制信道	Xiàxíng zhuānyòng wùlǐ kòngzhì xìndào	Dedicated physical control channel/downlink	DPCCH/D
下行专用物理数据信道	Xiàxíng zhuānyòng wùlǐ shùjù xìn dào	Dedicated physical data channel/downlink	DPDCH/D
下行专用物理信道	Xiàxíng zhuānyòng wùlǐ xìndào	Dedicated physical channel/downlink	DPCH/D
下页键	Xiàyè jiàn	Page down key	
下溢	Xiàyì	Underflow	
下一步	Xiàyībù	Next (WP command)	
下一代本地交换系统	Xiàyīdài běndì jiāohuàn xìtǒng	Next generation local switch	

下一代电信运营系统和软件	Xiàyīdài diànxìn yùnyíng xìtǒng hé ruǎnjiàn	Next generation operating system and software	NGOSS
下一代网络	Xiàyīdài wǎngluò	Next generation network	NGN
下一代因特网	Xiàyīdài Yīntèwǎng	Next generation Internet	NGI
下引线	Xiàyǐnxiàn	Down-lead (of an antenna)	
下一跳标记转发条目	Xiàyītiào biāojì zhuǎnfā tiáomù	Next hop label forwarding entry	NHLFE
下一跳地址解析协议	Xiàyītiào dìzhǐ jiěxī xiéyì	Next-hop (address) resolution protocol	NHRP
下一跳服务器	Xiàyītiào fúwùqì	Next-hop server	NHS
下一跳级	Xiàyītiào jí	Next-hop	
下一跳解析协议	Xiàyītiào jiěxī xiéyì	Next-hop resolution protocol	NHRP
下一跳客户	Xiàyītiào kèhù	Next hop client	NHC
下一跳路由协议	Xiàyītiào lùyóu xiéyì	Next hop routing protocol	NHRP
下游法	Xiàyóu fǎ	Downstream slope	
下游路由器	Xiàyóu lùyóuqì	Downstream router	Rd
下游物理部件	Xiàyóu wùlǐ bùjiàn	Downstream physical unit	DSPU
下载	Xiàzài	Download	
细胞自动机	Xìbāo zìdòngjī	Cellular automata	CA
西部数子	Xībù shùzǐ	Western Digital (US disk drive maker)	
吸顶式	Xīdǐng-shì	Ceiling mounted type	C
吸顶式天线	Xīdǐng-shì tiānxiàn	Ceiling suction antenna, ceiling-mount antenna	
斜缝隙天线阵	Xié fèngxì tiānxiàn zhèn	Inclined slot array for antenna	
泄荷	Xiè hé	Load shedding	
写后读	Xiě hòu dú	Read after write	RAW
写启用	Xiě qǐyòng	Write enable (for database)	
写数据	Xiě shùjù	Write data	WD
斜探头	Xié tàntóu	Angle probe	
斜 V 形天线	Xié V-xíng tiānxiàn	Inclined-V antenna	
斜效率	Xié xiàolǜ	Slope efficiency (FOC)	
谐波	Xiébō	Harmonic	
谐波传动	Xiébō chuándòng	Harmonic drive gearing	
谐波次数	Xiébō cìshù	Harmonic number	
谐波发射	Xiébō fāshè	Harmonic emission	
谐波分量	Xiébō fènliàng	Harmonic component	
谐波共轭信号	Xiébō gòng'è xìnhào	Harmonic conjugate signal	
谐波含量	Xiébō hánliàng	Harmonic content	
谐波和杂波抑制	Xiébō hé zábō yìzhì	Harmonic and noise suppression	
谐波雷达	Xiébō léidá	Harmonic radar	
谐波滤波器	Xiébō lǜbōqì	Harmonic filter	
谐波失真	Xiébō shīzhēn	Harmonic distortion	HD
谐波失真系数	Xiébō shīzhēn xìshù	Harmonic distortion factor	
谐波输出功率	Xiébō shūchū gōnglǜ	Harmonic output power	
卸除	Xièchú	Dismount	
携带式电话机	Xiédàishì diànhuàjī	Portable telephone set	
卸焊	Xièhàn	Desoldering (in SMT)	
写回	Xiěhuí	Write-back	
斜角法	Xiéjiǎo fǎ	Angle beam technique/angle beam testing	
斜角平面连接	Xiéjiǎo píngmiàn liánjiē	Angle plane connection	APC

斜口钳	Xiékǒuqián	Diagonal pliers	
泄漏	Xièlòu	Compromise (IPsec)	
泄漏电缆	Xièlòu diànlǎn	Radiating cable	
泄漏电流	Xièlòu diànliú	Leakage current	
泄漏发射	Xièlòu fāshè	Compromising emanation (IPsec)	
斜率	Xiélǜ	Slope	
希尔伯特变换	Xī-ěr-bó-tè biànhuàn	Hilbert transform	
希尔伯特曲线	Xī-ěr-bó-tè qūxiàn	Hilbert curve	
希尔伯特数组	Xī-ěr-bó-tè shùzǔ	Hilbert array	
协商数据单元	Xiéshāng shùjù dānyuán	Protocol data unit	PDU
协调处理机	Xiétiáo chǔlǐjī	Coordination processor	CP
协调等值线	Xiétiáo děngzhíxiàn	Coordination contour	
协调功能	Xiétiáo gōngnéng	Mediation function	
协调距离	Xiétiáo jùlí	Coordination distance	
协调区	Xiétiáo qū	Coordination area	
协调设备	Xiétiáo shèbèi	Mediation device	MD
协调世界时	Xiétiáo shìjièshí	Coordinated Universal Time	UTC
协调宇宙时	Xiétiáo yǔzhòu shí	Coordinated universal time	UTC
协调装置	Xiétiáo zhuāngzhì	Mediation device	
写通	Xiětōng	Write-through	
协同编程系统	Xiétóng biānchéng xìtǒng	Collaborative editing system	
协同产品商务	Xiétóng chǎnpǐn shāngwù	Collaborative product commerce	CPC
协同反馈	Xiétóng fǎnkuì	Collaborative feedback	
协同管理模型	Xiétóng guǎnlǐ móxíng	Cooperative management model	
协同过滤	Xiétóng guòlǜ	Collaborative filtering	
协同检测	Xiétóng jiǎncè	Collaborative detection	
协同克里格法	Xiétóng kè-lǐ-gé fǎ	Co-Kriging (in remote sensing)	
协同商务	Xiétóng shāngwù	Cooperative commerce, collaborative commerce	
协同通信	Xiétóng tōngxìn	Cooperative communication	
斜向频率探测	Xiéxiàng pínlǜ tàncè	Frequency sounding at oblique incidence	
协议	Xiéyì	Protocol	
协议版本消息	Xiéyì bǎnběn xiāoxi	Protocol version message (IPsec TLS)	
协议编译码器	Xiéyì biānyìmǎqì	Protocol encoder/decoder	PED
协议标识符	Xiéyì biāozhì fú	Protocol discriminator	PD
协议标识符	Xiéyì biāozhì fú	Protocol identifier	PI
协议参考模型	Xiéyì cānkǎo móxíng	Protocol reference model	PRM
协议独立稠密模式组播	Xiéyì dúlì chóumì móshì zǔbō	Protocol-independent multicast dense mode	PIM-DM
协议独立稀疏模式组播	Xiéyì dúlì xīshū móshì zǔbō	Protocol-independent multicast sparse mode	PIM-SM
协议分析	Xiéyì fēnxī	Protocol analysis	
协议分析器	Xiéyì fēnxīqì	Protocol analyzer	
协议攻击	Xiéyì gōngjī	Protocol attack (crypto)	
协议和参数选择	Xiéyì hé cānshù xuǎnzé	Protocol and parameter select	PPS
协议鉴别器	Xiéyì jiànbiéqì	Protocol discriminator	PD
协议集成测试系统	Xiéyì jíchéng cèshì xìtǒng	Protocol integrated test system	PITS
协议控制信息	Xiéyì kòngzhì xìnxī	Protocol control information	PCI
协议控制字节	Xiéyì kòngzhì zìjié	Protocol control byte	PCB

协议控制器	Xiéyì kòngzhìqì	Protocol controller	PC
协议捆绑	Xiéyì kǔnbǎng	Protocol binding	
协议类型	Xiéyì lèixíng	Protocol type	PT
协议类型选择	Xiéyì lèixíng xuǎnzé	Protocol type select	PTS
协议轮廓	Xiéyì lúnkuò	Protocol profile	
协议事件	Xiéyì shìjiàn	Protocol event	PE
协议实体	Xiéyì shítǐ	Protocol entity	PE
协议实现附加测试信息	Xiéyì shíxiàn fùjiā cèshì xìnxī	Protocol implementation extra information for testing	PIXIT
协议实现一致性声明	Xiéyì shíxiàn yīzhìxìng shēngmíng	Protocol implementation conformance statement	PICS
协议实现一致性说明	Xiéyì shíxiàn yīzhìxìng shuōmíng	Protocol implementation conformity statement	PICS
协议实现的测试补充材料	Xiéyì shíxiànde cèshì bǔchōng cáiliào	Protocol implementation extra information for testing	PIXIT
协议实现的一致性陈述	Xiéyì shíxiànde yīzhìxìng chénshù	Protocol implementation conformance statement	PICS
协议书	Xiéyì shū	Interface specification	
协议数据单元	Xiéyì shùjù dānyuán	Protocol data unit	PDU,PDY
协议隧道	Xiéyì suìdào	Protocol tunneling (in IP)	
协议套	Xiéyì tào	Protocol suite	
协议无关多点广播	Xiéyì wúguān duōdiǎn guǎngbō	Protocol-independent multicast	PIM
协议无关组播协议组播边界路由器	Xiéyì wúguān zǔbō xiéyì zǔbō biānjiè lùyóuqì	Protocol-independent multicast (PIM) multicast border router	PMBR
协议无关组播-密集模式	Xiéyì wúguān zǔbō--mìjí móshì	Protocol-independent multicast--dense mode	PIM-DM
协议无关组播-稀疏模式	Xiéyì wúguān zǔbō--xīshū móshì	Protocol-independent multicast--sparse mode	PIM-SM
协议一致性测试报告	Xiéyì yīzhìxìng cèshì bàogào	Protocol conformance test report	PCTR
协议栈	Xiéyì zhàn	Protocol stack	
协议转换	Xiéyì zhuǎnhuàn	Protocol conversion	
协议转换器	Xiéyì zhuǎnhuànqì	Protocol converter	
协议子树标识	Xiéyì zishù biāozhì	Protocol sub-tree identification	PI
谐振窗	Xiézhèn chuāng	Resonant window	
谐振滤模器	Xiézhèn lǜmóqì	Resonant mode filter	
谐振模	Xiézhèn mó	Resonance mode (in a cavity resonator)	
谐振膜片	Xiézhèn mópiàn	Resonant iris	
谐振频率	Xiézhèn pínlǜ	Resonance frequency (in a cavity resonator)	
谐振腔	Xiézhèn qiāng	Cavity resonator	
谐振阻抗	Xiézhèn zǔkàng	Resonant impedance	
谐振腔频率计	Xiézhènqiāng pínlǜjì	Cavity frequency meter	
谐振式隔离器	Xiézhèn-shì gélíqì	Resonance isolator	
协作命令引擎	Xiézuò mìnglìng yǐnqíng	Concurrent command engine	
协作网络清单	Xiézuò wǎngluò qīngdān	Cooperative network list	CNL
协作虚拟原型环境	Xiézuò xūnǐ yuánxíng huánjìng	Collaborative virtual prototyping environment (CAD/CAM)	CVPE
隙缝辐射器	Xìfèng fúshèqì	Slot radiator	
隙缝天线	Xìfèng tiānxiàn	Slot antenna	
隙缝阵	Xìfèng zhèn	Slot array (antenna)	
吸附力	Xīfù lì	Cohesion	
析构函数	Xīgòu hánshù	Destructor (function in software)	dtor
析构器	Xīgòuqì	Destructor	Dtor
细化	Xìhuà	Thinning	
希捷公司	Xījié gōngsī	SeaGate (US hard drive maker)	

希捷公司的静电防撞击外壳	Xījié gōngsīde jìngdiàn fáng zhuàngjī wàiké	SeaShield (Seagate's static shielding, trademark)	
西康	Xī-kāng	Siecor (JV between Siemens and Corning)	
细颗粒	Xìkēlì	Fine-grained	
吸缆机	Xīlǎnjī	Cable blowing machine (to install FOC)	
系列观测	Xìliè guāncè	Array observation	
系流气球通信	Xìliú qìqiú tōngxìn	Captive balloon communication	
西门子	Xī-mén-zǐ	Siemens (German company)	
新定型咨询台	Xīn dìngxíng zīxún tái	New type approval advisory board	NTAAB
信干比	Xìn gān bǐ	Signal-to-interference ratio	
信干噪比	Xìn gānzào bǐ	Signal-to-interference noise ratio	SINR
新规范的格式表示	Xīn guīfànde géshi biǎoshì	Non-canonical format indication	NCFI
新技术	Xīn jìshù	Neotechnology	
信码速率	Xìn mǎ sùlǜ	Channel encoding speed, short for 信道编码速率	
信纳比	Xìn nà bǐ	Signal to noise ratio	S/N
信骚比	Xìn sāo bǐ	Signal-to-disturbance ratio	
新视分类资讯	Xīn shì fēnlèi zīxùn	Classitext	
新数据标帜	Xīn shùjù biāozhì	New data flag	NDF
新数据标志	Xīn shùjù biāozhì	New data flag (in SDH)	NDF
新数据标识	Xīn shùjù biāozhì	New data flag	NDF
新数据型	Xīn shùjù xíng	New data type	
新协议	Xīn xiéyì	New deal	
新一代输入/输出标准	Xīn yīdài shūrù/shūchū biāozhǔn	Next generation input/output	NGIO
新因特网智能系统	Xīn Yīntèwǎng zhìnéng xìtǒng	New Internet knowledge system	NIKOS
信杂比	Xìn zá bǐ	Signal-to-complexity ratio	SCR
信噪比	Xìn zào bǐ	Signal-to-noise ratio	SNR
新宝	Xīnbǎo	Sampo (Taiwan company)	
信报传递应用程序接口	Xìnbào chuándì yìngyòng chéngxù jiēkǒu	Messaging application programming interface	MAPI
芯包同心度误差	Xīnbāo tóngxīndù wùchā	Core/cladding concentric error	
信标	Xìnbiāo	Beacon	
信道	Xìndào	Channel	
信道编解码单元	Xìndào biānjiěmǎ dānyuán	Channel coding unit	CCU
信道编码	Xìndào biānmǎ	Channel coding	
信道编码速率	Xìndào biānmǎ sùlǜ	Channel encoding speed	
信道编码器	Xìndào biānmǎqì	Channel encoder	CHE
信道标志	Xìndào biāozhì	Channel identification	
信道标识	Xìndào biāozhì	Channel identification	
信道参数	Xìndào cānshù	Channel parameter	CP
信道测试仪	Xìndào cèshìyí	Channel tester	CT
信道访问码	Xìndào fǎngwèn mǎ	Channel access code	CAC
信道访问协议	Xìndào fǎngwèn xiéyì	Channel access protocol	CAP
信道分配失败率	Xìndào fēnpèi shībài lǜ	Channel allocation failure rate	
信道服务单元	Xìndào fúwù dānyuán	Channel service unit	CSU
信道负载	Xìndào fùzài	Channel loading	
信道间隔	Xìndào jiàngé	Channel spacing	
信道交织	Xìndào jiāozhī	Channel interleaving	

信道接口处理器	Xìndào jiēkǒu chǔlǐqì	Channel interface processor	CIP
信道接口电路	Xìndào jiēkǒu diànlù	Channel interface circuit	
信道解码器	Xìndào jiěmǎqì	Channel decoder	CHD
信道卡管理器	Xìndào kǎ guǎnlǐqì	Channel card manager	CCM
信道卡接口控制器	Xìndào kǎ jiēkǒu kòngzhìqì	Channel card interface controller	CIC
信道捆绑	Xìndào kǔnbǎng	Channel bundle (or binding) (IPsec)	
信道类型	Xìndào lèixíng	Channel type	
信道流标识符	Xìndào liú biāozhì fú	Channel stream identifier	CSI
信道门	Xìndào mén	Channel gate	
信道模式	Xìndào móshì	Channel mode	
信道模式修改	Xìndào móshì xiūgǎi	Channel mode modify	
信道请求	Xìndào qǐngqiú	Channel request	
信道容量	Xìndào róngliàng	Channel capacity	
信道扫描	Xìndào sǎomiáo	Scan channel	
信道释放	Xìndào shìfàng	Channel release	
信道时隙	Xìndào shíxì	Channel time slot	
信道数据块长度	Xìndào shùjù kuài chángdù	Channel data block length	
信道速率	Xìndào sùlǜ	Channel rate	CR
信道跳频序列	Xìndào tiàopín xùliè	Channel hopping sequence	
信道相连	Xìndào xiānglián	Channel-attached	
信道效率	Xìndào xiàolǜ	Channel efficiency	
信道选接方式	Xìndào xuǎnjiē fāngshì	Channel selective mode	
信道选配单板	Xìndào xuǎnpèi dānbǎn	Channel selection unit	CSU
信道选择方式	Xìndào xuǎnzé fāngshì	Channel selective mode	
信道元件	Xìndào yuánjiàn	Channel element	CE
信道元件单元机架	Xìndào yuánjiàn dānyuán jījià	Channel element unit rack	CEUR
信道元件后面板	Xìndào yuánjiàn hòumian bǎn	Channel element back board	CEBB
信道元件控制管理器	Xìndào yuánjiàn kòngzhì guǎnlǐqì	Channel element control manager	CECM
信道指配	Xìndào zhǐpèi	Channel assignment	
信道化接收机	Xìndàohuà jiēshōujī	Channelized receiver	
信道间串话	Xìndào-jiān chuànhuà, chuàn sè	Inter-channel cross-talk	
信道间串色	Xìndào-jiān chuànsè	Inter-channel cross-color	
信道间干扰	Xìndào-jiān gānrǎo	Inter-channel interference	ICI
隙内信令	Xì-nèi xìnlìng	In-slot signaling	
信封	Xìnfēng	Envelope	
型叠置法	Xíng diézhì fǎ	Mode superposition method	
型分析法	Xíng fēnxī fǎ	Modal analysis	
行波	Xíngbō	Traveling wave (in a transmission line)	
行波天线	Xíngbō tiānxiàn	Traveling wave antenna	TWA
行波系数	Xíngbō xìshù	Travelling wave coefficient	
行波管	Xíngbōguǎn	Traveling wave tube	TWT
行波管放大器	Xíngbōguǎn fàngdàqì	Traveling wave tube amplifier	TWTA
行波形调变器	Xíngbō-xíng tiáobiànqì	Travelling wave modulator	
形参	Xíngcān	Formal parameter	
行程编码	Xíngchéng biānmǎ	Run length encoding	RLE
行程限制开关	Xíngchéng xiànzhì kāiguān	Position-limiting switch	

星关卫星网路接入节点	Xīngguān wèixīng wǎnglù jiērù jiédiǎn	Stargate satellite network access point	SSNAP
星号	Xīnghào	Asterisk *	
型号批准码	Xínghào pīzhǔn mǎ	Type approval code	TAC
性能	Xìngnéng	Performance, capability, property, facility	
性能表示	Xìngnéng biǎoshì	Performance indicator	
性能比率	Xìngnéng bǐlǜ	Performance rate	PR
性能测试基金会	Xìngnéng cèshì jījīnhuì	Foundation for Performance Measurement	FPM
性能分析显示系统	Xìngnéng fēnxī xiǎnshì xìtǒng	Performance analysis display system	PADS
性能管理	Xìngnéng guǎnlǐ	Performance management	
性能管理构件	Xìngnéng guǎnlǐ gòujiàn	Properties management building block	PMBB
性能管理信元	Xìngnéng guǎnlǐ xìnyuán	Performance management cell	
性能价格比	Xìngnéng jiàgé bǐ	Cost-performance ratio	
性能监测	Xìngnéng jiāncè	Performance monitoring	
性能降低	Xìngnéng jiàngdī	Performance degradation	
性能监视	Xìngnéng jiānshì	Performance monitoring	
性能拒绝	Xìngnéng jùjué	Facility reject (ISUP)	FRJ
性能可用性	Xìngnéng kěyòngxìng	Performance availability	
性能判据	Xìngnéng pànjù	Performance criterion	
性能评测器	Xìngnéng píngcèqì	Profiler	
性能评价	Xìngnéng píngjià	Performance evaluation	
性能请求消息	Xìngnéng qǐngqiú xiāoxi	Facility request message (ISUP)	FAR
性能下降	Xìngnéng xiàjiàng	Performance degradation	
性能/结构参数	Xìngnéng/jiégòu cānshù	Capability/configuration parameter	CCP
形式辨识	Xíngshì biànshí	Pattern recognition	
形式化描述技术	Xíngshì huà miáoshù jìshù	Formal description technology	FDT
形式逻辑	Xíngshì luójì	Formal logic	
形式识别	Xíngshì shíbié	Pattern recognition	
形式验证	Xíngshì yànzhèng	Formal verification (IPsec)	
形式证明	Xíngshì zhèngmíng	Formal proof (IPsec)	
形态描影	Xíngtài miáoyǐng	Shading	
信关设备	Xìnguān shèbèi	Gateway	
行为测试	Xíngwéi cèshì	Behavior test	
形位偏差	Xíngwèi piānchā	Misalignment	
行为时间序列	Xíngwéi shíjiān xùliè	Behavioral time sequence	
形相似多边	Xíngxiàngsì duōbiān	Shape similarity	
形心曲线	Xíngxīn qǔxiàn	Centroid	
行星波	Xíngxīng bō	Planetary wave	
星形分配网	Xīngxíng fēnpèi wǎng	Distributed star network	DSN
星型架构	Xīngxíng jiàgòu	Star schema	
星形接口	Xīngxíng jiēkǒu	Star interface	
星型联接	Xīngxíng liánjiē	Star join	
行星轮减速器	Xíngxīng lún jiǎnsùqì	Planetary gear reductor	
星型耦合器	Xīngxíng ǒuhéqì	Star coupler	
星形拓扑	Xīngxíng tuòpū	Star topology	
形状分析	Xíngzhuàng fēnxī	Shape analysis	
星状光纤耦合器	Xīngzhuàng guāngxiān ǒuhéqì	Star optical coupler	

信函	Xìnhán	Letter	
信号	Xìnhào	Signal	
信号变换装置	Xìnhào biànhuàn zhuāngzhì	Signal conversion equipment	SCE
信号标记失配	Xìnhào biāojì shīpèi	Signal label mismatch	SLM
信号标签	Xìnhào biāoqiān	Signal label	SL
信号捕获	Xìnhào bǔhuò	Acquisition of signal	AOS
信号参考地	Xìnhào cānkǎo dì	Signal reference ground	
信号操作平台服务提供(操作系统)	Xìnhào cāozuò píngtái fúwù tígōng (cāozuò xìtǒng)	Signal operations platforms-provisioning (operating system)	SOP
信号场强	Xìnhào chǎngqiáng	Signal strength	
信号成分	Xìnhào chéngfèn	Signal component (in AC signaling)	
信号传送	Xìnhào chuánsòng	Signal transfer	SIGTRAN
信号传送点	Xìnhào chuánsòng diǎn	Signal transfer point	STP
信号处理天线	Xìnhào chǔlǐ tiānxiàn	Signal processing antenna	
信号处理器公用卡	Xìnhào chǔlǐqì gōngyòng kǎ	Signal processor card common	SPCC
信号单元	Xìnhào dānyuán	Signal unit	
信号单元表示语	Xìnhào dānyuán biǎoshìyǔ	Signal unit indicator	
信号单元差错率监视	Xìnhào dānyuán chācuò lǜ jiānshì	Signal unit error rate monitor	SUERM
信号电平	Xìnhào diànpíng	Signal level	
信号电平中值	Xìnhào diànpíng zhōng zhí	Median of signal level	
信号丢失	Xìnhào diūshī	Loss of signal	LOS
信号丢失告警	Xìnhào diūshī gàojǐng	Loss of signal alarm	LOS
信号丢失缺陷	Xìnhào diūshī quēxiàn	Loss of signal defect	dLOS
信号对干扰比（信干比）	Xìnhào duì gānrǎo bǐ (xìn gān bǐ)	Signal-to-interference ratio	SIR
信号对剩余输出电平比	Xìnhào duì shèngyú shūchū diànpíng bǐ	Signal-to-residual output-power ratio	
信号对剩余输出功率比	Xìnhào duì shèngyú shūchū gōnglǜ bǐ	Signal-to-residual output-power ratio	
信号发生器	Xìnhào fāshēngqì	Signal generator	
信号分割	Xìnhào fēngē	Signal split	
信号分路器	Xìnhào fēnlùqì	Signal splitter	
信号分配	Xìnhào fēnpèi	Signal distribution	
信号分析	Xìnhào fēnxī	Signal analysis	
信号干扰比	Xìnhào gānrǎo bǐ	Signal to interference ratio	
信号功率噪声功率密度比	Xìnhào gōnglǜ zàoshēng gōnglǜ mìdù bǐ	Signal power-to-noise power density ratio	SNDR
信号功能	Xìnhào gōngnéng	Signal function	
信号检测器	Xìnhào jiǎncèqì	Signal detector	
信号交替变换	Xìnhào jiāotì biànhuàn	Alternate mark inversion	AMI
信号交替反转码	Xìnhào jiāotì fǎnzhuǎn mǎ	Alternate mark inversion	AMI
信号交替翻转码	Xìnhào jiāotì fānzhuǎn mǎ	Alternate mark inversion	AMI
信号结构波束成型	Xìnhào jiégòu bōshù chéngxíng	Signal structure beamforming	SSBF
信号极限长度	Xìnhào jíxiàn chángdù	Signal limit length	
信号基准网	Xìnhào jīzhǔn wǎng	Signal reference grid	
信号量	Xìnhào liàng	Semaphore	
信号劣化	Xìnhào lièhuà	Signal degrade	SD
信号劣化门限	Xìnhào lièhuà ménxiàn	Signal degrade threshold	SDT
信号路径	Xìnhào lùjìng	Signal trail	
信号路由法	Xìnhào lùyóu fǎ	Pass-along method	

信号码元	Xìnhào mǎyuán	Signal element	
信号强度	Xìnhào qiángdù	Signal strength	
信号清单	Xìnhào qīngdān	Repertoire of signals	
信号设备	Xìnhào shèbèi	Signaling equipment	
信号失败门限	Xìnhào shībài ménxiàn	Signal failure threshold	SFT
信号失效	Xìnhào shīxiào	Signal fail	SF
信号特性错误	Xìnhào tèxìng cuòwù	Signal quality error	SQE
信号网关	Xìnhào wǎngguān	Signal gateway	SG
信号网关单元	Xìnhào wǎngguān dānyuán	Signal gateway unit	SGU
信号网络层	Xìnhào wǎngluò céng	Signaling network layer	SNL
信号稳定度的路由算法	Xìnhào wěndìngdùde lùyóu suànfǎ	Signal stability routing	SSR
信号握手	Xìnhào wòshǒu	Handshake	
信号消息	Xìnhào xiāoxi	Signal message	
信号消息处理子系统	Xìnhào xiāoxi chǔlǐ zixìtǒng	Signaling message handling sub-system	SMHS
信号泄漏	Xìnhào xièlòu	Signal spill-over (in VF signaling)	
信号信躁比	Xìnhào xìn zào bǐ	Signal-to-noise ratio of strong signal	
信号星座	Xìnhào xīngzuò	Signal constellation (in digital modulation)	
信号压扩器	Xìnhào yākuòqì	Signal compander	
信号掩蔽比	Xìnhào yǎnbì bǐ	Signal-to-masking ratio	SMR
信号音	Xìnhào yīn	Signal tone	
信号音接收器	Xìnhào yīn jiēshōuqì	Signal tone receiver	
信号与噪声之比	Xìnhào yǔ zàoshēng zhī bǐ	Signal-to-noise ratio	
信号元	Xìnhào yuán	Signal element	
信号源	Xìnhào yuán	Signal source, annunciator	
信号运算器	Xìnhào yùnsuànqì	Signal arithmetic unit	
信号杂波比	Xìnhào zábō bǐ	Signal-to-clutter ratio	SCR
信号噪声比	Xìnhào zàoshēng bǐ	Signal-to-noise ratio	SNR
信号噪声密度比	Xìnhào zàoshēng mìdù bǐ	Signal-to-noise density ratio	SNDR
信号增益	Xìnhào zēngyì	Signal gain	
信号整形回路	Xìnhào zhěngxíng huílù	Signal conditioner	SGC
信号质量错误	Xìnhào zhìliàng cuòwù	Signal quality error	SQE
信号质量检测	Xìnhào zhìliàng jiǎncè	Signal quality detection	
信号质量检测器	Xìnhào zhìliàng jiǎncèqì	Signal quality detector	SQD
信号转换设备	Xìnhào zhuǎnhuàn shèbèi	Signal conversion equipment	
信号转接点	Xìnhào zhuǎnjiē diǎn	Signal transfer point	
信号字节扩展	Xìnhào zìjié kuòzhǎn	Signal byte expansion	SBE
信号组合设备	Xìnhào zǔhé shèbèi	Signal combining equipment	SCE
信号灯	Xìnhàodēng	Semaphore	
新加坡电信	Xīnjiāpō diànxìn	Singapore Telecom	
新加坡电信移动通信	Xīnjiāpō diànxìn yídòng tōngxìn	SingTel Mobile (Singapore GSM network operator)	
新加坡亚洲第一通信	Xīnjiāpō Yàzhōu dìyī tōngxìn	Singapore MobileOne Asia (GSM network operator)	
信赖度测试	Xìnlàidù cèshì	Reliability testing	
心理旋转	Xīnlǐ xuánzhuǎn	Mental rotation	
信令	Xìnlìng	Signaling	
信令安全性	Xìnlìng ānquánxìng	Signaling security (in common channel signaling)	
信令 ATM 适配层	Xìnlìng ATM shìpèi céng	Signaling asynchronous transfer mode adaptation layer	SAAL

信令传送	Xìnlìng chuánsòng	Signaling transport	SIGTRAN
信令传送层	Xìnlìng chuánsòng céng	Signaling transport layer	STL
信令传送点	Xìnlìng chuánsòng diǎn	Signaling transfer point	STP
信令传送转换器	Xìnlìng chuánsòng zhuǎnhuànqì	Signaling transport converter	STC
信令单元	Xìnlìng dānyuán	Signaling unit	
信令点	Xìnlìng diǎn	Signaling point	SP
信令点编码	Xìnlìng diǎn biānmǎ	Signaling point code	SPC
信令点管理簇	Xìnlìng diǎn guǎnlǐ cù	Signaling point management cluster	SPMC
信令端点	Xìnlìng duāndiǎn	Signaling end point	SEP
信令发送增益	Xìnlìng fāsòng zēngyì	Signaling transmission gain	
信令服务子系统	Xìnlìng fúwù zi xìtǒng	Signaling service sub-system	SSS
信令管理设备	Xìnlìng guǎnlǐ shèbèi	Signaling management equipment	SME
信令互通	Xìnlìng hùtōng	Signaling interworking	
信令控制器	Xìnlìng kòngzhìqì	Signaling controller	SC
信令连接控制部分	Xìnlìng liánjiē kòngzhì bùfen	Signaling connection control part	SCCP
信令连接控制部分用户适配层	Xìnlìng liánjiē kòngzhì bùfen yònghù shìpèi céng	Signaling connection control part user adaptation layer	SUA
信令链路	Xìnlìng liànlù	Signaling link	
信令链路测试消息	Xìnlìng liànlù cèshì xiāoxi	Signaling link test message	SLTM
信令链路级	Xìnlìng liànlù jí	Signaling link level	
信令链路码	Xìnlìng liànlù mǎ	Signaling link code	SLC
信令链路选择	Xìnlìng liànlù xuǎnzé	Signaling link selection	SLS
信令链路终端	Xìnlìng liànlù zhōngduān	Signaling link terminal	SLT
信令链路终端板 A	Xìnlìng liànlù zhōngduān bǎn A	Signaling link terminal board A	SLTA
信令链路终端控制	Xìnlìng liànlù zhōngduān kòngzhì	Signaling link terminal control	SILTC
信令逻辑通路	Xìnlìng luóji tōnglù	Logical signaling channel	
信令路由	Xìnlìng lùyóu	Signaling route	
信令路由选定	Xìnlìng lùyóu xuǎndìng	Signaling routing	
信令码转换	Xìnlìng mǎ zhuǎnhuàn	Signaling code transition	
信令模块	Xìnlìng mókuài	Signaling module	
信令模块分散	Xìnlìng mókuài fēnsàn	Diversity of a signaling module	
信令时隙	Xìnlìng shíxì	Signaling time slot	
信令数据链路级	Xìnlìng shùjù liànlù jí	Signaling data link level	
信令通道	Xìnlìng tōngdào	Signaling path (in common channel signaling)	
信令网	Xìnlìng wǎng	Signaling network	XLW
信令网管理	Xìnlìng wǎng guǎnlǐ	Signaling network management	
信令网关	Xìnlìng wǎngguān	Signaling gateway	SG
信令网关单元	Xìnlìng wǎngguān dānyuán	Signaling gateway unit	SGU
信令网关功能	Xìnlìng wǎngguān gōngnéng	Signaling gateway function	SGF
信令网关进程	Xìnlìng wǎngguān jìnchéng	Signaling gateway process	SGP
信令网络	Xìnlìng wǎngluò	Signaling network	
信令网络级	Xìnlìng wǎngluò jí	Signaling network level	
信令消息	Xìnlìng xiāoxi	Signaling message	
信令信道	Xìnlìng xìndào	Signaling channel	
信令信道控制器	Xìnlìng xìndào kòngzhìqì	Signaling channel controller	SCC
信令信息	Xìnlìng xìnxī	Signaling information	

信令信息段	Xìnlìng xìnxī duàn	Signaling information field	SIF
信令信息元素	Xìnlìng xìnxī yuánsù	Signaling information element	IE
信令系统	Xìnlìng xìtǒng	Signaling system	
信令虚通路	Xìnlìng xū tōnglù	Signaling virtual channel	SVC
信令虚信道	Xìnlìng xū xìndào	Signaling virtual channel	SVC
信令音	Xìnlìng yīn	Signaling tone	ST
信令音峰值频偏	Xìnlìng yīn fēngzhí pínpiān	Signaling tone peak frequency deviation	
信令终端	Xìnlìng zhōng duān	Signaling terminal	STE
信令终端控制集成板	Xìnlìng zhōngduān kòngzhì jíchéngbǎn	Signaling terminal control board assembly	STCA
信令终端网络接口集成板	Xìnlìng zhōngduān wǎngluò jiēkǒu jíchéngbǎn	Signaling terminal network interface board assembly	STNI
信令终结点	Xìnlìng zhōngjié diǎn	Signaling end point	SEP
信令转换处理器	Xìnlìng zhuǎnhuàn chǔlǐqì	Signaling transfer processor	STP
信令转换设备	Xìnlìng zhuǎnhuàn shèbèi	Signaling transfer equipment	STE
信令转换器	Xìnlìng zhuǎnhuànqì	Signaling converter	
信令转接点	Xìnlìng zhuǎnjiē diǎn	Signaling transfer point	STP
信令转接终结点	Xìnlìng zhuǎnjiē zhōngjié diǎn	Signaling transfer end point	STEP
信令的插入	Xìnlìngde chārù	Signaling insertion	
信令的提取	Xìnlìngde tíqǔ	Signaling extraction	
芯片	Xìnpiàn	Wafer (semiconductor mfg)	
芯片反转	Xìnpiàn fǎnzhuǎn	Flip-chip	
芯片封装系统	Xìnpiàn fēngzhuāng xìtǒng	Wafer packaging system (semiconductor mfg)	
芯片组	Xìnpiàn zǔ	Chip set	
芯片内集成缓存	Xìnpiàn-nèi jíchéng huǎncún	Cache on die	COD
芯片上集成缓存	Xìnpiàn-shàng jíchéng huǎncún	Cache on a chip	
信任	Xìnrèn	Trust	
信任策略	Xìnrèn cèlüè	Trust policy	TP
信任连接	Xìnrèn liánjiē	Trusted connection	
新手	Xīnshǒu	Newbie (Internet novice)	
信宿	Xìnsù	Information sink	
信体	Xìntǐ	Body (of a message)	
信筒	Xìntǒng	Post box (to send letters)	
信头	Xìntóu	Cell header	
信头	Xìntóu	Header; heading (of a data block)	
信头差错校验	Xìntóu chācuò jiàoyàn	Header error check	HEC
信头差错控制码	Xìntóu chācuò kòngzhì mǎ	Header error control	HEC
信头差错控制域	Xìntóu chācuò kòngzhì yù	Header error control	HEC
信头误码控制	Xìntóu wùmǎ kòngzhì	Header error control	HEC
新闻栏	Xīnwén lán	Newsgroup	
新闻组	Xīnwén zǔ	Newsgroup	
信息	Xìnxī	Information (ISUP message)	INF
信息安全	Xìnxī ānquán	Information security	INFOSEC
信息安全技术工程研究中心	Xìnxī ānquán jìshù gōngchéng yánjiū zhōngxīn	Engineering Research Center of Information Security Technology	ERCIST
信息安全协议	Xìnxī ānquán xiéyì	Message security protocol	MSP
信息巴恩	Xìnxī bā-ēn	Infobahn	
信息包	Xìnxī bāo	Packet	

信息保障	Xìnxī bǎozhàng	Information assurance	IA
信息保障技术框架	Xìnxī bǎozhàng jìshù kuàngjià	Information assurance technical framework	IATF
信息比特	Xìnxī bǐtè	Information bit	
信息产业部	Xìnxī chǎnyè bù	Ministry of Information Industry (China)	MII
信息查询	Xìnxī cháxún	Information request	IRQ
信息查询否认	Xìnxī cháxún fǒurèn	Information request negative acknowledge	INAK
信息查询确认	Xìnxī cháxún quèrèn	Information request acknowledge	IACK
信息查询响应	Xìnxī cháxún xiǎngyìng	Information request response	IRR
信息插座	Xìnxī chāzuò	Telecommunication outlet (as RS-232, RJ-11)	TO
信息插座	Xìnxī chāzuò	Information outlet	IO
信息传达	Xìnxī chuándá	Dissemination of information	
信息传递	Xìnxī chuándì	Information transfer	
信息传递部分	Xìnxī chuándì bùfen	Message transport part	MTP
信息传输部分	Xìnxī chuánshū bùfen	Message transfer part	MTP
信息传输系统	Xìnxī chuánshū xìtǒng	Information transmission system	
信息传送容量	Xìnxī chuánsòng róngliàng	Information transfer capability	ITC
信息传送通道	Xìnxī chuánsòng tōngdào	Information transfer channel	ITC
信息处理	Xìnxī chǔlǐ	Information processing	
信息单位	Xìnxī dānwèi	Information unit	
信息单元	Xìnxī dānyuán	Information element	IE
信息单元标识符	Xìnxī dānyuán biāozhìfú	Information element identifier	IEI
信息单元识别	Xìnxī dānyuán shíbié	Information element identity	IEI
信息丢失	Xìnxī diūshī	Loss of information	
信息反馈重发纠错	Xìnxī fǎnkuì chóngfā jiūcuò	Error correction information feedback and repetition	
信息负荷能力	Xìnxī fùhè nénglì	Information payload capacity	
信息服务业	Xìnxī fúwùyè	Information service trades	
信息高速公路	Xìnxī gāosù gōnglù	Information highway	
信息工程	Xìnxī gōngchéng	Information engineering	
信息管理	Xìnxī guǎnlǐ	Information management	
信息获取	Xìnxī huòqǔ	Information acquisition	
信息集	Xìnxī jí	Information set	
信息加密	Xìnxī jiāmì	Information security	
信息建模	Xìnxī jiànmó	Information modeling	
信息检索系统	Xìnxī jiǎnsuǒ xìtǒng	Information retrieval system	
信息交换中心	Xìnxī jiāohuàn zhōngxīn	Message switching center	MSC
信息交换用国际标准代码	Xìnxī jiāohuàn-yòng guójì biāozhǔn dàimǎ	International Standard Code for Information Interchange	ISCII
信息交换站	Xìnxī jiāohuànzhàn	Message clearinghouse	
信息基础设施	Xìnxī jīchǔ shèshī	Information infrastructure	
信息计费通知	Xìnxī jìfèi tōngzhī	Advice of charge information	AoCI
信息净负荷	Xìnxī jìngfùhè	Information payload	
信息净荷能力	Xìnxī jìnghé nénglì	Information payload capacity	
信息净荷容量	Xìnxī jìnghé róngliàng	Information payload capacity	
信息技术	Xìnxī jìshù	Information technology	IT
信息技术安全评级准则	Xìnxī jìshù ānquán píngjí zhǔnzé	Information technology security evaluation criteria	
信息技术设备	Xìnxī jìshù shèbèi	Information technology equipment	ITE
信息科学	Xìnxī kēxué	Information science	

信息空间	Xìnxī kōngjiān	Cyberspace	
信息块	Xìnxī kuài	Information block	
信息块字头	Xìnxī kuài zìtóu	Block header	
信息理论密码学	Xìnxī lǐlùn mìmǎxué	Information theoretic cryptography	
信息流	Xìnxī liú	Information flow	IF
信息流程图	Xìnxī liúchéngtú	Information flow chart	
信息码组	Xìnxī mǎzǔ	Information block	I-Block
信息描述符记录	Xìnxī miáoshù fú jìlù	Information descriptor record	IDR
信息模型	Xìnxī móxíng	Information model	IM
信息内容	Xìnxī nèiróng	Information content	
信息破坏	Xìnxī pòhuài	Corruption of information	
信息请求	Xìnxī qǐngqiú	Information request (computer term)	IRQ
信息请求	Xìnxī qǐngqiú	Information request (ISUP message)	INR
信息请求否认	Xìnxī qǐngqiú fǒurèn	Information request negative acknowledge	INAK
信息请求响应	Xìnxī qǐngqiú xiǎngyìng	Information request response	IRR
信息请求消息	Xìnxī qǐngqiú xiāoxi	Information request message (ISUP)	INR
信息请求原因	Xìnxī qǐngqiú yuányīn	Information request reason	IRR
信息请求证实	Xìnxī qǐngqiú zhèngshí	Information request acknowledged	IACK
信息融合	Xìnxī rónghé	Information fusion	
信息熵	Xìnxī shāng	Information entropy	
信息社会	Xìnxī shèhuì	Information-oriented society	
信息施用	Xìnxī shīyòng	Information utilization	
信息顺序图	Xìnxī shùnxù tú	Message sequence chart	MSC
信息属性	Xìnxī shǔxìng	Information attribute	
信息速率	Xìnxī sùlǜ	Information rate	
信息提取	Xìnxī tíqǔ	Information extraction	
信息通信网	Xìnxī tōngxìn wǎng	Information network	
信息通信系统	Xìnxī tōngxìn xìtǒng	Information network system	INS
信息挖掘	Xìnxī wājué	Data mining, information mining	
信息完整性编码	Xìnxī wánzhěngxìng biānmǎ	Message integrity code	MIC
信息位	Xìnxī wèi	Information bit	
信息文件	Xìnxī wénjiàn	Information file	INF File
信息消息	Xìnxī xiāoxi	Information message (ISUP)	INF
信息协议识别符	Xìnxī xiéyì shíbiéfú	Information protocol identifier	IPI
信息系统	Xìnxī xìtǒng	Information system	
信息系统安全	Xìnxī xìtǒng ānquán	Information system security	
信息系统安全工程	Xìnxī xìtǒng ānquán gōngchéng	Information systems security engineering	ISSE
信息系统工程	Xìnxī xìtǒng gōngchéng	Information system engineering	
信息音	Xìnxī yīn	Information tone	
信息隐藏	Xìnxī yǐncáng	Information hiding	
信息应用过程接口	Xìnxī yìngyòng guòchéng jiēkǒu	Messaging application procedure interface	MAPI
信息隐匿技术	Xìnxī yǐnnì jìshù	Information concealment, steganography	
信息有效负荷能力	Xìnxī yǒuxiào fùhè nénglì	Information payload capacity	
信息与通信技术	Xìnxī yǔ tōngxìn jìshù	Information and communications technology	ICT
信息元素	Xìnxī yuánsù	Information element	IE
信息娱乐	Xìnxī yúlè	Infotainment	

信息摘要	Xìnxī zhāiyào	Hash (in encryption)	
信息帧	Xìnxī zhèng	Information frame	I
信息指示业务	Xìnxī zhǐshì yèwù	Message indication service	
信息转换功能	Xìnxī zhuǎnhuàn gōngnéng	Information conversion function	ICF
信息字段	Xìnxī zìduàn	Information field	INF
信息字段大小	Xìnxī zìduàn dàxiǎo	Information field sizes	IFS
信息咨询	Xìnxī zīxún	Information consultant	
信息自由	Xìnxī zìyóu	Freedom of information	FOI
信息资源词典系统	Xìnxī zīyuán cídiǎn xìtǒng	Information resource dictionary system	
信息资源管理	Xìnxī zīyuán guǎnlǐ	Information resource management	
信息组	Xìnxī zǔ	Information group	IG
芯线直径	Xīnxiàn zhíjìng	Conductor diameter	
信息量管理	Xìnxīliàng guǎnlǐ	Traffic management	TM
信息论	Xìnxīlùn	Information theory	
新型通信系统	Xīnxíng tōngxìn xìtǒng	Advanced communication system	ACS
信息网	Xìnxīwǎng	Information network	IN
信息学	Xìnxīxué	Informatics	
信用卡呼叫	Xìnyòngkǎ hūjiào	Credit card calling	CRED
信元	Xìnyuán	Cell (of a digital information block or digital signal)	
信源	Xìnyuán	Information source	
信源编码	Xìnyuán biānmǎ	Source coding	
信元标明丢失优先度	Xìnyuán biāomíng diūshī yōuxiān dù	Cell loss priority	CLP
信元差错率	Xìnyuán chācuò lǜ	Cell error rate	CER
信元传输时延	Xìnyuán chuánshū shíyán	Cell transfer delay	CTD
信元传送时延	Xìnyuán chuánsòng shíyán	Cell transfer delay	CTD
信元传送延迟	Xìnyuán chuánsòng yánchí	Cell transfer delay	CTD
信元错误率	Xìnyuán cuòwù lǜ	Cell error rate	CER
信元定界	Xìnyuán dìngjiè	Cell delineation	
信元定界丢失	Xìnyuán dìngjiè diūshī	Loss of cell delineation	LCD
信元定界失同步	Xìnyuán dìngjiè shī tóngbù	Out of cell delineation	OCD
信元定界失步	Xìnyuán dìngjiè shībù	Out of cell delineation	OCD
信元丢弃优先级	Xìnyuán diūqì yōuxiān jí	Cell loss priority	CLP
信元丢失率	Xìnyuán diūshī lǜ	Cell loss rate	CLR
信元丢失优先	Xìnyuán diūshī yōuxiān	Cell loss priority	CLP
信元丢失优先级	Xìnyuán diūshī yōuxiān jí	Cell loss priority	CLP
信元丢失优先权	Xìnyuán diūshī yōuxiānquán	Cell loss priority	CLP
信元交换路由器	Xìnyuán jiāohuàn lùyóuqì	Cell switching router	CSR
信元描述	Xìnyuán miáoshù	Cell delineation	
信元时延变化	Xìnyuán shíyán biànhuà	Cell delay variation	CDV
信元时延变化容限	Xìnyuán shíyán biànhuà róngxiàn	Cell delay variation tolerance	CDVT
信元数据加密	Xìnyuán shùjù jiāmì	Cell payload encryption or scrambling	
信元速率边际	Xìnyuán sùlǜ biānjì	Cell rate margin	CRM
信元速率解耦	Xìnyuán sùlǜ jiě'ǒu	Cell rate decoupling	
信元头	Xìnyuán tóu	Cell header	
信元误插率	Xìnyuán wùchā lǜ	Cell mis-insertion rate	CMR
信元延迟变化	Xìnyuán yánchí biànhuà	Cell delay variation	CDV

信元延迟变化容限	Xìnyuán yánchí biànhuà róngxiàn	Cell delay variation tolerance	CDVT
信元转移时延	Xìnyuán zhuǎnyí shí yán	Cell transfer delay	CTD
心轴直径	Xīnzhóu zhíjìng	Center axis diameter	
雄猫	Xióngmāo	Tomcat (U.S. F-14 aircraft)	
熊猫电子	Xióngmāo diànzǐ	Panda Electronics (PRC company)	
洗牌	Xǐpái	Shuffle (from mahjong slang)	
锡桥	Xīqiáo	Bridge (in SMT)	
膝上型电脑	Xīshàngxíng diànnǎo	Laptop computer	
吸声能力	Xīshēng nénglì	Sound absorption ability	SAA
吸收	Xīshōu	Absorption	
吸收比	Xīshōu bǐ	Absorptance	
吸收边	Xīshōu biān	Absorption edges	
吸收池	Xīshōu chí	Absorption cell	
吸收带	Xīshōu dài	Absorption band	
吸收峰	Xīshōu fēng	Absorption peak	
吸收光度计	Xīshōu guāngdùjì	Absorptiometer	
吸收光谱	Xīshōu guāngpǔ	Absorption spectrum	
吸收率	Xīshōu lǜ	Absorptivity	
吸收钳	Xīshōu qián	Absorbing clamp	
吸收损耗	Xīshōu sǔnhào	Absorption loss	
吸收调制	Xīshōu tiáozhì	Absorption modulation	
吸收系数	Xīshōu xìshù	Absorption coefficient; absorption factor	
吸收修正	Xīshōu xiūzhèng	Absorption correction	
吸收指数	Xīshōu zhǐshù	Absorption index	
吸收式隔离器	Xīshōu-shì gélíqì	Absorption isolator	
吸收式频率计	Xīshōu-shì pínlǜjì	Absorption frequency meter	
吸收式衰减器	Xīshōu-shì shuāijiǎnqì	Absorptive attenuator	
吸收性	Xīshōuxìng	Absorptivity	
吸收性复盖层	Xīshōuxìng fùgài céng	Absorption overlay (coverage) (radar term)	
系数	Xìshù	Coefficient	
稀疏度	Xīshū dù	Sparsity	
稀疏二元矩阵	Xīshū èryuán jǔzhèn	Sparse binary matrix	
稀疏规则库	Xīshū guīzé kù	Sparse rule base	
稀疏矩阵	Xīshū jǔzhèn	Sparse matrix	
稀疏模式	Xīshū móshì	Sparse mode	SM
稀疏天线阵	Xīshū tiānxiàn zhèn	Thinned array antenna	TAA
稀疏图	Xīshū tú	Sparse graph	
稀疏型 PIM	Xīshū-xíng PIM	Sparse mode PIM	
系统保护	Xìtǒng bǎohù	System protection	
系统变更号码	Xìtǒng biàngēng hàomǎ	System change number (in ORACLE)	SCN
系统编码控制	Xìtǒng biānmǎ kòngzhì	System coding control	
系统编码容量	Xìtǒng biānmǎ róngliàng	System coding capacity	
系统表	Xìtǒng biǎo	System table	
系统标识	Xìtǒng biāozhì	System identification	SID
系统测试	Xìtǒng cèshì	System testing	
系统程序	Xìtǒng chéngxù	System program	

系统承载器	Xìtǒng chéngzàiqì	System loader	
系统初始化	Xìtǒng chūshǐhuà	System initialization	
系统存储过程	Xìtǒng cúnchǔ guòchéng	System stored procedures	
系统方法	Xìtǒng fāngfǎ	System approach	
系统访问控制列表	Xìtǒng fǎngwèn kòngzhì lièbiǎo	System access control list	SACL
系统仿真	Xìtǒng fǎngzhēn	System simulation	
系统仿真器	Xìtǒng fǎngzhēnqì	System simulator	SS
系统分析	Xìtǒng fēnxī	System analysis	SA
系统服务控制点	Xìtǒng fúwù kòngzhì diǎn	System services control point	SSCP
系统服务控制点格式	Xìtǒng fúwù kòngzhì diǎn géshi	System services control point format	SSCPFM
系统辅助设计	Xìtǒng fǔzhù shèjì	System-aided design	SAD
系统工程	Xìtǒng gōngchéng	Systems engineering	SE
系统工程师	Xìtǒng gōngchéng hī	System engineer	SE
系统工程组	Xìtǒng gōngchéng zǔ	System Engineering Group (CMM)	SEG
系统功能	Xìtǒng gōngnéng	System function	
系统管理	Xìtǒng guǎnlǐ	System management	
系统管理表	Xìtǒng guǎnlǐ biǎo	System table	
系统管理服务	Xìtǒng guǎnlǐ fúwù	System management service	
系统管理功能	Xìtǒng guǎnlǐ gōngnéng	System management function	SMF
系统管理功能单位	Xìtǒng guǎnlǐ gōngnéng dānwèi	System management function unit	
系统管理进程	Xìtǒng guǎnlǐ jìnchéng	Systems management process	
系统管理模式	Xìtǒng guǎnlǐ móshì	System management mode	SMM
系统管理内核	Xìtǒng guǎnlǐ nèihé	System management kernel	SMK
系统管理协会	Xìtǒng guǎnlǐ xiéhuì	Association for System Management	ASM
系统管理业务接口	Xìtǒng guǎnlǐ yèwù jiēkǒu	System management service interface	SMSI
系统管理应用程序	Xìtǒng guǎnlǐ yìngyòng chéngxù	System management application process	SMAP
系统管理应用服务单元	Xìtǒng guǎnlǐ yìngyòng fúwù dānyuán	System management application service element	SMASE
系统管理应用实体	Xìtǒng guǎnlǐ yìngyòng shítǐ	System management application entity	SMAE
系统管理应用协议机	Xìtǒng guǎnlǐ yìngyòng xiéyì jī	System management application protocol machine	SMAPM
系统管理中断	Xìtǒng guǎnlǐ zhōngduàn	System management interrupt	SMI
系统管理终端	Xìtǒng guǎnlǐ zhōngduān	System manager terminal	
系统管理总线	Xìtǒng guǎnlǐ zǒngxiàn	System management bus	SMB
系统管理员	Xìtǒng guǎnlǐyuán	System administrator	
系统规范	Xìtǒng guīfàn	System specification	
系统规划	Xìtǒng guīhuà	Systems planning	
系统故障	Xìtǒng gùzhàng	System failure	
系统函数	Xìtǒng hánshù	System function	
系统恢复时间	Xìtǒng huīfù shíjiān	System recovery time	
系统监视	Xìtǒng jiānshì	System monitoring	
系统加载	Xìtǒng jiāzài	System loading	SL
系统集成	Xìtǒng jíchéng	System integration	
系统集成测试	Xìtǒng jíchéng cèshì	System integration test	SIT
系统集成多功能芯片	Xìtǒng jíchéng duōgōngnéng xìnpiàn	System on a chip	SOAC
系统集成商	Xìtǒng jíchéng shāng	System integrator	
系统集成芯片	Xìtǒng jíchéng xìnpiàn	System-on-a-chip	SONC
系统结构	Xìtǒng jiégòu	System architecture	

系统开发方法	Xìtǒng kāifā fāngfǎ	Systems development methodology	
系统可行性论证	Xìtǒng kěxíngxìng lùnzhèng	System feasibility study	
系统可用性信息点	Xìtǒng kěyòngxìng xìnxī diǎn	System availability information point	
系统控制	Xìtǒng kòngzhì	System control	
系统控制板	Xìtǒng kòngzhì bǎn	System control board	SCB
系统控制盘	Xìtǒng kòngzhì pán	System control panel	SCP
系统利用率监控器	Xìtǒng lìyònglǜ jiānkòngqì	System utilization monitor	SUM
系统描述语言	Xìtǒng miáoshù yǔyán	System description language	SDL
系统模块	Xìtǒng mókuài	System module	
系统模拟	Xìtǒng mónǐ	System simulation	
系统模拟器	Xìtǒng mónǐqì	System simulator	SS
系统默认配置文件	Xìtǒng mòrèn pèizhì wénjiàn	System default profile	
系统模型	Xìtǒng móxíng	System model	
系统目录	Xìtǒng mùlù	System catalog	
系统内存	Xìtǒng nèicún	System memory	
系统评估	Xìtǒng pínggū	System evaluation	
系统启动	Xìtǒng qǐdòng	System initiation	
系统全呼	Xìtǒng quánhū	System-wide call	
系统任务	Xìtǒng rènwu	System task	
系统设计	Xìtǒng shèjì	Systems design	
系统设计评审	Xìtǒng shèjì píngshěn	System design review	
系统生成	Xìtǒng shēngchéng	System generation	SYSGEN
系统识别码	Xìtǒng shíbié mǎ	System identification	SID
系统时间	Xìtǒng shíjiān	System time	
系统试验	Xìtǒng shìyàn	System testing	
系统失真	Xìtǒng shīzhēn	System distortion	SD
系统数据库	Xìtǒng shùjùkù	System database (for database)	
系统损耗	Xìtǒng sǔnhào	System loss	SL
系统通信语句	Xìtǒng tōngxìn yǔjù	System communication statement	
系统网络建筑	Xìtǒng wǎngluò jiànzhù	System network architecture	SNA
系统网络结构	Xìtǒng wǎngluò jiégòu	System network architecture	
系统网络体系结构	Xìtǒng wǎngluò tǐxì jiégòu	System network architecture	SNA
系统网络体系结构及其协议	Xìtǒng wǎngluò tǐxì jiégòu jí qí xiéyì	Systems network architecture and protocols (IBM use)	SNA
系统完整性	Xìtǒng wánzhěngxìng	System integrity	
系统完整性规程	Xìtǒng wánzhěngxìng guīchéng	System integrity procedure	
系统误差	Xìtǒng wùchā	Systematic error	
系统信息	Xìtǒng xìnxī	System information	SI
系统信息观察器	Xìtǒng xìnxī guāncháqì	System information viewer	SIV
系统信息类型	Xìtǒng xìnxī lèixíng	System information type	
系统业务层	Xìtǒng yèwù céng	System service layer	SSL
系统一致性测试报告	Xìtǒng yīzhìxìng cèshì bàogào	System conformance test report	SCTR
系统一致性陈述	Xìtǒng yīzhìxìng chénshù	System conformance statement	SCS
系统优化	Xìtǒng yōuhuà	System optimization	
系统余量	Xìtǒng yúliàng	System margin	SM
系统增益	Xìtǒng zēngyì	System gain	SG
系统帧号码	Xìtǒng zhèng hàomǎ	System frame number	SFN

系统支援机器	Xìtǒng zhīyuán jīqì	System support machine	SSM
系统中断期	Xìtǒng zhōngduàn qī	Total system downtime	
系统自检	Xìtǒng zì jiǎn	System self-check	
系统总工作时间	Xìtǒng zǒnggōngzuò shíjiān	System overall operating time	
系统总线接口集成件	Xìtǒng zǒngxiàn jiēkǒu jíchéng jiàn	System bus interface assembly	SBIA
系统坐标系	Xìtǒng zuòbiāo xì	System coordinate system	
系统间电磁兼容性	Xìtǒng-jiān diàncí jiānróngxìng	Inter-system electromagnetic compatibility	
系统间干扰	Xìtǒng-jiān gānrǎo	Inter-system interference	
系统论	Xìtǒnglùn	System theory	
系统内电磁兼容性	Xìtǒng-nèi diàncí jiānróngxìng	Intra-system electromagnetic compatibility	
系统内干扰	Xìtǒng-nèi gānrǎo	Intra-system interference	
系统内噪声	Xìtǒng-nèi zàoshēng	Intra-system noise	
系统性故障	Xìtǒngxìng gùzhàng	Systematic fault	
系统性失效	Xìtǒngxìng shīxiào	Systematic failure	
稀土族材料	Xītǔ zú cáiliào	Rare earth material	
袖珍铃	Xiù zhēnlíng	Pocket bell	
修补	Xiūbǔ	Patch	
修复	Xiūfù	Restore	
修复范围	Xiūfù fànwéi	Repair coverage	
修复性维护	Xiūfùxìng wéihù	Corrective maintenance	
修复性维护时间	Xiūfùxìng wéihù shíjiān	Corrective maintenance time	
修改量	Xiūgǎi liàng	Modifier	
修改完成	Xiūgǎi wánchéng	Modify complete	
修改，排除，共享，废弃	Xiūgǎi, páichú, gòngxiǎng, fèiqì	Modified, exclusive, shared, invalid	MESI
溴化硼	Xiùhuàpéng	Boron bromide	BBr_3
修理	Xiūlǐ	Repair	
修理产品(装备)	Xiūlǐ chǎnpǐn (zhuāngbèi)	Repaired item	
修理时间	Xiūlǐ shíjiān	Repair time	
修理中心	Xiūlǐ zhōngxīn	Repair center	RC
修饰符	Xiūshì fú	Modifier	
修饰符	Xiūshì fú	Qualifier	
修饰字	Xiūshì zì	Modifier	
休斯公司	Xiū-sī gōngsī	Hughes Corp.	
嗅探器	Xiùtànqì	Sniffer (hacker program)	
袖珍设备	Xiùzhēn shèbèi	Pocket (personal) equipment	
修正艾伦偏差	Xiūzhèng ài-lún piānchā	Modified Allan deviation	MADEV
修正参考当量	Xiūzhèng cānkǎo dāngliàng	Corrected reference equivalent	
修正哈达玛方差	Xiūzhèng hǎ-dá-mǎ fāngchà	Modified Hadama variance	MHV
修正的相对元素位置指示编码	Xiūzhèngde xiāngduì yuánsù wèizhì zhǐshì biānmǎ	Modified relative element address designator code	MR
修正的正交重叠基座余弦调制	Xiūzhèngde zhèngjiāo chóngdié jīzuò yúxián tiáozhì	Modified quadrature overlapped raised-cosine modulation	MQORC
隙外信令	Xì-wài xìnlìng	Out-slot signaling	
吸引	Xīyǐn	Snap (ARCView term)	
吸引力	Xīyǐnlì	Attractiveness	
吸嘴	Xīzuǐ	Nozzle	

XML 密钥管理规范	XML mìyào guǎnlǐ guīfàn	Extensible markup language key management specification	XKMS
虚电路	Xū diànlù	Virtual circuit	
虚电路标志	Xū diànlù biāozhì	Virtual path identifier	VPI
虚调用	Xū diàoyòng	Virtual call (computer software term)	VC
虚光路	Xū guāng lù	Virtual optical path	
虚函数	Xū hánshù	Virtual function	
虚呼叫	Xū hūjiào	Virtual call (telecom term)	VC
虚呼叫控制	Xū hūjiào kòngzhì	Virtual call control	VCC
虚呼叫连接	Xū hūjiào liánjiē	Virtual call connection	VCC
虚级联	Xū jílián	Virtual concatenation	
虚境	Xū jìng	Virtuality	
虚警概率	Xū jǐng gàilǜ	False alarm probability	
虚连接	Xū liánjiē	Virtual connect	VC
虚连接的基本段	Xū liánjiēde jīběn duàn	Basic section of a virtual connection	
虚路径	Xū lùjìng	Virtual path	
虚判决值	Xū pànjué zhí	Virtual decision values	
虚频特性	Xū pín tèxìng	Imaginary frequency characteristic	
虚取	Xū qǔ	Virtual fetch	VF
虚取向量表	Xū qǔ xiàngliáng biǎo	Virtual fetch vector table	VFVT
虚容器	Xū róngqì	Virtual container	VC
虚容器通道开销	Xū róngqì tōngdào kāixiao	Virtual container path overhead	VC POH
虚通道	Xū tōngdào	Virtual path	
虚通道标志	Xū tōngdào biāozhì	Virtual channel identifier	VCI
虚通道标识	Xū tōngdào biāozhì	Virtual path identifier	VPI
虚通道复用实体	Xū tōngdào fùyòng shítǐ	Virtual path multiplex entity	VPME
虚通道告警指示信号	Xū tōngdào gàojǐng zhǐshì xìnhào	Virtual path--alarm indication signal	VP-AIS
虚通道级	Xū tōngdào jí	Virtual path level	
虚通道连接	Xū tōngdào liánjiē	Virtual path connection	VPC
虚通道连接标识符--连续性检验	Xū tōngdào liánjiē biāozhì fú--liánxùxìng jiǎnyàn	Virtual path connection identifier--continuous checking	VPCI-CC
虚通道连接终接	Xū tōngdào liánjiē zhōngjiē	Virtual path connection termination	VPCT
虚通道链路	Xū tōngdào liànlù	Virtual path link	
虚通道识别码	Xū tōngdào shíbié mǎ	Virtual channel identifier	VCI
虚通道识别码	Xū tōngdào shíbié mǎ	Virtual path identifier	VPI
虚通道实体	Xū tōngdào shítǐ	Virtual path entity	VPE
虚通道远端故障指示	Xū tōngdào yuǎnduān gùzhàng zhǐshì	Virtual path--remote defect indicator	VP-RDI
虚通道组	Xū tōngdào zǔ	Virtual path group	VPG
虚通路	Xū tōnglù	Virtual path (preferred)	VP
虚通路包	Xū tōnglù bāo	Virtual container	VC
虚通路标志	Xū tōnglù biāozhì	Virtual path identifier	VPI
虚通路标识	Xū tōnglù biāozhì	Virtual channel identifier	VCI
虚通路标识符	Xū tōnglù biāozhì fú	Virtual path identifier	VPI
虚通路复用实体	Xū tōnglù fùyòng shítǐ	Virtual channel multiplex entity	VCME
虚通路告警指示信号	Xū tōnglù gàojǐng zhǐshì xìnhào	Virtual channel--alarm indication signal	VC-AIS
虚通路级	Xū tōnglù jí	Virtual channel level	
虚通路级	Xū tōnglù jí	Virtual path level	

虚通路连接	Xū tōnglù liánjiē	Virtual path connection (preferred)	VPC
虚通路连接	Xū tōnglù liánjiē	Virtual channel connection	VCC
虚通路连接端点	Xū tōnglù liánjiē duāndiǎn	Virtual path connection endpoint	VPCE
虚通路连接终接	Xū tōnglù liánjiē zhōngjiē	Virtual channel connection termination	VCCT
虚通路连接的有关功能	Xū tōnglù liánjiēde yǒuguān gōngnéng	Virtual path connection related function	CRF(VP)
虚通路链路	Xū tōnglù liànlù	Virtual path link	VPL
虚通路链路	Xū tōnglù liànlù	Virtual channel link	
虚通路路径终接点	Xū tōnglù lùjìng zhōng jiēdiǎn	Virtual channel trail termination point	vcTTP
虚通路识别码	Xū tōnglù shíbié mǎ	Virtual channel indicator	VCI
虚通路实体	Xū tōnglù shítǐ	Virtual channel entity	VCE
虚通路远端故障指示	Xū tōnglù yuǎn duān gùzhàng zhǐshì	Virtual channel--remote defect indication	VC-RDI
虚信道	Xū xìndào	Virtual channel	VC
虚信道标志	Xū xìndào biāozhì	Virtual channel identifier	VCI
虚信道标识	Xū xìndào biāozhì	Virtual channel identifier	VCI
虚信道级	Xū xìndào jí	Virtual channel level	
虚信道连接	Xū xìndào liánjiē	Virtual channel connection	
虚信道连接端点	Xū xìndào liánjiē duāndiǎn	Virtual channel connection endpoint	VCCE
虚信道连接的有关功能	Xū xìndào liánjiēde yǒuguān gōngnéng	Virtual channel connection related function	CRF(VC)
虚信道链路	Xū xìndào liànlù	Virtual channel link	VCL
虚信道识别幅	Xū xìndào shíbié fú	Virtual channel identifier	VCI
虚终端客户和服务器	Xū zhōngduān kèhù hé fúwùqì	Virtual terminal clients and servers	
虚终端客户机和服务器	Xū zhōngduān kèhùjī hé fúwùqì	Virtual terminal clients and servers	
虚中继	Xū zhōngjì	Virtual trunk	
旋磁材料	Xuáncí cáiliào	Gyromagnetic material	
旋磁功率限制器	Xuáncí gōnglǜ xiànzhìqì	Gyromagnetic power limiter	
旋磁滤波器	Xuáncí lǜbōqì	Gyromagnetic filter	
旋磁媒质	Xuáncí méizhì	Gyromagnetic medium	
旋磁器件	Xuáncí qìjiàn	Gyromagnetic device	
旋磁效应	Xuáncí xiàoyìng	Gyromagnetic effects	
旋磁谐振	Xuáncí xiézhèn	Gyromagnetic resonance	
旋磁谐振器	Xuáncí xiézhènqì	Gyromagnetic resonator	
旋磁比	Xuáncíbǐ	Gyromagnetic ratio	
选单	Xuǎndān	Menu	
悬挂	Xuánguà	Dangle	
悬挂长度	Xuánguà chángdù	Dangle length	
悬挂节点	Xuánguà jiédiǎn	Dangling node	
悬挂容差	Xuánguà róngchā	Dangle tolerance	
悬空式光缆	Xuánkōng-shì guānglǎn	Aerial fiber optic cable	
选路策略	Xuǎnlù cèlüè	Routing policy	
选路关键字	Xuǎnlù guānjiàn zì	Routing keyword	
选路上下文	Xuǎnlù shangxiàwén	Routing context	
选路验证测试	Xuǎnlù yànzhèng cèshì	Route verify test	RVT
选配器	Xuǎnpèiqì	Selector	
选频放大器	Xuǎnpín fàngdàqì	Bandpass amplifier	
选频直防站	Xuǎnpín zhífángzhàn	Selective frequency repeater	
渲染	Xuànrǎn	Render (video term)	

选通	Xuǎntōng	Gating	
选项	Xuǎnxiàng	Option	
选择	Xuǎnzé	Select, selection, selective	
选择查询	Xuǎnzé cháxún	Select query	
选择重发ARQ	Xuǎnzé chóngfā ARQ	Selective repeat ARQ	
选择发送分集	Xuǎnzé fāsòng fēn jí	Selection transmission diversity	STD
选择呼叫设备	Xuǎnzé hūjiào shèbèi	Selective-calling equipment	
选择呼叫系统	Xuǎnzé hūjiào xìtǒng	Selective-calling system	
选择拒绝	Xuǎnzé jùjué	Selective reject	SREJ
选择可用性	Xuǎnzé kěyòngxing	Selective availability	SA
选择列表	Xuǎnzé lièbiǎo	Select list	
选择密文攻击	Xuǎnzé mìwén gōngjī	Chosen ciphertext attack (IPsec)	
选择排序	Xuǎnzé páixù	Selection sort	
选择全部	Xuǎnzé quánbù	Select all (WP command)	
选择声码处理器	Xuǎnzé shēngmǎ chǔlǐqì	Selector vocoder processor	SVP
选择输入装载控制	Xuǎnzé shūrù zhuāngzài kòngzhì	Selective incoming load control	SILC
选择通信模式	Xuǎnzé tōngxìn móshì	Selected communications mode	SCM
选择图层	Xuǎnzé tú céng	Selection coverage	
选择位置分集发射	Xuǎnzé wèizhì fēnjí fāshè	Site selection diversity transmission	SSDT
选择易码集成件	Xuǎnzé yìmǎ jíchéng jiàn	Selector transcoder assembly	SXOA
选择易码接口集成件	Xuǎnzé yìmǎ jiēkǒu jíchéng jiàn	Selector transcoder interface assembly	SXIA
选择域保护	Xuǎnzé yù bǎohù	Selective field protection (IPsec)	
选择域机密性	Xuǎnzé yù jīmìxìng	Selective field confidentiality (IPsec)	
选择域连接完整性	Xuǎnzé yù liánjiē wánzhěngxìng	Selective field connection integrity (IPsec)	
选择域无连接完整性	Xuǎnzé yù wúliánjiē wánzhěngxìng	Selective field connectionless integrity (IPsec)	
选择语句	Xuǎnzé yǔjù	Selective statement	
选择器	Xuǎnzéqì	Selector	
选择器接口卡管理器	Xuǎnzéqì jiēkǒu kǎ guǎnlǐqì	Selector interface card manager	SCM
选择器子系统	Xuǎnzéqì zixìtǒng	Selector bank sub-system	SBS
选择器子系统机架	Xuǎnzéqì zixìtǒng jījià	Selector bank sub-system rack	SBSR
选择器/声码器	Xuǎnzéqì/shēngmǎqì	Selector/vocoder	S/V
选择性	Xuǎnzéxìng	Selectivity	
选择性供给	Xuǎnzéxìng gōngjǐ	Selective availability	SA
选择性广播信令虚通路	Xuǎnzéxìng guǎngbō xìnlìng xū tōnglù	Selective broadcast signaling virtual path	
选择性广播信令虚通路	Xuǎnzéxìng guǎngbō xìnlìng xū tōnglù	Selective broadcast signaling virtual channel	
选择性广播信令虚信道	Xuǎnzéxìng guǎngbō xìnlìng xū xìndào	Selective broadcast signaling virtual channel	SBSVC
选择性呼叫	Xuǎnzéxìng hūjiào	Selective calling	
选址信道	Xuǎnzhǐ xìndào	Access channel (in CDMA)	
选址-配置模型	Xuǎnzhǐ—pèizhì móxíng	Location and allocation model	
旋转变压器	Xuánzhuǎn biànyāqì	Rotary transformer	
旋转场天线	Xuánzhuǎn cháng tiānxiàn	Rotating-field antenna	
旋转动力学理论	Xuánzhuǎn dònglìxué lǐlùn	Rotation dynamics theory	
旋转关节	Xuánzhuǎn guānjié	Rotary joint	
旋转加速伺服系统	Xuánzhuǎn jiāsù sìfú xìtǒng	Rotary acceleration feed forward (Western Digital Corp. hard drive technology)	RAFF
旋转异常	Xuánzhuǎn yìcháng	Rotation anomaly	
旋转式偏转线圈	Xuánzhuǎn-shì piānzhuǎn xiànquān	Rotary deflection coil	

旋转式相位变换器	Xuánzhuǎnshì xiàngwèi biànhuànqì	Rotary phase changer	
旋转式选择器	Xuánzhuǎnshì xuǎnzéqì	Rotary selector	
旋转式翼形衰减器	Xuánzhuǎnshì yìxíng shuāijiǎnqì	Rotary vane attenuator	
选组器	Xuǎnzǔqì	Pre-selector	
虚报概率	Xūbào gàilǜ	Probability of false report	
雪崩二极管	Xuěbēng èrjíguǎn	Avalanche diode	AD
雪崩光二极管	Xuěbēng guāng èrjíguǎn	Avalanche photo diode	APD
雪崩光电二极管	Xuěbēng guāngdiàn èrjíguǎn	Avalanche diode	AD
雪崩光电二极管耦合器	Xuěbēng guāngdiàn èrjíguǎn ǒuhéqì	Avalanche photodiode coupler	APC
雪崩光电检测器	Xuěbēng guāngdiàn jiǎncèqì	Avalanche photo-detector	APD
雪崩光电探测器	Xuěbēng guāngdiàn tàncèqì	Avalanche photo-detector	APD
雪崩可控整流器	Xuěbēng kěkòng zhěngliúqì	Avalanche controlled rectifier	ACR
雪花架构	Xuěhuā jiàgòu	Snowflake schema	
雪花模型	Xuěhuā móxíng	Snowflake model	
雪茄形天线	Xuějiāxíng tiānxiàn	Cigar antenna	
学位等级记录审验考试	Xuéwèi děngjí jìlù shěnyàn kǎoshì	Graduate record examination	GRE
序贯估计快速捕获	Xùguàn gūji kuàisù bǔhuò	Rapid acquisition by sequential estimation	RASE
序号	Xùhào	Serial number	SNR
序号保护	Xùhào bǎohù	Sequence number protection	SNP
序号攻击	Xùhào gōngjī	Sequence number attack (cryptology)	
序号检测装置	Xùhào jiǎncè zhuāngzhì	Serial presence detect	SPD
序号码	Xùhào mǎ	Serial number	
虚假包比例	Xūjiǎ bāo bǐlì	Spurious packet ratio	SPR
虚假信号	Xūjiǎ xìnhào	Signal imitation (in VF signaling)	
许可证	Xǔkězhèng	License	
序列	Xùliè	Sequence	
序列发起方	Xùliè fāqǐ fāng	Sequence initiator	
序列分组交换协议	Xùliè fēnzǔ jiāohuàn xiéyì	Sequenced packet exchange protocol (Novell usage)	SPX
序列号码	Xùliè hàomǎ	Sequence number	SN
序列号码机制	Xùliè hàomǎ jīzhì	Sequential numbering scheme	SEQN
序列接收方	Xùliè jiēshōu fāng	Sequence recipient	
序列路由更新协议	Xùliè lùyóu gēngxīn xiéyì	Sequenced routing update protocol	SRTP
序列密码	Xùliè mìmǎ	Stream cipher	
序列完整性	Xùliè wánzhěngxìng	Integrity sequencing	
序列细化	Xùliè xìhuà	Sequential thinning	
序列号协议数据单元	Xùlièhào xiéyì shùjù dānyuán	Sequence numbers protocol data unit	SNP
序列化	Xùlièhuà	Serialization/serialize	
序列式容器	Xùlièshì róngqì	Sequential container	
寻呼	Xúnhū	Page (verb)	
寻呼闭塞周期性	Xúnhū bìsè zhōuqīxìng	Paging block periodicity	PBP
寻呼分组计算	Xúnhū fēnzǔ jìsuàn	Paging packet calculation	
寻呼规程	Xúnhū guīchéng	Paging procedure	
寻呼接收机	Xúnhū jiēshōujī	Paging receiver	
寻呼控制信道	Xúnhū kòngzhì xìndào	Paging control channel	PCCH
寻呼模式	Xúnhū móshì	Pager mode	
寻呼请求	Xúnhū qǐngqiú	Paging request	PR

寻呼请求类型	Xúnhū qǐngqiú lèixíng	Paging request type	
寻呼响应	Xúnhū xiǎngyìng	Paging response	
寻呼信道	Xúnhū xìndào	Paging channel	PC, PCH
寻呼系统	Xúnhū xìtǒng	Paging system	
寻呼指示信道	Xúnhū zhǐshì xìndào	Paging indicator channel	PICH
寻呼指示器	Xúnhū zhǐshìqì	Page indicator	PI
循环	Xúnhuán	Loop, cycle, circular	
循环不定位	Xúnhuán bùdìngwèi	Cyclic unfixed (channel assignment)	
循环定位	Xúnhuán dìngwèi	Cyclic fixed (channel assignment)	
循环对称网络	Xúnhuán duìchèn wǎngluò	Cyclically symmetric network	CSN
循环队列	Xúnhuán duìliè	Cirular queue	
循环概率误差	Xúnhuán gàilǜ wùchā	Circular probable error	CPE
循环校正字节	Xúnhuán jiàozhèng zìjié	Cyclic check byte	CCB
循环冷却机	Xúnhuán lěngquèjī	Recirculating chiller (semiconductor mfg)	
循环链表	Xúnhuán liàn biǎo	Circular linked list	
循环连接	Xúnhuán liánjiē	Loop join (in SQL Server)	
循环码	Xúnhuán mǎ	Cyclic code	
循环码移键控	Xúnhuán mǎyí jiànkòng	Cyclic code-shift keying	CCSK
循环排队系统	Xúnhuán páiduì xìtǒng	Cyclic queuing system	
循环启/闭环转换控制	Xúnhuán qǐ/bìhuán zhuǎnhuàn kòngzhì	Cyclic on/off switching control	
循环曲线	Xúnhuán qūxiàn	Recurrence curve	
循环冗余编码	Xúnhuán rǒngyú biānmǎ	Cyclical redundancy code	CRC
循环冗余差错	Xúnhuán rǒngyú chācuò	Cyclical redundancy error	CRE
循环冗余检查	Xúnhuán rǒngyú jiǎnchá	Cyclical redundancy check	CRC
循环冗余检验	Xúnhuán rǒngyú jiǎnyàn	Cyclical redundancy check	CRC
循环冗余校验	Xúnhuán rǒngyú jiàoyàn	Cyclical redundancy correction	CRC
循环冗余校验码	Xúnhuán rǒngyú jiàoyàn mǎ	Cyclic redundancy check code	CRC
循环时间	Xúnhuán shíjiān	Cycle time	
循环寿命	Xúnhuán shòumìng	Cycle life	
循环输入输出程序	Xúnhuán shūrù shūchū chéngxù	Circular input-output routine	CIO
循环速率	Xúnhuán sùlǜ	Cycle rate (in SMT)	
循环误差概率	Xúnhuán wùchā gàilǜ	Circular error probability	CEP
循环序列	Xúnhuán xùliè	Circular sequence	
寻呼机标识码	Xúnhūjī biāozhì mǎ	Radio pager identity code	RIC
虚拟表	Xūnǐ biǎo	Virtual table	
虚拟拨号专网	Xūnǐ bōhào zhuānwǎng	Virtual private dial-up network	VPDN
虚拟拨号专用网络	Xūnǐ bōhào zhuānyòng wǎngluò	Virtual private dial-up network	VPDN
虚拟操作系统	Xūnǐ cāozuò xìtǒng	Virtual operating system	VOS
虚拟程序状态字	Xūnǐ chéngxù zhuàngtài zì	Virtual program status word	VPSW
虚拟存储	Xūnǐ cúnchǔ	Virtual memory	
虚拟存储	Xūnǐ cúnchǔ	Virtual storage	VS
虚拟存储管理	Xūnǐ cúnchǔ guǎnlǐ	Virtual storage management	VSM
虚拟存储环境	Xūnǐ cúnchǔ huánjìng	Virtual memory environment	VME
虚拟存储器分配	Xūnǐ cúnchǔqì fēnpèi	Virtual memory allocation	VMA
虚拟 DOS 机	Xūnǐ DOS jī	Virtual DOS machine	VDM
虚拟多维数据集	Xūnǐ duōwéi shùjùjí	Virtual datacube	

虚拟分组终端	Xūnǐ fēnzǔ zhōngduān	Virtual packet terminal	VPT
虚拟服务器	Xūnǐ fúwùqì	Virtual server	
虚拟根	Xūnǐ gēn	Virtual root	
虚拟工作场所	Xūnǐ gōngzuò chángsuǒ	Virtual workplace	
虚拟归属环境	Xūnǐ guīshǔ huánjìng	Virtual home environment	VHE
虚拟呼叫	Xūnǐ hūjiào	Virtual call	VC
虚拟机	Xūnǐ jī	Virtual machine	
虚拟交互控制器	Xūnǐ jiāohù kòngzhìqì	Virtual interaction controller	VIC
虚拟家区环境	Xūnǐ jiāqū huánjìng	Virtual home environment	VHE
虚拟家庭环境	Xūnǐ jiātíng huánjìng	Virtual home environment	VHE
虚拟接口模板	Xūnǐ jiēkǒu múbǎn	Virtual interface template	
虚拟接口体系	Xūnǐ jiēkǒu tǐxì	Virtual interface architecture	VIA
虚拟机器	Xūnǐ jīqì	Virtual machine	
虚拟局域网	Xūnǐ júyù wǎng	Virtual local area network	VLAN
虚拟局域网标识符	Xūnǐ júyù wǎng biāozhìfú	Virtual local area network (LAN) identifier	VID
虚拟空间会议系统	Xūnǐ kōngjiān huìyì xìtǒng	Virtual space teleconferencing system	VST
虚拟连接	Xūnǐ liánjiē	Virtual connection	VC
虚拟连接树	Xūnǐ liánjiē shù	Virtual connection tree	
虚拟连接树切换	Xūnǐ liánjiē shù qiēhuàn	Virtual connection tree handoff	
虚拟路径标识符	Xūnǐ lùjìng biāozhì fú	Virtual path identifier	VPI
虚拟路由标识符	Xūnǐ lùyóu biāozhì fú	Virtual route identifier	VRID
虚拟路由器	Xūnǐ lùyóuqì	Virtual router	VR
虚拟路由器冗余协议	Xūnǐ lùyóuqì rǒngyú xiéyì	Virtual router redundancy protocol (in LINUX and an IETF protocol)	VRRP
虚拟码	Xūnǐ mǎ	Pseudo code	
虚拟脉冲串	Xūnǐ màichōng chuàn	Dummy burst	DB
虚拟内存	Xūnǐ nèicún	Virtual memory	
虚拟配置管道	Xūnǐ pèizhì guǎndào	Virtual provisioned pipe	VPrP
虚拟配置网	Xūnǐ pèizhì wǎng	Virtual provisioned network	VPrN
虚拟企业	Xūnǐ qǐyè	Virtual enterprise	
虚拟冗余路由器协议	Xūnǐ rǒngyú lùyóuqì xiéyì	Virtual redundant router protocol	VRRP
虚拟设备驱动程序	Xūnǐ shèbèi qūdòng chéngxù	Virtual device drivers	VxD
虚拟实境	Xūnǐ shíjìng	Virtual reality	
虚拟输出排队	Xūnǐ shūchū páiduì	Virtual output queue	VOQ
虚拟私有拨号网络	Xūnǐ sīyǒu bōhào wǎngluò	Virtual private dial network	VPDN
虚拟通道标识符	Xūnǐ tōngdào biāozhìfú	Virtual channel identifier	VCI
虚拟通道内存结构	Xūnǐ tōngdào nèicún jiégòu	Virtual channel memory architecture	VCMA
虚拟突发脉冲序列	Xūnǐ tūfā màichōng xùliè	Dummy burst	DB
虚拟网	Xūnǐ wǎng	Virtual network service	VNS
虚拟网络地址转换	Xūnǐ wǎngluò dìzhǐ zhuǎnhuàn	Virtual network address translation	VNAT
虚拟网元	Xūnǐ wǎngyuán	Virtual network element	
虚拟维度	Xūnǐ wéidù	Virtual dimension	
虚拟文件分配表	Xūnǐ wénjiàn fēnpèi biǎo	Virtual file allocation table	VFAT
虚拟线交换环	Xūnǐ xiàn jiāohuàn huán	Virtual line switching ring	VLSR
虚拟现实	Xūnǐ xiànshí	Virtual reality	VR
虚拟现实标记语言	Xūnǐ xiànshí biāojì yǔyán	Virtual reality mark-up language	VRML
虚拟现实建模语言	Xūnǐ xiànshí jiànmó yǔyán	Virtual reality modeling language	VRML

虚拟现实模型语言	Xūnǐ xiànshí móxíng yǔyán	Virtual reality modeling language	VRML
虚拟信道标识符	Xūnǐ xìndào biāozhì fú	Virtual channel identifier	VCI
虚拟信道连接	Xūnǐ xìndào liánjiē	Virtual channel connection	VCC
虚拟硬件描述语言	Xūnǐ yìngjiàn miáoshù yǔyán	Virtual hardware description language	VHDL
虚拟用户端口	Xūnǐ yònghù duānkǒu	Virtual user port	VUP
虚拟用户专网	Xūnǐ yònghù zhuānwǎng	Virtual private network	VPN
虚拟远程通信存取法	Xūnǐ yuǎnchéng tōngxìn cúnqǔ fǎ	Virtual telecommunication access method	VTAM
虚拟源点	Xūnǐ yuándiǎn	Virtual source	VS
虚拟原型	Xūnǐ yuánxíng	Virtual prototype	
虚拟原型建模语言	Xūnǐ yuánxíng jiànmó yǔyán	Virtual prototype modeling language (CAD/CAM)	VPML
虚拟执行引擎	Xūnǐ zhíxíng yǐnqíng	Virtual execution engine	VEE
虚拟终点	Xūnǐ zhōngdiǎn	Virtual destination	VD
虚拟终端	Xūnǐ zhōngduān	Virtual terminal	VT
虚拟终端规约	Xūnǐ zhōngduān guīyuē	Virtual terminal protocol	VTP
虚拟终端协议	Xūnǐ zhōngduān xiéyì	Virtual terminal protocol (a Cisco protocol)	VTP
虚拟专网	Xūnǐ zhuānwǎng	Virtual private network	VPN
虚拟专线	Xūnǐ zhuānxiàn	Virtual leased line	VLL
虚拟专用拨号网络	Xūnǐ zhuānyòng bōhào wǎngluò	Virtual private dial network	VPDN
虚拟专用局域网业务	Xūnǐ zhuānyòng júyùwǎng yèwù	Virtual private LAN service	VPLS
虚拟专用 LAN 网段	Xūnǐ zhuānyòng LAN wǎngduàn	Virtual private LAN segment	VPLS
虚拟专用 LAN 子网段	Xūnǐ zhuānyòng LAN ziwǎng duàn	Virtual private LAN segment	VPLS
虚拟专用路由网络	Xūnǐ zhuānyòng lùyóu wǎngluò	Virtual private routed network	VPRN
虚拟专用网	Xūnǐ zhuānyòng wǎng	Virtual private network	VPN
虚拟专用网业务	Xūnǐ zhuānyòng wǎng yèwù	Virtual private network service	VPNS
虚拟专用线业务	Xūnǐ zhuānyòng xiàn yèwù	Virtual private wire service	VPWS
虚拟专用移动网	Xūnǐ zhuānyòng yídòng wǎng	Virtual private mobile network	VPMN
虚拟综合通信存取法	Xūnǐ zōnghé tōngxìn cúnqǔ fǎ	Virtual integrated communications access method	VICAM
虚拟租用线路	Xūnǐ zūyòng xiànlù	Virtual leased line	VLL
虚拟组织	Xūnǐ zǔzhī	Virtual organization	
虚拟化	Xūnǐhuà	Virtualization	
训练	Xùnliàn	Training	
训练系列号	Xùnliàn xìliè hào	Training sequence code	TSC
训练序列码	Xùnliàn xùliè mǎ	Training sequence code	TSC
训练样本	Xùnliàn yàngběn	Training sample	
询问	Xúnwèn	Enquiry (inquiry), interrogate	ENQ
询问电路群信息	Xúnwèn diànlù qún xìnxī	Circuit group query message (ISUP message)	CQM
询问机	Xúnwèn jī	Interrogator	
询问节点	Xúnwèn jiédiǎn	Interrogating node (GSM term)	
询问信息交换	Xúnwèn xìnxī jiāohuàn	Inquiry message exchange	IMX
寻线	Xúnxiàn	Line hunting	LH
寻线组	Xúnxiànzǔ	Line finding	
寻找呼叫信号	Xúnzhǎo hūjiào xìnhào	Find calling party	FC
寻找邻居	Xúnzhǎo línjū	Neighborhood discovery	ND
寻找邻居守护程序	Xúnzhǎo línjū shǒuhù chéngxù	Neighborhood discovery daemon	
寻找页	Xúnzhǎo yè	Go to page (WP command)	
寻找组	Xúnzhǎo zǔ	Hunt group	

需求发送	Xūqiú fāsòng	Request to send	RTS
需求工程	Xūqiú gōngchéng	Requirements engineering	
需求管理	Xūqiú guǎnlǐ	Request management (CMM)	RM
需求优先级	Xūqiú yōuxiān jí	Demand priority	
序数逻辑回归	Xùshù luóji huíguī	Ordinal logistic regression	
序数数据	Xùshù shùjù	Ordinal data	
嘘音	Xūyīn	Hiss	
许用不平衡量	Xǔyòng bùpínghéng liàng	Allowable imbalance	
许用码组	Xǔyòng mǎzǔ	Permissible code block	

Y

亚临界流	Yà línjiè liú	Sub-critical flow	
氩离子激光	Yà lízǐ jīguāng	Argon laser	
压差式	Yāchā-shì	Pressure gradient	PG
压电定位设备	Yādiàn dìngwèi shèbèi	Piezoelectric positioning equipment	
压电效应	Yādiàn xiàoyìng	Piezoelectric effect	
亚毫米波长	Yàháomǐ bōcháng	Submillimeter wavelength	
雅虎	Yǎhǔ	Yahoo! ©	
雅虎通	Yǎhǔ tōng	Yahoo! Messenger ©	
雅虎中文	Yǎhǔ Zhōngwén	Chinese Yahoo! ©	
压接工具	Yājiē gōngjù	Crimping tool	
压接机	Yājiējī	Pressure fastener	
压接机	Yājiējī	Hardware insert press (in SMT)	
压控晶振	Yākòng jīngzhèn	Voltage controlled crystal oscillator (short for 电压控制晶体振荡器)	VCXO
压控振荡器	Yākòng zhèndàngqì	Voltage controlled oscillator	VCO
压控振荡器输入控制电压	Yākòng zhèndàngqì shūrù kòngzhì diànyā	Voltage controlled oscillator input control voltage	
压扩	Yākuò	Companding (abbrev. of 压缩扩展)	
压扩单边带调幅	Yākuò dānbiāndài tiáofú	Companded single sideband amplitude modulation	CSSB-AM
压扩调频繁	Yākuò tiáopín fán	Companded frequency modulation	CFM
压扩预测增量调制	Yākuò yùcè zēngliàng tiáozhì	Companded predictive delta modulation	CPDM
压扩器	Yākuòqì	Compander	
压力	Yālì	Pressure	
压力控制阀	Yālì kòngzhì fá	Pressure control valve	
压力梯度	Yālì tīdù	Pressure gradient	
压力计	Yālìjì	Manometer	
亚历山大	Yà-lì-shān-dà	Alexandrite	
亚历山大激光	Yà-lì-shān-dà jīguāng	Alexandrite laser	
亚历山大激光晶体	Yà-lì-shān-dà jīguāng jīngtǐ	Alexandrite laser crystal	
亚硫酸气	Yàliúsuān qì	Sulfuric acid gas	
亚伦电信集团	Yà-lún diànxìn jítuán	Allen Group (US company)	
雅马哈	Yǎ-mǎ-hā	Yamaha (Japanese company)	
沿顶板面敷设	Yán dǐngbǎnmiàn fūshè	Along roof slab (in telecom cabling installation)	
研华	Yán huá	Advantech Ltd. (China company)	
沿梁敷设	Yán liáng fūshè	Along beam (telecom installation)	AB
沿墙面敷设	Yán qiángmiàn fūshè	On wall surface (telecom installation)	WS

沿天棚面敷设	Yán tiānpéngmiàn fūshè	Along ceiling (telecom installation)	CE
沿珠敷设	Yán zhū fūshè	Along column (telecom installation)	AC
掩蔽模型通用子带综合编码和复用	Yǎnbì móxíng tōngyòng zidài zōnghé biānmǎ hé fùyòng	Masking-pattern universal sub-band integrated coding and multiplexing	MUSICAM
延长导线	Yáncháng dǎoxiàn	Extension lead	
延迟	Yánchí	Delay	DELAY
延迟拨号信号	Yánchí bōhào xìnhào	Delay-dialing signal	
延迟传输	Yánchí chuánshū	Delay transmission	DT
延迟发送分集	Yánchí fāsòng fēnjí	Delay transmission diversity	DTD
延迟角	Yánchí jiǎo	Delay angle	
延迟释放	Yánchí shìfàng	Delayed release (ISUP message)	DRS
延迟锁定环	Yánchí suǒdìng huán	Delay-locked loop	DLL
延迟线对消器	Yánchí xiàn duìxiāoqì	Delay line canceller	
延迟线滤波器	Yánchí xiàn lǜbōqì	Delay line filter	
延迟移位键控	Yánchí yíwèi jiànkòng	Delay shift keying	DSK
延迟转换	Yánchí zhuǎnhuàn	Delay transition	
延迟自适应差分脉码调制	Yánchí zìshìyìng chāfēn màimǎ tiáozhì	Delay adaptive differential pulse code modulation	DADPCM
样本偏差	Yàngběn piānchā	Sample bias	
样方	Yàngfāng	Quadrat	
样方框	Yàngfāng kuàng	Quadrat frame	
氧化设备	Yǎnghuà shèbèi	Oxidation furnace	
氧化锆	Yǎnghuàgào	Zirconium oxide	ZrO_2
氧化锆高频感应炉	Yǎnghuàgào gāopín gǎnyìng lú	Zirconia induction furnace	
氧化锆陶瓷	Yǎnghuàgào táocí	Zirconia ceramic	
氧化物对准晶体管	Yǎnghuàwù duìzhǔn jīngtǐguǎn	Oxide aligned transistor (product of TRW)	OAT
氧化铟锡	Yǎnghuàyīnxī	Indium-tin-oxide	ITO
阳极	Yángjí	Anode	
阳极氧化钝化法	Yángjí yǎnghuà dùnhuàfǎ	Anodic oxidation passivation	
阳极化金属-氧化物-半导体	Yángjíhuà jīnshǔ—yǎnghuàwù bàndǎotǐ	Anodized metal-oxide semiconductor	AMOS
扬声电话机	Yángshēng diànhuàjī	Speaker telephone set	
扬声器额定阻抗	Yángshēngqì édìng zǔkàng	Rated impedance of loudspeaker	
扬声器功率	Yángshēngqì gōnglǜ	Power of loudspeaker	
杨氏模量	Yáng-shì móliàng	Young's modulus	
样条插值曲线	Yàngtiáo chāzhí qūxiàn	Spline	
样条方法	Yàngtiáo fāngfǎ	Splining	
样条平滑	Yàngtiáo pínghuá	Spline smoothing	
样值	Yàngzhí	Sample	
掩护媒体	Yǎnhù méitǐ	Cover-media	
延缓维护	Yánhuǎn wéihù	Deferred maintenance	
延缓维护告警	Yánhuǎn wéihù gàojǐng	Deferred maintenance alarm	DMA
严酷度等级	Yánkùdù děngjí	Characteristic severity	
掩码	Yǎnmǎ	Mask	
掩埋异质结	Yǎnmái yìzhìjié	Buried heterogeneous (fiber or cable)	BH
研磨	Yánmó	Polishing (optical device processing)	
淹没	Yānmò	Flooding (IPsec)	
研磨化合物	Yánmó huàhéwù	Polishing compound	

延期支付	Yánqī zhīfù	Moratorium	
眼球大战	Yǎnqiú dàzhàn	Battle for eyeballs (the competition between makers of computer 3D graphics cards)	
衍射	Yǎnshè	Diffraction	
衍射编码加密技术	Yǎnshè biānmǎ jiāmì jìshù	Diffraction code encryption	
衍射光栅	Yǎnshè guāng shān	Diffraction grating	
延伸馈电器	Yánshēn kuìdiànqì	Extended feed	
延伸系统	Yánshēn xìtǒng	Stretch system	
延伸率	Yánshēnlǜ	Elongation	
延时充电电路	Yánshí chōngdiàn diànlù	Delayed charging circuit	
延时抖动	Yánshí dǒudòng	Latent jitter	
延时交互式视频点播	Yánshí jiāohùshì shìpín diǎnbō	Interactive video on demand with delayed access	IVOD-d
延时线	Yánshí xiàn	Delay line	
验收测试	Yànshōu cèshì	Acceptance test	
验收检验设备	Yànshōu jiǎnyàn shèbèi	Acceptance checkout equipment	ACE
验收试验	Yànshōu shìyàn	Acceptance test	
演算法	Yǎnsuànfǎ	Algorithm	
眼图	Yǎntú	Eye pattern	
眼图模板	Yǎntú múbǎn	Eye diagram mask	
盐雾试验	Yánwù shìyàn	Salt fog test	
延性率	Yánxìng lǜ	Ductility factor	
延性率反应谱	Yánxìng lǜ fǎnyìng pǔ	Ductility factor response spectrum	
延续媒体	Yánxù méitǐ	Continuation media	
验证服务	Yànzhèng fúwù	Authentication service	
验证密钥	Yànzhèng mìyào	Authentication key	
验证牌	Yànzhèng pái	Authentication token	
验证试验	Yànzhèng shìyàn	Compliance test	
验证授权机构	Yànzhèng shòuquán jīgòu	Certification authority	
验证响应	Yànzhèng xiǎngyìng	Authentication response	AUTHR
验证中心	Yànzhèng zhōngxīn	Authentication center	AUC
验证、授权、计费	Yànzhèng、shòuquán、jìfèi	Authentication, authorization, accounting	AAA
研制阶段	Yánzhì jiēduàn	Development phase (of product life cycle)	
严重差错秒	Yánzhòng chācuò miǎo	Severely errored second	SES
严重差错秒比	Yánzhòng chācuò miǎo bǐ	Severely errored second ratio	SESR
严重差错信元块比	Yánzhòng chācuò xìnyuán kuài bǐ	Severely errored cell block ratio	SECBR
严重错误	Yánzhòng cuòwù	Fatal error	
严重错误帧	Yánzhòng cuòwù zhèng	Severely errored frame	SEF
严重告警	Yánzhòng gàojǐng	Major alarm	
严重故障	Yánzhòng gùzhàng	Major fault	
严重级别	Yánzhòng jíbié	Severity level	
严重扰动期	Yánzhòng rǎodòng qī	Severely disturbed period	SDP
严重误信元块	Yánzhòng wù xìnyuán kuài	Severely errored cell block	SECB
严重误块秒	Yánzhòng wùkuài miǎo	Severely errored second	SES
严重误块秒比	Yánzhòng wùkuài miǎo bǐ	Severely errored second ratio	SESR
严重误码秒	Yánzhòng wùmǎ miǎo	Severely errored second	SES
严重误码秒比	Yánzhòng wùmǎ miǎo bǐ	Severely errored second ratio	SESR
严重误信元块比例	Yánzhòng wùxìn yuán kuài bǐlì	Severely errored cell block ratio	SECBR

严重误信元块比例	Yánzhòng wùxìn yuán kuài bǐlì	Seriously errored cell block ratio	SECBR
要传送的后向序号	Yào chuánsòngde hòuxiàng xùhào	Backward sequence number to be transmitted	BSNT
遥测	Yáocè	Telemetering	
遥测技术	Yáocè jìshù	Telemetry	
遥测学	Yáocè xué	Telemetry	
遥测业务	Yáocè yèwù	Telemetry service	
遥察	Yáochá	Telemonitoring	
遥导	Yáodǎo	Teleguidance	
摇动	Yáodòng	Wander, sloshing, rocking	
摇杆	Yáogǎn	Joystick	
遥感	Yáogǎn	Remote sensing	
遥接	Yáojiē	Remote access	
遥警	Yáojǐng	Remote alarm	
遥控	Yáokòng	Telecontrol	
遥控操作业务单元	Yáokòng cāozuò yèwù dānyuán	Remote operation service element	ROSE
遥控市场推广	Yáokòng shìchǎng tuīguǎng	Telemarketing	
遥控台	Yáokòng tái	Remote control radio	
遥控维护	Yáokòng wéihù	Remote maintenance	
遥控线	Yáokòng xiàn	Remote control line	YX
遥令	Yáolìng	Telecommand	
要求连接	Yāoqiú liánjiē	Request for connection	RFC
钥匙环	Yàoshi huán	Keyring	
遥信	Yáoxìn	Telecommand	
遥信业务	Yáoxìn yèwù	Teleaction service	
压强式	Yāqiáng-shì	Pressure operated	PO
压入	Yārù	Push	
压伸与调频	Yāshēn yǔ tiáopín	Companding and frequency modulation	CFM
压缩	Yāsuō	Compress	
压缩	Yāsuō	Zip	
压缩安全有效载荷	Yāsuō ānquán yǒuxiào zàihè	Compressed effective security payload	
压缩波导段	Yāsuō bōdǎo duàn	Squeeze section (of a waveguide)	
压缩串联因特网协议	Yāsuō chuànlián Yīntèwǎng xiéyì	Compressed serial link Internet protocol	CSLIP
压缩出局访问	Yāsuō chūjú fǎngwèn	Suppress outgoing access	SOA
压缩方式	Yāsuō fāngshì	Compressed mode	CM
压缩光盘只读存储器	Yāsuō guāngpán zhǐ dú cúnchǔqì	Compact disk read only memory	CD-ROM
压缩控制协议	Yāsuō kòngzhì xiéyì	Compression control protocol	CCP
压缩扩展	Yāsuō kuòzhǎn	Companding (usually just 压扩)	
压缩强度	Yāsuō qiángdù	Compressive strength	
压缩算法	Yāsuō suànfǎ	Compression algorithm (IPsec)	
压缩文件	Yāsuō wénjiàn	Compressed file, ZIP file	
压缩纹理	Yāsuō wénlǐ	Compressed textures (video term)	
压缩应力	Yāsuō yìnglì	Compression stress	
压缩增量调制	Yāsuō zēngliàng tiáozhì	Compressed delta modulation	CDM
压缩器	Yāsuōqì	Compressor	
压缩性	Yāsuōxìng	Compressibility	
亚太电缆网络	Yàtài diànlǎn wǎngluò	Asia-Pacific Cable Network	APCN

亚太地区网络-中文分组	Yàtài dìqū wǎngluò--zhōngwén fēnzǔ	Asian Pacific Networking Group-Chinese characters	APNA-CC
亚信科技中国公司	Yàxìn kējì zhōngguó gōngsī	AsiaInfo Technology China Ltd.	
压应力	Yāyìnglì	Compressive stress	
哑元突发	Yǎyuán tūfā	Dummy burst (GSM term)	
压制	Yāzhì	Squelching (on SDH)	
压制性干扰	Yāzhìxìng gānrǎo	Blanket jamming; blanking jamming	
亚洲电脑展	Yàzhōu diànnǎo zhǎn	COMDEX Asia (trade exhibition)	
亚洲第一站	Yàzhōu dìyī zhàn	AsiaOne (Singapore web site)	
亚洲多媒体展	Yàzhōu duōméitǐ zhǎn	Inter Media Asia	
亚洲商业（网络）	Yàzhōu shāngyè (wǎngluò)	CommerceAsia	
亚洲线上	Yàzhōu xiànshàng	AsiaOnLine (Internet service)	
亚洲信息通信委员会	Yàzhōu xìnxī tōngxìn wěiyuánhuì	Asian Info-Communications Committee	AIC
亚洲信息系统安全服务	Yàzhōu xìnxī xìtǒng ānquán fúwù	Asia Information System Security Service	AIS3
哑子变量	Yǎzi biànliàng	Dummy argument (in FORTRAN)	
叶	Yè	Leaf	
页	Yè	Page	
页拆分	Yè chāifēn	Page split	
页长	Yè cháng	Page length	
叶成员	Yè chéngyuán	Leaf member	
页翻转	Yè fānzhuǎn	Page flipping	
页分界线	Yè fēnjièxiàn	Page break (WP command)	
叶互联网络	Yè hùlián wǎngluò	Leaf internetwork	
叶级	Yè jí	Leaf level	
页集	Yè jí	Page set	
页坐标系统	Yè zuòbiāo xìtǒng	Page coordinate system	
页/分	Yè/ fēn	Pages per minute (printer term)	ppm
液晶	Yèjīng	Liquid crystal	
液晶电视	Yèjīng diànshì	Liquid crystal (LCD) TV	
液晶监视器	Yèjīng jiānshìqì	Liquid crystal (LCD) monitor	
液晶可调滤波器	Yèjīng kětiáo lǜbōqì	Liquid crystal adjustable (tunable) filter	
液晶投影机	Yèjīng tóuyǐngjī	Liquid crystal (LCD) projector	
液晶显示屏	Yèjīng xiǎnshì píng	Liquid crystal display	LCD
液晶显示器	Yèjīng xiǎnshìqì	Liquid crystal display	LCD
液晶注入装置	Yèjīng zhùrù zhuāngzhì	Liquid crystal injection equipment	
页面尺寸扩展模式	Yèmiàn chǐcùn kuòzhǎn móshì	Page size extension	PSE
页面尺寸扩展模式, 36 位	Yèmiàn chǐcùn kuòzhǎn móshì, 36 wèi	Page size extension 36-bit (chip)	PSE36
页面等待	Yèmiàn děngdài	Page wait	
页面顶栏	Yèmiàn dǐnglán	Top margin	
页面方式 RAM	Yèmiàn fāngshì RAM	Page mode RAM	
页面范围	Yèmiàn fànwéi	Page extent	
叶面积指数	Yèmiàn jī zhǐshù	Leaf area index	
页面设置	Yèmiàn shèzhì	Page setup (WP command)	
液态轴承马达	Yètài zhóuchéng mǎdá	Fluid dynamic bearing motor	FDBM
液体冷却	Yètǐ lěngquè	Liquid cooling	
野外采集器	Yěwài cǎijíqì	Field collector, field data collector	
野外观测	Yěwài guāncè	Field observation	

业务保障	Yèwù bǎozhàng	Service assurance	SA
业务编程代码	Yèwù biānchéng dàimǎ	Service programming code	SPC
业务标识符	Yèwù biāozhì fú	Service identifier	SID
业务比特率	Yèwù bǐtè lǜ	Service bit rate	
业务创建环境功能	Yèwù chuàngjiàn huánjìng gōngnéng	Service creation environment function	SCEF
业务创造环境	Yèwù chuàngzào huánjìng	Service creation environment	SCE
业务处理模块	Yèwù chǔlǐ mókuài	Service processing module	SPM
业务到用户信息	Yèwù dào yònghù xìnxī	Service to user information	STUI
业务等级协商	Yèwù děngjí xiéshāng	Service level agreement	SLA
业务等级协议	Yèwù děngjí xiéyì	Service-level agreement	SLA
业务电路	Yèwù diànlù	Service circuit	
业务端口	Yèwù duānkǒu	Service port	
业务端口功能	Yèwù duānkǒu gōngnéng	Service port function	SPF
业务独立构件	Yèwù dúlì gòujiàn	Service-independent building blocks	SIB
业务访问功能	Yèwù fǎngwèn gōngnéng	Access to the services function	ASF
业务负荷分散控制	Yèwù fùhè fēnsàn kòngzhì	Traffic-load divided control	
业务负荷控制	Yèwù fùhè kòngzhì	Traffic-load control	
业务告警	Yèwù gàojǐng	Service alarm	SA
业务工程	Yèwù gōngchéng	Traffic engineering	TE
业务管理层	Yèwù guǎnlǐ céng	Service management layer	SML
业务管理点	Yèwù guǎnlǐ diǎn	Service management point	SMP
业务管理功能	Yèwù guǎnlǐ gōngnéng	Service management function	SMF
业务管理接入点	Yèwù guǎnlǐ jiērù diǎn	Service management access point	SMAP
业务管理接入功能	Yèwù guǎnlǐ jiērù gōngnéng	Service management access function	SMAF
业务管理控制平台	Yèwù guǎnlǐ kòngzhì píngtái	Service management control platform	SMCP
业务管理平台	Yèwù guǎnlǐ píngtái	Service management platform	SMP
业务管理系统	Yèwù guǎnlǐ xìtǒng	Service management system	SMS
业务规则	Yèwù guīzé	Business rules	
业务互通	Yèwù hùtōng	Service interworking	SI
业务交换点	Yèwù jiāohuàn diǎn	Service switching point	SSP
业务交换功能	Yèwù jiāohuàn gōngnéng	Service switching function	SSF
业务交换眯	Yèwù jiāohuàn mí	Service switching point	SSP
业务交换中心	Yèwù jiāohuàn zhōngxīn	Service switching center	SSC
业务级别协议	Yèwù jíbié xiéyì	Service level agreement	SLA
业务接概率	Yèwù jiē gàilǜ	Service access probability	
业务节点	Yèwù jiédiǎn	Service node	SN
业务节点接口	Yèwù jiédiǎn jiēkǒu	Service node interface	SNI
业务接口和协议处理	Yèwù jiēkǒu hé xiéyì chǔlǐ	Services interface and protocol processing	SIPP
业务接口和协议处理单元	Yèwù jiēkǒu hé xiéyì chǔlǐ dānyuán	Service interface and protocol processing unit	SIPP
业务接入点	Yèwù jiērù diǎn	Service access point	SAP
业务接入点标志	Yèwù jiērù diǎn biāozhì	Service access point identifier	SAPI
业务接入点识符	Yèwù jiērù diǎn shífú	Service access point identifier	SAPI
业务接入复用器	Yèwù jiērù fùyòngqì	Service access multiplexer	SAM
业务接入复用器接口	Yèwù jiērù fùyòngqì jiēkǒu	Service access multiplexer interface	SAMI
业务接入识别码	Yèwù jiērù shíbié mǎ	Service access point identity	SAPI
业务计数器	Yèwù jìshùqì	Traffic meter (in telecommunication)	

业务计算机	Yèwù jìsuànjī	Service computer (in telecommunication)	
业务基准	Yèwù jīzhǔn	Base-lining	
业务拒绝	Yèwù jùjué	Service reject	SRJ
业务开通	Yèwù kāitōng	Service fulfillment	SF
业务可保持性	Yèwù kěbǎochíxìng	Service retainability	
业务可保持性性能	Yèwù kěbǎochíxìng xìngnéng	Service retainability performance	
业务可操作性	Yèwù kěcāozuòxìng	Service operability	
业务可操作性性能	Yèwù kěcāozuòxìng xìngnéng	Service operability performance	
业务可接入性	Yèwù kějiērùxìng	Service accessibility	
业务可接入性性能	Yèwù kějiērùxìng xìngnéng	Service accessibility performance	
业务可用性	Yèwù kěyòngxìng	Service availability	
业务控制点	Yèwù kòngzhì diǎn	Service control point	SCP
业务控制功能	Yèwù kòngzhì gōngnéng	Service control function	SCF
业务控制功能 － 业务交换功能	Yèwù kòngzhì gōngnéng – yèwù jiāohuàn gōngnéng	Service control function - service switching function	SCF-SSF
业务控制功能 － 业务数据功能	Yèwù kòngzhì gōngnéng – yèwù shùjù gōngnéng	Service control function - service data function	SCF-SDF
业务控制功能 －业务控制功能	Yèwù kòngzhì gōngnéng - yèwù kòngzhì gōngnéng	Service control function - service control function	SCF-SCF
业务控制功能-不相干呼叫业务功能	Yèwù kòngzhì gōngnéng-bùxiānggān hūjiào yèwù gōngnéng	Service control function - call unrelated service function	SCF-CUSF
业务控制功能 专用资源功能	Yèwù kòngzhì gōngnéng-zhuānyòng zīyuán gōngnéng	Service control function - specialized resource function	SCF-SRF
业务控制网关功能	Yèwù kòngzhì wǎngguān gōngnéng	Service control gateway function	SCGF
业务控制网守	Yèwù kòngzhì wǎngshǒu	Gatekeeper for service control	GKc
业务控制用户代理功能	Yèwù kòngzhì yònghù dàilǐ gōngnéng	Service control user agent function	SCUAF
业务控制子系统	Yèwù kòngzhì zixìtǒng	Traffic control sub-system	TCS
业务口功能	Yèwù kǒu gōngnéng	Service port function	SPF
业务类别	Yèwù lèibié	Type of service	ToS
业务类型	Yèwù lèixíng	Class of service	COS
业务连线阻抗	Yèwù liánxiàn zǔkàng	Service connection impedance	
业务流程重组	Yèwù liúchéng chóngzǔ	Business process re-engineering	BPR
业务轮廓	Yèwù lúnkuò	Service profile	
业务轮廓管理	Yèwù lúnkuò guǎnlǐ	Service profile management	
业务逻辑	Yèwù luóji	Business logic	
业务逻辑	Yèwù luóji	Service logic	SL
业务逻辑程序	Yèwù luóji chéngxù	Service logic program	SLP
业务逻辑处理实例	Yèwù luóji chǔlǐ shílì	Service logic processing instance	SLPI
业务逻辑进程	Yèwù luóji jìnchéng	Service logic program	SLP
业务逻辑进程实例	Yèwù luóji jìnchéng shílì	Service logic program instance	SLPI
业务逻辑执行环境	Yèwù luóji zhíxíng huánjìng	Service logic execution environment	SLEE
业务码	Yèwù mǎ	Feature code	FC
业务码	Yèwù mǎ	Service code	SC
业务码	Yèwù mǎ	Service code	SC
业务能力服务器	Yèwù nénglì fúwùqì	Service capability server	SCS
业务能力特征	Yèwù nénglì tèzhēng	Service capability feature	SCF

业务能力性能	Yèwù nénglì xìngnéng	Serviceability performance	
业务请求	Yèwù qǐngqiú	Service request	SRQ
业务请求报告	Yèwù qǐngqiú bàogào	Service request report	SRQR
业务确认	Yèwù quèrèn	Service confirmation	SCF
业务容许控制	Yèwù róngxǔ kòngzhì	Service allowance control	SAC
业务生成工程环境	Yèwù shēngchéng gōngchéng huánjìng	Service creation engineering environment	SCREEN
业务生成环境	Yèwù shēngchéng huánjìng	Service creation environment	SCE
业务生成环境点	Yèwù shēngchéng huánjìng diǎn	Service creation environment point	SCEP
业务生成环境功能	Yèwù shēngchéng huánjìng gōngnéng	Service creation environment function	SCEF
业务使用率	Yèwù shǐyònglǜ	Service usage	SU
业务使用者系统	Yèwù shǐyòngzhě xìtǒng	Service consumer system	SCS
业务数据单元	Yèwù shùjù dānyuán	Service data unit	SDU
业务数据点	Yèwù shùjù diǎn	Service data point	SDP
业务数据功能	Yèwù shùjù gōngnéng	Service data function	SDF
业务属性	Yèwù shǔxìng	Service attribute	
业务搜索协议	Yèwù sōusuǒ xiéyì	Service discovery protocol	SDP
业务特定会聚子层	Yèwù tèdìng huìjù zicéng	Service-specific convergence sub-layer	SSCS
业务特定面向连接功能	Yèwù tèdìng miànxiàng liánjiē gōngnéng	Service-specific connection-oriented function	SSCOF
业务特定面向连接协议	Yèwù tèdìng miànxiàng liánjiē xiéyì	Service-specific connection-oriented protocol	SSCOP
业务特定的协调功能	Yèwù tèdìngde xiétiáo gōngnéng	Service-specific coordination function	SSCF
业务特有会聚层	Yèwù tèyǒu huìjù céng	Service-specific convergence layer	SSCS
业务特征	Yèwù tèzhēng	Service feature	SF
业务提供点	Yèwù tígōng diǎn	Point of presence	PoP
业务提供商	Yèwù tígōngshāng	Service provider	SP
业务提供者	Yèwù tígòngzhě	Service provider	SP
业务提供者标识符	Yèwù tígòngzhě biāozhìfú	Service provider identifier	SPI
业务提供者接口	Yèwù tígòngzhě jiēkǒu	Service provider interface	SPI
业务提供者控制键	Yèwù tígòngzhě kòngzhì jiàn	Service provider control key	SPCK
业务提供者链路	Yèwù tígòngzhě liànlù	Service provider link	SPL
业务提供者网络	Yèwù tígòngzhě wǎngluò	Service provider network	SPN
业务提供者网络标识符	Yèwù tígòngzhě wǎngluò biāozhìfú	Service provider network identifier	SPNI
业务提供者之间的接口	Yèwù tígòngzhě-zhījiānde jiēkǒu	Inter-service provider interface	
业务网关控制协议	Yèwù wǎngguān kòngzhì xiéyì	Service gateway control protocol	SGCP
业务网络接口	Yèwù wǎngluò jiēkǒu	Service network interface	SNI
业务完善性	Yèwù wánshànxìng	Service integrity	
业务位	Yèwù wèi	Service digit	
业务相互作用管理	Yèwù xiānghù zuòyòng guǎnlǐ	Service interaction manager	SIM
业务消息八位位组	Yèwù xiāoxi bāwèi wèizǔ	Service information octet	SIO
业务协调	Yèwù xiétiáo	Service interworking	
业务信道	Yèwù xìndào	Traffic channel	TCH
业务信道/半速 4.8kbit/s	Yèwù xìndào/bànsù 4.8kbit/s	Traffic channel/half-rate 4.8kbit/s	TCH/H4.8
业务信道/半速话音	Yèwù xìndào/bànsù huàyīn	Traffic channel/half-rate speech	TC/HS
业务信道/全速 4.8kbit/s	Yèwù xìndào/quánsù 4.8kbit/s	Traffic channel/full rate 4.8kbit/s	TCH/H4.8
业务信道/全速 9.6kbit/s	Yèwù xìndào/quánsù 9.6kbit/s	Traffic channel/full rate 9.6kbit/s	TCH/F9.6
业务信道/全速话音	Yèwù xìndào/quánsù huàyīn	Traffic channel/full rate speech	TCH/FS
业务信号失效	Yèwù xìnhào shīxiào	Service signal failure	SSF

业务信息八位位组	Yèwù xìnxī bāwèi wèizǔ	Service information octet	SIO
业务信息字节	Yèwù xìnxī zìjié	Service information byte	
业务选择服务器	Yèwù xuǎnzé fúwùqì	Service selection server	SSS
业务选择器	Yèwù xuǎnzéqì	Service selector (in SDH)	
业务应用网关功能	Yèwù yìngyòng wǎngguān gōngnéng	Service application gateway function	SAGF
业务用户差错概率	Yèwù yònghù chācuò gàilǜ	Service user mistake probability	
业务用户弃用概率	Yèwù yònghù qìyòng gàilǜ	Service user abandonment probability	
业务运营支撑系统	Yèwù yùnyíng zhīchēng xìtǒng	Operation support system/business support system	OSS/BSS, BOSS
业务运营支援系统	Yèwù yùnyíng zhīyuán xìtǒng	Business operation supporting system	BOSS
业务支撑传输协议	Yèwù zhīchēng chuánshū xiéyì	Service support transmission protocol	SSTP
业务支持性能	Yèwù zhīchí xìngnéng	Service support performance	
业务质量	Yèwù zhìliàng	Quality of service	QoS
业务指示	Yèwù zhǐshì	Service indicator	
业务指示表示语	Yèwù zhǐshì biǎoshì yǔ	Service indicator	
业务中心	Yèwù zhōngxīn	Service center	SC
业务专家组	Yèwù zhuānjiāzǔ	Services Experts Rapporteurs Group (GSM MoU)	SERG
业务子段	Yèwù zìduàn	Sub-service field	
业务组标识符	Yèwù zǔ biāozhì fú	Service set identity	SSID
业务组合	Yèwù zǔhé	Service mix	
业务的非透明支持	Yèwùde fēitòumíng zhīchí	Non-transparent support of services	
业务量工程	Yèwùliàng gōngchéng	Traffic engineering	TE
业务量合约	Yèwùliàng héyuē	Traffic contract	
业务量控制	Yèwùliàng kòngzhì	Traffic control	
业务量描述语	Yèwùliàng miáoshù yǔ	Traffic descriptor	
业务量模式	Yèwùliàng móshì	Traffic pattern	
业务量疏导	Yèwùliàng shūdǎo	Traffic grooming	
业务流标识符	Yèwùliú biāoshífú	Service flow identifier	SFID
业务流机密性	Yèwùliú jīmìxìng	Traffic flow confidentiality (IPsec)	
业务流设计	Yèwùliú shèjì	Traffic engineering	TE
业务流样板	Yèwùliú yàngbǎn	Traffic flow template	TFT
页下空白	Yè-xià kòngbái	Bottom margin	
液相外延	Yèxiàng wàiyán	Liquid phase epitaxy	LPE
液压泵	Yèyā bèng	Hydraulic pump	
液压放大器	Yèyā fàngdàqì	Hydraulic amplifier	
液压缓冲器	Yèyā huǎnchōngqì	Hydraulic buffer	
液压马达	Yèyā mǎdá	Hydraulic motor	
液压随动装置	Yèyā suídòng zhuāngzhì	Hydraulic follow-up unit	
液压式装卸过桥	Yèyā-shì zhuāngxiè guòqiáo	Hydraulic loading and unloading foot walk	
业余电台	Yèyú diàntái	Amateur station	
业余业务	Yèyú yèwù	Amateur service	
野战通信系统	Yězhàn tōngxìn xìtǒng	Tactical communication system	
以...为模	Yǐ ...wéi mó	Modulo ...	
依比人之见	Yī bǐ rén zhī jiàn	In my humble opinion (computer chat)	IMHO
以测链量得的距离	Yǐ cè liànliàng dédé jùlí	Chainage (distance obtained using surveyor chain)	
一单元	Yī dānyuán	Single cell	
一单元消息	Yī dānyuán xiāoxi	Single-unit message	

一对多关系	Yī duì duō guānxi	One-to-many relationship (for database)	
一对多联系	Yī duì duō liánxì	One-to-many relationship	
一对一关系	Yī duì yī guānxi	One-to-one relationship (for database)	
一对一行销	Yī duì yī xíngxiāo	One to one marketing	OOM
以行为主的顺序分配	Yǐ háng wéi zhǔde shùnxù fēnpèi	Row major order	
以列为主的顺序分配	Yǐ liè wéi zhǔde shùnxù fēnpèi	Column major order	
以 RP 为树跟的共享树	Yǐ RP wéi shùgēnde gòngxiǎng shù	RP-rooted share tree	RPT
以三人之姓所名的码	Yǐ sānrénzhīxìng suǒmíngde mǎ	Bose-Chaudhuri-Hocquenghem code	BCH
铱系统	Yī xìtǒng	Iridium system	
一般保护性错误	Yībān bǎohùxìng cuòwù	General protection fault	GPF
一般布局结构	Yībān bùjú jiégòu	Generic layout structure	
一般程序时间公式	Yībān chéngxù shíjiān gōngshì	Generalized timing formula	GTF
一般点光源	Yībān diǎn guāngyuán	Point light	
一般服务资源	Yībān fúwù zīyuán	Generic service resource	
一般告警	Yībān gàojǐng	Minor alarm	
一般可计算均衡模型	Yībān kějìsuàn jūnhéng móxíng	Computable general equilibrium model	CGEM
一般流量控制码	Yībān liúliàng kòngzhì mǎ	Generic flow control	GFC
一般逻辑结构	Yībān luóji jiégòu	Generic logical structure	
一般内容组成部分	Yībān nèiróng zǔchéng bùfen	Generic content portion	
一般内容组成部分描述	Yībān nèiróng zǔchéng bùfen miáoshù	Generic content portion description	
一般前向建立信息消息	Yībān qiánxiàng jiànlì xìnxī xiāoxi	General forward set-up information message	GSM
一般请求消息	Yībān qǐngqiú xiāoxi	General request message	GRQ
一般属性注册协议	Yībān shǔxìng zhùcè xiéyì	General attribute registration protocol	GARP
一般似然比	Yībān sìrán bǐ	Generalized likelihood ratio	GLR
一般文件	Yībān wénjiàn	Generic document	
一般文件传输协议	Yībān wénjiàn chuánshū xiéyì	Trivial file transfer protocol	TFTP
一般信息安全	Yībān xìnxī ānquán	General message security	GMS
一般要素	Yībān yàosù	General features	
一般应用程序资源	Yībān yìngyòng chéngxù zīyuán	Generic application resource	
一般的布线系统	Yībānde bùxiàn xìtǒng	Generic cabling system	GCS
一般化的	Yībānhuàde	Generic	
异边聚合	Yìbiān jùhé	Different-edge aggregation (CAD/CAM)	
仪表着陆系统	Yíbiǎo zhuólù xìtǒng	Instrument landing system	ILS
仪表着陆系统航向信标	Yíbiǎo zhuólù xìtǒng hángxiàng xìnbiāo	Instrument landing system localizer	
仪表着陆系统下滑信标	Yíbiǎo zhuólù xìtǒng xiàhuá xìnbiāo	Instrument landing system glide path	
异波长双工	Yìbōcháng shuānggōng	Heterogeneous frequency diplex	
异步拆线方式	Yìbù chāixiàn fāngshì	Asynchronous disconnected mode	ADM
异步传递方式	Yìbù chuándì fāngshì	Asynchronous transfer mode	ATM
异步传递方式无源光网络	Yìbù chuándì fāngshì wúyuán guāng wǎngluò	Asynchronous transfer mode passive optical network	APON
异步传递模式	Yìbù chuándì móshì	Asynchronous transfer mode	ATM
异步传递模式-交叉连接	Yìbù chuándì móshì - jiāochā liánjiē	Asynchronous transfer mode -cross-connect	ATM-XC
异步传递模式交叉连接	Yìbù chuándì móshì jiāochā liánjiē	Asynchronous transfer mode cross connect	AXC
异步传递模式交换	Yìbù chuándì móshì jiāohuàn	Asynchronous transfer mode switch	ATM-SW
异步传递模式网络接入子系统	Yìbù chuándì móshì wǎngluò jiērù zixìtǒng	Asynchronous transfer mode network access sub-system	ANAS

异步传递模式业务数据单元	Yìbù chuándì móshì yèwù shùjù dānyuán	Asynchronous transfer mode service data unit	ATM-SDU
异步传递模式用户网络接口	Yìbù chuándì móshì yònghù wǎngluò jiēkǒu	Asynchronous transfer mode user network interface	ATM-UNI
异步传递模式用户线接口电路	Yìbù chuándì móshì yònghùxiàn jiēkǒu diànlù	Asynchronous transfer mode subscriber line interface circuit	ATM-SLIC
异步传递区	Yìbù chuándì qū	Asynchronous transfer region	ATR
异步传输模式	Yìbù chuánshū móshì	Asynchronous transfer mode	ATM
异步传送方式	Yìbù chuánsòng fāngshì	Asynchronous transfer mode	ATM
异步传送方式适配层	Yìbù chuánsòng fāngshì shìpèi céng	Asynchronous transfer mode adaptation layer	AAL
异步传送模式	Yìbù chuánsòng móshì	Asynchronous transfer mode	ATM
异步传送模式适配层	Yìbù chuánsòng móshì shìpèi céng	Asynchronous transfer mode adaptation layer	AAL
异步地址通信系统	Yìbù dìzhǐ tōngxìn xìtǒng	Asynchronous address communications system	AACS
异步断开方式	Yìbù duànkāi fāngshì	Asynchronous disconnected mode	ADM
异步多线路控制器	Yìbù duō xiànlù kòngzhìqì	Asynchronous multi-line controller	AMLC
异步接口模块	Yìbù jiēkǒu mókuài	Asynchronous interface module	ASIM
一步激活	Yībù jīhuó	One-step activation	
异步控制字符影射	Yìbù kòngzhì zìfú yǐngshè	Asynchronous control character map	ACCM
异步链路	Yìbù liànlù	Asynchronous connecting link	ACL
异步码分多址	Yìbù mǎfēn duōzhǐ	Asynchronous code division multiple access	A-CDMA
异步平衡方式	Yìbù pínghéng fāngshì	Asynchronous balanced mode	ABM
异步平衡类别	Yìbù pínghéng lèibié	Balanced asynchronous class	BAC
异步平衡模式	Yìbù pínghéng móshì	Asynchronous balanced mode	ABM
一步去激活	Yībù qù jīhuó	One-step deactivation	
异步时分	Yìbù shífèn	Asynchronous time division	ATD
异步时分多路复用器	Yìbù shífèn duōlù fùyòngqì	Asynchronous time division multiplexer	ATDM
异步时分复用	Yìbù shífèn fùyòng	Asynchronous time division multiplexing	
异步事物控制程序	Yìbù shìwù kòngzhì chéngxù	Asynchronous transaction control program	ATCP
异步时序网络	Yìbù shíxù wǎngluò	Asynchronous sequential network	ASN
异步数据传递	Yìbù shùjù chuándì	Asynchronous data transfer	ADT
异步数据单元	Yìbù shùjù dānyuán	Asynchronous data unit	ADU
异步数据电路	Yìbù shùjù diànlù	Asynchronous data circuit	CDA
异步数据多路复用同步器	Yìbù shùjù duōlù fùyòng tóngbùqì	Asynchronous data multiplexer synchronizer	ADMS
异步数据收发机	Yìbù shùjù shōufājī	Asynchronous data transceiver	ADT
异步数据通信信道	Yìbù shùjù tōngxìn xìndào	Asynchronous data communication channel	ADCC
异步数据业务	Yìbù shùjù yèwù	Asynchronous data service	ADS
异步数据转移	Yìbù shùjù zhuǎnyí	Asynchronous data transfer	ADT
异步数字分级	Yìbù shùzì fēnjí	Asynchronous digital hierarchy	
异步数字系列	Yìbù shùzì xìliè	Asynchronous digital hierarchy	
异步数字用户线	Yìbù shùzì yònghù xiàn	Asynchronous digital subscriber line	ADSL
异步送代方法	Yìbù sòngdài fāngfǎ	Asynchronous iteration method	
异步通信	Yìbù tōngxìn	Asynchronous communication	
异步通信控制	Yìbù tōngxìn kòngzhì	Asynchronous communication control	ACC
异步通信控制模块	Yìbù tōngxìn kòngzhì mókuài	Asynchronous communication control module	ACM
异步通信适配	Yìbù tōngxìn shìpèi	Asynchronous communications adapter	ACA
异步网	Yìbù wǎng	Nonsynchronized network	
异步无连接	Yìbù wúliánjiē	Asynchronous connectionless	

异步响应方式	Yìbù xiǎngyìng fāngshì	Asynchronous response mode	ARM
异步序列网络	Yìbù xùliè wǎngluò	Asynchronous sequential network	ASN
异步延迟线	Yìbù yánchí xiàn	Asynchronous delay line	ADL
异步应答方式	Yìbù yìngdá fāngshì	Asynchronous response mode	ARM
异步用户模块	Yìbù yònghù mókuài	Asynchronous user module	AUM
异步终端转接器	Yìbù zhōngduān zhuǎnjiēqì	Asynchronous terminal adapter	ATA
异步转换模式	Yìbù zhuǎnhuàn móshì	Asynchronous transfer mode	ATM
异步转移模式	Yìbù zhuǎnyí móshì	Asynchronous transfer mode	ATM
异步转移模式-交叉连接	Yìbù zhuǎnyí móshì - jiāochā liánjiē	Asynchronous transfer mode -cross-connect	ATM-XC
异步转移模式交叉连接	Yìbù zhuǎnyí móshì jiāochā liánjiē	Asynchronous transfer mode cross connect	AXC
异步转移模式交换	Yìbù zhuǎnyí móshì jiāohuàn	Asynchronous transfer mode switch	ATM-SW
异步转移模式数据网络	Yìbù zhuǎnyí móshì shùjù wǎngluò	Asynchronous transfer mode data network	ADN
异步转移模式-网络接口卡	Yìbù zhuǎnyí móshì -wǎngluò jiēkǒu kǎ	Asynchronous transfer mode-netwrk interface card	ATM-NIC
异步转移模式网络接入子系统	Yìbù zhuǎnyí móshì wǎngluò jiērù zixìtǒng	Asynchronous transfer mode network access sub-system	ANAS
异步转移模式 - 业务接入点	Yìbù zhuǎnyí móshì- yèwù jiērù diǎn	Asynchronous transfer mode -service access point	ATM-SAP
异步转移模式业务数据单元	Yìbù zhuǎnyí móshì yèwù shùjù dānyuán	Asynchronous transfer mode service data unit	ATM-SDU
异步转移模式用户单元	Yìbù zhuǎnyí móshì yònghù dānyuán	Asynchronous transfer mode subscriber unit	ASU
异步转移模式用户网络接口	Yìbù zhuǎnyí móshì yònghù wǎngluò jiēkǒu	Asynchronous transfer mode user network interface	ATM-UNI
异步转移模式用户线接口电路	Yìbù zhuǎnyí móshì yònghùxiàn jiēkǒu diànlù	Asynchronous transfer mode subscriber line interface circuit	ATM-SLIC
异步转移区	Yìbù zhuǎnyí qū	Asynchronous transfer region	ATR
异步的	Yìbùde	Asynchronous	
异步的	Yìbùde	Heterochronous	
已裁定的环路	Yǐcáidìngde huánlù	Arbitrated loop	
异常	Yìcháng	Anomaly, anomalous	
异常	Yìcháng	Exception	
异常安全的	Yìcháng ānquánde	Exception-safe	
异常传播	Yìcháng chuánbō	Anomalous propagation	AP
异常处理	Yìcháng chǔlǐ	Exception handling	
异常处理机制	Yìcháng chǔlǐ jīzhì	Exception handling mechanism	
异常规范	Yìcháng guīfàn	Exception specification	
异常检测	Yìcháng jiǎncè	Anomaly detection	
异常空情	Yìcháng kōngqíng	Anomalous air situation, “bogey” on a radar screen	
异常声明	Yìcháng shēngmíng	Exception declaration	
异常值	Yìcháng zhí	Outlier	
一重保存方式	Yīchóng bǎocún fāngshì	Single-save system	
移出	Yíchū	Shift out	SO
溢出	Yìchū	Overflow	OVF
溢出程序	Yìchū chéngxù	Exploit (software program)	
遗传规划	Yíchuán guīhuà	Genetic programming	GP
遗传算法	Yíchuán suànfǎ	Genetic algorithm	
一次被覆层 (预涂层)	Yīcì bèifù céng (yù túcéng)	Primary coating (procoated)	
一次被覆光纤	Yīcì bèifù guāngxiān	Primary coating fiber	
一次拨号音	Yīcì bōhào yīn	Direct outward dialing one	DOD-1

一次电路	Yīcì diànlù	Primary circuit	
一次复用器	Yīcì fùyòngqì	Primary multiplexer	
一次雷达	Yīcì léidá	Primary radar	
一次群	Yīcì qún	Digital standard one (lowest data rate = 2Mbps)	DS-1
一次群接口	Yīcì qún jiēkǒu	Primary rate interface	PRI
一次群速率接口结构	Yīcì qún sùlǜ jiēkǒu jiégòu	Primary rate interface structure	
一次群速率接入	Yīcì qún sùlǜ jiērù	Primary rate access	PRA
一次群速率入口	Yīcì qún sùlǜ rùkǒu	Primary rate access	PRA
一次写入多次读出（光盘）	Yīcì xiěrù duōcì dú chū (guāngpán)	Write only read many (optical disk)	WORM
一次写入光盘	Yīcì xiěrù guāngpán	Write-once optical disk	
一次正常抽样方案	Yīcì zhèngcháng chōuyàng fāng'àn	Normal primary sampling plan (in quality standards)	
一次性编程	Yīcìxìng biānchéng	One-time programmable	
一次性登录	Yīcìxìng dēnglù	Single sign-on	SSO
一次性口令	Yīcìxìng kǒulìng	One-time password (crypto)	OTP
一次性签名方案	Yīcìxìng qiānmíng fāng'àn	One-time signature scheme	
一次性写入	Yīcìxìng xiěrù	Write once	WO
移带倒频	Yídài dǎopín	Band-shift inversion	
一等幅报	Yīděng fúbào	Continuous wave	CW
已登记访问	Yǐdēngjì fǎngwèn	Registered access	
一点多址通信	Yīdiǎn duōzhǐ tōngxìn	One-point multiple access communications	DZ
已调度备份	Yǐdiàodù bèifèn	Scheduled backup	
移动	Yídòng	Motion, mobile	
移动安全关联	Yídòng ānquán guānlián	Mobility security association (in mobile IP)	
移动绑定	Yídòng bǎngdìng	Mobility binding	
移动被叫	Yídòng bèijiào	Mobile terminating call	MTC
移动标识号码	Yídòng biāozhì hàomǎ	Mobile identification number	MIN
移动拨号电话系统	Yídòng bōhào diànhuà xìtǒng	Mobile dial telephone system	MDTS
移动代理	Yídòng dàilǐ	Mobile agent	MA
移动代理系统	Yídòng dàilǐ xìtǒng	Mobile agent system	MOGENT
移动到移动（呼叫）	Yídòng dào yídòng (hūjiào)	Mobile-to-mobile (call)	MTM
移动电话交换局	Yídòng diànhuà jiāohuànjú	Mobile telephone switching office	MTSO
移动电话网号码	Yídòng diànhuà wǎng hàomǎ	Mobile network code	MNC
移动电话系统	Yídòng diànhuà xìtǒng	Mobile Telephone System (Canada)	MTS
移动电台	Yídòng diàntái	Mobile station	MS
移动地球站	Yídòng dìqiúzhàn	Mobile (satellite) earth station	MES
移动地址搜索附加业务	Yídòng dìzhǐ sōusuǒ fùjiā yèwù	Mobile access hunting supplementary service	MAH
移动端系统	Yídòng duān xìtǒng	Mobile end system	M-ES
移动发端呼叫	Yídòng fāduān hūjiào	Mobile originating call	MOC
移动访问捕获	Yídòng fǎngwèn bǔhuò	Mobile access hunting	MAH
移动发起	Yídòng fāqǐ	Mobile originated	MO
移动发起定位请求	Yídòng fāqǐ dìngwèi qǐngqiú	Mobile originating location request	MO-LR
移动发起的点对点短消息	Yídòng fāqǐde diǎn duì diǎn duǎn xiāoxi	Short message mobile-originated point-to-point	SM MO
移动蜂窝电话	Yídòng fēngwō diànhuà	Mobile cellular telephony	
移动分配	Yídòng fēnpèi	Mobile allocation	MA
移动分配索引	Yídòng fēnpèi suǒyǐn	Mobile allocation index	MAI
移动分配索引偏移	Yídòng fēnpèi suǒyǐn piānyí	Mobile allocation index offset	MAIO

移动分配信道号	Yídòng fēnpèi xìndàohào	Mobile allocation channel number	MACN
移动管理实体	Yídòng guǎnlǐ shítǐ	Mobile management entity	MME
移动管理实体-数据链路层	Yídòng guǎnlǐ shítǐ - shùjù liànlù céng	Mobile management entity - data link layer	MDL
移动管理实体-物理层	Yídòng guǎnlǐ shítǐ - wùlǐ céng	Mobile management entity - physical layer	MPH
移动归属功能	Yídòng guīshǔ gōngnéng	Mobile home function	MHF
移动国家号码	Yídòng guójiā hàomǎ	Mobile country code	MCC
移动国家码	Yídòng guójiā mǎ	Mobile country code	MCC
移动号码可携	Yídòng hàomǎ kěxié	Mobile number portability	MNP
移动号码可携带性	Yídòng hàomǎ kěxiédàixìng	Mobile number portability	MNP
移动汇接中心	Yídòng huìjiē zhōngxīn	Tandem mobile switching center	TMSC
移动回音控制	Yídòng huíyīn kòngzhì	Mobile echo control	MEC
移动互通控制单元	Yídòng hùtōng kòngzhì dānyuán	Mobile interwork control element	MICE
移动互通模块	Yídòng hùtōng mókuài	Mobile interwork module	MIM
移动交换中心	Yídòng jiāohuàn zhōngxīn	Mobile switching center	MSC
移动交换机	Yídòng jiāohuànjī	Mobile switching center	MSC
移动交换局	Yídòng jiāohuànjú	Mobile switching center	MSC
移动节点	Yídòng jiédiǎn	Mobile node	MN
移动接口控制器	Yídòng jiēkǒu kòngzhìqì	Mobile interface controller	MIC
移动接入	Yídòng jiērù	Mobile access	MA
移动计算设备	Yídòng jìsuàn shèbèi	Mobile computing device	MCD
移动控制站	Yídòng kòngzhìzhàn	Mobile control station	MCS
移动宽带系统	Yídòng kuāndài xìtǒng	Mobile broadband system	MBS
移动宽带业务	Yídòng kuāndài yèwù	Mobile broadband service	MBS
移动连接产品	Yídòng liánjiē chǎnpǐn	Mobile connectivity product	
移动目录号码	Yídòng mùlù hàomǎ	Mobile directory number	MDN
移动切换估算	Yídòng qiēhuàn gūsuàn	Mobile evaluated handover	MEHO
移动商务	Yídòng shāngwù	Mobile commerce	MC
移动设备	Yídòng shèbèi	Mobile equipment	ME
移动设备识别寄存器	Yídòng shèbèi shíbié jìcúnqì	Mobile equipment identity register	EIR
移动识别码	Yídòng shíbié mǎ	Mobile identification number	MIN
移动始发呼叫	Yídòng shǐfā hūjiào	Mobile originating	MO
移动衰减码	Yídòng shuāijiǎn mǎ	Mobile attenuation code	MAC
移动数据传输	Yídòng shùjù chuánshū	Mobile data transmission	
移动数据基站	Yídòng shùjù jīzhàn	Mobile data base station	MDBS
移动数据链路连接	Yídòng shùjù liànlù liánjiē	Mobile data link connection	MDLC
移动数据链路连接标识符	Yídòng shùjù liànlù liánjiē biāozhìfú	Mobile data link connection identifier	MDLCI
移动数据链路协议	Yídòng shùjù liànlù xiéyì	Mobile data link protocol	MDLP
移动数据中介系统	Yídòng shùjù zhōngjiè xìtǒng	Mobile data intermediate system	MD-IS
移动特设网络	Yídòng tèshè wǎngluò	Mobile ad hoc network	MANET
移动通信	Yídòng tōngxìn	Mobile telecommunication	YD
移动通信地址分配	Yídòng tōngxìn dìzhǐ fēnpèi	Mobile address allocation	MA
移动通信附加功能	Yídòng tōngxìn fùjiā gōngnéng	Mobile additional function	MAF
移动通信国家码	Yídòng tōngxìn guójiā mǎ	Mobile country code	MCC
移动通信特别小组	Yídòng tōngxìn tèbié xiǎozǔ	Groupe Special Mobile (est. 1982)	GSM
移动通信系统	Yídòng tōngxìn xìtǒng	Mobile communication system	
移动通信应用部分	Yídòng tōngxìn yìngyòng bùfen	Mobile application part	MAP

移动通信指配信道号码	Yídòng tōngxìn zhǐpèi xìndào hàomǎ	Mobile allocation channel number	MACN
移动图象专家组	Yídòng túxiàng zhuānjiāzǔ	Moving Pictures Experts Group	MPEG
移动网编号	Yídòng wǎng biānhào	Mobile network code	MNC
移动网登记协议	Yídòng wǎng dēngjì xiéyì	Mobile network registration protocol	MNRP
移动网号	Yídòng wǎng hào	Mobile network code	MNC
移动网位置协议	Yídòng wǎng wèizhì xiéyì	Mobile network location protocol	MNLP
移动网增强逻辑定制应用	Yídòng wǎng zēngqiáng luóji dìngzhì yìngyòng	Customized application for mobile network enhanced logic	CAMEL
移动网增强逻辑的定做应用	Yídòng wǎng zēngqiáng luójide dìngzuò yìngyòng	Customized applications for mobil network enhanced logic	CAMEL
移动网络码	Yídòng wǎngluò mǎ	Mobile network code	MNC
移动网络增强逻辑的客户化应用	Yídòng wǎngluò zēngqiáng luójide kèhùhuà yìngyòng	Customized applications for mobile network enhanced logic	CAMEL
移动卫星通讯	Yídòng wèixīng tōngxùn	Mobile satellite communications	MSC
移动卫星业务	Yídòng wèixīng yèwù	Mobile satellite service	MSS
移动无线接入	Yídòng wúxiàn jiērù	Mobile wireless access	MWA
移动无线局	Yídòng wúxiàn jú	Mobile switching center	MSC
移动无线系统 ACE	Yídòng wúxiàn xìtǒng ACE	Mobile radio system ACE	MRSACE
移动虚拟网络运营商	Yídòng xūnǐ wǎngluò yùnyíngshāng	Mobile virtual network operator	MVNO
移动虚拟专用网	Yídòng xūnǐ zhuānyòng wǎng	Mobile virtual private network	MVPN
移动业务	Yídòng yèwù	Mobile service	
移动业务功能	Yídòng yèwù gōngnéng	Mobile serving function	MSF
移动业务交换中心	Yídòng yèwù jiāohuàn zhōngxīn	Mobile service switching center	MSC, MSSC
移动业务控制子系统	Yídòng yèwù kòngzhì zixìtǒng	Mobile traffic control sub-system	MTCS
移动应用部分	Yídòng yìngyòng bùfen	Mobile application part	MAP
移动应用单元	Yídòng yìngyòng dānyuán	Mobile application part	MAP
移动应用子系统	Yídòng yìngyòng zixìtǒng	Mobile application sub-system	MAS
移动因特网技术的体系结构	Yídòng Yīntèwǎng jìshùde tǐxì jiégòu	Mobile internet technical architecture	MITA
移动用户	Yídòng yònghù	Mobile subscriber	MS
移动用户标识符	Yídòng yònghù biāozhìfú	Mobile user identifier	MUI
移动用户不可及呼叫前转	Yídòng yònghù bùkějí hūjiào qiánzhuǎn	Call forwarding on mobile subscriber not reachable	CFNRk
移动用户单元	Yídòng yònghù dānyuán	Mobile subscriber unit	MSU
移动用户电话码	Yídòng yònghù diànhuà mǎ	Mobile subscriber directory number	DN
移动用户号码簿号码	Yídòng yònghù hàomǎbù hàomǎ	Mobile user directory number	DN
移动用户 ISDN 号码	Yídòng yònghù ISDN hàomǎ	Mobile subscriber ISDN number	MSISDN
移动用户接入权限识别码	Yídòng yònghù jiērù quánxiàn shíbié mǎ	Portable access rights key	PARK
移动用户临时本地电话号码	Yídòng yònghù línshí běndì diànhuà hàomǎ	Mobile subscriber temporary local directory number	TLDN
移动用户忙呼叫前转	Yídòng yònghù máng hujiào qiánzhuǎn	Call forwarding on mobile subscriber busy	CFB
移动用户漫游号码	Yídòng yònghù mànyóu hàomǎ	Mobile subscriber roaming number	MSRN
移动用户识别码	Yídòng yònghù shíbié mǎ	Mobile user identification number	MIN
移动运行环境	Yídòng yùnxíng huánjìng	Mobile execution environment	MexE
移动终端	Yídòng zhōngduān	Mobile terminal	MT
移动终端定位请求	Yídòng zhōngduān dìngwèi qǐngqiú	Mobile terminal location request	MT-LR
移动终端定位中心	Yídòng zhōngduān dìngwèi zhōngxīn	Mobile terminal locating center	MLC
移动终端呼叫	Yídòng zhōngduān hūjiào	Mobile termination call	MTC
移动终接	Yídòng zhōngjiē	Mobile terminated	MT

移动终止	Yídòng zhōngzhǐ	Mobile terminated	MT
移动终止呼叫	Yídòng zhōngzhǐ hūjiào	Mobile terminated call	MT
移动终止的点对点短消息	Yídòng zhōngzhǐde diǎn duì diǎn duǎn xiāoxi	Short message mobile-terminated point-to-point	SM MT
移动主叫	Yídòng zhǔjiào	Mobile originating call	MOC
移动住宅	Yídòng zhùzhái	Mobile home	
移动式存储设备	Yídòng-shì cúnchǔ shèbèi	Removable storage device	RSD
移动式电子电话交换局	Yídòng-shì diànzǐ diànhuà jiāohuànjú	Electronic mobile exchange	EMX
移动式连续图像专家组	Yídòng-shì liánxù túxiàng zhuānjiāzǔ	Motion Joint Photographic Experts Group	MJPEG
移动式信包无线电通信网	Yídòng-shì xìnbāo wúxiàndiàn tōngxìn wǎng	Mobile packet radio network	MPRN
移动式子卡	Yídòng-shì zikǎ	Mobile daughter card	MDC
移动台	Yídòngtái	Mobile station	MS
移动台（频率）分配	Yídòngtái (pínlǜ) fēnpèi	Mobile (frequency) allocation	MA
移动台被叫	Yídòngtái bèijiào	Mobile (station) terminating	MT
移动台被叫	Yídòngtái bèijiào	Mobile terminating call	MTC
移动台标志号码	Yídòngtái biāozhì hàomǎ	Mobile identification number	MIN
移动台标识符	Yídòngtái biāozhìfú	Mobile station identifier	MSID
移动台存储能力溢出标志	Yídòngtái cúnchǔ nénglì yìchū biāozhì	Mobile station memory capacity exceeded flag	MCEF
移动台等级标	Yídòngtái děngjí biāo	Mobile station class mark	MSCM
移动台发起的	Yídòngtái fāqǐde	Mobile originated	MO
移动台辅助切换	Yídòngtái fǔzhù qiēhuàn	Mobile assisted handover	MAHO
移动台功率电平	Yídòngtái gōnglǜ diànpíng	Mobile station power level	PL
移动台国际 ISDN 号码	Yídòngtái guójì ISDN hàomǎ	Mobile station International ISDN number	MSISDN
移动台划分	Yídòngtái huàfēn	Mobile allocation	
移动台 ISDN 号码	Yídòngtái ISDN hàomǎ	Mobile station ISDN number	MSISDN
移动台级别标志	Yídòngtái jíbié biāozhì	Station class mark	SCM
移动台接入寻找	Yídòngtái jiērù xúnzhǎo	Mobile access hunting	MAH
移动台控制单元	Yídòngtái kòngzhì dānyuán	Mobile station control unit	MSCU
移动台控制切换	Yídòngtái kòngzhì qiēhuàn	Mobile-controlled handoff	MCHO
移动台漫游号码	Yídòngtái mànyóu hàomǎ	Mobile station roaming number	MSRN
移动台起始点对点短消息业务	Yídòngtái qǐshǐ diǎn duì diǎn duǎn xiāoxi yèwù	Short message service-mobile originating/point-to-point	SMS-MO/PP
移动台识别号码	Yídòngtái shíbié hàomǎ	Mobile station identification number	MSIN
移动台始呼	Yídòngtái shǐhū	Mobile originated	MO
移动台特性	Yídòngtái tèxìng	Mobile station feature	
移动台终接点对点短消息业务	Yídòngtái zhōngjiēdiǎn duì diǎn duǎn xiāoxi yèwù	Short message service-mobile terminating/point-to-point	SMS-MT/PP
移动台终止的	Yídòngtái zhōngzhǐde	Mobile terminated	MT
移动台主叫	Yídòngtái zhǔ jiào	Mobile originating call	MOC
移动性管理	Yídòngxìng guǎnlǐ	Mobility management	MM
移动性应用部分	Yídòngxìng yìngyòng bùfen	Mobility application part	MAP
移动站	Yídòngzhàn	Mobile station	MS
移动站国际 ISDN 号	Yídòngzhàn guójì ISDN hào	Mobile station international ISDN number	MSISDN
移动站识别号	Yídòngzhàn shíbié hào	Mobile station identification number	MSIN
已发布数据	Yǐfābù shùjù	Published data	
移幅键控	Yífú jiànkòng	Amplitude shift keying	ASK

已复制数据	Yǐfùzhì shùjù	Replicated data	
异构	Yìgòu	Heterogeneous	
异构环境	Yìgòu huánjìng	Heterogenous environment	
异构网络	Yìgòu wǎngluò	Heterogenous network	
异构性	Yìgòuxìng	Heterogeneity	
一号可处理方式	Yīhào kěchǔlǐ fāngshì	Processable mode number one	PM1
1 号数字用户信令	Yīhào shùzì yònghù xìnlìng	Digital subscriber signaling no1	DSS1
一号数字用户信令系统	Yīhào shùzì yònghù xìnlìng xìtǒng	Digital subscriber signaling system one	DSS1
移后	Yíhòu	Back, zoom back (as in internet Explorer)	
以后见	Yǐhòu jiàn	See you later (computer chat)	CUL
溢呼表	Yìhū biǎo	Overflow meter	
溢呼路由	Yìhū lùyóu	Overflow route	
"异或"门	Yìhuò mén	Exclusive-OR gate	
"异或非"门	Yìhuòfēi mén	Exclusive-NOR gate	
移交测试	Yíjiāo cèshì	Handover test	
一阶谷	Yījiē gǔ	First order valley (GIS)	
一阶锁相环	Yījiē suǒxiānghuán	First-order phase-locked loop	
一阶微分环节	Yījiē wēifēn huánjié	First derivative element	
一阶无差系统	Yījiē wúchā xìtǒng	First order astatic system	
一阶效应	Yījiē xiàoyìng	First order effect	
已纠正块	Yǐjiūzhèng kuài	Corrected block	
一卡在手	Yīkǎ zàishǒu	All-in-one	
异类复用	Yìlèi fùyòng	Heterogeneous multiplex	
异类数据	Yìlèi shùjù	Heterogeneous data	
译码	Yìmǎ	Transcode, decode; translate	
译码和选择集成件	Yìmǎ hé xuǎnzé jíchéng jiàn	Transcoding and selector board assembly	TASA
译码和选择器	Yìmǎ hé xuǎnzéqì	Transcoder and selector bank	TSB
译码和选择器机架	Yìmǎ hé xuǎnzéqì jījià	Transcoder and selector bank rack	TSBR
译码类型	Yìmǎ lèixíng	Transcode type	TT
译码约束长度	Yìmǎ yuēshù chángdù	Decoding constraint length	
译码器	Yìmǎqì	Decoder	DEC
译码器	Yìmǎqì	Translator (in switching)	
译密码	Yìmìmǎ	Decipher	
隐马尔科夫模型	Yǐn mǎ-ěr-kē-fū móxíng	Hidden Markovian model	HMM
隐蔽存储信道	Yǐnbì cúnchǔ xìndào	Covert storage channel (IPsec)	
隐蔽计时信道	Yǐnbì jìshí xìndào	Covert timing channel (IPsec)	
隐蔽面消除	Yǐnbì miàn xiāochú	Hidden surface removal	
隐蔽调谐	Yǐnbì tiáoxié	Concealed tuning	
隐蔽线	Yǐnbì xiàn	Hidden line	
隐蔽线消除	Yǐnbì xiàn xiāochú	Hidden line removal	
隐蔽信道	Yǐnbì xìndào	Covert channel (IPsec)	
隐蔽系统	Yǐnbì xìtǒng	Concealment system (IPsec)	
隐蔽锥扫	Yǐnbì zhuī sǎo	Hide conical-scan	
隐藏文字	Yǐncáng wénzì	Hidden text (WP command)	
隐层神经元	Yǐncéng shénjīngyuán	Hidden neuron	
引出电缆	Yǐnchū diànlǎn	Drop cable	

引出光纤	Yǐnchū guāngxiān	Tail optical fiber	
引出线	Yǐnchū xiàn	Lead-out line	
引出线端子	Yǐnchū xiàn duānzi	Outlet line terminal	
引导	Yǐndǎo	Bootstrap, boot (verb)	
引导重试	Yǐndǎo chóngshì	Directed retry	
引导符号	Yǐndǎo fúhào	Aiming symbol	
引导雷达	Yǐndǎo léidá	Director radar	
引导路由器	Yǐndǎo lùyóuqì	Bootstrap router	BSR
引导设备	Yǐndǎo shèbèi	Guiding device	
引导图	Yǐndǎo tú	Deriviation graph	
引导协议	Yǐndǎo xiéyì	Bootstrap protocol	BOOTP
引导域	Yǐndǎo yù	Aiming field	
引导圆	Yǐndǎo yuán	Aiming circle	
引导指令	Yǐndǎo zhǐlìng	Bootstrap	
引导式干扰	Yǐndǎo-shì gānrǎo	Directed jamming	
音调代码调制	Yīndiào dàimǎ tiáozhì	Tone code modulation	TCM
音调调制	Yīndiào tiáozhì	Tone modulation	TM
引发	Yǐnfā	Raise (as 'to raise an exception')	
引发	Yǐnfā	Throw (as causing an exception, in software)	
硬编码的	Yìng biānmǎde	Hard-coded	
硬反馈	Yìng fǎnkuì	Rigid feedback	
硬故障	Yìng gùzhàng	Solid fault	
硬行终止符	Yìng háng zhōngzhǐ fú	Hard line terminator	
硬判决译码	Yìng pànjué yìmǎ	Hard decision decoding	
硬切换	Yìng qiēhuàn	Hard handover	HHO
硬同轴线	Yìng tóngzhóu xiàn	Rigid coaxial line	
硬限幅器	Yìng xiànfúqì	Hard limiter	
应变	Yìngbiàn	Strain	
应变层多量子阱	Yìngbiàn céng duō liàngzǐ jiē	Strained layer multiple quantum well	SLMQW
应变范围	Yìngbiàn fànwéi	Strain range	
应变能	Yìngbiàn néng	Strain energy	
应变限量	Yìngbiàn xiànliàng	Strain margin	
应变张量	Yìngbiàn zhāngliàng	Strain tensor	
应变计	Yìngbiànjì	Strain meter	
应答	Yìngdá	Acknowledgement	ACK
应答不计费信号	Yìngdá bùjìfèi xìnhào	Answer signal, no charge	ANN
应答单音	Yìngdá dānyīn	Answering tone	
应答电码	Yìngdá diànmǎ	Answer back code	ABC
应答检测图形	Yìngdá jiǎncè túxíng	Answer detection pattern	ADP
应答计费	Yìngdá jìfèi	Answer charging	ANC
应答免费	Yìngdá miǎnfèi	Answer no charge	ANN
应答模式	Yìngdá móshì	Acknowledged mode	AM
应答时间记录器	Yìngdá shíjiān jìlùqì	Answering time recorder	ATR
应答试占比	Yìngdá shìzhàn bǐ	Answer bid ratio	ABR
应答消息	Yìngdá xiāoxi	Answer message (SS7 ISUP message)	ANM
应答信号	Yìngdá xìnhào	Acknowledgement	ACK

应答信号	Yìngdá xìnhào	Answer signal	
应答信号（不计费）	Yìngdá xìnhào (bùjìfèi)	Answer signal (with no charge)	
应答信号、计费	Yìngdá xìnhào、jìfèi	Answer signal, charge	ANC
应答信号、免费	Yìngdá xìnhào、miǎnfèi	Answer signal, no charge	ANN
应答占用率	Yìngdá zhànyòng lǜ	Answer-seizure ratio	ASR
应答装置	Yìngdá zhuāngzhì	Call back apparatus	CBA
应当信号、计费未说明	Yīngdāng xìnhào、jìfèi wèi shuōmíng	Answer signal, unqualified	ANU
应答性	Yìngdáxìng	Responsiveness	
硬度	Yìngdù	Stiffness	
硬度率	Yìngdù lǜ	Rigidity	
硬度计	Yìngdùjì	Durometer (in SMT)	
英飞凌科技	Yīng-fēi-líng kējì	Infineon Technologies AG	
英孚美	Yīng-fú-měi	Informix (IBM software)	
英孚美软件有限公司	Yīng-fú-měi ruǎnjiàn yǒuxiàn gōngsī	Infomix Software Corp. (China)	
萤光放射晶体	Yíngguāng fàngshè jīngtǐ	Fluorescent emission crystal	
荧光质只读存储器	Yíngguāng zhì zhǐ dú cúnchǔqì	Fluorescent material read only memory	FMD ROM
英国标准所	Yīngguó biāozhǔn suǒ	British Standards Institute	BSI
英国伯明翰线规	Yīngguó bó-míng-hàn xiànguī	Birmingham Wire gauge (UK)	BWG
英国电脑学会	Yīngguó diànnǎo xuéhuì	British Computer Society	BCS
英国电信公司	Yīngguó diànxìn gōngsī	British Telecom Corp.	
英国联合电子制造公司	Yīngguó liánhé diànzǐ zhìzào gōngsī	Unifab Electronics Inc. (UK company)	
英国邮政与电信标准	Yīngguó yóuzhèng yǔ diànxìn biāozhǔn	British Posts and Telecommunications Standard	BPT
硬化规则	Yìnghuà guīzé	Hardening rule	
硬化剂	Yìnghuàjì	Hardener (in SMT)	
英华美电脑学校	Yīng-huá-měi diànnǎo xuéxiào	Informatics Computer School (Singapore)	
应急	Yìngjí	Emergency	
应急插座	Yìngjí chāzuò	Emergency socket	
应急电源	Yìngjí diànyuán	Emergency power	EP
应急动作	Yìngjí dòngzuò	Emergency action	
应急计划	Yìngjí jìhuà	Contingency plan	
应急示位无线电信标	Yìngjí shìwèi wúxiàndiàn xìnbiāo	Emergency position-indicating radio beacon	EPIRB
应急示位无线电信标电台	Yìngjí shìwèi wúxiàndiàn xìnbiāo diàntái	Emergency position-indication radio beacon station	
应急通信	Yìngjí tōngxìn	Emergency communication	
应急信息自动传输系统	Yìngjí xìnxī zìdòng chuánshū xìtǒng	Emergency message automatic transmission system	EMATS
硬件	Yìngjiàn	Hardware	
硬件抽象层	Yìngjiàn chōuxiàng céng	Hardware abstraction layer	HAL
硬件抽像化层	Yìngjiàn chōuxiànghuà céng	Hardware abstraction layer	HAL
硬件地址	Yìngjiàn dìzhǐ	Hardware address	
硬件仿真层	Yìngjiàn fǎngzhēn céng	Hardware emulation layer	HEL
硬件环境	Yìngjiàn huánjìng	Hardware environment	
硬件兼容性测试	Yìngjiàn jiānróngxìng cèshì	Hardware compatibility test	HCT
硬件兼容性列表	Yìngjiàn jiānróngxìng lièbiǎo	Hardware compatibility list	HCL
硬件描述语言	Yìngjiàn miáoshù yǔyán	Hardware description language	HDL
硬件模拟层	Yìngjiàn mónǐ céng	Hardware emulation layer	HEL
硬件时钟	Yìngjiàn shízhōng	Hardware timer	

硬件虚拟器	Yìngjiàn xūnǐqì	Hardware virtualizer	HV
硬件优先级	Yìngjiàn yōuxiān jí	Hardware priority level	
硬件运动补偿	Yìngjiàn yùndòng bǔcháng	Hardware motion compensation	
迎角	Yíngjiǎo	Angle of attack (in SMT)	
营救器电台	Yíngjiùqì diàntái	Survival craft station	
硬拷贝	Yìngkǎobèi	Hard copy	
应力	Yìnglì	Stress	
应力测定	Yìnglì cèdìng	Stress measurement	
应力场	Yìnglì cháng	Stress field	
应力分析	Yìnglì fēnxī	Stress analysis	
应力腐蚀	Yìnglì fǔshí	Stress corrosion	
应力感应双折射纤维	Yìnglì gǎnyìng shuāngzhéshè xiānwéi	Stress-induced birefringence fiber	SIF
应力集中	Yìnglì jízhōng	Stress concentration	
应力模型	Yìnglì móxíng	Stress model	
应力强度系数	Yìnglì qiángdù xìshù	Stress intensity factor	
应力释放法	Yìnglì shìfàng fǎ	Stress relief method	
应力松弛模型	Yìnglì sōngchí móxíng	Stress relaxation model	
应力下降	Yìnglì xiàjiàng	Stress drop	
应力应变曲线	Yìnglì yìngbiàn qūxiàn	Stress-strain curve	
应力张量	Yìnglì zhāngliàng	Stress tensor	
硬盘	Yìngpán	Hard disk	
硬盘控制器	Yìngpán kòngzhìqì	Hard disk controller	HDC
营商标识码	Yíngshāng biāoshí mǎ	Carrier identification code	CIC
映射	Yìngshè	Mapping	
映射抖动	Yìngshè dǒudòng	Mapping jitter	
映射复用	Yìngshè fùyòng	Mapping multiplexing	
影视点播	Yǐngshì diǎnbō	Video on demand	VOD
硬水	Yìngshuǐ	Hard water	
英特尔	Yīng-tè-ěr	Intel ® (US company)	
英特尔架构	Yīng-tè-ěr jiàgòu	Intel ® architecture	IA
英特尔开发者论坛	Yīng-tè-ěr kāifāzhě lùntán	Intel Developer forum	IDF
英特尔移动模块	Yīng-tè-ěr yídòng mókuài	Intel ® mobile module	IMM
英特网	Yīng-tè-wǎng	Internet	
英特网工程任务阻	Yīng-tè-wǎng gōngchéng rènwu zǔ	Internet Engineering Task Force	IETF
英特网缓存协议	Yīng-tè-wǎng huǎncún xiéyì	Internet cache protocol	ICP
英特网协议组织	Yīng-tè-wǎng xiéyì zǔzhī	World Wide Web Consortium	W3C
英特网业务提供者	Yīng-tè-wǎng yèwù tígòngzhě	Internet service provider	ISP
映象	Yìngxiàng	Mapping	
影像	Yǐngxiàng	Imagery	
影像处理	Yǐngxiàng chǔlǐ	Image processing	
影像处理设备	Yǐngxiàng chǔlǐ shèbèi	Image processing facility	
影像地图	Yǐngxiàng dìtú	Photographic map; photomap	
影响范围	Yǐngxiǎng fànwéi	Range of influence	
影像分割	Yǐngxiàng fēngē	Image division	
影像分类	Yǐngxiàng fēnlèi	Image classification	
影像复原	Yǐngxiàng fùyuán	Image restoration	

影响功能性维护	Yǐngxiǎng gōngnéngxìng wéihù	Function-affecting maintenance	
影像集成	Yǐngxiàng jíchéng	Image integration	
影像集成器	Yǐngxiàng jíchéngqì	Image integrator	
影像判读	Yǐngxiàng pàndú	Image interpretation	
影像配准	Yǐngxiàng pèizhǔn	Image registration	
影像匹配	Yǐngxiàng pǐpèi	Image matching	
影像扫描器	Yǐngxiàng sǎomiáoqì	Image scanner	
影像数据	Yǐngxiàng shùjù	Image data	
影像纹理	Yǐngxiàng wénlǐ	Image texture	
影像信息	Yǐngxiàng xìnxī	Image information	
影像系统	Yǐngxiàng xìtǒng	Video system	
影像增强	Yǐngxiàng zēngqiáng	Image enhancement	
影音光碟	Yǐngyīn guāngdié	Compact disk-read only memory	CD-ROM
影印机	Yǐngyìnjī	Copy machine	
应用	Yìngyòng	Application	
应用本体	Yìngyòng běntǐ	Applied ontology	
应用编程接口	Yìngyòng biānchéng jiēkǒu	Application programming interface	API
应用标识符	Yìngyòng biāozhì fú	Application identifier	AID
应用参数控制	Yìngyòng cānshù kòngzhì	Application parameter control	
应用层	Yìngyòng céng	Application layer	
应用层分帧	Yìngyòng céng fēnzhèng	Application-level framing	ALF
应用层结构	Yìngyòng céng jiégòu	Application layer structure	ALS
应用层用户标示	Yìngyòng céng yònghù biāoshì	Application level subscriber identity	ALSI
应用层语义可靠的自适应多播体系	Yìngyòng céng yǔyì kěkàode zìshìyìng duōbō tǐxì	Application-level semantics-reliable multicast	ASRM
应用层帧协议	Yìngyòng céng zhèng xiéyì	Application level framing	ALF
应用程序	Yìngyòng chéngxù	Application program	
应用程序包	Yìngyòng chéngxù bāo	Application package	
应用程序接口	Yìngyòng chéngxù jiēkǒu	Application program interface	API
应用程序角色	Yìngyòng chéngxù juésè	Application role	
应用程序框架	Yìngyòng chéngxù kuàngjià	Application framework	
应用程序请求	Yìngyòng chéngxù qǐngqiú	Application process invocation	API
应用程序生成器	Yìngyòng chéngxù shēngchéngqì	Application generator	AG
应用程序卸载环境	Yìngyòng chéngxù xièzài huánjìng	Application offload environment	
应用程序系统	Yìngyòng chéngxù xìtǒng	Application program system	APS
应用传送参数	Yìngyòng chuánsòng cānshù	Application transport parameter	APP
应用传送机制	Yìngyòng chuánsòng jīzhì	Application transport mechanism	APM
应用传送指导指示语	Yìngyòng chuánsòng zhǐdǎo zhǐshì yǔ	Application transport instruction indicator	ATII
应用代理	Yìngyòng dàilǐ	Application proxy	
应用二进制式接口	Yìngyòng èrjìnzhìshì jiēkǒu	Application binary interface	ABI
应用方	Yìngyòng fāng	User	
应用范围	Yìngyòng fànwéi	Application context	AC
应用分解	Yìngyòng fēnjiě	Application decomposition (in CORBA)	
应用服务单元	Yìngyòng fúwù dānyuán	Application service element	ASE
应用服务目标	Yìngyòng fúwù mùbiāo	Application service object	ASO
应用服务目标请求	Yìngyòng fúwù mùbiāo qǐngqiú	Application service object invocation	ASOI

应用服务提供商	Yìngyòng fúwù tígōngshāng	Application service provider	ASP
应用服务提供商	Yìngyòng fúwù tígōngshāng	Application service provider	ASP
应用服务提供者	Yìngyòng fúwù tígòngzhě	Application service provider	ASP
应用服务元素	Yìngyòng fúwù yuánsù	Application service element	ASE
应用服务器	Yìngyòng fúwùqì	Application server	AS
应用服务器进程	Yìngyòng fúwùqì jìnchéng	Application server process	ASP
应用服务器进程维护	Yìngyòng fúwùqì jìnchéng wéihù	Application server process maintenance	ASPM
应用服务商	Yìngyòng fúwùshāng	Application service provider	ASP
应用共享	Yìngyòng gòngxiǎng	Application sharing (in CSCW)	
应用管理	Yìngyòng guǎnlǐ	Application management	
应用管理构件	Yìngyòng guǎnlǐ gòujiàn	Applications management building block	AMBB
应用管理规范	Yìngyòng guǎnlǐ guīfàn	Application management specification	AMS
应用管理接口	Yìngyòng guǎnlǐ jiēkǒu	Application management interface	AMI
应用管理用户图形接口	Yìngyòng guǎnlǐ yònghù túxíng jiēkǒu	Applications manager graphical user interface	AMGUI
应用互通功能	Yìngyòng hùtōng gōngnéng	Application interworking function	
应用级网关	Yìngyòng jí wǎngguān	Application-level gateway	ALG
应用进程	Yìngyòng jìnchéng	Application process or program	AP
应用进程调用	Yìngyòng jìnchéng diàoyòng	Application-process-invocation	
应用进程类型	Yìngyòng jìnchéng lèixíng	Application-process-type	
应用控制操作系统	Yìngyòng kòngzhì cāozuò xìtǒng	Application control operating system	ACOS
应用控制及管理系统	Yìngyòng kòngzhì jí guǎnlǐ xìtǒng	Application control and management system	ACMS
应用链指针控制块	Yìngyòng liàn zhǐzhēn kòngzhì kuài	Application anchor block	AAB
应用联系	Yìngyòng liánxì	Application-association	
应用模式	Yìngyòng móshì	Application schema	
应用模型	Yìngyòng móxíng	Application model	
应用平台	Yìngyòng píngtái	Application platform	
应用软件	Yìngyòng ruǎnjiàn	Application software	
应用软件单元管理	Yìngyòng ruǎnjiàn dānyuán guǎnlǐ	Application software element manager	AEM
应用软件介面	Yìngyòng ruǎnjiàn jièmiàn	Application program interface	API
应用软件包	Yìngyòng ruǎnjiànbāo	Application software package	ASP
应用上下文	Yìngyòng shàngxiàwén	Application context	AC
应用上下文名称	Yìngyòng shàngxiàwén míngchēng	Application context name	ACN
应用实体	Yìngyòng shítǐ	Application entity	AE
应用实体安装和拆除	Yìngyòng shítǐ ānzhuāng hé chāichú	Application entity installer and remover	AEIR
应用实体调用	Yìngyòng shítǐ diàoyòng	Application entity invocation	AEI
应用实体类型	Yìngyòng shítǐ lèixíng	Application entity type	
应用数据单元	Yìngyòng shùjù dānyuán	Application data unit	ADU
应用托管	Yìngyòng tuōguǎn	Application hosting	
应用网关	Yìngyòng wǎngguān	Application-level gateway	
应用位置登记	Yìngyòng wèizhì dēngjì	Application location register	ALR
应用物理组	Yìngyòng wùlǐ zǔ	Applied physics group	GAP
应用向导服务	Yìngyòng xiàngdǎo fúwù	Application courier service	
应用协议	Yìngyòng xiéyì	Application protocol	
应用协议控制信息	Yìngyòng xiéyì kòngzhì xìnxī	Application protocol control information	APCI
应用协议数据单位	Yìngyòng xiéyì shùjù dānwèi	Application protocol data unit	
应用协议数据单元	Yìngyòng xiéyì shùjù dānyuán	Application protocol data unit	APDU

应用系统	Yìngyòng xìtǒng	Application system	
应用业务单元	Yìngyòng yèwù dānyuán	Application service element	ASE
应用业务接入点	Yìngyòng yèwù jiērù diǎn	Application service access point	ASAP
应用业务提供商	Yìngyòng yèwù tígōng shāng	Application service provider	ASP
应用业务元素	Yìngyòng yèwù yuánsù	Application service element	ASE
应用域	Yìngyòng yù	Application domain	
应用中间件	Yìngyòng zhōngjiān jiàn	Application middleware	
应用专用文件	Yìngyòng zhuānyòng wénjiàn	Application dedicated file	ADF
营运服务区	Yíngyùn fúwùqū	Carrier service area	CSA
营帐系统	Yíngzhàng xìtǒng	Billing system	
隐含令牌寄存器	Yǐnhán lìngpái jìcúnqì	Implicit token register	ITR
隐含文件	Yǐnhán wénjiàn	Hidden file	
隐含文件属性	Yǐnhán wénjiàn shǔxìng	Hidden file attributes	
引航者	Yǐnhángzhě	Navigator ® (Netscape software product)	
阴极脉冲调制器	Yīnjí màichōng tiáozhìqì	Cathode modulator	
阴极射线管	Yīnjí shèxiàn guǎn	Cathode ray tube	CRT
阴极线管	Yīnjí xiàn guǎn	Cathode ray tube	CRT
阴极栅	Yīnjí zhà	Cathode grid	CG
引脚	Yǐnjiǎo	Pin (on a connector)	
引脚外形	Yǐnjiǎo wàixíng	Lead configuration (in SMT)	
引脚网格阵列	Yǐnjiǎo wǎnggé zhènliè	Pin grid array	PGA
隐焦点节点	Yǐnjiāodiǎn jiédiǎn	Concealed focus node (in CSCW)	
音节清晰度	Yīnjié qīngxīdù	Syllable articulation	
音节压扩	Yīnjié yākuò	Syllabic companding	
音节压缩扩展	Yīnjié yāsuō kuòzhǎn	Syllabic companding	
音节表	Yīnjiébiǎo	Syllable chart	
音量控制	Yīnliàng kòngzhì	Volume control	
印码	Yìnmǎ	Printing code	
隐面消除	Yǐnmiàn xiāochú	Backface culling (video)	
印尼卫星公司	Yìnní wèixīng gōngsī	Indonesian Satellite Corp.	Indosat
音频	Yīnpín	Audio frequency, voice frequency	AF
音频	Yīnpín	Audio frequency	AF
音频板	Yīnpín bǎn	Voice frequency board	VFB
音频保护比	Yīnpín bǎohù bǐ	Audio-frequency protection ratio	
音频编码	Yīnpín biānmǎ	Voice coding	
音频编码器	Yīnpín biānmǎqì	Voice coder	VOCODER
音频处理器单元	Yīnpín chǔlǐqì dānyuán	Audio processor unit	APU
音频带通滤波器	Yīnpín dàitōng lǜbōqì	Audio bandpass filter	ABF
音频电话会议	Yīnpín diànhuà huìyì	Audio conference	
音频多媒体数字信号编解码器	Yīnpín duōméitǐ shùzì xìnhào biān jiěmǎqì	Audio codec	AC
音频放大器	Yīnpín fàngdàqì	Audio frequency amplifier	
音频复用电报	Yīnpín fùyòng diànbào	Voice-frequency multiplex telegraphy	VFT
音频负载	Yīnpín fùzài	Audio-frequency load	
音频互调失真	Yīnpín hùtiáo shīzhēn	Audio frequency intermodulation distortion	
音频配线	Yīnpín pèixiàn	Voice distribution frame	VDF

音频视频插入	Yīnpín shìpín chārù	Audio video interleave	AVI
音频试验负载	Yīnpín shìyàn fùzài	Audio-frequency test load	
音频数据复用板	Yīnpín shùjù fùyòng bǎn	Voice data multiplexer	VDM
音频数字叠加	Yīnpín shùzì diéjiā	Voice overlaying digital (data)	
音频数字叠加板	Yīnpín shùzì diéjiā bǎn	Voice data multiplexer (literally "voice frequency digital overlay board")	VDM
音频响应	Yīnpín xiǎngyìng	Audio-frequency response	
音频信道	Yīnpín xìndào	Voice frequency channel	VFC
音频信号干扰比	Yīnpín xìnhào gānrǎo bǐ	Audio-frequency signal-to-interference ratio	
音频信令	Yīnpín xìnlìng	Voice-frequency signaling	
音频压缩	Yīnpín yāsuō	Audio compression	
音频移频键控	Yīnpín yípín jiànkòng	Audio frequency shift keying	AFSK
音频终端设备	Yīnpín zhōngduān shèbèi	Audio terminal unit	ATU
音频子系统	Yīnpín zixìtǒng	Audio sub-system	ASS
音频-视频支持系统	Yīnpín-shìpín zhīchí xìtǒng	Audio-video support system	AVSS
引起注意中断	Yǐnqǐ zhùyì zhōngduàn	Attention interrupt	
引擎	Yǐnqíng	Engine	
引入设备	Yǐnrù shèbèi	Entrance facility	
引入线	Yǐnrùxiàn	Drop line	
引入线	Yǐnrùxiàn	Lead-in line	
隐身技术	Yǐnshēn jìshù	Stealth technology	
隐式	Yǐnshì	Implicit	
隐式调用	Yǐnshì diàoyòng	Implicit invocation	
隐式地址	Yǐnshì dìzhǐ	Implicit addressing	
隐失模	Yǐnshī mó	Evanescent mode (in a waveguide)	
隐式事务	Yǐnshì shìwù	Implicit transaction (for database)	
隐式拓扑记述	Yǐnshì tuòpū jìshù	Implicit topological description	
隐式转换	Yǐnshì zhuǎnhuàn	Implicit conversion	
引数	Yǐnshù	Argument	
印刷电路板	Yìnshuā diànlù bǎn	Printed circuit board	PCB
印刷电路板装配	Yìnshuā diànlù bǎn zhuāngpèi	Printed circuit board assembly	PCBA
印刷振子	Yìnshuā zhènzǐ	Printed oscillator	
印刷板式插座	Yìnshuābǎn-shi chāzuò	Printed circuit board slot	
因素	Yīnsù	Factor	
因素分析	Yīnsù fēnxī	Factor analysis	
因特网	Yīntèwǎng	Internet	
因特网安全连接和密钥管理协议	Yīntèwǎng ānquán liánjiē hé mìyào guǎnlǐ xiéyì	Internet security association and key management protocol	ISAKMP
因特网编号分配委员会	Yīntèwǎng biānhào fēnpèi wěiyuánhuì	Internet Assigned Numbers Authority	IANA
因特网编号管理局	Yīntèwǎng biānhào guǎnlǐjú	Internet Assigned Numbers Authority	IANA
因特网编号收授权委员会	Yīntèwǎng biānhào shōu shòuquán wěiyuánhuì	Internet Assigned Numbers Authority	IANA
因特网草案	Yīntèwǎng cǎo'àn	Internet draft	ID
因特网测试员	Yīntèwǎng cèshìyuán	Internet explorer	IE
因特网导航	Yīntèwǎng dǎoháng	Internet navigation	
因特网打印协议	Yīntèwǎng dǎyìn xiéyì	Internet printing protocol	IPP
因特网电话网关	Yīntèwǎng diànhuà wǎngguān	Internet telephone gateway	ITG

因特网电视会议	Yīntèwǎng diànshì huìyì	Internet videoconference	
因特网电子商务	Yīntèwǎng diànzǐ shāngwù	Electronic commerce over Internet	ECoI
因特网短消息网关	Yīntèwǎng duǎn xiāoxi wǎngguān	Internet short message gateway	ISMG
因特网多媒体子网	Yīntèwǎng duōméitǐ ziwǎng	Internet multiedia sub-system	IMS
因特网服务提供商	Yīntèwǎng fúwù tígōngshāng	Internet service provider	ISP
因特网服务提供者	Yīntèwǎng fúwù tígòngzhě	Internet service provider	ISP
因特网工程备忘录	Yīntèwǎng gōngchéng bèiwànglù	Internet Engineering Note	IEN
因特网工程部	Yīntèwǎng gōngchéng bù	Internet Engineering Task Force	IETF
因特网工程管理组	Yīntèwǎng gōngchéng guǎnlǐ zǔ	Internet Engineering Steering group	IESG
因特网工程任务组	Yīntèwǎng gōngchéng rènwu zǔ	Internet Engineering Task Force	IETF
因特网工程作业推动	Yīntèwǎng gōngchéng zuòyè tuīdòng	Internet Engineering Task Force	IETF
因特网工作委员会	Yīntèwǎng gōngzuò wěiyuánhuì	Internet Activities Board	IAB
因特网号码分配部门	Yīntèwǎng hàomǎ fēnpèi bùmén	Internet Assigned Numbers Authority	IANA
因特网会议电视	Yīntèwǎng huìyì diànshì	Internet videoconference	
因特网呼叫等待	Yīntèwǎng hūjiào děngdài	Internet call waiting	
因特网呼叫筛选	Yīntèwǎng hūjiào shāixuǎn	Internet call screening	
因特网呼叫中心	Yīntèwǎng hūjiào zhōngxīn	Internet call center	ICC
因特网活动委员会	Yīntèwǎng huódòng wěiyuánhuì	Internet activities board	IAB
因特网简单密钥交换协议	Yīntèwǎng jiǎndān mìyào jiāohuàn xiéyì	Simple key exchange Internet protocol	SKIP
因特网结构委员会	Yīntèwǎng jiégòu wěiyuánhuì	Internet Architecture Board	IAB
因特网接力闲谈	Yīntèwǎng jiēlì xiántán	Internet relay chat	IRC
因特网接入提供者	Yīntèwǎng jiērù tígòngzhě	Internet access provider	IAP
因特网控制报文协议	Yīntèwǎng kòngzhì bàowén xiéyì	Internet control message protocol	ICMP
因特网控制报文协议发现路由器	Yīntèwǎng kòngzhì bàowén xiéyì fāxiàn lùyóuqì	Internet control message protocol router discovery	IRD
因特网控制信息协议	Yīntèwǎng kòngzhì xìnxī xiéyì	Internet control message protocol	ICMP
因特网连接服务器	Yīntèwǎng liánjiē fúwùqì	Internet connection server	ICS
因特网密钥交换	Yīntèwǎng mìyào jiāohuàn	Internet key exchange	IKE
因特网密钥交换协议	Yīntèwǎng mìyào jiāohuàn xiéyì	Internet key exchange protocol	IKE
因特网内容提供商	Yīntèwǎng nèiróng tígōngshāng	Internet content provider	ICP
因特网内容提供者	Yīntèwǎng nèiróng tígòngzhě	Internet content provider	ICP
因特网内容选择平台	Yīntèwǎng nèiróng xuǎnzé píngtái	Platform for Internet content selection	PICS
因特网 ORB 间协议	Yīntèwǎng ORB-jiān xiéyì	Internet inter-ORB protocol (CORBA term)	IIOP
因特网平台提供者	Yīntèwǎng píngtái tígòngzhě	Internet presence provider	IPP
因特网商业中心	Yīntèwǎng shāngyè zhōngxīn	Internet business center	IBC
因特网适配器	Yīntèwǎng shìpèiqì	Internet adapter	IA
因特网视频会议	Yīntèwǎng shìpín huìyì	Internet videoconference	
因特网实验备忘录	Yīntèwǎng shíyàn bèiwànglù	Internet experiment note	IEN
因特网数据中心	Yīntèwǎng shùjù zhōngxīn	Internet data center	IDC
因特网提供的八比特组流量业务	Yīntèwǎng tígōngde bābǐtèzǔ liúliàng yèwù	Internet hosted octet stream service	IHOSS
因特网体系结构委员会	Yīntèwǎng tǐxì jiégòu wěiyuánhuì	Internet Architecture Board	IAB
因特网图像协议	Yīntèwǎng túxiàng xiéyì	Internet imaging protocol	IIP
因特网网络地址	Yīntèwǎng wǎngluò dìzhǐ	Internet address	IA
因特网协会	Yīntèwǎng xiéhuì	Internet Society	ISOC
因特网协议	Yīntèwǎng xiéyì	Internet protocol	IP

因特网协议版本 4	Yīntèwǎng xiéyì bǎnběn 4	Internet protocol version 4	Ipv4
因特网协议版本 6	Yīntèwǎng xiéyì bǎnběn 6	Internet protocol version 6	IPv6
因特网信息访问协议	Yīntèwǎng xìnxī fǎngwèn xiéyì	Internet message access protocol	IMAP
因特网信息服务	Yīntèwǎng xìnxī fúwù	Internet information services (in SQL Server)	IIS
因特网信息服务器	Yīntèwǎng xìnxī fúwùqì	Internet information server	IIS
因特网信息控制协议	Yīntèwǎng xìnxī kòngzhì xiéyì	Internet control message protocol	ICMP
因特网学会	Yīntèwǎng xuéhuì	Internet Society	ISOC
因特网研究部	Yīntèwǎng yánjiū bù	Internet Research Task Force	IRTF
因特网研究管理组	Yīntèwǎng yánjiū guǎnlǐ zǔ	Internet Research Steering group	IRSG
因特网研究指导组	Yīntèwǎng yánjiū zhǐdǎo zǔ	Internet Research Steering group	IRSG
因特网业务提供商	Yīntèwǎng yèwù tígōng shāng	Internet service provider	ISP
因特网业务提供者	Yīntèwǎng yèwù tígòngzhě	Internet service provider	ISP
因特网移动/多媒体通信	Yīntèwǎng yídòng/duōméitǐ tōngxìn	Internet mobile/multimedia telecommunication	IMT-2000
因特网邮件组织	Yīntèwǎng yóujiàn zǔzhī	Internet mail consortium	IMC
因特网月度报告	Yīntèwǎng yuèdù bàogào	Internet monthly report	IMR
因特网语音网关	Yīntèwǎng yǔyīn wǎngguān	Voice over Internet protocol (VoIP) gateway	
因特网支付提供商	Yīntèwǎng zhīfù tígōng shāng	Internet payment provider	IPP
因特网中继闲谈	Yīntèwǎng zhōngjì xiántán	Internet relay chat	IRC
因特网组成员协议	Yīntèwǎng zǔchéngyuán xiéyì	Internet group membership protocol	IGMP
因特网上传真	Yīntèwǎng-shàng chuánzhēn	Fax over Internet	
因特网上电子商务	Yīntèwǎng-shàng diànzi shāngwù	Electronic commerce over Internet	
音图会议业务	Yīntú huìyì yèwù	Audiographic conference service	
因为它是时代网络	Yīnwei tā shì shídài wǎngluò	Because it's Time Network	BITNET
印务馆	Yìnwùguǎn	PrintShop © (graphics software)	
引线焊接温度	Yǐnxiàn hànjiē wēndù	Lead soldering temperature	
引向单元	Yǐnxiàng dānyuán	Director element (of an antenna)	
音像多媒体业务执行协议	Yīnxiàng duōméitǐ yèwù zhíxíng xiéyì	Audio-visual multimedia service implementation agreement	AMSIA
音响光碟	Yīnxiǎng guāngdié	Audio CD	
音像控制装置	Yīnxiàng kòngzhì zhuāngzhì	Audio and video control device	AVCD
音响设备	Yīnxiǎng shèbèi	Sound installation	SI
音响输出	Yīnxiǎng shūchū	Audio output	
引向器	Yǐnxiàngqì	Director element (of an antenna)	
音效调制解调器主机板附加直立插卡	Yīnxiào tiáozhì jiětiáoqì zhǔjī bǎn fùjiā zhílì chā kǎ	Audio/modem riser	AMR
音效/数据主机板附加直立插卡	Yīnxiào/shùjù zhǔjī bǎn fùjiā zhílì chā kǎ	Audio/modem riser	AMR
音效/调制解调器主机板附加直立插卡	Yīnxiào/tiáozhì jiětiáoqì zhǔjī bǎn fùjiā zhílì chā kǎ	Audio/modem riser	AMR
音效卡	Yīnxiàokǎ	Audio card; sound card	
引信干扰	Yǐnxìn gānrǎo	Fuse jamming	
隐性事务	Yǐnxìng shìwù	Implicit transaction	
阴影	Yīnyǐng	Shadowing (in SMT)	
引用	Yǐnyòng	Refer	
引用	Yǐnyòng	Reference	
引用键	Yǐnyòng jiàn	Referenced key	
引用计数	Yǐnyòng jìshù	Reference counting	

引用完整性	Yĭnyòng wánzhěngxìng	Referential integrity	
音邮	Yīnyóu	Voicemail; voice message	
音源	Yīnyuán	Sound source	SS
音载负载	Yīnzài fùzài	Audio frequency load	
阴罩式	Yīnzhàoshì	Shadow mask (video term)	
印制板	Yìnzhì băn	Printed circuit board	PCB
印制电路	Yìnzhì diànlù	Printed circuit	
印制电路板组件	Yìnzhì diànlù băn zŭjiàn	Printed circuit board assembly	PCBA
印制电路集成板	Yìnzhì diànlù jíchéngbăn	Printed circuit board assembly	PBA
印制电路天线	Yìnzhì diànlù tiānxiàn	Printed circuit antenna	PCA
音质控制	Yīnzhì kòngzhì	Tone control	
音质评价	Yīnzhì píngjià	Assessment of acoustics	
印字电报	Yìnzì diànbào	Printing telegraphy	
因子分解	Yīnzĭ fēnjiě	Factorization	
因子分解/质数判定	Yīnzĭ fēnjiě/zhìshù pàndìng	Factoring and primality testing	
因子分析	Yīnzĭ fēnxī	Factor analysis	
因子集	Yīnzĭ jí	Factor set	
移频电报技术	Yípín diànbào jìshù	Frequency-shift telegraphy	
移频键控	Yípín jiànkòng	Frequency-shift keying	FSK
移频直防站	Yípín zhífángzhàn	Frequency shift repeater	FSR
移频中继机	Yípín zhōngjìjī	Frequency shift repeater	
仪器 BASIC 语言	Yíqì BASIC yŭyán	Instrument BASIC language	IBASIC
移前	Yíqián	Zoom in	
移入	Yírù	Shift in	SI
易失存储器	Yìshī cúnchŭqì	Volatile memory	
溢失功率	Yìshī gōnglǜ	Spill-over power	
溢失因数	Yìshī yīnshù	Spill-over factor	
易矢性存储器	Yìshĭxìng cúnchŭqì	Volatile memory	
一手包办	Yīshŏu bāo bàn	All-in-one	
以太环路	Yĭtài huánlù	EtherLoop	
以太数字用户线	Yĭtài shùzì yònghù xiàn	Ethernet digital subscriber line	EDSL
以太网	Yĭtàiwăng	Ethernet	
以太网交换机	Yĭtàiwăng jiāohuànjī	Ethernet switch	
以太网接口处理器	Yĭtàiwăng jiēkŏu chŭlĭqì	Ethernet interface processor	EIP
以太网溶解	Yĭtàiwăng róngjiě	Ethernet meltdown	
以太网文件传送协议	Yĭtàiwăng wénjiàn chuánsòng xiéyì	Ethernet file transfer protocol	EFTP
以太网无源光网络	Yĭtàiwăng wúyuán guāng wăngluò	Ethernet passive optical network	EPON
以太网上传送 PPP 协议	Yĭtàiwăng-shàng chuánsòng PPP xiéyì	Point-to-point protocol over Ethernet	PPPOE
以太网上点到点链路协议	Yĭtàiwăng-shàng diăn dàodiăn liànlù xiéyì	Point-to-point protocol over Ethernet	PPPOE
以太网上点到点协议	Yĭtàiwăng-shàng diăn dàodiăn xiéyì	Point-to-point protocol over Ethernet	PPPoE
以太网上 PPP 协议	Yĭtàiwăng-shàng PPP xiéyì	Point-to-point protocol over Ethernet	PPPoE
已调波	Yĭtiáo bō	Modulated wave	
已调信号	Yĭtiáo xìnhào	Modulated signal	
已调振荡	Yĭtiáo zhèndàng	Modulated oscillation	
一体化按需网络	Yītĭhuà ànxū wăngluò	Integrated on-demand network	ION
一体化服务数字网络	Yītĭhuà fúwù shùzì wăngluò	Integrated services digital network	ISDN

一体化天线的设备	Yītǐhuà tiānxiànde shèbèi	Integral antenna equipment	
一体化拓扑地理编码和参照	Yītǐhuà tuòpū dìlǐ biānmǎ hé cānzhào	Topologically integrated geographical encoding and reference	TIGER
一体化型设备	Yītǐhuàxíng shèbèi	Integrated equipment	
易通话	Yìtōnghuà	SPEAKeasy (software radio developed by US military and Hazeltine Corporation)	
意外消息	Yìwài xiāoxi	Unexpected message (IPsec TLS)	
移位	Yíwèi	Shift	
一位出错	Yīwèi chūcuò	Single bit error	SBE
移位加法器	Yíwèi jiāfǎqì	Displacement adder	Da
移位键	Yíwèi jiàn	Shift key	
移位寄存器	Yíwèi jìcúnqì	Shift register	
移位脉冲	Yíwèi màichōng	Shift pulse	SP
一维数据	Yīwéi shùjù	One-dimensional datum	
一维线阵	Yīwéi xiàn zhèn	One-dimensional linear array	
一维相扫有源相控阵天线	Yīwéi xiàngsǎo yǒuyuán xiàngkòngzhèn tiānxiàn	One-dimensional phase-sweep active phase-controlled array antenna	
一线通	Yīxiàn tōng	Integrated services digital network	ISDN
移相键控	Yíxiāng jiànkòng	Phase shift keying	PSK
意向锁	Yìxiàng suǒ	Intent lock	
移相网络	Yíxiàng wǎngluò	Phase shift network	
移相器	Yíxiàngqì	Phase shifter, phase changer	
移相式环行器	Yíxiàng-shì huánxíngqì	Phase-shifting circulator	
一写多读机	Yīxiě duōdú jī	Write one read many	WORM
翼形衰减器	Yìxíng shuāijiǎnqì	Vane attenuator	
翼形瓦特计	Yìxíng wǎtèjì	Vane wattmeter	
铱星系统	Yīxīng xìtǒng	Iridium Star System (satellite telephony)	
一氧化碳激光	Yīyǎnghuàtàn jīguāng	Carbon monoxide (CO) laser	
医药网络	Yīyào wǎngluò	MediNet	
一元操作符	Yīyuán cāozuò fú	Unary operator (in computer programming)	
抑噪输入信号电平	Yìzào shūrù xìnhào diànpíng	Noise-quieting input-signal level	
抑躁输入信号电平	Yìzào shūrù xìnhào diànpíng	Noise-quieting input-signal level	
一站购齐	Yīzhàn gòuqí	One-stop shopping	
抑制出访	Yìzhì chūfǎng	Suppress outgoing access	SOA
抑制电容器	Yìzhì diànróngqì	Suppression capacitor	
抑制方式	Yìzhì fāngshì	Containment type	
一致管理项目	Yīzhì guǎnlǐ xiàngmù	Conformant management entity	CME
一致化	Yīzhì huà	Homologation	
已知密文攻击	Yǐzhī mìwén gōngjī	Known plaintext attack (in cryptography)	
已知信息源	Yǐzhī xìnxī yuán	Recognized source	
抑制元件	Yìzhì yuánjiàn	Suppression element	
抑制载单边带发射	Yìzhì zài dānbiāndài fāshè	Suppressed carrier single-sideband emission	
抑制载波	Yìzhì zàibō	Suppressed carrier	
抑制载波单边带发射	Yìzhì zàibō dānbiāndài fāshè	Suppressed carrier single-sideband emission	
抑制载波幅度/相位编码	Yìzhì zàibō fúdù/xiàngwèi biānmǎ	Carrierless amplitude/phase (CAP) coding	
移植资料格式	Yízhí zīliào géshi	Portable document format (Adobe)	.pdf
抑制器	Yìzhìqì	Suppressor	
一致性	Yīzhìxìng	Conformance	

一致性	Yīzhìxìng	Congruence	
一致性测试	Yīzhìxìng cèshì	Conformance test	CT
一致性测试套	Yīzhìxìng cèshì tào	Conformance test suite	
一致性管理	Yīzhìxìng guǎnlǐ	Consistency management	
一致性规范	Yīzhìxìng guīfàn	Conformity specification	
抑制型火化塞	Yìzhìxíng huǒhuà sāi	Suppressed spark plug	
一致性检查	Yīzhìxìng jiǎnchá	Uniformity check	
一致性建模语言	Yīzhìxìng jiànmó yǔyán	Unified modeling language	UML
一致性结论测试	Yīzhìxìng jiélùn cèshì	Conformance resolution test	
一致性几何绕射理论	Yīzhìxìng jǐhé ràoshè lǐlùn	Uniform geometric theory of diffraction	UTD
一致性判定进程	Yīzhìxìng pàndìng jìnchéng	Conformance assessment process	
一致性实现	Yīzhìxìng shíxiàn	Conforming implementation	
一致性误差	Yīzhìxìng wùchā	Conformity error	
一致性需求"n"	Yīzhìxìng xūqiú "n"	Conformance requirement 'n'	CRn
一周预报	Yīzhōu yùbào	One week forecast	
用符合 ITU-T 建议 O.41 定的噪声计测量到的电压	Yòng fúhé ITU-T jiànyì O.41 guīdìngde zàoshēng jì cèliáng dàode diànyā	Voltage measured with a psophometer conforming to ITU-T Recommendation O.41	Upso
用集成电路加强的仿真程序	Yòng jíchéng diànlù jiāqiángde fǎngzhēn chéngxù	Simulation program with integrated circuit emphasis	SPIC
用脉冲进行调制	Yòng màichōng jìnxíng tiáozhì	Modulation by pulse	
用于 BS 接口的子复用器	Yòng yú BS jiēkǒude zifùyòngqì	Sub-multiplexer for base station interface	SMBS
用于重发的肯定应答	Yòng yú chóngfāde kěndìng yìngdá	Positive acknowledgment with retransmission	PAR
用于 IP 协议的光纤通道	Yòng yú IP xiéyìde guāngxiān tōngdào	Fiber channel over IP protocol	FC-IP
用法参数控制	Yòngfǎ cānshù kòngzhì	Usage parameter control	
用户	Yònghù	Subscriber, customer	
用户	Yònghù	User	
用户安装维护实体	Yònghù ānzhuāng wéihù shítǐ	Customer installation maintenance entities	CIME
用户板处理机	Yònghù bǎn chǔlǐjī	Line card processor	LCP
用户本地忙信号	Yònghù běndì máng xìnhào	Subscriber local busy signal	SLB
用户编号计划	Yònghù biānhào jìhuà	Private numbering plan	PNP
用户边缘	Yònghù biānyuán	Customer edge	CE
用户标识	Yònghù biāozhì	User identity	
用户标识号	Yònghù biāozhì hào	User identity	
用户标识模块	Yònghù biāozhì mókuài	Subscriber identity module	SIM
用户标识模块接口	Yònghù biāozhì mókuài jiēkǒu	Subscriber identity module interface	SIMI
用户部分	Yònghù bùfen	User part	UP
用户不能进行演示单独控制的分配型业务	Yònghù bùnéng jìnxíng yǎnshì dāndú kòngzhìde fēnpèi xíng yèwù	Distribution service without user individual presentation control	
用户参数控制/网络参数控制	Yònghù cānshù kòngzhì/ wǎngluò cānshù kòngzhì	User parameter control/network parameter control	UPC/NPC
用户侧的 CRF	Yònghù cede CRF	Subscriber-side CRF	CRF-S
用户测试后面板	Yònghù cèshì hòumian bǎn	Subscriber test back panel	STBP
用户长忙信号	Yònghù cháng máng xìnhào	Subscriber toll busy signal	STB
用户长途忙信号	Yònghù chángtú máng xìnhào	Subscriber toll busy signal	STB
用户超时请求消息	Yònghù chāoshí qǐngqiú xiāoxi	Subscriber timeout request message (in multicast)	
用户程序	Yònghù chéngxù	User program	
用户传真站	Yònghù chuánzhēnzhàn	Subscriber facsimile station	

用户存储器	Yònghù cúnchǔqì	Subscriber storage	
用户代理	Yònghù dàilǐ	User agent	UA
用户代理服务器	Yònghù dàilǐ fúwùqì	User agent server	UAS
用户代理客户	Yònghù dàilǐ kèhù	User agent client	UAC
用户单元	Yònghù dānyuán	Subscriber unit	SU
用户到业务信息	Yònghù dào yèwù xìnxī	User-to-service information	UTSI
用户到用户消息	Yònghù dào yònghù xiāoxi	User-to-user message (ISUP)	USR
用户到用户信令	Yònghù dào yònghù xìnlìng	User-to-user signaling	UUS
用户到用户信息	Yònghù dào yònghù xìnxī	User-to-user information (ISUP message)	USR
用户到用户业务	Yònghù dào yònghù yèwù	User-to-user service	UUS
用户到用户指示	Yònghù dào yònghù zhǐshì	User-to-user iindicator	
用户电报	Yònghù diànbào	Telex	
用户电报电传	Yònghù diànbào diànchuán	Telex	
用户电话交换机	Yònghù diànhuà jiāohuànjī	Customer telephone exchange	CTX
用户电路	Yònghù diànlù	Line circuit	
用户电子总线	Yònghù diànzǐ zǒngxiàn	Consumer electronics bus	CEBus
用户定位服务	Yònghù dìngwèi fúwù	User location service	ULS
用户定义功能	Yònghù dìngyì gōngnéng	User defined function	UDF
用户定义函数	Yònghù dìngyì hánshù	User defined function	UDF
用户定义事件	Yònghù dìngyì shìjiàn	User-defined event	
用户定义数据类型	Yònghù dìngyì shùjù lèixíng	User-defined data type	
用户定制队列	Yònghù dìngzhì duìliè	Custom queue	CQ
用户端	Yònghù duān	Subscriber's premises	
用户端 ADSL 收发单元	Yònghù duān ADSL shōufā dānyuán	ADSL Transciever unit-recever end	ATU-R
用户端设备	Yònghù duān shèbèi	Customer premises equipment	CPE
用户端口	Yònghù duānkǒu	User port	
用户端口功能	Yònghù duānkǒu gōngnéng	User port function	UPF
用户分支器	Yònghù fēnzhīqì	Subscriber's tap	ST
用户服务控制模块	Yònghù fúwù kòngzhì mókuài	Subscriber service control block	SSCO
用户服务中心	Yònghù fúwù zhōngxīn	Customer care center	
用户干线拨号	Yònghù gànxiàn bōhào	Subscriber trunk dialing	STD
用户个人资料识别码	Yònghù gèrén zīliào shíbié mǎ	Personal identification number	PIN
用户功能	Yònghù gōngnéng	User facility	
用户光纤网	Yònghù guāngxiān wǎng	Subscriber optical network	YGQ
用户管理点	Yònghù guǎnlǐ diǎn	Customer management point	CMP
用户管理平面	Yònghù guǎnlǐ píngmiàn	Customer management plane	CMP
用户管理信息接口	Yònghù guǎnlǐ xìnxī jiēkǒu	Customer management information port	CMIP
用户管理系统	Yònghù guǎnlǐ xìtǒng	Subscriber management systtem	SMS
用户号	Yònghù hào	Subscriber number	SN
用户号码	Yònghù hàomǎ	Subscriber number	SN
用户环路	Yònghù huánlù	Subscriber loop	
用户环路载波系统	Yònghù huánlù zàibō xìtǒng	Subscriber loop carrier system	SLC
用户环路终端单元	Yònghù huánlù zhōngduān dānyuán	Subscriber loop termination unit	SLTU
用户回路光通讯系统	Yònghù huílù guāng tōngxùn xìtǒng	Subscriber loop optical communication system	
用户呼叫处理	Yònghù hūjiào chǔlǐ	Subscribers call processing	SCP
用户加密	Yònghù jiāmì	User encipherment	

用户鉴别	Yònghù jiànbié	User authentication (in sense of identification)	
用户鉴权	Yònghù jiànquán	User authentication (in sense of authorization)	
用户鉴权密码	Yònghù jiànquán mìmǎ	Subscriber authentication key	Ki
用户鉴权密钥	Yònghù jiànquán mìyào	Subscriber authentication key	Ki
用户交互对话	Yònghù jiāohù duìhuà	User interactive dialogue	UID
用户交换机	Yònghù jiāohuànjī	Private branch exchange	PBX
用户交流网	Yònghù jiāoliú wǎng	Usenet	
用户寄存器	Yònghù jìcúnqì	Subscriber register	SR
拥护节点接口	Yōnghù jiédiǎn jiēkǒu	User node interface	UNI
用户接口	Yònghù jiēkǒu	User interface	UI
用户接口管理器	Yònghù jiēkǒu guǎnlǐqì	User interface manager	UIM
用户接口后面板	Yònghù jiēkǒu hòumian bǎn	Subscriber interface back panel	SIBP
用户界面	Yònghù jièmiàn	User interface	
用户接入	Yònghù jiērù	User access	
用户接入管理功能	Yònghù jiērù guǎnlǐ gōngnéng	Subscriber access management function	SAMF
用户接入维护中心	Yònghù jiērù wéihù zhōngxīn	Customer access maintenance center	CAMC
用户计数器	Yònghù jìshùqì	Subscriber meter	
用户集线比	Yònghù jíxiàn bǐ	Subscriber line concentration ratio	
用户集线器	Yònghù jíxiànqì	Subscriber line concentrator	
用户集中器	Yònghù jízhōngqì	Subscriber concentrator	
用户可编程阵列	Yònghù kěbiānchéng zhènliè	User programmable array	
用户可编程阵列综合编译器	Yònghù kěbiānchéng zhènliè zōnghé biānyìqì	Software compiler for user programmable arrays	
用户控制	Yònghù kòngzhì	User control	UC
用户口功能	Yònghù kǒu gōngnéng	User port function	UPF
用户连接网络	Yònghù liánjiē wǎngluò	Subscriber connection network	SCN
用户连接器	Yònghù liánjiēqì	Subscriber connector	SC
用户忙信号（电的）	Yònghù máng xìnhào (diànde)	Subscriber busy (electrical)	SSB
用户媒体网关	Yònghù méitǐ wǎngguān	Subscriber media gateway	SMG
用户面	Yònghù miàn	User plane	
用户名	Yònghù míng	User name	
用户模式	Yònghù móshì	User mode	
用户能进行演示单独控制的分配型业务	Yònghù néng jìnxíng yǎnshì dāndú kòngzhìde fēnpèi xíng yèwù	Distribution service with user individual presentation control	
用户平面	Yònghù píngmiàn	User plane	UP
用户亲和性	Yònghù qīnhéxìng	User-friendly	
用户确定用户忙	Yònghù quèdìng yònghù máng	User determined user busy	UDUB
用户缺席服务	Yònghù quēxí fúwù	Absent subscriber service	
用户取消消息	Yònghù qǔxiāo xiāoxi	User cancelled message (IPsec TLS)	
用户设备	Yònghù shèbèi	Customer equipment	CEQ
用户设备能使用 ODMA 中继	Yònghù shèbèi néng shǐyòng ODMA zhōngjì	User equipment with ODMA relay operation enabled	Uer
用户设计数据寄存器	Yònghù shèjì shùjù jìcúnqì	User designed data register	UDTR
用户身份保密	Yònghù shēnfen bǎomì	Subscriber identity confidentiality	
用户身份鉴权	Yònghù shēnfen jiànquán	Subscriber identity authentication	
用户身份模块	Yònghù shēnfen mókuài	Subscriber identity module	SIM
用户身份模组	Yònghù shēnfen mózǔ	Subscriber identity module	SIM

用户市忙信号	Yònghù shì máng xìnhào	Subscriber local busy signal	SLB
用户识别模块	Yònghù shíbié mókuài	Subscriber identification module	SIM
用户识别模组	Yònghù shíbié mózǔ	Subscriber identity module	SIM
用户识别应用发展工具	Yònghù shíbié yìngyòng fāzhǎn gōngjù	SimToolKit	STK
用户识别卡	Yònghù shíbiékǎ	Subscriber identity module	SIM
用户室内设备	Yònghù shìnèi shèbèi	Customer premises equipment	CPE
用户室内网	Yònghù shìnèi wǎng	Subscriber premises network	SPN
用户数据报头指示	Yònghù shùjù bàotóu zhǐshì	User data header indicator	UDHI
用户数据报文协议	Yònghù shùjù bàowén xiéyì	User datagram protocol	UDP
用户数据协议	Yònghù shùjù xiéyì	User data protocol	UDP
用户数据报协议	Yònghù shùjùbào xiéyì	User datagram protocol	UDP
用户数据库	Yònghù shùjùkù	User database	
用户数字接口设备	Yònghù shùzi jiēkǒu shèbèi	Subscriber's digital interface unit	SDIU
用户所在地	Yònghù suǒzàidì	Customer premises	
用户提示音	Yònghù tíshì yīn	Subscriber alerting signal	SAS
用户图问通信	Yònghù túwèn tōngxìn	Videotex	
用户网	Yònghù wǎng	Usenet	
用户网络	Yònghù wǎngluò	Customer network	CN
用户网络管理接口	Yònghù wǎngluò guǎnlǐ jiēkǒu	Customer network management interface	
用户网络管理业务的基于电子数据交换管理的接口实现	Yònghù wǎngluò guǎnlǐ yèwùde jīyú diànzi shùjù jiāohuàn guǎnlǐde jiēkǒu shíxiàn	Electronic data interchange (EDI) management-based interface realization for customer network management service	CNMe
用户网络管理业务的基于开放式系统互连参考模型管理的接口实现	Yònghù wǎngluò guǎnlǐ yèwùde jīyú kāifàngshì xìtǒng hùlián cānkǎo móxíng guǎnlǐde jiēkǒu shíxiàn	Open systems interconnect (OSI) management-based interface realization for customer cetwork management service	CNMc
用户网络接口	Yònghù wǎngluò jiēkǒu	Subscriber network interface	SNI
用户网络接口	Yònghù wǎngluò jiēkǒu	User network interface	UNI
用户网络接口结构	Yònghù wǎngluò jiēkǒu jiégòu	User network interface structure	
用户–网络协议	Yònghù— wǎngluò xiéyì	User-network protocol	
用户位置服务器	Yònghù wèizhì fúwùqì	Subscriber location server	
用户位置的灵活计账系统	Yònghù wèizhìde línghuó jìzhàng xìtǒng	Location sensitive billing system	LSBS
用户无线数字业务单元	Yònghù wúxiàn shùzì yèwù dānyuán	Digital service unit-radio	DSU-R
用户线	Yònghù xiàn	Subscriber line	
用户线	Yònghù xiàn	Subscriber feeder	SF
用户线测试设备	Yònghù xiàn cèshì shèbèi	Subscriber line measurement equipment	SLME
用户线话务量	Yònghù xiàn huàwùliàng	Subscriber line traffic	
用户线接口电路	Yònghù xiàn jiēkǒu diànlù	Subscriber line interface circuit	SLIC
用户线接口控制器	Yònghù xiàn jiēkǒu kòngzhìqì	Subscriber line interface controller	SLIC
用户线接入协议	Yònghù xiàn jiērù xiéyì	Subscriber line access protocol	SLAP
用户线集中交换机	Yònghù xiàn jízhōng jiāohuànjī	Subscriber line concentration switch	SLCS
用户线忙时试呼	Yònghù xiàn mángshí shì hū	Subscriber call attempts on busy hour	
用户线自动测试装置	Yònghù xiàn zìdòng cèshì zhuāngzhì	Automatic subscriber line test equipment	ASLTE
用户线路	Yònghù xiànlù	Subscriber line	
用户线路接口电路	Yònghù xiànlù jiēkǒu diànlù	Subscriber line interface circuit	
用户线路设备	Yònghù xiànlù shèbèi	Subscriber's line equipment	SLE

用户线路声频信息处理电路	Yònghù xiànlù shēngpín xìnxī chǔlǐ diànlù	Subscriber line audio processing circuit	SLAC
用户小交换机	Yònghù xiǎo jiāohuànjī	Private branch exchange	PBX
用户信报箱	Yònghù xìnbàoxiāng	Private letter box	
用户信号	Yònghù xìnhào	Subscriber signal	
用户信令	Yònghù xìnlìng	Subscriber line signaling	
用户信息	Yònghù xìnxī	User information	
用户信息控制系统	Yònghù xìnxī kòngzhì xìtǒng	Customer information control system	CICS
用户信息协议	Yònghù xìnxī xiéyì	User information protocol (IETF use)	
用户需求分析	Yònghù xūqiú fēnxī	User requirements analysis	
用户业务	Yònghù yèwù	User service	
用户业务类别	Yònghù yèwù lèibié	User class of service	
用户业务信息	Yònghù yèwù xìnxī	User service information	USI
用户移动性服务器	Yònghù yídòngxìng fúwùqì	User mobility server	UMS
用户应用	Yònghù yìngyòng	Subscriber application	SA
用户元素	Yònghù yuánsù	User element	
用户帐号	Yònghù zhànghào	User account	
用户至用户信令业务 1	Yònghù zhì yònghù xìnlìng yèwù 1	User-to-user signaling service 1	UUS1
用户指定型 DTE 业务	Yònghù zhǐdìngxíng DTE yèwù	Customized data termination equipment (DTE) service	
用户终端	Yònghù zhōngduān	Terminal equipment	TE
用户终端设备	Yònghù zhōngduān shèbèi	Subscriber terminal equipment	STE
用户终端设备提示信号	Yònghù zhōngduān shèbèi tíshì xìnhào	Customer premises equipment (CPE) alerting signal	CAS
用户终端业务	Yònghù zhōngduān yèwù	Teleservice	
用户中继群	Yònghù zhōngjì qún	Line/trunk group	LTG
用户装备	Yònghù zhuāngbèi	Subscriber installation	
用户装置	Yònghù zhuāngzhì	Subscriber installation	SI
用户装置管理功能	Yònghù zhuāngzhì guǎnlǐ gōngnéng	Subscriber installation management function	SIMF
用户装置运行系统	Yònghù zhuāngzhì yùnxíng xìtǒng	Subscriber installation operation system	SI-OpS
用户注册区域	Yònghù zhùcè qūyù	User registration area	URA
用户驻地设备	Yònghù zhùdì shèbèi	Customer premises equipment	CPE
用户驻地网	Yònghù zhùdì wǎng	Customer premises network	CPN
用户住宅网	Yònghù zhùzhái wǎng	Subscriber premises network	SPN
用户自定义函数	Yònghù zìdìngyì hánshù	User-defined functions (in SQL Server)	
用户自动交换机	Yònghù zìdòng jiāohuànjī	Private automatic branch exchange	PABX
用户自动小交换机	Yònghù zìdòng xiǎo jiāohuànjī	Private automatic branch exchange	PABX
用户化	Yònghùhuà	Customization	
用户-网络接口	Yònghù—wǎngluò jiēkǒu	Subscriber network interface	SNI
用户-网络接入	Yònghù—wǎngluò jiērù	User-network access	
用户-用户接口	Yònghù—yònghù jiēkǒu	User-network interface	UNI
用户-用户接口	Yònghù—yònghù jiēkǒu	User-to-user interface	UUI
用户-用户连接	Yònghù—yònghù liánjiē	User-to-user connection	
用户-用户消息	Yònghù—yònghù xiāoxi	User to user signaling	UUS
用户-用户协议	Yònghù—yònghù xiéyì	User-to-user protocol	
用户-用户信令	Yònghù—yònghù xìnlìng	User-to-user signaling	UUS
拥挤	Yōngjǐ	Congestion	
拥挤控制	Yōngjǐ kòngzhì	Congestion control	
永久存储器	Yǒngjiǔ cúnchǔqì	Permanent storage	

永久电路电信业务	Yǒngjiǔ diànlù diànxìn yèwù	Permanent circuit telecommunication service	
永久电路业务	Yǒngjiǔ diànlù yèwù	Permanent circuit service	
永久激活	Yǒngjiǔ jīhuó	Permanent activation	
永久链路	Yǒngjiǔ liànlù	Permanent link	
永久链路层	Yǒngjiǔ liànlù céng	Permanent link layer	PLL
永久逻辑链路	Yǒngjiǔ luóji liànlù	Permanent logical link	PLL
永久虚电路	Yǒngjiǔ xū diànlù	Permanent virtual circuit	PVC
永久虚电路	Yǒngjiǔ xū diànlù	Permanent virtual path	PVP
永久虚连接	Yǒngjiǔ xū liánjiē	Permanent virtual connection	PVC
永久虚通道	Yǒngjiǔ xū tōngdào	Permanent virtual path	PVP
永久虚通路连接	Yǒngjiǔ xū tōnglù liánjiē	Permanent virtual path connection	PVPC
永久虚信道	Yǒngjiǔ xū xìndào	Permanent virtual channel	PVC
永久虚信道连接	Yǒngjiǔ xū xìndào liánjiē	Permanent virtual channel connection	PVCC
永久虚拟连接	Yǒngjiǔ xūnǐ liánjiē	Permanent virtual connection	PVC
永久性电可变存储器	Yǒngjiǔxìng diàn kěbiàn cúnchǔqì	Non-volatile electrically alterable memory	NEAM
永久性锁	Yǒngjiǔxìng suǒ	Persistent lock	
涌浪	Yǒnglàng	Surge	
拥塞	Yōngsè	Congestion	
拥塞窗口	Yōngsè chuāngkǒu	Congestion window	CWND
拥塞等级	Yōngsè děngjí	Congestion level	
拥塞电平	Yōngsè diànpíng	Congesting level (of power)	
拥塞控制	Yōngsè kòngzhì	Congestion control	
拥塞控制机制	Yōngsè kòngzhì jīzhì	Congestion control mechanism	
拥塞通知	Yōngsè tōngzhī	Congestion notification	CN
拥塞信号	Yōngsè xìnhào	Congestion signal	
拥塞音	Yōngsè yīn	Congestion tone	
拥塞指示	Yōngsè zhǐshì	Congestion indication	CI
拥有总成本	Yōngyǒu zǒngchéngběn	Total cost of ownership	TCO
有保证帧速率	Yǒu bǎozhèng zhèng sùlǜ	Guaranteed frame rate	GFR
右边缘	Yòu bianyuán	Right-hand edge	
有标号复用	Yǒu biāohào fùyòng	Labeled multiplexing	
有标号确定性通路	Yǒu biāohào quèdìngxìng tōnglù	Labeled deterministic channel	
有标号通路	Yǒu biāohào tōnglù	Labeled channel	
有标号的接口结构	Yǒu biāohàode jiēkǒu jiégòu	Labeled interface structure	
有标号的统计性通路	Yǒu biāohàode tǒngjìxìng tōnglù	Labeled statistical channel	
有触点电动执行机构	Yǒu chùdiǎn diàndòng zhíxíng jīgòu	Contact-controlled electric actuator	
有触点位置发送器	Yǒu chùdiǎn wèizhì fāsòngqì	Contact electric position transmitter	
有出口的闭合用户群	Yǒu chūkǒude bìhé yònghù qún	Closed user group with outgoing access	
有固定位置的接口结构	Yǒu gùdìng wèizhìde jiēkǒu jiégòu	Positioned interface structure	
有固定位置的通路	Yǒu gùdìng wèizhìde tōnglù	Positioned channel	
有故障的咨询信道	Yǒu gùzhàngde zīxún xìndào	Abort advisory channel	AAC
有恢复连接完整性	Yǒu huīfù liánjiē wánzhěngxìng	Connection integrity with recovery (IPsec)	
有监护释放	Yǒu jiānhù shìfàng	Guarded release	
有聚焦结的光纤（缆）连接器	Yǒu jùjiāojiéde guāngxiān (lǎn) liánjiē qì	Optical fiber (cable) connector with focusing junction	
有如口的闭合用户群	Yǒu rúkǒude bìhé yònghù qún	Closed user group with incoming access	

有损耗的	Yǒu sǔnhàode	Lossy	
有条件前向转移	Yǒu tiáojiàn qiánxiàng zhuǎnyí	Call forwarding conditional	CFC
有条件的最大似然估计	Yǒu tiáojiànde zuìdà sìrán gūjì	Conditional maximum likelihood estimate	CMLE
有替换试验	Yǒu tìhuan shìyàn	Test with substitution	
右外部连接	Yòu wàibù liánjiē	Right outer join (in SQL Server)	
有无话鉴别	Yǒu wú huà jiànbié	Speech vs silence discrimination	
右向外联接	Yòu xiàngwài liánjiē	Right outer join (for database)	
有要求时间	Yǒu yāoqiú shíjiān	Required time	
有用户各自控制的分配性业务	Yǒu yònghù gèzì kòngzhìde fēnpèixìng yèwù	Distributed service with user individual presentation control	
由远端第二级接受的最后一个消息的前向序号	Yóu yuǎnduān dì'èrjí jiēshòude zuìhòu yīgè xiāoxide qiánxiàng xùhào	Forward sequence number of last message accepted by remote level 2	FSNC
油泵车	Yóubèng chē	Oil pump carriage	
游标	Yóubiāo	Cursor (for database)	
游标库	Yóubiāo kù	Cursor library	
诱标	Yòubiāo	Decoy target	
诱捕	Yòubǔ	Entrapment (IPsec)	
游程	Yóuchéng	Run path	
游程编码	Yóuchéng biānmǎ	Run length encoding	RLE
游程长度编码	Yóuchéng chángdù biānmǎ	Run-length coding	RLC
邮单	Yóudān	Mailing list	
邮递名单	Yóudì míngdān	Mailing list	
邮电服务系统	Yóudiàn fúwù xìtǒng	Listserv (computer term)	
诱发	Yòufā	Invocation	
有关转接连接功能	Yǒuguān zhuǎnjiē liánjiē gōngnéng	Transit connection-related function	TCRF
有害干扰	Yǒuhài gānrǎo	Harmful interference	
有核树	Yǒuhé shù	Center-based tree	
有核树组播路由协议	Yǒuhéshù zǔbō lùyóu xiéyì	Core-based tree multicast routing protocol	CBT
优化程序	Yōuhuà chéngxù	Optimizer (program)	
优化模型	Yōuhuà móxíng	Optimization model	
优化生产技术	Yōuhuà shēngchǎn jìshù	Optimized production technology	OPT
优化衰减光纤	Yōuhuà shuāijiǎn guāngxiān	Attenuation optimized fiber	AOF
优化同步	Yōuhuà tóngbù	Optimize synchronization	
优化器	Yōuhuàqì	Optimizer (device)	
油机	Yóujī	Diesel generator	YJ
右击	Yòujī	Right click (computer mouse command)	
有机薄膜场效晶体管	Yǒujī bómó cháng xiào jīngtǐguǎn	Organic thin-film field effect transistor	OTFT
有机发光二极管	Yǒujī fāguāng èrjíguǎn	Organic light-emitting diode	OLED
有机感光鼓	Yǒujī gǎnguāng gǔ	Organic photo conductor drum	
有机光学材料	Yǒujī guāngxué cáiliào	Organic optical materials	
有机活性的	Yǒujī huóxìngde	Organic activated (in SMT)	OA
邮件	Yóujiàn	Mail	
邮件安全传输格式	Yóujiàn ānquán chuánshū géshi	Mail-safe transfer format	MSTF
邮件传输代理	Yóujiàn chuánshū dàilǐ	Mail transfer agent	MTA
邮件循环	Yóujiàn xúnhuán	Mail loop	
有界滞后函数	Yǒujiè zhìhòu hánshù	Bounded lag function	

邮局协议	Yóujú xiéyì	Post office protocol	POP
邮局协议的第 3 个版本	Yóujú xiéyìde dìsangè bǎnběn	Post office protocol 3	POP3
邮局信箱地址	Yóujú xìnxiāng dìzhǐ	Post office box address (P.O. box address)	
有孔反射面	Yǒukǒng fǎnshè miàn	Orifice reflecting surface	
优利	Yōulì	Unisys (US company)	
优良保密协议	Yōuliáng bǎomì xiéyì	Pretty good privacy	PGP
游牧式无线接入	Yóumù shì wúxiàn jiērù	Nomadic wireless access	
优盘	Yōupán	Flash memory, thumb drive, jump drive	
有穷自动机简化	Yǒuqióng zìdòngjī jiǎnhuà	Finite state machine minimization	
有色玻璃滤光镜	Yǒusè bōli lǜguāngjìng	Colored-glass filter	
右上角	Yòushàngjiǎo	Top right corner	
右手习惯	Yòushǒu xíguàn	Right-handed	
游戏	Yóuxì	Game	
游戏发展商会议	Yóuxì fāzhǎn shāng huìyì	Game developer conference	GDC
右下角	Yòuxiàjiǎo	Bottom right corner	
优先（权）呼叫	Yōuxiān (quán) hūjiào	Priority call	
有限查询访问码	Yǒuxiàn cháxún fǎngwèn mǎ	Limited inquiry access code	LIAC
有限带宽的白噪声	Yǒuxiàn dàikuānde bái zàoshēng	Limited bandwidth white noise	
有线等价保密	Yǒuxiàn děngjià bǎomì	Wired equivalent privacy	WEP
有线等效协议	Yǒuxiàn děngxiào xiéyì	Wired equivalent protocol	WEP
有线电缆数据服务接口规范	Yǒuxiàn diànlǎn shùjù fúwù jiēkǒu guīfàn	Data over cable service interface specification	DOCSIS
有线电视	Yǒuxiàn diànshì	Cable television	CATV
有线电视光传输系统	Yǒuxiàn diànshì guāng chuánshū xìtǒng	Cable television optical transmission system	
有线电视网络上的数据接口规格	Yǒuxiàn diànshì wǎngluò-shàngde shùjù jiēkǒu guīgé	Data over cable service interface specification	DOCSIS
有线对等保密	Yǒuxiàn duìděng bǎomì	Wired equivalent privacy	WEP
优先队列	Yōuxiān duìliè	Priority queuing	PQ
有限辐射频率	Yǒuxiàn fúshè pínlǜ	Restricted-radiation frequency (for ISM apparatus)	
有限服务	Yǒuxiàn fúwù	Restricted service	
有线广播	Yǒuxiàn guǎngbō	Wired broadcasting	
有线管理	Yǒuxiàn guǎnlǐ	Wired for management	WfM
优先级	Yōuxiān jí	Priority	
优先级控制	Yōuxiān jí kòngzhì	Priority control	PC
优先级的公平服务曲线	Yōuxiān jíde gōngping fúwù qūxiàn	Hierarchical fair service curve	H-FSC
优先机动	Yōuxiān jīdòng	Priority maneuver	
优先接入及信道指配	Yōuxiān jiērù jí xìndào zhǐpèi	Priority access and channel assignment	PACA
优先接收者	Yōuxiān jiēshōuzhě	Preferred recipient	
有限路由探测器数据分组	Yǒuxiàn lùyóu tàncèqì shùjù fēnzǔ	Limited-route explorer packet	
有线数字段	Yǒuxiàn shùzì duàn	Digital line section	
有线数字通道	Yǒuxiàn shùzì tōngdào	Digital line path	
有线数字系统	Yǒuxiàn shùzì xitǒng	Digital line system	
有限推进响应	Yǒuxiàn tuījìn xiǎngyìng	Finite impulse response	FIR
有线线路分配器	Yǒuxiàn xiànlù fēnpèiqì	Landline trunk controller	LTC
有限消息机器	Yǒuxiàn xiāoxi jīqì	Finite message machine	FMM
有限元素法	Yǒuxiàn yuánsù fǎ	Finite element method	

有限增益灵敏度	Yǒuxiàn zēngyì língmǐndù	Gain limited sensitivity	
有限振幅波	Yǒuxiàn zhènfú bō	Finite amplitude wave	
优先中断	Yōuxiān zhōngduàn	Priority interrupt	
有限状态层叠	Yǒuxiàn zhuàngtài céngdié	Finite-state cascades	
有限状态机	Yǒuxiàn zhuàngtài jī	Finite state machine	FSM
有限状态模型	Yǒuxiàn zhuàngtài móxíng	Finite state module	FSM
有限状态转换系统	Yǒuxiàn zhuàngtài zhuǎnhuàn xìtǒng	Finite state transition system	FSTS
有限状态自动机	Yǒuxiàn zhuàngtài zìdòngjī	Finite state automaton	
有限状态器	Yǒuxiàn zhuàngtàiqì	Finite state machine	
有限资源链接	Yǒuxiàn zīyuán liànjiē	Limited resource link	
有线/无线转接器	Yǒuxiàn/wúxiàn zhuǎnjiēqì	Wired/wireless switcher	
优先的 CUG 连锁码	Yōuxiānde CUG liánsuǒ mǎ	Interlock code of the preferential CUG (closed user group)	IC(pref)
有线电	Yǒuxiàndiàn	Wired telecommunications	
有线电通信	Yǒuxiàndiàn tōngxìn	Wire communication	
邮箱	Yóuxiāng	Mail box	
有向连接	Yǒuxiàng liánjiē	Directed link	
有向面	Yǒuxiàng miàn	Directed face	
有向体	Yǒuxiàng tǐ	Directed solid	
有向图	Yǒuxiàng tú	Directed graph	
有向网络	Yǒuxiàng wǎngluò	Directed network	
有向无环图	Yǒuxiàng wúhuán tú	Directed acyclic graph	DAG
有向无循环图	Yǒuxiàng wúxúnhuán tú	Directed acyclic graph	DAG
有向线	Yǒuxiàng xiàn	Directed edge	
优先权排队	Yōuxiānquán páiduì	Priority queuing	PQ
优先序	Yōuxiānxù	Precedence	
有效报文	Yǒuxiào bàowén	Payload	
有效波	Yǒuxiào bō	Significant wave	
有效长度	Yǒuxiào chángdù	Effective length (of an antenna)	
有效传输率	Yǒuxiào chuánshū lǜ	Actual transfer rate	
有效传送速率	Yǒuxiào chuánsòng sùlǜ	Effective transfer rate	
有效单极辐射功率	Yǒuxiào dānjí fúshè gōnglǜ	Effective monopole radiated power	EMRP
有效地址	Yǒuxiào dìzhǐ	Effective address	EA
有效段	Yǒuxiào duàn	Active section	
有效兑付期	Yǒuxiào duìfù qī	Valid period of payment	
有效负荷	Yǒuxiào fùhè	Payload	
有效负荷模块	Yǒuxiào fùhè mókuài	Payload module	
有效辐射功率	Yǒuxiào fúshè gōnglǜ	Effective radiated power	ERP
有效负载单元	Yǒuxiào fùzài dānyuán	Payload unit	PU
有效改正力	Yǒuxiào gǎizhènglì	Effective margin (of a given apparatus)	
有效高度	Yǒuxiào gāodù	Effective height (of an antenna)	
有效各向同性辐射功率	Yǒuxiào gèxiàng tóngxìng fúshè gōnglǜ	Effective isotropically radiated power	EIRP
有效功能组	Yǒuxiào gōngnéng zǔ	Active function set	AFS
有效基长	Yǒuxiào jīcháng	Active gauge length	
有效基宽	Yǒuxiào jīkuān	Active gauge width	
有效客户反应	Yǒuxiào kèhù fǎnying	Efficient customer response	ECR

有效空隙率	Yǒuxiào kòngxì lǜ	Effective porosity	
有效路径	Yǒuxiào lùjìng	Active trail	
有效面积	Yǒuxiào miànjī	Effective area	
有效纤芯	Yǒuxiào qiànxīn	Effective core	
有效纤芯直径	Yǒuxiào qiànxīn zhíjìng	Effective core diameter	
有效全向辐射功率	Yǒuxiào quánxiàng fúshè gōnglǜ	Effective isotropic radiated power	EiRP
有效冗余	Yǒuxiào rǒngyú	Active redundancy	
有效时宽	Yǒuxiào shíkuān	Effective time width	
有效衰减系数	Yǒuxiào shuāijiǎn xìshù	Effective attenuation factor	EAF
有效数据传送速率	Yǒuxiào shùjù chuánsòng sùlǜ	Effective date transfer rate	
有效瞬时视野	Yǒuxiào shùnshí shìyě	Effective instantaneous field of view	EIFOV
有效输入	Yǒuxiào shūrù	Effective input	
有效数值孔径	Yǒuxiào shùzhí kǒngjìng	Effective numerical aperture	
有效数字	Yǒuxiào shùzì	Significant figure	
有效通道	Yǒuxiào tōngdào	Active path	
有效位	Yǒuxiào wèi	Active bit	AB
有效位	Yǒuxiào wèi	Significant digit	
有效维护时间	Yǒuxiào wéihù shíjiān	Active maintenance time	
有效信元	Yǒuxiào xìnyuán	Valid cell	
有效修复性维护时间	Yǒuxiào xiūfùxìng wéihù shíjiān	Active corrective maintenance time	
有效选择性	Yǒuxiào xuǎnzéxìng	Effective selectivity	
有效页寄存器	Yǒuxiào yè jìcúnqì	Active page register	APR
有效应力	Yǒuxiào yìnglì	Effective stress	
有效用户地址	Yǒuxiào yònghù dìzhǐ	Valid user address	VUA
有效预防性维修时间	Yǒuxiào yùfángxìng wéixiū shíjiān	Active preventive maintenance time	
有效噪声带宽	Yǒuxiào zàoshēng dàikuān	Effective noise bandwidth	ENB
有效性方向	Yǒuxiàoxìng fāngxiàng	Validity direction	
有效性周期	Yǒuxiàoxìng zhōuqī	Validity period	
右斜杠	Yòuxié gàng	Backslash (\ )	
有序参照系	Yǒuxù cānzhào xì	Ordinal reference system	
有序对	Yǒuxù duì	Ordered pair	
有序集	Yǒuxù jí	Ordered set	
有序时间标度	Yǒuxù shíjiān biāodù	Ordinal time scale	OTS
有序数	Yǒuxù shù	Ordered tree	
右旋极化	Yòuxuán jíhuà	Right hand polarization	RHP
右旋极化波	Yòuxuán jíhuà bō	Clockwise polarized wave	
右旋极化波	Yòuxuán jíhuà bō	Right-hand polarized wave	
右旋圆极化	Yòuxuán yuán jíhuà	Right-hand circular polarization	RCP
右旋圆极化(波,信号)	Yòuxuán yuán jíhuà (bō, xìnhào)	Right hand circular polarized (wave, signal)	RHCP
右旋转化	Yòuxuán zhuǎnhuà	Right-hand polarization	
有源	Yǒuyuán	Active	
有源干扰	Yǒuyuán gānrǎo	Active jamming	
有源光器件	Yǒuyuán guāng qìjiàn	Active optical device	AOD
有源光网络	Yǒuyuán guāng wǎngluò	Active optical network	AON
有源光纤	Yǒuyuán guāngxiān	Active optical fiber	AOF
有源校正网络	Yǒuyuán jiàozhèng wǎngluò	Active corrective network	

有源集线器	Yǒuyuán jíxiànqì	Active hub	
有源滤波器	Yǒuyuán lǜbōqì	Active filter	
有源滤波器网络	Yǒuyuán lǜbōqì wǎngluò	Active filter network	AFN
有源模板库	Yǒuyuán múbǎn kù	Active template library	ATL
有源天线	Yǒuyuán tiānxiàn	Active antenna	
有源天线阵系统	Yǒuyuán tiānxiàn zhèn xìtǒng	Active array antenna system	AAAS
有源通信卫星	Yǒuyuán tōngxìn wèixīng	Active communications satellite	ACS
有源网络	Yǒuyuán wǎngluò	Active network	AN
有源卫星	Yǒuyuán wèixīng	Active satellite	
有源遥感器	Yǒuyuán yáogǎnqì	Active sensor	
有源中继站	Yǒuyuán zhōngjìzhàn	Active relay station	
邮政	Yóuzhèng	Post and telecommunications	PTT
邮政编码	Yóuzhèng biānmǎ	Postal code	
邮政编码	Yóuzhèng biānmǎ	Postal code	
邮政电机械	Yóuzhèng diànjīxiè	Post and telecoms machinery	YJX
由政电控	Yóuzhèng diànkòng	Post and telecoms electrical control	YDK
邮政 O/R 地址	Yóuzhèng O/R dìzhǐ	Postal O/R address	
邮政 O/R 地址组成成份	Yóuzhèng O/R dìzhǐ zǔchéng chéngfèn	Postal O/R address components	
邮政信箱	Yóuzhèng xìnxiāng	Mail box	
邮政信箱	Yóuzhèng xìnxiāng	Letter box	
邮政与电信部	Yóuzhèng yǔ diànxìn bù	Ministry of Post and Telecommunications (PRC)	MPT
邮政总局寻码标准化咨询组	Yóuzhèng zǒngjú xúnmǎ biāozhǔnhuà zīxúnzǔ	Post Office Code Standardization Advisory Group (UK)	POCSAG
右值	Yòuzhí	Right value (rvalue)	
邮资明信片	Yóuzī míngxìnpiàn	Stamped postcard	
邮资票品	Yóuzī piàopǐn	Postage item	
邮资凭证	Yóuzī píngzhèng	Postage certificate	
邮资信封	Yóuzī xìnfēng	Stamped envelope	
邮资信卡	Yóuzī xìnkǎ	Stamped letter card	
域	Yù	Domain (in computers and telecommuncations)	
域	Yù	Field (in software)	
与承载无关呼叫控制	Yǔ chéngzài wúguān hūjiào kòngzhì	Bearer-independent call control	BICC
与电路	Yǔ diànlù	And circuit (usually "与")	AND
域定义属性	Yù dìngyì shǔxìng	Domain defined attributes	
与非	Yǔ fēi	"Not and" (a logical operator)	NAND
域后缀	Yù hòuzhuì	Domain suffix	
与呼叫无关的业务功能	Yǔ hūjiào wúguānde yèwù gōngnéng	Call unrelated service function	CUSF
与呼叫相关的通路外的用户交互作用	Yǔ hūjiào xiāngguānde tōnglù wàide yònghù jiāohù zuòyòng	Out-channel call related user interaction	OCCRUI
与或非"门	Yǔ huò fēi mén	AND-OR-INVERT gate	
遇忙回叫	Yù máng huíjiào	Completion of calls to busy subscriber	CCBS
遇忙呼叫前转	Yù máng hujiào qiánzhuǎn	Call forwarding busy	CFB
"与"门	Yǔ mén	AND gate	
域名服务器	Yù míng fúwùqì	Domain name server	DNS
与频率无关的天线	Yǔ pínlǜ wúguānde tiānxiàn	Frequency independent antenna	
域特定部分	Yù tèdìng bùfen	Domain specific part	DSP
域完整性	Yù wánzhěngxìng	Domain integrity	

遇移动用户忙呼叫前向转移	Yù yídòng yònghù máng hujiào qiánxiàng zhuǎnyí	Call forwarding on mobile subscriber busy	CFB
遇移动用户忙呼叫前转	Yù yídòng yònghù máng hujiào qiánzhuǎn	Call forwarding on mobile subscriber busy	CFB
域自动机	Yù zìdòngjī	Region automaton	
源	Yuán	Source	
圆波导	Yuán bōdǎo	Circular waveguide	
远操作规范数结构生成器	Yuǎn cāozuò guīfàn shù jiégòu shēngchéngqì	Remote operations stub generator	ROSY
源程序	Yuán chéngxù	Source code	
源程序	Yuán chéngxù	Source program	
源程序库	Yuán chéngxù kù	Source library	
源程序库更新	Yuán chéngxù kù gēngxīn	Source library update	SLU
源代码	Yuán dàimǎ	Source code	
原地形	Yuán dìxíng	Original topography	
源地址	Yuán dìzhǐ	Source address	SA
源地址段	Yuán dìzhǐ duàn	Origin address field	OAF
源端口	Yuán duānkǒu	Source port	
源对象	Yuán duìxiàng	Source object	
源多维数据集	Yuán duōwéi shùjùjí	Source datacube	
源分区	Yuán fēnqū	Source partition	
圆概率误差	Yuán gàilǜ wùchā	Circular error probable	CEP
圆轨道	Yuán guǐdào	Circular orbit (of a satellite)	
源和目标	Yuán hé mùbiāo	Source and target	
远红外线激光	Yuǎn hóngwàixiàn jīguāng	Far-infrared laser	
源呼叫信令地址	Yuán hūjiào xìnlìng dìzhǐ	Source call signal address	
圆极化	Yuán jíhuà	Circular polarized or polarization	
圆极化波	Yuán jíhuà bō	Circular polarization wave	CPW
圆极化场矢量	Yuán jíhuà cháng shǐliàng	Circularly polarized field vector	
圆极化馈电器	Yuán jíhuà kuìdiànqì	Circular polarization feed	
圆极化喇叭	Yuán jíhuà lǎba	Circular polarization horn	
圆极化平面波	Yuán jíhuà píngmiànbō	Circularly polarized plane wave	CPPW
源计算机	Yuán jìsuànjī	Source computer	
圆括号	Yuán kuòhào	Parentheses ( )	
圆括弧	Yuán kuòhú	Parentheses ( )	
源类	Yuán lèi	Source category	SC
源路由	Yuán lùyóu	Source routing (computer attack)	
源路由平移桥接	Yuán lùyóu píngyí qiáojiē	Source-route translational bridging	SR/TLB
源路由桥接	Yuán lùyóu qiáojiē	Source-route bridging	SRB
源路由透明桥接	Yuán lùyóu tòumíng qiáojiē	Source-route transparent bridging	SRT
源路由选择	Yuán lùyóu xuǎnzé	Source routing selection	
源路由选择并透明	Yuán lùyóu xuǎnzé bìng tòumíng	Source routing and transparency	SRT
源路由转换桥接	Yuán lùyóu zhuǎnhuàn qiáojiē	Source-route translational bridging	SRTLB
源路由器	Yuán lùyóuqì	Seed router	
源媒体接入控制	Yuán méitǐ jiērù kòngzhì	Source media access control	SMAC
源盘	Yuán pán	Source disk	
圆腔天线	Yuán qiāng tiānxiàn	Circular cavity antenna	
元数据服务	Yuán shùjù fúwù	Meta data services (in SQL Server)	

源数据库	Yuán shùjùkù	Source database	
源宿关系	Yuán sù guānxi	Source/sink relationship	
源小区	Yuán xiǎoqū	Cell of origin	COO
圆芯光纤	Yuán xīn guāngxiān	Circular core fiber	CCF
源信令点	Yuán xìnlìng diǎn	Origination point code	OPC
源信令点编码	Yuán xìnlìng diǎn biānmǎ	Origination point code	OPC
源业务量描述语	Yuán yèwùliàng miáoshù yǔ	Source traffic descriptor	
源业务量描述语	Yuán yèwùliáng miáoshùyǔ	Source traffic descriptor	
源因特网协议地址	Yuán Yīntèwǎng xiéyì dìzhǐ	Source Internet protocol (IP) address	
源于交换机单元	Yuán yú jiāohuànjī dānyuán	From switch unit	FSU
源语言	Yuán yǔyán	Source language	
源主机	Yuán zhǔjī	Source host	SRC
源最短路径树	Yuán zuìduǎn lùjìng shù	Shortest path tree	STP
元胞自动机	Yuánbāo zìdòngjī	Cellular automaton	
元编程	Yuánbiānchéng	Metaprogramming	
远场	Yuǎncháng	Far field	
远场区（佛累和费区）	Yuǎncháng qū (Fó-lěi-hé-fèi qū)	Far field region (Fraunhofer region)	
远场区方向图	Yuǎncháng qū fāngxiàng tú	Far field region pattern	
远场图	Yuǎncháng tú	Far field pattern	FFP
远程	Yuǎnchéng	Remote	
远程表	Yuǎnchéng biǎo	Remote table	
远程拨号用户认证服务	Yuǎnchéng bōhào yònghù rènzhèng fúwù	Remote authentication dial-in user service	Radius
远程操作	Yuǎnchéng cāozuò	Remote operation	
远程操作服务元素	Yuǎnchéng cāozuò fúwù yuánsù	Remote operation service element	ROSE
远程操作业务单元	Yuǎnchéng cāozuò yèwù dānyuán	Remote operations service element	ROSE
远程重定向攻击	Yuǎnchéng chóngdìngxiàng gōngjī	Remote redirection attack (in IPsec)	
远程传输单元	Yuǎnchéng chuánshū dānyuán	Remote transmission unit	RTU
远程传像	Yuǎnchéng chuánxiàng	Tele-imaging	
远程处理	Yuǎnchéng chǔlǐ	Teleprocessing	
远程处理安全	Yuǎnchéng chǔlǐ ānquán	Teleprocessing security	
远程存储过程	Yuǎnchéng cúnchǔ guòchéng	Remote stored procedure	
远程存取	Yuǎnchéng cúnqǔ	File transfer protocol	FTP
远程登录	Yuǎnchéng dēnglù	Telnet	
远程登录标识	Yuǎnchéng dēnglù biāozhì	Remote login identification	
远程登录命令	Yuǎnchéng dēnglù mìnglìng	Remote login (in Unix)	RLOGIN
远程电调	Yuǎnchéng diàntiáo	Remote electrical tilt	RET
远程调用接口	Yuǎnchéng diàoyòng jiēkǒu	Remote method interface	RMI
远程方法调度	Yuǎnchéng fāngfǎ diàodù	Remote method invocation	RMI
远程访问服务	Yuǎnchéng fǎngwèn fúwù	Remote access service	
远程分发服务器	Yuǎnchéng fēnfā fúwùqì	Remote distribution server	
远程分区	Yuǎnchéng fēnqū	Remote partition	
远程服务器	Yuǎnchéng fúwùqì	Remote server	
远程辅助总中心	Yuǎnchéng fǔzhù zǒng zhōngxīn	Total remote assistance center	TRACE
远程光传输设备	Yuǎnchéng guāng chuánshū shèbèi	Long-haul optical transmission set	LHOTS
远程光缆监测系统	Yuǎnchéng guānglǎn jiāncè xìtǒng	Remote fiber test system	RFTS
远程过程调用	Yuǎnchéng guòchéng diàoyòng	Remote procedure call	RPC

远程过程调用协议	Yuǎnchéng guòchéng diàoyòng xiéyì	Remote procedure call protocol (IETF use)	RPC
远程呼叫转移	Yuǎnchéng hūjiào zhuǎnyí	Remote call forwarding	RCF
远程监控	Yuǎnchéng jiānkòng	Remote monitoring (in SNMP)	RMON
远程监控系统	Yuǎnchéng jiānkòng xìtǒng	Remote supervision system	
远程交换机	Yuǎnchéng jiāohuànjī	Remote switch	
远程教学	Yuǎnchéng jiàoxué	Electronic learning; E-learning	
远程教学	Yuǎnchéng jiàoxué	Distance learning	
远程教育	Yuǎnchéng jiàoyù	Distance learning	
远程假脱机通信系统	Yuǎnchéng jiǎtuōjī tōngxìn xìtǒng	Remote spooling communication system	RSCS
远程接入服务	Yuǎnchéng jiērù fúwù	Remote access service	RAS
远程接入服务器	Yuǎnchéng jiērù fúwùqì	Remote access server	RAS
远程接入连接单元	Yuǎnchéng jiērù liánjiē dānyuán	Remote access connection element	
远程接入/拨号用户业务	Yuǎnchéng jiērù/bōhào yònghù yèwù	Remote access dial-in user service	RADIUS
远程计算业务	Yuǎnchéng jìsuàn yèwù	Remote computing service	RCS
远程拷贝协议	Yuǎnchéng kǎobèi xiéyì	Remote copy protocol	RCP
远程目录访问协议	Yuǎnchéng mùlù fǎngwèn xiéyì	Remote whois protocol	
远程桥连接	Yuǎnchéng qiáo liánjiē	Remote bridge	
远程桥接	Yuǎnchéng qiáojiē	Remote bridging	
远程请求	Yuǎnchéng qǐngqiú	Remote request	
远程认证拨号用户服务	Yuǎnchéng rènzhèng bōhào yònghù fúwù	Remote authentication dial--in user service	RADIUS
远程认证拨入用户服务	Yuǎnchéng rènzhèng bōrù yònghù fúwù	Remote authentication dial-in user service	RADIUS
远程身份验证拨入用户服务	Yuǎnchéng shēnfen yànzhèng bōrù yònghù fúwù	Remote authentication dial-in user service	RADIUS
远程视频监视	Yuǎnchéng shìpín jiānshì	Remote video surveillance	RVS
远程授权拨入用户服务	Yuǎnchéng shòuquán bōrù yònghù fúwù	Remote authorization dial in user service	RADIUS
远程数据	Yuǎnchéng shùjù	Remote data	
远程数据对象	Yuǎnchéng shùjù duìxiàng	Remote data object	RDO
远程数字回送	Yuǎnchéng shùzì huísòng	Remote digital loopback	RDL
远程数组集中器	Yuǎnchéng shùzǔ jízhōngqì	Remote packet concentrator	RPC
远程同步终端控制程序	Yuǎnchéng tóngbù zhōngduān kòngzhì chéngxù	Remote synchronous terminal control program	RSTCP
远程通信维护中心	Yuǎnchéng tōngxìn wéihù zhōngxīn	Telecommunication maintenance center	TMC
远程通信网存取控制器	Yuǎnchéng tōngxìnwǎng cúnqǔ kòngzhìqì	Telenet access controller	TAC
远程文件传送	Yuǎnchéng wénjiàn chuánsòng	Remote file transfer	RFT
远程文件访问	Yuǎnchéng wénjiàn fǎngwèn	Remote document access	
远程文件管理	Yuǎnchéng wénjiàn guǎnlǐ	Remote document management	
远程文件浏览器	Yuǎnchéng wénjiàn liúlǎnqì	Remote file browser	RFB
远程线路集线器	Yuǎnchéng xiànlù jíxiànqì	Remote line concentrator	RLC
远程消息业务	Yuǎnchéng xiāoxi yèwù	Telematic service	
远程协作	Yuǎnchéng xiézuò	Telecooperation	
远程信息	Yuǎnchéng xìnxī	Remote information	RI
远程信息处理	Yuǎnchéng xìnxī chǔlǐ	Teleprocessing	
远程信息处理	Yuǎnchéng xìnxī chǔlǐ	Telematics	
远程引导	Yuǎnchéng yǐndǎo	Remote boot	
远程用户拨号认证系统	Yuǎnchéng yònghù bōhào rènzhèng xìtǒng	Remote authentication dial-in user service	RADIUS
远程载入	Yuǎnchéng zǎirù	Telnet	

远程站	Yuǎnchéng zhàn	Remote station	RST
远程站数据终端	Yuǎnchéng zhàn shùjù zhōngduān	Remote station data terminal	RSDT
远程直接拨号	Yuǎnchéng zhíjiē bōhào	Direct distance dialing	DDD
远程直接自动拨号系统	Yuǎnchéng zhíjiē zìdòng bōhào xìtǒng	Automatic direct distance dialing system	ADDDS
远程终端仿真器	Yuǎnchéng zhōngduān fǎngzhēnqì	Remote terminal emulator	RTE
远程终端识别	Yuǎnchéng zhōngduān shíbié	Remote terminal identification	RTI
远地前端	Yuǎndì qiánduān	Remote head end	RHE
远地视在	Yuǎndì shìzài	Telepresence	
源点	Yuándiǎn	Source	
原电池	Yuándiànchí	Primary cell	
远地点	Yuǎndìdiǎn	Apogee	
远地点高度	Yuǎndìdiǎn gāodù	Altitude of the apogee	
远端	Yuǎnduān	Remote, far end	
远端背景块差错	Yuǎnduān bèijǐng kuài chācuò	Far-end background block error	FBBE
远端背景误块	Yuǎnduān bèijǐng wù kuài	Far-end background block error	FBBE
远端比特和增益信息	Yuǎnduān bǐtè hé zēngyì xìnxī	Remote bit and gain information	R-B&G
远端拨入用户验证服务	Yuǎnduān bōrù yònghù yànzhèng fúwù	Remote authentication dial-in user service	RADIUS
远端操作服务要素	Yuǎnduān cāozuò fúwù yàosù	Remote operation service element	ROSE
远端操作业务单元	Yuǎnduān cāozuò yèwù dānyuán	Remote operation service element	ROSE
远端操作业务元素	Yuǎnduān cāozuò yèwù yuánsù	Remote operations service element	ROSE
远端差错指示	Yuǎnduān chācuò zhǐshì	Remote error indication	REI
远端程序调度	Yuǎnduān chéngxù diàodù	Remote procedure call	RPC
远端程序调用	Yuǎnduān chéngxù diàoyòng	Remote procedure call	RPC
远端串话	Yuǎnduān chuànhuà	Far-end crosstalk	FEXT
远端串扰	Yuǎnduān chuànrǎo	Far-end crosstalk	FEXT
远端串音	Yuǎnduān chuànyīn	Far-end crosstalk	FEXT
远端单元	Yuǎnduān dānyuán	Remote unit	RU
远端点	Yuǎnduān diǎn	Remote point	RP
远端访问服务器	Yuǎnduān fǎngwèn fúwùqì	Remote access server	RAS
远端复制程序	Yuǎnduān fùzhì chéngxù	Remote copy program	RCP
远端复制协议	Yuǎnduān fùzhì xiéyì	Remote copy protocol	rcp
远端告警指示	Yuǎnduān gàojǐng zhǐshì	Remote alarm indication	RAI
远端工作站	Yuǎnduān gōngzuòzhàn	Remote workstation	RWS
远端过程调用	Yuǎnduān guòchéng diàoyòng	Remote-procedure call	RPC
远端故障指示	Yuǎnduān gùzhàng zhǐshì	Remote defect indicator	RDI
远端环路接口	Yuǎnduān huánlù jiēkǒu	Loop interface-remote terminal end	U-R
远端回声消除	Yuǎnduān huíshēng xiāochú	Far-end echo cancellation	FECC
远端机	Yuǎnduān jī	Remote terminal	RT
远端降质指示	Yuǎnduān jiàng zhì zhǐshì	Remote degradation indicator	RDI
远端监控	Yuǎnduān jiānkòng	Remote monitoring	RMON
远端鉴权拨号接入用户业务	Yuǎnduān jiànquán bōhào jiērù yònghù yèwù	Remote authentication dial-in user service	RADIUS
远端交换单元	Yuǎnduān jiāohuàn dānyuán	Remote switching unit	RSU
远端交换模块	Yuǎnduān jiāohuàn mókuài	Remote switch unit	RSU
远端畸变	Yuǎnduān jībiàn	Teledistortion	
远端接入	Yuǎnduān jiērù	Remote access	
远端接入连接单元	Yuǎnduān jiērù liánjiē dānyuán	Remote access connection element	

远端接入虚拟专用网	Yuǎnduān jiērù xūnǐ zhuānyòng wǎng	Remote access VPN (virtual private network)	RAVPN
远端接入终端	Yuǎnduān jiērù zhōngduān	Remote access terminal	RET
远端接收故障	Yuǎnduān jiēshōu gùzhàng	Far-end receive fault	FERF
远端接收失败	Yuǎnduān jiēshōu shībài	Far-end receive failure	FERF
远端集线器	Yuǎnduān jíxiànqì	Remote concentrator	
远端块差错	Yuǎnduān kuài chācuò	Far-end block error	FEBE
远端块误码	Yuǎnduān kuài wùmǎ	Far-end block error	FEBE
远端联机	Yuǎnduān liánjī	Remote login	
远端码组差错	Yuǎnduān mǎzǔ chācuò	Far-end block error	FEBE
远端模块错误	Yuǎnduān mókuài cuòwù	Far-end block error	FEBE
远端模块局	Yuǎnduān mókuài jú	Remote switch unit	RSU
远端缺陷秒	Yuǎnduān quēxiàn miǎo	Far-end defective second	FDS
远端缺陷指示	Yuǎnduān quēxiàn zhǐshì	Remote defect indication	RDI
远端任务入口	Yuǎnduān rènwu rùkǒu	Remote job entry	RJE
远端认证拨入用户业务	Yuǎnduān rènzhèng bōrù yònghù yèwù	Remote authentication dial-in user service (IPsec)	RADIUS
远端 S 参考点	Yuǎnduān S cānkǎo diǎn	Remote S reference point	T/S
远端失效指示	Yuǎnduān shīxiào zhǐshì	Remote failure indication	RFI
远端失效指示	Yuǎnduān shīxiào zhǐshì	Remote defect indication	RDI
远端数据库访问	Yuǎnduān shùjùkù fǎngwèn	Remote database access	RDA
远端数据库管理系统	Yuǎnduān shùjùkù guǎnlǐ xìtǒng	Remote database management system	RDBMS
远端 T 参考点	Yuǎnduān T cānkǎo diǎn	Remote T reference point	T/R
远端外壳协议	Yuǎnduān wàiké xiéyì	Remote shell protocol	rsh
远端网桥	Yuǎnduān wǎngqiáo	Remote bridge	
远端误块计数	Yuǎnduān wùkuài jìshù	Far-end error block counter	FEBC
远端误块秒	Yuǎnduān wùkuài miǎo	Far-end errored second	FES
远端误码指示	Yuǎnduān wùmǎ zhǐshì	Remote error indication	REI
远端线路 U 参考点	Yuǎnduān xiànlù U cānkǎo diǎn	Remote circuit U reference point	U-R
远端线路 U 参考点 2	Yuǎnduān xiànlù U cānkǎo diǎn 2	Remote circuit U reference point 2	U-R2
远端限质指示	Yuǎnduān xiànzhì zhǐshì	Remote defect indication	RDI
远端信头差错控制	Yuǎnduān xìntóu chācuò kòngzhì	Far-end header error control	FHEC
远端信息	Yuǎnduān xìnxī	Remote information	RI
远端信元定界丢失	Yuǎnduān xìnyuán dìngjiè diūshī	Far-end loss of cell delineation	FLCD
远端信源路由网桥	Yuǎnduān xìnyuán lùyóu wǎngqiáo	Remote source-route bridging	RSRB
远端严重误块秒	Yuǎnduān yánzhòng wùkuài miǎo	Far-end severely errored second	FSES
远端用户处理	Yuǎnduān yònghù chǔlǐ	Remote subscriber processing	RSP
远端用户单元	Yuǎnduān yònghù dānyuán	Remote subscriber unit	RSU
远端用户接入	Yuǎnduān yònghù jiērù	Far-end subscriber access	SA-F
远端用户接入	Yuǎnduān yònghù jiērù	Remote subscriber access	RSA
远端用户模块	Yuǎnduān yònghù mókuài	Remote subscriber module	RSM
远端用户设备	Yuǎnduān yònghù shèbèi	Far-end subscriber installation	SI-F
远端运行环境	Yuǎnduān yùnxíng huánjìng	Terminal operation environment	TOE
远端站连接	Yuǎnduān zhàn liánjiē	Distant station connected	DSC
远端帧处理器	Yuǎnduān zhèng chǔlǐqì	Remote frame handler	RFH
远端帧处理器接口	Yuǎnduān zhèng chǔlǐqì jiēkǒu	Remote frame handler interface	RFHI
源端证据	Yuánduān zhèngjù	Proof of origin (IPsec)	
员工考勤	Yuángōng kǎoqín	Attendance	

远拱点	Yuǎngǒngdiǎn	Apoapsis	
圆环激光陀螺仪	Yuánhuán jīguāng tuólúoyí	Ring laser gyroscope	
圆环面	Yuánhuán miàn	Torus	
原级速率界面	Yuánjí sùlǜ jièmiàn	Primary rate interface	PRI
原籍位置登记器	Yuánjí wèizhì dēngjìqì	Home location register	HLR
原籍位置注册处	Yuánjí wèizhì zhùcèchù	Home location register	HLR
原籍移动无线局	Yuánjí yídòng wúxiàn jú	Home mobile services switching center	HMSC
原籍移动用户	Yuánjí yídòng yònghù	Home mobile subscriber	
元件	Yuánjiàn	Component	
元件立起	Yuánjiàn lìqǐ	Tombstoning (in SMT)	
元件密度	Yuánjiàn mìdù	Component density	
元件压力试验	Yuánjiàn yālì shìyàn	Component stress testing (semiconductor mfg)	
元计算	Yuánjìsuàn	Meta-computing	
远距离供电	Yuǎnjùlí gōngdiàn	Remote power-feeding	
远距离监视	Yuǎnjùlí jiānshì	Distant surveillance	DS
原理图输入器	Yuánlǐ tú shūrùqì	Schematic capture	
原谅我的参与	Yuánliàng wǒde cānyù	Pardon my jumping in (computer chat)	PMJI
源码	Yuánmǎ	Source code	
元脉码调制	Yuánmàimǎ tiáozhì	Raw pulse code modulated	Raw PCM
元模型	Yuánmóxíng	Meta-model	
园区网	Yuánqū wǎng	Campus network	
原生的	Yuánshēngde	Native	
原始被叫号码	Yuánshǐ bèijiào hàomǎ	Original called number	
原始类型	Yuánshǐ lèixíng	Primitive type	
原始模板	Yuánshǐ múbǎn	Primary template	
原始设备制造厂家	Yuánshǐ shèbèi zhìzào chǎngjiā	Original equipment manufacturer	OEM
原始设备制造商	Yuánshǐ shèbèi zhìzàoshāng	Original equipment manufacturer	OEM
原始域	Yuánshǐ yù	Domain of origin	
原始资料	Yuánshǐ zīliào	Source material	
元数据	Yuánshùjù	Metadata	
元数据包	Yuánshùjù bāo	Metadata package	
元数据模式	Yuánshùjù móshì	Metadata schema	
元数据目录	Yuánshùjù mùlù	Metadata catalogue	
元数据实体	Yuánshùjù shítǐ	Metadata entity	
元数据实体类型	Yuánshùjù shítǐ lèixíng	Metadata entity type	
元数据型	Yuánshùjù xíng	Metadata type	
元数据元素	Yuánshùjù yuánsù	Metadata element	
元数据元素字典	Yuánshùjù yuánsù zìdiǎn	Metadata element dictionary	
元数据集	Yuánshùjùjí	Metadata dataset	
原素	Yuánsù	Primitive (noun)	
原素实体	Yuánsù shítǐ	Primitive entitiy	
圆筒隙缝盘	Yuántǒng xìfèng pán	Slotted cylinder panel	
圆筒隙缝天线	Yuántǒng xìfèng tiānxiàn	Slotted cylinder antenna	
圆筒形抛物面天线	Yuántǒngxíng pāowùmiàn tiānxiàn	Cylindrical parabola antenna	CPA
原型	Yuánxíng	Prototype	
原形	Yuánxíng	Root form	

圆形波导	Yuánxíng bōdǎo	Circular waveguide	
圆形滑动	Yuánxíng huádòng	Circular slide	
圆形软波导	Yuánxíng ruǎn bōdǎo	Circular flexible waveguide	
原型实验	Yuánxíng shíyàn	Prototype experiment	
圆形阵	Yuánxíng zhèn	Circular array	
圆形阵	Yuánxíng zhèn	Ring array	
元信令	Yuánxìnlìng	Meta-signaling	
元信令信元	Yuánxìnlìng xìnyuán	Meta-signaling cell	
元音	Yuányīn	Vowels	
原因	Yuányīn	Factor	FACT
原语	Yuányǔ	Primitive (in OSI reference model)	
原语信号	Yuányǔ xìnhào	Primitive signal	
原语序列	Yuányǔ xùliè	Primitive sequence	
元语言	Yuányǔyán	Meta-language	
原址代码	Yuánzhǐ dàimǎ	Primary address code	PAC
元指代	Yuánzhǐdài	Meta-anaphora	
圆周扫描	Yuánzhōu sǎomiáo	Circular sweep	
圆柱投影	Yuánzhù tóuyǐng	Cylindrical projection	
圆柱阵	Yuánzhù zhèn	Cylindrical array	
圆锥喇叭	Yuánzhuī lǎba	Conical horn	
圆锥扫描雷达	Yuánzhuī sǎomiáo léidá	Conical scan radar	
圆锥扫描雷达接收机	Yuánzhuī sǎomiáo léidá jiēshōujī	Conical scanning radar receiver	
圆锥扫描天线	Yuánzhuī sǎomiáo tiānxiàn	Conical scan antenna	
圆锥透镜	Yuánzhuī tòujìng	Conical lens	
圆锥投影	Yuánzhuī tóuyǐng	Conic projection	
圆锥形喇叭天线	Yuánzhuīxíng lǎba tiānxiàn	Conical horn antenna	
圆锥形阵	Yuánzhuīxíng zhèn	Conical array	
圆柱面反射器	Yuánzhùmiàn fǎnshèqì	Cylindrical reflector	
圆柱形阵	Yuánzhùxíng zhèn	Cylindrical array	
原子操作	Yuánzi cāozuò	Atomic operation	
原子功能	Yuánzǐ gōngnéng	Atomic function (smallest indivisible function)	
元组	Yuánzǔ	Tuple	
元组空间查找算法	Yuánzǔ kōngjiān cházhǎo suànfǎ	Tuple space search (for IP packet classification)	
预测	Yùcè	Prediction	
预测差分量化器	Yùcè chāfēn liànghuàqì	Predictive differential quantizer	PDQ
预测误差	Yùcè wùchā	Prediction error	
预测执行	Yùcè zhíxíng	Speculative execution	
预处理器	Yùchǔlǐqì	Pre-processor	
预调干扰机	Yùdiào gànrǎojī	Preset jammer	
预定	Yùdìng	Reserved	RES
预订电路业务	Yùdìng diànlù yèwù	Reserved circuit service	
预定字	Yùdìng zì	Reserved word	
越电离层传播	Yuè diànlícéng chuánbō	Trans-inospheric propagation	
跃变时刻	Yuèbiàn shíkè	Transition time	
跃点	Yuèdiǎn	Hop (noun)	
约定突发速率	Yuēdìng tūfā sùlǜ	Committed burst rate	CBR

约定信息率	Yuēdìng xìnxī lǜ	Committed information rate	CIR
约定信息速率	Yuēdìng xìnxī sùlǜ	Committed information rate	CIR
阅读次数	Yuèdú cìshù	Hits, visits (on a web page)	
阅读器	Yuèdúqì	Browser	
越局切换号码	Yuèjú qiēhuàn hàomǎ	Temporary handover number	HOT
乐器数位介面	Yuèqì shùwèi jièmiàn	Musical instrument digital interface	MIDI
乐器数字接口	Yuèqì shùzì jiēkǒu	Musical instrument digital interface	MIDI
越区切换	Yuèqū qiēhuàn	Handover, handoff (inter-cell)	HO
越区切换策略	Yuèqū qiēhuàn cèlüè	Handover strategy	
越区切换接入突发	Yuèqū qiēhuàn jiērù tūfā	Handover access burst	
越区切换界限	Yuèqū qiēhuàn jièxiàn	Handover margin	
越区切换执行	Yuèqū qiēhuàn zhíxíng	Handover execution	
约束	Yuēshù	Constraint (for database)	
约束规划	Yuēshù guīhuà	Constraint programming (CAD/CAM)	CP
约束金属板透镜天线	Yuēshù jīnshǔ bǎn tòujìng tiānxiàn	Constrained metal-plate lens antenna	
约束路由	Yuēshù lùyóu	Constraint-based routing	
约束满足问题	Yuēshù mǎnzú wèntí	Constraint satisfaction problem	CSP
约束透镜	Yuēshù tòujìng	Constrained lens	
越限告警	Yuèxiàn gàojǐng	Threshold crossing alarm	TCA
越站干扰	Yuèzhàn gānrǎo	Overreach interference	
语法	Yǔfǎ	Syntax	
语法类库	Yǔfǎ lèi kù	Syntax class library	
语法图	Yǔfǎ tú	Syntax diagram	
预放	Yùfàng	Pre-amplifier	PA
预放大器	Yùfàngdàqì	Pre-amplifier	PA
预防性维护	Yùfángxìng wéihù	Preventive maintenance	PM
预防性维护时间	Yùfángxìng wéihù shíjiān	Preventive maintenance time	
预防性维修	Yùfángxìng wéixiū	Preventive maintenance	
预防性的循环重发	Yùfángxìngde xúnhuán chóngfā	Preventive cyclic retransmission	
"与非"门	Yǔfēi mén	N-AND gate	
预分配	Yùfēnpèi	Early allocation	EA
预分配	Yùfēnpèi	Pre-assignment	
预分配多址	Yùfēnpèi duōzhǐ	Preassigned multiple access	PMA
预分配分时多路存取	Yùfēnpèi fēnshí duōlù cúnqǔ	Preassigned time division multiple access	PA-TDMA
预付费平台	Yùfùfèi píngtái	Prepaid billing platform	
预付费业务	Yùfùfèi yèwù	Pre-payment billing service	
预付费业务	Yùfùfèi yèwù	Prepaid charging	PPC
预付票底制	Yùfùpiào dǐzhì	Pre-payment rule	
余割平方射束天线	Yúgē píngfāng shèshù tiānxiàn	Cosecant-square beam antenna	
余割平方天线	Yúgē píngfāng tiānxiàn	Cosecant-squared antenna	
鱼骨表天线	Yúgǔ biǎo tiānxiàn	Fish-bone antenna	
迂回来路选择	Yūhuí láilù xuǎnzé	Alternative routing from	ARF
迂回路由	Yūhuí lùyóu	Alternate routing	
迂回路由波长	Yūhuí lùyóu bōcháng	Re-routing wavelength	
迂回路由选定	Yūhuí lùyóu xuǎndìng	Alternative routing	
迂回路由选择	Yūhuí lùyóu xuǎnzé	Alternative routing	AR

迂回去路选择	Yūhuí qùlù xuǎnzé	Alternative routing to	ART
余辉时间	Yúhuī shíjiān	Persistence	
迂回选择路由	Yūhuí xuǎnzé lùyóu	Alternative select route	ASRTE
预获取	Yùhuòqǔ	Pre-fetch	
域际策略路由选择	Yùjì cèlüè lùyóu xuǎnzé	Inter-domain policy routing	IDPR
域间策略路由选择	Yùjiān cèlüè lùyóu xuǎnzé	Inter-domain policy routing	IDPR
域间路由协议	Yùjiān lùyóu xiéyì	Inter-domain routing protocol	IDRP
域间路由选择协议	Yùjiān lùyóu xuǎnzé xiéyì	Inter-domain routing protocol (ISO use)	IDRP
域间选路协议	Yùjiān xuǎnlù xiéyì	Inter-domain routing protocol	IDRP
预缴无线服务	Yùjiǎo wúxiàn fúwù	Prepaid wireless service	
预校正	Yùjiàozhèng	Pre-correction	
预加重	Yùjiāzhòng	Pre-emphasis (radio term)	
预畸变	Yùjībiàn	Predicted distortion	
预警飞机	Yùjǐng fēijī	Airborne warning and control system aircraft	AWACS
预警机	Yùjǐng jī	Early warning aircraft	AWACS
语句	Yǔjù	Statement	
语句编号	Yǔjù biānhào	Statement number	
语句函数	Yǔjù hánshù	Statement function	
语句块	Yǔjù kuài	Statement block	
语句清晰度	Yǔjù qīngxīdù	Sentence articulation	
语句权限	Yǔjù quánxiàn	Statement permission	
预均衡	Yùjūnhéng	Pre-equalization	
语块句法分析	Yǔkuài jùfǎ fēnxī	Chunk parsing	
预览	Yùlǎn	Preview	
余量	Yúliàng	Allowance; margin	
预连接	Yùliánjiē	Pre-connect	
遇忙回叫	Yùmáng huíjiào	Call back on busy	
遇忙呼叫前转	Yùmáng hujiào qiánzhuǎn	Call forward on busy	CFB
遇忙呼叫完成	Yùmáng hujiào wánchéng	Completion of calls to busy subscribers	CCBS
遇忙呼叫转发	Yùmáng hujiào zhuǎnfā	Call forwarding busy	CFB
遇忙呼叫转送	Yùmáng hujiào zhuǎnsòng	Call forwarding busy	CFB
遇忙寄存呼叫	Yùmáng jìcún hūjiào	Registered call	
遇忙前转	Yùmáng qiánzhuǎn	Call forwarding on busy	CFB
域名	Yùmíng	Domain name	
域名服务	Yùmíng fúwù	Domain name service	DNS
域名服务器	Yùmíng fúwùqì	Domain name system server	DNS
域名服务器电子欺骗	Yùmíng fúwùqì diànzǐ qīpiàn	Domain name server (DNS) spoofing (IPsec)	
域名解析	Yùmíng jiěxī	Domain name resolution	
域名系统	Yùmíng xìtǒng	Domain name system	DNS
运动	Yùndòng	Movement	
运动补偿	Yùndòng bǔcháng	Motion compensation (video term)	MC
运动跟踪	Yùndòng gēnzōng	Motion tracking	
运动规划	Yùndòng guīhuà	Motion planning	
运动估值	Yùndòng gūzhí	Motion estimation (video term)	
运动类游戏	Yùndòng lèi yóuxì	Sports games (computer game)	SPG
运动力学	Yùndòng lìxué	Kinematic model	

运动盘	Yùndòng pán	Dip slope	
运动图像专家组	Yùndòng túxiàng zhuānjiāzǔ	Motion Picture Experts Group	MPEG
运费付至	Yùnfèi fù zhì	Carriage paid to	CPT
运费、保险费付至	Yùnfèi、bǎoxiǎnfèi fù zhì	Carriage and insurance paid	CIP
运输层	Yùnshū céng	Transport layer	
运输层联接端点	Yùnshū céng liánjiē duāndiǎn	Transport connection endpoint	TCEP
运输服务	Yùnshū fúwù	Transport service	TS
运输服务访问点	Yùnshū fúwù fǎngwèn diǎn	Transport service access point	TSAP
运输服务数据单元	Yùnshū fúwù shùjù dānyuán	Transport service data unit	TSDU
运输连接	Yùnshū liánjiē	Transport connection	TC
运输试验	Yùnshū shìyàn	Transport test	
运输协议数据单元	Yùnshū xiéyì shùjù dānyuán	Transport protocol data unit	TPDU
运算参数	Yùnsuàn cānshù	Operation parameter	
运算地址指令	Yùnsuàn dìzhǐ zhǐlìng	Operational-address instruction	OAI
运算放大器	Yùnsuàn fàngdàqì	Operational amplifier	
运算符	Yùnsuàn fú	Operator (computational)	
运算函数标志符	Yùnsuàn hánshù biāozhìfú	Arithmetic function designator	AFD
运算控制器	Yùnsuàn kòngzhìqì	Arithmetic control unit	ACU
运算轮数	Yùnsuàn lúnshù	Number of calculation rounds	
运算屏蔽寄存器	Yùnsuàn píngbì jìcúnqì	Arithmetic mask register	AMR
运算数	Yùnsuàn shù	Operand	
运算指示符	Yùnsuàn zhǐshìfú	Operation indicator	
运算总线	Yùnsuàn zǒngxiàn	Arithmetic bus	AB
运算器	Yùnsuànqì	Arithmetic unit (on main processor chip)	
云台及云台控制器	Yúntái jí yúntái kòngzhìqì	Pan unit and controller	PAC
运行	Yùnxíng	Operation	
运行程序	Yùnxíng chéngxù	Run-time	
运行管理维护和预置	Yùnxíng guǎnlǐ wéihù hé yùzhì	Operation, administration, maintenance, and provisioning	OAM&P
运行和维护	Yùnxíng hé wéihù	Operation and maintenance	OAM
运行库	Yùnxíng kù	Run-time repository (in CORBA)	
运行期	Yùnxíng qī	Run-time	
运行时	Yùnxíng shí	Run-time	
运行时间支撑系统	Yùnxíng shíjiān zhīchēng xìtǒng	Run-time infrastructure	RTI
运行条件	Yùnxíng tiáojiàn	Operating conditions	
运行位	Yùnxíng wèi	Active bit	AB
运行系统	Yùnxíng xìtǒng	Operation system	OS
运行系统功能	Yùnxíng xìtǒng gōngnéng	Operation system function	OSF
运行系统功能块	Yùnxíng xìtǒng gōngnéng kuài	Operation system function block	OSF
运行与维护	Yùnxíng yǔ wéihù	Operation and maintenance	O&M
运行支持系统	Yùnxíng zhīchí xìtǒng	Operating support system	OSS
运行，管理和维护	Yùnxíng, guǎnlǐ hé wéihù	Operation, administration and maintenance	OAM
运行、管理和维护中心	Yùnxíng、guǎnlǐ hé wéihù zhōngxīn	Operation, administration and maintenance center	OAMC
允许处理	Yǔnxǔ chǔlǐ	Permit processing	
允许带宽	Yǔnxǔ dàikuān	Allowed bandwidth	
允许带外功率	Yǔnxǔ dàiwài gōnglǜ	Permissible out-of-band power	
允许带外频谱	Yǔnxǔ dàiwài pínpǔ	Permissible out-of-band spectrum	

允许发送协议	Yǔnxǔ fāsòng xiéyì	Clear to send	CTS
允许附加寄存器的范围位	Yǔnxǔ fùjiā jicúnqìde fànwéi wèi	Allow additional register range bit	AARR
允许干扰	Yǔnxǔ gānrǎo	Permissible interference	
允许接入信道	Yǔnxǔ jiērù xìndào	Access grant channel	AGCH
允许接续信道	Yǔnxǔ jiēxù xìndào	Access grant channel	AGCH
允许偏差	Yǔnxǔ piānchā	Permissible deviation	
允许信元速率	Yǔnxǔ xìnyuán sùlǜ	Allowed cell rate	ACR
允许转接	Yǔnxǔ zhuǎnjiē	Transfer allowed	TFA
允许最大发射功率	Yǔnxǔ zuìdà fāshè gōnglǜ	Permissible maximum transmit power	
允许最小接收功率	Yǔnxǔ zuìxiǎo jiēshōu gōnglǜ	Permissible minimum receive power	
允许的负载阻抗	Yǔnxǔde fùzài zǔkàng	Allowable load impedance	
允许的缺陷标准	Yǔnxǔde quēxiàn biāozhǔn	Acceptable defect level	ADL
允许的信元率	Yǔnxǔde xìnyuán lǜ	Allowed cell rate	ACR
允许的信元速率	Yǔnxǔde xìnyuán sùlǜ	Allowed cell rate	ACR
运营成本	Yùnyíng chéngběn	Operating expenses	OPEX
运营支撑系统	Yùnyíng zhīchēng xìtǒng	Operation support system	OSS
运营支持系统	Yùnyíng zhīchí xìtǒng	Operation support system	OSS
运营商边缘路由器	Yùnyíngshāng biānyuán lùyóuqì	Provider edge router	PE
运营商标识码	Yùnyíngshāng biāoshí mǎ	Carrier identification code	CIC
运营商路由器	Yùnyíngshāng lùyóuqì	Provider router	P
运营商数字	Yùnyíngshāng shùzì	Carrier digits	CD
运营者决定的闭锁业务	Yùnyíngzhě juédìngde bìsuǒ yèwù	Operator determined barring	Odb
运营者融合组	Yùnyíngzhě rónghé zǔ	Operators harmonization group	OHG
运营者特定业务	Yùnyíngzhě tèdìng yèwù	Operator specific service	OSS
语篇机器理解	Yǔpiān jīqì lǐjiě	Computational linguistics	
预期值	Yùqī zhí	Desired value	
语声处理	Yǔshēng chǔlǐ	Speech processing	
预失真	Yùshīzhēn	Predistortion	
阈下信道	Yùxià xìndào	Subliminal channel	
余弦发射定律	Yúxián fāshè dìnglǜ	Cosine emission law	
遇险频率	Yùxiǎn pínlǜ	Distress frequency	
预写日志	Yùxiě rìzhì	Write-ahead log (for database)	
预型体	Yùxíngtǐ	Preform (noun)	
预型体	Yùxíngtǐ	Preform rod (FOC mfg)	
预型体研磨加工设备	Yùxíngtǐ yánmó jiāgōng shèbèi	Preform rod polishing equipment (FOC)	
预型体制造设备	Yùxíngtǐ zhìzào shèbèi	Preform rod manufacturing equipment (FOC)	
预选信道	Yùxuǎn xìndào	Pre-selected channel	
预选器	Yùxuǎnqì	Pre-selector	
语言处理器	Yǔyán chǔlǐqì	Language processor (device)	LP
语言加工程序	Yǔyán jiāgōng chéngxù	Language processor (program)	
语言交换单元	Yǔyán jiāohuàn dānyuán	Voice switching unit	VSU
语言接入单元	Yǔyán jiērù dānyuán	Voice access unit	VAU
语言识别处理器	Yǔyán shíbié chǔlǐqì	Speech recognition processor	SRP
语言预测编码	Yǔyán yùcè biānmǎ	Speech-predictive coding	SPEC
语言自然度	Yǔyán zìrándù	Naturalness of speech	
语义	Yǔyì	Semantics	

语义串行化图	Yǔyì chuànhánghuà tú	Semantic serialization graph	SeSG
语义单元	Yǔyì dānyuán	Semantic unit	
语义对象	Yǔyì duìxiàng	Semantic object	
语义关系	Yǔyì guānxi	Semantic relationship	
语义可串行性	Yǔyì kěchuànhángxìng	Semantic serializability	
语义数据建模	Yǔyì shùjù jiànmó	Semantic data modeling	
语义透明	Yǔyì tòumíng	Semantic transparency	
语义信息	Yǔyì xìnxī	Semantic information	
语义知识	Yǔyì zhīshi	Semantic knowledge	
预译码器	Yùyìmǎqì	Pre-translator	PX
语音保密	Yǔyīn bǎomì	Speech security	
语音编码	Yǔyīn biānmǎ	Speech coding	
语音编码器	Yǔyīn biānmǎqì	Speech encoder	SPE
语音辨识	Yǔyīn biànshí	Voice recognition	
语音采编器	Yǔyīn cǎibiānqì	Speech compiler	
语音采编台	Yǔyīn cǎibiāntái	Speech compiler console	
语音处理系统	Yǔyīn chǔlǐ xìtǒng	Voice processing system	VPS
语音带宽	Yǔyīn dàikuān	Speech bandwidth	
语音导航	Yǔyīn dǎoháng	Voice browser	VB
语音分割算法	Yǔyīn fēngē suànfǎ	Speech segmentation algorithm	
语音分组处理程序（器）	Yǔyīn fēnzǔ chǔlǐ chéngxù (qì)	Packet handler for voice	PHV
语音广播业务	Yǔyīn guǎngbō yèwù	Voice broadcast service	VBS
语音合成	Yǔyīn héchéng	Speech synthesis	
语音交互设备	Yǔyīn jiāohù shèbèi	Interactive voice response (equipment)	IVR
语音解码器	Yǔyīn jiěmǎqì	Speech decoder	SPD
语音接入信息	Yǔyīn jiērù xìnxī	Voice access to content	
语音激活因子	Yǔyīn jīhuó yīnzǐ	Voice activity factor	VA
宇音卡	Yǔyīn kǎ	Sound Galaxy © card	
语音扩展标记语言	Yǔyīn kuòzhǎn biāojì yǔyán	Voice eXtensible markup language	VXML
语音门户	Yǔyīn ménhù	Voice portal	VP
语音模块	Yǔyīn mókuài	Voice module	VM
语音平衡单词表	Yǔyīn pínghéng dāncí biǎo	Phonetically balanced word list	
语音拼写法	Yǔyīn pīnxiěfǎ	Soundex	
语音清晰度	Yǔyīn qīngxīdù	Sound articulation	
语音群呼叫业务	Yǔyīn qún hūjiào yèwù	Voice group call service	VGCS
语音商务	Yǔyīn shāngwù	Voice commerce	VC
语音识别	Yǔyīn shíbié	Speech recognition	
语音数位信令	Yǔyīn shùwèi xìnlìng	Speech digit signaling	
语音数字化	Yǔyīn shùzìhuà	Voice digitization	
语音网关	Yǔyīn wǎngguān	Audio gateway	AG
语音位信令	Yǔyīn wèi xìnlìng	Speech digit signaling	
语音信息处理点	Yǔyīn xìnxī chǔlǐ diǎn	Voice message handling point	VMHP
语音信箱	Yǔyīn xìnxiāng	Voice mail	
语音信箱系统	Yǔyīn xìnxiāng xìtǒng	Voice mail system	VMS
语音信箱业务	Yǔyīn xìnxiāng yèwù	Voice mail service	VMS
语音压缩算法	Yǔyīn yāsuō suànfǎ	Voice compression algorithm	

语音应用服务提供商	Yǔyīn yìngyòng fúwù tígōngshāng	Voice application service provider	VASP
语音邮件提示	Yǔyīn yóujiàn tíshì	Voicemail alert	VMA
语音邮箱	Yǔyīn yóuxiāng	Voice mailbox	VM
语音邮箱业务	Yǔyīn yóuxiāng yèwù	Voice mail service	VMS
语音置乱	Yǔyīn zhìluàn	Speech scrambling	
语音组呼业务	Yǔyīn zǔ hū yèwù	Voice group call service	VGCS
语音组呼叫业务	Yǔyīn zǔ hūjiào yèwù	Voice group call service	VGCS
语音+单工设备	Yǔyīn+dāngōng shèbèi	Speech+simplex equipment	
语音+双工设备	Yǔyīn+shuānggōng shèbèi	Speech+duplex equipment	
预映射	Yùyìngshè	Pre-image (in hash signature technology)	
语义学内容	Yǔyìxué nèiróng	Semantic content	
预约电路电信业务	Yùyuē diànlù diànxìn yèwù	Reserved circuit telecommunication service	
预约字	Yùyuē zì	Reserved word	
预置	Yùzhì	Preset	
阈值电流	Yùzhí diànliú	Threshold current	
域值区间	Yùzhí qūjiān	Domain range	
阈值时间	Yùzhí shíjiān	Threshold time	
预制棒	Yùzhìbàng	Preform (noun) (of FOC)	
预支付	Yùzhīfù	Prepay	
宇宙飞船	Yǔzhòu fēichuán	Spacecraft	
宇宙干扰	Yǔzhòu gānrǎo	Cosmic interference	
宇宙射线	Yǔzhòu shèxiàn	Cosmic ray	
宇宙时	Yǔzhòu shí	Universal time	UT
宇宙噪声	Yǔzhòu zàoshēng	Cosmic noise	
预啁啾	Yùzhōujiū	Pre-chirp	PCH
预住机密	Yùzhù jīmì	Pre-master secret (IPsec)	

Z

杂波	Zábō	Clutter	
杂波地图	Zábō dìtú	Clutter map	
杂波滤波器	Zábō lǜbōqì	Clutter filter	
杂波锁定	Zábō suǒdìng	Clutter lock	
杂波抑制	Zábō yìzhì	Clutter suppression	
杂波间可见度	Zábō-jiān kějiàndù	Inter-clutter visibility	
在 ATM 上逆多路复用	Zài ATM-shàng nì duōlù fùyòng	Inverse multiplexing on ATM	IMA
在 ATM 上的话音	Zài ATM-shàngde huà yīn	Voice over ATM	VOATM
在闭锁用户群中禁止出局呼叫	Zài bìsuǒ yònghù qún zhōng jìnzhǐ chūjú hūjiào	Outgoing call barred within the closed user group	OCB
在测试实现	Zài cèshì shíxiàn	Implementation under test	IUT
在测试系统	Zài cèshì xìtǒng	System under test	SUT
在 Dm 信道上链路接入协议	Zài Dm xìndàoshàng liànlù jiērù xiéyì	Link access protocol on the Dm channel	LAPDm
在 DSL 上传话音	Zài DSL-shàng chuán huàyīn	Voice over DSL	VoDSL
载干比	Zài gān bǐ	Carrier to interference ratio	CIR
在 IP 上传输的光纤信道数据帧	Zài IP-shàng chuánshūde guāngxiān xìndào shùjùzhèng	Entire fiber channel frame over IP (IETF use)	FCIP
在 IP 上的光纤信道	Zài IP-shàngde guāngxiān xìndào	Fibre channel over IP	FCIP

在 IP 上的话音	Zài IP-shàngde huàyīn	Voice over IP	VOIP
在 IPX 上的路由信息协议	Zài IPX-shàngde lùyóu xìnxī xiéyì	Routing information protocol over Internet packet exchange	RIPX
在两个段的边界之间的呼叫建立延迟	Zài liǎnggè duànde biānjiè zhījiānde hūjiào jiànlì yánchí	Call set-up delay between two section boundaries	
在同步数字系统上传输分组	Zài tóngbù shùzì xìtǒng-shàng chuánshū fēnzǔ	Packet over synchronous digital hierarchy	PoS
在网际协议上传输传真	Zài wǎngjì xiéyì-shàng chuánshū chuánzhēn	Fax over Internet protocol	FoIP
在无回答时呼叫转发	Zài wúhuídá shí hūjiào zhuǎnfā	Call forwarding on no reply	CFNRy
在移动用户不可达到时转发	Zài yídòng yònghù bùkě dádào shí zhuǎnfā	Call forwarding on mobile subscriber not reachable	CFNRc
在一个段的边界 Bi 处呼叫建立延迟	Zài yīgè duànde biānjiè Bi chù hūjiào jiànlì yánchí	Call set-up delay at a section boundary Bi	
在一个多连接和无连接环境中业务特定面向连接协议	Zài yīgè duō liánjiē hé wú liánjiē huánjìng zhōng yèwù tèdìng miànxiàng liánjiē xiéyì	Service-specific connection oriented protocol in a multi-link and connectionless environment	SSCOPMCE
在用	Zài yòng	Active	
载噪比	Zài zào bǐ	Carrier to noise ratio	C/N
灾变性失效	Zāibiànxìng shīxiào	Catastrophic failure, cataleptic failure	
载波	Zàibō	Carrier wave	CW
载波比	Zàibō bǐ	Carrier-to-noise ratio	CTNR
载波传输	Zàibō chuánshū	Carrier transmission	
载波电话	Zàibō diànhuà	Carrier frequency telephony	CFT
载波电话	Zàibō diànhuà	Carrier telephone	CT, ZH
载波电话增音机	Zàibō diànhuà zēngyīnjī	Carrier telephone repeater	
载波电话终端机	Zàibō diànhuà zhōngduānjī	Carrier telephone terminal	
载波电话中继器	Zàibō diànhuà zhōngjìqì	Carrier frequency telephone repeater	CRF
载波跌落	Zàibō diēluò	Carrier drop	
载波分量	Zàibō fènliàng	Carrier component	
载波分配架	Zàibō fēnpèi jià	Carrier distribution frame	CDF
载波复合二次差拍比	Zàibō fùhé èrcì chāpāi bǐ	Carrier/composite second order beat	C/CSO
载波复合三次差拍比	Zàibō fùhé sāncì chāpāi bǐ	Carrier/composite triple beat	C/CTB
载波服务	Zàibō fúwù	Bearer service	
载波干扰比	Zàibō gānrǎo bǐ	Carrier to interference ratio	CIR
载波功率	Zàibō gōnglǜ	Carrier power (of a radio transmitter)	PZ
载波恢复	Zàibō huīfù	Carrier recovery	
载波恢复环路	Zàibō huīfù huánlù	Carrier recovery loop	CRL
载波检测	Zàibō jiǎncè	Carrier detect	CD
载波检测多址	Zàibō jiǎncè duōzhǐ	Carrier sense multiple access	CSMA
载波检测失败率	Zàibō jiǎncè shībài lǜ	Carrier detection failure rate	
载波检测器	Zàibō jiǎncèqì	Carrier detector	CD
载波降低度	Zàibō jiàngdīdù	Carrier reduction	
载波控制多路存取	Zàibō kòngzhì duōlù cúnqǔ	Carrier sense multiple access	CSMA
载波频率偏置	Zàibō pínlǜ piānzhì	Carrier frequency offset	
载波频偏	Zàibō pínpiān	Carrier frequency deviation	
载波相位	Zàibō xiàngwèi	Carrier phase	
载波虚拟电路	Zàibō xūnǐ diànlù	Carrier virtual circuit	CVC
载波抑制度	Zàibō yìzhìdù	Carrier suppression	
载波侦听多址访问	Zàibō zhēntīng duōzhǐ fǎngwèn	Carrier sense multiple access	CSMA

载波侦听多址接入/避免冲撞协议	Zàibō zhēntīng duōzhǐ jiērù/ bìmiǎn chōngzhuàng xiéyì	Carrier sense multiple access with collision avoidance	CSMA/CA
载波侦听多址接入/碰撞检测协议	Zàibō zhēntīng duōzhǐ jiērù/ pèngzhuàng jiǎncè xiéyì	Carrier sense multiple access with collision detection	CSMA/CD
载波主群调制	Zàibō zhǔqún tiáozhì	Carrier master-group modulation	
载波-热噪声比	Zàibō—rè zàoshēng bǐ	Carrier-to-thermal noise ratio	CTNR
载出	Zàichū	Logout	
再次发布	Zàicì fābù	Republish	
再次发布者	Zàicì fābùzhě	Republisher	
再定时	Zàidìngshí	Retiming	
再定位	Zàidìngwèi	Re-locate	
再分配命令	Zàifēnpèi mìnglìng	Reallocation command	
再辐射	Zàifúshè	Re-radiation	
载荷	Zàihè	Payload	
再呼叫信号	Zàihūjiào xìnhào	Recall signal	
再开发	Zàikāifā	Redevelopment	
载码电路	Zàimǎ diànlù	Code-carrying circuit	
灾难应急计划	Zāinàn yìngjí jìhuà	Disaster plan	
载频	Zàipín	Carrier frequency	
载频单元框背板	Zàipín dānyuán kuàngbèibǎn	Carrier unit mother board	CUB
载频电话中继器	Zàipín diànhuà zhōngjìqì	Carrier frequency telephone repeater	CRF
载频接口控制器	Zàipín jiēkǒu kòngzhìqì	Carrier interface controller	CIC
再起动规程	Zàiqǐdòng guīchéng	Restart procedure	
载入	Zǎirù	Login, load	
载入器	Zǎirùqì	Loader	
再生	Zàishēng	Regeneration	
再生段	Zàishēng duàn	Regenerator section	RS
再生段开销	Zàishēng duàn kāixiao	Regenerator section overhead	RSOH
再生段网络连接	Zàishēng duàn wǎngluò liánjiē	Regenerator section network connection	RS NC
再生段终端	Zàishēng duàn zhōngduān	Regenerator section termination	RST
再生段路踪识别失配	Zàishēng duànlù zōng shíbié shīpèi	Regenerator section trace identification mismatch	RS-TIM
再生反馈	Zàishēng fǎnkuì	Regenerative feedback	
再生接收机	Zàishēng jiēshōujī	Regenerative receiver	
再生设备	Zàishēng shèbèi	Regenerator	RG
再生中继段	Zàishēng zhōngjì duàn	Regenerator relay section	
再生中继段级	Zàishēng zhōngjì duàn jí	Regenerator relay section level	
再生中继设备	Zàishēng zhōngjì shèbèi	Trunk regenerator	REG
再生中继器	Zàishēng zhōngjìqì	Regenerative repeater	REG
再生中继站	Zàishēng zhōngjìzhàn	Regenerative relay station	
再生转发器	Zàishēng zhuǎnfāqì	Regenerating transponder	
再生、重整形和重定时	Zàishēng、chóngzhěngxíng hé chóngdìngshí	Regeneration, reshaping, retiming	3R
再生器	Zàishēngqì	Regenerator	REG
再生器定时发生器	Zàishēngqì dìngshí fāshēngqì	Regenerator timing generator	RTG
载体设备	Zàitǐ shèbèi	Vehicle equipment	
在席	Zàixí	Presence	

在线帮助	Zàixiàn bāngzhù	Online help	
在线变换	Zàixiàn biànhuàn	Online transformation	
在线测试	Zàixiàn cèshì	On-line testing	
在线测试	Zàixiàn cèshì	In-circuit test (in SMT)	
在线测试仪	Zàixiàn cèshìyí	In-line tester	
在线插入和拆卸	Zàixiàn chārù hé chāixiè	Online insertion and removal	OIR
在线查询	Zàixiàn cháxún	Online query	
在线订货体系	Zàixiàn dìnghuò tǐxì	Electronic order system	E0S
在线分析与处理	Zàixiàn fēnxī yǔ chǔlǐ	Online analysis and processing	OAP
在线服务提供者	Zàixiàn fúwù tígòngzhě	Online service provider	OSP
在线格网控制	Zàixiàn géwǎng kòngzhì	Online grid control	OGC
在线计费服务器	Zàixiàn jìfèi fúwùqì	Online billing server	OBS
在线模拟量输出	Zàixiàn mónǐliàng shūchū	Online analog output	OAO
再现期间	Zàixiàn qījiān	Return period	
在线事务进程	Zàixiàn shìwù jìnchéng	Online transaction processing	OLTP
在线手写签名认证	Zàixiàn shǒuxiě qiānmíng rènzhèng	On-line handwriting signature verification	
在线自动测试功能	Zàixiàn zìdòng cèshì gōngnéng	Online automatic testing function	
再现性	Zàixiànxìng	Reproducibility	
再应答时间监视	Zàiyìngdá shíjiān jiānshì	Reanswer time supervision	
再应答信号	Zàiyìngdá xìnhào	Reanswer signal	RAN
再振铃	Zàizhènlíng	Reringing	
杂乱脉冲干扰	Záluàn màichōng gānrǎo	Random pulse jamming	
脏读	Zàng dú	Dirty read (for database)	
脏页	Zàng yè	Dirty page (for database)	
暂时存储器	Zànshí cúnchǔqì	Scratchpad memory	SPM
暂时降敏抑制	Zànshí jiàngmǐn yìzhì	Temporary desensitizing suppression	
暂时偏移	Zànshí piānyí	Temporary offset	TO
暂停	Zàntíng	Lock out (used for computer login or malfunction)	LO
暂停	Zàntíng	Park (verb) (used for computer hard disk)	
暂停	Zàntíng	Suspend	SUS
暂停消息	Zàntíng xiāoxi	Suspend message (ISUP)	SUS
皂化剂	Zàohuàjì	Saponifier (in SMT)	
早期报文丢弃	Zǎoqī bàowén diūqì	Early packet discard	EPD
早期故障期	Zǎoqī gùzhàng qī	Early fault period	
早期令牌释放	Zǎoqī lìngpái shìfàng	Early token release	ETR
早期失效期	Zǎoqī shīxiào qī	Early failure period	
噪声	Zàoshēng	Noise	
噪声场强	Zàoshēng chǎngqiáng	Noise field strength	
噪声传递	Zàoshēng chuándì	Noise transfer	
躁声带宽	Zàoshēng dàikuān	Noise bandwidth	
噪声等效带宽	Zàoshēng děngxiào dàikuān	Noise equivalent bandwidth	NEB
噪声等效辐射率	Zàoshēng děngxiào fúshè lǜ	Noise equivalent radiance	NER
噪声等效功率	Zàoshēng děngxiào gōnglǜ	Noise equivalent power	NEP
噪声等效功率密度	Zàoshēng děngxiào gōnglǜ mìdù	Noise equivalent power density	NEPD
噪声等效流密度	Zàoshēng děngxiào liú mìdù	Noise equivalent flux density	NEFD
噪声等效强度	Zàoshēng děngxiào qiángdù	Noise equivalent intensity	NEI

噪声等效输入信号	Zàoshēng děngxiào shūrù xìnhào	Noise equivalent input signal	NES
噪声等效通量	Zàoshēng děngxiào tōngliàng	Noise equivalent flux	NEF
噪声等效温差	Zàoshēng děngxiào wēnchā	Noise equivalent temperature difference	NETD
噪声等效温度	Zàoshēng děngxiào wēndù	Noise equivalent temperature	NET
噪声电动势	Zàoshēng diàndòngshì	Noise electromotive force	
噪声电流	Zàoshēng diànliú	Noise current	
噪声电压	Zàoshēng diànyā	Noise voltage	
噪声反馈控制	Zàoshēng fǎnkuì kòngzhì	Noise feedback control	NFC
噪声功率	Zàoshēng gōnglǜ	Noise power	
噪声功率比	Zàoshēng gōnglǜ bǐ	Noise power ratio	NPR
噪声计加权噪声	Zàoshēng jì jiāquán zàoshēng	Psophometrically weighted noise	
噪声调幅干扰	Zàoshēng tiáofú gānrǎo	Noise amplitude modulation (AM) jamming	
噪声调幅调相干扰	Zàoshēng tiáofú tiáoxiàng gānrǎo	Noise amplitude modulation-phase modulation jamming	
噪声调频干扰	Zàoshēng tiáopín gānrǎo	Noise frequency modulation (FM) jamming	
噪声调频有效频移	Zàoshēng tiáopín yǒuxiào pínyí	Noise frequency modulation effective frequency shift	
噪声调相干扰	Zàoshēng tiáoxiàng gānrǎo	Noise phase modulation (PM) jamming	
噪声调制干扰	Zàoshēng tiáozhì gānrǎo	Noise-modulated jamming	
噪声温度	Zàoshēng wēndù	Noise temperature (of a receiving antenna)	
噪声温度比	Zàoshēng wēndù bǐ	Noise-temperature ratio	NTR
噪声限制灵敏度	Zàoshēng xiànzhì língmǐndù	Noise limited sensitivity	
噪声系数	Zàoshēng xìshù	Noise figure	NF
噪声掩蔽比	Zàoshēng yǎnbì bǐ	Noise to masking ratio	NMR
噪声抑制	Zàoshēng yìzhì	Muting	
噪声抑制	Zàoshēng yìzhì	Noise suppression	
噪声抑制电路	Zàoshēng yìzhì diànlù	Noise suppression circuit	NSC
噪声源	Zàoshēng yuán	Noise source	
噪声余度	Zàoshēng yúdù	Noise margin	
早熟收敛	Zǎoshú shōuliǎn	Premature convergence	
造型转换	Zàoxíng zhuǎnhuàn	Casting	
噪音	Zàoyīn	Noise	
杂散发射	Zásǎn fāshè	Spurious emission	
杂散骚扰	Zásǎn sāorǎo	Spurious emissions	
杂散输出功率	Zásǎn shūchū gōnglǜ	Spurious-wave output power	
杂散响应抗扰性	Zásǎn xiǎngyìng kàngrǎoxìng	Spurious response immunity	
杂散响应频率	Zásǎn xiǎngyìng pínlǜ	Spurious response frequency	
杂散响应抑制比	Zásǎn xiǎngyìng yìzhì bǐ	Spurious response rejection ratio	
杂散窄带（射频）分量	Zásǎn zhǎidài (shèpín) fènliàng	Spurious narrow-band (RF) components	
杂项	Záxiàng	Miscellaneous	
增幅管	Zēngfú guǎn	Amplitron	
增广路径	Zēngguǎng lùjìng	Augmenting path	
增广路径图	Zēngguǎng lùjìng tú	Augmenting path graph	
增加操作符	Zēngjiā cāozuò fú	Increment operator	
增扩实境	Zēngkuò shíjìng	Augmented reality	
增扩虚境	Zēngkuò xūjìng	Augmented virtuality	
增量备份	Zēngliàng bèifèn	Incremental backup	
增量更新	Zēngliàng gēngxīn	Incremental update (for database)	

增量脉码调制	Zēngliàng màimǎ tiáozhì	Delta pulse code modulation	DPCM
增量区域传送	Zēngliàng qūyù chuánsòng	Incremental zone transfer	IXFR
增量调制	Zēngliàng tiáozhì	Delta modulation	
增量调制编码	Zēngliàng tiáozhì biānmǎ	Delta modulation code	
增量相位调制	Zēngliàng xiàngwèi tiáozhì	Incremental phase modulation	IPM
增配网络资源	Zēngpèi wǎngluò zīyuán	Add network resource	ADDNR
增强	Zēngqiáng	Reinforcement	
增强单位数据	Zēngqiáng dānwèi shùjù	Extended unit data (in SS7)	XUDT
增强单位数据业务	Zēngqiáng dānwèi shùjù yèwù	Extended unit data service (in SS7)	XUDTS
增强电路交换数据	Zēngqiáng diànlù jiāohuàn shùjù	Enhanced circuit switched data	ECSD
增强观察时间差定位	Zēngqiáng guānchá shíjiān chà dìngwèi	Enhanced observation time difference	EOTD
增强光盘	Zēngqiáng guāngpán	Compact disk-PLUS	CD-PLUS
增强链路状态	Zēngqiáng liànlù zhuàngtài	Enhanced link state	
增强内部网关路由协议	Zēngqiáng nèibù wǎngguān lùyóu xiéyì	Enhanced interior gateway routing protocol	EIGRP
增强桥	Zēngqiáng qiáo	Expander bridge	
增强清晰度电视	Zēngqiáng qīngxīdù diànshì	Enhanced definition television	EDTV
增强数据速率业务	Zēngqiáng shùjù sùlǜ yèwù	Enhanced data rate service (enhanced data rate for GSM evolution)	EDGE
增强数字无绳通讯	Zēngqiáng shùzì wúshéng tōngxùn	Digital enhanced cordless telecommunication	DECT
增强小型设备接口	Zēngqiáng xiǎoxíng shèbèi jiēkǒu	Enhanced small device interface	ESDI
增强载波接收	Zēngqiáng zàibō jiēshōu	Enhanced carrier reception	
增强质量的电视	Zēngqiáng zhìliàngde diànshì	Enhanced-quality television	
增强自适应运动补偿算法	Zēngqiáng zìshìyìng yùndòng bǔcháng suànfǎ	Enhanced adaptive motion compensation algorithm	EAMC
增强的电路交换数据	Zēngqiángde diànlù jiāohuàn shùjù	Enhanced circuit switched data	ECSD
增强的内部网关路由选择协议	Zēngqiángde nèibù wǎngguān lùyóu xuǎnzé xiéyì	Enhanced interior gateway routing protocol	EIGRP
增强的内部子层服务	Zēngqiángde nèibù zicéng fúwù	Enhanced internal sub-layer service	E-ISS
增强器	Zēngqiángqì	Booster	
增强式突发处理	Zēngqiáng-shì tūfā chǔlǐ	Extended burst transactions	
增强型不归零制	Zēngqiáng-xíng bùguīlíng zhì	Enhanced non-return-to-zero	ENRZ
增强形超薄高速金属媒体	Zēngqiáng-xíng chāobáo gāosù jīnshǔ méitǐ	Advanced super thin-layer and high-output metal media	ATOMM
增强形电子集成驱动器	Zēngqiáng-xíng diànzǐ jíchéng qūdòngqì	Enhanced integrated drive electronics	EIDE
增强型定位报告系统	Zēngqiáng-xíng dìngwèi bàogào xìtǒng	Enhanced position location reporting system	EPLRS
增强型多级优先和先占业务	Zēngqiáng-xíng duōjí yōuxiān hé xiānzhàn yèwù	Enhanced multilevel precedence and preemption service	EMLPP
增强型多级优先和占先业务	Zēngqiáng-xíng duōjí yōuxiān hé zhànxiān yèwù	Enhanced multi-level precedence and pre-emption service	eMLPP
增强型 GGSN	Zēngqiáng-xíng GGSN	Enhanced GGSN	E-GGSN
增强形工业标准架构	Zēngqiáng-xíng gōngyè biāozhǔn jiàgòu	Enhanced industry standard architecture	EISA
增强形光学存储器	Zēngqiáng-xíng guāngxué cúnchǔqì	Advanced storage magneto-optical	ASMO
增强型 HLR	Zēngqiáng-xíng HLR	Enhanced HLR	E-HLR
增强型呼叫选路	Zēngqiáng-xíng hūjiào xuǎnlù	Enhanced call routing	ECR
增强型局部管理接口	Zēngqiáng-xíng júbù guǎnlǐ jiēkǒu	Enhanced local management interface	ELMI
增强型可变速率编码器	Zēngqiáng-xíng kěbiàn sùlǜ biānmǎqì	Enhanced variable rate coder	EVRC
增强形扩充身份辨识数据	Zēngqiáng-xíng kuòchōng shēnfen biànshí shùjù	Enhanced extended identification data	E-EDID
增强形平行端口	Zēngqiáng-xíng píngxíng duānkǒu	Enhanced parallel port	EPP

增强型全速率	Zēngqiáng-xíng quánsùlǜ	Enhanced full rate	EFR
增强形视频数据通道协议	Zēngqiáng-xíng shìpín shùjù tōngdào xiéyì	Enhanced display data channel	E-DDC
增强型图形适配器	Zēngqiáng-xíng túxíng shìpèiqì	Enhanced graphics adapter	EGA
增强型相关跳频扩频	Zēngqiáng-xíng xiāngguān tiàopín kuòpín	Correlated hopping enhanced spread spectrum	CHESS
增强型寻呼码	Zēngqiáng-xíng xúnhū mǎ	Enhanced paging operators code	EPOC
增强形帧解析引擎	Zēngqiáng-xíng zhèng jiěxī yǐnqíng	Advanced packet parsing engine	APPE
增强型专用交换通信业务	Zēngqiáng-xíng zhuānyòng jiāohuàn tōngxìn yèwù	Enhanced private switched communications service	EPSCS
增添	Zēngtiān	Append	
增压式双工	Zēngyāshì shuānggōng	Incremental duplex	
增益	Zēngyì	Gain	G
增益带宽	Zēngyì dàikuān	Gain bandwidth	GB_W,GBW
增益交叉浸透	Zēngyì jiāochā jìntòu	Gain cross-saturation	
增益均衡	Zēngyì jūnhéng	Gain equilibrium	GEQ
增益均衡滤波器	Zēngyì jūnhéng lǜbōqì	Gain equilibrium filter	GEF
增益均衡器	Zēngyì jūnhéngqì	Gain equalizer	GEQ
增益控制	Zēngyì kòngzhì	Gain control	
增益平坦滤波器	Zēngyì píngtǎn lǜbōqì	Gain flattening filters	GFFs
增益平移	Zēngyì píngyí	Gain shifted	
增益平移掺饵光纤放大器	Zēngyì píngyí chān'ěr guāngxiān fàngdàqì	Gain shifted erbium-doped fiber amplifier	GS-EDFA
增益-带宽乘积	Zēngyì-dàikuān chéngjī	Gain-bandwidth product (of an avalanche photodiode)	
增长收益债卷	Zēngzhǎng shōuyì zhàijuàn	Growth and income securities	GAINS
增值分销商	Zēngzhí fēnxiāo shāng	Value added resellers	VAR
增值网	Zēngzhí wǎng	Value added network	VAN
增值业务	Zēngzhí yèwù	Value added service	VAS
增值业务提供商	Zēngzhí yèwù tígōngshāng	Value added service provider	VASP
增值转售商	Zēngzhí zhuǎnshòushāng	Value added reseller	VAR
增质型电视	Zēngzhì-xíng diànshì	Enhanced quality television	
栅瓣	Zhàbàn	Grating lobe	
栅瓣图	Zhàbàn tú	Grating lobe pattern	
栅板线馈电	Zhàbǎn xiàn kuìdiàn	Grid-plate line-feed	
铡刀式衰减器	Zhádāo-shì shuāijiǎnqì	Flap attenuator	
栅格	Zhàgé	Raster	
栅格地图	Zhàgé dìtú	Raster map	
栅格对象	Zhàgé duìxiàng	Raster object	
栅格结构	Zhàgé jiégòu	Raster structure	
栅格抛物面天线	Zhàgé pāowùmiàn tiānxiàn	Grid parabolic antenna	
栅格矢量转换	Zhàgé shǐliàng zhuǎnhuàn	Raster to vector conversion	
栅格数据	Zhàgé shùjù	Raster data	
栅格数据结构	Zhàgé shùjù jiégòu	Raster data structure	
栅格数据模型	Zhàgé shùjù móxíng	Raster data model	
窄带	Zhǎidài	Narrowband	
窄带（频）过程	Zhǎidài (pín) guòchéng	Narrowband process	
窄带发射	Zhǎidài fāshè	Narrowband emission	
窄带干扰	Zhǎidài gānrǎo	Narrowband interference	
窄带广播	Zhǎidài guǎngbō	Narrowcast; narrowcasting	

窄带 ISDN 用户部分	Zhǎidài ISDN yònghù bùfen	Narrowband ISDN user part	N-ISUP
窄带器件	Zhǎidài qìjiàn	Narrowband device	
窄带设备	Zhǎidài shèbèi	Narrowband device	
窄带数据链(线路)	Zhǎidài shùjù liàn (xiànlù)	Narrowband data link (line)	NBDL
窄带调频	Zhǎidài tiáopín	Narrowband frequency modulation	NFM
窄带调相	Zhǎidài tiáoxiàng	Narrowband phase modulation	NBPM
窄带调制	Zhǎidài tiáozhì	Narrowband frequency modulation	NBFM
窄带无源光网络	Zhǎidài wúyuán guāng wǎngluò	Narrowband passive optical network	NPON
窄带正交移频键控	Zhǎidài zhèngjiāo yípín jiànkòng	Narrowband quadrature frequency shift keying	N-QFSK
窄带正交移相键控	Zhǎidài zhèngjiāo yíxiàng jiànkòng	Narrowband quadrature phase shift keying	N-QPSK
窄带综合业务数字网	Zhǎidài zōnghé yèwù shùzì wǎng	Narrowband integrated services digital network	N-ISDN
窄带综合业务网	Zhǎidài zōnghé yèwù wǎng	Narrowband integrated services digital network	N-ISDN
摘挂机	Zhāiguàjī	Switch hook	
窄盒形天线	Zhǎihéxíng tiānxiàn	Pill-box antenna	
摘机	Zhāijī	Off-hook, pick up a telephone	
摘机等候	Zhāijī děnghòu	Off-hook waiting	
摘机后久不拨号	Zhāijī hòu jiǔ bù bōhào	No dialing after off-hook for a long time	
摘机信号	Zhāijī xìnhào	Off-hook signal	
窄频带时分多路存取	Zhǎipíndài shífèn duōlù cúnqǔ	Narrowband time division multiple access	NBTDMA
摘要	Zhāiyào	Digest	
摘要认证协议	Zhāiyào rènzhèng xiéyì	Summary authentication protocol (IPsec)	
栅控正交场放大器	Zhàkòng zhèngjiāo cháng fàngdàqì	Gridded crossed-field amplifier	GFCA
栈	Zhàn	Stack	
栈底	Zhàn dǐ	Bottom (of a stack)	
栈定	Zhàn dìng	Top (of a stack)	
站管理	Zhàn guǎnlǐ	Station management	SMT
栈控制指令	Zhàn kòngzhì zhǐlìng	Stacker control instruction	SCI
栈满	Zhàn mǎn	Stack full	SF
栈溢出	Zhàn yìchū	Stack overflow	
栈指示字	Zhàn zhǐshìzì	Stack pointer	SP
站钟	Zhàn zhōng	Station clock	
战场侦察雷达	Zhànchǎng zhēnchá léidá	Battlefield search radar	
站点层次聚集标识符	Zhàndiǎn céngcì jùjí biāozhìfú	Site-level aggregation identifier	SLAID
站点关守	Zhàndiǎn guānshǒu	Gatekeeper	
站点线路	Zhàndiǎn xiànlù	Line of sites	LOS
障碍台	Zhàng'ài tái	Fault desk	
障碍物检测	Zhàng'àiwù jiǎncè	Obstacle detection	
张弛振荡器	Zhāngchí zhèndàngqì	Relaxation oscillator	
帐号封锁	Zhànghào fēngsuǒ	Account lockout	
帐号管理	Zhànghào guǎnlǐ	Accounting management	AM
账户	Zhànghù	Account	
帐户锁定	Zhànghù suǒdìng	Account lockout	
涨价	Zhǎngjià	Mark up (in price) (verb and noun)	MU
章节分界线	Zhāngjié fēnjièxiàn	Section break (WP command)	
张力	Zhānglì	Tensile strength	
张力测试	Zhānglì cèshì	Tensile testing (FOC)	

张力节理	Zhānglì jiélǐ	Tension joint	
掌上型电脑	Zhǎngshàngxíng diànnǎo	Palmtop computer	
占机信号	Zhànjī xìnhào	Seizing signal	
占机证实信号	Zhànjī zhèngshí xìnhào	Seizing-acknowledgement signal	
站间联络公务电路	Zhàn-jiān liánluò gōngwù diànlù	Omnibus service circuit	
站间消息传递服务	Zhàn-jiān xiāoxi chuándì fúwù	Inter-site messaging service	ISM
展开式探测包	Zhǎnkāishì tàncè bāo	Spanning explorer packet	
占空建立呼叫	Zhànkōng jiànlì hūjiào	On-air-call-set-up	
战略防御计划	Zhànlüè fángyù jìhuà	Strategic Defense Initiative (US)	SDI
战略角色扮演游戏	Zhànlüè juésè bànyǎn yóuxì	Strategy role play games (computer game)	SRPG
战略密码体制	Zhànlüè mìmǎ tǐzhì	Strategic cipher system	
展期签证	Zhǎnqī qiānzhèng	Extended authorization period	
展示指示器	Zhǎnshì zhǐshìqì	Presentation indicator	PI
战术电台	Zhànshù diàntái	Tactical radio	
战术多网网间连接器	Zhànshù duōwǎng wǎng jiān liánjiēqì	Tactical multi-net gateway	TMG
战术密码体制	Zhànshù mìmǎ tǐzhì	Tactical cipher system	
战术名字服务器	Zhànshù míngzì fúwùqì	Tactical name server	TNS
战术数据信息链	Zhànshù shùjù xìnxī liàn	Tactical Data Information Link (US military)	TADIL
战术通信电子对抗系统	Zhànshù tōngxìn diànzǐ duìkàng xìtǒng	Tactical communication electronic warfare system	
战术作战中心	Zhànshù zuòzhàn zhōngxīn	Tactical operations center	TOC
粘贴	Zhāntiē	Paste (WP command)	
粘贴跟踪	Zhāntiē gēnzōng	Glue chasing	
粘贴记录	Zhāntiē jìlù	Glue records	
粘贴为	Zhāntiē wéi	Paste special (WP command)	
占位符	Zhànwèifú	Placeholder	
占线	Zhànxiàn	Occupied, busy	
占线测试	Zhànxiàn cèshì	Engaged test	
占线前标	Zhànxiàn qiánbiāo	Seizure precursor	
占用	Zhànyòng	Seize, seizure	
占用带宽	Zhànyòng dàikuān	Occupied bandwidth	
占用频带	Zhànyòng píndài	Occupied band	
占用信号	Zhànyòng xìnhào	Seizing signal	
占用证实信号时间监视	Zhànyòng zhèngshí xìnhào shíjiān jiānshì	Seizure acknowledged signal time supervision	
占有带宽	Zhànyǒu dàikuān	Occupied bandwidth	OBW
占有率	Zhànyǒu lǜ	Occupancy rate	
兆	Zhào	Mega- (prefix meaning 10^6)	
兆比特每秒	Zhàobǐtè měi miǎo	Megabits per second	Mb/s
兆赫	Zhàohè	MegaHertz	MHZ
兆赫兹	Zhàohè-zī	MegaHertz	MHz
召集人	Zhàojírén	Convenor	
照明设备	Zhàomíng shèbèi	Emergency lighting	
照明智能控制器	Zhàomíng zhìnéng kòngzhìqì	Intelligent fire controller	IFC
照射图形	Zhàoshè túxíng	Illumination pattern, illumination diagram	
爪哇语言	Zhǎo-wā yǔyán	Java language ©	
兆位	Zhàowèi	Megabit (10^6 bit)	MB
照像用滤光镜	Zhàoxiàng-yòng lǜguāngjìng	Photographic filter	

兆兆	Zhàozhào	Tera- (prefix meaning 10^{12})	T, TERA
照准仪	Zhàozhǔnyí	Alidade	
兆字节	Zhàozìjié	Megabyte (10^6 bytes)	MB, mb
栅状反射面	Zhàzhuàng fǎnshèmiàn	Grid reflecting surface	
栅状反射器	Zhàzhuàng fǎnshèqì	Lattice reflector	
渐变梯度光纤	Zhèbiàn tīdù guāngxiān	Graded index fiber	GIF
渐变折射率聚合物光纤	Zhèbiàn zhéshèlǜ jùhéwù guāngxiān	Graded index polymer optical fiber	GI-POF
折叠单极天线	Zhédié dānjí tiānxiàn	Folded monopole antenna	
折叠法	Zhédié fǎ	Folding method	
折叠偶极天线	Zhédié ǒují tiānxiàn	Folded dipole antenna	
锗硅	Zhěguī	Silicon germanium	SiGe
折合单极子	Zhéhé dānjízi	Folded monopole, folded unipole (antenna)	
折合偶极子	Zhéhé ǒujízi	Folded dipole (antenna)	
折合振子	Zhéhé zhènzǐ	Folded dipole	
折合的平衡/不平衡变换器	Zhéhéde pínghéng/bùpínghéng biànhuànqì	Folded balun (balanced/unbalanced device) converter	
渐近稳定性	Zhèjìn wěndìngxìng	Asymptotic stability	
渐进最大似然	Zhèjìn zuìdà sìrán	Asymptotic maximum likelihood	AML
遮拦	Zhēlán	Barrier	
阵排列	Zhèn páiliè	Array configuration	
阵因子	Zhèn yīnzǐ	Array factor	
针栅阵列	Zhēn zhà zhènliè	Pin grid array (electronics mfg)	PGA
阵，天线阵	Zhèn, tiānxiàn zhèn	Array, antenna array	
真波光纤	Zhēnbō guāngxiān	True Wave fiber © (Lucent product)	
侦察与控制数据链	Zhēnchá yǔ kòngzhì shùjù liàn	Surveillance and control Data link (US military)	SCDL
振荡	Zhèndàng	Oscillation	
振荡环节	Zhèndàng huánjié	Oscillating element	
振荡模式	Zhèndàng móshì	Oscillation mode	
振荡器	Zhèndàngqì	Oscillator	O, OSC
振动	Zhèndòng	Vibration	
震动传感器	Zhèndòng chuángǎnqì	Shock sensor	SS
振动实验	Zhèndòng shíyàn	Vibration test	
诊断	Zhěnduàn	Diagnosis, diagnostic	
诊断测试	Zhěnduàn cèshì	Diagnostic tests	
诊断程序	Zhěnduàn chéngxù	Diagnostic program	
诊断功能测试	Zhěnduàn gōngnéng cèshì	Diagnostic function test	DFT
诊断和监测	Zhěnduàn hé jiāncè	Diagnosis and monitoring	DIAG
诊断控制程序	Zhěnduàn kòngzhì chéngxù	Diagnostic control program	DCP
振幅传输系数	Zhènfú chuánshū xìshù	Amplitude transmission factor (in a transmission line)	
振幅反射系数	Zhènfú fǎnshè xìshù	Amplitude reflection factor (in a transmission line)	
振幅概率分布	Zhènfú gàilǜ fēnbù	Amplitude probability distribution	APD
振幅键控	Zhènfú jiànkòng	Amplitude shift keying	ASK
振幅量化	Zhènfú liànghuà	Amplitude quantization	
振幅频率失真	Zhènfú pínlǜ shīzhēn	Amplitude-frequency distortion	AFD
振幅特性	Zhènfú tèxìng	Amplitude characteristics	
振幅调制	Zhènfú tiáozhì	Amplitude modulation	AM
振幅相位键控	Zhènfú xiàngwèi jiànkòng	Amplitude phase keying	APK

振幅压扩单边带	Zhènfú yākuò dānbiāndài	Amplitude companded single sideband	ACSSB
镇幅压扩单边带	Zhènfú yākuò dānbiāndài	Amplitude companded single sideband	ACSB
振幅移相键控	Zhènfú yíxiāng jiànkòng	Amplitude phase shift keying	APSK
振幅与相位键控	Zhènfú yǔ xiàngwèi jiànkòng	Amplitude and phase keying	APK
振幅-相位调制	Zhènfú/xiàngwèi tiáozhì	Amplitude-phase modulation	APM
帧	Zhèng	Frame	FR
帧比率控制	Zhèng bǐlǜ kòngzhì	Frame rate control	FRC
帧擦除标识	Zhèng cāchú biāozhì	Frame erase identity	FEI
帧擦除率	Zhèng cāchú lǜ	Frame erase rate	FER
帧层参考事件	Zhèng céng cānkǎo shìjiàn	Frame-layer reference event	FE
帧差错率	Zhèng chācuò lǜ	Frame error rate	FER
帧长	Zhèng cháng	Frame length	
帧传送延迟	Zhèng chuánsòng yánchí	Frame transfer delay	FTD
帧处理单元（板）	Zhèng chǔlǐ dānyuán (bǎn)	Frame processing unit (board)	FPU
帧处理器	Zhèng chǔlǐqì	Frame handler	FH
帧单元	Zhèng dānyuán	Frame unit	FU
帧单元控制器	Zhèng dānyuán kòngzhìqì	Frame unit controller	FUC
帧定位	Zhèng dìngwèi	Frame alignment	
帧定位恢复时间	Zhèng dìngwèi huīfù shíjiān	Frame alignment recovery time	
帧定位时隙	Zhèng dìngwèi shíxì	Frame alignment time slot	
帧定位信号	Zhèng dìngwèi xìnhào	Frame alignment signal	FAS
帧丢失	Zhèng diūshī	Loss of frame	LOF
帧丢失告警	Zhèng diūshī gàojǐng	Loss of frame alarm	LOF
帧丢失率	Zhèng diūshī lǜ	Frame loss rate	FLR
帧丢失率	Zhèng diūshī lǜ	Frame loss rate	FLR
帧丢失秒	Zhèng diūshī miǎo	Frame loss second	FLS
帧方式承载业务	Zhèng fāngshì chéngzài yèwù	Frame mode bearer service	FMBS
正反馈	Zhèng fǎnkuì	Positive feedback	
正关联规则	Zhèng guānlián guīzé	Positive association rule	
帧号	Zhèng hào	Frame number	FN
帧缓冲缓存	Zhèng huǎnchōng huǎncún	Frame buffer cache	FBC
帧检序列	Zhèng jiǎn xùliè	Frame check sequence	FCS
帧检测序列	Zhèng jiǎncè xùliè	Frame check sequence	FCS
帧检查序列	Zhèng jiǎnchá xùliè	Frame check sequence	FCS
帧检验顺序	Zhèng jiǎnyàn shùnxù	Frame check sequence	FCS
帧检验序列	Zhèng jiǎnyàn xùliè	Frame check sequence	FCS
帧交换	Zhèng jiāohuàn	Frame switching	
帧交换承载业务	Zhèng jiāohuàn chéngzài yèwù	Frame switching bearer service	FSBS
帧校验序列	Zhèng jiàoyàn xùliè	Frame check sequence	FCS
帧交织	Zhèng jiāozhī	Frame inter-leaving	
帧结构型接口	Zhèng jiégòuxíng jiēkǒu	Framed interface	
帧结束序列	Zhèng jiéshù xùliè	End frame series	EFS
整据元	Zhěng jù yuán	Frame reject element	
帧拒收	Zhèng jùshōu	Frame reject	FRMR
帧开始	Zhèng kāishǐ	Frame start (timing information)	
帧控除标识码	Zhèng kòngchú biāozhì mǎ	Frame erase identity	FEI

帧控制	Zhèng kòngzhì	Frame control	FC
帧控制	Zhèng kòngzhì	Frame control	FC
正逻辑	Zhèng luójí	Positive logic	
正脉冲塞入	Zhèng màichōng sāirù	Positive pulse stuffing	
正码速调整	Zhèng mǎsù tiáozhěng	Positive justification	
政密	Zhèng mì	Government encryption or cryptography (short for 政府用的密码)	
帧模式承载业务	Zhèng móshì chéngzài yèwù	Frame mode bearer service	FMBS
帧模式承载业务链路接入规程	Zhèng móshì chéngzài yèwù liànlù jiērù guīchéng	Link access procedure to frame mode bearer service	LAPF
帧起始信号	Zhèng qǐshǐ xìnhào	Frame start signal	FS
帧起始序列	Zhèng qǐshǐ xùliè	Start frame sequence	SFS
帧起始符	Zhèng qǐshǐfú	Start of frame	SOF
正色散位移单模光纤	Zhèng sèsàn wèiyí dān ó guāngxiān	Non-zero dispersion-shifted single mode optical fiber	
帧删除标识	Zhèng shānchú biāozhì	Frame erase identifier	FEI
帧删除率	Zhèng shānchú lǜ	Frame erase rate	FER
帧失步	Zhèng shībù	Out-of-frame	OOF
帧失步秒	Zhèng shībù miǎo	Out-of-frame second	OFS
正失配	Zhèng shīpèi	Positive mismatching	
帧失位	Zhèng shīwèi	Loss of alignment	LOA
帧失位时间	Zhèng shīwèi shíjiān	Out-of-frame alignment time	
帧数为王	Zhèng shù wéi wáng	Frame rate is king (see "Battle for eyeballs")	
帧同步	Zhèng tóngbù	Frame alignment	
帧同步码	Zhèng tóngbù mǎ	Frame synchronization code	
帧同步字	Zhèng tóngbù zì	Frame synchronization word	FSW
帧头校验序列	Zhèng tóu jiàoyàn xùliè	Frame header check sequence	HCS
帧协议	Zhèng xiéyì	Frame protocol	FP
征印量差	Zhēng yìn liáng chà	Positive printing amount percent	
帧用户网络接口	Zhèng yònghù wǎngluò jiēkǒu	Frame-based user-to-network interface	FUNI
帧中继	Zhèng zhōngjì	Frame relay	FR
帧中继层管理实体	Zhèng zhōngjì céng guǎnlǐ shítǐ	Frame relay layer management entity	FRLME
帧中继承载业务	Zhèng zhōngjì chéngzài yèwù	Frame relay bearer service	FRBS
帧中继访问设备	Zhèng zhōngjì fǎngwèn shèbèi	Frame relay access device	FRAD
帧中继服务	Zhèng zhōngjì fúwù	Frame relay service	
帧中继交换虚电路	Zhèng zhōngjì jiāohuàn xū diànlù	Frame relay switched virtual circuit	
帧中继接入	Zhèng zhōngjì jiērù	Frame relay access	
帧中继接入器件	Zhèng zhōngjì jiērù qìjiàn	Frame relay access device	FRAD
帧中继论坛	Zhèng zhōngjì lùntán	Frame relay forum	FRF
帧中继数据传输业务	Zhèng zhōngjì shùjù chuánshū yèwù	Frame relay data transmission service	FRDTS
帧中继信息字段	Zhèng zhōngjì xìnxī zìduàn	Frame relay information field	FRIF
帧中继业务	Zhèng zhōngjì yèwù	Frame relay service	
帧中继业务特定会聚子层	Zhèng zhōngjì yèwù tèdìng huìjù zicéng	Frame relay-service-specific convergence sub-layer	FR-SSCS
帧中继永久虚电路	Zhèng zhōngjì yǒngjiǔ xū diànlù	Frame relay permanent virtual circuit	
帧中继中的点到点协议	Zhèng zhōngjì zhòngde diǎn dàodiǎn xiéyì	Point-to-point protocol in frame relay	PPPIFR
帧中继装拆	Zhèng zhōngjì zhuāngchāi	Frame relay assembly disassembly	FRAD

帧终止符	Zhèng zhōngzhǐfú	End of frame	EOF
帧周期	Zhèng zhōuqī	Frame time; frame duration (in switching)	
帧转发	Zhèng zhuǎnfā	Frame forwarding	
帧状态	Zhèng zhuàngtài	Frame status	FS
帧字段	Zhèng zìduàn	Frame segment	FS
正作用	Zhèng zuòyòng	Direct action	
帧/秒	Zhèng/miǎo	Frames per second	Fps
整版	Zhěngbǎn	Justified (in word processing)	
政策法规司	Zhèngcè fǎguī sī	Department of Policies and Regulations (MII)	
政策法规组	Zhèngcè fǎguī zǔ	Legal and Regulatory Group (GSM MoU)	L&G
政策集团	Zhèngcè jítuán	Strategies group	
正常充电	Zhèngcháng chōngdiàn	Normal charging	
正常断开方式	Zhèngcháng duànkāi fāngshì	Normal disconnected mode	NDM
正常服务	Zhèngcháng fúwù	Nominal service	
正常负载	Zhèngcháng fùzài	Normal load	
正常工作时触电防护	Zhèngcháng gōngzuò shí chùdiàn fánghù	Protection against shock in normal service	
正常固结	Zhèngcháng gùjié	Normal consolidation	
正常检查	Zhèngcháng jiǎnchá	Normal inspection	
正常计算流量系数	Zhèngcháng jìsuàn liúliàng xìshù	Calculated normal flow coefficient	
正常耦合转矩	Zhèngcháng ǒuhé zhuànjǔ	Normal coupling torque	
正常突发	Zhèngcháng tūfā	Normal burst	
正常响应方式	Zhèngcháng xiǎngyìng fāngshì	Normal response mode	NRM
正常信号	Zhèngcháng xìnhào	Normal signal	
正常运行承载器	Zhèngcháng yùnxíng chéngzàiqì	Sanity loader	
正常运行管理器	Zhèngcháng yùnxíng guǎnlǐqì	Sanity manager	
正常状态	Zhèngcháng zhuàngtài	Normal condition	
正常化管理器	Zhèngchánghuà guǎnlǐqì	Sanity manager	SM
正反码	Zhèng-fǎn mǎ	Positive and inverse code	
正方形天线	Zhèngfāngxíng tiānxiàn	Quadrant antenna	
正方形正射图片	Zhèngfāngxíng zhèngshè túpiàn	Ortho-photoquad	
政府成品	Zhèngfǔ chéngpǐn	Government off-the-shelf products	GOTS
政府电信组织	Zhèngfǔ diànxìn zǔzhī	Government Telecommunications Organization	GTO
政府顾问委员会	Zhèngfǔ gùwèn wěiyuánhuì	Government advisory committee	GAC
政府开放系统互连协议	Zhèngfǔ kāifàng xìtǒng hùlián xiéyì	Government Open system interconnection protocol	GOSIP
政府间协议	Zhèngfǔ-jiān xiéyì	Inter-governmental agreement	
正规分布	Zhèngguī fēnbù	Normal distribution	
正规散射	Zhèngguī sǎnshè	Normal dispersion	
整合	Zhěnghé	Conformity	
整合	Zhěnghé	Integrate	
证件	Zhèngjiàn	Certificate	
帧间变换	Zhèng-jiān biànhuàn	Inter-frame transform	
证件授权机构	Zhèngjiàn shòuquán jīgòu	Certification authority	CA
证件途径	Zhèngjiàn tújìng	Certification path	
正交编码	Zhèngjiāo biānmǎ	Orthogonal code	
正交部分响应键控	Zhèngjiāo bùfen xiǎngyìng jiànkòng	Quadrature partial response keying	QPRK
正交场平衡混频器	Zhèngjiāo cháng pínghéng hùnpínqì	Crossed-field balanced mixer	

正交场器件	Zhèngjiāo cháng qìjiàn	Crossed-field device	
正交发送分集	Zhèngjiāo fāsòng fēnjí	Orthogonal transmission diversity	OTD
正交幅度调制	Zhèngjiāo fúdù tiáozhì	Quadrature amplitude modulation	QAM
正交极化	Zhèngjiāo jíhuà	Orthogonal polarization	OP
正交极化方向图	Zhèngjiāo jíhuà fāngxiàng tú	Cross-polarization pattern (of an antenna)	
正交极化鉴别率	Zhèngjiāo jíhuà jiànbié lǜ	Cross-polarization discrimination rate (of an antenna)	
正交镜象滤波器	Zhèngjiāo jìngxiàng lǜbōqì	Quadrature mirror filter	QMF
正交可变扩频系数码	Zhèngjiāo kěbiàn kuòpín xìshù mǎ	Orthogonal variable spread factor codes	OVSF
正交可变扩频因子	Zhèngjiāo kěbiàn kuòpín yīnzǐ	Orthogonal variable spreading factor	OVSF
正交扩频	Zhèngjiāo kuòpín	Orthogonal frequency spread	
正交码偏移键控	Zhèngjiāo mǎ piānyí jiànkòng	Orthogonal code-shift keying	OCSK
正交模	Zhèngjiāo mó	Orthogonal modes	
正交模耦合器	Zhèngjiāo mó ǒuhéqì	Orthogonal mode coupler	
正交模耦合器	Zhèngjiāo mó ǒuhéqì	Orthomode transducer	OMT
正交模转换器	Zhèngjiāo mó zhuǎnhuànqì	Orthomode transducer	
正交频分复用	Zhèngjiāo pínfēn fùyòng	Orthogonal frequency division multiplexing	OFDM
正交频分复用论坛	Zhèngjiāo pínfēn fùyòng lùntán	Orthogonal frequency division multiplexing forum	OFDMF
正交频分调制	Zhèngjiāo pínfēn tiáozhì	Orthogonal frequency division modulation	OFDM
正交双线极化	Zhèngjiāo shuāngxiàn jíhuà	Orthogonal dual linear polarization	
正交数组处理程序	Zhèngjiāo shùzǔ chǔlǐ chéngxù	Orthogonal array processor	OAP
正交四相相移键控	Zhèngjiāo sìxiàng xiàngyí jiànkòng	Orthogonal quaternary phase shift keying	OQPSK
正交调幅	Zhèngjiāo tiáofú	Quadrature amplitude modulation	QAM
正交调幅器	Zhèngjiāo tiáofúqì	Quadrature modulator	
正交跳频	Zhèngjiāo tiàopín	Quadrature frequency hopping	
正交调制	Zhèngjiāo tiáozhì	Quadrature modulation	QM
正交同频率的	Zhèngjiāo tóng pínlǜde	Orthogonal co-frequency (adjective)	
正交通道	Zhèngjiāo tōngdào	Quadrature channel	
正交相干解调器	Zhèngjiāo xiānggān jiětiáoqì	Quadrature coherent demodulator	
正交相移键控	Zhèngjiāo xiāngyí jiànkòng	Quadrature phase shift keying	QPSK
正交信道	Zhèngjiāo xìndào	Orthogonal channels	
正交信道噪声仿真器	Zhèngjiāo xìndào zàoshēng fǎngzhēnqì	Orthogonal channel noise simulator	OCNS
正交信号	Zhèngjiāo xìnhào	Quadrature signal	
正交移相键控	Zhèngjiāo yíxiàng jiànkòng	Quadrature phase shift keying	QPSK
正交性	Zhèngjiāoxìng	Orthogonality	
证据	Zhèngjù	Evidence	
整理碎片	Zhěnglǐ suìpiàn	Degragment; defrag	
整理与合并	Zhěnglǐ yǔ hébìng	Consolidation and grooming	
整流	Zhěngliú	Rectification	
帧内变换	Zhèng-nèi biànhuàn	Intra-frame transform	
蒸汽软件	Zhēngqì ruǎnjiàn	Vaporware	
争抢判决	Zhēngqiǎng pànjué	Contention resolution	
征求意见	Zhēngqiú yìjiàn	Request for comment	RFC
正确性	Zhèngquèxìng	Validity	
正确性证明	Zhèngquèxìng zhèngmíng	Justification	
正射投影图像	Zhèngshè tóuyǐng túxiàng	Ortho-rectification	
正射投影像片	Zhèngshè tóuyǐng xiàngpiàn	Ortho-photography	

正射投影仪	Zhèngshè tóuyǐngyí	Ortho-photoscope	
正射影像地图	Zhèngshè yǐngxiàng dìtú	Ortho-photo map	
证实	Zhèngshí	Confirm	
证实（原语）	Zhèngshí (yuán yǔ)	Confirm (primtive)	
正式代码	Zhèngshì dàimǎ	Official code	
证实服务	Zhèngshí fúwù	Confirmed-service	
正式街道名称	Zhèngshì jiēdào míngchēng	Official street name	
正式街道名称本体	Zhèngshì jiēdào míngchēng běntǐ	Official street name body	
正式街道名称文字	Zhèngshì jiēdào míngchēng wénzì	Official street name text	
帧式接口	Zhèng-shì jiēkǒu	Framed interface	
正式名称	Zhèngshì míngchēng	Official name	
正式名称本体	Zhèngshì míngchēng běntǐ	Official name body	
正式名称文字	Zhèngshì míngchēng wénzì	Official name text	
证实时间	Zhèngshí shíjiān	Confirmation time	Tc
证实信号	Zhèngshí xìnhào	Acknowledgement signal	
证实信号单元	Zhèngshí xìnhào dānyuán	Acknowledgement signal unit	
证实信息传送方式	Zhèngshí xìnxī chuánsòng fāngshì	Acknowledged information transfer mode	
证实音	Zhèngshí yīn	Verification tone	
证实型服务	Zhèngshíxíng fúwù	Confirmed service	
证书	Zhèngshū	Certificate	
证书撤回消息	Zhèngshū chèhuí xiāoxi	Certificate withdrawn message (IPsec TLS)	
证书撤销列表	Zhèngshū chèxiāo lièbiǎo	Certificate revocation list (IPsec)	CRL
证书废除列表	Zhèngshū fèichú lièbiǎo	Certificate revocation list	CRL
证书管理机构	Zhèngshū guǎnlǐ jīgòu	Certification authority	CA
证书黑名单	Zhèngshū hēimíngdān	Certificate blacklist	
证书库	Zhèngshū kù	Certificate library	CL
证书期满消息	Zhèngshū qīmǎn xiāoxi	Certificate expired message (IPsec TLS)	
证书授权	Zhèngshū shòuquán	Certificate authority	CA
证书未知消息	Zhèngshū wèizhī xiāoxi	Certificate unknown message (IPsec TLS)	
证书协议	Zhèngshū xiéyì	Certificate agreement	
证书信任列表	Zhèngshū xìnrèn lièbiǎo	Certificate trust list	CTL
整数执行单元	Zhěngshù zhíxíng dānyuán	Integer execution unit	IEU
证书作废表	Zhèngshū zuòfèi biǎo	Certificate revocation list	CRL
正态分布	Zhèngtài fēnbù	Normal distribution	
整体发送	Zhěngtǐ fāsòng	En bloc sending	
正投影视图	Zhèngtóuyǐng shìtú	Orthographic view	
正文结束	Zhèngwén jiéshù	End of text	ETX
正文开始	Zhèngwén kāishǐ	Start of text	STX
正文开头	Zhèngwén kāitóu	Start of text	STX
正弦	Zhèngxián	Sine	
正弦变换	Zhèngxián biànhuàn	Sinusoidal transfer	
正弦变换编码	Zhèngxián biànhuàn biānmǎ	Sine transform coding	STC
正弦变换编码奇	Zhèngxián biànhuàn biānmǎqí	Sinusoidal transfer coder	STC
正弦波形分布	Zhèngxián bōxíng fēnbù	Sinusoidal distribution (of a current in an antenna)	
正弦曲线频移键控	Zhèngxián qūxiàn pínyí jiànkòng	Sinusoidal frequency shift keying	SFSK
正弦相位变化	Zhèngxián xiàngwèi biànhuà	Sinusoidal phase variation	

正弦波	Zhèngxiánbō	Sine wave	
正弦波测试信号	Zhèngxiánbō cèshì xìnhào	Sine wave test signal	
正弦波发生器	Zhèngxiánbō fāshēngqì	Sine wave generator	
正向	Zhèngxiàng	Forward direction (in a circulator or isolator)	
正向话终信号	Zhèngxiàng huàzhōng xìnhào	Clear-forward signal	
正向搜索	Zhèngxiàng sōusuǒ	Forward lookup	
正向损耗	Zhèngxiàng sǔnhào	Forward loss (in a circulator or isolator)	
正向误差控制	Zhèngxiàng wùchā kòngzhì	Forward error control	FEC
正向信道	Zhèngxiàng xìndào	Forward channel	
整型	Zhěngxíng	Integer	
正压	Zhèngyā	Barotropy	
正移	Zhèngyí	Right-sizing	
争用	Zhēngyòng	Contention	
征用	Zhēngyòng	Condemnation	
正则表达式	Zhèngzé biǎodá shì	Regular expression	
征值	Zhēngzhí	Value	
帧中中间码	Zhèng-zhōng zhōngjiān mǎ	Midamble (center section of a frame)	
整字换行	Zhěngzì huànháng	Word wrap	
真迹电报	Zhēnjī diànbào	Telewriting	
真空泵浦	Zhēnkōng bèngpǔ	Vacuum pump	
真空电容器	Zhēnkōng diànróngqì	Vacuum capacitor	
真空电子器件	Zhēnkōng diànzǐ qìjiàn	Vacuum electron device	
针孔滤光镜	Zhēnkǒng lǜguāngjìng	Pinhole filter (optical)	
真空萤光显示器	Zhēnkōng yíngguāng xiǎnshìqì	Vacuum fluorescent display	VFD
真空蒸镀化学药品	Zhēnkōng zhēngdù huàxué yàopǐn	Vacuum evaporation chemicals	
真空蒸镀设备	Zhēnkōng zhēngdù shèbèi	Vacuum evaporation equipment	
真空紫外线光源	Zhēnkōng zǐwàixiàn guāngyuán	Vacuum ultraviolet light source	
真空紫外线激光	Zhēnkōng zǐwàixiàn jīguāng	Vacuum ultraviolet laser	
针孔型自动亮度补偿镜头	Zhēnkǒng-xíng zìdòng liàngdù bǔcháng jìngtóu	Pinhole automatic light compensation (ALC) lens	PAL
阵列	Zhènliè	Array	
阵列波导光栅	Zhènliè bōdǎo guāngshān	Array waveguide grating	AWG
阵列处理机	Zhènliè chǔlǐjī	Array processor	AP
阵列天线	Zhènliè tiānxiàn	Array antenna	
振铃	Zhènlíng	Ring, ringing, alerting	
震铃产生器后面板	Zhènlíng chǎnshēngqì hòumianbǎn	Ring generator back panel	RGBP
振铃电流	Zhènlíng diànliú	Ringing current supply (the R in BORSCHT)	
振铃电压	Zhènlíng diànyā	Ring voltage	
震铃信号产生单元	Zhènlíng xìnhào chǎnshēng dānyuán	Ring signal generate unit	RSGU
振铃音	Zhènlíng yīn	Ringing tone	
振铃振荡器	Zhènlíng zhèndàngqì	Ring oscillator	RO
振鸣	Zhènmíng	Singing	
真瑞	Zhēn-ruì	GenRad Corp. (US)	
真实媒体文件格式	Zhēnshí méitǐ wénjiàn géshi	Real media file format	RMFF
真实世界电脑	Zhēnshí shìjiè diànnǎo	Real world computing	RWC
真正简单的整合	Zhēnzhèng jiǎndānde zhěnghé	Really simple syndication	RSS
真值表	Zhēnzhíbiǎo	Truth table	

折射	Zhéshè	Refraction	
折射近场	Zhéshè jìncháng	Refracted near field	
折射指数	Zhéshè zhǐshù	Refractive index	
折射波	Zhéshèbō	Refracted wave	
折射角	Zhéshèjiǎo	Angle of refraction	
折射率	Zhéshèlǜ	Index of refraction	
折射率分布	Zhéshèlǜ fēnbù	Refractive index profile	
折射率匹配材料	Zhéshèlǜ pǐpèi cáiliào	Index matching material	
折射率液	Zhéshèlǜ yè	Refractive index liquid	
折射率仪	Zhéshèlǜ yí	Refractive index meter	
折线编码律	Zhéxiàn biānmǎ lǜ	Segmented encoding law	
折线图	Zhéxiàntú	Line graph	
值	Zhí	Value	
制棒	Zhì bàng	Rod making (FOC mfg)	
值表达式	Zhí biǎodá shì	Value expression	
致颤电流阈值	Zhì chàn diànliú yùzhí	Threshold of ventricular fibrillation current	
指触光敏装置	Zhǐ chù guāngmǐn zhuāngzhì	Digilux touch mask	
置初始化方式	Zhì chūshǐhuà fāngshì	Set initialization mode	SIM
只存	Zhǐ cún	Storage-only	
只读	Zhǐ dú	Read only	RO
只读 CD 存储器	Zhǐ dú CD cúnchǔqì	Compact disk read only memory	CD-ROM
只读存储器	Zhǐ dú cúnchǔqì	Read-only memory	ROM
只读光盘存储器	Zhǐ dú guāngpán cúnchǔqì	Compact disk read only memory	CD-ROM
只读内储	Zhǐ dú nèichǔ	Read only memory	ROM
秩和滑窗检测器	Zhì hé huáchuāng jiǎncèqì	Rank sum slide-window detector	
止节点	Zhǐ jiédiǎn	To-node	
只进游标	Zhǐ jìn yóubiāo	Forward-only cursor	
置扩展的异步平衡方式	Zhì kuòzhǎnde yìbù pínghéng fāngshì	Set asynchronous balanced mode extended	SABME
值类型	Zhí lèixíng	Value types	
至忙用户的呼叫的完成	Zhì máng yònghùde hūjiàode wánchéng	Completion of calls to busy subscribers	CCBS
值属性表	Zhí shǔxìng biǎo	Value attribute table	VAT
只向前游标	Zhǐ xiàngqián yóubiāo	Forward-only cursor (for database)	
只向前的	Zhǐ xiàngqiánde	Forward-only	
只写	Zhǐ xiě	Write only	WO
置异步平衡方式	Zhì yìbù pínghéng fāngshì	Set asynchronous balanced mode	SABM
置异步平衡扩展模式	Zhì yìbù pínghéng kuòzhǎn móshì	Set asynchronous balanced mode extended	SABME
值域	Zhí yù	Co-domain (in CORBA)	
值域	Zhí yù	Value domain	
置正常响应方式	Zhì zhèngcháng xiǎngyìng fāngshì	Set normal response mode	SNRM
指标	Zhǐbiāo	Pointer	
制表对准	Zhìbiǎo duìzhǔn	Tabulation alignment	
指标字	Zhǐbiāo zì	Pointer	
指标字变量	Zhǐbiāo zì biànliàng	Pointer variable	
制表点	Zhìbiǎodiǎn	Tabulation stop	
直拨电话系统	Zhíbō diànhuà xìtǒng	Direct dialing telephone system	DDTS
直播卫星	Zhíbō wèixīng	Direct broadcast satellite	DBS

支撑	Zhīchēng	Brace	
支撑矢量机	Zhīchēng shǐliàngjī	Support vector machine	
支撑网	Zhīchēng wǎng	Supporting network	
支持	Zhīchí	Support	
支持对象	Zhīchí duìxiàng	Support object	
支持节点	Zhīchí jiédiǎn	Support node	
支持群集的应用程序	Zhīchí qúnjíde yìngyòng chéngxù	Cluster-aware application	
支持实体	Zhīchí shítǐ	Support entity	SE
支持实体功能	Zhīchí shítǐ gōngnéng	Support entity function	SEF
支持用户网络接口的业务特定协调功能	Zhīchí yònghù wǎngluò jiēkǒude yèwù tèdìng xiétiáo gōngnéng	Service specific coordination function supporting user-to-network interface	SSCF-UNI
支持中心网络管理	Zhīchí zhōngxīn wǎngluò guǎnlǐ	Support centralized network management	SCNM
直达波	Zhídá bō	Direct wave	
直达线路	Zhídá xiànlù	Direct route	
指代	Zhǐdài	Anaphora	
纸带穿孔机	Zhǐdài chuānkǒngjī	Paper tape punch	PTP
指代消解	Zhǐdài xiāojiě	Anaphoric resolution	
纸带阅读机	Zhǐdài yuèdújī	Paper tape reader	PTR
制导雷达	Zhìdǎo léidá	Guidance radar	
指点	Zhǐdiǎn	Point-and-click	
指点信标	Zhǐdiǎn xìnbiāo	Marker beacon	
指定路由器	Zhǐdìng lùyóuqì	Designated router	
指定路由器	Zhǐdìng lùyóuqì	Designated router	DR
指定批准人签名方案	Zhǐdìng pīzhǔn rén qiānmíng fāng'àn	Designated confirmer signature scheme	
指定桥	Zhǐdìng qiáo	Designated bridge	
指定网桥	Zhǐdìng wǎngqiáo	Designated bridge	
指定转发路由器	Zhǐdìng zhuǎnfā lùyóuqì	Designated forwarder	DF
指定转发者	Zhǐdìng zhuǎnfā zhě	Designated router	DR
指定转接列表	Zhǐdìng zhuǎnjiē lièbiǎo	Designated transit list	DTL
指定转接序列	Zhǐdìng zhuǎnjiē xùliè	Designated transit list	DTL
指定的桥	Zhǐdìngde qiáo	Designated bridge	
指定的认证机构	Zhǐdìngde rènzhèng jīgòu	Appointed certification body	CAB
指定的转接一览表	Zhǐdìngde zhuǎnjiē yīlǎnbiǎo	Designated transit list	DTL
止兑	Zhǐduì	Suspension of payment	
直方图	Zhífāngtú	Bar graph	
直方图	Zhífāngtú	Histogram	
直方图规定化	Zhífāngtú guīdìnghuà	Histogram specification	
直方图均衡化	Zhífāngtú jūnhénghuà	Histogram equalization	
直方图调整	Zhífāngtú tiáozhěng	Histogram adjust	
直方图正态化	Zhífāngtú zhèngtàihuà	Histogram normalization	
直放站	Zhífàngzhàn	Repeater station	
直观合计	Zhíguān héjì	Visual total	
直观贮存管	Zhíguān zhùcún guǎn	Direct-view storage tube	
滞后不等时并行畸变度	Zhìhòu bùděngshí bìngxíng jībiàndù	Degree of late anisochronous parallel distortion	
滞后时间	Zhìhòu shíjiān	Latency	
置换密码	Zhìhuàn mìmǎ	Substitution cipher	

置换频移键控	Zhìhuàn pínyí jiànkòng	Permutation frequency shift keying	PFSK
置换群理论	Zhìhuàn qún lǐlùn	Permutation group theory	
置换选择排序	Zhìhuàn xuǎnzé páixù	Replacement selection sort	
指挥控制中心	Zhǐhuī kòngzhì zhōngxīn	Command control center	CCC
指挥中心	Zhǐhuī zhōngxīn	Command center	CC
直角棱镜	Zhíjiǎo léngjìng	Rectangular prism	
直角棱镜	Zhíjiǎo léngjìng	Right-angle prism	
直角频率部分多路复用	Zhíjiǎo pínlǜ bùfen duōlù fùyòng	Orthogonal frequency division multiplexing	OFDM
直角坐标网	Zhíjiǎo zuòbiāo wǎng	Rectangular grid	
直角坐标显示器	Zhíjiǎo zuòbiāo xiǎnshìqì	Rectangular coordinate indicator	
直角坐标轴	Zhíjiǎo zuòbiāozhóu	Orthogonal coordinate axes	
直接安装压力表	Zhíjiē ānzhuāng yālìbiǎo	Direct mounting gauge	
直接包交换技术	Zhíjiē bāo jiāohuàn jìshù	Cut-through packet switching	
直接被害	Zhíjiē bèihài	Direct damage	
直接波	Zhíjiē bō	Direct wave	
直接拨出	Zhíjiē bōchū	Direct outward dialing	DOD
直接拨号	Zhíjiē bōhào	Direct dialing in	DDI
直接拨号去话呼叫	Zhíjiē bōhào qùhuà hūjiào	Directly dialed outgoing call	DDOC
直接拨号系统	Zhíjiē bōhào xìtǒng	Direct dialing system	DDS
直接拨入	Zhíjiē bōrù	Direct dialing in	DDI
直接拨入	Zhíjiē bōrù	Direct inward dialing	DID
直接长途拨号网	Zhíjiē chángtú bōhào wǎng	Direct distance dial network	
直接传递查询	Zhíjiē chuándì cháxún	Pass-through query	
直接传递应用部分	Zhíjiē chuándì yìngyòng bùfen	Direct transfer application part	DTAP
直接传递语句	Zhíjiē chuándì yǔjù	Pass-through statement	
直接传输恢复	Zhíjiē chuánshū huīfù	Direct transmission restoration	
直接传输应用部分	Zhíjiē chuánshū yìngyòng bùfen	Direct transmission application part	DTAP
直接存储器存取	Zhíjiē cúnchǔqì cúnqǔ	Direct memory access	DMA
直接存储器存取传送	Zhíjiē cúnchǔqì cúnqǔ chuánsòng	Direct memory access transfer	DMAT
直接存储器存取请求	Zhíjiē cúnchǔqì cúnqǔ qǐngqiú	Direct memory access request	DMAR
直接存储器存取通道	Zhíjiē cúnchǔqì cúnqǔ tōngdào	Direct memory access channel	DMAC
直接存储器地址	Zhíjiē cúnchǔqì dìzhǐ	Direct memory address	DMA
直接存取	Zhíjiē cúnqǔ	Direct access (to memory)	
直接存取存储器	Zhíjiē cúnqǔ cúnchǔqì	Direct access storage	
直接存取法	Zhíjiē cúnqǔ fǎ	Direct access method	DAM
直接存取数据通道	Zhíjiē cúnqǔ shùjù tōngdào	Direct access data channel	DADC
直接存取通信信道	Zhíjiē cúnqǔ tōngxìn xìndào	Direct access communication channel	DACC
直接存取文件	Zhíjiē cúnqǔ wénjiàn	Direct access file	
直接电话系统	Zhíjiē diànhuà xìtǒng	Direct dialing telephone system	DDTS
直接电缆连接	Zhíjiē diànlǎn liánjiē	Direct cable connect	DCC
直接定位	Zhíjiē dìngwèi	Explicit position	
直接定址法	Zhíjiē dìngzhǐ fǎ	Immediately allocating method	
直接地址	Zhíjiē dìzhǐ	Direct address	
直接对外拨号	Zhíjiē duìwài bōhào	Direct dialing overseas	DDO
直接对象	Zhíjiē duìxiàng	Direct object	
直接分配	Zhíjiē fēnpèi	Direct distribution	

直接广播卫星	Zhíjiē guǎngbō wèixīng	Direct broadcast satellite	DBS
直接挂网的存储器	Zhíjiē guàwǎngde cúnchǔqì	Network-attached storage	NAS
直接后继	Zhíjiē hòujì	Immediate successor	
直接呼叫	Zhíjiē hūjiào	Direct call	
直接基类	Zhíjiē jī lèi	Immediate base	
直接检测	Zhíjiē jiǎncè	Direct detection	
直接接触	Zhíjiē jiēchù	Direct contact	
直接接触防护	Zhíjiē jiēchù fánghù	Protection against direct contact	
直接接入	Zhíjiē jiērù	Direct access	
直接接入连接单元	Zhíjiē jiērù liánjiē dānyuán	Direct access connection element	
直接接收	Zhíjiē jiēshōu	Direct reception (US); straight reception (UK)	
直接接收者	Zhíjiē jiēshōuzhě	Immediate recipient	
直接可视数据	Zhíjiē kěshì shùjù	What you see is what you get	WYSIWYG
直接控制	Zhíjiē kòngzhì	Direct control	
直接扩频	Zhíjiē kuòpín	Direct spread spectrum	DS
直接扩频的码分多址	Zhíjiē kuòpínde mǎfēn duōzhǐ	Direct frequency spread spectrum code division multiple access	DF-SS-CDMA
直接连接	Zhíjiē liánjiē	Direct connect	
直接脉码调制	Zhíjiē màimǎ tiáozhì	Straight pulse-code modulation	SPCM
直接埋设	Zhíjiē máishè	Direct burial	DB
直接模拟存储技术	Zhíjiē mónǐ cúnchǔ jìshù	Direct analog storage technology	DAST
直接模式	Zhíjiē móshì	Immediate mode	
直接内存存取	Zhíjiē nèicún cúnqǔ	Direct memory access	DMA
直接内存访问	Zhíjiē nèicún fǎngwèn	Direct memory access	DMA
直接内存执行	Zhíjiē nèicún zhíxíng	Direct memory execute	DME
直接耦合放大器	Zhíjiē ǒuhé fàngdàqì	Direct-coupled amplifier	
直接派生类	Zhíjiē pàishēng lèi	Immediate derived	
直接评价法	Zhíjiē píngjià fǎ	Direct evaluation method	
直接强度调制	Zhíjiē qiángdù tiáozhì	Intensity modulation-direction modulation	IM-DM
直接前趋	Zhíjiē qiánqū	Immediate predecessor	
直接 RAMbus 内存	Zhíjiē Rambus nèicún	Direct RAMbus DRAM	DRDRAM
直接熔融法	Zhíjiē róngróng fǎ	Direct melt method (fiber optic mfg)	DM
直接上级	Zhíjiē shàngjí	Immediate superior	
直接时序扩展频谱	Zhíjiē shíxù kuòzhǎn pínpǔ	Direct sequence spread spectrum	DSSS
直接数字控制	Zhíjiē shùzì kòngzhì	Direct digital control	DDC
直接数字控制器	Zhíjiē shùzì kòngzhìqì	Direct digital controller	DDC
直接数字频率合成器	Zhíjiē shùzì pínlǜ héchéngqì	Direct digital (frequency) synthesizer	DDS
直接数字输入	Zhíjiē shùzì shūrù	Direct digital input	
直接数字信号流	Zhíjiē shùzì xìnhào liú	Direct stream digital	DSD
直接数字式频率合成器	Zhíjiē shùzìshì pínlǜ héchéngqì	Direct digital synthesizer	DDS
直接宿主	Zhíjiē sùzhǔ	Direct hosting	
直接探头进样	Zhíjiē tàntóu jìnyàng	Direct probe inlet	
直接调频	Zhíjiē tiáopín	Direct frequency modulation	DFM
直接提交	Zhíjiē tíjiāo	Direct submission	
直接同步协议	Zhíjiē tóngbù xiéyì	Direct synchronization (in CORBA)	DS
直接通话拨号	Zhíjiē tōnghuà bōhào	Direct distance dialing	DDD
直接位置	Zhíjiē wèizhì	Direct position	

直接相邻信道干扰	Zhíjiē xiānglín xìndào gānrǎo	Direct adjacent channel interference	DACI
直接响应模式	Zhíjiē xiǎngyìng móshì	Direct response mode	
直接序列扩频	Zhíjiē xùliè kuòpín	Direct sequence spread spectrum	DSSS
直接序列扩频码分多址接入	Zhíjiē xùliè kuòpín mǎfēn duōzhǐ jiērù	Direct sequence spread spectrum code division multiple access	DS-SS-CDMA
直接序列扩频调制	Zhíjiē xùliè kuòpín tiáozhì	Direct sequence spread spectrum modulation	
直接序列码分多址	Zhíjiē xùliè mǎfēn duōzhǐ	Direct sequence code division multiple access	DS-CDMA
直接序列展频技术	Zhíjiē xùliè zhǎnpín jìshù	Direct sequence spread spectrum	DSSS
直接因特网消息封装	Zhíjiē Yīntèwǎng xiāoxi fēngzhuāng	Direct Internet message encapsulation	DIME
直接用户	Zhíjiē yònghù	Direct user	
直接至家庭	Zhíjiē zhì jiātíng	Direct to home	DTH
直接中继方式	Zhíjiē zhōngjì fāngshì	Direct inward dialing	DID
直接中频数字化接收机	Zhíjiē zhōngpín shùzìhuà jiēshōujī	Direct intermediate frequency (IF) sampling receiver (for GSM/EDGE base station system)	
直接转换应用部分	Zhíjiē zhuǎnhuàn yìngyòng bùfen	Direct transfer application part	DTAP
直接注入燃烧器	Zhíjiē zhùrù ránshāoqì	Direct injection burner	
直接型 RambusRAM	Zhíjiē-xíng Rambus RAM	Rambus direct random access memory	RDRAM
指积分	Zhǐjīfēn	Convolution integral	
直径比	Zhíjìng bǐ	Diameter ratio	
知觉话音质量度量	Zhījué huàyīn zhìliàng dùliàng	Perceptual speech quality measure	PSQM
知觉语言质量度量	Zhījué yǔyán zhìliàng dùliàng	Perceptual speech quality measure	PSQM
直扩码分多址	Zhíkuò mǎfēn duōzhǐ	Direct-sequence code division multiple access	DS-CDMA
致冷参量放大器	Zhìlěng cānliàng fàngdàqì	Cooled parametric amplifier	
致冷电流	Zhìlěng diànliú	Cooling current	
直联信令方式	Zhílián xìnlìng fāngshì	Associated signaling	
质量	Zhìliàng	Mass	
质量	Zhìliàng	Quality	
质量保证	Zhìliàng bǎozhèng	Quality assurance	QA
质量测试	Zhìliàng cèshì	Quality test	
质量等级	Zhìliàng děngjí	Quality level	QL
质量等级下限	Zhìliàng děngjí xiàxiàn	Quality minimum	
质量功能配置	Zhìliàng gōngnéng pèizhì	Quality function deployment	QFD
质量管理	Zhìliàng guǎnlǐ	Quality management	
质量监督	Zhìliàng jiāndū	Quality monitoring	
质量控制	Zhìliàng kòngzhì	Quality control	QC
质量流量	Zhìliàng liúliàng	Mass flow-rate	
质量模式	Zhìliàng móshì	Quality schema	
质量输送	Zhìliàng shūsòng	Mass transport	
质量因子	Zhìliàng yīnzǐ	Quality factor	
直列制表	Zhíliè zhìbiǎo	Vertical tabulation	VT
指令	Zhǐlìng	Command, instruction	
指令存储单元	Zhǐlìng cúnchǔ dānyuán	Instruction cache	
指令存储器	Zhǐlìng cúnchǔqì	Instruction storage unit	ISU
指令地址 A 寄存器	Zhǐlìng dìzhǐ A jìcúnqì	Instruction address A-register	IAA
指令地址字	Zhǐlìng dìzhǐ zì	Command address word	CAW
指令发送	Zhǐlìng fāsòng	Instruction issue	
指令分类	Zhǐlìng fēnlèi	Instruction coloring	

指令缓存	Zhǐlìng huǎncún	Instructions cache	
指令集处理机语言	Zhǐlìng jí chǔlǐjī yǔyán	Instruction set processor language	ISPL
指令集架构	Zhǐlìng jí jiàgòu	Instruction set architecture	ISA
指令寄存器	Zhǐlìng jìcúnqì	Function register	FR
指令计数器	Zhǐlìng jìshùqì	Location counter	
指令控制单元	Zhǐlìng kòngzhì dānyuán	Instruction control unit	ICU
指令引退	Zhǐlìng yǐntuì	Retirement	
指令与数据发射系统	Zhǐlìng yǔ shùjù fāshè xìtǒng	Command and data transmission system	CDTS
指令/时钟周期	Zhǐlìng/sízhōng zhōuqī	Instructions per clock cycle	IPC
直流	Zhíliú	Direct current	DC
直流传输	Zhíliú chuánshū	Direct current transmission	
直流电阻	Zhíliú diànzǔ	Direct current resistance	
直流放大器	Zhíliú fàngdàqì	Direct current amplifier	
直流进样器	Zhíliú jìnyàngqì	Direct injector	
直流谐振充电	Zhíliú xiézhèn chōngdiàn	Direct current resonant charging	
直流谐振二极管充电	Zhíliú xiézhèn èrjíguǎn chōngdiàn	Direct current resonant diode charge	
直流信令	Zhíliú xìnlìng	Direct current signaling	
支路	Zhīlù	Tributary (SDH term)	TR
支路单元	Zhīlù dānyuán	Tributary unit	TU
支路单元复帧丢失	Zhīlù dānyuán fù zhèng diūshī	Tributary unit-loss of multi-frame	TU-LOM
支路单元告警指示信号	Zhīlù dānyuán gàojǐng zhǐshì xìnhào	Tributary unit alarm indication signal	TU-AIS
支路单元指针	Zhīlù dānyuán zhǐzhēn	Tributary unit pointer	TU PTR
支路单元指针	Zhīlù dānyuán zhǐzhēn	Tributary unit pointer	TUP
支路单元指针丢失	Zhīlù dānyuán zhǐzhēn diūshī	Tributary unit loss of pointer	TU-LOP
支路单元组	Zhīlù dānyuán zǔ	Tributary unit group	TUG
支路单元/管理单元	Zhīlù dānyuán/guǎnlǐ dānyuán	Tributary unit/administrative unit	TU/AU
支路净荷处理	Zhīlù jìnghé chǔlǐ	Tributary unit payload processing	TUPP
置乱	Zhìluàn	Scramble	
直埋缆	Zhímái lǎn	Direct buried cable	
直埋式光缆	Zhímái-shì guānglǎn	Direct buried fiber optic cable	
直埋式光缆	Zhímái-shì guānglǎn	Buried service lightguide (cable)	BSL
置忙	Zhìmáng	Set (verb, in switching)	
指明	Zhǐmíng	Designate (verb)	
职能	Zhínéng	Accountability	
止能	Zhǐnéng	Disable	
智能本地搜索算法	Zhìnéng běndì sōusuǒ suànfǎ	Intelligent local search algorithm	ILSA
智能代理	Zhìnéng dàilǐ	Intelligent agent	
智能大楼	Zhìnéng dàlóu	Intelligent building	ZNL
智能大楼布线系统	Zhìnéng dàlóu bùxiàn xìtǒng	Intelligent building system	IBS
智能大厦	Zhìnéng dàshà	Intelligent building	IB
智能打印机数据流	Zhìnéng dǎyìnjī shùjùliú	Intelligent printer data stream (IBM use)	IPDS
智能多业务光传送平台	Zhìnéng duō yèwù guāng chuánsòng píngtái	Intelligent multi-service transport platform	IMTP
智能分层覆盖	Zhìnéng fēncéng fùgài	Intelligent underlay overlay	IUO
智能工作台	Zhìnéng gōngzuòtái	Intelligent workstation	IWS
智能工作站	Zhìnéng gōngzuòzhàn	Intelligent workstation	IWS
智能光交换	Zhìnéng guāng jiāohuàn	Intelligent optical switching	IOS

智能光网络	Zhìnéng guāng wǎngluò	Intelligent optical network	OIN
智能过滤	Zhìnéng guòlǜ	Smart filter	
智能终端	Zhìnéng hōngduān	Intelligent terminal	
智能建筑	Zhìnéng jiànzhù	Intelligent building	IB
智能建筑管理系统	Zhìnéng jiànzhù guǎnlǐ xìtǒng	Intelligent building management system	IBMS
智能家园	Zhìnéng jiāyuán	Smart home	
智能接入功能	Zhìnéng jiērù gōngnéng	Intelligent access function	IAF
智能决策支持系统	Zhìnéng juécè zhīchí xìtǒng	Intelligent decision support system	IDSS
智能卡	Zhìnéng kǎ	Smart card	
智能卡读取器	Zhìnéng kǎ dúqǔqì	Smart card reader	
智能控制	Zhìnéng kòngzhì	Intelligent control	
智能排队系统	Zhìnéng páiduì xìtǒng	Intelligent queuing system	
智能驱动电子仪器	Zhìnéng qūdòng diànzǐyíqì	Intelligent drive electronics	IDE
智能时分多路复用器	Zhìnéng shífèn duōlù fùyòngqì	Intelligent time division multiplexer	ITDM
智能双层网	Zhìnéng shuāngcéng wǎng	Intelligent underlay-overlay (network)	IUO
智能天线	Zhìnéng tiānxiàn	Smart antenna	SA
智能跳频	Zhìnéng tiàopín	Intelligent frequency hopping	
智能铁路系统	Zhìnéng tiělù xìtǒng	Intelligent railway system	IRS
智能外设	Zhìnéng wàishè	Intelligent peripheral	IP
智能外设接口	Zhìnéng wàishè jiēkǒu	Intelligent peripheral interface	IPI
智能外围设备	Zhìnéng wàiwéi shèbèi	Intelligent peripheral	IP
智能外围站	Zhìnéng wàiwéizhàn	Intelligent out station	IOS
智能网	Zhìnéng wǎng	Intelligent network	IN
智能网业务节点	Zhìnéng wǎng yèwù jiédiǎn	Intelligent network service node	
职能网应用部分	Zhínéng wǎng yìngyòng bùfen	Intelligent network application part	INAP
职能网应用规程	Zhínéng wǎng yìngyòng guīchéng	Intelligent network application procedure	INAP
职能网应用协议	Zhínéng wǎng yìngyòng xiéyì	Intelligent network application protocol	INAP
智能网络	Zhìnéng wǎngluò	Intelligent network	IN
智能文档处理	Zhìnéng wéndàng chǔlǐ	Intelligent document processing	
智能用户电报	Zhìnéng yònghù diànbào	Teletex	TTX
智能用户电报基本控制功能总表	Zhìnéng yònghù diànbào jīběn kòngzhì gōngnéng zǒngbiǎo	Teletex basic control function repertoire	
智能用户电报基本图形字符总表	Zhìnéng yònghù diànbào jīběn túxíng zìfú zǒngbiǎo	Teletex basic graphic character repertoire	
智能用户电报控制功能总表	Zhìnéng yònghù diànbào kòngzhì gōngnéng zǒngbiǎo	Teletex control function repertoire	
智能用户电报设备	Zhìnéng yònghù diànbào shèbèi	Teletex equipment	
智能用户电报图形字符总表	Zhìnéng yònghù diànbào túxíng zìfú zǒngbiǎo	Teletex graphic character repertoire	
智能用户电报文件	Zhìnéng yònghù diànbào wénjiàn	Teletex document	
智能用户电报字符总表	Zhìnéng yònghù diànbào zìfú zǒngbiǎo	Teletex character repertoire	
智能运输系统	Zhìnéng yùnshū xìtǒng	Intelligent transportation system	ITS
智能栅格	Zhìnéng zhàgé	Intelligent raster	
智能指针	Zhìnéng zhǐzhēn	Smart pointer	
智能化滤波	Zhìnénghuà lǜbō	Intelligent filtering	
智能化内容配送	Zhìnénghuà nèiróng pèisòng	Intelligent content distribution	
智能型分散控制器	Zhìnéng-xíng fēnsàn kòngzhìqì	Distributed control panel - intelligent	DCP-I

指派基线	Zhǐpài jīxiàn	Allocated baseline	
指派路由器	Zhǐpài lùyóuqì	Designated router	DR
直排天线阵	Zhípái tiānxiàn zhèn	Collinear array antenna	CAA
指配	Zhǐpèi	Assignment (of a radio frequency or radio frequency channel	
指配变量	Zhǐpèi biànliàng	Provision variant	
指配故障	Zhǐpèi gùzhàng	Assignment failure	
指配命令	Zhǐpèi mìnglìng	Assignment command	
指配频带	Zhǐpèi píndài	Assigned frequency band	
指配频率	Zhǐpèi pínlǜ	Assigned frequency	
指配请求	Zhǐpèi qǐngqiú	Assignment request	
指配完成	Zhǐpèi wánchéng	Assignment complete	
指配信道	Zhǐpèi xìndào	Assigned channel	
指示	Zhǐshì	Indication, indicator	
知识表示	Zhīshi biǎoshì	Knowledge expression	
指示比特	Zhǐshì bìtè	Indicator bit	IB
知识查询管理语言	Zhīshi cháxún guǎnlǐ yǔyán	Knowledge query management language	KQML
指示灯盘	Zhǐshì dēngpán	Indicator lamp panel	
知识发现	Zhīshi fāxiàn	Knowledge discovery	
指示符	Zhǐshì fú	Directive (in programming)	
知识工程师	Zhīshi gōngchéngshī	Knowledge engineer	
知识获取	Zhīshi huòqǔ	Knowledge acquisition	
直视棱镜	Zhíshì léngjìng	Direct vision prism	
制式无线电台	Zhìshì wúxiàndiàntái	Compulsory fitted radio station	
知识系统	Zhīshi xìtǒng	Knowledge-based system	
知识约简	Zhīshi yuējiǎn	Knowledge reduction	
知识库	Zhīshikù	Knowledge base	
知识库	Zhīshikù	Repository	
知识库对象	Zhīshikù duìxiàng	Repository object	
知识库结构化查询语言架构	Zhīshikù jiégòuhuà cháxún yǔyán jiàgòu	Repository structured query language (SQL) schema	
知识库类型信息模型	Zhīshikù lèixíng xìnxī móxíng	Repository type information model	RTIM
知识库引擎	Zhīshikù yǐnqíng	Repository engine	
指数	Zhǐshù	Exponent	
指数分布	Zhǐshù fēnbù	Exponential distribution	
指数分布随机变量	Zhǐshù fēnbù suíjī biànliàng	Exponential random variable	
指数式传输线	Zhǐshùshì chuánshū xiàn	Exponential transmission line	
直通超群连接点	Zhítōng chāoqún liánjiē diǎn	Through-supergroup connection point	
直通超群组连接点	Zhítōng chāoqún zǔ liánjiē diǎn	Through-supergroup assembly connection point	
直通超主群连接点	Zhítōng chāozhǔqún liánjiē diǎn	Through-supermastergroup connection point	
直通法兰	Zhítōng fǎlán	Through flange	
直通交叉连接	Zhítōng jiāochā liánjiē	Straight-through cross-connection	
直同连接延时	Zhítóng liánjiē yánshí	Through-connection delay	
直通络连接点	Zhítōng luò liánjiē diǎn	Through-group connection point	
直通转发	Zhítōng zhuǎnfā	Cut-through	
直通主群连接点	Zhítōng zhǔqún liánjiē diǎn	Through-mastergroup connection point	
直通式光纤连接器	Zhítōng-shì guāngxiān liánjiēqì	Straight tip (optical fiber connector)	ST

制图符号	Zhìtú fúhào	Cartographic symbol	
制图数据	Zhìtú shùjù	Cartographic data	
制图专家系统	Zhìtú zhuānjiā xìtǒng	Cartographic expert system	
制图综合	Zhìtú zōnghé	Cartographic generalization	
置位	Zhìwèi	Set (in switching)	
指纹	Zhǐwén	Fingerprint	
置闲	Zhìxián	Reset	
支线	Zhīxiàn	Branch feeder	
直线检测	Zhíxiàn jiǎncè	Line detection	
直线阵	Zhíxiàn zhèn	Linear array (antenna)	
指向点	Zhǐxiàng diǎn	Pointer	
指向角	Zhǐxiàng jiǎo	Angle of spread	
指向精度	Zhǐxiàng jīngdù	Station-keeping (of a satellite)	
指向累计检测器	Zhǐxiàng lěijì jiǎncèqì	Integration detector	
指向性	Zhǐxiàng-xìng	Directional	
指向性响应特性	Zhǐxiàng-xìng xiǎngyìng tèxìng	Directional response characteristics	DRC
直线台定位设备	Zhíxiàntái dìngwèi shèbèi	Linear stage positioning equipment	
质心	Zhìxīn	Centroid	
置信度	Zhìxìndù	Confidence	
执行	Zhíxíng	Execute	E
执行	Zhíxíng	Run	
执行 A3 和 A8 功能的一个单一算法	Zhíxíng A3 hé A8 gōngnéngde yīgè dānyī suànfǎ	A single algorithm performing the functions of A3 and A8	A38
执行档	Zhíxíng dàng	Executable file	.exe
执行董事	Zhíxíng dǒngshì	Executive director	
执行额外信息	Zhíxíng éwài xìnxī	Implementation extra information	IXIT
执行方 CMISE 服务用户	Zhíxíng fāng CMISE fúwù yònghù	Performing CMISE-service-user	
执行缓冲区	Zhíxíng huǎnchōngqū	Execute buffers	
执行机构	Zhíxíng jīgòu	Actuator	
执行期	Zhíxíng qī	Runtime	
执行时	Zhíxíng shí	Runtime	
执行态	Zhíxíng tài	Execution state (IPsec)	
执行元件	Zhíxíng yuánjiàn	Actuator (driving) element	
执行周期	Zhíxíng zhōuqī	Execution cycle	
执行器	Zhíxíngqì	Actuator	
质询握手验证协议	Zhìxún wòshǒu yànzhèng xiéyì	Challenge handshake authentication protocol	CHAP
指引	Zhǐyǐn	Direction	
支援通信站	Zhīyuán tōngxìn zhàn	Support communication post	SCP
制约最短路径优选	Zhìyuē zuìduǎn lùjìng yōuxuǎn	Constrained shortest path first	CSPF
制造故障	Zhìzào gùzhàng	Manufacturing fault	
制造失效	Zhìzào shīxiào	Manufacturing failure	
制造自动化协议	Zhìzào zìdònghuà xiéyì	Manufacturing automation protocol	MAP
制造资源规划系统	Zhìzào zīyuán guīhuà xìtǒng	Manufacturing resource planning	MRP
制造资源计划	Zhìzào zīyuán jìhuà	Manufacturing resource planning	MRP
指针	Zhǐzhēn	Pointer	PTR
指针处理	Zhǐzhēn chǔlǐ	Pointer processing (SDH term)	

指针处理器	Zhǐzhēn chǔlǐqì	Pointer processor (SDH)	
指针丢失	Zhǐzhēn diūshī	Loss of pointer	LOP
制振对策	Zhìzhèn duìcè	Vibration (suppression) methods	
指针调整记数	Zhǐzhēn tiáozhěng jìshù	Pointer justification count	PJC
指针调整事件	Zhǐzhēn tiáozhěng shìjiàn	Pointer justification event	PJE
指针同步	Zhǐzhēn tóngbù	Pointer synchronization	
指针域	Zhǐzhēn yù	Pointer field (in software)	
直正声	Zhízheng shēng	Direct sound	
纸质地图	Zhǐzhì dìtú	Paper map	
质子交换	Zhìzǐ jiāohuàn	Proton exchange	PE
中尺变分析	Zhōng chǐbiàn fēnxī	Meso-analysis	
中地球轨道	Zhōng dìqiú guǐdào	Medium earth orbit	MEO
终地形	Zhōng dìxíng	Ultimate form	
中高空通信卫星	Zhōng gāokōng tōngxìn wèixīng	Intermediate altitude communication satellite	IACS
中高空通信卫星	Zhōng gāokōng tōngxìn wèixīng	Medium altitude communication satellite	MACS
中规模集成电路	Zhōng guīmó jíchéng diànlù	Medium-scale integrated circuit	MSI
中括号	Zhōng kuòhào	Bracket (square bracket) [ ]	
中密集聚乙烯	Zhōng mìjí jùyǐxī	Medium density polyethylene	MDPE
中速率	Zhōng sùlǜ	Intermediate data rate	IDR
中速率数据	Zhōng sùlǜ shùjù	Medium rate data	DM
中西文终端	Zhōng/xī wén zhōngduān	Chinese/English terminal	
中波传输	Zhōngbō chuánshū	Medium wave propagation	
仲裁	Zhòngcái	Arbitration	
仲裁环路	Zhòngcái huánlù	Arbitrated loop	
中档路由器	Zhōngdàng lùyóuqì	Modular router	
中等数据率	Zhōngděng shùjù lǜ	Intermediate data rate (between 64kbps and 44.763Mbps)	IDR
终点	Zhōngdiǎn	Destination	
终点	Zhōngdiǎn	End point	
终点端点标志	Zhōngdiǎn duāndiǎn biāozhì	Terminal endpoint identifier	TEI
终点码	Zhōngdiǎn mǎ	End node	
终点目标	Zhōngdiǎn mùbiāo	Destination object	
终点网络	Zhōngdiǎn wǎngluò	Destination network	DN
中断	Zhōngduàn	Interrupt (computer term)	
终端	Zhōngduān	Terminal	
终端标志	Zhōngduān biāozhì	Terminal token	
终端标识	Zhōngduān biāozhì	Terminal endpoint identifier	Tei
终端标识	Zhōngduān biāozhì	Terminal identification	TID
终端标识符	Zhōngduān biāozhìfú	Terminal identifier	
终端别名	Zhōngduān biémíng	Terminal alias	
终端不平衡电压	Zhōngduān bùpínghéng diànyā	Asymmetrical terminal voltage	
终端 CAMEL 签约信息	Zhōngduān CAMEL qiānyuē xìnxī	Terminating camel subscription information	T-CSI
终端操作方式	Zhōngduān cāozuò fāngshì	Terminal operating mode	
终端长途电话局	Zhōngduān chángtú diànhuàjú	Terminating toll center	TTC
中断持续时间	Zhōngduàn chíxù shíjiān	Interruption duration	
中断处理	Zhōngduàn chùlǐ	Interrupt processing or handling	
终端电子邮寄	Zhōngduān diànzǐ yóujì	Terminal based electronic mail	TBEM

终端地址寄存器	Zhōngduān dìzhǐ jìcúnqì	Terminal address register	TAR
终端端点标志	Zhōngduān duāndiǎn biāozhì	Terminal end point identifier	TEI
终端端点标识符	Zhōngduān duāndiǎn biāozhìfú	Terminal end point identifier	TEPI
终端多路复用器	Zhōngduān duōlù fùyòngqì	Terminal multiplexer	TM
终端访问控制器	Zhōngduān fǎngwèn kòngzhìqì	Terminal access controller	TAC
终端访问控制器访问控制系统	Zhōngduān fǎngwèn kòngzhìqì fǎngwèn kòngzhì xìtǒng	Terminal access controller access control system (Cisco protocol)	TACACS
终端仿真协议	Zhōngduān fǎngzhēn xiéyì	Terminal emulation protocol	
终端仿真器	Zhōngduān fǎngzhēnqì	Terminal emulator	
中断服务程序	Zhōngduàn fúwù chéngxù	Interrupt service routine	ISR
终端复用	Zhōngduān fùyòng	Terminal multiplexing	TM
终端复用器	Zhōngduān fùyòngqì	Terminal multiplexer	TM
终端工作组	Zhōngduān gōngzuòzǔ	Terminal Working Group (GSM MoU)	TWG
终端国际中心	Zhōngduān guójì zhōngxīn	Terminal international center	TIC
终端国内段	Zhōngduān guónèi duàn	Terminal national section	
终端国内中心	Zhōngduān guónèi zhōngxīn	Terminal national center	TNC
中断盒	Zhōngduàn hé	Breakout box	
中断级	Zhōngduàn jí	Interrupt level (computer term)	
中断级状态表	Zhōngduàn jí zhuàngtài biǎo	Interrupt level status table	ILST
中断间隔时间	Zhōngduàn jiàngé shíjiān	Time between interruptions	
终端结点	Zhōngduān jiédiǎn	Terminal node	
终端可携带性	Zhōngduān kěxiédà xìng	Terminal portability	TP
中断控制寄存器	Zhōngduàn kòngzhì jìcúnqì	Interrupt control register	INCR
中断控制器	Zhōngduàn kòngzhìqì	Interrupt control unit	ICU
终端控制器	Zhōngduān kòngzhìqì	Remote control unit	RCU
终端块	Zhōngduān kuài	Terminal block	
终端连接点	Zhōngduān liánjiē diǎn	Termination connection point	TCP
中断描述符表基地址	Zhōngduàn miáoshùfú biǎo jī dìzhǐ	Interrupt descriptor table base address	IDT Base Address
终端能力集	Zhōngduān nénglì jí	Terminal capacity set	TCS
终端能力集拒绝	Zhōngduān nénglì jí jùjué	Terminal capacity set reject	TCSR
终端能力集确认	Zhōngduān nénglì jí quèrèn	Terminal capacity set acknowledge	TCSA
终端 O/R 地址	Zhōngduān O/R dìzhǐ	Terminal O/R address	
终端配置设备	Zhōngduān pèizhì shèbèi	Terminal configuration facilities	TCF
中断屏弊寄存器	Zhōngduàn píngbì jìcúnqì	Interrupt mask register	IMR
终端平衡电压	Zhōngduān pínghéng diànyā	Symmetrical terminal voltage	
终端平衡回波损耗	Zhōngduān pínghéng huíbō sǔnhào	Terminal balance return loss	TBRL
终端平衡回损	Zhōngduān pínghéng huísǔn	Terminal balanced return loss	TBRL
中断启动	Zhōngduàn qǐdòng	Interrupt enable	INTE
终端启动通信测试	Zhōngduān qǐdòng tōngxìn cèshì	Terminal activated channel test	TACT
中断请求	Zhōngduàn qǐngqiú	Interrupt request	IRQ
中断请求向量	Zhōngduàn qǐngqiú xiàngliàng	Interrupt request vector	IRV
终端设备	Zhōngduān shèbèi	Terminal equipment	TE
终端设备提示信号	Zhōngduān shèbèi tíshì xìnhào	Customer premises equipment alert signal	CAS
终端设备/用户驻地网	Zhōngduān shèbèi/yònghù zhùdì wǎng	Terminal equipment/customer premises network	TE/CPN
终端识别符	Zhōngduān shíbiéfú	Terminal identifier	
终端适配	Zhōngduān shìpèi	Terminal adaptation	TA

终端适配功能	Zhōngduān shìpèi gōngnéng	Terminal adapter function	TAF
终端适配功能	Zhōngduān shìpèi gōngnéng	Terminal adaptation function	TAF
终端适配设备	Zhōngduān shìpèi shèbèi	Terminal adapter equipment	TAE
终端适配器	Zhōngduān shìpèiqì	Terminal adapter	TA
中断通道控制块	Zhōngduàn tōngdào kòngzhì kuài	Interrupt channel control block	INTCCB
终端透明度	Zhōngduān tòumíngdù	Terminal transparency	
终端网络	Zhōngduān wǎngluò	Terminating network	
终端无线电台	Zhōngduān wúxiàndiàntái	Terminal radio station	RST
中断信号	Zhōngduàn xìnhào	Interrupt signal	
终端信息字段大小	Zhōngduān xìnxī zìduàn dàxiǎo	Information field sizes for the terminal	IFST
终端系统	Zhōngduān xìtǒng	End system	ES
终端系统到中间系统	Zhōngduān xìtǒng dào zhōngjiān xìtǒng	End system-to-intermediate system	ES-IS
终端系统对中间系统路由选择交换协议	Zhōngduān xìtǒng duì zhōngjiān xìtǒng lùyóu xuǎnzé jiāohuàn xiéyì	End system to intermediate system routing exchange protocol	ES-IS
终端系统和中间系统路由交换协议	Zhōngduān xìtǒng hé zhōngjiān xìtǒng lùyóu jiāohuàn xiéyì	End system to intermediate system routing exchange protocol	ES-IS
终端业务	Zhōngduān yèwù	Teleservice	
终端移动无线局	Zhōngduān yídòng wúxiànjú	Terminal mobile services switching center	
终端移动性	Zhōngduān yídòngxìng	Terminal mobility	
终端用户	Zhōngduān yònghù	End user	
终端站	Zhōngduān zhàn	Terminal station	TS
中断状态字	Zhōngduàn zhuàngtài zì	Interrupt status word	ISW
终端机	Zhōngduānjī	Terminal machine (telecom term)	ZD
中断器开关选择器	Zhōngduànqì kāiguān xuǎnzéqì	Switching select repeater	SSR
中轨	Zhōngguǐ	Medium earth orbit	MEO
中国电波传播研究所	Zhōngguó diànbō chuánbō yánjiūsuǒ	China Research Institute of Radio Wave Propagation	
中国电信认证中心	Zhōngguó diànxìn rènzhèng zhōngxīn	China Telecommunications Certificate Authority	CTCA
中国电子技术进出口公司	Zhōngguó diànzǐ jìshù jìnchūkǒu gōngsī	China Electronics Import and Export Corp.	CEIEC
中国东方通信卫星有限责任公司	Zhōngguó Dōngfāng tōngxìn wèixīng yǒuxiàn zérèn gōngsī	China Orient Telecommunications Satellite Company, Ltd.	
中国高速信息示范网	Zhōngguó gāosù xìnxī shìfàn wǎng	China Advanced Info-optical Network	CAINONET
中国工程技术信息网	Zhōngguó gōngchéng jìshù xìnxīwǎng	China Engineering and Technology Information Network	CNTIN
中国公用分组交换数据网	Zhōngguó gōngyòng fēnzǔ jiāohuàn shùjù wǎng	China Packet Switched Data Network	ChinaPAC
中国公用数字数据网	Zhōngguó gōngyòng shùzì shùjù wǎng	China Digital Data Network	ChinaDDN
中国国家标准局	Zhōngguó Guójiā Biāozhǔnjú	China State Bureau of Standards	CSBS
中国国家金融网络	Zhōngguó guójiā jīnróng wǎngluò	China National Financial Network	CNFN
中国国家网络信息中心	Zhōngguó guójiā wǎngluò xìnxī zhōngxīn	China National Network Information Center	CNNIC
中国国家现代支付系统	Zhōngguó guójiā xiàndài zhīfù xìtǒng	China National Advanced Payment System	CNAPS
中国国家现代化支持系统	Zhōngguó guójiā xiàndàihuà zhīchí xìtǒng	Chinese National Advanced Payment System	CNAPS
中国惠普有限公司	Zhōngguó Huìpǔ yǒuxiàn gōngsī	China Hewlett-Packard Co. Ltd.	
中国教育和科研网	Zhōngguó jiàoyù hé kēyán wǎng	China Education and Research Network	CERnet
中国金桥信息网络	Zhōngguó jīnqiáo xìnxī wǎnglùo	China Golden Bridge Network	ChinaGBN
中国金融认证中心	Zhōngguó jīnróng rènzhèng zhōngxīn	China Financial Certification Authority	CFCA
中国科技网	Zhōngguó kējì wǎng	China Science and Technology Network	CSTnet

中国科学院	Zhōngguó Kēxuéyuàn	Chinese Academy of Sciences	CAS
中国科学院软件所	Zhōngguó Kēxuéyuàn ruǎnjiàn suǒ	China Academy of Sciences, Institute of Software	CAS IOS
中国普天信息产业集团公司	Zhōngguó pǔtiān xìnxī chǎnyè jítuán gōngsī	China PTIC Information Industry Corp.	
中国软件专业协会	Zhōngguó ruǎnjiàn zhuānyè xiéhuì	Chinese Software Professionals Association	CSPA
中国数字集群标准工作小组	Zhōngguó shùzì jíqún biāozhǔn gōngzuò xiǎozǔ	China Digital Tetra Standards Working Group	CDTSWG
中国铁路信息系统	Zhōngguó tiělù xìnxī xìtǒng	China Railway Information System	CRIS
中国铁路综合信息系统	Zhōngguó tiělù zōnghé xìnxī xìtǒng	China Railway Information System	CRIS
中国通信企业协会	Zhōngguó tōngxìn qǐyè xiéhuì	China Association of Communications Enterprises	CACE
中国通信学会	Zhōngguó tōngxìn xuéhuì	China Institute of Communications	CIC
中国网络通信有限公司	Zhōngguó wǎngluò tōngxìn yǒuxiàn gōngsī	China Network Communications Corp.,	CNC
中国网络信息中心	Zhōngguó wǎngluò xìnxī zhōngxīn	China Network Information Center	CNNIC
中国网通	Zhōngguó wǎngtōng	China Network Communications Corp., China Netcom	CNC
中国网通高速互联网	Zhōngguó wǎngtōng gāosù hùliánwǎng	China Networking Corp. Highspeed Interactive Network	CNCnet
中国网通公司	Zhōngguó wǎngtōng gōngsī	China Networking Corp.	CNC
中国无线通信标准研究组	Zhōngguó wúxiàn tōngxìn biāozhǔn yánjiū zǔ	China Wireless Telecommunication Standards Research Group	CWTS
中国无线通信标准组织	Zhōngguó wúxiàn tōngxìn biāozhǔn zǔzhī	China Wireless Telecommunications Standards Group	CWTS
中国线规	Zhōngguó xiànguī	Chinese Wire Gauge	CWG
中国信息安全产品测评认证中心	Zhōngguó xìnxī ānquán chǎnpǐn cèpíng rènzhèng zhōngxīn	China National Information Technology Security Certification Center	CNITSEC
中国信息产业商会	Zhōngguó xìnxī chǎnyè shānghuì	China Information Industry Trade Association	CIITA
中国信息基础设施	Zhōngguó xìnxī jīchǔ shèshī	China National Information Infrastructure	CNII
中国移动点对点协议	Zhōngguó yídòng diǎn duì diǎn xiéyì	China Mobile Peer to Peer Protocol	CMPP
中国移动互联网	Zhōngguó yídòng hùliánwǎng	China Mobile Net	CMnet
中国移动互联网应用协议特别组	Zhōngguó yídòng hùliánwǎng yìngyòng xiéyì tèbiézǔ	China Mobile Internet Application Protocol special group	CMIS
中国移动通信	Zhōngguó yídòng tōngxìn	China Mobile	CM
中国移动通信网络	Zhōngguó yídòng tōngxìn wǎngluò	China Mobile Network	CMNET
中国邮电工业总公司	Zhōngguó yóudiàn gōngyè zǒnggōngsī	China Post and Telecommunications Industry Corporation	PTIC
中和	Zhōnghé	Neutral, neutralization	
中和元件	Zhōnghé yuánjiàn	Neutrodyne	
中继	Zhōngjì	Trunk; relay	
中继测试单元	Zhōngjì cèshì dānyuán	Trunk test unit	
中继电路	Zhōngjì diànlù	Trunk circuit	
中继段	Zhōngjì duàn	Repeater section	
中继放大器	Zhōngjì fàngdàqì	Trunk amplifier	TA
中继接入-总线	Zhōngjì jiērù—zǒngxiàn	Trunk access – bus	TA-BUS
中继集线器	Zhōngjì jíxiànqì	Trunk concentrator	
中继链路开关	Zhōngjì liànlù kāiguān	Trunk line switch	TLSW
中级配线架	Zhōngjí pèixiànjià	Intermediate distributing frame	IDF
中继网关	Zhōngjì wǎngguān	Trunk gateway	TGW
中继再进入	Zhōngjì zàijìnrù	Re-entrant trunking	
中间标志交换路由器	Zhōngjiān biāozhì jiāohuàn lùyóuqì	Transit label switching router	
中间层	Zhōngjiān céng	Middle tier	
中间件	Zhōngjiān jiàn	Middleware	

中间节点	Zhōngjiān jiédiǎn	Intermediate node	
中间介绍人	Zhōngjiān jièshàorén	Meta introducer	
中间配线架	Zhōngjiān pèixiànjià	Intermediate distribution frame	IDF
中间设备	Zhōngjiān shèbèi	Intermediate equipment	
中间设备	Zhōngjiān shèbèi	Middleware	
中间网络节点	Zhōngjiān wǎngluò jiédiǎn	Intermediate network node	INN
中间协调组	Zhōngjiān xiétiáo zǔ	Interim coordination group	ICG
中间型号批准	Zhōngjiān xínghào pīzhǔn	Interim type approval	ITA
中间系统	Zhōngjiān xìtǒng	Intermediate system	IS
中间系统到中间系统路由交换协议	Zhōngjiān xìtǒng dào zhōngjiān xìtǒng lùyóu jiāohuàn xiéyì	Intermediate system to intermediate system routing exchange protocol	IS-IS
中间系统到中间系统协议	Zhōngjiān xìtǒng dào zhōngjiān xìtǒng xiéyì	Intermediate system to intermediate system protocol (ISO, IETF usage)	IS-IS
中间业务部分	Zhōngjiān yèwù bùfen	Intermediate services part	ISP
中间语言	Zhōngjiān yǔyán	Intermediate language	IL
中间载波	Zhōngjiān zàibō	Intermediate carrier	
中间帧比特	Zhōngjiān zhèng bǐtè	Intermediate frame bit	I
中间字符	Zhōngjiān zìfú	Intermediate character	
中间人攻击	Zhōngjiānrén gōngjī	Man-in-the-middle attack (cryptology term)	
中间商	Zhōngjiānshāng	Middleman (in business)	
终结	Zhōngjié	Finalization	
终结并常驻内存	Zhōngjié bìng chángzhù nèicún	Terminate and stay resident	TSR
终接 CAMEL 签约信息	Zhōngjiē CAMEL qiānyuē xìnxī	T-CAMEL subscription information	T-CSI
终结点	Zhōngjié diǎn	Destination node	
中介分布设备	Zhōngjiè fēnbù shèbèi	Intermediate distribution facility	IDF
中介功能块	Zhōngjiè gōngnéng kuài	Mediation function block	MF
中介会话路由选择	Zhōngjiè huìhuà lùyóu xuǎnzé	Intermediate session routing	ISR
中介交叉联接	Zhōngjiè jiāochā liánjiē	Intermediate cross connect	ICC
终接基本呼叫状态模式	Zhōngjiē jīběn hūjiào zhuàngtài móshì	Terminating basic call state model	T-BCSM
终结节点	Zhōngjié jiédiǎn	Termination node (SDH)	
终结连接点	Zhōngjié liánjiē diǎn	Termination connection point	TCP
中介路由选择节点	Zhōngjiè lùyóu xuǎnzé jiédiǎn	Intermediate routing node	IRN
中介软件	Zhōngjiè ruǎnjiàn	Middleware	
中介设备	Zhōngjiè shèbèi	Mediation device	MD
中介系统	Zhōngjiè xìtǒng	Intermediate system	IS
中介系统到中介系统	Zhōngjiè xìtǒng dào zhōngjiè xìtǒng	Intermediate system-to-intermediate system	IS-IS
中介语言	Zhōngjiè yǔyán	Intermediate language	IL
中介装置	Zhōngjiè zhuāngzhì	Mediation device	MD
终结器	Zhōngjiéqì	Finalizer	
终接器	Zhōngjiēqì	Final selector	
中继器	Zhōngjìqì	Repeater	
中继器	Zhōngjìqì	Relay	
中继器和辅助射频放大器的连续骚扰性能判据	Zhōngjìqì hé fǔzhù shèpín fàngdàqìde liánxù sāorǎo xìngnéng pànjù	Performance criteria for continuous phenomena applied to repeaters and ancillary RF amplifiers	CRptr
中继器和辅助射频放大器的瞬态骚扰性能判据	Zhōngjìqì hé fǔzhù shèpín fàngdàqìde shùntài sāorǎo xìngnéng pànjù	Performance criteria for transient phenomena applied to repeaters and ancillary RF amplifiers	TRptr
中继式无线电	Zhōngjìshì wúxiàndiàn	Trunked radio	TR

中继线	Zhōngjìxiàn	Trunk line	
中继线配线架	Zhōngjìxiàn pèixiànjià	Trunk distribution frame	TDF
中继线全忙	Zhōngjìxiàn quánmáng	All trunks busy	ATB
中继线群	Zhōngjìxiàn qún	Trunk group	
中继线网络	Zhōngjìxiàn wǎngluò	Trunk line network	TLN
中继线无人赠音站	Zhōngjìxiàn wúrén zèngyīn zhàn	Trunk line unmanned re-amplifier	ZW
中继站	Zhōngjìzhàn	Relay station	
中继站	Zhōngjìzhàn	Repeater station	Rep
中馈天线	Zhōngkuì tiānxiàn	Intermediate feed antenna	
种类解析代理	Zhǒnglèi jiěxī dàilǐ	Class parser agent (in Java)	CPA
中立第三方	Zhōnglì dìsānfāng	Trusted third party	TTP
中频	Zhōngpín	Medium frequency	MF
中频	Zhōngpín	Intermediate frequency	IF
中频对消器	Zhōngpín duìxiāoqì	Intermediate frequency canceller	
中频放大器	Zhōngpín fàngdàqì	Intermediate frequency amplifier	
中频放大器增益	Zhōngpín fàngdàqì zēngyì	Intermediate frequency amplifier gain	
中频放大器的中心频率	Zhōngpín fàngdàqìde zhōngxīn pínlǜ	Intermediate frequency amplifier center frequency	
中频干扰	Zhōngpín gānrǎo	Intermediate frequency jamming (interference)	
中频滑环	Zhōngpín huá huán	Medium frequency slip ring	
中频交换矩阵	Zhōngpín jiāohuàn jǔzhèn	Intermediate frequency switching matrix	IF-SM
中频积累	Zhōngpín jīlěi	Intermediate frequency integration	
中频抑制比	Zhōngpín yìzhì bǐ	Intermediate frequency rejection ratio	
中期交换机间的信令协议	Zhōngqī jiāohuànjī jiānde xìnlìng xiéyì	Interim inter-switch signaling protocol	iisp
中期预测	Zhōngqī yùcè	Medium-term prediction	
中枢站	Zhōngshū zhàn	Hub (station)	
钟速	Zhōngsù	Clock cycle/speed	
中卫一号	Zhōngwèi yīhào	ChinaStar-1 (telecommunications satellite)	
中位数	Zhōngwèishù	Median	
中文操作系统	Zhōngwén cāozuò xìtǒng	Chinese Unix Operating system	COSIX
中文视窗	Zhōngwén shìchuāng	Chinese Windows ©	C-Win
中文信息处理系统	Zhōngwén xìnxī chǔlǐ xìtǒng	Chinese Information Processing system	CHIPS
中文与东方语言信息处理学会	Zhōngwén yǔ Dōngfāng yǔyán xìnxī chǔlǐ xuéhuì	Chinese and Oriental Languages Information Processing Society	COLIPS
中文之星	Zhōngwén zhī xīng	Chinese Star; Cstar © (software)	
中文终端	Zhōngwén zhōngduān	Chinese terminal	
中线	Zhōngxiàn	Neutral wire	
中小型企业	Zhōngxiǎoxíng qǐyè	Small and medium-sized enterprises	SME
重心	Zhòngxīn	Center of gravity	
中心	Zhōngxīn	Center	
中心波长	Zhōngxīn bōcháng	Central wavelength	
中心波长容限	Zhōngxīn bōcháng róngxiàn	Central wavelength tolerance	
中心出版者	Zhōngxīn chūbǎnzhě	Central publisher (in SQL Server)	
中心订购者	Zhōngxīn dìnggòuzhě	Central subscriber (in SQL Server)	
中心辐射	Zhōngxīn fúshè	Center radiation	
中心管式	Zhōngxīn guǎn shì	Central tube type (FOC mfg)	
中心管式光纤带光缆	Zhōngxīn guǎn shì guāngxiān dài guānglǎn	Center loose tube optical fiber ribbon cable	

中心交换机	Zhōngxīn jiāohuànjī	Core switch	
中心加强件	Zhōngxīn jiāqiáng jiàn	Central strength member (FOC)	CSM
中心局	Zhōngxīn jú	Central office	CO
中心控制站	Zhōngxīn kòngzhì zhàn	Central control station	CCS
中心流形	Zhōngxīn liúxíng	Center manifold	
中心频率	Zhōngxīn pínlǜ	Central frequency	CF
中心频率偏移	Zhōngxīn pínlǜ piānyí	Central frequency deviation (or offset)	
中心频率容限	Zhōngxīn pínlǜ róngxiàn	Central frequency tolerance	
中心频率信号强度	Zhōngxīn pínlǜ xìnhào qiángdù	Signal strength on center frequency	SS/CF
中心设备识别寄存器	Zhōngxīn shèbèi shíbié jìcúnqì	Central equipment identity register	CEIR
中心射频站	Zhōngxīn shèpínzhàn	Central radio station	CRS
中心束管	Zhōngxīn shùguǎn	Central loose tube (FOC)	
中心束管光缆	Zhōngxīn shùguǎn guānglǎn	Unitube optical cable	
中心束管式光缆	Zhōngxīn shùguǎnshì guānglǎn	Central bundled optical cable	
中心束管式光纤带光缆	Zhōngxīn shùguǎnshì guāngxiān dài guānglǎn	Bundled light optical cable with ribbon fibers	
中心四边形像片	Zhōngxīn sìbiānxíng xiàngpiàn	Quad-centered photograph	
中心削波	Zhōngxīn xiāobō	Center clipping	
重心字符串	Zhòngxīn zìfúchuàn	Center of gravity character string	
中心点	Zhōngxīndiǎn	Center point	
中性导体	Zhōngxìng dǎotǐ	Neutral conductor	
中型服务器	Zhōngxíng fúwùqì	Midrange server	MRS
中型工作站	Zhōngxíng gōngzuòzhàn	Midrange workstation	MRW
中性密度滤光镜	Zhōngxìng mìdù lǜguāngjìng	Neutral density filter (optical)	
中兴通讯	Zhōngxīng tōngxùn	Zhongxing Telecommunications Enterprise (Chinese company)	ZTE
中性线	Zhōngxìng xiàn	Neutral wire	
中性消息语言	Zhōngxìng xiāoxi yǔyán	Neutral message language	NML
中性点非有效接地系统	Zhōngxìngdiǎn fēiyǒuxiào jiēdì xìtǒng	System with non-effectively grounded neutral	
中性点有效接地系统	Zhōngxìngdiǎn yǒuxiào jiēdì xìtǒng	System with effectively grounded neutral	
中心线	Zhōngxīnxiàn	Center line	
中心站	Zhōngxīnzhàn	Central station	CS
中序遍历	Zhōngxù biànlì	In-order traversal	
中央处理单元	Zhōngyāng chǔlǐ dānyuán	Central processor element	
中央处理机	Zhōngyāng chǔlǐjī	Central processor	
中央处理器	Zhōngyāng chǔlǐqì	Central processor unit	CPU
中央处理器占用率	Zhōngyāng chǔlǐqì zhànyòng lǜ	Central processing unit utilization	
中央级管理中心	Zhōngyāng jí guǎnlǐ zhōngxīn	Central-level management center	C-PMS
中央交换子系统	Zhōngyāng jiāohuàn zixìtǒng	Central switching sub-system	CSS
中央交换式集线器	Zhōngyāng jiāohuànshì jíxiànqì	Central switching hub	CSH
中央控制维护子系统	Zhōngyāng kòngzhì wéihù zixìtǒng	Central control maintenance sub-system	CCMS
中央控制器	Zhōngyāng kòngzhìqì	Central controller	
中央控制台	Zhōngyāng kòngzhìtái	Central control post	
中央设备识别寄存器	Zhōngyāng shèbèi shíbié jìcúnqì	Central equipment identity register	CEIR
重要软件	Zhòngyào ruǎnjiàn	Critical software	
重要性系数	Zhòngyàoxìng xìshù	Importance factor	
重载	Zhòngzài	Overload	

重载	Zhòngzài	Override	
重载决议	Zhòngzài juéyì	Overload resolution	
重载的函数	Zhòngzàide hánshù	Overloaded function	
中止	Zhōngzhǐ	Hang up	
终止并驻留内存程序	Zhōngzhǐ bìng zhùliú nèicún chéngxù	Terminate-and-stay-resident program	TSR
终止电压	Zhōngzhǐ diànyā	End voltage	
种植工程	Zhòngzhí gōngchéng	Planting works	
中值滤波器	Zhōngzhí lǜbōqì	Median filter	
终止失效率	Zhōngzhǐ shīxiào lǜ	Wear-out failure rate	
终止字符	Zhōngzhǐ zìfú	Final character	
中轴变换	Zhōngzhóu biànhuàn	Medial-axis transformation	
中转呼叫	Zhōngzhuǎn hūjiào	Transit call	
中转站	Zhōngzhuǎnzhàn	Hub	
种子点	Zhǒngzǐ diǎn	Seed	
种子函数	Zhǒngzǐ hánshù	Seed function	
种子路由器	Zhǒngzǐ lùyóuqì	Seed router	
轴	Zhóu	Axis	
轴比	Zhóu bǐ	Axial ratio (radar term)	
周边器材	Zhōubiān qìcái	Peripheral	
周边器材互联	Zhōubiān qìcái hùlián	Peripheral component interconnect	PCI
洲际研究网络协调委员会	Zhōujì yánjiū wǎngluò xiétiáo wěiyuánhuì	Coordinating Committee for Intercontinental Research Networking	CCIRN
啁啾	Zhōujiū	Chirp	Chirp
啁啾声	Zhōujiū shēng	Chirping	
周期	Zhōuqī	Cycle time	
周期	Zhōuqī	Period (of a satellite)	
周期检定	Zhōuqī jiǎndìng	Periodic verification	
周期挪用	Zhōuqī nuóyòng	Cycle stealing	
周期挪用缓冲器	Zhōuqī nuóyòng huǎnchōngqì	Cycle steal control buffer	CSCB
周期挪用请求	Zhōuqī nuóyòng qǐngqiú	Cycle steal request	CSR
周期挪用信息计数器	Zhōuqī nuóyòng xìnxī jìshùqì	Cycle stealing message counter	CSMC
周期挪用许可低	Zhōuqī nuóyòng xǔkě dī	Cycle steal grant low	CSGL
周期挪用许可高	Zhōuqī nuóyòng xǔkě gāo	Cycle steal grant high	CSGH
周期时间	Zhōuqī shíjiān	Periodic time	
周期试验	Zhōuqī shìyàn	Periodic test	
周期位置更新定时器	Zhōuqī wèizhì gēngxīn dìngshíqì	Periodic location re-timer (timing refresher)	
周期位置更新时限值	Zhōuqī wèizhì gēngxīn shíxiàn zhí	Time limit on periodic location refreshes	
周期信号	Zhōuqī xìnhào	Periodic signal	
周期帧	Zhōuqī zhèng	Periodic frame	
周期资源分配	Zhōuqī zīyuán fēnpèi	Cyclic resource allocation	
周期资源分配	Zhōuqī zīyuán fēnpèi	Periodic resource distribution	PRD
周期-频率谱	Zhōuqī—pínlǜ pǔ	Period-frequency spectrum	
周期性	Zhōuqīxìng	Periodicity	
周期性定时信号	Zhōuqīxìng dìngshí xìnhào	Cyclic timing signal	
周期性加载波导	Zhōuqīxìng jiāzài bōdǎo	Periodically loaded waveguide	
周期性畸变	Zhōuqīxìng jībiàn	Cyclic distortion	
周期性时标	Zhōuqīxìng shíbiāo	Cyclic time-scale	

周期性通/断开关控制	Zhōuqīxìng tōng/duànkāi guān kòngzhì	Cyclic on/off switching control	
周期性帧	Zhōuqīxìng zhèng	Periodic frame	
周速	Zhōusù	Cycle time	
轴系精度	Zhóuxì jīngdù	Axis train precision	
轴向和横向等离子化学汽相沉积法	Zhóuxiàng hé héngxiàng děnglízǐ huàxué qìxiàng chénjī fǎ	Axial and linear plasma [Chemical vapor] deposition	ALPD
轴向化学气相沉积法	Zhóuxiàng huàxué qìxiàng chénjī fǎ	Vapor axial deposition (for FOC)	VAD
轴向偏焦	Zhóuxiàng piānjiāo	Axial offset focus (radar term)	
轴向气相沉积法	Zhóuxiàng qìxiàng chénjī fǎ	Vapor axial deposition	VAD
帚形喇叭天线	Zhǒuxíng lǎba tiānxiàn	Hoghorn antenna	
周转时间	Zhōuzhuǎn shíjiān	Turn-around time	
主瓣	Zhǔ bàn	Major lobe, main lobe	
主表	Zhǔ biǎo	Primary table (for database)	
主波长	Zhǔ bōcháng	Dominant wavelength	DWL
主波束宽度	Zhǔ bōshù kuāndù	Principle half-power beamwidths	
主波束杂波	Zhǔ bōshù zábō	Main beam clutter	MBC
主菜单	Zhǔ càidān	Main menu	
主参考时钟	Zhǔ cānkǎo shízhōng	Primary reference clock	PRC
主成分分析	Zhǔ chéngfèn fēnxī	Principle component analysis	
主程序	Zhǔ chéngxù	Main routine	
主处理单元	Zhǔ chǔlǐ dānyuán	Main processor unit	MPU
主处理机	Zhǔ chǔlǐjī	Master processor	
主处理器复制管理器	Zhǔ chǔlǐqì fùzhì guǎnlǐqì	Main processor duplication manager	MPDM
主处理器后面板	Zhǔ chǔlǐqì hòumianbǎn	Main processor back panel	MPBP
主处理器 SCSI BUS 接口	Zhǔ chǔlǐqì SCSI Bus jiēkǒu	Main processor SCSI BUS interface	MSBI
主从触发器	Zhǔ cóng chùfāqì	Master-slave flip-flop	MSFF
主从同步	Zhǔ cóng tóngbù	Master-slave synchronization	
主从系统	Zhǔ cóng xìtǒng	Client/server network	
主存储器	Zhǔ cúnchǔqì	Main memory	
主存储器数据寄存器	Zhǔ cúnchǔqì shùjù jìcúnqì	Main storage data register	MSDR
主定义位置	Zhǔ dìngyì wèizhì	Master definition site	
主段	Zhǔ duàn	Main section	
主反射器	Zhǔ fǎnshèqì	Main reflector	
主反射体	Zhǔ fǎnshètǐ	Main reflector	
主分区	Zhǔ fēnqū	Primary partition	
主供电	Zhǔ gōngdiàn	Primary supply	
主关键字	Zhǔ guānjiàn zì	Primary keyword	
主关键字约束	Zhǔ guānjiàn zì yuēshù	Primary key constraint (in SQL Server)	
主管理代理	Zhǔ guǎnlǐ dàilǐ	Master management agent	MMA
主呼线识别提供	Zhǔ hūxiàn shíbié tígōng	Calling line identification presentation	CLIP
主呼线识别限制	Zhǔ hūxiàn shíbié xiànzhì	Calling line identification restriction	CLIR
主键	Zhǔ jiàn	Primary keyword (for database)	PK
主交叉连接	Zhǔ jiāochā liánjiē	Main cross connect	MCC
主交换机	Zhǔ jiāohuànjī	Host exchange	
主接地端子	Zhǔ jiēdì duānzi	Main grounding terminal	
主接地排	Zhǔ jiēdì pái	Main grounding bar	

主节点	Zhǔ jiédiǎn	Primary node	
主机密	Zhǔ jīmì	Master secret (IPsec)	
助记忆码	Zhù jìyì mǎ	Mnemonic code	
主基准时钟	Zhǔ jīzhǔn shízhōng	Primary reference clock	PRC
主控制单元机架	Zhǔ kòngzhì dānyuán jījià	Main control unit rack	MCUR
主控制集成板	Zhǔ kòngzhì jíchéngbǎn	Main control board assembly	MCPA
主控制器接口	Zhǔ kòngzhìqì jiēkǒu	Host controller interface	HCI
柱率	Zhù lǜ	Column area index	
主密钥	Zhǔ mìyào	Master key enciphering key	KKM
主模	Zhǔ mó	Fundamental mode	
主模	Zhǔ mó	Dominant mode (in a waveguide)	
主配置表	Zhǔ pèizhì biǎo	Master configuration table	MCT
主偏振态	Zhǔ piānzhèn tài	Principal state of polarization	PSP
主前端	Zhǔ qiánduān	Master headend	
主群	Zhǔ qún	Mastergroup	
主群段	Zhǔ qún duàn	Mastergroup section	
主群链路	Zhǔ qún liànlù	Mastergroup link	
主群速率	Zhǔ qún sùlǜ	Primary rate access	PRA
主群速率接口	Zhǔ qún sùlǜ jiēkǒu	Primary rate interface (North America and Japan)	PRI
主射束	Zhǔ shèshù	Main beam (of an antenna)	
主时钟	Zhǔ shízhōng	Master clock	
主时钟板	Zhǔ shízhōng bǎn	Main clock board	MCK
主时钟发生器	Zhǔ shízhōng fāshēngqì	Master clock generator	MCG
主时钟脉冲发生器	Zhǔ shízhōng màichōng fāshēngqì	Primary clock pulse generator	PCPG
主索引	Zhǔ suǒyǐn	Master index	
主同步码	Zhǔ tóngbù mǎ	Primary synchronization code	PSC
主通道发送参考点	Zhǔ tōngdào fāsòng cānkǎo diǎn	Main path interface at the transmitter	MPI-S
主通道发送端	Zhǔ tōngdào fāsòng duān	Main path interface at the transmitter	MPI-S
主通道接口	Zhǔ tōngdào jiēkǒu	Main path interface	MPI
主通道接收参考点	Zhǔ tōngdào jiēshōu cānkǎo diǎn	Main path interface at the receiver	MPI-R
主通道接收端	Zhǔ tōngdào jiēshōu duān	Main path interface at the receiver	MPI-R
主通路接口	Zhǔ tōnglù jiēkǒu	Main path interface	MPI
主维度表	Zhǔ wéidù biǎo	Primary dimension table	
主卫星天线电视/主天线电视	Zhǔ wèixīng tiānxiàn diànshì/zhǔ tiānxiàn diànshì	Satellite master antenna television /master antenna television	SMATV/MATV
主位置	Zhǔ wèizhì	Master site	
主文件	Zhǔ wénjiàn	Master file	
主文件	Zhǔ wénjiàn	Master file	MF
主文件表	Zhǔ wénjiàn biǎo	Master file table	MFT
主向量标示	Zhǔ xiàngliàng biāoshì	Main vector identifier	MVID
主星体	Zhǔ xīngtǐ	Primary body (in relation to a satellite)	
主信号	Zhǔ xìnhào	Host signal	
主选单	Zhǔ xuǎndān	Main menu	
主压力轴	Zhǔ yālì zhóu	Principal axis of pressure	
主页	Zhǔ yè	Home page	
主因	Zhǔ yīn	Primary cause	

主引导记录	Zhǔ yǐndǎo jìlù	Master boot record	MBR
主域控制器	Zhǔ yù kòngzhìqì	Primary domain controller	PDC
主载波	Zhǔ zàibō	Main carrier	
主站	Zhǔ zhàn	Host station	HST
主张力轴	Zhǔ zhānglì zhóu	Principal axis of tension	
主振放大式发射机	Zhǔ zhèn fàngdàshì fāshèjī	Master oscillator power amplifier transmitter	MOPA
主振荡器	Zhǔ zhèndàngqì	Master oscillator	
主钟	Zhǔ zhōng	Master clock	
主轴	Zhǔ zhóu	Principal axis	
抓包器	Zhuābāoqì	Packet grabber (hacker tool)	
转/分	Zhuǎn/fēn	Rotations per minute	RPM
转播发射机	Zhuǎnbō fāshèjī	Re-broadcast transmitter	
转储	Zhuǎnchǔ	Dump	
转出	Zhuǎnchū	Roll out	
转储文件	Zhuǎnchǔ wénjiàn	Dump file	
转动惯量	Zhuàndòng guànliàng	Moment of inertia	
转发代理	Zhuǎnfā dàilǐ	Forward proxy	
转发等价类	Zhuǎnfā děngjià lèi	Forwarding equivalence class	FEC
转发等效类	Zhuǎnfā děngxiào lèi	Forward equivalence class	FEC
转发启动抗扰性	Zhuǎnfā qǐdòng kàngrǎoxìng	Repeating attack rejection	
转发启动灵敏度	Zhuǎnfā qǐdòng língmǐndù	Repeating attack sensitivity	
转发台	Zhuǎnfā tái	Repeater	
转发调制灵敏度	Zhuǎnfā tiáozhì língmǐndù	Repeating modulation sensitivity	
转发信息表	Zhuǎnfā xìnxī biǎo	Forwarding information base	FIB
转发信息库	Zhuǎnfā xìnxī kù	Forwarding information base	FIB
转发延迟间隔	Zhuǎnfā yánchí jiàngé	Forward delay interval	
转发音频失真	Zhuǎnfā yīnpín shīzhēn	Repeating distortion	
转发器	Zhuǎnfāqì	Repeater	
转发器	Zhuǎnfāqì	Transponder (in radio communication)	
撞击式打印机	Zhuàngjīshì dǎyìnjī	Impact printer	
状况	Zhuàngkuàng	Status	
装配密度	Zhuāngpèi mìdù	Packaging density	
装配件	Zhuāngpèijiàn	Assembly	
装配件清单	Zhuāngpèijiàn qīngdān	Assembly manifest	
装入	Zhuāngrù	Loading, to load (software)	
装入	Zhuāngrù	Mount (hardware)	
装入程序	Zhuāngrù chéngxù	Loader	
装入程序语言	Zhuāngrù chéngxù yǔyán	Loader language	
装入模块	Zhuāngrù mókuài	Load module	
状态	Zhuàngtài	Mode, status, state	
状态变量法	Zhuàngtài biànliàng fǎ	Method of state variable	
状态查询	Zhuàngtài cháxún	Status inquiry	
状态窗口	Zhuàngtài chuāngkǒu	Status bar (WP command)	
状态处理	Zhuàngtài chǔlǐ	Status handling	
状态段	Zhuàngtài duàn	Status field	SF
状态改变注册	Zhuàngtài gǎibiàn zhùcè	Status change registration	SCR

状态管理	Zhuàngtài guǎnlǐ	Status manager	STM
状态合并环节	Zhuàngtài hébìng huánjié	State merging technique	
状态恢复序列	Zhuàngtài huīfù xùliè	Restitution sequence of conditions	
状态机	Zhuàngtài jī	State machine	
状态机对象	Zhuàngtài jī duìxiàng	State machine object	SMO
状态检查	Zhuàngtài jiǎnchá	Stateful inspection (IPsec)	
状态截断环节	Zhuàngtài jiéduàn huánjié	State space truncation	
状态控制寄存器	Zhuàngtài kòngzhì jìcúnqì	State control register	SCR
状态栏	Zhuàngtài lán	Status bar	
状态码	Zhuàngtài mǎ	Condition code	CC
状态请求	Zhuàngtài qǐngqiú	State request (SS7)	
状态确认	Zhuàngtài quèrèn	State confirm (SS7)	
状态条	Zhuàngtài tiáo	Status bar	
状态信息帧	Zhuàngtài xìnxī zhèng	Status information frame	SIF
状态询问	Zhuàngtài xúnwèn	Status inquiry	
状态指示	Zhuàngtài zhǐshì	State indication (SS7)	
状态转换系统	Zhuàngtài zhuǎnhuàn xìtǒng	Status transition system	
状态转移图	Zhuàngtài zhuǎnyí tú	State-transition diagram	
状态字	Zhuàngtài zì	Status word	SW
状态字段	Zhuàngtài zìduàn	Status field	SF
装箱单	Zhuāngxiāng dān	Packing list	P/L
装箱问题	Zhuāngxiāng wèntí	Bin packing	
装卸式器材	Zhuāngxièshì qìcái	Removable storage device	
装载	Zhuāngzài	Loading	LD
装载器	Zhuāngzàiqì	Loader	
装置地址	Zhuāngzhì dìzhǐ	Device address	DVA
装置控制字	Zhuāngzhì kòngzhì zì	Device control word	DCW
装置连线阻抗	Zhuāngzhì liánxiàn zǔkàng	Installation wiring impedance	
装置驱动器	Zhuāngzhì qūdòngqì	Unit driver	UD
转换	Zhuǎnhuàn	Conversion, changeover	
转换	Zhuǎnhuàn	Transformation	
转换	Zhuǎnhuàn	Change-over	
转换	Zhuǎnhuàn	Conversion	
转换本表	Zhuǎnhuàn běn biǎo	Convert present table	
转换表	Zhuǎnhuàn biǎo	Conversion list	
转换格式	Zhuǎnhuàn géshi	Transfer format	
转换功能	Zhuǎnhuàn gōngnéng	Conversion facility	CF
转换结束	Zhuǎnhuàn jiéshù	End of conversion	EOC
转换计划	Zhuǎnhuàn jihuà	Transfer schema	
转换计划	Zhuǎnhuàn jihuà	Transformation schema	
转换记录	Zhuǎnhuàn jilù	Conversion record	
转换全部	Zhuǎnhuàn quánbù	Convert all	
转换缺口	Zhuǎnhuàn quēkǒu	Commutation notch	
转换设备	Zhuǎnhuàn shèbèi	Conversion facility	CF
转换速度	Zhuǎnhuàn sùdù	Slew rate (video term)	
转换循环	Zhuǎnhuàn xúnhuán	Conversion cycle	

转换座外壳	Zhuǎnhuàn zuòwàiké	Adapter body	
转换器	Zhuǎnhuànqì	Converter (electrical or digital signal use)	
转换器	Zhuǎnhuànqì	Transponder (telecom)	
转换器损耗	Zhuǎnhuànqì sǔnhào	Transducer loss	
专家系统	Zhuānjiā xìtǒng	Expert system	
转角处	Zhuǎnjiǎo chù	Corner; nook	
转交地址	Zhuǎnjiāo dìzhǐ	Care-of address	
转接	Zhuǎnjiē	Transit	
转接点	Zhuǎnjiē diǎn	Transit point	
转接服务节点	Zhuǎnjiē fúwù jiédiǎn	Transit service node	TSN
转接交换机	Zhuǎnjiē jiāohuànjī	Transit exchange	TE
转接节点时钟	Zhuǎnjiē jiédiǎn shízhōng	Transit node clock	TNC
转接连接单元	Zhuǎnjiē liánjiē dānyuán	Transit connection element	TCE
转接时延	Zhuǎnjiē shíyán	Transit delay	
转接网	Zhuǎnjiē wǎng	Transit network	
转接网络段	Zhuǎnjiē wǎngluò duàn	Transit network segment	TNS
转接网络选择	Zhuǎnjiē wǎngluò xuǎnzé	Transit network selection	
转接延迟	Zhuǎnjiē yánchí	Transit delay	
转接点	Zhuǎnjiēdiǎn	Transition point	TP
专门化	Zhuānménhuà	Specialization	
专权网	Zhuānquán wǎng	Despotic network	
转让协定书	Zhuǎnràng xiédìng shū	Transfer protocol	
转入	Zhuǎnrù	Roll in	
转收	Zhuǎnshōu	Retrieve (verb)	
转送号码	Zhuǎnsòng hàomǎ	Forward-to number	ftn
转速	Zhuànsù	Rotational speed	
专题地图	Zhuāntí dìtú	Thematic map (GIS term)	
专题绘图	Zhuāntí huìtú	Thematic mapping	
专题数据	Zhuāntí shùjù	Thematic data	
专题属性	Zhuāntí shǔxìng	Thematic attribute	
专线	Zhuānxiàn	Dedicated line, private line	
转向表	Zhuǎnxiàng biǎo	Turntable	
转向符	Zhuǎnxiàng fú	Pipe symbol (|)	
转向阻抗	Zhuǎnxiàng zǔkàng	Turn impedance	
转信增益	Zhuǎnxìn zēngyì	Information transfer gain	
转型	Zhuǎnxíng	Casting	
转移	Zhuǎnyí	Migrate	
转移	Zhuǎnyí	Transfer	
转义	Zhuǎnyì	Escape	ESC
转移比	Zhuǎnyí bǐ	Transfer ratio	
转移导抗	Zhuǎnyí dǎokàng	Transfer immittance	
转移导纳	Zhuǎnyí dǎonà	Transfer admittance	
转移点	Zhuǎnyí diǎn	Escapement point	
转义符	Zhuǎnyì fú	Escape character	
转移概率密度	Zhuǎnyí gàilǜ mìdù	Transition probability density	
转移和连接	Zhuǎnyí hé liánjiē	Branch and link	BAL

转移控制	Zhuǎnyí kòngzhì	Transfer of control	TOC
转义码	Zhuǎnyì mǎ	Escape code	
转移模	Zhuǎnyí mó	Transfer-molded (FOC mfg)	
转移模式	Zhuǎnyí móshì	Translative mode	
转移时间	Zhuǎnyí shíjiān	Transfer time	Tt
转移网	Zhuǎnyí wǎng	Transit network	TN
转义序列	Zhuǎnyì xùliè	Escape sequence	
转义字符	Zhuǎnyì zìfú	Escape character	
转移阻抗	Zhuǎnyí zǔkàng	Transfer impedance (of a screened circuit)	
专用保护环	Zhuānyòng bǎohù huán	Dedicated protection ring (optical network term)	DPR
专用编号计划	Zhuānyòng biānhào jìhuà	Private numbering plan	PNP
专用查询识别码	Zhuānyòng cháxún shíbié mǎ	Dedicated inquiry access code	DIAC
专用存储器	Zhuānyòng cúnchǔqì	Private memory	PM
专用单工	Zhuānyòng dāngōng	Dedicated simplex	
专用电路数字数据业务	Zhuānyòng diànlù shùzì shùjù yèwù	Private circuit digital data service	PCDDS
专用电子自动交换分机	Zhuānyòng diànzǐ zìdòng jiāohuàn fēnjī	Electronic private automatic branch exchange	EPABX
专用电子战飞机	Zhuānyòng diànzǐzhàn fēijī	Special purpose electronic warfare aircraft	
专用调度集群移动通信网	Zhuānyòng diàodù jíqún yídòng tōngxìnwǎng	Private mobile radio	PMR
专用功能块	Zhuānyòng gōngnéng kuài	Application specific functional block	ASFB
专用管理信息业务单元	Zhuānyòng guǎnlǐ xìnxī yèwù dānyuán	Special management information service element	SMISE
专用管理域	Zhuānyòng guǎnlǐ yù	Private management domain	PRMD
专用号码簿管理域	Zhuānyòng hàomǎbù guǎnlǐ yù	Private directory management domain	PRDMD
专用环路	Zhuānyòng huánlù	Private loop	
专用环路设备	Zhuānyòng huánlù shèbèi	Private loop device	
专用交换机	Zhuānyòng jiāohuànjī	Private branch exchange	PBX
专用集成电路/芯片	Zhuānyòng jíchéng diànlù/xìnpiàn	Application specific integrated circuit/chip	ASIC
专用集群移动通信网	Zhuānyòng jíqún yídòng tōngxìnwǎng	Private mobile radio	PMR
专用控制	Zhuānyòng kòngzhì	Dedicated control	DC
专用控制程序	Zhuānyòng kòngzhì chéngxù	Dedicated control program	DCP
专用控制信道	Zhuānyòng kòngzhì xìndào	Dedicated control channel	DCCH
专用模式	Zhuānyòng móshì	Standby mode	
专用设备	Zhuānyòng shèbèi	Private device	
专用数据链路	Zhuānyòng shùjù liànlù	Dedicated data link	
专用数据网络	Zhuānyòng shùjù wǎngluò	Private data network	
专用通信公共载波	Zhuānyòng tōngxìn gōnggòng zàibō	Specialized-communication common carrier	SCCC
专用通信网	Zhuānyòng tōngxìnwǎng	Private telecommunication network	PTN
专用投币电话鉴别音	Zhuānyòng tóubì diànhuà jiànbié yīn	Special coinbox discriminating tone	
专用图形适配器	Zhuānyòng túxíng shìpèiqì	Professional graphics adapter	PGA
专用网编号计划	Zhuānyòng wǎng biānhào jìhuà	Private numbering plan	PNP
专用网接口	Zhuānyòng wǎng jiēkǒu	Private user network interface	PUNI
专用网间接口	Zhuānyòng wǎngjiàn jiēkǒu	Private network-to-network interface	PNNI
专用网络 Q 参考点信令系统	Zhuānyòng wǎngluò Q cānkǎodiǎn xìnlìng xìtǒng	Private network Q reference point signaling system	PSS
专用网络-网络接口	Zhuānyòng wǎngluò—wǎngluò jiēkǒu	Private network-network interface	PNNI
专用网上的传真	Zhuānyòng wǎngshàngde chuánzhēn	Facsimile on private networks	
专用维度	Zhuānyòng wéidù	Private dimension	

专用文件	Zhuānyòng wénjiàn	Dedicated file	DF
专用物理控制信道	Zhuānyòng wùlǐ kòngzhì xìndào	Dedicated physical control channel	DPCCH
专用物理数据信道	Zhuānyòng wùlǐ shùjù xìndào	Dedicated physical data channel	DPDCH
专用物理信道	Zhuānyòng wùlǐ xìndào	Physical dedicated channel	PDCH
专用线路	Zhuānyòng xiànlù	Private line	PL
专用小交换机	Zhuānyòng xiǎo jiāohuànjī	Private branch exchange	PBX
专用信道	Zhuānyòng xìndào	Dedicated channel	DCH
专用信令信道	Zhuānyòng xìnlìng xìndào	Dedicated signaling channel	DSC
专用选项	Zhuānyòng xuǎnxiàng	Private use option	
专用业务信道	Zhuānyòng yèwù xìndào	Dedicated traffic channel	DTCH
专用移动通信系统	Zhuānyòng yídòng tōngxìn xìtǒng	Private mobile communication system	
专用移动无线电	Zhuānyòng yídòng wúxiàndiàn	Private mobile radio	PMR
专用移动无线电	Zhuānyòng yídòng wúxiàndiàn	Special mobile radio	SMR
专用移动无线电系统	Zhuānyòng yídòng wúxiàndiàn xìtǒng	Specialized mobile radio system	SMRS
专用域名	Zhuānyòng yùmíng	Private domain name	
专用智能外设	Zhuānyòng zhìnéng wài shè	Private intelligent peripheral	PIP
专用支线电子交换机	Zhuānyòng zhīxiàn diànzǐ jiāohuànjī	Electronic private branch exchange	EPBX
专用终端设备	Zhuānyòng zhōngduān shèbèi	Application dedicated terminal	ADT
专用自动交换分机	Zhuānyòng zìdòng jiāohuàn fēnjī	Private automatic branch exchange	PABX
专用自动小交换机	Zhuānyòng zìdòng xiǎo jiāohuànjī	Private automatic branch exchange	PABX
专用自动用户交换机	Zhuānyòng zìdòng yònghù jiāohuànjī	Private automatic branch exchange	PABX
专用资源报告	Zhuānyòng zīyuán bàogào	Specialized resource report	SRR
专用资源功能	Zhuānyòng zīyuán gōngnéng	Special resource function	SRF
专用综合处理器	Zhuānyòng zōnghé chǔlǐqì	Application specific integrated processor	ASIP
专用的资源处理函数	Zhuānyòngde zīyuán chǔlǐ hánshù	Specialized resource function	SRF
转折频率	Zhuǎnzhé pínlǜ	Breakover frequency	
转置矩阵	Zhuǎnzhì jǔzhèn	Transposed matrix	
专指度	Zhuānzhǐdù	Specificity	
驻波	Zhùbō	Standing wave	
驻波保护电路	Zhùbō bǎohù diànlù	Standing wave protection ciruit	
驻波测量计	Zhùbō cèliángjì	Standing-wave meter	
驻波电压比	Zhùbō diànyā bǐ	Standing wave voltage-ratio	SWVR
驻波检波器	Zhùbō jiǎnbōqì	Standing-wave detector	
驻波声光调制	Zhùbō shēngguāng tiáozhì	Standing-wave acousto-optical modulation	SWAOM
驻波天线	Zhùbō tiānxiàn	Standing-wave antenna	SWA
驻波最大点	Zhùbō zuìdà diǎn	Standing-wave maximum	
驻波最小点	Zhùbō zuìxiǎo diǎn	Standing-wave minimum	
驻波比	Zhùbōbǐ	Standing-wave ratio	SWR
驻波比功率计	Zhùbōbǐ gōnglǜjì	Standing-wave ratio dynamometer	
驻波比切断器	Zhùbōbǐ qiēduànqì	Standing-wave ratio trip	
逐步增加冗余	Zhúbù zēngjiā rǒngyú	Incremental redundancy	
注册	Zhùcè	Login	
注册表	Zhùcè biǎo	Registered table	
注册表	Zhùcè biǎo	Registry (in Windows)	
注册表大小限制	Zhùcè biǎo dàxiǎo xiànzhì	Registry size limit	RSL
注册表启动	Zhùcè biǎo qǐdòng	Registry boot	

注册服务器	Zhùcè fúwùqì	Registrar server	
注册回应消息	Zhùcè huíyìng xiāoxi	Registration reply message (in IP)	
注册拒绝	Zhùcè jùjué	Registration reject (packet protocol)	RRJ
注册请求	Zhùcè qǐngqiú	Registration request (packet protocol)	RRQ
注册请求消息	Zhùcè qǐngqiú xiāoxi	Registration request message (in IP)	
注册确认	Zhùcè quèrèn	Registration confirm (packet protocol)	RCF
注册应答	Zhùcè yìngdá	Registration reply	RR
注册用户管理系统	Zhùcè yònghù guǎnlǐ xìtǒng	Subscriber management system	SMS
注册，接入和状态	Zhùcè, jiērù hé zhuàngtài	Registration, admission and status	RAS
注册，认证，状态	Zhùcè, rènzhèng, zhuàngtài	Registration, admission, status	RAS
注册的插座连接器	Zhùcède chāzuò liánjiēqì	Registered jack connector	RJ Connector
贮存寿命	Zhùcún shòumìng	Storage life	
住地代理	Zhùdì dàilǐ	Home agent	
驻地网关	Zhùdì wǎngguān	Residential gateway	RG
逐点选择	Zhúdiǎn xuǎnzé	Node-by-node selecting	
主动搭线窃听	Zhǔdòng dāxiàn qiètīng	Active wiretapping	
主动定位系统	Zhǔdòng dìngwèi xìtǒng	Active locating systems	
主动地址自动配置	Zhǔdòng dìzhǐ zìdòng pèizhì	Stateless address auto-configuration	
主动对抗	Zhǔdòng duìkàng	Active countermeasures	ACM
主动队列管理	Zhǔdòng duìliè guǎnlǐ	Active queue management	
主动授权同步包头	Zhǔdòng shòuquán tóngbù bāotóu	Unsolicited grant synchronization header	UGSH
主动授权业务	Zhǔdòng shòuquán yèwù	Unsolicited grant service	UGS
主动数据库	Zhǔdòng shùjùkù	Active database	
主动网络	Zhǔdòng wǎngluò	Active networks	
主动威胁	Zhǔdòng wēixié	Active threat (IPsec)	
主动追踪	Zhǔdòng zhuīzōng	Active homing	AH
主动式管理线路	Zhǔdòngshì guǎnlǐ xiànlù	Wired for management initiative	WMI
主动式遥感器	Zhǔdòngshì yáogǎnqì	Active sensor	
逐段转发信令	Zhúduàn zhuǎnfā xìnlìng	Link-by-link signaling	
逐段转接	Zhúduàn zhuǎnjiē	Link by link	LXL
主干电缆	Zhǔgàn diànlǎn	Backbone cable (in building)	BC
主干电缆接入	Zhǔgàn diànlǎn jiērù	Primary cable access	
主干光缆	Zhǔgàn guānglǎn	Backbone fiber optic cable	
主干网	Zhǔgàn wǎng	Backbone network	
主干子系统	Zhǔgàn zixitǒng	Riser backbone sub-system	RBS
主干组	Zhǔgàn zǔ	Trunk group (in multicast)	
主管部门	Zhǔguǎn bùmén	Administration	
主管部门号码簿管理域	Zhǔguǎn bùmén hàomǎbù guǎnlǐ yù	Administration directory management domain	ADDMD
主管当局	Zhǔguǎn dāngjú	Administrative authority	
主观平均得分	Zhǔguān píngjūn défēn	Mean opinion score	MOS
烛光	Zhúguāng	Candle (unit of measurement of light)	
珠海高凌信息科技有限公司	Zhūhǎi gāolíng xìnxī kējì yǒuxiàn gōngsī	Zhuhai Comleader Information Science & Technology Co. Ltd.	
逐行倒相制式	Zhúháng dǎoxiāng zhìshì	Phase alternating line (European television broadcast standard)	PAL
住户网关	Zhùhù wǎngguān	Residential gateway	RGW
锥削分布	Zhuīxiāo fēnbù	Tapered distribution	

追踪识别符失配	Zhuīzōng shíbiéfú shīpèi	Trace identifier mismatch	TIM
注记	Zhùjì	Annotation	
主机	Zhǔjī	Host, master (of networked computers)	
主机板	Zhǔjī bǎn	Motherboard; system board	
逐级比较模/数转换器	Zhújí bǐjiào mó/shù zhuǎnhuànqì	Successive comparison A/D converter	
注记层	Zhùjì céng	Annotation layer	
注记放置	Zhùjì fàngzhì	Annotation placement	
注记分组	Zhùjì fēnzǔ	Annotation group	
主机控制接口	Zhǔjī kòngzhì jiēkǒu	Host controller interface	HCI
注记类	Zhùjì lèi	Annotation class	
主机漏洞扫描器	Zhǔjī lòudòng sǎomiáoqì	Host vulnerability scanner	
主机托管	Zhǔjī tuōguǎn	Web hosting	
逐级选择	Zhújí xuǎnzé	Stage-by-stage selecting	
注记要素类	Zhùjì yàosù lèi	Annotation feature class	
主机总线适配器	Zhǔjī zǒngxiàn shìpèiqì	Host bus adapter	HBA
主叫	Zhǔjiào	Originating call	OC
主叫标识	Zhǔjiào biāozhì	Origination indicator	OI
主叫号码	Zhǔjiào hàomǎ	Calling party number	
主叫号码识别显示	Zhǔjiào hàomǎ shíbié xiǎnshì	Calling number identification presentation	CNIP
主叫号码识别限制	Zhǔjiào hàomǎ shíbié xiànzhì	Calling line identification restriction	CLIR
主叫号码识别限制	Zhǔjiào hàomǎ shíbié xiànzhì	Calling number presentation restriction	CNIR
主叫号码通知	Zhǔjiào hàomǎ tōngzhī	Calling line identification presentation	CLIP
主叫呼叫控制器	Zhǔjiào hūjiào kòngzhìqì	Calling party call controller	
主叫控制释放	Zhǔjiào kòngzhì shìfàng	Calling party release	
主叫类别	Zhǔjiào lèibié	Calling party's category	
主叫识别	Zhǔjiào shíbié	Caller identification	CID
主叫识别	Zhǔjiào shíbié	Calling line identity	CLI
主叫识别提供补充业务	Zhǔjiào shíbié tígōng bǔchōng yèwù	Calling line identification presentation supplementary service	CLIP
主叫识别限制补充业务	Zhǔjiào shíbié xiànzhì bǔchōng yèwù	Calling line identification restriction supplementary service	CLIR
主叫识别信息传送	Zhǔjiào shíbié xìnxī chuánsòng	Caller identity delivery	CID
主叫识别信息显示	Zhǔjiào shíbié xìnxī xiǎnshì	Call identification display	CID
主叫线路识别	Zhǔjiào xiànlù shíbié	Calling line identification	CLI
主叫线路识别显示	Zhǔjiào xiànlù shíbié xiǎnshì	Calling line identification presentation	CLIP
主叫线路识别限制	Zhǔjiào xiànlù shíbié xiànzhì	Calling line identification restriction	CLIR
主叫用户	Zhǔjiào yònghù	Calling party (in telecommunication)	
主叫用户挂机信号	Zhǔjiào yònghù guàjī xìnhào	Calling party clear signal	CCL
主叫终端	Zhǔjiào zhōngduān	Calling terminal	
主叫子地址	Zhǔjiào zidìzhǐ	Calling party sub-address	
主叫方编号	Zhǔjiào-fāng biānhào	Calling party number	
主叫线识别	Zhǔjiàoxiàn shíbié	Calling line identification presentation	CLIP
主叫线识别提供	Zhǔjiàoxiàn shíbié tígōng	Calling line identification presentation	CLIP
主叫线识别显示	Zhǔjiàoxiàn shíbié xiǎnshì	Calling line identification presentation	CLIP
主叫线识别限制	Zhǔjiàoxiàn shíbié xiànzhì	Calling line identification restriction	CLIR
注解	Zhùjiě	Annotation	
注解正射航片	Zhùjiě zhèngshè háng piàn	Annotation aerial orthophoto	

注解字段	Zhùjiě zìduàn	Comment field	
助记符	Zhùjìfú	Mnemonic	
驻极体	Zhùjítǐ	Electret	
驻极体传声器	Zhùjítǐ chuánshēngqì	Electret microphone	
主控站	Zhǔkòngzhàn	Main control station	
柱面波	Zhùmiàn bō	Cylindrical wave	
柱面坐标核	Zhùmiàn zuòbiāo hé	Cylinder coordinate kernel	
柱面 / 磁头 / 扇区	Zhùmiàn/cítóu/shàn qū	Cylinder/head/sector (of a computer hard disk)	CHS
准传输集群	Zhǔn chuánshū jíqún	Quasi-transmission trunking	
准点播电视	Zhǔn diǎnbō diànshì	Near video on demand	NVOD
准峰值	Zhǔn fēngzhí	Quasi-peak	QP
准峰值电压表	Zhǔn fēngzhí diànyābiǎo	Quasi-peak voltmeter	
准峰值检波器	Zhǔn fēngzhí jiǎnbōqì	Quasi-peak detector	
准分子激光	Zhǔn fènzi jīguāng	Excimer laser	
准分子激光加工机	Zhǔn fènzi jīguāng jiāgōngjī	Excimer laser processing equipment	
准光	Zhǔn guāng	Quasi-optical	
准近端	Zhǔn jìnduān	Quasi-nearby terminal	
准可逆行	Zhǔn kěnìxíng	Quasi-reversability	
准脉冲骚扰	Zhǔn màichōng sāorǎo	Quasi-impulsive disturbance (noise)	
准脉冲噪声	Zhǔn màichōng zàoshēng	Quasi-impulsive noise	
准同步连接管理	Zhǔn tóngbù liánjiē guǎnlǐ	Plesiochronous connection supervision	PCS
准同步连接监督	Zhǔn tóngbù liánjiē jiāndū	Plesiochronous connection supervision	PCS
准同步数字分级	Zhǔn tóngbù shùzì fēnjí	Pseudo-synchronous digital hierarchy	PDH
准同步数字体系	Zhǔn tóngbù shùzì tǐxì	Plesiochronous digital hierarchy	PDH
准同步数字体系	Zhǔn tóngbù shùzì tǐxì	Pseudo-synchronous digital hierarchy	PDH
准同步数字系列	Zhǔn tóngbù shùzì xìliè	Plesiochronous digital hierarchy	PDH
准同步的	Zhǔn tóngbùde	Plesiochronous	
准影视点播	Zhǔn yǐngshì diǎnbō	Near video on demand	NVOD
准远端	Zhǔn yuǎnduān	Quasi-remote terminal	
准直联信令方式	Zhǔn zhílián xìnlìng fāngshì	Quasi-associated signaling	
准备后续切换	Zhǔnbèi hòuxù qiēhuàn	Prepare subsequent handover	
准备切换	Zhǔnbèi qiēhuàn	Prepare handover	
准确度	Zhǔnquèdù	Accuracy	
准入/禁入盒	Zhǔnrù/jìnrù hé	GO/NO-GO box (semiconductor mfg)	
准时制生产	Zhǔnshí zhì shēngchǎn	Just in time	JIT
准予接入信道	Zhǔnyǔ jiērù xìndào	Access grant channel	AGCH
准予接续信道	Zhǔnyǔ jiēxù xìndào	Access grant channel	AGCH
准直透镜	Zhǔnzhí tòujìng	Collimator lens	
准直器	Zhǔnzhíqì	Collimator	
桌棋类游戏	Zhuō qí lèi yóuxì	Table chess (computer game)	TAB
桌面地理信息系统	Zhuōmiàn dìlǐ xìnxī xìtǒng	Desktop geographic information system	
桌面个人计算机	Zhuōmiàn gèrén jìsuànjī	Desktop personal computer	DPC
桌面管理接口	Zhuōmiàn guǎnlǐ jiēkǒu	Desktop management interface	DMI
桌面引擎	Zhuōmiàn yǐnqíng	Desktop engine (in SQL Server)	
着色	Zhuósè	Render (video term)	
着色 Petri 网	Zhuósè Petri wǎng	Colored Petri net	CPN

浊音	Zhuóyīn	Voiced sounds	
注入	Zhùrù	Injection	
注入光纤	Zhùrù guāngxiān	Launching fiber	
注入角	Zhùrù jiǎo	Injector angle	
注入井	Zhùrù jǐng	Injection well	
注入模	Zhùrù mó	Injection-molded (FOC mfg)	
注入锁定本地振荡器	Zhùrù suǒdìng běndì zhèndàngqì	Injection locked local oscillator	
注入装置	Zhùrù zhuāngzhì	Injection equipment	
注入式激光二极管	Zhùrùshì jīguāng èrjíguǎn	Inject light diode	ILD
注射成形机	Zhùshè chéngxíngjī	Injection molding equipment	
注射器	Zhùshèqì	Syringe (in SMT)	
注释	Zhùshì	Comment	
注释符	Zhùshì fú	Annotation (in SQL Server)	
注释匹配模式文件	Zhùshì pǐpèi móshì wénjiàn	Annotated mapping schema files (in SQL Server)	
注释请求	Zhùshì qǐngqiú	Request for comments	RFC
主题	Zhǔtí	Subject	
主体	Zhǔtǐ	Subject	
主题探查	Zhǔtí tànchá	Subject probe	
主题消息	Zhǔtí xiāoxi	Subject message	
逐条链路	Zhútiáo liànlù	Link by link	
逐条链路加密	Zhútiáo liànlù jiāmì	Link by link encipherment (IPsec)	
逐跳路由	Zhútiào lùyóu	Hop-by-hop route	
逐跳转发行为	Zhútiào zhuǎnfā xíngwéi	Per-hop behavior	PHB
逐跳式	Zhútiàoshì	Hop-by-hop	
助听器	Zhùtīngqì	Audiophone	
主席节点	Zhǔxí jiédiǎn	Chairman node (in CSCW)	
注销	Zhùxiāo	Logout	
注销	Zhùxiāo	Cancellation	
注销拒绝	Zhùxiāo jùjué	Unregistration reject (packet protocol)	URJ
注销请求	Zhùxiāo qǐngqiú	Unregistration request (packet protocol)	URQ
注销确认	Zhùxiāo quèrèn	Unregistration confirmed (packet protocol)	UCF
逐行	Zhúxíng	Progressive (video term)	
主要结点地面终端	Zhǔyào jiédiǎn dìmiàn zhōngduān	Major node earth terminal	MNT
主要设计	Zhǔyào shèjì	Primary design	
主要数据源	Zhǔyào shùjù yuán	Primary data source	
主要文件	Zhǔyào wénjiàn	Master file	MF
主要的交换中心	Zhǔyàode jiāohuàn zhōngxīn	Main switching center	MSC
主页	Zhǔyè	Home page	
柱状节理	Zhùzhuàng jiélǐ	Columnar joint	
字处理器	Zì chǔlǐqì	Word processor	
子对象	Zi duìxiàng	Child object	
自校准	Zì jiàozhǔn	Self-calibrating	
自联接	Zì liánjiē	Self-join	
字生成	Zì shēngchéng	Word generation	
自变量指针	Zìbiànliàng zhǐzhēn	Argument pointer	AP
自补偿网络	Zìbǔcháng wǎngluò	Self-compensating network	SCN

子层	Zicéng	Sub-layer	
子层监视	Zicéng jiānshì	Sub-layer monitoring	
自测试	Zìcèshì	Self-test	
资产周转率	Zīchǎn zhōuzhuǎnlǜ	Asset turnover rate	
字长	Zìcháng	Word length	
自差式接收	Zìchāshì jiēshōu	Autodyne reception	
子查询	Zicháxún	Sub-query (for database)	
自承式	Zìchéngshì	Self-supporting (FOC mfg)	
子程序	Zǐchéngxù	Sub-program, sub-routine	
子程序调用表	Zǐchéngxù diàoyòng biǎo	Sub-routine call table	SCT
自持(光纤电缆)	Zìchí (guāngxiān diànlǎn)	Self-sustained (optical fiber cable)	SS
子串	Zichuàn	Sub-string	
子代	Zǐdài	Child	
子带编码	Zidài biānmǎ	Sub-band coding	SBC
字典条目	Zìdiǎn tiáomù	Dictionary entry	
字典式攻击	Zìdiǎnshì gōngjī	Dictionary attack (IPsec)	
自定安装	Zìdìng ānzhuāng	Customize	
自定界带标号的接口	Zìdìngjiè dài biāohàode jiēkǒu	Self-delineating labeled interface	
自定界块	Zìdìngjiè kuài	Self-delineating block	
自定义	Zìdìngyì	Custom	
自定义规则	Zìdìngyì guīzé	Custom rule	
自定义汇总	Zìdìngyì huìzǒng	Custom rollup	
自定义排队	Zìdìngyì páiduì	Custom queuing	CQ
自定义数据包	Zìdìngyì shùjùbāo	Crafting packet(s)	
子地址	Zidìzhǐ	Sub-address	
子地址寻址	Zidìzhǐ xúnzhǐ	Sub-addressing	SUB
子地址业务	Zidìzhǐ yèwù	Sub-addressing service	
自动安全监控	Zìdòng ānquán jiānkòng	Automated security monitoring	
自动保护倒换	Zìdòng bǎohù dǎohuàn	Automatic protection switching	APS
自动保护切换	Zìdòng bǎohù qiēhuàn	Automatic protection switching	APS
自动报警	Zìdòng bàojǐng	Automatic alarm	AA
自动报警状态	Zìdòng bàojǐng zhuàngtài	Automatic alarm state	AAS
自动编码机	Zìdòng biānmǎjī	Automatic coding machine	ACOM
自动编码器	Zìdòng biānmǎqì	Automatic coding translator (in COBOL)	ACTRAN
自动比特率选择	Zìdòng bìtè lǜ xuǎnzé	Automatic bit rate selection	ABRS
自动拨号传号线	Zìdòng bōhào chuánhàoxiàn	Automatic dial order wire	ADOW
自动拨号设备	Zìdòng bōhào shèbèi	Automatic dialing unit	ADU
自动拨号装置	Zìdòng bōhào zhuāngzhì	Automatic dialing unit	ADU
自动拨号器	Zìdòng bōhàoqì	Automatic dialer	
自动操作监控器	Zìdòng cāozuò jiānkòngqì	Automatic operation monitor	AOM
自动操作控制	Zìdòng cāozuò kòngzhì	Automated operator control	AOC
自动操作台	Zìdòng cāozuò tái	Automated operator console	AOC
自动测试	Zìdòng cèshì	Automatic test	
自动测试设备	Zìdòng cèshì shèbèi	Automatic test equipment	ATE
自动测试设备	Zìdòng cèshì shèbèi	Automated test equipment	ATE
自动长话交换	Zìdòng chánghuà jiāohuàn	Automatic toll switch	CHZ

自动长途电话记录	Zìdòng chángtú diànhuà jìlù	Automatic toll ticketing	ATT
自动抄表	Zìdòng chāo biǎo	Automatic meter reading	AMR
自动车辆定位系统	Zìdòng chēliàng dìngwèi xìtǒng	Automatic vehicle location system	AVL
自动程序控制	Zìdòng chéngxù kòngzhì	Automatic program control	APC
自动程序设计与记录	Zìdòng chéngxù shèjì yǔ jìlù	Automatic programming and recording	APR
自动程序设计装置	Zìdòng chéngxù shèjì zhuāngzhì	Automatic program unit	APU
自动重发请求	Zìdòng chóngfā qǐngqiú	Automatic repeat request	ARQ
自动重复请求	Zìdòng chóngfù qǐngqiú	Automatic repeat request	ARQ
自动传输测量	Zìdòng chuánshū cèliáng	Automatic call measuring (equipment)	ATME
自动传输测量和信令测试设备	Zìdòng chuánshū cèliáng hé xìnlìng cèshì shèbèi	Automatic transmission measuring and signaling test equipment	ATME
自动传输再选路	Zìdòng chuánshū zàixuǎnlù	Automatic transmission rerouting	
自动 CPU 过热保护	Zìdòng CPU guòrè bǎohù	Automatic central processor unit overheat prevention system	ACOPS
自动 CPU 过热预防系统	Zìdòng CPU guòrè yùfáng xìtǒng	Automatic central processor unit overheat prevention system	ACOPS
自动错误询问	Zìdòng cuòwù xúnwèn	Automatic error interrogation	AEI
自动带宽控制	Zìdòng dàikuān kòngzhì	Automatic bandwidth control	ABC
自动电话呼叫	Zìdòng diànhuà hūjiào	Automatic telephone call	ATC
自动电话业务	Zìdòng diànhuà yèwù	Dial service	DS
自动电话机	Zìdòng diànhuàjī	Automatic telephone set	
自动电路分析程序	Zìdòng diànlù fēnxī chéngxù	Automatic circuit analysis program	ACAP
自动电路恢复	Zìdòng diànlù huīfù	Automatic circuit restoration	ACR
自动电路交换机	Zìdòng diànlù jiāohuànjī	Automatic circuit exchange	ACE
自动电路质量监视	Zìdòng diànlù zhìliàng jiānshì	Automatic circuit quality monitoring	ACQM
自动电平控制	Zìdòng diànpíng kòngzhì	Automatic level control	ALC
自动电压箝位	Zìdòng diànyā qiánwèi	Automatic voltage clamp	AVC
自动地名配置	Zìdòng dìmíng pèizhì	Automated name placement	
自动定时控制	Zìdòng dìngshí kòngzhì	Automatic timing control	ATC
自动定位装置	Zìdòng dìngwèi zhuāngzhì	Automatic positioning equipment (semiconductor mfg)	
自动二进制数据链路	Zìdòng èrjìnzhì shùjù liànlù	Automatic binary data link	ABDL
自动防空情报系统	Zìdòng fángkōng qíngbào xìtǒng	Automatic air defense information system	AADIS
自动反偏压	Zìdòng fǎnpiānyā	Automatic back bias	ABB
自动发射功率控制	Zìdòng fāshè gōnglǜ kòngzhì	Automatic transmission power control	ATPC
自动发射机识别	Zìdòng fāshèjī shíbié	Automatic transmitter identification	ATI
自动发送功率控制	Zìdòng fāsòng gōnglǜ kòngzhì	Automatic transmit power control	ATPC
自动发信功率控制	Zìdòng fāxìn gōnglǜ kòngzhì	Automatic transmission power control	ATPC
自动分行	Zìdòng fēnháng	Wrap	
自动分配话务	Zìdòng fēnpèi huàwù	Automatic call distribution	ACD
自动跟踪	Zìdòng gēnzōng	Automatic track following	ATF
自动跟踪校正	Zìdòng gēnzōng jiàozhèng	Automatic tracking correction	ATC
自动功率降低	Zìdòng gōnglǜ jiàngdī	Automatic power reduction	APR
自动功率减少	Zìdòng gōnglǜ jiǎnshǎo	Automatic power reduction	APR
自动功率控制	Zìdòng gōnglǜ kòngzhì	Automatic power control	APC
自动功率切断	Zìdòng gōnglǜ qiēduàn	Automatic power shutdown	APSD
自动光功率关断	Zìdòng guāng gōnglǜ guānduàn	Automatic (optical) power shut down	APSD
自动光功率减少	Zìdòng guāng gōnglǜ jiǎnshǎo	Automatic (optical) power reduction	APR

自动光控制	Zìdòng guāng kòngzhì	Automatic light control	ALC
自动光圈	Zìdòng guāngquān	Auto-iris	A-I
自动光学检测设备	Zìdòng guāngxué jiǎncè shèbèi	Automatic optical inspection equipment	AOI
自动光学检查	Zìdòng guāngxué jiǎnchá	Automatic optical inspection	AOI
自动挂装	Zìdòng guàzhuāng	Automount (Unix command)	
自动柜员机	Zìdòng guìyuánjī	Automatic teller machine	ATM
自动过载控制	Zìdòng guòzài kòngzhì	Automated overload control	AOC
自动故障查找	Zìdòng gùzhàng cházhǎo	Automatic fault finding	AFF
自动故障定位	Zìdòng gùzhàng dìngwèi	Automatic fault location	AFL
自动号码分析	Zìdòng hàomǎ fēnxī	Automatic number analysis	ANA
自动号码识别	Zìdòng hàomǎ shíbié	Automatic number identification	ANI
自动话务量记录器	Zìdòng huàwùliáng jìlùqì	Automatic traffic recorder	ATR
自动恢复	Zìdòng huīfù	Failback	
自动恢复	Zìdòng huīfù	Automatic recovery	
自动呼叫	Zìdòng hūjiào	Automatic calling	
自动呼叫重连	Zìdòng hūjiào chónglián	Automatic call reconnect	
自动呼叫分布远程截获	Zìdòng hūjiào fēnbù yuǎnchéng jiéhuò	Automatic call distribution remote capture	ADRC
自动呼叫分配	Zìdòng hūjiào fēnpèi	Automatic call distribution	ACD
自动呼叫分配远程截获	Zìdòng hūjiào fēnpèi yuǎnchéng jiéhuò	Automatic call distribution remote capture	ADRC
自动呼叫分配器	Zìdòng hūjiào fēnpèiqì	Automatic call distributor	ACD
自动呼叫号识别	Zìdòng hūjiào hào shíbié	Automatic called number identification	ACNI
自动呼叫记录	Zìdòng hūjiào jìlù	Automatic call recording	ACR
自动呼叫设备转接器	Zìdòng hūjiào shèbèi zhuǎnjiēqì	Automatic calling unit adapter	ACUA
自动呼叫识别	Zìdòng hūjiào shíbié	Automatic call identification	
自动呼叫应答	Zìdòng hūjiào yìngdá	Automatic call acceptance	ACA
自动呼叫装置	Zìdòng hūjiào zhuāngzhì	Automatic calling equipment	ACE
自动检测分析及报告技术	Zìdòng jiǎncè fēnxī jí bàogào jìshù	Self-monitoring analysis and report technology	SMART
自动交换	Zìdòng jiāohuàn	Automatic switching	
自动交换传送网络	Zìdòng jiāohuàn chuánsòng wǎngluò	Automatic switched transport network	ASTN
自动交换光网络	Zìdòng jiāohuàn guāng wǎngluò	Automatic switched optical network	ASON
自动交换节点	Zìdòng jiāohuàn jiédiǎn	Automatic switching node	ASN
自动交换设备	Zìdòng jiāohuàn shèbèi	Automatic switching equipment	
自动校正技术	Zìdòng jiàozhèng jìshù	Automatic correction technology	ACT
自动校准	Zìdòng jiàozhǔn	Automatic registration (in GIS)	
自动接入多信道无绳电话	Zìdòng jiērù duōxìndào wúshéng diànhuà	Autoaccess multiple channel cordless telephone	
自动激光关闭	Zìdòng jīguāng guānbì	Automatic laser shutdown	ALS
自动激光关断	Zìdòng jīguāng guānduàn	Automatic laser shutdown	ALS
自动警报呼叫	Zìdòng jǐngbào hūjiào	Automatic alarm call	AAC
自动静态更新	Zìdòng jìngtài gēngxīn	Auto-static updates	
自动静态路由	Zìdòng jìngtài lùyóu	Auto-static routing	
自动计算设备	Zìdòng jìsuàn shèbèi	Automatic computing equipment	ACE
自动纠错系统	Zìdòng jiūcuò xìtǒng	Automatic error correction system	AEC
自动均衡器	Zìdòng jūnhéngqì	Automatic equalizer	AEQ
自动控制	Zìdòng kòngzhì	Automatic control	ZK
自动亮度补偿	Zìdòng liàngdù bǔcháng	Automatic light compensation	ALC
自动链路转移	Zìdòng liànlù zhuǎnyí	Automatic link transfer	ALT

自动灵敏度控制	Zìdòng língmǐndù kòngzhì	Automatic sensitivity control	ASC
自动流程分析	Zìdòng liúchéng fēnxī	Automatic flow process analysis	AFPA
自动路由选择	Zìdòng lùyóu xuǎnzé	Automatic route selection	ARS
自动忙时保留呼叫装置	Zìdòng mángshí bǎoliú hūjiào zhuāngzhì	Automatic camp-on busy	ACB
自动喷水灭火系统	Zìdòng pēnshuǐ mièhuǒ xìtǒng	Sprinkler system	SS
自动偏振控制	Zìdòng piānzhèn kòngzhì	Automatic polarization control	APC
自动批处理文件	Zìdòng pīchǔlǐ wénjiàn	Auto-executing batch (autoexec.bat) file	
自动平衡控制	Zìdòng pínghéng kòngzhì	Automatic level control	ALC
自动平衡系统	Zìdòng pínghéng xìtǒng	Auto balance system (computer disk)	ABS
自动频率公用	Zìdòng pínlǜ gōngyòng	Automatic frequency sharing	
自动频率控制	Zìdòng pínlǜ kòngzhì	Automatic frequency control	AFC
自动频率控制的灵敏度门限	Zìdòng pínlǜ kòngzhìde língmǐndù ménxiàn	Sensitivity threshold of automatic frequency control	
自动频率调谐	Zìdòng pínlǜ tiáoxié	Automatic frequency tuning	AFT
自动频率微调	Zìdòng pínlǜ wēitiáo	Automatic frequency fine control	AFC
自动频率微调捕捉范围	Zìdòng pínlǜ wēitiáo bǔzhuō fànwéi	Automatic frequency fine control pull-in range	
自动频率微调捕捉时间	Zìdòng pínlǜ wēitiáo bǔzhuō shíjiān	Automatic frequency fine control pull-in time	
自动频率微调剩余误差	Zìdòng pínlǜ wēitiáo shèngyú wùchā	Automatic frequency fine control residual error	
自动频率微调同步范围	Zìdòng pínlǜ wēitiáo tóngbù fànwéi	Automatic frequency fine control locking-in range	
自动频率微调最大跟踪速率	Zìdòng pínlǜ wēitiáo zuìdà gēnzōng sùlǜ	Automatic frequency fine control maximum tracking rate	
自动请求重传	Zìdòng qǐngqiú chóngchuán	Automatic repeat request	ARQ
自动请求重发	Zìdòng qǐngqiú chóngfā	Automatic repeat request	ARQ
自动扫描接收机	Zìdòng sǎomiáo jiēshōujī	Automatic-scanning receiver	
自动色彩监视器	Zìdòng sècǎi jiānshìqì	Automatic color monitor	ACM
自动生成工具	Zìdòng shēngchéng gōngjù	Auto-build tool	ABT
自动声音识别	Zìdòng shēngyīn shíbié	Automatic speech recognition	ASR
自动时间校正器	Zìdòng shíjiān jiàozhèngqì	Automatic timing corrector	ATC
自动矢量化	Zìdòng shǐliànghuà	Automated vectorization	
自动收发	Zìdòng shōufā	Automatic send and receive	ASR
自动收发机	Zìdòng shōufājī	Automatic send-receiver	ASR
自动输出控制	Zìdòng shūchū kòngzhì	Automated output control	AOC
自动数据变换器	Zìdòng shùjù biànhuànqì	Automatic data translator	ADT
自动数据处理	Zìdòng shùjù chǔlǐ	Automatic data processing	ADP
自动数据处理程序	Zìdòng shùjù chǔlǐ chéngxù	Automatic data processing program	ADPP
自动数据处理设备	Zìdòng shùjù chǔlǐ shèbèi	Automatic data processing equipment	ADPE
自动数据处理系统	Zìdòng shùjù chǔlǐ xìtǒng	Automatic data processing system	ADPS
自动数据跟踪	Zìdòng shùjù gēnzōng	Automatic data tracking	ADT
自动数据交换	Zìdòng shùjù jiāohuàn	Automatic data exchange	ADX
自动数据交换系统	Zìdòng shùjù jiāohuàn xìtǒng	Automatic data exchange system	ADXS
自动数据交换系统	Zìdòng shùjù jiāohuàn xìtǒng	Automatic data switching system	ADSS
自动数据均衡电路调制解调器	Zìdòng shùjù jūnhéng diànlù tiáozhì jiětiáoqì	Automatic data equalizer modem	ADEM
自动数据速率变换器	Zìdòng shùjù sùlǜ biànhuànqì	Automatic data rate changer	ADRC
自动数据远程通信服务	Zìdòng shùjù yuǎnchéng tōngxìn fúwù	Automated data and telecommunications service	ADTS
自动数字网络交换中心	Zìdòng shùzì wǎngluò jiāohuàn zhōngxīn	Automatic digital network switching center	ASC
自动隧道	Zìdòng suìdào	Automated tunneling	AT

自动锁相	Zìdòng suǒxiāng	Automatic phase lock	APL
自动索引技术	Zìdòng suǒyǐn jìshù	Automated indexing technology	
自动台	Zìdòng tái	Auto system	AS
自动特征识别	Zìdòng tèzhēng shíbié	Automated feature recognition	
自动调效屏幕尺寸和中心位置	Zìdòng tiáoxiào píngmù chǐcùn hé zhōngxīn wèizhì	Auto-sizing and centering (video term)	ASC
自动调谐控制	Zìdòng tiáoxié kòngzhì	Automatic tuning control	ATC
自动同步设备（单元）	Zìdòng tóngbù shèbèi (dānyuán)	Automatic synchronizing unit	ASU
自动图象传输系统	Zìdòng túxiàng chuánshū xìtǒng	Automatic picture transmission system	APTS
自动图象控制	Zìdòng túxiàng kòngzhì	Automatic picture control	APC
自动网络拨号	Zìdòng wǎngluò bōhào	Automatic network dialing	AND
自动维护	Zìdòng wéihù	Automatic maintenance	am
自动维护运行（操作）	Zìdòng wéihù yùnxíng (cāozuò)	Automatic maintenance operation	AMO
自动位置报告	Zìdòng wèizhì bàogào	Automatic position reporting	APR
自动位置识别	Zìdòng wèizhì shíbié	Automatic location identification	ALI
自动文件传递	Zìdòng wénjiàn chuándì	Automatic file transfer	AFT
自动误差分析	Zìdòng wùchā fēnxī	Automatic error analysis	AEA
自动相关监视	Zìdòng xiāngguān jiānshì	Automatic dependent surveillance (civil air)	ADS
自动相关声码器	Zìdòng xiāngguān shēngmǎqì	Automatic correlation vocoder	ACV
自动相位补偿	Zìdòng xiàngwèi bǔcháng	Automatic phase compensation	APC
自动相位控制	Zìdòng xiàngwèi kòngzhì	Automatic phase control	APC
自动相位同步	Zìdòng xiàngwèi tóngbù	Automatic phase synchronization	APS
自动响应	Zìdòng xiǎngyìng	Automated response	
自动线路识别	Zìdòng xiànlù shíbié	Automatic line identification	ALI
自动斜率控制	Zìdòng xiélǜ kòngzhì	Automatic slope control	ASC
自动信道选择	Zìdòng xìndào xuǎnzé	Automatic channel selection	
自动信息交换	Zìdòng xìnxī jiāohuàn	Automatic message exchange	AME
自动选择性控制	Zìdòng xuǎnzéxìng kòngzhì	Automatic selectivity control	ASC
自动寻呼系统	Zìdòng xúnhū xìtǒng	Automatic paging system	
自动遥控	Zìdòng yáokòng	Automatic remote control	ARC
自动压缩	Zìdòng yāsuō	Automatic compression	
自动业务发现	Zìdòng yèwù fāxiàn	Automatic service discovery	ASD
自动译码	Zìdòng yìmǎ	Automatic code translation	ACT
自动译码器	Zìdòng yìmǎqì	Automatic data translator	ADT
自动引导装入程序	Zìdòng yǐndǎo zhuāngrù chéngxù	Automatic bootstrap loader	ABL
自动音调校正	Zìdòng yīndiào jiàozhèng	Automatic tone correction	ATC
自动音调控制	Zìdòng yīndiào kòngzhì	Automatic tone control	ATC
自动应答	Zìdòng yìngdá	Automatic answerback	AAB
自动应答	Zìdòng yìngdá	Automatically answer	AA
自动应答干线	Zìdòng yìngdá gànxiàn	Automatic answer trunk	AAT
自动应答自动呼叫	Zìdòng yìngdá zìdòng hūjiào	Automatic answering automatic calling	AAAC, A3C
自动应用开发系统	Zìdòng yìngyòng kāifā xìtǒng	Automatic applications development system	AADS
自动音量控制	Zìdòng yīnliàng kòngzhì	Automatic volume control	AVC
自动音频交换	Zìdòng yīnpín jiāohuàn	Automatic audio switching	AAS
自动移相器	Zìdòng yíxiàngqì	Automatic phase shifter	APS
自动拥塞控制	Zìdòng yōngsè kòngzhì	Automatic congestion control	ACC

自动拥塞控制信息消息	Zìdòng yōngsè kòngzhì xìnxī xiāoxi	Automatic congestion control information massage	ACC
自动远端数据终端	Zìdòng yuǎnduān shùjù zhōngduān	Automatic remote data terminal	ARDT
自动语音识别	Zìdòng yǔyīn shíbié	Automatic speech recognition	ASR
自动语音应答系统	Zìdòng yǔyīn yìngdá xìtǒng	Automatic voice response system	AVRS
自动阈值控制	Zìdòng yùzhí kòngzhì	Auto-threshold control	ATC
自动杂波消除电路	Zìdòng zábō xiāochú diànlù	Automatic noise canceller	ANC
自动增益控制	Zìdòng zēngyì kòngzhì	Automatic gain control	AGC
自动增益控制特性	Zìdòng zēngyì kòngzhì tèxìng	Automatic gain-control (AGC) characteristic	
自动增益控制的[灵敏度]门限	Zìdòng zēngyì kòngzhìde língmǐndù ménxiàn	Sensitivity threshold of automatic gain control	
自动障碍分析	Zìdòng zhàng'ài fēnxī	Automatic trouble analysis	ATA
自动振幅控制	Zìdòng zhènfú kòngzhì	Automatic amplitude control	AAC
自动制图/设施管理	Zìdòng zhìtú/shèshī guǎnlǐ	Automated mapping and facilities management	AM/FM
自动中继线测试	Zìdòng zhōngjìxiàn cèshì	Automatic trunk testing	ATT
自动转报	Zìdòng zhuǎnbào	Automatic transit telegram (Telex)	ZB
自动转发	Zìdòng zhuǎnfā	Automatic retransmission	
自动转发服务	Zìdòng zhuǎnfā fúwù	Automatic retransmission service	ARX
自动专用分路交换机	Zìdòng zhuānyòng fēnlù jiāohuànjī	Automatic private branch exchange	APBX
自动专用 IP 寻址	Zìdòng zhuānyòng IP xúnzhǐ	Automatic private IP addressing	APIPA
自动化	Zìdònghuà	Automation	
自动化对象	Zìdònghuà duìxiàng	Automation object (for database)	
自动化服务器	Zìdònghuà fúwùqì	Automation server (for database)	
自动化数字网络系统	Zìdònghuà shùzì wǎngluò xìtǒng	Automated digital network system	ADNS
自动化制图	Zìdònghuà zhìtú	Automated cartography	
字段	Zìduàn	Field (in a database, in Java)	
字段长度	Zìduàn chángdù	Field length (for database)	
字段定义	Zìduàn dìngyì	Field definition	
字段地址	Zìduàn dìzhǐ	Field address (computer term)	FA
字段名	Zìduàn míng	Field name	
字段目录	Zìduàn mùlù	Field catalogue	
字段说明	Zìduàn shuōmíng	Field specifications	
字段索引	Zìduàn suǒyǐn	Item indexing	
字段终止符	Zìduàn zhōngzhǐ fú	Field terminator	
子对象	Zǐduìxiàng	Sub-object	
自对准法兰	Zìduìzhǔn fǎlán	Socket flange	
子多路复用器	Zǐduōlù fùyòngqì	Sub-multiplexer unit	SMX
自发辐射噪声系数	Zìfā fúshè zàoshēng xìshù	Spontaneous noise figure	
自放电	Zìfàngdiàn	Self-discharge	
自返式取样器	Zìfǎnshì qǔyàngqì	Boomerang grabber (sampler)	
自返式深海取样管	Zìfǎnshì shēnhǎi qǔyàng guǎn	Boomerang gravity corer	
字符	Zìfú	Alphanumeric character	
字符	Zìfú	Character	
字符差错率	Zìfú chācuò lǜ	Character error ratio	
字符长度	Zìfú chángdù	Character size	
字符出错误率测试	Zìfú chū cuòwùlǜ cèshì	Character error rate test	CERT
字符出错误率测试器	Zìfú chū cuòwùlǜ cèshìqì	Character error rate tester	CERT

字符串	Zìfú chuàn	Character string	
字符串函数	Zìfú chuàn hánshù	Character string function	
字符串类型	Zìfú chuàn lèixíng	Character string type	
字符等待时间	Zìfú děngdài shíjiān	Character waiting time	CWT
字符等待整体	Zìfú děngdài zhěngtǐ	Character waiting integer	CWI
字符电报	Zìfú diànbào	Alphabetic telegraphy	
字符定位	Zìfú dìngwèi	Character alignment	
字符地址字	Zìfú dìzhǐ zì	Character address word	CAW
字符方式通信适配器	Zìfú fāngshì tōngxìn shìpèiqì	Character mode communications adapter	CMCA
字符格式	Zìfú géshi	Character format	
字符集	Zìfú jí	Character set	
字符间距（仅对固定间距字模而言）	Zìfú jiānjù (jǐn duì gùdìng jiānjù zìmú éryán)	Character spacing (for constant spacing fonts only)	
字符间隙	Zìfú jiànxì	Inter-character space	
字符检验	Zìfú jiǎnyàn	Character check	
字符校验位	Zìfú jiàoyàn wèi	Character check bit	
字符基线	Zìfú jīxiàn	Character baseline	
字符取向	Zìfú qǔxiàng	Character orientation	
字符属性	Zìfú shǔxìng	Character attribute	CA
字符速率	Zìfú sùlǜ	Character rate	
字符同步	Zìfú tóngbù	Character alignment	
字符同相	Zìfú tóngxiāng	Character in phase	
字符图像	Zìfú túxiàng	Character image	
字符信号	Zìfú xìnhào	Character signal	
字符序列	Zìfú xùliè	Character sequence	
字符周期	Zìfú zhōuqī	Character cycle	
字符走向	Zìfú zǒuxiàng	Character path	
子复合型	Zifùhéxíng	Sub-complex	
字符间休止状态	Zìfú-jiān xiūzhǐ zhuàngtài	Inter-character rest condition	
子复用板	Zifùyòng bǎn	Sub-multiplexer interface	SMI
子复用器	Zifùyòngqì	Sub-multiplexer	SMUX,SM
字符-字节串行传输	Zìfú—zijié chuànháng chuánshū	Character-byte serial transmission	CBST
资格级别	Zīge jíbié	Qualification level (IPsec)	
子公共信道多路复用和多路分解器	Zigōnggòng xìndào duōlù fùyòng hé duōlù fēnjiěqì	Sub-highway multiplexer and demultiplexer	SMDX
自构形	Zìgòuxíng	Autoform	
字冠	Zìguān	Prefix	
子环	Zihuán	Sub-loop	
自回归频谱估计捕获技术	Zìhuíguī pínpǔ gūjì bǔhuò jìshù	Autoregressive spectral estimation acquisition technique	ASEAT
子集	Zǐjí	Subset	
自激荡器	Zìjī dàngqì	Self-excited oscillation	
自己动手作	Zìjǐ dòngshǒu zuò	Do it yourself	DIY
子集句式	Zǐjí jùshì	Subset phrasing	
子集生成	Zǐjí shēngchéng	Generating subsets	
自激振荡	Zìjī zhèndàng	Self-excited oscillation	
子架	Zijià	Shelf	

子基地台	Zijīdìtái	Sub-base station	
字节	Zìjié	Byte	
字节	Zìjié	Octet	
字节串行	Zìjié chuànháng	Byte serial	
字节代替	Zìjié dàitì	Byte substitution	
字节代替变换	Zìjié dàitì biànhuàn	Byte substitution	
字节间插和消间插	Zìjié jiānchā hé xiāojiānchā	Byte interleaving and disinterleaving	
字节流协议用于因特网的主机字节流业务	Zìjié liú xiéyì yòng yú Yīntèwǎngde zhǔjī zìjié liú yèwù	Octet stream protocol for Internet-hosted octet stream service	OSP:IHOSS
字节替换	Zìjié tìhuan	Byte substitution	
自解文件	Zìjiě wénjiàn	Self-expanding file	
字节帧	Zìjié zhèng	Byte frame	
子记录的顺序	Zijìlùde shùnxù	Order of sub-records	
子句	Zijù	Clause	
自举路由器	Zìjǔ lùyóuqì	Bootstrap router	BSR
子卡	Zikǎ	Daughter card	
子空间	Zikōngjiān	Sub-space	
字库	Zìkù	Character palette	
字块	Zìkuài	Block	
字块检验序列	Zìkuài jiǎnyàn xùliè	Block check sequence	BCS
子类	Zǐlèi	Sub-class	
子类	Zǐlèi	Child class	
子类同步传输模式	Zǐlèi tóngbù chuánshū móshì	Sub-STM (synchronous transfer mode)	sSTM
子类别	Zǐlèibié	Sub-class	
子类型	Zǐlèixíng	Sub-type	
自量负载指数	Zìliàng fùzài zhǐshù	Vector load index	
资料勘探	Zīliào kāntàn	Data mining	
子例程	Zilìchéng	Sub-routine	
字面常数	Zìmiàn chángshù	Literal constant	
字模	Zìmú	Font	
字模大小	Zìmú dàxiǎo	Font size	
字母键位	Zìmǔ jiànwèi	Letter case	
字母数字	Zìmǔ shùzì	Alphanumeric	
字母转移	Zìmǔ zhuǎnyí	Letter shift	
字母转移信号	Zìmǔ zhuǎnyí xìnhào	Letter-shift signal	
子目录	Zǐmùlù	Sub-directory	
子配置模式	Zipèizhì móshì	Sub-configuration mode	
自平衡桥式功率计	Zìpínghéng qiáoshì gōnglǜjì	Self-balancing power bridge	
自然地图	Zìrán dìtú	Physical map (GIS term)	
自然对流	Zìrán duìliú	Natural convection	
自然二进制编码的十进制	Zìrán èrjìnzhì biānmǎde shíjìnzhì	Natural binary-coded decimal	NBCD
自然二进制编码的十六进制	Zìrán èrjìnzhì biānmǎde shíliùjìnzhì	Natural binary-coded hexadecimal	NBCH
自然辐射源	Zìrán fúshèyuán	Natural radiator	
自然干扰	Zìrán gānrǎo	Natural interference	
自然空间辐射	Zìrán kōngjiān fúshè	Natural space radiation	
自然冷却	Zìrán lěngquè	Natural cooling	

自然频率	Zìrán pínlǜ	Natural frequency	
自然谐振频率	Zìrán xiézhèn pínlǜ	Natural resonance frequency	
自然语言处理	Zìrán yǔyán chǔlǐ	Natural language processing	
自然语言汉语查询界面	Zìrán yǔyán hànyǔ cháxún jièmiàn	Natural language Chinese query interface	NLCQI
自然语言理解	Zìrán yǔyán lǐjiě	Natural language processing	NLP
自然噪声	Zìrán zàoshēng	Natural noise	
子矢量	Zishǐliàng	Sub-vector	
自适应	Zìshìyìng	Adaptation, adaptive; auto-negotiation (modem function)	
自适应变换编码	Zìshìyìng biànhuàn biānmǎ	Adaptive transform coding	ATC
自适应差分脉冲编码调制	Zìshìyìng chāfēn màichōng biānmǎ tiáozhì	Adaptive differential pulse code modulation	ADPCM
自适应差分脉码调制	Zìshìyìng chāfēn màimǎ tiáozhì	Adaptive differential pulse code modulation	ADPCM
自适应带宽	Zìshìyìng dàikuān	Self-adaptive bandwidth	
自适应动目标显示	Zìshìyìng dòng mùbiāo xiǎnshì	Adaptive mobile target indicator	Adaptive MTI
自适应动态分析和维修	Zìshìyìng dòngtài fēnxī hé wéixiū	Adaptive dynamic analysis and maintenance	ADAM
自适应动态模糊系统	Zìshìyìng dòngtài móhú xìtǒng	Adaptive dynamic fuzzy system	
自适应短波电台	Zìshìyìng duǎnbō diàntái	Adaptive HF station	
自适应多码率编译码器	Zìshìyìng duōmǎlǜ biānyìmǎqì	Adaptive multirate codec	AMRC
自适应多速率	Zìshìyìng duōsùlǜ	Adaptive multirate	AMR
自适应放大器	Zìshìyìng fàngdàqì	Adaptive amplifier	AA
自适应非线性增强器	Zìshìyìng fēixiànxìng zēngqiángqì	Adaptive non-linear enhancer	ANLE
自适应功率控制	Zìshìyìng gōnglǜ kòngzhì	Adaptive power control	APC
自适应横向滤波器	Zìshìyìng héngxiàng lǜbōqì	Adaptive transversal filter	ATF
自适应接收机	Zìshìyìng jiēshōujī	Adaptive receiver	
自适应计算机试验	Zìshìyìng jìsuànjī shìyàn	Adaptive computer experiment	ACE
自适应均衡	Zìshìyìng jūnhéng	Adaptive equalization	
自适应控制系统	Zìshìyìng kòngzhì xìtǒng	Adaptive control system	
自适应控制优化	Zìshìyìng kòngzhì yōuhuà	Adaptive control optimization	ACO
自适应量化	Zìshìyìng liànghuà	Adaptive quantization	AQ
自适应脉冲编码调制	Zìshìyìng màichōng biānmǎ tiáozhì	Adaptive differential pulse code modulation	ADPCM
自适应脉码调制	Zìshìyìng màimǎ tiáozhì	Adaptive pulse code modulation	APCM
自适应忙	Zìshìyìng máng	Adaptive busy	
自适应判决反馈均衡器	Zìshìyìng pànjué fǎnkuì jūnhéngqì	Adaptive decree feedback equalizer	ADFE
自适应判决反馈均衡器	Zìshìyìng pànjué fǎnkuì jūnhéngqì	Automatic decision feedback equalizer	ADFE
自适应散射干扰衰减器	Zìshìyìng sǎnshè gānrǎo shuāijiǎnqì	Adaptive clutter attenuator	ACA
自适应时域均衡器	Zìshìyìng shíyù jūnhéngqì	Adaptive time domain equalizer	ATDE
自适应数字接入协议	Zìshìyìng shùzì jiērù xiéyì	Adaptive digital access protocol	ADAPt
自适应数字滤波	Zìshìyìng shùzì lǜbō	Adaptive digital filtering	ADF
自适应数字声码器	Zìshìyìng shùzì shēngmǎqì	Adaptive digital vocoder	ADV
自适应算法	Zìshìyìng suànfǎ	Adaptive algorithm	
自适应速度等级调整	Zìshìyìng sùdù děngjí tiáozhěng	Adaptive speed leveling	
自适应天线	Zìshìyìng tiānxiàn	Adaptive antenna	AA
自适应天线系统	Zìshìyìng tiānxiàn xìtǒng	Adaptive antenna system	AAS
自适应调制	Zìshìyìng tiáozhì	Adaptive modulation	
自适应调制编码	Zìshìyìng tiáozhì biānmǎ	Adaptive modulation and coding	AMC
自适应调制系统	Zìshìyìng tiáozhì xìtǒng	Adaptive modulation system	AMS

自适应通道分配	Zìshìyìng tōngdào fēnpèi	Adaptive channel allocation	ACA
自适应通信	Zìshìyìng tōngxìn	Adaptive communication	
自适应图像分析	Zìshìyìng túxiàng fēnxī	Adaptive image analysis	
自适应图像压缩	Zìshìyìng túxiàng yāsuō	Adaptive image compression	
自适应微分脉码调制的部分波段编码	Zìshìyìng wēifēn màimǎ tiáozhìde bùfen bōduàn biānmǎ	Sub-band coding for adaptive differential pulse-code modulation	SBC-ADPCM
自适应无线拥塞控制	Zìshìyìng wúxiàn yōngsè kòngzhì	Adaptive wireless congestion control	
自适应相位代码调制	Zìshìyìng xiàngwèi dàimǎ tiáozhì	Adaptive phase code modulation	APCM
自适应预测	Zìshìyìng yùcè	Adaptive prediction	
自适应预测编码	Zìshìyìng yùcè biānmǎ	Adaptive predictive coding	APC
自适应预测编码器	Zìshìyìng yùcè biānmǎqì	Adaptive predictive coder	APC
自适应运动补偿算法	Zìshìyìng yùndòng bǔcháng suànfǎ	Adaptive motion compensation algorithm	AMC
自适应阈值控制	Zìshìyìng yùzhí kòngzhì	Adaptive threshold control	ATC
自适应噪声消除	Zìshìyìng zàoshēng xiāochú	Adaptive noise cancellation	ANC
自适应增量调制	Zìshìyìng zēngliàng tiáozhì	Adaptive delta modulation	ADM
自适应帧校准	Zìshìyìng zhèng jiàozhǔn	Adaptive frame alignment	
自适应阵列天线	Zìshìyìng zhènliè tiānxiàn	Adaptive array antenna	
子树	Zishù	Sub-tree	
子速率复用器	Zisùlǜ fùyòngqì	Trans-multiplexer	TMUX
子速率解复用器	Zisùlǜ jiěfùyòngqì	Trans-demultiplexer	TDMUX
自锁	Zìsuǒ	Latching	
姿态稳定卫星	Zītài wěndìng wèixīng	Attitude-stabilized satellite	
字体	Zìtǐ	Font (WP command)	
字体彩色	Zìtǐ cǎisè	Text color (WP command)	
字体盒	Zìtǐ hé	Font cartridge	
自同步扰码器	Zìtóngbù rǎomǎqì	Self-synchronous scrambler	
子图	Zitú	Sub-graph	
字凸	Zìtū	Kern	
紫外辐射	Zǐwài fúshè	Ultraviolet radiation	UV
紫外光二极体	Zǐwài guāng èrjítǐ	Ultraviolet photodiode	
紫外固化炉	Zǐwài gùhuà lú	Ultra-violet curing oven (semiconductor mfg)	
紫外硫化炉	Zǐwài liúhuà lú	Ultra-violet curing oven (semiconductor mfg)	
紫外透过滤光镜	Zǐwài tòuguò lǜguāngjìng	Ultraviolet transmitting filter	
紫外吸收滤光镜	Zǐwài xīshōu lǜguāngjìng	Ultraviolet absorbing filter	
紫外线材料	Zǐwàixiàn cáiliào	Ultraviolet materials	
紫外线光源	Zǐwàixiàn guāngyuán	Ultraviolet light source	
紫外线硬化设备	Zǐwàixiàn yìnghuà shèbèi	Ultraviolet curing equipment	
子网	Ziwǎng	Sub-network, sub-net	
子网从属会聚功能	Ziwǎng cóngshǔ huìjù gōngnéng	Sub-network dependent convergence function	SNDCF
子网带宽管理	Ziwǎng dàikuān guǎnlǐ	Sub-net bandwidth management	SBM
子网导向广播地址	Ziwǎng dǎoxiàng guǎngbō dìzhǐ	Sub-net-directed broadcast address (in IP)	
子网地址	Ziwǎng dìzhǐ	Sub-net address	
子网访问协议	Ziwǎng fǎngwèn xiéyì	Sub-network access protocol	SNAP
子网服务数据单元	Ziwǎng fúwù shùjù dānyuán	Sub-network service data unit	SNSDU
子网管理系统	Ziwǎng guǎnlǐ xìtǒng	Sub-network management system	SNM
子网接入点	Ziwǎng jiērù diǎn	Sub-network point of access	SNPA

子网接入协议	Ziwǎng jiērù xiéyì	Sub-network access protocol	SNAP
子网连接	Ziwǎng liánjiē	Sub-network connection	SNC
子网连接保护	Ziwǎng liánjiē bǎohù	Sub-network connection protection	SNCP
子网连接点	Ziwǎng liánjiē diǎn	Sub-network point of attachment	SNPA
子网连接点地址	Ziwǎng liánjiē diǎn dìzhǐ	Sub-network point of attachment address	
子网收敛	Ziwǎng shōuliǎn	Sub-network convergence	
子网相关收敛协议	Ziwǎng xiāngguān shōuliǎn xiéyì	Sub-network dependent convergence protocol	SNDCP
子网协议数据单元	Ziwǎng xiéyì shùjù dānyuán	Sub-network protocol data unit	SNPDU
子网掩码	Ziwǎng yǎnmǎ	Sub-net mask	
子网依赖汇聚	Ziwǎng yīlài huìjù	Sub-network dependent convergence	SNDC
子网依赖汇聚协议	Ziwǎng yīlài huìjù xiéyì	Sub-network dependent convergence protocol	SNDCP
子网依赖汇聚协议分组数据单元	Ziwǎng yīlài huìjù xiéyì fēnzǔ shùjù dānyuán	Sub-network dependent convergence protocol data unit	SN-PDU
子网依赖结合层	Ziwǎng yīlài jiéhé céng	Sub-network dependent convergence layer	SNDC
子午光线	Ziwǔ guāngxiàn	Meridian ray	
子午面	Ziwǔ miàn	Meridian plane	
自陷协议	Zìxiàn xiéyì	Bootstrap protocol	BOOTP
自相关	Zìxiāngguān	Auto-correlation	
自相关预测	Zìxiāngguān yùcè	Auto-correlation prediction	AP
自相关器	Zìxiāngguānqì	Auto-correlator	
子向量	Zixiàngliàng	Sub-vector	SV
子向量标识符	Zixiàngliàng biāozhìfú	Sub-vector indicator	SVI
子向量长度	Zixiàngliàng chángdù	Sub-vector length	SVL
自相位调制	Zìxiàngwèi tiáozhì	Self-phase modulation	SPM
自协方差	Zixiéfāngchà	Auto-covariance	
子信道	Zixìndào	Sub-channel	
子信道号码	Zixìndào hàomǎ	Sub-channel number	SCN
子信道同相传输	Zixìndào tóngxiāng chuánshū	Sub-channel phase transmission	
字型	Zìxíng	Font	
自省	Zìxǐng	Introspection	
字星	Zìxīng	WordStar © (software)	
自行通知汇款业务	Zìxíng tōngzhī huìkuǎn yèwù	Remittance service where sender informs the payee	
子系统复合表示语	Zixìtǒng fùhé biǎoshì yǔ	Sub-system multiplicity indicator (in SS7)	
子系统号码	Zixìtǒng hàomǎ	Sub-system number	SSN
子系统拥塞	Zixìtǒng yōngsè	Sub-system congestion	SSC
自选传真服务	Zìxuǎn chuánzhēn fúwù	Fax on demand	
自选路由标签	Zìxuǎn lùyóu biāoqiān	Self routing tag	SRTR
自学网桥	Zìxué wǎngqiáo	Learning Bridge	
自学习系统	Zìxuéxí xìtǒng	Self-learning system	
子序列越区规程	Zixùliè yuèqū guīchéng	Subsequent handover procedure	
资讯超速公路	Zīxùn chāosù gōnglù	Information superhighway	
资讯查找	Zīxùn cházhǎo	Infoseek	
咨询节点	Zīxún jiédiǎn	Interrogating node	IN
资讯科技展	Zīxùn kējì zhǎn	Informatics	
资讯商业	Zīxùn shāngyè	Infomercial	
资讯化空间	Zīxùnhuà kōngjiān	Infocosm	

子业务字段	Ziyèwù zìduàn	Sub-service field	SSF
资用功率	Zīyòng gōnglǜ	Available power	
自用呼叫中心	Ziyòng hūjiào zhōngxīn	In-house call center	
自由波长解决方案	Ziyóu bōcháng jiějué fāng'àn	Free wavelength solution	FWS
自由电子激光	Ziyóu diànzǐ jīguāng	Free electron laser	
自由访问控制列表	Ziyóu fǎngwèn kòngzhì lièbiǎo	Discretionary access control list	DACL
自由辐射频率	Ziyóu fúshè pínlǜ	Free-radiation frequency (for ISM apparatus)	
自由交换区	Ziyóu jiāohuàn qū	Free trade zone	
自由空间	Ziyóu kōngjiān	Free space	
自由空间波长	Ziyóu kōngjiān bōcháng	Free space wavelength	
自由空间传播	Ziyóu kōngjiān chuánbō	Free space propagation	
自由空间光系统	Ziyóu kōngjiān guāng xìtǒng	Free space optical system	
自由空间光纤	Ziyóu kōngjiān guāngxiān	Free space optics	FSO
自由空间光学通信	Ziyóu kōngjiān guāngxué tōngxìn	Free space optical communications	FSO
自由空间基本传输损耗	Ziyóu kōngjiān jīběn chuánshū sǔnhào	Free space basic transmission loss	
自由空间衰减	Ziyóu kōngjiān shuāijiǎn	Free space attenuation	
自由谱宽	Ziyóu pǔ kuān	Free spectral range	
自由振荡	Ziyóu zhèndàng	Free-run oscillation	
子域	Ziyù	Sub-area	
自愈	Ziyù	Self-healing	
自愈环	Ziyù huán	Self-healing hybrid ring (SDH term)	SHR
子域节点	Ziyù jiédiǎn	Sub-area node	
自愈网	Ziyù wǎng	Self-healing network	
资源	Zīyuán	Resources	
资源保留协议	Zīyuán bǎoliú xiéyì	Resource reserVation protocol	RRVP
资源冲突	Zīyuán chōngtū	Resource contention	
资源单位	Zīyuán dānwèi	Resource unit	RU
资源访问功能	Zīyuán fǎngwèn gōngnéng	Access to the resources function	ARF
资源附加网络	Zīyuán fùjiā wǎngluò	Attached resource computer net	ARCnet
资源管理	Zīyuán guǎnlǐ	Resource management	RM
资源管理构件	Zīyuán guǎnlǐ gòujiàn	Resource management building block	RMBB
资源管理和运营	Zīyuán guǎnlǐ hé yùnyíng	Resource management and operations	
资源管理信元	Zīyuán guǎnlǐ xìnyuán	Resource management cell	
资源管理系统	Zīyuán guǎnlǐ xìtǒng	Property management system	PMS
资源管理器	Zīyuán guǎnlǐqì	Resource manager	RM
资源监视器	Zīyuán jiānshìqì	Resource monitor	
资源记录	Zīyuán jìlù	Resource record	RR
资源可用性确认	Zīyuán kěyòngxìng quèrèn	Resources available confirmation	RAC
资源可用性指示	Zīyuán kěyòngxìng zhǐshì	Resource availability indication	RAI
资源控制对象	Zīyuán kòngzhì duìxiàng	Resource control object	RCO
资源描述方式	Zīyuán miáoshù fāngshì	Resource description format	RDF
资源描述框架	Zīyuán miáoshù kuàngjià	Resource description framework	RDF
资源派生	Zīyuán pàishēng	Resource fork	
资源请求表	Zīyuán qǐngqiú biǎo	Resource request table	RRT
资源文件	Zīyuán wénjiàn	Resource document	
资源限制	Zīyuán xiànzhì	Resource constraint	

资源异构集群系统模拟器	Zīyuán yìgòu jíqún xìtǒng mónǐqì	Cluster system simulator of heterogeneous resources	CSSHR
资源域	Zīyuán yù	Resource domain	
资源预留协议	Zīyuán yùliú xiéyì	Resource reservation protocol	RSVP
资源组成段	Zīyuán zǔchéng duàn	Resource configuration fragment	RCF
子载波复用	Zizàibō fùyòng	Sub-carrier multiplex	SCM
子帧	Zizhèng	Sub-frame	
自治系统	Zìzhì xìtǒng	Autonomous system	AS
自治系统边界路由器	Zìzhì xìtǒng biānjiè lùyóuqì	Autonomous system border router	ASBR
自治区系统边界路由器	Zìzhìqū xìtǒng biānjiè lùyóuqì	Autonomous system boundary router	ASBR
资助	Zīzhù	Subsidy	
自主存取控制	Zìzhǔ cúnqǔ kòngzhì	Discretionary access control (Linux)	DAC
自主代理	Zìzhǔ dàilǐ	Autonomous agent	
自主访问控制	Zìzhǔ fǎngwèn kòngzhì	Discretionary access control (IPsec)	
自助汇款	Zìzhù huìkuǎn	Self-service remitting	
自主交换	Zìzhǔ jiāohuàn	Autonomous switching	
资助金	Zīzhù jīn	Grant-in-aid	
自主隧道	Zìzhǔ suìdào	Voluntary tunnel	
自主显示器	Zìzhǔ xiǎnshìqì	Autonomous indicator (radar term)	
自主系统边界路由器	Zìzhǔ xìtǒng biānjiè lùyóuqì	Autonomous system boundary router	ASBR
自转周期	Zìzhuàn zhōuqī	Sidereal period of rotation (of an object in space)	
子组安全控制器	Zizǔ ānquán kòngzhìqì	Sub-group security controller	SGSC
字组传送指令	Zìzǔ chuánsòng zhǐlìng	Block transfer instruction	BTI
自阻抗	Zìzǔkàng	Self impedance (of antenna elements)	
自组织无线电通信网	Zìzǔzhī wúxiàndiàn tōngxìn wǎng	Self-organizing radio communication network	
纵电动势	Zòng diàndòngshì	Longitudinal electromotive force	
总电子含量	Zǒng diànzǐ hánliàng	Total electron content	TEC
总监测中心	Zǒng jiāncè zhōngxīn	General monitoring center	GMC
总建筑面积	Zǒng jiànzhù miànjī	Gross floor area	
总流量控制	Zǒng liúliàng kòngzhì	Global flow control	GFC
总配线架	Zǒng pèixiànjià	Main distributing frame	
总起止畸变度	Zǒng qǐzhǐ jībiàndù	Degree of gross start-stop distortion	
总失真系数	Zǒng shīzhēn xìshù	Total distortion factor	
总输出功率	Zǒng shūchū gōnglǜ	Total output power	
总损耗（无线电链路的）	Zǒng sǔnhào (wúxiàndiàn liànlùde)	Total loss (of a radio link)	
总效用最大化	Zǒng xiàoyòng zuìdàhuà	Maximization of total utility	
总谐波失真	Zǒng xiébō shīzhēn	Total harmonic distortion	THD
总谐波失真加噪音	Zǒng xiébō shīzhēn jiā zàoyīn	Total harmonic distortion plus noise	THD+N
总谐波系数	Zǒng xiébō xìshù	Total harmonic factor	
总有效面积	Zǒng yǒuxiào miànjī	Total effective area (of an antenna for a given direction)	
总噪声	Zǒng zàoshēng	Overall noise	
总噪声级	Zǒng zàoshēng jí	Total noise level	TNL
总状况	Zǒng zhuàngkuàng	Global status	
纵波	Zòngbō	Longitudinal wave	
总额定响度	Zǒng'é dìngxiǎngdù	Overall loudness rating	OLR
综合办公室自动化系统	Zōnghé bàngōngshì zìdònghuà xìtǒng	Integrated automated office system	
综合布线	Zōnghé bùxiàn	Generic cabling	

综合布线网络系统	Zōnghé bùxiàn wǎngluò xìtǒng	Integrated distribution network system	IDNS
综合布线系统	Zōnghé bùxiàn xìtǒng	Premises distribution system	PDS
综合参考点	Zōnghé cānkǎo diǎn	Integrated reference point	IRP
综合测试和检查程序	Zōnghé cèshì hé jiǎnchá chéngxù	Integrated test and checkout procedures	ITCP
综合测试仪	Zōnghé cèshìyí	General-purpose tester	
综合电缆、光缆	Zōnghé diànlǎn、guānglǎn	Hybrid cable	
综合电器介面	Zōnghé diànqì jièmiàn	Integrated devices electronics	IDE
综合电子信号处理机	Zōnghé diànzi xìnhào chǔlǐjī	Integrated electronic signal processor	IESP
综合电子战系统	Zōnghé diànzǐzhàn xìtǒng	Integrated electronic warfare system	
综合定位系统	Zōnghé dìngwèi xìtǒng	Integrated positioning system	
综合地形单元制图	Zōnghé dìxíng dānyuán zhìtú	Integrated terrain unit mapping	ITUM
综合符号调式程序	Zōnghé fúhào diàoshì chéngxù	Integrated symbolic debugger	ISD
综合服务	Zōnghé fúwù	Integrated service	
综合服务数字网络	Zōnghé fúwù shùzì wǎngluò	Integrated services digital network	ISDN
综合服务数字终端	Zōnghé fúwù shùzì zhōngduān	Integrated services digital terminal	ISDT
综合光缆	Zōnghé guānglǎn	Hybrid cable	
综合规划司	Zōnghé guīhuà sī	Department of Planning (MII)	
综合环境试验	Zōnghé huánjìng shìyàn	Combined environment test	
综合交换和传输网络	Zōnghé jiāohuàn hé chuánshū wǎngluò	Integrated switching and transmission network	ISTN
综合接地	Zōnghé jiēdì	Integrated ground	
综合结点信息	Zōnghé jiédiǎn xìnxī	Integrated node information	
综合接口局	Zōnghé jiēkǒujú	Integrated gateway	
综合接入服务器	Zōnghé jiērù fúwùqì	Unified access server	UAS
综合接入设备	Zōnghé jiērù shèbèi	Integrated access device	IAD
综合计划	Zōnghé jìhuà	Comprehensive plan	
综合近端串扰	Zōnghé jìnduān chuànrǎo	Power sum near-end crosstalk	PS-NEXT
综合宽带接入系统	Zōnghé kuāndài jiērù xìtǒng	Integrated broadband access system	IBAS
综合宽带通信系统	Zōnghé kuāndài tōngxìn xìtǒng	Integrated wideband communication system	IWCS
综合链信息	Zōnghé liàn xìnxī	Integrated link information	
综合链路层管理	Zōnghé liànlù céng guǎnlǐ	Consolidated link layer management	CLLM
综合流程图	Zōnghé liúchéngtú	General flow chart	GF
综合年度增长率	Zōnghé niándù zēngzhǎnglǜ	Combined annual growth rate	CAGR
综合配线架	Zōnghé pèixiànjià	Combined distribution frame	
综合声音信息系统	Zōnghé shēngyīn xìnxī xìtǒng	Integrated voice-messaging system	IVMS
综合税务系统	Zōnghé shuìwù xìtǒng	Inland Revenue integrated system	IRIS
综合数据网	Zōnghé shùjù wǎng	Integrated data network	IDN
综合数字传输和交换	Zōnghé shùzì chuánshū hé jiāohuàn	Integrated digital transmission and switching	
综合数字环路载波	Zōnghé shùzì huánlù zàibō	Integrated digital loop carrier	IDLC
综合数字通信系统	Zōnghé shùzì tōngxìn xìtǒng	Integrated digital communication system	IDCS
综合数字网	Zōnghé shùzì wǎng	Integrated digital network	IDN
综合通信控制板	Zōnghé tōngxìn kòngzhì bǎn	Integrated communications control panel	ICCP
综合图	Zōnghé tú	Composite map; integrated map	
综合网关模块	Zōnghé wǎng guān mókuài	Integrated gateway boards	IGW
综合网络管理	Zōnghé wǎngluò guǎnlǐ	Integrated network management	INM
综合网络管理系统	Zōnghé wǎngluò guǎnlǐ xìtǒng	Integrated network management system	INMS
综合网络的 Java API	Zōnghé wǎngluòde Java API	Java APIs for integrated networks	JAIN

综合相位控制	Zōnghé xiàngwèi kòngzhì	Integrated phase control	
综合性能分析	Zōnghé xìngnéng fēnxī	General performance analysis	
综合信息系统	Zōnghé xìnxī xìtǒng	Integrated information system	
综合业务单元	Zōnghé yèwù dānyuán	Integrated services unit	ISU
综合业务管理点	Zōnghé yèwù guǎnlǐ diǎn	Integrated service management point	ISMP
综合业务管理功能	Zōnghé yèwù guǎnlǐ gōngnéng	Integrated service management function	ISMF
综合业务管理接入点	Zōnghé yèwù guǎnlǐ jiērù diǎn	Integrated service management access point	ISMAP
综合业务接入网	Zōnghé yèwù jiērù wǎng	Integrated service access network	ISAN
综合业务控制点	Zōnghé yèwù kòngzhì diǎn	Integrated services control point	ISCP
综合业务控制功能	Zōnghé yèwù kòngzhì gōngnéng	Integrated service control function	ISCF
综合业务企业交换	Zōnghé yèwù qǐyè jiāohuàn	Integrated services business exchange	ISBX
综合业务生成环境点	Zōnghé yèwù shēngchéng huánjìng diǎn	Integrated service creation environment point	ISCEP
综合业务数据点	Zōnghé yèwù shùjù diǎn	Integrated service data point	ISDN
综合业务数据网络	Zōnghé yèwù shùjù wǎngluò	Integrated service data network	ISDN
综合业务数字网	Zōnghé yèwù shùzì wǎng	Integrated services digital network	ISDN
综合业务数字网用户部分	Zōnghé yèwù shùzì wǎng yònghù bùfen	Integrated services digital network user part	ISUP
综合业务网	Zōnghé yèwù wǎng	Integrated services network	
综合业务用户交换机	Zōnghé yèwù yònghù jiāohuànjī	Integrated services private branch exchange	ISPBX
综合终端计划	Zōnghé zhōngduān jìhuà	Integrated terminal plan or program	ITP
综合化通信导航识别航空电子系统	Zōnghéhuà tōngxìn dǎoháng shíbié hángkōng diànzǐ xìtǒng	Integrated communication, navigation and identification avionics	ICNIA
纵横比	Zònghéng bǐ	Aspect ratio	
纵横机	Zònghéng jī	Crossbar switch	CBS
纵横接线器	Zònghéng jiēxiànqì	Crossbar switch	
纵横制	Zònghéng zhì	Crossbar	XB
纵横式同轴波导变换器	Zònghéng-shì tóngzhóu bōdǎo biànhuànqì	Crossbar coaxial waveguide transformer	
综合器	Zōnghéqì	Synthesizer	
综合式光缆连接器	Zōnghé-shì guānglǎn liánjiēqì	Hybrid optical cable connector	
踪迹识别符失配	Zōngjī shíbiéfú shīpèi	Trace identifier mismatch	TIM
踪迹终结点	Zōngjī zhōngjié diǎn	Trail termination point	TTP
踪迹线	Zōngjīxiàn	Trace (on an oscilloscope)	
总局代码	Zǒngjú dàimǎ	Central office code	COC
纵模变换损耗	Zòngmó biànhuàn sǔnhào	Longitudinal conversion loss	LCL
总体规划	Zǒngtǐ guīhuà	Master plan	
总体平均	Zǒngtǐ píngjūn	Ensemble average	
总体设计	Zǒngtǐ shèjì	General design	
总体增益	Zǒngtǐ zēngyì	Unity gain	
总体最小二乘法	Zǒngtǐ zuìxiǎo èrchéngfǎ	Total least squares method	
总线	Zǒngxiàn	Bus (usually for computers); trunk line (in telecom)	
总线从设备	Zǒngxiàn cóng shèbèi	Bus slave	
总线调度	Zǒngxiàn diàodù	Bus scheduling	
总线和标记信道	Zǒngxiàn hé biāojì xìndào	Bus and tag channel	
总线交换线路	Zǒngxiàn jiāohuàn xiànlù	Bus exchange line	BEL
总线母板	Zǒngxiàn mǔbǎn	Bus motherboard	
总线请求中断	Zǒngxiàn qǐngqiú zhōngduàn	Bus request interrupt enable	BRIE

总线适配器	Zǒngxiàn shìpèiqì	Bus adapter	BA
总线拓扑	Zǒngxiàn tuòpū	Bus topology	
总线系统	Zǒngxiàn xìtǒng	Bus system	
总线主设备	Zǒngxiàn zhǔ shèbèi	Bus master	
纵向变换损耗	Zòngxiàng biànhuàn sǔnhào	Longitudinal conversion loss	LCL
纵向变换转移损耗	Zòngxiàng biànhuàn zhuǎnyí sǔnhào	Longitudinal conversion transfer loss	LCTL
纵向并联缝隙非谐振式天线阵	Zòngxiàng bìnglián fèngxì fēixiézhèn-shì tiānxiàn zhèn	Longitudinal shunt slot non-resonance array	
纵向并联缝隙谐振式天线阵	Zòngxiàng bìnglián fèngxì xiézhèn-shì tiānxiàn zhèn	Longitudinal shunt slot resonance array	
纵向抖动	Zòngxiàng dǒudòng	Longitudinal judder	
纵向过电压	Zòngxiàng guòdiànyā	Longitudinal over-voltage	
纵向平铺视窗	Zòngxiàng píng pū shìchuāng	Tile vertically (Windows command)	
纵向冗余(码)校验	Zòngxiàng rǒngyú (mǎ) jiàoyàn	Longitudinal redundancy check	LRC
纵向扫描	Zòngxiàng sǎomiáo	Along-track scanning	
纵向制表	Zòngxiàng zhìbiǎo	Horizontal tabulation	
纵向转换衰减	Zòngxiàng zhuǎnhuàn shuāijiǎn	Longitudinal conversion loss	LCL
纵向转换损耗	Zòngxiàng zhuǎnhuàn sǔnhào	Longitudinal conversion loss	LCL
总线型接口	Zǒngxiàn-xíng jiēkǒu	Bus-type interface	
走时曲线	Zǒushí qūxiàn	Travel-time curve	
走向	Zǒuxiàng	Strike	
走向线	Zǒuxiàng xiàn	Strikeout	
走线架	Zǒuxiànjià	Cableway	
族	Zú	Family (IPsec)	
组	Zǔ	Group	
组安全控制器	Zǔ ānquán kòngzhìqì	Group security controller	GSC
组地址	Zǔ dìzhǐ	Group address	
组管理	Zǔ guǎnlǐ	Group management	GM
组关系	Zǔ guānxi	Group relationships	
组交换密钥	Zǔ jiāohuàn mìyào	Group interchange key (IPsec)	GIK
阻流体	Zǔ liútǐ	Bluff body	
组密钥管理协议	Zǔ mìyào guǎnlǐ xiéyì	Group key management protocol	GKMP
组延迟	Zǔ yánchí	Group delay	
钻取	Zuānqǔ	Drill through	
组播	Zǔbō	Multicast	
组播边界网关协议	Zǔbō biānjiè wǎngguān xiéyì	Multicast border gateway protocol	MBGP
组播策略服务器	Zǔbō cèlüè fúwùqì	Multicast service policy server	MuPS
组播传送协议/自组织	Zǔbō chuánsòng xiéyì/zìzǔzhī	Multicast transmission protocol/self-ordering	MTP/SO
组播地址解析服务	Zǔbō dìzhǐ jiěxī fúwù	Multicast address resolution server (IETF usage)	MARS
组播会议媒体流提供程序	Zǔbō huìyì méitǐ liú tígōng chéngxù	Multicast conferencing media stream provider	
组播会议名称	Zǔbō huìyì míngchēng	Multicast conference name	
组播会议模型	Zǔbō huìyì móxíng	Multicast conferencing model	
组播呼叫	Zǔbō hūjiào	Multicast call	
组播互联网协议	Zǔbō hùliánwǎng xiéyì	Multicast internet protocol	MIP
组播敏感的第二层交换机	Zǔbō mǐngǎnde dì'èrcéng jiāohuànjī	Multicast aware level 2 switch	MAS
组播群	Zǔbō qún	Multicast group	

组播区域范围公告协议	Zǔbō qūyù fànwéi gōnggào xiéyì	Multicast scope zone announcement protocol (IETF usage)	MZAP
组播适配协议	Zǔbō shìpèi xiéyì	Multicast adaptation protocol	MAP
组播适配协议--服务接入点	Zǔbō shìpèi xiéyì/fúwù jiērù diǎn	Multicast adaptation protocol/service access point	MAPSAP
组播适配协议-协议数据单元	Zǔbō shìpèi xiéyì/xiéyì shùjù dānyuán	Multicast adaptation protocol/protocol data unit	MAPPDU
组播委托	Zǔbō wěituō	Multicast delegate	
组播业务	Zǔbō yèwù	Multicast service	
组播源发现协议	Zǔbō yuán fāxiàn xiéyì	Multicast source discovery protocol	MSDP
组播主干网	Zǔbō zhǔgàn wǎng	Multicast backbone network	MBONE
阻持	Zǔchí	Holddown	
阻档层密封	Zǔdàng céng mìfēng	Barrier seal	
阻挡物	Zǔdǎngwù	Obstacle	
阻断/解阻	Zǔduàn/jiězǔ	Blocking/deblocking	
阻焊	Zǔhàn	Soldermask (in SMT)	
组合	Zǔhé	Composition	
组合布局客体	Zǔhé bùjú kètǐ	Composite layout object	
组合电路	Zǔhé diànlù	Combinatorial circuit	
组合对象模型	Zǔhé duìxiàng móxíng	Component object model	COM
组合符号时间	Zǔhé fúhào shíjiān	United symbol time	UST
组合干扰	Zǔhé gānrǎo	Combination interference	
组合构成体	Zǔhé gòuchéngtǐ	Composite component	
组合键	Zǔhé jiàn	Composite key (for database)	
组合框	Zǔhé kuàng	Combination box	
组合逻辑客体	Zǔhé luójì kètǐ	Composite logical object	
组合频率	Zǔhé pínlǜ	Combination frequency	
组合切换	Zǔhé qiēhuàn	Bank switching	
组合索引	Zǔhé suǒyǐn	Composite index (for database)	
组合问题	Zǔhé wèntí	Combinatorial problems	
组合音	Zǔhé yīn	Combination tone	
组合音响	Zǔhé yīnxiǎng	Combined speaker cabinet	CSC
组合式光纤（缆）连接器	Zǔhé-shì guāngxiān (lǎn) liánjiēqì	Optical fiber (cable) composite connector	
组呼	Zǔhū	Talkgroup call	
组呼叫寄存器	Zǔhūjiào jìcúnqì	Group call record	GCR
嘴参考点	Zuǐ cānkǎo diǎn	Mouth reference point	MRP
最长公共子串	Zuìcháng gōnggòng zichuàn	Longest common sub-string	
最长前缀匹配	Zuìcháng qiánzhuì pǐpèi	Longest prefix matching	
最长移位寄存器	Zuìcháng yíwèi jìcúnqì	Maximum-length shift register	MLSR
最大包寿命时间	Zuìdà bāo shòumìng shíjiān	Maximum packet lifetime	MPL
最大包络法	Zuìdà bāoluò fǎ	Maximum envelope method	MEM
最大比合并	Zuìdà bǐ hébìng	Maximum ratio consolidation	MRC
最大比值合并	Zuìdà bǐzhí hébìng	Maximal ratio combining	MRC
最大波	Zuìdà bō	Extreme wave	
最大波压	Zuìdà bōyā	Maximum wave pressure	
最大长度移位寄存器	Zuìdà chángdù yíwèi jìcúnqì	Maximum-length shift register	MLSR
最大重发次数	Zuìdà chóngfā cìshù	Maximum number of re-tries	
最大充许拉力	Zuìdà chōngxǔ lālì	Maximum allowed tension	MAT

最大充许使用张力	Zuìdà chōngxǔ shǐyòng zhānglì	Maximum allowable tension	MAT
最大传输单元	Zuìdà chuánshū dānyuán	Maximum transmission unit	MTU
最大等待时延	Zuìdà děngdài shíyán	Maximum waiting delay	MWD
最大段寿命	Zuìdà duàn shòumìng	Maximum segment lifetime	MSL
最大反应位移	Zuìdà fǎnyìng wèiyí	Maximum response displacement	
最大副/主瓣比	Zuìdà fù/zhǔ bàn bǐ	Maximum relative side lobe level	
最大后验概率	Zuìdà hòuyàn gàilǜ	Maximum *a posteriori* probability	MAP
最大环路阻抗	Zuìdà huánlù zǔkàng	Maximum loop resistance	
最大加速度	Zuìdà jiāsùdù	Peak acceleration	
最大接收单元	Zuìdà jiēshōu dānyuán	Maximum receive unit	MRU
最大计算流量系数	Zuìdà jìsuàn liúliàng xìshù	Calculated maximum flow coefficient	
最大可能部分反应	Zuìdà kěnéng bùfen fǎnyìng	Partial response maximum likelihood	PRML
最大可行速率	Zuìdà kěxíng sùlǜ	Maximum attainable rate	
最大可用幅偏	Zuìdà kěyòng fúpiān	Maximum usable amplitude deviation	
最大理论带宽	Zuìdà lǐlùn dàikuān	Maximum theoretical bandwidth	MTB
最大理论数值孔径	Zuìdà lǐlùn shùzhí kǒngjìng	Maximum theoretical numerical aperture	NAMAX.TH
最大灵敏度	Zuìdà língmǐndù	Maximum sensitivity	
最大流量	Zuìdà liúliàng	Maximum discharge	
最大匹配	Zuìdà pǐpèi	Maximum matching	
最大冗余带宽适应路由选择	Zuìdà rǒngyú dàikuān shìyìng lùyóu xuǎnzé	Most redundant bandwidth adaptive route selecting	RBAR
最大塞入率	Zuìdà sāirùlǜ	Maximum stuffing rate	
最大时间间隔误差	Zuìdà shíjiān jiàngé wùchā	Maximum timing interval error	MTIE
最大似然	Zuìdà sìrán	Maximum likelihood	ML
最大似然序列估计	Zuìdà sìrán xùliè gūjì	Maximum likelihood sequence estimation	MLSE
最大似然序列估值	Zuìdà sìrán xùliè gūzhí	Maximum likelihood sequence estimation	MLSE
最大似然译码	Zuìdà sìrán yìmǎ	Maximum likelihood decoding	
最大探测距离	Zuìdà tàncè jùlí	Maximum detection range (of radar)	
最大调整率	Zuìdà tiáozhěnglǜ	Maximum justification rate	
最大团	Zuìdà tuán	Clique	
最大突发量	Zuìdà tūfāliàng	Maximum burst size	MBS
最大位转发率	Zuìdà wèi zhuǎnfā lǜ	Maximum bit forwarding rate	MBFR
最大相对旁瓣电平	Zuìdà xiāngduì pángbàn diànpíng	Maximum relative side lobe level	MRSLL
最大相对时间间隔误差	Zuìdà xiāngduì shíjiān jiàngé wùchā	Maximum relative time interval error	MRTIE
最大相位偏移	Zuìdà xiàngwèi piānyí	Maximum phase deviation	MPD
最大小信号增益	Zuìdà xiǎo xìnhào zēngyì	Maximum small-signal gain	
最大小信号增益波长	Zuìdà xiǎo xìnhào zēngyì bōcháng	Maximum small-signal gain wavelength	
最大有用功率	Zuìdà yǒuyòng gōnglǜ	Maximum useful power	
最大允许频偏	Zuìdà yǔnxǔ pínpiān	Maximum permissible frequency deviation	
最大允许相偏	Zuìdà yǔnxǔ xiāngpiān	Maximum permissible phase deviation	
最大噪声功率	Zuìdà zàoshēng gōnglǜ	The greatest noise power	TGNP
最大振幅	Zuìdà zhènfú	Maximum amplitude	
最大的传输单元	Zuìdàde chuánshū dānyuán	Maximum transmission unit	MTU
最大的传送单元	Zuìdàde chuánsòng dānyuán	Maximum transmission unit	MTU
最大的信元率	Zuìdàde xìnyuán lǜ	Maximum cell rate	maxCR
最大化	Zuìdàhuà	Maximize	
最低可用频率	Zuìdī kěyòng pínlǜ	Lowest useful frequency	LUF

最低位	Zuìdī wèi	Least significant bit	LSB
最低有效比特	Zuìdī yǒuxiào bǐtè	Least significant bit	LSB
最低有效位	Zuìdī yǒuxiào wèi	Least significant bit	LSB
最低有效位	Zuìdī yǒuxiào wèi	Least significant digit	LSD
最底层的派生类	Zuìdǐcéngde pàishēng lèi	Most derived class	
最短公共父串	Zuìduǎn gōnggòng fùchuàn	Shortest common superstring	
最短路径	Zuìduǎn lùjìng	Shortest path	
最短路径树	Zuìduǎn lùjìng shù	Shortest path tree	SPT
最短路径先开协议	Zuìduǎn lùjìng xiān kāi xiéyì	Open shortest path first [Protocol]	OSPF
最短路径优先	Zuìduǎn lùjìng yōuxiān	Shortest path first	SPF
最短路径优先算法	Zuìduǎn lùjìng yōuxiān suànfǎ	Shortest path first algorithm	SPF
最短路由选择	Zuìduǎn lùyóu xuǎnzé	Shortest-path routing	
最短寻道时间优先	Zuìduǎn xúndào shíjiān yōuxiān	Shortest searching time first	SSTF
最高可用频率	Zuìgāo kěyòng pínlǜ	Maximum usable frequency	MUF
最高位	Zuìgāo wèi	Most significant bit	MSB
最高有效比特	Zuìgāo yǒuxiào bǐtè	Most significant bit	MSB
最高有效位	Zuìgāo yǒuxiào wèi	Most significant bit	MSB
最高有效字节	Zuìgāo yǒuxiào zìjié	Most significant byte	MSB
最高振荡频率	Zuìgāo zhèndàng pínlǜ	Maximum frequency of oscillation	
最后拨号存储	Zuìhòu bōhào cúnchǔ	Last number dialed	LND
最后一英里以太网呼叫兴趣	Zuìhòu yīyīnglǐ yǐtàiwǎng hūjiào xìngqu	Ethernet in the last mile call for interest	ELMCFI
最后帧地址寄存器	Zuìhòu zhèng dìzhǐ jìcúnqì	Last frame address register	LFAR
最后的组合码	Zuìhòude zǔhé mǎ	Final assembly code	FAC
最佳参差比	Zuìjiā cēncī bǐ	Optimum stagger ratio	
最佳干扰样式	Zuìjiā gānrǎo yàngshì	Optimum jamming type	
最佳工作频率	Zuìjiā gōngzuò pínlǜ	Optimum working frequency	OWF
最佳可用频率	Zuìjiā kěyòng pínlǜ	Optimum usable frequency	OUF
最佳路由选择	Zuìjiā lùyóu xuǎnzé	Optimal routing	OR
最佳门限	Zuìjiā ménxiàn	Optimum threshold	
最佳调幅和调相	Zuìjiā tiáofú hétiáo xiāng	Optimal amplitude and phase modulation	OAPM
最近点对查询	Zuìjìn diǎn duì cháxún	Nearest neighbor search	
最近邻	Zuìjìn lín	Nearest neighbor (CAD/CAM)	NN
最近邻域	Zuìjìn línyù	Nearest neighbor	
最近特征线	Zuìjìn tèzhēng xiàn	Nearest feature line (CAD/CAM)	NFL
最近的，运行着的上行邻居	Zuìjìnde, yùnxíngzhede shàngxíng línjū	Nearest active upstream neighbor	NAUM
最快存取时间	Zuìkuài cúnqǔ shíjiān	Minimum access time	
最少花费路径	Zuìshǎo huāfèi lùjìng	Least-cost path	
最小（代价）生成树	Zuìxiǎo (dàijià) shēngchéng shù	Minimum (cost) spanning tree	
最小安装	Zuìxiǎo ānzhuāng	Minimum installation (of software)	
最小测试距离	Zuìxiǎo cèshì jùlí	Minimum measure distance	
最小冲突启发式修补	Zuìxiǎo chōngtū qǐfāshì xiūbǔ	Minimum-conflict heuristic repair	MCHR
最小冲突权值学习算法	Zuìxiǎo chōngtū quán zhí xuéxí suànfǎ	Minimum-conflict weight learning algorithm	MCWLA
最小二乘法	Zuìxiǎo èrchéngfǎ	Least square method	
最小干扰距离	Zuìxiǎo gānrǎo jùlí	Minimum jamming range	
最小画面间隔	Zuìxiǎo huàmiàn jiàngé	Minimum picture interval	MPI
最小均芳	Zuìxiǎo jūn fāng	Least mean square	LMS

最小均方（算法）	Zuìxiǎo jūn fāng (suànfǎ)	Least mean square (algorithm)	LMS
最小均方误差	Zuìxiǎo jūn fāng wùchā	Minimum mean square error	MMSE
最小均方根	Zuìxiǎo jūn fānggēn	Least mean squares	LMS
最小均方根差	Zuìxiǎo jūn fānggēn chà	Minimum (root) mean square error	MMSE
最小矩形	Zuìxiǎo jǔxíng	Minimum bounding rectangle	MBR
最小可检测信噪比	Zuìxiǎo kějiǎncè xìnzào bǐ	Minimum detectable signal-to-noise ratio	
最小可探测信号	Zuìxiǎo kětàncè xìnhào	Minimum detectable signal	MDS
最小可用场强	Zuìxiǎo kěyòng chǎngqiáng	Minimum usable field-strength	Emin
最小可用功率通量密度	Zuìxiǎo kěyòng gōnglǜ tōngliàng mìdù	Minimum usable power flux density	Pmin
最小码距	Zuìxiǎo mǎjù	Minimum distance (for coding)	
最小描述长度	Zuìxiǎo miáoshù chángdù	Minimum description length	MDL
最小密码长度	Zuìxiǎo mìmǎ chángdù	Minimum password length	
最小频移键控	Zuìxiǎo pínyí jiànkòng	Minimal shift keying	MSK
最小容差	Zuìxiǎo róngchā	Proximal tolerance	
最小生成树	Zuìxiǎo shēngchéng shù	Minimum spanning tree	
最小特权	Zuìxiǎo tèquán	Least privilege (IPsec)	
最小相位频移键控	Zuìxiǎo xiàngwèi pínyí jiànkòng	Minimum-phase frequency shift keying	MSK
最小相位谐波	Zuìxiǎo xiàngwèi xiébō	Minimum-phase harmonics	
最小信元速率	Zuìxiǎo xìnyuán sùlǜ	Minimum cell rate	MCR
最小移频键控	Zuìxiǎo yípín jiànkòng	Minimum (frequency) shift keying	MSK
最小制图单元	Zuìxiǎo zhìtú dānyuán	Minimum mapping units	
最小中值法	Zuìxiǎo zhōng zhí fǎ	Least median square	LMS
最小作用距离	Zuìxiǎo zuòyòng jùlí	Minimum detection range	
最小化	Zuìxiǎohuà	Minimize	
最新信息	Zuìxīn xìnxī	Update information	
最优传送	Zuìyōu chuánsòng	Best effort delivery	
最优内插	Zuìyōu nèichā	Optimal interpolation	OI
最优区位	Zuìyōu qūwèi	Optimal location	OL
最优线性无偏估计	Zuìyōu xiànxìng wúpiān gūjì	Best linear unbiased estimate	BLUE
最优信息率	Zuìyōu xìnxī lǜ	Optimal information rate	
最优化	Zuìyōuhuà	Optimization	
最优化方法	Zuìyōuhuà fāngfǎ	Optimization method	
最早的限优选算法	Zuìzǎode xiàn yōuxuǎn suànfǎ	Earliest deadline first	EDF
最终检验	Zuìzhōng jiǎnyàn	Final inspection	
最终集结码	Zuìzhōng jíjié mǎ	Final assembly code (GSM term)	
最终全面型号认证	Zuìzhōng quánmiàn xínghào rènzhèng	Final type approval	FTA
最终信号单元	Zuìzhōng xìnhào dānyuán	Final signaling unit	FSU
最终用户	Zuìzhōng yònghù	End user	
组件	Zǔjiàn	Component (IPsec)	
组件对象模式	Zǔjiàn duìxiàng móshì	Component object model	COM
组件对象模型	Zǔjiàn duìxiàng móxíng	Component object model	COM
阻抗	Zǔkàng	Impedance	
阻抗比	Zǔkàng bǐ	Impedance ratio	
阻抗变换器	Zǔkàng biànhuànqì	Impedance converter	
阻抗变换器	Zǔkàng biànhuànqì	Impedance transformer	
阻抗耦合	Zǔkàng ǒuhé	Impedance coupling	IC

阻抗匹配	Zǔkàng pǐpèi	Impedance matching	IM
阻抗圆图（导纳圆图）	Zǔkàng yuán tú (dǎonà yuán tú)	Polar impedance diagram; Smith chart (polar admittance diagram)	
阻力	Zǔlì	Drag	
阻尼	Zǔní	Damping	
阻尼振荡	Zǔní zhèndàng	Damped oscillation	
阻尼正弦瞬变	Zǔní zhèngxián shùnbiàn	Damped sinusoidal transient	
阻尼最小二乘法	Zǔní zuìxiǎo èrchéngfǎ	Damped least square method	DLS
左边界	Zuǒ bianjiè	Left margin	
左边缘	Zuǒ bianyuán	Left hand edge	
作进一步研究	Zuò jìnyībù yánjiū	For further study	FFS
左上角	Zuǒ shàngjiǎo	Top left corner	
左外部连接	Zuǒ wàibù liánjiē	Left outer join (in SQL Server)	
左下角	Zuǒ xiàjiǎo	Bottom left corner	
左向外联接	Zuǒ xiàngwài liánjiē	Left outer join (for database)	
坐标	Zuòbiāo	Coordinate (in GIS)	
坐标变换	Zuòbiāo biànhuàn	Coordinate transformation	
坐标变换核	Zuòbiāo biànhuàn hé	Coordinate transform kernel	
坐标参照系	Zuòbiāo cānzhàoxì	Coordinate reference system	
坐标格网	Zuòbiāo géwǎng	Coordinate grid (GIS term)	
坐标几何	Zuòbiāo jǐhé	Coordinate geometry	COGO
坐标控制点	Zuòbiāo kòngzhì diǎn	Coordinate control point, tic	
坐标维数	Zuòbiāo wéishù	Coordinate dimension	
坐标系统	Zuòbiāo xìtǒng	Coordinate system	
坐标原点	Zuòbiāo yuándiǎn	Coordinate origin	
坐标转换	Zuòbiāo zhuǎnhuàn	Transformation	
左手习惯	Zuǒshǒu xíguàn	Left-handed	
坐席记发器	Zuòxí jìfāqì	Position register	
左旋极化波	Zuǒxuán jíhuà bō	Anti-clockwise polarized wave	
左旋极化波	Zuǒxuán jíhuà bō	Left-hand polarized wave	
左漩圆极化	Zuǒxuán yuán jíhuà	Left hand circular polarization	LHCP
左旋转化	Zuǒxuán zhuǎnhuà	Left hand polarization	
作业	Zuòyè	Job	
作用域	Zuòyòng yù	Scope	
作用指示器	Zuòyòng zhǐshìqì	Action indicator	AI
左值	Zuǒzhí	Left value (lvalue)	
阻燃材料	Zǔrán cáiliào	Flame retardant material	
阻燃缆	Zǔrán lǎn	Flame retardant cable	
阻塞	Zǔsè	Blocking	
阻塞包	Zǔsè bāo	Choke packet	
阻塞多路复用信道	Zǔsè duōlù fùyòng xìndào	Block multiplexer channel	
阻塞滤波器	Zǔsè lǜbōqì	Stop filter	
阻塞现象	Zǔsè xiànxiàng	Blocking phenomena	
阻塞式干扰	Zǔsè-shì gānrǎo	Barrage jamming	
阻水带	Zǔshuǐ dài	Waterblock tape (FOC mfg)	
组态	Zǔtài	Configuration	
组网协议	Zǔwǎng xiéyì	Internetworking protocol	IP

租用电路数据传输业务	Zūyòng diànlù shùjù chuánshū yèwù	Leased circuit data transmission service	
租用线路	Zūyòng xiànlù	Leased line	
租用线路业务	Zūyòng xiànlù yèwù	Leased line service	
租用线路转换器	Zūyòng xiànlù zhuǎnhuànqì	Leased line adapter	LLA
租用虚线路	Zūyòng xū xiànlù	Virtual leased lines	VLL
阻止	Zǔzhǐ	Reject, rejection	REJ
阻止出呼叫	Zǔzhǐ chū hūjiào	Outgoing call barred	
组织名	Zǔzhī míng	Organization name	
阻止入呼叫	Zǔzhǐ rù hūjiào	Incoming call barred	
组织主管	Zǔzhī zhǔguǎn	Organization authority (CMM)	OA
组织性唯一标示符	Zǔzhīxìng wéiyī biāoshìfú	Organizational unique identifier	OUI
组装	Zǔzhuāng	Packet assembly	PA
组装	Zǔzhuāng	Reassembly	
组装效率	Zǔzhuāng xiàolǜ	Packaging efficiency	

Part 2
English-Chinese

Alphabetically by English Term with Chinese Pinyin Characters and English Abbreviations

A

A element	A 码元	A mǎyuán	
A horizon	A 层位	A céngwèi	
A interface	A 接口	A jiēkǒu	
a posteriori probability	后验概率	Hòuyàn gàilǜ	APP
A single algorithm performing the functions of A3 and A8	执行 A3 和 A8 功能的一个单一算法	Zhíxíng A3 hé A8 gōngnéngde yīgè dānyī suànfǎ	A38
A&B bit signaling	A&B 比特信令	A&B bǐtè xìnling	
AAL protocol control information	AAL 协议控制信息	AAL xiéyì kòngzhì xìnxī	AAL-PCI
AAL protocol data unit	AAL 协议数据单元	AAL xiéyì shùjù dānyuán	AAL-PDU
AAL service access point	AAL 业务接入点	AAL yèwù jiērù diǎn	AAL-SAP
AAL service data unit	AAL 业务数据单元	AAL yèwù shùjù dānyuán	AAL-SDU
AARP probe packets	AARP 探测数据包	AARP tàncè shùjù bāo	
Abandon	舍弃	Shěqì	
Abandon call	放弃呼叫	Fàngqì hūjiào	
Abbe comparator	阿贝比长仪	Ā-bèi bǐ cháng yí	
Abbe constant	阿贝常数	Ā-bèi chángshù	
Abbe number	阿贝数	Ā-bèi shù	
Abbe prism	阿贝棱镜	Ā-bèi léngjìng	
Abbe refractometer	阿贝折射率计	Ā-bèi zhéshèlǜ jì	
Abbe's sine condition	阿贝正弦条件	A-bèi zhèngxián tiáojiàn	
Abbreviated address	短缩地址	Duǎnsuō dìzhǐ	AA
Abbreviated dialing	简明拨号	Jiǎnmíng bōhào	ABD
Abbreviated dialing	缩位拨号	Suōwèi bōhào	AD
Abbreviated dialling numbers	数位拨号	Shùwèi bōhào	ADN
Abbreviation	缩略	Suōlüè	
Abbreviation	缩写词	Suōxiěcí	
Abbreviation record	缩写记录	Suōxiě jìlù	
Abbreviations	缩写	Suōxiě	
A-bedplate	A 形底座	A-xíng dǐzuò	
Abel's integral	阿贝尔积分	A-bèi'ěr jīfēn	
Abilene Project (US high-speed Internet project)	阿比林计划	Ābǐlín jìhuà	
Able and disable	使能和止能	Shǐnéng hé zhǐnéng	
Abnormal frame count	非正常帧计数	Fēizhèngcháng zhèng jìshù	AFC
Abort advisory channel	有故障的咨询信道	Yǒu gùzhàngde zīxún xìndào	AAC
Abort sequence	放弃序列	Fàngqì xùliè	
Abrasion resistance; wear resistance	耐磨性	Nàimóxìng	
Abscissa	横坐标	Héngzuòbiāo	
Absent subscriber	缺席用户	Quēxí yònghù	
Absent subscriber service	缺席用户服务	Quēxí yònghù fúwù	
Absent subscriber service	用户缺席服务	Yònghù quēxí fúwù	
Absolute accuracy	绝对精度	Juéduì jīngdù	
Absolute address	绝对地址	Juéduì dìzhǐ	
Absolute assembler	绝对汇编程序	Juéduì huìbiān chéngxù	AA

Absolute assembly language	绝对汇编语言	Juédui huìbiān yǔyán	AAL
Absolute coil	独立线圈	Dúlì xiànquān	
Absolute coordinate	绝对坐标	Juédui zuòbiāo	
Absolute error	绝对误差	Juédui wùchā	
Absolute frequency reference	绝对参考频率	Juédui cānkǎo pínlǜ	AFR
Absolute frequency reference	绝对基准频率	Juédui jīzhǔn pínlǜ	AFR
Absolute frequency reference	绝对频率参考	Juédui pínlǜ cānkǎo	AFR
Absolute gain (of an antenna)	绝对增益	Juédui zēngyì	
Absolute luminance threshold	绝对发光率阀	Juédui fāguāng lǜ fá	
Absolute luminance threshold	绝对亮度阀	Juédui liàngdù fá	
Absolute luminosity curve	绝对发光度曲线	Juédui fāguāngdù qūxiàn	
Absolute magnetic permeability	绝对磁导率	Juédui cídǎolǜ	
Absolute magnification	绝对放大率	Juédui fàngdàlǜ	
Absolute map accuracy	绝对地图精度	Juédui dìtú jīngdù	
Absolute mode	绝对模式	Juédui móshì	
Absolute order	绝对命令	Juédui mìnglìng	
Absolute phase shift keying	绝对相移键控	Juédui xiāngyí jiànkòng	APSK
Absolute position	绝对位置	Juédui wèizhì	
Absolute power level	绝对功率电平	Juédui gōnglǜ diànpíng	
Absolute radio frequency channel number	绝对频道号	Juédui píndào hào	ARFCN
Absolute radio frequency channel number	绝对射频频道号	Juédui shèpín píndào hào	ARFCN
Absolute radio frequency channel number	绝对无线载频号	Juédui wúxiàn zàipín hào	ARFCN
Absolute radio frequency channel number	完全的无线频率信道号码	Wánquánde wúxiàn pínlǜ xìndào hàomǎ	ARFCN
Absolute read-out	单独读出	Dāndú dúchū	
Absolute refractive index	绝对折射率	Juédui zhéshèlǜ	
Absolute RF channel number	绝对射频信道号	Juédui shèpín xìndàohào	ARFCN
Absolute signal delay	绝对信号延时	Juédui xìnhào yánshí	
Absolute single polarization optical fiber	绝对单偏振光纤	Juédui dānpiānzhèn guāngxiān	
Absolute temperature	绝对温度	Juédui wēndù	
Absolute vector	绝对矢量	Juédui shǐliàng	
Absolute voltage level	绝对电压电平	Juédui diànyā diànpíng	
Absorbing clamp	吸收钳	Xīshōu qián	
Absorptance	吸收比	Xīshōu bǐ	
Absorptiometer	吸收光度计	Xīshōu guāngdùjì	
Absorption	吸收	Xīshōu	
Absorption band	吸收带	Xīshōu dài	
Absorption cell	吸收池	Xīshōu chí	
Absorption coefficient; absorption factor	吸收系数	Xīshōu xìshù	
Absorption correction	吸收修正	Xīshōu xiūzhèng	
Absorption edges	吸收边	Xīshōu biān	
Absorption filter (optical)	色吸收滤光镜	Sè xīshōu lǜguāngjìng	
Absorption frequency meter	吸收式频率计	Xīshōu-shì pínlǜjì	
Absorption index	吸收指数	Xīshōu zhǐshù	
Absorption isolator	吸收式隔离器	Xīshōu-shì gélíqì	
Absorption loss	吸收损耗	Xīshōu sǔnhào	
Absorption modulation	吸收调制	Xīshōu tiáozhì	

Absorption of electromagnetic wave	电磁波吸收	Diàncíbō xīshōu	
Absorption overlay (coverage) (radar term)	吸收性复盖层	Xīshōuxìng fùgài céng	
Absorption peak	吸收峰	Xīshōu fēng	
Absorption spectrum	吸收光谱	Xīshōu guāngpǔ	
Absorptive attenuator	吸收式衰减器	Xīshōu-shì shuāijiǎnqì	
Absorptivity	吸收率	Xīshōu lǜ	
Absorptivity	吸收性	Xīshōuxìng	
Abstract base class	抽象基类	Chōuxiàng jī lèi	ABC
Abstract class	抽象类	Chōuxiàng lèi	
Abstract data type	抽象数据类型	Chōuxiàng shùjù lèixíng	
Abstract logic structure diagram	抽象逻辑结构图	Chōuxiàng luóji jiégòutú	
Abstract service primitive	抽象服务原语	Chōuxiàng fúwù yuányǔ	ASP
Abstract service primitive	抽象业务原语	Chōuxiàng yèwù yuányǔ	ASP
Abstract syntax	抽象句法	Chōuxiàng jùfǎ	
Abstract syntax notation	抽象句表记法	Chōuxiàng jùbiǎo jìfǎ	ASN
Abstract syntax notation	抽象句法符号	Chōuxiàng jùfǎ fúhào	ASN
Abstract syntax notation	抽象语法编码	Chōuxiàng yǔfǎ biānmǎ	ASN
Abstract syntax notation	抽象语法标记	Chōuxiàng yǔfǎ biāojì	ASN
Abstract syntax notation	抽象语法定义	Chōuxiàng yǔfǎ dìngyì	ASN
Abstract syntax notation	抽象语法记法	Chōuxiàng yǔfǎ jìfǎ	ASN
Abstract syntax notation 1	抽象句法表示法 1	Chōuxiàng jùfǎ biǎoshì fǎ 1	ASN.1
Abstract test case	抽象测试实例	Chōuxiàng cèshì shílì	
Abstract test case	抽象测试项	Chōuxiàng cèshì xiàng	
Abstract test method	抽象测试法	Chōuxiàng cèshì fǎ	ATM
Abstract test module	抽象测试模块	Chōuxiàng cèshì mókuài	
Abstract test suite	抽象测试套	Chōuxiàng cèshì tào	ATS
Abstract Windows Toolkit	抽象窗口工具库	Chōuxiàng chuāngkǒu gōngjù kù	
Abstraction	抽象	Chōuxiàng	
Abstraction	抽象物	Chōuxiàng wù	
Abstraction	抽象性	Chōuxiàng xìng	
Abstraction level	抽象级	Chōuxiàng jí	
Academy of Telecommunications Research (MII)	电信研究院	Diànxìn yánjiūyuàn	
Academy of Telecommunications Research and Planning (MII)	电信规划研究院	Diànxìn guīhuà yánjiūyuàn	
Accelerated graphics port	加速图形端口	Jiāsù túxíng duānkǒu	AGP
Accelerated graphics port	图形加速接口	Túxíng jiāsù jiēkǒu	AGP
Accelerated hub architecture	加速中心架构	Jiāsù zhōngxīn jiàgòu	AHA
Accelerated test	加速试验	Jiāsù shìyàn	
Acceleration	加速度	Jiāsùdù	
Acceleration response spectrum	加速度响应谱	Jiāsùdù xiǎngyìng pǔ	
Accelerator (chip)	加速器	Jiāsùqì	
Accelerometer	加速计	Jiāsùjì	
Accentuated contrast	加重对比度	Jiāzhòng duìbǐdù	
Acceptable defect level	允许的缺陷标准	Yǔnxǔde quēxiàn biāozhǔn	ADL
Acceptable quality level (in quality standards)	可接收质量水平	Kějiēshōu zhìliàng shuǐpíng	AQL
Acceptable reliability level	合格的可靠性	Hégéde kěkàoxìng	ARL
Acceptable use policy	可接受使用政策	Kějiēshòu shǐyòng zhèngcè	AUP

Acceptance angle	接收角	Jiēshōu jiǎo	
Acceptance angle plotter	接收角绘图器	Jiēshōu jiǎo huìtúqì	
Acceptance characteristic pattern	接收特性图	Jiēshōu tèxìng tú	
Acceptance checkout equipment	验收检验设备	Yànshōu jiǎnyàn shèbèi	ACE
Acceptance cone	接受光锥	Jiēshòu guāng zhuī	
Acceptance one-half angle	接收半角	Jiēshōu bàn jiǎo	
Acceptance pattern	接收图	Jiēshōu tú	
Acceptance test	接收测试	Jiēshōu cèshì	
Acceptance test	验收测试	Yànshōu cèshì	
Acceptance test	验收试验	Yànshōu shìyàn	
Accepted interference	可接受干扰	Kějiēshòu gānrǎo	
Acceptor	受主	Shòuzhǔ	
Access (computer term)	存取	Cúnqǔ	
Access (database and networking term)	访问	Fǎngwèn	
Access (telecom term)	接入	Jiērù	
Access adaptation function	接入适配功能	Jiērù shìpèi gōngnéng	AAF
Access and transport layer	接入和传输层	Jiērù hé chuánshū céng	
Access barred	接入受阻	Jiērù shòuzǔ	
Access barred signal	接入拒绝信号	Jiērù jùjué xìnhào	ACB
Access bearer capability	接入承载能力	Jiērù chéngzài nénglì	
Access bearer structure	接入承载结构	Jiērù chéngzài jiégòu	
Access burst	访问突发	Fǎngwèn tūfā	AB
Access burst	接入猝发比特群	Jiērù cùfā bǐtè qún	AB
Access burst	接入突发脉冲序列	Jiērù tūfā màichōng xùliè	AB
Access burst (GSM term)	突发访问	Tūfā fǎngwèn	
Access capability	接入能力	Jiērù nénglì	
Access category	访问类别	Fǎngwèn lèibié	
Access channel	接入通路	Jiērù tōnglù	
Access channel	接入信道	Jiērù xìndào	
Access channel	接续信道	Jiēxù xìndào	A-CH
Access channel	入网信道	Rùwǎng xìndào	
Access channel (in CDMA)	选址信道	Xuǎnzhǐ xìndào	
Access charge	接入费	Jiērù fèi	
Access circuit section	接入电路段	Jiērù diànlù duàn	
Access class	接入分类	Jiērù fēnlèi	AC
Access code (to computer memory)	存储码	Cúnchǔ mǎ	AC
Access concentrator (VPN/networking term)	访问集中器	Fǎngwèn jízhōngqì	
Access condition	接入条件	Jiērù tiáojiàn	AC
Access connection element	接入连接单元	Jiērù liánjiē dānyuán	ACE
Access contention	接入竞争	Jiērù jìngzhēng	
Access contention	接入争用	Jiērù zhēngyòng	
Access contention resolution	接入竞争解决	Jiērù jìngzhēng jiějué	
Access contention resolution	接入争用裁决	Jiērù zhēngyòng cáijué	
Access control	存取控制	Cúnqǔ kòngzhì	
Access control	访问控制	Fǎngwèn kòngzhì	AC
Access control (to computer memory)	存储控制	Cúnchǔ kòngzhì	AC

Access control center	接入控制中心	Jiērù kòngzhì zhōngxīn	ACC
Access control entry	访问控制项	Fǎngwèn kòngzhì xiàng	ACE
Access control information	访问控制信息	Fǎngwèn kòngzhì xìnxī	ACI
Access control information	接入控制信息	Jiērù kòngzhì xìnxī	ACI
Access control list	存取控制表	Cúnqǔ kòngzhì biǎo	ACL
Access control list	访问控制表	Fǎngwèn kòngzhì biǎo	ACL
Access control list	接入控制列表	Jiērù kòngzhì lièbiǎo	ACL
Access control mechanism (IPsec)	访问控制机制	Fǎngwèn kòngzhì jīzhì	
Access control system	出入控制系统	Chūrù kòngzhì xìtǒng	ACS
Access controller	存取控制器	Cúnqǔ kòngzhìqì	
Access coupler	通路耦合器	Tōnglù ǒuhéqì	
Access cycle (to computer memory)	存储周期	Cúnchǔ zhōuqī	AC
Access delay	接入延迟	Jiērù yánchí	
Access denied message (IPsec tLS)	访问拒绝消息	Fǎngwèn jùjué xiāoxi	
Access digital section	接入数字段	Jiērù shùzì duàn	
Access directory	访问目录	Fǎngwèn mùlù	
Access facility	接入设施	Jiērù shèshī	AF
Access function	访问函数	Fǎngwèn hánshù	
Access gatekeeper	接入网守	Jiērù wǎngshǒu	AGK
Access gateway	接入网关	Jiērù wǎngguān	AGW
Access grant	接入允许	Jiērù yǔnxǔ	
Access grant channel	接入允许信道	Jiērù yǔnxǔ xìndào	AGCH
Access grant channel	接入准许信道	Jiērù zhǔnxǔ xìndào	AGCH
Access grant channel	允许接入信道	Yǔnxǔ jiērù xìndào	AGCH
Access grant channel	允许接续信道	Yǔnxǔ jiēxù xìndào	AGCH
Access grant channel	准予接入信道	Zhǔnyǔ jiērù xìndào	AGCH
Access grant channel	准予接续信道	Zhǔnyǔ jiēxù xìndào	AGCH
Access group	访问组	Fǎngwèn zǔ	
Access group	接入组	Jiērù zǔ	
Access interface platform	接入接口平台	Jiērù jiēkǒu píngtái	AIP
Access key	存取键	Cúnqǔ jiàn	AKEY
Access key	访问关键字	Fǎngwèn guānjiàn zì	
Access layer	接入层	Jiērù céng	
Access level	访问级别	Fǎngwèn jíbié	
Access link	接入链路	Jiērù liànlù	AL
Access link control application protocol	接入链路控制应用协议	Jiērù liànlù kòngzhì yìngyòng xiéyì	ALCAP
Access list	访问表	Fǎngwèn biǎo	
Access method	存取方法	Cúnqǔ fāngfǎ	
Access network	接入网	Jiērù wǎng	AN
Access network	接入网络	Jiērù wǎngluò	
Access network coaxial drop cable	接入网用同轴电缆	Jiērù wǎng-yòng tóngzhóu diànlǎn	
Access network fault manager	接入网故障管理	Jiērùwǎng gùzhàng guǎnlǐ	AFM
Access network management system	接入网管理系统	Jiērùwǎng guǎnlǐ xìtǒng	ANMS
Access network –network management system	接入网网管系统	Jiērùwǎng wǎngguǎn xìtǒng	AN-NMS
Access network section	接入网络段	Jiērù wǎngluò duàn	
Access network system	接入网系统	Jiērùwǎng xìtǒng	ANS

Access network system management function	接入网系统管理功能	Jiērùwǎng xìtǒng guǎnlǐ gōngnéng	AN-SMF
Access node	接入节点	Jiērù jiédiǎn	
Access overload class	访问过载等级	Fǎngwèn guòzài děngjí	ACCOLC
Access path	访问路径	Fǎngwèn lùjìng	
Access period	访问期	Fǎngwèn qī	
Access point	接入站	Jiērùzhàn	AP
Access point (database usage)	访问点	Fǎngwèn diǎn	AP
Access point (telecom network usage)	接入点	Jiērùdiǎn	AP
Access point identifier	接入点标识符	Jiērùdiǎn biāozhìfú	APID
Access point identifier	接入点识别符	Jiērùdiǎn shíbié fú	APID
Access point identifier accepted	接入点接收标识	Jiērùdiǎn jiēshōu biāoshí	
Access point identifier expected	期望接收的接入点标识	Qīwàng jiēshōude jiērù diǎn biāozhì	
Access point identifier transmit	接入点发送标识	Jiērùdiǎn fāsòng biāozhì	
Access point name	接入点名	Jiērùdiǎn míng	APN
Access point name	接入点名	Jiērùdiǎn míng	APN
Access preamble	接入段首标记	Jiērùduàn shǒubiāojì	AP
Access privilege	访问权	Fǎngwèn quán	
Access protocol	访问协议	Fǎngwèn xiéyì	AP
Access protocol	接入协议	Jiērù xiéyì	
Access ramp	接入引擎	Jiērù yǐnqíng	
Access rate	接入率	Jiērù lǜ	AR
Access rate	接入速率	Jiērù sùlǜ	AR
Access request address	访问请求地址	Fǎngwèn qǐngqiú dìzhǐ	AR-ADDR
Access rights	存取权限	Cúnqǔ quánxiàn	
Access rights identity	存取权识别	Cúnqǔ quán shíbié	ARI
Access security	访问安全性	Fǎngwèn ānquánxìng	
Access server	接入服务器	Jiērù fúwùqì	AS
Access service class	接入业务分类	Jiērù yèwù fēnlèi	ASC
Access service request	访问业务请求	Fǎngwèn yèwù qǐngqiú	ASR
Access signaling	存取信令	Cúnqǔ xìnling	AS
Access signaling	接入信令	Jiērù xìnlìng	AS
Access significance	接入意义	Jiērù yìyì	
Access switching control sub-system	接入交换控制子系统	Jiērù jiāohuàn kòngzhì zixìtǒng	ASCS
Access switching maintenance sub-system	接入交换维护子系统	Jiērù jiāohuàn wéihù zixìtǒng	ASMS
Access switching management processor	接入交换管理处理器	Jiērù jiāohuàn guǎnlǐ chùlǐqì	ASMP
Access technology	访问技术	Fǎngwèn jìshù	
Access time	访问时间	Fǎngwèn shíjiān	
Access time (computer)	存取时间	Cúnqǔ shíjiān	
Access time from clock (in RAM or ROM)	时钟存取时间	Shízhōng cúnqǔshíjiān	ATC
Access to the resources function	资源访问功能	Zīyuán fǎngwèn gōngnéng	ARF
Access to the services function	业务访问功能	Yèwù fǎngwèn gōngnéng	ASF
Access token	访问令牌	Fǎngwèn lìngpái	
Access transport	接入信息传送	Jiērù xìnxī chuánsòng	
Access trunk	接入中继线	Jiērù zhōngjìxiàn	AT
Access type	访问类型	Fǎngwèn lèixíng	
Access unit	访问单元	Fǎngwèn dānyuán	AU

Access unit	接入单元	Jiērù dānyuán	AU
Access unit	入口单元	Rùkǒu dānyuán	AU
Access unit's access point	接入单元的接入点	Jiērù dānyuánde jiērùdiǎn	AUAP
Accessability	可接入性	Kějiērùxìng	
Accessibility	可达性	Kědá-xìng	
Accessibility	可及性	Kějíxìng	
Accessory hardware	附属硬件	Fùshǔ yìngjiàn	
Accessory use	附属用途	Fùshǔ yòngtú	
Accident	事故	Shìgù	
Accident date	事故日期	Shìgù rìqī	
Accident identifier	事故标识符	Shìgù biāozhìfú	
Accomodation	调节	Tiáojié	
Account	账户	Zhànghù	
Account credit card	记帐信用卡	Jìzhàng xìnyòngkǎ	ACC
Account lockout	帐号封锁	Zhànghào fēngsuǒ	
Account lockout	帐户锁定	Zhànghù suǒdìng	
Account to account	财户到财户	Cáihù dào cáihù	
Account to cash	财户到现金	Cáihù dào xiànjīn	
Accountability	职能	Zhínéng	
Accounting card call	记帐卡呼叫	Jìzhàng kǎ hūjiào	ACC
Accounting management	计费管理	Jìfèi guǎnlǐ	
Accounting management	帐号管理	Zhànghào guǎnlǐ	AM
Accreditation (computer systems)	审批	Shěnpī	
Accumulated call meter	累积呼叫计量器	Lěijī hūjiào jìliàngqì	ACM
Accumulated call meter	累积呼叫计数	Lěijī hūjiào jìshù	ACM
Accumulated call meter	累计呼叫表	Lěijì hūjiàobiǎo	ACM
Accumulated call meter max	累积呼叫计量器最大值	Lěijī hūjiào jìliàngqì zuìdàzhí	ACMM
Accumulated down time	累积不可用时间	Lěijī bùkěyòng shíjiān	
Accumulated jitter	累积抖动	Lěijī dǒudòng	
Accumulated time	累积时间	Lěijī shíjiān	
Accumulator	累加器	Lěijiāqì	
Accuracy	准确度	Zhǔnquèdù	
Accurate position indicator	精确位置指示器	Jīngquè wèizhì zhǐshìqì	API
Acer Lab (Taiwan computer company)	宏棋实验室	Hóng qí shíyànshì	
Acer Lab (Taiwan computer maker)	宏基实验室	Hóngjī shíyànshì	
Achromatic	消色差	Xiāosèchā	
Acknowledge	肯定字符	Kěndìng zìfú	ACK
Acknowledge	确认	Quèrèn	ACK
Acknowledge interrupt	肯定中断	Kěndìng zhōngduàn	AKI
Acknowledged information transfer mode	证实信息传送方式	Zhèngshí xìnxī chuánsòng fāngshì	
Acknowledged information transfer service	确认式信息传送服务	Quèrèn-shì xìnxī chuánsòng fúwù	AITS
Acknowledged mode	应答模式	Yìngdá móshì	AM
Acknowledgement	肯定应答	Kěndìng yìngdá	ACK
Acknowledgement	确认	Quèrèn	ACK
Acknowledgement	应答	Yìngdá	ACK
Acknowledgement	应答信号	Yìngdá xìnhào	ACK

Acknowledgement message	认可消息	Rènkě xiāoxi	ACK
Acknowledgement signal	证实信号	Zhèngshí xìnhào	
Acknowledgement signal unit	确认信号单元	Quèrèn xìnhào dānyuán	ASU
Acknowledgement signal unit	证实信号单元	Zhèngshí xìnhào dānyuán	
Acknowledgement window	确认窗口	Quèrèn chuāngkǒu	
Acome (French company)	爱克工业集团	Ài-kè gōngyè jítuán	
Acoustic amplitude logger	声波幅度测井仪	Shēngbō fúdù cèjǐngyí	
Acoustic coupler	声耦合器	Shēng ǒuhéqì	AC
Acoustic echo canceler	回波消除器	Huíbō xiāochúqì	AEC
Acoustic echo control	回音控制	Huíyīn kòngzhì	
Acoustic echo controller	回波控制器	Huíbō kòngzhìqì	AEC
Acoustic echo path	回波通道	Huíbō tōngdào	AEP
Acoustic emission	声发射	Shēng fāshè	
Acoustic fatigue	声疲劳	Shēng píláo	
Acoustic feedback	声反馈	Shēng fǎnkuì	AF
Acoustic fiber sensor	光纤声传感器	Guāngxiān shēng chuángǎnqì	
Acoustic hologram	声全息图	Shēng quánxī tú	
Acoustic impedance	声阻抗	Shēng zǔkàng	
Acoustic matching layer	声匹配层	Shēng pǐpèi céng	
Acoustic ratio	声比	Shēngbǐ	
Acoustic releaser	声释放器	Shēng shìfàngqì	
Acoustic transducer	声换能器	Shēng huànnéngqì	
Acoustical absorption coefficient	声吸收系数	Shēng xīshōu xìshù	AAC
Acoustical conduction	声导	Shēngdǎo	
Acoustical control and telemetry system	声控和遥测系统	Shēngkòng hé yáocè xìtǒng	ACTS
Acoustical delay line	声延迟线	Shēng yánchíxiàn	ADL
Acoustic-optic tunable filter	声光可调滤波器	Shēngguāng kětiáo lǜbōqì	AOTF
Acousto-optic crystal	声光光学晶体	Shēngguāng guāngxué jīngtǐ	
Acousto-optic deflector	声光偏折器	Shēngguāng piānzhéqì	
Acousto-optic filter	声光率波器	Shēngguāng lǜbōqì	AOF
Acousto-optic glass	声光玻璃	Shēngguāng bōli	
Acousto-optic modulator	声光调变器	Shēngguāng tiáobiànqì	
Acousto-optic modulator	声光调制器	Shēngguāng tiáozhìqì	AOM
Acousto-optic scanner	声光扫描器	Shēngguāng sǎomiáoqì	
Acousto-optic switch	声光开关	Shēngguāng kāiguān	AOS
Acousto-optical	声光	Shēngguāng	
Acquisition	采集	Cǎijí	
Acquisition indicator	扑获指示器	Pūhuò zhǐshìqì	AI
Acquisition indicator channel	扑获指示信道	Pūhuò zhǐshì xìndào	AICH
Acquisition of signal	信号捕获	Xìnhào bǔhuò	AOS
Acquisition probability test (radar term)	截获概率试验	Jiéhuò gàilǜ shìyàn	
Across beam (in telecom installation)	跨梁敷设	Kuà liáng fūshè	AB
Across column (in telecom installation)	跨珠敷设	Kuà zhū fūshè	AC
Across-track scanning	横向扫描	Héngxiàng sǎomiáo	
Actinoelectric effect	光化电效应	Guānghuà diàn xiàoyìng	AE
Action	操作	Cāozuò	

Action game	动作类游戏	Dòngzuò lèi yóuxì	
Action indicator	动作指示符	Dòngzuò zhǐshì fú	Ai
Action indicator	作用指示器	Zuòyòng zhǐshìqì	AI
Action invocation	动作调用	Dòngzuò diàoyòng	
Action role play games (computer game)	动作角色扮演游戏	Dòngzuò juésè bànyǎn yóuxì	ARPG
Activate indication	激活指示	Jīhuó zhǐshì	AI
Activate request	激活请求	Jīhuó qǐngqiú	AR
Activate trace mode	激活跟踪方式	Jīhuó gēnzōng fāngshì	
Activated chemical vapor deposition process	激活化学汽相沉积工艺	Jīhuó huàxué qìxiàng chénjī gōngyì	
Activation	激活	Jīhuó	
Activation analysis	激动分析	Jīdòng fēnxī	AA
Activation analysis	激活分析	Jīhuó fēnxī	AA
Active	活动的	Huódòngde	
Active	有源	Yǒuyuán	
Active	在用	Zài yòng	
Active antenna	有源天线	Yǒuyuán tiānxiàn	
Active array antenna system	有源天线阵系统	Yǒuyuán tiānxiàn zhèn xìtǒng	AAAS
Active bit	有效位	Yǒuxiào wèi	AB
Active bit	运行位	Yùnxíng wèi	AB
Active comm channel	活动 C 通路	Huódòng C tōnglù	
Active communications satellite	有源通信卫星	Yǒuyuán tōngxìn wèixīng	ACS
Active content	活动内容	Huódòng nèiróng	
Active copper cable	活动铜缆	Huódòng tónglǎn	
Active corrective maintenance time	有效修复性维护时间	Yǒuxiào xiūfùxìng wéihù shíjiān	
Active corrective network	有源校正网络	Yǒuyuán jiàozhèng wǎngluò	
Active countermeasures	主动对抗	Zhǔdòng duìkàng	ACM
Active database	主动数据库	Zhǔdòng shùjùkù	
Active directory	活动目录	Huódòng mùlù	
Active file	活动文件	Huódòng wénjiàn	
Active filter	有源滤波器	Yǒuyuán lǜbōqì	
Active filter network	有源滤波器网络	Yǒuyuán lǜbōqì wǎngluò	AFN
Active function set	有效功能组	Yǒuxiào gōngnéng zǔ	AFS
Active gauge length	有效基长	Yǒuxiào jīcháng	
Active gauge width	有效基宽	Yǒuxiào jīkuān	
Active homing	主动追踪	Zhǔdòng zhuīzōng	AH
Active hub	有源集线器	Yǒuyuán jíxiànqì	
Active jamming	有源干扰	Yǒuyuán gānrǎo	
Active laser medium	激光激活媒质	Jīguāng jīhuó méizhì	
Active locating systems	主动定位系统	Zhǔdòng dìngwèi xìtǒng	
Active maintenance time	有效维护时间	Yǒuxiào wéihù shíjiān	
Active medium	激活材料	Jīhuó cáiliào	
Active medium	激活媒质	Jīhuó méizhì	
Active member address	活动的成员地址	Huódòngde chéngyuán dìzhǐ	AM-ADDR
Active mode	活动模式	Huódòng móshì	
Active mode	激活模式	Jīhuó móshì	
Active mode lock	活动模锁定	Huódòng mó suǒdìng	AML

Active network	有源网络	Yǒuyuán wǎngluò	AN
Active networks	主动网络	Zhǔdòng wǎngluò	
Active optical device	有源光器件	Yǒuyuán guāng qìjiàn	AOD
Active optical fiber	有源光纤	Yǒuyuán guāngxiān	AOF
Active optical network	有源光网络	Yǒuyuán guāng wǎngluò	AON
Active packet filtering	动态包过滤	Dòngtài bāo guòlǜ	
Active page register	有效页寄存器	Yǒuxiào yè jìcúnqì	APR
Active part of timeslot	时隙的活动部分	Shíxìde huódòng bùfen	
Active partition	活动分区	Huódòng fēnqū	
Active path	有效通道	Yǒuxiào tōngdào	
Active position	操作位置	Cāozuò wèizhì	
Active position home	操作位置复位	Cāozuò wèizhì fùwèi	
Active preventive maintenance time	有效预防性维修时间	Yǒuxiào yùfángxìng wéixiū shíjiān	
Active queue management	主动队列管理	Zhǔdòng duìliè guǎnlǐ	
Active redundancy	有效冗余	Yǒuxiào rǒngyú	
Active relay station	有源中继站	Yǒuyuán zhōngjìzhàn	
Active satellite	有源卫星	Yǒuyuán wèixīng	
Active section	有效段	Yǒuxiào duàn	
Active sensor	有源遥感器	Yǒuyuán yáogǎnqì	
Active sensor	主动式遥感器	Zhǔdòngshì yáogǎnqì	
Active server page	激活服务器页	Jīhuó fúwùqì yè	ASP
Active server pages	活动服务器页面	Huódòng fúwùqì yèmiàn	
Active sharing mechanism (in CSCW)	活动共享机制	Huódòng gòngxiǎng jīzhì	
Active statement	活动语句	Huódòng yǔjù	
Active template library	有源模板库	Yǒuyuán múbǎn kù	ATL
Active threat (IPsec)	主动威胁	Zhǔdòng wēixié	
Active trail	有效路径	Yǒuxiào lùjìng	
Active window	激活窗口	Jīhuó chuāngkǒu	
Active wiretapping	主动搭线窃听	Zhǔdòng dāxiàn qiètīng	
Active, ad hoc	现役	Xiànyì	
ActiveX	网络化多媒体对象技术	Wǎngluòhuà duōméitǐ duìxiàng jìshù	
ActiveX data object	访问服务器专用对象集	Fǎngwèn fúwùqì zhuānyòng duìxiàng jí	ADO
Actual argument (in FORTRAN)	实自变量	Shí zìbiànliàng	
Actual argument (in FORTRAN)	实际变元	Shíjì biànyuán	
Actual crystal	实际晶体	Shíjì jīngtǐ	
Actual parameter	实参	Shícān	
Actual recipient	实际接收者	Shíjì jiēshōuzhě	
Actual transfer rate	实际传送速率	Shíjì chuánsòng sùlǜ	
Actual transfer rate	有效传输率	Yǒuxiào chuánshū lǜ	
Actual work time	实际占用时间	Shíjì zhànyòng shíjiān	AWT
Actuation method	驱动方法	Qūdòng fāngfǎ	
Actuator	驱动机构	Qūdòng jīgòu	
Actuator	执行机构	Zhíxíng jīgòu	
Actuator	执行器	Zhíxíngqì	
Actuator (driving) element	执行元件	Zhíxíng yuánjiàn	
ad hoc connector name	特殊连接器名称	Tèshū liánjiēqì míngchēng	

English	Chinese	Pinyin	Abbreviation
Ad hoc network	临时组网	Línshí zǔwǎng	
Ad hoc on-demand distance vector	按序距离矢量	Ànxù jùlí shǐliàng	AODV
Ada (computer language)	Ada 语言	Ada yǔyán	
Adaptability	可适应性	Kěshìyìngxìng	
Adaptation function	适配功能	Shìpèi gōngnéng	AF
Adaptation information	适配信息	Shìpèi xìnxī	AI
Adaptation layer (for ATM)	适配层	Shìpèi céng	
Adaptation unit	适配单元	Shìpèi dānyuán	AU
Adaptation, adaptive; auto-negotiation (modem function)	自适应	Zìshìyìng	
Adapter	监控器	Jiānkòngqì	
Adapter	适配器	Shìpèiqì	
Adapter body	转换座外壳	Zhuǎnhuàn zuòwàiké	
Adapter card	适配器卡	Shìpèiqì kǎ	
Adapter signal processing	适配器信号处理	Shìpèiqì xìnhào chǔlǐ	ASP
Adaption layer	适应层	Shìyìng céng	
Adaptive algorithm	自适应算法	Zìshìyìng suànfǎ	
Adaptive amplifier	自适应放大器	Zìshìyìng fàngdàqì	AA
Adaptive antenna	自适应天线	Zìshìyìng tiānxiàn	AA
Adaptive antenna system	自适应天线系统	Zìshìyìng tiānxiàn xìtǒng	AAS
Adaptive array antenna	自适应阵列天线	Zìshìyìng zhènliè tiānxiàn	
Adaptive busy	自适应忙	Zìshìyìng máng	
Adaptive channel allocation	自适应通道分配	Zìshìyìng tōngdào fēnpèi	ACA
Adaptive clutter attenuator	自适应散射干扰衰减器	Zìshìyìng sǎnshè gānrǎo shuāijiǎnqì	ACA
Adaptive communication	自适应通信	Zìshìyìng tōngxìn	
Adaptive computer experiment	自适应计算机试验	Zìshìyìng jìsuànjī shìyàn	ACE
Adaptive control optimization	自适应控制优化	Zìshìyìng kòngzhì yōuhuà	ACO
Adaptive control system	自适应控制系统	Zìshìyìng kòngzhì xìtǒng	
Adaptive decree feedback equalizer	自适应判决反馈均衡器	Zìshìyìng pànjué fǎnkuì jūnhéngqì	ADFE
Adaptive delta modulation	自适应增量调制	Zìshìyìng zēngliàng tiáozhì	ADM
Adaptive differential pulse code modulation	自适应差分脉冲编码调制	Zìshìyìng chāfēn màichōng biānmǎ tiáozhì	ADPCM
Adaptive differential pulse code modulation	自适应差分脉码调制	Zìshìyìng chāfēn màimǎ tiáozhì	ADPCM
Adaptive differential pulse code modulation	自适应脉冲编码调制	Zìshìyìng màichōng biānmǎ tiáozhì	ADPCM
Adaptive digital access protocol	自适应数字接入协议	Zìshìyìng shùzì jiērù xiéyì	ADAPt
Adaptive digital filtering	自适应数字滤波	Zìshìyìng shùzì lǜbō	ADF
Adaptive digital vocoder	自适应数字声码器	Zìshìyìng shùzì shēngmǎqì	ADV
Adaptive dynamic analysis and maintenance	自适应动态分析和维修	Zìshìyìng dòngtài fēnxī hé wéixiū	ADAM
Adaptive dynamic fuzzy system	自适应动态模糊系统	Zìshìyìng dòngtài móhú xìtǒng	
Adaptive equalization	自适应均衡	Zìshìyìng jūnhéng	
Adaptive frame alignment	自适应帧校准	Zìshìyìng zhèng jiàozhǔn	
Adaptive HF station	自适应短波电台	Zìshìyìng duǎnbō diàntái	
Adaptive image analysis	自适应图像分析	Zìshìyìng túxiàng fēnxī	
Adaptive image compression	自适应图像压缩	Zìshìyìng túxiàng yāsuō	
Adaptive mobile target indicator	自适应动目标显示	Zìshìyìng dòng mùbiāo xiǎnshì	Adaptive MTI
Adaptive modulation	自适应调制	Zìshìyìng tiáozhì	
Adaptive modulation and coding	自适应调制编码	Zìshìyìng tiáozhì biānmǎ	AMC
Adaptive modulation system	自适应调制系统	Zìshìyìng tiáozhì xìtǒng	AMS

Adaptive motion compensation algorithm	自适应运动补偿算法	Zìshìyìng yùndòng bǔcháng suànfǎ	AMC
Adaptive multirate	自适应多速率	Zìshìyìng duōsùlǜ	AMR
Adaptive multirate codec	自适应多码率编译码器	Zìshìyìng duōmǎlǜ biānyìmǎqì	AMRC
Adaptive noise cancellation	自适应噪声消除	Zìshìyìng zàoshēng xiāochú	ANC
Adaptive non-linear enhancer	自适应非线性增强器	Zìshìyìng fēixiànxìng zēngqiángqì	ANLE
Adaptive phase code modulation	自适应相位代码调制	Zìshìyìng xiàngwèi dàimǎ tiáozhì	APCM
Adaptive power control	自适应功率控制	Zìshìyìng gōnglǜ kòngzhì	APC
Adaptive prediction	自适应预测	Zìshìyìng yùcè	
Adaptive predictive coder	自适应预测编码器	Zìshìyìng yùcè biānmǎqì	APC
Adaptive predictive coding	自适应预测编码	Zìshìyìng yùcè biānmǎ	APC
Adaptive predictive coding with adaptive bit allocation	具有可适应比特分配的自适应预测编码	Jùyǒu kěshìyìng bǐtè fēnpèide zìshìyìng yùcè biānmǎ	APC-AB
Adaptive predictive coding with adaptive bit allocation	具有自适应比特分配的自适应预测编码	Jùyǒu zìshìyìng bǐtè fēnpèide zìshìyìng yùcè biānmǎ	APC-AB
Adaptive pulse code modulation	自适应脉码调制	Zìshìyìng màimǎ tiáozhì	APCM
Adaptive quantization	自适应量化	Zìshìyìng liànghuà	AQ
Adaptive quantization with backward estimation	采用反向估计的自适应量化	Cǎiyòng fǎnxiàng gūjìde zìshìyìng liànghuà	AQBE
Adaptive quantization with forward estimation	采用正向评判的自适应量化	Cǎiyòng zhèngxiàng píngpànde zìshìyìng liànghuà	AQFE
Adaptive receiver	自适应接收机	Zìshìyìng jiēshōujī	
Adaptive speed leveling	自适应速度等级调整	Zìshìyìng sùdù děngjí tiáozhěng	
Adaptive threshold control	自适应阈值控制	Zìshìyìng yùzhí kòngzhì	ATC
Adaptive time domain equalizer	自适应时域均衡器	Zìshìyìng shíyù jūnhéngqì	ATDE
Adaptive transform coding	自适应变换编码	Zìshìyìng biànhuàn biānmǎ	ATC
Adaptive transversal filter	自适应横向滤波器	Zìshìyìng héngxiàng lǜbōqì	ATF
Adaptive wireless congestion control	自适应无线拥塞控制	Zìshìyìng wúxiàn yōngsè kòngzhì	
Adcock array antenna	爱德科克阵天线	Ài-dé-kē-kè zhèn tiānxiàn	
Add carry	加法进位	Jiāfǎ jìnwèi	AC
Add control unit	加法控制器	Jiāfǎ kòngzhìqì	ACU
Add drop multiplexer	插/分复用器	Chā/fēn fùyòngqì	ADM
Add key round	加密钥轮	Jiā mìyào lún	
Add network resource	增配网络资源	Zēngpèi wǎngluò zīyuán	ADDNR
Add/drop cross-connection	分/插交叉连接	Fēn/chā jiāochā liánjiē	
Add/drop multiplexer	插入/分出复接设备	Chārù/fēnchū fù jiē shèbèi	ADM
Add/drop multiplexer	分/插复用设备	Fēn/chā fùyòng shèbèi	ADM
Add/drop multiplexer	分插复用器	Fēnchā fùyòngqì	ADM
Add/drop multiplexer	上/下复用器	Shàng/xià fùyòngqì	ADM
Add/drop multiplexer	上/下路复用器	Shàng/xià lù fùyòngqì	ADM
Add/drop optical module	上/下路光模块	Shàng/xià lù guāng mókuài	ADOM
Add-compare-select	加选比	Jiā xuǎn bǐ	ACS
Add-compare-select	相加-比较-选择，加选比	Xiāngjiā-bǐjiào-xuǎnzé, jiā xuǎn bǐ	ACS
Adder	加法器	Jiāfǎqì	
Adder output buffer	加法器输出缓冲器	Jiāfǎqì shūchū huǎnchōngqì	AOB
Adder output bus	加法器输出总线	Jiāfǎqì shūchū zǒngxiàn	AOB
Add-in	插件	Chājiàn	
Add-in	加载项	Jiāzài xiàng	
Additional assignment	附加指配	Fùjiā zhǐpèi	

Additional character	附加符号	Fùjiā fúhào	
Additional elementary functions	补充基本功能	Bǔchōng jīběn gōngnéng	AEF
Additional global function	附加的全局功能	Fùjiāde quánjú gōngnéng	AGF
Additional high layer function	附加的高层功能	Fùjiāde gāocéng gōngnéng	AHLF
Additional information transfer supplementary service	外加信息转送附加业务	Wàijiā xìnxī zhuǎnsòng fùjiā yèwù	
Additional low layer function	附加的低层功能	Fùjiāde dīcéng gōngnéng	ALLF
Additive outlier series	加性异常值序列	Jiāxìng yìchángzhí xùliè	
Additive primary colors	加色法三原色	Jiāsèfǎ sānyuánsè	
Additive Process (in SMT)	加成工艺	Jiāchéng gōngyì	
Additive white Gaussian noise	附加白高斯噪声	Fùjiā bái gāo-sī zàoshēng	AWGN
Additive white Gaussian noise	附加高斯白噪声	Fùjiā gāo-sī bái zàoshēng	AWGN
Additive white Gaussian noise	加性高斯白噪声	Jiāxìng gāo-sī bái zàoshēng	AWGN
Add-on card	加置卡	Jiāzhì kǎ	
Add-on header	添加标题	Tiānjiā biāotí	AOH
Add-on security	后加安全措施	Hòujiā ānquán cuòshī	
Address	地址	Dìzhǐ	
Address adder	地址加法器	Dìzhǐ jiāfǎqì	AAD
Address allocation plan	地址分配方案	Dìzhǐ fēnpèi fāng'àn	AAP
Address area	地址区	Dìzhǐ qū	
Address arithmetic unit	地址运算器	Dìzhǐ yùnsuànqì	AAU
Address bit permutating	地址位序列改变	Dìzhǐ wèi xùliè gǎibiàn	ABP
Address bus	地址总线	Dìzhǐ zǒngxiàn	
Address byte	地址字节	Dìzhǐ zìjié	AB
Address carry	地址进位	Dìzhǐ jìnwèi	AC
Address coding	地址编码	Dìzhǐ biānmǎ	
Address compare register	地址比较寄存器	Dìzhǐ bǐjiào jìcúnqì	ACR
Address complete message	地址全消息	Dìzhǐ quán xiāoxi	ACM
Address complete message (ISUP message)	地址接收完毕	Dìzhǐ jiēshōu wánbì	ACM
Address completion message	地址收全消息	Dìzhǐ shōuquán xiāoxi	ACM
Address constant	地址常数	Dìzhǐ chángshù	
Address control unit	地址控制器	Dìzhǐ kòngzhìqì	ACU
Address control vector	地址控制向量	Dìzhǐ kòngzhì xiàngliàng	ACV
Address data strobe	地址数据选通	Dìzhǐ shùjù xuǎntōng	ADS
Address decoder	地址译码器	Dìzhǐ yìmǎqì	AD
Address detector	地址探测器	Dìzhǐ tàncèqì	AD
Address digital receiver	数字地址接收器	Shùzì dìzhǐ jiēshōuqì	ADR
Address display sub-system	地址显示子系统	Dìzhǐ xiǎnshì zìxìtǒng	ADS
Address field	地址字段	Dìzhǐ zìduàn	AF
Address field extension	地址字段扩展	Dìzhǐ zìduàn kuòzhǎn	EA
Address function	地址函数	Dìzhǐ hánshù	ADDR
Address generation unit (CPU term)	地址产成单元	Dìzhǐ chǎnchéng dānyuán	
Address geocoding	地址地理编码	Dìzhǐ dìlǐ biānmǎ	
Address identification bit	地址识别比特	Dìzhǐ shíbié bǐtè	A
Address identifier	地址识别符	Dìzhǐ shíbié fú	
Address incomplete signal	地址不全信号	Dìzhǐ bùquán xìnhào	ADI
Address information	地址信息	Dìzhǐ xìnxī	

Address mapping list	地址映射表	Dìzhǐ yìngshè biǎo	AML
Address mapping table	地址映射表	Dìzhǐ yìngshè biǎo	AMT
Address mask	地址掩码	Dìzhǐ yǎnmǎ	
Address matching	地址匹配	Dìzhǐ pǐpèi	
Address over error	地址引起的错误	Dìzhǐ yǐnqǐde cuòwù	
Address pool	地址池	Dìzhǐ chí	
Address range definition block	地址范围定义块	Dìzhǐ fànwéi dìngyì kuài	ARDB
Address recoding protocol	地址解析协议	Dìzhǐ jiěxī xiéyì	ARP
Address relief protocol	地址解折协议	Dìzhǐ jiězhé xiéyì	ARP
Address resolution	地址解析	Dìzhǐ jiěxī	
Address resolution protocol	地址解析协议	Dìzhǐ jiěxī xiéyì	ARP
Address resolution server	地址解析服务器	Dìzhǐ jiěxī fúwùqì	ARS
Address selection	地址选择	Dìzhǐ xuǎnzé	ADSEL
Address sequencing	地址定序	Dìzhǐ dìngxù	
Address signal	地址信号	Dìzhǐ xìnhào	
Address space	地址空间	Dìzhǐ kōngjiān	
Address template	地址模板	Dìzhǐ múbǎn	AT
Address translation buffer	地址转换缓冲器	Dìzhǐ zhuǎnhuàn huǎnchōngqì	ATB
Address translation memory	地址翻译存储器	Dìzhǐ fānyì cúnchǔqì	ATM
Addressable detector	地址探测器	Dìzhǐ tàncèqì	AD
Addressable optical storage	光束寻址存储	Guāngshù xúnzhǐ cúnchǔ	
Addressable point	可寻址点	Kěxúnzhǐ diǎn	
Address-complete signal	地址全信号	Dìzhǐ quán xìnhào	
Address-complete signal (with charge)	地址全信号（计费）	Dìzhǐ quán xìnhào (jì fèi)	
Address-complete signal (with no charge)	地址全信号（不计费）	Dìzhǐ quán xìnhào (bùjì fèi)	
Addressed packet system	编址分组系统	Biānzhǐ fēnzǔ xìtǒng	APS
Address-of operator	取地址操作符	Qǔ dìzhǐ cāozuò fú	
Adhesion (in SMT)	附着力	Fùzhuólì	
Adiabatic change	绝热变化	Juérè biànhuà	
Adiabatic chart	绝热图	Juérè tú	
Adiabatic device	绝热器件	Juérè qìjiàn	
Adiabatic process	绝热过程	Juérè guòchéng	
Adjacency	邻接	Línjiē	
Adjacency	邻近	Línjìn	
Adjacency analysis	邻接分析	Línjiē fēnxī	
Adjacency areas	邻接区域	Línjiē qūyù	
Adjacency effect	邻界效应	Línjiè xiàoyìng	
Adjacency list	邻接表	Línjiē biǎo	
Adjacency matrix	邻接矩阵	Línjiē jǔzhèn	
Adjacency multi-list	邻接多重表	Línjiē duōzhòng biǎo	
Adjacent bit interference	邻位干扰	Línwèi gānrǎo	ABI
Adjacent cell interference	邻小区干扰	Línxiǎoqū gānrǎo	ACI
Adjacent cell interference	相临小区干扰	Xiānglín xiǎoqū gānrǎo	ACI
Adjacent channel	相邻频道	Xiānglín píndào	C/A, AC
Adjacent channel	相邻信道	Xiānglín xìndào	
Adjacent channel attenuation	相邻信道衰减	Xiānglín xìndào shuāijiǎn	ACA

Adjacent channel interference	邻频干扰	Línpín gānrǎo	ACI
Adjacent channel interference ratio	邻信道干扰比	Línxìndào gānrǎobǐ	ACIR
Adjacent channel leakage power ratio	邻信道泄漏功率比	Línxìndào xièlòu gōnglǜ bǐ	ACLR
Adjacent channel leakage ratio	邻信道泄漏比	Línxìndào xièlòubǐ	ACLR
Adjacent channel power	邻道功率	Líndào gōnglǜ	ACP
Adjacent channel selectivity	邻频选择性	Línpín xuǎnzéxìng	
Adjacent edge	相邻边	Xiānglín biān	
Adjacent frequency interference suppression	邻频干扰抑制	Línpín gānrǎo yìzhì	
Adjacent nodes	相邻节点	Xiānglín jiédiǎn	
Adjacent vertex	相邻顶点	Xiānglín dǐngdiǎn	
Adjacent-channel selectivity	邻道选择性	Líndào xuǎnzéxìng	
Adjacent-channel selectivity	邻频道选择性	Línpíndào xuǎnzéxìng	
Adjacent-channel selectivity	邻信道选择性	Línxìndào xuǎnzéxìng	ACS
Adjacent-signal selectivity	邻信号选择性	Línxìnhào xuǎnzéxìng	
Adjoining sheets	图幅拼接	Túfú pīnjiē	
Adjustable digit time slot	可调数位时隙	Kětiáo shùwèi shíxì	
Adjusted decibels	调准分贝	Tiáozhǔn fēnbèi	dBA
Adjustment standard accuracy	标准准确度校正	Biāozhǔn zhǔnquèdù jiàozhèng	
Administration	主管部门	Zhǔguǎn bùmén	
Administration and maintenance sub-system	管理维护子系统	Guǎnlǐ wéihù zixìtǒng	AMS
Administration center	管理中心	Guǎnlǐ zhōngxīn	ADC
Administration directory management domain	公用号码簿管理域	Gōngyòng hàomǎbù guǎnlǐ yù	ADDMD
Administration directory management domain	主管部门号码簿管理域	Zhǔguǎn bùmén hàomǎbù guǎnlǐ yù	ADDMD
Administration domain name	公用域名	Gōngyòng yùmíng	
Administration management domain	公用管理域	Gōngyòng guǎnlǐ yù	ADMD
Administration module	管理模块	Guǎnlǐ mókuài	AM
Administration module/communication module	管理/通信模块	Guǎnlǐ/Tōngxìn mókuài	AM/CM
Administration queue	管理队列	Guǎnlǐ duìliè	
Administrative area	管理区	Guǎnlǐqū	AA
Administrative authority	主管当局	Zhǔguǎn dāngjú	
Administrative delay (for corrective maintenance)	管理耽误	Guǎnlǐ dānwù	
Administrative distance	管理位距	Guǎnlǐ wèi jù	
Administrative domain	管理域	Guǎnlǐ yù	AD
Administrative domain name	管理域名	Guǎnlǐ yùmíng	
Administrative point	管理点	Guǎnlǐ diǎn	AP
Administrative processor	管理处理器	Guǎnlǐ chùlǐqì	AP
Administrative security	管理安全	Guǎnlǐ ānquán	
Administrative structure definition	管理结构定义	Guǎnlǐ jiégòu dìngyì	
Administrative structure identifier	管理结构标识符	Guǎnlǐ jiégòu biāozhì fú	
Administrative support system	管理支持系统	Guǎnlǐ zhīchí xìtǒng	ASS
Administrative terminal system	管理终端系统	Guǎnlǐ zhōngduān xìtǒng	ATS
Administrative unit	管理单元	Guǎnlǐ dānyuán	AU
Administrative unit alarm indication signal	管理单元告警指示信号	Guǎnlǐ dānyuán gàojǐng zhǐshì xìnhào	AU-AIS
Administrative unit group	管理单元组	Guǎnlǐ dānyuán zǔ	AUG
Administrative unit loss of pointer	管理单元指针丢失	Guǎnlǐ dānyuán zhǐzhēn diūshī	AU-LOP
Administrative unit pointer	管理单元指针	Guǎnlǐ dānyuán zhǐzhēn	AU PTR

Administrative unit pointer	管理单元指针	Guǎnlǐ dānyuán zhǐzhēn	AUP
Administrative unit pointer justification event	AU 指针调整事件	AU zhǐzhēn tiáozhěng shìjiàn	AUPJE
Administrative unit pointer negative justification	管理单元负指针调整	Guǎnlǐ dānyuán fù zhǐzhēn tiáozhěng	AU-NPJE
Administrative unit pointer positive justification	管理单元正指针调整	Guǎnlǐ dānyuán zhèng zhǐzhēn tiáozhěng	AU-PPJE
Administrative weight	管理加权	Guǎnlǐ jiāquán	AW
Administrator account	管理员帐号	Guǎnlǐyuán zhànghào	
Admission confirm	接入确认	Jiērù quèrèn	ACF
Admission control	接纳控制	Jiēnà kòngzhì	
Admissions confirmed (packet network protocol message)	接主确认	Jiēzhǔ quèrèn	ACF
Admissions rejected	接入拒绝	Jiērù jùjué	ARJ
Admissions request	接入请求	Jiērù qǐngqiú	ARQ
Admittance	导纳	Dǎonà	
ADSL overhead control channel	ADSL 开销控制信道	ADSL kāixiao kòngzhì xìndào	AOC
ADSL termination unit	ADSL 终端设备	ADSL zhōngduān shèbèi	
ADSL transceiver unit	ADSL 收发单元	ADSL shōufā dānyuán	ATU
ADSL transceiver unit, central office end	ADSL 局端发送接收单元	ADSL júduān fāsòng jiēshōu dānyuán	ATU-C
ADSL transceiver unit, remote terminal end	ADSL 远端发送接收单元	ADSL yuǎnduān fāsòng jiēshōu dānyuán	ATU-T
ADSL Transciever unit-recever end	用户端 ADSL 收发单元	Yònghù duān ADSL shōufā dānyuán	ATU-R
ADSL transmission unit-central	ADSL 中央传输单元	ADSL zhōngyāng chuánshū dānyuán	ATU-C
ADSL transmission unit-remote	ADSL 远端传输单元	ADSL yuǎnduān chuánshū dānyuán	ATU-R
Advanced acoustic signal processor	先进声信号处理器	Xiānjìn shēng xìnhào chǔlǐqì	AASP
Advanced audio coding	先进音频编码	Xiānjìn yīnpín biānmǎ	AAC
Advanced binary-coded decimal interchange code	高级二-十进制交换代码	Gāojí èr-shíjìnzhì jiāohuàn dàimǎ	ABCDIC
Advanced communication service	高级通信业务	Gāojí tōngxìn yèwù	
Advanced communication system	新型通信系统	Xīnxíng tōngxìn xìtǒng	ACS
Advanced communication technologies and services	现代通信技术和业务	Xiàndài tōngxìn jìshù hé yèwù	ACTS
Advanced communication technologies and services	先进的通信技术业务	Xiānjìnde tōngxìn jìshù yèwù	ATCS
Advanced communications function	高级通信功能	Gāojí tōngxìn gōngnéng	ACF
Advanced communications function	先进通信功能	Xiānjìn tōngxìn gōngnéng	ACF
Advanced configuration and power interface	高级配置和电源接口	Gāojí pèizhì hé diànyuán jiēkǒu	ACPI
Advanced configuration and power interface	先进设置和电源管理	Xiānjìn shèzhì hé diànyuán guǎnlǐ	ACPI
Advanced continuous simulation language	高级连续仿真语言	Gāojí liánxù fǎngzhēn yǔyán	ACSL
Advanced data communication control protocol	高级数据通信控制协议	Gāojí shùjù tōngxìn kòngzhì xiéyì	ADCCP
Advanced data communications procedure	先进数据通信规程	Xiānjìn shùjù tōngxìn guīchéng	ADCCP
Advanced data handler for on-line control	联机控制用先进数据处理程序	Liánjī kòngzhì-yòng xiānjìn shùjùchǔlǐ chéngxù	ADHOC
Advanced data processing	高级数据处理	Gāojí shùjù chǔlǐ	ADP
Advanced data system	高级数据系统	Gāojí shùjù xìtǒng	ADS
Advanced digital opticai control system	高级数据光控制系统	Gāojí shùjù guāng kòngzhì xìtǒng	ADOCS
Advanced dual in-line memory modules	高级双重内嵌式内存模块	Gāojí shuāngchóng nèiqiàn-shì nèicún mókuài	ADIMM
Advanced encryption standard	高级加密标准	Gāojí jiāmì biāozhǔn	AES
Advanced encryption standard	先进加密标准	Xiānjìn jiāmì biāozhǔn	AES
Advanced encryption system	先进的加密系统	Xiānjìnde jiāmì xìtǒng	AES
Advanced fetch	先行取指令	Xiānxíng qǔ zhǐlìng	
Advanced flexible access multiplex system	高级灵活接入复用系统	Gāojí línghuó jiērù fùyòng xìtǒng	AFMS

Advanced freephone service	高级免费电话业务	Gāojí miǎnfèi diànhuà yèwù	AFS
Advanced graphics port	高级图形端口	Gāojí túxíng duānkǒu	AGP
Advanced graphics system	高级图形系统	Gāojí túxíng xìtǒng	AGS
Advanced guidance system	高级制导系统	Gāojí zhìdǎo xìtǒng	AGS
Advanced intelligent network	高级智能网	Gāojí zhìnéng wǎng	AIN
Advanced local area network	高级局域网	Gāojí júyùwǎng	ALAN
Advanced macro processor	宏指令处理程序	Hóng zhǐlìng chǔlǐ chéngxù	AMP
Advanced Micro Devices	超微科技	Chāowēi kējì	AMD
Advanced Micro Devices (US computer company)	超微半导体	Chāowēi bàndǎotǐ	AMD
Advanced mobile phone service	高级移动电话服务	Gāojí yídòng diànhuà fúwù	AMPS
Advanced mobile phone service	高级移动电话业务	Gāojí yídòng diànhuà yèwù	AMPS
Advanced mobile phone service	先进移动电话业务	Xiānjìn yídòng diànhuà yèwù	AMPS
Advanced mobile phone system	高极移动电话系统	Gāojí yídòng diànhuà xìtǒng	AMPS
Advanced mobile phone system	先进的移动电话系统	Xiānjìnde yídòng diànhuà xìtǒng	AMPS
Advanced mobile security architecture	先进移动安全体系结构	Xiānjìn yídòng ānquán tǐxì jiégòu	AMSA
Advanced mobile telephone system	高级移动电话系统	Gāojí yídòng diànhuà xìtǒng	AMTS
Advanced network integration	高级网络集成	Gāojí wǎngluò jíchéng	ANI
Advanced network integration	高级网络综合	Gāojí wǎngluò zōnghé	ANI
Advanced network system architecture	高级网络系统结构	Gāojí wǎngluò xìtǒng jiégòu	ANSA
Advanced networks and services	高级网络和服务	Gāojí wǎngluò hé fúwù	ANS
Advanced packet parsing engine	增强形帧解析引擎	Zēngqiáng-xíng zhèng jiěxī yǐnqíng	APPE
Advanced paging operator code	先进寻呼操作码	Xiānjìn xúnhū cāozuòmǎ	APOC
Advanced peer to peer networking	高级对等网络	Gāojí duìděng wǎngluò	APPN
Advanced peer-to-peer communications	先进的同层通信	Xiānjìnde tóngcéng tōngxìn	APPC
Advanced peer-to-peer internetworking	先进的同层互联网	Xiānjìnde tóngcéng hùliánwǎng	APPI
Advanced personal communication system	高级个人通信系统	Gāojí gèrén tōngxìn xìtǒng	APCS
Advanced power management	高级能源管理	Gāojí néngyuán guǎnlǐ	APM
Advanced programmable interrupt controller	高级程序中断控制器	Gāojí chéngxù zhōngduàn kòngzhìqì	APIC
Advanced programming interface	高级编程接口	Gāojí biānchéng jiēkǒu	API
Advanced program-to-program communication (IBM protocol)	高级程序间通信	Gāojí chéngxù-jiān tōngxìn	APPC
Advanced real-time processing system	高级实时处理系统	Gāojí shíshí chǔlǐ xìtǒng	
Advanced Research Project Agency	先进研究计划局	Xiānjìn yánjiū jìhuàjú	ARPA
Advanced Research Projects Agency (US)	高级研究计划局	Gāojí yánjiū jìhuàjú	ARPA
Advanced Research Projects Agency (US)	高级研究计划署	Gāojí yánjiū jìhuàshǔ	ARPA
Advanced Research Projects Agency Network	高级研究计划局网络	Gāojí yánjiū jìhuàjú wǎngluò	ARPAnet
Advanced Research Projects Agency network (US)	阿帕网	Ā-pà wǎng	ARPANET
Advanced Research Projects Agency network (US)	高级研究规划局网络	Gāojí yánjiū guīhuàjú wǎngluò	ARPANET
Advanced Research Projects Agency network (US)	高级研究计划署网络	Gāojí yánjiū jìhuàshǔ wǎngluò	ARPANET
Advanced SCSI program interface	高级 SCSI 编程接口	Gāojí SCSI biānchéng jiēkǒu	ASPI
Advanced signal processing	高级信号处理	Gāojí xìnhào chǔlǐ	ASP
Advanced software technology and algorithms	高级软件技术与算法	Gāojí ruǎnjiàn jìshù yǔ suànfǎ	ASTA
Advanced speech call items	先进的语音呼叫项目	Xiānjìnde yǔyīn hūjiào xiàngmù	ASCI
Advanced storage magneto-optical	增强形光学存储器	Zēngqiáng-xíng guāngxué cúnchǔqì	ASMO
Advanced streaming (media) format	先进流媒体格式	Xiānjìn liúméitǐ géshi	ASF

Advanced super thin-layer and high-output metal media	增强形超薄高速金属媒体	Zēngqiáng-xíng chāobáo gāosù jīnshǔ méitǐ	ATOMM
Advanced technology attachment packet interface	AT 封包連接介面	AT fēngbāo liánjiē jièmiàn	ATAPI
Advanced technology storage	先进技术存储	Xiānjìn jìshù cúnchǔ	ADTX
Advanced teleprocessing system	高级远程信息处理系统	Gāojí yuǎnchéng xìnxī chǔlǐ xìtǒng	ATS
Advanced text management system	高级文本管理系统	Gāojí wénběn guǎnlǐ xìtǒng	ATMS
Advanced very high resolution radiometer	其它分辨率辐射计	Qítā fēnbiànlǜ fúshèjì	AVHRR
Advanced, modern	先进	Xiānjìn	
Advantech Ltd. (China company)	研华	Yán huá	
Adventure genre (computer game)	冒险类游戏	Màoxiǎn lèi yóuxì	AVG
Advice of charge	计费通知	Jìfèi tōngzhī	AOC
Advice of charge	收费通知	Shōufèi tōngzhī	AOC
Advice of charge charging	计费收费通知	Jìfèi shōufèi tōngzhī	AoC
Advice of charge charging supplementary service	计费通知（记费）补充业务	Jìfèi tōngzhī (jìfèi) bǔchōng yèwù	AoCC
Advice of charge for charging	计费通知(计费)	Jìfèi tōngzhī (jìfèi)	AoCc
Advice of charge for information	计费通知(信息)	Jìfèi tōngzhī (xìnxī)	AoCi
Advice of charge information	信息计费通知	Xìnxī jìfèi tōngzhī	AoCI
Advice of charge information supplementary service	计费通知（信息）补充业务	Jìfèi tōngzhī (xìnxī) bǔchōng yèwù	AoCI
Advice of charge, charging level	计费通知, 计费类	Jìfèi tōngzhī, jìfèi lèi	AoCC
Advice of charge, information level	计费通知, 信息类	Jìfèi tōngzhī, xìnxī lèi	AoCI
Advisory Committee on Electronics and Telecommunications	电子电信咨询委员会	Diànzǐ diànxìn zīxún wěiyuánhuì	ACET
Advisory route	建议路由	Jiànyì lùyóu	ADR
Aeolian vibration	风积振动	Fēngjī zhèndòng	
Aerial (or airborne) remote sensing (GIS)	航空遥感	Hángkōng yáogǎn	
Aerial cable	架空缆	Jiàkōng lǎn	
Aerial fiber optic cable	架空光缆	Jiàkōng guānglǎn	AOFC
Aerial fiber optic cable	悬空式光缆	Xuánkōng-shì guānglǎn	
Aerial insert	架空插入段	Jiàkōng chārù duàn	
Aerodynamic admittance	空气动力导纳	Kōngqì dònglì dǎonà	
Aerodynamic force	空气动力	Kōngqì dònglì	
Aeronautical earth station	航空地球站	Hángkōng dìqiúzhàn	
Aeronautical fixed service	航空固定业务	Hángkōng gùdìng yèwù	
Aeronautical fixed station	航空固定电台	Hángkōng gùdìng diàntái	
Aeronautical mobile satellite service	航空移动卫星通信	Hángkōng yídòng wèixīng tōngxìn	AMSS
Aeronautical mobile service	航空移动业务	Hángkōng yídòng yèwù	
Aeronautical mobile-satellite service	航空卫星移动业务	Hángkōng wèixīng yídòng yèwù	
Aeronautical mobile-satellite service	卫星航空移动业务	Wèixīng hángkōng yídòng yèwù	
Aeronautical radio navigation satellite service	卫星航空无线电导航业务	Wèixīng hángkōng wúxiàndiàn dǎoháng yèwù	
Aeronautical radio navigation service	航空无线电导航业务	Hángkōng wúxiàndiàn dǎoháng yèwù	
Aeronautical station	对空台	Duìkōng tái	
Aeronautical station	航空电台	Hángkōng diàntái	
Aeronautics Advisory Committee (US, part of NASA)	航空咨询委员会	Hángkōng zīxún wěiyuánhuì	AAC
Aeronautics and Astronautics Coordinating Board (US, part of NASA)	航空与宇航协调局	Hángkōng yǔ yǔháng xiétiáo jú	AACB
Aerosol (in SMT)	气溶剂	Qìróngjì	
AF protection ratio	AF 保护比	AF bǎohù bǐ	

AF signal-to-interference ratio	AF 信号干扰比	AF xìnhào gānrǎo bǐ	
Affine transformation	仿射变换	Fǎngshè biànhuàn	
Affinity	相似性	Xiāngsìxìng	
Affordability	可购性	Kěgòuxìng	
Aftermarket	配件市场	Pèijiàn shìchǎng	
Afternoon effect	下午效应	Xiàwǔ xiàoyìng	
AGC attack time	AGC 启动时间	AGC qǐdòng shíjiān	
AGC recovery time	AGC 恢复时间	AGC huīfù shíjiān	
Ageing failure	老化失效	Lǎohuà shīxiào	
Ageing fault	老化故障	Lǎohuà gùzhàng	
Ageing test	老化测试	Lǎohuà cèshì	
Agencia Nacional de Telecomunicaoes (Brazil)	国家电信管理局	Guójiā diànxìn guǎnlǐjú	ANATEL
Agent	代理商	Dàilǐshāng	
Agent advertisement	代理通告	Dàilǐ tōnggào	AA
Agent advertisement (in mobile IP)	代理广告	Dàilǐ guǎnggào	
Agent advertisement (message)	代理广播消息	Dàilǐ guǎngbō xiāoxi	
Agent advertisement extension	代理广播扩展	Dàilǐ guǎngbō kuòzhǎn	AAE
Agent communication	代理通信	Dàilǐ tōngxìn	
Agent discovery (in mobile IP)	代理发现	Dàilǐ fāxiàn	
Agent request	代理请求	Dàilǐ qǐngqiú	AR
Agent role	代表角色	Dàibiǎo juésè	
Agent solicitation (message)	代理请求消息	Dàilǐ qǐngqiú xiāoxi	
Agent, proxy	代理	Dàilǐ	A
Agent-based software service framework	基于代理软件服务框架	Jīyú dàilǐ ruǎnjiàn fúwù kuàngjià	ASF
Agere Systems Corp. (US company)	杰尔系统有限公司	Jié-ěr xìtǒng yǒuxiàn gōngsī	
Agfa (Belgian company)	爱克发	Ài-kè-fā	
Aggregate channel	聚合信道	Jùhé xìndào	
Aggregate domain	集合域	Jíhé yù	
Aggregate function	聚合函数	Jùhé hánshù	
Aggregate query	聚合查询	Jùhé cháxún	
Aggregate route-based IP switching	集中式基于路由的 IP 交换	Jízhōng-shì jīyú lùyóude IP jiāohuàn	ARIS
Aggregate signal	集合信号	Jíhé xìnhào	
Aggregation	聚合	Jùhé	
Aggregation	码聚焦	Mǎ jùjiāo	
Aggregation prefix	聚合前缀	Jùhé qiánzhuì	
Aggregation relationship	集合关系	Jíhé guānxi	
Aggregation wrapper	聚合包装	Jùhé bāozhuāng	
Agile manufacturing (British concept)	敏捷制造	Mǐnjié zhìzào	AM
Agile radar, frequency agile radar	捷变频雷达	Jiébiànpín léidá	
Agilent Technologies Co. Ltd. (China)	安捷伦科技（中国）有限公司	Ān-jié-lún kējì (Zhōngguó) yǒuxiàn gōngsī	
Agilent Technologies Software Co. Ltd.	安捷伦科技软件有限公司	Ān-jié-lún kējì ruǎnjiàn yǒuxiàn gōngsī	
Agreed on by both parties	甲乙双方商定	Jiǎ yǐ shuāngfāng shāngdìng	
Aigo (Chinese-made MP3 player)	爱国者	Àiguózhě	
Aiming circle	引导圆	Yǐndǎo yuán	
Aiming field	引导域	Yǐndǎo yù	

Aiming symbol	引导符号	Yǐndǎo fúhào	
Air blown fiber	气吹光纤	Qìchuī guāngxiān	ABF
Air conditioning ducting	空调通风	Kōngtiáo tōngfēng	FK
Air core deflection coil (radar term)	空心偏转线圈	Kōngxīn piānzhuǎn xiànquān	
Air duct	风道	Fēngdào	
Air Force Flight Safety Guidance Commission	空军飞行安全指导委员会	Kōngjūn fēixíng ānquán zhǐdǎo wěiyuánhuì	
Air Force Science and Research Commission	空军学术研究委员会	Kōngjūn xuéshù yánjiū wěiyuánhuì	
Air handling unit	空气处理机组	Kōngqì chǔlǐjī zǔ	AHU
Air interface	空间接口	Kōngjiān jiēkǒu	
Air interface	空中接口	Kōngzhōng jiēkǒu	
Air interface user rate	空中接口用户速率	Kōngzhōng jiēkǒu yònghù sùlǜ	AIUR
Air link	空中链路	Kōngzhōng liànlù	
Air route traffic control center (civil aviation)	航路交管中心	Háng lù jiāo guǎn zhōngxīn	ARTCC
Air route traffic control center (civil aviation)	航空路途交通管理中心	Hángkōng lùtú jiāotōng guǎnlǐ zhōngxīn	ARTCC
Air seizure time (telecom billing)	空中信道获取时刻	Kōngzhōng xìndào huòqǔ shíkè	
Air Traffic Control (short for 航空交通调度)	航调	Háng diào	
Air Traffic Control	航空交通调度	Hángkōng jiāotōng diàodù	
Air traffic control (civil aviation)	空中交通管制	Kōngzhōng jiāotōng guǎnzhì	ATC
Air traffic control radar	空中交通管制雷达	Kōngzhōng jiāotōng guǎnzhì léidá	
Air traffic flow management (civil aviation)	空中交通量管理	Kōngzhōng jiāotōngliàng guǎnlǐ	ATFM
Air traffic management (civil aviation)	空中交通管理	Kōngzhōng jiāotōng guǎnlǐ	ATM
Air traffic services (civil aviation)	空中交通服务	Kōngzhōng jiāotōng fúwù	ATS
Airborne flux gate magnetometer	航空磁通门磁力仪	Hángkōng cítōng mén cílìyí	
Airborne radar	机载雷达	Jīzài léidá	
Airborne range-finding radar	机载测距雷达	Jīzài cèjù léidá	
Airborne self-protection electronic warfare system	机载自卫电子战系统	Jīzài zìwèi diànzǐzhàn xìtǒng	
Airborne warning and control system aircraft	预警飞机	Yùjǐng fēijī	AWACS
Airborne warning radar	机载警戒雷达	Jīzài jǐngjiè léidá	
Aircraft earth station	航空器地球站	Hángkōngqì dìqiúzhàn	
Aircraft station	航空器电台	Hángkōngqì diàntái	
Aircraft station	机载电台	Jīzài diàntái	
Aircraft tail warning radar	护尾雷达	Hùwěi léidá	ATWR
Airspace management (civil aviation)	空域管理	Kōngyù guǎnlǐ	ASM
Air-spaced doublet	空气隙双分离透镜	Kōngqì xì shuāng fēnlí tòujìng	
Air-spaced doublet	空气隙双合透镜	Kōngqì xì shuānghé tòujìng	
Air-supported fiber	空气间隙光纤	Kōngqì jiànxì guāngxiān	
Air-tight	气密式	Qìmì-shì	
Air-to-air communication	空对空通信	Kōngduìkōng tōngxìn	A/A
Air-to-air missile	空对空导弹	Kōngduìkōng dǎodàn	A/A
Alarm	报讯	Bàoxùn	
Alarm	告警	Gàojǐng	ALM
Alarm access control board assembly	告警接入控制集成板	Gàojǐng jiērù kòngzhì jíchéngbǎn	AACA
Alarm acknowledgement	告警确认	Gàojǐng quèrèn	
Alarm alignment	告警核对	Gàojǐng héduì	
Alarm clock service	闹钟服务	Nàozhōng fúwù	
Alarm control board assembly	告警控制集成板	Gàojǐng kòngzhì jíchéngbǎn	

Alarm control process	告警控制处理	Gàojǐng kòngzhì chǔlǐ	ACP
Alarm display	告警显示	Gàojǐng xiǎnshì	ALD
Alarm filtering	告警过滤	Gàojǐng guòlǜ	
Alarm indication signal	告警指示信号	Gàojǐng zhǐshì xìnhào	AIS
Alarm indicator signal	故障警报信号	Gùzhàng jǐngbào xìnhào	AIS
Alarm inhibition	告警屏蔽	Gàojǐng píngbì	
Alarm lock	告警锁定	Gàojǐng suǒdìng	
Alarm log	告警日志	Gàojǐng rìzhì	
Alarm panel control block	告警面板控制模块	Gàojǐng miànbǎn kòngzhì mókuài	APC
Alarm panel control unit assembly	告警面板控制集成单元	Gàojǐng miànbǎn kòngzhì jíchéng dānyuán	APCU
Alarm reporting telephone	报警电话	Bàojǐng diànhuà	ART
Alarm seconds	告警秒	Gàojǐng miǎo	ALS
Alarm severity	告警等级	Gàojǐng děngjí	
Alarm standby	告警预投入	Gàojǐng yù tóurù	
Alarm statement	告警语句	Gàojǐng yǔjù	AS
Alarm statistics	告警统计	Gàojǐng tǒngjì	
Alarm status	告警状况	Gàojǐng zhuàngkuàng	
Alarm summary panel	报警汇总画面	Bàojǐng huìzǒng huàmiàn	
Alarm surveillance	告警监视	Gàojǐng jiānshì	AS
A-law	A 律	A lǜ	
A-law encoding	A 律编码	A lǜ biānmǎ	
Albedograph	反射计	Fǎnshèjì	
Alcatel (French company)	阿尔卡特	Ā-ěr-kǎ-tè	
Alcatel Carrier Environment Internet System	阿尔卡特运营环境因特网系统	Ā-ěr-kǎ-tè yùnyíng huánjìng Yīntèwǎng xìtǒng	ACEIS
Alcatel China Ltd.	阿尔卡特中国公司	Ā-ěr-kǎ-tè Zhōngguó gōngsī	
Alert	警报	Jǐngbào	
Alerting	警觉	Jǐngjué	
Alerting	提醒	Tíxǐng	
Alexandrite	亚历山大	Yà-lì-shān-dà	
Alexandrite laser	亚历山大激光	Yà-lì-shān-dà jīguāng	
Alexandrite laser crystal	亚历山大激光晶体	Yà-lì-shān-dà jīguāng jīngtǐ	
Alford loop antenna	爱尔福德环形天线	Ài-ěr-fú-dé huánxíng tiānxiàn	
Algebraic code excited linear prediction	代数码激励线性预测	Dàishù mǎ jīlì xiànxìng yùcè	ACELP
Algebraic code excited linear prediction	代数码本激励线性预测编码	Dàishù mǎběn jīlì xiànxìng yùcè biānmǎ	ACELP
Algebraic coding theory	代数编码理论	Dàishù biānmǎ lǐlùn	ACT
Algebraic compiler	代数编译程序	Dàishù biānyì chéngxù	ACOM
Algebraic topology	代数拓朴	Dàishù tuòpò	
Algorithm	算法	Suànfǎ	
Algorithm	演算法	Yǎnsuànfǎ	
Algorithm analysis	算法分析	Suànfǎ fēnxī	
Algorithm state machine	算法状态机	Suànfǎ zhuàngtài jī	ASM
Algorithmic language	算法语言	Suànfǎ yǔyán	ALGOL
Alias address	别名地址	Biémíng dìzhǐ	
Alias entry	别名登录项	Biémíng dēnglù xiàng	
Alias server	别名服务器	Biémíng fúwùqì	

Alias, nickname	别名	Biémíng	
Aliasing	命名别名	Mìngmíng biémíng	
Aliasing distortion	混叠失真	Hùndié shīzhēn	
Aliasing error	交叠误差	Jiāodié wùchā	
Alidade	照准仪	Zhàozhǔnyí	
Align	对齐	Duìqí	
Align	排列	Páiliè	
Align template	对齐模板	Duìqí múbǎn	
Aligned bundle	定位光纤束	Dìngwèi guāngxiānshù	
Alignment	定位	Dìngwèi	
Alignment	校准	Jiàozhǔn	AL
Alignment	套刻	Tàokè	
Alignment coating equipment (semiconductor mfg)	配向膜涂布装置	Pèixiàng mótú bù zhuāngzhì	
Alignment error	调整错误	Tiáozhěng cuòwù	
Alignment error rate monitor	定位差错率监视	Dìngwèi chācuòlǜ jiānshì	AERM
Alignment film	配向膜	Pèixiàng mó	
Alignment jitter	定位抖动	Dìngwèi dǒudòng	
Alignment jitter	对准抖动	Duìzhǔn dǒudòng	
Alignment jitter	校正抖动	Jiàozhèng dǒudòng	AJ
Alignment network	校正网络	Jiàozhèng wǎngluò	AN
Alignment sensor	校准传感器	Jiàozhǔn chuángǎnqì	
All barring of outgoing call	闭锁全部出呼叫	Bìsuǒ quánbù chū hūjiào	BO
All call forwarding services	全呼叫前转业务	Quán hūjiào qiánzhuǎn yèwù	CF
All call forwarding services	所有的呼叫前转业务	Suǒyǒude hūjiào qiánzhuǎn yèwù	CF
All channel signaling	全部信道传输信令	Quánbù xìndào chuánshū xìnlìng	ACS
All dielectric lashed cable (FOC)	全介质捆绑光缆	Quán jièzhì kǔnbǎng guānglǎn	ADL
All dielectric self-supporting fiber optic cable	全介质自乘式光缆	Quán jièzhì zìchéng-shì guānglǎn	ADSS
All digital phase-locked loop	全数子锁相环	Quán shùzi suǒxiàng huán	ADPLL
All digital phase-locked loop	全数子锁相环	Quánshùzǐ suǒxiānghuán	ADPLL
All number calling	全号码呼叫	Quán hàomǎ hūjiào	ANC
All ones	全"1"	Quán "1"	
All optical fiber and optical components	全光纤型光器件	Quán guāngxiānxíng guāng qìjiàn	
All optical network	全光网络	Quán guāng wǎngluò	AON
All optical wave converter	全光波长转换器	Quán guāng bōcháng zhuǎnhuànqì	AOWC
All passive optical network	全无源光网络	Quán wúyuán guāng wǎngluò	APON
All plastic optical fiber	全塑光纤	Quánsù guāngxiān	APOF
All routes busy	路由全忙	Lùyóu quán máng	ARB
All suspend	全部中止	Quánbù zhōngzhǐ	ASUSP
All trunks busy	中继线全忙	Zhōngjìxiàn quánmáng	ATB
All wave antenna	全波天线	Quánbō tiānxiàn	AWA
Allan deviation	艾伦偏差	Ài-lún piānchā	ADEV
All-band intercept receiver	全频段侦察接收机	Quán pínduàn zhēnchá jiēshōujī	ABIR
Allen Group (US company)	亚伦电信集团	Yà-lún diànxìn jítuán	
All-glass fiber	全玻璃光纤	Quán bōli guāngxiān	
Allied Command Channel (NATO usage)	盟军指挥信道	Méngjūn zhǐhuī xìndào	ACCHAN
All-in-one	一卡在手	Yīkǎ zàishǒu	

All-in-one	一手包办	Yīshǒu bāo bàn	
Allocate	分配	Fēnpèi	
Allocate	配置	Pèizhì	
Allocated baseline	指派基线	Zhǐpài jīxiàn	
Allocated frequency band	划分的频带	Huàfēnde píndài	
Allocation (of a frequency band)	划分	Huàfēn	
Allocation model	分配模型	Fēnpèi móxíng	
Allocation unit size	分配单位大小	Fēnpèi dānwèi dàxiǎo	
Allocator	分配器	Fēnpèiqì	
Allocator	配置器	Pèizhìqì	
Allomorphism	多态性	Duōtàixìng	
All-optical communication	全光通信	Quán guāng tōngxìn	AOC
All-optical towed array	全光牵引阵列	Quán guāng qiānyǐn zhènliè	AOTA
Allotment (of a radio frequency or channel)	分配	Fēnpèi	
Allow additional register range bit	允许附加寄存器的范围位	Yǔnxǔ fùjiā jìcúnqìde fànwéi wèi	AARR
Allowable criterion	容许标准	Róngxǔ biāozhǔn	
Allowable imbalance	许用不平衡量	Xǔyòng bùpínghéng liàng	
Allowable load impedance	允许的负载阻抗	Yǔnxǔde fùzài zǔkàng	
Allowable settlement	容许沉积量	Róngxǔ chénjī liàng	
Allowable stress	容许应力	Róngxǔ yìnglì	
Allowable stress design method	容许应力设计法	Róngxǔ yìnglì shèjì fǎ	
Allowance; margin	余量	Yúliàng	
Allowed bandwidth	允许带宽	Yǔnxǔ dàikuān	
Allowed cell rate	允许信元速率	Yǔnxǔ xìnyuán sùlǜ	ACR
Allowed cell rate	允许的信元率	Yǔnxǔde xìnyuán lǜ	ACR
Allowed cell rate	允许的信元速率	Yǔnxǔde xìnyuán sùlǜ	ACR
All-path-busy	通路全忙	Tōnglù quánmáng	APB
All-plastic fiber	全塑料光纤	Quán sùliào guāngxiān	
All-rings explorer packet	全环探测数据分组	Quánhuán tàncè shùjù fēnzǔ	
All-routes explorer packet	全程数据探测包	Quánchéng shùjù tàncè bāo	
All-silica fiber	全石英光纤	Quán shíyīng guāngxiān	
All-silicon fiber	全硅光纤	Quánguī guāngxiān	
Alluvial fan	扇形地	Shànxíng dì	
Allwave fiber (Lucent product)	全波光纤	Quánbō guāngxiān	
All-zone extraction	全空域录取	Quán kōngyù lùqǔ	
ALOHA system	ALOHA 系统	ALOHA xìtǒng	
Along beam (telecom installation)	沿梁敷设	Yán liáng fūshè	AB
Along ceiling (telecom installation)	沿天棚面敷设	Yán tiānpéngmiàn fūshè	CE
Along column (telecom installation)	沿珠敷设	Yán zhū fūshè	AC
Along roof slab (in telecom cabling installation)	沿顶板面敷设	Yán dǐngbǎnmiàn fūshè	
Along-track scanning	纵向扫描	Zòngxiàng sǎomiáo	
Alphabetic telegraphy	字符电报	Zìfú diànbào	
Alphanumeric	字母数字	Zìmǔ shùzì	
Alphanumeric character	字符	Zìfú	
Alpine Electronics (China) Co. Ltd.	阿尔派电子（中国）有限公司	Ā-ěr-pài diànzǐ (Zhōngguó) yǒuxiàn gōngsī	

Alt key	交替键	Jiāotì jiàn	
Alternate address	替代地址	Tìdài dìzhǐ	AADR
Alternate billing service	可选记帐业务	Kěxuǎn jìzhàng yèwù	ABS
Alternate digital inversion coding	数字交替反转码	Shùzì jiāotì fǎnzhuǎn mǎ	ADI
Alternate frame rendering (video)	交替渲染技术	Jiāotì xuànrǎn jìshù	AFR
Alternate mark inversion	传号交替变换码	Chuánhào jiāotì biànhuàn mǎ	AMI
Alternate mark inversion	信号交替变换	Xìnhào jiāotì biànhuàn	AMI
Alternate mark inversion	信号交替反转码	Xìnhào jiāotì fǎnzhuǎn mǎ	AMI
Alternate mark inversion	信号交替翻转码	Xìnhào jiāotì fǎnzhuǎn mǎ	AMI
Alternate mark inversion code	交替传号反转码	Jiāotì chuánhào fǎnzhuǎn mǎ	AMI
Alternate mark inversion code	交替代号反转码	Jiāotì dàihào fǎnzhuǎn mǎ	
Alternate mark inversion coding	交替极性翻转码	Jiāotì jíxìng fǎnzhuǎn mǎ	AMI
Alternate mark inversion coding	极性交替反转双极性码	Jíxìng jiāotì fǎnzhuǎn shuāng jíxìng mǎ	AMI
Alternate mark inversion violation	交替信号反转破坏点	Jiāotì xìnhào fǎnzhuǎn pòhuàidiǎn	
Alternate name	替换名字	Tìhuan míngzì	
Alternate name body	替换名字体	Tìhuan míngzì tǐ	
Alternate name text	替换名字文本	Tìhuan míngzì wénběn	
Alternate recipient	交替接收者	Jiāotì jiēshōuzhě	
Alternate recipient	替换接收者	Tìhuan jiēshōuzhě	
Alternate routing	迂回路由	Yūhuí lùyóu	
Alternate street name	替换通路名	Tìhuan tōnglù míng	
Alternate synchronization partners (in SQL Server)	代替同步伙伴	Dàitì tóngbù huǒbàn	
alternate synchronization partners (in SQL Server)	交替同步伙伴	Jiāotì tóngbù huǒbàn	
Alternate the batch number (radar term)	换批	Huàn pī	
Alternated polarization (adjective)	交替极化的	Jiāotì jíhuàde	
Alternating (exchange) load	交变负荷	Jiāobiàn fùhè	
Alternating code	交变码	Jiāobiàn mǎ	
Alternating current	交流	Jiāoliú	AC
Alternating current (AC) secondary interface	二次 AC 接口	Èrcì AC jiēkǒu	
Alternating current (AC) secondary voltage	二次 AC 电压	Èrcì AC diànyā	
Alternating current component	交流分量	Jiāoliú fènliàng	
Alternating current diode charging	交流二极管充电	Jiāoliú èrjíguǎn chōngdiàn	
Alternating current hum and noise suppression	交流声和噪声抑制	Jiāoliú shēng hé zàoshēng yìzhì	
Alternating current phase tracking	交流相位跟踪法	Jiāoliú xiàngwèi gēnzōng fǎ	
Alternating current polarograph	交流极谱仪	Jiāoliú jípǔyí	
Alternating current relay	交流继电器	Jiāoliú jìdiànqì	ACR
Alternating current signaling	交流信令	Jiāoliú xìnlìng	
Alternating current voltage stabilizer	交流稳压器	Jiāoliú wěnyāqì	
Alternating humidity-heat test	交变温热试验	Jiāobiàn wēnrè shìyàn	
Alternating non-return to zero	交替不归零制	Jiāotì bù guī líng zhì	ANRZ
Alternative address	可选择的地址	Kěxuǎnzéde dìzhǐ	
Alternative address usage subscription	替代地址使用预约	Tìdài dìzhǐ shǐyòng yùyuē	
Alternative alias address	可选择的别名地址	Kěxuǎnzéde biémíng dìzhǐ	
Alternative code	交替码	Jiāotì mǎ	
Alternative route cancel	消除迂回路由	Xiāochú yūhuí lùyóu	ARC
Alternative routing	迂回路由选定	Yūhuí lùyóu xuǎndìng	

Alternative routing	迂回路由选择	Yūhuí lùyóu xuǎnzé	AR
Alternative routing from	从迂回路由来	Cóng yūhuí lùyóu lái	ARF
Alternative routing from	迂回来路选择	Yūhuí láilù xuǎnzé	ARF
Alternative routing to	从迂回路由去	Cóng yūhuí lùyóu qù	ART
Alternative routing to	迂回去路选择	Yūhuí qùlù xuǎnzé	ART
Alternative select route	迂回选择路由	Yūhuí xuǎnzé lùyóu	ASRTE
Alternative test method	替代测试法	Tìdài cèshì fǎ	ATM
Alternative test method	替代试验方法	Tìdài shìyàn fāngfǎ	ATM
Altitude of the apogee	远地点高度	Yuǎndìdiǎn gāodù	
Altitude of the perigee	近地点高度	Jìndìdiǎn gāodù	
Aluminum gallium nitride	铝镓氮	Lǚjiādàn	AlGaN
Aluminum nitride	氮化铝	Dànhuà lǚ	AlN
Aluminum trichloride	三氯化铝	Sānlǜhuàlǚ	$AlCl_3$
Aluminum-polyethylene adhesive (FOC)	铝-聚乙烯粘结	Lǚjùyǐxī niánjié	
Always on	始终保持	Shǐzhōng bǎochí	AO
Always on server	始终保持服务器	Shǐzhōng bǎochí fúwùqì	AOS
Amateur satellite service	卫星业余业务	Wèixīng yèyú yèwù	
Amateur service	业余业务	Yèyú yèwù	
Amateur station	业余电台	Yèyú diàntái	
Ambient electromagnetic level	电磁环境电平	Diàncí huánjìng diànpíng	
Ambient noise	环境躁声	Huánjìng zàoshēng	
Ambient vibration	环境振动	Huánjìng zhèndòng	
Ambiguity error	模糊误差	Móhu wùchā	
Ambiguity function (radar term)	模糊函数	Móhu hánshù	
Ambiguity pattern (radar term)	模糊图	Móhu tú	
America Online	美国线上	Měiguó xiànshàng	AOL
America On-Line	美国在线服务	Měiguó zàixiàn fúwù	AOL
America Online ® (US company)	线上美国	Xiànshàng Měiguó	AOL
American Academy of Science	美国科学院	Měiguó kēxuéyuàn	AAS
American Association for Artificial Intelligence	美国人工智能协会	Měiguó réngōng zhìnéng xiéhuì	AAAI
American Association for the Advancement of Science	美国科学促进协会	Měiguó kēxué cùjìn xiéhuì	AAAS
American Association of Engineers	美国工程师协会	Měiguó gōngchéngshī xiéhuì	AAE
American Astronautical Society	美国宇航学会	Měiguó yǔháng xuéhuì	AAS
American Automatic Control Council	美国自动控制委员会	Měiguó zìdòng kòngzhì wěiyuánhuì	AACC
American Broadcasting Corp. (US company)	美国广播公司	Měiguó guǎngbō gōngsī	ABC
American Bureau of Standards	美国标准局	Měiguó biāozhǔnjú	ABS
American Communication Association	美国通信协会	Měiguó tōngxìn xiéhuì	ACA
American Congress on Surveying and Mapping	美国测绘委员会	Měiguó cèhuì wěiyuánhuì	ACSM
American Federation of Information processing Societies	美国信息处理学会联合会	Měiguó xìnxī chǔlǐ xuéhuì liánhéhuì	AFIPS
American Intelligent Building Institute	美国智能建筑学会	Měiguó zhìnéng jiànzhù xuéhuì	AIBI
American National Standard for Information Systems	美国信息系统国家标准	Měiguó xìnxī xìtǒng guójiā biāozhǔn	ANSI
American National Standards Institute	美国国家标准协会	Měiguó guójiā biāozhǔn xiéhuì	ANSI
American National Standards Institute	美国国家标准研究所	Měiguó guójiā biāozhǔn yánjiūsuǒ	ANSI
American National Standards Institute	美国国家标准组织	Měiguó guójiā biāozhǔn zǔzhī	ANSI
American National Standards Institute	美国国家标准局	Měiguó guójiā biāozhǔnjú	ANSI

American standard code	美标码	Měi biāo mǎ	ASCII
American Standard Code for Information Interchange	美国国家标准信息交换代码	Měiguó guójiā biāozhǔn xìnxī jiāohuàn dàimǎ	ASCII
American Standard Code for Information Interchange	美国信息交换标准代码	Měiguó xìnxī jiāohuàn biāozhǔn dàimǎ	ASCII
American Standard Code for Information Interchange	美国信息交换标准码	Měiguó xìnxī jiāohuàn biāozhǔn mǎ	ASCII
American Standards Association	美国标准协会	Měiguó biāozhǔn xiéhuì	ASA
American Telephone and Telegraph (AT&T) (US company)	美国电报电话公司	Měiguó diànbào diànhuà gōngsī	ATT
American Translators Association	美国翻译协会	Měiguó fānyì xiéhuì	ATA
American Wire Gauge	美国线规	Měiguó xiànguī	AWG
American Wire Gauge	美国线缆规格	Měiguó xiànlǎn guīgé	AWG
Ammeter	电流表	Diànliúbiǎo	
Amount of discharge	排出量	Páichū liàng	
Ampere-hour meter	安时计	Ānshí jì	
Amplification, zoom	放大	Fàngdà	
Amplified spontaneous emission	放大自发辐射	Fàngdà zìfā fúshè	ASE
Amplified spontaneous emission	放大自激辐射信号	Fàngdà zìjī fúshè xìnhào	AME
Amplified spontaneous emission noise	放大自激发射噪声	Fàngdà zìjīfāshè zàoshēng	ASEN
Amplifier	放大器	Fàngdàqì	A
Amplifier bias current	放大器偏压电流	Fàngdàqì piānyā diànliú	ABC
Amplifier linear dynamic range	放大器线性动态范围	Fàngdàqì xiànxìng dòngtài fànwéi	
Amplifier/divider assembly	放大/分配集成件	Fàngdà/fēnpèi jíchéngjiàn	IADA
Amplitron	增幅管	Zēngfú guǎn	
Amplitude	幅度	Fúdù	A
Amplitude	幅值	Fúzhí	
Amplitude and phase keying	振幅与相位键控	Zhènfú yǔ xiàngwèi jiànkòng	APK
Amplitude characteristic	幅度特性	Fúdù tèxìng	
Amplitude characteristics	振幅特性	Zhènfú tèxìng	
Amplitude companded single sideband	振幅压扩单边带	Zhènfú yākuò dānbiāndài	ACSSB
Amplitude companded single sideband	镇幅压扩单边带	Zhènfú yākuò dānbiāndài	ACSB
Amplitude demodulation	幅度解调	Fúdù jiětiáo	
Amplitude detection	幅度检波	Fúdù jiǎnbō	
Amplitude discriminator	鉴幅器	Jiànfúqì	
Amplitude distortion	幅度失真	Fúdù shīzhēn	
Amplitude distortion	幅度失真	Fúdù shīzhēn	
Amplitude limiter	限幅器	Xiànfúqì	AL
Amplitude limiting circuit	限幅电路	Xiànfú diànlù	
Amplitude limiting sensitivity	限幅灵敏度	Xiànfú língmǐndù	
Amplitude modulation	幅度调制	Fúdù tiáozhì	AM
Amplitude modulation	调幅	Tiáofú	AM
Amplitude modulation	振幅调制	Zhènfú tiáozhì	AM
Amplitude modulation (AM) noise	调幅躁声	Tiáofú zàoshēng	
Amplitude modulation (AM) station	调幅电台	Tiáofú diàntái	
Amplitude modulation (AM) telegraph	调幅电报	Tiáofú diànbào	
Amplitude modulation (AM) transmitter	调幅发射机	Tiáofú fāshèjī	
Amplitude modulation jamming (radar term)	调幅干扰	Tiáofú gānrǎo	
Amplitude of fading	衰落幅度	Shuāiluò fúdù	

Amplitude phase conversion	幅度相位变换	Fúdù xiāngwèi biànhuàn	APC
Amplitude phase conversion	幅相变换	Fú-xiāng biànhuàn	APC
Amplitude phase keying	幅相键控	Fú-xiāng jiànkòng	APK
Amplitude phase keying	振幅相位键控	Zhènfú xiàngwèi jiànkòng	APK
Amplitude phase shift keying	振幅移相键控	Zhènfú yíxiāng jiànkòng	APSK
Amplitude probability distribution	幅度概率分布	Fúdù gàilǜ fēnbù	APD
Amplitude probability distribution	振幅概率分布	Zhènfú gàilǜ fēnbù	APD
Amplitude quantization	振幅量化	Zhènfú liànghuà	
Amplitude quantized control	幅度量化控制	Fúdù liànghuà kòngzhì	
Amplitude quantizing	幅度分层	Fúdù fēncéng	
Amplitude reflection coefficient	幅度反射系数	Fúdù fǎnshè xìshù	
Amplitude reflection factor (in a transmission line)	振幅反射系数	Zhènfú fǎnshè xìshù	
Amplitude shift keyed infrared	长波形可移动输入红外线	Chángbō-xíng kěyídòng shūrù hóngwàixiàn	ASK IR
Amplitude shift keying	幅移键控	Fúyí jiànkòng	ASK
Amplitude shift keying	移幅键控	Yífú jiànkòng	ASK
Amplitude shift keying	振幅键控	Zhènfú jiànkòng	ASK
Amplitude spectrum	幅度谱	Fúdù pǔ	
Amplitude transmission factor (in a transmission line)	振幅传输系数	Zhènfú chuánshū xìshù	
Amplitude/frequency characteristic	幅度频率特性	Fúdù pínlǜ tèxìng	
Amplitude/frequency characteristic	幅频特性	Fú-pín tèxìng	
Amplitude/frequency distortion	幅度频率失真	Fúdù pínlǜ shīzhēn	
Amplitude-comparison monopulse radar	比幅单脉冲雷达	Bǐ fú dān màichōng léidá	
Amplitude-frequency distortion	幅频失真	Fú-pín shīzhēn	AFD
Amplitude-frequency distortion	振幅频率失真	Zhènfú pínlǜ shīzhēn	AFD
Amplitude-frequency equalization	幅频一致性	Fú-pín yīzhìxìng	
Amplitude-frequency response	幅频响应	Fú-pín xiǎngyìng	AFR
Amplitude-phase error	幅相误差	Fú-xiàng wùchā	
Amplitude-phase meter	幅值-相位仪	Fúzhí—xiàngwèiyí	
Amplitude-phase modulation	振幅-相位调制	Zhènfú/xiàngwèi tiáozhì	APM
Anaglyph	互补色立体影像	Hùbǔsè lìtǐ yǐngxiàng	
Anaglyph	互补色立体图	Hùbǔsè lìtǐtú	
Anaglyph	立体照片	Lìtǐ zhàopiàn	
Anaglyphographic photomap	互补色立体影象地图	Hùbǔsè lìtǐ yǐngxiàng dìtú	
Analog	模拟	Mónǐ	
Analog cellular system	模拟蜂窝系统	Mónǐ fēngwō xìtǒng	
Analog channel	模拟通路	Mónǐ tōnglù	
Analog color code	模拟色码	Mónǐ sèmǎ	
Analog common channel assembly	模拟公共信道集成板	Mónǐ gōnggòng xìndào jíchéngbǎn	ACCA
Analog common channel processor	模拟公共信道处理器	Mónǐ gōnggòng xìndào chǔlǐqì	ACCP
Analog controller	模拟控制器	Mónǐ kòngzhìqì	AC
Analog data recognition	模拟数据识别	Mónǐ shùjù shíbié	ADR
Analog delay unit	模拟延迟装置	Mónǐ yánchí zhuāngzhì	ADU
Analog expansion bus	模拟扩展总线	Mónǐ kuòzhǎn zǒngxiàn	AEB
Analog filter	模拟滤波器	Mónǐ lǜbōqì	
Analog front-end	模拟前端	Mónǐ qiánduān	AFE
Analog input	模拟输入	Mónǐ shūrù	

Analog integrated circuit	模拟集成电路	Mónǐ jíchéng diànlù	
Analog lines unit	模拟用户线单元	Mónǐ yònghùxiàn dānyuán	ALU
Analog map	模拟图	Mónǐ tú	
Analog microwave	模拟微波	Mónǐ wēibō	WBM
Analog modulation	模拟调制	Mónǐ tiáozhì	
Analog multiplexer quantizer	模拟复用器量化器	Mónǐ fùyòngqì liànghuàqì	AMQ
Analog output	模拟输出	Mónǐ shūchū	
Analog paging system	模拟式寻呼系统	Mónǐ-shì xúnhū xìtǒng	
Analog phase shifter	模拟移相器	Mónǐ yíxiàngqì	
Analog phase-locked loop	模拟锁相环	Mónǐ suǒxiàng huán	APLL
Analog ranging	模拟测距	Mónǐ cèjù	
Analog repeater	模拟中继器	Mónǐ zhōngjìqì	
Analog screen	模拟屏	Mónǐ píng	
Analog signal	模拟信号	Mónǐ xìnhào	
Analog signal processing	模拟信号处理	Mónǐ xìnhào chǔlǐ	ASP
Analog signaling	模拟信令	Mónǐ xìn lìng	
Analog subscriber line board	模拟用户电路板	Mónǐ yònghù diànlù bǎn	ASL
Analog subscriber line circuit	模拟用户线电路	Mónǐ yònghùxiàn diànlù	ASLC
Analog subscriber module	模拟用户模块	Mónǐ yònghù mókuài	ASM
Analog sweep (i.e. a continuous sweep)	模拟式扫描	Mónǐ-shì sǎomiáo	
Analog switching	模拟交换	Mónǐ jiāohuàn	
Analog switching sub-system	模拟交换子系统	Mónǐ jiāohuàn zixìtǒng	ASS
Analog terminal adapter	模拟终端适配器	Mónǐ zhōngduān shìpèiqì	ATA
Analog time division multiplexing system	模拟时分复用系统	Mónǐ shífèn fùyòng xìtǒng	ATDMS
Analog to digital converter	模数转换器	Móshù zhuǎnhuànqì	ADC
Analog trunk unit	模拟中继单元	Mónǐ zhōngjì dānyuán	ATU
Analog trunked mobile radio	模拟集群流动通讯	Mónǐ jíqún liúdòng tōngxùn	TMR
Analog video	模拟电视	Mónǐ diànshì	AV
Analog video	模拟视频	Mónǐ shìpín	AV
Analog/digital conversion	模/数转换	Mó/shù zhuǎnhuàn	A/D
Analog/digital converter	模/数变换器	Mó/shù biànhuànqì	A/D
Analog/digital converter	模/数变换器	Mó/shù biànhuànqì	ADC
Analog/digital converter	模/数转换器	Mó/shù zhuǎnhuànqì	A/D
Analog/digital/analog (conversion)	模/数/模（变换）	Mó/shù/mó (biànhuàn)	A/D/A
Analog/intensity modulator	模拟/强度调变器	Mónǐ/qiángdù tiáobiànqì	
Analog-digital conversion	模/数变换	Mó/shù biànhuàn	A/D
Analog-digital processor	模-数处理器	Mó-shù chǔlǐqì	ADP
Analog-digital recorder	模拟-数字记录器	Mónǐ/shùzì jìlù qì	ADR
Analog-digital recorder	模拟-数字记录器	Mónǐ-shùzì jìlùqì	ADR
Analog-intensity modulation	模拟强度调制	Mónǐ qiángdù tiáozhì	
Analog-to-digital converter	类比数位转化器	Lèibǐ shùwèi zhuǎnhuàqì	
Analysis engine	分析引擎	Fēnxī yǐnqíng	
Analysis server	分析服务器	Fēnxī fúwùqì	
Analytic signal	解析信号	Jiěxī xìnhào	
Analytical geometry	解析几何	Jiěxī jǐhé	
Analytical plotter	解析测图仪	Jiěxī cètúyí	

Analytical triangulation	解析三角测量	Jiěxī sānjiǎo èliáng	
Analyzer tube	分析管	Fēnxī guǎn	
Anaphora	指代	Zhǐdài	
Anaphoric resolution	指代消解	Zhǐdài xiāojiě	
Anchor	锚子	Máozi	
Anchor point	锚点	Máodiǎn	
Ancillary data	辅助数据	Fǔzhù shùjù	
Ancillary equipment	辅助设备	Fǔzhù shèbèi	AE
And circuit (usually "与")	与电路	Yǔ diànlù	AND
AND gate	"与"门	Yǔ mén	
Andersen Consulting	安盛咨询	An-shèng zīxún	
AND-OR-INVERT gate	与或非"门	Yǔ huò fēi mén	
Andrew Antenna Corp (UK company)	安德鲁天线公司	Ān-dé-lǔ tiānxiàn gōngsī	
Anechoic chamber	消声室	Xiāoshēng shì	
Anechoic enclosure	电波暗室	Diànbō ànshì	
Anechoic tank	消声水池	Xiāoshēng shuǐchí	
Anelasticity	非弹性	Fēitánxìng	
Angle beam technique/angle beam testing	斜角法	Xiéjiǎo fǎ	
Angle bracket < >	尖括号	Jiānkuòhào	
Angle diversity (in reception)	角度分集	Jiǎodù fēnjí	
Angle form	角型	Jiǎo-xíng	
Angle intercept probability (radar term)	角度截获概率	Jiǎodù jiéhuò gàilǜ	
Angle modulation	角度调制	Jiǎodù tiáozhì	
Angle noise	角度噪声	Jiǎodù zàoshēng	
Angle of arrival	到达角度	Dàodá jiǎodù	AOA
Angle of arrival	入射角	Rùshèjiǎo	
Angle of attack (in SMT)	迎角	Yíngjiǎo	
Angle of emergence	出射角	Chūshè jiǎo	
Angle of incidence	入射角	Rùshèjiǎo	
Angle of refraction	折射角	Zhéshèjiǎo	
Angle of spread	指向角	Zhǐxiàng jiǎo	
Angle plane connection	斜角平面连接	Xiéjiǎo píngmiàn liánjiē	APC
Angle probe	斜探头	Xié tàntóu	
Angle strain	角应变	Jiǎo yìngbiàn	
Angstrom	埃	Āi	
Angular displacement	角位移	Jiǎowèiyí	
Angular displacement grating	角位移光栅	Jiǎowèiyí guāngshān	
Angular distance	角距离	Jiǎojùlí	
Angular encoder	角编码器	Jiǎo biānmǎqì	
Angular misalignment	角偏差	Jiǎo piānchā	
Angular misalignment loss	角偏差损耗	Jiǎo piānchā sǔnhào	
Angular momentum	角动量	Jiǎo dòngliàng	
Angular sensitivity	角灵敏度	Jiǎo língmǐndù	
Animated graphics	动画图形	Dònghuà túxíng	
Animation	动画	Dònghuà	
Anisochronism	不等时	Bùděngshí	

Anisochronous	非等步的	Fēiděngbùde	
Anisochronous transmission	不等时传输	Bùděngshí chuánshū	
Anisotropic adhesive (in SMT)	各异向性胶	Gèyìxiàngxìng jiāo	
Anisotropic filtering (video)	各向异性过滤	Gèxiàngyìxìng guòlǜ	
Anisotropic propagation medium	各向异性传播媒质	Gèxiàng yìxìng chuánbō méizhì	
Anisotropic, anisotropy	各向异性	Gèxiàng yìxìng	
Annotated mapping schema files (in SQL Server)	注释匹配模式文件	Zhùshì pǐpèi móshì wénjiàn	
Annotation	评注	Píngzhù	
Annotation	注记	Zhùjì	
Annotation	注解	Zhùjiě	
Annotation (in SQL Server)	注释符	Zhùshì fú	
Annotation aerial orthophoto	注解正射航片	Zhùjiě zhèngshè háng piàn	
Annotation class	注记类	Zhùjì lèi	
Annotation feature class	注记要素类	Zhùjì yàosù lèi	
Annotation group	注记分组	Zhùjì fēnzǔ	
Annotation layer	注记层	Zhùjì céng	
Annotation placement	注记放置	Zhùjì fàngzhì	
Annotational property	批注属性	Pīzhù shǔxìng	
Announcement call	通播	Tōngbō	
Annular chamber	环室	Huán shì	
Annular ring (in SMT)	环状圈	Huánzhuàng quān	
Annular slot antenna	环形隙缝天线	Huánxíng xìfèng tiānxiàn	
Annular slot antenna	环状缝隙天线	Huánzhuàng fèngxì tiānxiàn	ASA
Anode	阳极	Yángjí	
Anodic oxidation passivation	阳极氧化钝化法	Yángjí yǎnghuà dùnhuàfǎ	
Anodized metal-oxide semiconductor	阳极化金属-氧化物-半导体	Yángjíhuà jīnshǔ—yǎnghuàwù bàndǎotǐ	AMOS
Anomalistic period	近点周期	Jìndiǎn zhōuqī	
Anomalous air situation, “bogey” on a radar screen	异常空情	Yìcháng kōngqíng	
Anomalous propagation	异常传播	Yìcháng chuánbō	AP
Anomaly detection	异常检测	Yìcháng jiǎncè	
Anomaly, anomalous	异常	Yìcháng	
Anonymity key	无名键	Wúmíng jiàn	AK
Anonymous access	匿名接入	Nìmíng jiērù	AA
Anonymous file transfer protocol	匿名文件传送协议	Nìmíng wénjiàn chuánsòng xiéyì	AFTP
Anonymous FTP	无记名文件存取	Wújìmíng wénjiàn cúnqǔ	
Anonymous subscription	匿名订阅	Nìmíng dìngyuè	
Anonymous user	匿名用户	Nìmíng yònghù	
Answer back code	应答电码	Yìngdá diànmǎ	ABC
Answer bid ratio	应答试占比	Yìngdá shìzhàn bǐ	ABR
Answer charging	应答计费	Yìngdá jìfèi	ANC
Answer detection pattern	应答检测图形	Yìngdá jiǎncè túxíng	ADP
Answer message (SS7 ISUP message)	应答消息	Yìngdá xiāoxi	ANM
Answer message (ISUP message)	被较应答	Bèijiào yìngdá	ANM
Answer no charge	应答免费	Yìngdá miǎnfèi	ANN
Answer signal	应答信号	Yìngdá xìnhào	
Answer signal (with no charge)	应答信号(不计费)	Yìngdá xìnhào (bùjìfèi)	

Answer signal, charge	应答信号、计费	Yìngdá xìnhào、jìfèi	ANC
Answer signal, no charge	应答不计费信号	Yìngdá bùjìfèi xìnhào	ANN
Answer signal, no charge	应答信号、免费	Yìngdá xìnhào、miǎnfèi	ANN
Answer signal, unqualified	应当信号、计费未说明	Yīngdāng xìnhào、jìfèi wèi shuōmíng	ANU
Answer to reset	复位响应	Fùwèi xiǎngyìng	ATR
Answer to reset	复位应答	Fùwèi yìngdá	ATR
Answer to reset	回答到复位	Huídá dào fùwèi	ATR
Answering time recorder	应答时间记录器	Yìngdá shíjiān jìlùqì	ATR
Answering tone	应答单音	Yìngdá dānyīn	
Answer-seizure ratio	应答占用率	Yìngdá zhànyòng lǜ	ASR
Antenna	天线	Tiānxiàn	
Antenna admittance	天线导纳	Tiānxiàn dǎonà	
Antenna amplifier	天线放大器	Tiānxiàn fàngdàqì	AA
Antenna aspect processor	天线方位处理机	Tiānxiàn fāngwèi chǔlǐjī	AAP
Antenna automatic tuning	天线自动调谐	Tiānxiàn zìdòng tiáoxié	
Antenna bandwidth	天线带宽	Tiānxiàn dàikuān	
Antenna bay	天线子阵	Tiānxiàn zizhèn	
Antenna beam	天线波束	Tiānxiàn bōshù	
Antenna capture area	天线收集面	Tiānxiàn shōují miàn	
Antenna combiner	天线合路器	Tiānxiàn hélùqì	ACOM
Antenna combining unit	天线合成单元	Tiānxiàn héchéng dānyuán	
Antenna combining unit	天线组合单元	Tiānxiàn zǔhé dānyuán	ACU
Antenna control unit	天线控制部件	Tiānxiàn kòngzhì bùjiàn	ACU
Antenna control unit	天线控制器	Tiānxiàn kòngzhìqì	ACU
Antenna coupler unit	天线耦合器单元	Tiānxiàn ǒuhéqì dānyuán	ACU
Antenna current	天线电流	Tiānxiàn diànliú	
Antenna directivity diagram	天线方向性图	Tiānxiàn fāngxiàngxìng tú	
Antenna dynamics	天线动态特性	Tiānxiàn dòngtài tèxìng	
Antenna efficiency (for an aperture-type antenna)	天线效率	Tiānxiàn xiàolǜ	
Antenna electrical boresight	天线电轴	Tiānxiàn diànzhóu	
Antenna elevating/subsiding machine	天线升降机构	Tiānxiàn shēngjiàng jīgòu	
Antenna feed line	天馈线	Tiānkuìxiàn	
Antenna front end block	天线前端模块	Tiānxiàn qiánduān mókuài	AFEB
Antenna front end unit	天线前端单元	Tiānxiàn qiánduān dānyuán	AFEU
Antenna gain	天线增益	Tiānxiàn zēngyì	
Antenna harmonic and spurious output radiated emissions (Mil-Std-461E, RE103)	天线谐波和乱真输出辐射发射	Tiānxiàn xiébō hé luànzhēn shūchū fúshè fāshè	
Antenna illumination efficiency	天线照射效率	Tiānxiàn zhàoshè xiàolǜ	AIE
Antenna impedance	天线阻抗	Tiānxiàn zǔkàng	
Antenna input admittance	天线输入导纳	Tiānxiàn shūrù dǎonà	
Antenna input impedance	天线输入阻抗	Tiānxiàn shūrù zǔkàng	
Antenna locking device	天线锁定装置	Tiānxiàn suǒdìng zhuāngzhì	
Antenna matching device	天线匹配装置	Tiānxiàn pǐpèi zhuāngzhì	
Antenna noise temperature	天线噪声温度	Tiānxiàn zàoshēng wēndù	
Antenna optical boresight	天线光轴	Tiānxiàn guāngzhóu	
Antenna pedestal	天线座	Tiānxiàn zuò	

English	Chinese	Pinyin	Abbr.
Antenna pointing (boresight) error	天线指向误差	Tiānxiàn zhǐxiàng wùchā	
Antenna polarization	天线极化	Tiānxiàn jíhuà	
Antenna port signal rejection conducted susceptibility (Mil-Std-461E, CS104)	天线端子无用信号抑制传导传敏感	Tiānxiàn duānzi wúyòng xìnhào yìzhì chuándǎo chuán mǐngǎn	
Antenna power rating	天线额定功率	Tiānxiàn édìng gōnglǜ	
Antenna realized gain	天线实际增益	Tiānxiàn shíjì zēngyì	
Antenna resonance frequency	天线谐振频率	Tiānxiàn xiézhèn pínlǜ	
Antenna switching matrix	天线转换矩阵	Tiānxiàn zhuǎnhuàn jǔzhèn	
Antenna system	天线系统	Tiānxiàn xìtǒng	
Antenna terminal conducted emissions (Mil-Std-461E, CE106)	天线端子传导发射	Tiānxiàn duānzi chuándǎo fāshè	
Antenna terminal cross-modulation conducted susceptibility (Mil-Std-461E, CS105)	天线端子交调传导敏感度	Tiānxiàn duānzi jiāotiáo chuándǎo mǐngǎndù	
Antenna terminal intermodulation conducted susceptibility (Mil-Std-461E, CS103)	天线端子互调传导敏感度	Tiānxiàn duānzi hùtiáo chuándǎo mǐngǎndù	
Antenna transmit-receive (T-R) switch	天线收发开关	Tiānxiàn shōufā kāiguān	
Antenna tuning housing	天线调谐室	Tiānxiàn tiáoxié shì	
Antenna voltage rating	天线额定电压	Tiānxiàn édìng diànyā	
Antenna wavelength	天线波长	Tiānxiàn bōcháng	
Anti T-R cell	反 T-R 盒	Fǎn T-R hé	
Anti-alias	平滑	Pínghuá	
Anti-aliasing	去阶梯法	Qù jiētī fǎ	
Anti-cavitation valve	防空化阀	Fángkōnghuà fá	
Anti-click circuit	消喀呖音电路	Xiāokā-liyīn diànlù	
Anticlinal valley	背斜谷	Bèixié gǔ	
Anticline	背斜	Bèixié	
Anticlockwise polarized electromagnetic wave	反时针偏振电磁波	Fǎnshízhēn piānzhèn diàncíbō	
Anti-clockwise polarized wave	逆时针极化波	Nìshízhēn jíhuà bō	
Anti-clockwise polarized wave	左旋极化波	Zuǒxuán jíhuà bō	
Anti-clutter test against the sea (radar term)	抗海浪试验	Kànghǎilàng shìyàn	
Anti-coupling bi-frequency induced polarization instrument	抗耦双频激电仪	Kàng'ǒu shuāngpín jīdiànyí	
Anti-eavesdropping (IPsec)	防窃听	Fángqiètīng	
Anti-interference, anti-jamming	抗干扰	Kànggānrǎo	
Anti-jamming	抗干扰	Kànggānrǎo	AJ
Anti-jamming array	抗干扰阵	Kànggānrǎo zhèn	
Anti-jamming frequency	抗干扰频率	Kànggānrǎo pínlǜ	AJF
Anti-magnetized varistor	消磁电压敏电阻器	Xiāocí diànyā mǐn diànzǔqì	
Anti-noise microphone	抗躁声送话器	Kàngzàoshēng sònghuàqì	
Anti-radiation missile	反复射导弹	Fǎnfùshè dǎodàn	ARM
Anti-reflection coating	防反射涂层	Fángfǎnshè túcéng	
Anti-replay protection (IPsec)	防重放保护	Fángchóngfàng bǎohù	
Anti-repudiation (IPsec)	抗抵赖性	Kàngdǐlàixìng	
Anti-resonance	反共振	Fǎn gòngzhèn	
Anti-saturation (Radar term)	抗饱和	Kàngbǎohé	
Anti-sidetone circuit	消侧音电路	Xiāocèyīn diànlù	
Anti-spam	反垃圾邮件	Fǎnlājī yóujiàn	
Anti-spoofing	反电子欺骗	Fǎn diànzǐ qīpiàn	

Anti-stealth technology	反隐身技术	Fǎnyǐnshēn jìshù	
Anti-Stokes line	反斯托克斯线	Fǎn Sī-tuō-kè-sī xiàn	
Anti-submarine aircraft	反潜机	Fǎnqián jī	
Anti-submarine patrol aircraft	反潜巡逻及	Fǎnqián xúnluó jí	
Anti-symmetric biorthogonal wavelet	反对称双正交小波	Fǎn duìchēng shuāng zhèngjiāo xiǎobō	
Anti-symmetric filter	非对称滤波器	Fēiduìchèn lǜbōqì	AFL
Anti-tampering (IPsec)	防篡改	Fángcuàngǎi	
Anti-vibration	抗振	Kàngzhèn	
Antivirus software	抗毒软件	Kàngdú ruǎnjiàn	
Anti-virus software	防病毒软件	Fángbìngdú ruǎnjiàn	
Anycast addressing	任意广播地址	Rènyì guǎngbō dìzhǐ	AA
Aomega (US company)	奥美嘉	Ào-měi-jiā	
Aperiodic antenna	非调谐天线	Fēitiáoxié tiānxiàn	AA
Aperiodic circular grid array	非周期环栅阵	Fēizhōuqī huán zhàzhèn	
Aperiodic element	非周期环节	Fēizhōuqī huánjié	
Aperture	孔径	Kǒngjìng	
Aperture (of an antenna)	口面	Kǒumiàn	
Aperture aberration	孔径像差	Kǒngjìng xiàngchā	
Aperture blockage	口面阻挡	Kǒumiàn zǔdǎng	
Aperture blockage loss	口面阻挡损失	Kǒumiàn zǔdǎng sǔnshī	
Aperture blocking factor (in a reflector antenna)	口面阻挡因数	Kǒumiàn zǔdǎng yīnshù	
Aperture distortion	孔径失真	Kǒngjìng shīzhēn	
Aperture effect	孔径效应	Kǒngjìng xiàoyìng	AE
Aperture illumination efficiency	口面照射效率	Kǒumiàn zhàoshè xiàolǜ	
Aperture illumination function	口面照射函数	Kǒumiàn zhàoshè hánshù	
Aperture ratio	孔径比	Kǒngjìng bǐ	
Aperture-type antenna	口面天线	Kǒumiàn tiānxiàn	
Aplanatic lens	齐明透镜	Qímíng tòujìng	
Aplanatic lens	消球差透镜	Xiāoqiúchā tòujìng	
Apoapsis	远拱点	Yuǎngǒngdiǎn	
Apogee	远地点	Yuǎndìdiǎn	
Apparent line error ratio	视在线路误差码率	Shìzài xiànlù wùchā mǎ lǜ	
Apparent luminance	视在亮度	Shìzài liàngdù	
Apparent power	视在功率	Shìzài gōnglǜ	
Appear on the market (verb phrase)	投市	Tóushì	
Appearance	外观	Wàiguān	
Appearance potential	出现电位	Chūxiàn diànwèi	
Append	附加	Fùjiā	
Append	增添	Zēngtiān	
Apple Chinese Dictation Kit ©	苹果中文译写器	Píngguǒ zhōngwén yìxiěqì	ACDK
Apple Computer Inc. (US company)	苹果电脑集团	Píngguǒ diànnǎo jítuán	
Applet (computer mini-program)	小应用程序	Xiǎo yìngyòng chéngxù	
AppleTalk address resolution protocol	AppleTalk 地址解析协议	AppleTalk dìzhǐ jiěxī xiéyì	AARP
AppleTalk data stream protocol	AppleTalk 数据流协议	AppleTalk shùjù liú xiéyì	ADSP
AppleTalk echo protocol	AppleTalk 回声协议	AppleTalk huíshēng xiéyì	AEP
AppleTalk echo protocol	AppleTalk 回应协议	AppleTalk huíyìng xiéyì	AEP

English	Chinese	Pinyin	Abbreviation
AppleTalk Ethernet interface	AppleTalk 以太网接口	AppleTalk yǐtàiwǎng jiēkǒu	EtherTalk
AppleTalk filing protocol	AppleTalk 文件协议	AppleTalk wénjiàn xiéyì	AFP
AppleTalk remote access	AppleTalk 远程访问	AppleTalk yuǎnchéng fǎngwèn	ARA
AppleTalk session protocol	AppleTalk 会话协议	AppleTalk huìhuà xiéyì	ASP
AppleTalk transaction protocol	AppleTalk 事务协议	AppleTalk shìwù xiéyì	ATP
AppleTalk update-based routing protocol	AppleTalk 基于更新的路由选择协议	AppleTalk jīyú gēngxīnde lùyóu xuǎnzé xiéyì	AURP
Appliance impedance	设备阻抗	Shèbèi zǔkàng	
Application	应用	Yìngyòng	
Application anchor block	应用链指针控制块	Yìngyòng liàn zhǐzhēn kòngzhì kuài	AAB
Application binary interface	应用二进制式接口	Yìngyòng èrjinzhìshì jiēkǒu	ABI
Application context	应用范围	Yìngyòng fànwéi	AC
Application context	应用上下文	Yìngyòng shàngxiàwén	AC
Application context name	应用上下文名称	Yìngyòng shàngxiàwén míngchēng	ACN
Application control and management system	应用控制及管理系统	Yìngyòng kòngzhì jí guǎnlǐ xìtǒng	ACMS
Application control operating system	应用控制操作系统	Yìngyòng kòngzhì cāozuò xìtǒng	ACOS
Application courier service	应用向导服务	Yìngyòng xiàngdǎo fúwù	
Application data unit	应用数据单元	Yìngyòng shùjù dānyuán	ADU
Application decomposition (in CORBA)	应用分解	Yìngyòng fēnjiě	
Application dedicated file	应用专用文件	Yìngyòng zhuānyòng wénjiàn	ADF
Application dedicated terminal	专用终端设备	Zhuānyòng zhōngduān shèbèi	ADT
Application domain	应用域	Yìngyòng yù	
Application entity	应用实体	Yìngyòng shítǐ	AE
Application entity installer and remover	应用实体安装和拆除	Yìngyòng shítǐ ānzhuāng hé chāichú	AEIR
Application entity invocation	应用实体调用	Yìngyòng shítǐ diàoyòng	AEI
Application entity type	应用实体类型	Yìngyòng shítǐ lèixíng	
Application form of subscription	报刊订阅单	Bàokān dìngyuè dān	
Application framework	应用程序框架	Yìngyòng chéngxù kuàngjià	
Application generator	应用程序生成器	Yìngyòng chéngxù shēngchéngqì	AG
Application hosting	应用托管	Yìngyòng tuōguǎn	
Application identifier	应用标识符	Yìngyòng biāozhì fú	AID
Application interworking function	应用互通功能	Yìngyòng hùtōng gōngnéng	
Application layer	应用层	Yìngyòng céng	
Application layer structure	应用层结构	Yìngyòng céng jiégòu	ALS
Application level framing	应用层帧协议	Yìngyòng céng zhèng xiéyì	ALF
Application level subscriber identity	应用层用户标示	Yìngyòng céng yònghù biāoshì	ALSI
Application location register	应用位置登记	Yìngyòng wèizhì dēngjì	ALR
Application management	应用管理	Yìngyòng guǎnlǐ	
Application management interface	应用管理接口	Yìngyòng guǎnlǐ jiēkǒu	AMI
Application management specification	应用管理规范	Yìngyòng guǎnlǐ guīfàn	AMS
Application middleware	应用中间件	Yìngyòng zhōngjiān jiàn	
Application model	应用模型	Yìngyòng móxíng	
Application offload environment	应用程序卸载环境	Yìngyòng chéngxù xièzài huánjìng	
Application package	应用程序包	Yìngyòng chéngxù bāo	
Application parameter control	应用参数控制	Yìngyòng cānshù kòngzhì	
Application platform	应用平台	Yìngyòng píngtái	

Application process invocation	应用程序请求	Yìngyòng chéngxù qǐngqiú	API
Application process or program	应用进程	Yìngyòng jìnchéng	AP
Application program	应用程序	Yìngyòng chéngxù	
Application program interface	应用程序接口	Yìngyòng chéngxù jiēkǒu	API
Application program interface	应用软件介面	Yìngyòng ruǎnjiàn jièmiàn	API
Application program system	应用程序系统	Yìngyòng chéngxù xìtǒng	APS
Application programming interface	应用编程接口	Yìngyòng biānchéng jiēkǒu	API
Application protocol	应用协议	Yìngyòng xiéyì	
Application protocol control information	应用协议控制信息	Yìngyòng xiéyì kòngzhì xìnxī	APCI
Application protocol data unit	应用协议数据单位	Yìngyòng xiéyì shùjù dānwèi	
Application protocol data unit	应用协议数据单元	Yìngyòng xiéyì shùjù dānyuán	APDU
Application proxy	应用代理	Yìngyòng dàilǐ	
Application role	应用程序角色	Yìngyòng chéngxù juésè	
Application schema	应用模式	Yìngyòng móshì	
Application server	应用服务器	Yìngyòng fúwùqì	AS
Application server process	应用服务器进程	Yìngyòng fúwùqì jìnchéng	ASP
Application server process maintenance	应用服务器进程维护	Yìngyòng fúwùqì jìnchéng wéihù	ASPM
Application service access point	应用业务接入点	Yìngyòng yèwù jiērù diǎn	ASAP
Application service element	应用服务单元	Yìngyòng fúwù dānyuán	ASE
Application service element	应用服务元素	Yìngyòng fúwù yuánsù	ASE
Application service element	应用业务单元	Yìngyòng yèwù dānyuán	ASE
Application service element	应用业务元素	Yìngyòng yèwù yuánsù	ASE
Application service object	应用服务目标	Yìngyòng fúwù mùbiāo	ASO
Application service object invocation	应用服务目标请求	Yìngyòng fúwù mùbiāo qǐngqiú	ASOI
Application service provider	应用服务提供商	Yìngyòng fúwù tígōngshāng	ASP
Application service provider	应用服务提供者	Yìngyòng fúwù tígòngzhě	ASP
Application service provider	应用服务商	Yìngyòng fúwùshāng	ASP
Application service provider	应用业务提供商	Yìngyòng yèwù tígōng shāng	ASP
Application sharing (in CSCW)	应用共享	Yìngyòng gòngxiǎng	
Application software	应用软件	Yìngyòng ruǎnjiàn	
Application software element manager	应用软件单元管理	Yìngyòng ruǎnjiàn dānyuán guǎnlǐ	AEM
Application software package	应用软件包	Yìngyòng ruǎnjiànbāo	ASP
Application specific functional block	专用功能块	Zhuānyòng gōngnéng kuài	ASFB
Application specific integrated circuit	特殊应用集成电路	Tèshū yìngyòng jíchéng diànlù	ASIC
Application specific integrated circuit/chip	专用集成电路/芯片	Zhuānyòng jíchéng diànlù/xìnpiàn	ASIC
Application specific integrated processor	专用综合处理器	Zhuānyòng zōnghé chǔlǐqì	ASIP
Application system	应用系统	Yìngyòng xìtǒng	
Application transport instruction indicator	应用传送指导指示语	Yìngyòng chuánsòng zhǐdǎo zhǐshì yǔ	ATII
Application transport mechanism	应用传送机制	Yìngyòng chuánsòng jīzhì	APM
Application transport parameter	应用传送参数	Yìngyòng chuánsòng cānshù	APP
Application-association	应用联系	Yìngyòng liánxì	
Application-level framing	应用层分帧	Yìngyòng céng fēnzhèng	ALF
Application-level gateway	应用级网关	Yìngyòng jí wǎngguān	ALG
Application-level gateway	应用网关	Yìngyòng wǎngguān	
Application-level semantics-reliable multicast	应用层语义可靠的自适应多播体系	Yìngyòng céng yǔyì kěkàode zìshìyìng duōbō tǐxì	ASRM

Application-process-invocation	应用进程调用	Yìngyòng jìnchéng diàoyòng	
Application-process-type	应用进程类型	Yìngyòng jìnchéng lèixíng	
Applications management building block	应用管理构件	Yìngyòng guǎnlǐ gòujiàn	AMBB
Applications manager graphical user interface	应用管理用户图形接口	Yìngyòng guǎnlǐ yònghù túxíng jiēkǒu	AMGUI
Application-specific schema	特定应用模式	Tèdìng yìngyòng móshì	
Applied ontology	应用本体	Yìngyòng běntǐ	
Applied physics group	应用物理组	Yìngyòng wùlǐ zǔ	GAP
Applique	附板	Fùbǎn	
Apply charging	申请计费	Shēnqǐng jìfèi	AC
Apply charging report	申请计费报告	Shēnqǐng jìfèi bàogào	ACR
Appointed certification body	指定的认证机构	Zhǐdìngde rènzhèng jīgòu	CAB
Approximate interpolation	近似内插	Jìnsì nèichā	
Approximate reasoning	近似推理	Jìnsì tuīlǐ	
Approximate string matching	模糊匹配	Móhu pǐpèi	
Approximation algorithm	近似算法	Jìnsì suànfǎ	
Approximation error	近误差	Jìnwùchā	
Aramid fiber	芳纶纤维	Fānglún xiānwéi	
Arbitrary device handler	任意设备处理程序	Rènyì shèbèi chǔlǐ chéngxù	ADH
Arbitrary precision arithmetic	高精度计算	Gāojīngdù jìsuàn	
Arbitrary projection (GIS)	任意投影	Rènyì tóuyǐng	
Arbitrary transmission on MPLS	MPLS 上的任意传输	MPLS-shàngde rènyì chuánshū	AtoM
Arbitrated loop	已裁定的环路	Yǐcáidìngde huánlù	
Arbitrated loop	仲裁环路	Zhòngcái huánlù	
Arbitration	仲裁	Zhòngcái	
Arc	弧段	Húduàn	
Arc attribute table	弧属性表	Hú shǔxìng biǎo	AAT
Arc automation server	Arc 自动服务器	Arc zìdòng fúwùqì	
Arc code file	弧段编码文件	Húduàn biānmǎ wénjiàn	
Arc digitizing system	弧段数字化系统	Húduàn shùzìhuà xìtǒng	ADS
Arc light source	弧光灯	Húguāngdēng	
Arc spatial database engine	Arc 空间数据库引擎	Arc kōngjiān shùjùkù yǐnqíng	ArcSDE
Arc standard raster graph	Arc 标准栅格图	Arc biāozhǔn zhàgé tú	ASRG
Arc/Info facility manager	Arc/Info 公共设施管理器	Arc/Info gōnggòng shèshī guǎnlǐqì	ArcFM
Arc/Info macro language	Arc/Info 宏语言	Arc/Info hóng yǔyán	AML
Arc/Info Tools	Arc/Info 工具模块	Arc/Info gōngjù mókuài	
Arcade game	电子游戏	Diànzǐ yóuxì	
Arc-control device	灭弧装置	Mièhú zhuāngzhì	
Archie (Internet search engine)	档案搜索软件	Dàng'àn sōusuǒ ruǎnjiàn	
Archie (Internet tool)	文件搜寻站	Wénjiàn sōuxúnzhàn	
Archie file search engine	阿奇文件搜寻站	Ā-qí wénjiàn sōuxúnzhàn	
Architectural acoustics	建筑声学	Jiànzhù shēngxué	AA
Architecture	架构	Jiàgòu	
Architecture	建筑学	Jiànzhùxué	
Archival data	存档数据	Cúndàng shùjù	
Archive	档案	Dàng'àn	
Archive file	存档文件	Cúndàng wénjiàn	

Archive file	归档文件	Guīdàng wénjiàn	
Archive parser agent (in Java)	文档解析代理	Wéndàng jiěxī dàilǐ	APA
Arc-node structure	弧段-节点结构	Húduàn—jiédiǎn jiégòu	
Arc-node topology	弧段-节点拓扑	Húduàn—jiédiǎn tuòpū	
Area border router	区域边界路由器	Qūyù biānjiè lùyóuqì	ABR
Area buffer	面缓冲区	Miàn huǎnchōngqū	
Area centroid	面质心	Miàn zhìxīn	
Area chain	面链	Miàn liàn	
Area clutter switch	区域杂波开关	Qūyù zábō kāiguān	
Area code	地区码	Dìqū mǎ	
Area color code	区域色码	Qūyù sèmǎ	
Area communications network	地区通信网	Dìqū tōngxìnwǎng	ACN
Area generalization	面要素综合	Miàn yàosù zōnghé	
Area networking system	区域网络系统	Qūyù wǎngluò xìtǒng	ANS
Area, face	面	Miàn	
Argon laser	氩离子激光	Yà lízǐ jīguāng	
Argument	变元	Biànyuán	
Argument	引数	Yǐnshù	
Argument pointer	自变量指针	Zìbiànliàng zhǐzhēn	AP
Argument, parameter	参数	Cānshù	
Arithmetic and logic unit	算术及逻辑运算部件	Suànshù jí luóji yùnsuàn bùjiàn	ALU
Arithmetic average	算术平均	Suànshù píngjūn	AA
Arithmetic bus	运算总线	Yùnsuàn zǒngxiàn	AB
Arithmetic control unit	运算控制器	Yùnsuàn kòngzhìqì	ACU
Arithmetic flag	算术标志	Suànshù biāozhì	AF
Arithmetic function designator	运算函数标志符	Yùnsuàn hánshù biāozhìfú	AFD
Arithmetic logic unit	算术逻辑单元	Suànshù luóji dānyuán	ALU
Arithmetic mask register	运算屏蔽寄存器	Yùnsuàn píngbì jìcúnqì	AMR
Arithmetic unit (on main processor chip)	运算器	Yùnsuànqì	
Arleigh Burke (US Navy destroyer class)	阿利伯克	Ālì Bókè	
Armature	动铁芯	Dòngtiěxīn	
Armored cable	铠装电缆	Kǎizhuāng diànlǎn	AC
Arm's reach	伸臂范围	Shēnbì fànwéi	
Army Alaska Communications System (US system built in WWII)	陆军阿拉斯加通信系统	Lùjūn Ā-lā-sī-jiā tōngxìn xìtǒng	AACS
Army Area Communications System	陆军地（区）域通讯系统	Lùjūn dì (qū) yù tōngxùn xìtǒng	AACS
Army Data Distribution System (US)	美国陆军数据分发系统	Měiguó lùjūn shùjù fēnfā xìtǒng	ADDS
Army Tactical Data Link (US military)	陆军战术数据链	Lùjūn zhànshù shùjù liàn	ATDL
Arrange icons (Windows command)	排列图标	Páiliè túbiāo	
Array	列阵	Lièzhèn	
Array	阵列	Zhènliè	
Array (mathematical)	数组	Shùzǔ	
Array antenna	阵列天线	Zhènliè tiānxiàn	
Array configuration	阵排列	Zhèn páiliè	
Array declarator	数组说明符	Shùzǔ shuōmíng fú	
Array element	数组元件	Shùzǔ yuánjiàn	
Array factor	阵因子	Zhèn yīnzǐ	

English	Chinese	Pinyin	Abbreviation
Array observation	系列观测	Xìliè guāncè	
Array processing instruction set	数组处理指令系统	Shùzǔ chǔlǐ zhǐlìng xìtǒng	APIS
Array processor	阵列处理机	Zhènliè chǔlǐjī	AP
Array structure	数组结构体	Shùzǔ jiégòu tǐ	
Array transform processor	数组变换处理机	Shùzǔ biànhuàn chǔlǐjī	ATP
Array waveguide grating	阵列波导光栅	Zhènliè bōdǎo guāngshān	AWG
Array, antenna array	阵，天线阵	Zhèn, tiānxiàn zhèn	
Arrayed waveguide grating	列阵波导光栅	Lièzhèn bōdǎo guāngshān	AWG
Arrow key, direction key	方向键	Fāngxiàng jiàn	
Arrow operator	箭头操作符	Jiàntóu cāozuòfú	
Arrowheads	箭头	Jiàntóu	
Articulation	清晰度	Qīngxīdù	
Articulation point	连接点	Liánjiēdiǎn	
Articulation reference equivalent	清晰度参考当量	Qīngxīdù cānkǎo dāngliàng	
Articulation test	清晰度试验	Qīngxīdù shìyàn	
Artificial balancing line	仿真平衡线	Fǎngzhēn pínghéng xiàn	
Artificial dielectric	人工介质	Réngōng jièzhì	
Artificial dielectric	人造介质	Rénzào jièzhì	
Artificial ear	仿真耳	Fǎngzhēn'ěr	
Artificial hand	模拟手	Mónǐ shǒu	
Artificial head	仿真头	Fǎngzhēn tóu	
Artificial intelligence	人工智能	Réngōng zhìnéng	AI
Artificial life	人工生命	Réngōng shēngmìng	AL
Artificial mains network	人工电源网络	Réngōng diànyuán wǎngluò	AMN
Artificial mouth	仿真嘴	Fǎngzhēn zuǐ	
Artificial neural network	人工神经网络	Réngōng shénjīng wǎngluò	ANN
Artificial space ionization jamming	人工空间电离干扰	Réngōng kōngjiān diànlí gānrǎo	
Artwork (in SMT)	布线图	Bùxiàntú	
As soon as possible (computer chat)	尽快	Jǐnkuài	ASAP
Ascending node (of a satellite)	升交点	Shēngjiāodiǎn	
ASE sub-system	ASE 子系统	ASE zìxìtǒng	ASES
Ashing equipment (optical fiber mfg)	灰烬设备	Huījìn shèbèi	
Ashton-Tate (US company purchased by Borland)	安信达	Ān-xìn-dá	
Asia Information System Security Service	亚洲信息系统安全服务	Yàzhōu xìnxī xìtǒng ānquán fúwù	AIS3
AsiaInfo Technology China Ltd.	亚信科技中国公司	Yàxìn kējì zhōngguó gōngsī	
Asian Info-Communications Committee	亚洲信息通信委员会	Yàzhōu xìnxī tōngxìn wěiyuánhuì	AIC
Asian Pacific Networking Group-Chinese characters	亚太地区网络-中文分组	Yàtài dìqū wǎngluò--zhōngwén fēnzǔ	APNA-CC
AsiaOne (Singapore web site)	亚洲第一站	Yàzhōu dìyī zhàn	
AsiaOnLine (Internet service)	亚洲线上	Yàzhōu xiànshàng	
Asia-Pacific Cable Network	亚太电缆网络	Yàtài diànlǎn wǎngluò	APCN
Aspatial data	非空间数据	Fēikōngjiān shùjù	
Aspect ratio	纵横比	Zònghéng bǐ	
Aspheric mirror	非球面镜	Fēiqiú miànjìng	
Aspherical lens	非球面透镜	Fēiqiú miàntòujìng	
Assemble	汇编	Huìbiān	
Assembler instruction	汇编指令	Huìbiān zhǐlìng	

Assembler program	汇编程序	Huìbiān chéngxù	
Assembly	配件	Pèijiàn	
Assembly	装配件	Zhuāngpèijiàn	
Assembly buffer	汇编程序缓冲器	Huìbiān chéngxù huǎnchōngqì	AB
Assembly language	汇编语言	Huìbiān yǔyán	
Assembly manifest	装配件清单	Zhuāngpèijiàn qīngdān	
Assert acknowledge	断言应答	Duànyán yìngdá	AA
Assert(ion)	断言	Duànyán	
Assessment of acoustics	音质评价	Yīnzhì píngjià	
Asset turnover rate	资产周转率	Zīchǎn zhōuzhuǎnlǜ	
Assign	赋值	Fùzhí	
Assign network address	分配网络地址	Fēnpèi wǎngluò dìzhǐ	ANA
Assigned channel	指配信道	Zhǐpèi xìndào	
Assigned frequency	指配频率	Zhǐpèi pínlǜ	
Assigned frequency band	指配频带	Zhǐpèi píndài	
Assignment	分配	Fēnpèi	
Assignment (of a radio frequency or radio frequency channel	指配	Zhǐpèi	
Assignment command	分配命令	Fēnpèi mìnglìng	
Assignment command	指配命令	Zhǐpèi mìnglìng	
Assignment complete	分配完成	Fēnpèi wánchéng	
Assignment complete	指配完成	Zhǐpèi wánchéng	
Assignment failure	指配故障	Zhǐpèi gùzhàng	
Assignment operator	赋值操作符	Fùzhí cāozuòfú	
Assignment request	指配请求	Zhǐpèi qǐngqiú	
Assignment source point	分配资源点	Fēnpèi zīyuán diǎn	ASP
Assignment statements (in SQL Server)	赋值语句	Fùzhí yǔjù	
Assimilation	同化	Tónghuà	
Assist request instruction	辅助请求指令	Fǔzhù qǐngqiú zhǐlìng	ARI
Assist request instruction	辅助请求指示	Fǔzhù qǐngqiú zhǐshì	ARI
Assistance service control	辅助业务控制	Fǔzhù yèwù kòngzhì	ASC
Assistive technology program	辅助技术程序	Fǔzhù jìshù chéngxù	
Associated control channel	辅助控制信道	Fǔzhù kòngzhì xìndào	ACCH
Associated control channel	随路控制信道	Suílù kòngzhì xìndào	ACCH
Associated control channel	相关控制信道	Xiāngguān kòngzhì xìndào	ACCH
Associated data	关联数据	Guānlián shùjù	
Associated object	相关目标	Xiāngguān mùbiāo	AO
Associated signaling	直联信令方式	Zhílián xìnlìng fāngshì	
Association (IPsec)	关联	Guānlián	
Association control protocol machine	联系控制协议机	Liánxì kòngzhì xiéyìjī	ACPM
Association control service element	关联控制服务单元	Guānlián kòngzhì fúwù dānyuán	ACSE
Association control service element	连接控制服务单元	Liánjiē kòngzhì fúwù dānyuán	ACSE
Association control service element	连接控制服务元素	Liánjiē kòngzhì fúwù yuánsù	ACSE
Association control service element	联系控制服务单元	Liánxì kòngzhì fúwù dānyuán	ACSE
Association control service element	联系控制服务要素	Liánxì kòngzhì fúwù yàosù	ACSE
Association control service element (an ISO standard)	关联控制服务元素	Guānlián kòngzhì fúwù yuánsù	ACSE

Association for System Management	系统管理协会	Xìtǒng guǎnlǐ xiéhuì	ASM
Association Francaise des Informaticiens (French association of persons in the information industry)	法国信息工作人员协会	Fǎguó xìnxī gōngzuò rényuán xiéhuì	AFIN
Association of public safety communication officials international	国际公共安全通信官方协议	Guójì gōnggòng ānquán tōngxìn guānfāng xiéyì	APCO
Association of Radio Industry Businesses (Japan)	无线行业企业协会	Wúxiàn hángyè qǐyè xiéhuì	ARIB
Association rule	关联规则	Guānlián guīzé	
Associative array processor	相连阵列处理机	Xiānglián zhènliè chǔlǐjī	AAP
Associative capacitive read-only memory	关联电容只读存储器	Guānlián diànróng zhǐ dú cúnchǔqì	ACROM
Associative container	关联式容器	Guānlián-shì róngqì	
Associative content addressable memory	相关内容可寻止存储器	Xiāngguān nèiróng kěxúnzhǐ cúnchǔqì	ACAM
Associative data processing	相关数据处理	Xiāngguān shùjù chǔlǐ	ADP
Associative processor computer system	相联处理机计算系统	Xiānglián chǔlǐjī jìsuàn xìtǒng	APCS
Associativity-based routing	基于关联性的路由算法	Jīyú guānlián xìngde lùyóu suànfǎ	ABR
Assumed sliding plane	假想滑移面	Jiǎxiǎng huáyí miàn	
Assurance level	可信级别	Kěxìn jíbié	
Assured forwarding	确保转发	Quèbǎo zhuǎnfā	AF
Assured operations	确保工作过程	Quèbǎo gōngzuò guòchéng	
Assured reproduction area	确保复制区	Quèbǎo fùzhì qū	
Asterisk *	星号	Xīnghào	
Astronomical mirror	天文用面镜	Tiānwén-yòng miànjìng	
Astronomical radar	天文雷达	Tiānwén léidá	
Asymmetric algorithm (IPsec)	不对称算法	Bùduìchèn suànfǎ	
Asymmetric amplitude modulation	不对称调幅	Bùduìchèn tiáofú	AAM
Asymmetric communications	非对称双路通信	Fēiduìchèn shuānglù tōngxìn	AC
Asymmetric crypto algorithm	非对称加密算法	Fēiduìchèn jiāmì suànfǎ	
Asymmetric data exchange	非对称数据交换	Fēiduìchèn shùjù jiāohuàn	ADX
Asymmetric digital subscriber line	不对称数字订阅线路	Bùduìchèn shùzì dìngyuè xiànlù	ADSL
Asymmetric digital subscriber line	不对称数字用户线	Bùduìchèn shùzì yònghù xiàn	ADSL
Asymmetric digital subscriber line	非对称数字用户线路	Fēiduìchèn shùzì yònghù xiànlù	ADSL
Asymmetric digital subscriber loop	非对称数字用户环路	Fēiduìchèn shùzì yònghù huánlù	ADSL
Asymmetric encryption	非对称加密	Fēiduìchèn jiāmì	
Asymmetric flow control	不对称流量控制	Bùduìchèn liúliàng kòngzhì	AFC
Asymmetrical control	不对称控制	Bùduìchèn kòngzhì	
Asymmetrical terminal voltage	不对称端子电压	Bùduìchèn duānzi diànyā	
Asymmetrical terminal voltage	终端不平衡电压	Zhōngduān bùpínghéng diànyā	
Asymmetrical voltage	不平衡电压	Bùpínghéng diànyā	
Asymmetry of AM envelope	调幅度不对称性	Tiáofúdù bùduìchènxìng	
Asymptotic availability	渐近可用性	Jiànjìn kěyòngxìng	A
Asymptotic coding gain	渐进编码增益	Jiànjìn biānmǎ zēngyì	ACG
Asymptotic maximum likelihood	渐进最大似然	Zhèjìn zuìdà sìrán	AML
Asymptotic mean availability	渐近平均可用性	Jiànjìn píngjūn kěyòngxìng	
Asymptotic mean unavailability	渐近平均不可用性	Jiànjìn píngjūn bùkěyòngxìng	
Asymptotic stability	浙近稳定性	Zhèjìn wěndìngxìng	
Asymptotic unavailability	渐近不可用性	Jiànjìn bùkěyòngxìng	U
Asynchronous	异步的	Yìbùde	
Asynchronous address communications system	异步地址通信系统	Yìbù dìzhǐ tōngxìn xìtǒng	AACS

Asynchronous balanced mode	异步平衡方式	Yìbù pínghéng fāngshì	ABM
Asynchronous balanced mode	异步平衡模式	Yìbù pínghéng móshì	ABM
Asynchronous code division multiple access	异步码分多址	Yìbù mǎfēn duōzhǐ	A-CDMA
Asynchronous communication	异步通信	Yìbù tōngxìn	
Asynchronous communication control	异步通信控制	Yìbù tōngxìn kòngzhì	ACC
Asynchronous communication control module	异步通信控制模块	Yìbù tōngxìn kòngzhì mókuài	ACM
Asynchronous communications adapter	异步通信适配	Yìbù tōngxìn shìpèi	ACA
Asynchronous connecting link	异步链路	Yìbù liànlù	ACL
Asynchronous connectionless	异步无连接	Yìbù wúliánjiē	
Asynchronous control character map	异步控制字符影射	Yìbù kòngzhì zìfú yǐngshè	ACCM
Asynchronous data circuit	异步数据电路	Yìbù shùjù diànlù	CDA
Asynchronous data communication channel	异步数据通信信道	Yìbù shùjù tōngxìn xìndào	ADCC
Asynchronous data multiplexer synchronizer	异步数据多路复用同步器	Yìbù shùjù duōlù fùyòng tóngbùqì	ADMS
Asynchronous data service	异步数据业务	Yìbù shùjù yèwù	ADS
Asynchronous data transceiver	异步数据收发机	Yìbù shùjù shōufājī	ADT
Asynchronous data transfer	异步数据传递	Yìbù shùjù chuándì	ADT
Asynchronous data transfer	异步数据转移	Yìbù shùjù zhuǎnyí	ADT
Asynchronous data unit	异步数据单元	Yìbù shùjù dānyuán	ADU
Asynchronous delay line	异步延迟线	Yìbù yánchí xiàn	ADL
Asynchronous digital hierarchy	异步数字分级	Yìbù shùzì fēnjí	
Asynchronous digital hierarchy	异步数字系列	Yìbù shùzì xìliè	
Asynchronous digital subscriber line	异步数字用户线	Yìbù shùzì yònghù xiàn	ADSL
Asynchronous disconnected mode	异步拆线方式	Yìbù chāixiàn fāngshì	ADM
Asynchronous disconnected mode	异步断开方式	Yìbù duànkāi fāngshì	ADM
Asynchronous interface module	异步接口模块	Yìbù jiēkǒu mókuài	ASIM
Asynchronous iteration method	异步送代方法	Yìbù sòngdài fāngfǎ	
Asynchronous multi-line controller	异步多线路控制器	Yìbù duō xiànlù kòngzhìqì	AMLC
Asynchronous response mode	异步响应方式	Yìbù xiǎngyìng fāngshì	ARM
Asynchronous response mode	异步应答方式	Yìbù yìngdá fāngshì	ARM
Asynchronous sequential network	异步时序网络	Yìbù shíxù wǎngluò	ASN
Asynchronous sequential network	异步序列网络	Yìbù xùliè wǎngluò	ASN
Asynchronous terminal adapter	异步终端转接器	Yìbù zhōngduān zhuǎnjiēqì	ATA
Asynchronous time division	异步时分	Yìbù shífēn	ATD
Asynchronous time division multiplexer	异步时分多路复用器	Yìbù shífēn duōlù fùyòngqì	ATDM
Asynchronous time division multiplexing	异步时分复用	Yìbù shífēn fùyòng	
Asynchronous transaction control program	异步事物控制程序	Yìbù shìwù kòngzhì chéngxù	ATCP
Asynchronous transfer mode	异步传递方式	Yìbù chuándì fāngshì	ATM
Asynchronous transfer mode	异步传递模式	Yìbù chuándì móshì	ATM
Asynchronous transfer mode	异步传输模式	Yìbù chuánshū móshì	ATM
Asynchronous transfer mode	异步传送方式	Yìbù chuánsòng fāngshì	ATM
Asynchronous transfer mode	异步传送模式	Yìbù chuánsòng móshì	ATM
Asynchronous transfer mode	异步转换模式	Yìbù zhuǎnhuàn móshì	ATM
Asynchronous transfer mode	异步转移模式	Yìbù zhuǎnyí móshì	ATM
Asynchronous transfer mode adaptation layer	异步传送方式适配层	Yìbù chuánsòng fāngshì shìpèi céng	AAL
Asynchronous transfer mode adaptation layer	异步传送模式适配层	Yìbù chuánsòng móshì shìpèi céng	AAL
Asynchronous transfer mode cross connect	异步传递模式交叉连接	Yìbù chuándì móshì jiāochā liánjiē	AXC

Asynchronous transfer mode cross connect	异步转移模式交叉连接	Yìbù zhuǎnyí móshì jiāochā liánjiē	AXC
Asynchronous transfer mode -cross-connect	异步传递模式-交叉连接	Yìbù chuándì móshì - jiāochā liánjiē	ATM-XC
Asynchronous transfer mode -cross-connect	异步转移模式-交叉连接	Yìbù zhuǎnyí móshì - jiāochā liánjiē	ATM-XC
Asynchronous transfer mode data network	异步转移模式数据网络	Yìbù zhuǎnyí móshì shùjù wǎngluò	ADN
Asynchronous transfer mode network access subsystem	异步传递模式网络接入子系统	Yìbù chuándì móshì wǎngluò jiērù zixìtǒng	ANAS
Asynchronous transfer mode network access subsystem	异步转移模式网络接入子系统	Yìbù zhuǎnyí móshì wǎngluò jiērù zixìtǒng	ANAS
Asynchronous transfer mode passive optical network	异步传递方式无源光网络	Yìbù chuándì fāngshì wúyuán guāng wǎngluò	APON
Asynchronous transfer mode -service access point	异步转移模式 - 业务接入点	Yìbù zhuǎnyí móshì- yèwù jiērù diǎn	ATM-SAP
Asynchronous transfer mode service data unit	异步传递模式业务数据单元	Yìbù chuándì móshì yèwù shùjù dānyuán	ATM-SDU
Asynchronous transfer mode service data unit	异步转移模式业务数据单元	Yìbù zhuǎnyí móshì yèwù shùjù dānyuán	ATM-SDU
Asynchronous transfer mode subscriber line interface circuit	异步传递模式用户线接口电路	Yìbù chuándì móshì yònghùxiàn jiēkǒu diànlù	ATM-SLIC
Asynchronous transfer mode subscriber line interface circuit	异步转移模式用户线接口电路	Yìbù zhuǎnyí móshì yònghùxiàn jiēkǒu diànlù	ATM-SLIC
Asynchronous transfer mode subscriber unit	异步转移模式用户单元	Yìbù zhuǎnyí móshì yònghù dānyuán	ASU
Asynchronous transfer mode switch	异步传递模式交换	Yìbù chuándì móshì jiāohuàn	ATM-SW
Asynchronous transfer mode switch	异步转移模式交换	Yìbù zhuǎnyí móshì jiāohuàn	ATM-SW
Asynchronous transfer mode user network interface	异步传递模式用户网络接口	Yìbù chuándì móshì yònghù wǎngluò jiēkǒu	ATM-UNI
Asynchronous transfer mode user network interface	异步转移模式用户网络接口	Yìbù zhuǎnyí móshì yònghù wǎngluò jiēkǒu	ATM-UNI
Asynchronous transfer mode-netwrk interface card	异步转移模式-网络接口卡	Yìbù zhuǎnyí móshì -wǎngluò jiēkǒu kǎ	ATM-NIC
Asynchronous transfer region	异步传递区	Yìbù chuándì qū	ATR
Asynchronous transfer region	异步转移区	Yìbù zhuǎnyí qū	ATR
Asynchronous user module	异步用户模块	Yìbù yònghù mókuài	AUM
Atemporal data	非时域数据	Fēishíyù shùjù	
Atemporal database	非时域数据库	Fēishíyù shùjùkù	
Atlantic cable	大西洋海底电缆	Dàxīyáng hǎidǐ diànlǎn	AC
Atlas	地图册	Dìtúcè	
ATM adaptation layer	ATM 匹配层	ATM pǐpèi céng	AAL
ATM adaptation layer	ATM 适配层	ATM shìpèi céng	AAL
ATM adaptation layer common part	ATM 适配层公用部分	ATM shìpèi céng gōngyòng bùfen	CP-AAL
ATM adaptation layer service specific part	ATM 适配层业务特定部分	ATM shìpèi céng yèwù tèdìng bùfen	SSP-AAL
ATM adaptation layer type 2	ATM 匹配层类型 2	ATM pǐpèi céng lèixíng 2	AAL2
ATM adaptation layer,common part	ATM 适配层公共部分	ATM shìpèicéng gōnggòng bùfen	CP-AAL
ATM block transfer	ATM 块传送	ATM kuài chuánsòng	ABT
ATM deterministic bit rate	ATM 固定比特率	ATM gùdìng bǐtè lǜ	
ATM end system address	ATM 终端系统地址	ATM zhōngduān xìtǒng dìzhǐ	AESA
ATM inverse multiplexing	ATM 反向复用	ATM fǎnxiàng fùyòng	AIMUX
ATM layer connection	ATM 层连接	ATM céng liánjiē	
ATM link	ATM 链路	ATM liànlù	
ATM passive optical network	ATM 无源光网络	ATM wúyuán guāng wǎngluò	APON
ATM service data unit	ATM 业务数据单元	ATM yèwù shùjù dānyuán	ATM-SDU
ATM traffic descriptor	ATM 业务量描述语	ATM yèwùliáng miáoshù yǔ	

ATM transfer capability	ATM 传送功能	ATM chuánsòng gōngnéng	ATC
ATM wireless access communication system	ATM 无线接入通信系统	ATM wúxiàn jiērù tōngxìn xìtǒng	AWACS
Atmospheric absorption loss	大气吸收损耗	Dàqì xīshōu sǔnhào	
Atmospheric effects	雾化效果	Wùhuà xiàoguǒ	AE
Atmospheric interference	天电干扰	Tiāndiàn gānrǎo	
Atmospheric noise	大气噪声	Dàqì zàoshēng	
Atmospheric radio noise	大气无线电噪声	Dàqì wúxiàndiàn zàoshēng	
Atmospheric transmission loss	空间传播损耗	Kōngjiān chuánbō sǔnhào	
Atmospherics	天电	Tiāndiàn	
Atomic data type	基本数据类型	Jīběn shùjù lèixíng	
Atomic function (smallest indivisible function)	原子功能	Yuánzǐ gōngnéng	
Atomic operation	原子操作	Yuánzi cāozuò	
Attach	附着	Fùzhuó	ATT
Attach	挂接	Guàjiē	
Attach and detach permission	附着分离允许	Fùzhuó fēnlí yǔnxǔ	
Attached resource computer net	资源附加网络	Zīyuán fùjiā wǎngluò	ARCnet
Attached resource computer network	附加资源计算机网络	Fùjiā zīyuán jìsuànjī wǎngluò	ARCnet
Attached tab	附票	Fùpiào	
Attachment unit interface	附加单元接口	Fùjiā dānyuán jiēkǒu	AUI
Attachment unit interface	连接单元接口	Liánjiē dānyuán jiēkǒu	AUI
Attack	攻击	Gōngjī	
Attack Registry & intelligence service	攻击事件注册及智能服务	Gōngjī shìjiàn zhùcè jí zhìnéng fúwù	ARIS
Attendance	员工考勤	Yuángōng kǎoqín	
Attention interrupt	引起注意中断	Yǐnqǐ zhùyì zhōngduàn	
Attenuation	衰耗	Shuāihào	
Attenuation	衰减	Shuāijiǎn	
Attenuation coefficient	衰减系数	Shuāijiǎn xìshù	
Attenuation coefficient (FOC)	衰减常数	Shuāijiǎn chángshù	
Attenuation crosstalk	衰减串扰	Shuāijiǎn chuànrǎo	
Attenuation crosstalk ratio	衰减串扰比	Shuāijiǎn chuànrǎo bǐ	ACR
Attenuation crosstalk ratio	衰减串音比	Shuāijiǎn chuànyīn bǐ	ACR
Attenuation crosstalk ratio power sum	衰减串音功率和	Shuāijiǎn chuànyīn gōnglǜ hé	PSACR
Attenuation curve	衰减曲线	Shuāijiǎn qūxiàn	
Attenuation equalization	衰减均衡	Shuāijiǎn jūnhéng	
Attenuation optimized fiber	优化衰减光纤	Yōuhuà shuāijiǎn guāngxiān	AOF
Attenuation outside a channel	带外衰减	Dàiwài shuāijiǎn	
Attenuation resolution	衰减分辦率	Shuāijiǎn fēnbàn lǜ	
Attenuation spectral dependency	衰减光谱特性	Shuāijiǎn guāngpǔ tèxìng	
Attenuation to crosstalk ratio	衰减与串扰比	Shuāijiǎn yǔ chuànrǎo bǐ	ACR
Attenuation to crosstalk ratio	衰减-串音比率	Shuāijiǎn—chuànyīn bǐlǜ	ACR
Attenuation/frequency distortion	衰减频率失真	Shuāijiǎn pínlǜ shīzhēn	
Attenuator	衰减器	Shuāijiǎnqì	
Atterberg limit	阿特伯界限	Ā-tè-bó jièxiàn	
Attitude-stabilized satellite	姿态稳定卫星	Zītài wěndìng wèixīng	
Attract and intercept	收集和截获	Shōují hé jiéhuò	
Attractiveness	吸引力	Xīyǐnlì	

Attribute	属性	Shǔxìng	
Attribute	特性	Tèxìng	
Attribute accuracy	属性精度	Shǔxìng jīngdù	
Attribute accuracy	属性准确度	Shǔxìng zhǔnquèdù	
Attribute association	属性关联	Shǔxìng guānlián	
Attribute catalogue	属性目录	Shǔxìng mùlù	
Attribute certificate	属性证书	Shǔxìng zhèngshū	
Attribute class	属性类型	Shǔxìng lèixíng	
Attribute code	属性编码	Shǔxìng biānmǎ	
Attribute consistency checking	属性一致性检验	Shǔxìng yīzhìxìng jiǎnyàn	
Attribute data	属性数据	Shǔxìng shùjù	
Attribute definition	属性定义	Shǔxìng dìngyì	
Attribute domain	属性域	Shǔxìng yù	
Attribute error	属性错误	Shǔxìng cuòwù	
Attribute file	属性文件	Shǔxìng wénjiàn	
Attribute header	属性标题	Shǔxìng biāotí	
Attribute identifier	属性标识符	Shǔxìng biāozhìfú	
Attribute linkage	属性连接	Shǔxìng liánjiē	
Attribute list	属性表	Shǔxìng biǎo	
Attribute matching	属性匹配	Shǔxìng pǐpèi	
Attribute query	属性查询	Shǔxìng cháxún	
Attribute record	属性记录	Shǔxìng jìlù	
Attribute reduction	属性约简	Shǔxìng yuējiǎn	
Attribute sampling	属性抽样	Shǔxìng chōuyàng	
Attribute similarity	属性相似性	Shǔxìng xiāngsìxìng	
Attribute table	属性表	Shǔxìng biǎo	
Attribute type	属性类型	Shǔxìng lèixíng	
Attribute type codes	属性类型码	Shǔxìng lèixíng mǎ	
Attribute type name	属性类型名称	Shǔxìng lèixíng míngchēng	
Attribute validation rule	属性检验规则	Shǔxìng jiǎnyàn guīzé	
Attribute value	属性值	Shǔxìng zhí	
Attribute value assertion	属性值断言	Shǔxìng zhí duànyán	
Attribute value assertion	属性值判断语	Shǔxìng zhí pànduàn yǔ	AVA
Attribute value codes	属性值代码	Shǔxìng zhí dàimǎ	
Attribute value definition	属性值定义	Shǔxìng zhí dìngyì	
Attribute; tag; feature; trait	特征	Tèzhēng	
Attributed adjacency graph (CAD/CAM)	属性邻接图	Shǔxìng línjiē tú	AAG
Audible noise	可闻噪声	Kěwén zàoshēng	
Audible signal	可闻信号	Kěwén xìnhào	
Audible sound	可听声	Kětīngshēng	
Audio and video control device	音像控制装置	Yīnxiàng kòngzhì zhuāngzhì	AVCD
Audio bandpass filter	音频带通滤波器	Yīnpín dàitōng lǜbōqì	ABF
Audio card; sound card	音效卡	Yīnxiàokǎ	
Audio CD	音响光碟	Yīnxiǎng guāngdié	
Audio codec	音频多媒体数字信号编解码器	Yīnpín duōméitǐ shùzì xìnhào biān jiěmǎqì	AC

English	Chinese	Pinyin	Abbr.
Audio compression	音频压缩	Yīnpín yāsuō	
Audio conference	音频电话会议	Yīnpín diànhuà huìyì	
Audio frequency	声频	Shēngpín	AF
Audio frequency	音频	Yīnpín	AF
Audio frequency amplifier	音频放大器	Yīnpín fàngdàqì	
Audio frequency intermodulation distortion	音频互调失真	Yīnpín hùtiáo shīzhēn	
Audio frequency load	音载负载	Yīnzài fùzài	
Audio frequency shift keying	音频移频键控	Yīnpín yípín jiànkòng	AFSK
Audio frequency, voice frequency	音频	Yīnpín	AF
Audio gateway	语音网关	Yǔyīn wǎngguān	AG
Audio output	音响输出	Yīnxiǎng shūchū	
Audio processor unit	音频处理器单元	Yīnpín chǔlǐqì dānyuán	APU
Audio signal	声频信号	Shēngpín xìnhào	
Audio signal	声讯	Shēngxùn	
Audio sub-system	音频子系统	Yīnpín zixìtǒng	ASS
Audio terminal unit	音频终端设备	Yīnpín zhōngduān shèbèi	ATU
Audio tone decoder	声调译码器	Shēngdiào yìmǎqì	ATD
Audio video interleave	音频视频插入	Yīnpín shìpín chārù	AVI
Audio/modem riser	音效调制解调器主机板附加直立插卡	Yīnxiào tiáozhì jiětiáoqì zhǔjī bǎn fùjiā zhílì chā kǎ	AMR
Audio/modem riser	音效/数据主机板附加直立插卡	Yīnxiào/shùjù zhǔjī bǎn fùjiā zhílì chā kǎ	AMR
Audio/modem riser	音效/调制解调器主机板附加直立插卡	Yīnxiào/tiáozhì jiětiáoqì zhǔjī bǎn fùjiā zhílì chā kǎ	AMR
Audio-frequency load	音频负载	Yīnpín fùzài	
Audio-frequency protection ratio	音频保护比	Yīnpín bǎohù bǐ	
Audio-frequency response	音频响应	Yīnpín xiǎngyìng	
Audio-frequency signal-to-interference ratio	音频信号干扰比	Yīnpín xìnhào gānrǎo bǐ	
Audio-frequency test load	音频试验负载	Yīnpín shìyàn fùzài	
Audiographic conference service	声音图像会议业务	Shēngyīn túxiàng huìyì yèwù	
Audiographic conference service	音图会议业务	Yīntú huìyì yèwù	
Audio-on-demand	按需点播音频	Ànxū diǎnbō yīnpín	AOD
Audiophone	助听器	Zhùtīngqì	
Audio-video support system	音频-视频支持系统	Yīnpín-shìpín zhīchí xìtǒng	AVSS
Audio-visual	声视	Shēng shì	AV
Audio-visual	视听	Shìtīng	AV
Audio-visual multimedia service implementation agreement	音像多媒体业务执行协议	Yīnxiàng duōméitǐ yèwù zhíxíng xiéyì	AMSIA
Audit logging	审核记录	Shěnhé jìlù	
Audit trail	审计跟踪	Shěnjì gēnzōng	
Auditing	审核	Shěnhé	
Auditory distance	听觉距离	Tīngjué jùlí	
Augmentation data embedding	扩充数据的嵌入	Kuòchōng shùjùde qiànrù	
Augmented content-addressed memory	可扩充的内容定止存储器	Kěkuòchōngde nèiróng dìngzhǐ cúnchǔqì	ACAM
Augmented parity check	扩充的奇偶校验	Kuòchōngde jīǒu jiàoyàn	APC
Augmented reality	增扩实境	Zēngkuò shíjìng	
Augmented virtuality	增扩虚境	Zēngkuò xūjìng	

Augmenting path	增广路径	Zēngguǎng lùjìng	
Augmenting path graph	增广路径图	Zēngguǎng lùjìng tú	
Aural and visual code	听觉和视觉信号编码	Tīngjué hé shìjué xìnhào biānmǎ	AVC
Authenticated network file system	认证式网络文件系统	Rènzhèng-shì wǎngluò wénjiàn xìtǒng	
Authentication	鉴别	Jiànbié	
Authentication	身份验证	Shēnfen yànzhèng	
Authentication algorithm	鉴权算法 A3	Jiànquán suànfǎ	
Authentication algorithm A3	认证算法 A3	Rènzhèng suànfǎ A3	A3
Authentication and key agreement	鉴权和密钥同意	Jiànquán hé mìyuè tóngyì	AKA
Authentication center	鉴权中心	Jiànquán zhōngxīn	AC, AUC
Authentication center	验证中心	Yànzhèng zhōngxīn	AUC
Authentication code	认证码	Rènzhèng mǎ	
Authentication exchange mechanism (IPsec)	认证交换机制	Rènzhèng jiāohuàn jīzhì	
Authentication header	鉴定文件头	Jiàndìng wénjiàn tóu	AH
Authentication header	签定文件头	Qiāndìng wénjiàn tóu	
Authentication header (in IPsec)	认证头	Rènzhèng tóu	AH
Authentication header (in IPSec)	认证头	Rènzhèng tóu	
Authentication information (IPsec)	认证信息	Rènzhèng xìnxī	
Authentication key	验证密钥	Yànzhèng mìyào	
Authentication management field	认证管理范围	Rènzhèng guǎnlǐ fànwéi	AMF
Authentication protocol	认证协议	Rènzhèng xiéyì	
Authentication random number	身份验证随机号	Shēnfen yànzhèng suíjī hào	ARN
Authentication reject	鉴权拒绝	Jiànquán jùjué	
Authentication response	鉴权响应	Jiànquán xiǎngyìng	
Authentication response	验证响应	Yànzhèng xiǎngyìng	AUTHR
Authentication sequence number	身份验证序列号	Shēnfen yànzhèng xùlièhào	ASN
Authentication server	鉴别服务器	Jiànbié fúwùqì	
Authentication server	认证服务器	Rènzhèng fúwùqì	
Authentication service	验证服务	Yànzhèng fúwù	
Authentication token	认证标记	Rènzhèng biāojì	AUTN
Authentication token	验证牌	Yànzhèng pái	
Authentication, authorization, accounting	认证、授权、计费	Rènzhèng、shòuquán、jì fèi	AAA
Authentication, authorization, accounting	验证、授权、计费	Yànzhèng、shòuquán、jìfèi	AAA
Authentication/security data (in FTP)	认证/安全数据	Rènzhèng/ānquán shùjù	ADAT
Authentication/security mechanism (in FTP)	认证/安全机制	Rènzhèng/ānquán jīzhì	AUTH
Authentication; certification	认证	Rènzhèng	
Authenticator	鉴别符	Jiànbié fú	
Authoritative restore	强制性还原	Qiángzhìxìng huányuán	
Authority and format identifier	授权和格式标识符	Shòuquán hé géshi biāozhìfú	AFI
Authority domain	权限域	Quánxiàn yù	
Authority frame identifier	规范帧标识	Guīfàn zhèng biāozhì	AFI
Authority relationship	权限关系	Quánxiàn guānxi	
Authority relationship set	权限关系集	Quánxiàn guānxi jí	
Authorization	授权	Shòuquán	
Authorization key (cipher key)	认证密钥	Rènzhèng mìyào	
Authorization state (status)	授权状态	Shòuquán zhuàngtài	

Auto balance system (computer disk)	自动平衡系统	Zìdòng pínghéng xìtǒng	ABS
Auto system	自动台	Zìdòng tái	AS
Autoaccess multiple channel cordless telephone	自动接入多信道无绳电话	Zìdòng jiērù duōxìndào wúshéng diànhuà	
Auto-build tool	自动生成工具	Zìdòng shēngchéng gōngjù	ABT
AutoCAD (engineering drawing software)	欧特克	Ōu-tè-kè	
Auto-clamp assembly (surface mount technology)	电钳装	Diànqiánzhuāng	
Auto-correlation	自相关	Zìxiāngguān	
Auto-correlation prediction	自相关预测	Zìxiāngguān yùcè	AP
Auto-correlator	自相关器	Zìxiāngguānqì	
Auto-covariance	自协方差	Zìxiéfāngchà	
Auto-dialer	接拨器	Jiēbōqì	
Autodyne reception	自差式接收	Zìchāshì jiēshōu	
Auto-executing batch (autoexec.bat) file	自动批处理文件	Zìdòng pīchǔlǐ wénjiàn	
Autoform	自构形	Zìgòuxíng	
Auto-iris	自动光圈	Zìdòng guāngquān	A-I
Automated cartography	自动化制图	Zìdònghuà zhìtú	
Automated data and telecommunications service	自动数据远程通信服务	Zìdòng shùjù yuǎnchéng tōngxìn fúwù	ADTS
Automated digital network system	自动化数字网络系统	Zìdònghuà shùzì wǎngluò xìtǒng	ADNS
Automated feature recognition	自动特征识别	Zìdòng tèzhēng shíbié	
Automated indexing technology	自动索引技术	Zìdòng suǒyǐn jìshù	
Automated mapping and facilities management	自动制图/设施管理	Zìdòng zhìtú/shèshī guǎnlǐ	AM/FM
Automated meteorological data acquisition system	气象数据自动采集系统	Qìxiàng shùjù zìdòng cǎijí xìtǒng	
Automated name placement	自动地名配置	Zìdòng dìmíng pèizhì	
Automated operator console	自动操作台	Zìdòng cāozuò tái	AOC
Automated operator control	自动操作控制	Zìdòng cāozuò kòngzhì	AOC
Automated output control	自动输出控制	Zìdòng shūchū kòngzhì	AOC
Automated overload control	自动过载控制	Zìdòng guòzài kòngzhì	AOC
Automated response	自动响应	Zìdòng xiǎngyìng	
Automated security monitoring	自动安全监控	Zìdòng ānquán jiānkòng	
Automated test equipment	自动测试设备	Zìdòng cèshì shèbèi	ATE
Automated tunneling	自动隧道	Zìdòng suìdào	AT
Automated vectorization	自动矢量化	Zìdòng shǐliànghuà	
Automatic (optical) power reduction	自动光功率减少	Zìdòng guāng gōnglǜ jiǎnshǎo	APR
Automatic (optical) power shut down	自动光功率关断	Zìdòng guāng gōnglǜ guānduàn	APSD
Automatic air defense information system	自动防空情报系统	Zìdòng fángkōng qíngbào xìtǒng	AADIS
Automatic alarm	自动报警	Zìdòng bàojǐng	AA
Automatic alarm call	自动警报呼叫	Zìdòng jǐngbào hūjiào	AAC
Automatic alarm state	自动报警状态	Zìdòng bàojǐng zhuàngtài	AAS
Automatic amplitude control	自动振幅控制	Zìdòng zhènfú kòngzhì	AAC
Automatic answer trunk	自动应答干线	Zìdòng yìngdá gànxiàn	AAT
Automatic answerback	自动应答	Zìdòng yìngdá	AAB
Automatic answering automatic calling	自动应答自动呼叫	Zìdòng yìngdá zìdòng hūjiào	AAAC, A3C
Automatic applications development system	自动应用开发系统	Zìdòng yìngyòng kāifā xìtǒng	AADS
Automatic audio switching	自动音频交换	Zìdòng yīnpín jiāohuàn	AAS
Automatic back bias	自动反偏压	Zìdòng fǎnpiānyā	ABB
Automatic bandwidth control	自动带宽控制	Zìdòng dàikuān kòngzhì	ABC

Automatic base communication system	基地自动通信系统	Jīdì zìdòng tōngxìn xìtǒng	ABCS
Automatic binary data link	自动二进制数据链路	Zìdòng èrjìnzhì shùjù liànlù	ABDL
Automatic bit rate selection	自动比特率选择	Zìdòng bǐtè lǜ xuǎnzé	ABRS
Automatic bootstrap loader	自动引导装入程序	Zìdòng yǐndǎo zhuāngrù chéngxù	ABL
Automatic call acceptance	自动呼叫应答	Zìdòng hūjiào yìngdá	ACA
Automatic call accounting	电话自动计费系统	Diànhuà zìdòng jìfèi xìtǒng	ACA
Automatic call distribution	自动分配话务	Zìdòng fēnpèi huàwù	ACD
Automatic call distribution	自动呼叫分配	Zìdòng hūjiào fēnpèi	ACD
Automatic call distribution remote capture	自动呼叫分布远程截获	Zìdòng hūjiào fēnbù yuǎnchéng jiéhuò	ADRC
Automatic call distribution remote capture	自动呼叫分配远程截获	Zìdòng hūjiào fēnpèi yuǎnchéng jiéhuò	ADRC
Automatic call distributor	自动呼叫分配器	Zìdòng hūjiào fēnpèiqì	ACD
Automatic call identification	自动呼叫识别	Zìdòng hūjiào shíbié	
Automatic call measuring (equipment)	自动传输测量	Zìdòng chuánshū cèliáng	ATME
Automatic call reconnect	自动呼叫重连	Zìdòng hūjiào chónglián	
Automatic call recording	自动呼叫记录	Zìdòng hūjiào jìlù	ACR
Automatic called number identification	自动呼叫号识别	Zìdòng hūjiào hào shíbié	ACNI
Automatic calling	自动呼叫	Zìdòng hūjiào	
Automatic calling equipment	自动呼叫装置	Zìdòng hūjiào zhuāngzhì	ACE
Automatic calling unit adapter	自动呼叫设备转接器	Zìdòng hūjiào shèbèi zhuǎnjiēqì	ACUA
Automatic camp-on busy	自动忙时保留呼叫装置	Zìdòng mángshí bǎoliú hūjiào zhuāngzhì	ACB
Automatic central processor unit overheat prevention system	自动 CPU 过热保护	Zìdòng CPU guòrè bǎohù	ACOPS
Automatic central processor unit overheat prevention system	自动 CPU 过热预防系统	Zìdòng CPU guòrè yùfáng xìtǒng	ACOPS
Automatic channel selection	自动信道选择	Zìdòng xìndào xuǎnzé	
Automatic circuit analysis program	自动电路分析程序	Zìdòng diànlù fēnxī chéngxù	ACAP
Automatic circuit exchange	自动电路交换机	Zìdòng diànlù jiāohuànjī	ACE
Automatic circuit quality monitoring	自动电路质量监视	Zìdòng diànlù zhìliàng jiānshì	ACQM
Automatic circuit restoration	自动电路恢复	Zìdòng diànlù huīfù	ACR
Automatic code translation	自动译码	Zìdòng yìmǎ	ACT
Automatic coding machine	自动编码机	Zìdòng biānmǎjī	ACOM
Automatic coding translator (in COBOL)	自动编码器	Zìdòng biānmǎqì	ACTRAN
Automatic color monitor	自动色彩监视器	Zìdòng sècǎi jiānshìqì	ACM
Automatic compression	自动压缩	Zìdòng yāsuō	
Automatic computing equipment	自动计算设备	Zìdòng jìsuàn shèbèi	ACE
Automatic congestion control	自动拥塞控制	Zìdòng yōngsè kòngzhì	ACC
Automatic congestion control information massage	自动拥塞控制信息消息	Zìdòng yōngsè kòngzhì xìnxī xiāoxi	ACC
Automatic control	自动控制	Zìdòng kòngzhì	ZK
Automatic correction technology	自动校正技术	Zìdòng jiàozhèng jìshù	ACT
Automatic correlation vocoder	自动相关声码器	Zìdòng xiāngguān shēngmǎqì	ACV
Automatic CPU overheat prevention system	CPU 过热预防系统	CPU guòrè yùfáng xìtǒng	ACOPS
Automatic data equalizer modem	自动数据均衡电路调制解调器	Zìdòng shùjù jūnhéng diànlù tiáozhì jiětiáoqì	ADEM
Automatic data exchange	自动数据交换	Zìdòng shùjù jiāohuàn	ADX
Automatic data exchange system	自动数据交换系统	Zìdòng shùjù jiāohuàn xìtǒng	ADXS
Automatic data processing	自动数据处理	Zìdòng shùjù chǔlǐ	ADP
Automatic data processing equipment	自动数据处理设备	Zìdòng shùjù chǔlǐ shèbèi	ADPE

Automatic data processing program	自动数据处理程序	Zìdòng shùjù chǔlǐ chéngxù	ADPP
Automatic data processing system	自动数据处理系统	Zìdòng shùjù chǔlǐ xìtǒng	ADPS
Automatic data rate changer	自动数据速率变换器	Zìdòng shùjù sùlǜ biànhuànqì	ADRC
Automatic data switching system	自动数据交换系统	Zìdòng shùjù jiāohuàn xìtǒng	ADSS
Automatic data tracking	自动数据跟踪	Zìdòng shùjù gēnzōng	ADT
Automatic data translator	自动数据变换器	Zìdòng shùjù biànhuànqì	ADT
Automatic data translator	自动译码器	Zìdòng yìmǎqì	ADT
Automatic decision feedback equalizer	自适应判决反馈均衡器	Zìshìyìng pànjué fǎnkuì jūnhéngqì	ADFE
Automatic dependent surveillance (civil air)	自动相关监视	Zìdòng xiāngguān jiānshì	ADS
Automatic dial order wire	自动拨号传号线	Zìdòng bōhào chuánhàoxiàn	ADOW
Automatic dialer	自动拨号器	Zìdòng bōhàoqì	
Automatic dialing unit	自动拨号设备	Zìdòng bōhào shèbèi	ADU
Automatic dialing unit	自动拨号装置	Zìdòng bōhào zhuāngzhì	ADU
Automatic digital network switching center	自动数字网络交换中心	Zìdòng shùzì wǎngluò jiāohuàn zhōngxīn	ASC
Automatic direct distance dialing system	远程直接自动拨号系统	Yuǎnchéng zhíjiē zìdòng bōhào xìtǒng	ADDDS
Automatic equalizer	自动均衡器	Zìdòng jūnhéngqì	AEQ
Automatic error analysis	自动误差分析	Zìdòng wùchā fēnxī	AEA
Automatic error correction system	自动纠错系统	Zìdòng jiūcuò xìtǒng	AEC
Automatic error interrogation	自动错误询问	Zìdòng cuòwù xúnwèn	AEI
Automatic fault finding	自动故障查找	Zìdòng gùzhàng cházhǎo	AFF
Automatic fault location	自动故障定位	Zìdòng gùzhàng dìngwèi	AFL
Automatic file transfer	自动文件传递	Zìdòng wénjiàn chuándì	AFT
Automatic flow process analysis	自动流程分析	Zìdòng liúchéng fēnxī	AFPA
Automatic frequency control	自动频率控制	Zìdòng pínlǜ kòngzhì	AFC
Automatic frequency fine control	自动频率微调	Zìdòng pínlǜ wēitiáo	AFC
Automatic frequency fine control locking-in range	自动频率微调同步范围	Zìdòng pínlǜ wēitiáo tóngbù fànwéi	
Automatic frequency fine control maximum tracking rate	自动频率微调最大跟踪速率	Zìdòng pínlǜ wēitiáo zuìdà gēnzōng sùlǜ	
Automatic frequency fine control pull-in range	自动频率微调捕捉范围	Zìdòng pínlǜ wēitiáo bǔzhuō fànwéi	
Automatic frequency fine control pull-in time	自动频率微调捕捉时间	Zìdòng pínlǜ wēitiáo bǔzhuō shíjiān	
Automatic frequency fine control residual error	自动频率微调剩余误差	Zìdòng pínlǜ wēitiáo shèngyú wùchā	
Automatic frequency sharing	自动频率公用	Zìdòng pínlǜ gōngyòng	
Automatic frequency tuning	自动频率调谐	Zìdòng pínlǜ tiáoxié	AFT
Automatic gain control	自动增益控制	Zìdòng zēngyì kòngzhì	AGC
Automatic gain-control (AGC) characteristic	自动增益控制特性	Zìdòng zēngyì kòngzhì tèxìng	
Automatic interpretation of structural drawings (CAD/CAM)	建筑结构图自动识别系统	Jiànzhù jiégòutú zìdòng shíbié xìtǒng	AISD
Automatic laser shutdown	激光器自动关闭	Jīguāngqì zìdòng guānbì	ALS
Automatic laser shutdown	自动激光关闭	Zìdòng jīguāng guānbì	ALS
Automatic laser shutdown	自动激光关断	Zìdòng jīguāng guānduàn	ALS
Automatic level control	自动电平控制	Zìdòng diànpíng kòngzhì	ALC
Automatic level control	自动平衡控制	Zìdòng pínghéng kòngzhì	ALC
Automatic light compensation	自动亮度补偿	Zìdòng liàngdù bǔcháng	ALC
Automatic light control	自动光控制	Zìdòng guāng kòngzhì	ALC
Automatic line identification	自动线路识别	Zìdòng xiànlù shíbié	ALI
Automatic link transfer	自动链路转移	Zìdòng liànlù zhuǎnyí	ALT
Automatic location identification	自动位置识别	Zìdòng wèizhì shíbié	ALI

Automatic maintenance	自动维护	Zìdòng wéihù	am
Automatic maintenance operation	自动维护运行（操作）	Zìdòng wéihù yùnxíng (cāozuò)	AMO
Automatic map registration (in GIS)	地图自动配准	Dìtú zìdòng pèizhǔn	
Automatic message exchange	自动信息交换	Zìdòng xìnxī jiāohuàn	AME
Automatic meter reading	自动抄表	Zìdòng chāo biǎo	AMR
Automatic network dialing	自动网络拨号	Zìdòng wǎngluò bōhào	AND
Automatic noise canceller	自动杂波消除电路	Zìdòng zábō xiāochú diànlù	ANC
Automatic number analysis	自动号码分析	Zìdòng hàomǎ fēnxī	ANA
Automatic number identification	自动号码识别	Zìdòng hàomǎ shíbié	ANI
Automatic operation monitor	自动操作监控器	Zìdòng cāozuò jiānkòngqì	AOM
Automatic optical inspection	自动光学检查	Zìdòng guāngxué jiǎnchá	AOI
Automatic optical inspection equipment	自动光学检测设备	Zìdòng guāngxué jiǎncè shèbèi	AOI
Automatic paging system	自动寻呼系统	Zìdòng xúnhū xìtǒng	
Automatic phase compensation	自动相位补偿	Zìdòng xiàngwèi bǔcháng	APC
Automatic phase control	自动相位控制	Zìdòng xiàngwèi kòngzhì	APC
Automatic phase lock	自动锁相	Zìdòng suǒxiāng	APL
Automatic phase shifter	自动移相器	Zìdòng yíxiàngqì	APS
Automatic phase synchronization	自动相位同步	Zìdòng xiàngwèi tóngbù	APS
Automatic picture control	自动图象控制	Zìdòng túxiàng kòngzhì	APC
Automatic picture transmission system	自动图象传输系统	Zìdòng túxiàng chuánshū xìtǒng	APTS
Automatic polarization control	自动偏振控制	Zìdòng piānzhèn kòngzhì	APC
Automatic position reporting	自动位置报告	Zìdòng wèizhì bàogào	APR
Automatic positioning equipment (semiconductor mfg)	自动定位装置	Zìdòng dìngwèi zhuāngzhì	
Automatic power control	自动功率控制	Zìdòng gōnglǜ kòngzhì	APC
Automatic power reduction	自动功率降低	Zìdòng gōnglǜ jiàngdī	APR
Automatic power reduction	自动功率减少	Zìdòng gōnglǜ jiǎnshǎo	APR
Automatic power shutdown	自动功率切断	Zìdòng gōnglǜ qiēduàn	APSD
Automatic private branch exchange	自动专用分路交换机	Zìdòng zhuānyòng fēnlù jiāohuànjī	APBX
Automatic private IP addressing	自动专用 IP 寻址	Zìdòng zhuānyòng IP xúnzhǐ	APIPA
Automatic program control	自动程序控制	Zìdòng chéngxù kòngzhì	APC
Automatic program unit	自动程序设计装置	Zìdòng chéngxù shèjì zhuāngzhì	APU
Automatic programming and recording	自动程序设计与记录	Zìdòng chéngxù shèjì yǔ jìlù	APR
Automatic protection switching	自动保护倒换	Zìdòng bǎohù dǎohuàn	APS
Automatic protection switching	自动保护切换	Zìdòng bǎohù qiēhuàn	APS
Automatic recovery	自动恢复	Zìdòng huīfù	
Automatic registration (in GIS)	自动校准	Zìdòng jiàozhǔn	
Automatic remote control	自动遥控	Zìdòng yáokòng	ARC
Automatic remote data terminal	自动远端数据终端	Zìdòng yuǎnduān shùjù zhōngduān	ARDT
Automatic repeat request	自动重发请求	Zìdòng chóngfā qǐngqiú	ARQ
Automatic repeat request	自动重复请求	Zìdòng chóngfù qǐngqiú	ARQ
Automatic repeat request	自动请求重传	Zìdòng qǐngqiú chóngchuán	ARQ
Automatic repeat request	自动请求重发	Zìdòng qǐngqiú chóngfā	ARQ
Automatic repetition Verdan system	弗丹自动重发系统	Fú-dān zìdòng chóngfā xìtǒng	
Automatic retransmission	自动转发	Zìdòng zhuǎnfā	
Automatic retransmission service	自动转发服务	Zìdòng zhuǎnfā fúwù	ARX
Automatic route selection	自动路由选择	Zìdòng lùyóu xuǎnzé	ARS

Automatic selectivity control	自动选择性控制	Zìdòng xuǎnzéxìng kòngzhì	ASC
Automatic send and receive	自动收发	Zìdòng shōufā	ASR
Automatic send-receiver	自动收发机	Zìdòng shōufājī	ASR
Automatic sensitivity control	自动灵敏度控制	Zìdòng língmǐndù kòngzhì	ASC
Automatic service discovery	自动业务发现	Zìdòng yèwù fāxiàn	ASD
Automatic slope control	自动斜率控制	Zìdòng xiélǜ kòngzhì	ASC
Automatic speech recognition	自动声音识别	Zìdòng shēngyīn shíbié	ASR
Automatic speech recognition	自动语音识别	Zìdòng yǔyīn shíbié	ASR
Automatic subscriber line test equipment	用户线自动测试装置	Yònghù xiàn zìdòng cèshì zhuāngzhì	ASLTE
Automatic switched optical network	自动交换光网络	Zìdòng jiāohuàn guāng wǎngluò	ASON
Automatic switched transport network	自动交换传送网络	Zìdòng jiāohuàn chuánsòng wǎngluò	ASTN
Automatic switching	自动交换	Zìdòng jiāohuàn	
Automatic switching equipment	自动交换设备	Zìdòng jiāohuàn shèbèi	
Automatic switching node	自动交换节点	Zìdòng jiāohuàn jiédiǎn	ASN
Automatic synchronizing unit	自动同步设备（单元）	Zìdòng tóngbù shèbèi (dānyuán)	ASU
Automatic target recognition	目标自动识别	Mùbiāo zìdòng shíbié	ATR
Automatic telephone call	自动电话呼叫	Zìdòng diànhuà hūjiào	ATC
Automatic telephone set	自动电话机	Zìdòng diànhuàjī	
Automatic teletype message switching (system)	电传电报自动报文交换系统	Diànchuán diànbào zìdòng bàowén jiāohuàn xìtǒng	ATMS
Automatic teller machine	自动柜员机	Zìdòng guìyuánjī	ATM
Automatic test	自动测试	Zìdòng cèshì	
Automatic test equipment	自动测试设备	Zìdòng cèshì shèbèi	ATE
Automatic timing control	自动定时控制	Zìdòng dìngshí kòngzhì	ATC
Automatic timing corrector	自动时间校正器	Zìdòng shíjiān jiàozhèngqì	ATC
Automatic toll switch	自动长话交换	Zìdòng chánghuà jiāohuàn	CHZ
Automatic toll ticketing	自动长途电话记录	Zìdòng chángtú diànhuà jìlù	ATT
Automatic tone control	自动音调控制	Zìdòng yīndiào kòngzhì	ATC
Automatic tone correction	自动音调校正	Zìdòng yīndiào jiàozhèng	ATC
Automatic track following	自动跟踪	Zìdòng gēnzōng	ATF
Automatic tracking correction	自动跟踪校正	Zìdòng gēnzōng jiàozhèng	ATC
Automatic traffic recorder	自动话务量记录器	Zìdòng huàwùliáng jìlùqì	ATR
Automatic transit telegram (Telex)	自动转报	Zìdòng zhuǎnbào	ZB
Automatic transmission measuring and signaling test equipment	自动传输测量和信令测试设备	Zìdòng chuánshū cèliáng hé xìnlìng cèshì shèbèi	ATME
Automatic transmission power control	自动发射功率控制	Zìdòng fāshè gōnglǜ kòngzhì	ATPC
Automatic transmission power control	自动发信功率控制	Zìdòng fāxìn gōnglǜ kòngzhì	ATPC
Automatic transmission rerouting	自动传输再选路	Zìdòng chuánshū zàixuǎnlù	
Automatic transmit power control	自动发送功率控制	Zìdòng fāsòng gōnglǜ kòngzhì	ATPC
Automatic transmitter identification	自动发射机识别	Zìdòng fāshèjī shíbié	ATI
Automatic trouble analysis	自动障碍分析	Zìdòng zhàng'ài fēnxī	ATA
Automatic trunk testing	自动中继线测试	Zìdòng zhōngjìxiàn cèshì	ATT
Automatic tuning control	自动调谐控制	Zìdòng tiáoxié kòngzhì	ATC
Automatic vehicle location system	自动车辆定位系统	Zìdòng chēliàng dìngwèi xìtǒng	AVL
Automatic voice response system	自动语音应答系统	Zìdòng yǔyīn yìngdá xìtǒng	AVRS
Automatic voltage clamp	自动电压箝位	Zìdòng diànyā qiánwèi	AVC
Automatic volume control	自动音量控制	Zìdòng yīnliàng kòngzhì	AVC

Automatically answer	自动应答	Zìdòng yìngdá	AA
Automatic-scanning receiver	自动扫描接收机	Zìdòng sǎomiáo jiēshōujī	
Automation	自动化	Zìdònghuà	
Automation object (for database)	自动化对象	Zìdònghuà duìxiàng	
Automation of bibliography through computerization	计算机化自动编目	Jìsuànjīhuà zìdòng biānmù	ABC
Automation server (for database)	自动化服务器	Zìdònghuà fúwùqì	
Automotive ignition interference	汽车点火干扰	Qìchē diǎnhuǒ gānrǎo	
Automotive network eXchange	汽车网络交换中心	Qìchē wǎngluò jiāohuàn zhōngxīn	ANX
Automount (Unix command)	自动挂装	Zìdòng guàzhuāng	
Autonomous agent	自主代理	Zìzhǔ dàilǐ	
Autonomous decentralized loop network	独立分散循环网络	Dúlì fēnsàn xúnhuán wǎngluò	ADL-Net
Autonomous fireproofing	个体防火	Gètǐ fánghuǒ	
Autonomous indicator (radar term)	自主显示器	Zìzhǔ xiǎnshìqì	
Autonomous switching	自主交换	Zìzhǔ jiāohuàn	
Autonomous system	自治系统	Zìzhì xìtǒng	AS
Autonomous system border router	自治系统边界路由器	Zìzhì xìtǒng biānjiè lùyóuqì	ASBR
Autonomous system boundary router	自治区系统边界路由器	Zìzhìqū xìtǒng biānjiè lùyóuqì	ASBR
Autonomous system boundary router	自主系统边界路由器	Zìzhǔ xìtǒng biānjiè lùyóuqì	ASBR
Autonomy, autonomous, independent	独立	Dúlì	
Autoregressive spectral estimation acquisition technique	自回归频谱估计捕获技术	Zìhuíguī pínpǔ gūjì bǔhuò jìshù	ASEAT
Auto-sizing and centering (video term)	自动调效屏幕尺寸和中心位置	Zìdòng tiáoxiào píngmù chǐcùn hé zhōngxīn wèizhì	ASC
Auto-static routing	自动静态路由	Zìdòng jìngtài lùyóu	
Auto-static updates	自动静态更新	Zìdòng jìngtài gēngxīn	
Auto-threshold control	自动阈值控制	Zìdòng yùzhí kòngzhì	ATC
Auxiliary attachment	辅件	Fǔjiàn	
Auxiliary clock board	辅助时钟板	Fǔzhù shízhōng bǎn	ACK
Auxiliary communications facility (military usage)	备用通信设备	Bèiyòng tōngxìn shèbèi	ACF
Auxiliary control element	辅助控制单元	Fǔzhù kòngzhì dānyuán	ACE
Auxiliary controller bus	辅助控制器总线	Fǔzhù kòngzhìqì zǒngxiàn	
Auxiliary crate controller	辅助机箱控制器	Fǔzhù jīxiāng kòngzhìqì	
Auxiliary data processing equipment	辅助数据处理设备	Fǔzhù shùjù chǔlǐ shèbèi	ADPE
Auxiliary data processing system	辅助数据处理系统	Fǔzhù shùjù chǔlǐ xìtǒng	ADPS
Auxiliary deflection coil	辅助偏转线圈	Fǔzhù piānzhuǎn xiànquān	
Auxiliary deflection plate	辅助偏转板	Fǔzhù piānzhuǎn bǎn	
Auxiliary display unit	辅助显示装置（单元）	Fǔzhù xiǎnshì zhuāngzhì (dānyuán)	ADU
Auxiliary executable statement	辅助执行语句	Fǔzhù zhíxíng yǔjù	
Auxiliary input	辅助输入接口	Fǔzhù shūrù jiēkǒu	
Auxiliary memory	辅助存储器	Fǔzhù cúnchǔqì	
Auxiliary output signal	辅助输出信号	Fǔzhù shūchū xìnhào	
Auxiliary power source	辅助电源	Fǔzhù diànyuán	APS
Auxiliary storage unit	辅助存储单元	Fǔzhù cúnchǔ dānyuán	ASU
Auxiliary switch	辅助开关	Fǔzhù kāiguān	ASW
Availability	存取性	Cúnqǔxìng	
Availability	可获性	Kěhuòxìng	

Availability (IPsec)	可用性	Kěyòngxìng	
Available area	可用区	Kěyòng qū	
Available bit rate	可获得比特率	Kěhuòdé bǐtèlǜ	ABR
Available bit rate	可用比特率	Kěyòng bǐtè lǜ	ABR
Available cell rate	可用的信元率	Kěyòngde xìnyuán lǜ	AVCR
Available power	可用功率	Kěyòng gōnglǜ	
Available power	资用功率	Zīyòng gōnglǜ	
Available power gain (of two-port network)	可用功率增益	Kěyòng gōnglǜ zēngyì	
Avalanche controlled rectifier	雪崩可控整流器	Xuěbēng kěkòng zhěngliúqì	ACR
Avalanche diode	雪崩二极管	Xuěbēng èrjíguǎn	AD
Avalanche diode	雪崩光电二极管	Xuěbēng guāngdiàn èrjíguǎn	AD
Avalanche photo diode	雪崩光二极管	Xuěbēng guāng èrjíguǎn	APD
Avalanche photo-detector	雪崩光电检测器	Xuěbēng guāngdiàn jiǎncèqì	APD
Avalanche photo-detector	雪崩光电探测器	Xuěbēng guāngdiàn tàncèqì	APD
Avalanche photodiode coupler	雪崩光电二极管耦合器	Xuěbēng guāngdiàn èrjíguǎn ǒuhéqì	APC
Average access time	平均访问时间	Píngjūn fǎngwèn shíjiān	
Average access time (computer disk)	平均存取时间	Píngjūn cúnqǔ shíjiān	AAT
Average cell rate	平均信元率	Píngjūn xìnyuán lǜ	ACR
Average detector	平均值检波器	Píngjūnzhí jiǎnbōqì	
Average envelope detection	平均包络检波	Píngjūn bāoluò jiǎnbō	
Average fade duration	平均衰落时间	Píngjūn shuāiluò shíjiān	AFD
Average failure number	平均故障数	Píngjūn gùzhàng shù	AFN
Average handling time	平均处理时间	Píngjūn chǔlǐ shíjiān	AHT
Average holding time	平均保持时间	Píngjūn bǎochí shíjiān	AHT
Average holding time	平均占用时间	Píngjūn zhànyòng shíjiān	AHT
Average latency	平均潜伏期	Píngjūn qiánfúqī	
Average latency time	平均潜伏时间	Píngjūn qiánfú shíjiān	
Average life expectancy	平均寿命预期值	Píngjūn shòumìng yùqīzhí	ALE
Average nominal characteristic	平均名义特性	Píngjūn míngyì tèxìng	
Average picture level	平均图象电平	Píngjūn túxiàng diànpíng	APL
Average power (in a transmission line)	平均功率	Píngjūn gōnglǜ	
Average response amplitude	平均响应幅度	Píngjūn xiǎngyìng fúdù	ARA
Average response spectrum	平均反应谱	Píngjūn fǎnyìng pǔ	
Average restoration time	平均恢复时间	Píngjūn huīfù shíjiān	ART
Average search length	平均查找长度	Píngjūn cházhǎo chángdù	
Average seek time	平均寻道时间	Píngjūn xúndào shíjiān	
Average sidelobe level	平均旁瓣电平	Píngjūn pángbàn diànpíng	ASL
Average time between maintenance	平均维修间隔时间	Píngjūn wéixiū jiàngé shíjiān	ATBM
Average time delay	平均时延	Píngjūn shíyán	ATD
Average useful life	平均使用寿命	Píngjūn shǐyòng shòumìng	AUL
Average value	平均值	Píngjūnzhí	AV
Aviation Product Design Finalization Commission	航空产品定型委员会	Hángkōng chǎnpǐn dìngxíng wěiyuánhuì	
Aviation weather service (civil aviation)	航空气象服务	Hángkōng qìxiàng fúwù	AWS
Away from the keyboard (computer chat)	离开键盘	Líkāi jiànpán	AFK
Axial and lateral plasma deposition (process)	双向等离子体沉积(工艺)	Shuāngxiàng děnglí zǐtǐ chénjī (gōngyì)	

Axial and linear plasma [Chemical vapor] deposition	轴向和横向等离子化学汽相沉积法	Zhóuxiàng hé héngxiàng děnglízǐ huàxué qìxiàng chénjī fǎ	ALPD
Axial offset focus (radar term)	轴向偏焦	Zhóuxiàng piānjiāo	
Axial ratio (radar term)	轴比	Zhóu bǐ	
Aximuth axis	方位轴	Fāngwèi zhóu	
Axis	轴	Zhóu	
Axis train precision	轴系精度	Zhóuxì jīngdù	
Azimuth	方位角	Fāngwèi jiǎo	
Azimuthal projection (GIS)	方位投影	Fāngwèi tóuyǐng	
Aztech (Singapore company)	爱捷特	Ài-jié-tè	

B

B interface	B 接口	B jiēkǒu	
B scope	B 型显示器	B-xíng xiǎnshìqì	
Bachman	贝克曼	Bèi-kè-màn	
Back (or background) administrative module	后管理模块	Hòu guǎnlǐ mókuài	BAM
Back (WP command)	前一步	Qián yībù	
Back at the keyboard (computer chat)	回到键盘	Huídào jiànpán	BAK
Back board	后面板	Hòumian bǎn	BCBB
Back buffer	后置缓冲	Hòuzhì huǎnchōng	
Back buffering	后台缓冲	Hòutái huǎnchōng	
Back lobe	背瓣	Bèibàn	
Back lobe	后瓣	Hòubàn	
Back off	退避	Tuìbì	
Back office, back end, background	后台	Hòutái	
Back plane	底板	Dǐbǎn	
Back Pressure	背压	Bèiyā	
Back pressure	后向压力	Hòuxiàng yālì	
Back reflection (FOC)	回波反射	Huíbō fǎnshè	
Back reflector antenna, backfire antenna	背射天线	Bèishè tiānxiàn	
Back scattering (FOC)	回波散射	Huíbō sǎnshè	
Back scattering technique	向后散射法	Xiànghòu sǎnshè fǎ	
Back scattering wave	反向散乱波	Fǎnxiàng sànluàn bō	
Back, zoom back (as in internet Explorer)	移后	Yíhòu	
Backboard insertion socket	背板式插座	Bèibǎnshi chāzuò	
Backbone bearer	骨干网载体	Gǔgànwǎng zàitǐ	BB
Backbone cable (in building)	垂直电缆	Chuízhí diànlǎn	BC
Backbone cable (in building)	主干电缆	Zhǔgàn diànlǎn	BC
Backbone fiber optic cable	主干光缆	Zhǔgàn guānglǎn	
Backbone network	骨干网络	Gǔgàn wǎngluò	
Backbone network	主干网	Zhǔgàn wǎng	
Backbone network connection	骨干网连接	Gǔgànwǎng liánjiē	BNC
Backbone network connection identifier	骨干网连接识别符	Gǔgànwǎng liánjiē shíbiéfú	BNC-ID
Backbone network connection link	骨干网连接链路	Gǔgànwǎng liánjiē liànlù	BNCL
Backdoor	后门	Hòumén	
Back-end	后端	Hòuduān	

Back-end processor	后端处理机	Hòuduān chǔlǐjī	BEP
Back-end server	后端服务器	Hòuduān fúwùqì	
Backface culling (video)	隐面消除	Yǐnmiàn xiāochú	
Back-fill	回填土	Huítiántǔ	
Backfire antenna	反向辐射天线	Fǎnxiàng fúshè tiānxiàn	
Back-flushing	反吹	Fǎnchuī	
Background	背景	Bèijǐng	
Background	后台	Hòutái	
Background bit error ratio	背景误块秒比	Bèijǐng wùkuài miǎo bǐ	BBER
Background block error	背景差错块	Bèijǐng chācuò kuài	BBE
Background block error	背景块误码	Bèijǐng kuài wùmǎ	BBE
Background block error	背景误块	Bèijǐng wùkuài	BBE
Background block error ratio	背景差错块比	Bèijǐng chācuò kuài bǐ	BBER
Background block error ratio	背景块误码比	Bèijǐng kuài wùmǎ bǐ	BBER
Background block error ratio	背景误块比	Bèijǐng wùkuài bǐ	BBER
Background block errored second ratio	背景块差错秒比	Bèijǐng kuài chācuò miǎo bǐ	BBESR
Background color (WP command)	背景彩色	Bèijǐng cǎisè	
Background current	基流	Jīliú	
Background mass spectrum	本底质谱	Běndǐ zhìpǔ	
Background memory controller	后台存储控制器	Hòutái cúnchǔ kòngzhìqì	BMC
Background noise	背景噪声	Bèijǐng zàoshēng	BGN
Background noise conditioning	背景噪音调节	Bèijǐng zàoyīn tiáojié	BNC
Background noise reduction	背景噪音降低	Bèijǐng zàoyīn jiàngdī	BNR
Background program	后台程序	Hòutái chéngxù	
Background sound	背景音响	Bèijǐng yīnxiǎng	BGS
Backlash \	回差	Huíchà	
Backlight	背光源	Bèiguāng yuán	
Backpack-type	背负式	Bēifù-shì	
Backplane	背板	Bèibǎn	
Backpressure	反压	Fǎnyā	
Backscatter	后向散射	Hòuxiàng sǎnshè	
Backscattered electron image	背散射电子象	Bèisǎnshè diànzǐ xiàng	
Back-scattering cross section, back-scattering area (of an antenna)	后散射截面	Hòusǎnshè jiémiàn	
Backslash \	反斜线	Fǎnxiéxiàn	
Backslash (\ )	右斜杠	Yòuxié gàng	
Backslash key (\ )	退位键	Tuìwèi jiàn	
Backspace	反向键	Fǎnxiàng jiàn	
Backspace	退格	Tuìgé	BS
Backtrace (IT term)	回溯跟踪	Huísù gēnzōng	
Backup and restore (in SQL Server)	备份和恢复	Bèifèn hé huīfù	
Backup device	备份设备	Bèifèn shèbèi	
Backup domain controller	备份域控制器	Bèifèn yù kòngzhìqì	BDC
Backup file	备份文件	Bèifèn wénjiàn	
Backup lighting	备用照明	Bèiyòng zhàomíng	BUL
Backup media	备份媒体	Bèifèn méitǐ	
Backup media pool	备份媒体池	Bèifèn méitǐ chí	

Backup plan	备份计划	Bèifèn jìhuà	
Backup procedure	备份规程	Bèifèn guīchéng	
Back-up relationships	备用关系	Bèiyòng guānxi	
Backup set	备份集	Bèifèn jí	
Backup, reserve, spare	备份	Bèifèn	
Backward	后向	Hòuxiàng	
Backward busying	后向忙	Hòuxiàng máng	
Backward chaining	反向链	Fǎnxiàng liàn	
Backward compatibility	后向兼容性	Hòuxiàng jiānróngxìng	
Backward compatible	向下兼容	Xiàngxià jiānróng	
Backward explicit congestion notification	后向显式拥塞通知	Hòuxiàng xiǎnshì yōngsè tōngzhī	BECN
Backward explicit congestion notification	后向显示拥塞指示	Hòuxiàng xiǎnshì yōngsè zhǐshì	BECN
Backward explicit congestion notification	向后显式拥挤通告	Xiànghòu xiǎn-shì yōngjǐ tōnggào	BECN
Backward indicator bit	后向指示比特	Hòuxiàng zhǐshì bǐtè	BIB
Backward indicator bit	后向指示位	Hòuxiàng zhǐshì wèi	BIB
Backward interworking telephone events	后向互通电话事件	Hòuxiàng hùtōng diànhuà shìjiàn	BITEs
Backward learning	后向学习	Hòuxiàng xuéxí	
Backward motion vector (video term)	后向运动矢量	Hòuxiàng yùndòng shǐliàng	
Backward pump (FOC)	后向泵浦	Hòuxiàng bèngpǔ	
Backward sequence number	后向顺序号	Hòuxiàng shùnxù hào	BSN
Backward sequence number to be transmitted	要传送的后向序号	Yào chuánsòngde hòuxiàng xùhào	BSNT
Backward set-up message	后向建立消息	Hòuxiàng jiànlì xiāoxi	BSM
Backward setup signal	后向建立信号	Hòuxiàng jiànlì xìnhào	BSM
Backward signal	后向信号	Hòuxiàng xìnhào	
Backward signal unit	后向信令单元	Hòuxiàng xìnling dānyuán	BSU
Backward wave	反向波	Fǎnxiàng bō	
Backward wave tube	返波管	Fǎnbōguǎn	
Bad certificate message (IPsec TLS)	坏证书消息	Huài zhèngshū xiāoxi	
Bad frame identity	坏帧标识	Huàizhèng biāozhì	BFI
Bad frame identity	坏帧识别	Huàizhèng shíbié	BFI
Bad frame indication	坏帧标志	Huàizhèng biāozhì	BFI
Bad frame indication	坏帧指示	Huàizhèng zhǐshì	BFI
Bad frame indicator function	坏帧指示性能	Huàizhèng zhǐshì xìngnéng	
Bad record MAC message (IPsec TLS)	坏纪录消息	Huài jìlù xiāoxi	
Baffle wall	隔板	Gébǎn	
Balance merging sort	平衡归并排序	Pínghéng guībìng páixù	
Balance rule	差额请领制度	Chā'é qǐnglǐng zhìdù	
Balance two-way merging sort	二路平衡归并排序	Èrlù pínghéng guībìng páixù	
Balanced aggregate signal	平衡集合信号	Pínghéng jíhé xìnhào	
Balanced antenna	平衡天线	Pínghéng tiānxiàn	
Balanced asynchronous class	异步平衡类别	Yìbù pínghéng lèibié	BAC
Balanced binary tree	平衡二叉树	Pínghéng èrchā shù	
Balanced code	平衡码	Pínghéng mǎ	
Balanced data link	平衡数据链路	Pínghéng shùjù liànlù	
Balanced hierarchy	均衡层次结构	Jūnhéng céngcì jiégòu	
Balanced mixer	平衡混频器	Pínghéng hùnpínqì	

Balanced output	对称输出	Duìchèn shūchū	
Balanced parametric amplifier	平衡型参量放大器	Pínghéng-xíng cānliàng fàngdàqì	
Balanced plug	平衡型阀芯	Pínghéng-xíng fáxīn	
Balanced return loss	平衡回损	Pínghéng huísǔn	
Balance-unbalance switch	平衡 - 不平衡转换器	Pínghéng-bùpínghéng zhuǎnhuànqì	Balun
Balancing inductor	平衡电感	Pínghéng diàngǎn	
Balancing network	平衡网络	Pínghéng wǎngluò	
Ball grid array	球状矩阵排列	Qiúzhuàng jǔzhèn páiliè	BGA
Ball grid array	球状网格阵列	Qiúzhuàng wǎnggé zhènliè	BGA
Ball grid array (electronics mfg)	球栅阵列	Qiú zhà zhènliè	BGA
Ball grid array (in SMT)	球栅列阵	Qiú zhà lièzhèn	BGA
Ball lens	球透镜	Qiú tòujìng	
Balloon for correction (radar term)	校正气球	Jiàozhèng qìqiú	
Balloon tracking test (radar term)	气球跟踪试验	Qìqiú gēnzōng shìyàn	
Balun (balanced/unbalanced devce)	平衡/不平衡变换器	Pínghéng/bùpínghéng biànhuànqì	
Balun (balanced-unbalanced transformer)	巴伦	Bā-lún	
Band	边界文件	Biānjiè wénjiàn	
Band	波段	Bōduàn	
Band allocation	频带划分	Píndài huàfēn	
Band number	区域号码	Qūyù hàomǎ	
Band ratio	波段比	Bōduàn bǐ	
Band scrambling	频带置乱	Píndài zhìluàn	
Band spread	频带扩展	Píndài kuòzhǎn	
Banding	条带效应	Tiáodài xiàoyìng	
Bandpass	带通	Dàitōng	
Bandpass (operating wavelength range)	工作波长范围	Gōngzuò bōcháng fànwéi	
Bandpass amplifier	选频放大器	Xuǎnpín fàngdàqì	
Bandpass filter	带通滤波器	Dàitōng lǜbōqì	BF
Bandpass filter isolator	带通滤波器/隔离器	Dàitōng lǜbōqì/gélíqì	BPFI
Band-shift inversion	移带倒频	Yídài dǎopín	
Band-spreading	波段扩展	Bōduàn kuòzhǎn	
Bandwidth	带宽	Dàikuān	
Bandwidth allocation	带宽分配	Dàikuān fēnpèi	
Bandwidth allocation control protocol	带宽分配控制协议	Dàikuān fēnpèi kòngzhì xiéyì	BACP
Bandwidth allocation protocol	带宽分配协议	Dàikuān fēnpèi xiéyì	BAP
Bandwidth assignment	带宽批发	Dàikuān pīfā	
Bandwidth broker	带宽代理	Dàikuān dàilǐ	
Bandwidth compression technique	带宽压缩技术	Dàikuān yāsuō jìshù	BCT
Bandwidth confirm	带宽确认	Dàikuān quèrèn	
Bandwidth delay product	带宽时延乘积	Dàikuān shíyán chéngjī	BDP
Bandwidth expansion ratio	带宽扩展比	Dàikuān kuòzhǎn bǐ	
Bandwidth Hotel	带宽酒店	Dàikuān jiǔdiàn	
Bandwidth of a device	器件带宽	Qìjiàn dàikuān	
Bandwidth on demand	弹性带宽运用	Tánxìng dàikuān yùnyòng	BOD
Bandwidth reject	带宽拒绝	Dàikuān jùjué	
Bandwidth reject	带宽请求拒绝	Dàikuān qǐngqiú jùjué	BRJ

Bandwidth request	带宽请求	Dàikuān qǐngqiú	
Bandwidth reservation	带宽预留	Dàikuān yùliú	
Bandwidth time	带宽时间	Dàikuān shíjiān	BT
Bandwidth-on-demand	按需分配带宽	Ànxū fēnpèi dàikuān	BoD
Bank (of a selector)	线弧	Xiànhú	
Bank (unit of memory)	存储体	Cúnchǔ tǐ	
Bank switching	组合切换	Zǔhé qiēhuàn	
Banner	横幅	Héngfú	
Banner	网页标识	Wǎngyè biāozhì	
Banyan Systems, Inc. (US company)	企业网系统公司	Qǐyèwǎng xìtǒng gōngsī	
Bar chart	条形图	Tiáoxíng tú	
Bar code	条码	Tiáomǎ	
Bar code label for registered correspondence	挂号函件条码标签	Guàhào hánjiàn tiáomǎ biāoqiān	
Bar code reader	条码阅读器	Tiáomǎ yuèdúqì	
Bar code scanner	条码扫描器	Tiáomǎ sǎomiáoqì	
Bar code scanning lens	条码扫描器镜头	Tiáomǎ sǎomiáoqì jìngtóu	
Bar graph	棒图	Bàngtú	
Bar graph	线条图	Xiàntiáo tú	
Bar graph	直方图	Zhífāngtú	
Bare fiber	裸光纤	Luǒ guāngxiān	
Bare optical fiber network	裸光纤网	Luǒ guāngxiān wǎng	
Barotropy	正压	Zhèngyā	
Barrage jamming	阻塞式干扰	Zǔsè-shì gānrǎo	
Barred dialling number	禁止拨号	Jìnzhǐ bōhào	BDN
Barrel theory (the contents of a barrel can reach only to the top of the shortest stave)	木桶理论	Mùtǒng lǐlùn	
Barretter	热线检流计	Rèxiàn jiǎnliújì	
Barrier	遮拦	Zhēlán	
Barrier seal	阻档层密封	Zǔdàng céng mìfēng	
Barring of all incoming calls	闭锁所有呼入业务	Bìsuǒ suǒyǒu hūrù yèwù	BAIC
Barring of all incoming calls	闭锁所有入呼叫	Bìsuǒ suǒyǒu rù hūjiào	BAIC
Barring of all incoming calls	闭锁所有入局呼叫	Bìsuǒ suǒyǒu rùjú hūjiào	BAIC
Barring of all incoming calls	禁止所有呼入呼叫	Jìnzhǐ suǒyǒu hūrù hūjiào	BAIC
Barring of all incoming calls	禁止所有入局呼叫	Jìnzhǐ suǒyǒu rùjú hūjiào	BAIC
Barring of all incoming calls	全闭锁入呼叫	Quán bìsuǒ rùhūjiào	BI
Barring of all incoming calls roam	当漫游出归属 PLMN 国家后，闭锁所有入局呼叫	Dāng mànyóu chū guīshǔ PLMN guójiā hòu, bìsuǒ suǒyǒu rùjú hūjiào	BAIC-Roam
Barring of all incoming calls supplementary service	闭锁所有附加业务入呼叫	Bìsuǒ suǒyǒu fùjiā yèwù rù hūjiào	BAIC
Barring of all incoming calls supplementary service	所有入局禁止补充业务	Suǒyǒu rùjú jìnzhǐ bǔchōng yèwù	BI
Barring of all outgoing calls	闭锁所有出呼叫	Bìsuǒ suǒyǒu chū hūjiào	BAOC
Barring of all outgoing calls	闭锁所有出局呼叫	Bìsuǒ suǒyǒu chūjú hūjiào	BAOC
Barring of all outgoing calls	禁止所有对外呼叫	Jìnzhǐ suǒyǒu duìwài hūjiào	BAOC
Barring of all outgoing calls supplementary service	闭锁所有附加业务出呼叫	Bìsuǒ suǒyǒu fùjiā yèwù chū hūjiào	BAOC
Barring of all outgoing calls supplementary service	禁止所有出局呼叫补充业务	Jìnzhǐ suǒyǒu chūjú hūjiào bǔchōng yèwù	BAOC
Barring of all outgoing calls supplementary service	所有出局禁止补充业务	Suǒyǒu chūjú jìnzhǐ bǔchōng yèwù	BO
Barring of all outgoing international calls	闭锁所有国际呼出业务	Bìsuǒ suǒyǒu guójì hūchū yèwù	BOIC

Barring of GPRS interworking profile(s)	闭锁 GPRS 互通文件	Bìsuǒ GPRS hùtōng wénjiàn	BGIWP
Barring of incoming calls when roaming outside the home PLMN country	闭锁在 PLMN 归属国家外漫游时的入呼叫	Bìsuǒ zài PLMN guīshǔ guójiā wài mànyóu shíde rù hūjiào	BIC-Roam
Barring of incoming calls when roaming outside the home PLMN country supplementary service	当漫游出归属 PLMN 国家后,闭锁入呼叫	Dāng mànyóu chū guīshǔ PLMN guójiā hòu, bìsuǒ rù hūjiào	BIC-Roam
Barring of incoming calls when roaming outside the home PLMN country	当漫游出归属 PLMN 国家时,闭锁入呼叫	Dāng mànyóu chū guīshǔ PLMN guójiā shí, bìsuǒ rù hūjiào	BIC-Roam
Barring of incoming calls when roaming outside the home PLMN country	当漫游到原籍PLMN国家以外时禁止所有入呼	Dāng mànyóu dào yuánjí PLMN guójiā yǐwài shí jìnzhǐ suǒyǒu rùhū	BIC-Roam
Barring of outgoing international calls	闭锁出局国际呼叫	Bìsuǒ chūjú guójì hūjiào	BOIC
Barring of outgoing international calls	闭锁国际出呼叫	Bìsuǒ guójì chū hūjiào	BOIC
Barring of outgoing international calls	禁止对国际的呼叫	Jìnzhǐ duì guójìde hūjiào	BOIC
Barring of outgoing international calls except those direct to the home PLMN	闭锁除直接到归属 PLMN 国家外国际呼叫	Bìsuǒ chú zhíjiē dào guīshǔ PLMN guójiā-wài guójì hūjiào	BOIC-exHC
Barring of outgoing international calls except those directed to the home PLMN country	闭锁除直接到 PLMN 归属国以外的国际出呼叫	Bìsuǒ chú zhíjiē dào PLMN guīshǔ guó yǐwàide guójì chū hūjiào	BOIC-exHC
Barring of outgoing international calls except those directed to the home PLMN country	除至归属公共陆地移动通信网国家外,闭锁国际出呼叫	Chú zhì guīshǔ gōnggòng lùdì yídòng tōngxìnwǎng guójiā wài, bìsuǒ guójì chū hūjiào	BOIC-exHC
Barring of outgoing international calls except those directed to the home PLMN country	除至归属 PLMN 国家外,闭锁国际出呼叫	Chú zhì guīshǔ PLMN guójiā wài, bìsuǒ guójì chū hūjiào	BOIC-exHC
Barring of outgoing international calls except those directed to the home PLMN country supplementary service	禁止所有除归属国外的国际出局呼叫补充业务	Jìnzhǐ suǒyǒu chú guīshǔ guówàide guójì chūjú hūjiào bǔchōng yèwù	BOIC-exHC
Barring of outgoing international calls except those directed towards the home PLMN country	除直接到归属 PLMN 国家外的呼叫外,闭锁国际出呼叫	Chú zhíjiē dào guīshǔ PLMN guójiā wàide hūjiào wài, bìsuǒ guójì chū hūjiào	BOIC-exHC
Barring of outgoing international calls supplementary service	禁止国际出局呼叫补充业务	Jìnzhǐ guójì chūjú hūjiào bǔchōng yèwù	BOIC
Base address	基地址	Jī dìzhǐ	
Base aeronautical equipment	基地航空设备	Jīdì hángkōng shèbèi	
Base class	基类	Jī lèi	
Base class library	基类库	Jī lèi kù	BCL
Base data type	基本数据类型	Jīběn shùjù lèixíng	
Base key (cryptography)	基本密钥	Jīběn mìyào	
Base limiter	基值限幅器	Jīzhí xiànfúqì	
Base limiting	基值限幅	Jīzhí xiànfú	
Base map	底图	Dǐtú	
Base map	基础地图	Jīchǔ dìtú	
Base mode field strength (FOC)	基模场强	Jīmó chǎngqiáng	
Base peak	基峰	Jī fēng	
Base priority	基本优先级	Jīběn yōuxiān jí	
Base rack	基本架	Jīběn jià	BCBR
Base radio identification code	基本寻呼机标识码	Jīběn xúnhūjī biāozhìmǎ	
Base register	基地址寄存器	Jī dìzhǐ jìcúnqì	BR
Base standard	基本标准	Jīběn biāozhǔn	
Base station	基站	Jīzhàn	BS
Base station application part	基站应用部分	Jīzhàn yìngyòng bùfen	BSSAP

Base station area	基站区	Jīzhàn qū	
Base station control function (module)	基站控制功能（模块）	Jīzhàn kòngzhì gōngnéng (mókuài)	BCF
Base station controller	基站控制器	Jīzhàn kòngzhìqì	BSC
Base station identification	基站识别码	Jīzhàn shíbié mǎ	BSID
Base station identity code	基站标识码	Jīzhàn biāozhì mǎ	BSIC
Base station interface	基站接口	Jīzhàn jiēkǒu	BSI
Base station interface equipment	基站接口设备	Jīzhàn jiēkǒu shèbèi	BIE
Base station management application part	基站管理应用部分	Jīzhàn guǎnlǐ yìngyòng bùfen	BSSMAP
Base station manager	基站管理器	Jīzhàn guǎnlǐqì	BSM
Base station mobile application part	基站移动应用部分	Jīzhàn yídòng yìngyòng bùfen	BSMAP
Base station module	基站模块	Jīzhàn mókuài	BSM
Base station operation and maintenance application part	BSS 操作维护应用部分	BSS cāozuò wéihù yìngyòng bùfen	BSSOMAP
Base station originating	基站主叫	Jīzhàn zhǔ jiào	BO
Base station sub-system	基站子系统	Jīzhàn zixìtǒng	BSS
Base station sub-system	基站子系统	Jīzhàn zixìtǒng	BSS
Base station sub-system application part	基站子系统应用部分	Jīzhàn zixìtǒng yìngyòng bùfen	BSSAP
Base station sub-system management application part	基站子系统管理应用部分	Jīzhàn zixìtǒng guǎnlǐ yìngyòng bùfen	BSSMAP
Base station sub-system test equipment	基站测试设备	Jīzhàn cèshì shèbèi	BSSTE
Base station system	基站系统	Jīzhàn xìtǒng	BSS
Base station system application part	基站系统应用部分	Jīzhàn xìtǒng yìngyòng bùfen	BSSAP
Base station system application part+	基站应用部分加	Jīzhàn yìngyòng bùfen jiā	BSSAP+
Base station system GPRS protocol	基站子系统 GPRS 协议	Jīzhàn zixìtǒng GPRS xiéyì	BSSGP
Base station system management application part	基站系统管理应用部分	Jīzhàn xìtǒng guǎnlǐ yìngyòng bùfen	BSSMAP
Base station system operation and maintenance application part	基站系统运营和维护应用部分	Jīzhàn xìtǒng yùnyíng hé wéihù yìngyòng bùfen	BSSOMAP
Base station system operation and maintenance application part	基站子系统操作与维护应用部分	Jīzhàn zixìtǒng cāozuò yǔ wéihù yìngyòng bùfen	BSSOMAP
Base station telephonic control element	基站电话控制单元	Jīzhàn diànhuà kòngzhì dānyuán	BSTCE
Base station terminating	基站被叫	Jīzhàn bèi jiào	BT
Base station test assembly	基站测试集成件	Jīzhàn cèshì jíchéng jiàn	BSTA
Base station test block	基站测试模块	Jīzhàn cèshì mókuài	BSTB
Base station test unit	基站测试单元	Jīzhàn cèshì dānyuán	BSTU
Base station transceiver system	基站收发信机系统	Jīzhàn shōufāxìnjī xìtǒng	BTS
Base station transmission sub-system	基站传输子系统	Jīzhàn chuánshū zixìtǒng	BTS
Base station transmitter power	基站发射器功率	Jīzhàn fāshèqì gōnglǜ	BSTXPWR
Base station-controlled handoff	基站控制切换	Jīzhàn kòngzhì qiēhuàn	BCHO
Base table	基表	Jī biǎo	
Base transceiver station	基站收发信机	Jīzhàn shōufā xìn jī	BTS
Base transceiver station	基站收发信台	Jīzhàn shōufāxìntái	BTS
Base transceiver station color code	基站色码	Jīzhàn sèmǎ	BCC
Base transceiver station color code	基站收发信机色码	Jīzhàn shōufāxìnjī sèmǎ	BCC
Base transceiver station identity code	基站收发信机识别码	Jīzhàn shōufāxìnjī shíbié mǎ	BSIC
Base transceiver station management	基站收发信台管理	Jīzhàn shōufāxìntái guǎnlǐ	BTSM
Base transmitter station	基站	Jīzhàn	BTS
Base type	基类型	Jī lèixíng	

Baseband	基带	Jīdài	
Baseband and signal processing	基带和信号处理	Jīdài hé xìnhào chǔlǐ	BBSIG
Baseband arragement	基带安排	Jīdài ānpái	BBA
Baseband bandwidth	基带带宽	Jīdài dàikuān	
Baseband filter	基带滤波器	Jīdài lǜbōqì	BBF
Baseband modem	基带调制解调器	Jīdài tiáozhì jiětiáoqì	BM
Baseband modem	基带调制解调制器	Jīdài tiáozhì jiětiáozhìqì	BM
Baseband processing unit	基带处理单元	Jīdài chǔlǐ dānyuán	BPU
Baseband processor mother board	基带处理框背板	Jīdài chǔlǐ kuàng bèibǎn	BPB
Baseband protocol	基带协议	Jīdài xiéyì	BB
Baseband response	基带频率响应	Jīdài pínlǜ xiǎngyìng	
Baseband signal processor	基带信号处理器	Jīdài xìnhào chǔlǐqì	
Baseline	基线	Jīxiàn	
Baseline drift	基线漂移	Jīxiàn piāoyí	
Baseline implementation capabilities	设备能力底线	Shèbèi nénglì dǐxiàn	BIC
Baseline implementation capabilities	设备能力基线	Shèbèi nénglì jīxiàn	BIC
Baseline potential	空白电位	Kòngbái diànwèi	
Baseline privacy key management -response	保密协议密钥管理响应消息	Bǎomì xiéyì mìyào guǎnlǐ xiǎngyìng xiāoxi	BPKM-RSP
Baseline privacy key management-request	保密协议密钥管理请求消息	Bǎomì xiéyì mìyào guǎnlǐ qǐngqiú xiāoxi	BPKM-REQ
Baseline protocol indicator	保密协议标识符	Bǎomì xiéyì biāozhì fú	BPI
Baseline value	空白值	Kòngbái zhí	
Base-lining	业务基准	Yèwù jīzhǔn	
Baseplate	基板	Jībǎn	
Basic access	基本接入	Jīběn jiērù	BA
Basic access	基本入口	Jīběn rùkǒu	
Basic arithmetic module	基本算术模块	Jīběn suànshù mókuài	BAM
Basic call state model	基本呼叫状态模型	Jīběn hūjiào zhuàngtài móxíng	BCSM
Basic call status model	基本呼叫状态模型	Jīběn hūjiào zhuàngtài móxíng	BCSM
Basic call unrelated state model	基本呼叫不相关状态模型	Jīběn hūjiào bùxiāngguān zhuàngtài móxíng	BCUSM
Basic call unrelated state model	基本呼叫无关状态模型	Jīběn hūjiào wúguān zhuàngtài móxíng	BCUSM
Basic clock pulse frequency	基本时钟脉冲频率	Jīběn shízhōng màichōng pínlǜ	BCPF
Basic coding rules	基本编码规则	Jīběn biānmǎ guīzé	
Basic command interpreter	基本命令解调程序	Jīběn mìnglìng jiětiáo chéngxù	BCI
Basic communication access method	基本通信存取法	Jīběn tōngxìn cúnqǔ fǎ	BCAM
Basic component	基本构成体	Jīběn gòuchéng tǐ	
Basic control function	基本控制功能	Jīběn kòngzhì gōngnéng	BCF
Basic control function	基本控制功能	Jīběn kòngzhì gōngnéng	BCF
Basic cryptographic function	基本加密函数	Jīběn jiāmì hánshù	
Basic data management	基本数据管理	Jīběn shùjù guǎnlǐ	
Basic data type	基本数据型	Jīběn shùjù-xíng	
Basic encoding rules	基本编码规则	Jīběn biānmǎ guīzé	BER
Basic external function	基本外部函数	Jīběn wàibù hánshù	
Basic function	基本功能	Jīběn gōngnéng	
Basic global function	基本的全局功能	Jīběnde quánjú gōngnéng	BGF
Basic handover procedure	基本切换程序	Jīběn qiēhuàn chéngxù	
Basic handover procedure	基本越区切换规程	Jīběn yuèqū qiēhuàn guīchéng	

Basic high layer function	基本的高层功能	Jīběnde gāocéng gōngnéng	BHLF
Basic input/output system	基本输入输出系统	Jīběn shūrù shūchū xìtǒng	BIOS
Basic insulation	基本绝缘	Jīběn juéyuán	
Basic interconnection test	基本互连测试	Jīběn hùlián cèshì	BIT
Basic interface structure	基本接口结构	Jīběn jiēkǒu jiégòu	
Basic layout object	基本布局客体	Jīběn bùjú kètǐ	
Basic logical object	基本逻辑客体	Jīběn luóji kètǐ	
Basic low layer function	基本的底层功能	Jīběnde dǐcéng gōngnéng	BLLF
Basic maximun usable frequency	基本最高可用频率	Jīběn zuìgāo kěyòng pínlǜ	
Basic measurement unit	基本测量单位	Jīběn cèliáng dānwèi	BMU
Basic mode control procedure	基本型控制规程	Jīběn-xíng kòngzhì guīchéng	BMCP
Basic multilingual plane	基本多文种平面	Jīběn duō wénzhǒng píngmiàn	BMP
Basic noise	基本噪声	Jīběn zàoshēng	
Basic primitive interface model	基本的简单接口模型	Jīběnde jiǎndān jiēkǒu móxíng	BPIM
Basic processing unit	基本处理装置	Jīběn chǔlǐ zhuāngzhì	BPU
Basic rate access	基本速率接入	Jīběn sùlǜ jiērù	BRA
Basic rate integrated services digital network	基本速率的综合业务数字网	Jīběn sùlǜde zōnghé yèwù shùzì wǎng	BRI
Basic rate interface	基本速率接口	Jīběn sùlǜ jiēkǒu	BRI
Basic rate interface	基群速率接口	Jīqún sùlǜ jiēkǒu	BRI
Basic reference model	基本参考模型	Jīběn cānkǎo móxíng	
Basic section of a virtual connection	虚连接的基本段	Xū liánjiēde jīběn duàn	
Basic service	基本服务	Jīběn fúwù	
Basic service group	基本业务群	Jīběn yèwù qún	BSG
Basic service group	基本业务组	Jīběn yèwù zǔ	BSG
Basic session reference	基本会话参考	Jīběn huìhuà cānkǎo	
Basic spatial unit	基本空间单元	Jīběn kōngjiān dānyuán	BSU
Basic spectral subtraction	基本谱减法	Jīběn pǔ jiǎnfǎ	BSS
Basic switching element	基本交换单元	Jīběn jiāohuàn dānyuán	
Basic test	基本测试	Jīběn cèshì	
Basic throughput class negotiation	基本的吞吐量等级协商	Jīběnde tūntǔliàng děngjí xiéshāng	
Basic transmission header	基本传输标题	Jīběn chuánshū biāotí	BTH
Basic transmission loss (of a radio link)	基本传输损耗	Jīběn chuánshū sǔnhào	
Basic user-network interface	基本的用户-网络接口	Jīběnde yònghù—wǎngluò jiēkǒu	BUNI
Basic value	基本值	Jīběn zhí	
Basin	盆地	Péndì	
Batch data	批量数据	Pīliàng shùjù	
Batch data exchange service	成批数据交换业务	Chéngpī shùjù jiāohuàn yèwù	BDES
Batch file	批处理文件	Pī chǔlǐ wénjiàn	
Batch file	批次档案	Pīcì dàng'àn	
Batch inlet	分批进样	Fēnpī jìnyàng	
Batch model	批模式	Pī móshì	
Batch operations	批块操作	Pī kuài cāozuò	
Batch parameters	批处理参数	Pī chǔlǐ cānshù	
Batch processing	成批处理	Chéngpī chǔlǐ	
Batch processing	批处理	Pī chǔlǐ	
Batch processing	批次处理	Pīcì chǔlǐ	

Batch queue	批处理队列	Pī chǔlǐ duìliè	
Baton handover	接力切换	Jiēlì qiēhuàn	
Battery capacity	电池容量	Diànchí róngliàng	
Battery power	电池功率	Diànchí gōnglǜ	
Battery supply to subscriber line (the B in BORSCHT, q.v.)	馈电	Kuìdiàn	
Battery testing	碰电源测试	Pèng diànyuán cèshì	
Battle for eyeballs (the competition between makers of computer 3D graphics cards)	眼球大战	Yǎnqiú dàzhàn	
Battlefield search radar	战场侦察雷达	Zhànchǎng zhēnchá léidá	
Bat-wing antenna	蝙蝠翼形天线	Biānfúyìxíng tiānxiàn	
Bat-wing panel	蝙蝠翼盘	Biānfúyì pán	
Baud	波德	Bō-dé	
Baud	波特	Bōtè	
Baud rate	波特率	Bōtèlǜ	
Baudot language	博多语言	Bó-duō yǔyán	
Bay (computer term)	底板	Dǐbǎn	
Bay Area Regional Research Network (US)	海湾地区的区域性研究网络	Hǎiwān dìqūde qūyùxìng yánjiū wǎngluò	BARRNet
Bayesian estimate	贝叶斯估计	Bèi-yè-sī gūjì	
Bayesian information criterion	贝叶斯信息准则	Bèi-yè-sī xìnxī zhǔnzé	BIC
Bayesian network	贝叶斯网络	Bèi-yè-sī wǎngluò	
Bayesian theory	贝叶理论	Bèi-yè lǐlùn	
Bayonet fiber optic connector	大口式光纤连接器	Dàkǒushì guāngxiān liánjiēqì	BFOC
BCCH allocation	BCCH 配置	BCCH pèizhì	BA
BCP back board	BCP 后面板	BCP hòumian bǎn	BCBB
BDA China (US firm in Beijing that tracks China telecom market)	BDA 中国	BDA Zhōngguó	
Beacon	信标	Xìnbiāo	
Bead (in a coaxial line)	垫	Diàn	
Beam	束流	Shùliú	
Beam antenna	束流天线	Shùliú tiānxiàn	
Beam axis (of an antenna)	射束轴	Shèshù zhóu	BA
Beam collimation error	射束准直误差	Shèshù zhǔnzhí wùchā	BCE
Beam conical angle	波束圆锥角	Bōshù yuánzhuī jiǎo	
Beam deflection	波束偏转	Bōshù piānzhuǎn	
Beam diameter	光束直径	Guāngshù zhíjìng	
Beam divergence	光束发散度	Guāngshù fāsàndù	
Beam footprint (of a satellite antenna)	波束覆盖区	Bōshù fùgàiqū	
Beam forming	波束成型	Bōshù chéngxíng	
Beam landing area (video term)	电子束落区	Diànzǐshù luò qū	BLA
Beam solid angle	射束立体角	Shèshù lìtǐjiǎo	BSA
Beam splitter	分束器	Fēnshùqì	
Beam transmission line	射束传输线	Shèshù chuánshūxiàn	
Beam waveguide	射束波导	Shèshù bōdǎo	
Beam width	射束宽度	Shèshù kuāndù	
Beam-shape loss	波束形状损耗	Bōshù xíngzhuàng sǔnhào	
Beamwidth	光束宽度	Guāngshù kuāndù	
Bearer association transport	承载偶联传送	Chéngzài ǒulián chuánsòng	BAT

Bearer capability	承载能力	Chéngzài nénglì	BC
Bearer capability	传递能力	Chuándì nénglì	BC
Bearer capability identity element	承载能力标示单元	Chéngzài nénglì biāoshì dānyuán	BC_IE
Bearer capability information element	承载能力信息单元	Chéngzài nénglì xìnxī dānyuán	BCIE
Bearer capacity information element	承载容量信息单元	Chéngzài róngliàng xìnxī dānyuán	BCIE
Bearer channel	承载信道	Chéngzài xìndào	B-channel
Bearer channel connection	承载通道连接	Chéngzài tōngdào liánjiē	BCC
Bearer channel connection	承载通路连接	Chéngzài tōnglù liánjiē	BCC
Bearer channel connection control	承载通路连接控制	Chéngzài tōnglù liánjiē kòngzhì	BCC
Bearer control function	承载控制功能	Chéngzài kòngzhì gōngnéng	BCF
Bearer gateway control function	承载控制网关功能	Chéngzài kòngzhì wǎngguān gōngnéng	BCF-G
Bearer independent call control	独立于承载的呼叫控制	Dúlì yú chéngzàide hūjiào kòngzhì	BICC
Bearer Independent Call Control protocol	承载独立呼叫控制协议	Chéngzài dúlì hūjiào kòngzhì xiéyì	BICC
Bearer interworking function	承载互通功能	Chéngzài hùtōng gōngnéng	BIWF
Bearer node control function	承载控制节点功能	Chéngzài kòngzhì jiédiǎn gōngnéng	BCF-N
Bearer service	承载业务	Chéngzài yèwù	BS
Bearer service	载波服务	Zàibō fúwù	
Bearer service not provided	不提供承载业务	Bùtígōng chéngzài yèwù	
Bearer transmission control function	承载控制转接功能	Chéngzài kòngzhì zhuǎnjiē gōngnéng	BCF-T
Bearer-independent call control	承载无关的呼叫控制	Chéngzài wúguānde hūjiào kòngzhì	BICC
Bearer-independent call control	与承载无关呼叫控制	Yǔ chéngzài wúguān hūjiào kòngzhì	BICC
Bearing capacity	承受力	Chéngshòulì	
Bearing capacity factor	承受力系数	Chéngshòulì xìshù	
Bearing marker	方位标志	Fāngwèi biāozhì	
Bearing of station	电台方位	Diàntái fāngwèi	
Beat jamming	差拍干扰	Chāpāi gānrǎo	
Beat reception	差拍式接收	Chāpāi-shì jiēshōu	
Beat-frequency oscillator	拍频振荡器	Pāipín zhèndàngqì	BFO
Beaver-tail beam antenna	獭尾形射束天线	Tǎwěixíng shèshù tiānxiàn	
Because it's Time Network	因为它是时代网络	Yīnwei tā shì shídài wǎngluò	BITNET
Beep	响铃	Xiǎnglíng	
Begin subscriber activity	开始用户激活	Kāishǐ yònghù jīhuó	
Beginner's All-purpose Symbolic Instruction Code	初学者通用符号指令码	Chūxuézhě tōngyòng fúhào zhǐlìng mǎ	BASIC
Beginning of message	消息开始	Xiāoxi kāishǐ	BOM
Beginning tag	开始标签	Kāishǐ biāoqiān	B tag
Behavior test	特征测试	Tèzhēng cèshì	
Behavior test	行为测试	Xíngwéi cèshì	
Behavioral time sequence	行为时间序列	Xíngwéi shíjiān xùliè	
Behavior-based aggregation	基于行为的汇集	Jīyú xíngwéide huìjí	
Beijing Concord International Economic Consulting Co. Ltd.	北京康德国际经济咨询公司	Běijīng kāngdé guójì jīngjì zīxún gōngsī	
Beijing Ericsson Communication System Co. Ltd.	北京爱立信通信系统有限公司	Běijīng ài-lì-xìn tōngxìn xìtǒng yǒuxiàn gōngsī	
Beijing Gaohong Telecommunications Technology Co. Ltd.	北京高鸿通信技术有限公司	Běijīng gāohóng tōngxìn jìshù yǒuxiàn gōngsī	
Beijing Lucent Technologies Fiber Optic Co. Ltd.	北京朗讯科技光缆有限公司	Běijīng Lǎng-xùn kējì guānglǎn yǒuxiàn gōngsī	BFOC
Beijing University of Post & Telecommunications	北京邮电大学	Běijīng yóudiàn dàxué	

Bel	贝	Bèi	B
Belgacom, the Belgian Telecommunications Authority	比利时电信	Bǐ-lì-shí diànxìn	
Bell	告警	Gàojǐng	BEL
Bell Administrative Network Communications System	贝尔行政管理网络通信系统	Bèi'ěr xíngzhèng guǎnlǐ wǎngluò tōngxìn xìtǒng	BANCS
Bell Communications Research Lab	贝尔通信研究所	Bèi'ěr tōngxìn yánjiūsuǒ	BELLCORE
Bell Labs	贝尔试验室	Bèi'ěr shìyànshì	
Bell layered space-time architecture	分层空时结构	Fēncéng kōng shí jiégòu	BLAST
Bell operating company	贝尔运营公司	Bèi'ěr yùnyíng gōngsī	BOC
Bell South	南方贝尔	Nánfāng bèi-ěr	
Bellini-Tosi antenna	贝里尼-托西天线	Bèi-lǐ-ní--tuō-xī tiānxiàn	
Benchmark	基值	Jīzhí	
Benchmark	基准程序	Jīzhǔn chéngxù	
Benchmark	水准点	Shuǐzhǔndiǎn	
Benchmark test	基准测试	Jīzhǔn cèshì	
Benchmark test	基准评测	Jīzhǔn píngcè	
Benchmark test program values	基准测试程序数值	Jīzhǔn cèshì chéngxù shùzhí	
Bench-top oven	工作台炉	Gōngzuòtái lú	
Benchtop Venturi forced convection infrared reflow oven (semiconductor mfg)	台式文氏强制对流红外回流炉	Táishì wén-shì qiángzhì duìliú hóngwài huíliú lú	
Bend attenuation	弯曲衰耗	Wānqū shuāihào	
Bend radius	弯曲半径	Wānqū bànjìng	
Bendable waveguide	可弯波导	Kěwān bōdǎo	
Bending	弯曲	Wānqū	
Bending loss (FOC)	弯曲损耗	Wānqū sǔnhào	
Bending moment	弯曲率	Wānqū lǜ	
Bending strength	弯曲强度	Wānqū qiángdù	
Bending vibration	弯曲振动	Wānqū zhèndòng	
Bendix (US company)	本迪克斯公司	Běn-dí-kè-sī gōngsī	
Berkeley Internet Naming Domain Service (software)	柏克利因特网名域服务	Bǎi-kè-lì Yīntèwǎng míngyù fúwù	BINDS
Berkeley software distribution	伯克利软件分配代号	Bó-kè-lì ruǎnjiàn fēnpèi dàihào	BSD
Best effort	尽力而为	Jìnlì ér wéi	BE
Best effort	尽力服务	Jìnlì fúwù	
Best effort delivery	最优传送	Zuìyōu chuánsòng	
Best linear unbiased estimate	最优线性无偏估计	Zuìyōu xiànxìng wúpiān gūjì	BLUE
Beta software	测试版软件	Cèshìbǎn ruǎnjiàn	
Beta version	测试版	Cèshìbǎn	
Bethe hole coupler	贝塞孔耦合器	Bèi-sāi kǒng ǒuhéqì	
Between-the-lines entry (IPsec)	线间侵入	Xiàn-jiān qīnrù	
Beverage antenna	贝佛莱日天线	Bèi-fó-lái-rì tiānxiàn	
Beyond line of sight	超视距	Chāoshìjù	BLOS
Bezel ring	盖环	Gài huán	
Bezier curve	贝塞尔曲线	Bèi-sāi-ěr qūxiàn	
Bhattacharyya distance	巴特查里亚距离	Bā-tè-chá-lǐ-yà jùlí	BD
Bhattacharyya distance	B 距离	B-jùlí	BD
Bias (of voltage)	偏压	Piānyā	

Bias distortion	偏畸变	Piānjī biàn	
Bias test	拉偏测试	Lāpiān cèshì	
Bi-axial stable system	二轴稳定系统	Èrzhóu wěndìng xìtǒng	
Biconic connector	双锥形连接器	Shuāng zhuīxíng liánjiēqì	
Biconical antenna	双锥形天线	Shuāng zhuīxíng tiānxiàn	
Biconnected graph	重连通图	Chóngliántōng tú	
Bidirectional approximate reasoning	双向近似推力	Shuāngxiàng jìnsì tuīlì	
Bidirectional data bus	双向数据总线	Shuāngxiàng shùjù zǒngxiàn	BDB
Bidirectional data transfer	双向数据传送	Shuāngxiàng shùjù chuánsòng	BDT
Bidirectional line switching ring	双向线路倒换环	Shuāngxiàng xiànlù dǎohuàn huán	BLSR
Bi-directional mapping (in Visual Basic)	双向映射	Shuāngxiàng yìngshè	
Bidirectional path protection ring	双向通道保护环	Shuāngxiàng tōngdào bǎohù huán	
Bidirectional protection switching	双向保护倒换	Shuāngxiàng bǎohù dǎohuàn	
Bidirectional trail/connection type	双向路径/连接类型	Shuāngxiàng lùjìng/liánjiē lèixíng	
Bidirectional transmission	双向传输	Shuāngxiàng chuánshū	
Bidirectionally-predictive coded picture (video term)	双向预测编码图像	Shuāngxiàng yùcè biānmǎ túxiàng	
Bids per circuit hour	没电路每小时的试占次数	Méi diànlù měi xiǎoshíde shìzhàn cìshù	BCH
Bifurcation	分岔	Fēnchà	
Big 5 code (computer coding of Chinese characters)	五大码	Wǔ dà mǎ	
Big Blue (nickname for IBM, Inc.)	蓝色巨人	Lánsè jùrén	
Big-5 code	大五码	Dàwǔ mǎ	
Big-endian (data storage format)	低地址高字节顺序	Dīdìzhǐ gāozìjié shùnxù	
Bilateral closed user group	双边闭合用户群	Shuāngbiān bìhé yònghù qún	BCUG
Bilateral closed user group	双向封闭用户集团	Shuāngxiàng fēngbì yònghù jítuán	BCUG
Bilateral control	双向控制	Shuāngxiàng kòngzhì	
Bilateral current stabilizer	双向稳流器	Shuāngxiàng wěnliúqì	
Bi-level pulse	双电平脉冲	Shuāng diànpíng màichōng	
Bilinear filtering (video)	双线性过滤	Shuāng xiànxìng guòlǜ	
Bilinear interpolation	双线性内插法	Shuāng xiànxìng nèichāfǎ	
Bilinear model	双线型模型	Shuāng xiànxíng móxíng	
Bill management platform	计费管理平台	Jìfèi guǎnlǐ píngtái	BMP
Bill of lading	提单	Tídān	B/L
Bill of materials	材料清单	Cáiliào qīngdān	BoM
Bill of refund	报刊退款单	Bàokān tuìkuǎndān	
Billing and account rapporteurs group (GSM MoU)	计费核算组	Jìfèi hésuàn zǔ	BARG
Billing and management system	计费和管理系统	Jìfèi hé guǎnlǐ xìtǒng	BMS
Billing center	计费中心	Jìfèi zhōngxīn	BC
Billing error probabillity	记帐差错概率	Jìzhàng chācuò gàilǜ	
Billing integrity	记费完整性	Jìfèi wánzhěngxìng	
Billing management point	记帐管理点	Jìzhàng guǎnlǐ diǎn	BMP
Billing mediation software	计费中介软件	Jìfèi zhōngjiè ruǎnjiàn	
Billing system	计费系统	Jìfèi xìtǒng	BS
Billing system	营帐系统	Yíngzhàng xìtǒng	
Billion operations per second	十亿次运算/秒	Shíyì cì yùnsuàn/miǎo	BOPS
Bi-metallic	双金属	Shuāng jīnshǔ	

Bin packing	装箱问题	Zhuāngxiāng wèntí	
Binary	二进制	Èrjìnzhì	
Binary asymmetric channel	二进制不对称通道	Èrjìnzhì bùduìchèn tōngdào	BAC
Binary check character	二进制校验字符	Èrjìnzhì jiàoyàn zìfú	BCC
Binary code	二进制码	Èrjìnzhì mǎ	
Binary code	脉码调整二元码	Màimǎ tiáozhěng èryuán mǎ	
Binary code frequency shift keying	二进制码频移键控	Èrjìnzhì mǎ pínyí jiànkòng	BCFSK
Binary coded decimal	二/十进制代码	Èr/shíjìnzhì dàimǎ	BCD
Binary coded decimal	二进制编码的十进制	Èrjìnzhì biānmǎde shíjìnzhì	BCD
Binary coded decimal	十进制数的二进制编码	Shíjìnzhì shùde èrjìnzhì biānmǎ	BCD
Binary coded Hollerith	何勒内四二进制代码	Hé-lè-nèi-sì èrjìnzhì dàimǎ	BCH
Binary coded octal	二进制编码的八进制	Èrjìnzhì biānmǎde bājìnzhì	BCO
Binary coherent phase shift keying	二进制相干相移键控	Èrjìnzhì xiānggān xiāngyí jiànkòng	BCPSK
Binary collaboration	二元合作	Èryuán hézuò	
Binary delta modulation	二进制增量调制	Èrjìnzhì zēngliàng tiáozhì	BDM
Binary detection	二进检测	Èrjìn jiǎncè	
Binary differential phase shift keying	二相差分相移键控	Èrxiāng chàfēn xiàngyí jiànkòng	BDPSK
Binary digit, bit	二进制比特	Èrjìnzhì bǐtè	
Binary digit, bit	二进制数位	Èrjìnzhì shùwèi	
Binary digit, bit	二进制位	Èrjìnzhì wèi	
Binary elastic scattering event	双弹性散射过程	Shuāng tánxìng sǎnshè guòchéng	
Binary elastic scattering peak	双弹性散射峰	Shuāng tánxìng sǎnshè fēng	
Binary exponential backoff system (in mobile IP)	二进制数级回退机制	Èrjìnzhì shùjí huítuì jīzhì	
Binary figure	二进制符号	Èrjìnzhì fúhào	
Binary figure	二进制数字	Èrjìnzhì shùzì	
Binary file	二进制文件	Èrjìnzhì wénjiàn	
Binary file	二位元文件	Èrwèiyuán wénjiàn	
Binary file transfer	二进制文件传输	Èrjìnzhì wénjiàn chuánshū	
Binary floating point arithmetic	二进制浮点运算	Èrjìnzhì fúdiǎn yùnsuàn	BFPA
Binary frequency modulated differentially coherent phase shift keying	二进制调频差动相干相移键控	Èrjìnzhì tiáopín chādòng xiānggān xiāngyí jiànkòng	B-FMDCPSK
Binary frequency shift keying	二进制频移键控	Èrjìnzhì pínyí jiànkòng	BFSK
Binary function	双参函数	Shuāngcān hánshù	
Binary image (GIS)	二值图像	Èrzhí túxiàng	
Binary Intersystem transmission standard	二进制系统间传输标准	Èrjìnzhì xìtǒng-jiān chuánshū biāozhǔn	BITS
Binary large object	大块二进制数据目标	Dàkuài èrjìnzhì shùjù mùbiāo	BLOB
Binary large object	二进制大对象	Èrjìnzhì dà duìxiàng	
Binary large object	二进制大目标	Èrjìnzhì dà mùbiāo	BLOB
Binary large object identifier	大块二进制数据目标标识	Dàkuài èrjìnzhì shùjù mùbiāo biāozhì	BLOBID
Binary logging	二进制记录	Èrjìnzhì jìlù	
Binary logistic regression	二元逻辑回归	Èryuán luójì huíguī	
Binary notation	二进制备记数法	Èrjìnzhì bèijì shùfǎ	
Binary number	二进制数	Èrjìnzhì shù	
Binary operator	二元操作符	Èryuán cāozuò fú	
Binary phase shift keying	二进制相移键控	Èrjìnzhì xiāngyí jiànkòng	BPSK
Binary phase shift keying	二相相移键控	Èrxiàng xiàngyí jiànkòng	BPSK

Binary phase shift keying	二相移相键控	Èrxiàng yíxiàng jiànkòng	BPSK
Binary rate	二进制速率	Èrjìnzhì sùlǜ	
Binary running environment for wireless	无线二进制运行环境	Wúxiàn èrjìnzhì yùnxíng huánjìng	BREW
Binary running environment for wireless platforms	无线平台二进制运行环境	Wúxiàn píngtái èrjìnzhì yùnxíng huánjìng	BREW
Binary search	二分查找	Èrfēn cházhǎo	
Binary search tree	二叉查找树	Èrchā cházhǎo shù	
Binary segmentation	二进制分割	Èrjìnzhì fēngē	
Binary sort tree	二叉排序树	Èrchā páixù shù	
Binary symmetric channel	二进制对称信道	Èrjìnzhì duìchèn xìndào	BSC
Binary symmetric channel	二元对称信道	Èryuán duìchèn xìndào	
Binary synchronous communication	二进制同步通信	Èrjìnzhì tóngbù tōngxìn	BSC
Binary synchronous control	二进制同步控制	Èrjìnzhì tóngbù kòngzhì	BSC
Binary tree	二叉树	Èrchā shù	
Binary-coded decimal (BCD) code	二十进制码	Èrshí jìnzhì mǎ	
Binary-decimal converter	二-十进制交换器	Èr-shíjìnzhì jiāohuànqì	BDC
Binary-to-hexadecimal conversion	二十六进制转换	Èrshíliù jìnzhì zhuǎnhuàn	
Bind, binding	关联	Guānlián	
Binding	绑定	Bǎngdìng	
Binding	汇集	Huìjí	
Binding	捆绑	Kǔnbǎng	
Binding	联编	Liánbiān	
Binding	连结	Liánjié	
Binding acknowledgement	绑定应答	Bǎngdìng yìngdá	BA
Binding identity	包装识别	Bāozhuāng shíbié	BID
Binding request	绑定请求	Bǎngdìng qǐngqiú	
Binding update	绑定更新	Bǎngdìng gēngxīn	
Binomial corner	二项式弯头	Èrxiàngshì wāntóu	
Binomial distribution	二项式分布	Èrxiàngshì fēnbù	
Binomial twist waveguide	二项式扭波导	Èrxiàngshì niǔ bōdǎo	
BioMed net	生物医药网络	Shēngwù yīyào wǎngluò	
Biometric authentication	生物特性认证	Shēngwù tèxìng rènzhèng	BA
Bipartite graph	二部图	Èrbù tú	
Biphase coding	二相编码	Èrxiàng biānmǎ	
Biphase coding	双相编码	Shuāngxiàng biānmǎ	
Bipolar 3-zero substitution	双极 3 零替代	Shuāng jí san líng tìdài	
Bipolar transistor	双极型晶体管	Shuāngjíxíng jīngtǐguǎn	
Bipolar violation	双极性破坏	Shuāng jíxìng pòhuài	BPV
Bipolar violation	双极性破坏点	Shuāngjíxìng pòhuài diǎn	
Bipolar with three-zero substitution	三零取代双极性码	Sān líng qǔdài shuāng jíxìng mǎ	B3ZS
Biprism	双棱镜	Shuāng léngjìng	
Birdies (noise in telecommunications)	尖叫声	Jiānjiàoshēng	
Birefringent crystal	双折射光晶体	Shuāng zhéshè guāng jīngtǐ	
Birmingham Wire gauge (UK)	英国伯明翰线规	Yīngguó bó-míng-hàn xiànguī	BWG
Bisector	双分（复用）器	Shuāng fēn (fù yòng) qì	
Bistable trigger circuit	双稳态触发电路	Shuāng wěntài chùfā diànlù	
Bistatic radar	双基地雷达	Shuāng jīdì léidá	

Bisynchronous communications adapter	双同步通信转接器	Shuāng tóngbù tōngxìn zhuǎnjiēqì	BCA
Bit	比特	Bǐtè	
Bit	位	Wèi	
Bit block transfer	位块传输	Wèikuài chuánshū	Blit
Bit combination	位组	Wèi zǔ	
Bit control block	位控制序块	Wèi kòngzhì xùkuài	BCB
Bit energy to noise spectral density ratio	比特能量与噪声谱密度比	Bǐtè néngliàng yǔ zàoshēng pǔ mìdù bǐ	
Bit error rate	比特差错率	Bǐtè chācuò lǜ	BER
Bit error rate	比特错误率	Bǐtè cuòwù lǜ	BER
Bit error rate	比特误码率	Bǐtè wùmǎ lǜ	BER
Bit error rate	误比特率	Wù bǐtè lǜ	BER
Bit error rate	误码率	Wùmǎlǜ	BER
Bit error rate tester	误码率测试仪	Wùmǎlǜ cèshìyí	BERT
Bit error ratio	比特差错比	Bǐtè chācuò bǐ	BER
Bit interleaved parity	比特间插奇偶校验	Bǐtè jiānchā jīǒu jiàoyàn	BIP
Bit interleaved parity	比特间插奇偶性	Bǐtè jiānchā jīǒu xìng	BIP
Bit interleaved parity	比特交织奇偶性	Bǐtè jiāozhī jīǒu xìng	BIP
Bit interleaved parity	比特间插奇偶性	Bǐtè-jiān chā jīǒu xìng	BIP
Bit interleaved parity check	比特交叉奇偶校验	Bǐtè jiāochā jīǒu jiàoyàn	BIP
Bit interleaved parity check	比特奇偶校验码	Bǐtè jīǒu jiàoyàn mǎ	BIP
Bit interleaved parity check	比特间插奇偶校验	Bǐtè-jiān chā jīǒu jiàoyàn	BIP
Bit interleaved parity check N code	比特间插奇偶校验 N 位码	Bǐtè-jiān chā jīǒu jiàoyàn N wèi mǎ	BIP-N
Bit loss probability	位损耗概率	Wèi sǔnhào gàilǜ	BLP
Bit loss rate	比特丢失率	Bǐtè diūshī lǜ	BLR
Bit mapping	位图	Wèitú	
Bit mapping protocol	位映射协议	Wèi yìngshè xiéyì	BMP
Bit mask	位屏蔽	Wèi píngbì	
Bit number	比特号码	Bǐtè hàomǎ	BN
Bit parallel	比特并行	Bǐtè bìngxíng	
Bit pattern	位模式	Wèi móshì	
Bit protocol control	位协议控制	Wèi xiéyì kòngzhì	
Bit rate	比特率	Bǐtè lǜ	
Bit rate	码速率	Mǎ sùlǜ	
Bit rate multiplier	位速率乘法器	Wèi sùlǜ chéngfǎqì	BRM
Bit rate tolerance	比特率容差	Bǐtè lǜ róngchā	
Bit sequence independence	比特序列独立性	Bǐtè xùliè dúlìxìng	
Bit serial	位串行	Wèi chuànháng	
Bit stream	比特流	Bǐtè liú	
Bit stream	位流	Wèiliú	
Bit string	比特串	Bǐtè chuàn	
Bit string type	比特串类型	Bǐtè chuàn lèixíng	
Bit type	二进位型	Èrjìnwèi-xíng	
BITBUS © (Intel product)	位总线网	Wèi zǒngxiàn wǎng	
Bit-load condition-based traffic distortion rate	基于比特的符合条件的业务量失真率	Jīyú bǐtède fúhé tiáojiànde yèwù liáng shīzhēn lǜ	BCTDR
Bitmap	点阵图	Diǎnzhèntú	

Bitmap file	位图文件	Wèitú wénjiàn	.bmp
Bitnet	比特网	Bǐtè wǎng	
Bit-oriented link control procedure	面向比特的链路控制规程	Miànxiàng bǐtède liànlù kòngzhì guīchéng	
Bit-rate allocation signal	比特率定位信号	Bǐtè lǜ dìngwèi xìnhào	BAS
Bits per second	位每秒	Wèi měi miǎo	bps
Bits per second	位/秒	Wèi/miǎo	Bps
Bitwise	按位	Àn wèi	
Bitwise copy	按位拷	Àn wèi kǎo	
Bitwise copy	为单元进行复制	Wéi dānyuán jìnxíng fùzhì	
Bitwise copy	位元逐一复制	Wèiyuán zhúyī fùzhì	
Bitwise operation	按位运算	Àn wèi yùnsuàn	
Bi-variate correlation	二变量相关	Èrbiànliàng xiāngguān	
Black hole	黑洞	Hēidòng	
Blade antenna	刀型天线	Dāoxíng tiānxiàn	
Bland test	空白试验	Kòngbái shìyàn	
Blank field descriptor	空白字段描述符	Kòngbái zìduàn miáoshù fú	
Blank money order	空白汇票	Kòngbái huìpiào	
Blank string	空白串	Kòngbái chuàn	
Blank string	空格串	Kònggé chuàn	
Blanket jamming; blanking jamming	压制性干扰	Yāzhìxìng gānrǎo	
Blend, blending	混和	Hùnhé	
Blind carbon copy	密件抄送	Mìjiàn chāosòng	BCC
Blind digitizing	盲目数字化	Mángmù shùzìhuà	
Blind landing-aid radar	盲目着陆雷达	Mángmù zháolù léidá	
Blind literature	盲人读物	Mángrén dúwù	
Blind phase	盲相	Mángxiàng	
Blind retrieval	盲提取	Máng tíqǔ	
Blind speed	盲速	Mángsù	
Blind spot	盲点	Mángdiǎn	
Blind transport format detection	盲目传输格式检测	Mángmù chuánshū géshì jiǎncè	BTFD
Blind via (in SMT)	盲通路孔	Máng tōnglù kǒng	
Blind zone	盲区	Mángqū	
Block	区块	Qūkuài	
Block	字块	Zìkuài	
Block (digital signal processing)	码组	Mǎzǔ	
Block (noun)	块	Kuài	
Block adaptive algorithm	块字适应算法	Kuài zìshìyìng suànfǎ	BAA
Block cell rate	块信元速率	Kuài xìnyuán sùlǜ	BCR
Block check	码组检验	Mǎzǔ jiǎnyàn	
Block check character	块检验字符	Kuài jiǎnyàn zìfú	BCC
Block check procedure	块校验规程	Kuài jiàoyàn guīchéng	
Block check sequence	数据块检查序列	Shùjù kuài jiǎnchá xùliè	BCS
Block check sequence	字块检验序列	Zìkuài jiǎnyàn xùliè	BCS
Block cipher	分组密码	Fēnzǔ mìmǎ	
Block cipher	块密码	Kuài mìmǎ	
Block code	定长编码	Dìngcháng biānmǎ	

Block code	分组代码	Fēnzǔ dàimǎ	
Block code	分组码	Fēnzǔ mǎ	
Block code	块码	Kuài mǎ	
Block cycle	块周期	Kuài zhōuqī	
Block cyclic distributed channel assignment	分组循环分散定位	Fēnzǔ xúnhuán fēnsàn dìngwèi	
Block data check mode	块数据校验方式	Kuài shùjù jiàoyàn fāngshì	BDCM
Block diagram editor	框图编辑器	Kuàngtú biānjíqì	
Block error rate	块差错率	Kuài chācuò lǜ	
Block error rate	块误码率	Kuài wùmǎ lǜ	BLER
Block error rate	码组差错率	Mǎzǔ chācuò lǜ	BLER
Block floating-point distributed	块浮点分布式	Kuài fúdiǎn fēnbùshì	BFD
Block glide	块滑移	Kuài huáyí	
Block guard time	块保护时间	Kuài bǎohù shíjiān	BGT
Block header	信息块字头	Xìnxī kuài zìtóu	
Block move	搬移区块	Bānyí qūkuài	
Block multiplexer channel	阻塞多路复用信道	Zǔsè duōlù fùyòng xìndào	
Block payload	块净负荷	Kuài jìng fùhè	
Block payload	块净荷	Kuài jìnghé	
Block payload	块有效负荷	Kuài yǒuxiào fùhè	
Block protection	块保护	Kuài bǎohù	
Block search	分块查找	Fēnkuài cházhǎo	
Block signal	码组信号	Mǎzǔ xìnhào	
Block transfer instruction	字组传送指令	Zìzǔ chuánsòng zhǐlìng	BTI
Block turbo codes	分组 turbo 码	Fēnzǔ turbo mǎ	BTC
Block waiting time	块等待时间	Kuài děngdài shíjiān	BWT
Blocked passage	封闭通道	Fēngbì tōngdào	
Blocked passage location	封闭通道位置	Fēngbì tōngdào wèizhì	
Blocked passage type	封闭通道类型	Fēngbì tōngdào lèixíng	
Blocking	拼块	Pīnkuài	
Blocking	阻塞	Zǔsè	
Blocking phenomena	阻塞现象	Zǔsè xiànxiàng	
Blocking signal	闭塞信号	Bìsè xìnhào	BLO
Blocking/deblocking	阻断/解阻	Zǔduàn/jiězǔ	
Blocking-acknowledgement signal	闭塞证实信号	Bìsè zhèngshí xìnhào	BLA
Blocking-tube oscillator	电子管间歇振荡器	Diànzǐguǎn jiànxiē zhèndàngqì	BTO
Blog (web log)	博客日记	Bókè rìjì	
Blower	风机	Fēngjī	
Blowtorch	喷灯	Pēndēng	
Bluetooth	蓝牙	Lányá	
Bluetooth access point	蓝牙接入点	Lányá jiērù diǎn	BAP
Bluetooth qualification program	蓝牙质量鉴定程序	Lányá zhìliàng jiàndìng chéngxù	
Bluetooth Special Interest Group (SIG)	蓝牙特殊利益集团	Lányá tèshū lìyì jítuán	
Bluetooth technology	蓝牙技术	Lányá jìshù	
Bluff body	阻流体	Zǔ liútǐ	
Board flipper (in component assembly process)	翻扳机	Fānbānjī	
Board inward dialing	板自动拨入	Bàn zìdòng bōrù	BID

Bode diagram	博德图	Bó-dé tú	
Body (of a message)	信体	Xìntǐ	
Body capacitance	身体电容	Shēntǐ diànróng	
Body entity	体实体	Tǐ shítǐ	
Body wave	实体波	Shítǐ bō	
Body-wave magnitude (Mb)	体波大小	Tǐbō dàxiǎo	
BOIC except those directed to the home PLMN country	除了指向本地 PLMN 国家之外的 BOIC	Chúle zhǐxiàng běndì PLMN guójiā zhīwàide BOIC	BOIC-exHC
Bold (WP command)	粗体	Cūtǐ	
Bolometer	辐射热测定器	Fúshè rè cèdìngqì	
Bolometer	辐射热计	Fúshè rèjì	
Bolometer	辐射式测量计	Fúshè-shì cèliángjì	
Bolometer	热副射仪	Rè fùshèyí	
Bolometer mount	辐射测量计座	Fúshè cèliángjì zuò	
Bolometric power meter	辐射式功率计	Fúshè-shì gōnglǜjì	
Bolt cutter	断线钳	Duànxiàn qián	
Bombing radar	轰炸雷达	Hōngzhà léidá	
Bond	联结	Liánjié	
Bond lift-off (in SMT)	焊接升离	Hànjiē shēnglí	
Bonding	等电位连接	Děngdiànwèi liánjiē	
Bonding agent (in SMT)	粘合剂	Niánhéjì	
Bonnet	上阀盖	Shàng fágài	
Bonneville Satellite Corp. (US)	波尼韦尔卫星公司	Bō-ní-wéi-ěr wèixīng gōngsī	
Bookkeeping	簿记	Bùjì	
Bookmark (for Web browser)	书签	Shūqiān	
Boolean	布尔型	Bù-ěr-xíng	
Boolean algebra	布尔代数	Bù-ěr dàishù	
Boolean algebra	布林代数	Bù-lín dàishù	
Boolean assignment statement	布尔赋值语句	Bù-ěr fùzhí yǔjù	BAS
Boolean equation	逻辑方程	Luójì fāngchéng	
Boolean expression	布尔表达式	Bù-ěr biǎodá shì	
Boolean operation	布尔运算	Bù-ěr yùnsuàn	
Boolean operator	布尔操作符	Bù-ěr cāozuò fú	
Boolean operator	布尔算子	Bù-ěr suànzi	
Boolean value	布林值	Bù-lín zhí	
Boomerang grabber (sampler)	自返式取样器	Zìfǎnshì qǔyàngqì	
Boomerang gravity corer	自返式深海取样管	Zìfǎnshì shēnhǎi qǔyàng guǎn	
Boost charge	急充电	Jíchōngdiàn	
Booster	增强器	Zēngqiángqì	
Booster (power) amplifier (for optical fiber)	光功率放大器	Guāng gōnglǜ fàngdàqì	BA
Booster amplifier	功率放大器	Gōnglǜ fàngdàqì	BA
Booster battery	升压电池组	Shēngyā diànchízǔ	
Booster converter	升压式变换器	Shēngyā-shì biànhuànqì	
Booster-distribution amplifier	升压器-分布放大器	Shēngyāqì—fēnbù fàngdàqì	BDA
Boot catalog file	启动目录文件	Qǐdòng mùlù wénjiàn	BCF
Boot disk	启动盘	Qǐdòng pán	

English	Chinese	Pinyin	Abbreviation
Boot file	启动文件	Qǐdòng wénjiàn	
Boot image file	启动映像文件	Qǐdòng yìngxiàng wénjiàn	BIF
Boot information negotiation layer	启动信息协商层	Qǐdòng xìnxī xiéshāng céng	BINL
Boot logging	启动记录	Qǐdòng jilù	
Boot partition	启动分区	Qǐdòng fēnqū	
Boot sector	启动区	Qǐdòng qū	
Boot volume	启动卷	Qǐdòng juàn	
Bootstrap	引导指令	Yǐndǎo zhǐling	
Bootstrap protocol	引导协议	Yǐndǎo xiéyì	BOOTP
Bootstrap protocol	自陷协议	Zixiàn xiéyì	BOOTP
Bootstrap router	引导路由器	Yǐndǎo lùyóuqì	BSR
Bootstrap router	自举路由器	Zìjǔ lùyóuqì	BSR
Bootstrap, boot (verb)	引导	Yǐndǎo	
Border	边框	Biānkuàng	
Border element	边缘设备	Biānyuán shèbèi	BE
Border gateway	边界网关	Biānjiè wǎngguān	BG
Border gateway	边沿网关	Biānyán wǎngguān	BG
Border gateway	边缘网关	Biānyuán wǎngguān	
Border gateway multicast protocol	边界网关组播协议	Biānjiè wǎngguān zǔbō xiéyì	BGMP
Border gateway protocol	边界路由协议	Biānjiè lùyóu xiéyì	BGP
Border gateway protocol	边界网关协议	Biānjiè wǎngguān xiéyì	BGP
Border information	图廓注记	Túkuò zhùjì	
Border intermediate system	边界中介系统	Biānjiè zhōngjiè xìtǒng	BIS
Border line	图廓线	Túkuòxiàn	
Border matching	边缘匹配	Biānyuán pǐpèi	
Border protection	边界保护	Biānjiè bǎohù	
Border scanning register	边界扫描寄存器	Biānjiè sǎomiáo jìcúnqì	BSR
Borehole logging method	孔内测井法	Kǒng-nèi cèjǐngfǎ	
Boresight error	瞄准误差	Miáozhǔn wùchā	
Boresight error (of an antenna)	视轴误差	Shìzhóu wùchā	
Boresight tower	校准塔	Jiàozhǔn tǎ	
Borland (US software company)	宝兰	Bǎo-lán	
Boron bromide	溴化硼	Xiùhuàpéng	BBr_3
Boron trichloride	三氯化硼	Sānlǜhuàpéng	BCl_3
Bose-Chaudhuri-Hocquenghem code	博斯-乔赫里-霍克文黑木码	Bó-sī—Qiáo-hè-lǐ—Huò-kè-wén-hēi-mù mǎ	BCH
Bose-Chaudhuri-Hocquenghem code	以三人之姓所名的码	Yǐ sānrénzhīxìng suǒmíngde mǎ	BCH
Both way call setup	双向建立呼叫	Shuāngxiàng jiànlì hūjiào	
Both-ways trunk	双方中继	Shuāngfāng zhōngjì	BWT
Bottleneck	瓶径	Píngjìng	
Bottleneck	瓶颈	Píngjǐng	
Bottom (of a stack)	栈底	Zhàn dǐ	
Bottom edge	下边缘	Xiàbianyuán	
Bottom field	底场	Dǐcháng	
Bottom left corner	左下角	Zuǒ xiàjiǎo	
Bottom margin	页下空白	Yè-xià kòngbái	
Bottom of stack	堆栈底部	Duīzhàn dǐbù	

Bottom right corner	右下角	Yòuxiàjiǎo	
Boundary	边界	Biānjiè	
Boundary condition	边界条件	Biānjiè tiáojiàn	
Boundary edge set	边界边集	Biānjiè biān jí	
Boundary effects	边界效应	Biānjiè xiàoyìng	
Boundary element	边界要素	Biānjiè yàosù	
Boundary element method	边界要素法	Biānjiè yàosù fǎ	
Boundary function	边界函数	Biānjiè hánshù	
Boundary junction	边界接合	Biānjiè jiēhé	
Boundary layer	边界层	Biānjiècéng	
Boundary monument	边界标志	Biānjiè biāozhì	
Boundary radiation	边角辐射	Biānjiǎo fúshè	
Boundary scan test	边界扫描测试	Biānjiè sǎomiáo cèshì	
Boundary state gelatinization (FOC mfg)	界面凝胶法	Jièmiàn níngjiāo fǎ	BSG
Boundary type	边界类型	Biānjiè lèixíng	
Bounded lag function	有界滞后函数	Yǒujiè zhìhòu hánshù	
Bounds checking	边界检查	Biānjiè jiǎnchá	
Bounds checking	界限检查	Jièxiàn jiǎnchá	
Boxcarring or batching of messages	批量消息传输/处理	Pīliàng xiāoxi chuánshū/chǔlǐ	
Brace	支撑	Zhīchēng	
Brace (curly brace) { }	大括号	Dàkuòhào	
Brace (curly brace) { }	花括号	Huā kuòhào	
Bracket [ ]	括号	Kuòhào	
Bracket (square bracket) [ ]	中括号	Zhōng kuòhào	
Bracket (square bracket) [ ]	方括号	Fāng kuòhào	
Bragg optic fiber grating	布拉格光纤光栅	Bù-lā-gé guāngxiān guāngshān	
Brain-state-in-a-box (neural networking term)	盒中脑	Hé-zhōng nǎo	
Branch amplifier	分路放大器	Fēnlù fàngdàqì	BA
Branch and link	转移和连接	Zhuǎnyí hé liánjiē	BAL
Branch antenna transceiver switch	分支式天线收发开关	Fēnzhī-shì tiānxiàn shōufā kāiguān	
Branch feeder	支线	Zhīxiàn	
Branch fuse	分路熔丝	Fēnlù róngsī	
Branch hybrid junction	分支式电桥	Fēnzhī-shì diànqiáo	
Branch prediction	分支预测	Fēnzhī yùcè	
Branch prediction table	分支预测表	Fēnzhī yùcè biǎo	
Branch processing unit	分支处理单元	Fēnzhī chǔlǐ dānyuán	BPU
Branch target buffer/cache	分支目标缓冲	Fēnzhī mùbiāo huǎnchōng	BTB/C
Branch, tributary	分支	Fēnzhī	
Branched cable	分支光缆	Fēnzhī guānglǎn	
Branching filter	分路滤波器	Fēnlù lǜbōqì	
Breach (IPsec)	攻破	Gōngpò	
Breakable (i.e. cipher algorithm, etc.)	可破密的	Kěpòmìde	
Breakdown	击穿	Jīchuān	
Breakdown	强拆	Qiángchāi	
Breakdown after intrusion	插入后的强拆	Chārù hòude qiáng chāi	
Breakdown power	击穿功率	Jīchuān gōnglǜ	

English	Chinese	Pinyin	Abbr.
Breakdown voltage	击空电压	Jīkōng diànyā	
Breaking length	裂断长	Lièduàn cháng	
Breaking load	破坏承载	Pòhuài chéngzài	
Breaking off for subscription	报刊退订	Bàokān tuìdìng	
Breakline	分割线	Fēngē xiàn	
Break-make ratio	断续比	Duànxù bǐ	
Breakout	分支点	Fēnzhī diǎn	
Breakout box	中断盒	Zhōngduàn hé	
Breakout cable	分支光缆	Fēnzhī guānglǎn	
Breakover frequency	转折频率	Zhuǎnzhé pínlǜ	
Breakpoint	断点	Duàndiǎn	
Bremsstrahlung	韧致辐射	Rèn zhì fúshè	
Brevity list (IPsec)	简码表	Jiǎnmǎ biǎo	
Bridge	桥接	Qiáojiē	
Bridge	桥接器	Qiáojiēqì	
Bridge	网桥	Wǎngqiáo	
Bridge (in SMT)	锡桥	Xīqiáo	
Bridge amplifier	桥接放大器	Qiáojiē fàngdàqì	BA
Bridge control protocol	桥式控制协议	Qiáo-shì kòngzhì xiéyì	BCP
Bridge converter	桥式变换器	Qiáo-shì biànhuànqì	
Bridge forwarding	网桥转发	Wǎngqiáo zhuǎnfā	
Bridge group	网桥组	Wǎngqiáo zǔ	
Bridge number	网桥号	Wǎngqiáo hào	
Bridge protocol data unit	桥接协议数据单元	Qiáojiē xiéyì shùjù dānyuán	BPDU
Bridge protocol data unit	网桥协议数据单元	Wǎngqiáo xiéyì shùjù dānyuán	BPDU
Bridge rectifier	桥式整流器	Qiáo-shì zhěngliúqì	
Bridge static filtering	网桥静态过滤	Wǎngqiáo jìngtài guòlǜ	
Bridge tap	桥接抽头	Qiáojiē chōutóu	
Bridged tap equalizer	桥接抽头均衡器	Qiáojiē chōutóu jūnhéngqì	BTEQ
Bridge-router (brouter)	网桥路由器	Wǎngqiáo lùyóuqì	
Bridging amplifier	桥式放大器	Qiáo-shì fàngdàqì	BA
Bridging control protocol (in PPP)	桥接控制协议	Qiáojiē kòngzhì xiéyì	BCP
Bridging loss	跨接损耗	Kuàjiē sǔnhào	
Brief catalogue of newspapers and periodicals	报刊简明目录	Bàokān jiǎnmíng mùlù	
Brillouin scattering	布里渊散射	Bù-lǐ-yuān sǎnshè	
Brinell hardness test	布氏硬度试验	Bù-shì yìngdù shìyàn	
Bring into service performance objective	投入业务性能指标	Tóurù yèwù xìngnéng zhǐbiāo	BISPO
British Computer Society	英国电脑学会	Yīngguó diànnǎo xuéhuì	BCS
British Posts and Telecommunications Standard	英国邮政与电信标准	Yīngguó yóuzhèng yǔ diànxìn biāozhǔn	BPT
British Standards Institute	英国标准所	Yīngguó biāozhǔn suǒ	BSI
British Telecom Corp.	英国电信公司	Yīngguó diànxìn gōngsī	
Broad band switching system	宽带交换系统	Kuāndài jiāohuàn xìtǒng	BSS
Broadband access	宽带接入	Kuāndài jiērù	
Broadband access network	宽带接入网	Kuāndài jiērù wǎng	BAN
Broadband access server	带宽接入服务器	Dàikuān jiērù fúwùqì	BAS
Broadband access server	宽带接入服务器	Kuāndài jiērù fúwùqì	BRAS

Broadband access unit	宽带接入单元	Kuāndài jiērù dānyuán	BAU
Broadband adapter	宽带适配器	Kuāndài shìpèiqì	BBA
Broadband amplifier	宽频放大器	Kuānpín fàngdàqì	
Broadband antenna	宽带天线	Kuāndài tiānxiàn	
Broadband communication channel	宽带通信通路	Kuāndài tōngxìn tōnglù	
Broadband communication channel	宽带通信信道	Kuāndài tōngxìn xìndào	
Broadband confirmed	宽带确认	Kuāndài quèrèn	BCF
Broadband coupler	宽带耦合器	Kuāndài ǒuhéqì	BBC
Broadband data multipexer	宽带数据复用器	Kuāndài shùjù fùyòngqì	BDM
Broadband device	宽带器件	Kuāndài qìjiàn	
Broadband device	宽带设备	Kuāndài shèbèi	
Broadband emission	宽带发射	Kuāndài fāshè	
Broadband exchange service	宽带交换业务	Kuāndài jiāohuàn yèwù	BES
Broadband exchange termination	宽带交换终接	Kuāndài jiāohuàn zhōngjiē	B-ET
Broadband fixed wireless access	宽带固定无线接入	Kuāndài gùdìng wúxiàn jiērù	BFWA
Broadband generalized radio access network	通用宽带无线接入网络	Tōngyòng kuāndài wúxiàn jiērù wǎngluò	BGRAN
Broadband integrated services digital network	广带综合业务数字网	Guǎngdài zōnghé yèwù shùzì wǎng	B-ISDN
Broadband integrated services digital network	宽带综合业务数字网	Kuāndài zōnghé yèwù shùzì wǎng	B-ISDN
Broadband integrated services digital network-user part	宽带综合业务数字网用户部分	Kuāndài zōnghé yèwù shùzìwǎng yònghù bùfen	B-ISUP
Broadband interference	宽带干扰	Kuāndài gānrǎo	
Broadband intermediate frequency amplifier	宽带中频放大器	Kuāndài zhōngpín fàngdàqì	
Broadband ISDN user part	宽带 ISDN 用户部分	Kuāndài ISDN yònghù bùfen	B-ISUP
Broadband ISDN user part	宽带 ISDN 用户部分	Kuāndài ISDN yònghù bùfen	BISUP
Broadband local exchange	宽带本地交换	Kuāndài běndì jiāohuàn	B-LEX
Broadband message transfer part level 3 (in SS7)	宽带消息传递部三层	Kuāndài xiāoxi chuándì bù sāncéng	MTPL3-b
Broadband network	宽带网络	Kuāndài wǎngluò	
Broadband network access server	宽带网络接入服务器	Kuāndài wǎngluò jiērù fúwùqì	BNAS
Broadband operation center	宽带运行中心	Kuāndài yùnxíng zhōngxīn	BBOC
Broadband optical fiber amplifier	宽带光放大器	Kuāndài guāng fàngdàqì	BOFA
Broadband optical full service network	宽带光全业务接入网	Kuāndài guāng quán yèwù jiērù wǎng	BOFSN
Broadband passive optical network	宽带无源光网络	Kuāndài wúyuán guāng wǎngluò	B-PON
Broadband rejected	宽带拒绝	Kuāndài jùjué	BRJ
Broadband remote access server	宽带远程接入服务器	Kuāndài yuǎnchéng jiērù fúwùqì	BRAS
Broadband request	宽带请求	Kuāndài qǐngqiú	BRQ
Broadband switching unit	宽带交换单元	Kuāndài jiāohuàn dānyuán	BSU
Broadband user-network interface	宽带用户 - 网络接口	Kuāndài yònghù-wǎngluò jiēkǒu	B-UNI
Broadband wireless ATM system	宽带无线 ATM 系统	Kuāndài wúxiàn ATM xìtǒng	BWAN
Broadband wireless MAN standard (IEEE 802.16)	宽带无线 MAN 标准	Kuāndài wúxiàn MAN biāozhǔn	WiMAX
Broadband, wideband	宽带	Kuāndài	BW
Broadcast	广播	Guǎngbō	
Broadcast and select network	广播与选择网	Guǎngbō yǔ xuǎnzé wǎng	
Broadcast and unknown server	广播和未知地址服务器	Guǎngbō hé wèizhī dìzhǐ fúwùqì	BUS
Broadcast and unknown server	广播和未知服务器	Guǎngbō hé wèizhī fúwùqì	BUS
Broadcast channel	广播信道	Guǎngbō xìndào	BCH
Broadcast connection type	广播式连接	Guǎngbōshì liánjiē	

Broadcast control channel	广播控制信道	Guǎngbō kòngzhì xìndào	BCCH
Broadcast control channel (BCCH) allocation	广播控制信道划分	Guǎngbō kòngzhì xìndào huàfēn	
Broadcast control functional entity	广播控制功能实体	Guǎngbō kòngzhì gōngnéng shítǐ	BCFE
Broadcast cross-connection	广播交叉连接	Guǎngbō jiāochā liánjiē	
Broadcast paging system	广播寻呼系统	Guǎngbō xúnhū xìtǒng	
Broadcast search	广播搜索	Guǎngbō sōusuǒ	
Broadcast storm	广播风暴	Guǎngbō fēngbào	
Broadcast transmission	广播传输	Guǎngbō chuánshū	
Broadcast videography	图文广播	Túwén guǎngbō	
Broadcast/multicast control	广播/多播控制	Guǎngbō/duōbō kòngzhì	BMC
Broadcasting satellite service	广播卫星业务	Guǎngbō wèixīng yèwù	BSS
Broadcasting service	广播业务	Guǎngbō yèwù	
Broadcasting station	广播电台	Guǎngbō diàntái	
Broadcasting-satellite service	卫星广播业务	Wèixīng guǎngbō yèwù	
Broadside array	边射阵	Biānshè zhèn	
Broadside array antenna	垂射天线阵	Chuíshè tiānxiànzhèn	BAA
Bronzing, bronze plating	镀青铜	Dùqīngtóng	
Browse mode	浏览模式	Liúlǎn móshì	
Browser	阅读器	Yuèdúqì	
Browser (Internet tool)	浏览器	Liúlǎnqì	
Browser applications (programs)	浏览器应用	Liúlǎnqì yìngyòng	
Browser-accessible application	可经由浏览器访问的应用程序	Kějīng yóu liúlǎnqì fǎngwènde yìngyòng chéngxù	
Browsing data	浏览数据	Liúlǎn shùjù	
BrushWriter (Chinese software)	大学士	Dàxuéshì	
Brute force attack (cryptology)	强力攻击	Qiánglì gōngjī	
BSC clock distribution board assembly	BSC 时钟分配集成板	BSC shízhōng fēnpèi jíchéngbǎn	BCDA
BSC clock rack panel	BSC 时钟机架面板	BSCshízhōng jījià miànbǎn	BCBP
BSC main processor back panel	BSC 主处理器后面板	BSC zhǔ chǔlǐ qì hòumian bǎn	BMBP
BSM initialization and maintenance	BSM 初始化和维护	BSM chūshǐhuà hé wéihù	BIM
B-spline	B 样条曲线	B-yàng tiáoqūxiàn	
BTS call control	BTS 呼叫控制	BTS hūjiào kòngzhì	BCO
BTS CDMA base rack	CDMA BTS 基本架	CDMA BTS jīběn jià	BCBR
BTS CDMA extended rack	CDMA BTS 扩展架	CDMA BTS kuòzhǎn jià	BCER
BTS communication interconnect network	BTS 通信互联网络	BTS tōngxìn hùliánwǎng luò	BCIN
BTS configure and resource management	BTS 配置和资源管理	BTS pèizhì hé zīyuán guǎnlǐ	BRM
BTS control and interface board assembly	BTS 控制和接口集成板	BTS kòngzhì hé jiēkǒu jíchéngbǎn	BCIA
BTS control and maintenance	BTS 控制和维护	BTS kòngzhì hé wéihù	BCM
BTS control and maintenance block	BTS 控制和维护模块	BTS kòngzhì hé wéihù mókuài	BCMB
BTS control processor	BTS 控制处理器	BTS kòngzhì chǔlǐ qì	BCP
BTS data access	BTS 数据存取	BTS shùjù cúnqǔ	BDA
BTS diagnosis	BTS 诊断	BTS zhěnduàn	BDIA
BTS fault management	BTS 故障管理	BTS gùzhàng guǎnlǐ	BFM
BTS high capacity IPC processor	BTS 高容量 IPC 处理器	BTS gāo róngliàng IPC chǔlǐqì	BHIP
BTS interconnect back board	BTS 互联后面板	BTS hù lián hòumian bǎn	BIBB
BTS measurement	BTS 测量	BTS cèliáng	BMEA

BTS message router	BTS 消息路由器	BTS xiāoxi lùyóu qì	BMR
BTS resource allocation	BTS 资源分配	BTS zīyuán fēnpèi	BRA
BTS sanity management	BTS 正常运行管理器	BTS zhèngcháng yùnxíng guǎnlǐqì	BSMN
BTS status handling	BTS 状态处理	BTS zhuàngtài chǔlǐ	BSH
BTS system time	BTS 系统时间	BTS xìtǒng shíjiān	BSTM
BTS test processor	BTS 测试处理器	BTS cèshì chǔlǐqì	BTP
Bubblejet printer	喷泡式打印机	Pēnpào-shì dǎyìnjī	
Buffalo Laboratories application of digitally exact spectra	数字化精确谱 Buffalo 实验室应用（系统)	Shùzìhuà jīngquè pǔ Buffalo shíyànshì yìngyòng (xìtǒng)	BLADES
Buffer	缓冲器	Huǎnchōngqì	
Buffer address	缓冲地址	Huǎnchōng dìzhǐ	BA
Buffer allocation size	缓冲区分配容量	Huǎnchōng qū fēnpèi róngliàng	
Buffer amplifier	缓冲放大器	Huǎnchōng fàngdàqì	
Buffer counter reset	缓冲计数器	Huǎnchōng jìshùqì	BCR
Buffer overflow attack (type of hacker attack)	缓冲区溢出攻击	Huǎnchōng qū yìchū gōngjī	
Buffer stage	缓冲级	Huǎnchōng jí	
Buffer store	缓冲存储器	Huǎnchōng cúnchǔqì	
Buffer tube (FOC)	缓冲管	Huǎnchōng guǎn	
Buffer zone	缓冲区	Huǎnchōng qū	
Buffer-to-buffer credit	缓冲区到缓冲区信用数	Huǎnchōng qū dào huǎnchōng qū xìnyòng shù	BB_Credit
Bug	臭虫	Chòuchóng	
Bug	缺陷	Quēxiàn	
Build (noun, usually a computer application)	编译和连接	Biānyì hé liánjiē	
Build (noun, usually a computer application, short for compile and connect 编译和连接)	编连	Biānlián	
Building	建筑物	Jiànzhùwù	
Building area	建筑面积	Jiànzhù miànjī	
Building automatic system	楼宇自动化系统	Lóuyǔ zìdònghuà xìtǒng	BAS
Building automation	楼宇自动化	Lóuyǔ zìdònghuà	BA
Building automation and control net	建筑物自动化和控制网络	Jiànzhùwù zìdònghuà hé kòngzhì wǎngluò	BAC
Building backbone cable	建筑物主干电缆	Jiànzhùwù zhǔgàn diànlǎn	
Building backbone optical cable	建筑物主干光缆	Jiànzhùwù zhǔgàn guānglǎn	
Building block signal processor	积木块信号处理机	Jīmù kuài xìnhào chǔlǐjī	BBSP
Building code (regulations)	建筑法规	Jiànzhù fǎguī	
Building code (standards)	建筑标准法	Jiànzhù biāozhǔn fǎ	
Building construction	房室建筑	Fángshì jiànzhù	FJ
Building distributor	建筑物配线架	Jiànzhùwù pèixiànjià	BD
Building entrance facility	建筑物入口设施	Jiànzhùwù rùkǒu shèshī	BEF
Building Ethernet access system	数字以太网接入系统	Shùzì yǐtàiwǎng jiērù xìtǒng	BEAS
Building integrated time supply	楼内综合定时供给设备	Lóunèi zōnghé dìngshí gōngjǐ shèbèi	BITS
Building integrated timing supply	大楼综合定时供给设备	Dàlóu zōnghé dìngshí gōngjǐ shèbèi	BITS
Building integrated timing supply	大楼内综合定时源	Dàlóu-nèi zōnghé dìngshí yuán	BITS
Building integrated timing supply	局内综合定时供给系统	Jú-nèi zōnghé dìngshí gōngjǐ xìtǒng	BITS
Building integrated timing system	大楼综合定时供给系统	Dàlóu zōnghé dìngshí gōngjǐ xìtǒng	BITS
Building integrated timing system	通信楼综合定时供给系统	Tōngxìn lóu zōnghé dìngshí gōngjǐ xìtǒng	BITS
Building line	建筑线	Jiànzhù xiàn	

Building local exchange carrier	数字本地交换运营	Shùzì běndì jiāohuàn yùnyíng	BLEC
Building management automation	建筑管理自动化	Jiànzhù guǎnlǐ zìdònghuà	
Building management system	建筑管理系统	Jiànzhù guǎnlǐ xìtǒng	BMS
Building penetration loss	建筑物穿透损耗	Jiànzhùwù chuāntòu sǔnhào	
Building plumbing	房室给排水	Fángshì gěi páishuǐ	FS
Building restrictions	建筑限制	Jiànzhù xiànzhì	
Building structure	房室结构	Fángshì jiégòu	FG
Building structure	建筑构造	Jiànzhù gòuzào	
Built-in	内建	Nèijiàn	
Built-in	内置	Nèizhì	
Built-in function	内部函数	Nèibù hánshù	
Built-in function	内置函数	Nèizhì hánshù	
Built-in test	内置测试	Nèizhì cèshì	BIT
Bulk acoustic wave	体声波	Tǐ shēngbō	BAW
Bulk cable injection conducted susceptibility (Mil-Std-461E, CS114)	电缆束注入传导敏感度	Diànlǎn shù zhùrù chuándǎo mǐngǎndù	
Bulk cable injection impulse excitation conducted susceptibility (Mil-Std-461E, CS115)	电缆束注入脉冲激励传导敏感度	Diànlǎn shù zhùrù màichōng jīlì chuándǎo mǐngǎndù	
Bulk effect diode local oscillator	体效应二极管本地振荡器	Tǐ xiàoyìng èrjíguǎn běndì zhèndàngqì	
Bulk memory	大容量存储器	Dàróngliàng cúnchǔqì	
Bulk modulus	体积弹性模量	Tǐjī tánxìng móliàng	
Bulk remittance	大宗汇款	Dàzōng huìkuǎn	
Bulk sub-routine	辅助存储器子程序	Fǔzhù cúnchǔqì zǐchéngxù	
Bulk update	批量更新	Pīliàng gēngxīn	
Bulk-logged recovery (in SQL Server)	批日志恢复	Pī rìzhì huīfù	
Bulk-posted correspondence	大宗函件	Dàzōng hánjiàn	
Bulletin board service	布告板服务	Bùgàobǎn fúwù	BBS
Bulletin board service	公告板服务	Gōnggào bǎn fúwù	BBS
Bulletin board service	公告板业务	Gōnggào bǎn yèwù	BBS
Bulletin board system	布告栏系统	Bùgàolán xìtǒng	BBS
Bulletin board system	电子公告栏	Diànzǐ gōnggào lán	BBS
Bunched frame alignment signal	集中式帧定位信号	Jízhōngshì zhèng dìngwèi xìnhào	
Bundle jacket	光纤束护套	Guāngxiān shù hùtào	
Bundled light optical cable with ribbon fibers	中心束管式光纤带光缆	Zhōngxīn shùguǎnshì guāngxiān dài guānglǎn	
Bundled services	捆绑式服务	Kǔnbǎng-shì fúwù	
Bundled software	批套附送软件	Pītào fùsòng ruǎnjiàn	
Bureau of Radio Regulation (MII)	无线电管理局	Wúxiàndiàn guǎnlǐjú	
Burial in wall (telecom installation)	墙内埋设	Qiáng-nèi máishè	BW
Buried depth	埋深	Mái shēn	
Buried heterogeneous (fiber or cable)	掩埋异质结	Yǎnmái yìzhìjié	BH
Buried service lightguide (cable)	直埋式光缆	Zhímái-shì guānglǎn	BSL
Buried structure	埋设结构	Máishè jiégòu	
Buried via (in SMT)	埋入的通路孔	Máirùde tōnglù kǒng	
Buried works	埋设工	Máishè gōng	
Burn through	烧穿	Shāo chuān	
Burn-in	老化	Lǎohuà	

Burn-in test	拷机实验	Kǎojī shíyàn	
Burst	猝发	Cùfā	
Burst	突发	Tūfā	
Burst	突发脉冲	Tūfā màichōng	
Burst and random error correction codes	纠突发错和随机错码	Jiū tūfā cuò hé suíjī cuò mǎ	
Burst data transfer rate	突发数据传输率	Tūfā shùjù chuánshū lǜ	
Burst error	猝发差错	Cùfā chācuò	
Burst error	突发差错	Tūfā chācuò	
Burst error channel	猝发错误通道	Cùfā cuòwù tōngdào	BEC
Burst error correction codes	纠突发错码	Jiū tūfā cuò mǎ	
Burst firing control	猝发导通控制	Cùfā dǎotōng kòngzhì	
Burst firing control	猝发点火控制	Cùfā diǎnhuǒ kòngzhì	
Burst length	突发长度	Tūfā chángdù	
Burst method	突发方法	Tūfā fāngfǎ	
Burst modem	突发式调制解调器	Tūfā-shì tiáozhì jiětiáoqì	
Burst packet attribute	突发包特征	Tūfā bāo tèzhēng	BPA
Burst period	突发脉冲序列周期	Tūfā màichōng xùliè zhōuqī	BP
Burst pipelined synchronous static RAM	突发式管道同步静态存储器	Tūfā-shì guǎndào tóngbù jìngtài cúnchǔqì	BSRAM
Burst tolerance	突发容限	Tūfā róngxiàn	BT
Burst traffic	突发业务	Tūfā yèwù	
Burst transmission	突发式传输	Tūfā-shì chuánshū	
Burst-error processor	突发错误处理程序	Tūfā cuòwù chǔlǐ chéngxù	BEP
Burstiness	突发性	Tūfāxìng	
Burst-mode controller	突发模式控制器	Tūfā móshì kòngzhìqì	BMC
Burst-mode optical receiver	突发模式光接收机	Tūfā móshì guāng jiēshōujī	
Bursty data services	突发数据业务	Tūfā shùjù yèwù	
Bus	汇流排	Huìliú pái	
Bus (usually for computers); trunk line (in telecom)	总线	Zǒngxiàn	
Bus adapter	总线适配器	Zǒngxiàn shìpèiqì	BA
Bus and tag channel	总线和标记信道	Zǒngxiàn hé biāojì xìndào	
Bus bar	汇流条母线	Huìliútiáo mǔxiàn	BB
Bus exchange line	总线交换线路	Zǒngxiàn jiāohuàn xiànlù	BEL
Bus master	总线主设备	Zǒngxiàn zhǔ shèbèi	
Bus motherboard	总线母板	Zǒngxiàn mǔbǎn	
Bus network	串列网络	Chuànliè wǎngluò	
Bus request interrupt enable	总线请求中断	Zǒngxiàn qǐngqiú zhōngduàn	BRIE
Bus scheduling	总线调度	Zǒngxiàn diàodù	
Bus slave	总线从设备	Zǒngxiàn cóng shèbèi	
Bus system	总线系统	Zǒngxiàn xìtǒng	
Bus topology	总线拓扑	Zǒngxiàn tuòpū	
Busied out; blocked	闭塞	Bìsè	
Business group	商业组群	Shāngyè zǔqún	BG
Business group complex	复合商业组群	Fùhé shāngyè zǔ qún	BGC
Business intelligence	商业智能化	Shāngyè zhìnénghuà	BI
Business logic	业务逻辑	Yèwù luóji	
Business management	商业管理	Shāngyè guǎnlǐ	BM

Business management layer	商业管理层	Shāngyè guǎnlǐ céng	BML
Business management layer	事务管理层	Shìwù guǎnlǐ céng	BML
Business operation supporting system	业务运营支援系统	Yèwù yùnyíng zhīyuán xìtǒng	BOSS
Business process definition	商务处理流程定义	Shāngwù chǔlǐ liúchéng dìngyì	
Business process model	企业过程模型	Qǐyè guòchéng móxíng	
Business process re-engineering	企业经营过程重组	Qǐyè jīngyíng guòchéng chóngzǔ	
Business process re-engineering	业务流程重组	Yèwù liúchéng chóngzǔ	BPR
Business rules	业务规则	Yèwù guīzé	
Business Software Alliance	商业软件联盟	Shāngyè ruǎnjiàn liánméng	BSA
Business-critical application	企业要害应用	Qǐyè yàohài yìngyòng	
Business-to-business	企业对企业	Qǐyè duì qǐyè	B2B
Bus-type interface	总线型接口	Zǒngxiàn-xíng jiēkǒu	
Busy condition	忙状态	Máng zhuàngtài	
Busy hour	忙时	Mángshí	
Busy hour call attempts	忙时话务量	Mángshí huàwùliàng	BHCA
Busy hour call completed	忙时呼叫完成	Mángshí hūjiào wánchéng	BHCC
Busy hour calling attempts	忙时呼叫尝试	Mángshí hūjiào chángshì	BHCA
Busy hour calling attempts	忙时试呼次数	Mángshí shìhū cìshù	BHCA
Busy hour calls	忙时呼叫	Mángshí hūjiào	BHC
Busy hour load	忙时负载	Mángshí fùzài	BHL
Busy hour usage	忙时应用	Mángshí yìngyòng	BHU
Busy queuing /callback	繁忙排队/自动回叫	Fánmáng páiduì/zìdòng huíjiào	
Busy state	忙状态	Máng zhuàngtài	
Busy test	忙闲测试	Mángxián cèshì	
Busy tone	忙音	Mángyīn	
Busy tone trunk	忙音中继线	Mángyīn zhōngjìxiàn	BTT
Busy/idle bit	忙闲比特	Máng xián bǐtè	
Busy/idle check	忙闲检测	Mángxián jiǎncè	
Busy/Idle flag	忙/闲标志	Máng/xián biāozhì	
Butt joint	对头连接	Duìtou liánjiē	
Butting optical fiber (cable) connector	对接式光纤（缆）连接器	Duìjiē-shì guāngxiān (lǎn) liánjiēqì	
Buttons	按钮	Ànniǔ	
Buzz, crackle	蜂音	Fēngyīn	
Buzzer	蜂鸣器	Fēngmíngqì	BZ
Buzzer	蜂音器	Fēngyīnqì	BZ
Bypass	旁通	Pángtōng	
Bypass	透传	Tòuchuán	
Bypass circuitry	旁路电路	Pánglù diànlù	
Bypass mode	旁路方式	Pánglù fāngshì	
Bypass queue	旁通队列	Pángtōng duìliè	
Bypass relay	旁路中继	Pánglù zhōngjì	
Bypass switching	旁路交换	Pánglù jiāohuàn	
Byte	位元组	Wèiyuánzǔ	
Byte	字节	Zìjié	
Byte frame	字节帧	Zìjié zhèng	
Byte interleaving and disinterleaving	字节间插和消间插	Zìjié jiānchā hé xiāojiānchā	

Byte serial	字节串行	Zìjié chuànháng	
Byte substitution	字节代替	Zìjié dàitì	
Byte substitution	字节代替变换	Zìjié dàitì biànhuàn	
Byte substitution	字节替换	Zìjié tìhuan	

C

C interface	C 接口	C jiēkǒu	
C language	C 语言	C yǔyán	
Cabinet	列柜	Lièguì	
Cabinet radiation	机壳辐射	Jīké fúshè	
Cable access point	电缆接入点	Diànlǎn jiērù diǎn	CAP
Cable adapter	电缆附加器	Diànlǎn fùjiāqì	
Cable assembly	光缆组件	Guānglǎn zǔjiàn	
Cable blowing machine (to install FOC)	吸缆机	Xīlǎnjī	
Cable broadband forum	电缆宽带论坛	Diànlǎn kuāndài lùntán	CBF
Cable carrier wave	电缆载波	Diànlǎn zàibō	LZ
Cable chute	电缆槽	Diànlǎn cáo	
Cable chute	电缆沟	Diànlǎn gōu	
Cable drum	电缆盘	Diànlǎn pán	
Cable drum hand cart	电缆手推车	Diànlǎn shǒutuīchē	
Cable fault locator	电缆故障探测器	Diànlǎn gùzhàng tàncèqì	CFL
Cable interface unit	电缆接口组件	Diànlǎn jiēkǒu zǔjiàn	CIU
Cable modem	电缆调制解调器	Diànlǎn tiáozhì jiětiáoqì	
Cable modem	缆调制解调器	Lǎn tiáozhì jiětiáoqì	CM
Cable modem termination system	电缆调制解调器终端系统	Diànlǎn tiáozhì jiětiáoqì zhōngduān xìtǒng	CMTS
Cable MODEM termination system	线缆调制解调器终端系统	Xiànlǎn tiáozhì jiětiáoqì zhōngduān xìtǒng	CMTS
Cable or harness branch	光缆或光缆捆束分支	Guānglǎn huò guānglǎn kǔnshù fēnzhī	
Cable or harness run	光缆或光缆捆束主干	Guānglǎn huò guānglǎn kǔnshù zhǔgàn	
Cable phone	电缆电话	Diànlǎn diànhuà	CAP
Cable port	电缆端口	Diànlǎn duānkǒu	
Cable replacement protocol	电缆替代协议	Diànlǎn tìdài xiéyì	CRP
Cable television	电缆电视	Diànlǎn diànshì	CATV
Cable television	有线电视	Yǒuxiàn diànshì	CATV
Cable television optical transmission system	有线电视光传输系统	Yǒuxiàn diànshì guāng chuánshū xìtǒng	
Cable tension transducer	电缆张力传感器	Diànlǎn zhānglì chuángǎnqì	
Cable termination frame	电缆终端配线架	Diànlǎn zhōngduān pèixiànjià	CTF
Cable thermal detector	缆式线型感温探测器	Lǎnshìxiànxíng gǎnwēn tàncèqì	CTD
Cable unit	电缆单位	Diànlǎn dānwèi	
Cable unit	光缆单元	Guānglǎn dānyuán	
Cabletron Spectrum (description of this network management software)	旧纳档块化技术	Jiù nà dàng kuàihuà jìshù	CS
Cableway	走线架	Zǒuxiànjià	
Cabling	布缆	Bùlǎn	
Cache array routing protocol	缓存集群路由协议	Huǎncún jíqún lùyóu xiéyì	CARP
Cache directory	缓存目录	Huǎncún mùlù	
Cache on a chip	芯片上集成缓存	Xìnpiàn-shàng jíchéng huǎncún	
Cache on board	板上集成缓存	Bǎn-shàng jíchéng huǎncún	COB

English	Chinese	Pinyin	Abbreviation
Cache on die	芯片内集成缓存	Xìnpiàn-nèi jíchéng huǎncún	COD
Cache-coherent non-uniform memory access	连贯缓冲非统一内存寻址	Liánguàn huǎnchōng fēi tǒngyī nèicún xúnzhǐ	cc-NUMA
Caching	缓存	Huǎncún	
Caching resolver	缓存解析程序	Huǎncún jiěxī chéngxù	
Cadastral map	地籍图	Dìjí tú	
Cage antenna	笼形天线	Lóngxíng tiānxiàn	
Calculated field	计算字段	Jìsuàn zìduàn	
Calculated maximum flow coefficient	最大计算流量系数	Zuìdà jìsuàn liúliàng xìshù	
Calculated member	计算所得成员	Jìsuàn suǒdé chéngyuán	
Calculated normal flow coefficient	正常计算流量系数	Zhèngcháng jìsuàn liúliàng xìshù	
Calculation condition	计算条件	Jìsuàn tiáojiàn	
Calculation formula	计算公式	Jìsuàn gōngshì	
Calculation pass	计算传递	Jìsuàn chuándì	
Calculation sub-cube	计算子多维数据集	Jìsuàn ziduōwéi shùjùjí	
Calendar year	历年	Lìnián	
Calibrate	定标	Dìngbiāo	
Calibrated error	标定误差	Biāodìng wùchā	
Calibration	校准	Jiàozhǔn	
California Education and Research Federation Network	加州教育与研究协会网	Jiāzhōu jiàoyù yǔ yánjiū xiéhuì wǎng	CERFnet
Call (noun, in computer use, invoking a program or sub-routine, in telecom use, initiating a protocol or sub-routine)	调用	Diàoyòng	
Call abandonment probability	呼叫放弃概率	Hūjiào fàngqì gàilǜ	
Call accepted signal	呼叫接受信号	Hūjiào jiēshòu xìnhào	
Call accounting	呼叫计费	Hūjiào jìfèi	
Call agent	呼叫代理	Hūjiào dàilǐ	
Call agent server	呼叫代理服务器	Hūjiào dàilǐ fúwùqì	
Call analysis program	呼叫分析程序	Hūjiào fēnxī chéngxù	CAP
Call attempt (by a user)	试呼	Shìhū	
Call attempts per second	每秒试呼数	Měi miǎo shìhūshù	CAPS
Call attempts per second	每移试呼数	Měi yíshì hūshù	CAPS
Call back	回叫	Huíjiào	
Call back apparatus	应答装置	Yìngdá zhuāngzhì	CBA
Call back on busy	遇忙回叫	Yùmáng huíjiào	
Call center	呼叫中心	Hūjiào zhōngxīn	
Call center engineering	呼叫中心工程	Hūjiào zhōngxīn gōngchéng	
Call center manager	呼叫中心管理	Hūjiào zhōngxīn guǎnlǐ	CCM
Call center software	呼叫中心软件	Hūjiào zhōngxīn ruǎnjiàn	
Call clear failure probability	呼叫清除失败概率	Hūjiào qīngchú shībài gàilǜ	
Call clearing delay	呼叫清除延时	Hūjiào qīngchú yánshí	
Call clearing message	呼叫清除消息	Hūjiào qīngchú xiāoxi	
Call collision	呼叫碰撞	Hūjiào pèngzhuàng	
Call completed to busy subscriber	忙用户的呼叫完成	Máng yònghùde hūjiào wánchéng	CCBS
Call completion probability	呼通概率	Hūtōng gàilǜ	
Call completion service setup	呼叫完成业务建立	Hūjiào wánchéng yèwù jiànlì	CCSS
Call completion supplementary services	呼叫完成附加业务	Hūjiào wánchéng fùjiā yèwù	

Call confirmation protocol	呼叫确认协议	Hūjiào quèrèn xiéyì	CCP
Call confirmed	呼叫确认	Hūjiào quèrèn	
Call congestion ratio	呼损率	Hū sǔn lǜ	
Call connection maintenance service accept	呼叫连接管理业务 接入	Hūjiào liánjiē guǎnlǐ yèwù jiērù	
Call connection maintenance service request	呼叫连接管理业务 请求	Hūjiào liánjiē guǎnlǐ yèwù qǐngqiú	
Call control	呼叫控制	Hūjiào kòngzhì	CC
Call control access function	呼叫控制接入功能	Hūjiào kòngzhì jiērù gōngnéng	CCAF
Call control agent functioning	呼叫控制代理功能	Hūjiào kòngzhì dàilǐ gōngnéng	CCAF
Call control block	呼叫控制块	Hūjiào kòngzhì kuài	CCB
Call control function	呼叫控制功能	Hūjiào kòngzhì gōngnéng	CCF
Call control manager	拔号控制管理	Bōhào kòngzhì guǎnlǐ	CCM
Call control processor	呼叫控制处理器	Hūjiào kòngzhì chǔlǐqì	CCP
Call control processor board assembly	呼叫控制处理集成板	Hūjiào kòngzhì chǔlǐ jíchéngbǎn	CCPA
Call control processor board assembly	呼叫控制处理器集成板	Hūjiào kòngzhì chǔlǐqì jíchéngbǎn	CCPA
Call control server	呼叫控制服务器	Hūjiào kòngzhì fúwùqì	
Call control signal	呼叫控制信号	Hūjiào kòngzhì xìnhào	
Call deflection	呼叫改向	Hūjiào gǎixiàng	CD
Call deflection	呼叫偏斜	Hūjiào piānxié	
Call deflection	呼叫转向	Hūjiào zhuǎnxiàng	CD
Call deflection selection	呼叫改发选择	Hūjiào gǎifā xuǎnzé	
Call deflection subscription	呼叫改发预约	Hūjiào gǎifā yùyuē	
Call detail record	呼叫详细记录	Hūjiào xiángxì jìlù	CDR
Call detail record charging identifier	呼叫详细记录计费标识（话单）	Hūjiào xiángxì jìlù jìfèi biāozhì (huà dān)	CDR
Call detail recording	呼叫细节记录	Hūjiào xìjié jìlù	CDR
Call detail recording	通话明细记录	Tōnghuà míngxì jìlù	CDR
Call disestablishment message	呼叫拆线消息	Hūjiào chāixiàn xiāoxi	
Call emulator	呼叫仿真	Hūjiào fǎngzhēn	
Call establishment	呼叫建立	Hūjiào jiànlì	
Call establishment message	呼叫建立消息	Hūjiào jiànlì xiāoxi	
Call failure signal	呼叫故障信号	Hūjiào gùzhàng xìnhào	CFL
Call flow	呼叫流量	Hūjiào liúliàng	
Call forward on busy	遇忙呼叫前转	Yùmáng hujiào qiánzhuǎn	CFB
Call forward unconditional	无条件呼叫转移	Wútiáojiàn hūjiào zhuǎnyí	
Call forwarding	呼叫前向转移	Hūjiào qiánxiàng zhuǎnyí	CF
Call forwarding	呼叫前转	Hūjiào qiánzhuǎn	
Call forwarding	呼叫转送	Hūjiào zhuǎnsòng	CF
Call forwarding busy	遇忙呼叫前转	Yù máng hujiào qiánzhuǎn	CFB
Call forwarding busy	遇忙呼叫转发	Yùmáng hujiào zhuǎnfā	CFB
Call forwarding busy	遇忙呼叫转送	Yùmáng hujiào zhuǎnsòng	CFB
Call forwarding conditional	有条件前向转移	Yǒu tiáojiàn qiánxiàng zhuǎnyí	CFC
Call forwarding not reachable	不可及呼叫前转	Bùkějí hūjiào qiánzhuǎn	CFNRc
Call forwarding on busy	遇忙前转	Yùmáng qiánzhuǎn	CFB
Call forwarding on mobile subscriber busy	当移动用户忙时呼叫转发	Dāng yídòng yònghù mángshí hūjiào zhuǎnfā	CFB
Call forwarding on mobile subscriber busy	移动用户忙呼叫前转	Yídòng yònghù máng hujiào qiánzhuǎn	CFB

Call forwarding on mobile subscriber busy	遇移动用户忙呼叫前向转移	Yù yídòng yònghù máng hujiào qiánxiàng zhuǎnyí	CFB
Call forwarding on mobile subscriber busy	遇移动用户忙呼叫前转	Yù yídòng yònghù máng hujiào qiánzhuǎn	CFB
Call forwarding on mobile subscriber not reachable	对找不到移动用户的呼叫转移	Duì zhǎobudào yídòng yònghùde hūjiào zhuǎnyí	CFNRc
Call forwarding on mobile subscriber not reachable	移动用户不可及呼叫前转	Yídòng yònghù bùkějí hūjiào qiánzhuǎn	CFNRk
Call forwarding on mobile subscriber not reachable	在移动用户不可达到时转发	Zài yídòng yònghù bùkě dádào shí zhuǎnfā	CFNRc
Call forwarding on mobile subscriber not reachable supplementary service	不可及呼叫前转补充业务	Bùkě jí hūjiào qiánzhuǎn bǔchōng yèwù	CFNRc
Call forwarding on mobile subscriber not reachable supplementary service	当移动用户不可及前转补充业务	Dāng yídòng yònghù bùkějí qiánzhuǎn bǔchōng yèwù	CFNRc
Call forwarding on no reply	无应答呼叫前向转移	Wúyìngdá hūjiào qiánxiàng zhuǎnyí	CFNRy, CFNREP
Call forwarding on no reply	无应答呼叫前转	Wúyìngdá hūjiào qiánzhuǎn	CFNR
Call forwarding on no reply	无应答呼叫转发	Wúyìngdá hūjiào zhuǎnfā	CFNR
Call forwarding on no reply	无应答呼叫转送	Wúyìngdá hūjiào zhuǎnsòng	CFNR
Call forwarding on no reply	无应答前转	Wúyìngdá qiánzhuǎn	CFNRP
Call forwarding on no reply	在无回答时呼叫转发	Zài wúhuídá shí hūjiào zhuǎnfā	CFNRy
Call forwarding on no reply supplementary service	补充业务无应答呼叫前转	Bǔchōng yèwù wúyìngdá hūjiào qiánzhuǎn	CFNRy
Call forwarding on no reply supplementary service	无应答前转补充业务	Wúyìngdá qiánzhuǎn bǔchōng yèwù	CFU
Call forwarding on not reachable	呼叫不可及前转	Hūjiào bùkě jí qiánzhuǎn	CFNRA
Call forwarding on subscriber busy	当用户忙时呼叫转发	Dāng yònghù mángshí hūjiào zhuǎnfā	CFB
Call forwarding unconditional	无条件呼叫前向转移	Wútiáojiàn hūjiào qiánxiàng zhuǎnyí	CFU
Call forwarding unconditional	无条件呼叫前转	Wútiáojiàn hūjiào qiánzhuǎn	CFU
Call forwarding unconditional	无条件呼叫转发	Wútiáojiàn hūjiào zhuǎnfā	CFU
Call forwarding unconditional	无条件呼叫转送	Wútiáojiàn hūjiào zhuǎnsòng	CFU
Call forwarding unconditional	无条件前转	Wútiáojiàn qiánzhuǎn	CFU
Call forwarding unconditional supplementary service	无条件呼叫前转补充业务	Wútiáojiàn hūjiào qiánzhuǎn bǔchōng yèwù	CFU
Call forwarding when called mobile subscriber does not reply	当被呼移动用户不回答时的呼叫转移	Dāng bèihū yídòng yònghù bù huídá shíde hūjiào zhuǎnyí	CFNRy
Call gapping	呼叫中断	Hūjiào zhōngduàn	
Call hold	呼叫保持	Hūjiào bǎochí	HOLD
Call hold supplementary service	呼叫保持补充业务	Hūjiào bǎochí bǔchōng yèwù	HOLD
Call identification display	主叫识别信息显示	Zhǔjiào shíbié xìnxī xiǎnshì	CID
Call identifier	呼叫标识符	Hūjiào biāozhì fú	
Call identity	呼叫身份	Hūjiào shēnfen	
Call information phase message	呼叫信息阶段消息	Hūjiào xìnxī jiēduàn xiāoxi	
Call information processing	调用信息处理	Diàoyòng xìnxī chǔlǐ	CIP
Call information processing	呼叫信息处理	Hūjiào xìnxī chǔlǐ	CIP
Call information system	呼叫信息系统	Hūjiào xìnxī xìtǒng	CIS
Call instance code	呼叫实例码	Hūjiào shílì mǎ	CIC
Call loss rate	呼损率	Hū sǔn lǜ	
Call lost system	呼损制	Hū sǔn zhì	
Call management	呼叫管理	Hūjiào guǎnlǐ	CM
Call manager	呼叫管理器	Hūjiào guǎnlǐqì	CM
Call mediation node	呼叫协调功能	Hūjiào xiétiáo gōngnéng	CMN
Call mediation node	呼叫协调节点	Hūjiào xiétiáo jiédiǎn	CMN

Call modification completed (ISUP message)	呼叫特性改变完毕	Hūjiào tèxìng gǎibiàn wánbì	CMC
Call modification reject (ISUP message)	拒绝改变呼叫特性	Jùjué gǎibiàn hūjiào tèxìng	CMRJ
Call modification request (ISUP message)	改变呼叫特性请求	Gǎibiàn hūjiào tèxìng qǐngqiú	CMR
Call offering supplementary services	呼叫提供附加业务	Hūjiào tígōng fùjiā yèwù	
Call operator	调用操作符	Diàoyòng cāozuò fú	
Call packing	呼叫暂停	Hūjiào zàntíng	
Call phases	呼叫阶段	Hūjiào jiēduàn	
Call proceeding	呼叫进程	Hūjiào jìnchéng	
Call proceeding	呼叫进行	Hūjiào jìnxíng	
Call process	呼叫进程	Hūjiào jìnchéng	CALL PROC
Call processing	呼叫处理	Hūjiào chǔlǐ	
Call processing control system	呼叫处理控制系统	Hūjiào chǔlǐ kòngzhì xìtǒng	CPCS
Call processing language	呼叫处理语言	Hūjiào chǔlǐ yǔyán	CPL
Call progress	呼叫进展	Hūjiào jìnzhǎn	
Call progress (ISUP message)	呼叫过程	Hūjiào guòchéng	CPG
Call progress message (ISUP)	呼叫进程消息	Hūjiào jìnchéng xiāoxi	CPG
Call progress signal	呼叫进行信号	Hūjiào jìnxíng xìnhào	
Call progressing (message)	呼叫进展消息	Hūjiào jìnzhǎn xiāoxi	CPG
Call quality test	呼叫质量拨打测试	Hūjiào zhìliàng bōdǎ cèshì	CQT
Call redirecting number	呼叫转移号码	Hūjiào zhuǎnyí hàomǎ	
Call redirection	呼叫改发	Hūjiào gǎifā	
Call redirection information	呼叫转移信息	Hūjiào zhuǎnyí xìnxī	
Call re-establishment permission	呼叫重建允许	Hūjiào chóngjiàn yǔnxǔ	
Call reference	呼叫参考	Hūjiào cānkǎo	CR
Call reference value	呼叫参考值	Hūjiào cānkǎo zhí	CRV
Call release	呼叫释放	Hūjiào shìfàng	
Call request signal	呼叫请求信号	Hūjiào qǐngqiú xìnhào	
Call screening	呼叫筛选	Hūjiào shāixuǎn	
Call screening	通话播放	Tōnghuà bōfàng	
Call server control function	呼叫服务器控制功能	Hūjiào fúwùqì kòngzhì gōngnéng	CSCF
Call service function	呼叫业务功能	Hūjiào yèwù gōngnéng	CSF
Call service gateway function	呼叫业务网关功能	Hūjiào yèwù wǎngguān gōngnéng	CSF-G
Call service mediation function	呼叫业务协调功能	Hūjiào yèwù xiétiáo gōngnéng	CSF-C
Call service node function	呼叫业务节点功能	Hūjiào yèwù jiédiǎn gōngnéng	CSF-N
Call service transit function	呼叫业务转接功能	Hūjiào yèwù zhuǎnjiē gōngnéng	CSF-T
Call setup	呼叫初始化	Hūjiào chūshǐhuà	
Call set-up delay	呼叫建立延迟	Hūjiào jiànlì yánchí	
Call set-up delay at a section boundary Bi	在一个段的边界 Bi 处呼叫建立延迟	Zài yīgè duànde biānjiè Bi chù hūjiào jiànlì yánchí	
Call set-up delay between two section boundaries	在两个段的边界之间的呼叫建立延迟	Zài liǎnggè duànde biānjiè zhījiānde hūjiào jiànlì yánchí	
Call set-up error probability	呼叫建立差错概率	Hūjiào jiànlì chācuò gàilǜ	
Call set-up failure probability	呼叫建立失败概率	Hūjiào jiànlì shībài gàilǜ	
Call set-up failure probability	叫建立失败概率	Jiào jiànlì shībài gàilǜ	
Call set-up time	呼叫建立时间	Hūjiào jiànlì shíjiān	
Call simulator	呼叫模拟器	Hūjiào mónǐqì	

Call spill-over	呼叫泄漏	Hūjiào xièlòu	
Call state	呼叫状态	Hūjiào zhuàngtài	
Call state control function	呼叫状态控制功能	Hūjiào zhuàngtài kòngzhì gōngnéng	CSCF
Call store	呼叫存储	Hūjiào cúnchǔ	
Call supervision message	呼叫监视消息	Hūjiào jiānshì xiāoxi	CSM
Call time-out	呼叫超时	Hūjiào chāoshí	
Call tracing	呼叫跟踪	Hūjiào gēnzōng	
Call transfer	呼叫转送	Hūjiào zhuǎnsòng	CT
Call transfer	呼叫转移	Hūjiào zhuǎnyí	CT
Call transfer supplementary service	呼叫传送补充业务	Hūjiào chuánsòng bǔchōng yèwù	CT
Call unrelated service function	与呼叫无关的业务功能	Yǔ hūjiào wúguānde yèwù gōngnéng	CUSF
Call waiting	呼叫待时	Hūjiào dàishí	CW
Call waiting	呼叫等待	Hūjiào děngdài	CW
Call waiting supplementary service	呼叫等待补充业务	Hūjiào děngdài bǔchōng yèwù	CW
Call/bearer gateway function	呼叫/承网关功能	Hūjiào/chéng wǎngguān gōngnéng	C/BGF
Call/bearer gateway function	呼叫/承载网关功能	Hūjiào/chéngzài wǎngguān gōngnéng	C/B GF
Call/service processing	呼叫/服务处理	Hūjiào/fúwù chǔlǐ	
Call-arrival signal	呼叫到达信号	Hūjiào dàodá xìnhào	
Callback	回调	Huídiào	
Callback control protocol	回叫控制协议	Huíjiào kòngzhì xiéyì	CCP
Call-directing character	定向呼叫字符	Dìngxiàng hūjiào zìfú	CDC
Call-directing character	定向调入字符	Dìngxiàng tiáorù zìfú	CDC
Called address modified notification	被呼地址修改通知	Bèihū dìzhǐ xiūgǎi tōngzhī	
Called line identity	被叫线路标识	Bèijiào xiànlù biāozhì	CLI
Called party (in telecommunication)	被叫用户	Bèijiào yònghù	
Called party call controller	被叫呼叫控制器	Bèijiào hūjiào kòngzhìqì	
Called party number	被叫号码	Bèijiào hàomǎ	
Called party number	被叫方编号	Bèijiàofāng biānhào	
Called party release	被叫控制释放	Bèijiào kòngzhì shìfàng	
Called party sub-address	被叫子地址	Bèijiào zidìzhǐ	
Called station identifier	被呼叫站标识符	Bèihūjiào zhàn biāoshífú	CED
Called subscriber held signal	被叫拥护不挂机信号	Bèijiào yōnghù bùguàjī xìnhào	CSH
Called terminal	被叫终端	Bèijiào zhōngduān	
Caller identification	主叫识别	Zhǔjiào shíbié	CID
Caller identity delivery	主叫识别信息传送	Zhǔjiào shíbié xìnxī chuánsòng	CID
Call-failure loop	呼叫故障循环	Hūjiào gùzhàng xúnhuán	CFL
Calling forward on mobile subscriber not reachable	当无线信道拥挤时的呼叫转移	Dāng wúxiàn xindào yōngjǐ shíde hūjiào zhuǎnyí	CENRc
Calling forwarding on mobile subscriber busy	当被呼移动用户忙时的呼叫转	Dāng bèihū yídòng yònghù máng shíde hūjiào zhuǎn	CFB
Calling line identification	主叫线路识别	Zhǔjiào xiànlù shíbié	CLI
Calling line identification presentation	呼叫线标识显示	Hūjiào xiàn biāozhì xiǎnshì	CLIP
Calling line identification presentation	呼叫消息（线）识别显示	Hūjiào xiāoxi (xiàn) shíbié xiǎnshì	CLIP
Calling line identification presentation	主呼线识别提供	Zhǔ hūxiàn shíbié tígōng	CLIP
Calling line identification presentation	主叫号码通知	Zhǔjiào hàomǎ tōngzhī	CLIP
Calling line identification presentation	主叫线路识别显示	Zhǔjiào xiànlù shíbié xiǎnshì	CLIP

Calling line identification presentation	主叫线识别	Zhǔjiàoxiàn shíbié	CLIP
Calling line identification presentation	主叫线识别提供	Zhǔjiàoxiàn shíbié tígōng	CLIP
Calling line identification presentation	主叫线识别显示	Zhǔjiàoxiàn shíbié xiǎnshì	CLIP
Calling line identification presentation supplementary service	主叫识别提供补充业务	Zhǔjiào shíbié tígōng bǔchōng yèwù	CLIP
Calling line identification restriction	呼叫线标识限制	Hūjiào xiàn biāozhì xiànzhì	CLIR
Calling line identification restriction	呼叫消息（线）识别限制	Hūjiào xiāoxi (xiàn) shíbié xiànzhì	CLIR
Calling line identification restriction	主呼线识别限制	Zhǔ hūxiàn shíbié xiànzhì	CLIR
Calling line identification restriction	主叫号码识别限制	Zhǔjiào hàomǎ shíbié xiànzhì	CLIR
Calling line identification restriction	主叫线路识别限制	Zhǔjiào xiànlù shíbié xiànzhì	CLIR
Calling line identification restriction	主叫线识别限制	Zhǔjiàoxiàn shíbié xiànzhì	CLIR
Calling line identification restriction supplementary service	主叫识别限制补充业务	Zhǔjiào shíbié xiànzhì bǔchōng yèwù	CLIR
Calling line identity	呼叫消息（线）识别	Hūjiào xiāoxi (xiàn) shíbié	CLI
Calling line identity	主叫识别	Zhǔjiào shíbié	CLI
Calling name presentation	呼叫名显示	Hūjiào míng xiǎnshì	CNAP
Calling number identification presentation	主叫号码识别显示	Zhǔjiào hàomǎ shíbié xiǎnshì	CNIP
Calling number presentation restriction	主叫号码识别限制	Zhǔjiào hàomǎ shíbié xiànzhì	CNIR
Calling party (in telecommunication)	主叫用户	Zhǔjiào yònghù	
Calling party call controller	主叫呼叫控制器	Zhǔjiào hūjiào kòngzhìqì	
Calling party clear signal	主叫用户挂机信号	Zhǔjiào yònghù guàjī xìnhào	CCL
Calling party handling	呼叫方控制	Hūjiào fāng kòngzhì	CPH
Calling party number	主叫号码	Zhǔjiào hàomǎ	
Calling party number	主叫方编号	Zhǔjiào-fāng biānhào	
Calling party release	主叫控制释放	Zhǔjiào kòngzhì shìfàng	
Calling party sub-address	主叫子地址	Zhǔjiào zidìzhǐ	
Calling party's category	主叫类别	Zhǔjiào lèibié	
Calling sequence	呼叫序列	Hūjiào xùliè	
Calling station response	呼叫站响应	Hūjiào zhàn xiǎngyìng	
Calling terminal	主叫终端	Zhǔjiào zhōngduān	
Calling tone	呼叫单音	Hūjiào dānyīn	
Call-level interface	调用级接口	Diàoyòng jí jiēkǒu	CLI
Call-waiting tone	呼叫等待音	Hūjiào děngdài yīn	
Calorimetric power meter	量热计式功率计	Liángrèjì-shì gōnglǜjì	
Cambridge ring	剑桥环	Jiànqiáo huán	CR
CAMEL application part	CAMEL 应用部分	CAMEL yìngyòng bùfen	CAP CAMEL
CAMEL service environment	CAMEL 业务环境	CAMEL yèwù huánjìng	CSE
Camera	摄像机	Shèxiàngjī	
Camera lens	摄像机镜头	Shèxiàngjī jìngtóu	
Camera tube	摄像管	Shèxiàng guǎn	
Campus	建筑群	Jiànzhùqún	
Campus backbone cable	建筑群主干电缆	Jiànzhùqún zhǔgàn diànlǎn	
Campus backbone optical cable	建筑群主干光缆	Jiànzhùqún zhǔgàn guānglǎn	
Campus backbone sub-system	建筑群主干子系统	Jiànzhùqún zhǔgàn zixìtǒng	
Campus distributor	建筑群配线架	Jiànzhùqún pèixiànjià	CD
Campus network	园区网	Yuánqū wǎng	
Campus sub-system	建筑群子系统	Jiànzhùqún zixìtǒng	CS

Canadian Broadcasting Corp.	加拿大广播公司	Jiā-ná-dà Guǎngbō Gōngsī	CBC
Canadian Geography Information System	加拿大地理信息系统	Jiā-ná-dà dìlǐ xìnxī xìtǒng	CGIS
Canadian Institute of Geomatics	加拿大测量工程研究所	Jiā-ná-dà cèliáng gōngchéng yánjiūsuǒ	CIG
Canadian Standards Association	加拿大标准联合会	Jiā-ná-dà biāozhǔn liánhéhuì	CSA
Canadian Standards Association	加拿大标准协会	Jiā-ná-dà biāozhǔn xiéhuì	CSA
Cancel location	删除位置	Shānchú wèizhì	
Cancellation	注销	Zhùxiāo	
Cancellation after verification	核销	Héxiāo	
Cancellation ratio	对消比	Duìxiāo bǐ	
Candidate bootstrap router	候选自举路由器	Hòuxuǎn zìjǔ lùyóuqì	CBSR
Candidate key (for database)	候选键	Hòuxuǎn jiàn	
Candidate key (in SQL Server)	侯选关键字	Hóuxuǎn guānjiàn zì	
Candle (unit of measurement of light)	烛光	Zhúguāng	
Canon (Japanese company)	佳能	Jiā-néng	
Canonical correlation analysis	典型相关分析	Diǎnxíng xiāngguān fēnxī	
Canonical format indicator	经典格式指示符	Jīngdiǎn géshi zhǐshìfú	CFI
Capability	负荷能力	Fùhè nénglì	
Capability Maturity Model	能力成熟模型	Nénglì chéngshú móxíng	CMM
Capability set	能力集	Nénglì jí	CS
Capability set 1	能力集 1	Nénglì jí 1	CS1
Capability set 2	能力集 2	Nénglì jí 2	CS2
Capability test	功能测试	Gōngnéng cèshì	
Capability test	机能检测	Jīnéng jiǎncè	
Capability test	能力测试	Nénglì cèshì	
Capability/configuration parameter	能力配置参数	Nénglì pèizhì cānshù	CCP
Capability/configuration parameter	性能/结构参数	Xìngnéng/jiégòu cānshù	CCP
Capacitance balance	电容平衡	Diànróng pínghéng	
Capacitive transducer/sensor	电容式传感器	Diànróng-shì chuángǎnqì	
Capacitor for voltage protection	保护电容器	Bǎohù diànróngqì	
Capacity	容量	Róngliàng	
Capacity allocation	容量配置	Róngliàng pèizhì	CA
Capacity allocation acknowledgement	容量配置认可	Róngliàng pèizhì rènkě	CAA
Capacity deallocation	容量重新分配	Róngliàng chóngxīn fēnpèi	CD
Capacity deallocation acknowledgement	容量重新分配认可	Róngliàng chóngxīn fēnpèi rènkě	CDA
Capacity volume ratio	容积率	Róngjī lǜ	
Capillary action (in SMT)	毛细管作用	Máoxìguǎn zuòyòng	
Capital expenses	投资成本	Tóuzī chéngběn	CAPEX
Caps lock	大写锁定	Dàxiě suǒdìng	
CapsLock key	打字锁定键	Dǎzì suǒdìng jiàn	
Capsule resource unit	包装资源单位	Bāozhuāng zīyuán dānwèi	CRU
Captive balloon communication	系流气球通信	Xìliú qìqiú tōngxìn	
Captive network portal	强制网络门户	Qiángzhì wǎngluò ménhù	
Capture	捕获	Bǔhuò	
Capture area	捕获区	Bǔhuò qū	
Capture area (of a terrestrial receiving station)	捕捉区	Bǔzhuō qū	
Capture effect	捕获效应	Bǔhuò xiàoyìng	

Capture trigger	捕获触发器	Bǔhuò chùfāqì	
Carbon coated fiber	碳涂层光纤	Tàntúcéng guāngxiān	CCF
Carbon copy	抄送	Chāosòng	
Carbon dioxide (CO_2) laser	二氧化碳激光	Èryǎnghuàtàn jīguāng	
Carbon dioxide (CO_2) laser processing equipment	二氧化碳激光加工机	Èryǎnghuàtàn jīguāng jiāgōngjī	
Carbon dioxide extinguishing system	二氧化碳系统	Èryǎnghuàtàn xìtǒng	CDES
Carbon monoxide (CO) laser	一氧化碳激光	Yīyǎnghuàtàn jīguāng	
Card adapter register	卡片适配器寄存器	Kǎpiàn shìpèiqì jìcúnqì	CAR
Card holder verification	持卡人校验信息	Chíkǎrén jiàoyàn xìnxī	CHV
Card holder verification information	卡支持器检验信息	Kǎ zhīchíqì jiǎnyàn xìnxī	CHV
Card punch	卡片穿孔机	Kǎpiàn chuānkǒngjī	C/P
Card reader	读片机	Dúpiànjī	
Card reader	卡片阅读机	Kǎpiàn yuèdújī	C/R
Card reader/encoder	卡读写器/编码器	Kǎ dúxiěqì/biānmǎqì	CR/E
Card-to-card interleaving	卡到卡交错存取	Kǎ dào kǎ jiāocuò cúnqǔ	C2C
Care-of address	转交地址	Zhuǎnjiāo dìzhǐ	
Carpal tunnel sydrome	计算机腕管综合症	Jìsuànjī wànguǎn zōnghézhèng	CTS
Carriage and insurance paid	运费、保险费付至	Yùnfèi、bǎoxiǎnfèi fù zhì	CIP
Carriage for cabling	电缆敷设车	Diànlǎn fūshè chē	
Carriage for frequency converting	变频车	Biànpín chē	
Carriage for repair equipment	工程修理车	Gōngchéng xiūlǐ chē	
Carriage paid to	运费付至	Yùnfèi fù zhì	CPT
Carriage return	回车	Huíchē	CR
Carrier component	载波分量	Zàibō fènliàng	
Carrier detect	载波检测	Zàibō jiǎncè	CD
Carrier detection failure rate	载波检测失败率	Zàibō jiǎncè shībài lǜ	
Carrier detector	载波检测器	Zàibō jiǎncèqì	CD
Carrier digits	运营商数字	Yùnyíngshāng shùzì	CD
Carrier distribution frame	载波分配架	Zàibō fēnpèi jià	CDF
Carrier drop	载波跌落	Zàibō diēluò	
Carrier frequency	载频	Zàipín	
Carrier frequency deviation	载波频偏	Zàibō pínpiān	
Carrier frequency offset	载波频率偏置	Zàibō pínlǜ piānzhì	
Carrier frequency telephone repeater	载波电话中继器	Zàibō diànhuà zhōngjìqì	CRF
Carrier frequency telephone repeater	载频电话中继器	Zàipín diànhuà zhōngjìqì	CRF
Carrier frequency telephony	载波电话	Zàibō diànhuà	CFT
Carrier identification code	承载者标识码	Chéngzàizhě biāozhì mǎ	CIC
Carrier identification code	营商标识码	Yíngshāng biāoshí mǎ	CIC
Carrier identification code	运营商标识码	Yùnyíngshāng biāoshí mǎ	CIC
Carrier interface controller	载频接口控制器	Zàipín jiēkǒu kòngzhìqì	CIC
Carrier master-group modulation	载波主群调制	Zàibō zhǔqún tiáozhì	
Carrier phase	载波相位	Zàibō xiàngwèi	
Carrier power (of a radio transmitter)	载波功率	Zàibō gōnglǜ	PZ
Carrier recovery	载波恢复	Zàibō huīfù	
Carrier recovery loop	载波恢复环路	Zàibō huīfù huánlù	CRL
Carrier reduction	载波降低度	Zàibō jiàngdīdù	

Carrier sense multiple access	载波检测多址	Zàibō jiǎncè duōzhǐ	CSMA
Carrier sense multiple access	载波控制多路存取	Zàibō kòngzhì duōlù cúnqǔ	CSMA
Carrier sense multiple access	载波侦听多址访问	Zàibō zhēntīng duōzhǐ fǎngwèn	CSMA
Carrier sense multiple access with collision avoidance	载波侦听多址接入/避免冲撞协议	Zàibō zhēntīng duōzhǐ jiērù/ bìmiǎn chōngzhuàng xiéyì	CSMA/CA
Carrier sense multiple access with collision detection	载波侦听多址接入/碰撞检测协议	Zàibō zhēntīng duōzhǐ jiērù/ pèngzhuàng jiǎncè xiéyì	CSMA/CD
Carrier service area	电信公司服务区	Diànxìn gōngsī fúwùqū	CSA
Carrier service area	电信公司营运服务区	Diànxìn gōngsī yíngyùn fúwùqū	CSA
Carrier service area	营运服务区	Yíngyùn fúwùqū	CSA
Carrier suppression	载波抑制度	Zàibō yìzhìdù	
Carrier telephone	载波电话	Zàibō diànhuà	CT, ZH
Carrier telephone repeater	载波电话增音机	Zàibō diànhuà zēngyīnjī	
Carrier telephone terminal	载波电话终端机	Zàibō diànhuà zhōngduānjī	
Carrier to interference ratio	载干比	Zài gān bǐ	CIR
Carrier to interference ratio	载波干扰比	Zàibō gānrǎo bǐ	CIR
Carrier to noise ratio	载噪比	Zài zào bǐ	C/N
Carrier transmission	载波传输	Zàibō chuánshū	
Carrier unit mother board	载频单元框背板	Zàipín dānyuán kuàngbèibǎn	CUB
Carrier virtual circuit	载波虚拟电路	Zàibō xūnǐ diànlù	CVC
Carrier wave	载波	Zàibō	CW
Carrier/composite second order beat	载波复合二次差拍比	Zàibō fùhé èrcì chāpāi bǐ	C/CSO
Carrier/composite triple beat	载波复合三次差拍比	Zàibō fùhé sāncì chāpāi bǐ	C/CTB
Carrierless amplitude and phase modulation	无线波调幅与调相	Wúxiànbō tiáofú yǔ tiáoxiàng	CAP
Carrierless amplitude and phase modulation	无载波幅相调制	Wúzàibō fú xiāng tiáozhì	CAP
Carrierless amplitude/phase (CAP) coding	抑制载波幅度/相位编码	Yìzhì zàibō fúdù/xiàngwèi biānmǎ	
Carrierless amplitude/phase modulation	无载波调幅/调相	Wúzàibō tiáofú/tiáoxiàng	CAP
Carrier-sense multiple access with collision detection	带碰撞检测的载波侦听多址访问	Dài pèngzhuàng jiǎncède zàibō zhēntīng duōzhǐ fǎngwèn	CSMA/CD
Carrier-to-noise ratio	载波比	Zàibō bǐ	CTNR
Carrier-to-thermal noise ratio	载波-热噪声比	Zàibō—rè zàoshēng bǐ	CTNR
Carry (mathematical term)	进位	Jìnwèi	CAR
Cartogram	比较统计地图	Bǐjiào tǒngjì dìtú	
Cartographic analysis	地图分析	Dìtú fēnxī	
Cartographic communication	地图传输	Dìtú chuánshū	
Cartographic data	制图数据	Zhìtú shùjù	
Cartographic database	地图数据库	Dìtú shùjùkù	
Cartographic expert system	制图专家系统	Zhìtú zhuānjiā xìtǒng	
Cartographic generalization	制图综合	Zhìtú zōnghé	
Cartographic information	地图信息	Dìtú xìnxī	
Cartographic information system	地图信息系统	Dìtú xìnxī xìtǒng	
Cartographic language	地图语言	Dìtú yǔyán	
Cartographic modeling	地图模拟	Dìtú mónǐ	
Cartographic semantics	地图语义	Dìtú yǔyì	
Cartographic semiology	地图符号学	Dìtú fúhàoxué	
Cartographic symbol	制图符号	Zhìtú fúhào	

English	Chinese	Pinyin	Abbr.
Cartographic syntax	地图句法	Dìtú jùfǎ	
Cartographic syntax	地图语法	Dìtú yǔfǎ	
Cartography	地图学	Dìtúxué	
Cartometry	地图测量学	Dìtú cèliángxué	
Cascade	串级	Chuànjí	
Cascade (Windows command)	层叠视窗	Céngdié shìchuāng	
Cascade amplifier	级联放大器	Jílián fàngdàqì	CA
Cascade amplifier transmitter	级联放大发射机	Jílián fàngdà fāshèjī	
Cascaded network	级联网络	Jílián wǎngluò	
Cascaded operation (in SQL Server)	级联运行	Jílián yùnxíng	
Cascading delete (for database)	级联删除	Jílián shānchú	
Cascading referential integrity constraints (in SQL Server)	级联参考完整性约束	Jílián cānkǎo wánzhěng xìng yuēshù	
Cascading style sheets	层叠格式表	Céngdié géshi biǎo	CSS
Cascading update (for database)	级联更新	Jílián gēngxīn	
Cascading, cascade connection	级联	Jílián	
Case key	事例键	Shìlì jiàn	
Case set	事例集	Shìlì jí	
Case shift	键位转移	Jiànwèi zhuǎnyí	
Case study	案例分析	Ànlì fēnxī	
Case; casing; shell; housing	外壳	Wàiké	
Case-based reasoning	案例推理	Ànlì tuīlǐ	CBR
Case-based reasoning	基于案例推理	Jīyú ànlì tuīlǐ	
Case-based reasoning	基于范例推理	Jīyú fànlì tuīlǐ	CBR
Case-sensitive	区分大小写	Qūfēn dàxiǎo xiě	
Cash to account	现金到财户	Xiànjīn dào cáihù	
Cash to cash	现金到现金	Xiànjīn dào xiànjīn	
Casing	套管	Tàoguǎn	
Casio (Japanese company)	卡西鸥	Kǎ-xī-ōu	
Cassegrain reflector antenna	卡塞格伦反射器天线	Kǎ-sāi-gé-lún fǎnshè qì tiānxiàn	
Casting	造型转换	Zàoxíng zhuǎnhuàn	
Casting	转型	Zhuǎnxíng	
Casual inspection	不定期检查	Bùdìngqī jiǎnchá	
Catadioptric lens	反射折射透镜	Fǎnshè zhéshè tòujìng	
Catalog	目录	Mùlù	
Catalogue of newspapers and periodicals	报刊目录	Bàokān mùlù	
Catastrophic failure, cataleptic failure	灾变性失效	Zāibiànxìng shīxiào	
Categorical attribute	类型属性	Lèixíng shǔxìng	
Categories of access	接入种类	Jiērù zhǒnglèi	
Category 1 cabling	第一类电缆	Dìyīlèi diànlǎn	Cat-1
Category 2 cabling	第二类电缆	Dì'èrlèi diànlǎn	Cat-2
Category 3 cabling	第三类电缆	Dìsānlèi diànlǎn	Cat-3
Category 4 cabling	第四类电缆	Dìsìlèi diànlǎn	Cat-4
Category 5 wiring	五类线	Wǔ lèi xiàn	
Category analysis	类别分析	Lèibié fēnxī	
Category code	类型码	Lèixíng mǎ	
Cathode grid	阴极栅	Yīnjí zhà	CG

Cathode modulator	阴极脉冲调制器	Yīnjí màichōng tiáozhìqì	
Cathode ray tube	阴极射线管	Yīnjí shèxiàn guǎn	CRT
Cathode ray tube	阴极线管	Yīnjí xiàn guǎn	CRT
Cavitation	空化	Kōnghuà	
Cavity filter	控腔滤波器	Kòngqiāng lǜbōqì	
Cavity frequency meter	谐振腔频率计	Xiézhènqiāng pínlǜjì	
Cavity oscillator	空腔型振荡器	Kōngqiāng-xíng zhèndàngqì	
Cavity resonator	空腔谐器	Kōngqiāng xiéqì	
Cavity resonator	空腔谐振器	Kōngqiāng xiézhèn	
Cavity resonator	空腔谐振器	Kōngqiāng xiézhènqì	
Cavity resonator	谐振腔	Xiézhèn qiāng	
Cavity-stabilized local oscillator	空腔稳频本地振荡器	Kōngqiāng wěnpín běndì zhèndàngqì	
CCP call control	CCP 呼叫控制	CCP hūjiào kòngzhì	CCC
CCP data access	CCP 数据存取	CCP shùjù cúnqǔ	CDA
CCP diagnostics	CCP 诊断	CCP zhěnduàn	CDIA
CCP fault manager	CCP 故障管理	CCP gùzhàng guǎnlǐ	CFM
CCP measurement	CCP 测量	CCP cèliáng	CMEA
CCP message handling	CCP 消息处理	CCP xiāoxi chǔlǐ	CMH
CCP processor loader	CCP 处理器承载器	CCP chǔlǐqì chéngzàiqì	CPL
CCP resource allocation	CCP 资源分配	CCP zīyuán fēnpèi	CRA
CCP resource manager	CCP 资源管理器	CCP zīyuán guǎnlǐqì	CRM
CCP sanity loader	CCP 正常运行承载器	CCP zhèngcháng yùnxíng chéngzàiqì	CSM
CCP sanity manager	CCP 正常运行管理器	CCP zhèngcháng yùnxíng guǎnlǐqì	CSMN
CCP status handling	CCP 状态处理	CCP zhuàngtài chǔlǐ	CSH
CCP system loader	CCP 系统承载器	CCP xìtǒng chéngzàiqì	CSL
CD recordable	可记录光盘	Kějìlù guāngpán	CDR
CDMA channel element assembly	CDMA 信道元件	CDMA xìndào yuánjiàn	CCEA
CDMA development group	CDMA 发展组织	CDMA fāzhǎn zǔzhī	CDG
CDMA Development Group (North America)	CDMA 发展集团	CDMA fāzhǎn jítuán	CDG
CDMA digital channel sub-system	CDMA 数字信道子系统	CDMA shùzì xìndào zixìtǒng	CDCS
CDMA modulation and demodulation block	CDMA 调制与解调模块	CDMA tiáozhì yǔ jiětiáo mókuài	CMDB
CDPD network entity identifier authentication protocol	CDPD 网络实体标识符证实协议	CDPD wǎngluò shítǐ biāozhìfú zhèngshí xiéyì	CNA-P
CDPD network entity identifier authentication service user	CDPD 网络实体标识符服务用户证实	CDPD wǎngluò shítǐ biāozhìfú fúwù yònghù zhèngshí	CNA-SU
Ceiling mounted type	吸顶式	Xīdǐng-shì	C
Ceiling suction antenna, ceiling-mount antenna	吸顶式天线	Xīdǐng-shì tiānxiàn	
Cell	单元	Dānyuán	
Cell (frequency) allocation	小区（频率）分配	Xiǎoqū (pínlǜ) fēnpèi	CA
Cell (mobile telephone coverage area)	小区	Xiǎoqū	
Cell (of a digital information block or digital signal)	信元	Xìnyuán	
Cell access permission	小区存取允许	Xiǎoqū cúnqǔ yǔnxǔ	
Cell allocation	蜂窝配置	Fēngwō pèizhì	CA
Cell allocation	小区配置	Xiǎoqū pèizhì	CA
Cell allocation (GSM term)	小区分配	Xiǎoqū fēnpèi	
Cell and time discount service	分区分时计费业务	Fēnqū fēnshí jìfèi yèwù	

Cell antenna unit	小区天线单元	Xiǎoqū tiānxiàn dānyuán	CAU
Cell bar qualify	小区禁止限制	Xiǎoqū jìnzhǐ xiànzhì	CBQ
Cell border (WP command)	方格边框	Fānggé biānkuàng	
Cell broadcast	小区广播	Xiǎoqū guǎngbō	CB
Cell broadcast center	小区广播短消息中心	Xiǎoqū guǎngbō duǎnxiāoxi zhōngxīn	CBC
Cell broadcast center	小区广播中心	Xiǎoqū guǎngbō zhōngxīn	CBC
Cell broadcast channel	小区广播信道	Xiǎoqū guǎngbō xìndào	
Cell broadcast control channel	小区广播控制信道	Xiǎoqū guǎngbō kòngzhì xìndào	CBCH
Cell broadcast entity	小区广播实体	Xiǎoqū guǎngbō shítǐ	CBE
Cell broadcast message identifier	小区广播消息识别符	Xiǎoqū guǎngbō xiāoxi shíbiéfú	CBMI
Cell broadcast service	小区广播业务	Xiǎoqū guǎngbō yèwù	CBS
Cell broadcast short message	小区广播短消息	Xiǎoqū guǎngbō duǎnxiāoxi	CBSM
Cell broadcast short message service	小区广播短消息业务	Xiǎoqū guǎngbō duǎnxiāoxi yèwù	CBSMS
Cell channel description	小区信道描述	Xiǎoqū xìndào miáoshù	
Cell code (video term)	像元码	Xiàngyuán mǎ	
Cell coverage area	小区覆盖范围	Xiǎoqū fùgài fànwéi	
Cell delay variation	信元时延变化	Xìnyuán shíyán biànhuà	CDV
Cell delay variation	信元延迟变化	Xìnyuán yánchí biànhuà	CDV
Cell delay variation tolerance	信元时延变化容限	Xìnyuán shíyán biànhuà róngxiàn	CDVT
Cell delay variation tolerance	信元延迟变化容限	Xìnyuán yánchí biànhuà róngxiàn	CDVT
Cell delineation	信元定界	Xìnyuán dìngjiè	
Cell delineation	信元描述	Xìnyuán miáoshù	
Cell description	小区描述	Xiǎoqū miáoshù	
Cell error rate	误信元率	Wùxìnyuán lǜ	CER
Cell error rate	信元差错率	Xìnyuán chācuò lǜ	CER
Cell error rate	信元错误率	Xìnyuán cuòwù lǜ	CER
Cell global identification	全球小区识别	Quánqiú xiǎoqū shíbié	CGI
Cell global identification	小区全球识别	Xiǎoqū quánqiú shíbié	CGI
Cell header	信头	Xìntóu	
Cell header	信元头	Xìnyuán tóu	
Cell identity	小区标识号	Xiǎoqū biāozhì hào	CI
Cell identity	小区身份	Xiǎoqū shēnfen	
Cell identity	小区识别	Xiǎoqū shíbié	CI
Cell loss priority	信元标明丢失优先度	Xìnyuán biāomíng diūshī yōuxiān dù	CLP
Cell loss priority	信元丢弃优先级	Xìnyuán diūqì yōuxiān jí	CLP
Cell loss priority	信元丢失优先	Xìnyuán diūshī yōuxiān	CLP
Cell loss priority	信元丢失优先级	Xìnyuán diūshī yōuxiān jí	CLP
Cell loss priority	信元丢失优先权	Xìnyuán diūshī yōuxiānquán	CLP
Cell loss rate	信元丢失率	Xìnyuán diūshī lǜ	CLR
Cell loss rate (CLR) for high priority cells (only those with CLP=0)	CLP 为 0 信元的信元丢失率	CLP wéi 0 xìnyuánde xìnyuán diūshī lǜ	CLR0
Cell loss rate (CLR) for the aggregate cell stream containing both cell loss priority (CLP)=0 and CLP=1 cells	CLP 为 0 和 1 的总的信元丢失率	CLP wéi 0 hé 1de zǒngde xìnyuán diūshī lǜ	CLR0+1
Cell mis-insertion rate	信元误插率	Xìnyuán wùchā lǜ	CMR
Cell of origin	源小区	Yuán xiǎoqū	COO
Cell payload encryption or scrambling	信元数据加密	Xìnyuán shùjù jiāmì	
Cell radio network temporary identity	无线蜂窝网络临时识别	Wúxiàn fēngwō wǎngluò línshí shíbié	C-RNTI

Cell rate decoupling	信元速率解耦	Xìnyuán sùlǜ jiě'ǒu	
Cell rate margin	信元速率边际	Xìnyuán sùlǜ biānjì	CRM
Cell re-select offset	小区重选偏移量	Xiǎoqū chóngxuǎn piānyí liáng	CRO
Cell re-selection blocking	小区重选滞后	Xiǎoqū chóngxuǎn zhìhòu	
Cell re-selection hysteresis parameter	小区重选滞后参数	Xiǎoqū chóngxuǎn zhìhòu cānshù	
Cell reselection offset	小区重先偏置	Xiǎoqū chóngxiān piānzhì	CRO
Cell resolution	像元分辨率	Xiàngyuán fēnbiànlǜ	
Cell sectorize	网孔裂向	Wǎngkǒng lièxiàng	
Cell set	单元集	Dānyuán jí	
Cell shading (WP command)	方格背景	Fānggé bèijǐng	
Cell short message broadcasting	小区短消息广播	Xiǎoqū duǎnxiāoxi guǎngbō	
Cell site alarm assembly	小区告警集成件	Xiǎoqū gàojǐng jíchéng jiàn	CSAA
Cell site controller	小区控制器	Xiǎoqū kòngzhìqì	CSC
Cell site modem software	小区调制解调软件	Xiǎoqū tiáozhì jiětiáo ruǎnjiàn	CSMS
Cell size	删格大小	Shāngé dàxiǎo	
Cell split	网孔分裂	Wǎngkǒng fēnliè	
Cell switching router	信元交换路由器	Xìnyuán jiāohuàn lùyóuqì	CSR
Cell transfer delay	信元传输时延	Xìnyuán chuánshū shíyán	CTD
Cell transfer delay	信元传送时延	Xìnyuán chuánsòng shíyán	CTD
Cell transfer delay	信元传送延迟	Xìnyuán chuánsòng yánchí	CTD
Cell transfer delay	信元转移时延	Xìnyuán zhuǎnyí shí yán	CTD
Cell-based	基于信元	Jīyú xìnyuán	
Cellular authentication and voice encryption	蜂窝鉴权及话音加密	Fēngwō jiànquán jí huàyīn jiāmì	CAVE
Cellular automata	单元自动机	Dānyuán zìdòngjī	CA
Cellular automata	细胞自动机	Xìbāo zìdòngjī	CA
Cellular automaton	元胞自动机	Yuánbāo zìdòngjī	
Cellular digital packet data	蜂窝数字分组数据	Fēngwō shùzì fēnzǔ shùjù	CDPD
Cellular digital packet data	数字蜂窝分组数据	Shùzì fēngwō fēnzǔ shùjù	CDPD
Cellular geographic service area	蜂窝地理服务区	Fēngwō dìlǐ fúwùqū	CGSA
Cellular handset	蜂窝手持机	Fēngwō shǒuchíjī	
Cellular message encryption algorithm	蜂窝信息加密算法	Fēngwō xìnxī jiāmì suànfǎ	CEMA
Cellular mobile radio	蜂窝式移动通信系统	Fēngwō-shì yídòng tōngxìn xìtǒng	CMR
Cellular mobile radiotelephone service	蜂窝式移动无线电话业务	Fēngwō-shì yídòng wúxiàn diànhuà yèwù	CMRS
Cellular mobile system	蜂窝式移动通信系统	Fēngwō-shì yídòng tōngxìn xìtǒng	CMS
Cellular model (CAD/CAM)	单元体模型	Dānyuántǐ móxíng	
Cellular network administrator	蜂窝网络管理器	Fēngwō wǎngluò guǎnlǐqì	CAN
Cellular network administrator interface	蜂窝网络管理器界面	Fēngwō wǎngluò guǎnlǐqì jièmiàn	CNAI
Cellular radiotelephone service	蜂窝无线电话服务	Fēngwō wúxiàn diànhuà fúwù	CRS
Cellular system	蜂窝系统	Fēngwō xìtǒng	
Cellular Telecommunications Industry Association	蜂窝通信工业协会	Fēngwō tōngxìn gōngyè xiéhuì	CTIA
Cellular Telecommunications Industry Association (US)	蜂窝电信工业协会	Fēngwō diànxìn gōngyè xiéhuì	CTIA
Center	中心	Zhōngxīn	
Center axis diameter	心轴直径	Xīnzhóu zhíjìng	
Center clipping	中心削波	Zhōngxīn xiāobō	
Center for Innovative Computer Application	计算机应用开发中心	Jìsuànjī yìngyòng kāifā zhōngxīn	CICA
Center line	中心线	Zhōngxīnxiàn	

Center loose tube optical fiber ribbon cable	中心管式光纤带光缆	Zhōngxīn guǎn shì guāngxiān dài guānglǎn	
Center manifold	中心流形	Zhōngxīn liúxíng	
Center of gravity	重心	Zhòngxīn	
Center of gravity character string	重心字符串	Zhòngxīn zìfúchuàn	
Center of International Cooperation for Computerization (Japan)	计算机化国际合作中心	Jìsuànjīhuà guójì hézuò zhōngxīn	CICC
Center point	中心点	Zhōngxīndiǎn	
Center radiation	中心辐射	Zhōngxīn fúshè	
Center-based tree	有核树	Yǒuhé shù	
Centered	居中	Jūzhōng	
Central bundled optical cable	中心束管式光缆	Zhōngxīn shùguǎnshì guānglǎn	
Central control maintenance sub-system	中央控制维护子系统	Zhōngyāng kòngzhì wéihù zixìtǒng	CCMS
Central control post	中央控制台	Zhōngyāng kòngzhìtái	
Central control station	中心控制站	Zhōngxīn kòngzhì zhàn	CCS
Central controller	中央控制器	Zhōngyāng kòngzhìqì	
Central equipment identity register	中心设备识别寄存器	Zhōngxīn shèbèi shíbié jìcúnqì	CEIR
Central equipment identity register	中央设备识别寄存器	Zhōngyāng shèbèi shíbié jìcúnqì	CEIR
Central frequency	中心频率	Zhōngxīn pínlǜ	CF
Central frequency deviation (or offset)	中心频率偏移	Zhōngxīn pínlǜ piānyí	
Central frequency tolerance	中心频率容限	Zhōngxīn pínlǜ róngxiàn	
Central loose tube (FOC)	中心束管	Zhōngxīn shùguǎn	
Central office	中心局	Zhōngxīn jú	CO
Central office ADSL transmission unit	局端 ADSL 收发单元	Júduān ADSL shōufā dānyuán	ATU-C
Central office code	总局代码	Zǒngjú dàimǎ	COC
Central office line U reference point	局端线路 U 参考点	Júduān xiànlù U cānkǎo diǎn	U-C
Central office line U reference point 2	局端线路 U 参考点 2	Júduān xiànlù U cānkǎo diǎn 2	U-C2
Central office terminal	局端机	Júduānjī	COT
Central office termination	局端	Júduān	COT
Central office V reference point	局端 V 参考点	Júduān V cānkǎo diǎn	V-C
Central processing unit utilization	中央处理器占用率	Zhōngyāng chǔlǐqì zhànyòng lǜ	
Central processor	中央处理机	Zhōngyāng chǔlǐjī	
Central processor element	中央处理单元	Zhōngyāng chǔlǐ dānyuán	
Central processor unit	中央处理器	Zhōngyāng chǔlǐqì	CPU
Central publisher (in SQL Server)	中心出版者	Zhōngxīn chūbǎnzhě	
Central publisher with remote distributor (in SQL Server)	带有远程分发者的中心出版者	Dàiyǒu yuǎnchéng fēnfā zhěde zhōngxīn chūbǎnzhě	
Central radio station	中心射频站	Zhōngxīn shèpínzhàn	CRS
Central station	中心站	Zhōngxīnzhàn	CS
Central strength member (FOC)	中心加强件	Zhōngxīn jiāqiáng jiàn	CSM
Central subscriber (in SQL Server)	中心订购者	Zhōngxīn dìnggòuzhě	
Central switching hub	中央交换式集线器	Zhōngyāng jiāohuànshì jíxiànqì	CSH
Central switching sub-system	中央交换子系统	Zhōngyāng jiāohuàn zixìtǒng	CSS
Central switching-network control	集中交换网络控制	Jízhōng jiāohuàn wǎngluò kòngzhì	CSC
Central tube (FOC mfg)	缆中心管	Lǎn zhōngxīn guǎn	
Central tube type (FOC mfg)	中心管式	Zhōngxīn guǎn shì	
Central wavelength	中心波长	Zhōngxīn bōcháng	
Central wavelength tolerance	中心波长容限	Zhōngxīn bōcháng róngxiàn	

Centrality	集中性	Jízhōngxìng	
Centralized automatic message accounting	集中自动处理记帐	Jízhōng zìdòng chǔlǐ jìzhàng	CAMA
Centralized automatic message accounting	集中式自动电报计费	Jízhōng-shì zìdòng diànbào jìfèi	CAMA
Centralized automatic message accounting system	集中式自动通话记帐系统	Jízhōng-shì zìdòng tōnghuà jìzhàng xìtǒng	CAMA
Centralized control	集中控制	Jízhōng kòngzhì	
Centralized database	集中式数据库	Jízhōng-shì shùjùkù	CDB
Centralized multipoint	集中式多点	Jízhōng-shì duōdiǎn	
Centralized overlay function	集中叠加功能	Jízhōng diéjiā gōngnéng	
Centralized processing	集中式处理	Jízhōng-shì chǔlǐ	
Centralized real-time database	集中式实时数据库	Jízhōng-shì shíshí shùjùkù	CRTDB
Centralized service control	集中业务控制	Jízhōng yèwù kòngzhì	CSC
Centralized supervisory and control equipment	集中监控设备	Jízhōng jiānkòng shèbèi	CSC
Centralized supervisory and control equipment	集中监视和控制设备	Jízhōng jiānshì hé kòngzhì shèbèi	CSC
Central-level management center	中央级管理中心	Zhōngyāng jí guǎnlǐ zhōngxīn	C-PMS
Centroid	形心曲线	Xíngxīn qǔxiàn	
Centroid	质心	Zhìxīn	
CEPT digital trunk interface	CEPT 数字中继接口	CEPT shùzì zhōngjì jiēkǒu	CDIT
Ceramic ferrule (pipe)	陶瓷套管	Táocí tàoguǎn	
Ceramic ferrule (ring)	陶瓷箍	Táocí gū	
Ceramic pin grid array	陶瓷针型栅格阵列	Táocí zhēn-xíng zhàgé zhènliè	CPGA
Certainty factor	可信度	Kěxìndù	
Certificate	证件	Zhèngjiàn	
Certificate	证书	Zhèngshū	
Certificate agreement	证书协议	Zhèngshū xiéyì	
Certificate authority	认证管理机构	Rènzhèng guǎnlǐ jīgòu	CA
Certificate authority	证书授权	Zhèngshū shòuquán	CA
Certificate blacklist	证书黑名单	Zhèngshū hēimíngdān	
Certificate configuration message	检验机构消息	Jiǎnyàn jīgòu xiāoxi	CCM
Certificate configuration message	认证机构消息	Rènzhèng jīgòu xiāoxi	CCM
Certificate expired message (IPsec TLS)	证书期满消息	Zhèngshū qīmǎn xiāoxi	
Certificate issuer	签发机构名	Qiānfā jīgòu míng	
Certificate library	证书库	Zhèngshū kù	CL
Certificate of conformity	合格证书	Hégé zhèngshū	
Certificate revocation list	证书废除列表	Zhèngshū fèichú lièbiǎo	CRL
Certificate revocation list	证书作废表	Zhèngshū zuòfèi biǎo	CRL
Certificate revocation list (IPsec)	证书撤销列表	Zhèngshū chèxiāo lièbiǎo	CRL
Certificate trust list	证书信任列表	Zhèngshū xìnrèn lièbiǎo	CTL
Certificate unknown message (IPsec TLS)	证书未知消息	Zhèngshū wèizhī xiāoxi	
Certificate withdrawn message (IPsec TLS)	证书撤回消息	Zhèngshū chèhuí xiāoxi	
Certificate, credential (IPsec)	凭证	Píngzhèng	
Certification authority	认证当局	Rènzhèng dāngjú	CA
Certification authority	认证管理部门	Rènzhèng guǎnlǐ bùmén	CA
Certification authority	认证职权	Rènzhèng zhíquán	CA
Certification authority	认证中心	Rènzhèng zhōngxīn	CA
Certification authority	验证授权机构	Yànzhèng shòuquán jīgòu	
Certification authority	证件授权机构	Zhèngjiàn shòuquán jīgòu	CA

English	Chinese	Pinyin	Abbr.
Certification authority	证书管理机构	Zhèngshū guǎnlǐ jīgòu	CA
Certification path	证件途径	Zhèngjiàn tújìng	
Certification practice statement	使用证明书	Shǐyòng zhèngmíngshū	CPS
Chaff	箔条	Bótiáo	
Chaff	干扰物	Gānrǎo wù	
Chaff cloud	干扰云	Gānrǎo yún	
Chaff dipole	干扰偶极子	Gānrǎo ǒujízi	
Chaff package	干扰包	Gānrǎo bāo	
Chaff simulator	干扰物模拟器	Gānrǎo wù mónǐqì	
Chain code	链代码	Liàn dàimǎ	
Chain (function calls)	链	Liàn	
Chainage (distance obtained using surveyor chain)	以测链量得的距离	Yǐ cè liànliàng déde jùlí	
Chainage offset	测链支距	Cèliàn zhījù	
Chainage referencing	测链参照	Cèliàn cānzhào	
Chainage referencing features	测链参照地物	Cèliàn cānzhào dìwù	
Chainage referencing section	测链参照区段	Cèliàn cānzhào qūduàn	
Chained addressing	链式寻址	Liàn-shì xúnzhǐ	CA
Chaining search	链搜索	Liàn sōusuǒ	
Chaining, join	链接	Liànjiē	
Chairman node (in CSCW)	主席节点	Zhǔxí jiédiǎn	
Chalcogenide	硫屬化合物	Liúshǔhuà héwù	
Chalcogenide glass optical fiber	掺磷光纤	Chān lín guāngxiàn	
Challenge handshake authentication protocol	质询握手验证协议	Zhìxún wòshǒu yànzhèng xiéyì	CHAP
Challenge handshake authentication protocol (IPsec)	挑战握手认证协议	Tiǎozhàn wòshǒu rènzhèng xiéyì	CHAP
Challenge response mechanism (IPsec)	挑战应答机制	Tiǎozhàn yìngdá jīzhì	
Challenge-handshake authentication protocol	盘问握手认证协议	Pánwèn wòshǒu rènzhèng xiéyì	CHAP
Challenge-handshake authentication protocol	握手认证协议	Wòshǒu rènzhèng xiéyì	CHAP
Change back acknowledgement	返回正常信道应答	Fǎnhuí zhèngcháng xìndào yìngdá	CBA
Change back declaration signal	返回正常通道说明信号	Fǎnhuí zhèngcháng tōngdào shuōmíng xìnhào	CBD
Change of power line voltage	电源电压变化试验	Diànyuán diànyā biànhuà shìyàn	
Change script	更改脚本	Gēnggǎi jiǎoběn	
Changeback	倒回	Dǎohuí	
ChangeCipherSpec protocol (IPsec)	改变密码说明协议	Gǎibiàn mìmǎ shuōmíng xiéyì	
Changed address interception	更改地址窃取	Gēnggǎi dìzhǐ qièqǔ	
Changed polarization feed	变极化馈电器	Biànjíhuà kuìdiànqì	
Changeover	倒换	Dǎohuàn	
Change-over	转换	Zhuǎnhuàn	
Changeover acknowledge signal	倒换证实信号	Dǎohuàn zhèngshí xìnhào	COA
Changeover signal	倒换信号	Dǎohuàn xìnhào	COO
Changing address of delivery for newspapers and periodicals	报刊改寄	Bàokān gǎijì	
Changing dimension	可更改维度	Kěgēnggǎi wéidù	
Changing number acknowledge	改号通知	Gǎihào tōngzhī	CAN
Channel	通道	Tōngdào	
Channel	信道	Xìndào	
Channel (preferred), path	通路	Tōnglù	

Channel access code	信道访问码	Xìndào fǎngwèn mǎ	CAC
Channel access protocol	通道存取协议	Tōngdào cúnqǔ xiéyì	CAP
Channel access protocol	信道访问协议	Xìndào fǎngwèn xiéyì	CAP
Channel adapter mode register	通道适配器方式寄存器	Tōngdào shìpèiqì fāngshì jìcúnqì	CAMR
Channel addition	波道增	Bōdào zēng	
Channel address register	通道地址寄存器	Tōngdào dìzhǐ jìcúnqì	CAR
Channel address translator	通道地址翻译器	Tōngdào dìzhǐ fānyìqì	CAT
Channel allocation	波道配置	Bōdào pèizhì	
Channel allocation failure rate	信道分配失败率	Xìndào fēnpèi shībài lǜ	
Channel assignment	信道指配	Xìndào zhǐpèi	
Channel assignment order	通道分配命令	Tōngdào fēnpèi mìnglìng	CAO
Channel associated signaling	随路信令	Suílù xìnlìng	CAS
Channel associated signaling	相联通道信号传输	Xiānglián tōngdào xìnhào chuánshū	CAS
Channel availability table	通道可用性表	Tōngdào kěyòngxìng biǎo	CAT
Channel buffer pointer	通道缓冲器指针	Tōngdào huǎnchōngqì zhǐzhēn	CBP
Channel buffer storage	通道缓冲存储器	Tōngdào huǎnchōng cúnchǔqì	CBS
Channel buffer table	通道缓冲区表	Tōngdào huǎnchōngqū biǎo	CBT
Channel bundle (or binding) (IPsec)	信道捆绑	Xìndào kǔnbǎng	
Channel capacity	信道容量	Xìndào róngliàng	
Channel card interface controller	信道卡接口控制器	Xìndào kǎ jiēkǒu kòngzhìqì	CIC
Channel card manager	信道卡管理器	Xìndào kǎ guǎnlǐqì	CCM
Channel check test	通道检测	Tōngdào jiǎncè	CCT
Channel coding	信道编码	Xìndào biānmǎ	
Channel coding unit	信道编解码单元	Xìndào biānjiěmǎ dānyuán	CCU
Channel command word	通道命令字	Tōngdào mìnglìng zì	CCW
Channel data block length	信道数据块长度	Xìndào shùjù kuài chángdù	
Channel decoder	信道解码器	Xìndào jiěmǎqì	CHD
Channel division multiplexer	通道分组多路器	Tōngdào fēnzǔ duōlùqì	CDM
Channel efficiency	信道效率	Xìndào xiàolǜ	
Channel element	信道元件	Xìndào yuánjiàn	CE
Channel element back board	信道元件后面板	Xìndào yuánjiàn hòumian bǎn	CEBB
Channel element control manager	信道元件控制管理器	Xìndào yuánjiàn kòngzhì guǎnlǐqì	CECM
Channel element unit rack	信道元件单元机架	Xìndào yuánjiàn dānyuán jījià	CEUR
Channel encoder	信道编码器	Xìndào biānmǎqì	CHE
Channel encoding speed	信道编码速率	Xìndào biānmǎ sùlǜ	
Channel encoding speed, short for 信道编码速率	信码速率	Xìn mǎ sùlǜ	
Channel evaluation and call	通道坚定和呼叫	Tōngdào jiāndìng hé hūjiào	CHEC
Channel flow control	通道信息流控制	Tōngdào xìnxī liú kòngzhì	CFC
Channel gain	波道增益	Bōdào zēngyì	
Channel gate	信道门	Xìndào mén	
Channel grant	通道许可	Tōngdào xǔkě	CG
Channel hop	跳信道	Tiào xìndào	
Channel hopping sequence	信道跳频序列	Xìndào tiàopín xùliè	
Channel identification	通路确认	Tōnglù quèrèn	
Channel identification	信道标志	Xìndào biāozhì	
Channel identification	信道标识	Xìndào biāozhì	

Channel interface circuit	信道接口电路	Xìndào jiēkǒu diànlù	
Channel interface processor	信道接口处理器	Xìndào jiēkǒu chǔlǐqì	CIP
Channel interleaving	信道交织	Xìndào jiāozhī	
Channel loading	信道负载	Xìndào fùzài	
Channel mode	信道模式	Xìndào móshì	
Channel mode modify	信道模式修改	Xìndào móshì xiūgǎi	
Channel noise figure	波道噪声系数	Bōdào zàoshēng xìshù	
Channel parameter	信道参数	Xìndào cānshù	CP
Channel rate	信道速率	Xìndào sùlǜ	CR
Channel reconfiguration hardware	通道重配置硬件	Tōngdào chóng pèizhì yìngjiàn	CRH
Channel release	信道释放	Xìndào shìfàng	
Channel removal	波道减	Bōdào jiǎn	
Channel request	信道请求	Xìndào qǐngqiú	
Channel request priority	通道请求优先	Tōngdào qǐngqiú yōuxiān	CRP
Channel selection unit	信道选配单板	Xìndào xuǎnpèi dānbǎn	CSU
Channel selective mode	信道选接方式	Xìndào xuǎnjiē fāngshì	
Channel selective mode	信道选择方式	Xìndào xuǎnzé fāngshì	
Channel separating filter	分路滤波器	Fēnlù lǜbōqì	CSF
Channel separation	声道分离	Shēngdào fēnlí	CS
Channel service unit	信道服务单元	Xìndào fúwù dānyuán	CSU
Channel signal-spontaneous noise figure	波道信号自发辐射噪声系数	Bōdào xìnhào zìfā fúshè zàoshēng xìshù	
Channel spacing	信道间隔	Xìndào jiàngé	
Channel status byte	通道状态字节	Tōngdào zhuàngtài zìjié	CSB
Channel status indicator	通道状态指示器	Tōngdào zhuàngtài zhǐshìqì	CSI
Channel stream identifier	信道流标识符	Xìndào liú biāozhì fú	CSI
Channel tester	信道测试仪	Xìndào cèshìyí	CT
Channel time slot	信道时隙	Xìndào shíxì	
Channel type	信道类型	Xìndào lèixíng	
Channel vocoder	通道音码器	Tōngdào yīnmǎqì	CV
Channel-attached	信道相连	Xìndào xiānglián	
Channeled substrate planar structure	沟道衬底平面结构	Gōudào chèndǐ píngmiàn jiégòu	CSP
Channelized E1	分时隙 E1	Fēnshíxì E1	
Channelized receiver	信道化接收机	Xìndàohuà jiēshōujī	
Chaos cryptography	混沌密码学	Hùndùn mìmǎ xué	
Chaos theory	混沌理论	Hùndùn lǐlùn	
Chaotic modulation	混沌调制	Hùndùn tiáozhì	
Chaotic spread spectrum communication system	混沌扩频通信系统	Hùndùn kuòpín tōngxìn xìtǒng	
Chaotic synchronization	混沌同步	Hùndùn tóngbù	
Character	字符	Zìfú	
Character address word	字符地址字	Zìfú dìzhǐ zì	CAW
Character alignment	字符定位	Zìfú dìngwèi	
Character alignment	字符同步	Zìfú tóngbù	
Character attribute	字符属性	Zìfú shǔxìng	CA
Character baseline	字符基线	Zìfú jīxiàn	
Character check	字符检验	Zìfú jiǎnyàn	
Character check bit	字符校验位	Zìfú jiàoyàn wèi	

Character cycle	字符周期	Zìfú zhōuqī	
Character error rate test	字符出错误率测试	Zìfú chū cuòwùlǜ cèshì	CERT
Character error rate tester	字符出错误率测试器	Zìfú chū cuòwùlǜ cèshìqì	CERT
Character error ratio	字符差错率	Zìfú chācuò lǜ	
Character format	字符格式	Zìfú géshi	
Character image	字符图像	Zìfú túxiàng	
Character in phase	字符同相	Zìfú tóngxiāng	
Character mode communications adapter	字符方式通信适配器	Zìfú fāngshì tōngxìn shìpèiqì	CMCA
Character orientation	字符取向	Zìfú qǔxiàng	
Character palette	字库	Zìkù	
Character path	字符走向	Zìfú zǒuxiàng	
Character rate	字符速率	Zìfú sùlǜ	
Character sequence	字符序列	Zìfú xùliè	
Character set	字符集	Zìfú jí	
Character signal	字符信号	Zìfú xìnhào	
Character size	字符长度	Zìfú chángdù	
Character spacing (for constant spacing fonts only)	字符间距（仅对固定间距字模而言）	Zìfú jiānjù (jǐn duì gùdìng jiānjù zìmú éryán)	
Character string	字符串	Zìfú chuàn	
Character string function	字符串函数	Zìfú chuàn hánshù	
Character string type	字符串类型	Zìfú chuàn lèixíng	
Character waiting integer	字符等待整体	Zìfú děngdài zhěngtǐ	CWI
Character waiting time	字符等待时间	Zìfú děngdài shíjiān	CWT
Character-byte serial transmission	字符-字节串行传输	Zìfú—zìjié chuànháng chuánshū	CBST
Characteristic distortion	特性畸变	Tèxìng jībiàn	
Characteristic frequency	特征频率	Tèzhēng pínlǜ	
Characteristic impedance	特性阻抗	Tèxìng zǔkàng	
Characteristic information	标识信息	Biāozhì xìnxī	CI
Characteristic information	特征信息	Tèzhēng xìnxī	CI
Characteristic polynomial	特征多项式	Tèzhēng duōxiàngshì	
Characteristic severity	严酷度等级	Yánkùdù děngjí	
Characteristic wave impedance (of a transmission line)	特性波阻抗	Tèxìng bō zǔkàng	
Characteristic waveform interpolation	特征波形内插	Tèzhēng bōxíng nèichā	CWI
Characterization test	鉴定测试	Jiàndìng cèshì	
Character-oriented communications controller	面向字符的通信控制器	Miànxiàng zìfúde tōngxìn kòngzhìqì	COC
Characters per inch	每寸多少字	Měi cùn duōshao zì	CPI
Characters per second	每秒多少字	Měi miǎo duōshao zì	CPS
Characters per second	每秒字符数	Měi miǎo zìfúshù	CPS
Charge (as a battery)	充电	Chōngdiàn	
Charge advice information	计费建议信息	Jìfèi jiànyì xìnxī	CAI
Charge advice information	收费通知信息	Shōufèi tōngzhī xìnxī	CAI
Charge coupled device	电荷连接设备	Diànhè liánjiē shèbèi	CCD
Charge coupled device	电荷耦合器件	Diànhè ǒuhé qìjiàn	CCD
Charge coupled device canceller	电荷耦合器件对消器	Diànhè ǒuhé qìjiàn duìxiāoqì	
Charge efficiency	充电效率	Chōngdiàn xiàolǜ	
Charge for reply to advice of non-delivery	答复无法投递通知单费	Dáfù wúfǎtóudì tōngzhīdān fèi	

Charge information (ISUP message)	计费信息	Jìfèi xìnxī	CRG
Charge neutralization	电荷中和	Diànhè zhōnghé	
Charge rate	充电率	Chōngdiànlǜ	
Charging	计费	Jìfèi	
Charging accounting sub-system	计费子系统	Jìfèi zixìtǒng	CAS
Charging circuit	充电电路	Chōngdiàn diànlù	
Charging equipment	计费设备	Jìfèi shèbèi	
Charging gateway	计费网关	Jìfèi wǎngguān	CG
Charging gateway function	计费网关功能	Jìfèi wǎngguān gōngnéng	CGF
Charging gateway functionality	计费网关功能性	Jìfèi wǎngguān gōngnéngxìng	CGF
Charging inductor	充电电感	Chōngdiàn diàngǎn	
Charging message	计费消息	Jìfèi xiāoxi	CHG
Charging of additional publishing	报刊增版、增刊发行费	Bàokān zēngbǎn、zēngkān fāxíngfèi	
Charging point	收费点	Shōufèi diǎn	CHP
Charging point (GSM term)	计费点	Jìfèi diǎn	
Charging record (telecom billing term)	计费记录	Jìfèi jìlù	
Charging supplementary services	计费附加业务	Jìfèi fùjiā yèwù	
Charpy notch impact test	夏比缺口冲击试验	Xià-bǐ quēkǒu chōngjī shìyàn	
Chat	聊天	Liáotiān	
Chat channel	闲谈频道	Xiántán píndào	
Chat room	聊天室	Liáotiānshì	
Chat script	会话脚本	Huìhuà jiǎoběn	
Chebyshev array	契比雪夫阵	Qì-bǐ-xuě-fū zhèn	
Check (in SS7)	标验码	Biāoyàn mǎ	CK
Check bit	检查比特	Jiǎnchá bǐtè	CK
Check bit	检验比特	Jiǎnyàn bǐtè	
Check bit	检验位	Jiǎnyàn wèi	
Check bit	校验比特	Jiàoyàn bǐtè	CK
Check bit	较验位	Jiàoyàn wèi	CB
Check bit	校验位	Jiàoyàn wèi	
Check bit generator	校验位发生器	Jiàoyàn wèi fāshēngqì	CBG
Check box	复选框	Fùxuǎn kuàng	
Check button	复选按钮	Fùxuǎn ànniǔ	
Check character	校验字符	Jiàoyàn zìfú	
Check constraint (in SQL Server)	检查约束	Jiǎnchá yuēshù	
Check plot	检验样区	Jiǎnyàn yàngqū	
Check sum error	检查和错误	Jiǎnchá hé cuòwù	CSE
Checkmark √	复选标记	Fùxuǎn biāojì	
Checkout and fault isolation	检查与故障隔离	Jiǎnchá yǔ gùzhàng gélí	COFI
Check-out time	检查时间	Jiǎnchá shíjiān	
Checkpoint	检验点	Jiǎnyàn diǎn	
Checkpoint (for database)	检查点	Jiǎnchá diǎn	
Checksum	校验和	Jiàoyàn hé	
Check-sum	加总比对法	Jiā zǒngbǐduì fǎ	
Cheese antenna (for centimetric radar)	盒形天线	Héxíng tiānxiàn	
Chemical barrier	化学阻挡层	Huàxué zǔdǎng céng	

English	Chinese	Pinyin	Abbreviation
Chemical laser	化学激光器	Huàxué jīguāngqì	
Chemical vapor deposition (CVD) equipment	化学气相沉积法设备	Huàxué qìxiàng chénjī fǎ shèbèi	
Chief executive officer	首席执行官	Shǒuxí zhíxíng guān	CEO
Chief financial officer	首席财务官	Shǒuxí cáiwù guān	CFO
Chief information officer	首席信息官	Shǒuxí xìnxī guān	CIO
Chief operating officer	首席运营官	Shǒuxí yùnyíng guān	COO
Chief organizing officer	首席管理官	Shǒuxí guǎnlǐ guān	COO
Chief technical officer	首席技术官	Shǒuxí jìshù guān	CTO
Chief technology officer	首席技术官	Shǒuxí jìshù guān	CTO
Child	子代	Zǐdài	
Child class	子类	Zǐlèi	
Child object	子对象	Zi duìxiàng	
Child Online Protection Act (US)	儿童在线保护法	Értóng zàixiàn bǎohù fǎ	
China 3G Technical Experts Group	第三代移动通信技术试验专家组	Dìsāndài yídòng tōngxìn jìshù shìyàn zhuānjiāzǔ	3GTEG
China Academy of Sciences, Institute of Software	中国科学院软件所	Zhōngguó Kēxuéyuàn ruǎnjiàn suǒ	CAS IOS
China Academy of Telecommunications Technology	电信科学技术研究院	Diànxìn kēxué jìshù yánjiūyuàn	CATT
China Advanced Info-optical Network	中国高速信息示范网	Zhōngguó gāosù xìnxī shìfàn wǎng	CAINONET
China Association of Communications Enterprises	中国通信企业协会	Zhōngguó tōngxìn qìyè xiéhuì	CACE
China Digital Data Network	中国公用数字数据网	Zhōngguó gōngyòng shùzì shùjù wǎng	ChinaDDN
China Digital Tetra Standards Working Group	中国数字集群标准工作小组	Zhōngguó shùzì jíqún biāozhǔn gōngzuò xiǎozǔ	CDTSWG
China Education and Research Network	中国教育和科研网	Zhōngguó jiàoyù hé kēyán wǎng	CERnet
China Electronics Import and Export Corp.	中国电子技术进出口公司	Zhōngguó diànzǐ jìshù jìnchūkǒu gōngsī	CEIEC
China Engineering and Technology Information Network	中国工程技术信息网	Zhōngguó gōngchéng jìshù xìnxīwǎng	CNTIN
China Financial Certification Authority	中国金融认证中心	Zhōngguó jīnróng rènzhèng zhōngxīn	CFCA
China Golden Bridge Network	中国金桥信息网络	Zhōngguó jīnqiáo xìnxī wǎnglùo	ChinaGBN
China Hewlett-Packard Co. Ltd.	中国惠普有限公司	Zhōngguó Huìpǔ yǒuxiàn gōngsī	
China Information Industry Trade Association	中国信息产业商会	Zhōngguó xìnxī chǎnyè shānghuì	CIITA
China Institute of Communications	中国通信学会	Zhōngguó tōngxìn xuéhuì	CIC
China Mobile	中国移动通信	Zhōngguó yídòng tōngxìn	CM
China Mobile Internet Application Protocol special group	中国移动互联网应用协议特别组	Zhōngguó yídòng hùliánwǎng yìngyòng xiéyì tèbiézǔ	CMIS
China Mobile Net	中国移动互联网	Zhōngguó yídòng hùliánwǎng	CMnet
China Mobile Network	中国移动通信网络	Zhōngguó yídòng tōngxìn wǎngluò	CMNET
China Mobile Peer to Peer Protocol	中国移动点对点协议	Zhōngguó yídòng diǎn duì diǎn xiéyì	CMPP
China National Advanced Payment System	中国国家现代支付系统	Zhōngguó guójiā xiàndài zhīfù xìtǒng	CNAPS
China National Financial Network	中国国家金融网络	Zhōngguó guójiā jīnróng wǎngluò	CNFN
China National Information Infrastructure	中国信息基础设施	Zhōngguó xìnxī jīchǔ shèshī	CNII
China National Information Technology Security Certification Center	中国信息安全产品测评认证中心	Zhōngguó xìnxī ānquán chǎnpǐn cèpíng rènzhèng zhōngxīn	CNITSEC
China National Network Information Center	中国国家网络信息中心	Zhōngguó guójiā wǎngluò xìnxī zhōngxīn	CNNIC
China Netcom	网通	Wǎngtōng	CNC
China Network Communications Corp.,	中国网络通信有限公司	Zhōngguó wǎngluò tōngxìn yǒuxiàn gōngsī	CNC
China Network Communications Corp., China Netcom	中国网通	Zhōngguó wǎngtōng	CNC
China Network Information Center	中国网络信息中心	Zhōngguó wǎngluò xìnxī zhōngxīn	CNNIC

China Networking Corp.	中国网通公司	Zhōngguó wǎngtōng gōngsī	CNC
China Networking Corp. Highspeed Interactive Network	中国网通高速互联网	Zhōngguó wǎngtōng gāosù hùliánwǎng	CNCnet
China Orient Telecommunications Satellite Company, Ltd.	中国东方通信卫星有限责任公司	Zhōngguó Dōngfāng tōngxìn wèixīng yǒuxiàn zérèn gōngsī	
China Packet Switched Data Network	中国公用分组交换数据网	Zhōngguó gōngyòng fēnzǔ jiāohuàn shùjù wǎng	ChinaPAC
China Post and Telecommunications Industry Corporation	中国邮电工业总公司	Zhōngguó yóudiàn gōngyè zǒnggōngsī	PTIC
China PTIC Information Industry Corp.	中国普天信息产业集团公司	Zhōngguó pǔtiān xìnxī chǎnyè jítuán gōngsī	
China Railway Information System	中国铁路信息系统	Zhōngguó tiělù xìnxī xìtǒng	CRIS
China Railway Information System	中国铁路综合信息系统	Zhōngguó tiělù zōnghé xìnxī xìtǒng	CRIS
China Research Institute of Radio Wave Propagation	中国电波传播研究所	Zhōngguó diànbō chuánbō yánjiūsuǒ	
China Science and Technology Network	中国科技网	Zhōngguó kējì wǎng	CSTnet
China State Bureau of Standards	中国国家标准局	Zhōngguó Guójiā Biāozhǔnjú	CSBS
China Telecommunications Certificate Authority	中国电信认证中心	Zhōngguó diànxìn rènzhèng zhōngxīn	CTCA
China Unicom Corp.	联通	Liántōng	
China Wireless Telecommunication Standards Research Group	中国无线通信标准研究组	Zhōngguó wúxiàn tōngxìn biāozhǔn yánjiū zǔ	CWTS
China Wireless Telecommunications Standards Group	中国无线通信标准组织	Zhōngguó wúxiàn tōngxìn biāozhǔn zǔzhī	CWTS
ChinaStar-1 (telecommunications satellite)	中卫一号	Zhōngwèi yīhào	
Chinese Academy of Sciences	中国科学院	Zhōngguó Kēxuéyuàn	CAS
Chinese and Oriental Languages Information Processing Society	中文与东方语言信息处理学会	Zhōngwén yǔ Dōngfāng yǔyán xìnxī chǔlǐ xuéhuì	COLIPS
Chinese character DOS	汉字操作系统	Hànzì cāozuò xìtǒng	CCDOS
Chinese information processing system	汉字信息处理系统	Hànzì xìnxī chǔlǐ xìtǒng	CHIPS
Chinese Information Processing system	中文信息处理系统	Zhōngwén xìnxī chǔlǐ xìtǒng	CHIPS
Chinese localization	汉化	Hànhuà	
Chinese National Advanced Payment System	中国国家现代化支持系统	Zhōngguó guójiā xiàndàihuà zhīchí xìtǒng	CNAPS
Chinese Software Professionals Association	中国软件专业协会	Zhōngguó ruǎnjiàn zhuānyè xiéhuì	CSPA
Chinese Star; Cstar © (software)	中文之星	Zhōngwén zhī xīng	
Chinese terminal	中文终端	Zhōngwén zhōngduān	
Chinese Unix Operating system	中文操作系统	Zhōngwén cāozuò xìtǒng	COSIX
Chinese Windows ©	中文视窗	Zhōngwén shìchuāng	C-Win
Chinese Wire Gauge	中国线规	Zhōngguó xiànguī	CWG
Chinese Yahoo! ©	雅虎中文	Yǎhǔ Zhōngwén	
Chinese/English terminal	中西文终端	Zhōng/xī wén zhōngduān	
Chip	晶片	Jīngpiàn	
Chip	码片	Mǎpiàn	
Chip capacitor	片装电容器	Piànzhuāng diànróngqì	
Chip component	片状元件	Piànzhuàng yuánjiàn	
Chip component encapsulation	片状元件封装	Piànzhuàng yuánjiàn fēngzhuāng	
Chip mounter	贴片机	Tiēpiànjī	
Chip on board (in SMT)	板面芯片	Bǎnmiàn xìnpiàn	COB
Chip paster (in component assembly process)	贴片机	Tiēpiànjī	
Chip set	芯片组	Xìnpiàn zǔ	
Chip swap	晶片切换	Jīngpiàn qiēhuàn	
Chipset	晶片组	Jīngpiàn zǔ	

Chireix-Mesny antenna	其列克斯-麦斯尼天线	Qí-liè-kè-sī--mài-sī-ní tiānxiàn	
Chirp	啁啾	Zhōujiū	Chirp
Chirping	啁啾声	Zhōujiū shēng	
Chi-squared distribution	X^2分布	X^2 fēnbù	
Choke	扼流器	Èliúqì	
Choke flange	扼流法兰	Èliú fǎlán	
Choke joint	扼流连接	Èliú liánjiē	
Choke packet	慢递信息包	Màndì xìnxī bāo	
Choke packet	阻塞包	Zǔsè bāo	
Choke piston	扼流活塞	Èliú huósāi	
Choropleth	等值线图	Děngzhíxiàn tú	
Choropleth map (GIS)	等值区域图	Děngzhí qūyù tú	
Choropleth map (GIS)	分区首色图	Fēnqū shǒusè tú	
Chosen ciphertext attack (IPsec)	选择密文攻击	Xuǎnzé mìwén gōngjī	
Chromatic dispersion	色度色散	Sèdù sèsàn	
Chromatic dispersion coefficient (FOC)	色散系数	Sèsàn xìshù	
Chrominance	色度	Sèdù	C, CHR
Chromination format (video term)	色度格式	Sèdù géshi	
Chunk parsing	语块句法分析	Yǔkuài jùfǎ fēnxī	
Cigar antenna	雪茄形天线	Xuějiāxíng tiānxiàn	
Cipher	密码	Mìmǎ	
Cipher block chaining	密码分组链接	Mìmǎ fēnzǔ liàn jiē	CPB
Cipher block chaining (IPsec)	密码块链	Mìmǎ kuài liàn	CBC
Cipher chain (IPsec)	密码链	Mìmǎ liàn	
Cipher check value (IPsec)	密码校检值	Mìmǎ jiàojiǎn zhí	
Cipher feedback	密文反馈	Mìwén fǎnkuì	CFB
Cipher key (IPsec) (usually only key in English)	密钥	Mìyào	
Cipher key agreement scheme	密钥协同方案	Mìyào xiétóng fāng'àn	
Cipher key certificate management center	密钥证书管理中心	Mìyào zhèngshū guǎnlǐ zhōngxīn	KCMC
Cipher key distribution center	密钥分配中心	Mìyào fēnpèi zhōngxīn	KDC
Cipher key escrow system (cryptology)	密钥托管系统	Mìyào tuōguǎn xìtǒng	KES
Cipher key exchange algorithm	密钥交换算法	Mìyào jiāohuàn suànfǎ	KEA
Cipher key injection device, key injector	密钥注入器	Mìyào zhùrùqì	KID
Cipher key management (IPsec)	密钥管理	Mìyào guǎnlǐ	
Cipher key management center	密钥管理中心	Mìyào guǎnlǐ zhōngxīn	KMC
Cipher key management infrastructure	密钥管理基础设施	Mìyào guǎnlǐ jīchǔ shèshī	KMI
Cipher key management mechanism (IPsec)	密钥管理机制	Mìyào guǎnlǐ jīzhì	
Cipher key scheduling	密钥编排	Mìyào biānpái	
Cipher key sequence number	密钥序号	Mìyào xùhào	
Cipher key sequence/number	加密键序列数/号	Jiāmì jiàn xùliè shù/hào	CKSN
Cipher key variable	密钥捷变	Mìyào jiébiàn	
Cipher mode command	加密模式命令	Jiāmì móshì mìnglìng	
Cipher mode complete	加密模式完成	Jiāmì móshì wánchéng	
Cipher mode reject	加密模式拒绝	Jiāmì móshì jùjué	
Cipher mode setting	加密模式设置	Jiāmì móshì shèzhì	
Cipher stream	密文流	Mìwén liú	

Ciphering key	密码本	Mìmǎ běn	Kc
Ciphering key generating algorithm	密码本生成算法	Mìmǎ běn shēngchéng suànfǎ	
Ciphering key sequence number	密码本序列号	Mìmǎ běn xùlièhào	CKSN
Ciphering key sequence number	密码索引序列号	Mìmǎ suǒyǐn xùlièhào	CKSN
Ciphering offset	加密补偿	Jiāmì bǔcháng	COF
Cipherkey setting	密钥设置	Mìyào shèzhì	
CipherSpec (IPsec)	密码说明	Mìmǎ shuōmíng	
Ciphertext (IPsec)	密文	Mìwén	
Ciphertext, message code	密信码	Mìxìn mǎ	
Ciphertext-only attack	惟密文攻击	Wéi mìwén gōngjī	
Circuit	电路	Diànlù	
Circuit access points	电路接入点	Diànlù jiērù diǎn	
Circuit activation order	线路启用命令	Xiànlù qǐyòng mìnglìng	CAO
Circuit allocation order	线路分配命令	Xiànlù fēnpèi mìnglìng	CAO
Circuit breaker	断路器	Duànlùqì	
Circuit condition indicator	电路状态指示器	Diànlù zhuàngtài zhǐshìqì	CCI
Circuit configuration monitor	电路配置监测器	Diànlù pèizhì jiāncèqì	CCM
Circuit control station	电路控制站	Diànlù kòngzhì zhàn	
Circuit emulation access card	电路模拟接入卡	Diànlù mónǐ jiērù kǎ	CEMAC
Circuit emulation over transport	传送电路仿真	Chuánsòng diànlù fǎngzhēn	CEOT
Circuit emulation service	电路仿真业务	Diànlù fǎngzhēn yèwù	CES
Circuit grade	电路等级	Diànlù děngjí	
Circuit group	电路群	Diànlù qún	
Circuit group block	电路群阻塞	Diànlù qún zǔsè	
Circuit group blocking acknowledge	电路群阻塞证实	Diànlù qún zǔsè zhèngshí	
Circuit group blocking acknowledgement (ISUP message)	电路群闭塞认可	Diànlù qún bìsè rènkě	CGBA
Circuit group blocking request (ISUP message)	电路群闭塞请求	Diànlù qún bìsè qǐngqiú	CGB
Circuit group congestion signal	电路群拥塞信号	Diànlù qún yōngsè xìnhào	CGC
Circuit group query message (ISUP message)	询问电路群信息	Xúnwèn diànlù qún xìnxī	CQM
Circuit group reset message	电路群复原消息	Diànlù qún fùyuán xiāoxi	GRS
Circuit group reset-acknowledgement message	电路群复原证实消息	Diànlù qún fùyuán zhèngshí xiāoxi	GRA
Circuit group supervision message	电路群监视消息	Diànlù qún jiānshì xiāoxi	GRM
Circuit group unblock	电路群解闭	Diànlù qún jiěbì	
Circuit group unblocking acknowledge	电路群解闭证实	Diànlù qún jiěbì zhèngshí	
Circuit group unblocking acknowledgement (ISUP message)	解除电路群闭塞认可	Jiěchú diànlùqún bìsè rènkě	CGUA
Circuit group unblocking request (ISUP message)	解除电路群闭塞请求	Jiěchú diànlùqún bìsè qǐngqiú	CGU
Circuit identification code	电路识别码	Diànlù shíbié mǎ	CIC
Circuit identity code list	电路识别码表	Diànlù shíbiémǎ biǎo	
Circuit interrupter	电路中断器	Diànlù zhōngduànqì	CI
Circuit layer network	电路层网络	Diànlù-céng wǎngluò	
Circuit merit rating	通信线路品质评分	Tōngxìn xiànlù pǐnzhì píngfēn	
Circuit mode bearer service	电路方式承载业务	Diànlù fāngshì chéngzài yèwù	CMBS
Circuit network management message group	电路网管理消息	Diànlù wǎng guǎnlǐ xiāoxi	CNM
Circuit number	电路号码	Diànlù hàomǎ	
Circuit pool	电路组	Diànlù zǔ	

Circuit pool list	电路组表	Diànlù zǔ biǎo	
Circuit proxy	线路代理	Xiànlù dàilǐ	
Circuit quality monitoring system	电路质量监测系统	Diànlù zhìliàng jiāncè xìtǒng	CQMS
Circuit reset signal	电路复原消息	Diànlù fùyuán xiāoxi	RSC
Circuit sub-control station	电路副控制站	Diànlù fùkòngzhìzhàn	
Circuit supervision message	电路监视消息	Diànlù jiānshì xiāoxi	CCM
Circuit supervision signal	电路监视信号	Diànlù jiānshì xìnhào	CCS
Circuit switched data	电路交换数据	Diànlù jiāohuàn shùjù	CSD
Circuit switched data transmission service	电路交换数据传输业务	Diànlù jiāohuàn shùjù chuánshū yèwù	
Circuit switched digital circuitry	线路交换数字电路	Xiànlù jiāohuàn shùzì diànlù	CSDC
Circuit switched gateway	电路交换网关	Diànlù jiāohuàn wǎngguān	CS-GW
Circuit switched network	电路交换网	Diànlù jiāohuàn wǎng	CSN
Circuit switched public data network	电路交换公共数据网	Diànlù jiāohuàn gōnggòng shùjù wǎng	CSPDN
Circuit switched public data network	电路交换公用数据网	Diànlù jiāohuàn gōngyòng shùjù wǎng	CSPDN
Circuit switched service	电路交换业务	Diànlù jiāohuàn yèwù	CS
Circuit switched voice	线路交换声	Xiànlù jiāohuàn shēng	CSV
Circuit switching	电路交换	Diànlù jiāohuàn	CS
Circuit tester (in SMT)	电路测试机	Diànlù cèshìjī	
Circuit tracing	电路跟踪	Diànlù gēnzōng	
Circuit transfer mode	电路传递方式	Diànlù chuándì fāngshì	
Circuit transfer mode	电路传送模式	Diànlù chuánsòng móshì	
Circuit validation test	电路有效测试	Diànlù yǒuxiào cèshì	CVT
Circuit, line, route	线路	Xiànlù	
Circuit-switched data network	线路转接数据网络	Xiànlù zhuǎnjiē shùjù wǎngluò	CSDN
Circular antenna array	环形天线阵列	Huánxíng tiānxiàn zhènliè	
Circular array	圆形阵	Yuánxíng zhèn	
Circular cavity antenna	圆腔天线	Yuán qiāng tiānxiàn	
Circular core fiber	圆芯光纤	Yuán xīn guāngxiān	CCF
Circular error average	平均循环误差	Píngjūn xúnhuán wùchā	CEA
Circular error probability	循环误差概率	Xúnhuán wùchā gàilǜ	CEP
Circular error probable	圆概率误差	Yuán gàilǜ wùchā	CEP
Circular flexible waveguide	圆形软波导	Yuánxíng ruǎn bōdǎo	
Circular grid array	环栅阵	Huán zhàzhèn	
Circular input-output routine	循环输入输出程序	Xúnhuán shūrù shūchū chéngxù	CIO
Circular linked list	循环链表	Xúnhuán liàn biǎo	
Circular orbit (of a satellite)	圆轨道	Yuán guǐdào	
Circular polarization feed	圆极化馈电器	Yuán jíhuà kuìdiànqì	
Circular polarization horn	圆极化喇叭	Yuán jíhuà lǎba	
Circular polarization wave	圆极化波	Yuán jíhuà bō	CPW
Circular polarized or polarization	圆极化	Yuán jíhuà	
Circular probable error	循环概率误差	Xúnhuán gàilǜ wùchā	CPE
Circular sequence	循环序列	Xúnhuán xùliè	
Circular slide	圆形滑动	Yuánxíng huádòng	
Circular sweep	圆周扫描	Yuánzhōu sǎomiáo	
Circular waveguide	圆波导	Yuán bōdǎo	
Circular waveguide	圆形波导	Yuánxíng bōdǎo	

Circularly polarized field vector	圆极化场矢量	Yuán jíhuà cháng shǐliàng	
Circularly polarized plane wave	圆极化平面波	Yuán jíhuà píngmiànbō	CPPW
Circulation rate of postal distribution	报刊发行费率	Bàokān fāxíng fèilǜ	
Circulator	环行器	Huánxíngqì	
Cirular queue	循环队列	Xúnhuán duìliè	
Cisco discovery protocol	思科发现协议	Sī-kē fāxiàn xiéyì	CDP
Cisco group management protocol	思科组管理协议	Sī-kē zǔ guǎnlǐ xiéyì	CGMP
Cisco internetwork operating system	思科网络操作系统	Sī-kē wǎngluò cāozuò xìtǒng	
Cisco inter-switch link protocol	思科交换链路内协议	Sī-kē jiāohuàn liànlù-nèi xiéyì	ISL
Cisco router port group management protocol	思科路由器端口组管理协议	Sī-kē lùyóuqì duānkǒuzǔ guǎnlǐ xiéyì	RGMP
Cisco Systems (US company)	思科系统公司	Sī-kē xìtǒng gōngsī	
Citizens band	民用频带	Mínyòng píndài	CB
City telephone cable lines	市话电缆线路	Shìhuà diànlǎn xiànlù	SXD
City telephone optical cable lines	市话光缆线路	Shìhuà guānglǎn xiànlù	SXG
City-level clearance and processing center	城市级清算和处理中心	Chéngshì jí qīngsuàn hé chǔlǐ zhōngxīn	CCPC
Cladding	包层	Bāocéng	
Cladding (in SMT)	覆盖层	Fùgàicéng	
Cladding center	包层中心	Bāocéng zhōngxīn	
Cladding diameter (FOC term)	包层直径	Bāocéng zhíjìng	
Cladding ellipticity (FOC term)	包层不圆度	Bāocéng bùyuándù	
Cladding mode stripper	包层模消除器	Bāocéng mó xiāochúqì	
Cladding/coating concentricity (FOC term)	包层/涂层同心度误差	Bāocéng/ túcéng tóngxīndù wùchā	
Clamp	钳位器	Qiánwèiqì	
Clamp assembly (surface mount technology)	钳装	Qiánzhuāng	
Clamping	钳流	Qiánliú	
Clamping	钳位	Qiánwèi	
Class	类	Lèi	
Class	类别	Lèibié	
Class A (of an amplifying stage)	A 类（放大级的）	A lèi (fàngdà jíde)	
Class A workstation	A 类工作站	A lèi gōngzuòzhàn	
Class AB (of an amplifying stage)	AB 类	AB-lèi	
Class B (of an amplifying stage)	B 类（放大级的）	B lèi (fàngdà jíde)	
Class B workstation	B 类工作站	B-lèi gōngzuòzhàn	
Class C (of an amplifying stage)	C 类（放大级的）	C lèi (fàngdà jíde)	
Class declaration	类声明	Lèi shēngmíng	
Class definition	类定义	Lèi dìngyì	
Class derivation list	类继承列表	Lèi jìchéng lièbiǎo	
Class factory	类厂	Lèi chǎng	
Class hierarchy	类层次结构	Lèi céngcì jiégòu	
Class identifier	类标识符	Lèi biāozhìfú	
Class II equipment	II 类设备	II-lèi shèbèi	
Class library	类库	Lèi kù	
Class loader	类装载器	Lèi zhuāngzàiqì	
Class of emission	发射类别	Fāshè lèibié	
Class of service	服务类别	Fúwù lèibié	CoS
Class of service	业务类型	Yèwù lèixíng	COS

Class parser agent (in Java)	种类解析代理	Zhǒnglèi jiěxī dàilǐ	CPA
Class template	类模板	Lèi múbǎn	
Class template partial specializations	类模板部分特化	Lèi múbǎn bùfen tèhuà	
Class template specializations	类模板特化	Lèi múbǎn tèhuà	
Classical IP over ATM	ATM 上的经典 IP 规范	ATM-shàngde jīngdiǎn IP guīfàn	IPOA
Classical process algebra	经典进程代数	Jīngdiǎn jìnchéng dàishù	
Classification	分类	Fēnlèi	
Classification	清分	Qīngfēn	
Classification accuracy	分类精度	Fēnlèi jīngdù	
Classification code	分类码	Fēnlèi mǎ	
Classification error	分类误差	Fēnlèi wùchā	
Classification map	分类图	Fēnlèi tú	
Classification rule	分类规则	Fēnlèi guīzé	
Classification scheme	分类方案	Fēnlèi fāng'àn	
Classified image	分类影像	Fēnlèi yǐngxiàng	
Classified minimum cost path first	分类的最小代价路径优先	Fēnlèide zuìxiǎo dàijià lùjìng yōuxiān	CCPF
Classifier (for QoS)	分类其	Fēnlèi qí	
Classifier (IPsec)	分类器	Fēnlèiqì	
Classitext	新视分类资讯	Xīn shì fēnlèi zīxùn	
Classless addressing (IPsec)	无类地址分配	Wúlèi dìzhǐ fēnpèi	
Classless inter-domain routing	无类域间路由选择	Wúlèi yùjiān lùyóu xuǎnzé	CIDR
Classless inter-domain routing	无类别域际路由选择	Wúlèibié yùjì lùyóu xuǎnzé	CIDR
Classless inter-domain routing	无类别域间选路	Wúlèibié yùjiān xuǎnlù	CIDR
Classless speed-rate adjustment	无级调速	Wújí tiáosù	
Classmark change	等级改变	Děngjí gǎibiàn	
Classmark request	级别请求	Jíbié qǐngqiú	
Classmark update	级别更新	Jíbié gēngxīn	
Class-of-service tone	服务等级信号音	Fúwù děngjí xìnhào yīn	
Clause	子句	Zijù	
Clean data	无错数据	Wúcuò shùjù	
Clean room	无尘室	Wúchénshì	
Clean room supplies	无尘室用机具	Wúchénshì-yòng jījù	
Cleanroom oven (semiconductor mfg)	洁净室炉	Jiéjìngshì lú	
Cleanup	清除	Qīngchú	
Cleanup	清理	Qīnglǐ	
Clear (WP command)	清除	Qīngchú	
Clear back signal	后向挂机信号	Hòuxiàng guàjī xìnhào	CBK
Clear cache	清缓存	Qīng huǎncún	
Clear command	请除命令	Qīngchú mìnglìng	
Clear command channel (in FTP)	清除命令信道	Qīngchú mìnglìng xìndào	CCC
Clear complete	清除完成	Qīngchú wánchéng	
Clear confirmation delay	清除证实延迟	Qīngchú zhèngshí yánchí	
Clear forward	前向拆线	Qiánxiàng chāixiàn	CLF
Clear forward signal	前向拆线信号	Qiánxiàng chāixiàn xìnhào	CLF
Clear indication delay	清除指示延迟	Qīngchú zhǐshì yánchí	
Clear point	清除点	Qīngchú diǎn	CLR

Clear request	清除请求	Qīngchú qǐngqiú	
Clear request delay	清除请求延迟	Qīngchú qǐngqiú yánchí	
Clear to send	清除发送	Qīngchú fāsòng	CTS
Clear to send	允许发送协议	Yǔnxǔ fāsòng xiéyì	CTS
Clearance	电气间隙	Diànqì jiànxì	
Clear-back signal	拆除信号	Chāichú xìnhào	CBK
Clear-back signal	挂机信号	Guàjī xìnhào	CBK
Clear-back signal	后向拆线信号	Hòuxiàng chāixiàn xìnhào	
Clear-forward signal	拆线信号	Chāixiàn xìnhào	CLF
Clear-forward signal	正向话终信号	Zhèngxiàng huàzhōng xìnhào	
Clearing	拆线	Chāixiàn	
Cleartext (IPsec)	明文	Míngwén	
Clear-to-zero control word	清零控制字	Qīng líng kòngzhì zì	
Cleavage (not *that* kind!)	切开	Qiēkāi	
Click (the sound)	喀呖声	Kālì shēng	
Click (in telecommunications)	喀声	Kā shēng	
Click (on a computer mouse)	按压	Ànyā	
Click (using a computer mouse)	点击	Diǎnjī	
Click and copy [copy using a computer mouse]	使用鼠标拷贝对象	Shǐyòng shǔbiāo kǎobèi duìxiàng	
Click rate	喀呖声率	Kālì shēng lǜ	
Click rate	喀声率	Kāshēnglǜ	
Click to dial	点击拨号	Diǎnjī bōhào	
Click to fax	点击传真	Diǎnjī chuánzhēn	CTF
Click to fax	点击发传真	Diǎnjī fā chuánzhēn	
Click to fax	点击发送传真	Diǎnjī fāsòng chuánzhēn	CTF
Click to fax back	点击回送传真	Diǎnjī huísòng chuánzhēn	
Click-through	点进次数	Diǎnjin cìshù	
Click-through rate	点进率	Diǎnjin lǜ	
Client	客户端	Kèhù duān	
Client application	客户端应用程序	Kèhù duān yìngyòng chéngxù	
Client area	客户区	Kèhù qū	
Client cursor (for database)	客户端游标	Kèhù duān yóubiāo	
Client network	顾主网	Gùzhǔ wǎng	
Client network	客户网	Kèhù wǎng	
Client request	客户请求	Kèhù qǐngqiú	
Client, customer	客户	Kèhù	
Client/browser/server	客户机/浏览器/服务器	Kèhùjī/liúlǎnqì/fúwùqì	C/B/S
Client/server	客户机/服务器	Kèhùjī/fúwùqì	C/S
Client/server computing	客户机-服务器计算	Kèhùjī/fúwùqì jìsuàn	
Client/server format	客户机/服务器方式	Kèhùjī/fúwùqì fāngshì	
Client/server layer	客户/服务器层	Kèhù/ fúwùqì céng	
Client/server network	主从系统	Zhǔ cóng xìtǒng	
Client/server relationship	客户/服务器关系	Kèhù/fúwùqì guānxi	
Clipart	剪贴画	Jiǎntiē huà	
Clipboard	剪贴板	Jiǎntiē bǎn	
Clipped pixel array	剪切像素阵列	Jiǎnqiē xiàngsù zhènliè	

Clipper	削波器	Xiāobōqì	
Clipping	剪音	Jiǎnyīn	
Clipping	削波	Xiāobō	
Clipping (video term)	剪贴纹理	Jiǎntiē wénlǐ	
Clique	最大团	Zuìdà tuán	
Clobbering	文件数据误操作	Wénjiàn shùjù wùcāozuò	
Clock control signal	时钟控制信号	Shízhōng kòngzhì xìnhào	
Clock cycle time	时钟周期	Shízhōng zhōuqī	CCT
Clock cycle/speed	钟速	Zhōngsù	
Clock device	时钟设备	Shízhōng shèbèi	CKD
Clock distribution back panel	时钟分配后面板	Shízhōng fēnpèi hòumian bǎn	
Clock distribution board assembly	时钟分配集成板	Shízhōng fēnpèi jíchéngbǎn	BCDA
Clock frequency dividing circuit	时钟分频电路	Shízhōng fēnpín diànlù	
Clock generation board assembly	时钟产生集成板	Shízhōng chǎnshēng jíchéngbǎn	
Clock generator	时钟发生器	Shízhōng fāshēngqì	CG
Clock monitoring and distribution /AGC bank assembly	时钟监测和分配/AGC 集成板	Shízhōng jiāncè hé fēnpèi/AGC jíchéngbǎn	CABA
Clock pulse	时钟脉冲	Shízhōng màichōng	
Clock pulse generator	时钟脉冲发生器	Shízhōng màichōng fāshēngqì	CPG
Clock rack panel	时钟机架面板	Shízhōng jījià miànbǎn	BCBP
Clock receiver	时钟接收机	Shízhōng jiēshōujī	
Clock relay board assembly	时延集成板	Shíyán jíchéngbǎn	BCRA
Clock shift register	时钟移位寄存器	Shízhōng yíwèi jìcúnqì	CSR
Clock signal (timing information)	时钟信号	Shízhōng xìnhào	CK
Clock source (timing information)	时钟源	Shízhōng yuán	CS
Clock source identifier	时钟源指示器	Shízhōng yuán zhǐshìqì	Csid
Clock source quality level	时钟源质量等级	Shízhōng yuán zhìliàng děngjí	
Clock start command	时钟起动命令	Shízhōng qǐdòng mìnglìng	CSC
Clock synthesizer	时钟合成器	Shízhōng héchéngqì	
Clock tone module	时钟与信号音模块	Shízhōng yǔ xìnhào yīn mókuài	CTM
Clock, timer	时钟	Shízhōng	
Clockwise polarized wave	顺时针极化波	Shùnshízhēn jíhuà bō	
Clockwise polarized wave	右旋极化波	Yòuxuán jíhuà bō	
Clog	拼块	Pīnkuài	
Clone	克隆	Kèlóng	
Clone computer	仿制电脑	Fǎngzhì diànnǎo	
Close logical channel	关闭逻辑通道	Guānbì luóji tōngdào	CLC
Close logical channel acknowledge	关闭逻辑通道确认	Guānbì luóji tōngdào quèrèn	CLCA
Close logical channel reject	关闭逻辑通道拒绝	Guānbì luóji tōngdào jùjué	CLCR
Close user group	闭合用户群	Bìhé yònghù qún	CUG
Closed area	闭合区	Bìhé qū	
Closed circuit television	闭路电视	Bìlù diànshì	CCTV
Closed circuit voltage	闭路电压	Bìlù diànyā	
Closed loop transfer function	闭环传递函数	Bìhuán chuándì hánshù	
Closed loop voltage gain	闭环电压增益	Bìhuán diànyā zēngyì	
Closed loop zero	闭环零点	Bìhuán língdiǎn	

Closed user group	闭合用户群组	Bìhé yònghù qúnzǔ	CUG
Closed user group	闭锁用户群	Bìsuǒ yònghù qún	CUG
Closed user group	封闭用户群	Fēngbì yònghù qún	CUG
Closed user group interlock code	闭合用户群联结码	Bìhé yònghù qún liánjié mǎ	
Closed user group supplementary service	闭合用户群补充业务	Bìhé yònghù qún bǔchōng yèwù	CUG SS
Closed user group with incoming access	有如口的闭合用户群	Yǒu rúkǒude bìhé yònghù qún	
Closed user group with outgoing access	有出口的闭合用户群	Yǒu chūkǒude bìhé yònghù qún	
Closed user network	闭域网	Bìyù wǎng	
Closed-loop bandwidth	闭环带宽	Bìhuán dàikuān	
Closed-loop control	闭环控制	Bìhuán kòngzhì	
Closed-loop control system	闭环控制系统	Bìhuán kòngzhì xìtǒng	
Closed-loop system frequency characteristic	闭环系统频率特性	Bìhuán xìtǒng pínlǜ tèxìng	
Close-in automatic route-restoral system	闭合自动路由恢复系统	Bìhé zìdòng lùyóu huīfùxì tǒng	CARRS
Closure	闭合	Bìhé	
Closure (FOC)	融接箱	Róngjiē xiāng	
Clover-leaf antenna	苜蓿叶形天线	Mùxu yèxíng tiānxiàn	
Cluster	磁区	Cíqū	
Cluster	集群	Jíqún	
Cluster	聚类	Jùlèi	
Cluster	群集	Qúnjí	
Cluster adapter	群集适配器	Qúnjí shìpèiqì	
Cluster address	群集地址	Qúnjí dìzhǐ	
Cluster administrator	群集管理器	Qúnjí guǎnlǐqì	
Cluster administrator extension	群集管理器扩展	Qúnjí guǎnlǐqì kuòzhǎn	
Cluster analysis	聚类分析	Jùlèi fēnxī	
Cluster computing	集群计算	Jíqún jìsuàn	
Cluster control function	簇控制功能	Cù kòngzhì gōngnéng	CCF
Cluster file system	机群文件系统	Jīqún wénjiàn xìtǒng	
Cluster log	群集日志	Qúnjí rìzhì	
Cluster system simulator of heterogeneous resources	资源异构集群系统模拟器	Zīyuán yìgòu jíqún xìtǒng mónǐqì	CSSHR
Cluster-aware application	支持群集的应用程序	Zhīchí qúnjíde yìngyòng chéngxù	
Clustered index	聚集索引	Jùjí suǒyǐn	
Clustered index (in SQL Server)	簇索引	Cù suǒyǐn	
Clustering	聚簇	Jùcù	
Clustering	聚集	Jùjí	
Clustering protocol	群集协议	Qúnjí xiéyì	
Cluster-unaware application	不支持群集的应用程序	Bùzhīchí qúnjíde yìngyòng chéngxù	
Clutter	杂波	Zábō	
Clutter filter	杂波滤波器	Zábō lǜbōqì	
Clutter lock	杂波锁定	Zábō suǒdìng	
Clutter map	杂波地图	Zábō dìtú	
Clutter suppression	杂波抑制	Zábō yìzhì	
Coarse wavelength division multiplexing	粗波分复用	Cū bōfēn fùyòng	CWDM
Coarse-fine measurement system	粗精测系统	Cū-jīng cè xìtǒng	
Coarse-grained	粗颗粒	Cū kēlì	
Coast aeronautical equipment	海岸航空设备	Hǎi'àn hángkōng shèbèi	

Coast earth station	海岸地球站	Hǎi'àn dìqiú zhàn	
Coast station	海岸电台	Hǎi'àn diàntái	
Coast station	海岸电台	Hǎi'àn diàntái	
Coastal earth station	海岸地球站	Hǎi'àn dìqiúzhàn	
Coating (FOC mfg)	涂层	Túcéng	
Coating (process)	镀膜加工	Dùmó jiāgōng	
Coating adhesion tester (semiconductor mfg)	涂层黏附力测定仪	Túcéng niánfùlì cèdìngyí	
Coating diameter (FOC mfg)	涂层直径	Túcéng zhíjìng	
Coating equipment	镀膜设备	Dùmó shèbèi	
Coating materials	镀膜材料	Dùmó cáiliào	
Coaxial	同轴的	Tóngzhóude	CA
Coaxial antenna	同轴天线	Tóngzhóu tiānxiàn	
Coaxial cable	同轴电缆	Tóngzhóu diànlǎn	CC
Coaxial cable carrier telephone	同轴电缆载波电话	Tóngzhóu diànlǎn zàibō diànhuà	
Coaxial cavity	同轴谐振腔	Tóngzhóu xiézhènqiāng	
Coaxial connector	同轴接头	Tóngzhóu jiētóu	
Coaxial directional coupler	同轴定向耦合器	Tóngzhóu dìngxiàng ǒuhéqì	
Coaxial filter	同轴滤波器	Tóngzhóu lǜbōqì	
Coaxial hybrid ring	同轴环行电桥	Tóngzhóu huánxíng diànqiáo	
Coaxial line	同轴线	Tóngzhóu xiàn	
Coaxial rotary joint	同轴旋转关节	Tóngzhóu xuánzhuǎn guānjié	
Coaxial switch	同轴转换开关	Tóngzhóu zhuǎnhuàn kāiguān	
Coaxial wire armored cable	通轴线铠装电缆	Tōngzhóu xiàn kǎizhuāng diànlǎn	WA
Coaxiality	同轴度	Tóngzhóu dù	
Coaxial-stripline transformer	同轴带线变换器	Tóngzhóu dàixiàn biànhuànqì	
Coaxial-waveguide transformer	同轴波导变换器	Tóngzhóu bōdǎo biànhuànqì	
Coboundary	上边缘	Shàngbianyuán	
Coboundary function	上边缘函数	Shàngbianyuán hánshù	
Co-channel	共频道	Gòng píndào	C/I
Co-channel (adjective)	同频道的	Tóngpíndàode	
Co-channel interference	同波道干扰	Tóngbōdào gānrǎo	CCI
Co-channel interference	同频干扰	Tóngpín gānrǎo	
Co-channel interference	同信道干扰	Tóngxìndào gānrǎo	
Co-channel interference protection ratio	同频干扰保护比	Tóngpín gānrǎo bǎohù bǐ	
Co-channel rejection	共道抑制	Gòngdào yìzhì	
Co-channel re-use distance	共信道再用距离	Gòngxìndào zàiyòng jùlí	
Co-channel signalling	共道信令	Gòngdào xìnlìng	
Co-channel station	同频信道电台	Tóngpín xìndào diàntái	
Co-channel suppression	共道抑制	Gòngdào yìzhì	
Coda wave	尾波	Wěibō	
Code	代码	Dàimǎ	
Code access security	代码访问安全	Dàimǎ fǎngwèn ānquán	
Code and time division multiple access	码时分多址	Mǎ shífèn duōzhǐ	CTDMA
Code book	码书	Mǎ shū	
Code breaking	密码破译	Mìmǎ pòyì	
Code buffer	代码缓冲器	Dàimǎ huǎnchōngqì	CB

Code combination	代码组合	Dàimǎ zǔhé	
Code conversion	代码变换	Dàimǎ biànhuàn	
Code conversion	码交换	Mǎ jiāohuàn	
Code conversion, transcoding	代码转换	Dàimǎ zhuǎnhuàn	
Code division	码分	Mǎfēn	
Code division exchange	码分交换	Mǎfēn jiāohuàn	
Code division multiple access	码分多址	Mǎfēn duōzhǐ	CDMA
Code division multiple access	码分多址接入	Mǎfēn duōzhǐ jiērù	CDMA
Code division multiple access cellular system	码分多址蜂窝系统	Mǎfēn duōzhǐ fēngwō xìtǒng	
Code division multiple access personal communications network	码分多址个人通信网	Mǎfēn duōzhǐ gèrén tōngxìnwǎng	CDMA PCN
Code division multiple access personal communications network	码分多址个人通讯网	Mǎfēn duōzhǐ gèrén tōngxùnwǎng	CDMA PCN
Code division multiplex	码分多路复用	Mǎfēn duōlù fùyòng	CDM
Code division multiplexing	码分复用	Mǎfēn fùyòng	CDM
Code excited linear prediction	代码激励线性预测	Dàimǎ jīlì xiànxìng yùcè	CELP
Code excited linear prediction	码激线性预测	M-jī xiànxìng yùcè	CELP
Code extension	代码扩充	Dàimǎ kuòchōng	
Code length	长码	Chángmǎ	
Code mark inversion	代码标记转换	Dàimǎ biāojì zhuǎnhuàn	CMI
Code modulation technology	编码调制技术	Biānmǎ tiáozhì jìshù	
Code modulus generator	代码模数发生器	Dàimǎ móshù fāshēngqì	CMG
Code number of newspapers and periodicals	报刊代号	Bàokān dàihào	
Code page	代码页	Dàimǎ yè	
Code path connect	码字通道连接	Mǎzì tōngdào liánjiē	CPC
Code path ID	码字通道值	Mǎzì tōngdào zhí	CPI
Code path link	码字通道链路	Mǎzì tōngdào liànlù	CPL
Code pattern	码型	Mǎ xíng	
Code reader (often short for bar code reader)	读码器	Dúmǎqì	
Code receiver	收码器	Shōumǎqì	
Code sender	发码器	Fāmǎqì	
Code set	代码集	Dàimǎ jí	
Code speed-rate transformation	码速率变换	Mǎ sùlǜ biànhuàn	
Code table	代码表	Dàimǎ biǎo	
Code transmission	编码传输	Biānmǎ chuánshū	
Code violation	代码违约	Dàimǎ wéiyuē	
Code violation	码违例	Mǎ wéilì	CV
Code word	码字	Mǎzì	
Codec (coder-decoder)	编译码器	Biānyì mǎqì	
Code-carrying circuit	载码电路	Zàimǎ diànlù	
Coded character set	编码字符集	Biānmǎ zìfú jí	
Coded composite transport channel	编码合成传输信道	Biānmǎ héchéng chuánshū xìndào	CCTrCH
Coded interrupt cause	代码化中断原因	Dàimǎhuà zhōngduàn yuányīn	CIC
Coded mark inversion	编码标记变换	Biānmǎ biāojì biànhuàn	CMI
Coded mark inversion	编码传号反转码	Biānmǎ chuánhào fǎnzhuǎn ma	CMI
Coded mark inversion	传号反转码	Chuánhào fǎnzhuǎn mǎ	CMI
Coded order (video term)	编码顺序	Biānmǎ shùnxù	

Coded orthogonal frequency division multiplexing	编码正交频分复用	Biānmǎ zhèngjiāo pínfēn fùyòng	COFDM
Coded signal (in multi-frequency signaling)	编码信号	Biānmǎ xìnhào	
Coded video bit stream (video term)	编码视频比特流	Biānmǎ shìpín bǐtè liú	
Code-excited	码激励	Mǎjīlì	
Code-excited linear prediction	码激励线性预测	Mǎjīlì xiànxìng yùcè	CELP
Coder and decoder (the C in BORSCHT)	编译码器	Biānyì mǎqì	
Coder sequential pulse	编码器时序脉冲	Biānmǎqì shíxù màichōng	CSP
Coder, encoder	编码器	Biānmǎqì	
Coder-decoder	编码解码器	Biānmǎ jiěmǎqì	CODEC
Coding efficiency	编码效率	Biānmǎ xiàolǜ	
Coding element	码元	Mǎyuán	
Coding gain	编码增益	Biānmǎ zēngyì	
Coding rectangle	编码矩形	Biānmǎ jǔxíng	
Coding violation	编码违列	Biānmǎ wéiliè	CV
Coding walk-through	代码走查	Dàimǎ zǒuchá	
Coding, code	编码	Biānmǎ	
Co-directional	同向	Tóngxiàng	
Co-directional interface	同向接口	Tóngxiàng jiēkǒu	
Co-domain (in CORBA)	值域	Zhí yù	
Coefficient	系数	Xìshù	
Coefficient of beam utilization	波束利用系数	Bōshù lìyòng xìshù	CBU
Coefficient of discharge	流量系数	Liúliàng xìshù	
Coefficient of network complexity	网络复杂性系数	Wǎngluò fùzáxìng xìshù	CNC
Coefficient of storage	储留系数	Chǔliú xìshù	
Coefficient of the thermal expansion	温度膨胀系数	Wēndù péngzhàng xìshù	
Coefficient of thermal expansion	热膨胀系数	Rè péngzhàng xìshù	CTE
Coefficient of variation	变动系数	Biàndòng xìshù	
Coevolutionary algorithm	共同进化算法	Gòngtóng jìnhuà suànfǎ	CoEA
Coexistent addess solution	混合地址解决方案	Hùnhé dìzhǐ jiějué fāng'àn	CAS
Cognitive science	认知科学	Rènzhī kēxué	
Coherence	相干性	Xiānggānxìng	
Coherent carrier keying	相干载波键控	Xiānggān zàibō jiànkòng	CCK
Coherent demodulation	相干解调	Xiānggān jiětiáo	
Coherent digital phased array system	相干数字相控阵列系统	Xiānggān shùzì xiàng kòng zhènliè xìtǒng	CODIPHASE
Coherent gain	干涉增益	Gānshè zēngyì	
Coherent jamming; coherent interference	相关干扰	Xiāngguān gānrǎo	
Coherent linear frequency modulation	相干线性调频	Xiānggān xiànxìng tiáopín	CLFM
Coherent mobile target indicator	相干动目标显示	Xiānggān dòngmùbiāo xiǎnshì	Coherent MTI
Coherent modulation	相干调制	Xiānggān tiáozhì	
Coherent optical communication	相干光通信	Xiānggān guāng tōngxìn	
Coherent oscillator	相干振荡器	Xiānggān zhèndàngqì	
Coherent phase shift keying modulation	相干相移键控调制	Xiānggān xiàngyí jiànkòng tiáozhì	CPSK
Coherent sidelobe cancellation	相干旁瓣消除法	Xiānggān pángbàn xiāochú fǎ	CSLC
Coherent signal processing system	相干信号处理系统	Xiānggān xìnhào chǔlǐ xìtǒng	CSPS
Coherent signal processor	相干信号处理机	Xiānggān xìnhào chǔlǐjī	CSP
Cohesion	吸附力	Xīfù lì	

English	Chinese	Pinyin	Abbr.
Coil gun	线圈炮	Xiànquān páo	
Coil rack, bobbin	线圈骨架	Xiànquān gǔjià	
Coinbox discriminating tone	公用投币电话鉴别音	Gōngyòng tóubì diànhuà jiànbiéyīn	
Coinbox identification tone	投币电话识别廛	Tóubì diànhuà shíbié chán	
Coin-value tone	币值音	Bìzhí yīn	
Co-Kriging (in remote sensing)	协同克里格法	Xiétóng kè-lǐ-gé fǎ	
Cold boot; cold start	冷启动	Lěng qǐdòng	
Cold cleaning (in SMT)	冷清洗	Lěng qingxǐ	
Cold mirror	冷镜	Lěng jìng	
Cold point (of a radiating element)	冷点	Lěngdiǎn	
Cold solder joint (in SMT)	冷焊锡点	Lěng hànxīdiǎn	
Cold-pressed pliers	冷压钳	Lěng yā qián	
Collaborative detection	协同检测	Xiétóng jiǎncè	
Collaborative editing system	协同编程系统	Xiétóng biānchéng xìtǒng	
Collaborative feedback	协同反馈	Xiétóng fǎnkuì	
Collaborative filtering	协同过滤	Xiétóng guòlǜ	
Collaborative product commerce	协同产品商务	Xiétóng chǎnpǐn shāngwù	CPC
Collaborative virtual prototyping environment (CAD/CAM)	协作虚拟原型环境	Xiézuò xūnǐ yuánxíng huánjìng	CVPE
Collapsed backbone	分级主干网	Fēnjí zhǔgàn wǎng	
Collapsing loss	丢失损耗	Diūshī sǔnhào	
Collation	排序规则	Páixù guīzé	
Collection	收集	Shōují	
Collection (noun)	集合	Jíhé	
Collective routing indicator	成组路由选择指示符	Chéngzǔ lùyóu xuǎnzé zhǐshìfú	CRI
Collimator	准直器	Zhǔnzhíqì	
Collimator lens	准直透镜	Zhǔnzhí tòujìng	
Collimator pigtail	单双光纤头	Dānshuāng guāngxiān tóu	
Collinear array	共线阵	Gòngxiàn zhèn	
Collinear array antenna	共线阵天线	Gòngxiàn zhèn tiānxiàn	
Collinear array antenna	直排天线阵	Zhípái tiānxiàn zhèn	CAA
Collision detection	碰撞检波	Pèngzhuàng jiǎnbō	CD
Collision-free Hash search (for IP packet classification)	无冲突哈希查找算法	Wúchōngtū hāxī cházhǎo suànfǎ	
Collision-free multiple access	无冲突多路存取	Wúchōngtū duōlù cúnqǔ	CFMA
Collision-free multiple access	无碰头多路存取	Wúpèngtóu duōlù cúnqǔ	CFMA
Colllision detection	碰撞测试	Pèngzhuàng cèshì	
Collocation	场地出租	Chǎngdì chūzū	
Color center	色心	Sè xīn	
Color code	色码	Sèmǎ	
Color composite	彩色合成	Cǎisè héchéng	
Color conversion filter	色温变换滤光镜	Sèwēn biànhuàn lǜguāngjìng	
Color filter	彩色滤光片	Cǎisè lǜguāngpiàn	
Color gamut	色阶	Sè jiē	
Color graphic adapter	彩色图像监控器	Cǎisè túxiàng jiānkòngqì	CGA
Color graphic adapter	彩色图形适配器	Cǎisè túxíng shìpèiqì	CGA
Color ribbon	彩墨带	Cǎimòdài	

Color separation	彩色分离	Cǎisè fēnlí	
Color video broadcast signal	彩色全电视信号	Cǎisè quán diànshì xìnhào	CVBS
Colored noise	色噪声	Sè zàoshēng	
Colored Petri net	着色 Petri 网	Zhuósè Petri wǎng	CPN
Colored-glass filter	有色玻璃滤光镜	Yǒusè bōli lǜguāngjìng	
Columbia Broadcasting Corp. (US)	哥伦比亚广播公司	Gē-lún-bǐ-yà guǎngbō gōngsī	CBS
Column	列	Liè	
Column address selection	列地址选定	Liè dìzhǐ xuǎndìng	CAS
Column address strobe	列地址控制器	Liè dìzhǐ kòngzhìqì	CAS
Column area index	柱率	Zhù lǜ	
Column break (WP command)	栏分界线	Lán fēnjièxiàn	
Column constraint (in SQL Server)	列约束	Liè yuēshù	
Column filter	列筛选	Liè shāixuǎn	
Column filter (in SQL Server)	列过滤	Liè guòlǜ	
Column major order	以列为主的顺序分配	Yǐ liè wéi zhǔde shùnxù fēnpèi	
Column mode	列方式	Liè fāngshì	COLM
Columnar joint	柱状节理	Zhùzhuàng jiélǐ	
Column-level collation	列级排序规则	Liè jí páixù guīzé	
Column-level constraint	列级约束	Liè jí yuēshù	
Combinable key	可组合键	Kězǔhé jiàn	
Combination box	组合框	Zǔhé kuàng	
Combination frequency	组合频率	Zǔhé pínlǜ	
Combination interference	组合干扰	Zǔhé gānrǎo	
Combination pulse and frequency coding system	脉冲与频率组合编码制	Màichōng yǔ pínlǜ zǔhé biānmǎ zhì	
Combination pulse and frequency-coding system	脉冲和频率组合编码制	Màichōng hé pínlǜ zǔhé biānmǎ zhì	
Combination tone	组合音	Zǔhé yīn	
Combination-loop control system	复合控制系统	Fùhé kòngzhì xìtǒng	
Combinatorial circuit	组合电路	Zǔhé diànlù	
Combinatorial jamming	混合干扰	Hùnhé gānrǎo	
Combinatorial problems	组合问题	Zǔhé wèntí	
Combined annual growth rate	综合年度增长率	Zōnghé niándù zēngzhǎnglǜ	CAGR
Combined distribution frame	综合配线架	Zōnghé pèixiànjià	
Combined environment test	综合环境试验	Zōnghé huánjìng shìyàn	
Combined input/output queuing	结合输入,输出排队	Jiéhé shūrù, shūchū páiduì	CIOP
Combined input/output queuing	输入输出结合排队	Shūrù shūchū jiéhé páiduì	CIOQ
Combined local/transit exchange	市话/中继混合交换局	Shìhuà/zhōngjì hùnhé jiāohuànjú	
Combined rack	混合架	Hùnhé jià	CMBR
Combined speaker cabinet	组合音响	Zǔhé yīnxiǎng	CSC
Combiner	合并器	Hébìngqì	
Combiner, mixer	混合器	Hùnhéqì	C
COMDEX Asia (trade exhibition)	亚洲电脑展	Yàzhōu diànnǎo zhǎn	
Command	命令	Mìnglìng	
Command address word	指令地址字	Zhǐlìng dìzhǐ zì	CAW
Command and data transmission system	指令与数据发射系统	Zhǐlìng yǔ shùjù fāshè xìtǒng	CDTS
Command and telemetry data handling	命令与遥测数据处理	Mìnglìng yǔ yáocè shùjùchǔlǐ	CTDH
Command APDU	APDU 命令	APDU mìnglìng	C-APDU

Command center	指挥中心	Zhǐhuī zhōngxīn	CC
Command control center	指挥控制中心	Zhǐhuī kòngzhì zhōngxīn	CCC
Command data buffer	命令数据缓冲器	Mìnglìng shùjù huǎnchōngqì	CDB
Command execution byte	命令执行字节	Mìnglìng zhíxíng zìjié	CEB
Command handling	命令处理	Mìnglìng chǔlǐ	COH
Command identifier	命令标识符	Mìnglìng biāozhìfú	CI
Command input buffer	命令输入缓冲器	Mìnglìng shūrù huǎnchōngqì	CIB
Command interpreter	命令解释程序	Mìnglìng jiěshì chéngxù	CI
Command language	命令语言	Mìnglìng yǔyán	
Command line	命令行	Mìnglìng háng	
Command line interface	命令行界面	Mìnglìng háng jièmiàn	CLI
Command line processor	命令行处理器	Mìnglìng háng chǔlǐqì	CLP
Command management information service element	命令管理信息业务元素	Mìnglìng guǎnlǐ xìnxī yèwù yuánsù	CMISE
Command procedure	命令程序	Mìnglìng chéngxù	
Command prompt	命令提示符	Mìnglìng tíshìfú	
Command prompt window	命令提示符窗口	Mìnglìng tíshìfú chuāngkǒu	
Command relationship	命令关系	Mìnglìng guānxi	
Command terminal (in DECnet)	命令终端	Mìnglìng zhōngduān	CTERM
Command TPDU	TPDU 命令	TPDU mìnglìng	C-TPDU
Command, instruction	指令	Zhǐlìng	
Command/response	命令/响应	Mìnglìng/xiǎngyìng	C/R
Command/response field bit	命令/响应比特	Mìnglìng/xiǎngyìng bǐtè	C/R
Command/response field bit	命令/响应字段比特	Mìnglìng/xiǎngyìng zìduàn bǐtè	C/R
Comment	注释	Zhùshì	
Comment field	注解字段	Zhùjiě zìduàn	
CommerceAsia	亚洲商业（网络）	Yàzhōu shāngyè (wǎngluò)	
Commercial access provider	商业访问提供者	Shāngyè fǎngwèn tígòngzhě	
Commercial encryption	商密	Shāng mì	
Commercial Internet exchange	商业因特网交换中心	Shāngyè Yīntèwǎng jiāohuàn zhōngxīn	CIX
Commercial Internet exchange	商用因特网交换中心	Shāngyòng Yīntèwǎng jiāohuàn zhōngxīn	CIX
Commercial Internet Exchange Association	商业因特网交易协会	Shāngyè Yīntèwǎng jiāoyì xiéhuì	CIEA
Commercial off-the-shelf products	商业成品	Shāngyè chéngpǐn	COTS
Commission (verb), put into commission	调侧	Diáocè	
Commission merchant	经销商	Jīngxiāoshāng	
Commit	提交	Tíjiāo	
Commité Européenne de Normalisation, European Committee for Standardization	欧洲标准化委员会	Oūzhōu biāozhǔnhuà wěiyuánhuì	CEN
Committed burst rate	约定突发速率	Yuēdìng tūfā sùlǜ	CBR
Committed burst size	承诺突发量	Chéngnuò tūfā liàng	Bc
Committed burst size	承诺的突发大小	Chéngnuòde tūfā dàxiǎo	Bc
Committed information rate	承诺信息速率	Chéngnuò xìnxī sùlǜ	CIR
Committed information rate	约定信息率	Yuēdìng xìnxī lǜ	CIR
Committed information rate	约定信息速率	Yuēdìng xìnxī sùlǜ	CIR
Committed rate measurement interval	承诺速率测量时间间隔	Chéngnuò sùlǜ cèliáng shíjiān jiàngé	Tc
Committed time interval	承诺的时间间隔	Chéngnuòde shíjiān jiàngé	Tc
Committee on Data for Science and Technology	科技数据委员会	Kējì shùjù wěiyuánhuì	CODATA

Commodore dynamic total vision	Commodore 公司的动态全视视盘	Commodore gōngsīde dòngtài quánshì shìpán	CDTV
Common (party) line telephone	共线电话	Gòngxiàn diànhuà	
Common access monitor program	通用存取监控程序	Tōngyòng cúnqǔ jiānkòng chéngxù	CAMP
Common access switching equipment	共用入口转接设备	Gòngyòng rùkǒu zhuǎnjiē shèbèi	CASE
Common access telecommunications system	共用存取远程通信系统	Gòngyòng cúnqǔ yuǎnchéng tōngxìn xìtǒng	CATS
Common air interface	公共空中接口	Gōnggòng kōngzhōng jiēkǒu	CAI
Common air interface (CDMA)	通用空中接口	Tōngyòng kōngzhōng jiēkǒu	CAI
Common application service	公共应用服务要素	Gōnggòng yìngyòng fúwù yàosù	CASE
Common battery telephone	共电电话	Gòngdiàn diànhuà	CB
Common bus branch adapter	通用总线分支适配器	Tōngyòng zǒngxiàn fēnzhī shìpèiqì	CBBA
Common business-oriented language	面向商业的通用语言	Miànxiàng shāngyède tōngyòng yǔyán	COBOL
Common business-oriented language	通用商业语言	Tōngyòng shāngyè yǔyán	COBOL
Common carrier	公共电信公司	Gōnggòng diànxìn gōngsī	
Common channel module	公共信道模块	Gōnggòng xìndào mókuài	CCM
Common channel network controller	公共信道网络控制器	Gōnggòng xìndào wǎngluò kòngzhìqì	CCNC
Common channel signal protocol	公共通道信号协议	Gōnggòng tōngdào xìnhào xiéyì	CCSP
Common channel signaling	公共信道信令	Gōnggòng xìndào xìnlìng	CCS
Common channel signaling	共路信令	Gònglù xìnlìng	
Common channel signaling back panel	公共信道信号后面板	Gōnggòng xìndào xìnhào hòumian bǎn	CSBP
Common channel signaling controller	公共通道信号控制器	Gōnggòng tōngdào xìnhào kòngzhìqì	CSC
Common channel signaling MTP processor	公共信道信号 MTP 处理器	Gōnggòng xìndào xìnhào MTP chǔlǐqì	CMP
Common channel signaling network	共路信令网	Gònglù xìnlìng wǎng	CCSN
Common channel signaling processor	公共信道信号处理器	Gōnggòng xìndào xìnhào chǔlǐqì	CSP
Common channel signaling system	公共信道信号系统	Gōnggòng xìndào xìnhào xìtǒng	CCSS
Common channel signaling system	共路信令系统	Gònglù xìnlìng xìtǒng	CCSS
Common channel signaling system no.7	七号共用信道信令系统	Qīhào gòngyòng xìndào xìnlìng xìtǒng	SS7
Common code impedance	共模阻抗	Gòngmó zǔkàng	
Common code interference	共模干扰	Gòngmó gānrǎo	
Common command set	通用指令集	Tōngyòng zhǐlìng jí	CCS
Common control	公共控制	Gōnggòng kòngzhì	
Common control and measurement plane	公共控制和测量平面	Gōnggòng kòngzhì hé cèliáng píngmiàn	CCAMP
Common control channel	公共控制信道	Gōnggòng kòngzhì xìndào	CCCH
Common control physical channel	公共控制物理信道	Gōnggòng kòngzhì wùlǐ xìndào	CCPCH
Common control physical channel	共用控制物理信道	Gòngyòng kòngzhì wùlǐ xìndào	CCPCH
Common coupling point, point of common coupling	公共耦合点	Gōnggòng ǒuhédiǎn	PCC
Common data security architecture	公共数据安全架构	Gōnggòng shùjù ānquán jiàgòu	CDSA
Common data security architecture	公用数据安全框架	Gōngyòng shùjù ānquán kuàngjià	CDSA
Common encryption (for public use)	普密	Pǔmì	
Common fields	公用字段	Gōngyòng zìduàn	
Common gateway interface	公共网关接口	Gōnggòng wǎngguān jiēkǒu	CGI
Common gateway interface	共用网关接口	Gòngyòng wǎngguān jiēkǒu	CGI
Common gateway interface	通用网关接口	Tōngyòng wǎngguān jiēkǒu	CGI
Common gateway interface (CGI) script	CGI 脚本文件	CGI jiǎoběn wénjiàn	
Common gateway interface-based attack (IPsec)	基于 CGI 攻击	Jīyú CGI gōngjī	
Common hardware reference platform	共用硬件参考平台	Gòngyòng yìngjiàn cānkǎo píngtái	CHRP

English	Chinese	Pinyin	Abbr.
Common HINA	公共 HINA	Gōnggòng HINA	CH
Common information model	公共信息模型	Gōnggòng xìnxī móxíng	CIM
Common information model	通用信息模型	Tōngyòng xìnxī móxíng	CIM
Common intermediate format	公共中介格式	Gōnggòng zhōngjiè géshi	CIF
Common intermediate language	通用中间语言	Tōngyòng zhōngjiān yǔyán	CIL
Common intermediate language	通用中介语言	Tōngyòng zhōngjiè yǔyán	CIL
Common Internet file system	通用 Internet 文件系统	Tōngyòng Internet wénjiàn xìtǒng	CIFS
Common intrusion detection framework	通用入侵检测框架	Tōngyòng rùqīn jiǎncè kuàngjià	CIDF
Common intrusion specification language	通用入侵规范语言	Tōngyòng rùqīn guīfàn yǔyán	CISL
Common key (in SQL Server)	公共关键字	Gōnggòng guānjiàn zì	
Common language	公用语言	Gōngyòng yǔyán	
Common language infrastructure	通用语言基础设施	Tōngyòng yǔyán jīchǔ shèshī	CLI
Common language specification	通用语言规范	Tōngyòng yǔyán guīfàn	CLS
Common link access for workstations	工作站的通用连接访问	Gōngzuòzhànde tōngyòng liánjiē fǎngwèn	CLAW
Common log format	公共日志格式	Gōnggòng rìzhì géshi	CLF
Common management	公共管理	Gōnggòng guǎnlǐ	COM
Common management information interface	公用管理信息接口	Gōngyòng guǎnlǐ xìnxī jiēkǒu	
Common management information protocol	公共管理信息协议	Gōnggòng guǎnlǐ xìnxī xiéyì	CMIP
Common management information protocol	通用管理信息协议	Tōngyòng guǎnlǐ xìnxī xiéyì	CMIP
Common management information service	公共管理信息服务	Gōnggòng guǎnlǐ xìnxī fúwù	CMIS
Common management information service	公共管理信息业务	Gōnggòng guǎnlǐ xìnxī yèwù	CMIS
Common management information service	公用管理信息服务	Gōngyòng guǎnlǐ xìnxī fúwù	CMIS
Common management information service element	公共管理信息服务单元	Gōnggòng guǎnlǐ xìnxī fúwù dānyuán	CMISE
Common management information service element	公共管理信息服务要素	Gōnggòng guǎnlǐ xìnxī fúwù yàosù	CMISE
Common management information service element	公共管理信息服务元素	Gōnggòng guǎnlǐ xìnxī fúwù yuánsù	CMISE
Common management information service element	公共管理信息业务单元	Gōnggòng guǎnlǐ xìnxī yèwù dānyuán	CMISE
Common management information service element	公用管理信息服务单元	Gōngyòng guǎnlǐ xìnxī fúwù dānyuán	CMISE
Common management information service element	公用管理信息协议服务单元	Gōngyòng guǎnlǐ xìnxī xiéyì fúwù dānyuán	CMISE
Common management information service element	公用管理信息业务单元	Gōngyòng guǎnlǐ xìnxī yèwù dānyuán	CMISE
Common management interface protocol	公共管理接口协议	Gōnggòng guǎnlǐ jiēkǒu xiéyì	CMIP
Common management interface service	公共管理接口服务	Gōnggòng guǎnlǐ jiēkǒu fúwù	CMIS
Common mobile radio	公用移动无线电	Gōngyòng yídòng wúxiàndiàn	CMR
Common mode	共模	Gòngmó	
Common mode conversion	共模转换	Gòngmó zhuǎnhuàn	
Common mode current	共模电流	Gòngmó diànliú	
Common mode gain	共模增益	Gòngmó zēngyì	
Common mode noise	共模噪声	Gòngmó zàoshēng	
Common mode range	公共模式区域	Gōnggòng móshì qūyù	
Common mode rejection	共模抑制	Gòngmó yìzhì	
Common mode rejection ratio	共模抑制比	Gòngmó yìzhì bǐ	CMRR
Common mode signal	共模信号	Gòngmó xìnhào	
Common mode voltage	共模电压	Gòngmó diànyā	
Common name	公共名	Gōnggòng míng	
Common object file format	通用对象文件格式	Tōngyòng duìxiàng wénjiàn géshi	COFF

Common object model	公用对象模型	Gōngyòng duìxiàng móxíng	COM
Common object modeling	通用对象模型	Tōngyòng duìxiàng móxíng	COM
Common object request broker	通用对象请求中间件	Tōngyòng duìxiàng qǐngqiú zhōngjiān jiàn	CORBA
Common object request broker architecture	公共对象请求代里体系结构	Gōnggòng duìxiàng qǐngqiú dàilǐ tǐxì jiégòu	CORBA
Common object request broker architecture	公共对象请求中介器体系结构	Gōnggòng duìxiàng qǐngqiú zhōngjièqì tǐxì jiégòu	CORBA
Common object request broker architecture	公共客体请求代理体系	Gōnggòng kètǐ qǐngqiú dàilǐ tǐxì	CORBA
Common object request broker architecture	公共目标请求掮客结构	Gōnggòng mùbiāo qǐngqiú qiánkè jiégòu	CORBA
Common object request broker architecture	通用对象请求代理结构	Tōngyòng duìxiàng qǐngqiú dàilǐ jiégòu	CORBA
Common object request broker architecture	通用对象请求代理体系结构	Tōngyòng duìxiàng qǐngqiú dàilǐ tǐxì jiégòu	CORBA
Common object request broker architecture	通用对象请求中介架构	Tōngyòng duìxiàng qǐngqiú zhōngjiè jiàgòu	CORBA
Common object request broker architecture	通用对象申请代理结构	Tōngyòng duìxiàng shēnqǐng dàilǐ jiégòu	CORBA
Common object request broker architecture	通用客体请求代理体系结构	Tōngyòng kètǐ qǐngqiú dàilǐ tǐxì jiégòu	CORBA
Common object services specification	公共对象服务规范	Gōnggòng duìxiàng fúwù guīfàn	COSS
Common open policy service	公共开放策略业务	Gōnggòng kāifàng cèlüè yèwù	COPS
Common open policy service	公共开放政策服务	Gōnggòng kāifàng zhèngcè fúwù	COPS
Common open policy service	通用开放策略服务	Tōngyòng kāifàng cèlüè fúwù	COPS
Common operating environment	公共操作环境	Gōnggòng cāozuò huánjìng	COE
Common packet channel	公用分组信道	Gōngyòng fēnzǔ xìndào	CPCH
Common part	公共部分	Gōnggòng bùfen	CP
Common part convergence sub-layer	公共部分会聚子层	Gōnggòng bùfen huìjù zi céng	CPCS
Common part convergence sub-layer	公共会聚子层	Gōnggòng huìjù zicéng	CPCS
Common part convergence sub-layer	通用部分会聚子层	Tōngyòng bùfen huìjù zicéng	CPCS
Common part indicator	公共部分指示	Gōnggòng bùfen zhǐshì	CPI
Common part sub-layer	公共部分字层	Gōnggòng bùfen zìcéng	CPS
Common pilot channel	公共导引信道	Gōnggòng dǎoyǐn xìndào	CPICH
Common power control channel	公共功率控制信道	Gōnggòng gōnglǜ kòngzhì xìndào	CPCCH
Common rack	公共机架	Gōnggòng jījià	COMR
Common resource	公共资源	Gōnggòng zīyuán	
Common route-label distribution protocol	局部路由标记分配协议	Júbù lùyóu biāojì fēnpèi xiéyì	CR-LDP
Common security service	公共安全服务	Gōnggòng ānquán fúwù	CSS
Common session user information	公用会化期用户信息	Gōngyòng huìhuà qī yònghù xìnxī	CSUI
Common signal channel	公用信号信道	Gōngyòng xìnhào xìndào	CSC
Common signal channel demodulator	公用信号通道解调器	Gōngyòng xìnhào tōngdào jiětiáoqì	CSCD
Common signaling channel	公共信令信道	Gōnggòng xìnlìng xìndào	CSC
Common signaling control board assembly	公共信号控制集成板	Gōnggòng xìnhào kòngzhì jíchéngbǎn	CSCA
Common TDMA terminal	公用时分多址终端	Gōngyòng shífēn duōzhǐ zhōngduān	CTTE
Common technical regulation	公共工程细则	Gōnggòng gōngchéng xìzé	CTR
Common technical regulation	通用技术规定	Tōngyòng jìshù guīdìng	CTR
Common traffic channel	公共业务信道	Gōnggòng yèwù xìndào	CTCH
Common transport semantic	通用传输语义	Tōngyòng chuánshū yǔyì	CTS
Common type system	通用类型系统	Tōngyòng lèixíng xìtǒng	CTS
Common user circuit	公共用户线路	Gōnggòng yònghù xiànlù	CUC
Common user data network	公共用户数据网络	Gōnggòng yònghù shùjù wǎngluò	CUDN
Common vulnerabilities and exposures	通用漏洞披露	Tōngyòng lòudòng pīlù	CVE
Common management information service (IETF standard)	通用管理信息服务	Tōngyòng guǎnlǐ xìnxī fúwù	CMIS

Commonwealth Pacific Cable	联邦太平洋电缆	Liánbāng tàipíngyáng diànlǎn	COMPAC
Communicated text area	通信文本区	Tōngxìn wénběn qū	
Communication area master station	通信区主控站	Tōngxìn qū zhǔkòngzhàn	CAMS
Communication automation	通信自动化	Tōngxìn zìdònghuà	CA
Communication automation, office automation, building management automation, fire automation and safety automation	通信自动化,办公自动化,建筑管理自动化,消防自动化和安全自动化	Tōngxìn zìdònghuà, Bàngōng zìdònghuà, jiànzhù guǎnlǐ zìdònghuà, xiāofáng zìdònghuà hé ānquán zìdònghuà	A5
Communication bus	通信总线	Tōngxìn zǒngxiàn	CB
Communication bus translator	通信总线转换器	Tōngxìn zǒngxiàn zhuǎnhuànqì	CBT
Communication capability	通信能力	Tōngxìn nénglì	
Communication control unit	通信控制单元	Tōngxìn kòngzhì dānyuán	CCU
Communication control unit	通信控制器	Tōngxìn kòngzhìqì	CCU
Communication Equipment Manufacturers Association	通信设备制造商协会	Tōngxìn shèbèi zhìzàoshāng xiéhuì	CEMA
Communication interconnect network	通信互联网络	Tōngxìn hùlián wǎngluò	BCIN
Communication interconnection network	通信互联网	Tōngxìn hùliánwǎng	CIN
Communication interconnection sub-system	通信互联子系统	Tōngxìn hùlián zìxìtǒng	CIS
Communication interconnection sub-system rack	通信互联子系统机架	Tōngxìn hùlián zìxìtǒng jījià	CISR
Communication line terminal	通信线路终端	Tōngxìniànlù zhōngduān	CLT
Communication link analysis system	通信链路分析系统	Tōngxìn liànlù fēnxī xìtǒng	CLAS
Communication linkage controller	通信连接控制器	Tōngxìn liánjiē kòngzhìqì	CLC
Communication management	通信管理	Tōngxìn guǎnlǐ	CM
Communication module	通信模块	Tōngxìn mókuài	CM
Communication network analysis program	通信网络分析程序	Tōngxìn wǎngluò fēnxī chéngxù	CNAP
Communication network architecture	通信网络结构	Tōngxìn wǎngluò jiégòu	CNA
Communication network management application	通信网络管理应用	Tōngxìn wǎngluò guǎnlǐ yìngyòng	CNMA
Communication network manager	通信网络管理程序	Tōngxìn wǎngluò guǎnlǐ chéngxù	CNM
Communication on-line testing system	通信联机测试系统	Tōngxìn liánjī cèshì xìtǒng	COLTS
Communication output interrupt handler	通信输出中断(信息)处理机	Tōngxìn shūchū zhōngduàn (xìnxī) chǔlǐjī	COIH
Communication protocol (computer term)	通信规约	Tōngxìn guīyuē	
Communication satellite	通信卫星	Tōngxìn wèixīng	CS
Communication satellite coverage area	通信卫星覆盖范围	Tōngxìn wèixīng fùgài fànwéi	
Communication satellite program	通信卫星计划	Tōngxìn wèixīng jìhuà	CSP
Communication satellite transponder	通信卫星转发器	Tōngxìn wèixīng zhuǎnfāqì	
Communication service	通信业务	Tōngxìn yèwù	
Communication service center	通信业务中心	Tōngxìn yèwù zhōngxīn	CSC
Communication signal distribution system	通信信号分配系统	Tōngxìn xìnhào fēnpèi xìtǒng	CSDS
Communication switch-board	通信交换机台	Tōngxìn jiāohuànjī tái	CSB
Communication system manager	通信系统管理程序	Tōngxìn xìtǒng guǎnlǐ chéngxù	CSM
Communication system manager interface	通信系统管理程序接口	Tōngxìn xìtǒng guǎnlǐ chéngxù jiēkǒu	CSMI
Communication system model	通信系统模型	Tōngxìn xìtǒng móxíng	
Communication system monitoring	通信系统监视	Tōngxìn xìtǒng jiānshì	CSM
Communication system planning element	通信系统计划环节	Tōngxìn xìtǒng jìhuà huánjié	CSPE
Communication, telecommmuncation	通信	Tōngxìn	
Communications and tracking sub-system	通信与跟踪子系统	Tōngxìn yǔ gēnzōng zìxìtǒng	CTS
Communications automatic processing equipment	通信自动处理设备	Tōngxìn zìdòng chǔlǐ shèbèi	CAPE
Communications buffer	通信缓冲器	Tōngxìn huǎnchōngqì	CB

Communications buffer memory	通信缓冲存储器	Tōngxìn huǎnchōng cúnchǔqì	CBM
Communications channel	通信通路	Tōngxìn tōnglù	
Communications control center	通信控制中心	Tōngxìn kòngzhì zhōngxīn	CCC
Communications file control block	通信文件控制块	Tōngxìn wénjiàn kòngzhì kuài	CFCB
Communications input/output multiplexer	通信输入/输出多路复用期	Tōngxìn shūrù/shūchū duōlù fùyòngqī	CIOM
Communications interrupt program	通信中断程序	Tōngxìn zhōngduàn chéngxù	CIP
Communications path	通信路径	Tōngxìn lùjìng	
Communications port (computers)	通讯端口	Tōngxùn duānkǒu	COM
Communications privacy	通信保密	Tōngxìn bǎomì	
Communications procedure-oriented language	面向通信过程的语言	Miànxiàng tōngxìn guòchéngde yǔyán	CPOL
Communications program	通信程序	Tōngxìn chéngxù	
Communications Satellite Corp.	通信卫星公司	Tōngxìn wèixīng gōngsī	COMSAT
Communications secrecy	通信保密	Tōngxìn bǎomì	COMSEC
Communications security	通信安全	Tōngxìn ānquán	COMSEC
Communications server	通信服务器	Tōngxìn fúwùqì	CS
Communications statistical network analysis procedure	通信统计网络分析过程	Tōngxìn tǒngjì wǎngluò fēnxī guòchéng	CSNAP
Communications status register	通信状态寄存器	Tōngxìn zhuàngtài jìcúnqì	CSR
Communications, navigation and identification (avionics)	通信导航识别	Tōngxìn dǎoháng shíbié	CNI
Communications, navigation and surveillance (GPS)	同心、导航、监视	Tóngxīn、dǎoháng、jiānshì	CNS
Communicopia	通讯社群	Tōngxùn shèqún	
Community	社区	Shèqū	
Community	团体	Tuántǐ	
Community antenna television	共用天线电视	Gòngyòng tiānxiàn diànshì	CATV
Community automatic exchange	共用自动交换机	Gòngyòng zìdòng jiāohuànjī	CAX
Community of interest supplementary services	社团性附加业务	Shètuánxìng fùjiā yèwù	
Community reception (in satellite broadcasting)	集体接收	Jítǐ jiēshōu	
Commutated antenna direction finder	换向天线测向仪	Huànxiàng tiānxiàn cèxiàngyí	CADF
Commutation	上班	Shàngbān	
Commutation notch	转换缺口	Zhuǎnhuàn quēkǒu	
Commuter	上班人	Shàngbān rén	
Compact analog line interface	小型模拟用户线接口	Xiǎoxíng mónǐ yònghù xiàn jiēkǒu	CALI
Compact assembler programming system	紧致汇编程序程序设计系统	Jǐnzhì huìbiānchéngxù chéngxù shèjì xìtǒng	CAPS
Compact casing	精巧机壳	Jīngqiǎo jīké	
Compact disc	光碟	Guāngdié	CD
Compact disk	激光唱片	Jīguāngchàngpiàn	CD
Compact disk (CD) player	激光唱机	Jīguāngchàngjī	
Compact disk burner	刻录机	Kèlùjī	
Compact disk drive	光碟驱动器	Guāngdié qūdòngqì	
Compact disk file system	光盘文件系统	Guāngpán wénjiàn xìtǒng	CDFS
Compact disk interactive	交互式 CD 盘	Jiāohùshì CD pán	CD-I
Compact disk plus graphics	CD 盘加图形	CD pán jiā túxíng	CD + G
Compact disk read only memory	压缩光盘只读存储器	Yāsuō guāngpán zhǐ dú cúnchǔqì	CD-ROM
Compact disk read only memory	只读 CD 存储器	Zhǐ dú CD cúnchǔqì	CD-ROM
Compact disk read only memory	只读光盘存储器	Zhǐ dú guāngpán cúnchǔqì	CD-ROM
Compact disk read-only memory	密盘只读存储器	Mìpán zhǐ dú cúnchǔqì	CDROM

English	Chinese	Pinyin	Abbrev.
Compact disk recordable	可刻录光盘	Kěkèlù guāngpán	CD-R
Compact disk recorder	光碟录制机	Guāngdié lùzhìjī	
Compact disk/read-write	光刻机	Guāngkèjī	CD-RW
Compact disk-interactive	互动式光碟	Hùdòngshì guāngdié	CD-I
Compact disk-PLUS	增强光盘	Zēngqiáng guāngpán	CD-PLUS
Compact disk-read only memory	唯读光碟	Wéidú guāngdié	CD-ROM
Compact disk-read only memory	影音光碟	Yǐngyīn guāngdié	CD-ROM
Compact disk-read only memory eXtended architecture	唯读光盘增强形架构	Wéidú guāngpán zēngqiáng-xíng jiàgòu	CD-ROM/XA
Compact disk-recordable	可录写光碟	Kělùxiě guāngdié	CD-R
Compact disk-rewritable	可重复刻录光盘	Kěchóngfù kèlù guāngpán	CDRW
Compact, wallmount (when referring to chassis)	精巧型	Jīngqiǎo-xíng	
Companded frequency modulation	压扩调频繁	Yākuò tiáopín fán	CFM
Companded predictive delta modulation	压扩预测增量调制	Yākuò yùcè zēngliàng tiáozhì	CPDM
Companded single sideband amplitude modulation	压扩单边带调幅	Yākuò dānbiāndài tiáofú	CSSB-AM
Compander	压扩器	Yākuòqì	
Companding (abbrev. of 压缩扩展)	压扩	Yākuò	
Companding (usually just 压扩)	压缩扩展	Yāsuō kuòzhǎn	
Companding and frequency modulation	压伸与调频	Yāshēn yǔ tiáopín	CFM
Companion chip	同伴芯片	Tóngbàn xìnpiàn	
Compaq (US company)	康拍公司	Kāng-pāi gōngsī	
Compaq (US computer company)	康柏公司	Kāng-bǎi gōngsī	
Comparative form	比较级	Bǐjiào jí	
Comparator coil	比较线圈	Bǐjiào xiànquān	
Comparators	比较器	Bǐjiào qì	CM
Compartmentalization (IPsec)	分割	Fēngē	
Compatibility mode	兼容方式	Jiānróng fāngshì	CM
Compatibility mode	相容方式	Xiāngróng fāngshì	CM
Compatibility test suite	兼容性测试法套件	Jiānróngxìng cèshìfǎ tàojiàn	
Compatibility testing	兼容性测试	Jiānróngxìng cèshì	CPT
Compatible	兼容	Jiānróng	
Compatible duplex system	兼容的双工系统	Jiānróngde shuānggōng xìtǒng	CDS
Compatible shift keying	兼容频移键控	Jiānróng pínyí jiànkòng	CSK
Compelled signaling	互控信令	Hùkòng xìnlìng	
Compensated micromanometer	补偿微压计	Bǔcháng wēiyājì	
Compensated pyrheliometer	补偿直接日射强度表	Bǔcháng zhíjiē rìshè qiángdù biǎo	
Compensating extension lead	补偿型延长导线	Bǔcháng xíng yáncháng dǎoxiàn	
Compensating network (of an antenna)	补偿网络	Bǔcháng wǎngluò	
Compensator	补偿器	Bǔchángqì	
Compile	编译	Biānyì	
Compile (verb)	编择	Biānzé	
Compile time	编译期	Biānyì qī	
Compile time	编译时	Biānyì shí	
Compile, edit	编制	Biānzhì	
Compiler	编译器	Biānyìqì	
Compiler (computer program)	编译程序	Biānyì chéngxù	COMP

Compiler generator	编译程序的生成程序	Biānyì chéngxùde shēngchéng chéngxù	
Compiler language	编程语言	Biānchéng yǔyán	
Complement	补数	Bǔshù	
Complement	互补	Hùbǔ	
Complementary error function	互补误差函数	Hùbǔ wùchā hánshù	erfc
Complementary metal oxide semiconductor	互补金属氧化物半导体	Hùbǔ jīnshǔ yǎnghuàwù bàndǎotǐ	CMOS
Complementary metal oxide semiconductor integrated circuit	互补金属氧化物半导体集成电路	Hùbǔ jīnshǔ yǎnghuàwù bàndǎotǐ jíchéng diànlù	CMOS-IC
Complementary straight binary code	标准二进制补码	Biāozhǔn èrjìnzhì bǔ mǎ	CSB
Complementary transistor logic circuit	互补晶体管逻辑电路	Hùbǔ jīngtǐguǎn luójì diànlù	CTL
Complete binary tree	完全二叉树	Wánquán èrchā shù	
Complete chain	完全链	Wánquán liàn	
Complete connection	完成接续	Wánchéng jiēxù	
Complete connection	完整接续	Wánzhěng jiēxù	
Complete failure	完全故障	Wánquán gùzhàng	
Complete failure	完全失效	Wánquán shīxiào	
Complete fault	完全	Wánquán gùzhàng	
Complete generator set	完全生成符集	Wánquán shēngchéngfú jí	
Complete graph	完全图	Wánquán tú	
Complete layer 3 information	完全第三层信息	Wánquán dìsāncéng xìnxī	
Complete loopback	完全环回	Wánquán huán huí	
Complete path index (in XML)	全部路径索引	Quánbù lùjìng suǒyǐn	CPI
Complete sequence numbers protocol data unit	完全序列号协议数据单元	Wánquán xùlièhào xiéyì shùjù dānyuán	CSNP
Complete spatial randomness	完全空间随机性	Wánquán kōngjiān suíjīxìng	CSR
Completed call	接通呼叫	Jiētōng hūjiào	
Completion of call busy subscriber	对遇忙用户完成呼叫	Duì yùmáng yònghù wánchéng hūjiào	CCBS
Completion of call to busy subscribers	对忙时用户的再呼叫	Duì mángshí yònghùde zài hūjiào	CCBS
Completion of calls on no reply	未应答的呼叫完成	Wèiyìngdáde hūjiào wánchéng	CCNR
Completion of calls to busy subscriber	完成到遇忙用户的呼叫	Wánchéng dào yùmáng yònghùde hūjiào	CCBS
Completion of calls to busy subscriber	遇忙回叫	Yù máng huíjiào	CCBS
Completion of calls to busy subscriber supplementary service	完成对状态忙用户的呼叫补充业务	Wánchéng duì zhuàngtài máng yònghùde hūjiào bǔchōng yèwù	CCBS
Completion of calls to busy subscribers	到忙用户的呼叫完成	Dào máng yònghùde hūjiào wánchéng	CCBS
Completion of calls to busy subscribers	完成到示忙用户呼叫	Wánchéng dào shìmáng yònghù hūjiào	CCBS
Completion of calls to busy subscribers	遇忙呼叫完成	Yùmáng hujiào wánchéng	CCBS
Completion of calls to busy subscribers	至忙用户的呼叫的完成	Zhì máng yònghùde hūjiàode wánchéng	CCBS
Complex functional equation	复函数方程	Fù hánshù fāngchéng	
Complex instruction set computer	复杂指令集计算机	Fùzá zhǐlìng jí jìsuànjī	CISC
Complex instruction set computer	复杂指令系统计算机	Fùzá zhǐlìng xìtǒng jìsuànjī	CISC
Complex instruction set computing	复杂指令集计算	Fùzá zhǐlìng jí jìsuàn	CISC
Complex modulated jamming	复调制干扰	Fù tiáozhì gānrǎo	
Complex object	复杂对象	Fùzá duìxiàng	
Complex polygon	复杂多边形	Fùzá duōbiānxíng	
Complex power (in a transmission line)	复数功率	Fùshù gōnglǜ	
Complex quaternary phase shift modulation	复四相调制	Fù sìxiāng tiáozhì	CQM
Complex reflection coefficient	复反射系数，	Fùfǎnshè xìshù,	

Complex signal	复信号	Fù xìnhào	
Complex sound	复合音	Fùhé yīn	
Complex spectrum	复频谱	Fùpínpǔ	
Complex surface	复杂面	Fùzá miàn	
Complex waveform modulated jamming	复合波形调制干扰	Fùhé bōxíng tiáozhì gānrǎo	
Compliance period	顺从周期	Shùncóng zhōuqī	
Compliance test	验证试验	Yànzhèng shìyàn	
Component	构成体	Gòuchéngtǐ	
Component	元件	Yuánjiàn	
Component (IPsec)	组件	Zǔjiàn	
Component density	元件密度	Yuánjiàn mìdù	
Component interconnection language	部件互连语言	Bùjiàn hùlián yǔyán	CIL
Component library management agent (in Java)	构件库管理代理	Gòujiàn kù guǎnlǐ dàilǐ	CLMA
Component object model	部件对象模型	Bùjiàn duìxiàng móxíng	
Component object model	部件目标模型	Bùjiàn mùbiāo móxíng	COM
Component object model	组合对象模型	Zǔhé duìxiàng móxíng	COM
Component object model	组件对象模式	Zǔjiàn duìxiàng móshì	COM
Component object model	组件对象模型	Zǔjiàn duìxiàng móxíng	COM
Component stress testing (semiconductor mfg)	元件压力试验	Yuánjiàn yālì shìyàn	
Component-based modeling	基于组件建模	Jīyú zǔjiàn jiànmó	
Component-based software development technology	基于构件的软件开发技术	Jīyú gòujiànde ruǎnjiàn kāifā jìshù	CBSDT
Composite application sharing mechanism (in CSCW)	混合式应用共享机制	Hùnhé-shì yìngyòng gòngxiǎng jīzhì	
Composite armor	复合装甲	Fùhé zhuāngjiǎ	
Composite component	组合构成体	Zǔhé gòuchéngtǐ	
Composite curve	合成曲线	Héchéng qūxiàn	
Composite gain (of a two-port network)	复合增益	Fùhé zēngyì	
Composite index (for database)	复合索引	Fùhé suǒyǐn	
Composite index (for database)	组合索引	Zǔhé suǒyǐn	
Composite intersection type	复合交会方式	Fùhé jiāohuì fāngshì	
Composite key (for database)	复合键	Fùhé jiàn	
Composite key (for database)	组合键	Zǔhé jiàn	
Composite layout object	组合布局客体	Zǔhé bùjú kètǐ	
Composite logical object	组合逻辑客体	Zǔhé luóji kètǐ	
Composite map; integrated map	综合图	Zōnghé tú	
Composite pronunciation	合成音	Héchéng yīn	
Composite signal dialing	复合信号拨号	Fùhé xìnhào bōhào	CSD
Composite solid	合成立体	Héchéng lìtǐ	
Composite stainless tube type (FOC)	复合不锈钢管型	Fùhé bùxiùgāng guǎnxíng	
Composite surface	合成曲面	Héchéng qūmiàn	
Composite triple beat	复合三价差拍	Fùhé sān jiàchā pāi	CTB
Composition	复合	Fùhé	
Composition	组合	Zǔhé	
Composition point	构成点	Gòuchéng diǎn	
Compound circular horn antenna	复合圆形喇叭天线	Fùhé yuánxíng lǎba tiānxiàn	
Compound coordinate reference system	复合坐标参照系	Fùhé zuòbiāo cānzhàoxì	

Compound element	复合元素	Fùhé yuánsù	
Compound fiber	复合光纤	Fùhé guāngxiān	
Compound function	复合功能	Fùhé gōngnéng	
Compound phase locked demodulator	复合锁相解调器	Fùhé suǒxiàng jiětiáoqì	CPLD
Compound rectangular horn antenna	复合矩形喇叭天线	Fùhé jǔxíng lǎba tiānxiàn	
Compound semiconductor material	化合物半导体材料	Huàhéwù bàndǎotǐ cáiliào	
Compound signal (in AC signaling)	复合信号	Fùhé xìnhào	
Compound statement	复合语句	Fùhé yǔjù	
Compound switching	复合交换	Fùhé jiāohuàn	
Comprehensive plan	综合计划	Zōnghé jìhuà	
Compress	压缩	Yāsuō	
Compressed delta modulation	压缩增量调制	Yāsuō zēngliàng tiáozhì	CDM
Compressed effective security payload	压缩安全有效载荷	Yāsuō ānquán yǒuxiào zàihè	
Compressed file, ZIP file	压缩文件	Yāsuō wénjiàn	
Compressed mode	压缩方式	Yāsuō fāngshì	CM
Compressed serial link Internet protocol	压缩串联因特网协议	Yāsuō chuànlián Yīntèwǎng xiéyì	CSLIP
Compressed textures (video term)	压缩纹理	Yāsuō wénlǐ	
Compressibility	压缩性	Yāsuōxìng	
Compressible multi-component flow	可压缩多组分驱动	Kěyāsuō duō zǔfèn qūdòng	
Compression algorithm (IPsec)	压缩算法	Yāsuō suànfǎ	
Compression control protocol	压缩控制协议	Yāsuō kòngzhì xiéyì	CCP
Compression stress	压缩应力	Yāsuō yìnglì	
Compressive strength	抗压强度	Kàngyā qiángdù	
Compressive strength	压缩强度	Yāsuō qiángdù	
Compressive stress	压应力	Yāyìnglì	
Compressor	压缩器	Yāsuōqì	
Compromise (IPsec)	泄漏	Xièlòu	
Compromised (as a security breach)	报知	Bàozhī	
Compromising emanation (IPsec)	泄漏发射	Xièlòu fāshè	
Compulsory fitted radio station	制式无线电台	Zhìshì wúxiàndiàntái	
CompuServe (an ISP)	电脑服务网	Diànnǎo fúwù wǎng	
Computable general equilibrium model	一般可计算均衡模型	Yībān kějìsuàn jūnhéng móxíng	CGEM
Computational fluid dynamics	计算流体力学	Jìsuàn liútǐ lìxué	CFD
Computational geometry	计算几何学	Jìsuàn jǐhéxué	
Computational linguistics	语篇机器理解	Yǔpiān jīqì lǐjiě	
Computational lingustics	计算语言学	Jìsuàn yǔyánxué	
Computational topology	计算形势拓扑学	Jìsuàn xíngshì tuòpūxué	
Computed column	计算列	Jìsuàn liè	
Computer address bus	计算机地址总线	Jìsuànjī dìzhǐ zǒngxiàn	CAB
Computer analog input	计算机模拟输入	Jìsuànjī mónǐ shūrù	CAI
Computer animation	计算机动画技术	Jìsuànjī dònghuà jìshù	
Computer Associate	电脑友伴	Diànnǎo yǒubàn	CA
Computer communication, compunication	算信	Suànxìn	
Computer compatible tape	计算机兼容磁带	Jìsuànjī jiānróng cídài	CCT
Computer distributors exposition	计算机代理分销业展览会	Jìsuànjī dàilǐ fēnxiāo yè zhǎnlǎnhuì	COMDEX
Computer emergency response team	计算机应急响应小组	Jìsuànjī yìngjí xiǎngyìng xiǎozǔ	CERT

Computer generated graphics	计算机生成图像	Jìsuànjī shēngchéng túxiàng	CGG
Computer graphics metafile	计算机图形元文件	Jìsuànjī túxíng yuán wénjiàn	CGM
Computer incident response team	计算机事件响应小组	Jìsuànjī shìjiàn xiǎngyìng xiǎozǔ	CIRT
Computer integrated manufacturing system	计算机集成制造系统	Jìsuànjī jíchéng zhìzào xìtǒng	CIMS
Computer language	计算机语言	Jìsuànjī yǔyán	
Computer network	计算机网络	Jìsuànjī wǎngluò	JWL
Computer output microfilm	计算机输出缩微胶片	Jìsuànjī shūchū suōwēijiāopiàn	COM
Computer peripheral device	计算机外围设备	Jìsuànjī wàiwéi shèbèi	
Computer peripheral module	计算机外设模块	Jìsuànjī wàishè mókuài	CPM
Computer recovery center	电脑修复中心	Diànnǎo xiūfù zhōngxīn	
Computer security	计算机安全	Jìsuànjī ānquán	COMPUSEC
Computer simulation	计算机模拟	Jìsuànjī mónǐ	
Computer software	计算机软件	Jìsuànjī ruǎnjiàn	RJ
Computer software configuration item	计算机软件配置项	Jìsuànjī ruǎnjiàn pèizhì xiàng	CSCI
Computer sub-system controller	计算机子系统控制器	Jìsuànjī zixìtǒng kòngzhìqì	CSC
Computer supported collaborative work	计算机支持的协同工作	Jìsuànjī zhīchíde xiétóng gōngzuò	CSCW
Computer supported cooperative work	计算机协同工作支持系统	Jìsuànjī xiétóng gōngzuò zhīchí xìtǒng	CSCW
Computer supported cooperative work	计算机支持协同工作	Jìsuànjī zhīchí xiétóng gōngzuò	CSCW
Computer telecommunication integration	计算机电信集成	Jìsuànjī diànxìn jíchéng	CTI
Computer telephony integration	电脑电话集成	Diànnǎo diànhuà jíchéng	CTI
Computer telephony integration	计算机通信技术	Jìsuànjī tōngxìn jìshù	CTI
Computer to print	计算机直接印刷	Jìsuànjī zhíjiē yìnshuā	CTP
Computer virus	计算机病毒	Jìsuànjī bìngdú	CV
Computer vision	计算机视觉	Jìsuànjī shìjué	
Computer vision syndrome	计算机视觉综合症	Jìsuànjī shìjué zōnghézhèng	CVS
Computer, command and control	计算机,指挥和控制	Jìsuànjī, zhǐhuī hé kòngzhì	C3
Computer, communication, control	计算机，通讯和控制	Jìsuànjī, tōngxùn hé kòngzhì	3C
Computer-aided architectural design	计算机辅助建筑设计	Jìsuànjī fǔzhù jiànzhù shèjì	CAAD
Computer-aided conceptual design	计算机辅助概念设计	Jìsuànjī fǔzhù gàiniàn shèjì	CACD
Computer-aided design	计算机辅助设计	Jìsuànjī fǔzhù shèjì	CAD
Computer-aided design drawing	计算机辅助制图	Jìsuànjī fǔzhù zhìtú	CADD
Computer-aided design/computer-aided manufacturing	计算机辅助设计/计算机辅助制造	Jìsuànjī fǔzhù shèjì/jìsuànjī fǔzhù zhìzào	CAD/CAM
Computer-aided engineering	计算机辅助工程	Jìsuànjī fǔzhù gōngchéng	CAE
Computer-aided geometric design	计算机辅助几何设计	Jìsuànjī fǔzhù jǐhé shèjì	CAGD
Computer-aided instruction	计算机辅助教学	Jìsuànjī fǔzhù jiàoxué	CAI
Computer-aided management	计算机辅助管理	Jìsuànjī fǔzhù guǎnlǐ	CAM
Computer-aided manufacturing	计算机辅助制造	Jìsuànjī fǔzhù zhìzào	CAM
Computer-aided planning	计算机辅助规划	Jìsuànjī fǔzhù guīhuà	CAP
Computer-aided planning and designing program	计算机辅助规划设计程序	Jìsuànjī fǔzhù guīhuà shèjì chéngxù	
Computer-aided process planning (CMM)	计算机辅助工艺过程设计	Jìsuànjī fǔzhù gōngyì guòchéng shèjì	CAPP
Computer-aided software engineering	计算机辅助软件工程	Jìsuànjī fǔzhù ruǎnjiàn gōngchéng	CASE
Computer-aided test	计算机辅助测试	Jìsuànjī fǔzhù cèshì	CAT
Computer-assisted accounting	计算机辅助会计计算	Jìsuànjī fǔzhù kuàijì jìsuàn	CAA
Computer-assisted mass appraisal	计算机辅助群体评估	Jìsuànjī fǔzhù qúntǐ pínggū	CAMA
Computer-based message system	计算机信息系统	Jìsuànjī xìnxī xìtǒng	CBMS

Computer-based training	电脑辅助培训	Diànnǎo fǔzhù péixùn	CBT
Computer-based training	基于计算机的训练	Jīyú jìsuànjīde xùnliàn	CBT
Computerized branch exchange	计算机化交换分机	Jìsuànjīhuà jiāohuàn fēnjī	CBX
Computerized digital switching system	计算机化数字交换系统	Jìsuànjīhuà shùzì jiāohuàn xìtǒng	CDSS
Computer-on-a-chip	单片计算机	Dānpiàn jìsuànjī	
Computer-telephone integration	计算机电话综合技术	Jìsuànjī diànhuà zōnghé jìshù	CTI
Computer-telephony integration	计算机电话集成	Jìsuànjī diànhuà jíchéng	CTI
Computing configuration management	计算组成管理	Jìsuàn zǔchéng guǎnlǐ	Com.CM
Computing network architecture technology	计算机网络结构技术	Jìsuànjī wǎngluò jiégòu jìshù	CNAT
Computing object	计算对象	Jìsuàn duìxiàng	CO
Comsat/RSI (US company)	美国通信卫星公司	Měiguó tōngxìn wèixīng gōngsī	
Concatenated code	级连码	Jílián mǎ	
Concatenated cross-connect matrix	级联交叉矩阵	Jílián jiāochā jǔzhèn	
Concatenated key	连接键	Liánjiē jiàn	
Concatenation	串联	Chuànlián	
Concatenation	级联	Jílián	
Concatenation	拼接	Pīnjiē	
Concave grating	面光栅	Miàn guāngshān	
Concealed focus node (in CSCW)	隐焦点节点	Yǐnjiāodiǎn jiédiǎn	
Concealed in beam	暗敷设在梁内	Àn fūshè zài liáng-nèi	BC
Concealed in ceiling	暗敷设在室面内	Àn fūshè zài shìmiàn-nèi	CC
Concealed in column	暗敷设在珠内	Àn fūshè zài zhū-nèi	CLC
Concealed in roof slab	暗敷设在顶板内	Àn fūshè zài dǐngbǎn-nèi	CC
Concealed tuning	隐蔽调谐	Yǐnbì tiáoxié	
Concealment system (IPsec)	隐蔽系统	Yǐnbì xìtǒng	
Concentrated resistive suppressor	集中电阻抑制器	Jízhōng diànzǔ yìzhìqì	
Concentrating flux plate	导磁板	Dǎocí bǎn	
Concentrating flux sleeve	导磁套	Dǎocí tào	
Concentration (in switching)	集中	Jízhōng	
Concentrator	集线器	Jíxiànqì	
Concentrator	集中器	Jízhōngqì	
Concentric orifice plate	同心孔板	Tóngxīn kǒngbǎn	
Concentricity	同心度	Tóngxīndù	
Concentricity error	同心度误差	Tóngxīndù wùchā	
Concept formation	概念发明	Gàiniàn fāmíng	
Concept node	概念节点	Gàiniàn jiédiǎn	
Concept phase (of product life cycle)	论证阶段	Lùnzhèng jiēduàn	
Concept-level design	概念级设计	Gàiniàn-jí shèjì	
Conceptual data model	概念数据模型	Gàiniàn shùjù móxíng	
Conceptual design	概念设计	Gàiniàn shèjì	
Conceptual formalism	概念形式	Gàiniàn xíngshì	
Conceptual model	概念模型	Gàiniàn móxíng	
Conceptual model of the mission space	任务空间概念模型	Rènwu kōngjiān gàiniàn móxíng	CMMS
Conceptual schema	概念数据模式	Gàiniàn shùjù móshì	
Conceptual schema language	概念数据模式语言	Gàiniàn shùjù móshì yǔyán	
Concrete class	具体类	Jùtǐ lèi	

English	Chinese	Pinyin	Abbreviation
Concrete syntax	具体句法	Jùtǐ jùfǎ	
Concurrency	并发	Bìngfā	
Concurrency	并发机制	Bìngfā jīzhì	
Concurrency control	并发控制	Bìngfā kòngzhì	
Concurrency management	并发管理	Bìngfā guǎnlǐ	
Concurrent algorithmic programming language/digital system design language	并行算法程序设计语言/数字系统设计语言	Bìngxíng suànfǎ chéngxù shèjì yǔyán/shùzì xìtǒng shèjì yǔyán	CAP/DSDL
Concurrent command engine	协作命令引擎	Xiézuò mìnglìng yǐnqíng	
Concurrent computing	并发计算	Bìngfā jìsuàn	
Concurrent connections	并发连结数	Bìngfā liánjié shù	
Concurrent engineering	并行工程	Bìngxíng gōngchéng	CE
Concurrent operating conflict	并发操作冲突	Bìngfā cāozuò chōngtū	
Concurrent processors	并发处理器	Bìngfā chǔlǐqì	
Concurrent push	并发推动	Bìngfā tuīdòng	
Concurrent real time operating system	并行实时操作系统	Bìngxíng shíshí cāozuò xìtǒng	CROS
Concurrent time domain multiple access	并行时域多路存取算法	Bìngxíng shíyù duōlù cúnqǔ suànfǎ	CTDMA
Condemnation	征用	Zhēngyòng	
Condenser lens	聚光透镜	Jùguāng tòujìng	
Condition bit	条件位	Tiáojiàn wèi	CB
Condition code	状态码	Zhuàngtài mǎ	CC
Conditional access	条件接入	Tiáojiàn jiērù	CA
Conditional access system	条件接收系统	Tiáojiàn jiēshōu xìtǒng	CAS
Conditional call forwarding	条件呼叫前转	Tiáojiàn hūjiào qiánzhuǎn	CCF
Conditional call forwarding	条件呼叫转移	Tiáojiàn hūjiào zhuǎnyí	CCF
Conditional dual phase coding	条件二相码	Tiáojiàn èr xiàng mǎ	CDP
Conditional instability	条件不稳定性	Tiáojiàn bùwěndìngxìng	
Conditional maximum likelihood estimate	有条件的最大似然估计	Yǒu tiáojiànde zuìdà sìrán gūjì	CMLE
Conditional operator	条件操作符	Tiáojiàn cāozuò fú	
Conditional package	条件特征包	Tiáojiàn tèzhēng bāo	
Conditionality branch address	条件转移地址	Tiáojiàn zhuǎnyí dìzhǐ	CBRA
Conditionally stable system	条件稳定系统	Tiáojiàn wěndìng xìtǒng	
Conductance	电导	Diàndǎo	
Conducted conference	受控会议	Shòukòng huìyì	
Conducted emission (in Mil-Std-461E)	传导发射	Chuándǎo fāshè	
Conducted interference	传导干扰	Chuándǎo gānrǎo	
Conducted spurious emission	传导杂散发射	Chuándǎo zásǎn fāshè	
Conducted susceptibility	传导敏感度	Chuándǎo mǐngǎndù	
Conduction port	导通端口	Dǎotōng duānkǒu	
Conductive epoxy (in SMT)	导电性环氧树脂	Dǎodiànxìng huányǎng shùzhī	
Conductive ink (in SMT)	导电墨水	Dǎodiàn mòshuǐ	
Conductive part	导电部分	Dǎodiàn bùfen	
Conductivity	电导率	Diàndǎolǜ	
Conductivity meter	电导仪	Diàndǎoyí	
Conductor	导体	Dǎotǐ	
Conductor diameter	芯线直径	Xīnxiàn zhíjìng	
Conduit	槽道	Cáodào	

Conduit	管道	Guǎndào	GD
Conduit suspension type	管吊式	Guǎndiào-shì	DS
Conference call	会议电话	Huìyì diànhuà	CONF
Conference call mix	会议电话呼叫混合	Huìyì diànhuà hūjiào hùnhé	CCMX
Conference calling	会议呼叫	Huìyì hūjiào	CONF
Conference conductor	会议主持者	Huìyì zhǔchízhě	
Conference des Administrations Européennes des Postes et Telecommunications	欧洲邮政和远程通信会议	Ōuzhōu yóuzhèng hé yuǎnchéng tōngxìn huìyì	
Conference of European Post and Telecommunication Administrations	欧洲邮电行政大会	Ōuzhōu yóudiàn xíngzhèng dàhuì	CEPT
Conference of European Post and Telecommunication Administrations	欧洲邮政和电信行政会议	Ōuzhōu yóuzhèng hé diànxìn xíngzhèng huìyì	CEPT
Conference of European Posts and Telecommunications	欧洲邮政和通信会议	Ōuzhōu yóuzhèng hé tōngxìn huìyì	CEPT
Conference of European Posts and Telecommunications Administrations	欧洲邮电行政会议	Ōuzhōu yóudiàn xíngzhèng huìyì	CEPT
Conference on laser electro-optical systems	激光器与光电系统会议	Jīguāngqì yǔ guāngdiàn xìtǒng huìyì	CLEOS
Conference telephone	会议电话	Huìyì diànhuà	HD
Conference television	会议电视	Huìyì diànshì	
Conference trunk	会议电话总线	Huìyì diànhuà zǒngxiàn	CFT
Confidence	置信度	Zhìxìndù	
Confidentiality	保密性	Bǎomì-xìng	
Confidentiality (IPsec)	机密性	Jīmìxìng	
Confidentiality protected command (in FTP)	机密性保护命令	Jīmìxìng bǎohù mìnglìng	CONF
Configurable logic block	可配置逻辑模块	Kěpèizhì luóji mókuài	CLB
Configuration	配置	Pèizhì	
Configuration	组态	Zǔtài	
Configuration and resource management	配置和资源管理	Pèizhì hé zīyuán guǎnlǐ	CRM
Configuration audit	配置检查	Pèizhì jiǎnchá	
Configuration control board	配置控制组	Pèizhì kòngzhì zǔ	
Configuration daemon (in VPN)	配置精灵	Pèizhì jīnglíng	CD
Configuration data manager	配置数据管理器	Pèizhì shùjù guǎnlǐqì	CDM
Configuration data set	配置数据集	Pèizhì shùjùjí	CDS
Configuration generator	配置生成器	Pèizhì shēngchéngqì	
Configuration identification	配置标识	Pèizhì biāozhì	
Configuration item	配置项	Pèizhì xiàng	
Configuration management	配置管理	Pèizhì guǎnlǐ	
Configuration register value	配置登记码	Pèizhì dēngjì mǎ	
Configuration report server	配置报告服务器	Pèizhì bàogào fúwùqì	CRS
Configuration space enable	可分配空间	Kěfēnpèi kōngjiān	CSE
Configuration status recording	配置状态记录	Pèizhì zhuàngtài jìlù	
Configured tunneling	配置隧道	Pèizhì suìdào	CT
Confining pressure	围压	Wéiyā	
Confirm	证实	Zhèngshí	
Confirm (primtive)	证实（原语）	Zhèngshí (yuán yǔ)	
Confirmation time	证实时间	Zhèngshí shíjiān	Tc
Confirmed service	证实型服务	Zhèngshíxíng fúwù	
Confirmed-service	证实服务	Zhèngshí fúwù	
Conflation, merge	合并	Hébìng	

Conflict analysis	冲突分析	Chōngtū fēnxī	
Conflict detection	冲突检测	Chōngtū jiǎncè	
Conflict resolution strategy	冲突解决策略	Chōngtū jiějué cèlüè	
Confluence	合流	Héliú	
Conformal antenna	共形天线	Gòngxíng tiānxiàn	
Conformal array	共形阵	Gòngxíng zhèn	
Conformal array antenna	共形阵天线	Gòngxíng zhèn tiānxiàn	
Conformal coat cure (semiconductor mfg)	保形涂层硫化	Bǎoxíng túcéng liúhuà	
Conformal coating (in SMT)	共形涂层	Gòngxíng túcéng	
Conformal projection	等角投影	Děngjiǎo tóuyǐng	
Conformance	一致性	Yīzhìxìng	
Conformance assessment process	适合性评价过程	Shìhéxìng píngjià guòchéng	
Conformance assessment process	一致性判定进程	Yīzhìxìng pàndìng jìnchéng	
Conformance clause	适合性的条款	Shìhéxìngde tiáokuǎn	
Conformance quality level	适合性品质水平	Shìhéxìng pǐnzhì shuǐpíng	
Conformance requirement 'n'	一致性需求"n"	Yīzhìxìng xūqiú "n"	CRn
Conformance resolution test	一致性结论测试	Yīzhìxìng jiélùn cèshì	
Conformance test	一致性测试	Yīzhìxìng cèshì	CT
Conformance test report	适合性检验报告	Shìhéxìng jiǎnyàn bàogào	
Conformance test suite	一致性测试套	Yīzhìxìng cèshì tào	
Conformance testing	适合性检验	Shìhéxìng jiǎnyàn	
Conformant management entity	一致管理项目	Yīzhì guǎnlǐ xiàngmù	CME
Conformant traffic	顺从流	Shùncóng liú	
Conforming implementation	适宜操作	Shìyí cāozuò	
Conforming implementation	一致性实现	Yīzhìxìng shíxiàn	
Conformity	整合	Zhěnghé	
Conformity error	一致性误差	Yīzhìxìng wùchā	
Conformity specification	一致性规范	Yīzhìxìng guīfàn	
Congested district	过密集地区	Guòmìjí dìqū	
Congesting level (of power)	拥塞电平	Yōngsè diànpíng	
Congestion	拥挤	Yōngjǐ	
Congestion	拥塞	Yōngsè	
Congestion control	拥挤控制	Yōngjǐ kòngzhì	
Congestion control	拥塞控制	Yōngsè kòngzhì	
Congestion control mechanism	拥塞控制机制	Yōngsè kòngzhì jīzhì	
Congestion indication	拥塞指示	Yōngsè zhǐshì	CI
Congestion level	拥塞等级	Yōngsè děngjí	
Congestion notification	拥塞通知	Yōngsè tōngzhī	CN
Congestion signal	拥塞信号	Yōngsè xìnhào	
Congestion tone	拥塞音	Yōngsè yīn	
Congestion window	拥塞窗口	Yōngsè chuāngkǒu	CWND
Congruence	一致性	Yīzhìxìng	
Conic projection	圆锥投影	Yuánzhuī tóuyǐng	
Conical array	圆锥形阵	Yuánzhuīxíng zhèn	
Conical dielectric horn-feed	介质导喇叭馈电器	Jièzhì dǎo lǎba kuìdiànqì	
Conical horn	圆锥喇叭	Yuánzhuī lǎba	

Conical horn antenna	圆锥形喇叭天线	Yuánzhuīxíng lǎba tiānxiàn	
Conical lens	圆锥透镜	Yuánzhuī tòujìng	
Conical scan antenna	圆锥扫描天线	Yuánzhuī sǎomiáo tiānxiàn	
Conical scan radar	圆锥扫描雷达	Yuánzhuī sǎomiáo léidá	
Conical scanning radar receiver	圆锥扫描雷达接收机	Yuánzhuī sǎomiáo léidá jiēshōujī	
Conjoint boundary	共同边界	Gòngtóng biānjiè	
Conjugate graduation method	共轭梯度法	Gòng'è tīdù fǎ	CGM
Conjugate selecting	联合选择	Liánhé xuǎnzé	
Conjugate structure-algebraic code excited linear prediction	共轭结构-代数码激励线性预测	Gòng'è jiégòu—dàishù mǎ jīlì xiànxìng yùcè	CS-ACELP
Conjunction	连词	Liáncí	
Conjunction analysis tool (software)	接近分析工具	Jiējìn fēnxī gōngjù	
Connect acknowledgement	连接认可	Liánjiē rènkě	CONNACK
Connect acknowledgement	连接证实	Liánjiē zhèngshí	CONNACK
Connect ID	连接号	Liánjiēhào	
Connect message (ISUP)	连接消息	Liánjiē xiāoxi	CON
Connect signal	接线信号	Jiēxiàn xìnhào	
Connect to resource	连接到资源	Liánjiē dào zīyuán	CTR
Connected component	连通分量	Liántōng fènliàng	
Connected component	连通分支	Liántōng fēnzhī	
Connected graph	连通图	Liántōng tú	
Connected line identification presentation	被叫线识别显示	Bèijiào xiàn shíbié xiǎnshì	COLP
Connected line identification presentation	被接线路识别显示	Bèijiē xiànlù shíbié xiǎnshì	COLP
Connected line identification presentation	连接线标识显示	Liánjiēxiàn biāozhì xiǎnshì	COLP
Connected line identification presentation	连接线识别提供	Liánjiēxiàn shíbié tígōng	COLP
Connected line identification presentation	连接线识别显示	Liánjiēxiàn shíbié xiǎnshì	COLP
Connected line identification presentation supplementary service	被叫识别提供补充业务	Bèijiào shíbié tígōng bǔchōng yèwù	COLP
Connected line identification restriction	被叫线识别限制	Bèijiào xiàn shíbié xiànzhì	COLR
Connected line identification restriction	被接线路识别限制	Bèijiē xiànlù shíbié xiànzhì	COLR
Connected line identification restriction	连接号码识别限制	Liánjiē hàomǎ shíbié xiànzhì	C0LR
Connected line identification restriction	连接线标识限制	Liánjiēxiàn biāozhì xiànzhì	COLR
Connected line identification restriction	连接线识别限制	Liánjiēxiàn shíbié xiànzhì	COLR
Connected line identification restriction supplementary service	被叫识别限制补充业务	Bèijiào shíbié xiànzhì bǔchōng yèwù	COLR
Connected line identity	被叫识别	Bèijiào shíbié	COLI
Connected line identity	连接线识别	Liánjiēxiàn shíbié	COLI
Connected node	连接节点	Liánjiē jiédiǎn	
Connected tone-controlled squelch system	连续单音控制静噪制	Liánxù dānyīn kòngzhì jìngzào zhì	
Connecting point	接续点	Jiēxùdiǎn	
Connection	接续	Jiēxù	
Connection	连接	Liánjiē	CONN
Connection acknowledged (SS7 message)	连接确认	Liánjiē quèrèn	COAK, CC
Connection admission control	接纳允许控制	Jiēnà yǔnxǔ kòngzhì	CAC
Connection admission control	连接接纳控制	Liánjiē jiēnà kòngzhì	CAC
Connection admission control	连接允许控制	Liánjiē yǔnxǔ kòngzhì	CAC
Connection attribute	连接属性	Liánjiē shǔxìng	

Connection confidentiality (IPsec)	连接机密性	Liánjiē jīmìxìng	
Connection configuration management	连接组成管理	Liánjiē zǔchéng guǎnlǐ	Con.CM
Connection confirm	连接证实	Liánjiē zhèngshí	CC
Connection control	连接控制	Liánjiē kòngzhì	
Connection control interface	连接控制接口	Liánjiē kòngzhì jiēkǒu	CCI
Connection controller	连接控制器	Liánjiē kòngzhìqì	CC
Connection element	连接单元	Liánjiē dānyuán	CE
Connection end point	连接端点	Liánjiē duāndiǎn	CEP
Connection endpoint identifier	连接端点标识符	Liánjiē duāndiǎn biāozhìfú	CEI
Connection establishment error probability	连接建立错误概率	Liánjiē jiànlì cuòwù gàilǜ	CEP
Connection establishment failure probability	连接建立失败概率	Liánjiē jiànlì shībài gàilǜ	CFP
Connection establishment protocol	建立联系协议	Jiànlì liánxì xiéyì	CEP
Connection fragment	连接段	Liánjiē duàn	CF
Connection frame number	接续帧号	Jiēxù zhènghào	CFN
Connection frame number	连接帧号	Liánjiē zhènghào	CFN
Connection function	连接功能	Liánjiē gōngnéng	C
Connection identifier	连接标识符	Liánjiē biāozhì fú	CID
Connection integrity with recovery (IPsec)	有恢复连接完整性	Yǒu huīfù liánjiē wánzhěngxìng	
Connection integrity without recovery (IPsec)	无恢复连接完整性	Wúhuīfù liánjiē wánzhěngxìng	
Connection management	接续管理	Jiēxù guǎnlǐ	CM
Connection management	连接管理	Liánjiē guǎnlǐ	CM
Connection matrix	连接矩阵	Liánjiē jǔzhèn	CM
Connection module	通信模块	Tōngxìn mókuài	CM
Connection network	接续网路	Jiēxù wǎnglù	
Connection oriented network service	面向连接网络业务	Miànxiàng liánjiē wǎngluò yèwù	CONS
Connection overhead	连接开销	Liánjiē kāixiao	CO
Connection point	连接点	Liánjiēdiǎn	CP
Connection pooling	连接池	Liánjiē chí	
Connection quality	连接质量	Liánjiē zhìliàng	
Connection refused (in SS7)	拒绝连接	Jùjué liánjiē	CREF
Connection related function	连接相关功能	Liánjiē xiāngguān gōngnéng	CRF
Connection related function	连接有关功能	Liánjiē yǒuguān gōngnéng	CRF
Connection released (in SS7)	释放连接	Shìfàng liánjiē	RLSD
Connection request	连接要求	Liánjiē yāoqiú	
Connection request (SS7 message)	连接请求	Liánjiē qǐngqiú	CORE, CR
Connection retainability (in telecommunication)	连接可保持性	Liánjiē kěbǎochíxìng	
Connection retention	连接保持	Liánjiē bǎochí	
Connection termination point	连接终结点	Liánjiē zhōngjiédiǎn	CTP
Connection type	连接类型	Liánjiē lèixíng	
Connection view	连接可视	Liánjiē kěshì	CV
Connection view state	连接可视状态	Liánjiē kěshì zhuàngtài	CVS
Connectionless	无连接	Wúliánjiē	CL
Connectionless bearer control	无连接承载控制	Wúliánjiē chéngzài kòngzhì	CBC
Connectionless broadband data service	无连接宽带数据服务	Wúliánjiē kuāndài shùjù fúwù	CBDS
Connectionless broadband data service	无连接型宽带数据业务	Wúliánjiēxíng kuāndài shùjù yèwù	CBDS
Connectionless confidentiality (IPsec)	无连接机密性	Wúliánjiē jīmìxìng	

Connectionless data acknowledged (SS7 message)	无连接数据确认	Wúliánjiē shùjù quèrèn	CLDA
Connectionless data transfer (SS7 message)	无连接数据传送	Wúliánjiē shùjù chuánsòng	CLDT
Connectionless integrity (IPsec)	无连接完整性	Wúliánjiē wánzhěngxìng	
Connectionless network layer protocol	无连接的网络层协议	Wúliánjiēde wǎngluò céng xiéyì	CLNP
Connectionless network layer service	无连接的网络层服务	Wúliánjiēde wǎngluò céng fúwù	CLNS
Connectionless network protocol	无连接模式网络层协议	Wúliánjiē móshì wǎngluò céng xiéyì	CLNP
Connectionless network protocol	无连接网络协议	Wúliánjiē wǎngluò xiéyì	CLNP
Connectionless network service	五连接网络服务	Wǔliánjiē wǎngluò fúwù	CLNS
Connectionless server	无连接服务器	Wúliánjiē fúwùqì	CLS
Connectionless service	无连接业务	Wúliánjiē yèwù	
Connectionless service	无连接型业务	Wúliánjiēxíng yèwù	
Connectionless service function	无连接业务功能	Wúliánjiē yèwù gōngnéng	CLSF
Connection-mode network service	点对点面向连接网络业务	Diǎn duì diǎn miànxiàng liánjiē wǎngluò yèwù	FTP-CONS PTP
Connection-mode network service	连接方式网络服务	Liánjiē fāngshì wǎngluò fúwù	CMNS
Connection-oriented	面向连接	Miànxiàng liánjiē	CO
Connection-oriented conference system	面向连接的会议系统	Miànxiàng liánjiēde huìyì xìtǒng	
Connection-oriented data acknowledge	面向连接数据确认	Miànxiàng liánjiē shùjù quèrèn	CODA
Connection-oriented data transport	面向连接数据传送	Miànxiàng liánjiē shùjù chuánsòng	CODT
Connection-oriented internetworking	面向连接的网络互联	Miànxiàng liánjiēde wǎngluò hùlián	
Connection-oriented network (layer) service	面向连接的网络层服务	Miànxiàng liánjiēde wǎngluò céng fúwù	CONS
Connection-oriented network layer protocol	面向连接的网络层协议	Miànxiàng liánjiēde wǎngluò céng xiéyì	CONP
Connection-oriented network protocol	定向连接网络协议	Dìngxiàng liánjiē wǎngluò xiéyì	CONP
Connection-oriented network protocol (ISO use)	面向连接的网络协议	Miànxiàng liánjiēde wǎngluò xiéyì	CONP
Connection-oriented network service	定向连接网络业务	Dìngxiàng liánjiē wǎngluò yèwù	CONS
Connection-oriented transport service	面向连接的运输服务	Miànxiàng liánjiēde yùnshū fúwù	COTS
Connection-related function	连接的有关功能	Liánjiēde yǒuguān gōngnéng	CRF
Connectivity check	连续性检测	Liánxùxìng jiǎncè	CC
Connectivity manager	连通管理器	Liántōng guǎnlǐqì	CM
Connectivity, linkage	连接性	Liánjiēxìng	
Connector	连接器	Liánjiēqì	
Connector insertion loss	连接器插入损耗	Liánjiēqì chārù sǔnhào	
Connector optical conductor loss	连接器光导损耗	Liánjiēqì guāngdǎo sǔnhào	
Consecutive identical digit	连续相同数字	Liánxù xiāngtóng shùzì	CID
Consecutive identical digits	连接相同数字	Liánjiē xiāngtóng shùzì	CID
Consecutive identical digits	连续恒等数字	Liánxù héngděng shùzì	CID
Consecutive severely errored second	连续严重误块秒	Liánxù yánzhòng wùkuài miǎo	CSES
Conservative busy tone multiple access	保护性忙音多路存取	Bǎohù-xìng mángyīn duōlù cúnqǔ	C-BTMA
Consistency management	一致性管理	Yīzhìxìng guǎnlǐ	
Console	控制台	Kòngzhìtái	
Console input/output	控制台输入输出装置	Kòngzhìtái shūrù shūchū zhuāngzhì	
Console interface board	控制台接口板	Kòngzhìtái jiēkǒu bǎn	CIB
Console typewriter	控制台打字机	Kòngzhìtái dǎzìjī	
Consolidated link layer management	加强的链路层管理	Jiāqiángde liànlùcéng guǎnlǐ	CLLM
Consolidated link layer management	综合链路层管理	Zōnghé liànlù céng guǎnlǐ	CLLM
Consolidation	归并/集中	Guībìng/jízhōng	

Consolidation	固结	Gùjié	
Consolidation and grooming	整理与合并	Zhěnglǐ yǔ hébìng	
Consolidation test	固结试验	Gùjié shìyàn	
Consolidation works	加固工程	Jiāgù gōngchéng	
Constant altitude plane position indicator	等高平面位置显示器	Děnggāo píngmiàn wèizhì xiǎnshìqì	PPI
Constant bit rate	固定比特率	Gùdìng bǐtèlǜ	CBR
Constant bit rate	恒定比特率	Héngdìng bǐtè lǜ	CBR
Constant bit rate service	固定比特率业务	Gùdìng bǐtèlǜ yèwù	
Constant bit rate service	恒定比特率业务	Héngdìng bǐtè lǜ yèwù	CBR
Constant current power supply	恒流电源	Héngliú diànyuán	
Constant failure intensity period	恒定失效频度期	Héngdìng shīxiào píndù qī	
Constant failure rate period	恒定失效率期	Héngdìng shīxiào lǜ qī	
Constant false alarm receiver	恒虚警接收机	Héng xūjǐng jiēshōujī	CFAR
Constant linear velocity (optical disk)	恒定线速度	Héngdìng xiànsùdù	CLV
Constant modulus algorithm	恒模算法	Héngmó suànfǎ	CMA
Constant ratio code	定比码	Dìngbǐmǎ	
Constant ratio code	恒比码	Héngbǐ mǎ	
Constant spacing	固定间距	Gùdìng jiānjù	
Constant temperature	恒温	Héngwēn	
Constant temperature and humidity test	恒温恒湿试验	Héngwēn héngshī shìyàn	
Constant voltage charge	恒压充电	Héngyā chōngdiàn	
Constant voltage power supply	恒压电源	Héngyā diànyuán	
Constant (noun)	常量	Chángliàng	
Constant-value control system	恒值控制系统	Héngzhí kòngzhì xìtǒng	
Constrained feed	强迫馈电	Qiǎngpò kuìdiàn	
Constrained lens	约束透镜	Yuēshù tòujìng	
Constrained metal-plate lens antenna	约束金属板透镜天线	Yuēshù jīnshǔ bǎn tòujìng tiānxiàn	
Constrained non-linear regression	受约束非线性回归	Shòuyuēshù fēixiànxìng huíguī	
Constrained shortest path first	制约最短路径优选	Zhìyuē zuìduǎn lùjìng yōuxuǎn	CSPF
Constraint length of the convolutional code	卷积码的约束长度	Juànjī mǎde yuēshù chángdù	K
Constraint programming (CAD/CAM)	约束规划	Yuēshù guīhuà	CP
Constraint satisfaction problem	约束满足问题	Yuēshù mǎnzú wèntí	CSP
Constraint (for database)	约束	Yuēshù	
Constraint-based label distribution protocol	受限标签分配协议	Shòuxiàn biāoqiān fēnpèi xiéyì	CR-LDP
Constraint-based LSP (label switching path)	基于约束 LSP	Jīyú yuēshù LSP	CR-LSP
Constraint-based routing	受限路由	Shòuxiàn lùyóu	
Constraint-based routing	约束路由	Yuēshù lùyóu	
Constraints	限制	Xiànzhì	
Construct (noun)	成分	Chéngfèn	
Construct (noun)	概念	Gàiniàn	
Construct (noun)	构件	Gòujiàn	
Construct (noun; for language)	构造	Gòuzào	
Construction and real estate network	建筑与房地产网络	Jiànzhù yǔ fángdìchǎn wǎngluò	CORENET
Construction drawing (CAD/CAM)	建筑工程图	Jiànzhù gōngchéng tú	
Construction industry	建筑业	Jiànzhùyè	
Constructor	构造函数	Gòuzào hánshù	Ctor

Constructor	构造器	Gòuzào qì	ctor
Consultative Committee on International Radio (a division of ITU)	国际无线电咨询委员会	Guójì wúxiàndiàn zīxún wěiyuánhuì	CCIR
Consultative Committee on Space Data Systems	空间数据系统咨询委宴会	Kōngjiān shùjù xìtǒng zīxún wěiyànhuì	CCSDS
Consumer digital subscriber line	消费者数字订阅线路	Xiāofèizhě shùzì dìngyuè xiànlù	CDSL
Consumer electronics	消费电子	Xiāofèi diànzǐ	
Consumer electronics bus	用户电子总线	Yònghù diànzǐ zǒngxiàn	CEBus
Consumer Electronics Manufacturing Association	消费者电子制造业协会	Xiāofèizhě diànzǐ zhìzàoyè xiéhuì	CEMA
Consumer electronics show	民用设备展览会	Mínyòng shèbèi zhǎnlǎnhuì	CES
Consumer package	消售包装	Xiāoshòu bāozhuāng	
Contact electric position transmitter	有触点位置发送器	Yǒu chùdiǎn wèizhì fāsòngqì	
Contact head	触头	Chùtóu	
Contact piston	接触式活塞	Jiēchù-shì huósāi	
Contact resistance	接触电阻	Jiēchù diànzǔ	
Contact voltage	接触电压	Jiēchù diànyā	
Contact-controlled electric actuator	有触点电动执行机构	Yǒu chùdiǎn diàndòng zhíxíng jīgòu	
Container (SDH term)	容器	Róngqì	C
Container object	所有者对象	Suǒyǒuzhě duìxiàng	
Containment	包容	Bāoróng	
Containment	牵制	Qiānzhì	
Containment hierarchy	牵制等级	Qiānzhì děngjí	
Containment tree	牵制树	Qiānzhì shù	
Containment type	抑制方式	Yìzhì fāngshì	
Content	内容	Nèiróng	
Content addressable file store	可按内容寻址的文件存储	Kě àn nèiróng xúnzhǐde wénjiàn cúnchǔ	CAFS
Content addressable memory	按内容编址的存储器	Àn nèiróng biānzhǐde cúnchǔqì	CAM
Content addressable storage	按内容的寻址的存储器	Àn nèiróngde xúnzhǐde cúnchǔqì	CAS
Content architecture	内容体系结构	Nèiróng tǐxì jiégòu	
Content architecture class	内容体系结构类别	Nèiróng tǐxì jiégòu lèibié	
Content architecture level	内容体系结构级	Nèiróng tǐxì jiégòu jí	
Content delivery network	内容分发网络	Nèiróng fēnfā wǎngluò	CDN
Content delivery services	内容分发业务	Nèiróng fēnfā yèwù	CDS
Content delivery services	内容配送业务	Nèiróng pèisòng yèwù	CDS
Content distribution network	内容分发网络	Nèiróng fēnfā wǎngluò	CDN
Content distribution service	内容分发服务	Nèiróng fēnfā fúwù	CDS
Content editing process	内容编辑处理	Nèiróng biānjí chǔlǐ	
Content element	内容元素	Nèiróng yuánsù	
Content layout process	内容布局处理	Nèiróng bùjú chǔlǐ	
Content manager	内容管理器	Nèiróng guǎnlǐqì	
Content portion	内容组成部分	Nèiróng zǔchéng bùfen	
Content portion description	内容组成部分描述	Nèiróng zǔchéng bùfen miáoshù	
Content service provider	内容服务提供者	Nèiróng fúwù tígòngzhě	CSP
Content standard for spatial metadata	空间元数据的内容标准	Kōngjiān yuánshùjùde nèiróng biāozhǔn	CSSM
Content type	内容类型	Nèiróng lèixíng	
Content-addressable memory	内容定址存储器	Nèiróng dìngzhǐ cúnchǔqì	CAM
Content-addressable memory	内容寻址存储器	Nèiróng xúnzhǐ cúnchǔqì	CAM
Content-based image retrieval	基于内容的图像检索技术	Jīyú nèiróngde túxiàng jiǎnsuǒ jìshù	CBIR

Contention	争用	Zhēngyòng	
Contention resolution	争抢判决	Zhēngqiǎng pànjué	
Context	环境	Huánjìng	
Context	上下文	Shàngxiàwén	
Context addressed segment sequential memory	按上下文编址的分段顺序存储器	Àn shàngxiàwén biānzhǐde fēnduàn shùnxù cúnchǔqì	CASSM
Contiguity	邻接性	Línjiē xìng	
Contingency plan	应急计划	Yìngjí jìhuà	
Continuation line	连续行	Liánxù háng	
Continuation media	延续媒体	Yánxù méitǐ	
Continuation of message	消息继续	Xiāoxi jìxù	COM
Continuation record	连续记录	Liánxù jìlù	
Continued fraction	连分式	Lián fēnshì	
Continuity check	导通检验	Dǎotōng jiǎnyàn	
Continuity check	连续性检查	Liánxùxìng jiǎnchá	
Continuity check	连续性检验	Liánxùxìng jiǎnyàn	
Continuity signal	导通消息	Dǎotōng xiāoxi	COT
Continuity signal	导通信号	Dǎotōng xìnhào	COT
Continuity-check incoming (signal)	连续性检验输入(信号)	Liánxù-xìng jiǎnyàn shūrù (xìnhào)	CCI
Continuity-check-request signal	请求导通检验信号	Qǐngqiú dǎotōng jiǎnyàn xìnhào	CCR
Continuity-failure signal	导通故障信号	Dǎotōng gùzhàng xìnhào	CCF
Continuity-recheck incoming	连续性重复检验输入信号	Liánxùxìng chóngfù jiǎnyàn shūrù xìnhào	CRI
Continuous averaging	连续平均法	Liánxù píngjūn fǎ	
Continuous checking	连续检查	Liánxù jiǎnchá	
Continuous concatenation	连续级联	Liánxù jílián	
Continuous current-carrying capacity (of a conductor)	连续载流量	Liánxù zàiliúliàng	
Continuous data	连续数据	Liánxù shùjù	
Continuous database	连续数据库	Liánxù shùjùkù	
Continuous disturbance	连续骚扰	Liánxù sāorǎo	
Continuous dynamic channel assign	连续的动态信道分配	Liánxùde dòngtài xìndào fēnpèi	CDCA
Continuous Fourier transform	连续傅里叶变换	Liánxù fùlǐyè biànhuàn	CFT
Continuous individual tone system	连续单音制	Liánxù dānyīnzhì	
Continuous mapping	连续制图	Liánxù zhìtú	
Continuous noise	连续噪声	Liánxù zàoshēng	
Continuous operating ability of the main power	电源连续工作能力	Diànyuán liánxù gōngzuò nénglì	
Continuous operation ability of the power supply	电源持续工作能力	Diànyuán chíxù gōngzuò nénglì	
Continuous phase frequency shift keying	连续相位频移键控	Liánxù xiàngwèi pínyí jiànkòng	CPFSK
Continuous phase modulation	连续相位调制	Liánxù xiàngwèi tiáozhì	CPM
Continuous replenishment program	连续库存补充计划	Liánxù kùcún bǔchōng jìhuà	CRP
Continuous severely errored second	连续严重误码秒	Liánxù yánzhòng wùmǎ miǎo	CSES
Continuous signal	连接信号	Liánjiē xìnhào	
Continuous slope delta modulation	连续斜率Δ调制	Liánxù xiélǜ Δ tiáozhì	CSDM
Continuous spectrum	连续谱	Liánxùpǔ	
Continuous tone	不间断色调	Bùjiànduàn sèdiào	
Continuous wave	连续波	Liánxù bō	CW
Continuous wave	一等幅报	Yīděng fúbào	CW

Continuous wave (CW) laser	连续式激光	Liánxù-shì jīguāng	
Continuous wave jamming	连续波干扰	Liánxù bō gānrǎo	
Continuous wave modulated signal	连续波调制信号	Liánxù bō tiáozhì xìnhào	
Continuous wave telegraph	等幅电报	Děngfú diànbào	
Continuous wave transmission	连续波传输	Liánxù bō chuánshū	CW
Continuously variable slope delta modulation	连续可变斜率增量方式	Liánxù kěbiàn xiélǜ zēngliàng fāngshì	CVSDM
Continuously variable slope delta modulation	连续可变斜率增量调制	Liánxù kěbiàn xiélǜ zēngliàng tiáozhì	CVSD
Continuously variable slope delta modulation	连续可变斜率 Δ 调制	Liánxù kěbiàn xiélǜ Δ tiáozhì	CVSD
Continuously variable slope delta modulation	连续可变的角变增量调制	Liánxù kěbiànde jiǎobiàn zēngliàng tiáozhì	CVSDM
Continuous-phase frequency shift keying	连续相位移频键控	Liánxù xiàngwèi yípín jiànkòng	CPFSK
Continuous-phase modulation	连续调相	Liánxù tiáoxiàng	CPM
Contour (GIS)	等高线	Děnggāoxiàn	
Contour interval	等高线间距	Děnggāoxiàn jiānjù	
Contour interval (GIS)	等高距	Děnggāojù	
Contour tagging	等高线标注	Děnggāoxiàn biāozhù	
Contoured-beam antenna	等强度线射束天线	Děngqiángdù xiàn shèshù tiānxiàn	
Contract level maintenance	维护服务合同等级	Wéihù fúwù hétong děngjí	
Contract selling	包销	Bāoxiāo	
Contraction	收缩流	Shōusuō liú	
Contradirectional	反向	Fǎnxiàng	
Contradirectional interface	反向接口	Fǎnxiàng jiēkǒu	
Contrast	对比度	Duìbǐdù	
Contrast stretching	反差扩展	Fǎnchā kuòzhǎn	
Contribution	素材	Sùcái	
Contribution	索材	Suǒcái	
Contribution	投送	Tóusòng	
Contribution application	素材应用	Sùcái yìngyòng	
Contribution application	索材应用	Suǒcái yìngyòng	
Contribution application	投送应用	Tóusòng yìngyòng	
Contribution link	贡献路线	Gòngxiàn lùxiàn	
Control and interface board assembly	控制和接口集成板	Kòngzhì hé jiēkǒu jíchéngbǎn	BCIA
Control and maintenance	控制和维护	Kòngzhì hé wéihù	BCM
Control and maintenance block	控制和维护模块	Kòngzhì hé wéihù mókuài	BCMB
Control and transmit assembly	控制和传输集成件	Kòngzhì hé chuánshū jíchéng jiàn	CATA
Control arithmetic unit	控制运算单元	Kòngzhì yùnsuàn dānyuán	CAU
Control back board	控制后面板	Kòngzhì hòumian bǎn	
Control block update facility	控制块更新设施	Kòngzhì kuài gēngxīn shèshī	CBUF
Control bus parity check error	控制总线寄偶校验错	Kòngzhì zǒngxiàn jì'ǒu jiàoyàn cuò	CPAR
Control channel (ISDN usage)	控制信道	Kòngzhì xìndào	CCH
Control character	控制字符	Kòngzhì zìfú	
Control command word	控制命令字	Kòngzhì mìnglìng zì	CCW
Control console	控制台	Kòngzhìtái	CON
Control dependence graph	控制依赖图	Kòngzhì yīlài tú	CDG
Control electronics	控制电路	Kòngzhì diànlù	CE
Control equipment	控制设备	Kòngzhì shèbèi	
Control flag	控制标志	Kòngzhì biāozhì	

Control flow graph	控制流图	Kòngzhì liú tú	CFG
Control function	控制功能	Kòngzhì gōngnéng	
Control gate photomultiplier	控制栅光电培增器	Kòngzhì zhà guāngdiàn péizēngqì	
Control interworking back panel	控制互通后面板	Kòngzhì hùtōng hòumian bǎn	CIBP
Control interworking node interface	控制互通节点接口	Kòngzhì hùtōng jiédiǎn jiēkǒu	CINI
Control interworking node manager	控制互通节点管理器	Kòngzhì hùtōng jiédiǎn guǎnlǐqì	CINM
Control layer	控制层	Kòngzhì céng	
Control logic circuit	控制逻辑电路	Kòngzhì luóji diànlù	
Control mapping	控制制图	Kòngzhì zhìtú	
Control panel	控制面板	Kòngzhì miànbǎn	
Control plane	控制面	Kòngzhì miàn	
Control plane	控制平面	Kòngzhì píngmiàn	CP
Control point, reference point	控制点	Kòngzhì diǎn	
Control processor	控制处理器	Kòngzhì chǔlǐqì	BCP
Control set	控制集	Kòngzhì jí	
Control signal	控制信号	Kòngzhì xìnhào	
Control signaling code	控制信令码	Kòngzhì xìnlìng mǎ	CSC
Control signaling rate	控制信号传送速率	Kòngzhì xìnhào chuánsòng sùlǜ	
Control statement	控制语句	Kòngzhì yǔjù	
Control station	控制站	Kòngzhìzhàn	
Control station	控制站	Kòngzhìzhàn	
Control system	控制系统	Kòngzhì xìtǒng	CE
Control system error	控制系统误差	Kòngzhì xìtǒng wùchā	
Control system message log	控制系统信息日志	Kòngzhì xìtǒng xìnxī rìzhì	CSML
Control system program	控制系统的程序	Kòngzhì xìtǒngde chéngxù	
Control unit	控制部件	Kòngzhì bùjiàn	
Control word	控制字	Kòngzhì zì	CW
Control zone	控制区	Kòngzhì qū	
Control-break report	控制中断报表	Kòngzhì zhōngduàn bàobiǎo	
Controllable isolation (IPsec)	可控隔离	Kěkòng gélí	
Controlled access	受控访问	Shòukòng fǎngwèn	
Controlled accessability	受控访问性	Shòukòng fǎngwènxìng	
Controlled data transfer element (DTE) not installed	受控 DTE 未装备好	Shòukòng DTE wèi zhuāngbèi hǎo	
Controlled load service	受控负载业务	Shòukòng fùzài yèwù	CLS
Controlled maintenance	受控维护	Shòukòng wéihù	
Controlled sharing (IPsec)	受控共享	Shòukòng gòngxiǎng	
Controlled slip	受控滑动	Shòukòng huádòng	
Controlled station	受控站	Shòukòng zhàn	
Controlled variable	被控变量	Bèikòng biànliàng	
Controlling radio network controller	控制无线网络的控制器	Kòngzhì wúxiàn wǎngluòde kòngzhìqì	CRNC
Control-of-flow language	控制流语言	Kòngzhì liú yǔyán	
Convection	对流	Duìliú	
Convective echo	对流形回音	Duìliúxíng huíyīn	
Convenor	召集人	Zhàojírén	
Conventional degree of distortion	常规畸变度	Chángguī jībiàn dù	
Conventional evolutionary algorithm	传统进化类算法	Chuántǒng jìnhuà lèi suànfǎ	CEA

Convergence	会合	Huìhé	
Convergence	会聚	Huìjù	
Convergence	收敛	Shōuliǎn	C
Convergence protocol	会聚协议	Huìjù xiéyì	
Convergence protocol entity	会聚协议实体	Huìjù xiéyì shítǐ	CPE
Convergence rate	收敛速度	Shōuliǎn sùdù	
Convergence ratio	收敛比	Shōuliǎn bǐ	
Convergence service	会聚服务	Huìjù fúwù	CS
Convergence sub-layer	会聚子层	Huìjù zicéng	CS
Convergence sub-layer protocol data unit	会聚子层协议数据单元	Huìjù zicéng xiéyì shùjù dānyuán	CS-PDU
Conversation (in telecommunication)	会话	Huìhuà	
Conversation (in telecommunication)	通话	Tōnghuà	
Conversation service	会话业务	Huìhuà yèwù	
Conversation test	会话测试	Huìhuà cèshì	
Conversational mode	对话方式	Duìhuà fāngshì	
Conversational service	会话型业务	Huìhuàxíng yèwù	
Conversion	转换	Zhuǎnhuàn	
Conversion cycle	转换循环	Zhuǎnhuàn xúnhuán	
Conversion facility	转换功能	Zhuǎnhuàn gōngnéng	CF
Conversion facility	转换设备	Zhuǎnhuàn shèbèi	CF
Conversion list	转换表	Zhuǎnhuàn biǎo	
Conversion precision	换算精度	Huànsuàn jīngdù	
Conversion record	转换记录	Zhuǎnhuàn jìlù	
Conversion rule	变换规则	Biànhuàn guīzé	
Conversion, changeover	转换	Zhuǎnhuàn	
Convert all	转换全部	Zhuǎnhuàn quánbù	
Convert present table	转换本表	Zhuǎnhuàn běn biǎo	
Converter (electrical or digital signal use)	转换器	Zhuǎnhuànqì	
Converter conversion loss	变频损耗	Biànpín sǔnhào	
Convex hull	凸包	Tū bāo	
Conveyer (in component assembly process)	输送带	Shūsòngdài	
Convolution	卷积	Juǎnjī	
Convolution integral	指积分	Zhǐjīfēn	
Convolutional code	卷积码	Juànjī mǎ	
Convolutor	卷积器	Juǎnjīqì	
Cookie	小甜饼	Xiǎo tiánbǐng	
Coolant	冷媒	Lěngméi	
Coolant	冷却剂	Lěngquèjì	
Cooled parametric amplifier	致冷参量放大器	Zhìlěng cānliàng fàngdàqì	
Cooling current	致冷电流	Zhìlěng diànliú	
Cooling system for laser	激光用冷却设备	Jīguāng-yòng lěngquè shèbèi	
Cooling test	冷却试验	Lěngquè shìyàn	
Cooperative commerce, collaborative commerce	协同商务	Xiétóng shāngwù	
Cooperative communication	协同通信	Xiétóng tōngxìn	
Cooperative management model	协同管理模型	Xiétóng guǎnlǐ móxíng	
Cooperative network list	协作网络清单	Xiézuò wǎngluò qīngdān	CNL

English	Chinese	Pinyin	Abbr.
Coopetition (buzzword formed from cooperation and competition)	合作竞争	Hézuò jìngzhēng	
Coordinate (in GIS)	坐标	Zuòbiāo	
Coordinate control point, tic	坐标控制点	Zuòbiāo kòngzhì diǎn	
Coordinate dimension	坐标维数	Zuòbiāo wéishù	
Coordinate geometry	坐标几何	Zuòbiāo jǐhé	COGO
Coordinate grid (GIS term)	坐标格网	Zuòbiāo géwǎng	
Coordinate origin	坐标原点	Zuòbiāo yuándiǎn	
Coordinate reference system	坐标参照系	Zuòbiāo cānzhàoxì	
Coordinate system	坐标系统	Zuòbiāo xìtǒng	
Coordinate transform kernel	坐标变换核	Zuòbiāo biànhuàn hé	
Coordinate transformation	坐标变换	Zuòbiāo biànhuàn	
Coordinated Universal Time	标准世界时	Biāozhǔn shìjièshí	
Coordinated Universal Time	协调世界时	Xiétiáo shìjièshí	UTC
Coordinated universal time	协调宇宙时	Xiétiáo yǔzhòu shí	UTC
Coordinating Committee for Intercontinental Research Networking	洲际研究网络协调委员会	Zhōujì yánjiū wǎngluò xiétiáo wěiyuánhuì	CCIRN
Coordination area	协调区	Xiétiáo qū	
Coordination contour	协调等值线	Xiétiáo děngzhíxiàn	
Coordination distance	协调距离	Xiétiáo jùlí	
Coordination processor	协调处理机	Xiétiáo chǔlǐjī	CP
Copier	复印机	Fùyìnjī	
Co-polar pattern (of an antenna)	同极化方向图	Tóngjíhuà fāngxiàngtú	
Copolymer steel tape	钢塑带	Gāng sù dài	
Copper cable	铜线电缆	Tóngxiàn diànlǎn	CC
Copper conductor	铜芯	Tóng xīn	
Copper distributed data interface	铜线分布式数据接口	Tóngxiàn Fēnbùshì shùjù jiēkǒu	CDDI
Copper foil (in SMT)	铜箔	Tóngbó	
Copper mirror test (in SMT)	铜镜测试	Tóngjìng cèshì	
Copper phthalo-cyanine	铜酞菁	Tóngtàijīng	CuPc
Copy (WP command)	复制	Fùzhì	
Copy as (WP command)	复制为	Fùzhì wéi	
Copy machine	影印机	Yǐngyìnjī	
Copy (usually a noun)	拷贝	Kǎobèi	
Copyright	版权	Bǎnquán	©
Copyright protection	版权保护	Bǎnquán bǎohù	
Cord	塞绳	Sāishéng	
Cord circuit	塞绳电路	Sāishéng diànlù	
Cord circuit	绳路	Shéng lù	
Cordless fixed part (telephone)	无绳座机	Wúshéng zuòjī	CFP
Cordless local area network	无绳局域网	Wúshéng júyùwǎng	CLAN
Cordless portable part (telephone)	无绳手机	Wúshéng shǒujī	CPP
Cordless switchboard	无绳交换台	Wúshéng jiāohuàntái	
Cordless telephone set	无绳电话机	Wúshéng diànhuàjī	
Cordless telephone system	无绳电话系统	Wúshéng diànhuà xìtǒng	
Cordless telephone system second generation	第二代无绳电话系统	Dì'èrdài wúshéng diànhuà xìtǒng	CT-2
Cordless telephony profile	无绳电话模型	Wúshéng diànhuà móxíng	

Core	核心	Héxīn	
Core [Network] QoS manager	核心网服务质量管理器	Héxīn wǎng fúwù zhìliàng guǎnlǐqì	CQM
Core center	纤芯中心	Qiànxīn zhōngxīn	
Core diameter	纤芯直径	Qiànxīn zhíjìng	
Core function	核心功能	Héxīn gōngnéng	CF
Core header	核心帧头域	Héxīn zhèng tóuyù	
Core memory	磁心存储器	Cíxīn cúnchǔqì	
Core network	核心网络	Héxīn wǎngluò	CN
Core network bearer service	核心网承载业务	Héxīn wǎng chéngzài yèwù	CNB
Core protocol	核心协议	Héxīn xiéyì	CP
Core rod (FOC mfg)	核心棒	Héxīn bàng	
Core router	核心路由器	Héxīn lùyóuqì	CR
Core switch	核心交换机	Héxīn jiāohuànjī	
Core switch	中心交换机	Zhōngxīn jiāohuànjī	
Core tandem node	核心汇接节点	Héxīn huìjiē jiédiǎn	
Core/cladding concentric error	芯包同心度误差	Xīnbāo tóngxīndù wùchā	
Core-based tree	核树	Hé shù	CBT
Core-based tree multicast routing protocol	有核树组播路由协议	Yǒuhéshù zǔbō lùyóu xiéyì	CBT
Core-based tree routing algorithm	基于心树路由算法	Jīyú xīn shù lùyóu suànfǎ	
Corner reflector	角反射器	Jiǎofǎnshèqì	
Corner reflector antenna	角反射天线	Jiǎo fǎnshè tiānxiàn	
Corner reflector antenna	角形反射器天线	Jiǎo-xíng fǎnshèqì tiānxiàn	
Corner; nook	转角处	Zhuǎnjiǎo chù	
Corning (US company)	康宁公司	Kāng-níng gōngsī	
Corporate control key	共同的控制键	Gòngtóngde kòngzhì jiàn	CCK
Corporate signing key (IPsec)	法人签名密钥	Fǎrén qiānmíng mìyào	
Correctable error	可校正差错	Kějiàozhèng chācuò	
Corrected block	已纠正块	Yǐjiūzhèng kuài	
Corrected reference equivalent	修正参考当量	Xiūzhèng cānkǎo dāngliàng	
Correction signal	校正信号	Jiàozhèng xìnhào	
Corrective maintenance	修复性维护	Xiūfùxìng wéihù	
Corrective maintenance time	修复性维护时间	Xiūfùxìng wéihù shíjiān	
Correlated frequency hopping	相关跳频	Xiāngguān tiàopín	
Correlated hopping enhanced spread spectrum	增强型相关跳频扩频	Zēngqiáng-xíng xiāngguān tiàopín kuòpín	CHESS
Correlated jjitter	相关抖动	Xiāngguān dǒudòng	
Correlated subquery	相关子查询	Xiāngguān zicháxún	
Correlation	相关	Xiāngguān	
Correlation alert	相关预警	Xiāngguān yùjǐng	
Correlation attack	相关攻击	Xiāngguān gōngjī	
Correlation coefficient	相关系数	Xiāngguān xìshù	
Correlation immunity	相关免疫	Xiāngguān miǎnyì	
Correlative analysis	相关分析	Xiāngguān fēnxī	
Correlative coding	相关编码	Xiāngguān biānmǎ	
Correlative phase shift keying	相关相移键控	Xiāngguān xiàngyí jiànkòng	CORPSK
Correlative phase shift keying	相关移相键控	Xiāngguān yíxiàng jiànkòng	CORPSK
Correlator (in GPS system)	相关器	Xiāngguānqì	

Correspondent (N)-entities	对应 N-实体	Duìyìng N-shítǐ	
Corridor	廊道	Lángdào	
Corrosion protection	防腐蚀	Fángfǔshí	
Corrosion resistant	抗蚀	Kàngshí	CRE
Corrugated horn	波纹喇叭	Bōwén lǎba	
Corrugated horn antenna	波纹喇叭天线	Bōwén lǎba tiānxiàn	
Corrugated laminated coaxial	多层皱纹金属带被覆同轴对	Duōcéng zhòuwén jīnshǔdài bèifù tóngzhóu duì	CLOAX
Corruption of information	信息破坏	Xìnxī pòhuài	
Cosecant-square beam antenna	余割平方射束天线	Yúgē píngfāng shèshù tiānxiàn	
Cosecant-squared antenna	余割平方天线	Yúgē píngfāng tiānxiàn	
Cosine emission law	余弦发射定律	Yúxián fāshè dìnglǜ	
Cosmic interference	宇宙干扰	Yǔzhòu gānrǎo	
Cosmic noise	宇宙噪声	Yǔzhòu zàoshēng	
Cosmic ray	宇宙射线	Yǔzhòu shèxiàn	
Cost and freight	成本加运费	Chéngběn jiā yùnfèi	C/F
Cost effectiveness analysis	费用效益分析	Fèiyòng xiàoyì fēnxī	
Cost of use	使用价格	Shǐyòng jiàgé	
Cost, insurance and freight	成本保险加运费付至	Chéngběn bǎoxiǎn jiā yùnfèi fù zhì	CIF
Cost, insurance and freight	成本加运保费	Chéngběn jiā yùnbǎo fèi	CIF
Costate variable	共态变量	Gòngtài biànliàng	
Costomer management plateform	客户管理平台	Kèhù guǎnlǐ píngtái	CMP
Cost-performance ratio	性能价格比	Xìngnéng jiàgé bǐ	
Cost-risk analysis	费用风险分析	Fèiyòng fēngxiǎn fēnxī	
Count to infinity	无穷计数	Wúqióng jìshù	
Counter, meter	计次表	Jìcìbiǎo	
Counter-audio device	防窃听装置	Fángqiètīng zhuāngzhì	
Countermeasure	对抗	Duìkàng	
Countermeasures	对策	Duìcè	
Counter-mortar radar	反迫击炮雷达	Fǎn pǎijīpào léidá	
Counterweight	配重	Pèizhòng	
Counterweight fill works	反压筑土工程	Fǎnyā zhùtǔ gōngchéng	
Counting internal interest	内部计息	Nèibù jìxī	
Countries (regions) exchanging international remittances	通汇国（地区）	Tōnghuì guó (dìqū)	
Country code	国家代码	Guójiā dàimǎ	CC
Country code	国家号码	Guójiā hàomǎ	CC
Country code	国家码	Guójiā mǎ	CC
Country name	国家名	Guójiā míng	
County level branch (of the financial network)	县级处理中心	Xiànjí chǔlǐ zhōngxīn	CLB
Coupled cavity traveling wave tube	耦合腔行波管	Ǒuhé qiāng xíngbōguǎn	
Coupled circuit	耦合电路	Ǒuhé diànlù	
Coupled factor	耦合度	Ǒuhédù	
Coupled vibration	耦合振动	Ǒuhé zhèndòng	
Coupler	耦合器	Ǒuhéqì	
Coupling	联轴器	Liánzhóuqì	
Coupling	耦合	Ǒuhé	

English	Chinese	Pinyin	Abbreviation
Coupling	偶联	Ǒulián	
Coupling and decoupling networks	耦合/去耦合网络	Ǒuhé/qù'ǒuhé wǎngluò	CDN
Coupling aperture	耦合口	Ǒuhé kǒu	
Coupling efficiency	耦合效率	Ǒuhé xiàolǜ	
Coupling factor	耦合系数	Ǒuhé xìshù	
Coupling loop	耦合环	Ǒuhé huán	
Coupling loss	耦合损耗	Ǒuhé sǔnhào	
Coupling path	耦合路径	Ǒuhé lùjìng	
Coupling path	耦合途径	Ǒuhé tújìng	
Coupling probe	耦合探针	Ǒuhé tànzhēn	
Coupling ratio	分光比	Fēnguāng bǐ	CR
Coupling, cabled	插索	Chāsuǒ	
Course marker	航向标志	Hángxiàng biāozhì	
Courseware	教材软件	Jiàocái ruǎnjiàn	
Courseware	课件	Kèjiàn	
Cover	涵盖	Hángài	
Cover flange	配用法兰盖片	Pèiyòng fǎlán gàipiàn	
Cover ID	图层单位	Túcéng dānwèi	
Cover; coverage; layer; coverage extent	图层	Túcéng	
Coverage area (of a space station)	覆盖区	Fùgài qū	
Coverage units	图层范围	Túcéng fànwéi	
Coverage, overlay	覆盖	Fùgài	
Cover-media	掩护媒体	Yǎnhù méitǐ	
Covert channel (IPsec)	隐蔽信道	Yǐnbì xìndào	
Covert storage channel (IPsec)	隐蔽存储信道	Yǐnbì cúnchǔ xìndào	
Covert timing channel (IPsec)	隐蔽计时信道	Yǐnbì jìshí xìndào	
Crack (break into, hack into)	闯入	Chuǎngrù	
Cracker (person or program that breaks passwords)	垮客	Kuǎ-kè	
Cracking pattern	碎裂图型	Suìliè túxíng	
Crafting packet(s)	自定义数据包	Zìdìngyì shùjùbāo	
Crash (i.e. computer or system crash)	崩溃	Bēngkuì	
Crash, hang (computer slang)	死机	Sǐjī	
Cray supercomputer	克雷超级电脑	Kè-léi chāojí diànnǎo	
Create extended DOS partition	创建扩展 DOS 分区	Chuàngjiàn kuòzhǎn DOS fēnqū	
Create primary DOS partition	创建 DOS 主分区	Chuàngjiàn DOS zhǔ fēnqū	
Create, creation	创建	Chuàngjiàn	
Creative Technology (US company)	创新科技	Chuàngxīn kējì	
Credit card calling	信用卡呼叫	Xìnyòngkǎ hūjiào	CRED
Creepage distance	爬电距离	Pádiàn jùlí	
Creeptrace resistance (lit. resists "electric scarring")	耐电痕	Nài diànhén	
Crest factor	波峰因数	Bōfēng yīnshù	
Crest factor	峰值系数	Fēngzhí xìshù	
Crest factor	峰值因数	Fēngzhí yīnshù	
Crimping tool	压接工具	Yājiē gōngjù	
Critical alarm	临界告警	Línjiè gàojǐng	

Critical damping	临界阻尼	Línjiè zǔní	
Critical failure	危险失效	Wēixiǎn shīxiào	
Critical fault	危险故障	Wēixiǎn gùzhàng	
Critical flicker frequency	临界闪变频率	Línjiè shǎnbiàn pínlǜ	
Critical frequency (of a mode in a waveguide)	临界频率	Línjiè pínlǜ	
Critical path	关键路径	Guānjiàn lùjìng	
Critical points	临界点	Línjièdiǎn	
Critical pressure differential	临界压差	Línjiè yāchā	
Critical pressure differential ratio	临界压差比	Línjiè yāchā bǐ	
Critical pressure ratio	临界压力比	Línjiè yālì bǐ	
Critical resistance	临界电阻	Línjiè diànzǔ	
Critical software	重要软件	Zhòngyào ruǎnjiàn	
Critical state	危险状态	Wēixiǎn zhuàngtài	
Critical velocity	临界流速	Línjiè liúsù	
Critical wavelength (of a mode in a waveguide)	临界波长	Línjiè bōcháng	
Criticality	紧急度	Jǐnjídù	
Cross assembler (computer program)	交叉汇编程序	Jiāochā huìbiān chéngxù	
Cross band diversity (reception)	跨频带分集[接收]	Kuà píndài fēnjí (jiēshōu)	
Cross compiler	交叉编译程序	Jiāochā biānyì chéngxù	
Cross compiling	交叉编译	Jiāochā biānyì	
Cross connection	交接	Jiāojiē	
Cross connections closet	交接间	Jiāojiē jiān	
Cross correlation function	互相关函数	Hùxiāngguān hánshù	
Cross coupling	互耦	Hù'ou	CC
Cross coupling	交叉耦合	Jiāochā ǒuhé	CC
Cross hatching, grid	格网	Géwǎng	
Cross levee	横堤	Héngdī	
Cross modulation	交叉调制	Jiāochā tiáozhì	
Cross modulation	交调	Jiāotiáo	
Cross polarization canceller	交叉极化抵消器	Jiāochā jíhuà dǐxiāoqì	
Cross polarization discrimination	交叉极化鉴别度	Jiāochā jíhuà jiànbié dù	XPD
Cross roller bearing	交叉滚子轴承	Jiāochā gǔnzi zhóuchéng	
Cross-assembling	交叉汇编	Jiāochā huìbiān	
Crossbar	纵横制	Zònghéng zhì	XB
Crossbar coaxial waveguide transformer	纵横式同轴波导变换器	Zònghéng-shì tóngzhóu bōdǎo biànhuànqì	
Crossbar switch	交叉开关	Jiāochā kāiguān	
Crossbar switch	纵横机	Zònghéng jī	CBS
Crossbar switch	纵横接线器	Zònghéng jiēxiànqì	
Cross-beam	横梁	Héngliáng	
Cross-connect element	交叉单元	Jiāochā dānyuán	XC
Cross-connect matrix	交叉连接矩阵	Jiāochā liánjiē jǔzhèn	CM
Cross-connect system	交叉连接系统	Jiāochā liánjiē xìtǒng	XC
Cross-correlation	互相关性	Hùxiāngguān-xìng	
Cross-correlator	互相关器	Hùxiāngguānqì	
Crossed slot antenna	十字缝隙天线	Shízì fèngxì tiānxiàn	
Crossed-field balanced mixer	正交场平衡混频器	Zhèngjiāo chǎng pínghéng hùnpínqì	

Crossed-field device	正交场器件	Zhèngjiāo cháng qìjiàn	
Cross-gain modulation	交叉增益调制	Jiāochā zēngyì tiáozhì	CGM
Cross-interleave Reed-Solomon code	交叉交织里德-所罗门编码	Jiāochā jiāozhī Lǐdé-Suǒluómén biānmǎ	CIRC
Cross-modulation factor	交叉调制因子	Jiāochā tiáozhì yīnzǐ	CMF
Cross-office check	跨局检验	Kuà jú jiǎnyàn	
Cross-over distortion	交叉失真	Jiāochā shīzhēn	
Crossover frequency	交越频率	Jiāoyuè pínlǜ	
Crossover of load characteristic	负载特性交叠	Fùzài tèxìng jiāodié	
Cross-phase modulation	交叉相位调制	Jiāochā xiàngwèi tiáozhì	CPM, XPM
Crosspoint	交叉点	Jiāochādiǎn	
Cross-polarization	交叉极化	Jiāochā jíhuà	
Cross-polarization discrimination rate (of an antenna)	正交极化鉴别率	Zhèngjiāo jíhuà jiànbié lǜ	
Cross-polarization interference counteracter	交叉极化干扰抵消器	Jiāochā jíhuà gānrǎo dǐxiāoqì	XPIC
Cross-polarization level	交叉极化电平	Jiāochā jíhuà diànpíng	
Cross-polarization loss	交叉极化损失	Jiāochā jíhuà sǔnshī	
Cross-polarization pattern (of an antenna)	正交极化方向图	Zhèngjiāo jíhuà fāngxiàng tú	
Cross-port affinity	交叉端口亲缘性	Jiāochā duānkǒu qīnyuánxìng	
Cross-reference object	交叉引用对象	Jiāochā yǐnyòng duìxiàng	
Cross-spectral density	交义密度	Jiāoyì mìdù	
Crosstab	交叉表	Jiāochā biǎo	
Crosstab query (for database)	交叉表查询	Jiāochā biǎo cháxún	
Crosstalk	串话	Chuànhuà	
Crosstalk	交叉干扰	Jiāochā gānrǎo	
Crosstalk	交扰	Jiāorǎo	
Crosstalk	交调失真	Jiāotiáo shīzhēn	
Cross-talk (IPsec)	串道	Chuàndào	
Crosstalk isolation	串扰隔离度	Chuànrǎo gélídù	
Crosstalk reference equivalent	串音参考当量	Chuànyīn cānkǎo dāngliàng	
Crosstalk, directivity	串扰	Chuànrǎo	
Cross-tile indexing	交叉分区	Jiāochā fēnqū	
Crossware	交叉件	Jiāochā jiàn	
Crown	顶部	Dǐngbù	
Crush load	侧压力	Cèyālì	
Cryptanalysis (IPsec)	密码分析	Mìmǎ fēnxī	
Crypto auxiliary unit	加密辅助单元	Jiāmì fǔzhù dānyuán	CAU
Crypto token	加密令牌	Jiāmì lìngpái	
Cryptographic algorithm	密码算法	Mìmǎ suànfǎ	
Cryptographic check value (IPsec)	密码校检值	Mìmǎ jiàojiǎn zhí	
Cryptographic message syntax	密码消息语法	Mìmǎ xiāoxi yǔfǎ	CMS
Cryptographic protocol	密码协议	Mìmǎ xiéyì	
Cryptographic service provider	加密服务提供者	Jiāmì fúwù tígòngzhě	CSP
Cryptographic system	加密系统	Jiāmì xìtǒng	CS
Cryptographic system	密码系统	Mìmǎ xìtǒng	
Cryptographically secure TINA	密码安全 TINA	Mìmǎ ānquán TINA	CrySTINA
Cryptography	密码术	Mìmǎshù	
Cryptography (IPsec)	密码体制	Mìmǎ tǐzhì	

Cryptologic security	密码安全	Mìmă ānquán	
Cryptologic variable, cryptovariable	密码变量	Mìmă biànliàng	
Cryptologic, cryptographic (adj.)	密码	Mìmă	
Cryptology	密码学	Mìmăxué	
Crypto-operation	密码操作	Mìmă cāozuò	
Crystal grating	晶体光栅	Jīngtǐ guāngshān	
Crystal growing material	结晶育成材料	Jiéjīng yùchéng cáiliào	
Crystal mixer	晶体混频器	Jīngtǐ hùnpínqì	
Crystal-controlled clock generator	晶体控制时钟脉冲发生器	Jīngtǐ kòngzhì shízhōng màichōng fāshēngqì	CCCG
Crystalline electrode	晶体电极	Jīngtǐ diànjí	
CSL Hong Kong (GSM network operator)	香港移动通信	Xiānggăng yídòng tōngxìn	
C-type spring tube	C 型弹簧管	C-xíng tánhuáng guăn	
Cube (for database)	多维数据集	Duōwéi shùjùjí	
Cube phase error	立方相差	Lìfāng xiàngchà	
Cubic contents	建筑容积	Jiànzhù róngjī	
Cubic spline interpolation	三次样条插值	Sāncì yàngtiáo chāzhí	CSI
Cueing tone gain	提示音增益	Tíshì yīn zēngyì	
Cumulus convection	积云对流	Jīyún duìliú	
Cure (in SMT)	烘焙固化	Hōngbèi gùhuà	
Curing oven	固化炉	Gùhuà lú	
Curing oven (semiconductor mfg)	硫化炉	Liúhuà lú	
Current call meter	通用的呼叫表	Tōngyòngde hūjiào biăo	CCM
Current cell rate	当前信元速率	Dāngqián xìnyuán sùlǜ	CCR
Current channel	当前信道	Dāngqián xìndào	
Current data bit	现行数据位	Xiànxíng shùjù wèi	CDB
Current density	密度流	Mìdù liú	
Current equalizer	电流均衡器	Diànliú jūnhéngqì	
Current gain	电流增益	Diànliú zēngyì	
Current layout position	当前布局位置	Dāngqián bùjú wèizhì	
Current limiting device	限流装置	Xiànliú zhuāngzhì	
Current meter	流速计	Liúsùjì	
Current mode logic	电流型逻辑电路	Diànliú-xíng luóji diànlù	CML
Current probe	电流探头	Diànliú tàntóu	
Current rate	当前速率	Dāngqián sùlǜ	
Current read state (IPsec)	当前读状态	Dāngqián dú zhuàngtài	
Current serving base station	当前服务的基站	Dāngqián fúwùde jīzhàn	
Current to voltage converter	电流-电压变换器	Diànliú/diànyā biànhuànqì	I / V
Current write state (IPsec)	当前写状态	Dāngqián xiě zhuàngtài	
Current-limiting protection	限流保护	Xiànliú băohù	
Cursor	光标	Guāngbiāo	
Cursor (for database)	游标	Yóubiāo	
Cursor library	游标库	Yóubiāo kù	
Cursor off	光标隐匿	Guāngbiāo yĭnnì	COF
Cursor on	光标显现	Guāngbiāo xiănxiàn	CON
Curtain antenna	幕形天线	Mùxíng tiānxiàn	
Curtain wall	屏蔽墙	Píngbì qiáng	

Curvature; buckling	曲率	Qūlǜ	
Curve	曲线	Qūxiàn	
Curve diagram	曲线图	Qūxiàntú	
Curve fitting	曲线拟合	Qūxiàn nǐhé	
Curve generator	曲线产生机	Qūxiàn chǎnshēngjī	
Curve interpolation (GIS)	曲线内插	Qūxiàn nèichā	
Curve segment	曲线部分	Qūxiàn bùfen	
Custodian	管理人	Guǎnlǐ rén	
Custom	定制	Dìngzhì	
Custom	自定义	Zìdìngyì	
Custom queue	用户定制队列	Yònghù dìngzhì duìliè	CQ
Custom queuing	自定义排队	Zìdìngyì páiduì	CQ
Custom rollup	自定义汇总	Zìdìngyì huìzǒng	
Custom rule	自定义规则	Zìdìngyì guīzé	
Customer	顾客	Gùkè	
Customer access maintenance center	用户接入维护中心	Yònghù jiērù wéihù zhōngxīn	CAMC
Customer care center	客户服务中心	Kèhù fúwù zhōngxīn	CCC
Customer care center	用户服务中心	Yònghù fúwù zhōngxīn	
Customer edge	用户边缘	Yònghù biānyuán	CE
Customer equipment	用户设备	Yònghù shèbèi	CEQ
Customer information control system	用户信息控制系统	Yònghù xìnxī kòngzhì xìtǒng	CICS
Customer installation maintenance entities	用户安装维护实体	Yònghù ānzhuāng wéihù shítǐ	CIME
Customer management information port	用户管理信息接口	Yònghù guǎnlǐ xìnxī jiēkǒu	CMIP
Customer management plane	用户管理平面	Yònghù guǎnlǐ píngmiàn	CMP
Customer management point	用户管理点	Yònghù guǎnlǐ diǎn	CMP
Customer network	用户网络	Yònghù wǎngluò	CN
Customer network management	客户管理系统	Kèhù guǎnlǐ xìtǒng	
Customer network management interface	用户网络管理接口	Yònghù wǎngluò guǎnlǐ jiēkǒu	
Customer network management interface using common management information protocol	使用通用管理信息协议的用户网络管理接口	Shǐyòng tōngyòng guǎnlǐ xìnxī xiéyìde yònghù wǎngluò guǎnlǐ jiēkǒu	CNMc
Customer network management interface using EDI/MHS	使用电子数据交换/消息处理系统的用户网络管理接口	Shǐyòng diànzi shùjù jiāohuàn/Xiāoxi chǔlǐ xìtǒngde yònghù wǎngluò guǎnlǐ jiēkǒu	CNMe
Customer premises	用户所在地	Yònghù suǒzàidì	
Customer premises equipment	客户端设备	Kèhù duān shèbèi	CPE
Customer premises equipment	用户端设备	Yònghù duān shèbèi	CPE
Customer premises equipment	用户室内设备	Yònghù shìnèi shèbèi	CPE
Customer premises equipment	用户驻地设备	Yònghù zhùdì shèbèi	CPE
Customer premises equipment (CPE) alerting signal	用户终端设备提示信号	Yònghù zhōngduān shèbèi tíshì xìnhào	CAS
Customer premises equipment alert signal	终端设备提示信号	Zhōngduān shèbèi tíshì xìnhào	CAS
Customer premises equipment-based VPN	基于客户端设备的 VPN	Jīyú kèhù duān shèbèide VPN	
Customer premises network	用户驻地网	Yònghù zhùdì wǎng	CPN
Customer relations manager	客户关系管理	Kèhù guānxi guǎnlǐ	CRM
Customer relationship management	客户关系管理	Kèhù guānxi guǎnlǐ	
Customer service representative	客户服务代表	Kèhù fúwù dàibiǎo	CSR
Customer telephone exchange	用户电话交换机	Yònghù diànhuà jiāohuànjī	CTX

Customizable	可定制化	Kědìngzhìhuà	
Customization	用户化	Yònghùhuà	
Customize	自定安装	Zìdìng ānzhuāng	
Customized application for mobile network enhanced logic	移动网增强逻辑定制应用	Yídòng wǎng zēngqiáng luóji dìngzhì yìngyòng	CAMEL
Customized applications for mobil network enhanced logic	移动网增强逻辑的定做应用	Yídòng wǎng zēngqiáng luójide dìngzuò yìngyòng	CAMEL
Customized applications for mobile network enhanced logic	GSM 的移动智能业务	GSM-de yídòng zhìnéng yèwù	CAMEL
Customized applications for mobile network enhanced logic	移动网络增强逻辑的客户化应用	Yídòng wǎngluò zēngqiáng luójide kèhùhuà yìngyòng	CAMEL
Customized data termination equipment (DTE) service	用户指定型 DTE 业务	Yònghù zhǐdìngxíng DTE yèwù	
Customized software	个别编写的软件	Gèbié biānxiěde ruǎnjiàn	
Cut (in GIS or telecom construction)	挖土	Wātǔ	
Cut (WP command)	剪切	Jiǎnqiē	
Cut parabolic antenna	切割抛物面天线	Qiēgē pāowùmiàn tiānxiàn	
Cut sheet	切片	Qiēpiàn	
Cut slope	挖方坡面	Wāfāng pōmiàn	
Cutler feed	卡特勒馈源	Kǎ-tè-lè kuìyuán	
Cut-off attenuator	截止衰减器	Jiézhǐ shuāijiǎnqì	
Cut-off attenuator	截止式衰减器	Jiézhǐ-shì shuāijiǎnqì	
Cut-off frequency	截止频率	Jiézhǐ pínlǜ	
Cut-off function	切断性能	Qiēduàn xìngnéng	
Cut-off wall	截水墙	Jiéshuǐ qiáng	
Cut-off wavelength	截止波长	Jiézhǐ bōcháng	
Cut-off wavelength shifted optical fiber	截止波长位移光纤	Jiézhǐ bōcháng wèiyí guāngxiān	CSF
Cutover	割接	Gējiē	
Cutover into operation	割接开通	Gējiē kāitōng	
Cut-sheet feeder	输纸装置	Shūzhǐ zhuāngzhì	
Cut-through	捷径交换	Jiéjìng jiāohuàn	
Cut-through	直通转发	Zhítōng zhuǎnfā	
Cut-through packet switching	直接包交换技术	Zhíjiē bāo jiāohuàn jìshù	
Cutting	开挖	Kāiwā	
Cutting machine (semiconductor mfg)	切削加工设备	Qiēxiāo jiāgōng shèbèi	
Cyber café	网际咖啡屋	Wǎngjì kāfēiwū	
Cyber carrier	网络空间运营商	Wǎngluò kōngjiān yùnyíng shāng	CC
Cyber citizen; netizen	网际公民	Wǎngjì gōngmín	
Cyber community	联网社群	Liánwǎng shèqún	
Cyber sales	网际行销	Wǎngjì xíngxiāo	
Cyber surfer	网际漫游者	Wǎngjì mànyóuzhě	
Cybercash	电子货币	Diànzǐ huòbì	
Cybercash, digicash	电子钱	Diànzǐ qián	
Cybernaut	网客	Wǎngkè	
Cybernaut	网友	Wǎngyǒu	
Cybernaut	网中人	Wǎng-zhōng rén	
Cybernetic	控制论	Kòngzhìlùn	
Cyberphobia	电脑恐惧症	Diànnǎo kǒngjùzhēng	
Cyberpunk	数字朋客	Shùzì péngkè	

Cybersex; cyberporn; cybersmut	网际色情	Wǎngjì sèqíng	
Cyberspace	网络空间	Wǎngluò kōngjiān	
Cyberspace	信息空间	Xìnxī kōngjiān	
Cyberworld	联网世界	Liánwǎng shìjiè	
Cycle	回路（环）	Huílù (huán)	
Cycle life	循环寿命	Xúnhuán shòumìng	
Cycle of operation	工作周期	Gōngzuò zhōuqī	
Cycle rate (in SMT)	循环速率	Xúnhuán sùlǜ	
Cycle steal control buffer	周期挪用缓冲器	Zhōuqī nuóyòng huǎnchōngqì	CSCB
Cycle steal grant high	周期挪用许可高	Zhōuqī nuóyòng xǔkě gāo	CSGH
Cycle steal grant low	周期挪用许可低	Zhōuqī nuóyòng xǔkě dī	CSGL
Cycle steal request	周期挪用请求	Zhōuqī nuóyòng qǐngqiú	CSR
Cycle stealing	周期挪用	Zhōuqī nuóyòng	
Cycle stealing message counter	周期挪用信息计数器	Zhōuqī nuóyòng xìnxī jìshùqì	CSMC
Cycle time	循环时间	Xúnhuán shíjiān	
Cycle time (period)	周期	Zhōuqī	
Cycle time (speed)	周速	Zhōusù	
Cycle-skipping	跳周	Tiàozhōu	
Cycle-skipping average time	跳周平均时间	Tiàozhōu píngjūn shíjiān	
Cyclic check byte	循环校正字节	Xúnhuán jiàozhèng zìjié	CCB
Cyclic code	循环码	Xúnhuán mǎ	
Cyclic code-shift keying	循环码移键控	Xúnhuán mǎyí jiànkòng	CCSK
Cyclic correlation	相关运算	Xiāngguān yùnsuàn	
Cyclic distortion	周期性畸变	Zhōuqīxìng jībiàn	
Cyclic fixed (channel assignment)	循环定位	Xúnhuán dìngwèi	
Cyclic on/off switching control	循环启/闭环转换控制	Xúnhuán qǐ/bìhuán zhuǎnhuàn kòngzhì	
Cyclic on/off switching control	周期性通/断开关控制	Zhōuqīxìng tōng/duànkāi guān kòngzhì	
Cyclic queuing system	循环排队系统	Xúnhuán páiduì xìtǒng	
Cyclic redundancy check	冗余循环校验	Rǒngyú xúnhuán jiàoyàn	
Cyclic redundancy check code	循环冗余校验码	Xúnhuán rǒngyú jiàoyàn mǎ	CRC
Cyclic resource allocation	周期资源分配	Zhōuqī zīyuán fēnpèi	
Cyclic time-scale	周期性时标	Zhōuqīxìng shíbiāo	
Cyclic timing signal	周期性定时信号	Zhōuqīxìng dìngshí xìnhào	
Cyclic unfixed (channel assignment)	循环不定位	Xúnhuán bùdìngwèi	
Cyclical redundancy check	循环冗余检查	Xúnhuán rǒngyú jiǎnchá	CRC
Cyclical redundancy check	循环冗余检验	Xúnhuán rǒngyú jiǎnyàn	CRC
Cyclical redundancy check for fragmented data load (in DOCSIS)	对分段数据净荷的 CRC	Duì fēnduàn shùjù jìnghéde CRC	FCRC
Cyclical redundancy code	循环冗余编码	Xúnhuán rǒngyú biānmǎ	CRC
Cyclical redundancy correction	循环冗余校验	Xúnhuán rǒngyú jiàoyàn	CRC
Cyclical redundancy error	循环冗余差错	Xúnhuán rǒngyú chācuò	CRE
Cyclically symmetric network	循环对称网络	Xúnhuán duìchèn wǎngluò	CSN
Cylinder coordinate kernel	柱面坐标核	Zhùmiàn zuòbiāo hé	
Cylinder/head/sector (of a computer hard disk)	柱面 / 磁头 / 扇区	Zhùmiàn/cítóu/shàn qū	CHS
Cylindrical array	圆柱阵	Yuánzhù zhèn	
Cylindrical array	圆柱形阵	Yuánzhùxíng zhèn	
Cylindrical parabola antenna	圆筒形抛物面天线	Yuántǒngxíng pāowùmiàn tiānxiàn	CPA

Cylindrical projection	圆柱投影	Yuánzhù tóuyǐng	
Cylindrical reflector	圆柱面反射器	Yuánzhùmiàn fǎnshèqì	
Cylindrical wave	柱面波	Zhùmiàn bō	
Cymomotive force	波动强度	Bōdòng qiángdù	c. m. f
Cymomotive force; field strength-distance product	场强-距离乘积	Chǎngqiáng--jùlí chéngjī	CMF

D

D4 framing	D4 成帧技术	D4 chéngzhèng jìshù	
Daemon	守护程序	Shǒuhù chéngxù	
Daemon	守护进程	Shǒuhù jìnchéng	
Daewoo Corp. (Korean company)	大宇	Dàyǔ	
Daily data manager record	数管日志	Shùguǎn rìzhì	
Daily maintenance record	维护日志	Wéihù rìzhì	
Damage	损伤	Sǔnshāng	
Damage factor	损坏率	Sǔnhuài lǜ	
Damp heat test	温热试验	Wēnrè shìyàn	
Damped least square method	阻尼最小二乘法	Zǔní zuìxiǎo èrchéngfǎ	DLS
Damped oscillation	阻尼振荡	Zǔní zhèndàng	
Damped sinusoidal transient	阻尼正弦瞬变	Zǔní zhèngxián shùnbiàn	
Damper	减振器	Jiǎnzhènqì	
Damping	阻尼	Zǔní	
Damping factor	衰减系数	Shuāijiǎn xìshù	
Dangle	悬挂	Xuánguà	
Dangle length	悬挂长度	Xuánguà chángdù	
Dangle tolerance	悬挂容差	Xuánguà róngchā	
Dangling node	悬挂节点	Xuánguà jiédiǎn	
Darcy's formula	达西公式	Dá-xī gōngshì	
Darcy's law	达西法则	Dá-xī fǎzé	
Dark current	暗电流	Àndiànliú	
Dash (in Morse code)	划	Huà	
Data	数据	Shùjù	D
Data above voice	话上数据	Huà-shàng shùjù	DAV
Data abstraction	数据抽象	Shùjù chōuxiàng	
Data access	数据存取	Shùjù cúnqǔ	DA
Data access language	数据访问语言	Shùjù fǎngwèn yǔyán	DAL
Data access object	数据访问对象	Shùjù fǎngwèn duìxiàng	DAO
Data access protocol (in DECnet)	数据访问协议	Shùjù fǎngwèn xiéyì	DAP
Data access security	数据访问安全性	Shùjù fǎngwèn ānquánxìng	
Data accessibility	数据可访问性	Shùjù kěfǎngwènxìng	
Data accumulation unit	数据采集器	Shùjù cǎijíqì	DQU
Data acquisition	数据获取	Shùjù huòqǔ	
Data acquisition circuit	数据采集电路	Shùjù cǎijí diànlù	
Data acquisition time	取数据时间	Qǔ shùjù shíjiān	
Data adaptive evaluator and monitor	数据自适应鉴别器与监视器	Shùjù zìshìyìng jiànbiéqì yǔ jiānshìqì	DAEMON
Data address	数据地址	Shùjù dìzhǐ	DA

English	Chinese	Pinyin	Abbreviation
Data address register	数据地址寄存器	Shùjù dìzhǐ jìcúnqì	DAR
Data administrator	数据管理	Shùjù guǎnlǐ	
Data aggregation	数据聚合	Shùjù jùhé	
Data analysis	数据分析	Shùjù fēnxī	
Data archive	数据档案	Shùjù dàng'àn	
Data attribute	数据属性	Shùjù shǔxìng	
Data availability	数据可用性	Shùjù kěyòngxìng	
Data backup	数据备份	Shùjù bèifèn	
Data bit	数据位	Shùjù wèi	
Data block	数据块	Shùjù kuài	
Data block address (in ORACLE)	数据块地址	Shùjù kuài dìzhǐ	DBAD
Data buffer cache (in SQL Server)	数据缓冲器	Shùjù huǎnchōngqì	
Data bus	数据总线	Shùjù zǒngxiàn	D-BUS
Data bus connector	数据总线连接器	Shùjù zǒngxiàn liánjiēqì	
Data cache	数据存储单元	Shùjù cúnchǔ dānyuán	
Data capture	数据获取	Shùjù huòqǔ	
Data carrier detect	数据载体监测	Shùjù zàitǐ jiāncè	DCD
Data carrier failure detector	数据载波故障检测器	Shùjù zàibō gùzhàng jiǎncèqì	DCF
Data catalog	数据目录	Shùjù mùlù	
Data cell	数据单元	Shùjù dānyuán	
Data cell length	数据单元的长度	Shùjù dānyuánde chángdù	LGTH
Data center	数据中心	Shùjù zhōngxīn	
Data center markup language	数据中心标记语言	Shùjù zhōngxīn biāojì yǔyán	DCML
Data channel (D channel)	数据信道	Shùjù xìndào	
Data channel protection level (in FTP)	数据信道保护级别	Shùjù xìndào bǎohù jíbié	PROT
Data channel unit	数据信道单元	Shùjù xìndào dānyuán	DCU
Data circuit	数据电路	Shùjù diànlù	
Data circuit (terminating) equipment	数据电路终接设备	Shùjù diànlù zhōngjiē shèbèi	DCE
Data circuit concentrator	数据电路集中器	Shùjù diànlù jízhōngqì	DCC
Data circuit equipment	数据电路设备	Shùjù diànlù shèbèi	DCE
Data circuit equipment	数据电路设备	Shùjù diànlù shèbèi	DCE
Data circuit terminating equipment	数据电路端接设备	Shùjù diànlù duānjiē shèbèi	DCI
Data circuit terminating equipment	数据电路终端设备	Shùjù diànlù zhōngduān shèbèi	DCE
Data circuit terminating equipment	数字电路终接设备	Shùzì diànlù zhōngjiē shèbèi	DCE
Data circuit transparency	数据电路透明性	Shùjù diànlù tòumíngxìng	
Data clearinghouse	数据仓库	Shùjù cāngkù	
Data code	数据代码	Shùjù dàimǎ	
Data coding scheme	数据编码方案	Shùjù biānmǎ fāng'àn	DCS
Data collection	数据采集	Shùjù cǎijí	
Data collection PC	数据收集 PC 机	Shùjù shōují PC-jī	DCP
Data collection processor	数据收集处理器	Shùjù shōují chǔlǐqì	
Data communication	数据通信	Shùjù tōngxìn	
Data communication channel	数据通信通路	Shùjù tōngxìn tōnglù	DCC
Data communication channel	数据通信信道	Shùjù tōngxìn xìndào	DCC
Data communication control procedure	数据通信控制规程	Shùjù tōngxìn kòngzhì guīchéng	DCCP
Data communication equipment	数据通信设备	Shùjù tōngxìn shèbèi	DCE

Data communication equipment monitoring and switching	数据通信设备监控与转换	Shùjù tōngxìn shèbèi jiānkòng yǔ zhuǎnhuàn	DACEMS
Data communication function	数据通信功能	Shùjù tōngxìn gōngnéng	DCF
Data communication interface	数据通信接口	Shùjù tōngxìn jiēkǒu	DCI
Data communication multiplexer	数据通信多路复用器	Shùjù tōngxìn duōlù fùyòngqì	DCM
Data communication network	数据通信网	Shùjù tōngxìnwǎng	DCN
Data communications channel	数据通信通道	Shùjù tōngxìn tōngdào	DCC
Data completeness	数据完全性	Shùjù wánquánxìng	
Data compression	数据压缩	Shùjù yāsuō	
Data concentrator	数据集中器	Shùjù jízhōngqì	
Data conferencing	数据会议	Shùjù huìyì	
Data confidentiality (IPsec)	数据机密性	Shùjù jīmìxìng	
Data confidentiality algorithm	数据保密算法	Shùjù bǎomì suànfǎ	C-ALG
Data connection (for database)	数据连接	Shùjù liánjiē	
Data contamination (IPsec)	数据损害	Shùjù sǔnhài	
Data control	数据控制	Shùjù kòngzhì	
Data control language (for database)	数据控制语言	Shùjù kòngzhì yǔyán	DCL
Data convergence (in SQL Server)	数据的集中性	Shùjùde jízhōngxìng	
Data conversion	数据转化	Shùjù zhuǎnhuà	
Data conversion module	数据转换模块	Shùjù zhuǎnhuàn mókuài	DCM
Data country code	数据国家代码	Shùjù guójiā dàimǎ	DCC
Data cube	多维数据集	Duōwéi shùjùjí	
Data cube	数据立方	Shùjù lìfāng	
Data cube file	多维数据集文件	Duōwéi shùjùjí wénjiàn	
Data cube role	多维数据集角色	Duōwéi shùjùjí juésè	
Data definition	数据定义	Shùjù dìngyì	
Data definition language	数据定义语言	Shùjù dìngyì yǔyán	DDL
Data definition query	数据定义查询	Shùjù dìngyì cháxún	
Data delimiter	数据定界符	Shùjù dìngjièfú	
Data dependence graph	数据依赖图	Shùjù yīlài tú	DDG
Data descripition word	数据描述字	Shùjù miáoshù zì	DDW
Data description language	数据描述语言	Shùjù miáoshù yǔyán	DDL
Data dictionary	数据词典	Shùjù cídiǎn	
Data dictionary (for database)	数据字典	Shùjù zìdiǎn	
Data dictionary view (for database)	数据字典视图	Shùjù zìdiǎn shìtú	
Data dissemination	数据发布	Shùjù fābù	
Data edit	数据编辑	Shùjù biānjí	
Data element	数据元	Shùjù yuán	
Data element	数据元素	Shùjù yuánsù	
Data encoding	数据编码	Shùjù biānmǎ	
Data encryption	数据加密	Shùjù jiāmì	
Data encryption algorithm	数据加密算法	Shùjù jiāmì suànfǎ	DEA
Data encryption key	数据加密键	Shùjù jiāmì jiàn	DEK
Data encryption standard	数据加密标准	Shùjù jiāmì biāozhǔn	DES
Data entry; data input	数据输入	Shùjù shūrù	
Data error	数据误差	Shùjù wùchā	
Data exchange format	数据交换格式	Shùjù jiāohuàn géshi	DXF

Data exchange input-output device	数据交换输入输出设备	Shùjù jiāohuàn shūrù shūchū shèbèi	DXIO
Data exchange interface	数据交换接口	Shùjù jiāohuàn jiēkǒu	DXI
Data exchange standard	数据交换标准	Shùjù jiāohuàn biāozhǔn	
Data exchange, data interchange	数据交换	Shùjù jiāohuàn	
Data exploration	数据探索	Shùjù tànsuǒ	
Data explosion	数据爆炸	Shùjù bàozhà	
Data export; data output	数据输出	Shùjù shūchū	
Data extraction	数据抽取	Shùjù chōuqǔ	
Data file (for database)	数据文件	Shùjù wénjiàn	
Data form1	数据形式 1	Shùjù xíngshì 1	DT1
Data format	数据格式	Shùjù géshi	
Data forwarding	数据前送	Shùjù qiánsòng	
Data frame	数据帧	Shùjù zhèng	DF
Data freeway	数据自由路	Shùjù zìyóu lù	DFW
Data freeway	数据自由通道	Shùjù zìyóu tōngdào	DFW
Data fusion	数据融合	Shùjù rónghé	
Data glove (robotics)	数据手套	Shùjù shǒutào	
Data grid	数据网格	Shùjù wǎnggé	
Data handling sub-system	数据处理子系统	Shùjù chǔlǐ zixìtǒng	DHS
Data hiding	数据隐藏	Shùjù yǐncáng	
Data indexing	数据索引	Shùjù suǒyǐn	
Data initialization (in FORTRAN)	数据初值语句	Shùjù chūzhí yǔjù	DATA
Data input voice output telephone system	数据输入话音输出电话系统	Shùjù shūrù huàyīn shūchū diànhuà xìtǒng	DIVOTS
Data integration	数据集成	Shùjù jíchéng	
Data integrity (IPsec)	数据完整性	Shùjù wánzhěngxìng	
Data integrity algorithm	数据完整性算法	Shùjù wánzhěngxìng suànfǎ	I-ALG
Data interception	数据窃取	Shùjù qièqǔ	
Data Interchange Standard Association	数据交换标准协会	Shùjù jiāohuàn biāozhǔn xiéhuì	DISA
Data interface board	数据接口板	Shùjù jiēkǒu bǎn	DDU
Data interleaving	数据交织	Shùjù jiāozhī	
Data interpolation	数据内插	Shùjù nèichā	
Data item	数据项	Shùjù xiàng	
Data item label	数据项标签	Shùjù xiàng biāoqiān	
Data key	数据密钥	Shùjù mìyào	DK
Data layer	数据层	Shùjù céng	DL
Data line multiplexer	数据线路复用器	Shùjù xiànlù fùyòngqì	DLM
Data lineage	数据沿袭	Shùjù yánxí	
Data link	数据链路	Shùjù liànlù	DL
Data link back panel	数据链路后面板	Shùjù liànlù hòumian bǎn	DLBP
Data link connection	数据链路连接	Shùjù liànlù liánjiē	DLC
Data link connection identifier	数据链路连接标志	Shùjù liànlù liánjiē biāozhì	DLCI
Data link connection identifier	数据链路连接标识	Shùjù liànlù liánjiē biāozhì	DLCI
Data link connection identifier	数据链路连接标识符	Shùjù liànlù liánjiē biāozhìfú	DLCI
Data link connection identity	数据链路连接识别	Shùjù liànlù liánjiē shíbié	DLCI
Data link connection identity	数据链路连接证实	Shùjù liànlù liánjiē zhèngshí	DLCI

Data link control	数据链路控制	Shùjù liànlù kòngzhì	DL-Control
Data link core	数据链路核心层	Shùjù liànlù héxīn céng	DL-CORE
Data link discriminator	数据链路鉴别器	Shùjù liànlù jiànbiéqì	DLD
Data link escape	数据链转义	Shùjù liàn zhuǎnyì	DLE
Data link escape character	数据链路转义字符	Shùjù liànlù zhuǎnyì zìfú	DLE
Data link layer	数据链路层	Shùjù liànlù céng	DLL
Data link protocol	数据链路协议	Shùjù liànlù xiéyì	
Data link service	数据链路服务	Shùjù liànlù fúwù	DLS
Data link service access point	数据链路服务访问点	Shùjù liànlù fúwù fǎngwèndiǎn	DLSAP
Data link service data unit	数据链路服务数据单元	Shùjù liànlù fúwù shùjù dānyuán	DLSDU
Data link switching client access protocol (IETF use)	数据转接客户访问协议	Shùjù zhuǎnjiē kèhù fǎngwèn xiéyì	DCAP
Data link switching protocol	数据链路交换协议	Shùjù liànlù jiāohuàn xiéyì	DLSw
Data logging	数据记事	Shùjù jìshì	
Data management	数据管理	Shùjù guǎnlǐ	
Data management terminal	数管台	Shùguǎntái	
Data management terminal	数据管理台	Shùjù guǎnlǐtái	
Data manipulation language	数据操纵语言	Shùjù cāozòng yǔyán	DML
Data manipulation language	数据操作语言	Shùjù cāozuò yǔyán	DML
Data mart	数据商场	Shùjù shāngchǎng	
Data mart (for database)	数据集市	Shùjù jíshì	
Data member	成员变量	Chéngyuán biànliàng	
Data member	数据成员	Shùjù chéngyuán	
Data message handler	数据消息处理器	Shùjù xiāoxi chǔlǐqì	DMH
Data message handling	数据消息处理	Shùjù xiāoxi chǔlǐ	DMH
Data message transmission	数据消息传送	Shùjù xiāoxi chuánsòng	DMT
Data mining	数据挖掘	Shùjù wājué	
Data mining	资料勘探	Zīliào kāntàn	
Data mining for customer service and sales	客户服务和客户行销的资料探测	Kèhù fúwù hé kèhù xíngxiāode zīliào tàncè	DMCSS
Data mining tool	数据挖掘工具	Shùjù wājué gōngjù	
Data mining, information mining	信息挖掘	Xìnxī wājué	
Data missing	数据丢失	Shùjù diūshī	
Data model	数据模型	Shùjù móxíng	
Data modification	数据修改	Shùjù xiūgǎi	
Data network identification code	数据网标别码	Shùjù wǎng biāobiémǎ	DNIC
Data network identification code	数据网标识码	Shùjù wǎng biāozhìmǎ	DNIC
Data network identification code	数据网络识别码	Shùjù wǎngluò shíbiémǎ	DNIC
Data network identifier	数据网络标识符	Shùjù wǎngluò biāozhìfú	DNID
Data normalization	数据规范化	Shùjù guīfànhuà	
Data number value	数字码值	Shùzì mǎ zhí	DNV
Data object	数据对象	Shùjù duìxiàng	
Data object	数据目标	Shùjù mùbiāo	DO
Data over cable service interface specification	电缆数据业务接口规范	Diànlǎn shùjù yèwù jiēkǒu guīfàn	DOCSIS
Data over cable service interface specification	有线电缆数据服务接口规范	Yǒuxiàn diànlǎn shùjù fúwù jiēkǒu guīfàn	DOCSIS

Data over cable service interface specification	有线电视网络上的数据接口规格	Yǒuxiàn diànshì wǎngluò-shàngde shùjù jiēkǒu guīgé	DOCSIS
Data over cable service interface specifications	线缆服务接口数据规格	Xiànlǎn fúwù jiēkǒu shùjù guīgé	DOCSIS
Data over cable system interface standard	电缆网上的数据接口规范	Diànlǎn wǎngshàngde shùjù jiēkǒu guīfàn	DOCSIS
Data over voice	话上数据	Huà-shàng shùjù	DOV
Data overrun error	数据溢出错误	Shùjù yìchū cuòwù	
Data packet assembly/disassembly function	数据包分组/重组功能	Shùjù bāo fēnzǔ/chóngzǔ gōngnéng	PAD
Data packet communications	数据分组通信	Shùjù fēnzǔ tōngxìn	DPC
Data packet transfer delay	数据分组传送延迟	Shùjù fēnzǔ chuánsòng yánchí	
Data page (in Sybase)	数据页	Shùjù yè	
Data path not provided signal	不提供数据通路信号	Bù tígōng shùjù tōnglù xìnhào	DPN
Data phone	数据电话机	Shùjù diànhuàjī	
Data post-processing system	数据后处理系统	Shùjù hòuchǔlǐ xìtǒng	DPPS
Data presentation	数据表达	Shùjù biǎodá	
Data processing	数据处理	Shùjù chǔlǐ	
Data product	数据产品	Shùjù chǎnpǐn	
Data protection engineering (IPsec)	数据保护工程	Shùjù bǎohù gōngchéng	
Data pump	数据泵	Shùjù bèng	
Data pump (for database)	数据抽取	Shùjù chōuqǔ	
Data quality	数据质量	Shùjù zhìliàng	
Data quality date	数据品质日期	Shùjù pǐnzhì rìqī	
Data quality element	数据品质要素	Shùjù pǐnzhì yàosù	
Data quality evaluation procedure	数据品质评价值程序	Shùjù pǐnzhì ping jiàzhí chéngxù	
Data quality measure	数据品质测定	Shùjù pǐnzhì cèdìng	
Data quality overview element	数据品质的浏览要素	Shùjù pǐnzhìde liúlǎn yàosù	
Data quality result	数据品质评价结果	Shùjù pǐnzhì píngjià jiéguǒ	
Data quality scope	数据品质的使用范围	Shùjù pǐnzhìde shǐyòng fànwéi	
Data quality sub-element	数据品质的次生要素	Shùjù pǐnzhìde cìshēng yàosù	
Data quality value type	数据品质评价值的类型	Shùjù pǐnzhì ping jiàzhíde lèixíng	
Data recorder	数据记录器	Shùjù jìlùqì	
Data redundancy	数据冗余度	Shùjù rǒngyúdù	
Data relativity	数据相关性	Shùjù xiāngguānxìng	
Data reliability	数据可靠性	Shùjù kěkàoxìng	
Data replay (IPsec)	数据重放	Shùjù chóngfàng	
Data retrieval complete indication (SS7)	数据恢复完成指示	Shùjù huīfù wánchéng zhǐshì	
Data retrieval confirm (SS7)	数据恢复确认	Shùjù huīfù quèrèn	
Data retrieval indication (SS7)	数据恢复指示	Shùjù huīfù zhǐshì	
Data retrieval request (SS7)	数据恢复请求	Shùjù huīfù qǐngqiú	
Data rights	数据权限	Shùjù quánxiàn	
Data roam	无线传讯	Wúxiàn chuánxùn	
Data safety	数字安全	Shùzì ānquán	
Data scrubbing (for database)	数据清理	Shùjù qīnglǐ	
Data security	数据安全	Shùjù ānquán	
Data security	数据安全性	Shùjù ānquánxìng	
Data security	数据保安	Shùjù bǎo'ān	
Data serial interface	数据串行接口	Shùjù chuànháng jiēkǒu	DSI

English	Chinese	Pinyin	Abbreviation
Data server	数据服务器	Shùjù fúwùqì	
Data service division	数据服务部门	Shùjù fúwù bùmén	DSD
Data service unit	数据服务单元	Shùjù fúwù dānyuán	DSU
Data services unit	数据业务单元	Shùjù yèwù dānyuán	DSU
Data set	数据集	Shùjù jí	
Data set ready	数据集就绪	Shùjù jí jiùxù	DSR
Data sharing	数据共享	Shùjù gòngxiǎng	
Data signal	数据信号	Shùjù xìnhào	
Data signal processor	数据信号处理器	Shùjù xìnhào chǔlǐqì	DSP
Data signal rate	数据信号速率	Shùjù xìnhào sùlǜ	
Data signal rate selection (signal)	数据信号率选择(信号)	Shùjù xìnhào lǜ xuǎnzé (xìnhào)	DSRS
Data signaling rate	数据信令速率	Shùjù xìnlìng sùlǜ	
Data sink	数据槽	Shùjù cáo	
Data sink	数据汇	Shùjù huì	
Data sink	数据宿	Shùjù sù	
Data smoothing	数据平滑	Shùjù pínghuá	
Data source	数据源	Shùjù yuán	
Data source authentication (IPsec)	数据源认证	Shùjù yuán rènzhèng	
Data source name (for database)	数据源名称	Shùjù yuán míngchēng	DSN
Data specification	数据说明	Shùjù shuōmíng	
Data standardization	数据标准化	Shùjù biāozhǔnhuà	
Data station	数据站	Shùjù zhàn	
Data storage	数据存贮	Shùjù cúnzhù	
Data storage device	数据存储器	Shùjù cúnchǔqì	DSD
Data storage library	数据存储库	Shùjù cúnchǔkù	DL
Data striping	条状分布数据	Tiáozhuàng fēnbù shùjù	
Data strobe link	数据选通连接	Shùjù xuǎntōng liánjiē	DSL
Data structure	数据结构	Shùjù jiégòu	
Data subscriber terminal equipment	数据用户终端设备	Shùjù yònghù zhōngduān shèbèi	DSTE
Data switch exchange	数据交换机	Shùjù jiāohuànjī	DSE
Data switching equipment	数据交换设备	Shùjù jiāohuàn shèbèi	DSE
Data switching exchange	数据传接交换台	Shùjù chuánjiē jiāohuàntái	DSE
Data switching exchange	数据转换交换机	Shùjù zhuǎnhuàn jiāohuànjī	DSE
Data symbol	数据符号	Shùjù fúhào	
Data table (for database)	数据表	Shùjù biǎo	
Data terminal (or termination) equipment	数据终端设备	Shùjù zhōngduān shèbèi	DTE
Data terminal equipment	数字终端设备	Shùzì zhōngduān shèbèi	DTE
Data terminal equipment/data circuit equipment (DTE/DCE) interface	数据终端设备与数据电路设备接口	Shùjù zhōngduān shèbèi yǔ shùjù diànlù shèbèi jiēkǒu	
Data terminal ready	数据终端就绪	Shùjù zhōngduān jiùxù	
Data time-slot distribution (board)	数据时隙分配板	Shùjù shíxì fēnpèi bǎn	DTD
Data transfer	数据传送	Shùjù chuánsòng	
Data transfer	数据对传	Shùjù duìchuán	
Data transfer	数据转移	Shùjù zhuǎnyí	
Data transfer protocol	数据传送协议	Shùjù chuánsòng xiéyì	DTP
Data transfer rate	数据传送速率	Shùjù chuánsòng sùlǜ	

Data transformation services (in SQL Server)	数据转换服务	Shùjù zhuǎnhuàn fúwù	DTS
Data transmission	数据传输	Shùjù chuánshū	
Data transmission equipment	数据传输设备	Shùjù chuánshū shèbèi	DTE
Data transmission function	数据传输函数	Shùjù chuánshū hánshù	DTF
Data transmission line	数据传输线路	Shùjù chuánshū xiànlù	
Data transmission protocol	数据传输协议	Shùjù chuánshū xiéyì	DTP
Data transmission radio	数传台	Shù chuán tái	
Data transmission radio	数传台	Shùchuántái	
Data transmission rate	数据传送速率	Shùjù chuánsòng sùlǜ	DTR
Data transmission speed	数据传输速度	Shùjù chuánshū sùdù	
Data transmission system	数据传输系统	Shùjù chuánshū xìtǒng	
Data transmission telecommunication	数据传输通信	Shùjù chuánshū tōngxìn	SC
Data transmitter	数传机	Shùchuánjī	
Data type	数据类型	Shùjù lèixíng	
Data uncertainty	数据不确定性	Shùjù bùquèdìngxìng	
Data under voice	话下数据	Huà-xià shùjù	DUV
Data under voice transmission	话下数据传输	Huà-xià shùjù chuánshū	DUV
Data updating	数据更新	Shùjù gēngxīn	
Data user part	数据用户部分	Shùjù yònghù bùfen	DUP
Data validation	数据确认	Shùjù quèrèn	
Data verification	数据检验	Shùjù jiǎnyàn	
Data view	数据视图	Shùjù shìtú	
Data visualization	数据可视化	Shùjù kěshìhuà	
Data warehouse	数据仓库	Shùjù cāngkù	DW
Data warehousing	数据储库	Shùjù chǔkù	
Data-aware control (for database)	数据感知控件	Shùjù gǎnzhī kòngjiàn	
Database	数据库	Shùjùkù	DB
Database administrator	数据库管理者	Shùjùkù guǎnlǐzhě	DBA
Database catalog	数据库目录	Shùjùkù mùlù	
Database consistency checker (in SQL Server)	数据库一致性检查程序	Shùjùkù yīzhìxìng jiǎnchá chéngxù	DBCC
Database control system nucleus	数据库控制系统核心	Shùjùkù kòngzhì xìtǒng héxīn	DCSN
Database design	数据库设计	Shùjùkù shèjì	
Database diagram	数据关系图	Shùjù guānxi tú	
Database directory	数据库目录	Shùjùkù mùlù	
Database engine	数据库引擎	Shùjùkù yǐnqíng	
Database fault management	数据库故障管理	Shùjùkù gùzhàng guǎnlǐ	DB-FM
Database file	数据库文件	Shùjùkù wénjiàn	
Database handling	数据库处理	Shùjùkù chǔlǐ	DBH
Database integrator	数据库集成器	Shùjùkù jíchéngqì	
Database integrity	数据库完整性	Shùjùkù wánzhěngxìng	
Database language	数据库语言	Shùjùkù yǔyán	
Database lock	数据库锁定	Shùjùkù suǒdìng	
Database longevity	数据库寿命	Shùjùkù shòumìng	
Database management system	数据库管理系统	Shùjùkù guǎnlǐ xìtǒng	DBMS
Database object	数据库对象	Shùjùkù duìxiàng	
Database organizing system	数据库组织系统	Shùjùkù zǔzhī xìtǒng	DBOS

Database overload	数据库溢出	Shùjùkù yìchū	DBOL
Database owner	数据库所有者	Shùjùkù suǒyǒuzhě	
Database portrayal catalog	数据库表述类型	Shùjùkù biǎoshù lèixíng	
Database project	数据库工程	Shùjùkù gōngchéng	
Database propagation software	数据库复制软件	Shùjùkù fùzhì ruǎnjiàn	
Database role	数据库角色	Shùjùkù juésè	
Database schema	数据库架构	Shùjùkù jiàgòu	
Database schema	数据库模式	Shùjùkù móshì	
Database script	数据库脚本	Shùjùkù jiǎoběn	
Database security system	数据库安全系统	Shùjùkù ānquán xìtǒng	DBSS
Data-bound (for database)	数据绑定	Shùjù bǎngdìng	
Datacube	数据立方体	Shùjù lìfāngtǐ	
Data-driven attack (IPsec)	数据驱动攻击	Shùjù qūdòng gōngjī	
Data-flow control layer	数据流控制层	Shùjù liú kòngzhì céng	
Data-flow, data stream	数据流	Shùjù liú	
Datagram	数据报	Shùjù bào	
Datagram	数据报文	Shùjù bàowén	
Datagram delivery protocol (Apple use)	数据报传送协议	Shùjùbào chuánsòng xiéyì	DDP
Data-link switching	数据链路交换	Shùjù liànlù jiāohuàn	DLSw
Data-link-connectionless-mode data transmission	数据链路无连接型数据传输	Shùjù liànlù wúliánjiēxíng shùjù chuánshū	
Data-link-connection-mode data transmission	数据链路连接型数据传输	Shùjù liànlù liánjiēxíng shùjù chuánshū	
Datang Telecom Multimedia Center	大唐电信多媒体中心	Dàtáng diànxìn duōméitǐ zhōngxīn	
Datang Telecom Technology Co. Ltd.	大唐电信科技股份有限公司	Dàtáng diànxìn kējì gǔfèn yǒuxiàn gōngsī	
Dataphone line formatter	数据电话编制器	Shùjù diànhuà biānzhìqì	DPLF
Dataphone switched digital service	数据电话交换数字业务	Shùjù diànhuà jiāohuàn shùzì yèwù	DSDS
Data-sensitive fault	数据敏感性故障	Shùjù mǐngǎnxìng gùzhàng	
Dataset series	数据库系列	Shùjùkù xìliè	
Dataset (for database)	数据集	Shùjùjí	
Datem	数据模块	Shùjù mókuài	
Datum	大地基准面	Dàdì jīzhǔn miàn	
Daughter card	子卡	Zikǎ	
Dawning (Chinese supercomputer maker)	曙光	Shǔguāng	
Daylight filter	日光滤光镜	Rìguāng lǜguāngjìng	
De facto standard	事实上标准	Shìshíshang biāozhǔn	
de Jure standard	法律上标准	Fǎlǜ-shàng biāozhǔn	
Deactivate	去活	Qùhuó	
Deactivate indication	解除激活指示	Jiěchú jīhuó zhǐshì	DI
Deactivate request	解除激活请求	Jiěchú jīhuó qǐngqiú	DR
Deactivate trace mode	去活跟踪方式	Qùhuó gēnzōng fāngshì	
Deactivation	去激活	Qùjīhuó	
Dead lock (for database)	死锁	Sǐsuǒ	
Dead sector	空段	Kōngduàn	
Dead storage	死库容	Sǐ kùróng	
Dead time	寂静时间	Jìjìng shíjiān	

Dead-letter queue	死信队列	Sǐxìn duìliè	
Deadline	截止期	Jiézhǐqī	
Deallocate	归还	Guīhuán	
Deblocking	分块	Fēnkuài	
Debugger	调试器	Tiáoshìqì	
Debugging	排除错误	Páichú cuòwù	
Debugging	调试	Tiáoshì	
Debugging aids	调试工具	Tiáoshì gōngjù	DA
Debugging computer program	调试计算机程序	Tiáoshì jìsuànjī chéngxù	DCP
Debugging helper	调试帮助程序	Tiáoshì bāngzhù chéngxù	DHP
Deburrer	去毛刺机	Qùmáocìjī	
Decade (10 Hertz interval)	十倍频程	Shíbèi pínchéng	
Decadic signal	十进制信号	Shíjìnzhì xìnhào	
Decapsulate, unwrap	解封	Jiěfēng	
Decapsulating agent (in IP)	拆封代理	Chāifēng dàilǐ	
Decapsulation	拆封	Chāifēng	
Decay	退化	Tuìhuà	
Decay-time broadening	下降时间展宽	Xiàjiàng shíjiān zhǎnkuān	
Decentralized control	分散控制方式	Fēnsàn kòngzhì fāngshì	
Decentralized multipoint	分散式多点	Fēnsàn-shì duōdiǎn	
Decentralized processing	分散处理	Fēnsàn chǔlǐ	
Decibel	分贝	Fēnbèi	dB
Decibels per milliwatt	分贝/毫瓦	Fēnbèi/háowǎ	dB/m
Decimal adder	十进制加法器	Shíjìnzhì jiāfǎqì	DA
Decimal degrees	十进制经纬度	Shíjìnzhì jīngwěi dù	
Decimal notation	十进制记数法	Shíjìnzhì jìshù fǎ	
Decipher	译密码	Yìmìmǎ	
Decipher, decrypt, decode, decryption (IPsec)	解密	Jiěmì	
Decision and support system	决策和支持系统	Juécè hé zhīchí xìtǒng	DSS
Decision circuit	判决电路	Pànjué diànlù	
Decision content	判定含量	Pàndìng hánliàng	
Decision data	判定数据	Pàndìng shùjù	
Decision index system	决策指标体系	Juécè zhǐbiāo tǐxì	
Decision instant of digital signal	数字信号的判决瞬时	Shùzì xìnhàode pànjué shùnshí	
Decision intelligence	决策智能化	Juécè zhìnénghuà	DI
Decision matrix	决策矩阵	Juécè jǔzhèn	
Decision support	决策支持	Juécè zhīchí	
Decision support system	决策支持系统	Juécè zhīchí xìtǒng	DSS
Decision tree	决策树	Juécè shù	
Decision tree	判定树	Pàndìng shù	
Decision value	判决值	Pànjué zhí	
Declaration	声明	Shēngmíng	
Declaration unit	说明部件	Shuōmíng bùjiàn	
Declarative referential integrity (for database)	声明引用完整性	Shēngmíng yǐnyòng wánzhěng xìng	DRI
Declination	偏差	Piānchā	DEC
DECnet routing protocol	DECnet 路由选择协议	DECnet lùyóu xuǎnzé xiéyì	DRP

Decode	解码	Jiěmǎ	
Decode error message (IPsec TLS)	解码错误消息	Jiěmǎ cuòwù xiāoxi	
Decode status flag	解码状态标志	Jiěmǎ zhuàngtài biāozhì	DSF
Decoder	解码器	Jiěmǎqì	
Decoder	译码器	Yìmǎqì	DEC
Decoder alarm time	解码器报讯时间	Jiěmǎqì bàoxùn shíjiān	
Decoder attack time	解码器启动时间	Jiěmǎqì qǐdòng shíjiān	
Decoder false code falsifying	解码器假码虚报	Jiěmǎqì jiǎmǎ xūbào	
Decoder input buffer (video term)	解码器输入缓冲器	Jiěmǎqì shūrù huǎnchōngqì	
Decoder noise falsifying	解码器噪声虚报	Jiěmǎqì zàoshēng xūbào	
Decoder operating level range	解码器工作电平范围	Jiěmǎqì gōngzuò diànpíng fànwéi	
Decoder recovery time	解码器恢复时间	Jiěmǎqì huīfù shíjiān	
Decoder required protection time	解码器保护时间	Jiěmǎqì bǎohù shíjiān	
Decoder selectivity	解码器的选择性	Jiěmǎqìde xuǎnzéxìng	
Decoding constraint length	译码约束长度	Yìmǎ yuēshù chángdù	
Decomposition	分解	Fēnjiě	
Decompression failure message (IPsec TLS)	解压失败消息	Jiěyā shībài xiāoxi	
Decoy target	诱标	Yòubiāo	
Decrypt error message (IPsec TLS)	解密错误消息	Jiěmì cuòwù xiāoxi	
Decrypt failure message (IPsec TLS)	解密失败消息	Jiěmì shībài xiāoxi	
DECT authentication module	DECT 认证模型	DECT rènzhèng móxíng	DAM
Dedicated channel	专用信道	Zhuānyòng xìndào	DCH
Dedicated control	专用控制	Zhuānyòng kòngzhì	DC
Dedicated control channel	专用控制信道	Zhuānyòng kòngzhì xìndào	DCCH
Dedicated control program	专用控制程序	Zhuānyòng kòngzhì chéngxù	DCP
Dedicated data link	专用数据链路	Zhuānyòng shùjù liànlù	
Dedicated file	专用文件	Zhuānyòng wénjiàn	DF
Dedicated inquiry access code	专用查询识别码	Zhuānyòng cháxún shíbié mǎ	DIAC
Dedicated line, private line	专线	Zhuānxiàn	
Dedicated ODMA channel	ODMA 专用信道	ODMA zhuānyòng xìndào	ODCH
Dedicated physical channel/downlink	下行专用物理信道	Xiàxíng zhuānyòng wùlǐ xìndào	DPCH/D
Dedicated physical control channel	专用物理控制信道	Zhuānyòng wùlǐ kòngzhì xìndào	DPCCH
Dedicated physical control channel/downlink	下行专用物理控制信道	Xiàxíng zhuānyòng wùlǐ kòngzhì xìndào	DPCCH/D
Dedicated physical data channel	专用物理数据信道	Zhuānyòng wùlǐ shùjù xìndào	DPDCH
Dedicated physical data channel/downlink	下行专用物理数据信道	Xiàxíng zhuānyòng wùlǐ shùjù xìn dào	DPDCH/D
Dedicated protection ring (optical network term)	专用保护环	Zhuānyòng bǎohù huán	DPR
Dedicated signaling channel	专用信令信道	Zhuānyòng xìnlìng xìndào	DSC
Dedicated simplex	专用单工	Zhuānyòng dāngōng	
Dedicated traffic channel	专用业务信道	Zhuānyòng yèwù xìndào	DTCH
Deduction	推导	Tuīdǎo	
De-emphasis	去加重	Qùjiāzhòng	
De-emphasis circuit	去加重电路	Qù jiāzhòng diànlù	
Deep buffer (in RAM or ROM)	深度缓冲	Shēndù huǎnchōng	DB
Deep scattering layer	深水散射层	Shēnshuǐ sǎnshè céng	DSL
Deep space	深度空间	Shēndù kōngjiān	
Deep space	深空	Shēnkōng	

Deep space communication	深空通信	Shēnkōng tōngxìn	
Deep space network	空深网	Kōngshēn wǎng	DSN
Deep space probe	深度空间探测器	Shēndù kōngjiān tàncèqì	
Deep space probe	深空探测器	Shēnkōng tàncèqì	
Deep trench silicon etch (semiconductor mfg)	半导体管沟深度蚀刻	Bàndǎotǐ guǎngōu shēndù shíkè	
Default	启始设置	Qǐshǐ shèzhì	
Default	缺省	Quēshěng	
Default attribute	默认属性	Mòrèn shǔxìng	
Default attribute values	默认属性值	Mòrèn shǔxìng zhí	
Default button	默认按钮	Mòrèn ànniǔ	
Default check initialization	缺省的检错初始值	Quēshěngde jiǎncuò chūshǐ zhí	
Default constraint (for database)	默认约束	Mòrèn yuēshù	
Default constraint (in SQL Server)	缺省约束	Quēshěng yuēshù	
Default database	默认数据库	Mòrèn shùjùkù	
Default entry	缺省填	Quēshěng tián	
Default host	默认主机	Mòrèn zhǔjī	
Default instance (for database)	默认实例	Mòrèn shílì	
Default language	默认语言	Mòrèn yǔyán	
Default member	默认成员	Mòrèn chéngyuán	
Default printer	默认打印机	Mòrèn dǎyìnjī	
Default result set (for database)	默认结果集	Mòrèn jiéguǒ jí	
Default route	缺省路由	Quēshěng lùyóu	
Default setting	缺省设置	Quēshěng shèzhì	
Default setup	内定设置	Nèidìng shèzhì	
Default share	缺省共享	Quēshěng gòngxiǎng	
Default value	默认值	Mòrèn zhí	
Default value	内定直	Nèidìng zhí	
Default value	缺省值	Quēshěng zhí	
Defect	降质	Jiàngzhì	
Defect	缺陷	Quēxiàn	
Defect management cell	降质管理信元	Jiàngzhì guǎnlǐ xìn yuán	
Defect management cell	缺陷管理信元	Quēxiàn guǎnlǐ xìnyuán	
Defect management cell	缺陷管理信元	Quēxiàn guǎnlǐ xìnyuán	
Defect second	缺陷秒	Quēxiàn miǎo	DS
Defense Acquisition Office (US)	国防采办	Guófáng cǎibàn	DAO
Defense Communication Agency (US)	国防部通信局	Guófángbù tōngxìn jú	DCA
Defense data network	防卫数据网	Fángwèi shùjù wǎng	DDN
Defense Information Systems Agency (US)	国防信息系统局	Guófáng xìnxī xìtǒngjú	DISA
Defense Modeling and Simulation Office (US)	国防建模和仿真办公室	Guófáng jiànmó hé fǎngzhēn bàngōngshì	DMSO
Defer	推迟	Tuīchí	
Deferred maintenance	延缓维护	Yánhuǎn wéihù	
Deferred maintenance alarm	延缓维护告警	Yánhuǎn wéihù gàojǐng	DMA
Define constant (assembler term)	定义常数	Dìngyì chángshù	DC
Define constant character	定义常数字符	Dìngyì chángshù zìfú	DCC
Define constant double	定义常数二字	Dìngyì chángshù èr zì	DCD
Define constant floating	定义常数浮动	Dìngyì chángshù fúdòng	DCF

Define event control block	定义事件控制字组	Dìngyì shìjiàn kòngzhì zì zǔ	DFECB
Definition	定义	Dìngyì	
Definition of management information	管理信息定义	Guǎnlǐ xìnxī dìngyì	DMI
Deflection channel bandwidth	偏转通道带宽	Piānzhuǎn tōngdào dàikuān	
Deflection coil	偏转线圈	Piānzhuǎn xiànquān	
Deflection modulation	偏转调制	Piānzhuǎn tiáozhì	DM
Deflection plate	偏转板	Piānzhuǎn bǎn	
Deflection settling time	偏转稳定时间	Piānzhuǎn wěndìng shíjiān	
Deflection setup time	偏转建立时间	Piānzhuǎn jiànlì shíjiān	
Defocusing protection circuit	散焦保护电路	Sànjiāo bǎohù diànlù	
Deformation	变形	Biànxíng	
Deformation coefficient	变形系数	Biànxíng xìshù	
Deformed postage item	变体票品	Biàntǐ piàopǐn	
Degenerate mode (in a cavity resonator or waveguide)	简并模	Jiǎnbìng mó	
Degeneration	退缩	Tuìsuō	
Degradation	降级	Jiàngjí	
Degradation	劣化	Lièhuà	
Degradation failure	退化失效	Tuìhuà shīxiào	
Degraded, down-graded	档次稍低	Dàngcì shāodī	
Degragment, defrag	碎片整理	Suìpiàn zhěnglǐ	
Degragment; defrag	整理碎片	Zhěnglǐ suìpiàn	
Degree of bias distortion	偏畸变度	Piānjī biàndù	
Degree of early anisochronous parallel distortion	超前不等时并行畸变度	Chāoqián bùděngshí bìngxíng jībiàndù	
Degree of gross start-stop distortion	总起止畸变度	Zǒng qǐzhǐ jībiàndù	
Degree of individual distortion (of a particular significant instant)	单个畸变度	Dāngè jībiàndù	
Degree of isochronous distortion	等时畸变度	Děngshí jībiàndù	
Degree of late anisochronous parallel distortion	滞后不等时并行畸变度	Zhìhòu bùděngshí bìngxíng jībiàndù	
Degree of polarization	偏振度	Piānzhèndù	DOP
Degree of radiant protection	辐射隔离度	Fúshè gélídù	
Degree of service	服务等级	Fúwù děngjí	
Degree of standardized distortion	标准化测试畸变度	Biāozhǔnhuà cèshì jībiàn dù	
Degree of start-stop distortion	起止畸变度	Qǐzhǐ jībiàndù	
Degree of synchronous start-stop distortion	同步起止畸变度	Tóngbù qǐzhǐ jībiàn dù	
Deinstall, uninstall	反装置	Fǎnzhuāngzhì	
Delamination (in SMT)	分层	Fēncéng	
Delaunay triangulation	德洛内三角	Dé-luò-nèi sānjiǎo	
Delay	时延	Shíyán	
Delay	延迟	Yánchí	DELAY
Delay adaptive differential pulse code modulation	延迟自适应差分脉码调制	Yánchí zìshìyìng chāfēn màimǎ tiáozhì	DADPCM
Delay angle	延迟角	Yánchí jiǎo	
Delay frequency characteristic	时延频率特性	Shíyán pínlǜ tèxìng	
Delay inequality	时延差	Shíyán chà	
Delay jitter	时延抖动	Shíyán dǒudòng	
Delay line	迟延线	Chíyán xiàn	
Delay line	延时线	Yánshí xiàn	

Delay line canceller	延迟线对消器	Yánchí xiàn duìxiāoqì	
Delay line filter	延迟线滤波器	Yánchí xiàn lǜbōqì	
Delay shift keying	延迟移位键控	Yánchí yíwèi jiànkòng	DSK
Delay transition	延迟转换	Yánchí zhuǎnhuàn	
Delay transmission	延迟传输	Yánchí chuánshū	DT
Delay transmission diversity	延迟发送分集	Yánchí fāsòng fēnjí	DTD
Delay-dialing signal	延迟拨号信号	Yánchí bōhào xìnhào	
Delayed charging circuit	延时充电电路	Yánshí chōngdiàn diànlù	
Delayed release (ISUP message)	延迟释放	Yánchí shìfàng	DRS
Delay-locked loop	延迟锁定环	Yánchí suǒdìng huán	DLL
Delegate (verb)	委托	Wěituō	
Delete cells (WP command)	删除方格	Shānchú fānggé	
Delete character	删除字符	Shānchú zìfú	DEL
Delete query	删除查询	Shānchú cháxún	
Delete subscriber data	删除用户数据	Shānchú yònghù shùjù	
Delete, erase, cancel	删除	Shānchú	
Deletion flag	删除标记	Shānchú biāojì	
Delimiter	界符	Jièfú	
Delimiter	界限符号	Jièxiàn fúhào	
Delimiter, separator	分隔符	Fēngé fú	
Delivered at frontier	边境交货	Biānjìng jiāohuò	
Delivered duplicate frame	传送后的重复帧	Chuánsòng-hòude chóngfù zhèng	
Delivered duplicate frames	递交后的重复帧	Dìjiāo hòude chóngfù zhèng	
Delivered duty paid	完税后交货	Wánshuì-hòu jiāohuò	
Delivered duty unpaid	完税前交货	Wánshuì-qián jiāohuò	DDU
Delivered duty unpaid	未完税交货	Wèiwánshuì jiāohuò	
Delivered errored frame	传送后的出错帧	Chuánsòng-hòude chūcuò zhèng	
Delivered errored frames	递交后的出错帧	Dìjiāo hòude chūcuò zhèng	
Delivered ex-ship	船上交货	Chuánshàng jiāohuò	DES
Delivered out-of-sequence frame	传送后的失序帧	Chuánsòng-hòude shīxù zhèng	
Delivered out-of-sequence frames	递交后的失序帧	Dìjiāo hòude shīxù zhèng	
Delivery	投递	Tóudì	
Delivery media integrated framework	传送媒体综合框架	Chuánsòng méitǐ zōnghé kuàngjià	DMIF
Delivery report	投递报告	Tóudì bàogào	
Delivery service partner	交付服务合伙人	Jiāofù fúwù héhuǒrén	DSP
Dell Computer Corp.	戴尔电脑集团	Dài-ěr diànnǎo jítuán	
Delphi (an ISP)	待尔发	Dài-ěr-fā	
Delta	三角洲	Sānjiǎozhōu	
Delta modulation	增量调制	Zēngliàng tiáozhì	
Delta modulation code	增量调制编码	Zēngliàng tiáozhì biānmǎ	
Delta pulse code modulation	增量脉码调制	Zēngliàng màimǎ tiáozhì	DPCM
Demand assignment	按需分配	Ànxū fēnpèi	
Demand assignment controller	按需分配控制器	Ànxū fēnpèi kòngzhìqì	DAC
Demand assignment multiple access	按申请分配-多址联接	Àn shēnqǐng fēnpèi-duō zhǐ liánjiē	DAMA
Demand assignment multiple access	按需分配多地址	Ànxū fēnpèi duōdìzhǐ	DAMA
Demand assignment multiple access	按需分配多址	Ànxū fēnpèi duōzhǐ	DAMA

Demand assignment protocol	按需分配协议	Ànxū fēnpèi xiéyì	DAP
Demand assignment signaling and switching (unit)	按需分配信令传送和交换（设备）	Ànxū fēnpèi xìnlìng chuánsòng hé jiāohuàn (shèbèi)	DASS
Demand assignment system	按需分配系统	Ànxū fēnpèi xìtǒng	
Demand assignment-digital speech interpolation	请求分配-数字式语音插入	Qǐngqiú fēnpèi—shùzì-shì yǔyīn chārù	DADSI
Demand priority	需求优先级	Xūqiú yōuxiān jí	
Demand service	即时业务	Jíshí yèwù	
Demand telecommunication service	按要求的电信业务	Àn yāoqiúde diànxìnyèwù	
Demand-assigned signaling and switching unit sub-system	请求分配信号发送与转换子系统	Qǐngqiú fēnpèi xìnhào fāsòng yǔ zhuǎnhuàn zìxìtǒng	DSSS
Demand-assignment time division multiple access	按需求分配时分多重存取	Àn xūqiú fēnpèi shífēn duōzhòng cúnqǔ	DA-TDMA
Demand-dial connection	请求拨号连接	Qǐngqiú bōhào liánjiē	
Demand-dial routing	请求拨号路由选择	Qǐngqiú bōhào lùyóu xuǎnzé	
Demapping	去映射	Qùyìngshè	
Demarcation	分界线	Fēnjièxiàn	
Demilitarized zone	隔离区	Gélí qū	DMZ
Democratic network	等权网	Děngquán wǎng	
Demodulation	解调	Jiětiáo	
Demodulation carrier frequency control	解调载频控制	Jiětiáo zàipín kòngzhì	
Demodulator	解调器	Jiětiáoqì	D
deMorgan's theorem	德-模定理	Dé-mó dìnglǐ	
deMorgan's theorem	德-模尔根定理	Dé-mó-ěr-gēn dìnglǐ	
Demultiplex	多路分用	Duōlù fēnyòng	DX
Demultiplexer	分接器	Fēnjiēqì	
Demultiplexer	分用器	Fēnyòngqì	
Demultiplexer	解复用器	Jiěfùyòngqì	DEMUX
Demultiplexing	分用	Fēnyòng	
Demultiplexing wavelength router	解复用波长选路器	Jiěfùyòng bōcháng xuǎnlùqì	
Denial (IPsec)	否认	Fǒurèn	
Denial of service	拒绝服务	Jùjué fúwù	
Denial of service (IPsec)	服务拒绝	Fúwù jùjué	
Denial of service attack	拒绝服务攻击	Jùjué fúwù gōngjī	DoS
Denormalize	使非规范化	Shǐ fēiguīfànhuà	
Denotational semantic model	标志语义模型	Biāozhì yǔyì móxíng	
Dense mode	密集模式	Mìjí móshì	DM
Dense graph	稠密图	Chóumì tú	
Dense mode PIM	密集型 PIM	Mìjí-xíng PIM	
Dense wavelength division multiplexing	密集型波分复用	Mìjíxíng bōfēn fùyòng	DWDM
Dense wavelength division multiplex	波长密集型复用技术	Bōcháng mìjíxíng fùyòng jìshù	DWDM
Dense wavelength division multiplexer	密集波分复用器	Mìjí bōfēn fùyòngqì	DWDM
Dense wavelength division multiplexer filter	密集波分复用滤波器	Mìjí bōfēn fùyòng lǜbōqì	DWFI
Dense wavelength division multiplexing	密集波分复用	Mìjí bōfēn fùyòng	DWDM
Density	密度	Mìdù	
Density detection	密度检测	Mìdù jiǎncè	
Density slicing	密度分割	Mìdù fēngē	
Deny	拒绝	Jùjué	

English	Chinese	Pinyin	Abbreviation
Department of Defense (DOD) kernel transition strategy	国防部总体过渡策略	Guófángbù zǒngtǐ guòdù cèlüè	DDKTS
Department of Planning (MII)	综合规划司	Zōnghé guīhuà sī	
Department of Policies and Regulations (MII)	政策法规司	Zhèngcè fǎguī sī	
Department of Science and Technology (MII)	科学技术司	Kēxué jìshù sī	
Department of Telecommunications Administration (MII)	电信管理局	Diànxìn guǎnlǐjú	
Dependability	广义可靠性	Guǎngyì kěkàoxìng	
Dependencies	相关性	Xiāngguānxìng	
Dependent object (GIS term)	附属对象	Fùshǔ duìxiàng	
Deploy	部署	Bùshǔ	
Depolarization	去极化	Qùjíhuà	
Depressed clad fiber	凹陷型包层光纤	Āoxiànxíng bāocéng guāngxiān	
Depth cueing	深度暗示	Shēndù ànshì	
Depth curve	深度曲线	Shēndù qūxiàn	
Depth of embedment	进尺	Jìnchǐ	
Depth of field	多重境深	Duōzhòng jìng shēn	DOF
De-Q-ing circuit	降优值电路	Jiàng yōuzhí diànlù	
Dequantization (video term)	反量化	Fǎnliànghuà	
Derating	降额	Jiàng‘é	
De-reference	解引用	Jiě yǐnyòng	
De-reference operator	提领运算子	Tílǐng yùnsuànzǐ	
Derived class	派生类	Pàishēng lèi	
Derived delta modulation	导出增量调制	Dǎochū zēngliàng tiáozhì	DDM
Derived delta modulation	二次增量调制	Èrcì zēngliàng tiáozhì	DDM
Derived map	派生地图	Pàishēng dìtú	
Deriviation graph	引导图	Yǐndǎo tú	
Descendant	后代	Hòudài	
Descending node (of a satellite)	降交点	Jiàngjiāodiǎn	
Descrambler	解扰码器	Jiěrǎomǎqì	
Descrambler	解扰器	Jiěrǎoqì	
Descrambling, descramble	解扰	Jiěrǎo	
Description logic	描述逻辑	Miáoshù luóji	
Descriptive data	描述性数据	Miáoshù-xìng shùjù	
Descriptor	描述符	Miáoshùfú	
Desensitization	降灵	Jiànglíng	
Desensitization	灵敏度降低	Língmǐndù jiàngdī	
Desensitizing	降敏	Jiàngmǐn	
Desieter telegraph translation	德西特电报转换器	Dé-xī-tè diànbào zhuǎnhuànqì	
Design	设计	Shèjì	
Design algorithm	设计算法	Shèjì suànfǎ	DA
Design by contract	契约式设计	Qìyuē-shì shèjì	
Design failure	设计失效	Shèjì shīxiào	
Design fault	设计故障	Shèjì gùzhàng	
Design formula	设计形式	Shèjì xíngshì	
Design impedance	设计阻抗	Shèjì zǔkàng	
Design pattern	设计模式	Shèjì móshì	

Design review	设计评审	Shèjì píngshěn	
Design standard	设计标准	Shèjì biāozhǔn	
Designate (verb)	指明	Zhǐmíng	
Designated bridge	指定桥	Zhǐdìng qiáo	
Designated bridge	指定网桥	Zhǐdìng wǎngqiáo	
Designated bridge	指定的桥	Zhǐdìngde qiáo	
Designated confirmer signature scheme	指定批准人签名方案	Zhǐdìng pīzhǔn rén qiānmíng fāng'àn	
Designated forwarder	指定转发路由器	Zhǐdìng zhuǎnfā lùyóuqì	DF
Designated router	指定路由器	Zhǐdìng lùyóuqì	
Designated router	指定路由器	Zhǐdìng lùyóuqì	DR
Designated router	指定转发者	Zhǐdìng zhuǎnfā zhě	DR
Designated router	指派路由器	Zhǐpài lùyóuqì	DR
Designated transit list	指定转接列表	Zhǐdìng zhuǎnjiē lièbiǎo	DTL
Designated transit list	指定转接序列	Zhǐdìng zhuǎnjiē xùliè	DTL
Designated transit list	指定的转接一览表	Zhǐdìngde zhuǎnjiē yīlǎnbiǎo	DTL
Designation of specific areas	区域设计	Qūyù shèjì	
Designed for the manufacturer (in SMT)	为制造着想的设计	Wéi zhìzàozhe xiǎngde shèjì	DFM
Designed return period	设计再现期间	Shèjì zàixiàn qījiān	
Designed speed	设计速度	Shèjì sùdù	
Desired value	预期值	Yùqī zhí	
Desktop computer	台式电脑	Tái-shì diànnǎo	
Desktop engine (in SQL Server)	桌面引擎	Zhuōmiàn yǐnqíng	
Desktop geographic information system	桌面地理信息系统	Zhuōmiàn dìlǐ xìnxī xìtǒng	
Desktop management interface	桌面管理接口	Zhuōmiàn guǎnlǐ jiēkǒu	DMI
Desktop personal computer	桌面个人计算机	Zhuōmiàn gèrén jìsuànjī	DPC
Desoldering (in SMT)	卸焊	Xièhàn	
Despotic network	专权网	Zhuānquán wǎng	
De-spreading	解扩	Jiěkuò	
Destination	终点	Zhōngdiǎn	
Destination address	目的地址	Mùdì dìzhì	DA
Destination audit	目的地状态查询	Mùdìdì zhuàngtài cháxún	DAUD
Destination available (SS7)	目的地可用	Mùdìdì kěyòng	DAVA
Destination category	目的类	Mùdì lèi	DC
Destination code	目的码	Mùdì mǎ	
Destination host	目标主机	Mùbiāo zhǔjī	DST
Destination information	目标信息	Mùbiāo xìnxī	
Destination Internet protocol (IP) address	目的因特网协议地址	Mùdì Yīntèwǎng xiéyì dìzhǐ	
Destination local exchange	目的地端局交换机	Mùdìdì duānjú jiāohuànjī	DLE
Destination location	目的地	Mùdìdì	
Destination MAC	目标 MAC	Mùbiāo MAC	
Destination network	终点网络	Zhōngdiǎn wǎngluò	DN
Destination node	终结点	Zhōngjié diǎn	
Destination object	目的对象	Mùdì duìxiàng	
Destination object	终点目标	Zhōngdiǎn mùbiāo	
Destination options	地址可选项	Dìzhǐ kěxuǎn xiàng	
Destination point code	目的点编码	Mùdì diǎn biānmǎ	DPC

Destination point code	目的地址编码	Mùdì dìzhǐ biānmǎ	DPC
Destination point code	目的信令点编码	Mùdì xìnlìng diǎn biānmǎ	DPC
Destination point code	目的地点码	Mùdìdì diǎnmǎ	DPC
Destination point code	目的地信令点编码	Mùdìdì xìnlìngdiǎn biānmǎ	DPC
Destination port	目的端口	Mùdì duānkǒu	
Destination unavailable (SS7)	目的地不可用	Mùdìdì bùkěyòng	DUNA
Destination user part unavailable (SS7)	目的地用户部分不可用	Mùdìdì yònghù bùfen bùkěyòng	DUPU
Destination, objective	目的	Mùdì	
Destination-sequenced distance vector	目的序列距离矢量	Mùdì xùliè jùlí shǐliàng	DSDV
Destroy	销毁	Xiāohuǐ	
Destructive read-out	破坏性读出	Pòhuàixìng dúchū	
Destructive test	破坏性试验	Pòhuàixìng shìyàn	
Destructor	析构器	Xīgòuqì	Dtor
Destructor (function in software)	析构函数	Xīgòu hánshù	dtor
Desynchronization	同步失效	Tóngbù shīxiào	
Desynchronizer	去同步器	Qùtóngbùqì	
Detach	除去	Chúqù	
Detach	分开	Fēnkāi	DET
Detach	分离	Fēnlí	DET
Detach indication	分离指示	Fēnlí zhǐshì	
Detail flowchart	详细流程图	Xiángxì liúchéngtú	DFC
Detailed items list of subscription	报刊订阅清单	Bàokān dìngyuè qīngdān	
Details view	详细视图	Xiángxì shìtú	
Detection	检波	Jiǎnbō	
Detection criterion	检测准则	Jiǎncè zhǔnzé	
Detection distortion	检波失真	Jiǎnbō shīzhēn	
Detection efficiency	检波效率	Jiǎnbō xiàolǜ	
Detection point	检测点	Jiǎncè diǎn	DP
Detection point	检出点	Jiǎnchū diǎn	
Detection probability	发现概率	Fāxiàn gàilǜ	
Detection time	检测时间	Jiǎncè shíjiān	T1
Detectivity	探测率	Tàncè lǜ	
Detector	检波器	Jiǎnbōqì	
Detector	检测器	Jiǎncèqì	
Detector	检光元件	Jiǎnguāng yuánjiàn	
Detector coupler	检测耦合器	Jiǎncè ǒuhéqì	
Detector current sensitivity	检波器的电流灵敏度	Jiǎnbōqìde diànliú língmǐndù	
Detector imbalance	传感器失衡	Chuángǎnqì shīhéng	
Detector mount	检波座	Jiǎnbō zuò	
Detector noise limited operation	受检测器噪声限制的工作状态	Shòu jiǎncèqì zàoshēng xiànzhìde gōngzuò zhuàngtài	
Detector voltage sensitivity	检波器的电压灵敏度	Jiǎnbōqìde diànyā língmǐndù	
Detention reservoir; regulating reservoir	调节水库	Tiáojié shuǐkù	
Determinate fault	确定性故障	Quèdìngxìng gùzhàng	
Determinate flow direction	确定性流向	Quèdìngxìng liúxiàng	
Determination test	测定试验	Cèdìng shìyàn	

Determined (adj), set	取定	Qǔdìng	
Deterministic	确定性	Quèdìngxìng	
Deterministic and stochastic Petri net	确定与随机 Petri 网	Quèdìng yǔ suíjī Petri wǎng	DSPN
Deterministic bit rate	固定比特率	Gùdìng bǐtèlǜ	DBR
Deterministic bit rate	确定比特率	Quèdìng bǐtè lǜ	DBR
Deterministic load distribution	确定性负载分担	Quèdìngxìng fùzài fēndān	
Deterministic method	定值论法	Dìngzhí lùnfǎ	
Deterministic method	确定方式	Quèdìng fāngshì	
Deterministic transfer mode	确定传递方式	Quèdìng chuándì fāngshì	
Deterministically	确定的	Quèdìngde	
Detuning	失调	Shītiáo	
Deutsche Industrie Norm	德国工业标准	Déguó gōngyè biāozhǔn	DIN
Deutsche Telekom	德国电信	Déguó Diànxìn	
Developable surface	可扩展平面	Kěkuòzhǎn píngmiàn	
Developer edition (of software)	开发者版	Kāifāzhě bǎn	
Development	开发	Kāifā	
Development phase (of product life cycle)	研制阶段	Yánzhì jiēduàn	
Development plan	开发计划	Kāifā jìhuà	
Development promotion area	开发促进地域	Kāifā cùjìn dìyù	
Development rights	开发权	Kāifā quán	
Development system	开发系统	Kāifā xìtǒng	
Deviation operation	位移式操作	Wèiyí-shì cāozuò	
Device access code	设备访问码	Shèbèi fǎngwèn mǎ	DCE
Device address	装置地址	Zhuāngzhì dìzhǐ	DVA
Device bay	设备插架	Shèbèi chājià	DB
Device control	设备控制	Shèbèi kòngzhì	DC
Device control word	装置控制字	Zhuāngzhì kòngzhì zì	DCW
Device coordinate	设备坐标	Shèbèi zuòbiāo	
Device descriptor table	设备描述符表	Shèbèi miáoshùfú biǎo	DDT
Device driver	设备驱动	Shèbèi qūdòng	
Device server	设备服务器	Shèbèi fúwùqì	
Device space	设备空间	Shèbèi kōngjiān	
Device start	设备启动	Shèbèi qǐdòng	DST
Device status bit	设备状态位	Shèbèi zhuàngtài wèi	DSB
Device status word	设备状态字	Shèbèi zhuàngtài zì	DSW
Device stop	设备停止	Shèbèi tíngzhǐ	DSP
Device under test	被测器件	Bèicè qìjiàn	DUT
Device under test	被测设备	Bèicè shèbèi	DUT
Device wait	设备等待	Shèbèi děngdài	DW
Device-independent bitmap	设备无关性位图	Shèbèi wúguānxìng wèi tú	DIB
Dew point test	露点试验	Lùdiǎn shìyàn	
Dewetting (in SMT)	去湿	Qùshī	
Diagnosis and monitoring	诊断和监测	Zhěnduàn hé jiāncè	DIAG
Diagnosis, diagnostic	诊断	Zhěnduàn	
Diagnostic control program	诊断控制程序	Zhěnduàn kòngzhì chéngxù	DCP
Diagnostic function test	诊断功能测试	Zhěnduàn gōngnéng cèshì	DFT

Diagnostic program	诊断程序	Zhěnduàn chéngxù	
Diagnostic tests	诊断测试	Zhěnduàn cèshì	
Diagonal	对角线	Duìjiǎoxiàn	
Diagonal pliers	斜口钳	Xiékǒuqián	
Dial	标度盘	Biāodùpán	
Dial (noun)	拨号盘	Bōhàopán	D
Dial (verb and noun)	拨号	Bōhào	
Dial access Information retrieval system	拨号存取信息检索系统	Bōhào cúnqǔ xìnxī jiǎnsuǒ xìtǒng	DAIRS
Dial backup	拨号备份	Bōhào bèifèn	
Dial backup auto answer unit	拨号盘备用自动应答设备	Bōhàopán bèiyòng zìdòng yìngdá shèbèi	DBAAU
Dial backup unit	拨号辅助设备	Bōhào fǔzhù shèbèi	DBU
Dial exchange	拨号交换机	Bōhào jiāohuànjī	
Dial pulse	号盘脉冲	Hàopán màichōng	DP
Dial pulse incoming register	拨号脉冲入局记发器	Bōhào màichōng rùjú jìfāqì	DPIR
Dial service	自动电话业务	Zìdòng diànhuà yèwù	DS
Dial switch (thumbwheel switch)	拨号开关	Bōhào kāiguān	
Dial system	拨号系统	Bōhào xìtǒng	DS
Dial system B-switchboard	拨号制 B 交换台	Bōhào zhì B jiāohuàntái	DSB
Dial tone	拨号音	Bōhào yīn	DT
Dial tone delay	拨号音延迟	Bōhào yīn yánchí	
Dial tone signal	拨号音信号	Bōhào yīn xìnhào	
Dial/dialed pulse	拨号脉冲	Bōhào màichōng	DP
Dial-in by the DTE	DTE 拨入	DTE bōrù	
Dialing mistake probability	拨号错误概率	Bōhào cuòwù gàilǜ	
Dialog box	对话栏	Duìhuà lán	
Dialog box	会话箱	Huìhuà xiāng	
Dialog box (in a GUI)	对话框	Duìhuà kuàng	
Dial-on-demand	按需拨号	Ànxū bōhào	
Dial-on-demand	随拨服务	Suíbō fúwù	
Dial-on-demand routing	按需拨号路由	Ànxū bōhào lùyóu	DDR
Dial-on-demand routing	拨号请求路由	Bōhào qǐngqiú lùyóu	DDR
Dial-on-demand routing	拨号选路	Bōhào xuǎnlù	DDR
Dial-out by the PSPDN	PSPDN 拨出	PSPDN bōchū	
Dial-up connection	拨号连接	Bōhào liánjiē	
Dial-up connection	拨接	Bōjiē	
Dial-up line	拨号线路	Bōhào xiànlù	
Dial-up network	拨号网络	Bōhào wǎngluò	
Dial-up networking	拨号上网	Bōhào shangwǎng	DUN
Dial-up terminal	拨号终端	Bōhào zhōngduān	
Diameter ratio	直径比	Zhíjìng bǐ	
Diamond (MP3 manufacturer)	帝盟	Dì-méng	
Dichotomizing search	二分法搜索	Èrfēnfǎ sōusuǒ	
Dichromic filter	双色向滤光镜	Shuāng sèxiàng lǜguāngjìng	
Dichromic mirror	双色向面镜	Shuāng sèxiàng miànjìng	
Dicke radiometer	地克型辐射计	Dì-kè-xíng fúshèjì	
Dictionary attack (IPsec)	字典式攻击	Zìdiǎnshì gōngjī	

Dictionary entry	字典条目	Zìdiǎn tiáomù	
Die cutting	模切	Móqiē	
Dielectric anisotropy	介电性能各向异性	Jièdiàn xìngnéng gèxiàng yìxìng	DA
Dielectric chaff rod	介质干扰杆	Jièzhì gānrǎo gǎn	
Dielectric lens	介质透镜	Jièzhì tòujìng	
Dielectric lens antenna	介质透镜天线	Jièzhì tòujìng tiānxiàn	
Dielectric loss	介电损耗	Jièdiàn sǔnhào	
Dielectric phase shifter	介质移相器	Jièzhì yíxiàngqì	
Dielectric resonator	介质谐振器	Jièzhì xiézhènqì	
Dielectric rod antenna	棒状介质天线	Bàngzhuàng jièzhì tiānxiàn	DRA
Dielectric rod antenna	介质棒天线	Jièzhì bàng tiānxiàn	
Dielectric strength	介电强度	Jièdiàn qiángdù	
Dielectric strength test	介质强度试验	Jièzhì qiángdù shìyàn	
Dielectric test	介质试验	Jièzhì shìyàn	
Dielectric test	绝缘试验	Juéyuán shìyàn	
Dielectric waveguide	介质波导	Jièzhì bōdǎo	
Dielectrics (semiconductor mfg)	介质材料	Jièzhì cáiliào	
Diesel generator	油机	Yóujī	YJ
Difference frequency distortion	差频失真	Chàpín shīzhēn	
Difference gain	差增益	Chà zēngyì	
Difference global positioning system	差分全球定位系统	Chāfēn quánqiú dìngwèi xìtǒng	DGPS
Difference service model	差分服务模型	Chāfēn fúwù móxíng	DiffServ
Difference signal	差信号	Chà xìnhào	
Difference slope	差斜率	Chà xiélǜ	
Different-edge aggregation (CAD/CAM)	异边聚合	Yìbiān jùhé	
Differential attack	差分攻击	Chāfēn gōngjī	
Differential backup	差异备份	Chāyì bèifèn	
Differential binary phase shift keying	差动二进制移相键控	Chādòng èrjìnzhì yíxiāng jiànkòng	DBPSK
Differential coil	差动线圈	Chādòng xiànquān	
Differential coupler	差分耦合器	Chāfēn ǒuhéqì	
Differential cryptanalysis	差分密码分析法	Chāfēn mìmǎ fēnxīfǎ	
Differential database backup	差异数据库备份	Chāyì shùjùkù bèifèn	
Differential duplex	差动式双工	Chādòng-shì shuānggōng	
Differential encoded coherent phase shift keying	微分编码相干移相键控	Wēifēn biānmǎ xiānggān yíxiàng jiànkòng	DECPSK
Differential encoding	差分编码	Chāfēn biānmǎ	
Differential frequency hopping	差分跳频	Chāfēn tiàopín	DFH
Differential gain	微分增益	Wēifēn zēngyì	DG
Differential gain distortion	微分增益失真	Wēifēn zēngyì shīzhēn	
Differential global navigation satellite system	差分全球卫星导航系统	Chāfēn quánqiú wèixīng dǎoháng xìtǒng	DGNSS
Differential group delay	差分群迟延	Chāfēn qún chíyán	DGD
Differential group delay	差分群时延	Chāfēn qún shíyán	DGD
Differential group delay	微分群时延	Wēifēn qún shíyán	DGD
Differential interface	差分接口	Chāfēn jiēkǒu	
Differential Manchester encoding	差分曼彻斯特编码	Chāfēn Màn-chè-sī-tè biānmǎ	
Differential mode coupler	差模耦合器	Chàmó ǒuhéqì	
Differential mode inversion (modulation)	微分反模调制	Wēifēn fǎnmó tiáozhì	DMI

English	Chinese	Pinyin	Abbreviation
Differential mode tracking	差模跟踪	Chàmó gēnzōng	
Differential mode voltage	差模电压	Chàmó diànyā	
Differential modulation	差分调制	Chāfēn tiáozhì	
Differential phase distortion	微分相位失真	Wēifēn xiàngwèi shīzhēn	
Differential phase pulse modulation	微分相位脉冲调制	Wēifēn xiàngwèi màichōng tiáozhì	DPPM
Differential phase shift keying	差分相移键控	Chāfēn xiāngyí jiànkòng	DPSK
Differential phase shift keying	差分移相键控	Chāfēn yíxiāng jiànkòng	DPSK
Differential phase-shift	差分相移	Chāfēn xiāngyí	
Differential preamplifier	差动前置放大器	Chādòng qiánzhì fàngdàqì	
Differential pressure	差压	Chàyā	
Differential protection	差动保护	Chādòng bǎohù	
Differential pulse code modulation	差分脉冲编码调制	Chāfēn màichōng biānmǎ tiáozhì	DPCM
Differential pulse code modulation	差分脉码调制	Chāfēn màimǎ tiáozhì	DPCM
Differential quadrature phase shift keying	差分正交相移键控	Chāfēn zhèngjiāo xiāngyí jiànkòng	DQPSK
Differential quadriphase shift keying	差分四相相移键控	Chāfēn sìxiāng xiāngyí jiànkòng	DQPSK
Differential quaternary phase shift keying	差分正交移相键控	Chāfēn zhèngjiāo yíxiāng jiànkòng	DQPSK
Differential rectification	图象微调	Túxiàng wēitiáo	
Differential timing	差分时钟	Chāfēn shízhōng	
Differential-encoded phase shift keying	差分编码移相键控	Chāfēn biānmǎ yíxiāng jiànkòng	DEPSK
Differentially coherent phase shift keying	差分相干移相键控	Chāfēn xiānggān yíxiāng jiànkòng	DCPSK
Differentially coherent pulse code modulation	差分相干脉码调制	Chāfēn xiānggān màimǎ tiáozhì	DCPCM
Differentially encoded quadrature phase-shift keying	差分编码正交移相键控	Chāfēn biānmǎ zhèngjiāo yíxiāng jiànkòng	DQPSK
Differentially encoded, quadriphase shift keying	差分编码四相相移键控	Chāfēn biānmǎ sìxiāng xiāngyí jiànkòng	DQPSK
Differentiated service	差分业务	Chāfēn yèwù	DS
Differentiated service	区分服务	Qūfēn fúwù	
Differentiated service	区分业务	Qūfēn yèwù	
Differentiated service (IETF use)	区分服务体系结构	Qūfēn fúwù tǐxì jiégòu	DiffServ
Differentiated service model (CAD/CAM)	区分服务模型	Qūfēn fúwù móxíng	DiffServ
Differentiated services	区别服务	Qūbié fúwù	Diff-serv
Differentiated services	区别业务	Qūbié yèwù	DiffServ
Differentiating circuit	微分电路	Wēifēn diànlù	
Differentiator	微分器	Wēifēnqì	
Diffraction	衍射	Yǎnshè	
Diffraction code encryption	衍射编码加密技术	Yǎnshè biānmǎ jiāmì jìshù	
Diffraction grating	衍射光删	Yǎnshè guāng shān	
Diffraction of electromagnetic wave	电磁波饶射	Diàncíbō ráoshè	
Diffraction-limited lens	绕射极限透镜	Ràoshè jíxiàn tòujìng	
Diffuse convolutional codes	扩展卷积码	Kuòzhǎn juànjī mǎ	
Diffuse reflection; scattering	散射	Sǎnshè	
Diffusing update algorithm	扩散修正算法	Kuòsàn xiūzhèng suànfǎ	DUAL
Diffusion	扩散	Kuòsàn	
Diffusion current	扩散电流	Kuòsàn diànliú	
Diffusion function	扩压函数	Kuòyā hánshù	
Diffusion furnace	扩散炉	Kuòsàn lú	
Digest	摘要	Zhāiyào	
Digilux touch mask	指触光敏装置	Zhǐ chù guāngmǐn zhuāngzhì	

Digit (in telecommunication signaling)	数位	Shùwèi	
Digit absorption	数位吸收	Shùwèi xīshōu	
Digit deletion	数位删除	Shùwèi shānchú	
Digit error ratio	数字差错率	Shùzì chācuò lǜ	
Digit rate	数字率	Shùzì lǜ	
Digit sequence integrity	数字序列完整性	Shùzì xùliè wánzhěngxing	DSI
Digit time slot	数位时隙	Shùwèi shíxì	
Digit time slot	数字时隙	Shùzì shíxì	
Digit, digital	数字	Shùzì	
Digital	数字形式的	Shùzì xíngshìde	
Digital	数字的	Shùzide	
Digital [Microwave] radio relay system	数字微波接力系统	Shùzì wēibō jiēlì xìtǒng	DRRS
Digital access and cross-connect system	数字存取和交叉连接系统	Shùzì cúnqǔ hé jiāochā liánjiē xìtǒng	DACS
Digital access protocol	数字访问协议	Shùzì fǎngwèn xiéyì	DAMPS
Digital accumulator	数字积累器	Shùzì jīlěiqì	
Digital advanced mobile phone service	数字先进移动电话业务	Shùzì xiānjìn yídòng diànhuà yèwù	D-AMPS
Digital advanced mobile phone service	数字化高级移动电话系统	Shùzìhuà gāojí yídòng diànhuà xìtǒng	DAMPS
Digital advanced mobile phone system	数字先进移动电话系统	Shùzì xiānjìn yídòng diànhuà xìtǒng	DAVID
Digital ammeter	数字电流表	Shùzì diànliúbiǎo	
Digital analysis method	数字分析法	Shùzì fēnxīfǎ	
Digital analyzer	数字分析器	Shùzì fēnxīqì	
Digital array	数字矩阵	Shùzì jǔzhèn	
Digital audio broadcast	数字音频广播	Shùzì yīnpín guǎngbō	DAB
Digital audio extraction	数子音频抓取	Shùzì yīnpín zhuāqǔ	DAE
Digital Audio Video committee	数字音频视频委员会	Shùzì yīnpín shìpín wěiyuánhuì	DAVIC
Digital Audio Video committee	数字音像委员会	Shùzì yīnxiàng wěiyuánhuì	DAVIC
Digital audio/video interactive decoder	数字音频/视频交互式译码器	Shùzì yīnpín/shìpín jiāohùshì yìmǎqì	DBF
Digital beam forming	数字波束行成	Shùzì bōshù xíngchéng	
Digital block	数字单元	Shùzì dānyuán	
Digital block	数字区段	Shùzì qūduàn	
Digital branch exchange	数字小型交换机	Shùzì xiǎoxíng jiāohuànjī	DBX
Digital branching board (2Mb/s)	数字分支板	Shùzì fēnzhī bǎn	DB2M
Digital broadcast satellite	数字广播卫星	Shùzì guǎngbō wèixīng	DBS
Digital business	数字企业	Shùzì qǐyè	
Digital camera	数码相机	Shùmǎ xiàngjī	
Digital cellular land mobile telecommunication system	数字蜂窝陆地移动通信系统	Shùzì fēngwō lùdì yídòng tōngxìn xìtǒng	DCLMTS
Digital cellular mobile	数字蜂窝移动	Shùzì fēngwō yídòng	
Digital cellular radio frequency sub-system	数字蜂窝无线频率子系统	Shùzì fēngwō wúxiàn pínlǜ zixìtǒng	DRFS
Digital cellular system	数字蜂窝系统	Shùzì fēngwō xìtǒng	DCS
Digital center	数字中心	Shùzì zhōngxīn	DC
Digital certificate	数字证书	Shùzì zhèngshū	
Digital channel	数字通路	Shùzì tōnglù	
Digital channel block	数字信道模块	Shùzì xìndào mókuài	DCB
Digital channel element assembly	数字信道集成件	Shùzì xìndào jíchéng jiàn	DCEA

Digital channel link	数字信道连接	Shùzì xìndào liánjiē	DCL
Digital channel sub-system	数字信道子系统	Shùzì xìndào zixìtǒng	
Digital chart of the world	世界数字化图	Shìjiè shùzìhuà tú	DCW
Digital circuit	数字电路	Shùzì diànlù	
Digital circuit multiplication equipment	数字电路倍增设备	Shùzì diànlù bèizēng shèbèi	DCME
Digital circuit multiplication equipment- adaptive differential pulse code modulation	数字电路倍增设备—自适应差分脉冲编码调制	Shùzì diànlù bèizēng shèbèi— zìshìyìng chāfēn màichōng biānmǎ tiáozhì	DCME-ADPCM
Digital circuit multiplication system	数字话路扩容系统	Shùzì huàlù kuòróng xìtǒng	
Digital circuit network	数字电路网	Shùzì diànlù wǎng	DCN
Digital code squelch	数字编码将净躁制	Shùzì biānmǎ jiāngjìngzào zhì	DCS
Digital color code	数字色码	Shùzì sèmǎ	DCC
Digital communication channel	数字通信通路	Shùzì tōngxìn tōnglù	DCC
Digital communication protocol	数字通信协议	Shùzì tōngxìn xiéyì	DCP
Digital communication terminal equipment	数字通信终端设备	Shùzì tōngxìn zhōngduān shèbèi	DCTE
Digital connection	数字连接	Shùzì liánjiē	
Digital control channel	数字控制信道	Shùzì kòngzhì xìndào	DBR
Digital cordless telephone system second generation	第二代数字无绳电话系统	Dì'èrdài shùzì wúshéng diànhuà xìtǒng	CT-2
Digital cross-connect	数字交叉连接	Shùzì jiāochā liánjiē	DXC
Digital cross-connect board (2Mb/s)	数字交换板	Shùzì jiāohuàn bǎn	DX2M
Digital cross-connect equipment	数字交叉连接设备	Shùzì jiāochā liánjiē shèbèi	DXC
Digital cross-connect equipment	数字交叉连接器	Shùzì jiāochā liánjiēqì	DXC
Digital cross-connect system	数据交叉连接系统	Shùjù jiāochā liánjiē xìtǒng	DCS
Digital cross-connect system	数字交叉连接系统	Shùzì jiāochā liánjiē xìtǒng	DCS
Digital cross-correct	数字交叉校正	Shùzì jiāochā jiàozhèng	DCC
Digital data	数字数据	Shùzì shùjù	
Digital data acquisition system	数字数据采集系统	Shùzì shùjù cǎijí xìtǒng	
Digital data communications message protocol (in DECnet)	数字数据通信报文协议	Shùzì shùjù tōngxìn bàowén xiéyì	DDCMP
Digital data exchange	数字数据交换局	Shùzì shùjù jiāohuànjú	DDX
Digital data measuring system	数字数据测量系统	Shùzì shùjù cèliáng xìtǒng	DDMS
Digital data multiplexer	数字数据多路复用器	Shùzì shùjù duōlù fùyòngqì	DDM
Digital data network	数字数据网	Shùzì shùjù wǎng	SSW
Digital data network	数字数据网	Shùzì shùjù wǎng	DDN
Digital data packet switching network	数字数据分组交换网络	Shùzì shùjù fēnzǔ jiāohuàn wǎngluò	DDX
Digital data packet switching network	数字数据信包交换网络	Shùzì shùjù xìnbāo jiāohuàn wǎngluò	DDX
Digital data service	数字数据业务	Shùzì shùjù yèwù	DDS
Digital data switching exchange	数字数据交换局	Shùzì shùjù jiāohuànjú	DDSE
Digital data switching matrix	数字数据开关矩阵	Shùzì shùjù kāiguān jǔzhèn	DDSM
Digital data switching service	数字数据交换业务	Shùzì shùjù jiāohuàn yèwù	DDXS
Digital data terminal equipment	数字数据终端设备	Shùzì shùjù zhōngduān shèbèi	DDTE
Digital data terminal equipment service module	数字数据终端设备服务模块	Shùzì shùjù zhōngduān shèbèi fúwù mókuài	DDTESM
Digital data transmission system	数字数据转输系统	Shùzì shùjù zhuǎnshū xìtǒng	DDTS
Digital decade	数字 10 年	Shùzì shí nián	
Digital demultiplexer	数字分接器	Shùzì fēnjiēqì	
Digital demultiplexing	数字分接	Shùzì fēnjiē	

Digital diary	电子记事本	Diànzǐ jìshìběn	
Digital dispatch security monitoring system	数字发送保密监控系统	Shùzì fāsòng bǎomì jiānkòng xìtǒng	DDSMS
Digital distribution frame	数字分配架	Shùzì fēnpèijià	DDF
Digital distribution frame	数字配线架	Shùzì pèixiàn jià	DDF
Digital down converter	数字下变频	Shùzì xiàbiànpín	DDC
Digital earphone	数字耳机	Shùzì ěrjī	
Digital earth	数字地球	Shùzì dìqiú	
Digital echo canceler	数字回声消除器	Shùzì huíshēng xiāochúqì	
Digital echo canceler board (A)	数字回波抑制器 A	Shùzì huíbō yìzhìqì A	DECA
Digital echo-canceling chip	回波消除数字电路芯片	Huíbō xiāochú shùzì diànlù xìnpiàn	DECC
Digital electric actuator	数字式电动执行机构	Shùzì-shì diàndòng zhíxíng jīgòu	
Digital electronic message service	数字电子报文业务	Shùzì diànzǐ bàowén yèwù	DEMS
Digital electronic switching system	数字式电子交换系统	Shùzì-shì diànzǐ jiāohuàn xìtǒng	DESS
Digital elevation model	数字高程模型	Shùzì gāochéng móxíng	DEM
Digital enhanced cordless telecommunication	增强数字无绳通讯	Zēngqiáng shùzì wúshéng tōngxùn	DECT
Digital enhanced cordless telecommunications	数字增强型无绳通信	Shùzì zēngqiáng-xíng wúshéng tōngxìn	DECT
Digital enhanced cordless telephone	数字增强无绳电话	Shùzì zēngqiáng wúshéng diànhuà	DECT
Digital error	数字差错	Shùzì chācuò	
Digital error monitor sub-system	数字式误差监控子系统	Shùzì-shì wùchā jiānkòng zixìtǒng	DEMS
Digital European Cordless Telecommunication	欧洲数字无绳电信	Oūzhōu shùzì wúshéng diànxìn	DECT
Digital European Cordless Telecommunication	欧洲数字无绳通信	Oūzhōu shùzì wúshéng tōngxìn	DECT
Digital European Cordless Telecommunication system	泛欧数字无绳通信系统	Fàn'ōu shùzì wúshéng tōngxìn xìtǒng	DECT
Digital European cordless telephone	泛欧数字无绳电话系统	Fàn'ōu shùzì wúshéng diànhuà xìtǒng	DECT
Digital European Cordless Telephone	数位式欧洲无绳电话	Shùwèi-shì Oūzhōu wúshéng diànhuà	DECT
Digital exchange	数字交换机	Shùzì jiāohuànjī	
Digital exchange	数字交换局	Shùzì jiāohuànjú	
Digital exchange format	数字交换标准	Shùzì jiāohuàn biāozhǔn	
Digital facsimile interface system	数字传真接口系统	Shùzì chuánzhēn jiēkǒu xìtǒng	DFIS
Digital feedback frequency modulation system	数字反馈调频系统	Shùzì fǎnkuì tiáopín xìtǒng	DFFMS
Digital ferrite phase shifter	数字式铁氧体移相器	Shùzì-shì tiěyǎngtǐ yíxiàngqì	DFPS
Digital filling	数字填充	Shùzì tiánchōng	
Digital filter	数字滤波器	Shùzì lǜbōqì	
Digital fingerprint	数字拇印	Shùzì mǔyìn	
Digital fingerprint	数字指纹	Shùzì zhǐwén	
Digital flat panel	数字式平面显示器	Shùzì-shì píngmiàn xiǎnshìqì	DFP
Digital flex scan (video term)	数字伸缩扫描	Shùzì shēnsuō sǎomiáo	DFS
Digital frequency division	数字分频	Shùzì fēnpín	
Digital frequency synthesizer	数字频率合成器	Shùzì pínlǜ héchéngqì	
Digital Geographic Information exchange Standard	数字化地理信息交换标准	Shùzìhuà dìlǐ xìnxī jiāohuàn biāozhǔn	DIGEST
Digital geospatial metadata	数字地理空间元数据	Shùzì dìlǐ kōngjiān yuán shùjù	DGM
Digital image	数字图像	Shùzì túxiàng	
Digital image control (video term)	数字图像控制	Shùzì túxiàng kòngzhì	DIC
Digital image processing	数字图象处理	Shùzì túxiàng chǔlǐ	DIP
Digital image watermark	数字图像水印	Shùzì túxiàng shuǐyìn	
Digital imaging group	数字成图组织	Shùzì chéngtú zǔzhī	DIG

Digital information transmission system	数字信息传输系统	Shùzì xìnxī chuánshū xìtǒng	DITS
Digital input	数字输入	Shùzì shūrù	DI
Digital input voice answer block	数字输入声音应答部件	Shùzì shūrù shēngyīn yìngdá bùjiàn	DIVA
Digital integrated circuit	数字集成电路	Shùzì jíchéng diànlù	
Digital landscape model	数字景观模型	Shùzì jǐngguān móxíng	DLM
Digital leased line service	数字租用线业务	Shùzì zūyòng xiàn yèwù	DLL
Digital light processing (video term)	数字光处理	Shùzì guāng chǔlǐ	DLP
Digital line graph	数字线划图	Shùzì xiàn huàtú	DLG
Digital line path	数字有线通道	Shùzì yǒuxiàn tōngdào	
Digital line path	有线数字通道	Yǒuxiàn shùzì tōngdào	
Digital line section	数字有线段	Shùzì yǒuxiàn duàn	
Digital line section	有线数字段	Yǒuxiàn shùzì duàn	
Digital line system	有线数字系统	Yǒuxiàn shùzì xìtǒng	
Digital line unit	数字线单元	Shùzì xiàn dānyuán	DLU
Digital link	数字链路	Shùzì liànlù	
Digital loop carrier	数字环路载波	Shùzì huánlù zàibō	DLC
Digital loopback	数字环回	Shùzì huánhuí	
Digital map	数字地图	Shùzì dìtú	
Digital map data	数字地图数据	Shùzì dìtú shùjù	
Digital mapping	数字制图	Shùzì zhìtú	
Digital matched filter	数字匹配滤波器	Shùzì pǐpèi lǜbōqì	
Digital mean square error (criteria)	数字均方误差(标准)	Shùzì jūn fāng wùchā (biāozhǔn)	DMSE
Digital microphone	数字传声器	Shùzì chuánshēngqì	
Digital microwave	数字微波	Shùzì wēibō	WBS
Digital microwave radio	数字微波传输设备	Shùzì wēibō chuánshū shèbèi	DMR
Digital microwave system	数字微波系统	Shùzì wēibō xìtǒng	DMS
Digital mobile radio	数字无线移动	Shùzì wúxiàn yídòng	DMR
Digital modularized radio	数字模块化无线电	Shùzì mókuàihuà wúxiàndiàn	DMR
Digital modulation	数字调制	Shùzì tiáozhì	
Digital modulator	数位调变器	Shùwèi tiáobiànqì	
Digital monochrome laser copy machine	单色激光数位影印机	Dānsè jīguāng shùwèi yǐngyìnjī	
Digital multiplex equipment	数字复用设备	Shùzì fùyòng shèbèi	
Digital multiplex hierarchy	数字复接体系	Shùzì fùjiē tǐxì	
Digital multiplex hierarchy	数字复用分级系统	Shùzì fùyòng fēnjí xìtǒng	
Digital multiplex hierarchy	数字复用系列	Shùzì fùyòng xìliè	
Digital multiplexer	数字复接器	Shùzì fùjiēqì	
Digital multiplexer	数字复用器	Shùzì fùyòngqì	
Digital multiplexing	数字复接	Shùzì fù jiē	
Digital multiplexing	数字复用	Shùzì fùyòng	
Digital multiscan II (video term)	数字式智能多频追踪	Shùzì-shì zhìnéng duōpín zhuīzōng	
Digital multi-wavelength transmission system	数字多波段传输系统	Shùzì duōbōduàn chuánshū xìtǒng	DWTS
Digital network	数字网	Shùzì wǎng	
Digital network architecture	数字网络体系结构	Shùzì wǎngluò tǐxì jiégòu	DNA
Digital network identification code	数字网标识码	Shùzì wǎng biāozhì mǎ	DNIC
Digital offset modulation	数字参差调制	Shùzì cēncī tiáozhì	
Digital on-screen display	同屏数字化显示	Tóngpíng shùzìhuà xiǎnshì	DOSD

Digital output	数字输出	Shùzì shūchū	DO
Digital packet network	数字分组网	Shùzì fēnzǔ wǎng	DPN
Digital paging system	数字式寻呼系统	Shùzì-shì xúnhū xìtǒng	
Digital patch unit	数字插入装置	Shùzì chārù zhuāngzhì	DPU
Digital path	数字通道	Shùzì tōngdào	
Digital path not provided signal	不提供数字通路信号	Bùtígōng shùzì tōnglù xìnhào	DPN
Digital phase lock loop	数字式锁相环	Shùzì-shì suǒxiàng huán	DPLL
Digital phase ramp feedback	数字相位斜波反馈	Shùzì xiàngwèi xiébō fǎnkuì	
Digital phase shifter	数字移相器	Shùzì yíxiàngqì	
Digital phase-locked loop	数字锁相环	Shùzì suǒxiāng huán	
Digital position	数字位置	Shùzì wèizhì	
Digital principal local exchange	数字式市内主交换机	Shùzì-shì shìnèi zhǔ jiāohuànjī	DPLE
Digital private branch exchange	数字式专用小交换机	Shùzì-shì zhuānyòng xiǎo jiāohuànjī	DPBX
Digital radio	数字无线电	Shùzì wúxiàndiàn	DR
Digital radio concentrator	数字无线电集中器	Shùzì wúxiàndiàn jízhōngqì	
Digital radio path	数字无线通道	Shùzì wúxiàn tōngdào	
Digital radio path	无线数字通道	Wúxiàn shùzì tōngdào	
Digital radio section	数字无线段	Shùzì wúxiàn duàn	
Digital radio section	无线数字段	Wúxiàn shùzì duàn	
Digital radio system	无线数字系统	Wúxiàn shùzì xìtǒng	
Digital ranging	数字测距	Shùzì cèjù	
Digital rate	数字速率	Shùzì sùlǜ	
Digital reference sequence	数字参考序列	Shùzì cānkǎo xùliè	DRS
Digital resolving	数字式分解	Shùzì-shì fēnjiě	
Digital rights management	数字权限管理	Shùzì quánxiàn guǎnlǐ	DRM
Digital satellite center	数字卫星中心	Shùzì wèixīng zhōngxīn	DSC
Digital satellite standard	数字卫星标准	Shùzì wèixīng biāozhǔn	DSS
Digital scene matching area correlation	数字式景象匹配区域相关制导	Shùzì-shì jǐngxiàng pǐpèi qūyù xiāngguān zhìdǎo	
Digital search tree	数字查找树	Shùzì cházhǎo shù	
Digital section level	数字段的级	Shùzì duànde jí	
Digital section or segment	数字段	Shùzì duàn	DS
Digital secure voice terminal	保密数字通信音频终端	Bǎomì shùzì tōngxìn yīnpín zhōngduān	DSVT
Digital segment extension	数字段拉远	Shùzì duàn lāyuǎn	
Digital selective calling system	数字选呼系统	Shùzì xuǎnhū xìtǒng	
Digital sense multiple access with collision detection	带碰撞检测的数字侦听多址访问	Dài pèngzhuàng jiǎncède shùzì zhēntīng duōzhǐ fǎngwèn	DSMA/CD
Digital sensor	数字传感器	Shùzì chuángǎnqì	
Digital sequence integrity	数字系列完整性	Shùzì xìliè wánzhěngxìng	
Digital service channel	数字公务通道	Shùzì gōngwù tōngdào	DSC
Digital service channels	数字业务信道	Shùzì yèwù xìndào	DSC
Digital service circuit	数字业务电路	Shùzì yèwù diànlù	DSC
Digital service unit	数字业务单元	Shùzì yèwù dānyuán	DSU
Digital service unit-radio	用户无线数字业务单元	Yònghù wúxiàn shùzì yèwù dānyuán	DSU-R
Digital signal	数字信号	Shùzì xìnhào	
Digital signal generater	数字信号发生器	Shùzì xìnhào fāshēngqì	

Digital signal processing	数字信号处理	Shùzì xìnhào chǔlǐ	DSP
Digital signal processor	数字信号处理器	Shùzì xìnhào chǔlǐqì	DSP
Digital signal receiver	数字信号接收器	Shùzì xìnhào jiēshōuqì	
Digital signaling	数字信令	Shùzì xìnlìng	
Digital signature (IPsec)	数字签名	Shùzì qiānmíng	
Digital signature algorithm	数字签名算法	Shùzì qiānmíng suànfǎ	DSA
Digital simulator computer system	数字模拟计算机系统	Shùzì mónǐ jìsuànjī xìtǒng	DSCS
Digital simultaneous voice and data (ITU-T Recommendation H.320)	声音和数据同时传输协议	Shēngyīn hé shùjù tóngshí chuánshū xiéyì	DSVD
Digital speech code	数字语音编码	Shùzì yǔyīn biānmǎ	
Digital speech interpolation	数字话音插空	Shùzì huàyīn chākōng	DSI
Digital speech interpolation	数字话音插入	Shùzì huàyīn chārù	DSI
Digital speech interpolation	数字语音插空	Shùzì yǔyīn chākōng	DSI
Digital speech interpolation	数字语音插值	Shùzì yǔyīn chāzhí	
Digital speech signal	数字话音信号	Shùzì huàyīn xìnhào	DSS
Digital staggered modulation	数字参差调制	Shùzì cēncī tiáozhì	
Digital standard 3 (3rd level digital standard transmission rate = 34Mbps)	三次群	Sāncì qún	DS-3
Digital standard 4 (4th digital standard rate =140Mbps)	四次群	Sìcì qún	DS-4
Digital standard one (lowest data rate = 2Mbps)	一次群	Yīcì qún	DS-1
Digital storage media - control command	数字存储媒体 - 控制命令	Shùzì cúnchǔ méitǐ-kòngzhì mìnglìng	DSM - CC
Digital storage media - control command, user-to-user	数字存储媒体 - 控制命令用户至用户	Shùzì cúnchǔ méitǐ-kòngzhì mìnglìng yònghù zhì yònghù	DSM-CC U-U
Digital storage media-control command	数字存储媒体-控制命令	Shùzì cúnchǔ méitǐ—kòngzhì mingling	DSM-CC
Digital subscriber controller	数字用户控制器	Shùzì yònghù kòngzhìqì	DSC
Digital subscriber line	数字用户线	Shùzì yònghù xiàn	DSL
Digital subscriber line access multiplexer	数字用户线接入复用器	Shùzì yònghù xiàn jiērù fùyòngqì	DSLAM
Digital subscriber line board	数字用户电路板	Shùzì yònghù diànlù bǎn	DSL
Digital subscriber loop	数字用户环路	Shùzì yònghù huánlù	DSL
Digital subscriber loop carrier	数字用户环路载波	Shùzì yònghù huánlù zàibō	SHZ
Digital subscriber signaling no1	1 号数字用户信令	Yihào shùzì yònghù xìnlìng	DSS1
Digital subscriber signaling system no. one	数字用户信令系统 1	Shùzì yònghù xìnlìng xìtǒng 1	DSS1
Digital subscriber signaling system one	一号数字用户信令系统	Yīhào shùzì yònghù xìnlìng xìtǒng	DSS1
Digital subscriber voice terminal	数字通信用户音频终端	Shùzì tōngxìn yònghù yīnpín zhōngduān	DSVT
Digital sum	数字和	Shùzì hé	
Digital sum variation	数字和之差	Shùzì hé zhīchà	
Digital sweep	数字式扫描	Shùzì-shì sǎomiáo	
Digital switch network	数字交换网络	Shùzì jiāohuàn wǎngluò	DSN
Digital switching	数字交换	Shùzì jiāohuàn	
Digital switching delay	数字交换时延	Shùzì jiāohuàn shíyán	
Digital switching node	数字交换节点	Shùzì jiāohuàn jiédiǎn	
Digital switching system	数字交换系统	Shùzì jiāohuàn xìtǒng	DSS
Digital synchronization	数字同步	Shùzì tóngbù	DS
Digital tandem	数字汇接局	Shùzì huìjiējú	DTm
Digital telecommunication circuit	数字电信电路	Shùzì diànxìn diànlù	
Digital television display system	数子电视显示系统	Shùzi diànshì xiǎnshì xìtǒng	DTDS
Digital terminal	数字终端	Shùzì zhōngduān	SZ

Digital termination multiplex unit	数字终端多路复用装置	Shùzì zhōngduān duōlù fùyòng zhuāngzhì	DTMU
Digital terrain model	数字地形模型	Shùzì dìxíng móxíng	DTM
Digital theater system	数字影院系统	Shùzì yǐngyuàn xìtǒng	DTS
Digital time assignment speech interpolation	数字时间分配语言内插入	Shùzì shíjiān fēnpèi yǔyán nèichārù	DTASI
Digital time delayer	数字延时器	Shùzì yánshíqì	
Digital to analog (D/A) conversion	数模变换	Shù mó biànhuàn	
Digital to analog conversion daughter board assembly	数模转换子集成板	Shù mó zhuǎnhuàn zǐjíchéng bǎn	DACD
Digital to analog converter	数模传换器	Shù mó chuánhuànqì	DAC
Digital to analog converter	数模转换器	Shù mó zhuǎnhuànqì	DAC
Digital transmission	数字传输	Shùzì chuánshū	
Digital transmission channel	数字传输通路	Shùzì chuánshū tōnglù	
Digital transmission channel	数字传输信道	Shùzì chuánshū xìndào	
Digital transmission link	数字传输链路	Shùzì chuánshū liànlù	
Digital transparency	数字透明性	Shùzì tòumíngxìng	
Digital trunk back panel	数字中继后面板	Shùzì zhōngjì hòumian bǎn	DTBP
Digital trunk board (module)	数字中继板(块)	Shùzì zhōngjì bǎn (kuài)	DTM
Digital trunk interface	数字中继接口	Shùzì zhōngjì jiēkǒu	DTI
Digital trunk module	数字中继板	Shùzì zhōngjì bǎn	DTM
Digital trunk/echo canceler module	数字中继/回波抑制模块	Shùzì zhōngjì/huíbō yìzhì mókuài	DT/ECM
Digital trunked radio	数字集群通信系统	Shùzì jíqún tōngxìn xìtǒng	
Digital unit	数字单元	Shùzì dānyuán	DU
Digital unit back board	数字单元后面板	Shùzì dānyuán hòumian bǎn	DUBB
Digital unit backplane board	数字单元底版	Shùzì dānyuán dǐbǎn	DUBB-A
Digital up-converter	数字上变频	Shùzì shàngbiànpín	DUC
Digital video	数字视频	Shùzì shìpín	DV
Digital video broadcast	数字电视广播	Shùzì diànshì guǎngbō	DVB
Digital video broadcast	数字视频广播	Shùzì shìpín guǎngbō	DVB
Digital video disk	数字视频光盘	Shùzì shìpín guāngpán	DVD
Digital video disk	数字式影视光盘	Shùzì-shì yǐngshì guāngpán	DVD
Digital video interface	数字视频接口	Shùzì shìpín jiēkǒu	DVI
Digital video recorder	数字录像机	Shùzì lùxiàngjī	DVR
Digital video services	数字视频业务	Shùzì shìpín yèwù	
Digital watermarking	数字水印	Shùzì shuǐyìn	
Digital wrapper	数字包封	Shùzì bāofēng	
Digital wrapper	数字封装器	Shùzì fēngzhuāngqì	
Digital/analog conversion	数字模拟转换	Shùzì mónǐ zhuǎnhuàn	D/A
Digital/analog converter	数/模转换器	Shù/mó zhuǎnhuànqì	D/A
Digital-advanced mobile phone system	数字式现代移动电话系统	Shùzì-shì xiàndài yídòng diànhuà xìtǒng	D-AMPS
Digital-analog (digilog) channel	数模信道	Shù mó xìndào	
Digital-analog (digilog) circuit	数模电路	Shù mó diànlù	
Digitally coded voice	数字编码语音	Shùzì biānmǎ yǔyīn	DCV
Digitally compressed direct satellite broadcast	数字压缩卫星直播	Shùzì yāsuō wèixīng zhíbō	DTH
Digitally controlled delta modulation	数字控制增量调制	Shùzì kòngzhì zēngliàng tiáozhì	DCDM
Digitial scale	数字比例尺	Shùzì bǐlìchǐ	
Digitize	数字化	Shùzìhuà	
Digitizer logic unit	数字化逻辑单元	Shùzìhuà luóji dānyuán	DLU

Digitizer; tablet	数字化仪	Shùzìhuàyí	
Digitizing capture device	数字化采集设备	Shùzìhuà cǎijí shèbèi	
Dihedral corner reflector	双面角形反射器	Shuāngmiàn jiǎoxíng fǎnshè qì	
Dilatational wave	疏密波	Shūmìbō	
Dilation (in image coding)	膨胀	Péngzhàng	
Dilution of precision	精度的降额	Jīngdùde jiàng'é	DOP
Dimension	维度	Wéidù	
Dimension hierarchy	维度层次结构	Wéidù céngcì jiégòu	
Dimension table	维度表	Wéidù biǎo	
Dimensional analysis	量刚分析	Liànggāng fēnxī	
Dimensionality of spatial data	空间数据维度	Kōngjiān shùjù wéidù	
Dimensionality reduction	维度约简技术	Wéidù yuējiǎn jìshù	
Diminishing increment sort	随小增量排序	Suíxiǎo zēngliàng páixù	
Diode	二极管	Èrjíguǎn	D
Diode laser	二极管激光器	Èrjíguǎn jīguāngqì	
Diode switch	二极管开关	Èrjíguǎn kāiguān	DS
Diode transistor logic circuit	二机管晶体管逻辑电路	Erjīguǎn jīngtǐguǎn luóji diànlù	DTL
Dip slope	运动盘	Yùndòng pán	
Diplexer	双工器	Shuānggōngqì	DPX
Diplexer (of an antenna)	双路复用器	Shuānglù fùyòngqì	
Dipole antenna	偶极天线	Ǒují tiānxiàn	
Dipole antenna	偶极子天线	Ǒujízi tiānxiàn	DA
Dipole antenna with feed points displaced transverse to dipole axis	馈电点沿轴的横向移动的偶极天线	Kuìdiàn diǎn yán zhóude héngxiàng yídòngde ǒují tiānxiàn	DAFDTA
Dipole flat plane (antenna)	偶极子平面(天线)	Ǒujízi píngmiàn (tiānxiàn)	DFP
Dipole-curtain antenna	偶极子-幕形天线	Ǒujízi-mùxíng tiānxiàn	
Dipole-disk antenna	偶极子盘形天线	Ǒujízi pánxíng tiānxiàn	DDA
Dipole-disk feed for rear-feed	后馈带反射盘的振子馈电器	Hòukuì dài fǎnshè pánde zhènzǐ kuìdiànqì	
Direct access	直接接入	Zhíjiē jiērù	
Direct access (to memory)	直接存取	Zhíjiē cúnqǔ	
Direct access communication channel	直接存取通信信道	Zhíjiē cúnqǔ tōngxìn xìndào	DACC
Direct access connection element	直接接入连接单元	Zhíjiē jiērù liánjiē dānyuán	
Direct access data channel	直接存取数据通道	Zhíjiē cúnqǔ shùjù tōngdào	DADC
Direct access file	直接存取文件	Zhíjiē cúnqǔ wénjiàn	
Direct access method	直接存取法	Zhíjiē cúnqǔ fǎ	DAM
Direct access storage	直接存取存储器	Zhíjiē cúnqǔ cúnchǔqì	
Direct action	正作用	Zhèng zuòyòng	
Direct address	直接地址	Zhíjiē dìzhǐ	
Direct adjacent channel interference	直接相邻信道干扰	Zhíjiē xiānglín xìndào gānrǎo	DACI
Direct analog storage technology	直接模拟存储技术	Zhíjiē mónǐ cúnchǔ jìshù	DAST
Direct broadcast satellite	直播卫星	Zhíbō wèixīng	DBS
Direct broadcast satellite	直接广播卫星	Zhíjiē guǎngbō wèixīng	DBS
Direct broadcast satellite PC	人造卫星直接广播式 PC	Rénzào wèixīng zhíjiē guǎngbō shì PC	DBS-PC
Direct broadcasting by satellite	卫星直播	Wèixīng zhíbō	DBS
Direct burial	直接埋设	Zhíjiē máishè	DB

Direct buried cable	直埋缆	Zhímái lǎn	
Direct buried fiber optic cable	直埋式光缆	Zhímái-shì guānglǎn	
Direct cable connect	直接电缆连接	Zhíjiē diànlǎn liánjiē	DCC
Direct call	直接呼叫	Zhíjiē hūjiào	
Direct connect	直接连接	Zhíjiē liánjiē	
Direct contact	直接接触	Zhíjiē jiēchù	
Direct control	直接控制	Zhíjiē kòngzhì	
Direct current	直流	Zhíliú	DC
Direct current (DC) secondary interface	二次 DC 接口	Èrcì DC jiēkǒu	
Direct current (DC) secondary voltage	二次 DC 电压	Èrcì DC diànyā	
Direct current amplifier	直流放大器	Zhíliú fàngdàqì	
Direct current resistance	直流电阻	Zhíliú diànzǔ	
Direct current resonant charging	直流谐振充电	Zhíliú xiézhèn chōngdiàn	
Direct current resonant diode charge	直流谐振二极管充电	Zhíliú xiézhèn èrjíguǎn chōngdiàn	
Direct current signaling	直流信令	Zhíliú xìnlìng	
Direct current transmission	直流传输	Zhíliú chuánshū	
Direct damage	直接被害	Zhíjiē bèihài	
Direct detection	直接检测	Zhíjiē jiǎncè	
Direct dialing in	直接拨号	Zhíjiē bōhào	DDI
Direct dialing in	直接拨入	Zhíjiē bōrù	DDI
Direct dialing overseas	直接对外拨号	Zhíjiē duìwài bōhào	DDO
Direct dialing system	直接拨号系统	Zhíjiē bōhào xìtǒng	DDS
Direct dialing telephone system	直拨电话系统	Zhíbō diànhuà xìtǒng	DDTS
Direct digital (frequency) synthesizer	直接数字频率合成器	Zhíjiē shùzì pínlǜ héchéngqì	DDS
Direct digital control	直接数字控制	Zhíjiē shùzì kòngzhì	DDC
Direct digital controller	直接数字控制器	Zhíjiē shùzì kòngzhìqì	DDC
Direct digital input	直接数字输入	Zhíjiē shùzì shūrù	
Direct digital synthesizer	直接数字式频率合成器	Zhíjiē shùzìshì pínlǜ héchéngqì	DDS
Direct distance dial network	直接长途拨号网	Zhíjiē chángtú bōhào wǎng	
Direct distance dialing	长途直拨	Chángtú zhíbō	DDD
Direct distance dialing	远程直接拨号	Yuǎnchéng zhíjiē bōhào	DDD
Direct distance dialing	直接通话拨号	Zhíjiē tōnghuà bōhào	DDD
Direct distribution	直接分配	Zhíjiē fēnpèi	
Direct evaluation method	直接评价法	Zhíjiē píngjià fǎ	
Direct frequency modulation	直接调频	Zhíjiē tiáopín	DFM
Direct frequency spread spectrum code division multiple access	直接扩频的码分多址	Zhíjiē kuòpínde mǎfēn duōzhǐ	DF-SS-CDMA
Direct hosting	直接宿主	Zhíjiē sùzhǔ	
Direct injection burner	直接注入燃烧器	Zhíjiē zhùrù ránshāoqì	
Direct injector	直流进样器	Zhíliú jìnyàngqì	
Direct intermediate frequency (IF) sampling receiver (for GSM/EDGE base station system)	直接中频数字化接收机	Zhíjiē zhōngpín shùzìhuà jiēshōujī	
Direct Internet message encapsulation	直接因特网消息封装	Zhíjiē Yīntèwǎng xiāoxi fēngzhuāng	DIME
Direct inward dialing	呼入直拨到分机用户	Hūrù zhíbō dào fēnjī yònghù	DID
Direct inward dialing	直接拨入	Zhíjiē bōrù	DID
Direct inward dialing	直接中继方式	Zhíjiē zhōngjì fāngshì	DID
Direct melt method (fiber optic mfg)	直接熔融法	Zhíjiē róngróng fǎ	DM

Direct memory access	直接存储器存取	Zhíjiē cúnchǔqì cúnqǔ	DMA
Direct memory access	直接内存存取	Zhíjiē nèicún cúnqǔ	DMA
Direct memory access	直接内存访问	Zhíjiē nèicún fǎngwèn	DMA
Direct memory access channel	直接存储器存取通道	Zhíjiē cúnchǔqì cúnqǔ tōngdào	DMAC
Direct memory access request	直接存储器存取请求	Zhíjiē cúnchǔqì cúnqǔ qǐngqiú	DMAR
Direct memory access transfer	直接存储器存取传送	Zhíjiē cúnchǔqì cúnqǔ chuánsòng	DMAT
Direct memory address	直接存储器地址	Zhíjiē cúnchǔqì dìzhǐ	DMA
Direct memory execute	直接内存执行	Zhíjiē nèicún zhíxíng	DME
Direct mounting gauge	直接安装压力表	Zhíjiē ānzhuāng yālìbiǎo	
Direct object	直接对象	Zhíjiē duìxiàng	
Direct orbit (of a satellite)	顺行轨道	Shùnxíng guǐdào	
Direct outward dialing	出局直接拨号	Chūjú zhíjiē bōhào	DOD
Direct outward dialing	直接拨出	Zhíjiē bōchū	DOD
Direct outward dialing one	一次拨号音	Yīcì bōhào yīn	DOD-1
Direct position	直接位置	Zhíjiē wèizhì	
Direct probe inlet	直接探头进样	Zhíjiē tàntóu jìnyàng	
Direct RAMbus DRAM	直接 RAMbus 内存	Zhíjiē Rambus nèicún	DRDRAM
Direct reception (US); straight reception (UK)	直接接收	Zhíjiē jiēshōu	
Direct rendering infrastructure (video term)	基层直接渲染	Jīcéng zhíjiē xuànrǎn	DIR
Direct response mode	直接响应模式	Zhíjiē xiǎngyìng móshì	
Direct route	直达线路	Zhídá xiànlù	
Direct sequence code division multiple access	直接序列码分多址	Zhíjiē xùliè mǎfēn duōzhǐ	DS-CDMA
Direct sequence spread spectrum	直接时序扩展频谱	Zhíjiē shíxù kuòzhǎn pínpǔ	DSSS
Direct sequence spread spectrum	直接序列扩频	Zhíjiē xùliè kuòpín	DSSS
Direct sequence spread spectrum	直接序列展频技术	Zhíjiē xùliè zhǎnpín jìshù	DSSS
Direct sequence spread spectrum code division multiple access	直接序列扩频码分多址接入	Zhíjiē xùliè kuòpín mǎfēn duōzhǐ jiērù	DS-SS-CDMA
Direct sound	直正声	Zhízheng shēng	
Direct spread spectrum	直接扩频	Zhíjiē kuòpín	DS
Direct stream digital	直接数字信号流	Zhíjiē shùzì xìnhào liú	DSD
Direct submission	直接提交	Zhíjiē tíjiāo	
Direct synchronization (in CORBA)	直接同步协议	Zhíjiē tóngbù xiéyì	DS
Direct to home	直接至家庭	Zhíjiē zhì jiātíng	DTH
Direct transfer application part	直接传递应用部分	Zhíjiē chuándì yìngyòng bùfen	DTAP
Direct transfer application part	直接转换应用部分	Zhíjiē zhuǎnhuàn yìngyòng bùfen	DTAP
Direct transmission application part	直接传输应用部分	Zhíjiē chuánshū yìngyòng bùfen	DTAP
Direct transmission restoration	直接传输恢复	Zhíjiē chuánshū huīfù	
Direct user	直接用户	Zhíjiē yònghù	
Direct vision prism	直视棱镜	Zhíshì léngjìng	
Direct wave	直达波	Zhídá bō	
Direct wave	直接波	Zhíjiē bō	
Direct X texture compression (video term)	DirectX 纹理压缩	DirectX wénlǐ yāsuō	DXTC
Direct-coupled amplifier	直接耦合放大器	Zhíjiē ǒuhé fàngdàqì	
Directed acyclic graph	有向无环图	Yǒuxiàng wúhuán tú	DAG
Directed acyclic graph	有向无循环图	Yǒuxiàng wúxúnhuán tú	DAG
Directed edge	有向线	Yǒuxiàng xiàn	

Directed energy weapon	定向能武器	Dìngxiàng néng wǔqì	DEW
Directed face	有向面	Yǒuxiàng miàn	
Directed graph	有向图	Yǒuxiàng tú	
Directed jamming	引导式干扰	Yǐndǎo-shì gānrǎo	
Directed link	有向连接	Yǒuxiàng liánjiē	
Directed network	有向网络	Yǒuxiàng wǎngluò	
Directed retry	引导重试	Yǐndǎo chóngshì	
Directed solid	有向体	Yǒuxiàng tǐ	
Directed tree	定向树	Dìngxiàng shù	
Direction	指引	Zhǐyǐn	
Direction angle (GIS)	方向角	Fāngxiàng jiǎo	
Direction division multiplexing	方向分割复用	Fāngxiàng fēngē fùyòng	DDM
Direction of arrival	到达方向	Dàodá fāngxiàng	DOA
Direction of arrival	入射方向	Rùshè fāngxiàng	DOA
Direction of polarization (in a waveguide)	极化方向	Jíhuà fāngxiàng	
Direction of propagation	传播方向	Chuánbō fāngxiàng	
Direction of propagation of energy (in a transmission line)	能量传播方向	Néngliàng chuánbō fāngxiàng	
Directional	指向性	Zhǐxiàng-xìng	
Directional (antenna) array	定向天线阵	Dìngxiàng tiānxiàn zhèn	DA
Directional antenna	定向天线	Dìngxiàng tiānxiàn	
Directional carrier sense multiple access	定向载波控制多路存取	Dìngxiàng zàibō kòngzhì duōlù cúnqǔ	D-CSMA
Directional coupler	定向耦合器	Dìngxiàng ǒuhéqì	
Directional filter	方向滤波器	Fāngxiàng lǜbōqì	
Directional gradient vector	方向梯度矢量	Fāngxiàng tīdù shǐliàng	
Directional gyroscope position	定向陀螺仪位置	Dìngxiàng tuóluóyí wèizhì	DGP
Directional light	方向性光源	Fāngxiàngxìng guāngyuán	
Directional mutual conductance	定向互导	Dìngxiàng hùdǎo	
Directional null	方向零点	Fāngxiàng língdiǎn	
Directional response characteristics	指向性响应特性	Zhǐxiàng-xìng xiǎngyìng tèxìng	DRC
Directionality	方向性	Fāngxiàngxìng	DL
Directional-null antenna	方向零点天线	Fāngxiàng língdiǎn tiānxiàn	
Direction-control valve	方向控制阀	Fāngxiàng kòngzhì fá	
Directive (in programming)	指示符	Zhǐshì fú	
Directive gain	方向性增益	Fāngxiàngxìng zēngyì	
Directivity (of a directional coupler)	方向性	Fāngxiàngxìng	
Directivity of an antenna	方向性系数	Fāngxiàngxìng xìshù	
Directly dialed outgoing call	直接拨号去话呼叫	Zhíjiē bōhào qùhuà hūjiào	DDOC
Director element (of an antenna)	引向单元	Yǐnxiàng dānyuán	
Director element (of an antenna)	引向器	Yǐnxiàngqì	
Director radar	引导雷达	Yǐndǎo léidá	
Directory (as a list of computer files)	目录	Mùlù	
Directory (as the telephone book)	号码簿	Hàomǎbù	
Directory access control domain	号码簿访问控制域	Hàomǎbù fǎngwèn kòngzhì yù	DACD
Directory access protocol	号码簿访问协议	Hàomǎbù fǎngwèn xiéyì	DAP
Directory access protocol	目录访问协议	Mùlù fǎngwèn xiéyì	
Directory assistance and messaging system	电话查号与通告系统	Diànhuà cháhào yǔ tōnggào xìtǒng	DAMSYS

Directory entry	号码簿登记项	Hàomǎbù dēngjì xiàng	
Directory entry	号码簿登录项	Hàomǎbù dēnglù xiàng	
Directory information base	号码簿信息库	Hàomǎbù xìnxīkù	DIB
Directory information tree	号码簿信息树	Hàomǎbù xìnxī shù	DIT
Directory information tree	目录信息树	Mùlù xìnxī shù	DIT
Directory management domain	号码簿管理域	Hàomǎbù guǎnlǐ yù	DMD
Directory name	号码簿名	Hàomǎbù míng	
Directory name service	查号业务	Cháhào yèwù	DNS
Directory number	电话号码	Diànhuà hàomǎ	DN
Directory number	号码簿号码	Hàomǎbù hàomǎ	DN
Directory replication	目录复制	Mùlù fùzhì	
Directory schema	号码簿体制	Hàomǎbù tǐzhì	
Directory service	目录服务	Mùlù fúwù	
Directory structure	目录结构	Mùlù jiégòu	
Directory system	号码簿系统	Hàomǎbù xìtǒng	DS
Directory system	目录服务系统	Mùlù fúwù xìtǒng	DS
Directory system agent	号码簿系统代理	Hàomǎbù xìtǒng dàilǐ	DSA
Directory system agent (program)	目录系统代理(程序)	Mùlù xìtǒng dàilǐ (chéngxù)	DSA
Directory system protocol	号码簿系统协议	Hàomǎbù xìtǒng xiéyì	DSP
Directory tree	目录树	Mùlù shù	
Directory user	号码簿用户	Hàomǎbù yònghù	
Directory user agent	号码簿用户代理	Hàomǎbù yònghù dàilǐ	DUA
Directory user agent	目录用户代理	Mùlù yònghù dàilǐ	DUA
Direct-sequence code division multiple access	直扩码分多址	Zhíkuò mǎfēn duōzhǐ	DS-CDMA
Direct-view storage tube	直观贮存管	Zhíguān zhùcún guǎn	
Dirty page (for database)	脏页	Zàng yè	
Dirty read (for database)	脏读	Zàng dú	
Disable	止能	Zhǐnéng	
Disable, disabled	禁用	Jīnyòng	
Disabled state; outage	不能工作状态	Bùnéng gōngzuò zhuàngtài	
Disabled time	不能工作时间	Bùnéng gōngzuò shíjiān	
Disassembler	反汇编器	Fǎnhuìbiānqì	
Disassembly	分装	Fēnzhuāng	
Disaster plan	灾难应急计划	Zāinàn yìngjí jìhuà	
Disc attenuator	盘式衰减器	Pánshì shuāijiǎnqì	
Discard eligibility	丢弃指示	Diūqì zhǐshì	DE
Discard eligibility (in frame relay)	丢弃许可	Diūqì xǔkě	DE
Discard eligibility (in frame relay)	丢失指示	Diūshī zhǐshì	DE
Discard eligible	可丢弃的	Kědiūqìde	
Discharge	放电	Fàngdiàn	
Discharge characteristic curve	放电特性曲线	Fàngdiàn tèxìng qūxiàn	
Discharge coefficient	流出系数	Liúchū xìshù	
Discharge depth	放电深度	Fàngdiàn shēndù	
Discharge gauging	流量观测站	Liúliàng guāncèzhàn	
Discharge lamp	放电灯	Fàngdiàn dēng	
Discharge measurement	流量观测	Liúliàng guāncè	

Discharge rate	放电率	Fàngdiànlǜ	
Discharge voltage	放电电压	Fàngdiàn diànyā	
Discone antenna	盘锥形天线	Pánzhuīxíng tiānxiàn	
Disconnect	拆开	Chāikāi	DISC
Disconnect	拆线	Chāixiàn	
Disconnect	断开	Duànkāi	DISC
Disconnect	断开连接	Duànkāi liánjiē	
Disconnect	断连	Duànlián	DISC
Disconnect	切断	Qiēduàn	DISC
Disconnect end of transmission	传输结束断开	Chuánshū jiéshù duànkāi	DEOT
Disconnect forward connection	切断前向连接	Qiēduàn qiánxiàng liánjiē	DFC
Disconnect mode	断连模式	Duànlián móshì	
Disconnected	断开的	Duànkāide	
Disconnected mode	断开方式	Duànkāi fāngshì	DM
Disconnecting switch	切断开关	Qiēduàn kāiguān	DS
Discontinous transmission	间断传输	Jiànduàn chuánshū	DTX
Discontinuous interference	不连续干扰	Bù liánxù gānrǎo	
Discontinuous interference	非连续干扰	Fēiliánxù gānrǎo	
Discontinuous reception	非连续接收	Fēiliánxù jiēshōu	DRX
Discontinuous reception (mechanism)	不连续接收（机制）	Bùliánxù jiēshōu (jīzhì)	DRX
Discontinuous transmission	非连续传输	Fēiliánxù chuánshū	DTX
Discontinuous transmission	非连续发射	Fēiliánxù fāshè	DTX
Discontinuous transmission	非连续发信	Fēiliánxù fāxìn	DTX
Discontinuous transmission (mechanism)	不连续发送（机制）	Bùliánxù fāsòng (jīzhì)	DTX
Discontinuous transmission permission	非连续发射允许	Fēiliánxù fāshè yǔnxǔ	
Discordancy test	不一致测试	Bùyīzhì cèshì	
Discovery complete	发现完成	Fāxiàn wánchéng	
Discrete address	离散地址	Lísàn dìzhǐ	DA
Discrete address communication system	离散地址通信系统	Lísàn dìzhǐ tōngxìn xìtǒng	DACS
Discrete component tester (semiconductor mfg)	分散测试系统	Fēnsàn cèshì xìtǒng	
Discrete control system	离散控制系统	Lísàn kòngzhì xìtǒng	
Discrete cosine transform	离散余弦变换	Lísàn yúxián biànhuàn	DCT
Discrete data	离散数据	Lísàn shùjù	
Discrete feature	离散特征	Lísàn tèzhēng	
Discrete Fourier transform	离散傅立叶变换	Lísàn fù-lì-yè biànhuàn	DFT
Discrete Fourier transform	离散付里叶变换	Lísàn fù-lǐ-yè biànhuàn	
Discrete fourier transform	离散傅氏变换	Lísàn fù-shì biànhuàn	DFT
Discrete logarithm	离散对数	Lísàn duìshù	
Discrete logarithm problem	离散对数问题	Lísàn duìshù wèntí	DLP
Discrete memoryless channel	离散无记忆信道	Lísàn wújìyì xìndào	DMC
Discrete multitone	不连续多基频模式	Bùliánxù duōjīpín móshì	DMT
Discrete multitone	离散多音	Lísàn duōyīn	DMT
Discrete multitone	离散多载波	Lísàn duōzàibō	DMT
Discrete signal	离散信号	Lísàn xìnhào	
Discrete wavelet multiTone	离散小波多音	Lísàn xiǎobō duō yīn	DWMT
Discretely timed signal	时间离散信号	Shíjiān lísàn xìnhào	

Discrete-time-pulse-frequency modulation	离散时间脉冲频率调制	Lísàn shíjiān màichōng pínlǜ tiáozhì	DPFM
Discretionary access control (IPsec)	自主访问控制	Zìzhǔ fǎngwèn kòngzhì	
Discretionary access control (Linux)	自主存取控制	Zìzhǔ cúnqǔ kòngzhì	DAC
Discretionary access control list	任意访问控制列表	Rènyì fǎngwèn kòngzhì lièbiǎo	DACL
Discretionary access control list	自由访问控制列表	Zìyóu fǎngwèn kòngzhì lièbiǎo	DACL
Discretization	离散化	Lísàn-huà	
Discriminating selector	鉴别选择器	Jiànbié xuǎnzéqì	
Discrimination ratio (of an antenna between two received waves)	分辨率	Fēnbiànlǜ	
Discriminator	鉴别程序	Jiànbié chéngxù	
Discriminator input object	鉴别程序输入客体	Jiànbié chéngxù shūrù kètǐ	
Discriminator sensitivity	鉴相灵敏度	Jiànxiāng língmǐndù	
Discussion group	讨论组	Tǎolùn zǔ	
DiscWizard	磁盘控制软件	Cípán kòngzhì ruǎnjiàn	
Disengage confirm	脱离确认	Tuōlí quèrèn	DCF
Disengage confirmed	退出确认	Tuìchū quèrèn	DCF
Disengage reject	脱离拒绝	Tuōlí jùjué	DRJ
Disengage rejected	退出拒绝	Tuìchū jùjué	DRJ
Disengage request	退出请求	Tuìchū qǐngqiú	DRQ
Disengage request	脱离请求	Tuōlí qǐngqiú	DRQ
Disk	盘	Pán	
Disk block sub-allocation	磁盘块再分配	Cípán kuài zàifēnpèi	
Disk dispatch arithmetic	磁盘调度算法	Cípán diàodù suànfǎ	
Disk jacket, disk sleeve	软盘外套	Ruǎnpán wàitào	
Disk mapping	磁盘映射	Cípán yìngshè	
Disk mirroring	磁盘镜像	Cípán jìngxiàng	
Disk operating system	磁盘操作系统	Cípán cāozuò xìtǒng	DOS
Disk space	磁盘空间	Cípán kōngjiān	
Disk storage	磁盘存贮	Cípán cúnzhù	
Disk storage device	磁盘存储器	Cípán cúnchǔqì	DSD
Disk unit	磁盘单元	Cípán dānyuán	DKU
Disk unit back panel	磁盘单元后面板	Cípán dānyuán hòumian bǎn	DKBP
Dislocation	位错	Wèicuò	
Dismount	卸除	Xièchú	
Dispatch	分派	Fēnpài	
Dispatch	派发	Pàifā	
Dispatch (program)	调度（程序）	Diàodù (chéngxù)	
Dispatch desk	调度台	Diàodùtái	
Dispatch identifier	分派标识符	Fēnpài biāozhì fú	DISPID
Dispatch routing	派遣路由	Pàiqiǎn lùyóu	
Dispatch station controller	调度台控制器	Diàodùtái kòngzhìqì	DCS
Dispatch telephone	调度电话	Diàodù diànhuà	D
Dispatcher	调度器	Diàodùqì	
Dispersant (in SMT)	分散剂	Fēnsànjì	
Dispersed wave	分散性波动	Fēnsàn-xìng bōdòng	
Dispersion	分散	Fēnsàn	
Dispersion	色散	Sèsàn	

Dispersion accommodation	色散容纳	Sèsàn róngnà	DA
Dispersion accommodation	色散容纳技术	Sèsàn róngnà jìshù	DA
Dispersion accommodation	色散调节	Sèsàn tiáojié	DA
Dispersion coefficient	色散系数	Sèsàn xìshù	
Dispersion compensation fiber	色散补偿光纤	Sèsàn bǔcháng guāngxiān	DCF
Dispersion compensation module	色散补偿模块	Sèsàn bǔcháng mókuài	DCM
Dispersion compensation single mode optical fiber	色散补偿单模光纤	Sèsàn bǔcháng dānmó guāngxiān	DCSM
Dispersion curve	分散曲线	Fēnsàn qūxiàn	
Dispersion dose	散射剂量	Sǎnshè jìliàng	
Dispersion filter	色散滤波器	Sèsàn lǜbōqì	
Dispersion flattened optical fiber	色散平坦光纤	Sèsàn píngtǎn guāngxiān	DFF
Dispersion flattened single mode optical fiber	色散平坦单模光纤	Sèsàn píngtǎn dānmó guāngxiān	DFSM
Dispersion managed fiber	色散管理光纤	Sèsàn guǎnlǐ guāngxiān	DMF
Dispersion multitone	离散多音	Lísàn duōyīn	DMT
Dispersion of electromagnetic wave	电磁波色射	Diàncíbō sèshè	
Dispersion power	色散本领	Sèsàn běnlǐng	
Dispersion slope compensating fiber	色散斜率补偿光纤	Sèsàn xiélǜ bǔcháng guāngxiān	DSCF
Dispersion supported transmission	色散支持传输	Sèsàn zhīchí chuánshū	DST
Dispersion-shift fiber	色散移位光纤	Sèsàn yíwèi guāngxiān	DSF
Dispersion-shifted fiber optic cable	色散位移光缆	Sèsàn wèiyí guānglǎn	
Dispersion-shifted optical fiber	色散漂移光纤	Sèsàn piāoyí guāngxiān	DSF
Dispersion-shifted optical fiber	色散位移光纤	Sèsàn wèiyí guāngxiān	DSF
Dispersion-shifted single mode optical fiber	色散位移单模光纤	Sèsàn wèiyí dānmó guāngxiān	DSSM
Dispersive crystal	分光晶体	Fēnguāng jīngtǐ	
Dispersive Rayleigh wave	分散性瑞利波	Fēnsàn-xìng Ruì-lì bō	
Displaced phase center antenna	相移中心天线	Xiàngyí zhōngxīn tiānxiàn	DPCA
Displacement	位移	Wèiyí	DISP
Displacement adder	移位加法器	Yíwèi jiāfǎqì	Da
Displacement code	位移码	Wèiyí mǎ	
Displacement response spectrum	位移反应谱	Wèiyí fǎnyìng pǔ	
Displacement vector	位移向量	Wèiyí xiàngliàng	
Display console	显示控制台	Xiǎnshì kòngzhìtái	DC
Display data channel (video term)	显示数据通道	Xiǎnshì shùjù tōngdào	DDC
Display generating software	显示发生软件	Xiǎnshì fāshēng ruǎnjiàn	DGS
Display panel	显示面板	Xiǎnshì miànbǎn	
Display power management signalling	显示能源管理信号	Xiǎnshì néngyuán guǎnlǐ xìnhào	DPMS
Display support software	显示支援软件	Xiǎnshì zhīyuán ruǎnjiàn	DSS
Display technology	显示技术	Xiǎnshì jìshù	
Display, (computer) monitor	显示	Xiǎnshì	
Disruptive discharge dielectric breakdown	介质击穿	Jièzhì jīchuān	
Disruptive technology	爆发性技术	Bàofāxìng jìshù	
Dissemination of information	信息传达	Xìnxī chuándá	
Dissipation factor	耗散因数	Hàosàn yīnshù	DF
Distance amplitude compensation	距离振幅补偿	Jùlí zhènfú bǔcháng	
Distance amplitude curve	距离振幅曲线	Jùlí zhènfú qūxiàn	
Distance learning	远程教学	Yuǎnchéng jiàoxué	

Distance learning	远程教育	Yuǎnchéng jiàoyù	
Distance measure	距离度量	Jùlí dùliàng	
Distance vector multicast routing protocol	距离矢量组播路由协议	Jùlí shǐliàng zǔbō lùyóu xiéyì	DVMRP
Distance vector multicast routing protocol	距离向量多点广播路由选择协议	Jùlí xiàngliàng duō diǎn guǎngbō lùyóu xuǎnzé xiéyì	DVMRP
Distance vector multicast routing protocol	距离向量组播路由协议	Jùlí xiàngliàng zǔbō lùyóu xiéyì	DVMRP
Distance vector routing algorithm	距离矢量路由算法	Jùlí shǐliàng lùyóu suànfǎ	
Distance vector routing algorithm	距离向量路由选择算法	Jùlí xiàngliàng lùyóu xuǎnzé suànfǎ	
Distance-decay function	距离衰减函数	Jùlí shuāijiǎn hánshù	
Distant station connected	远端站连接	Yuǎnduān zhàn liánjiē	DSC
Distant surveillance	远距离监视	Yuǎnjùlí jiānshì	DS
Distinguished encoding rules	唯一编码规则	Wéiyī biānmǎ guīzé	DER
Distinguished name	辨别名	Biànbiémíng	
Distinguished name	可识别名	Kěshíbié míng	DN
Distinguished name	识别名	Shíbié míng	DN
Distortion	失真度	Shīzhēndù	
Distortion (of a signal)	失真	Shīzhēn	
Distortion delay	变形时延	Biànxíng shíyán	
Distortion delay	失真时延	Shīzhēn shíyán	
Distortion detection loop	失真检测环路	Shīzhēn jiǎncè huánlù	DDL
Distortion detection loop	失真指示器	Shīzhēn zhǐshìqì	DDL
Distortion factor	失真因数	Shīzhēn yīnshù	DF
Distress call	呼救	Hūjiù	
Distress frequency	遇险频率	Yùxiǎn pínlǜ	
Distress system	呼救系统	Hūjiù xìtǒng	
Distributed active real-time database	分布式主动实时数据库	Fēnbùshì zhǔdòng shíshí shùjùkù	DARTDB
Distributed agent environment	分布式代理环境	Fēnbùshì dàilǐ huánjìng	DAE
Distributed analysis structure	分布式分析结构	Fēnbùshì fēnxī jiégòu	
Distributed application	分布式应用	Fēnbù shì yìngyòng	
Distributed array descriptor (Fortran)	分布数组描述	Fēnbù shù zǔ miáoshù	DAD
Distributed Bragg reflection	分布布拉格反射	Fēnbù Bùlāgé fǎnshè	DCA
Distributed channel assignment	分散定位	Fēnsàn dìngwèi	
Distributed common object model	分布式公共对象模型	Fēnbùshì gōnggòng duìxiàng móxíng	
Distributed communication architecture	分布式通信体系	Fēnbùshì tōngxìn tǐxì	DCA
Distributed communication architecture	公布式通信体系	Gōngbùshì tōngxìn tǐxì	DCA
Distributed component object model	分布式组件对象模型	Fēnbùshì zǔjiàn duìxiàng móxíng	DCOM
Distributed computing environment	分布式计算环境	Fēnbùshì jìsuàn huánjìng	DCE
Distributed connection management	分布式连接管理	Fēnbùshì liánjiē guǎnlǐ	DCM
Distributed control	分步式控制	Fēnbùshì kòngzhì	
Distributed control	分散控制	Fēnsàn kòngzhì	
Distributed control	分散式控制	Fēnsàn-shì kòngzhì	
Distributed control panel - intelligent	智能型分散控制器	Zhìnéng-xíng fēnsàn kòngzhìqì	DCP-I
Distributed control system	集散型控制系统	Jísàn xíng kòngzhì xìtǒng	DCS
Distributed coordination function (IEEE 802.11 protocol)	分布协调功能	Fēnbù xiétiáo gōngnéng	DCF
Distributed data	分布式数据	Fēnbùshì shùjù	
Distributed data management	分布式数据管理	Fēnbùshì shùjù guǎnlǐ	DDM

Distributed data network	分布式数据网	Fēnbùshì shùjù wǎng	DDN
Distributed database	分布式数据库	Fēnbùshì shùjùkù	
Distributed denial of service attack	分布拒绝服务攻击	Fēnbù jùjué fúwù gōngjī	DDoS
Distributed denial of service attack	分布式拒绝服务攻击	Fēnbùshì jùjué fúwù gōngjī	DDoS
Distributed double-loop computer network	分布式双环路计算机网络	Fēnbùshì shuāng huánlù jìsuànjī wǎngluò	DDLCN
Distributed evolutionary algorithm	分布式演化算法	Fēnbùshì yǎnhuà suànfǎ	
Distributed feedback	分布反馈	Fēnbù fǎnkuì	
Distributed feedback fair queuing	分布反馈公平排队算法	Fēnbù fǎnkuì gōngping páiduì suànfǎ	DF^2Q
Distributed feedback laser	分布反馈激光器	Fēnbù fǎnkuì jīguāngqì	DFB
Distributed feedback laser diode	分布反馈型激光器	Fēnbù fǎnkuìxíng jīguāngqì	DFB-LD
Distributed frame alignment signal	分散式帧定位信号	Fēnsànshì zhèng dìngwèi xìnhào	
Distributed function	分布式功能	Fēnbùshì gōngnéng	
Distributed functional plane	分布式功能平面	Fēnbùshì gōngnéng píngmiàn	DFP
Distributed garbage collection	分布式垃圾收集	Fēnbùshì lājī shōují	
Distributed interactive simulation	分布交互仿真	Fēnbù jiāohù fǎngzhēn	DIS
Distributed interNet application	分布式网间应用程序	Fēnbùshì wǎngjiān yìngyòng chéngxù	DNA
Distributed Internet application	分布式因特网应用程序	Fēnbùshì Yīntèwǎng yìngyòng chéngxù	DNA
Distributed internet application architecture	分布式互联网应用结构	Fēnbùshì hùliánwǎng yìngyòng jiégòu	DNA
Distributed intrusion detection system	分布式入侵检测系统	Fēnbùshì rùqīn jiǎncè xìtǒng	DIDS
Distributed loop computer network	分布式环形计算机网络	Fēnbùshì huánxíng jìsuànjī wǎngluò	DLCN
Distributed loop message communication protocol	分布式环形信息通信规约	Fēnbùshì huánxíng xìnxī tōngxìn guīyuē	DLMCP
Distributed management task force	分布管理程序	Fēnbù guǎnlǐ chéngxù	DMTF
Distributed management task force	公布式管理任务组	Gōngbùshì guǎnlǐ rènwuzǔ	DMTF
Distributed message queue	分布式消息队列	Fēnbùshì xiāoxi duìliè	DMQ
Distributed microwave communication system	分布式微波通信系统	Fēnbùshì wēibō tōngxìn xìtǒng	
Distributed mobile communication system	分布式移动通信系统	Fēnbùshì yídòng tōngxìn xìtǒng	
Distributed parameter network	分布参数网络	Fēnbù cānshù wǎngluò	
Distributed process control system	分布过程控制系统	Fēnbù guòchéng kòngzhì xìtǒng	DPCS
Distributed processing	分布式处理	Fēnbùshì chǔlǐ	
Distributed processing environment	分布式处理环境	Fēnbùshì chǔlǐ huánjìng	DPE
Distributed processing network	分布处理网络	Fēnbù chǔlǐ wǎngluò	DPN
Distributed processor sub-system	分配处理器子系统	Fēnpèi chǔlǐqì zixìtǒng	DPS
Distributed query (for database)	分布式查询	Fēnbùshì cháxún	
Distributed queue dual bus	分布排队双总线	Fēnbù páiduì shuāng zǒngxiàn	DQDB
Distributed queue dual bus	分布式队列双总线	Fēnbùshì duìliè shuāng zǒngxiàn	DQDB
Distributed queue dual bus	分布式排队双总线	Fēnbùshì páiduì shuāng zǒngxiàn	
Distributed queue, dual bus	分散队列双总线	Fēnsàn duìliè shuāng zǒngxiàn	DQDB
Distributed real-time database	分布式实时数据库	Fēnbùshì shíshí shùjùkù	DRTDB
Distributed relational database	分布式关系型数据库	Fēnbùshì guānxi xíng shùjùkù	
Distributed relational database structure	分布式关系数据库结构	Fēnbùshì guānxì shùjùkù jiégòu	DRDS
Distributed relational DBMS	分布式关系数据库管理系统	Fēnbùshì guānxì shùjùkù guǎnlǐ xìtǒng	DRDBMS
Distributed resistive suppressor	分布电阻抑制器	Fēnbù diànzǔ yìzhìqì	
Distributed scheduling multiple access	分布调度多路存取	Fēnbù diàodù duōlù cúnqǔ	DSMA
Distributed service	分配型业务	Fēnpèixíng yèwù	

Distributed service with user individual presentation control	有用户各自控制的分配性业务	Yǒu yònghù gèzì kòngzhìde fēnpèixìng yèwù	
Distributed shared memory mapping	分布式共享内存映射	Fēnbùshì gòngxiǎng nèicún yìngshè	
Distributed star network	星形分配网	Xīngxíng fēnpèi wǎng	DSN
Distributed system	分布式系统	Fēnbùshì xìtǒng	
Distributed time division multiple access	分布时分多重存取	Fēnbù shífèn duōzhòng cúnqǔ	DTDMA
Distributed transaction coordinator (in SQL Server)	分布式事务协调器	Fēnbùshì shìwù xiétiáo qì	DTC
Distributed transaction coordinator resource	分布式事务协调器资源	Fēnbùshì shìwù xiétiáoqì zīyuán	
Distribution	分配	Fēnpèi	
Distribution (of a software version)	分发版	Fēnfā bǎn	
Distribution agent (in SQL Server)	分发代理	Fēnfā dàilǐ	
Distribution amplifier	分配放大器	Fēnpèi fàngdàqì	DA
Distribution application	分配应用	Fēnpèi yìngyòng	
Distribution database	分发数据库	Fēnfā shùjùkù	
Distribution frame	分配架	Fēnpèi jià	
Distribution frame, distributor	配线架	Pèixiàn jià	DF
Distribution graph method	流量分布图	Liúliàng fēnbùtú	
Distribution header	分布标题	Fēnbù biāotí	
Distribution hub	分配中心	Fēnpèi zhōngxīn	
Distribution link	分布路线	Fēnbù lùxiàn	
Distribution list	分发表	Fēnfā biǎo	DL
Distribution list expansion	分发表扩充	Fēnfā biǎo kuòchōng	
Distribution list name	分发表名	Fēnfā biǎo míng	
Distribution point	分配点	Fēnpèi diǎn	
Distribution point	配线点	Pèixiàn diǎn	DP
Distribution requirements planning	配送需求计划	Pèisòng xūqiú jìhuà	DRP
Distribution resource planning	配送资源计划	Pèisòng zīyuán jìhuà	DRP
Distribution retention period	分发保持期	Fēnfā bǎochí qī	
Distribution service	分配业务	Fēnpèi yèwù	
Distribution service with user individual presentation control	用户能进行演示单独控制的分配型业务	Yònghù néng jìnxíng yǎnshì dāndú kòngzhìde fēnpèi xíng yèwù	
Distribution service without user individual presentation control	无用户各自控制的分配性业务	Wúyònghù gèzì kòngzhìde fēnpèi-xìng yèwù	
Distribution service without user individual presentation control	用户不能进行演示单独控制的分配型业务	Yònghù bùnéng jìnxíng yǎnshì dāndú kòngzhìde fēnpèi xíng yèwù	
Distribution shelf	分配架	Fēnpèi jià	DISS
Distribution switchboard	分配交换台	Fēnpèi jiāohuàntái	DSB
Distributive	分布式	Fēnbùshì	
Distributor	分发服务器	Fēnfā fúwùqì	
Distributor	分销商	Fēnxiāo shāng	
Distributor spark suppressor	点火分配器抑制器	Diǎnhuǒ fēnpèiqì yìzhìqì	
District	地区	Dìqū	
District coding	分区编码	Fēnqū biānmǎ	
District exchange center	地市局	Dìshìjú	
District switching center	区域交换中心	Qūyù jiāohuàn zhōngxīn	DSC
Disturbance	扰乱	Rǎoluàn	

Disturbance current	骚扰电流	Sāorǎo diànliú	
Disturbance field strength	骚扰场强	Sāorǎo chǎngqiáng	
Disturbance power	骚扰功率	Sāorǎo gōnglǜ	
Disturbance suppression	骚扰抑制	Sāorǎo yìzhì	
Disturbance voltage	骚扰电压	Sāorǎo diànyā	
Dithering	抖色处理	Dǒusè chǔlǐ	
Dithering (video term)	抖动	Dǒudòng	
Divergence, discrepancy	差异	Chāyì	
Diversity	多样性	Duōyàngxìng	
Diversity	分集	Fēnjí	
Diversity cell receiver board	分集小区接收板	Fēnjí xiǎoqū jiēshōu bǎn	DCRB
Diversity combiner	分集合并器	Fēnjí hébìngqì	
Diversity control unit	分集控制单元	Fēnjí kòngzhì dānyuán	DCU
Diversity gain	分集增益	Fēnjí zēngyì	
Diversity handover	分集切换	Fēnjí qiēhuàn	DHO
Diversity improvement factor	分集改善因数	Fēnjí gǎishàn yīnshù	
Diversity of a signaling module	信令模块分散	Xìnlìng mókuài fēnsàn	
Diversity receiver	分集接收	Fēnjí jiēshōu	
Diversity reception	分集接收	Fēnjí jiēshōu	
Diversity separation	分集间隔	Fēnjí jiàngé	
Divided junction	分隔点	Fēngé diǎn	
Divider type	间隔物类型	Jiàngéwù lèixíng	
Divider width	间隔物宽度	Jiàngéwù kuāndù	
Division method	除法	Chúfǎ	
Do Communication More (Japanese telecom provider)	沟通更多	Gōutōng gèng duō	DoCoMo
Do it yourself	自己动手作	Zìjǐ dòngshǒu zuò	DIY
Do not disturb service	免打扰服务	Miǎn dǎrǎo fúwù	
Docking station	插接站	Chājiē zhàn	
Document	文档	Wéndàng	
Document	文件	Wénjiàn	
Document against payment	付款交单	Fùkuǎn jiāodān	D/P
Document application profile	文件应用轮廓	Wénjiàn yìngyòng lúnkuò	
Document architecture	文件体系结构	Wénjiàn tǐxì jiégòu	
Document architecture class	文件体系结构类别	Wénjiàn tǐxì jiégòu lèibié	
Document architecture level	文件体系结构级	Wénjiàn tǐxì jiégòu jí	
Document bulk transfer	文件成批传送	Wénjiàn chéngpī chuánsòng	
Document bulk transfer and manipulation	文件成批传送和管理操作	Wénjiàn chéngpī chuánsòng hé guǎnlǐ cāozuò	
Document class	文件类别	Wénjiàn lèibié	
Document class description	文件类别描述	Wénjiàn lèibié miáoshù	
Document content description (in XML)	文件内容描述	Wénjiàn nèiróng miáoshù	DCD
Document facsimile	文件传真	Wénjiàn chuánzhēn	
Document file	文档文件	Wéndàng wénjiàn	
Document interchange architecture	文件交换体系结构	Wénjiàn jiāohuàn tǐxì jiégòu	DIA
Document layout process	文件布局处理	Wénjiàn bùjú chǔlǐ	
Document layout root	文件布局根	Wénjiàn bùjú gēn	

Document logical root	文件逻辑根	Wénjiàn luóji gēn	
Document maintenance Group (in CMM)	文档支持组	Wéndàng zhīchí zǔ	DMG
Document management	文件管理	Wénjiàn guǎnlǐ	
Document manipulation	文件管理操作	Wénjiàn guǎnlǐ cāozuò	
Document object model	文档对象模型	Wéndàng duìxiàng móxíng	DOM
Document profile	文件轮廓	Wénjiàn lúnkuò	
Document profile level	文件轮廓级	Wénjiàn lúnkuò jí	
Document subject, document body	文件主体	Wénjiàn zhǔtǐ	
Document transfer and interactive mode	文件传送及交互方式	Wénjiàn chuánsòng jí jiāohù fāngshì	
Document transfer and manipulation user	文件传送和管理操作用户	Wénjiàn chuánsòng hé guǎnlǐ cāozuò yònghù	DTAM
Document transfer mode	文件传送方式	Wénjiàn chuánsòng fāngshì	
Document type definition	文档类型定义	Wéndàng lèixíng dìngyì	DTD
Document type definition (in XML)	文件类型定义	Wénjiàn lèixíng dìngyì	DTD
Document window	文档窗口	Wéndàng chuāngkǒu	
Documentary records	文献资料	Wénxiàn zīliào	
Documentation	文件编制	Wénjiàn biānzhì	
Dolph-Chebyshev array	道尔夫-契比雪夫阵	Dào-ěr-fū--qì-bǐ-xuě-fū zhèn	
Dolph-Chebyshev array antenna	道尔夫-切比雪夫阵列天线	Dào-ěr-fū—qiē-bǐ-xuě-fū zhènliè tiānxiàn	
Dolph-Chebyshev array antenna	多尔夫-契比舍夫天线阵	Duō-ěr-fū—Qì-bǐ-shè-fū tiānxiàn zhèn	DCAA
Domain (in computers and telecommuncations)	域	Yù	
Domain defined attributes	域定义属性	Yù dìngyì shǔxìng	
Domain integrity	域完整性	Yù wánzhěngxìng	
Domain knowledge	领域知识	Lǐngyù zhīshi	
Domain name	网域地址	Wǎngyù dìzhǐ	
Domain name	域名	Yùmíng	
Domain name resolution	域名解析	Yùmíng jiěxī	
Domain name server	域名服务器	Yù míng fúwùqì	DNS
Domain name server (DNS) spoofing (IPsec)	域名服务器电子欺骗	Yùmíng fúwùqì diànzǐ qīpiàn	
Domain name service	域名服务	Yùmíng fúwù	DNS
Domain name system	域名系统	Yùmíng xìtǒng	DNS
Domain name system server	域名服务器	Yùmíng fúwùqì	DNS
Domain of origin	原始域	Yuánshǐ yù	
Domain range	域值区间	Yùzhí qūjiān	
Domain specific part	域特定部分	Yù tèdìng bùfen	DSP
Domain suffix	域后缀	Yù hòuzhuì	
Domestic communications satellite	国内通信卫星	Guónèi tōngxìn wèixīng	Domsat
Domestic package	内销包装	Nèixiāo bāozhuāng	
Domestic trunk interface	国内干线接口	Guónèi gànxiàn jiēkǒu	DTI
Dominant mode (in a waveguide)	主模	Zhǔ mó	
Dominant wavelength	主波长	Zhǔ bōcháng	DWL
Dongle	软件狗	Ruǎnjiàn gǒu	
Door contacts	大门传感器	Dàmén chuángǎnqì	DC
Door-knob transformer	门钮式同轴波导变换器	Ménniǔ-shì tóngzhóu bōdǎo biànhuànqì	
Door-open alarm	开门告警	Kāimén gàojǐng	
Doppler	多普勒	Duō-pǔ-lè	
Doppler frequency deviation correction	多普勒频偏校正	Duō-pǔ-lè pínpiān jiàozhèng	

Doppler radar	测速雷达	Cèsù léidá	
Doppler radar	多普勒雷达	Duō-pǔ-lè léidá	
Doppler shift	多普勒频移	Duō-pǔ-lè pínyí	
Doppler sonar	多普勒声纳	Duō-pǔ-lè shēngnà	
DOS shell	DOS 外壳	DOS wàiké	
Dose	剂量	Jìliàng	
Dot (in Morse code)	点	Diǎn	
Dot character (.)	点符	Diǎnfú	
Dot matrix printer	点阵式打印机	Diǎnzhèn-shì dǎyìnjī	
Dot method (GIS)	点值法	Diǎnzhí fǎ	
Dot operator (in graphics)	点操作符	Diǎn cāozuò fú	
Dot pitch	点距	Diǎn jù	
Dot texture blending (video term)	点型纹理混和	Diǎnxíng wénlǐ hùnhé	
Dots per inch	每英寸点数	Měi yīngcùn diǎnshù	Dpi
Dots per inch (printer term)	每英寸的打印像素	Měi yīngcùnde dǎyìn xiàngsù	dpi
Dotted decimal notation	十进制点格式	Shíjìnzhì diǎn géshi	
Dotted notation	点分符号	Diǎnfēn fúhào	
Dotted-decimal notation	点十进制表示法	Diǎn shíjìnzhì biǎoshì fǎ	
Dotting sequence	点序列	Diǎn xùliè	
Double balanced mixer	双重平衡混频器	Shuāngchóng pínghéng hùnpínqì	
Double bit	双位	Shuāng wèi	
Double bounce technique	二次反射法	Èrcì fǎnshè fǎ	
Double buffering	双缓冲区	Shuāng huǎnchōngqū	
Double canceller	二次对消器	Èrcì duìxiāoqì	
Double click (WP command)	双击	Shuāng jī	
Double conversion receiver	双变频接收机	Shuāngbiànpín jiēshōujī	
Double current return to zero system	双流归零制	Shuāngliú guīlíng zhì	
Double current transmission	双流传输	Shuāngliú chuánshū	
Double data rate	双倍数据速率	Shuāngbèi shùjù sùlǜ	DDR
Double data rate SDRAM	双数据率 SDRAM	Shuāng shùjù lǜ SDRAM	DDR-SDRAM
Double deflection CRT	双偏管	Shuāng piān guǎn	
Double density	双密度	Shuāng mìdù	DD
Double dither loop	双抖动环	Shuāng dǒudòng huán	DDL
Double diversity reception	双重分集接收	Shuāngchóng fēnjí jiēshōu	
Double dynamic suspension system	双悬浮动态减震系统	Shuāng xuánfú dòngtài jiǎnzhèn xìtǒng	DDSS
Double error	双位差错	Shuāngwèi chācuò	
Double frequency shift keying	双移频键控	Shuāng yípín jiànkòng	DFSK
Double gain stage logarithmic amplifier	双增益级对数放大器	Shuāng zēngyì jí duìshù fàngdàqì	
Double gate MOS four terminal device	双栅极MOS四极管	Shuāngshānjí MOS sìjíguǎn	
Double heterogeneous	双异质结	Shuāng yìzhì jié	
Double insulation	双重绝缘	Shuāngchóng juéyuán	
Double modification	双重修改方式	Shuāngchóng xiūgǎi fāngshì	
Double modulation	双重调制	Shuāngchóng tiáozhì	
Double phantom circuit	双幻线电路	Shuāng huànxiàn diànlù	
Double polarization receive	双极化接收	Shuāng jíhuà jiēshōu	
Double pole	双极点	Shuāng jídiǎn	

Double pole filter	双极点滤波器	Shuāng jídiǎn lùbōqì	
Double precision	双精度	Shuāng jīngdù	
Double quaternary modulation	双四相调制	Shuāng sìxiāng tiáozhì	DQM
Double seizure	同抢	Tóngqiǎng	
Double side/double density (disk)	双面双密度(磁盘)	Shuāngmiàn shuāng mìdù (cípán)	DS/DD
Double sideband	双边带	Shuāng biāndài	DSB
Double sideband	双边带	Shuāngbiāndài	DSB
Double sideband amplitude modulation	双边带幅度调制	Shuāng biāndài fúdù tiáozhì	DSBAM
Double sideband modulation	双边带调制	Shuāngbiāndài tiáozhì	
Double T junction	双 T 接头	Shuāng T jiētóu	
Double threshold detection	双门限检测	Shuāng ménxiàn jiǎncè	
Double threshold detector	双门限检测器	Shuāng ménxiàn jiǎncèqì	
Double time-stamp transaction-level synchronization	双时间印的事各级同步	Shuāng shíjiān yìnde shì gèjí tóngbù	DTSTLS
Double underline (WP command)	下划双线	Xiàhuà shuāngxiàn	
Double window fiber	双窗孔纤维	Shuāng chuāngkǒng xiānwéi	DWF
Double-adaptive file compression	双重自适应文卷压缩	Shuāngchóng zìshìyìng wénjuàn yāsuō	DAFC
Double-byte character set	双字节字符集	Shuāng zìjié zìfú jí	DBCS
Double-deflection	双偏转	Shuāng piānzhuǎn	
Double-ended queue	双端列表	Shuāngduān lièbiǎo	
Double-ended synchronization	双端同步	Shuāngduān tóngbù	
Double-horn feed for rear-feed	后馈双喇叭馈电器	Hòukuì shuāng lǎba kuìdiànqì	
Double-length word	双倍字长	Shuāngbèi zìcháng	
Double-pole, single-throw switch	双刀单掷开关	Shuāngdāo dānzhì kāiguān	DPST
Doublet antenna	偶极天线	Ǒují tiānxiàn	
Doublet byte	二位字节	Èrwèi zìjié	
Doubling up	共同居住	Gòngtóng jūzhù	
Doubly linked list	双向链表	Shuāngxiàng liàn biǎo	
Doubly linked tree	双链树	Shuāngliàn shù	
Douglas-Peucker algorithm	道格拉斯算法	Dào-gé-lā-sī suànfǎ	
Down converter	下变频器	Xiàbiànpínqì	
Down state	不可用状态	Bùkěyòng zhuàngtài	
Down-casing	小写转换	Xiǎoxiě zhuǎnhuàn	
Downhole instrument	下井仪器	Xiàjǐng yíqì	
Down-lead (of an antenna)	下引线	Xiàyǐnxiàn	
Downlink	下行	Xiàxíng	
Downlink	下行链路	Xiàxíng liànlù	
Downlink	下行线路	Xiàxíng xiànlù	DL
Downlink data channel	下行数据信道	Xiàxíng shùjù xìndào	
Downlink pilot time slot	下行导引时隙	Xiàxíng dǎoyǐn shíxì	DwPTS
Downlink pseudo-random data	下行伪随机数据	Xiàxíng wěisuíjī shùjù	DPRD
Downlink shared channel	下行共用信道	Xiàxíng gòngyòng xìndào	DSCH
Downlink shared channel	下行链路共享信道	Xiàxíng liànlù gòngxiǎng xìndào	DSCH
Download	下载	Xiàzài	
Downloadable sample (Internet audio)	可下载的取样音色	Kěxiàzàide qǔyàng yīnsè	
Downloadable sounds level 2	第二代可下载音色	Dì'èrdài kěxiàzài yīnsè	DLS-2
Downsizing	向下规模化	Xiàngxià guīmóhuà	

Downstream	下行方向	Xiàxíng fāngxiàng	
Downstream label switching router	下流标志交换路由器	Xiàliú biāozhì jiāohuàn lùyóuqì	
Downstream physical unit	下游物理部件	Xiàyóu wùlǐ bùjiàn	DSPU
Downstream router	下游路由器	Xiàyóu lùyóuqì	Rd
Downstream slope	下游法	Xiàyóu fǎ	
Downstream transmission	下行传输方向	Xiàxíng chuánshū fāngxiàng	
Downtime	关机时间	Guānjī shíjiān	
Downtime	停机时间	Tíngjī shíjiān	
Downward compatible	向下兼容	Xiàngxià jiānróng	
Downward link	下行线路	Xiàxíng xiànlù	DLINK
Downward radiation	向下辐射	Xiàngxià fúshè	
Downward regulation	向下调整	Xiàngxià tiáozhěng	
Draft mode (WP command)	标尺	Biāochǐ	
Draft mode (WP command)	草稿状态	Cǎogǎo zhuàngtài	
Draft proposal (in groupware document handling; originally a term in official circles meaning "to make a proposal for a settlement' or in legal circles meaning 'to publish a case')	拟办	Nǐbàn	
Drafting scale	绘图比例尺	Huìtú bǐlìchǐ	
Drag	拖动	Tuōdòng	
Drag	阻力	Zǔlì	
Drag and drop	即拖即用	Jítuō jíyòng	
Drag and drop	拖放	Tuō fàng	
Drag-and-drop [move using a computer mouse]	使用鼠标移动对象	Shǐyòng shǔbiāo yídòng duìxiàng	
Drape	叠加图	Diéjiā tú	
Draw (verb, FOC mfg)	拉丝	Lāsī	
Drawing	绘图	Huìtú	
Drawing board	绘图板	Huìtúbǎn	
Drawing entities	绘图实体	Huìtú shítǐ	
Drawing exchange format	绘图交换格式	Huìtú jiāohuàn géshi	
Drawing extent	绘图范围	Huìtú fànwéi	
Drawing file	绘图文件	Huìtú wénjiàn	
Drawing graphs nicely	图的描绘	Túde miáohuì	
Drawing trees	树的描绘	Shùde miáohuì	
Drect sequence spread spectrum modulation	直接序列扩频调制	Zhíjiē xùliè kuòpín tiáozhì	
Drift compensation	漂移补偿	Piāoyí bǔcháng	
Drift radio network controller	无线漂移网络控制器	Wúxiàn piāoyí wǎngluò kòngzhìqì	DRNC
Drift RNS [radio network sub-system]	RNS 漂移	RNS piāoyí	DRNS
Drift, wander	漂移	Piāoyí	DR
Drill down/drill up	深化/浅化	Shēnhuà/qiǎnhuà	
Drill through	钻取	Zuānqǔ	
Drive	激动	Jīdòng	DR
Drive	驱动	Qūdòng	DR
Drive letter	驱动器号	Qūdòngqì hào	
Drive name	驱动器名	Qūdòngqì míng	
Drive self test	磁盘自检程序	Cípán zìjiǎn chéngxù	DST
Drive, driver	驱动器	Qūdòngqì	

Driven element	受激单元	Shòujī dānyuán	
Driver (the computer program)	驱动	Qūdòng	
Drooping characteristic	下降特性	Xiàjiàng tèxìng	
Drop (noun)	分接点	Fēnjiēdiǎn	
Drop and insert equipment	分路机/设备	Fēnlù jī/shèbèi	
Drop cable	分接电缆	Fēnjiē diànlǎn	
Drop cable	引出电缆	Yǐnchū diànlǎn	
Drop line	引入线	Yǐnrùxiàn	
Drop-and-continue (SDH)	下路和继续传送	Xiàlù hé jìxù chuánsòng	
Drop-out	漏码	Lòumǎ	
Dropped call	掉话	Diàohuà	
Dropped scan line	丢失扫描线	Diūshī sǎomiáo xiàn	
Drum factor	滚筒因数	Gǔntǒng yīnshù	
Drum plotter	流向式绘图仪	Liúxiàng-shì huìtúyí	
Drum scanner	流向式扫描仪	Liúxiàng-shì sǎomiáoyí	
Dry density	干密度	Gān mìdù	
Dry-air filling machine	干燥充气机	Gānzào chōngqìjī	
DS-2 (2nd digital standard transmission rate = 8Mbps)	二次群	Èrcì qún	
D-star	D-星号	D-xīng hào	
Dual address cycle	双重地址周期	Shuāngchóng dìzhǐ zhōuqī	DAC
Dual attachment station	双向连接站	Shuāngxiàng liánjiē zhàn	DAS
Dual band	双频段	Shuāng pínduàn	
Dual band fiber amplifier	双波段光纤放大器	Shuāng bōduàn guāngxiān fàngdàqì	DBFA
Dual band fiber amplifier	双带光纤放大器	Shuāngdài guāngxiān fàngdàqì	DBFA
Dual boot	双重启动	Shuāngchóng qǐdòng	
Dual bus	双总线	Shuāng zǒngxiàn	
Dual counter-rotating ring	双反向旋转环	Shuāng fǎnxiàng xuánzhuǎn huán	
Dual hubbed service (SDH)	双汇接业务	Shuāng huìjiē yèwù	
Dual independent bus	双独立总线	Shuāng dúlì zǒngxiàn	DIB
Dual independent map encoding	双重独立地图编码文件	Shuāngchóng dúlì dìtú biānmǎ wénjiàn	DIME
Dual inline memory module	双边接触内存模组	Shuāngbiān jiēchù nèicún mózǔ	DIMM
Dual in-line memory module	双重内嵌式内存模块	Shuāngchóng nèiqiàn-shì nèicún mókuài	DIMM
Dual in-line package	双列直插式封装	Shuāng liè zhíchā-shì fēngzhuāng	DIP
Dual in-line package	双列直插	Shuāngliè zhíchā	DIP
Dual node interconnection (SDH)	双节点互连	Shuāng jiédiǎn hùlián	
Dual port memory	双端口存储器	Shuāng duānkǒu cúnchǔqì	DPM
Dual port RAM	双端口 RAM	Shuāng duānkǒu RAM	DPRAM
Dual processor	双机	Shuāng jī	
Dual rotating counter ring	双循环计数环	Shuāng xúnhuán jìshù huán	
Dual significance	双重意义	Shuāngchóng yìyì	
Dual sliding beam pick and placer (in SMT)	双滑动梁型贴片机	Shuāng huádòng liáng xíng tiēpiànjī	
Dual stack	双堆叠	Shuāng duīdié	
Dual stack transition mechanism (in IPv6)	双栈过渡机制	Shuāng zhàn guòdù jīzhì	DSTM
Dual stream	双码流	Shuāng mǎliú	
Dual system	双机系统	Shuāngjī xìtǒng	
Dual -technology sensor	双鉴传感器	Shuāng jiàn chuángǎnqì	DTS

Dual tone multi-frequency	双音多频	Shuāngyīn duōpín	DTMF
Dual-attached concentrator	双连接集中器	Shuāng liánjiē jízhōngqì	DAC
Dual-attachment station	双连接工作站	Shuāng liánjiē gōngzuòzhàn	DAS
Dual-channel asynchronous receiver/transmitter	双信道异步接受器/发射器	Shuāng xìndào yìbù jiēshòuqì/ fāshèqì	DART
Dual-homing	双归属	Shuāng guīshǔ	
Dual-in-line package	双列直插式封装	Shuānglièzhí chāshì fēngzhuāng	DIP
Dualized file	双重文件	Shuāngchóng wénjiàn	
Dual-mode jammer	双模式干扰机	Shuāng móshì gānrǎojī	
Dual-path multicast	双路径多播	Shuāng lùjìng duōbō	
Dual-polarity antenna	双极化天线	Shuāng jíhuà tiānxiàn	
Dual-train drive device	双链传动装置	Shuāngliàn chuándòng zhuāngzhì	
Dual-wavelength optical coupler	两波长光合波器	Liǎng bōcháng guāng hébōqì	
Duct	管道	Guǎndào	
Duct cable	管道缆	Guǎndào lǎn	
Duct fiber optic cable	管道光缆	Guǎndào guānglǎn	
Ducted fiber optic cable	管路式光缆	Guǎnlù-shì guānglǎn	
Ductility	韧性	Rènxìng	
Ductility factor	延性率	Yánxìng lǜ	
Ductility factor response spectrum	延性率反应谱	Yánxìng lǜ fǎnyìng pǔ	
Dumb	非智能型	Fēizhìnéngxíng	
Dummy antenna	仿真天线	Fǎngzhēn tiānxiàn	
Dummy antenna	假天线	Jiǎ tiānxiàn	
Dummy argument (in FORTRAN)	假变元	Jiǎ biànyuán	
Dummy argument (in FORTRAN)	哑子变量	Yǎzi biànliàng	
Dummy bits	伪比特	Wěibìtè	
Dummy burst	伪突发	Wěitūfā	DB
Dummy burst	虚拟脉冲串	Xūnǐ màichōng chuàn	DB
Dummy burst	虚拟突发脉冲序列	Xūnǐ tūfā màichōng xùliè	DB
Dummy burst (GSM term)	哑元突发	Yǎyuán tūfā	
Dummy lamp	模拟灯	Mónǐ dēng	
Dummy load	等效负载	Děngxiào fùzài	
Dummy load	假负载	Jiǎ fùzài	
Dump	转储	Zhuǎnchǔ	
Dump file	转储文件	Zhuǎnchǔ wénjiàn	
Duplex	双工	Shuānggōng	
Duplex frequency separation	双工频率间隔	Shuānggōng pínlǜ jiàngé	
Duplex operation	双工操作	Shuānggōng cāozuò	
Duplex radiotelephone	双工无线电话机	Shuānggōng wúxiàn diànhuà jī	
Duplex system	双重系统	Shuāngchóng xìtǒng	
Duplex transmission	双工传输	Shuānggōng chuánshū	
Duplex working	同波长双工	Tóngbōcháng shuānggōng	
Duplexer, diplexer (for antennas)	双工器	Shuānggōngqì	
Duplication communication control board assembly	双重通信控制集成板	Shuāngchóng tōngxìn kòngzhì jíchéngbǎn	DCCA
Durability	耐久性	Nàijiǔxìng	
Duration	持续时间	Chíxù shíjiān	
Duration of a voltage change	电压变化持续时间	Diànyā biànhuà chíxù shíjiān	

Duration of load	负荷保持时间	Fùhè bǎochí shíjiān	
Duration time modulation	持续时间调制	Chíxù shíjiān tiáozhì	DTM
Durometer (in SMT)	硬度计	Yìngdùjì	
Dust-protected	防尘	Fángchén	
Duty cycle	工作比	Gōngzuò bǐ	
D-valve	D 形阀	D-xíng fá	
Dwell time	停顿时间	Tíngdùn shíjiān	
Dye laser	染料激光	Rǎnliào jīguāng	
Dynamic address resolution	动态地址解析	Dòngtài dìzhǐ jiěxī	
Dynamic analysis	动力分析	Dònglì fēnxī	
Dynamic assembly	动态配件	Dòngtài pèijiàn	
Dynamic assembly	动态装配件	Dòngtài zhuāngpèijiàn	
Dynamic automatic gain control (AGC) characteristic	动态自动增益控制特性	Dòngtài zìdòng zēngyì kòngzhì tèxìng	
Dynamic bandwidth allocation	动态带宽分配	Dòngtài dàikuān fēnpèi	DBA
Dynamic binding	动态绑定	Dòngtài bǎngdìng	
Dynamic buffer	动态缓冲器	Dòngtài huǎnchōngqì	
Dynamic channel allocation	动态波道配置	Dòngtài bōdào pèizhì	DCA
Dynamic channel allocation	动态信道分配	Dòngtài xìndào fēnpèi	
Dynamic channel assignment	动态信道分配	Dòngtài xìndào fēnpèi	
Dynamic code grating holography	动态编码光栅全息	Dòngtài biānmǎ guāngshān quánxī	
Dynamic compression	动态压缩	Dòngtài yāsuō	
Dynamic conformance requirement	动态一致性要求	Dòngtài yīzhìxìng yāoqiú	
Dynamic connection management	动态连接管理	Dòngtài liánjiē guǎnlǐ	DCM
Dynamic cursor (for database)	动态游标	Dòngtài yóubiāo	
Dynamic data authentication	动态数据鉴别	Dòngtài shùjù jiànbié	
Dynamic data exchange	动态数据交换	Dòngtài shùjù jiāohuàn	DDX
Dynamic debugging system	动态调式系统	Dòngtài diàoshì xìtǒng	DDS
Dynamic disk	动态磁盘	Dòngtài cípán	
Dynamic enterprise modeling	动态企业建模	Dòngtài qǐyè jiànmó	DEM
Dynamic extended resolution	动态可扩展分辨率	Dòngtài kě kuòzhǎn fēnbiànlǜ	DxR
Dynamic filter (in SQL Server)	动态过滤	Dòngtài guòlǜ	
Dynamic filter (for database)	动态筛选	Dòngtài shāixuǎn	
Dynamic flat shading (video term)	动态平面描影	Dòngtài píngmiàn miáoyǐng	DFS
Dynamic focus lens (video term)	动态聚焦	Dòngtài jùjiāo	DFL
Dynamic focusing coil	动态聚焦线圈	Dòngtài jùjiāo xiànquān	
Dynamic focusing electrode	动态聚焦电极	Dòngtài jùjiāo diànjí	
Dynamic frequency allocation	动态频率分配	Dòngtài pínlǜ fēnpèi	
Dynamic fuzzy set	动态模糊集	Dòngtài móhu jí	
Dynamic gain equalizer	动态增益均衡器	Dòngtài zēngyì jūnhéngqì	DGE
Dynamic graphics	动态图形	Dòngtài túxíng	
Dynamic holography synthesis fabrication	动态全息合成制作	Dòngtài quánxī héchéng zhìzuò	
Dynamic host configuration protocol	动态宿主配置协议	Dòngtài sùzhǔ pèizhì xiéyì	DHCP
Dynamic host configuration protocol	动态主机分配协议	Dòngtài zhǔjī fēnpèi xiéyì	DHCP
Dynamic host configuration protocol	动态主机配置协议	Dòngtài zhǔjī pèizhì xiéyì	DHCP
Dynamic host control protocol	动态主机控制协议	Dòngtài zhǔjī kòngzhì xiéyì	DHCP
Dynamic hypertext markup language	动态超文本标记语言	Dòngtài chāowénběn biāojì yǔyán	DHTML

Dynamic hypertext markup language	动态超文本置标语言	Dòngtài chāowénběn zhìbiāo yǔyán	DHTML
Dynamic indexing structure	动态索引结构	Dòngtài suǒyǐn jiégòu	
Dynamic invocation interface (CORBA term)	动态调用接口	Dòngtài diàoyòng jiēkǒu	DII
Dynamic labels	动态标记	Dòngtài biāojì	
Dynamic laboratory test	室内动力实验	Shìnèi dònglì shíyàn	
Dynamic link library	动态链接库	Dòngtài liànjiēkù	DLL
Dynamic link library	动态链路库	Dòngtài liànlùkù	DLL
Dynamic locking (for database)	动态锁定	Dòngtài suǒ dìng	
Dynamic memory allocation	动态存储分配	Dòngtài cúnchǔ fēnpèi	DMA
Dynamic memory interface	动态存储器接口	Dòngtài cúnchǔqì jiēkǒu	DMI
Dynamic moll holography	动态莫尔全息	Dòngtài mò-ěr quánxī	
Dynamic network planning technique	动态网络规划技术	Dòngtài wǎngluò guīhuà jìshù	DYNET
Dynamic noise limiter	动态噪声限制器	Dòngtài zàoshēng xiànzhìqì	DNL
Dynamic operating range (of equipment)	动态工作范围	Dòngtài gōngzuò fànwéi	
Dynamic overload traffic control	动态话务量超载控制	Dòngtài huàwùliáng chāozài kòngzhì	
Dynamic packet transmission	动态分组传送	Dòngtài fēnzǔ chuánsòng	DPT
Dynamic packet transport	动态包传输	Dòngtài bāo chuánshū	DPT
Dynamic packet transport	动态分组传送	Dòngtài fēnzǔ chuánsòng	
Dynamic pressure	速度压	Sùdù yā	
Dynamic priority	动态优先级	Dòngtài yōuxiānjí	
Dynamic programming	动态规划	Dòngtài guīhuà	DP
Dynamic quadrapole lens	动态四极镜	Dòngtài sìjí jìng	DQL
Dynamic random access memory	动态随机存储器	Dòngtài suíjī cúnchǔqì	DRAM
Dynamic random access memory	动态随机存取存储器	Dòngtài suíjī cúnqǔ cúnchǔqì	DRAM
Dynamic range (of a signal)	动态范围	Dòngtài fànwéi	
Dynamic range control	动态范围控制	Dòngtài fànwéi kòngzhì	
Dynamic recovery (for database)	动态恢复	Dòngtài huīfù	
Dynamic regrouping	动态重组	Dòngtài chóngzǔ	
Dynamic resource allocation control	动态资源分配控制	Dòngtài zīyuán fēnpèi kòngzhì	DRAC
Dynamic response analysis	动力反应解析	Dònglì fǎnyìng jiěxī	
Dynamic segmentation	动态分段	Dòngtài fēnduàn	
Dynamic separation of duties	动态取责分离	Dòngtài qǔzé fènlí	DSD
Dynamic service addition acknowledgement request message	动态业务增加确认消息	Dòngtài yèwù zēngjiā quèrèn xiāoxi	DSA-ACK
Dynamic service addition request message	动态业务增加请求消息	Dòngtài yèwù zēngjiā qǐngqiú xiāoxi	DSA-REQ
Dynamic service addition response message	动态业务增加响应消息	Dòngtài yèwù zēngjiā xiǎngyìng xiāoxi	DSA-RSP
Dynamic service change acknowledgement message	动态业务改变确认消息	Dòngtài yèwù gǎibiàn quèrèn xiāoxi	DSC-ACK
Dynamic service change request message (for data over cable- docsis)	动态业务改变请求消息	Dòngtài yèwù gǎibiàn qǐngqiú xiāoxi	DSC-REQ
Dynamic service change response message	动态业务改变响应消息	Dòngtài yèwù gǎibiàn xiǎngyìng xiāoxi	DSC-RSP
Dynamic service deletion request message	动态业务删除请求消息	Dòngtài yèwù shānchú qǐngqiú xiāoxi	DSD-REQ
Dynamic service deletion response message	动态业务删除响应消息	Dòngtài yèwù shānchú xiǎngyìng xiāoxi	DSD-RSP
Dynamic simulation	动态模拟	Dòngtài mónǐ	
Dynamic single-longitudinal mode	动态单纵模	Dòngtài dānzòngmó	DSLM
Dynamic skeleton interface (CORBA term)	动态框架接口	Dòngtài kuàngjià jiēkǒu	DSI
Dynamic skeleton invocation (CORBA term)	动态骨架调用	Dòngtài gǔjià diàoyòng	DSI
Dynamic snapshot (for database)	动态快照	Dòngtài kuàizhào	

Dynamic source routing	动态源路由	Dòngtài yuán lùyóu	DSR
Dynamic structured query language (SQL) statements (for database)	动态结构化查询语言语句	Dòngtài jiégòuhuà cháxún yǔyán yǔjù	
Dynamic sub-grade stiffness	动力的地基刚性	Dònglìde dìjī gāngxìng	
Dynamic synchronous transfer mode	动态同步传送模式	Dòngtài tóngbù chuánsòng móshì	DTM
Dynamic Total Area Communications System (UK)	动态全地区通信系统	Dòngtài quán dìqū tōngxìn xìtǒng	DYNATACS
Dynamic trunk protocol	思科动态中继协议	Sī-kē dòngtài zhōngjì xiéyì	DTP
Dynamic Z-buffering (video term)	动态 Z 轴缓冲区	Dòngtài Z-zhóu huǎnchōngqū	
Dynamically redefinable character set	动态再定义字符集	Dòngtài zàidìngyì zìfú jí	DRCS
Dynamics theory	动力学理论	Dònglìxué lǐlùn	

E

E principal plane	E 主平面	E zhǔ píngmiàn	
Ear reference point	耳参考点	Ěr cānkǎo diǎn	ERP
Ear reference point	听力参考点	Tīnglì cānkǎo diǎn	
Earliest deadline first	最早的限优选算法	Zuìzǎode xiàn yōuxuǎn suànfǎ	EDF
Early allocation	预分配	Yùfēnpèi	EA
Early classmark sending control	尽早类别发送控制	Jǐnzǎo lèibié fāsòng kòngzhì	ECSC
Early failure period	早期失效期	Zǎoqī shīxiào qī	
Early fault period	早期故障期	Zǎoqī gùzhàng qī	
Early packet discard	早期报文丢弃	Zǎoqī bàowén diūqì	EPD
Early token release	令牌提前释放	Lìngpái tíqián shìfàng	
Early token release	早期令牌释放	Zǎoqī lìngpái shìfàng	ETR
Early warning aircraft	预警机	Yùjǐng jī	AWACS
Earphone	耳机	Ěrjī	
Earphone socket (on radio)	耳机插座	Ěrjī chāzuò	
Earth exploration-satellite service	卫星地球探测业务	Wèixīng dìqiú tàncè yèwù	
Earth observation system	对地观测系统	Duìdì guāncè xìtǒng	EOS
Earth station	地面站	Dìmiànzhàn	
Earth station	地球电台	Dìqiú diàntái	
Earth station	地球站	Dìqiúzhàn	
Earth-return double phantom circuit	地回双幻线电路	Dìhuí shuānghuànxiàn diànlù	
Earth-space path propagation	地-空路径传播	Dì-kōng lùjìng chuánbō	
Easy setting CPU dual jumper	简化 CPU 双重跳线法	Jiǎnhuà CPU shuāngchóng tiàoxiànfǎ	ESDJ
Easy setting dual jumper	简化双重跳线法	Jiǎnhuà shuāngchóng tiàoxiàn fǎ	ESDJ
Eavesdropping (IPsec)	窃取	Qièqǔ	
Eavesdropping (IPsec) (for RF communications)	窃听	Qiètīng	
E-business	电子商务	Diànzǐ shāngwù	
E-business advanced communication platform	先进的电子商务通信平台	Xiānjìnde diànzǐ shāngwù tōngxìn píngtái	EACP
E-cash, digital currency	电子现金	Diànzǐ xiànjīn	
Eccentric core fiber	偏心光纤	Piānxīn guāngxiān	ECF
Echo	回波	Huíbō	
Echo box	回波箱	Huíbō xiāng	
Echo canceling	回波抵消	Huíbō dǐxiāo	EC
Echo cancellation	回声消除	Huíshēng xiāochú	EC
Echo cancellation algorithm	回音抑制算法	Huíyīn yìzhì suànfǎ	

Echo cancellation hybrid	回波抵消四端网络	Huíbō dǐxiāo sìduān wǎngluò	ECH
Echo cancellation method	回波抵消法	Huíbō dǐxiāo fǎ	
Echo canceller	回波抵消器	Huíbō dǐxiāoqì	
Echo canceller	回声抑制单元	Huíshēng yìzhì dānyuán	EC
Echo channel, E channel	回波信道	Huíbō xìndào	
Echo reference equivalent	回声参考当量	Huíshēng cānkǎo dāngliàng	
Echo return loss	回波损耗	Huíbō sǔnhào	ERP
Echo suppress	回波抑制	Huíbō yìzhì	
Echo suppressor	回波抑制器	Huíbō yìzhìqì	
Echoplex	回显	Huíxiǎn	
Echoplex mode	回送方式	Huísòng fāngshì	
Ecosystem for ASP	ASP 发展环境	ASP fāzhǎn huánjìng	
Ecosystem for Media © (by AT&T)	媒体发展环境	Méitǐ fāzhǎn huánjìng	
Edge	边	Biān	
Edge	边界	Biānjiè	
Edge	边缘	Biānyuán	
Edge aggregation	边缘汇聚	Biānyuán huìjù	
Edge aggregation (CAD/CAM)	边聚合	Biān jùhé	EA
Edge and vertex connectivity	割边/割点连通性	Gēbiān/ gēdiǎn liántōng xìng	
Edge anti-aliasing (video term)	边缘抗锯齿失真	Biānyuán kàng jùchǐ shīzhēn	
Edge card	边缘卡	Biānyuán kǎ	
Edge card control	边缘卡控制	Biānyuán kǎ kòngzhì	ECC
EDGE circuit switched data	EDGE 电路交换传输 模式	EDGE diànlù jiāohuàn chuánshū móshì	ECSD
Edge coloring	边染色	Biān rǎnsè	
Edge crisping	边缘处理	Biānyuán chǔlǐ	
Edge deletion (CAD/CAM)	边删除	Biān shānchú	ED
Edge detection	边沿检测	Biānyán jiǎncè	
Edge detection	边缘检测	Biānyuán jiǎncè	
Edge detection filter	边缘检测滤波器	Biānyuán jiǎncè lǜbōqì	
Edge device	边缘设备	Biānyuán shèbèi	ED
Edge element	边缘元素	Biānyuán yuánsù	
Edge enhancement	边缘增强	Biānyuán zēngqiáng	
Edge feature	边缘特征	Biānyuán tèzhēng	
Edge flags	边标记	Biān biāojì	
EDGE general packet radio service	EDGE 分组交换传输 模式	EDGE fēnzǔ jiāohuàn chuánshū móshì	EGPRS
Edge generation (CAD/CAM)	边生成	Biān shēngchéng	EG
Edge jitter	边缘抖动	Biānyuán dǒudòng	
Edge join	边界连接	Biānjiè liánjiē	
Edge join	边缘拼接	Biānyuán pīnjiē	
EDGE label switching router	边界标志交换路由器	Biānjiè biāozhì jiāohuàn lùyóu qì	
Edge light emitting diode	边发射发光管	Biān fāshè fāguāng guǎn	ELED
Edge matching	边缘匹配	Biānyuán pǐpèi	
Edge mode suppression	边模抑制	Biānmó yìzhì	
Edge rail system (semiconductor mfg)	边缘钢轨系统	Biānyuán gāngguǐ xìtǒng	
Edge router	边缘路由器	Biānyuán lùyóuqì	ER
Edge sharpness	边缘锐度	Biānyuán ruìdù	

Edge switch	边缘交换机	Biānyuán jiāohuànjī	
Edge-dividing expansion (CAD/CAM)	边分享展开	Biān fēnxiǎng zhǎnkāi	
Edge-enabled	启用边缘	Qǐyòng biānyuán	
Edge-exclusive expansion (CAD/CAM)	边独享展开	Biān dúxiǎng zhǎnkāi	
Edge-guide mode isolator	边导模隔离器	Biān dǎo mó gélíqì	
Edge-node graph	边界结点图	Biānjiè jiédiǎn tú	
Edge-prepared	边缘就绪	Biānyuán jiùxù	
Edge-sharing expansion (CAD/CAM)	边共享展开	Biān gòngxiǎng zhǎnkāi	
Edit menu (WP command)	编辑菜单	Biānjí càidān	
Editing	编辑	Biānjí	
Editing process	编辑处理	Biānjí chǔlǐ	
Editor	编辑器	Biānjíqì	
Educational television hall	电教馆	Diànjiào guǎn	
Educational television hall	电视教育馆	Diànshì jiàoyù guǎn	
Effect	效果	Xiàoguǒ	
Effective address	有效地址	Yǒuxiào dìzhǐ	EA
Effective area	有效面积	Yǒuxiào miànjī	
Effective attenuation factor	有效衰减系数	Yǒuxiào shuāijiǎn xìshù	EAF
Effective core	有效纤芯	Yǒuxiào qiànxīn	
Effective core diameter	有效纤芯直径	Yǒuxiào qiànxīn zhíjìng	
Effective date transfer rate	有效数据传送速率	Yǒuxiào shùjù chuánsòng sùlǜ	
Effective gain in spectrum utilization	频谱利用有效增益	Pínpǔ liyòng yǒuxiào zēngyì	
Effective height (of an antenna)	有效高度	Yǒuxiào gāodù	
Effective input	有效输入	Yǒuxiào shūrù	
Effective instantaneous field of view	有效瞬时视野	Yǒuxiào shùnshí shìyě	EIFOV
Effective isotropic radiated power	有效全向辐射功率	Yǒuxiào quánxiàng fúshè gōnglǜ	EiRP
Effective isotropically radiated power	有效各向同性辐射功率	Yǒuxiào gèxiàng tóngxìng fúshè gōnglǜ	EIRP
Effective length (of an antenna)	有效长度	Yǒuxiào chángdù	
Effective margin (of a given apparatus)	有效改正力	Yǒuxiào gǎizhènglì	
Effective monopole radiated power	有效单极辐射功率	Yǒuxiào dānjí fúshè gōnglǜ	EMRP
Effective noise bandwidth	有效噪声带宽	Yǒuxiào zàoshēng dàikuān	ENB
Effective numerical aperture	有效数值孔径	Yǒuxiào shùzhí kǒngjìng	
Effective porosity	有效空隙率	Yǒuxiào kòngxì lǜ	
Effective radiated power	有效辐射功率	Yǒuxiào fúshè gōnglǜ	ERP
Effective selectivity	有效选择性	Yǒuxiào xuǎnzéxìng	
Effective stress	有效应力	Yǒuxiào yìnglì	
Effective time width	有效时宽	Yǒuxiào shíkuān	
Effective transfer rate	有效传送速率	Yǒuxiào chuánsòng sùlǜ	
Efficiency	效率	Xiàolǜ	
Efficient	高效	Gāoxiào	
Efficient customer response	有效客户反应	Yǒuxiào kèhù fǎnyìng	ECR
Egg crate lens	窗格式透镜	Chuānggé-shì tòujìng	
Egress LSR	边缘出节点	Biānyuán chū jiédiǎn	
E-H tuner	E-H 面调节器	E-H miàn tiáojiéqì	
Eigenket (in quantum cryptography)	本征态	Běnzhēngtài	
Eigenvalues	固有值	Gùyǒuzhí	

Eigenvibration, principal vibration	固有振动	Gùyǒu zhèndòng	
Elapsed time	过渡时间	Guòdù shíjiān	
Elastic asynchronous-to-synchronous interface	弹性异步-同步接口	Tánxìng yìbù—tóngbù jiēkǒu	EASI
Elastic body	弹性体	Tánxìngtǐ	
Elastic limit	弹性限度	Tánxìng xiàndù	
Elastic modulus (measured in Gpa)	弹性模量	Tánxìng móliàng	
Elastic rebound	弹性反应	Tánxìng fǎnyìng	
Elastic wave	弹性波	Tánxìng bō	
Elasticity	弹性	Tánxìng	
Elasto-plastic joint	弹塑性连接	Tánsùxìng liánjiē	
Elasto-plastic response spectrum	弹塑性反应谱	Tánsùxìng fǎnyìng pǔ	
Elasto-plasticity	弹塑性	Tánsùxìng	
Electret	驻极体	Zhùjítǐ	
Electret microphone	驻极体传声器	Zhùjítǐ chuánshēngqì	
Electric accident	电气事故	Diànqì shìgù	
Electric charge time constant (of a detector)	充电时间常数	Chōngdiàn shíjiān chángshù	
Electric conductor	导电体	Dǎodiàn tǐ	
Electric control attenuator	电调衰减器	Diàntiáo shuāijiǎnqì	
Electric echo loss	电回波损耗	Diàn huíbō sǔnhào	EEL
Electric field	电场	Diànchǎng	
Electric field radiated emissions (Mil-Std-461E, RE102)	电场辐射发射	Diànchǎng fúshè fāshè	
Electric field radiated susceptibility (Mil-Std-461E, RS103)	电场辐射敏感度	Diànchǎng fúshè mǐngǎndù	
Electric field strength	电场强度	Diànchǎng qiángdù	
Electric sequence number	电子序号	Diànzǐ xùhào	ESN
Electric shield	电屏蔽	Diàn píngbì	
Electric shielding	电屏蔽	Diànpíngbì	
Electric shock	电击	Diànjī	
Electrical boresight (of an antenna)	电的视轴	Diànde shìzhóu	
Electrical charge time constant of a detector	检波器的充电时间常数	Jiǎnbōqìde chōngdiàn shíjiān chángshù	
Electrical conductivity	导电率	Dǎodiànlǜ	
Electrical corrosion, erode by electricity	电蚀	Diànshí	
Electrical discharge time constant (of a detector)	放电时间常数	Fàngdiàn shíjiān chángshù	
Electrical discharge time constant (of a detector)	检波器的放电时间常数	Jiǎnbōqìde fàngdiàn shíjiān chángshù	
Electrical erosion	电腐蚀	Diànfǔshí	
Electrical fast transient/burst	电快速瞬变脉冲群	Diàn kuàisù shùnbiàn màichōng qún	EFT/B
Electrical impedance characteristics	电阻抗特性	Diànzǔkàng tèxìng	EIC
Electrical installation	电气装置	Diànqì zhuāngzhì	FD
Electrical length (of a waveguide element or component)	电长度	Diàn chángdù	
Electrical logging	电测井	Diàncèjǐng	
Electrical man machine interface	电的人机接口	Diànde rénjī jiēkǒu	EMMI
Electrical network	电网络	Diàn wǎngluò	
Electrical numerical integrator & calculator	电子数字综合计算机	Diànzǐ shùzì zōnghé jìsuànjī	ENIAC
Electrical prospecting	电气勘查	Diànqì kānchá	
Electrical time division multiplexing	电时分复用	Diàn shífēn fùyòng	ETDM
Electrical/optical conversion	电/光转变	Diàn/guāng zhuǎnbiàn	E/O

Electrical/optical signal converter	电光信号转换器	Diànguāng xìnhào zhuǎnhuànqì	E/O
Electrically alterable storage	电可改存储器	Diàn kěgǎi cúnchǔqì	
Electrically erasable programmable read only memory	电可擦可编程序的只读存储器	Diàn kěcā kěbiān chéngxùde zhǐdú cúnchǔqì	EEPROM
Electrically erasable programmable read-only memory	电可擦可编程只读存储器	Diàn kěcā kěbiānchéng zhǐdú cúnchǔqì	EEPROM
Electrically erasable programmable ROM	电擦写可编程只读存储器	Diàn cāxiě kěbiānchéng zhǐdú cúnchǔqì	EEPROM
Electrically steerable antenna	电控转向天线	Diànkòng zhuǎnxiàng tiānxiàn	
Electrically variable optical attenuator	电控可变光衰减器	Diànkòng kěbiàn guāng shuāijiǎnqì	EVOA
Electricity absorption - distributed feedback	电吸收分布反馈	Diànxīshōu fēnbù fǎnkuì	EA-DFB
Electricity absorption modulation	电吸收调制	Diànxīshōu tiáozhì	EAM
Electroabsorption modulated laser	电吸收调制激光器	Diànxīshōu tiáozhì jīguāngqì	EML
Electroabsorption modulator	电吸收调制器	Diànxīshōu tiáozhìqì	EAM
Electrochromic display	电铬显示器	Diàngè xiǎnshìqì	ECD
Electroluminescence display	电激发光显示器	Diànjī fāguāng xiǎnshìqì	ELD
Electroluminescent display panel	场致发光显示板	Chǎngzhì fāguāng xiǎnshìbǎn	
Electromagnetic	电磁	Diàncí	
Electromagnetic compatibility	电磁兼容性	Diàncí jiānróngxìng	EMC
Electromagnetic compatibility level	电磁兼容电平	Diàncí jiānróng diànpíng	
Electromagnetic compatibility margin	电磁兼容裕量	Diàncí jiānróng yùliàng	
Electromagnetic coupling	电磁耦合	Diàncí ǒuhé	
Electromagnetic disturbance	电磁骚扰	Diàncí sāorǎo	
Electromagnetic disturbance	电磁通扰	Diàncí tōngrǎo	
Electromagnetic emission	电磁发射	Diàncí fāshè	
Electromagnetic energy	电磁能量	Diàncí néngliàng	
Electromagnetic environment	电磁环境	Diàncí huánjìng	
Electromagnetic field	电磁场	Diàncíchǎng	
Electromagnetic induction	电磁感应	Diàncí gǎnyìng	
Electromagnetic interference	电磁干扰	Diàncí gānrǎo	EMI
Electromagnetic interference safety margin	电磁干扰安全裕度	Diàncí gānrǎo ānquán yùdù	
Electromagnetic mode	电磁模	Diàncí mó	
Electromagnetic noise	电磁噪声	Diàncí zàoshēng	
Electromagnetic noise	电磁噪声	Diàncí zàoshēng	
Electromagnetic pollution	电磁污染	Diàncí wūrǎn	
Electromagnetic pulse	电磁脉冲	Diàncí màichōng	EMP
Electromagnetic pulse jamming	电磁脉冲干扰	Diàncí màichōng gānrǎo	
Electromagnetic radiation	电磁辐射	Diàncí fúshè	
Electromagnetic screen	电磁屏蔽	Diàncí píngbì	
Electromagnetic sensibility	电磁敏感性	Diàncí mǐngǎnxìng	EMS
Electromagnetic shielding	电磁屏蔽	Diàncí píngbì	
Electromagnetic spectrum	电磁光谱	Diàncí guāngpǔ	
Electromagnetic survey	电磁勘查	Diàncí kānchá	
Electromagnetic susceptibility	电磁敏感度	Diàncí mǐngǎndù	
Electromagnetic susceptibility	电磁敏感性	Diàncí mǐngǎnxìng	
Electromagnetic wave	电磁波	Diàncíbō	
Electromotive force	电动势	Diàndòngshì	emf
Electron beam	电子束	Diànzǐ shù	

Electron frequency drift	电子频移	Diànzǐ pínyí	
Electronic atlas	电子地图集	Diànzǐ dìtújí	
Electronic attack (IW)	电子攻击	Diànzǐ gōngjī	EA
Electronic automatic tuning	电子自动调谐	Diànzǐ zìdòng tiáoxié	
Electronic beam focusing	电子注聚焦	Diànzǐ zhù jùjiāo	
Electronic bonding	电子传单	Diànzǐ chuándān	
Electronic camouflage	电子伪装	Diànzǐ wěizhuāng	
Electronic chart	电子海图	Diànzǐ hǎitú	
Electronic check, e-check	电子支票	Diànzǐ zhīpiào	
Electronic code book	电子密本	Diànzǐ mìběn	ECB
Electronic commerce over Internet	因特网电子商务	Yīntèwǎng diànzǐ shāngwù	ECoI
Electronic commerce over Internet	因特网上电子商务	Yīntèwǎng-shàng diànzi shāngwù	
Electronic commerce, e-commerce	电子商务	Diànzǐ shāngwù	EC
Electronic computer originated mail	面向计算机电子邮件	Miànxiàng jìsuànjī diànzi yóujiàn	ECOM
Electronic countermeasures	电子对抗	Diànzǐ duìkàng	ECM
Electronic crosspoint	电子交叉点	Diànzǐ jiāochādiǎn	
Electronic data interchange	电子数据交换	Diànzi shùjù jiāohuàn	EDI
Electronic data interchange (EDI) management-based interface realization for customer network management service	用户网络管理业务的基于电子数据交换管理的接口实现	Yònghù wǎngluò guǎnlǐ yèwùde jīyú diànzi shùjù jiāohuàn guǎnlǐde jiēkǒu shíxiàn	CNMe
Electronic data processing center	电子数据处理器	Diànzǐ shùjù chǔlǐqì	EDPC
Electronic design automation	电子设计自动化	Diànzǐ shèjì zìdònghuà	
Electronic distance measuring device	电子距离测量设备	Diànzǐ jùlí cèliáng shèbèi	EDMD
Electronic Engineers Association	电子工程师协会	Diànzǐ gōngchéngshī xiéhuì	EEA
Electronic entertainment expo	电子娱乐展览会	Diànzǐ yúlè zhǎnlǎnhuì	E3
Electronic Frontier Foundation	电子前线基金会	Diànzǐ qiánxiàn jījīnhuì	EFF
Electronic Industries Association	电子工业联合会	Diànzǐ gōngyè liánhéhuì	EIA
Electronic Industries Association	电子工业协会	Diànzǐ gōngyè xiéhuì	EIA
Electronic Industries Association (US)	美国电子工业协会	Měiguó diànzǐ gōngyè xiéhuì	EIA
Electronic integration, e-integration	电子集成	Diànzǐ jíchéng	
Electronic jamming	电子干扰	Diànzǐ gānrǎo	
Electronic key exchange	电子密匙交换	Diànzǐ mìshi jiāohuàn	
Electronic key telephone system	电子按键电话系统	Diànzǐ ànjiàn diànhuà xìtǒng	EKTS
Electronic learning; E-learning	远程教学	Yuǎnchéng jiàoxué	
Electronic mail	电子信箱	Diànzǐ xìnxiāng	E-mail
Electronic mail, e-mail	电子邮件	Diànzi yóujiàn	
Electronic mobile exchange	移动式电子电话交换局	Yídòng-shì diànzǐ diànhuà jiāohuànjú	EMX
Electronic news gathering	电子新闻收集	Diànzǐ xīnwén shōují	ENG
Electronic numbering	电子号码	Diànzǐ hàomǎ	ENUM
Electronic order system	在线订货体系	Zàixiàn dìnghuò tǐxì	E0S
Electronic packaging	电子组装	Diànzǐ zǔzhuāng	
Electronic private automatic branch exchange	专用电子自动交换分机	Zhuānyòng diànzǐ zìdòng jiāohuàn fēnjī	EPABX
Electronic private branch exchange	专用支线电子交换机	Zhuānyòng zhīxiàn diànzǐ jiāohuànjī	EPBX
Electronic reconnaissance	电子侦察	Diànzǐ zhēnchá	
Electronic scanning antenna	电扫描天线	Diànsǎomiáo tiānxiàn	
Electronic scanning radar	电扫描雷达	Diànsǎomiáo léidá	

Electronic sequence number	电子串号	Diànzǐ chuànhào	ESN
Electronic serial number	电子串号	Diànzǐ chuànhào	ESN
Electronic serial number	电子序列号	Diànzǐ xùlièhào	ECN
Electronic support (in electronic warfare)	电子支援	Diànzǐ zhīyuán	
Electronic sweep generator	电子扫描振荡器	Diànzǐ sǎomiáo zhèndàngqì	ESG
Electronic switching programming language	电子交换程序设计语言	Diànzǐ jiāohuàn chéngxù shèjì yǔyán	ESPL
Electronic system engineering	电子系统工程	Diànzǐ xìtǒng gōngchéng	
Electronic telephone switching system	电子电话交换系统	Diànzǐ diànhuà jiāohuàn xìtǒng	ETSS
Electronic voice processing	电子话音处理	Diànzǐ huàyīn chǔlǐ	
Electronic warfare	电子战	Diànzǐzhàn	EW
Electronic warfare (EW) simulation test range	电子战模拟试验场	Diànzǐzhàn mónǐ shìyànchǎng	
Electronic white board	电子白板	Diànzǐ báibǎn	
Electronic/optical conversion	电/光转换	Diàn/guāng zhuǎnhuàn	E/O
Electronically agile radar	机载相控阵天线雷达	Jīzài xiàngkòng zhèn tiānxiàn léidá	EAR
Electronically small antenna	电小天线	Diàn xiǎo tiānxiàn	
Electronically-controlled telephone exchange	电子控制的电话交换局	Diànzǐ kòngzhìde diànhuà jiāohuànjú	ECX
Electro-optic crystal	电光光学晶体	Diànguāng guāngxué jīngtǐ	
Electro-optic deflector	电光偏折器	Diànguāng piānzhéqì	
Electro-optic modulator	电光调变器	Diànguāng tiáobiànqì	
Electro-optic scanner	电光扫瞄器	Diànguāng sǎomiáoqì	
Electro-optical countermeasures	光电对抗	Guāngdiàn duìkàng	
Electroplating part	电镀零件	Diàndù língjiàn	
Electrostatic deflection	静电偏转	Jìngdiàn piānzhuǎn	
Electrostatic deflection tube	静电偏转管	Jìngdiàn piānzhuǎn guǎn	
Electrostatic discharge	静电放电	Jìngdiàn fàngdiàn	ESD
Electrostatic discharge	静电释放	Jìngdiàn shìfàng	ESD
Electrostatic discharge protection threshold	静电放电防护阈值	Jìngdiàn fàngdiàn fánghù yù zhí	
Electrostatic focus	静电聚焦	Jìngdiàn jùjiāo	
Electrostatic line scanner	电子扫描仪	Diànzǐ sǎomiáoyí	
Electrostatic plotter	静电绘图仪	Jìngdiàn huìtúyí	
Element cell	单元室	Dānyuán shì	
Element management	网元管理	Wǎngyuán guǎnlǐ	EM
Element management layer	网元管理层	Wǎngyuán guǎnlǐ céng	EML
Element management layer topology configurator	单元管理层拓扑结构	Dānyuán guǎnlǐcéng tuòpū jiégòu	EML-TC
Element management system	单元管理系统	Dānyuán guǎnlǐ xìtǒng	EMS
Element management system	网元管理系统	Wǎngyuán guǎnlǐ xìtǒng	EMS
Element manager	单元管理者	Dānyuán guǎnlǐzhě	EM
Element of service	服务要素	Fúwù yàosù	
Element stream	单元流	Dānyuán liú	ES
Element synchronization	码元同步	Mǎyuán tóngbù	
Elementary assignment	基本分配	Jīběn fēnpèi	EA
Elementary basic service group	基础单元业务群	Jīchǔ dānyuán yèwù qún	EBSG
Elementary cable section	单元电缆段	Dānyuán diànlǎn duàn	
Elementary data types	基本数据类型	Jīběn shùjù lèixíng	
Elementary electric dipole	基本电偶极子	Jīběn diàn'ǒujízǐ,	
Elementary file	基本文件	Jīběn wénjiàn	EF

Elementary file	基础文件	Jīchǔ wénjiàn	EF
Elementary magnetic dipole	基本磁偶极子	Jīběn cí'ǒujízi	
Elementary maintenance activity	基本维护作业	Jīběn wéihù zuòyè	
Elementary operation	基本操作	Jīběn cāozuò	EO
Elementary regenerator section	单元再生段	Dānyuán zàishēng duàn	
Elementary repeater section	单元中继段	Dānyuán zhōngjì duàn	
Elementary time unit	基本时间单元	Jīběn shíjiān dānyuán	ETU
Elevator seeking algorithm	电梯式查找（寻道）算法	Diàntī-shì cházhǎo (xúndào) suànfǎ	
Eliminating-edge aggregation (CAD/CAM)	消边聚合	Xiāobiān jùhé	
Elitech Datacom Co. Ltd., Shenzhen	安立达通信设备有限公司	Ānlìdá tōngxìn shèbèi yǒuxiàn gōngsī	
Ellipse; elliptic	椭圆	Tuǒyuán	
Ellipsoid	椭圆体	Tuǒyuántǐ	
Ellipsoid mirror	椭圆面镜	Tuǒyuán miànjìng	
Ellipsoidal height	椭圆体高度	Tuǒyuántǐ gāodù	
Ellipsometry (semiconductor mfg)	椭偏仪	Tuǒpiānyí	
Elliptic curve crypto	椭圆曲线加密	Tuǒyuán qūxiàn jiāmì	ECC
Elliptic curve cryptosystem	椭圆曲线密码体制	Tuǒyuán qūxiàn mìmǎ tǐzhì	
Elliptical curve discrete logarithm problem	椭圆曲线离散对数问题	Tuǒyuán qūxiàn lísàn duìshù wèntí	ECDLP
Elliptical flexible waveguide	椭圆软波导	Tuǒyuán ruǎn bōdǎo	
Elliptical orbit (of a satellite)	椭圆轨道	Tuǒyuán guǐdào	
Elliptical polarization	椭圆极化	Tuǒyuán jíhuà	
Elliptical variogram	椭球变异函数	Tuǒqiú biànyì hánshù	
Elliptical waveguide	椭圆波导管	Tuǒyuán bōdǎoguǎn	
Elliptical waveguide	椭圆形波导	Tuǒyuánxíng bōdǎo	
Elliptically polarized wave	椭圆极化波	Tuǒyuán jíhuà bō	
Elongation	延伸率	Yánshēnlǜ	
Emanation (IPsec)	发射	Fāshè	
Emanation security (IPsec)	发射安全	Fāshè ānquán	
E-marketplace	电子市场	Diànzǐ shìchǎng	
Embedded	嵌入式	Qiànrù-shì	
Embedded adaptive differential pulse code modulation	嵌入式自适应差分脉冲编码调制	Qiànrù-shì zìshìyìng chāfēn màichōng biānmǎ tiáozhì	E-ADPCM
Embedded block RAM	嵌入模块 RAM	Qiànrù mókuài RAM	
Embedded control channel	嵌入控制通道	Qiànrù kòngzhì tōngdào	ECC
Embedded control channel	嵌入控制通路	Qiànrù kòngzhì tōnglù	ECC
Embedded control set	内嵌控制集	Nèiqiàn kòngzhì jí	
Embedded controller	嵌入式控制器	Qiànrù-shì kòngzhìqì	EC
Embedded controller	微型控制器	Wēixíng kòngzhìqì	EC
Embedded industrial control computer	嵌入式工控机	Qiànrù-shì gōngkòngjī	
Embedded mobile database	嵌入移动数据库	Qiànrù yídòng shùjùkù	EMDB
Embedded object	内嵌对象	Nèiqiàn duìxiàng	
Embedded operating channel	嵌入操作通道	Qiànrù cāozuò tōngdào	EOC
Embedded operations channel	嵌入操作通路	Qiànrù cāozuò tōnglù	EOC
Embedded operations channel	嵌入操作信道	Qiànrù cāozuò xìndào	EOC
Embedded processor	嵌入式处理器	Qiànrù-shì chǔlǐqì	
Embedded real-time target	嵌入实时目标	Qiànrù shíshí mùbiāo	

Embedded SQL	嵌入式 SQL 语句	Qiànrù-shì SQL yǔjù	
Embedded standard products	嵌入标准产品	Qiànrù biāozhǔn chǎnpǐn	ESP
Embedded testing	嵌入测试	Qiànrù cèshì	
Embedded testing	嵌套测试	Qiàntào cèshì	
Embedded voice mail	嵌入式语音邮件	Qiànrù-shì yǔyīn yóujiàn	
Embedded watermark	嵌入水印	Qiànrù shuǐyìn	
Embedded zerotree wavelet coding method	嵌入式零树小波编码方法	Qiànrù-shì líng shù xiǎobō biānmǎ fāngfǎ	EZW
Embedding dimension	嵌入维数	Qiànrù wéishù	
Emergency	应急	Yìngjí	
Emergency action	应急动作	Yìngjí dòngzuò	
Emergency call	紧急呼叫	Jǐnjí hūjiào	
Emergency communication	应急通信	Yìngjí tōngxìn	
Emergency incident management port	紧急事件管理端口	Jǐnjí shìjiàn guǎnlǐ duānkǒu	EMP
Emergency lighting	照明设备	Zhàomíng shèbèi	
Emergency message automatic transmission system	应急信息自动传输系统	Yìngjí xìnxī zìdòng chuánshū xìtǒng	EMATS
Emergency position-indicating radio beacon	应急示位无线电信标	Yìngjí shìwèi wúxiàndiàn xìnbiāo	EPIRB
Emergency position-indicating radiobeacon station	紧急指位无线信标台	Jǐnjízhǐ wèi wúxiàn xìnbiāotái	
Emergency position-indication radio beacon station	应急示位无线电信标电台	Yìngjí shìwèi wúxiàndiàn xìnbiāo diàntái	
Emergency power	应急电源	Yìngjí diànyuán	EP
Emergency repair disk	紧急修复磁盘	Jǐnjí xiūfù cípán	ERD
Emergency socket	应急插座	Yìngjí chāzuò	
Emission	发射	Fāshè	
Emission beam angle between half-power points	半功率点的发射光束角	Bàn gōnglǜ diǎnde fāshè guāngshù jiǎo	
Emission level (of a disturbance source)	发射电平	Fāshè diànpíng	
Emission level of a disturbance source	骚扰源的发射电平	Sāorǎo yuánde fāshè diànpíng	
Emission limit	发射限值	Fāshè xiànzhí	
Emission limit from a disturbing source	来自骚扰源的发射限值	Láizì sāorǎoyuánde fāshè xiànzhí	
Emission limit of a disturbance source	骚扰源的发射限量	Sāorǎo yuánde fāshè xiànliàng	
Emission margin	发射裕量	Fāshè yùliàng	
Emitter	发射机	Fāshèjī	E
Emitter	发射器	Fāshèqì	E
Emitter	发送器	Fāsòngqì	E
Emitter (of electromagnetic disturbance)	辐射源	Fúshèyuán	
Emitter coupled logic	射极耦合逻辑	Shè jí ǒuhé luóji	ECL
Emoticon	表情符号	Biǎoqíng fúhào	
Emoticon	情感符号	Qínggǎn fúhào	
Empirical equation	经验公式	Jīngyàn gōngshì	
Empowering control message	授权控制消息	Shòuquán kòngzhì xiāoxi	ECM
Empowering management message	授权管理消息	Shòuquán guǎnlǐ xiāoxi	EMM
Empty base class optimization	空基类优化	Kōng jīlèi yōuhuà	EBCO
Emulator	仿真器	Fǎngzhēnqì	
En bloc sending	整体发送	Zhěngtǐ fāsòng	
Enablenet	能网	Néng wǎng	
En-bloc signaling	成组信令	Chéngzǔ xìnlìng	
Encapsulating security payload	封装安全荷	Fēngzhuāng ānquán hé	ESP

Encapsulating security payload	封装安全净荷	Fēngzhuāng ānquán jìnghé	ESP
Encapsulating security payload (in IPSec)	封装安全负载	Fēngzhuāng ānquán fùzài	ESP
Encapsulating security payload (protocol)	封装安全载荷(协议)	Fēngzhuāng ānquán zàihè (xiéyì)	ESP
Encapsulation	封装	Fēngzhuāng	
Encapsulation bridging	封装桥接	Fēngzhuāng qiáojiē	
Encapsulation test	密封试验	Mìfēng shìyàn	
Encapsulation test	密封性试验	Mìfēngxìng shìyàn	
Encipherment protection	加密保护	Jiāmì bǎohù	
Encipherment scheme	加密方案	Jiāmì fāng'àn	
Enclosing class	外围类别	Wàiwéi lèibié	
Enclosure	外壳	Wàiké	
Enclosure port	机箱端口	Jīxiāng duānkǒu	
Enclosure port	外部端口	Wàibù duānkǒu	
Encode	锁码	Suǒmǎ	
Encode by group	按组编码	Àn zǔbiān mǎ	
Encoded data string	编码数据串	Biānmǎ shùjù chuàn	
Encoded information type	编码信息类型	Biānmǎ xìnxī lèixíng	EIT
Encoder output	编码器输出	Biānmǎqì shūchū	
Encoder overall operating time	编码器总工作时间	Biānmǎqì zǒng gōngzuò shíjiān	
Encoding	编码	Biānmǎ	
Encoding constraint length	编码约束长度	Biānmǎ yuēshù chángdù	
Encoding law	编码律	Biānmǎ lǜ	
Encoding process	编码过程	Biānmǎ guòchéng	
Encoding rules	编码规则	Biānmǎ guīzé	
Encoding service	符号化服务	Fúhàohuà fúwù	
Encrypted trigger	加密触发器	Jiāmì chùfāqì	
Encryption algorithm	加密算法	Jiāmì suànfǎ	
Encryption control protocol	保密控制协议	Bǎomì kòngzhì xiéyì	ECP
Encryption control protocol	加密控制协议	Jiāmì kòngzhì xiéyì	ECP
Encryption control signal	加密控制信号	Jiāmì kòngzhì xìnhào	ECS
Encryption key	加密密钥	Jiāmì mìyào	
Encryption mechanism (IPsec)	加密机制	Jiāmì jīzhì	
Encryption, encipherment	加密	Jiāmì	
Encryption/decryption library	加密/解密库	Jiāmì/jiěmì kù	
End capacitor	端电容器	Duān diànróngqì	
End delimiter	结束定界符	Jiéshù dìngjiè fú	ED
End edge	结尾边缘	Jiéwěi biānyuán	
End finish	端面光洁度	Duānmiàn guāngjiédù	
End frame series	帧结束序列	Zhèng jiéshù xùliè	EFS
End node	终点码	Zhōngdiǎn mǎ	
End notice message (IPsec TLS)	结束通告消息	Jiéshù tōnggào xiāoxi	
End of block	块结束符	Kuài jiéshùfú	EOB
End of charge point	收费点的末端	Shōufèi diǎnde mòduān	CEND
End of conversion	转换结束	Zhuǎnhuàn jiéshù	EOC
End of dialing	拨号结束	Bōhào jiéshù	EOD
End of file	文件尾	Wénjiàn wěi	

End of frame	帧终止符	Zhèng zhōngzhǐfú	EOF
End of line	行尾	Háng wěi	
End of media	媒体结束	Méitǐ jiéshù	EM
End of message	消息结束	Xiāoxi jiéshù	EOM
End of optional parameters	可选参数结束标志	Kěxuǎn cānshù jiéshù biāozhì	
End of text	正文结束	Zhèngwén jiéshù	ETX
End of transmission	传输结束	Chuánshū jiéshù	EOT
End of transmission	发送结束	Fāsòng jiéshù	EOT
End of transmission block	码组传输结束	Mazǔ chuánshū jiéshù	ETB
End of transmission character	传输结束字符	Chuánshū jiéshù zifú	
End office	端局	Duān jú	EO
End office	市话端局	Shìhuà duān jú	EO
End plate on a computer board/card	拉手条	Lāshǒutiáo	
End point	端点	Duāndiǎn	
End point	终点	Zhōngdiǎn	
End point alias	端点别名	Duāndiǎn biémíng	
End point identifier	端点标识符	Duāndiǎn biāozhìfú	EID
End session command	结束会话命令	Jiéshù huìhuà mìnglìng	ESC
End system	端系统	Duān xìtǒng	ES
End system	末端系统	Mòduān xìtǒng	
End system	终端系统	Zhōngduān xìtǒng	ES
End system identifier	端系统标识符	Duān xìtǒng biāozhìfú	ESI
End system to intermediate system routing exchange protocol	终端系统对中间系统路由选择交换协议	Zhōngduān xìtǒng duì zhōngjiān xìtǒng lùyóu xuǎnzé jiāohuàn xiéyì	ES-IS
End system to intermediate system routing exchange protocol	终端系统和中间系统路由交换协议	Zhōngduān xìtǒng hé zhōngjiān xìtǒng lùyóu jiāohuàn xiéyì	ES-IS
End system-to-intermediate system	终端系统到中间系统	Zhōngduān xìtǒng dào zhōngjiān xìtǒng	ES-IS
End tag	结束标签	Jiéshù biāoqiān	E tag
End user	端用户	Duān yònghù	
End user	末端用户	Mòduān yònghù	
End user	终端用户	Zhōngduān yònghù	
End user	最终用户	Zuìzhōng yònghù	
End voltage	终止电压	Zhōngzhǐ diànyā	
End-aligned	结尾对准	Jiéwěi duìzhǔn	
End-fire array	端射阵	Duānshèzhèn	
End-guidance radar	末制导雷达	Mòzhìdǎo léidá	
Endless loop, infinite loop, deadloop	死循环	Sǐxúnhuán	
End-of charge voltage	充电终止电压	Chōngdiàn zhōngzhǐ diànyā	
End-of-file mark	文件结束标志	Wénjiàn jiéshù biāozhì	EOF
End-of-message code	电文结束代码	Diànwén jiéshù dàimǎ	
End-of-pulsing signal	脉冲终了信号	Màichōng zhōngliǎo xìnhào	
End-to-end authentication	端对端身份验证	Duān duì duān shēnfen yànzhèng	
End-to-end credit	端对端信用值	Duān duì duān xìnyòngzhí	
End-to-end encryption (IPsec)	端对端加密	Duān duì duān jiāmì	
End-to-end signaling	端到端信令	Duān dào duān xìnlìng	
End-to-end transmission	端到端传输	Duān dào duān chuánshū	

Endurance test	耐久性试验	Nàijiǔxìng shìyàn	
End-user device	末端使用设备	Mòduān shǐyòng shèbèi	
Energy density	能量密度	Néngliàng mìdù	
Energy dispersal technique	能量扩散技术	Néngliàng kuòsàn jìshù	
Energy Sciences Network	能源科学网	Néngyuán kēxué wǎng	Esnet
Energy spectral density	能量谱密度	Néngliàng pǔ mìdù	ESD
Energy Star ©	能源之星	Néngyuán zhī xīng	
Engaged test	占线测试	Zhànxiàn cèshì	
Engagement and separation torque	啮合和分离转矩	Nièhé hé fēnlí zhuànjǔ	
Engine	引擎	Yǐnqíng	
Engineering acceptance test	工程验收测试	Gōngchéng yànshōu cèshì	EAT
Engineering computing object	工程计算对象	Gōngchéng jìsuàn duìxiàng	ECO
Engineering data management	工程数据管理	Gōngchéng shùjù guǎnlǐ	EDM
Engineering datum	工程基准面	Gōngchéng jīzhǔnmiàn	
Engineering judgment	工程判定	Gōngchéng pàndìng	
Engineering map	工程规划图	Gōngchéng guīhuàtú	
Engineering object group	工程对象组	Gōngchéng duìxiàngzǔ	EOG
Engineering Research Center of Information Security Technology	信息安全技术工程研究中心	Xìnxī ānquán jìshù gōngchéng yánjiū zhōngxīn	ERCIST
Engineering simulation	工程仿真	Gōngchéng fǎngzhēn	
Enhanced adaptive motion compensation algorithm	增强自适应运动补偿算法	Zēngqiáng zìshìyìng yùndòng bǔcháng suànfǎ	EAMC
Enhanced call routing	增强型呼叫选路	Zēngqiáng-xíng hūjiào xuǎnlù	ECR
Enhanced carrier reception	增强载波接收	Zēngqiáng zàibō jiēshōu	
Enhanced circuit switched data	增强电路交换数据	Zēngqiáng diànlù jiāohuàn shùjù	ECSD
Enhanced circuit switched data	增强的电路交换数据	Zēngqiángde diànlù jiāohuàn shùjù	ECSD
Enhanced data GSM environment	高性能数据 GSM 环境	Gāoxìngnéng shùjù GSM huánjìng	
Enhanced data rate service (enhanced data rate for GSM evolution)	增强数据速率业务	Zēngqiáng shùjù sùlǜ yèwù	EDGE
Enhanced data rates for global evalution	全球演进增强数据速率	Quánqiú yǎnjìn zēngqiáng shùjù sùlǜ	EDGE
Enhanced data rates for global evolution	GSM 增强数据率改进	GSM zēngqiáng shùjù lǜ gǎijìn	EDGE
Enhanced data rates for GSM evalution	GSM 演进增强数据速率	GSM yǎnjìn zēngqiáng shùjù sùlǜ	EDGE
Enhanced data rates for GSM evolution	全球移动通信系统(GSM)演进的增强型数据率	Quánqiú yídòng tōngxìn xìtǒng (GSM) yǎnjìnde zēngqiángxíng shùjùlǜ	EDGE
Enhanced definition television	增强清晰度电视	Zēngqiáng qīngxīdù diànshì	EDTV
Enhanced digital access communications system	加强的数字接入通信系统	Jiāqiángde shùzì jiērù tōngxìn xìtǒng	EDACS
Enhanced display data channel	增强形视频数据通道协议	Zēngqiáng-xíng shìpín shùjù tōngdào xiéyì	E-DDC
Enhanced extended identification data	增强形扩充身份辨识数据	Zēngqiáng-xíng kuòchōng shēnfen biànshí shùjù	E-EDID
Enhanced full rate	增强型全速率	Zēngqiáng-xíng quánsùlǜ	EFR
Enhanced GGSN	增强型 GGSN	Zēngqiáng-xíng GGSN	E-GGSN
Enhanced graphics adapter	扩展的彩色图形显示适配器	Kuòzhǎnde cǎisè túxíng xiǎnshì shìpèiqì	EGA
Enhanced graphics adapter	增强型图形适配器	Zēngqiáng-xíng túxíng shìpèiqì	EGA
Enhanced HLR	增强型 HLR	Zēngqiáng-xíng HLR	E-HLR
Enhanced industry standard architecture	增强形工业标准架构	Zēngqiáng-xíng gōngyè biāozhǔn jiàgòu	EISA
Enhanced integrated drive electronics	增强形电子集成驱动器	Zēngqiáng-xíng diànzǐ jíchéng qūdòngqì	EIDE
Enhanced interior gateway routing protocol	增强内部网关路由协议	Zēngqiáng nèibù wǎngguān lùyóu xiéyì	EIGRP

Enhanced interior gateway routing protocol	增强的内部网关路由选择协议	Zēngqiángde nèibù wǎngguān lùyóu xuǎnzé xiéyì	EIGRP
Enhanced internal sub-layer service	增强的内部子层服务	Zēngqiángde nèibù zicéng fúwù	E-ISS
Enhanced link state	增强链路状态	Zēngqiáng liànlù zhuàngtài	
Enhanced local management interface	增强型局部管理接口	Zēngqiáng-xíng júbù guǎnlǐ jiēkǒu	ELMI
Enhanced man machine interface for videotex and other retrieval services	可视图文和其他可恢复业务的增强人机接口	Kěshì túwén hé qítā kěhuīfù yèwùde zēngqiáng rénjī jiēkǒu	VEMMI
Enhanced multilevel precedence and preemption service	增强型多级优先和先占业务	Zēngqiáng-xíng duōjí yōuxiān hé xiānzhàn yèwù	EMLPP
Enhanced multi-level precedence and pre-emption service	增强型多级优先和占先业务	Zēngqiáng-xíng duōjí yōuxiān hé zhànxiān yèwù	eMLPP
Enhanced non-return-to-zero	增强型不归零制	Zēngqiáng-xíng bùguīlíng zhì	ENRZ
Enhanced observation time difference	增强观察时间差定位	Zēngqiáng guānchá shíjiān chà dìngwèi	EOTD
Enhanced observed time difference	高级时差检测技术	Gāojí shíchā jiǎncè jìshù	EOTD
Enhanced paging operators code	增强型寻呼码	Zēngqiáng-xíng xúnhū mǎ	EPOC
Enhanced parallel port	增强形平行端口	Zēngqiáng-xíng píngxíng duānkǒu	EPP
Enhanced performance fiber unit	高性能光线单元	Gāoxìngnéng guāngxiàn dānyuán	EPFU
Enhanced position location reporting system	增强型定位报告系统	Zēngqiáng-xíng dìngwèi bàogào xìtǒng	EPLRS
Enhanced private switched communications service	增强型专用交换通信业务	Zēngqiáng-xíng zhuānyòng jiāohuàn tōngxìn yèwù	EPSCS
Enhanced quality television	增质型电视	Zēngzhì-xíng diànshì	
Enhanced small device interface	增强小型设备接口	Zēngqiáng xiǎoxíng shèbèi jiēkǒu	ESDI
Enhanced variable rate coder	增强型可变速率编码器	Zēngqiáng-xíng kěbiàn sùlǜ biānmǎqì	EVRC
Enhanced-quality television	增强质量的电视	Zēngqiáng zhìliàngde diànshì	
Enquiry (inquiry), interrogate	询问	Xúnwèn	ENQ
Ensemble average	总体平均	Zǒngtǐ píngjūn	
Enterprise application integration	企业应用程序集成	Qǐyè yìngyòng chéngxù jíchéng	EAI
Enterprise application integration	企业应用集成	Qǐyè yìngyòng jíchéng	EAI
Enterprise call server	企业呼叫服务器	Qǐyè hūjiào fúwùqì	
Enterprise content management	企业内容管理	Qǐyè nèiróng guǎnlǐ	ECM
Enterprise information management	企业信息管理	Qǐyè xìnxī guǎnlǐ	EIM
Enterprise intranet	企业内部网络	Qǐyè nèibù wǎngluò	
Enterprise process model	企业过程模型	Qǐyè guòchéng móxíng	
Enterprise process modeling system	企业过程模型系统	Qǐyè guòchéng móxíng xìtǒng	EPMS
Enterprise requirement planning	企业需求计划	Qǐyè xūqiú jìhuà	ERP
Enterprise resource plan	企业资源规划	Qǐyè zīyuán guīhuà	ERP
Enterprise resource planning	企业资源计划	Qǐyè zīyuán jìhuà	ERP
Enterprise resources program	企业资源规划	Qǐyè zīyuán guīhuà	ERP
Enterprise systems connection	企业系统互联	Qǐyè xìtǒng hùlián	ESCON
Entire fiber channel frame over IP (IETF use)	在 IP 上传输的光纤信道数据帧	Zài IP-shàng chuánshūde guāngxiān xìndào shùjùzhèng	FCIP
Entity	实体	Shítǐ	
Entity attribute	实体属性	Shítǐ shǔxìng	
Entity authentication (IPsec)	实体认证	Shítǐ rènzhèng	
Entity class	实体类	Shítǐ lèi	
Entity instance	实体实例	Shítǐ shílì	
Entity integrity	实体完整性	Shítǐ wánzhěngxìng	

English	Chinese	Pinyin	Abbreviation
Entity point	实体点	Shítǐ diǎn	
Entity set	实体集	Shítǐ jí	
Entity type	实体类型	Shítǐ lèixíng	
Entity-relationship diagram; ER diagram	实体关系图表	Shítǐ guānxi túbiǎo	
Entity-relationship model; ER model	实体关系模型	Shítǐ guānxi móxíng	
Entity-relationship modeling; ER modeling	实体关系建模	Shítǐ guānxi jiànmó	
Entrance facility	引入设备	Yǐnrù shèbèi	
Entrapment (IPsec)	诱捕	Yòubǔ	
Entropy leakage	熵漏	Shāng lòu	
Enumeration	列举	Lièjǔ	
Enumeration	枚举	Méijǔ	
Enumerator	枚举成员	Méijǔ chéngyuán	
Enumerator	枚举器	Méijǔqì	
Envelope	信封	Xìnfēng	
Envelope (of a signal)	包络	Bāoluò	
Envelope delay	包络时延	Bāoluò shíyán	
Envelope delay distortion	包络延时失真	Bāoluò yánshí shīzhēn	
Envelope demodulation	包络线解调	Bāoluò xiàn jiětiáo	
Envelope for insured letter	保价信封	Bǎojià xìnfēng	
Envelope negative feed-back	包络负反馈	Bāoluò fùfǎnkuì	
Envelope velocity	包络速度	Bāoluò sùdù	
Environment assumption	环境假设	Huánjìng jiǎshè	
Environment chamber	环境试验机	Huánjìng shìyànjī	
Environment factor	环境系数	Huánjìng xìshù	
Environment mapped bump mapping	环境凹凸映射	Huánjìng āotū yìngshè	
Environment module (in SPL)	环境模块	Huánjìng mókuài	
Environment parameters	环境参数	Huánjìng cānshù	
Environment stress screening	环境应力筛选	Huánjìng yìnglì shāixuǎn	ESS
Environment test	环境试验	Huánjìng shìyàn	
Environmental [and power supply] supervision and control (board)	环境电源监控(板)	Huánjìng diànyuán jiānkòng (bǎn)	ESC
Environmental audio extensions	环境音效扩展技术	Huánjìng yīn xiào kuòzhǎn jìshù	EAX
Environmental data	环境数据	Huánjìng shùjù	
Environmental Protection Agency (US)	环境保护局	Huánjìng bǎohù jú	EPA
Environmental remote sensing	环境遥感	Huánjìng yáogǎn	
Environmental Sciences Research Institute (US GIS organization)	环境科学研究所	Huánjìng kēxué yánjiūsuǒ	ESRI
Environmental Sciences Services Administration (US)	环境科学管理局	Huánjìng kēxué guǎnlǐjú	ESSA
Environmental stress cracking resistance	耐环境应力开裂	Nài huánjìng yìnglì kāiliè	ESCR
Environmental test	环境测试	Huánjìng cèshì	
Environmental variable	环境变量	Huánjìng biànliàng	
Epipolar geometry	对极几何	Duìjí jǐhé	
Episode rule discovery by sliding windows	基于滑动窗口的情景规则挖掘算法	Jīyú huádòng chuāngkǒude qíngjǐng guīzé wājué suànfǎ	ERDISWIN
Epistatic interaction	基因连锁	Jīyīn liánsuǒ	
E-plane corner	E-面弯头	E-miàn wāntóu	
E-plane lens	E 面透镜	E-miàn tòujìng	

E-plane sectoral horn antenna	E 面扇形喇叭天线	E-miàn shànxíng lǎba tiānxiàn	
E-plane T circulator	E 面 T 形环行器	E-miàn T-xíng huánxíngqì	
E-plane T-junction	E 面 T 形接头	E-miàn T-xíng jiētóu	
E-plane waveguide bend	E 面弯波导	E-miàn wān bōdǎo	
E-plane Y circulator	E 面 Y 形环行器	E-miàn Y-xíng huánxíngqì	
E-plane Y junction	E-面 Y 形接头	E-miàn Y-xíng jiētóu	
Epoxy resin	环氧树脂	Huányǎng shùzhī	
Epson (Japanese company)	爱普生	Ài-pǔ-shēng	
Equal	相等	Xiāngděng	
Equal area projection (GIS)	等面积投影	Děngmiànjī tóuyǐng	
Equal cash rule	等额现金请领制	Děng'é xiànjīn qǐnglǐng zhì	
Equal error protection	同等的错误保护	Tóngděngde cuòwù bǎohù	EEP
Equal interval classification	等距分类	Děngjù fēnlèi	
Equal length code	等长电码	Děngcháng diànmǎ	
Equal level far end crosstalk	等电平远端串音	Děngdiànpíng yuǎnduān chuànyīn	ELFEXT
Equal level far end crosstalk	等电位远端串扰	Děngdiànwèi yuǎnduān chuànrǎo	ELFEXT
Equal level far end crosstalk attenuation power sum	等电平远端串音衰减功率和	Děngdiànpíng yuǎnduān chuànyīn shuāijiǎn gōnglǜ hé	PSELFEXT
Equality	相等性	Xiāngděngxìng	
Equality gain control	等增益控制	Děngzēngyì kòngzhì	EGC
Equality operator	等号操作符	Děnghào cāozuòfú	
Equalization network	均衡网络	Jūnhéng wǎngluò	
Equalize	均衡	Jūnhéng	EQ
Equalizer	均衡器	Jūnhéngqì	
Equation item	方程项	Fāngchéng xiàng	
Equatorial orbit (of a satellite)	赤道轨道	Chìdào guǐdào	
Equiangle projection (GIS)	等角投影	Děngjiǎo tóuyǐng	
Equiangular spiral antenna	等角螺旋天线	Děngjiǎo luóxuán tiānxiàn	
Equiareal projection (GIS)	等积投影	Děngjī tóuyǐng	
Equidistant projection (GIS)	等距投影	Děngjù tóuyǐng	
Equidistant projection (GIS)	等距离投影	Děngjùlí tóuyǐng	
Equilibrium condition	稳态	Wěntài	
Equilibrium numerical aperture	稳态数值孔径	Wěntài shùzhí kǒngjìng	
Equilibrium slope	稳定斜面	Wěndìng xiémiàn	
Equiphase surface	等相位面	Děngxiàngwèi miàn	
Equipment cable	设备电缆	Shèbèi diànlǎn	
Equipment coding capacity	设备编码容量	Shèbèi biānmǎ róngliàng	
Equipment identification register	设备识别登记器	Shèbèi shíbié dēngjìqì	EIR
Equipment identifier	设备标识符	Shèbèi biāozhìfú	EID
Equipment identity center	设备识别中心	Shèbèi shíbié zhōngxīn	EIR
Equipment identity register	设备标示寄存器	Shèbèi biāoshì jìcúnqì	EIR
Equipment identity register	设备身份寄存器	Shèbèi shēnfen jìcúnqì	EIR
Equipment identity register	设备识别寄存器	Shèbèi shíbié jìcúnqì	EIR
Equipment identity register	设备识别注册处	Shèbèi shíbié zhùcèchù	EIR
Equipment management function	设备管理功能	Shèbèi guǎnlǐ gōngnéng	EMF
Equipment optical cable	设备光缆	Shèbèi guānglǎn	

English	Chinese	Pinyin	Abbr.
Equipment room	设备间	Shèbèi jiān	ER
Equipment under test	受试设备	Shòushì shèbèi	EUT
Equipment under test (ITU-T Recommendation O.161)	被测设备	Bèicè shèbèi	EUT
Equipotential bonding	等电位连接	Děngdiànwèi liánjiē	
Equipotential bonding conductor	等电位连接导体	Děngdiànwèi liánjiē dǎotǐ	
Equivalence	等价	Děngjià	
Equivalence predicate	等价谓词	Děngjià wèicí	
Equivalence relation	等价关系	Děngjià guānxi	
Equivalent (spot) noise temperature (of a linear two-port network)	等效（点）噪声温度（线性双端口网络的）	Děngxiào (diǎn) zàoshēng wēndù (xiànxìng shuāng duān kǒu wǎngluòde)	
Equivalent binary content	等效二进制数	Děngxiào èrjìn zhìshù	
Equivalent bit rate	等效比特率	Děngxiào bǐtèlǜ	
Equivalent dimensionality	等维	Děngwéi	
Equivalent earth radius	等效地球半径	Děngxiào dìqiú bànjìng	
Equivalent four-wire system	等效四线系统	Děngxiào sìxiàn xìtǒng	EFWS
Equivalent gain consolidation	等增益合并	Děngzēngyì hébìng	EGC
Equivalent isotropic radiated power	等效全向辐射功率	Děngxiào quánxiàng fúshè gōnglǜ	EIRP
Equivalent isotropically radiated power (in a given direction)	等效各向同性辐射功率	Děngxiào gèxiàng tóngxìng fúshè gōnglǜ	EIRP
Equivalent linearization method	等值线型化方法	Děngzhí xiànxínghuà fāngfǎ	
Equivalent noise	等效噪声	Děngxiào zàoshēng	EN
Equivalent noise input	等效噪声输入	Děngxiào zàoshēng shūrù	ENI
Equivalent noise resistance (of a one-port network)	等效噪声电阻	Děngxiào zàoshēng diànzǔ	
Equivalent noise voltage (of a one-port network)	等效噪声电压（单端口网络的）	Děngxiào zàoshēng diànyā	
Equivalent number of looks (radar)	等效视数	Děngxiào shìshù	ENL
Equivalent radiated power	等效辐射功率	Děngxiào fúshè gōnglǜ	ERP
Equivalent radius (of a conductor)	等效半径	Děngxiào bànjìng	
Equivalent radius (of a multi-wire element)	等效半径	Děngxiào bànjìng	
Equivalent satellite link noise temperature	等效卫星链路噪声温度	Děngxiào wèixīng liànlù zàoshēng wēndù	
Equivalent satellite link noise temperature	等效卫星线路躁声温度	Děngxiào wèixīng xiànlù zàoshēng wēndù	
Equivalent shear model	等值剪切模型	Děngzhí jiǎnqiē móxíng	
Erasable memory	可擦存储器	Kěcā cúnchǔqì	
Erasable programmable logic array	可擦程序控制逻辑阵列	Kěcā chéngxù kòngzhì luóji zhènliè	EPLA
Erasable programmable read only memory	可擦可编程只读存储器	Kěcā kěbiānchéng zhǐdú cúnchǔqì	EPROM
Erasable programmable read only memory	可擦除的可编程只读存储器	Kěcāchúde kěbiānchéng zhǐdú cúnchǔqì	EPROM
Erasable programmable read only memory	可擦掉的可编程只读存储器	Kěcādiàode kěbiānchéng zhǐdú cúnchǔqì	EPROM
Erasable read only memory	可擦只读存储器	Kěcā zhǐ dú cúnchǔqì	EROM
Erased silence descriptor rate	擦除的 SID 帧率	Cāchúde SID zhèng lǜ	ESIDR
Erased valid silence descriptor rate	擦除的有效 SID 帧率	Cāchúde yǒuxiào SID zhèng lǜ	EVSIDR
Erasure	抹除	Mǒchú	
Erbium laser	铒固体激光	Ěr gùtǐ jīguāng	
Erbium-doped fiber amplifier	掺铒光纤放大器	Chān'ěr guāngxiān fàngdàqì	EDFA
Erbium-doped fiber laser	掺铒光纤激光器	Chān'ěr guāngxiān jīguāngqì	

Erbium-doped fluoridized fiber amplifier	掺铒氟化光纤放大器	Chān'ěr fúhuà guāngxiān fàngdàqì	EDFFA
Ergonomics	人机工程学	Rén jī gōngchéngxué	
Ergonomics	人体工学	Réntǐ gōngxué	
Ericsson (Norwegian company)	爱立信	Ài-lì-xìn	
Ericsson cellular data converter	爱立信蜂窝数据转换器	Ài-lì-xìn fēngwō shùjù zhuǎnhuànqì	ECDC
Ericsson Engineering Tool	爱立信工程工具	Ài-lì-xìn gōngchéng gōngjù	EET
Erlang	爱尔兰	Aì'ěrlán	
Erroneous binary digit	差错二进制数字	Chācuò èrjìnzhì shùzì	
Erroneous block	差错码组	Chācuò mǎzǔ	
Erroneous character	差错字符	Chācuò zìfú	
Erroneous digit	差错数字	Chācuò shùzì	
Error	差错	Chācuò	ERR
Error	误差	Wùchā	
Error acceptance; error handling	容错	Róngcuò	
Error alert task	错误报警任务	Cuòwù bàojǐng rènwu	EAT
Error burst	差错突发	Chācuò tūfā	
Error burst length	差错突发长度	Chācuò tūfā chángdù	
Error check bit	差错检测比特	Chācuò jiǎncè bǐtè	E
Error checking	错误检测	Cuòwù jiǎncè	
Error checking (or correcting) code	纠错码	Jiūcuò mǎ	ECC
Error checking and correction	错误检查修正	Cuòwù jiǎnchá xiūzhèng	ECC
Error checking and correction	错误检验与校正	Cuòwù jiǎnyàn yǔ jiàozhèng	ECC
Error code	误码	Wùmǎ	
Error control	差错控制	Chācuò kòngzhì	
Error control coding	差错控制编码	Chācuò kòngzhì biānmǎ	
Error correcting (or checking) code	错误校正码	Cuòwù jiàozhèng mǎ	ECC
Error correcting capability	纠错能力	Jiūcuò nénglì	
Error correction	纠错	Jiūcuò	
Error correction code	纠错校正码	Jiūcuò jiàozhèng mǎ	ECC
Error correction information feedback and repetition	信息反馈重发纠错	Xìnxī fǎnkuì chóngfā jiūcuò	
Error correction mode (for facsimile)	错误校正模式	Cuòwù jiàozhèng móshì	ECM
Error correction Signal	纠错信号	Jiūcuò xìnhào	ECS
Error detecting and feedback system	检错及反馈重发系统	Jiǎncuò jí fǎnkuì chóngfā xìtǒng	ARQ
Error detection	差错检测	Chācuò jiǎncè	
Error detection	错误检测	Cuòwù jiǎncè	
Error detection	检错	Jiǎncuò	
Error detection and correction	误差检测和纠正	Wùchā jiǎncè hé jiūzhèng	
Error detection code	差错检测码	Chācuò jiǎncè mǎ	EDC
Error detection code	错误检测码	Cuòwù jiǎncè mǎ	
Error detection code	检错码	Jiǎncuòmǎ	
Error detection code byte	错误检波码字节	Cuòwù jiǎnbō mǎ zìjié	EDC
Error detection without repetition	不重发的差错检测	Bù chóngfāde chācuò jiǎncè	
Error free seconds	无差错秒	Wúchācuò miǎo	EFS
Error freezing	错误冻结	Cuòwù dòngjié	
Error function	误差函数	Wùchā hánshù	erf
Error handling	差错处理	Chācuò chǔlǐ	EH

Error handling	误差处理	Wùchā chǔlǐ	
Error indication	错误指示	Cuòwù zhǐshì	AI
Error interval monitor	差错时间段监视	Chācuò shíjiānduàn jiānshì	EIM
Error interval monitor	错误时段监视器	Cuòwù shíduàn jiānshìqì	EIM
Error log (for database)	错误日志	Cuòwù rìzhì	
Error message	出错信息	Chūcuò xìnxī	
Error message	错误信息	Cuòwù xìnxī	
Error modeling	误差模型	Wùchā móxíng	
Error multiplication	误码增殖	Wùmǎ zēngzhí	
Error multiplication factor	误码增殖因子	Wùmǎ zēngzhí yīnzǐ	
Error processing	错误处理	Cuòwù chǔlǐ	
Error propagation	误差传播	Wùchā chuánbō	
Error protection code	防错码	Fángcuòmǎ	
Error rate	差错率	Chācuò lǜ	
Error ratio	差错比	Chācuò bǐ	
Error recovery	错误恢复处理	Cuòwù huīfù chǔlǐ	
Error reporting code	报错码	Bào cuò mǎ	
Error second A	误码秒类型A	Wùmǎ miǎo lèixíng A	ESA
Error second B	误码秒类型B	Wùmǎ miǎo lèixíng B	ESB
Error signal	误差信号	Wùchā xìnhào	
Error signal resolver	误差信号分解器	Wùchā xìnhào fēnjiěqì	
Error spread	误码扩散	Wùmǎ kuòsàn	
Error state number	错误状态号	Cuòwù zhuàngtài hào	
Error status	错误状态	Cuòwù zhuàngtài	
Error, bug	错误	Cuòwù	
Error-detecting and feedback system	检错反馈系统	Jiǎncuò fǎnkuì xìtǒng	
Error-detecting capacity	检错能力	Jiǎncuò nénglì	
Errored block	差错块	Chācuò kuài	EB
Errored block	误块	Wùkuài	EB
Errored block count	误块计数	Wùkuài jìshù	EBC
Errored second	差错秒	Chācuò miǎo	ES
Errored second	误块秒	Wùkuài miǎo	ES
Errored second	误码秒	Wùmǎ miǎo	ES
Errored second (in-service condition)	差错秒（开业务状态）	Chācuò miǎo (kāiyè wù zhuàngtài)	ES
Errored second (out-of-service condition)	差错秒（停业务状态）	Chācuò miǎo (tíngyè wù zhuàngtài)	
Errored second rate	误块秒率	Wùkuài miǎo lǜ	
Errored second ratio	差错秒比	Chācuò miǎo bǐ	ESR
Errored second ratio	误块秒比	Wùkuài miǎo bǐ	ESR
Errored second ratio	误码秒比	Wùmǎ miǎo bǐ	ESR
Errored second ratio	误码秒比率	Wùmǎ miǎo bǐlǜ	ESR
Error-free communication link	无误通信线路	Wúwù tōngxìn xiànlù	EFCL
Error-free seconds	无误码秒	Wúwùmǎ miǎo	EFS
Escape	转义	Zhuǎnyì	ESC
Escape character	换码子复	Huàn mǎzifù	ESC
Escape character	换义子复	Huàn yìzīfù	ESC
Escape character	转义符	Zhuǎnyì fú	

Escape character	转义字符	Zhuǎnyì zìfú	
Escape code	转义码	Zhuǎnyì mǎ	
Escape sequence	转义序列	Zhuǎnyì xùliè	
Escapement point	转移点	Zhuǎnyí diǎn	
Escorted browsing	护航浏览	Hùháng liúlǎn	
Establish confirm (SS7)	建立确认	Jiànlì quèrèn	
Establish request (SS7)	建立请求	Jiànlì qǐngqiú	
Establish temporary connection	建立临时连接	Jiànlì línshí liánjiē	ETC
Estimated retail price	估计零售价	Gūjì língshòujià	ERP
Etched grating	蚀刻光栅	Shíkè guāngshān	
Etching machine (semiconductor mfg)	蚀刻设备	Shíkè shèbèi	
Etching services	蚀刻服务	Shíkè fúwù	
EtherLoop	以太环路	Yǐtài huánlù	
Ethernet	以太网	Yǐtàiwǎng	
Ethernet digital subscriber line	以太数字用户线	Yǐtài shùzì yònghù xiàn	EDSL
Ethernet file transfer protocol	以太网文件传送协议	Yǐtàiwǎng wénjiàn chuánsòng xiéyì	EFTP
Ethernet in the last mile call for interest	最后一英里以太网呼叫兴趣	Zuìhòu yīyīnglǐ yǐtàiwǎng hūjiào xìngqu	ELMCFI
Ethernet interface processor	以太网接口处理器	Yǐtàiwǎng jiēkǒu chǔlǐqì	EIP
Ethernet meltdown	以太网溶解	Yǐtàiwǎng róngjiě	
Ethernet passive optical network	以太网无源光网络	Yǐtàiwǎng wúyuán guāng wǎngluò	EPON
Ethernet switch	以太网交换机	Yǐtàiwǎng jiāohuànjī	
ETSI technical report	ETSI 技术报告	ETSI jìshù bàogào	ETR
Euclidean distance	欧几里得距离	Oū-jǐ-lǐ-dé jùlí	
Eulerian cycle / Chinese postman	Euler 回路/中国邮路	Euler huílù/ Zhōngguó yóulù	
European Academic and Research Network	欧洲科学与研究网	Oūzhōu kēxué yǔ yánjiū wǎng	EARN
European Area communications Plan	欧洲地区通信计划	Oūzhōu dìqū tōngxìn jìhuà	EACP
European Broadcasting Union	欧洲广播联盟	Oūzhōu guǎngbō liánméng	EBU
European Committee of Representatives of Official Cartography	欧洲官方地图学代表委员会	Oūzhōu guānfāng dìtúxué dàibiǎo wěiyuánhuì	CERCO
European Committee of Telecommunication Regulatory Affairs	欧洲通信事务管理委员会	Oūzhōu tōngxìn shìwù guǎnlǐ wěiyuánhuì	ECTRA
European Communications Coordinating Committee	欧洲通信协调委员会	Oūzhōu tōngxìn xiétiáo wěiyuánhuì	ECCC
European communications Satellite	欧洲通信卫星	Oūzhōu tōngxìn wèixīng	ECS
European Communications Satellite Organization	欧洲通信卫星组织	Oūzhōu tōngxìn wèixīng zǔzhī	ECSO
European Computer Manufacturers Association	欧洲计算机制造商协会	Oūzhōu jìsuànjī zhìzàoshāng xiéhuì	ECMA
European Conference of Posts and Telecommunications	欧洲邮政电信会议	Oūzhōu yóuzhèng diànxìn huìyì	ECPT
European Digital Cordless Telephone (DECT) standard cipher algorithm	欧洲数字无绳电话标准密码算法	Oūzhōu shùzì wúshéng diànhuà biāozhǔn mìmǎ suànfǎ	DSCA
European Particle Physics Laboratory	欧洲量子物理试验室	Oūzhōu liàngzǐ wùlǐ shìyànshì	CERN
European Radio Messaging System	欧洲无线电信息系统	Oūzhōu wúxiàndiàn xìnxī xìtǒng	ERMES
European Space Agency	欧洲航天局	Oūzhōu hángtiān jú	ESA
European Telecommunication Standards Institute	欧洲电信标准化委员会	Oūzhōu diànxìn biāozhǔnhuà wěiyuánhuì	ETSI
European Telecommunication Standards Institute	欧洲远程通信标准学会	Oūzhōu yuǎnchéng tōngxìn biāozhǔn xuéhuì	ETSI
European telecommunications numbering space	欧洲通信编号空间	Oūzhōu tōngxìn biānhào kōngjiān	ETNS
European Telecommunications Standard	欧洲电信标准	Oūzhōu diànxìn biāozhǔn	ETS

European Telecommunications Standard	欧洲通信标准	Oūzhōu tōngxìn biāozhǔn	ETS
European Telecommunications Standards Institute	欧洲电信标准组织/协会	Oūzhōu diànxìn biāozhǔn zǔzhī/xiéhuì	ETSI
European Telecommunications Standards Institute	欧洲通信标准研究院	Oūzhōu tōngxìn biāozhǔn yánjiūyuàn	ETSI
European Total Access Communication System	欧洲全向接入通信系统	Oūzhōu quánxiàng jiērù tōngxìn xìtǒng	ETACS
Eutectic solders (in SMT)	共晶焊锡	Gòngjīng hànxī	
Evaluate	评估	Pínggū	
Evanescent mode (in a waveguide)	隐失模	Yǐnshī mó	
Evanescent wave	渐消波	Jiànxiāo bō	
Even parity check	偶检验	Ǒu jiǎnyàn	
Even parity check	偶校验	Ǒu jiàoyàn	
Event	事件	Shìjiàn	
Event analyzer	事件分析器	Shìjiàn fēnxīqì	
Event control block	事件控制块	Shìjiàn kòngzhì kuài	ECB
Event control block	事件控制字组	Shìjiàn kòngzhì zìzǔ	ECB
Event database	事件数据库	Shìjiàn shùjùkù	
Event detection point	事件检出点	Shìjiàn jiǎnchū diǎn	EDP
Event detection point-notification	事件检测点 - 通知	Shìjiàn jiǎncè diǎn-tōngzhī	EDP-N
Event detection point-notification	事件检出点-通知	Shìjiàn jiǎnchū diǎn - tōngzhī	EDP-N
Event detection point-request	事件检测点 - 请求	Shìjiàn jiǎncè diǎn-qǐngqiú	EDP-R
Event detection point-request	事件检出点-请求	Shìjiàn jiǎnchū diǎn -qǐngqiú	EDP-R
Event dissemination	事件广播	Shìjiàn guǎngbō	
Event driven	事件驱动的	Shìjiàn qūdòngde	
Event forwarding discrimination	事件前向判别	Shìjiàn qiánxiàng pànbié	EFD
Event forwarding discriminator	事件黑心发鉴别器	Shìjiàn hēixīnfā jiànbiéqì	EFD
Event forwarding discriminator	事件转发鉴别程序	Shìjiàn zhuǎnfā jiànbié chéngxù	
Event forwarding discriminator	事件转发判定程度	Shìjiàn zhuǎnfā pàndìng chéngdù	
Event generator	事件发生器	Shìjiàn fāshēngqì	
Event handler	事件处理器	Shìjiàn chǔlǐqì	
Event report	事件报告	Shìjiàn bàogào	
Event report management function	事件报告管理功能	Shìjiàn bàogào guǎnlǐ gōngnéng	
Event source	事件源	Shìjiàn yuán	
Event time	事件时间	Shìjiàn shíjiān	
Evidence	证据	Zhèngjù	
Exact frequency	精确频率	Jīngquè pínlǜ	
Example-based machine translation	基于实例的机器翻译	Jīyú shílìde jīqì fānyì	EBMT
Exception	异常	Yìcháng	
Exception declaration	异常声明	Yìcháng shēngmíng	
Exception handler	例外处理器	Lìwài chǔlǐqì	
Exception handling	异常处理	Yìcháng chǔlǐ	
Exception handling mechanism	异常处理机制	Yìcháng chǔlǐ jīzhì	
Exception specification	异常规范	Yìcháng guīfàn	
Exception-safe	异常安全的	Yìcháng ānquánde	
Excess burst	超量突发	Chāoliàng tūfā	Be
Excess burst rate	超额突发速率	Chāo'é tūfā sùlǜ	EBR
Excess burst size	超额突发量	Chāo'é tūfā liáng	Be

Excess burst size	超诺突发量	Chāonuò tūfāliàng	Be
Excess fiber length	光纤余长	Guāngxiān yú cháng	EFL
Excess information rate	超额信息速率	Chāo'é xìnxī sùlǜ	EIR
Excess information rate	超越信息速率	Chāoyuè xìnxī sùlǜ	EIR
Excess loss	附加损耗	Fùjiā sǔnhào	
Excessive pumping	过量抽水	Guòliàng chōushuǐ	
Exchange	交换局	Jiāohuànjú	
Exchange connection	交换局连接	Jiāohuànjú liánjiē	
Exchange identification	交换标识	Jiāohuàn biāozhì	XID
Exchange identifier	交换标识符	Jiāohuàn biāozhì fú	XID
Exchange radio interface	交换机无线接口	Jiāohuànjī wúxiàn jiēkǒu	
Exchange room	交换机房	Jiāohuànjī fáng	
Exchange termination	交换终端	Jiāohuàn zhōngduān	ET
Exchange termination	交换终接	Jiāohuàn zhōngjiē	ET
Exchange termination	交换机终接	Jiāohuànjī zhōngjiē	ET
Exchange termination	交换局终端	Jiāohuànjú zhōngduān	ET
Exchangeable gain (of a two-port network)	可换功率增益	Kěhuàn gōnglǜ zēngyì	
Exchangeable noise power (of a one-port network)	可换噪声功率	Kěhuàn zàoshēng gōnglǜ	
Exchangeable power	可换功率	Kěhuàn gōnglǜ	
Excimer laser	准分子激光	Zhǔn fènzi jīguāng	
Excimer laser processing equipment	准分子激光加工机	Zhǔn fènzi jīguāng jiāgōngjī	
Exclusion range	排除范围	Páichú fànwéi	
Exclusive lock (for database)	排它锁	Páitā suǒ	
Exclusive-NOR gate	“异或非”门	Yìhuòfēi mén	
Exclusive-OR gate	“异或”门	Yìhuò mén	
Executable code	可执行代码	Kězhíxíng dàimǎ	
Executable file	可执行文件	Kězhíxíng wénjiàn	
Executable file	执行档	Zhíxíng dàng	.exe
Executable test case	可能实行的试验项目	Kěnéng shíxíngde shìyàn xiàngmù	
Executable test case	可执行测试实例	Kězhíxíng cèshì shílì	
Executable test suite	可能实行的试验项目组	Kěnéng shíxíngde shìyàn xiàngmù zǔ	
Executable test suite	可执行测试套	Kězhíxíng cèshì tào	ETS
Execute	执行	Zhíxíng	E
Execute buffers	执行缓冲区	Zhíxíng huǎnchōngqū	
Execution cycle	执行周期	Zhíxíng zhōuqī	
Execution state (IPsec)	执行态	Zhíxíng tài	
Executive director	执行董事	Zhíxíng dǒngshì	
Exhaustive means	穷举法	Qióngjǔfǎ	
Existing quality television	常规电视	Chángguī diànshì	
Existing-frame capacity count	现存帧总量计数	Xiàncún zhèng zǒngliàng jìshù	EFCC
Existing-quality television	现有质量的电视	Xiànyǒu zhìliàngde diànshì	
Exit (WP command)	退出	Tuìchū	
Exit/entrance angle	出射/入射角	Chūshè/rùshè jiǎo	
Exogenous factors	外因	Wàiyīn	
Expanded character set	扩展的字符组	Kuòzhǎnde zìfú zǔ	ECS
Expanded memory	扩充内存	Kuòchōng nèicún	

Expanded memory specification	扩展内存规范	Kuòzhǎn nèicún guīfàn	EMS
Expanded memory unit	扩展存储器	Kuòzhǎn cúnchǔqì	EMU
Expanded session reference	扩充的会话参考	Kuòchōngde huìhuà cānkǎo	
Expanded short message entity	扩展短消息实体	Kuòzhǎn duǎnxiāoxi shítǐ	ESME
Expanded transmission time slots	扩展传输时隙	Kuòzhǎn chuánshū shíxì	
Expander	扩展器	Kuòzhǎnqì	
Expander bridge	增强桥	Zēngqiáng qiáo	
Expansibility	可拓展性	Kětuòzhǎnxing	
Expansion (in switching)	扩散	Kuòsàn	
Expansion bus	扩展总线	Kuòzhǎn zǒngxiàn	EB
Expansion joint	扩展节理	Kuòzhǎn jiélǐ	
Expansion measurement	扩展测量	Kuòzhǎn cèliáng	EM
Expansion port	扩展端口	Kuòzhǎn duānkǒu	
Expansion slot	扩充槽	Kuòchōng cáo	
Expansion slot	扩充插槽	Kuòchōng chācáo	
Expectation	期望值	Qīwàngzhí	
Expected measured loss	期望的测量损耗	Qīwàngde cèliáng sǔnhào	EMIL
Expected user response	期待用户响应	Qīdài yònghù xiǎngyìng	XRES
Expedite (in groupware document handling)	催办	Cuībàn	
Expedited delivery	加速传送	Jiāsù chuánsòng	
Expedited forwarding	加速转发	Jiāsù zhuǎnfā	EF
Expedited message handler buffer	加速报文处理器缓冲器	Jiāsù bàowén chǔlǐqì huǎnchōngqì	EMHB
Expedited message handling	加速信息处理	Jiāsù xìnxī chǔlǐ	EMH
Experimental packet switched system	实验分组交换系统	Shíyàn fēnzǔ jiāohuàn xìtǒng	EPSS
Experimental packet switching network	实验包交换系统	Shíyàn bāo jiāohuàn xìtǒng	EPSN
Experimental programming method	试验设计法	Shìyàn shèjì fǎ	
Experimental radio station	实验无线电台	Shíyàn wúxiàndiàntái	
Experimental station	实验电台	Shíyàn diàntái	
Expert system	专家系统	Zhuānjiā xìtǒng	
Expire interval	过期间隔	Guòqī jiàngé	
Explicit addressing	显示地址	Xiǎnshì dìzhǐ	
Explicit call transfer supplementary service	显呼叫传送附加业务	Xiǎn hūjiào chuánsòng fùjiā yèwù	ECT
Explicit congestion notification	明确拥塞通知	Míngquè yōngsè tōngzhī	ECN
Explicit congestion notification	显示拥塞指标	Xiǎnshì yōngsè zhǐbiāo	ECN
Explicit conversion	显示转换	Xiǎnshì zhuǎnhuàn	
Explicit forward congestion indication	显示前向拥塞指示	Xiǎnshì qiánxiàng yōngsè zhǐshì	EFCI
Explicit forward congestion indication	显式前向阻塞指示	Xiǎnshì qiánxiàng zǔsè zhǐshì	EFCI
Explicit forward congestion indicator	明确前向拥塞指示	Míngquè qiánxiàng yōngsè zhǐshì	EFCI
Explicit forward congestion indicator	显式前向拥塞指示符	Xiǎnshì qiánxiàng yōngsè zhǐshìfú	EFCI
Explicit position	绝对位置	Juéduì wèizhì	
Explicit position	直接定位	Zhíjiē dìngwèi	
Explicit rate	显式率	Xiǎnshì lǜ	ER
Explicit routing	显示路由	Xiǎnshì lùyóu	
Explicit specialization	显式特化	Xiǎnshì tèhuà	
Explicit topological description	显式拓扑记述	Xiǎnshì tuòpū jìshù	
Explicit transaction (for database)	显式事务	Xiǎnshì shìwù	

English	Chinese	Pinyin	Abbreviation
Explicitly parallel instruction code	显示并行指令代码	Xiǎnshì bìngxíng zhǐlìng dàimǎ	EPIC
Explict call transfer	显式呼叫转接	Xiǎnshì hūjiào zhuǎnjiē	ECT
Exploit (software program)	溢出程序	Yìchū chéngxù	
Exploratory data analysis	探索数据分析	Tànsuǒ shùjù fēnxī	
Explorer frame	探测帧	Tàncè zhèng	
Explorer packet	探测数据分组	Tàncè shùjù fēnzǔ	
Explosion-proof telephone set	防爆电话机	Fángbào diànhuàjī	
Exponent	指数	Zhǐshù	
Exponential distribution	指数分布	Zhǐshù fēnbù	
Exponential random variable	指数分布随机变量	Zhǐshù fēnbù suíjī biànliàng	
Exponential transmission line	指数式传输线	Zhǐshùshì chuánshū xiàn	
Export	导出	Dǎochū	
Exposed conductive part	外露导电部分	Wàilù dǎodiàn bùfen	
Exposed zone	暴露区	Bàolù qū	
Exposure source	曝光设备	Bàoguāng shèbèi	
Expression	表达式	Biǎodá shì	
Expression folding	表达式折叠	Biǎodáshì zhédié	
Extended address	扩展地址	Kuòzhǎn dìzhǐ	EA
Extended addressing	扩充编址	Kuòchōng biānzhǐ	EA
Extended answer message indication	扩充应答信息指示	Kuòchōng yìngdá xìnxī zhǐshì	EAM
Extended area service (telephony term)	扩大区域服务	Kuòdà qūyù fúwù	EAS
Extended arithmetic module	扩充运算模块	Kuòchōng yùnsuàn mókuài	EAM
Extended assembler language coding	扩充的汇编语言编码	Kuòchōngde huìbiān yǔyán biānmǎ	XALC
Extended attribute adjacency graph (CAD/CAM)	扩展属性邻接图	Kuòzhǎn shǔxìng línjiē tú	EAAG
Extended authorization period	展期签证	Zhǎnqī qiānzhèng	
Extended band fiber amplifier	扩展带光纤放大器	Kuòzhǎn dài guāngxiān fàngdàqì	EBFA
Extended binary coded decimal code	扩充的二-十进制交换码	Kuòchōngde èr-shíjìnzhì jiāohuàn mǎ	EBCDIC
Extended binary coded decimal interchange code	扩展二进制编码的十进制交换格式	Kuòzhǎn èrjìnzhì biānmǎde shíjìnzhì jiāohuàn géshi	EBCDIC
Extended burst transactions	增强式突发处理	Zēngqiáng-shì tūfā chǔlǐ	
Extended capabilities port	扩充能力端口	Kuòchōng nénglì duān kǒu	ECP
Extended changeover acknowledgment	扩展的倒换证实	Kuòzhǎnde dǎohuàn zhèngshí	XCA
Extended changeover order	扩展的倒换命令	Kuòzhǎnde dǎohuàn mìngling	XCO
Extended character set	扩展字符集	Kuòzhǎn zìfú jí	
Extended common service area	扩充的公共服务区	Kuòchōngde gōnggòng fúwùqū	ECSA
Extended data	外延数据	Wàiyán shùjù	
Extended direct memory access	扩充的直接存储器存取	Kuòchōngde zhíjiē cúnchǔqì cúnqǔ	EDMA
Extended enterprise	外延的企业	Wàiyánde qǐyè	
Extended feed	延伸馈电器	Yánshēn kuìdiànqì	
Extended field elliptical aperture lens	可扩展扫描椭圆孔镜头	Kěkuòzhǎn sǎomiáo tuǒyuán kǒng jìngtóu	EFEAL
Extended header	扩展帧头	Kuòzhǎn zhèngtóu	EHDR
Extended industry standard architecture	扩充工业标准体系结构	Kuòchōng gōngyè biāozhǔn tǐxì jiégòu	EISA
Extended industry standard architecture	扩充的工业标准结构	Kuòchōngde gōngyè biāozhǔn jiégòu	EISA
Extended interaction amplifier	分布作用放大器	Fēnbù zuòyòng fàngdàqì	EIA
Extended interaction oscillator	分布作振荡器	Fēnbù zuò zhèndàngqì	EIO
Extended Markovian process algebra	扩展马尔科夫进程代数	Kuòzhǎn mǎ-ěr-kē-fū jìnchéng dàishù	EMPA

Extended memory	扩充存储器	Kuòchōng cúnchǔqì	EM
eXtended memory specification	扩充记忆体	Kuòchōng jìyìtǐ	XMS
Extended memory unit	扩充的存储器	Kuòchōngde cúnchǔqì	EMU
Extended packet sequence numbering	扩充包顺序编号	Kuòchōng bāo shùnxù biānhào	EPSN
Extended page table entry	扩充的页面表项	Kuòchōngde yèmiàn biǎoxiàng	XPTE
Extended partition	扩展分区	Kuòzhǎn fēnqū	
Extended rack	扩展架	Kuòzhǎn jià	BCER
Extended short message entity agent	扩展短消息试题代理	Kuòzhǎn duǎnxiāoxi shìtí dàilǐ	ESME Agent
Extended simple mail transfer protocol	扩展型简单邮件传输协议	Kuòzhǎn-xíng jiǎndān yóujiàn chuánshū xiéyì	ESMTP
Extended stored procedure	扩展存储过程	Kuòzhǎn cúnchǔ guòchéng	
Extended system configuration data	可扩展系统配置数据	Kěkuòzhǎn xìtǒng pèizhì shùjù	ESCD
Extended system configuration data	扩展系统配置数据	Kuòzhǎn xìtǒng pèizhì shùjù	ESCD
Extended telephone systems programming language	扩充的电话系统程序语言	Kuòchōngde diànhuà xìtǒng chéngxù yǔyán	ETSPL
Extended unit data (in SS7)	增强单位数据	Zēngqiáng dānwèi shùjù	XUDT
Extended unit data service (in SS7)	增强单位数据业务	Zēngqiáng dānwèi shùjù yèwù	XUDTS
Extended unsuccessful backward setup information message	扩充后向建立不成功消息	Kuòchōng hòuxiàng jiànlì bùchénggōng xiāoxi	EUM
Extensible access control markup language	扩展访问控制标记语言	Kuòzhǎn fǎngwèn kòngzhì biāojì yǔyán	XACML
Extensible authentication protocol	可扩展身份验证协议	Kěkuòzhǎn shēnfen yànzhèng xiéyì	EAP
Extensible authentication protocol (in PPP)	扩展认证协议	Kuòzhǎn rènzhèng xiéyì	EAP
Extensible markup language	可扩展标记语言	Kěkuòzhǎn biāojì yǔyán	XML
Extensible markup language	扩充标记语言	Kuòchōng biāojì yǔyán	XML
Extensible markup language	扩展性标识语言	Kuòzhǎn-xìng biāozhì yǔyán	XML
Extensible markup language (in SQL Server)	扩展标示语言支持	Kuòzhǎn biāoshì yǔyán zhīchí	XML
Extensible markup language key management specification	XML 密钥管理规范	XML mìyào guǎnlǐ guīfàn	XKMS
Extensible markup language message interface	可扩展标记语言消息接口	Kěkuòzhǎn biāojì yǔyán xiāoxi jiēkǒu	XMI
Extensible markup language schema definition	可扩展标记语言模式定义语言	Kěkuòzhǎn biāojì yǔyán móshì dìngyì yǔyán	XSD
Extensible object exchange model	可扩展对象交换模型	Kěkuòzhǎn duìxiàng jiāohuàn móxíng	EOEM
eXtensible rights markup language	可扩展权限标记语言	Kěkuòzhǎn quánxiàn biāojì yǔyán	XrML
Extensible style language (in SQL Server)	可扩展样式语言	Kěkuòzhǎn yàngshì yǔyán	XSL
Extensible stylesheet language	可扩展设计语言	Kěkuòzhǎn shèjì yǔyán	XSL
eXtensible stylesheet language	可扩展样式表语言	Kěkuòzhǎn yàngshì biǎo yǔyán	XSL
eXtensible stylesheet language transformation	可扩展样式表语言转换	Kěkuòzhǎn yàngshì biǎo yǔyán zhuǎnhuàn	XSLT
Extension (3-letter extension to a computer file name)	扩展名	Kuòzhǎn míng	
Extension (extra telephone set)	分机	Fēnjī	
Extension joint	外延点	Wàiyán diǎn	
Extension lead	延长导线	Yáncháng dǎoxiàn	
Extensometer	伸缩计	Shēnsuōjì	
Exterior gateway protocol	外部路由协议	Wàibù lùyóu xiéyì	EGB
Exterior gateway protocol	外部网点协议	Wàibù wǎngdiǎn xiéyì	EGP
Exterior gateway protocol	外部网关协议	Wàibù wǎngguān xiéyì	EGP
Exterior size	外形规格	Wàixíng guīgé	
External access equipment	外部接入设备	Wàibù jiērù shèbèi	EA
External alarms	外部报警	Wàibù bàojǐng	EA

English	Chinese	Pinyin	Abbreviation
External attribute database	外部属性数据库	Wàibù shǔxìng shùjùkù	
External command	外部命令	Wàibù mìnglìng	EXTCMD
External control set	外部控制集	Wàibù kòngzhì jí	
External data representation	外部数据表示	Wàibù shùjù biǎoshì	XDR
External data transfer rate	外部数据传输率	Wàibù shùjù chuánshū lǜ	
External disabled state	外因不能工作状态	Wàiyīn bùnéng gōngzuò zhuàngtài	
External disabled time; external loss time	外因不能工作时间	Wàiyīn bùnéng gōngzuò shíjiān	
External document class	外部文件类别	Wàibù wénjiàn lèibié	
External drive	外置磁盘驱动器	Wàizhì cípán qūdòngqì	
External file	外部文件	Wàibù wénjiàn	
External function	外部函数	Wàibù hánshù	
External hard drive	外置硬盘	Wàizhì yìngpán	
External host	外部主机	Wàibù zhǔjī	
External identifier	外部标识符	Wàibù biāozhì fú	
External immunity	外部抗扰性	Wàibù kàngrǎoxìng	
External interface	外部接口	Wàibù jiēkǒu	
External interference	外部干扰	Wàibù gānrǎo	
External memory	外部存储器	Wàibù cúnchǔqì	
External network	外部网络	Wàibù wǎngluò	
External network-node interface	外部网络节点接口	Wàibù wǎngluò jiédiǎn jiēkǒu	E-NNI
External noise	外界噪声	Wàijiè zàoshēng	
External reference	外部调用	Wàibù diàoyòng	
External reference	外部引用	Wàibù yǐnyòng	
External repository	外部仓库	Wàibù cāngkù	ER
External security audit (IPsec)	外部安全审计	Wàibù ānquán shěnjì	
External service broker (in VPN)	外部服务代理	Wàibù fúwù dàilǐ	ESB
External sort	外部排序	Wàibù páixù	
External storage	外存	Wàicún	
External system (outside the purview of the the official PTT networks)	外部系统	Wàibù xìtǒng	
External videotex application provider	可视图文应用外部提供者	Kěshì túwén yìngyòng wàibù tígòngzhě	
External videotex host computer	可视图文外部主机	Kěshì túwén wàibù zhǔjī	
Extinction ratio	消光比	Xiāoguāng bǐ	
Extra frame rate	额外帧速率	Éwài zhèng sùlǜ	EFR
Extra frame rate	额外帧率	Éwài zhènglǜ	EFR
Extra information for testing	试验用辅助信息	Shìyànyòng fǔzhù xìnxī	
Extra loss	附加损耗	Fùjiā sǔnhào	EL
Extra traffic signal	额外业务信号	Éwài yèwù xìnhào	
Extract	抽取	Chōuqǔ	
Extraction display	录取显示器	Lùqǔ xiǎnshìqì	
Extraction error	录取误差	Lùqǔ wùchā	
Extra-high frequency	极高频	Jígāopín	EHF
Extraneous conductive part	外部导电部分	Wàibù dǎodiàn bùfen	
Extranet	企业外部网络	Qǐyè wàibù wǎngluò	
Extranet	外联网	Wàiliánwǎng	
Extranet	外延网	Wàiyán wǎng	
Extrapolation (prediction)	外推(预测)	Wàituī (yùcè)	

Extra-short-pulse radar	极窄脉冲雷达	Jízhǎi màichōng léidá	
Extreme counting	极值计数	Jízhí jìshù	EC
Extreme value	极值	Jízhí	
Extreme value distribution	极值分布	Jízhí fēnbù	
Extreme wave	最大波	Zuìdà bō	
Extremely low frequency	极低频	Jídīpín	ELF
Extrusion line	挤出生产线	Jǐchū shēngchǎnxiàn	
Ex-works	工厂交货	Gōngchǎng jiāohuò	EXW
Eye diagram mask	眼图模板	Yǎntú múbǎn	
Eye pattern	眼图	Yǎntú	

F

Fabric address notification	架构地址通知	Jiàgòu dìzhǐ tōngzhī	FAN
Fabric loop port	架构环路端口	Jiàgòu huánlù duānkǒu	
Fabric port reject frame	架构端口拒绝帧	Jiàgòu duānkǒu jùjué zhèng	F_RJT
Fabric shortest path first	光纤最短路径优先协议	Guāngxiān zuìduǎn lùjìng yōuxiān xiéyì	FSPF
Fabry-Perot cavity laser device	法布里 - 泊罗腔激光器	Fǎ-bù-lǐ--pó-luó qiāng jīguāngqì	FP-LD
Fabry-Perot laser diode	法布里--珀罗激光二极管	Fǎ-bù-lǐ--pò-luó jīguāng èrjíguǎn	FP-LD
Fabry-Perot saturable absorber	发布里-珀罗饱和吸收器	Fā-bù-lǐ--pò-luó bǎohé xīshōu qì	FPSA
Face recognition	人脸识别	Rénliǎn shíbié	
Face to face	面对面	Miàn duì miàn	FTF
Facility	设施	Shèshī	
Facility accepted (ISUP message)	网络性能请求许可	Wǎngluò xìngnéng qǐngqiú xǔkě	FAA
Facility management	设施管理	Shèshī guǎnlǐ	
Facility mapping systems	设施制图系统	Shèshī zhìtú xìtǒng	
Facility not supported	设备不支持	Shèbèi bùzhīchí	
Facility reject (ISUP message)	网络性能请求拒绝	Wǎngluò xìngnéng qǐngqiú jùjué	FRJ
Facility reject (ISUP)	性能拒绝	Xìngnéng jùjué	FRJ
Facility request (ISUP message)	网络性能请求	Wǎngluò xìngnéng qǐngqiú	FAR
Facility request message (ISUP)	性能请求消息	Xìngnéng qǐngqiú xiāoxi	FAR
Facility restriction level	功能限制等级	Gōngnéng xiànzhì děngjí	FRL
Facsimile	传真	Chuánzhēn	FAX
Facsimile communication	传真通信	Chuánzhēn tōngxìn	CZ
Facsimile on private networks	专用网上的传真	Zhuānyòng wǎngshàngde chuánzhēn	
Facsimile packet assembly/disassembly	传真分组装拆设施	Chuánzhēn fēnzǔ zhuāngchāi shèshī	FPAD
Facsimile service	传真业务	Chuánzhēn yèwù	
Facsimile terminal; facsimile machine	传真终端	Chuánzhēn zhōngduān	
Fact	事实	Shìshí	
Fact table	事实数据表	Shìshí shùjù biǎo	
Factor	因素	Yīnsù	
Factor	原因	Yuányīn	FACT
Factor analysis	因素分析	Yīnsù fēnxī	
Factor analysis	因子分析	Yīnzǐ fēnxī	
Factor of cooperation	合作因数	Hézuò yīnshù	
Factor set	因子集	Yīnzǐ jí	
Factoring and primality testing	因子分解/质数判定	Yīnzǐ fēnjiě/zhìshù pàndìng	

Factorization	因子分解	Yīnzǐ fēnjiě	
Fading	衰落	Shuāiluò	
Fading bandwidth	衰落带宽	Shuāiluò dàikuān	
Fading channel	衰落信道	Shuāiluò xìndào	
Fading depth	衰落深度	Shuāiluò shēndù	
Fading duration	衰落周期	Shuāiluò zhōuqī	
Fading envelope	衰落包络	Shuāiluò bāoluò	
Fading rate	衰落率	Shuāiluòlǜ	
Fail safe	故障保护	Gùzhàng bǎohù	
Fail soft	故障弱化	Gùzhàng ruòhuà	
Fail verdict	不合格判定	Bùhégé pàndìng	
Failback	故障回复	Gùzhàng huífù	
Failback	自动恢复	Zìdòng huīfù	
Failback policy	故障回复策略	Gùzhàng huífù cèlüè	
Failover	故障转移	Gùzhàng zhuǎnyí	
Failover policy	故障转移策略	Gùzhàng zhuǎnyí cèlüè	
Fail-safe	保安性	Bǎo'ānxing	
Fail-safe	失效保护	Shīxiào bǎohù	
Fail-safe	失效保险	Shīxiào bǎoxiǎn	
Failure	失效	Shīxiào	
Failure access	故障访问	Gùzhàng fǎngwèn	
Failure analysis	失效分析	Shīxiào fēnxī	
Failure cause	失效原因	Shīxiào yuányīn	
Failure count	失效次数	Shīxiào cìshù	FC
Failure criterion	破坏标准	Pòhuài biāozhǔn	
Failure domain	失效区域	Shīxiào qūyù	
Failure intensity acceleration factor	失效频度加速因子	Shīxiào píndù jiāsù yīnzǐ	
Failure mechanism	失效机理	Shīxiào jīlǐ	
Failure mode	失效模式	Shīxiào móshì	
Failure prediction	失效预测	Shīxiào yùcè	
Failure rate	失效率	Shīxiàolǜ	
Failure rate acceleration factor	失效率加速因子	Shīxiào lǜ jiāsù yīnzǐ	
Failure rate test	故障率测试	Gùzhàng lǜ cèshì	
Failure recovery	失效恢复	Shīxiào huīfù	
Failure test	故障测试	Gùzhàng cèshì	
Failure to operate (electrical term)	拒动	Jùdòng	
Fair access	公平接入	Gōngping jiērù	
Fair dependence hierarchy (in Petri nets)	公平依赖体系	Gōngping yīlài tǐxì	
Fair dependence relation (in Petri nets)	公平依赖关系	Gōngping yīlài guānxi	
Fair queuing	公平排队	Gōngping páiduì	FQ
Fairness index	公平系数	Gōngping xìshù	
Fallback relationships	替换关系	Tìhuan guānxi	
False alarm probability	虚警概率	Xū jǐng gàilǜ	
False negatives	漏报	Lòubào	
False positives	误报	Wùbào	
False start	假启动	Jiǎ qǐdòng	

False transmit format detection ratio	假传送格式检波比率	Jiǎ chuánsòng géshi jiǎnbō bǐlǜ	FDR
Falsification (IW attack)	伪造	Wěizào	
Family (IPsec)	族	Zú	
Fan antenna	扇区天线	Shànqū tiānxiàn	
Fan coil unit	风机盘管	Fēngjī pánguǎn	FCU
Fan-beam antenna	扇形波束天线	Shànxíng bōshù tiānxiàn	
Fan-beam antenna	扇形射束天线	Shànxíng shèshù tiānxiàn	
Fan-in	扇入	Shànrù	
Fan-out	扇出	Shànchū	
Fan-out unit	扇出单元	Shànchū dānyuán	
Fantail	扇尾	Shànwěi	
Far field	远场	Yuǎnchǎng	
Far field pattern	远场图	Yuǎnchǎng tú	FFP
Far field region (Fraunhofer region)	远场区(佛累和费区)	Yuǎnchǎng qū (Fó-lěi-hé-fèi qū)	
Far field region pattern	远场区方向图	Yuǎnchǎng qū fāngxiàng tú	
Faraday effect	法拉弟效应	Fǎ-lā-dì xiàoyìng	
Faraday rotation circulator	法拉第旋转式环行器	Fǎ-lā-dì xuánzhuǎn-shì huánxíngqì	
Faraday rotation isolator	法拉第旋转效应隔离器	Fǎ-lā-dì xuánzhuǎn xiàoyìng gélíqì	
Far-end background block error	远端背景块差错	Yuǎnduān bèijǐng kuài chācuò	FBBE
Far-end background block error	远端背景误块	Yuǎnduān bèijǐng wù kuài	FBBE
Far-end block error	远端块差错	Yuǎnduān kuài chācuò	FEBE
Far-end block error	远端块误码	Yuǎnduān kuài wùmǎ	FEBE
Far-end block error	远端码组差错	Yuǎnduān mǎzǔ chācuò	FEBE
Far-end block error	远端模块错误	Yuǎnduān mókuài cuòwù	FEBE
Far-end crosstalk	远端串话	Yuǎnduān chuànhuà	FEXT
Far-end crosstalk	远端串扰	Yuǎnduān chuànrǎo	FEXT
Far-end crosstalk	远端串音	Yuǎnduān chuànyīn	FEXT
Far-end defective second	远端缺陷秒	Yuǎnduān quēxiàn miǎo	FDS
Far-end echo cancellation	远端回声消除	Yuǎnduān huíshēng xiāochú	FECC
Far-end error block counter	远端误块计数	Yuǎnduān wùkuài jìshù	FEBC
Far-end errored second	远端误块秒	Yuǎnduān wùkuài miǎo	FES
Far-end header error control	远端信头差错控制	Yuǎnduān xìntóu chācuò kòngzhì	FHEC
Far-end loss of cell delineation	远端信元定界丢失	Yuǎnduān xìnyuán dìngjiè diūshī	FLCD
Far-end receive failure	远端接收失败	Yuǎnduān jiēshōu shībài	FERF
Far-end receive fault	远端接收故障	Yuǎnduān jiēshōu gùzhàng	FERF
Far-end severely errored second	远端严重误块秒	Yuǎnduān yánzhòng wùkuài miǎo	FSES
Far-end subscriber access	远端用户接入	Yuǎnduān yònghù jiērù	SA-F
Far-end subscriber installation	远端用户设备	Yuǎnduān yònghù shèbèi	SI-F
Far-infrared laser	远红外线激光	Yuǎn hóngwàixiàn jīguāng	
Fast associated control channel	快速随路控制信道	Kuàisù suílù kòngzhì xìndào	FACCH
Fast associated control channel/full rate	快速随路控制信道/全速率	Kuàisù suílù kòngzhì xìndào/quánsùlǜ	FACCH/F
Fast associated control channel/full rate	快速相关控制信道/全速率	Kuàisù xiāngguān kòngzhì xìndào/quánsùlǜ	FACCH/F
Fast associated control channel/half rate	快速随路控制信道/半速率	Kuàisù suílù kòngzhì xìndào/bàn sùlǜ	FACCH/H
Fast cell selection	快速小区选择	Kuàisù xiǎoqū xuǎnzé	FCS
Fast circuit switching	快速电路交换	Kuàisù diànlù jiāohuàn	FCS
Fast entry/exit multimedia state	快速进入/退出多媒体状态	Kuàisù jìnrù/tuìchū duōméitǐ zhuàngtài	FEMMS

Fast ethernet (IEEE 802.3u)	快速以太网	Kuàisù yǐtàiwǎng	
Fast ethernet interface processor	快速以太网接口处理器	Kuàisù yǐtàiwǎng jiēkǒu chǔlǐqì	FEIP
Fast Fourier transform	快速傅利叶变换	Kuàisù fù-lì-yè biànhuàn	FFT
Fast Fourier transform	快速付里叶变换	Kuàisù fù-lǐ-yè biànhuàn	FFT
Fast Fourier transform	快速傅氏变换	Kuàisù fù-shì biànhuàn	FFT
Fast Fourier transform	快速热欧姆转换	Kuàisù rè Oū-mǔ zhuǎnhuàn	FFT
Fast frequency hopping	快跳频	Kuài tiàopín	FFH
Fast frequency hopping	快速跳频	Kuàisù tiàopín	FFH
Fast frequency shift keying	快速移频键控	Kuàisù yípín jiànkòng	FFSK
Fast frequency-shift keying	快速频移键控	Kuàisù pínyí jiànkòng	FFSK
Fast Hadamard transform	快速哈达码变换	Kuàisù hǎ-dá-mǎ biànhuàn	FHT
Fast link pulse	快链路脉冲	Kuài liànlù màichōng	FLP
Fast packet switching	快速分组交换	Kuàisù fēnzǔ jiāohuàn	FPS
Fast pattern processor	快速模式处理机	Kuàisù móshì chǔlǐjī	FPP
Fast pull-in range	快捕带	Kuài bǔ dài	
Fast reroute	快速重路由	Kuàisù chónglùyóu	
Fast response to load (semiconductor mfg)	负载快速响应	Fùzài kuàisù xiǎngyìng	
Fast select	快速选择	Kuàisù xuǎnzé	
Fast sequenced transport	快速连续传送	Kuàisù liánxù chuánsòng	FST
Fast sequenced transport (protocol)	快速有序运输(协议)	Kuàisù yǒuxù yùnshū (xiéyì)	FST
Fast serial interface processor	快速串行接口处理器	Kuàisù chuànháng jiēkǒu chǔlǐqì	FSIP
Fast switching thyristor	快速晶闸管	Kuàisù jīngzháguǎn	FST
Fast time constant circuit	快时间常数电路	Kuài shíjiān chángshù diànlù	FTC
Fast update request	快速更新请求	Kuàisù gēngxīn qǐngqiú	
Fast uplink signaling channel	上行链路快速信令信道	Shàngxíng liànlù kuàisù xìnlìng xìndào	FAUSCH
Fast Walsh transform	快速沃尔什变换	Kuàisù wò-ěr-shí biànhuàn	FWT
Fat client	胖客户端	Pàng kèhù duān	
Fatal error	严重错误	Yánzhòng cuòwù	
Fatigue factor	疲劳系数	Píláo xìshù	
Fault analysis	故障分析	Gùzhàng fēnxī	
Fault cause	故障原因	Gùzhàng yuányīn	
Fault configuration accounting performance security	故障组成计算性能安全	Gùzhàng zǔchéng jìsuàn xìngnéng ānquán	FCAPS
Fault control	故障控制	Gùzhàng kòngzhì	FC
Fault correction	故障修复	Gùzhàng xiūfù	
Fault corrective time	故障修复时间	Gùzhàng xiūfù shíjiān	
Fault coverage	故障范围	Gùzhàng fànwéi	
Fault criteria	故障准则	Gùzhàng zhǔnzé	
Fault current	事故电流	Shìgù diànliú	
Fault definition program	故障定义程序	Gùzhàng dìngyì chéngxù	
Fault desk	障碍台	Zhàng'ài tái	
Fault detection test	故障检测	Gùzhàng jiǎncè	FDT
Fault diagnosis time	故障诊断时间	Gùzhàng zhěnduàn shíjiān	
Fault diagnostics	故障诊断	Gùzhàng zhěnduàn	
Fault disconnection	故障解列	Gùzhàng jiěliè	
Fault grounding or earthing	故障接地	Gùzhàng jiēdì	
Fault interface	故障接口	Gùzhàng jiēkǒu	FI

Fault localization	故障定位	Gùzhàng dìngwèi	
Fault localization time	故障定位时间	Gùzhàng dìngwèi shíjiān	
Fault management	故障管理	Gùzhàng guǎnlǐ	BFM
Fault management	失效管理	Shīxiào guǎnlǐ	FM
Fault management building block	故障管理构件	Gùzhàng guǎnlǐ gòujiàn	FMBB
Fault manager	故障管理器	Gùzhàng guǎnlǐqì	FM
Fault masking	故障遮掩	Gùzhàng zhēyǎn	
Fault mode	故障模式	Gùzhàng móshì	
Fault modes and effects analysis	故障模式和影响分析	Gùzhàng móshì hé yǐngxiǎng fēnxī	FMEA
Fault modes, effects and criticality analysis	故障模式、影响和严重性分析	Gùzhàng móshì、yǐngxiǎng hé yánzhòngxìng fēnxī	FMECA
Fault protection	故障保护	Gùzhàng bǎohù	
Fault recognition	故障识别	Gùzhàng shíbié	
Fault report point	故障报告点	Gùzhàng bàogàodiǎn	
Fault simulation	故障模拟	Gùzhàng mónǐ	
Fault tolerance	故障耐受性	Gùzhàng nàishòuxìng	
Fault tolerance	容错	Róngcuò	
Fault tree	故障树	Gùzhàng shù	
Fault tree analysis	故障述分析	Gùzhàng shù fēnxī	FTA
Fault withstandability	耐故障能力	Nài gùzhàng nénglì	
Fault, bug	故障	Gùzhàng	
Fault-tolerant analysis	容差分析	Róngchā fēnxī	
Fault-tolerant technique	容错技术	Róngcuò jìshù	
Fax adaptor	传真适配器	Chuánzhēn shìpèiqì	FA
Fax on demand	随选传真	Suíxuǎn chuánzhēn	FOD
Fax on demand	自选传真服务	Zìxuǎn chuánzhēn fúwù	
Fax over Internet	因特网上传真	Yīntèwǎng-shàng chuánzhēn	
Fax over Internet protocol	在网际协议上传输传真	Zài wǎngjì xiéyì-shàng chuánshū chuánzhēn	FoIP
FDDI follow-on LAN	更高速率的 FDDI 网络	Gènggāo sùlǜde FDDI wǎngluò	FFOL
FDM transmitter module	FDM 发送器组件	FDM fāsòngqì zǔjiàn	FTM
Feasibility report, short for 可行性研究报告	可研	Kě yán	
Feasibility study	可行性研究	Kěxíngxìng yánjiū	
Feature activation	特性激活	Tèxìng jīhuó	
Feature association	特征关联	Tèzhēng guānlián	
Feature attribute	特征属性	Tèzhēng shǔxìng	
Feature attribute table	特征属性表	Tèzhēng shǔxìng biǎo	
Feature catalogue	特征类型	Tèzhēng lèixíng	
Feature catalogue element	特征类型要素	Tèzhēng lèixíng yàosù	
Feature catalogue entity	特征类型实体	Tèzhēng lèixíng shítǐ	
Feature class	特征类	Tèzhēng lèi	
Feature code	特征编码	Tèzhēng biānmǎ	
Feature code	业务码	Yèwù mǎ	FC
Feature division	特征分割	Tèzhēng fēngē	
Feature element	特征元素	Tèzhēng yuánsù	
Feature extraction	特征提取	Tèzhēng tíqǔ	
Feature function	特征功能	Tèzhēng gōngnéng	

Feature fusion	特征融合	Tèzhēng rónghé	
Feature identifer	特征标识码	Tèzhēng biāozhì mǎ	
Feature indication	特性指示	Tèxìng zhǐshì	
Feature line (CAD/CAM)	特征线	Tèzhēng xiàn	
Feature mergence check (CAD/CAM)	特征合并检查	Tèzhēng hébìng jiǎnchá	
Feature modeling	特征造型	Tèzhēng zàoxíng	
Feature operation	特征操作	Tèzhēng cāozuò	
Feature operation type	特征操作类型	Tèzhēng cāozuò lèixíng	
Feature portrayal	特征描述法	Tèzhēng miáoshù fǎ	
Feature relationship	特征关系	Tèzhēng guānxi	
Feature relationship type	特征关系类型	Tèzhēng guānxi lèixíng	
Feature selection	特征选取	Tèzhēng xuǎnqǔ	
Feature serial number	特征序列号	Tèzhēng xùlièhào	
Feature substitution	特征取代	Tèzhēng qǔdài	
Feature succession	特征延续	Tèzhēng yánxù	
Feature topology	特征拓扑	Tèzhēng tuòpū	
Feature type	特征类型	Tèzhēng lèixíng	
FEC to NHLFE map	FEC 至 NHLFE 的映射	FEC zhì NHLFE de yìngshè	FTN
Federal Communications Commission (US)	联邦通信委员会	Liánbāng tōngxìn wěiyuánhuì	FCC
Federal Geodetic Control Committee	联邦测量控制委员会	Liánbāng cèliáng kòngzhì wěiyuánhuì	FGCC
Federal Information Exchange (US)	联邦信息交换	Liánbāng xìnxī jiāohuàn	FIX
Federal Information Processing Standard (US)	联邦信息处理标准	Liánbāng xìnxī chǔlǐ biāozhǔn	FIPS
Federal Interagency Coordinating Committee on Digital Cartography	联邦数字制图协调委员会	Liánbāng shùzì zhìtú xiétiáo wěiyuánhuì	FICCDC
Federal Networking Council (US)	联邦网络技术委员会	Liánbāng wǎngluò jìshù wěiyuánhuì	FNC
Federal Networking Council (US)	联邦网络委员会	Liánbāng wǎngluò wěiyuánhuì	FNC
Federal Open Market Committee (US)	联邦开放市场委员会	Liánbāng kāifàng shìchǎng wěiyuánhuì	FOMC
Federal Research Internet Coordinating Committee	联邦调查因特网协调委员会	Liánbāng diàochá yīntèwǎng xiétiáo wěiyuánhuì	FRICC
Federal Trade Commission (US)	联邦贸易委员会	Liánbāng màoyì wěiyuánhuì	FTC
Federal Trade Commission (US)	联邦商业委员会	Liánbāng shāngyè wěiyuánhuì	FTC
Federated database	联合数据库	Liánhé shùjùkù	
Federated database servers (in SQL Server)	联合数据库服务器	Liánhé shùjùkù fúwùqì	
Federation execution data (in MSMP)	联邦执行数据	Liánbāng zhíxíng shùjù	FED
Fee for distribution of newspapers and periodicals	报刊发行费	Bàokān fāxíng fèi	
Fee for publishing delay of newspapers and periodicals	报刊延期出版损失补偿费	Bàokān yánqī chūbǎn sǔnshī bǔchángfèi	
Fee indicator	费用显示器	Fèiyòng xiǎnshìqì	FI
Feed	馈电器	Kuìdiànqì	
Feed (of an antenna)	馈源	Kuìyuán	
Feed line loss, feeder loss	馈线损耗	Kuìxiàn sǔnhào	
Feed line network	馈线网络	Kuìxiàn wǎngluò	
Feed network	馈电网络	Kuìdiàn wǎngluò	
Feed network for phase controlled array	相控阵馈电网络	Xiàngkòng zhèn kuìdiàn wǎngluò	
Feed, feeder, feed line	馈线	Kuìxiàn	
Feedback	反馈	Fǎnkuì	
Feedback control system	反馈控制系统	Fǎnkuì kòngzhì xìtǒng	

Feedback frequency modulation	反馈调频	Fǎnkuì tiáopín	FBFM
Feedback information	反馈信息	Fǎnkuì xìnxī	FBI
Feedback transmit diversity	反馈发射分集	Fǎnkuì fāshè fēnjí	FBTD
Feeder link	馈送链路	Kuìsòng liànlù	
Feeder link	馈线链路	Kuìxiàn liànlù	
Feedforward	前馈	Qiánkuì	
Femto-second	飞秒	Fēimiǎo	
Fermat's principle	费马原理	Fèi-mǎ yuánlǐ	
Ferrite	铁氧体	Tiěyǎngtǐ	
Ferrite antenna	铁氧体天线	Tiěyǎngtǐ tiānxiàn	
Ferrite duplexer	铁氧体天线收发开关	Tiěyǎngtǐ tiānxiàn shōufā kāiguān	
Ferrite phase shifter	铁氧体移相器	Tiěyǎngtǐ yíxiàngqì	
Ferrite rod antenna	铁氧体棒天线	Tiěyǎngtǐ bàng tiānxiàn	
Ferrite switch	铁氧体开关	Tiěyǎngtǐ kāiguān	
Ferrous-center laser	铁离子中心激光	Tiě lízǐ zhōngxīn jīguāng	
Ferrule	插针体	Chāzhēntǐ	
Ferrule	套管	Tàoguǎn	
Fetch	提取	Tíqǔ	
Fetch cycle	取周期	Qǔ zhōuqī	
Fetch element	读取单元	Dúqǔ dānyuán	
Fetch protection (IPsec)	取数保护	Qǔ shù bǎohù	
Fiber absorption	光纤吸收	Guāngxiān xīshōu	
Fiber attenuation	光纤衰减	Guāngxiān shuāijiǎn	
Fiber bend radius	尾纤弯曲半径	Wěixiān wānqū bànjìng	
Fiber Bragg grating	光纤布拉格光栅	Guāngxiān Bù-lā-gé guāngshān	FBG
Fiber buffer	光纤缓冲层	Guāngxiān huǎnchōngcéng	
Fiber channel	光纤通道	Guāngxiān tōngdào	
Fiber channel	光纤信道	Guāngxiān xìndào	FC
Fiber channel - arbitrated loop	光纤通道仲裁环路	Guāngxiān tōngdào zhòngcái huán lù	FC-AL
Fiber channel - common transport	光纤通道通用传输	Guāngxiān tōngdào tōngyòng chuánshū	FC-CT
Fiber channel - fabric generic requirements	光纤通道一般要求	Guāngxiān tōngdào yībān yāoqiú	FC-FG
Fiber channel - fabric loop attachment	光纤通道环路接入	Guāngxiān tōngdào huánlù jiērù	FC-FLA
Fiber channel - generic services	光纤通道通用服务	Guāngxiān tōngdào tōngyòng fúwù	FC-GS
Fiber channel and fiber channel protocol (ANSI use)	光纤信道和光纤信道协议	Guāngxiān xìndào hé guāngxiān xìndào xiéyì	FC & FCP
Fiber Channel Association	光纤通道协会	Guāngxiān tōngdào xiéhuì	FCA
Fiber Channel Industry Association	光纤通道工业协会	Guāngxiān tōngdào gōngyè xiéhuì	FCIA
Fiber channel loop community	光纤通道环路社团	Guāngxiān tōngdào huánlù shètuán	FCLC
Fiber channel over IP protocol	用于 IP 协议的光纤通道	Yòng yú IP xiéyìde guāngxiān tōngdào	FC-IP
Fiber channel protocol	光纤通道协议	Guāngxiān tōngdào xiéyì	FCP
Fiber channel second-generation generic services	光纤通道第二代通用服务	Guāngxiān tōngdào dì' èr dài tōngyòng fúwù	FC-GS-2
Fiber channel service protocol	光纤通道服务协议	Guāngxiān tōngdào fúwù xiéyì	FSP
Fiber channel single bytes	光纤通道单字节	Guāngxiān tōngdào dānzì jié	FC_SB
Fiber channel storage network	光纤通道存储网络	Guāngxiān tōngdào cúnchǔ wǎngluò	FCSN
Fiber channel switch fabric	光纤通道交换架构	Guāngxiān tōngdào jiāohuàn jiàgòu	FC-SW
Fiber channel third-generation generic services	光纤通道第三代通用服务	Guāngxiān tōngdào dì sān dài tōngyòng fúwù	FC-GS-3

Fiber channel virtual interface	光纤通道虚拟接口	Guāngxiān tōngdào xūnǐ jiēkǒu	FC-VI
Fiber cladding	光纤包层	Guāngxiān bāocéng	
Fiber connection	光纤互联	Guāngxiān hùlián	FICON
Fiber connection	光纤连接	Guāngxiān liánjiē	Ficon
Fiber core	纤芯	Qiànxīn	
Fiber core	纤芯	Xiānxīn	
Fiber dispersion	光纤色散	Guāngxiān sèsàn	
Fiber distributed data interface	光导数据介面	Guāngdǎo shùjù jièmiàn	FDDI
Fiber distributed data interface	光缆分布数据接口	Guānglǎn fēnbù shùjù jiēkǒu	FDDIF
Fiber distributed data interface	光缆分配式数据接口	Guānglǎn fēnpèishì shùjù jiēkǒu	FDDI
Fiber distributed data interface	光纤分布数据接口	Guāngxiān fēnbù shùjù jiēkǒu	FDDI
Fiber distributed data interface	光纤分布式数据接口	Guāngxiān Fēnbùshì shùjù jiēkǒu	FDDI
Fiber distributed data interface	光纤缆分布式数据接口	Guāngxiānlǎn Fēnbùshì shùjù jiēkǒu	FDDI
Fiber fusion splice	光纤熔接	Guāngxiān róngjiē	
Fiber grating outer chamber wavelength transformer	光纤光栅外腔波长转换器	Guāngxiān guāngshān wàiqiāng bōcháng zhuǎnhuànqì	
Fiber grating-type gain equalizer	光纤光栅型增益均衡器	Guāngxiān guāngshānxíng zēngyì jūnhéngqì	GEQ
Fiber in the loop	光纤环路系统	Guāngxiān huánlù xìtǒng	FITL
Fiber in the loop	光纤用户环路	Guāngxiān yònghù huánlù	FTTL
Fiber Instrument Sales, Inc (US)	光纤仪表销售公司	Guāngxiān yíbiǎo xiāoshòu gōngsī	FIS
Fiber interface module	光纤接口模块	Guāngxiān jiēkǒu mókuài	FIM
Fiber isolator, optical isolator	光隔离器	Guāng gélíqì	
Fiber isolator/wavelength division multiplexer	光隔离器/波分复用器	Guāng gélíqì/bōfēn fùyòngqì	IWDM
Fiber jack	光纤插孔	Guāngxiān chākǒng	FJ
Fiber kilometers (fiber-km)	光纤千米	Guāngxiān qiānmǐ	
Fiber laser	光纤激光器	Guāngxiān jīguāngqì	FL
Fiber Link around the Globe	国际海底光缆系统	Guójì hǎidǐ guānglǎn xìtǒng	FLAG
Fiber link negotiation pulses	光纤链路协商脉冲	Guāngxiān liànlù xiéshāng màichōng	FLNPs
Fiber management trays	光纤管理箱（碟）	Guāngxiān guǎnlǐ xiāng (dié)	FMT
Fiber node	光节点	Guāng jiédiǎn	FN
Fiber optic cable	纤维光缆	Xiānwéi guānglǎn	FOC
Fiber optic cable blower	光缆喷射器	Guānglǎn pēnshèqì	
Fiber optic cable communications	管缆通信	Guǎnlǎn tōngxìn	
Fiber optic cable digital equipment	光缆数字设备	Guānglǎn shùzì shèbèi	GS
Fiber optic cable line	光缆线路	Guānglǎn xiànlù	
Fiber optic cable manufacturing equipment	光缆制造设备	Guānglǎn zhìzào shèbèi	
Fiber optic cable strand	光缆线	Guānglǎn xiàn	FOC
Fiber optic circulator	纤维光学环行器	Xiānwéi guāngxué huánxíngqì	
Fiber optic closure	光纤接续盒	Guāngxiān jiēxùhé	
Fiber Optic Communication, Inc (Taiwan)	光纤通信公司	Guāngxiān tōngxìn gōngsī	FOCI
Fiber optic connector intermateability standards	可互相配对的光纤连接器标准	Kěhùxiāng pèiduìde guāngxiān liánjiēqì biāozhǔn	FOCIS
Fiber optic distribution box	光纤终端箱	Guāngxiān zhōngduān xiāng	
Fiber optic distribution panel	光纤分配板	Guāngxiān fēnpèibǎn	
Fiber optic faceplate	光纤面板	Guāngxiān miànbǎn	FOFP
Fiber optic furnace	光纤引线炉	Guāngxiān yǐnxiàn lú	

Fiber optic fusion splice equipment	光纤融接设备	Guāngxiān róngjiē shèbèi	
Fiber optic gyroscope	光纤陀螺	Guāngxiān tuóluó	
Fiber optic hybrid device	光纤混成元件	Guāngxiān hùnchéng yuánjiàn	
Fiber optic illuminator	光纤光源	Guāngxiān guāngyuán	
Fiber optic interferometric sensor	光纤干扰测量传感器	Guāngxiān gānrǎo cèliáng chuángǎnqì	FOIS
Fiber optic inter-repeater link	光纤中继器连接	Guāngxiān zhōngjìqì liánjiē	FOIRL
Fiber optic inter-repeater link	光纤中继站间连接	Guāngxiān zhōngjìzhàn-jiān liánjiē	FOIRL
Fiber optic lightguide	光导管	Guāngdǎoguǎn	
Fiber optic materials	光纤材料	Guāngxiān cáiliào	
Fiber optic modem	光纤调制解调器	Guāngxiān tiáozhì jiětiáoqì	FOM
Fiber optic net	光纤网	Guāngxiān wǎng	FON
Fiber Optic Network Solutions Corp. (US)	光纤网络承包公司	Guāngxiān wǎngluò chéngbāo gōngsī	FONS Corp
Fiber optic patchcord pigtail	光纤跳接线	Guāngxiān tiàojiēxiàn	
Fiber optic polishing machine	光纤端面研磨设备	Guāngxiān duānmiàn yánmó shèbèi	
Fiber optic preform	光纤预型体	Guāngxiān yùxíngtǐ	
Fiber optic Raman amplifier	光纤拉曼放大器	Guāngxiān lā-màn fàngdàqì	FRA
Fiber optic Raman amplifier	拉曼光纤放大器	Lā-màn guāngxiān fàngdàqì	FRA
Fiber optic ribbon	光纤带	Guāngxiān dài	
Fiber optic single window bandwidth coupler	光纤单窗口带宽耦合器	Guāngxiān dānchuāngkǒu dàikuān ǒuhéqì	
Fiber optic spinning equipment	光纤纺丝设备	Guāngxiān fǎngsī shèbèi	
Fiber optic stripper	光纤剥线夹	Guāngxiān bōxiàn jiā	
Fiber optic subscriber line terminal	光纤用户线路终端	Guāngxiān yònghù xiànlù zhōngduān	FSLT
Fiber optic test equipment and procedures	光纤测试设备与测试方法	Guāngxiān cèshì shèbèi yǔ cèshì fāngfǎ	FOTP
Fiber optic transmission system	光导纤维传输系统	Guāngdǎo xiānwéi chuánshū xìtǒng	FOTS
Fiber optics	纤维光学	Xiānwéi guāngxué	
Fiber optics connector	纤维光学连接器	Xiānwéi guāngxué liánjiēqì	
Fiber optics connector classification	纤维光学连接器分类	Xiānwéi guāngxué liánjiēqì fènlèi	
Fiber optics lan section (of TIA, US)	光纤局域网委员会	Guāngxiān júyùwǎng wěiyuánhuì	FOLS
Fiber organizer tape application	光纤编织带涂敷机	Guāngxiān biānzhīdài túfūjī	FOTA
Fiber polisher	光纤抛光机	Guāngxiān pāoguāngjī	FPOL
Fiber pulling test	光纤拉伸试验	Guāngxiān lāshēn shìyàn	
Fiber reference surface	光纤基准面	Guāngxiān jīzhǔnmiàn	
Fiber scattering	光纤散射	Guāngxiān sǎnshè	
Fiber service platform	光纤服务平台	Guāngxiān fúwù píngtái	FSP
Fiber storage center	光纤存储中心	Guāngxiān cúnchǔ zhōngxīn	FSC
Fiber to feeder	光纤到馈线	Guāngxiān dào kuìxiàn	FTF
Fiber to the building	光纤到大楼	Guāngxiān dào dàlóu	FTTB
Fiber to the building	光纤到楼	Guāngxiān dào lóu	FTTB
Fiber to the cabinet	光纤到机柜	Guāngxiān dào jī guì	FTTCab
Fiber to the cabinet	光纤到接线柜箱	Guāngxiān dào jiēxiàn guìxiāng	FTTCab
Fiber to the curb	光纤到近邻	Guāngxiān dào jìnlín	FTTC
Fiber to the curb	光纤到路边	Guāngxiān dào lùbiān	FTTC
Fiber to the customer	光纤到用户	Guāngxiān dào yònghù	FTTC
Fiber to the desk	光纤到办公桌	Guāngxiān dào bàngōngzhuō	FTTD
Fiber to the desk	光纤到桌面	Guāngxiān dào zhuōmiàn	FTTD
Fiber to the home	光纤到户	Guāngxiān dào hù	FTTH

Fiber to the home	光纤到家	Guāngxiān dào jiā	FTTH
Fiber to the home	光纤到家庭	Guāngxiān dào jiātíng	FTTH
Fiber to the last amplifier	光纤到最后一个放大器	Guāngxiān dào zuìhòu yīgè fàngdàqì	FTLA
Fiber to the loop	光纤用户环路	Guāngxiān yònghù huánlù	FTTL
Fiber to the node	光纤到节点	Guāngxiān dào jiédiǎn	FTTN
Fiber to the node	光纤到节点	Guāngxiān dào jiédiǎn	FTTN
Fiber to the office	光纤到办公室	Guāngxiān dào bàngōngshì	FTTO
Fiber to the premises	光纤到住地	Guāngxiān dào zhùdì	FTTP
Fiber to the service area	光纤到小区	Guāngxiān dào xiǎoqū	FTTSA
Fiber to the serving area	光纤到服务区	Guāngxiān dào fúwùqū	FSA
Fiber to the zone	光纤到小区	Guāngxiān dào xiǎoqū	FTTZ
Fiber torsion test	光纤扭力试验	Guāngxiān niǔlì shìyàn	
Fiber transmission module	光传输模块	Guāng chuánshū mókuài	FTM
Fiber-based distributed data interface	基于光纤的分布数据接口	Jīyú guāngxiānde fēnbù shùjù jiēkǒu	FDDI
Fiberglass reinforced plastic	玻璃纤维增强塑胶	Bōli xiānwéi zēngqiáng sùjiāo	FRP
Fiberglass rodent protection	玻璃光纤齿咬防护	Bōli guāngxiān chǐyǎo fánghù	FRP
FiberHome Telecommunication Technologies Co. Ltd.	烽火通信科技股份有限公司	Fēnghuǒ tōngxìn kējì gǔfèn yǒuxiàn gōngsī	
Fiber-kilometer	光纤-公里	Guāngxiān--gōnglǐ	F-km
Fibernet inbuilding network	光纤网络	Guāngxiān wǎngluò	FIN
Fiber-optic ground	光纤地线	Guāngxiān dìxiàn	FOG
Fiber-optic link around the globe	环球光纤链路	Huánqiú guāngxiān liànlù	FLAG
Fiber-optic microscope	光纤显微镜	Guāngxiān xiǎnwēijìng	FOMS
Fiberoptic undersea systems	海底光缆系统	Hǎidǐ guānglǎn xìtǒng	FUS
Fiberoptics Market Research Service (from KMI - Kinder Morgan Inc.)	纤维光学市场研究服务	Xiānwéi guāngxué shìchǎng yánjiū fúwù	FMRS
Fiberoptics Marketing Intelligence (from KMI - Kinder Morgan Inc.)	纤维光学市场情报	Xiānwéi guāngxué shìchǎng qíngbào	FMI
Fiber-to-the passive coaxial (network)	光纤到无源同轴（网络）	Guāngxiān dào wúyuán tóngzhóu (wǎngluò)	FTPC
Fiber-to-the power supply serving area	光纤到供电服务区	Guāngxiān dào gōngdiàn fúwùqū	FPSA
Fibre channel over IP	在 IP 上的光纤信道	Zài IP-shàngde guāngxiān xìndào	FCIP
Fictitious graticule	假想经纬网	Jiǎxiǎng jīngwěiwǎng	
Fidelity (audio)	清晰度	Qīngxīdù	
Fiducial (in SMT)	基准点	Jīzhǔndiǎn	
Field	栏位	Lánwèi	
Field (in a database, in Java)	字段	Zìduàn	
Field (in software)	域	Yù	
Field address (computer term)	字段地址	Zìduàn dìzhǐ	FA
Field address (of a computer program)	区段地址	Qūduàn dìzhǐ	FA
Field address (telecom term)	通信组地址	Tōngxìn zǔ dìzhǐ	FA
Field application engineer	现场应用工程师	Xiànchǎng yìngyòng gōngchéngshī	
Field bus	现场总线	Xiànchǎng zǒngxiàn	
Field bus datalink	现场总线数据链路	Xiànchǎng zǒngxiàn shùjù liànlù	FDL
Field catalogue	字段目录	Zìduàn mùlù	
Field collector, field data collector	野外采集器	Yěwài cǎijíqì	
Field control (refers to magnetic field)	激磁控制	Jīcí kòngzhì	
Field data	现场数据	Xiànchǎng shùjù	

Field definition	字段定义	Zìduàn dìngyì	
Field displacement	场移	Chángyí	
Field effect transistor	场效应晶体管	Cháng xiàoyìng jīngtǐguǎn	FET
Field emitter display	场发射显示器	Cháng fāshè xiǎnshìqì	FED
Field intensity sensibility	场强灵敏度	Chǎngqiáng língmǐndù	
Field length (for database)	字段长度	Zìduàn chángdù	
Field maintenance	现场维护	Xiànchǎng wéihù	
Field name	字段名	Zìduàn míng	
Field observation	野外观测	Yěwài guāncè	
Field observations	实地观测	Shídì guāncè	
Field programmable gate array	现场可编程门阵列	Xiànchǎng kěbiānchéng mén zhènliè	FPGA
Field programmable logic array	现场可编程逻辑阵列	Xiànchǎng kěbiānchéng luóji zhènliè	FPLA
Field programmable systems chip	现场可编程序系统芯片	Xiànchǎng kěbiān chéngxù xìtǒng xìnpiàn	FPSC
Field quantity	场量	Chángliàng	
Field reconnaissance	实地勘查	Shídì kānchá	
Field replaceable unit	可实地替换单元	Kěshídì tìhuan dānyuán	FRU
Field replaceable unit	现场可换件	Xiànchǎng kěhuàn jiàn	FRU
Field replaceable unit	现场可替换部件	Xiànchǎng kětìhuan bùjiàn	FRU
Field specifications	字段说明	Zìduàn shuōmíng	
Field strength	场强	Chǎngqiáng	
Field strength meter	场强计	Chǎngqiáng jì	FSM
Field strength-distance product; cymomotive force	场强-距离乘积	Chǎngqiáng--jùlí chéngjī	CMF
Field survey	实地调查	Shídì diàochá	
Field terminator	字段终止符	Zìduàn zhōngzhǐ fú	
Field test	现场试验	Xiànchǎng shìyàn	
Field vector	场矢量	Cháng shǐliàng	
Field vector polarization	场矢量极化	Cháng shǐliàng jíhuà	
Fieldbus control system	现场总线控制系统	Xiànchǎng zǒngxiàn kòngzhì xìtǒng	FCS
Field-controlled thyristor	场控晶闸管	Chángkòng jīngzháguǎn	
Field-displacement isolator	场移式隔离器	Chángyíshì gélíqì	
Field-programmable gate arrays	现场可编程序门阵列	Xiànchǎng kěbiān chéngxù mén zhènliè	FPGAs
Field-strength test analysis	场强测试分析	Chǎngqiáng cèshì fēnxī	
Fighting game (computer game)	格斗类游戏	Gédòu-lèi yóuxì	FTG
Figure of merit	品质因数	Pǐnzhì yīnshù	G/T
Filament winding	纤维缠线	Xiānwéi chánxiàn	
File	文件	Wénjiàn	
File access block	文件存取块	Wénjiàn cúnqǔ kuài	FAB
File address register	文件地址寄存器	Wénjiàn dìzhǐ jìcúnqì	FAR
File allocation table	文件分配表	Wénjiàn fēnpèi biǎo	FAT
File attribute	文件属性	Wénjiàn shǔxìng	
File compression	文件压缩	Wénjiàn yāsuō	
File control block	文件控制块	Wénjiàn kòngzhì kuài	FCB
File control information	行控制信息	Háng kòngzhì xìnxī	FCI
File extension	文件后缀	Wénjiàn hòuzhuì	
File fork	文件派生	Wénjiàn pàishēng	
File group	文件组	Wénjiàn zǔ	

File indexing	文件索引	Wénjiàn suǒyǐn	
File integrity checker	文件完整性检查器	Wénjiàn wánzhěngxìng jiǎncháqì	
File locking	文件锁定	Wénjiàn suǒdìng	
File management system	文件管理系统	Wénjiàn guǎnlǐ xìtǒng	FMS
File menu (WP command)	文件菜单	Wénjiàn càidān	
File name	文件名	Wénjiàn míng	
File number	文件编号	Wénjiàn biānhào	
File protection (IPsec)	文件保护	Wénjiàn bǎohù	
File replication service	文件复制服务	Wénjiàn fùzhì fúwù	
File separator	文件分隔	Wénjiàn fēngé	FS
File server	文件服务器	Wénjiàn fúwùqì	
File storage type	文件存储类型	Wénjiàn cúnchǔ lèixíng	
File structure	文件结构	Wénjiàn jiégòu	
File transfer access and management (ISO use)	文件传输访问和管理	Wénjiàn chuánshū fǎngwèn hé guǎnlǐ	FTAM
File transfer access management	文件传送存放与管理	Wénjiàn chuánsòng cúnfàng yǔ guǎnlǐ	FTAM
File transfer addressing and management	文件传送地址和管理	Wénjiàn chuánsòng dìzhǐ hé guǎnlǐ	FTAM
File transfer protocol	文件传输协议	Wénjiàn chuánshū xiéyì	FTP
File transfer protocol	文件传送协议	Wénjiàn chuánsòng xiéyì	FTP
File transfer protocol	远程存取	Yuǎnchéng cúnqǔ	FTP
File transfer protocol site (Internet location for downloading files using FTP)	文件传送点	Wénjiàn chuánsòng diǎn	FTP site
File transfer, access and management	文件传输、存取和管理	Wénjiàn chuánshū、cúnqǔ hé guǎnlǐ	FTAM
File transfer, access and management protocol	文件传送接入及管理协议	Wénjiàn chuánsòng jiērù jí guǎnlǐ xiéyì	FTAM
File transfer, access and manipulation	文件传输，接入和使用	Wénjiàn chuánshū, jiērù hé shǐyòng	FTAM
File transmission, access and management	文件传输访问管理	Wénjiàn chuánshū fǎngwèn guǎnlǐ	FTAM
File type	文件类型	Wénjiàn lèixíng	
Filing	存档	Cúndàng	
Fill factor	填充因子	Tiánchōng yīnzǐ	
Fill factor (SDH structure)	填充系数	Tiánchōng xìshù	
Fill rate	填充率	Tiánchōng lǜ	
Fill, pad (verb)	填充	Tiánchōng	
Filled (FOC type, usually jelly-filled)	填充式	Tiánchōng-shì	
Filled cable	填充电缆	Tiánchōng diànlǎn	
Fillet (in SMT)	焊角	Hànjiǎo	
Fill-in signal unit	填充信号单元	Tiánchōng xìnhào dānyuán	FISU
Filter (electrical or RF)	滤波器	Lǜbōqì	
Filter (for database)	筛选	Shāixuǎn	
Filter (optical)	滤光镜	Lǜguāngjìng	
Filter design and analysis tool	滤波器设计和分析工具	Lǜbōqì shèjì hé fēnxī gōngjù	
Filter identifer	滤波器标识符	Lǜbōqì biāozhìfú	FID
Filter identifier	过滤标识符	Guòlǜ biāozhìfú	FID
Filter output	滤波器输出	Lǜbōqì shūchū	
Filter software	过滤软件	Guòlǜ ruǎnjiàn	
Filter tap coupler	滤波型分路器	Lǜbō-xíng fēnlùqì	FTAP
Filter visualization tool	滤波器可视化工具	Lǜbōqì kěshìhuà gōngjù	
Filter wavelength division multiplexer	滤波型波分复用器	Lǜbō-xíng bōfēn fùyòngqì	FWDM
Filtering	滤波	Lǜbō	

Final assembly code	最后的组合码	Zuìhòude zǔhé mǎ	FAC
Final assembly code (GSM term)	最终集结码	Zuìzhōng jíjié mǎ	
Final character	终止字符	Zhōngzhǐ zìfú	
Final inspection	最终检验	Zuìzhōng jiǎnyàn	
Final selector	终接器	Zhōngjiēqì	
Final signaling unit	最终信号单元	Zuìzhōng xìnhào dānyuán	FSU
Final type approval	最终全面型号认证	Zuìzhōng quánmiàn xínghào rènzhèng	FTA
Finalization	终结	Zhōngjié	
Finalizer	终结器	Zhōngjiéqì	
Finance group (CMM)	财务组	Cáiwù zǔ	FG
Financial management system	财务管理系统	Cáiwù guǎnlǐ xìtǒng	FMS
Financial network association (China)	金融网络协会	Jīnróng wǎngluò xiéhuì	FNA
Financial Services Technology Consortium	金融服务技术联盟	Jīnróng fúwù jìshù liánméng	FSTC
Financial Times Stock Exchange top 100 companies	泰晤士金融股票交易 100 家顶级公司	Tàiwùshì jīnróng gǔpiào jiāoyì 100 jiā dǐngjí gōngsī	FTSE100
Find (WP command)	查寻	Cháxún	
Find calling party	寻找呼叫信号	Xúnzhǎo hūjiào xìnhào	FC
Find me/follow me	发现/跟踪	Fāxiàn/gēnzōng	
Finding	查找	Cházhǎo	
Fine mechanics	精密机械	Jīngmì jīxiè	
Fine pitch	细间距	Xì jiānjù	
Fine-grained	细颗粒	Xìkēlì	
Fine-pitch technology (in SMT)	密脚距技术	Mìjiǎojù jìshù	FPT
Finger	查索	Chásuǒ	
Finger (verb)	人名查询	Rénmíng cháxún	
Fingerprint	指纹	Zhǐwén	
Finite amplitude wave	有限振幅波	Yǒuxiàn zhènfú bō	
Finite element method	有限元素法	Yǒuxiàn yuánsù fǎ	
Finite impulse response	有限推进响应	Yǒuxiàn tuījìn xiǎngyìng	FIR
Finite message machine	有限消息机器	Yǒuxiàn xiāoxi jīqì	FMM
Finite state automaton	有限状态自动机	Yǒuxiàn zhuàngtài zìdòngjī	
Finite state machine	有限状态机	Yǒuxiàn zhuàngtài jī	FSM
Finite state machine	有限状态器	Yǒuxiàn zhuàngtàiqì	
Finite state machine minimization	有穷自动机简化	Yǒuqióng zìdòngjī jiǎnhuà	
Finite state module	有限状态模型	Yǒuxiàn zhuàngtài móxíng	FSM
Finite state transition system	有限状态转换系统	Yǒuxiàn zhuàngtài zhuǎnhuàn xìtǒng	FSTS
Finite-state cascades	有限状态层叠	Yǒuxiàn zhuàngtài céngdié	
Finland-Russia optical cable line (built 1993)	芬（兰）俄（国）光缆线路	Fēn (lán) é (guó) guānglǎn xiànlù	FRL
Finland-Russia optical gateway	芬俄光通路	Fēn é guāng tōnglù	FROG
Finland-Russia optical gateway	芬兰俄国光通路	Fēnlán éguó guāng tōnglù	FROG
Fire alarm	火警	Huǒjǐng	
Fire alarm automatic control unit	火灾自动报警控制装置	Huǒzāi zìdòng bàojǐng kòngzhì zhuāngzhì	FACU
Fire alarm bell	火警警铃	Huǒjǐng jǐnglíng	FAB
Fire alarm system	火灾报警系统	Huǒzāi bàojǐng xìtǒng	FCC
Fire automation	消防自动化	Xiāofáng zìdònghuà	

Fire control radar	火控雷达	Huǒkòng léidá	
Fire hydrant	消火栓	Xiāohuǒshuān	FH
Fire public address	火灾事故广播	Huǒzāi shìgù guǎngbō	FPA
Fire resistant damper	防火阀	Fánghuǒ fá	FRD
Fire resistant shutter	防火卷帘	Fánghuǒ juànlián	FRS
Firehose cursor	流水游标	Liúshuǐ yóubiāo	
Firewall	防火墙	Fánghuǒqiáng	
Firewall (lit : gateway guard)	门禁	Ménjìn	
Firewire (IEEE 1394)	火线	Huǒxiàn	
Firmware	固件	Gùjiàn	
Firmware channel	固件通道	Gùjiàn tōngdào	FMCH
Firmware hub	固件中心	Gùjiàn zhōngxīn	FWH
First choice set of circuits	首选电路组	Shǒuxuǎn diànlù zǔ	
First come first service	先到先服务	Xiān dào xiān fúwù	FCFS
First derivative element	一阶微分环节	Yījiē wēifēn huánjié	
First generation radio transmission technology	第一阶段无线传输技术	Dìyījiēduàn wúxiàn chuánshū jìshù	1XRTT
First in, first out	先进先出	Xiān jìn xiān chū	FIFO
First input first output	先入先出队列	Xiān rù xiān chū duìliè	FIFO
First level data multiplexer	第一级数据复用器	Dìyījí shùjù fùyòngqì	
First level interrupt handler	第一级中断处理程序	Dìyījí zhōngduàn chùlǐ chéngxù	FLIH
First motion	初动	Chūdòng	
First normal form	第 1 范式	Dìyī fànshì	1NF
First order astatic system	一阶无差系统	Yījiē wúchā xìtǒng	
First order effect	一阶效应	Yījiē xiàoyìng	
First order valley (GIS)	一阶谷	Yījiē gǔ	
First person game (computer game)	第一人称游戏	Dìyīrénchēng yóuxì	FPP
First ringing	初呼振铃	Chūhū zhènlíng	
First Wiener filter solution	第一维纳滤波器解	Dìyī wéinà lǜbōqì jiě	FWFS
First-come first service	先来先服务	Xiān lái xiān fúwù	
First-in first-out list	先进先出表（队列）	Xiān jìn xiān chū biǎo (duìliè)	
First-order phase-locked loop	一阶锁相环	Yījiē suǒxiānghuán	
First-party release	双方控制释放	Shuāngfāng kòngzhì shìfàng	
Fish tape	电缆牵引圈	Diànlǎn qiānyǐn quān	
Fish-bone antenna	鱼骨表天线	Yúgǔ biǎo tiānxiàn	
Fitness for use	适用度	Shìyòngdù	
Five tone sequential system	五音顺序制	Wǔyīn shùnxù zhì	
Five-horn feed	五喇叭馈电器	Wǔ lǎba kuìdiànqì	
Five-phase reservation protocol	五阶段预留协议	Wǔ jiēduàn yùliú xiéyì	FPRP
Fixed analyzer	固定分析器	Gùdìng fēnxīqì	FA
Fixed base station	固定基地电台	Gùdìng jīdì diàntái	
Fixed bit rate	固定比特率	Gùdìng bǐtèlǜ	FBR
Fixed channel allocation	固定信道分配	Gùdìng xìndào fēnpèi	FCA
Fixed channel assignment	固定信道指配	Gùdìng xìndào zhǐpèi	
Fixed control set	固定控制集	Gùdìng kòngzhì jí	
Fixed database role	固定数据库角色	Gùdìng shùjùkù juésè	
Fixed deflection coil	固定式偏转线圈	Gùdìng-shì piānzhuǎn xiànquān	

Fixed dialing number	固定拨号	Gùdìng bōhào	FDN
Fixed dispersion compensator	固定色散补偿器	Gùdìng sèsàn bǔchángqì	DCFG
Fixed end systems	固定端系统	Gùdìng duān xìtǒng	
Fixed laser bar code scanner	固定式激光条码扫描器	Gùdìng-shì jīguāng tiáomǎ sǎomiáoqì	
Fixed length one-way acknowledgement	定长单向确认	Dìngcháng dānxiàng quèrèn	
Fixed memory	固定存储器	Gùdìng cúnchǔqì	
Fixed network services	固定网络通讯服务	Gùdìng wǎngluò tōngxùn fúwù	FNS
Fixed network user rate	固定网用户率	Gùdìng wǎng yònghùlǜ	FNUR
Fixed object check	固定目标检查	Gùdìng mùbiāo jiǎnchá	
Fixed optical attenuator	固定光衰减器	Gùdìng guāng shuāijiǎnqì	
Fixed pad attenuator	固定衰减器	Gùdìng shuāijiǎnqì	
Fixed point representation	定点表示法	Dìngdiǎn biǎoshì fǎ	FPR
Fixed radio access	固定无线接入	Gùdìng wúxiàn jiērù	FRA
Fixed reference modulation	固定基准调制	Gùdìng jīzhǔn tiáozhì	
Fixed satellite communications	固定卫星通讯	Gùdìng wèixīng tōngxùn	FSC
Fixed satellite service	静止卫星业务	Jìngzhǐ wèixīng yèwù	FSS
Fixed satellite services	固定卫星业务	Gùdìng wèixīng yèwù	FSS
Fixed server role	固定服务器角色	Gùdìng fúwùqì juésè	
Fixed service	固定业务	Gùdìng yèwù	
Fixed station	固定电台	Gùdìng diàntái	
Fixed subscriber	固定用户	Gùdìng yònghù	FS
Fixed subscriber unit	单用户固定台	Dānyònghù gùdìng tái	FSU
Fixed subscriber unit	固定用户单元	Gùdìng yònghù dānyuán	FSU
Fixed temperature heat detector	定温控测器	Dìngwēn kòngcèqì	FTHD
Fixed terminal	固定终端	Gùdìng zhōngduān	FT
Fixed wireless access	固定无线接入	Gùdìng wúxiàn jiērù	FWA
Fixed wireless network	固定无线网络	Gùdìng wúxiàn wǎngluò	FWN
Fixed/mobile convergence	固定通信与移动通信相互靠拢	Gùdìng tōngxìn yǔ yídòng tōngxìn xiānghù kàolǒng	FMC
Fixed-aggregate data type	固定聚合数据类型	Gùdìng jùhé shùjù lèixíng	
Fixed-length	定长	Dìngcháng	
Fixed-length records	定长记录	Dìngcháng jìlù	F
Fixed-length two-way acknowledgement	定长双向确认	Dìngcháng shuāngxiàng quèrèn	
Fixed-mobile convergence	固定与移动通信融合	Gùdìng yǔ yídòng tōngxìn rónghé	FMC
Fixed-satellite service	卫星固定业务	Wèixīng gùdìng yèwù	
Fixture (in SMT)	夹具	Jiājù	
Flag	标记	Biāojì	
Flag (in a data packet)	标志段	Biāozhì duàn	F
Flag (in SS7)	标志码	Biāozhì mǎ	F
Flag (video term)	标志	Biāozhì	
Flag field	标记字段	Biāojì zìduàn	
Flag hunting	标志位插索	Biāozhì wèi chāsuǒ	
Flame (computer slang)	叫骂	Jiàomà	
Flame detector	火焰探测器	Huǒyàn tàncèqì	FD
Flame resistance test	耐燃烧试验	Nàiránshāo shìyàn	
Flame retardant cable	阻燃缆	Zǔrán lǎn	

Flame retardant material	阻燃材料	Zǔrán cáiliào	
Flame war (computer slang)	骂战	Màzhàn	
Flamethrower mini-bridger	小型桥接器	Xiǎoxíng qiáojiēqì	FTMB
Flange assembly	法兰组件	Fǎlán zǔjiàn	
Flange joint	法兰连接	Fǎlán liánjiē	
Flange type	法兰类型	Fǎlán lèixíng	
Flap attenuator	铡刀式衰减器	Zhádāo-shì shuāijiǎnqì	
Flash memory	快闪存储器	Kuàishǎn cúnchǔqì	FM
Flash memory	闪存	Shǎn cún	Flash
Flash memory	闪速存储器	Shǎnsù cúnchǔqì	
Flash memory, thumb drive, jump drive	优盘	Yōupán	
Flash programmable read only memory	块闪可编程只读存储器	Kuàishǎn kěbiānchéng zhǐdú cúnchǔqì	FLASH-PROM
Flash request	快闪要求	Kuàishǎn yāoqiú	
Flash technology	闪存技术	Shǎn cún jìshù	
Flashing frequency	停闪频率	Tíngshǎn pínlǜ	
Flashlamp pumped dye laser	闪光灯激发染料激光	Shǎnguāngdēng jīfā rǎnliào jīguāng	
Flat addressing	板存储地址	Bǎn cúnchǔ dìzhǐ	
Flat cathode ray tube (CRT)	平面阴极射线管	Píngmiàn yīnjí shèxiànguǎn	
Flat fading	平衰落	Píng shuāiluò	
Flat file	平面文件	Píngmiàn wénjiàn	
Flat flange	平面法兰	Píngmiàn fǎlán	
Flat headed antenna	平头缝隙天线	Píngtóu fèngxì tiānxiàn	
Flat random noise	平坦随机噪声	Píngtǎn suíjī zàoshēng	
Flat shading (video term)	平面描影	Píngmiàn miáoyǐng	
Flat-bed color image scanner	平台式彩色影像扫描器	Píngtái-shì cǎisè yǐngxiàng sǎomiáoqì	
Flatbed plotter	平板绘图机	Píngbǎn huìtújī	
Flat-bed transmitter	平面式发送机	Píngmiàn-shì fāsòngjī	
Flat-gain amplifier	平坦增益放大器	Píngtǎn zēngyì fàngdàqì	FA
Flatness	均匀性	Jūnyúnxìng	FL
Flat-panel-display	平板显示	Píngbǎn xiǎnshì	FPD
Flattened interface	平展界面	Píngzhǎn jièmiàn	
Flattened rowset	平展行集	Píngzhǎn háng jí	
Flattening	扁平率	Biǎnpíng lǜ	
Flat-top antenna	平顶天线	Píngdǐng tiānxiàn	
Flaw (IPsec)	缺陷	Quēxiàn	
Flaw hypothesis methodology	缺陷假设法	Quēxiàn jiǎshèfǎ	
Flaw hypothesis methodology (IPsec)	缺陷假设法	Quēxiàn jiǎshèfǎ	
Flexible access system	灵活接入系统	Línghuó jiērù xìtǒng	FA
Flexible access termination	灵活接入终端	Línghuó jiērù zhōngduān	FAT
Flexible coaxial line	软同轴线	Ruǎn tóngzhóu xiàn	
Flexible feedback	软反馈	Ruǎn fǎnkuì	
Flexible multiplexer	灵活复接器	Línghuó fùjiēqì	MUX
Flexible multiplexer	灵活复用设备	Línghuó fùyòng shèbèi	FM
Flexible multiplexer	灵活复用器	Línghuó fùyòngqì	FM
Flexible paging system	可变速寻呼系统	Kěbiànsù xúnhū xìtǒng	FLEX
Flexible point	灵活点	Línghuó diǎn	FP

Flexible topology data link	灵活拓扑数据链路	Línghuó tuòpū shùjù liànlù	FTDL
Flexible waveguide	软波导	Ruǎn bōdǎo	
Flexural shear model	弯曲剪切模型	Wānqū jiǎnqiē móxíng	
Flicker	闪变	Shǎnbiàn	
Flicker	闪烁	Shǎnshuò	
Flicker noise	闪烁噪声	Shǎnshuò zàoshēng	
Flickermeter	闪变计	Shǎnbiànjì	
Flickermeter	闪烁计	Shǎnshuòjì	
Flight information service (civil aviation)	飞行情报服务	Fēixíng qíngbào fúwù	FIS
Flip chip (in SMT)	倒装芯片	Dàozhuāng xìnpiàn	
Flip chip pin grid array	反转芯片针脚栅格阵列	Fǎnzhuǎn xìnpiàn zhēnjiao zhàgé zhènliè	FCPGA
Flip double buffered (video)	反转双缓存	Fǎnzhuǎn shuāng huǎncún	
Flip-chip	芯片反转	Xìnpiàn fǎnzhuǎn	
Flip-flop	触发器	Chùfāqì	FF
FLIR Systems, Inc	FLIR 系统公司	FLIR xìtǒng gōngsī	FSI
Floater	浮子	Fúzi	
Floating charge	浮充充电	Fúchōng chōngdiàn	
Floating mode	浮动模式	Fúdòng móshì	
Floating point	浮点	Fúdiǎn	
Floating point addition	浮点加	Fúdiǎn jiā	FADD
Floating point communications library	浮点通信库	Fúdiǎn tōngxìn kù	
Floating point division	浮点除	Fúdiǎn chú	FDIV
Floating point multiplication	浮点乘	Fúdiǎn chéng	FMUL
Floating point operations per second	浮点操作/秒	Fúdiǎn cāozuò/ miǎo	FLOP
Floating point operations per second	每秒浮点运算次数	Měi miǎo fúdiǎn yùnsuàn cìshù	FLOPS
Floating point representation	浮点表示法	Fúdiǎn biǎoshì fǎ	
Floating point subtraction	浮点减	Fúdiǎn jiǎn	FSUB
Floating point unit	浮点运算单元	Fúdiǎn yùnsuàn dānyuán	FPU
Floating structure	浮游结构物	Fúyóu jiégòu wù	
Floating voltage peak value	浮充电压峰值	Fúchōng diànyā fēngzhí	
Flooding	洪流	Hóngliú	
Flooding	洪水	Hóngshuǐ	
Flooding	流播	Liúbō	
Flooding (IPsec)	淹没	Yānmò	
Flooding attack (IW)	洪流攻击	Hóngliú gōngjī	
Flooding search	泛搜索	Fànsōusuǒ	
Floor distributor	楼层配线架	Lóucéng pèixiànjià	FD
Floor standing - Venturi forced convection infrared reflow oven (semiconductor mfg)	地轴架式-文氏强制对流红外回流炉	Dìzhóujiàshi-wén-shì qiángzhì duìliú hóngwài huíliú lú	
Floppy disk	软磁盘	Ruǎn cípán	
Floppy disk controller	软盘驱动器控制装置	Ruǎnpán qūdòngqì kòngzhì zhuāngzhì	FDC
Floppy disk driver	软盘驱动器	Ruǎnpán qūdòngqì	FDD
Flourided silicon oxide	二氧氟化硅	Èryǎng fúhuà guī	Si02F
Flow aggregation	流汇集	Liú huìjí	
Flow attribute notification protocol (Toshiba)	流属性通知协议	Liú shǔxìng tōngzhī xiéyì	FANP
Flow chart	流程图	Liúchéngtú	

Flow chart symbol	流程图符号	Liúchéngtú fúhào	
Flow classification algorithm (for IP packet classification)	流分类算法	Liú fēnlèi suànfǎ	
Flow control	流量控制	Liúliàng kòngzhì	
Flow control language (in SQL Server)	流程控制语言	Liúchéng kòngzhì yǔyán	
Flow control parameter negotiation	流量控制参数协商	Liúliàng kòngzhì cānshù xiéshāng	
Flow control protection circuit	流量控保电路	Liúliàng kòng bǎo diànlù	
Flow control statements (in SQL Server)	流程控制语句	Liúchéng kòngzhì yǔjù	
Flow meter	流量计	Liúliàngjì	
Flow net	流线网	Liúxiàn wǎng	
Flow rate control valve	流量控制阀	Liúliàng kòngzhì fá	
Flow relation (in Petri net)	流关系	Liú guānxi	
Flow table	流表	Liú biǎo	
Flow velocity	流速	Liúsù	
Flow visualization	流可视化	Liú kěshìhuà	
Flow visualization	流体视觉化	Liútǐ shìjuéhuà	
Fluctuating flow	波动气流	Bōdòng qìliú	
Fluid dynamic bearing motor	液态轴承马达	Yètài zhóuchéng mǎdá	FDBM
Fluke Networks Corp.	福禄克网络公司	Fú-lù-kè wǎngluò gōngsī	
Fluorated polyimide (FOC mfg)	氟化聚酸亚胺材料	Fúhuà jùsuān yà'àn cáiliào	FULPI
Fluorescent emission crystal	萤光放射晶体	Yíngguāng fàngshè jīngtǐ	
Fluorescent material read only memory	荧光质只读存储器	Yíngguāng zhì zhǐ dú cúnchǔqì	FMD ROM
Fluoride fiber	氟化物光纤	Fúhuàwù guāngxiān	FF
Fluoromaterial (semiconductor mfg)	氟材料	Fú cáiliào	
Flush	刷新	Shuāxīn	
Flush, purge	冲洗	Chōngxǐ	
Flush-mounted antenna	平嵌天线	Píngqiàn tiānxiàn	
Flush-mounted antenna	平镶天线	Píngxiāng tiānxiàn	
Flutter fading	急剧衰落	Jíjù shuāiluò	
Flying probe (PCB manufacture)	飞针式	Fēizhēn-shì	
Foam fire extinguishing system	泡沫灭火系统	Pàomò mièhuǒ xìtǒng	FFES
Focal length	焦距	Jiāojù	FL
Focal-length-to–diameter ratio of a satellite parabolic reflector	卫星抛物反射面焦距对天线口径之比	Wèixīng pāowù fǎnshè miàn jiāojù duì tiānxiàn kǒujìng zhī bǐ	f/D
Focus distance	焦距	Jiāojù	
Focus node (in CSCW)	焦点节点	Jiāodiǎn jiédiǎn	
Focusing reflector	聚焦反射器	Jùjiāo fǎnshèqì	
Focus-out	散焦	Sànjiāo	
Fog (video term)	雾化效果	Wùhuà xiàoguǒ	
Fog table quality (video)	雾化表画质	Wùhuà biǎohuà zhì	
Foil twisted pair	金属箔对线	Jīnshǔ bó duìxiàn	FTP
Foil twisted pair	金属箔双绞电缆	Jīnshǔ bó shuāngjiǎo diànlǎn	FTP
Folded balun (balanced/unbalanced device) converter	折合的平衡/不平衡变换器	Zhéhéde pínghéng/bùpínghéng biànhuànqì	
Folded dipole	折合振子	Zhéhé zhènzǐ	
Folded dipole (antenna)	折合偶极子	Zhéhé ǒujízi	
Folded dipole antenna	折叠偶极天线	Zhédié ǒují tiānxiàn	

Folded monopole antenna	折叠单极天线	Zhédié dānjí tiānxiàn	
Folded monopole, folded unipole (antenna)	折合单极子	Zhéhé dānjízi	
Folder	文件夹	Wénjiàn jiā	
Folding endurance	耐折度	Nàizhédù	
Folding method	折叠法	Zhédié fǎ	
Font	字模	Zìmú	
Font	字型	Zìxíng	
Font (WP command)	字体	Zìtǐ	
Font cartridge	字体盒	Zìtǐ hé	
Font size	字模大小	Zìmú dàxiǎo	
Foot wall	下盘	Xiàpán	
Footer (WP command)	尾页标	Wěiyè biāo	
Footnote	脚注	Jiǎozhù	
For further study	进一步研究	Jìnyībù yánjiū	FFS
For further study	为以后研究	Wéi yǐhòu yánjiū	FFS
For further study	作进一步研究	Zuò jìnyībù yánjiū	FFS
For your information	供参考	Gōng cānkǎo	FYI
For your information	供你用的信息	Gōng nǐ yòngde xìnxī	FYI
For your information	为您提供信息	Wéi nín tígōng xìnxī	FYI
For your reference (computer chat)	供你参考	Gōng nǐ cānkǎo	FYR
Forbes (US magazine)	福布斯	Fú-bù-sī	
Force feedback joystick	力量反匱式操纵杆	Lìliang fǎnkuì-shì cāozònggǎn	FFJ
Forced insertion (call pre-emption)	强插	Qiángchā	
Forced release	强迫释放	Qiǎngpò shìfàng	
Forced switch	强制倒换	Qiángzhì dǎohuàn	FSW
Forced switchover	强制切换	Qiángzhì qiēhuàn	FSw
Forced texture compression	强制纹理压缩	Qiángzhì wénlǐ yāsuō	
Forced ventilation	强迫通风	Qiǎngpò tōngfēng	
Foreground program	前台程序	Qiántái chéngxù	
Foreign agent	外部代理	Wàibù dàilǐ	FA
Foreign agent	外地代理	Wàidì dàilǐ	FA
Foreign agent	外区代理	Wàiqū dàilǐ	FA
Foreign agent care-of address	外地代理转交地址	Wàidì dàilǐ zhuǎnjiāo dìzhǐ	
Foreign exchange office	外部交换局	Wàibù jiāohuànjú	FXO
Foreign exchange station	外部交换站	Wàibù jiāohuàn zhàn	FXS
Foreign key	外关键字	Wài guānjiàn zì	
Foreign key (for database)	外键	Wàijiàn	FK
Foreign key constraint (in SQL Server)	外关键字约束	Wài guānjiàn zì yuēshù	
Foreign table	外表	Wàibiǎo	
Foreign trade processing zone	对外贸易加工区	Duìwài màoyì jiāgōng qū	
Foreign trade zone	对外贸易区	Duìwài màoyì qū	FTZ
Foreign-funded enterprise	外资企业	Wàizī qǐyè	
Forgery (IPsec)	伪造	Wěizào	
Form	窗体	Chuāngtǐ	
Form feed	换页	Huàn yè	FF
Form recognition	表格识别	Biǎogé shíbié	

Formal description technology	形式化描述技术	Xíngshì huà miáoshù jìshù	FDT
Formal logic	形式逻辑	Xíngshì luóji	
Formal parameter	形参	Xíngcān	
Formal proof (IPsec)	形式证明	Xíngshì zhèngmíng	
Formal verification (IPsec)	形式验证	Xíngshì yànzhèng	
Formalization of spatial concepts	空间概念构成	Kōngjiān gàiniàn gòuchéng	
Format	格式	Géshi	
Format (verb)	格式化	Géshihuà	
Format bar (WP command)	排版工具	Páibǎn gōngjù	
Format conversion	格式转换	Géshi zhuǎnhuàn	
Format effector	格式控制符	Géshi kòngzhìfú	
Format identifier	格式标识符	Géshi biāozhì fú	FI
Format menu (WP command)	排版菜单	Páibǎn càidān	
Format prefix	格式前缀	Géshi qiánzhuì	FP
Format translator programming language	公式翻译程序语言	Gōngshì fānyì chéngxù yǔyán	FORTRAN
Formation of image, imagery	成象	Chéngxiàng	
Formatted form	格式化形式	Géshihuà xíngshì	
Formatted processable form	格式化可处理形式	Géshihuà kěchǔlǐ xíngshì	
Formlines	地形线	Dìxíng xiàn	
Forms interface	窗口界面	Chuāngkǒu jièmiàn	
Formula	公式	Gōngshì	
Formula translator	公式翻译语言	Gōngshì fānyì yǔyán	FORTRAN
Formulary (IPsec)	定则	Dìngzé	
Fortuitous distortion	不规则畸变	Bùguīzé jībiàn	
Forum of Incident Response and Security Teams	事件响应和安全团队论坛	Shìjiàn xiǎngyìng hé ānquán tuánduì lùntán	FIRST
Forward	前向	Qiánxiàng	
Forward access channel	前向接入信道	Qiánxiàng jiērù xìndào	FACH
Forward access signaling	前转接入信令	Qiánzhuǎn jiērù xìnlìng	
Forward address message	前向地址消息	Qiánxiàng dìzhǐ xiāoxi	FAM
Forward address signal	前向地址信号	Qiánxiàng dìzhǐ xìnhào	
Forward busy	前向忙	Qiánxiàng máng	
Forward call indicator	前向呼叫指示	Qiánxiàng hūjiào zhǐshì	
Forward chaining	前向链	Qiánxiàng liàn	
Forward channel	前向信道	Qiánxiàng xìndào	
Forward channel	正向信道	Zhèngxiàng xìndào	
Forward check SS indication	前转检验 SS 指示	Qiánzhuǎn jiǎnyàn SS zhǐshì	
Forward code division multiple access channel	前向码分多址信道	Qiánxiàng mǎfēn duōzhǐ xìndào	
Forward compatibility	前向兼容性	Qiánxiàng jiānróngxìng	
Forward control channel	前向控制信道	Qiánxiàng kòngzhì xìndào	FOCC
Forward declaration	前置声明	Qiánzhì shēngmíng	
Forward delay interval	转发延迟间隔	Zhuǎnfā yánchí jiàngé	
Forward direction (in a circulator or isolator)	正向	Zhèngxiàng	
Forward equivalence class	转发等效类	Zhuǎnfā děngxiào lèi	FEC
Forward equivalent classification	前向等效类	Qiánxiàng děngxiào lèi	FEC
Forward error control	前向差错控制	Qiánxiàng chācuò kòngzhì	FEC
Forward error control	正向误差控制	Zhèngxiàng wùchā kòngzhì	FEC

Forward error correction	前向纠错	Qiánxiàng jiūcuò	FEC
Forward error correction code	前向纠错码	Qiánxiàng jiūcuò mǎ	FEC
Forward explicit congestion notification	前向显式拥塞通知	Qiánxiàng xiǎnshì yōngsè tōngzhī	FECN
Forward explicit congestion notification	显式正向阻塞通知	Xiǎnshì zhèngxiàng zǔsè tōngzhī	FECN
Forward feed equalizing	前馈均衡	Qiánkuì jūnhéng	
Forward indicator bit	前向指示比特	Qiánxiàng zhǐshì bǐtè	FIB
Forward interworking telephone events	前向互通电话事件	Qiánxiàng hùtōng diànhuà shìjiàn	FITEs
Forward link	前向链路	Qiánxiàng liànlù	
Forward lookup	正向搜索	Zhèngxiàng sōusuǒ	
Forward loss (in a circulator or isolator)	正向损耗	Zhèngxiàng sǔnhào	
Forward motion vector (video term)	前向运动矢量	Qiánxiàng yùndòng shǐliàng	
Forward proxy	转发代理	Zhuǎnfā dàilǐ	
Forward pump (FOC)	前向泵浦	Qiánxiàng bèngpǔ	
Forward seizure	前向占用	Qiánxiàng zhànyòng	
Forward sequence number	前向顺序号	Qiánxiàng shùnxù hào	FSN
Forward sequence number of last message accepted by remote level 2	由远端第二级接受的最后一个消息的前向序号	Yóu yuǎnduān dì'èrjí jiēshòude zuìhòu yīgè xiāoxide qiánxiàng xùhào	FSNC
Forward set-up	前向建立	Qiánxiàng jiànlì	
Forward setup message	前向建立信号	Qiánxiàng jiànlì xìnhào	FSM
Forward setup message (TUP)	前向建立消息	Qiánxiàng jiànlì xiāoxi	FSM
Forward signal	前向信号	Qiánxiàng xìnhào	
Forward traffic channel	前向业务信道	Qiánxiàng yèwù xìndào	
Forward transfer message (ISUP)	前向转移消息	Qiánxiàng zhuǎnyí xiāoxi	FOT
Forward validation	向前验证	Xiàngqián yànzhèng	FV
Forward voice channel	前向话音信道	Qiánxiàng huàyīn xìndào	FVC
Forward wave tube	前向波管	Qiánxiàng bō guǎn	
Forwarded-to number	前转号码	Qiánzhuǎn hàomǎ	Ftn
Forwarding equivalence class	转发等价类	Zhuǎnfā děngjià lèi	FEC
Forwarding information base	转发信息表	Zhuǎnfā xìnxī biǎo	FIB
Forwarding information base	转发信息库	Zhuǎnfā xìnxī kù	FIB
Forwarding violation	前转违例	Qiánzhuǎn wéilì	
Forward-only	只向前的	Zhǐ xiàngqiánde	
Forward-only cursor	只进游标	Zhǐ jìn yóubiāo	
Forward-only cursor (for database)	只向前游标	Zhǐ xiàngqián yóubiāo	
Forward-to number	转送号码	Zhuǎnsòng hàomǎ	ftn
Forward-transfer signal	前向转移信号	Qiánxiàng zhuǎnyí xìnhào	FOT
Fouled up beyound all recognition	混乱透顶，糟极了	Hùnluàn tòudǐng, zāo jíle	Fubar
Foundation for Performance Measurement	性能测试基金会	Xìngnéng cèshì jījīnhuì	FPM
Foundry Networks Inc.	网捷网络公司	Wǎngjié wǎngluò gōngsī	
Four wave mixing	四波混频	Sìbō hùnpín	FWM
Four-axial stable system	四轴稳定系统	Sìzhóu wěndìng xìtǒng	
Four-channel additional sequence control	四通道附加序列控制	Sì tōngdào fùjiā xùliè kòngzhì	FASC
Four-fiber multiplex section shared protection ring	四纤双向服用段共享保护环	Sìxiān shuāngxiàng fúyòng duàn gòngxiǎng bǎohù huán	
Four-horn feed	四喇叭馈电器	Sì lǎba kuìdiànqì	
Fourier analysis	付立叶分析	Fù-lì-yè fēnxī	

Fourier lens	傅利叶透镜	Fù-lì-yè tòujìng	
Fourier spectrum	付立叶谱	Fù-lì-yè pǔ	
Fourier transform	傅立叶变换	Fù-lì-yè biànhuàn	
Four-level frequency modulation	四电平调频	Sì diànpíng tiáopín	4-level FM
Four-level frequency modulation	四电平调频	Sìdiànpíng tiáopín	4-level FM
Four-part dotted notation	四元点分符号	Sìyuán diǎnfēn fúhào	
Four-state, four condition	四态	Sìtài	
Four-tap	四分支	Sì fēnzhī	
Fourth generation language	第四代语言	Dìsìdài yǔyán	4GL
Fourth order cumulant (in digital signal processing)	四阶累积量	Sìjiē lěijī liàng	
Four-way power divider	四路功率分配器	Sìlù gōnglǜ fēnpèiqì	4WPD
Four-wire switching	四线交换	Sìxiàn jiāohuàn	
Fractal	分形	Fēnxíng	
Fractal behavior	分形行为	Fēnxíng xíngwéi	
Fractal dimension	分维	Fēnwéi	
Fractal dimension model	分数维模型	Fēnshùwéi móxíng	
Fractal encoding	分形编码	Fēnxíng biānmǎ	
Fractal geometry	分形几何	Fēnxíng jǐhé	
Fractile	分位值	Fènwèizhí	
Fractional bandwidth	部分带宽	Bùfen dàikuān	
Fractional bit-plane	分数位平面	Fēnshùwèi píngmiàn	
Fractional T1 circuit	部分 T1 电路	Bùfen T1 diànlù	
Fragile watermark	脆弱型水印	Cuìruòxíng shuǐyìn	
Fragment	报片	Bào piàn	
Fragment (in generic network information model)	片段	Piànduàn	
Fragment attack	分片攻击	Fēnpiàn gōngjī	
Fragment, fragmentation	分片	Fēnpiàn	
Fragment, sliver	碎片	Suìpiàn	
Fragmentation (for database)	碎片	Suìpiàn	
Fragmented frame	分段帧	Fēnduàn zhèng	FRAG
Frame	帧	Zhèng	FR
Frame alignment	帧定位	Zhèng dìngwèi	
Frame alignment	帧同步	Zhèng tóngbù	
Frame alignment recovery time	帧定位恢复时间	Zhèng dìngwèi huīfù shíjiān	
Frame alignment signal	帧定位信号	Zhèng dìngwèi xìnhào	FAS
Frame alignment time slot	帧定位时隙	Zhèng dìngwèi shíxì	
Frame buffer cache	帧缓冲缓存	Zhèng huǎnchōng huǎncún	FBC
Frame check sequence	帧检序列	Zhèng jiǎn xùliè	FCS
Frame check sequence	帧检测序列	Zhèng jiǎncè xùliè	FCS
Frame check sequence	帧检查序列	Zhèng jiǎnchá xùliè	FCS
Frame check sequence	帧检验顺序	Zhèng jiǎnyàn shùnxù	FCS
Frame check sequence	帧检验序列	Zhèng jiǎnyàn xùliè	FCS
Frame check sequence	帧校验序列	Zhèng jiàoyàn xùliè	FCS
Frame control	帧控制	Zhèng kòngzhì	FC
Frame control	帧控制	Zhèng kòngzhì	FC
Frame erase identifier	帧删除标识	Zhèng shānchú biāozhì	FEI

Frame erase identity	帧擦除标识	Zhèng cāchú biāozhì	FEI
Frame erase identity	帧控除标识码	Zhèng kòngchú biāozhì mǎ	FEI
Frame erase rate	帧擦除率	Zhèng cāchú lǜ	FER
Frame erase rate	帧删除率	Zhèng shānchú lǜ	FER
Frame error rate	误帧率	Wùzhèng lǜ	FER
Frame error rate	帧差错率	Zhèng chācuò lǜ	FER
Frame forwarding	帧转发	Zhèng zhuǎnfā	
Frame handler	帧处理器	Zhèng chǔlǐqì	FH
Frame header check sequence	帧头校验序列	Zhèng tóu jiàoyàn xùliè	HCS
Frame inter-leaving	帧交织	Zhèng jiāozhī	
Frame length	帧长	Zhèng cháng	
Frame loss rate	丢帧率	Diūzhèng lǜ	
Frame loss rate	帧丢失率	Zhèng diūshī lǜ	FLR
Frame loss rate	帧丢失率	Zhèng diūshī lǜ	FLR
Frame loss second	帧丢失秒	Zhèng diūshī miǎo	FLS
Frame mode bearer service	帧方式承载业务	Zhèng fāngshì chéngzài yèwù	FMBS
Frame mode bearer service	帧模式承载业务	Zhèng móshì chéngzài yèwù	FMBS
Frame number	帧号	Zhèng hào	FN
Frame processing unit (board)	帧处理单元（板）	Zhèng chǔlǐ dānyuán (bǎn)	FPU
Frame protocol	帧协议	Zhèng xiéyì	FP
Frame rate control	帧比率控制	Zhèng bǐlǜ kòngzhì	FRC
Frame rate is king (see "Battle for eyeballs")	帧数为王	Zhèng shù wéi wáng	
Frame reject	帧拒收	Zhèng jùshōu	FRMR
Frame reject element	整据元	Zhěng jù yuán	
Frame relay	帧中继	Zhèng zhōngjì	FR
Frame relay access	帧中继接入	Zhèng zhōngjì jiērù	
Frame relay access device	帧中继访问设备	Zhèng zhōngjì fǎngwèn shèbèi	FRAD
Frame relay access device	帧中继接入器件	Zhèng zhōngjì jiērù qìjiàn	FRAD
Frame relay assembly disassembly	帧中继装拆	Zhèng zhōngjì zhuāngchāi	FRAD
Frame relay bearer service	帧中继承载业务	Zhèng zhōngjì chéngzài yèwù	FRBS
Frame relay data transmission service	帧中继数据传输业务	Zhèng zhōngjì shùjù chuánshū yèwù	FRDTS
Frame relay forum	帧中继论坛	Zhèng zhōngjì lùntán	FRF
Frame relay information field	帧中继信息字段	Zhèng zhōngjì xìnxī zìduàn	FRIF
Frame relay layer management entity	帧中继层管理实体	Zhèng zhōngjì céng guǎnlǐ shítǐ	FRLME
Frame relay permanent virtual circuit	帧中继永久虚电路	Zhèng zhōngjì yǒngjiǔ xū diànlù	
Frame relay service	帧中继服务	Zhèng zhōngjì fúwù	
Frame relay service	帧中继业务	Zhèng zhōngjì yèwù	
Frame relay switched virtual circuit	帧中继交换虚电路	Zhèng zhōngjì jiāohuàn xū diànlù	
Frame relay-service-specific convergence sub-layer	帧中继业务特定会聚子层	Zhèng zhōngjì yèwù tèdìng huìjù zicéng	FR-SSCS
Frame segment	帧字段	Zhèng zìduàn	FS
Frame start (timing information)	帧开始	Zhèng kāishǐ	
Frame start signal	帧起始信号	Zhèng qǐshǐ xìnhào	FS
Frame status	帧状态	Zhèng zhuàngtài	FS
Frame switching	帧交换	Zhèng jiāohuàn	
Frame switching bearer service	帧交换承载业务	Zhèng jiāohuàn chéngzài yèwù	FSBS
Frame synchronization code	帧同步码	Zhèng tóngbù mǎ	

Frame synchronization word	帧同步字	Zhèng tóngbù zì	FSW
Frame time; frame duration (in switching)	帧周期	Zhèng zhōuqī	
Frame transfer delay	帧传送延迟	Zhèng chuánsòng yánchí	FTD
Frame unit	帧单元	Zhèng dānyuán	FU
Frame unit controller	帧单元控制器	Zhèng dānyuán kòngzhìqì	FUC
Frame-based compliant traffic distortion ratio	基于帧和符合条件的业务量失真比	Jīyú zhèng hé fúhé tiáojiànde yèwùliàng shīzhēn bǐ	FCTDR
Frame-based generic cell rate algorithm	基于帧的通用信元速率算法	Jīyú zhèngde tōngyòng xìnyuán sùlǜ suànfǎ	F-GCRA
Frame-based user-to-network interface	帧用户网络接口	Zhèng yònghù wǎngluò jiēkǒu	FUNI
Framed interface	成帧接口	Chéngzhèng jiēkǒu	
Framed interface	帧结构型接口	Zhèng jiégòuxíng jiēkǒu	
Framed interface	帧式接口	Zhèng-shì jiēkǒu	
Framed structure	骨架结构	Gǔjià jiégòu	
Frame-layer reference event	帧层参考事件	Zhèng céng cānkǎo shìjiàn	FE
Frames per second	帧/秒	Zhèng/miǎo	Fps
Frames per second (video term)	每秒多少画面	Měi miǎo duōshao huàmiàn	FPS
Framework	框架	Kuàngjià	
Framing	成帧	Chéngzhèng	
Framing byte (STM term)	定帧字节	Dìngzhèng zìjié	
France Telecom Corp.	法国电信公司	Fǎguó diànxìn gōngsī	
Franklin antenna	富兰克林天线	Fù-lán-kè-lín tiānxiàn	
Fraunhofer region	弗朗和费区	Fú-lǎng-hé-fèi qū	
Fraunhofer region (far-field region)	佛累和费区	Fó-lěi-hé-fèi qū	
Free alongside ship	船边交货	Chuánbiān jiāohuò	
Free electron laser	自由电子激光	Zìyóu diànzǐ jīguāng	
Free media pool	可用媒体池	Kěyòng méitǐ chí	
Free of tax	免税	Miǎnshuì	FOT
Free on board	船上交货	Chuánshàng jiāohuò	FOB
Free phone	免费业务	Miǎnfèi yèwù	FPH
Free Software Foundation	免费软件基金会	Miǎnfèi ruǎnjiàn jījīnhuì	FSF
Free space	自由空间	Zìyóu kōngjiān	
Free space attenuation	自由空间衰减	Zìyóu kōngjiān shuāijiǎn	
Free space basic transmission loss	自由空间基本传输损耗	Zìyóu kōngjiān jīběn chuánshū sǔnhào	
Free space optical communications	自由空间光学通信	Zìyóu kōngjiān guāngxué tōngxìn	FSO
Free space optical system	自由空间光系统	Zìyóu kōngjiān guāng xìtǒng	
Free space optics	自由空间光纤	Zìyóu kōngjiān guāngxiān	FSO
Free space propagation	自由空间传播	Zìyóu kōngjiān chuánbō	
Free space wavelength	自由空间波长	Zìyóu kōngjiān bōcháng	
Free spectral range	自由谱宽	Zìyóu pǔ kuān	
Free to carrier	交至承运人	Jiāozhì chéngyùnrén	
Free trade zone	自由交换区	Zìyóu jiāohuàn qū	
Free wavelength solution	自由波长解决方案	Zìyóu bōcháng jiějué fāng'àn	FWS
Free world dial-up	全球随意拨号	Quánqiú suíyì bōhào	FWD
Free world dial-up	世界随意拨号	Shìjiè suíyì bōhào	FWD
Freedom of information	信息自由	Xìnxī zìyóu	FOI

English	Chinese	Pinyin	Abbreviation
Freenet	免费网	Miǎnfèi wǎng	
Freephone	被叫集中付费业务	Bèijiào jízhōng fùfèi yèwù	FPH
Free-radiation frequency (for ISM apparatus)	自由辐射频率	Zìyóu fúshè pínlǜ	
Free-run oscillation	自由振荡	Zìyóu zhèndàng	
Freeware	免费软件	Miǎnfèi ruǎnjiàn	
Freeze picture request	静态画请求	Jìngtài huà qǐngqiú	
Frequency	频率	Pínlǜ	F
Frequency accuracy	频率准确度	Pínlǜ zhǔnquèdù	
Frequency agility	频率捷变	Pínlǜ jiébiàn	
Frequency allotment	频率指配	Pínlǜ zhǐpèi	
Frequency and time division multiple access	频分和时分多址	Pínfēn hé shífēn duōzhǐ	FTDMA
Frequency assignment	频率分配	Pínlǜ fēnpèi	FA
Frequency assignment	频率指配	Pínlǜ zhǐpèi	
Frequency band	频带	Píndài	
Frequency band	频段	Pínduàn	
Frequency bandwidth	频率带宽	Pínlǜ dàikuān	
Frequency channel	频道	Píndào	
Frequency characteristic	频率特性	Pínlǜ tèxìng	
Frequency chirp	频率啁啾	Pínlǜ zhōujiū	FCH
Frequency compensation	频率补偿	Pínlǜ bǔcháng	
Frequency compression demodulator	频率压缩解调器	Pínlǜ yāsuō jiětiáoqì	FCD
Frequency control	频率控制	Pínlǜ kòngzhì	
Frequency conversion	频率变换	Pínlǜ biànhuàn	
Frequency conversion format	变频方式	Biànpín fāngshì	
Frequency conversion loss	变频损耗	Biànpín sǔnhào	
Frequency conversion product	频率变换产物	Pínlǜ biànhuàn chǎnwù	
Frequency converter	频率变换器	Pínlǜ biànhuànqì	FC
Frequency converter, frequency changer	变频器	Biànpínqì	
Frequency correction burst	频率校正短脉冲串	Pínlǜ jiàozhèng duǎnmàichōng chuàn	FB
Frequency correction burst	频率校正突发	Pínlǜ jiàozhèng tūfā	FB
Frequency correction burst	突发频率校正	Tūfā pínlǜ jiàozhèng	FB
Frequency correction channel	频率校正信道	Pínlǜ jiàozhèng xìndào	FCCH
Frequency correction channel	频率纠正信道	Pínlǜ jiūzhèng xìndào	FCCH
Frequency decorrelation	频率去相关	Pínlǜ qù xiāngguān	
Frequency demodulation	频率解调	Pínlǜ jiětiáo	
Frequency departure	频率偏离	Pínlǜ piānlí	
Frequency deviation	频偏	Pínpiān	
Frequency deviation correction	频偏校正	Pínpiān jiàozhèng	
Frequency deviation ratio	频率偏移率	Pínlǜ piānyílǜ	
Frequency discrimination	频率鉴别	Pínlǜ jiànbié	
Frequency discrimination figure	鉴频系数	Jiànpín xìshù	
Frequency discriminator	鉴频器	Jiànpínqì	
Frequency discriminator amplitude frequency symmetry	鉴频器幅度对称性	Jiànpínqì fúdù duìchènxìng	
Frequency discriminator crossover frequency	鉴频器交界频率	Jiànpínqì jiāojiè pínlǜ	
Frequency discriminator frequency symmetry	鉴频器频率对称性	Jiànpínqì pínlǜ duìchènxìng	
Frequency discriminator pass band	鉴频器通频带	Jiànpínqì tōngpíndài	

Frequency diversity	频率分集	Pínlǜ fēnjí	
Frequency diversity radar	频率分集雷达	Pínlǜ fēnjí léidá	
Frequency diversity reception	频率分集接收	Pínlǜ fēnjí jiēshōu	
Frequency diversity/spread spectrum multiple access	频率分集扩展频谱码分多址	Pínlǜ fēnjí kuòzhǎn pínpǔ mǎfēn duōzhǐ	FD/SSMA
Frequency divider	分频器	Fēnpínqì	FD
Frequency division	分频	Fēnpín	
Frequency division	频分	Pínfēn	
Frequency division	频率分割	Pínlǜ fēngē	
Frequency division data link	频分数据键	Pínfēn shùjù jiàn	FDDL
Frequency division duplex	频分双工	Pínfēn shuānggōng	FDD
Frequency division multiple access	频分多路存取	Pínfēn duōlù cúnqǔ	FDMA
Frequency division multiple access	频分多址	Pínfēn duōzhǐ	FDMA
Frequency division multiplexer	频分多路复用器	Pínfēn duōlù fùyòngqì	FDM
Frequency division multiplexing	频分多路复用	Pínfēn duōlù fùyòng	FDM
Frequency division multiplexing	频分复用	Pínfēn fùyòng	FDM
Frequency division multiplexing modulation	频分复用调制	Pínfēn fùyòng tiáozhì	
Frequency domain	频域	Pínyù	
Frequency domain analysis	频域分析	Pínyù fēnxī	
Frequency domain filter	频率域滤波器	Pínlǜ yù lǜbōqì	
Frequency domain filtering	频率域滤波	Pínlǜ yù lǜbō	
Frequency domain reflectometry	频域反射计	Pínyù fǎnshèjì	
Frequency drift	频率漂移	Pínlǜ piāoyí	
Frequency drift	频漂	Pínpiāo	
Frequency error	频率误差	Pínlǜ wùchā	
Frequency fine tuning	频率微调	Pínlǜ wēitiáo	
Frequency fluctuation	频率起伏	Pínlǜ qǐfú	
Frequency hop synchronization	跳频同步	Tiàopín tóngbù	FHS
Frequency hopping	跳频	Tiàopín	FH
Frequency hopping code division multiple access	跳频码分多址	Tiàopín mǎfēn duōzhǐ	FH-CDMA
Frequency hopping multiple access	跳频多重存取	Tiàopín duōzhòng cúnqǔ	FHMA
Frequency hopping sequence number	跳频序列号	Tiàopín xùlièhào	HSN
Frequency hopping spread spectrum	跳频扩频	Tiàopín kuòpín	FHSS
Frequency hopping spread spectrum modulation	跳频扩频调制	Tiàopín kuòpín tiáozhì	
Frequency hopping/differential quadriphase shift keying	跳频/差分四相移相键控	Tiàopín/chāfēn sìxiāng yíxiāng jiànkòng	FH/DQPSK
Frequency identity	频率鉴别号码	Pínlǜ jiànbié hàomǎ	FID
Frequency independent antenna	与频率无关的天线	Yǔ pínlǜ wúguānde tiānxiàn	
Frequency instability	频率不稳定度	Pínlǜ bùwěndìngdù	
Frequency inversion	频率倒置	Pínlǜ dàozhì	
Frequency locked loop	频率锁定环	Pínlǜ suǒdìng huán	FLL
Frequency locked loop	频率同步环路	Pínlǜ tóngbù huánlù	FLL
Frequency lock-loss range	频率失锁范围	Pínlǜ shīsuǒ fànwéi	
Frequency management	频率管理	Pínlǜ guǎnlǐ	
Frequency mixer	混频器	Hùnpínqì	
Frequency modulated continuous wave	调频连续波	Tiáopín liánxù bō	FMCW
Frequency modulated continuous wave	调频连续波	Tiáopín liánxù bō	FMCW

English	Chinese	Pinyin	Abbreviation
Frequency modulated jamming	调频干扰	Tiáopín gānrǎo	
Frequency modulated transmitter	调频发射机	Tiáopín fāshèjī	FMX
Frequency modulation	频率调制	Pínlǜ tiáozhì	FM
Frequency modulation	调频	Tiáopín	FM
Frequency modulation and differentially coherent PSK	调频差动相干相移键控	Tiáopín chādòng xiānggān xiàngyí jiànkòng	FM-DCPSK
Frequency modulation radar transmitter	调频雷达发射机	Tiáopín léidá fāshèjī	
Frequency modulation radio telephone	调频无线电话机	Tiáopín wúxiàn diànhuàjī	
Frequency modulation/frequency division multiple access	调频/频分多路存取	Tiáopín/pínfēn duōlù cúnqǔ	FM/FDMA
Frequency multiplication	倍频	Bèipín	
Frequency multiplication local oscillator	倍频本地振荡器	Bèipín běndì zhèndàngqì	
Frequency multiplier	倍频器	Bèipínqì	
Frequency offset	频率偏置	Pínlǜ piānzhì	
Frequency phase locked loop	频率相位同步环路	Pínlǜ xiàngwèi tóngbù huánlù	FPLL
Frequency pre-selection	频率预选	Pínlǜ yùxuǎn	
Frequency presetting device	频率预置器	Pínlǜ yùzhìqì	
Frequency pull-in range	频率捕捉范围	Pínlǜ bǔzhuō fànwéi	
Frequency pulling	频率牵引	Pínlǜ qiānyǐn	
Frequency pull-out range	频率失锁范围	Pínlǜ shīsuǒ fànwéi	
Frequency range (of equipment)	频率范围	Pínlǜ fànwéi	
Frequency redefinition	频率重定义	Pínlǜ zhòng dìngyì	
Frequency reference	基准频率	Jīzhǔn pínlǜ	
Frequency reference divide panel	频率参数分配面板	Pínlǜ cānshù fēnpèi miànbǎn	FRDP
Frequency response	频率响应	Pínlǜ xiǎngyìng	FR
Frequency response	频响	Pínxiǎng	FR
Frequency response characteristic	频率响应特性	Pínlǜ xiǎngyìng tèxìng	
Frequency response flatness	频响平坦度	Pínxiǎng píngtǎndù	
Frequency re-use	频率再用	Pínlǜ zàiyòng	
Frequency re-use satellite network	频率再利用卫星网络	Pínlǜ zàilìyòng wèixīng wǎngluò	
Frequency selection anti-jamming technique	频率选择抗干扰技术	Pínlǜ xuǎnzé kànggānrǎo jìshù	
Frequency selective fading	频率选择性衰落	Pínlǜ xuǎnzéxìng shuāiluò	
Frequency selectivity	频率选择性	Pínlǜ xuǎnzéxìng	
Frequency sensitivity	频率灵敏度	Pínlǜ língmǐndù	
Frequency shift (in keying)	频移	Pínyí	
Frequency shift mode	频率改变方式	Pínlǜ gǎibiàn fāngshì	FM
Frequency shift repeater	移频直防站	Yípín zhífángzhàn	FSR
Frequency shift repeater	移频中继机	Yípín zhōngjìjī	
Frequency shifter effect	频率转换效果	Pínlǜ zhuǎnhuàn xiàoguǒ	FSE
Frequency sounding at oblique incidence	斜向频率探测	Xiéxiàng pínlǜ tàncè	
Frequency spectrum	频谱	Pínpǔ	
Frequency spot error	频率瞄准误差	Pínlǜ miáozhǔn wùchā	
Frequency stability	频率稳定度	Pínlǜ wěndìngdù	
Frequency stabilization accuracy	频率稳准度	Pínlǜ wěnzhǔndù	
Frequency stabilized laser	稳频激光	Wěnpín jīguāng	
Frequency standard	频率标准	Pínlǜ biāozhǔn	
Frequency standard output (may be shortened to 频标输出)	频率标准输出	Pínlǜ biāozhǔn shūchū	

Frequency standard output (short for 频率标准输出)	频标输出	Pín biāo shūchū	
Frequency step size	频率步级	Pínlǜ bù jí	
Frequency sweep	扫频	Sǎopín	
Frequency synthesizer	频率合成器	Pínlǜ héchéngqì	
Frequency synthesizer	频率综合器	Pínlǜ zōnghéqì	
Frequency synthesizer	频率综合仪	Pínlǜ zōnghéyí	
Frequency synthesizer	频综器	Pínzōngqì	
Frequency synthesizer, short for 频率合成器	频合器	Pínhéqì	
Frequency time hopping multiple access	频率时间跳跃多路存取	Pínlǜ shíjiān tiàoyuè duōlù cúnqǔ	FTHMA
Frequency to voltage converter	频率 / 电压转换	Pínlǜ/diànyā zhuǎnhuàn	F / V
Frequency tolerance	频率容差	Pínlǜ róngchā	
Frequency tolerance	频率容限	Pínlǜ róngxiàn	
Frequency transmission band	发射频段	Fāshè pínduàn	
Frequency variation rate	频率变化速率	Pínlǜ biànhuà sùlǜ	
Frequency-amplitude modulation	频率振幅调制	Pínlǜ zhènfú tiáozhì	FAM
Frequency-coded pulse compression	频率编码脉冲压缩	Pínlǜ biānmǎ màichōng yāsuō	
Frequency-coding system	频率编码制	Pínlǜ biānmǎ zhì	
Frequency-conversion circuit	频率变换电路	Pínlǜ biànhuàn diànlù	
Frequency-modulation (FM) noise	调频躁声	Tiáopín zàoshēng	
Frequency-shift keying	频移键控	Pínyí jiànkòng	FSK
Frequency-shift keying	移频键控	Yípín jiànkòng	FSK
Frequency-shift modulation	频移调制	Pínyí tiáozhì	FSM
Frequency-shift telegraphy	频移电报	Pínyí diànbào	FST
Frequency-shift telegraphy	移频电报技术	Yípín diànbào jìshù	
Frequently asked questions	常见问题	Chángjiàn wèntí	FAQ
Fresnel lens	菲涅尔透镜	Fēi-niè-ěr tòujìng	
Fresnel lens antenna; zone-plate lens antenna	菲涅耳透镜天线	Fēi-niè-ěr tòujìng tiānxiàn	
Fresnel reflection	菲涅尔反射	Fēi-niè-ěr fǎnshè	
Fresnel reflection loss	菲涅尔反射损耗	Fēi-niè-ěr fǎnshè sǔnhào	
Fresnel region	菲涅耳区	Fēi-niè-ěr qū	
Friction	摩擦	Mócā	
Friction head	摩擦水头	Mócā shuǐtóu	
Friction layer	摩擦层	Mócā céng	
Friction pile	摩擦柱	Mócā zhù	
Friction velocity	摩擦速度	Mócā sùdù	
From switch unit	源于交换机单元	Yuán yú jiāohuànjī dānyuán	FSU
From-node	起始节点	Qǐshǐ jiédiǎn	
Front (of a queue)	队头	Duìtóu	
Front administrative module	前管理模块	Qián guǎnlǐ mókuài	FAM
Front buffer	前置缓冲	Qiánzhì huǎnchōng	
Front page	前页	Qiányè	
Front side bus	前置总线	Qiánzhì zǒngxiàn	FSB
Front-end	前端	Qiánduān	
Front-end communications processor	前端通信处理机	Qiánduān tōngxìn chùlǐjī	FECP
Front-end processor	前端处理机	Qiánduān chǔlǐjī	FEP

Front-end processor	前端处理器	Qiánduān chǔlǐqì	FEP
Front-end target driver	前端目标设备驱动	Qiánduān mùbiāo shèbèi qūdòng	FETD
Front-to-back ratio	前后比	Qiánhòu bǐ	
Fujian Malata Electronics Co. Ltd.	福建万利达电子有限公司	Fújiàn wàn-lì-dá diànzǐ yǒuxiàn gōngsī	
Fujitsu (Japan company)	富士通	Fù-shì-tōng	
Fujitsu Network Switching (Japan)	富士通网络交换	Fùshìtōng wǎngluò jiāohuàn	FNS
Fujitsu Network Transmission Systems Inc. (Japan)	富士通网络传输系统公司	Fùshìtōng wǎngluò chuánshū xìtǒng gōngsī	FNTS
Full adder	全加法器	Quán jiāfǎqì	FA
Full adder	全加器	Quán jiāqì	FA
Full allocation	全配置	Quán pèizhì	FA
Full binary tree	满二叉树	Mǎn èrchā shù	
Full carrier	全载波	Quán zàibō	
Full carrier emission	全载波发射	Quán zàibō fāshè	
Full carrier single sideband (SSB) emission	满载波单边带发射	Mǎnzàibō dānbiāndài fāshè	
Full carrier single-sideband emission	全载波单边带发射	Quán zàibō dānbiāndài fāshè	
Full channel broadcast videography	全通路广播可视图文	Quán tōnglù guǎngbō kěshì túwén	
Full duplex	全双工	Quánshuānggōng	
Full duplex data flow	全双工数据流	Quánshuānggōng shùjùliú	FDX
Full duplex transmission	全双工传输	Quánshuānggōng chuánshū	
Full fabric citizenship	全架构成员	Quán jiàgòu chéngyuán	
Full handshake authentication	完全握手证实	Wánquán wòshǒu zhèngshí	
Full installation (of software)	完全安装	Wánquán ānzhuāng	
Full liquidus temperature (in SMT)	完全液化温度	Wánquán yèhuà wēndù	
Full outer join	完整外部联接	Wánzhěng wàibù liánjiē	
Full phase correlation	全相关	Quánxiāng guān	FPC
Full rate	全速率	Quán sùlǜ	
Full rate	全速率	Quán sùlǜ	FR
Full rate	全速	Quánsù	FR
Full rate data traffic channel (2.4kbs)	全速率数据业务信道	Quánsùlǜ shùjù yèwù xìndào	TCH/F2.4
Full rate speech traffic channel (TCH)	全速率话音业务信道	Quánsùlǜ huàyīn yèwù xìndào	TCH/FS
Full rate traffic channel	全速业务信道	Quánsù yèwù xìndào	TCH/F
Full rate traffic channel	全速率业务信道	Quánsùlǜ yèwù xìndào	TCH/F
Full rate traffic channel	全速率业务信道	Quánsùlǜ yèwù xìndào	Bm
Full scale	满量程	Mǎn liángchéng	FS
Full scene anti-aliasing (video term)	全景抗锯齿失真	Quánjǐng kàng jùchǐ shīzhēn	FSAA
Full screen	全屏	Quánpíng	
Full service access network	全业务接入网络	Quán yèwù jiērù wǎngluò	FSAN
Full service network	全信息网络	Quán xìnxī wǎngluò	FSN
Full service network	全业务网络	Quán yèwù wǎngluò	
Full service set	全业务集	Quán yèwù jí	FSS
Full service set (of equipment)	全业务台	Quán yèwù tái	FSS
Full specialization	完全特化	Wánquán tèhuà	
Full type approval	全面型号认证	Quánmiàn xínghào rènzhèng	FTA
Full width at half maximum	半幅全宽	Bànfú quán kuān	FWHM
Full width half maximum	半幅值全宽	Bànfúzhí quán kuān	FWHM
Full width half maximum (pulse)	脉冲的半高宽度	Màichōngde bàngāo kuāndù	FWHM

Full zone transfer	完整区域传送	Wánzhěng qūyù chuánsòng	AXFR
Full-service access transmission	全业务接入传输	Quán yèwù jiērù chuánshūde	
Full-text catalog	全文目录	Quánwén mùlù	
Full-text enabling	全文启用	Quánwén qǐyòng	
Full-text index	全文索引	Quánwén suǒyǐn	
Full-text query	全文查询	Quánwén cháxún	
Full-text search (in SQL Server)	全文检索	Quánwén jiǎnsuǒ	
Full-text service	全文服务	Quánwén fúwù	
Full-wave dipole	全波偶极子	Quánbō ǒujízi	
Fully automatic operation	全自动操作	Quánzìdòng cāozuò	
Fully dissociated signaling	完全非直联信令方式	Wánquán fēizhílián xìnlìng fāngshì	
Fully intermateable optical fiber (cable) connector	全互配光纤（缆）连接器	Quán hùpèi guāngxiān (lǎn) liánjiē qì	
Fully polynomial time approximation	完全多项式时间近似	Wánquán duōxiàngshì shíjiān jìnsì	FPTA
Fully qualified domain name	全限定域名	Quán xiàndìng yùmíng	FQDN
Fully qualified domain name	完全合格域名	Wánquán hégé yùmíng	FQDN
Fume extraction system (electronics mfg)	排烟洁净系统	Páiyān jiéjìng xìtǒng	
Function	功能	Gōngnéng	FUN
Function	函数	Hánshù	
Function address	功能地址	Gōngnéng dìzhǐ	FA
Function address indicator	功能地址指示符	Gōngnéng dìzhǐ zhǐshì fú	FAI
Function attributes	功能属性	Gōngnéng shǔxìng	
Function block	功能块	Gōngnéng kuài	
Function call operator	函数调用操作符	Hánshù diàoyòng cāozuò fú	
Function card load	功能卡装载	Gōngnéng kǎ zhuāngzài	fcload
Function check-out	功能检查	Gōngnéng jiǎnchá	
Function element	功能单元	Gōngnéng dānyuán	FE
Function generator	函数发生器	Hánshù fāshēngqì	
Function key	功能键	Gōngnéng jiàn	
Function object	函数对象	Hánshù duìxiàng	
Function overloaded resolution	函数重载决议	Hánshù zhòngzài juéyì	
Function register	操作寄存器	Cāozuò jìcúnqì	
Function register	指令寄存器	Zhǐlìng jìcúnqì	FR
Function sharing	功能分担	Gōngnéng fēndān	
Function signal	功能信号	Gōngnéng xìnhào	
Function sub-program	函数子程序	Hánshù zǐchéngxù	
Function template	函数模板	Hánshù múbǎn	
Function unit	功能单元	Gōngnéng dānyuán	FU
Function unit (in SPL)	函数部件	Hánshù bùjiàn	
Function-affecting maintenance	影响功能性维护	Yǐngxiǎng gōngnéngxìng wéihù	
Functional architecture	功能体系结构	Gōngnéng tǐxì jiégòu	
Functional baseline	功能基线	Gōngnéng jīxiàn	
Functional component	功能成分	Gōngnéng chéngfèn	
Functional entity	功能实体	Gōngnéng shítǐ	FE
Functional entity access manager	功能实体接入管理	Gōngnéng shítǐ jiērù guǎnlǐ	FEAM
Functional group	功能群	Gōngnéng qún	

Functional group	功能组	Gōngnéng zǔ	
Functional loss	功能损失度	Gōngnéng sǔnshīdù	
Functional mode	功能方式	Gōngnéng fāngshì	
Functional operations process	功能运营过程	Gōngnéng yùnyíng guòchéng	
Functional programming language	函数程序设计语言	Hánshù chéngxù shèjì yǔyán	FPL
Functional standard	功能标准	Gōngnéng biāozhǔn	
Functional terminal	功能型终端	Gōngnéng-xíng zhōngduān	
Functional test	功能测试	Gōngnéng cèshì	
Function-degrading maintenance	功能下降性维护	Gōngnéng xiàjiàngxìng wéihù	
Function-divided control	功能分散控制	Gōngnéng fēnsàn kòngzhì	
Function-permitting maintenance	不影响功能性维护	Bùyǐngxiǎng gōngnéngxìng wéihù	
Function-preventing maintenance	妨碍功能性维护	Fáng'ài gōngnéngxìng wéihù	
Functor	仿函数	Fǎng hánshù	
Fundamental (component of a sound wave)	基波	Jībō	
Fundamental factor	基波系数	Jībō xìshù	
Fundamental mode	基本模式	Jīběn móshì	
Fundamental mode	主模	Zhǔ mó	
Fundamental period	基本周期	Jīběn zhōuqī	
Furnish charging information	提供计费信息	Tígōng jìfèi xìnxī	FCI
Furukawa Electric Industries (Japan)	古河电气工业	Gǔ-hé diànqì gōngyè	
Fuse	保险丝	Bǎoxiǎnsī	F
Fuse	熔断器	Róngduànqì	
Fuse assembly board	熔丝集成板	Róngsī jíchéngbǎn	FAB
Fuse jamming	引信干扰	Yǐnxìn gānrǎo	
Fuse unit	保险丝装置	Bǎoxiǎnsī zhuāngzhì	FU
Fused biconic taper (FOC)	熔融拉锥式	Róngróng lāzhuī-shì	FBT
Fused deposition modeling	熔融沉积法	Róngróng chénjī fǎ	FDM
Fused silica glass	石英镜片	Shíyīng jìngpiàn	
Fusion frequency (when flashes seem like a steady light)	视觉停闪频率	Shìjué tíngshǎn pínlǜ	
Fusion splicer (FOC)	熔接机	Róngjiējī	
Fusion technology of spatial data	空间数据融合	Kōngjiān shùjù rónghé	
Future public land mobile telecommunication system	未来公用陆地移动通信系统	Wèilái gōngyòng lùdì yídòng tōngxìn xìtǒng	FPLMTS
Future public land mobile telecommunication system	未来公众移动通信系统	Wèilái gōngzhòng yídòng tōngxìn xìtǒng	FPLMTS
Fuzzy analysis	模糊分析	Móhu fēnxī	
Fuzzy concept	模糊概念	Móhu gàiniàn	
Fuzzy control	模糊控制	Móhu kòngzhì	
Fuzzy feature	模糊要素	Móhu yàosù	
Fuzzy logic	模糊逻辑	Móhu luóji	
Fuzzy optimization	模糊优选	Móhu yōuxuǎn	
Fuzzy pattern analysis	模糊模式分析	Móhu móshì fēnxī	
Fuzzy reasoning	模糊推理	Móhu tuīlǐ	
Fuzzy relational database	模糊关系数据库	Móhu guānxì shùjùkù	
Fuzzy set	模糊集合	Móhu jíhé	
Fuzzy tolerance	模糊容差	Móhu róngchā	

Fuzzy variance	模糊分差	Móhu fēnchà	

G

G/T ratio	G/T 比	G/T bǐ	
Gain	增益	Zēngyì	G
Gain bandwidth	增益带宽	Zēngyì dàikuān	GB_W,GBW
Gain control	增益控制	Zēngyì kòngzhì	
Gain cross-saturation	增益交叉浸透	Zēngyì jiāochā jìntòu	
Gain equalizer	增益均衡器	Zēngyì jūnhéngqì	GEQ
Gain equilibrium	增益均衡	Zēngyì jūnhéng	GEQ
Gain equilibrium filter	增益均衡滤波器	Zēngyì jūnhéng lǜbōqì	GEF
Gain flattening filters	增益平坦滤波器	Zēngyì píngtǎn lǜbōqì	GFFs
Gain limited sensitivity	有限增益灵敏度	Yǒuxiàn zēngyì língmǐndù	
Gain relative to a half-wave dipole	相对于半波偶极振子的增益	Xiāngduì yú bànbō ǒují zhènzǐde zēngyì	
Gain relative to a short vertical antenna	相对于短垂直天线的增益	Xiāngduì yú duǎn chuízhí tiānxiànde zēngyì	
Gain shifted	增益平移	Zēngyì píngyí	
Gain shifted erbium-doped fiber amplifier	增益平移掺饵光纤放大器	Zēngyì píngyí chān’ěr guāngxiān fàngdàqì	GS-EDFA
Gain-bandwidth product (of an avalanche photodiode)	增益-带宽乘积	Zēngyì-dàikuān chéngjī	
Gallium arsenide	砷化镓	Shēnhuàjiā	GaAs
Gallium arsenide integrated circuit	砷化镓集成电路	Shēnhuàjiā jíchéng diànlù	
Gallium nitride	氮化镓	Dànhuà jiā	GaN
Galois field	伽罗华域	Jiāluóhuá yù	GF
Galvano-cautery, electrocorrosion	电腐蚀	Diànfǔshí	
Game	游戏	Yóuxì	
Game developer conference	游戏发展商会议	Yóuxì fāzhǎn shāng huìyì	GDC
Gantt chart/graph	甘特图	Gān-tè tú	
Gap	间隙	Jiànxì	
Gap loss	间隙损耗	Jiànxì sǔnhào	
Garbage collection	垃圾回收	Lājī huíshōu	GC
Garbage collection	垃圾收集	Lājī shōují	GC
Garbage in, garbage out	无用输入无用输出	Wúyòng shūrù wúyòng shūchū	GIGO
GARP information declaration	GARP 信息发布	GARP xìnxī fābù	GID
GARP information propagation	GARP 信息广播	GARP xìnxī guǎngbō	GIP
GARP multicast registration protocol (IEEE 802.1P)	GARP 组播注册协议	GARP zǔbō zhùcè xiéyì	GMRP
GARP protocol data unit	GARP 协议数据单元	GARP xiéyì shùjù dānyuán	GARP PDU
GARP VLAN registration protocol	GARP VLAN 注册协议	GARP VLAN zhùcè xiéyì	GVRP
Gas filled cable	充气电缆	Chōngqì diànlǎn	GFC
Gas flow CO_2 laser	气流型二氧化碳激光	Qìliú-xíng èryǎnghuàtàn jīguāng	
Gas handling equipment	气体填充设备	Qìtǐ tiánchōng shèbèi	
Gas laser	气体激光	Qìtǐ jīguāng	
Gas recycler	气体再生设备	Qìtǐ zàishēng shèbèi	
Gases for optical applications	光学用气体	Guāngxué-yòng qìtǐ	
Gate	门	Mén	
Gate array	门阵列	Mén zhènliè	GA

Gate switch	门开关	Mén kāiguān	
Gate turnoff thyristor	门极可关断晶体管	Ménjí kěguānduàn jīngtǐguǎn	GTO
Gated frequency position modulation	手控频率位置调制	Shǒukòng pínlǜ wèizhì tiáozhì	GFPM
Gatekeeper	关守	Guānshǒu	GK
Gatekeeper	网守	Wǎngshǒu	
Gatekeeper	网闸	Wǎngzhá	GK
Gatekeeper	站点关守	Zhàndiǎn guānshǒu	
Gatekeeper confirm	网守发现确认	Wǎngshǒu fāxiàn quèrèn	GCF
Gatekeeper confirm (packet protocol)	关守确认	Guānshǒu quèrèn	GCF
Gatekeeper for service control	业务控制网守	Yèwù kòngzhì wǎngshǒu	GKc
Gatekeeper function	网守功能	Wǎngshǒu gōngnéng	GKF
Gatekeeper identifier	关守标识	Guānshǒu biāozhì	
Gatekeeper reject	关守拒绝	Guānshǒu jùjué	GRJ
Gatekeeper reject	网守发现拒绝	Wǎngshǒu fāxiàn jùjué	GRJ
Gatekeeper request	关守请求	Guānshǒu qǐngqiú	GRQ
Gatekeeper request	网守发现请求	Wǎngshǒu fāxiàn qǐngqiú	GRQ
Gateway	出入口	Chūrùkǒu	
Gateway	关口	Guānkǒu	GW
Gateway	关口局	Guānkǒujú	GW
Gateway	门限路	Ménxiàn lù	
Gateway	信关设备	Xìnguān shèbèi	
Gateway (exchange)	关口局	Guānkǒu jú	GW
Gateway (on a network)	网关	Wǎngguān	GW
Gateway account	网关帐户	Wǎngguān zhànghù	
Gateway communication back panel	关口通信后面板	Guānkǒu tōngxìn hòumian bǎn	GCBP
Gateway communication interconnection network	关口通信互联网	Guānkǒu tōngxìn hùliánwǎng	GCIN
Gateway discovery protocol	网关查找协议	Wǎngguān cházhǎo xiéyì	GDP
Gateway discovery protocol	网关发现协议	Wǎngguān fāxiàn xiéyì	GDP
Gateway earth station	网关地球站	Wǎngguān dìqiúzhàn	GES
Gateway exchange	国际出口局	Guójì chūkǒujú	GE
Gateway GPRS support node	GPRS 网关支持节点	GPRS wǎngguān zhīchí jiédiǎn	GGSN
Gateway GPRS support node	网关 GPRS 支持节点	Wǎngguān GPRS zhīchí jiédiǎn	GGSN
Gateway host	网关主机	Wǎngguān zhǔjī	
Gateway mobile services switching center	关口移动交换中心	Guānkǒu yídòng jiāohuàn zhōngxīn	GMSC
Gateway mobile services switching center	网关移动业务交换中心	Wǎngguān yídòng yèwù jiāohuàn zhōngxīn	GMSC
Gateway mobile switch center	入口移动交换中心	Rùkǒu yídòng jiāohuàn zhōngxīn	GMSC
Gateway mobile switching center	关口移动业务交换中心	Guānkǒu yídòng yèwù jiāohuàn zhōngxīn	GMSC
Gateway mobile switching center	入口移动无线局	Rùkǒu yídòng wúxiànjú	GMSC
Gateway mobile switching center	网关移动交换中心	Wǎngguān yídòng jiāohuàn zhōngxīn	GMSC
Gateway mobile switching center (MSC)	入口 MSC	Rùkǒu MSC	GMSA
Gateway MSC	关口 MSC	Guānkǒu MSC	GMSC
Gateway network element	网关网元	Wǎngguān wǎngyuán	GNE
Gateway network element	网间接口单元	Wǎngjiàn jiēkǒu dānyuán	GNE
Gateway router	网关路由器	Wǎngguān lùyóuqì	GW
Gateway service node	关口服务节点	Guānkǒu fúwù jiédiǎn	GSN
Gateway services node	网关服务节点	Wǎngguān fúwù jiédiǎn	GSN

Gateway/interworking MSC	关口互连 MSC	Guānkǒu hùlián MSC	G/IW MSC
Gateway-to-gateway protocol	网关到网关连接协议	Wǎngguān dào wǎngguān liánjiē xiéyì	GGP
Gating	选通	Xuǎntōng	
Gauss map projection	高斯地图投影	Gāo-sī dìtú tóuyǐng	
Gauss plane coordinate system	高斯平面坐标系	Gāo-sī píngmiàn zuòbiāo xì	
Gauss-Fourier transform	高斯-傅里叶变换	Gāo-sī—Fù-lǐ-yè biànhuàn	GFT
Gaussian approximation method	高斯近似法	Gāo-sī jìnsìfǎ	
Gaussian channel	高斯信道	Gāo-sī xìndào	
Gaussian coordinate	高斯坐标	Gāo-sī zuòbiāo	
Gaussian distribution	高斯分布	Gāo-sī fēnbù	
Gaussian error	高斯误差	Gāo-sī wùchā	
Gaussian filtered minimum-shift keying	高斯滤波最小移频键控	Gāo-sī lǜbō zuìxiǎo yípín jiànkòng	GMSK
Gaussian frequency shift keying	高斯滤波频移键控	Gāo-sī lǜbō pínyí jiànkòng	GAP
Gaussian frequency shift keying	高斯频移键控	Gāo-sī pínyí jiànkòng	GFSK
Gaussian function	高斯函数	Gāo-sī hánshù	
Gaussian minimum shift keying	高斯最小频移键控	Gāo-sī zuìxiǎo pínyí jiànkòng	GMSK
Gaussian minimum-shift keying	高斯最小键移	Gāo-sī zuìxiǎo jiànyí	GMSK
Gaussian minimum-shift keying	高斯最小移频键控	Gāo-sī zuìxiǎo yípín jiànkòng	GMSK
Gaussian mixture model	高斯混合模型	Gāo-sī hùnhé móxíng	GMM
Gaussian noise	高斯噪声	Gāo-sī zàoshēng	
Gaussian passband arrayed waveguide grating multiplexer/demultiplexer	高斯型通带波导阵列光栅复用/解复用器	Gāo-sī-xíng tōngdài bōdǎo zhènliè guāngshān fùyòng/jiě fùyòngqì	
Gaussian white noise	高斯白噪声	Gāo-sī bái zàoshēng	
Gazetteer	地名录	Dìmíng lù	
GB code (computer code for Chinese characters)	国标码	Guóbiāo mǎ	
GBK encoding	国标扩展码	Guóbiāo kuòzhǎn mǎ	
General acceptance test software	通用验收测试软件	Tōngyòng yànshōu cèshì ruǎnjiàn	GATS
General Agreement on Tariffs and Trade	关税和贸易总协定	Guānshuì hé màoyì zǒngxiédìng	GATT
General Agreement on Trade in Services	服务贸易总协定	Fúwù màoyì zǒng xiédìng	GATS
General Agreement on Trade in Services	贸易服务总协定	Màoyì fúwù zǒngxiédìng	GATS
General attribute registration protocol	一般属性注册协议	Yībān shǔxìng zhùcè xiéyì	GARP
General broadcast signaling cell	通用广播信令信元	Tōngyòng guǎngbō xìnlìng xìnyuán	
General broadcast signaling virtual channel	通用广播信令虚通路	Tōngyòng guǎngbō xìnlìng xū tōnglù	
General broadcast signaling virtual channel	通用广播信令虚信道	Tōngyòng guǎngbō xìnlìng xū xìndào	GBSVC
General calling	全呼	Quán hū	
General conference control	通用会议控制	Tōngyòng huìyì kòngzhì	Gcc
General conference control- service access point	通用会议控制服务接入点	Tōngyòng huìyì kòngzhì fúwù jiērù diǎn	GccSAP
General control	通用控制	Tōngyòng kòngzhì	GC
General design	总体设计	Zǒngtǐ shèjì	
General features	一般要素	Yībān yàosù	
General flow chart	综合流程图	Zōnghé liúchéngtú	GF
General flow control	基本流量控制	Jīběn liúliàng kòngzhì	GFC
General format identifier	通用格式标识符	Tōngyòng géshi biāozhìfú	GFI
General forward set-up information message	一般前向建立信息消息	Yībān qiánxiàng jiànlì xìnxī xiāoxi	GSM
General hardware oriented system transfer	全面硬件导向系统转移	Quánmiàn yìngjiàn dǎoxiàng xìtǒng zhuǎnyí	GHOST
General inquiry access code	通用查询访问码	Tōngyòng cháxún fǎngwèn mǎ	GIAC

General inter-ORB protocol (CORBA term)	通用 ORB 间协议	Tōngyòng ORB-jiān xiéyì	GIOP
General linear model	通用线性模型	Tōngyòng xiànxìng móxíng	
General message security	一般信息安全	Yībān xìnxī ānquán	GMS
General MicroSystems Corp.	通用微波系统公司	Tōngyòng wēibō xìtǒng gōngsī	GMS
General monitoring center	总监测中心	Zǒng jiāncè zhōngxīn	GMC
General Motors Corporation (US company)	通用汽车公司	Tōngyòng qìchē gōngsī	GM
General overview	概观	Gàiguān	
General packet radio service	通用分组无线业务	Tōngyòng fēnzǔ wúxiàn yèwù	GPRS
General packet radio service	通用无线分组业务	Tōngyòng wúxiàn fēnzǔ yèwù	GPRS
General packet radio service	无线分组业务	Wúxiàn fēnzǔ yèwù	GPRS
General packet radio service (GPRS) tunneling protocol	GPRS 隧道协议	GPRS suìdào xiéyì	
General packet radio service- service switch function	通用分组无线业务交换功能	Tōngyòng fēnzǔ wúxiàn yèwù jiāohuàn gōngnéng	GPRSSSF
General performance analysis	综合性能分析	Zōnghé xìngnéng fēnxī	
General power supply unit	通用功率电源单元	Tōngyòng gōnglǜ diànyuán dānyuán	GPSU
General processor sharing	广义处理器共享	Guǎngyì chǔlǐqì gòngxiǎng	GPS
General protection fault	一般保护性错误	Yībān bǎohùxìng cuòwù	GPF
General purpose computer	通用计算机	Tōngyòng jìsuànjī	
General purpose input	普通操作输入	Pǔtōng cāozuò shūrù	GPI
General purpose optical fiber (cable) connector	普通光纤（缆）连接器	Pǔtōng guāngxiān (lǎn) liánjiēqì	
General register stack	通用寄存器堆栈	Tōngyòng jìcúnqì duīzhàn	GRS
General request message	一般请求消息	Yībān qǐngqiú xiāoxi	GRQ
General switch management protocol	通用交换管理协议	Tōngyòng jiāohuàn guǎnlǐ xiéyì	GSMP
General switch telephone network	同用电话交换网	Tóngyòng diànhuà jiāohuàn wǎng	GSTN
General switched telephone network	普通电话交换网	Pǔtōng diànhuà jiāohuàn wǎng	GSTN
General switched telephone network	同用交换电话网	Tóngyòng jiāohuàn diànhuà wǎng	GSTN
Generalization	概化	Gàihuà	
Generalized intrusion detection objects	通用入侵检测对象	Tōngyòng rùqīn jiǎncè duìxiàng	GIDO
Generalized inverse matrix	广义逆矩阵	Guǎngyì nì jǔzhèn	
Generalized likelihood ratio	一般似然比	Yībān sìrán bǐ	GLR
Generalized linear model	广义线性模型	Guǎngyì xiànxìng móxíng	
Generalized list	广义表	Guǎngyì biǎo	
Generalized multi-protocol label switching	通用多协议标志交换协议	Tōngyòng duōxiéyì biāozhì jiāohuàn xiéyì	GMPLS
Generalized phase control	广义相位控制	Guǎngyì xiàngwèi kòngzhì	
Generalized system of acceptance	普惠制	Pǔhuìzhì	GSP
Generalized tamed frequency modulation	通用平滑调频	Tōngyòng pínghuá tiáopín	GTFM
Generalized tamed frequency modulation	通用于滑调频	Tōngyòng yúhuá tiáopín	GTFM
Generalized timing formula	一般程序时间公式	Yībān chéngxù shíjiān gōngshì	GTF
Generally accepted accounting principles	公认会计原则	Gōngrèn kuàijì yuánzé	GAAP
General-purpose tester	综合测试仪	Zōnghé cèshìyí	
Generating graphs	图的生成	Túde shēngchéng	
Generating partitions	划分生成	Huàfēn shēngchéng	
Generating permutations	排列生成	Páiliè shēngchéng	
Generating subsets	子集生成	Zǐjí shēngchéng	
Generator	发电机	Fādiànjī	G
Generic	泛化的	Fànhuàde	

English	Chinese	Pinyin	Abbreviation
Generic	通用的	Tōngyòngde	
Generic	一般化的	Yībānhuàde	
Generic access profile	通用访问应用	Tōngyòng fǎngwèn yìngyòng	GAP
Generic access profile	通用接口配置	Tōngyòng jiēkǒu pèizhì	GAP
Generic access profile	通用接入图	Tōngyòng jiērù tú	GAP
Generic algorithm	通用算法	Tōngyòng suànfǎ	
Generic application resource	一般应用程序资源	Yībān yìngyòng chéngxù zīyuán	
Generic attribute registration protocol	通用属性注册协议	Tōngyòng shǔxìng zhùcè xiéyì	GARP
Generic cabling	综合布线	Zōnghé bùxiàn	
Generic cabling system	一般的布线系统	Yībānde bùxiàn xìtǒng	GCS
Generic cell rate algorithm	通用信元速率算法	Tōngyòng xìnyuán sùlǜ suànfǎ	GCRA
Generic cell rate algorithm	通用信元率算法	Tōngyòng xìnyuánlǜ suànfǎ	GCRA
Generic connection acceptance control	通用连接接纳控制	Tōngyòng liánjiē jiēnà kòngzhì	GCAC
Generic content portion	一般内容组成部分	Yībān nèiróng zǔchéng bùfen	
Generic content portion description	一般内容组成部分描述	Yībān nèiróng zǔchéng bùfen miáoshù	
Generic definition	通用定义	Tōngyòng dìngyì	
Generic document	一般文件	Yībān wénjiàn	
Generic flow control	通用流量控制	Tōngyòng liúliàng kòngzhì	GFC
Generic flow control	一般流量控制码	Yībān liúliàng kòngzhì mǎ	GFC
Generic framing procedure	通用成帧规程	Tōngyòng chéngzhèng guīchéng	GFP
Generic framing protocol	通用成帧协议	Tōngyòng chéng zhèng xiéyì	GFP
Generic information block	通用信息模块	Tōngyòng xìnxī mókuài	GIB
Generic layout structure	一般布局结构	Yībān bùjú jiégòu	
Generic logical structure	一般逻辑结构	Yībān luóji jiégòu	
Generic network information model	通用网络信息模型	Tōngyòng wǎngluò xìnxī móxíng	GNM
Generic object exchange profile	通用对象交换应用	Tōngyòng duìxiàng jiāohuàn yìngyòng	GOEP
Generic routing encapsulation	通用路由封装	Tōngyòng lùyóu fēngzhuāng	GRE
Generic routing encapsulation	通用路由选择封装	Tōngyòng lùyóu xuǎnzé fēngzhuāng	GRE
Generic routing encapsulation	通用选路封装	Tōngyòng xuǎnlù fēngzhuāng	GRE
Generic security service application program interface	通用安全服务应用程序接口	Tōngyòng ānquán fúwù yìngyòng chéngxù jiēkǒu	GSS-API
Generic service resource	一般服务资源	Yībān fúwù zīyuán	
Generic spatial analysis function	空间几何分析函数	Kōngjiān jǐhé fēnxī hánshù	
Generic specification	通用规范	Tōngyòng guīfàn	
Generic upper layer security	通用上层安全性	Tōngyòng shàngcéng ānquánxìng	GULS
Generic visual perception processor	常规视觉处理器	Chángguī shìjué chǔlǐqì	GVPP
Genetic algorithm	遗传算法	Yíchuán suànfǎ	
Genetic programming	遗传规划	Yíchuán guīhuà	GP
GenRad Corp. (US)	真瑞	Zhēn-ruì	
Geocentric coordinate system	地心坐标系	Dìxīn zuòbiāo xì	
Geodesic hierarchy	测量层次	Cèliáng céngcì	
Geodetic control	测地控制	Cèdì kòngzhì	
Geodetic control network	大地控制网	Dàdì kòngzhì wǎng	
Geodetic control point	大地控制点	Dàdì kòngzhì diǎn	
Geodetic coordinate	大地坐标	Dàdì zuòbiāo	
Geodetic coordinate system	大地坐标系	Dàdì zuòbiāo xì	

Geodetic datum	大地基准	Dàdì jīzhǔn	
Geodetic origin	大地原点	Dàdì yuándiǎn	
Geodetic reference system	大地参照系	Dàdì cānzhàoxì	
Geographic graticule (GIS)	地理坐标网	Dìlǐ zuòbiāo wǎng	
Geographical information system	地里信息系统	Dìli xìnxī xìtǒng	GIS
Geography markup language	地理标记语言	Dìlǐ biāojì yǔyán	GML
Geoid	大地水准面	Dàdì shuǐzhǔn miàn	
Geoidal reference	大地水准参照	Dàdì shuǐzhǔn cānzhào	
Geo-information	地学信息	Dìxué xìnxī	
Geometric axis of parabolic antenna	抛物面天线几何轴	Pāowùmiàn tiānxiàn jǐhé zhóu	
Geometric graphic element	几何图形元素	Jǐhé túxíng yuánsù	
Geomorphology	地形学	Dìxíngxué	
Geo-object	地学目标	Dìxué mùbiāo	
Geo-processing	地学处理	Dìxué chǔlǐ	
Geoscope	测地仪	Cèdìyí	
Geostationary earth orbit	对地静止轨道	Duìdì jìngzhǐ guǐdào	GEO
Geostationary earth orbit	静止地球轨道	Jìngzhǐ dìqiú guǐdào	GEO
Geostationary orbit	对地静止轨道	Duìdì jìngzhǐ guǐdào	
Geostationary satellite	地球静止卫星	Dìqiú jìngzhǐ wèixīng	
Geostationary satellite	对地静止卫星	Duìdì jìngzhǐ wèixīng	
Geostationary satellite	同步卫星	Tóngbù wèixīng	Geos
Geostationary satellite orbit	地球静止卫星轨道	Dìqiú jìngzhǐ wèixīng guǐdào	
Geostationary satellite orbit	对地静止卫星轨道	Duìdì jìngzhǐ wèixīng guǐdào	
Geosynchronous earth orbit	同步地球轨道	Tóngbù dìqiú guǐdào	GEO
Geosynchronous earth orbit satellite	同步地球轨道卫星	Tóngbù dìqiú guǐdào wèixīng	GEOS
Geosynchronous satellite	地球同步卫星	Dìqiú tóngbù wèixīng	
Geosynchronous satellite	对地同步卫星	Duìdì tóngbù wèixīng	
Germanium chlorate or tetrachloride	四氯化锗	Sìlǜhuàzhě	$GeCl_4$
Germanium content fiber	含锗光纤	Hánzhě guāngxiān	GF
Get nearest server	获取最近服务器	Huòqǔ zuìjìn fúwùqì	GNS
Get password	获得口令	Huòdé kǒulìng	
Getter (in software)	取值函数	Qǔzhí hánshù	
Giant magnetoresistive	巨型磁阻	Jù-xíng cízǔ	GMR
Giga- (prefix meaning 10^9)	千兆	Qiānzhào	G
Gigabaud	吉波特	Jíbōtè	GBd
Gigabaud	吉咖波特	Jígābōtè	GBd
Gigabaud	千兆波特	Qiānzhào bōtè	GBd
Gigabit ethernet	Gb 以太网	Gb Yǐtàiwǎng	GE, GbE
Gigabit ethernet	吉比以太网	Jíbǐ yǐtàiwǎng	
Gigabit ethernet	吉比特级以太网	Jíbǐtè jí yǐtàiwǎng	GbE,Gbe
Gigabit ethernet	吉比特以太网	Jíbǐtè yǐtàiwǎng	GE=GbE
Gigabit Ethernet	千兆比特以太网	Qiānzhào bǐtè yǐtàiwǎng	GE
Gigabit Ethernet	千兆以太网	Qiānzhào yǐtàiwǎng	GE
Gigabit Ethernet	千兆比以太网	Qiānzhàobǐ yǐtàiwǎng	GbE
Gigabit Ethernet	千兆位以太网	Qiānzhàowèi yǐtàiwǎng	GbE
Gigabit Ethernet switch	千兆比以太网交换机	Qiānzhàobǐ yǐtàiwǎng jiāohuànjī	

Gigabit interface converter	吉比特接口转换器	Jíbĭtè jiēkǒu zhuǎnhuànqì	GBIC
Gigabit interface converter	千兆比特接口转换器	Qiānzhào bĭtè jiēkǒu zhuǎnhuànqì	GBIC
Gigabit link module	千兆比特链路模块	Qiānzhào bĭtè liànlù mókuài	GLM
Gigabit media-independent interface	千兆比特媒体无关接口	Qiānzhào bĭtè méitĭ wúguān jiēkǒu	GMII
Gigabit serial logic products	吉比特系列产品	Jíbĭtè xìliè chǎnpĭn	GSL
Gigabit switch router	千兆位交换路油器	Qiānzhàowèi jiāohuàn lùyóuqì	GSR
Gigabit/sec serial transmitter and receiver	Gb/s 系列发射机与接收机	Gb/s xìliè fāshèjī yǔ jiēshōujī	GigSTAR
Gigabits	吉比特	Jíbĭtè	Gb
Gigabits per second	吉比特每秒	Jíbĭtè měi miǎo	Gb/s
Gigabits per second	吉位秒	Jíwèi miǎo	Gbit/s; Gbps
Gigabyte	吉咖字节	Jígāzìjié,	GB
Gigabyte	吉字节	Jízìjié	GB
Gigabyte	千兆字节	Qiānzhào zìjié	GB
Gigapop	千兆级交换节点	Qiānzhào-jí jiāohuàn jiédiǎn	
Gilbert code	吉尔伯特码	Jí-ěr-bó-tè mǎ	
Glass break sensor	玻璃破碎传感器	Bōli pòsuì chuángǎnqì	GBS
Glass generator (FOC mfg)	玻璃产生机	Bōli chǎnshēngjī	
Glass laser	玻璃激光	Bōli jīguāng	
Glass mirror	玻璃面镜	Bōli miànjìng	
Glass optical fiber	玻璃光纤	Bōli guāngxiān	GOF
Glass substrate	玻璃基板	Bōli jībǎn	
Glass-ceramic ferrules	玻璃陶瓷陶管	Bōli táocí táoguǎn	GCF
Glass-ceramic mirror	玻璃/陶瓷面镜	Bōli/táocí miànjìng	
Gleaning	搜集	Sōují	
Glitch capture	毛刺捕获	Máocì bǔhuò	
Glitch, burr (PCB manufacture)	毛刺	Máocì	
Global Access Ltd.	全球接入有限公司	Quánqiú jiērù yǒuxiàn gōngsī	GAL
Global account	全局帐户	Quánjú zhànghù	
Global area	共用区	Gòngyòng qū	
Global area coverage	全球覆盖	Quánqiú fùgài	
Global assembly cache	全局配件缓存	Quánjú pèijiàn huǎncún	GAC
Global assembly cache	全局装配件缓存	Quánjú zhuāngpèijiàn huǎncún	GAC
Global aviation traffic manager	全球航空管制系统	Quánqiú hángkōng guǎnzhì xìtǒng	GATM
Global base register	共用基址寄存器	Gòngyòng jīzhǐ jìcúnqì	GBR
Global catalog	全局编录	Quánjú biānlù	
Global cell identity	全球小区识别码	Quánqiú xiǎoqū shíbiémǎ	GCI
Global Communication Semiconductors Inc.	全球通信半导体公司	Quánqiú tōngxìn bàndǎotĭ gōngsī	GCS
Global Communications Satellite System	全球通信卫星系统	Quánqiú tōngxìn wèixīng xìtǒng	GCSS
Global computing	全球计算	Quánqiú jìsuàn	
Global configuration mode	全球配置模式	Quánqiú pèizhì móshì	
Global connection ID	全局连接 ID	Quánjú liánjiē ID	GCI
Global control	全局控制	Quánjú kòngzhì	GC
Global data collection PC	全球数据收集 PC 机	Quánqiú shùjù shōují PC-jī	GDCP
Global data table	全局数据表	Quánjú shùjù biǎo	GDP
Global default	全局默认值	Quánjú mòrèn zhí	
Global descriptor table	全局描述表	Quánjú miáoshù biǎo	GDP

Global descriptor table	全局描述符表	Quánjú miáoshùfú biǎo	GDT
Global digital service unit	全球数字单元	Quánqiú shùzì dānyuán	GDSU
Global European network	全球欧网络	Quánqiú ōu wǎngluò	GEN
Global flow control	总流量控制	Zǒng liúliàng kòngzhì	GFC
Global function	全局功能	Quánjú gōngnéng	GF
Global Grid Forum (formed by IBM, Microsoft, and Sun Microsystems)	全球网格论坛	Quánqiú wǎnggé lùntán	
Global group (in multicast)	全局组	Quánjú zǔ	
Global high capacity IPC processor	全球高容量 IPC 处理器	Quánqiú gāoróngliàng IPC chǔlǐqì	GHIP
Global information distribution	全局信息发布	Quánjú xìnxī fābù	GID
Global information distribution (GID) daemon	全局信息发布后台程序	Quánjú xìnxī fābù hòutái chéngxù	
Global information exchange	全球信息交换	Quánqiú xìnxī jiāohuàn	GIE
Global information grid	全球信息网格	Quánqiú xìnxī wǎnggé	GIG
Global information infrastructure	全球信息基础结构	Quánqiú xìnxī jīchǔ jiégòu	GII
Global information infrastructure	全球信息基础设施	Quánqiú xìnxī jīchǔ shèshī	GII
Global maritime distress and safety system	全球遇险与安全系统	Quánqiú yùxiǎn yǔ ānquán xìtǒng	
Global memory	共用存储器	Gòngyòng cúnchǔqì	
Global memory	全局存储器	Quánjú cúnchǔqì	
Global mobile personal communications by satellite	全球移动个人卫星通信	Quánqiú yídòng gèrén wèixīng tōngxìn	GMPCS
Global mobile personal communications services	全球移动个人通信业务	Quánqiú yídòng gèrén tōngxìn yèwù	GMPCS
Global Navigation Satellite System	全球导航卫星系统	Quánqiú dǎoháng wèixīng xìtǒng	GLONASS
Global navigation satellite system	全球卫星导航系统	Quánqiú wèixīng dǎoháng xìtǒng	GNSS
Global network addressing domain	全球网络编地域	Quánqiú wǎngluò biāndìyù	
Global network addressing domain	全球网络编址域	Quánqiú wǎngluò biānzhǐ yù	
Global network locator	全球网络探测器	Quánqiú wǎngluò tàncèqì	GNL
Global network service	全球网络服务	Quánqiú wǎngluò fúwù	GNS
Global network service	全球网络业务	Quánqiú wǎngluò yèwù	GNS
Global object	全局对象	Quánjú duìxiàng	
Global optimization	全球优化	Quánqiú yōuhuà	
Global Orbiting Navigation Satellite System	全球定轨导航卫星系统	Quánqiú dìngguǐ dǎoháng wèixīng xìtǒng	GLONASS
Global path index (in XML)	全局路径索引	Quánjú lùjìng suǒyǐn	GPI
Global personal communication system	全球个人通信系统	Quánqiú gèrén tōngxìn xìtǒng	GPCS
Global positioning satellite system	全球卫星定位系统	Quánqiú wèixīng dìngwèi xìtǒng	GPSS
Global positioning system	全球定位系统	Quánqiú dìngwèi xìtǒng	GPS
Global properties	全局属性	Quánjú shǔxìng	
Global reach internet connection	可通达全球因特网路连接	Kětōngdá quánqiú Yīntèwǎng lù liánjiē	GRIC
Global resource information system	全球资源信息系统	Quánqiú zīyuán xìnxī xìtǒng	
Global routing pool	全局布线池	Quánjú bùxiàn chí	
Global rule	全局规则	Quánjú guīzé	
Global scheduling multiple access	全局调度多路存取	Quánjú diàodù duōlù cúnqǔ	GSMA
Global scope resolution operator	全局范围解析操作符	Quánjú fànwéi jiěxī cāozuò fú	
Global Security Analysis Lab	全球安全性分析实验室	Quánqiú ānquánxìng fēnxī shíyànshì	GSAL
Global service back panel	全球服务后面板	Quánqiú fúwù hòumian bǎn	GSBP
Global significance	全球意义	Quánqiú yìyì	
Global status	总状况	Zǒng zhuàngkuàng	
Global subscriptions	全局订阅	Quánjú dìngyuè	

Global synchronization	全局同步	Quánjú tóngbù	
Global System for Mobile Communications	全球移动通信系统	Quánqiú yídòng tōngxìn xìtǒng	GSM
Global title	全局码	Quánjú mǎ	GT
Global title	全球名称	Quánqiú míngchēng	GT
Global title	全球题目	Quánqiú tímù	GT
Global title	全球寻址码	Quánqiú xúnzhǐ mǎ	GT
Global title indicator	全局码表示语	Quánjú mǎ biǎoshì yǔ	GTI
Global trading web	全球网上电子贸易市场	Quánqiú wǎngshàng diànzǐ màoyì shìcháng	GTW
Global validity condition (CAD/CAM)	全球有效性条件	Quánqiú yǒuxiàoxìng tiáojiàn	GVC
Global variable	全局变量	Quánjú biànliàng	
Global virtual network service	全局虚拟网业务	Quánjú xūnǐ wǎng yèwù	GVNS
Globally uniform identifier	全局统一标识	Quánjú tǒngyī biāozhì	GUID
Globally unique identifier	全局唯一标识符	Quánjú wéiyī biāozhìfú	GUID
Globally unique identifier	全球唯一标识符	Quánqiú wéiyī biāozhì fú	GUID
Globalstar (satellite system)	全球星	Quánqiú xīng	
Globe text telephone	全球文本电话	Quánqiú wénběn diànhuà	GTT
Glue chasing	粘贴跟踪	Zhāntiē gēnzōng	
Glue records	粘贴记录	Zhāntiē jìlù	
GNU's network object model environment	GNU 网络对象模型环境	GNU wǎngluò duìxiàng móxíng huánjìng	GNOME
Go on TV	上电视	Shàng diànshì	GOTV,G.O.T.V.
Go to page (WP command)	寻找页	Xúnzhǎo yè	
GO/NO-GO box (semiconductor mfg)	准入/禁入盒	Zhǔnrù/jìnrù hé	
Go-back-N ARQ	退N步ARQ	Tuì N-bù ARQ	
Golay code	戈莱码	Gē-lái mǎ	
Golay sequential coding	格雷码	Gé-léi mǎ	
Golden boy (in SMT)	金样	Jīnyàng	
Golden Bridge Network (China)	金桥网	Jīnqiáo wǎng	GB-Net
Gopher (an Internet tool)	考访服务	Kǎo-fǎng fúwù	
Gopher (Internet search engine)	地鼠	Dìshǔ	
Goppa codes	戈帕码	Gē-pà mǎ	
Gosudarstvennui Standart (Russian government standard) (used by the Chinese to indicate the agency	国家标准制定部	Guójiā biāozhǔn zhìdìng bù	ГОСТ
Goubau line	沟包线	Gōu-bāo xiàn	
Gouraud shading (video)	高洛德描影	Gāo-luò-dé miáo yǐng	
Gouraud shading (video)	内插法均匀涂色	Nèichāfǎ jūnyún túsè	
Government advisory committee	政府顾问委员会	Zhèngfǔ gùwèn wěiyuánhuì	GAC
Government encryption or cryptography (short for 政府用的密码)	政密	Zhèng mì	
Government off-the-shelf products	政府成品	Zhèngfǔ chéngpǐn	GOTS
Government Open system interconnection protocol	政府开放系统互连协议	Zhèngfǔ kāifàng xìtǒng hùlián xiéyì	GOSIP
Government Telecommunications Organization	政府电信组织	Zhèngfǔ diànxìn zǔzhī	GTO
G-polygon	G 多边形	G-duōbiānxíng	
GPRS mobility management	GPRS 移动性管理	GPRS yídòngxìng guǎnlǐ	GMM
GPRS support node	GPRS 支持节点	GPRS zhīchí jiédiǎn	GSN
GPRS tunneling protocol for user plane	GPRS 隧道协议用户平面	GPRS suìdào xiéyì yònghù píngmiàn	GTP-U
GPS receiver	GPS 接收机	GPS jiēshōujī	GPSR

GPS-inertial navigation system	全球定位 - 惯性导航系统	Quánqiú dìngwèi-guànxìng dǎoháng xìtǒng	
Gradation analysis curve	粒度曲线	Lìdù qūxiàn	
Grade of service	服务等级	Fúwù děngjí	GOS
Graded index (FOC)	梯度折射率	Tīdù zhéshèlǜ	
Graded index fiber	渐变梯度光纤	Jiànbiàn tīdù guāngxiān	GIF
Graded index fiber	渐变折射率光纤	Jiànbiàn zhéshèlǜ guāngxiān	GI
Graded index fiber	渐变型多模光纤	Jiànbiànxíng duōmó guāngxiān	GIF
Graded index fiber	渐变型光纤	Jiànbiànxíng guāngxiān	
Graded index fiber	浙变梯度光纤	Zhèbiàn tīdù guāngxiān	GIF
Graded index of refraction	渐变折射率	Jiànbiàn zhéshèlǜ	
Graded index polymer optical fiber	梯度折射率塑料光纤	Tīdù zhéshèlǜ sùliào guāngxiān	GI-POF
Graded index polymer optical fiber	浙变折射率聚合物光纤	Zhèbiàn zhéshèlǜ jùhéwù guāngxiān	GI-POF
Graded index profile	渐变折射率分布	Jiànbiàn zhéshèlǜ fēnbù	
Gradient	梯度	Tīdù	
Grading	分级复联	Fēnjí fùlián	
Grading	分品	Fēnpǐn	
Grading	平整	Píngzhěng	
Gradual failure; drift failure	渐变失效	Jiànbiàn shīxiào	
Graduate record examination	学位等级记录审验考试	Xuéwèi děngjí jìlù shěnyàn kǎoshì	GRE
Graduated symbol map	渐变符号图	Jiànbiàn fúhào tú	
Graduating impedance transformer	渐变式阻抗变换器	Jiànbiàn-shì zǔkàng biànhuànqì	
Grain size accumulation curve	粒度累积曲线	Lìdù lěijī qūxiàn	
Grain size analysis	粒度分析	Lìdù fēnxī	
Grain size distribution	粒径分布	Lìjìng fēnbù	
Grained analysis	纹理分析	Wénlǐ fēnxī	
Grant power down	授权掉电	Shòuquán diàodiàn	GNTPDN
Grant (for database)	授权	Shòuquán	
Grant-in-aid	资助金	Zīzhù jīn	
Granularity	粒度	Lìdù	
Graph isomorphism	图的同构	Túde tóng gòu	
Graph partition	图的划分	Túde huàfēn	
Graph problems -- polynomial	图论-多项式算法	Túlùn- duōxiàngshì suànfǎ	
Graph theory	图论	Túlùn	
Graph, graphic	图形	Túxíng	
Graphic address remapping table	图形地址重绘表	Túxíng dìzhǐ chónghuì biǎo	GART
Graphic character	图形字符	Túxíng zìfú	
Graphic code extension	图形代码扩充	Túxíng dàimǎ kuòchōng	
Graphic communication	图形通讯	Túxíng tōngxùn	
Graphic data	图形数据	Túxíng shùjù	
Graphic database	图形数据库	Túxíng shùjùkù	
Graphic display	显示器	Xiǎnshìqì	
Graphic distortion	图形失真	Túxíng shīzhēn	
Graphic distortion correction	图形失真校正	Túxíng shīzhēn jiàozhèng	
Graphic element	图形元素	Túxíng yuánsù	
Graphic entity	图形实体	Túxíng shítǐ	
Graphic file	图形文件	Túxíng wénjiàn	

English	Chinese	Pinyin	Abbreviation
Graphic fudging	图形插印	Túxíng chāyìn	
Graphic handler	图形处理器	Túxíng chǔlǐqì	GPH
Graphic information	图形信息	Tú-xíng xìnxī	
Graphic interchange format	图形交换格式	Túxíng jiāohuàn géshi	GIF
Graphic manipulation	图形操作	Túxíng cāozuò	
Graphic network browser	图形网浏览	Túxíng wǎng liúlǎn	GNB
Graphic network editor	图形网编辑	Túxíng wǎng biānjí	GNE
Graphic output circuit analysis program	图形输出电路分析程序	Túxíng shūchū diànlù fēnxī chéngxù	GOCAP
Graphic overlay	图形叠加	Túxíng diéjiā	
Graphic primitive	图形要素	Túxíng yàosù	
Graphic stability	图象稳定度	Túxiàng wěndìngdù	
Graphic symbol	图形符号	Túxíng fúhào	
Graphic terminal	图形终端	Túxíng zhōngduān	
Graphical information system	图形信息系统	Túxíng xìnxī xìtǒng	GIS
Graphical interface	图文界面	Túwén jièmiàn	
Graphical kernel system	计算机图形核心系统	Jìsuànjī túxíng héxīn xìtǒng	GKS
Graphical language	图形语言	Túxíng yǔyán	
Graphical user interface	图象使用者介面	Túxiàng shǐyòngzhě jièmiàn	GUI
Graphical user interface	图象用户介面	Túxiàng yònghù jièmiàn	GUI
Graphical user interface	图形界面	Túxíng jièmiàn	GUI
Graphical user interface	图形用户接口	Túxíng yònghù jiēkǒu	GUI
Graphical user interface	图形用户界面	Túxíng yònghù jièmiàn	GUI
Graphical user terminal	图形用户终端	Túxíng yònghù zhōngduān	
Graphics and memory controller hub	图形和内存控制中心	Túxíng hé nèicún kòngzhì zhōngxīn	GMCH
Graphics communications terminal	图形通信终端	Túxíng tōngxìn zhōngduān	GCT
Graphics device interface	图形设备接口	Túxíng shèbèi jiēkǒu	GDI
Graphics display terminal	图形显示终端	Túxíng xiǎnshì zhōngduān	
Graphics exchange specification	图形数据互换说明	Túxíng shùjù hùhuàn shuōmíng	GES
Graphics page	绘图区	Huìtú qū	
Graphics processing unit	图形处理器	Túxíng chǔlǐqì	GPU
Graphics table	图表	Túbiǎo	
Grating coupler sampled reflector	光栅耦合取样反射器	Guāngshān ǒuhé qǔyàng fǎnshèqì	GCSR
Grating light valves	光栅光阀	Guāngshān guāngfá	GLVs
Grating lobe	栅瓣	Zhàbàn	
Grating lobe pattern	栅瓣图	Zhàbàn tú	
Green Hills Software Co.	绿色希尔斯软件公司	Lǜsè Xī-ěr-sī ruǎnjiàn gōngsī	GHS
Green, oxygen, light and foot	绿色、氧气、阳光与漫步	Lǜsè、yǎngqì、yángguāng yǔ mànbù	GOLF
Greenwich electronic time	格林尼治电子时间	Gé-lín-ní-zhì diànzǐ shíjiān	GeT
Greenwich mean time	格林尼治时间	Gé-lín-ní-zhì shíjiān	GMT
Gregorian calendar	公历	Gōnglì	
Gregorian reflector antenna	格雷戈伦反射器天线	Gé-léi-gē-lún fǎnshèqì tiānxiàn	
Grid (as a grating)	栅极	Shānjí	G
Grid (as network); lattice; mesh	网格	Wǎnggé	G
Grid cell	网格单元	Wǎnggé dānyuán	
Grid computing	网格计算	Wǎnggé jìsuàn	
Grid coordinate system	格网坐标系	Géwǎng zuòbiāo xì	

Grid data	格网数据	Géwǎng shùjù	
Grid format	格网格式	Géwǎng géshi	
Grid map	格网地图	Géwǎng dìtú	
Grid middleware	网格中间件	Wǎnggé zhōngjiān jiàn	
Grid parabolic antenna	栅格抛物面天线	Zhàgé pāowùmiàn tiānxiàn	
Grid reference	格网参照	Géwǎng cānzhào	
Grid reflecting surface	栅状反射面	Zhàzhuàng fǎnshèmiàn	
Grid security infrastructure	网格安全基础设施	Wǎnggé ānquán jīchǔ shèshī	GSI
Grid square	方格网	Fānggé wǎng	
Grid structure	网格结构	Wǎnggé jiégòu	
Gridded crossed-field amplifier	栅控正交场放大器	Zhàkòng zhèngjiāo cháng fàngdàqì	GFCA
Grid-gated photomultiplier	控制栅光电培增器	Kòngzhì zhà guāngdiàn péizēngqì	GGPM
Grid-plate line-feed	栅板线馈电	Zhàbǎn xiàn kuìdiàn	
G-ring	G-环	G-huán	
Grooming (of a digital signal)	疏导	Shūdǎo	
Grooming and consolidation	疏导和合并	Shūdǎo hé hébìng	
Gross floor area	总建筑面积	Zǒng jiànzhù miànjī	
Ground fault circuit interrupter	接地故障电路中级器	Jiēdì gùzhàng diànlù zhōngjíqì	GFCI
Ground fault current	接地故障电流	Jiēdì gùzhàng diànliú	
Ground fault factor	接地故障因数	Jiēdì gùzhàng yīnshù	
Ground fault, earth fault	接地故障	Jiēdì gùzhàng	
Ground loop	接地环路	Jiēdì huánlù	
Ground mat	地面网	Dìmiàn wǎng	
Ground phantom circuit	地回幻线电路	Dì huíhuànxiàn diànlù	
Ground reference plane	接地参考平面	Jiēdì cānkǎo píngmiàn	
Ground short circuit current	接地短路电流	Jiēdì duǎnlù diànliú	
Ground testing	碰地气测试	Pèng dìqì cèshì	
Ground wave	地波	Dìbō	
Ground wire wound optical fiber cable	接地线缠绕光缆	Jiēdìxiàn chánrǎo guānglǎn	GWWOP
Ground, earth (electrical)	接地	Jiēdì	
Ground/air communication equipment	地-空通信设备	Dì-kōng tōngxìn shèbèi	
Ground-coupled interference	地耦合干扰	Dì'ǒuhé gānrǎo	
Grounded	被接地	Bèijiēdì	
Grounded circuit	接地电路	Jiēdì diànlù	
Grounded conductor	被接地的导体	Bèijiēdìde dǎotǐ	
Grounding conductor	接地导体	Jiēdì dǎotǐ	
Grounding conductor	接地线	Jiēdìxiàn	
Grounding inductor	接地电感器	Jiēdì diàngǎnqì	
Grounding resistance	接地电阻	Jiēdì diànzǔ	
Grounding switch	接地开关	Jiēdì kāiguān	
Grounding wire	地线	Dìxiàn	
Ground-plane antenna	地平面天线	Dìpíngmiàn tiānxiàn	
Ground-state absorption	基态吸收	Jītài xīshōu	GSA
Group	群	Qún	
Group	组	Zǔ	
Group 3 facsimile	三类传真	Sānlèi chuánzhēn	G3 FAX

Group 4 facsimile	四类传真	Sìlèi chuánzhēn	
Group address	组地址	Zǔ dìzhǐ	
Group box	分组框	Fēnzǔ kuàng	
Group call	集体呼叫	Jítǐ hūjiào	
Group call record	组呼叫寄存器	Zǔhūjiào jìcúnqì	GCR
Group call register	呼叫寄发器群	Hūjiào jìfāqì qún	GCR
Group delay	群时延	Qún shíyán	
Group delay	组延迟	Zǔ yánchí	
Group delay equalization	群时延均衡	Qún shíyán jūnhéng	
Group delay flatness (ripple)	群延平坦度	Qúnyán píngtǎndù	
Group delay/frequency distortion	群时延频率失真	Qún shíyán pínlǜ shīzhēn	
Group identification	群识别	Qún shíbié	GI
Group identifier	群标识符	Qún biāozhì fú	GI
Group identifier (level 1)	鉴别器群（电平 1）	Jiànbiéqì qún (diànpíng 1)	GID1
Group identifier (level 1)	鉴别器群（电平 2）	Jiànbiéqì qún (diànpíng 2)	GID2
Group interchange key (IPsec)	组交换密钥	Zǔ jiāohuàn mìyào	GIK
Group key management protocol	组密钥管理协议	Zǔ mìyào guǎnlǐ xiéyì	GKMP
Group link	群链路	Qún liànlù	
Group management	组管理	Zǔ guǎnlǐ	GM
Group of blocks	块群	Kuài qún	GOB
Group relationship	分类关系	Fēnlèi guānxi	
Group relationships	组关系	Zǔ guānxi	
Group routing and charging equipment	群路由选择和计价设备	Qún lùyóu xuǎnzé hé jìjià shèbèi	GRACE
Group section	群段	Qún duàn	
Group security controller	组安全控制器	Zǔ ānquán kòngzhìqì	GSC
Group signature scheme	小组签名方案	Xiǎozǔ qiānmíng fāng'àn	
Group switching center	分组交换中心	Fēnzǔ jiāohuàn zhōngxīn	GSC
Group switching center	群交换中心	Qún jiāohuàn zhōngxīn	GSC
Group terminal point	群终接点	Qún zhōngjiēdiǎn	GTP
Group velocity	群速	Qúnsù	
Group velocity	群速度	Qúnsùdù	
Group velocity dispersion	群速度分散	Qúnsùdù fēnsàn	
Group velocity dispersion	群速度色散	Qúnsùdù sèsàn	GVD
Groupe Special Mobile (est. 1982)	移动通信特别小组	Yídòng tōngxìn tèbié xiǎozǔ	GSM
Groupware	群件	Qúnjiàn	
Growth and income securities	增长收益债卷	Zēngzhǎng shōuyì zhàijuàn	GAINS
GSM certification forum	GSM 认可论坛	GSM rènkě lùntán	GCF
GSM global roaming forum	GSM 全球漫游论坛	GSM quánqiú mànyóu lùntán	GGRF
GSM PLMN area	GSM 公用陆地移动通信网覆盖面积	GSM gōngyòng lùdì yídòng tōngxìnwǎng fùgài miànjī	Gpa
GSM public land mobile network	GSM 公共陆地移动网络	GSM gōnggòng lùdì yídòng wǎngluò	GSM PLMN
GSM service area	GSM 业务区	GSM yèwù qū	
GSM service identity module	GSM 业务识别模块	GSM yèwù shíbié mókuài	GSIM
GSM subscriber identity module	GSM 用户识别模块	GSM yònghù shíbié mókuài	SIM
GSM system area	GSM 系统区域	GSM xìtǒng qūyù	GSA
GSM type approval advisory board	GSM 型号认证咨询委员会	GSM xínghào rènzhèng zīxún wěiyuánhuì	GSM TAAB

GSM/EDGE radio access network	GSM/EDGE 无线接入网	GSM/EDGE wúxiàn jiērù wǎng	GERAN
Gt-polygon	gt-多边形	gt-duōbiānxíng	
Gt-ring	gt-环	gt-huán	
Guaranteed bit rate	保证比特率	Bǎozhèng bǐtè lǜ	GBR
Guaranteed frame rate	有保证帧速率	Yǒu bǎozhèng zhèng sùlǜ	GFR
Guard band	间隔频带	Jiàngé píndài	
Guard period	保护时段	Bǎohù shíduàn	
Guard period	保护时隙	Bǎohù shíxì	GP
Guard period	防护周期	Fánghù zhōuqī	GP
Guarded release	有监护释放	Yǒu jiānhù shìfàng	
Guarding (in voice frequency signaling)	监护	Jiānhù	
Guest	来宾	Láibīn	
Guest account	来宾帐户	Láibīn zhànghù	
Guidance radar	制导雷达	Zhìdǎo léidá	
Guide wavelength	波导波长	Bōdǎo bōcháng	
Guided wave (in a transmission line)	导行波	Dǎoxíng bō	
Guidelines for the definition of managed objects	被管对象定义指南	Bèiguǎn duìxiàng dìngyì zhǐnán	GDMO
Guidelines for the definition of managed objects	对管理目标定义的指南	Duì guǎnlǐ mùbiāo dìngyìde zhǐnán	GDMO
Guidelines for the definition of managed objects	管理对象定义规范	Guǎnlǐ duìxiàng dìngyì guīfàn	GDMO
Guidelines for the definition of managed objects	管理目标定义指南	Guǎnlǐ mùbiāo dìngyì zhǐnán	GDMO
Guiding device	引导设备	Yǐndǎo shèbèi	
Guiding groove	导向槽	Dǎoxiàngcáo	
Guiding sleeve	导管	Dǎoguǎn	
Guilin Institute of Optical Communications	桂林光通信研究所	Guìlín guāngtōngxìn yánjiūsuǒ	GIOC
Guoxin Lucent Network Technologies Co. Ltd. (Sino-US joint venture)	国信朗讯科技网络技术有限公司	Guóxìn Lǎngxùn Kējì wǎngluò jìshù yǒuxiàn gōngsī	GXLU
Gutter	侧沟	Cègōu	
Gyromagnetic device	旋磁器件	Xuáncí qìjiàn	
Gyromagnetic effects	旋磁效应	Xuáncí xiàoyìng	
Gyromagnetic filter	旋磁滤波器	Xuáncí lǜbōqì	
Gyromagnetic material	旋磁材料	Xuáncí cáiliào	
Gyromagnetic medium	旋磁媒质	Xuáncí méizhì	
Gyromagnetic power limiter	旋磁功率限制器	Xuáncí gōnglǜ xiànzhìqì	
Gyromagnetic ratio	旋磁比	Xuáncíbǐ	
Gyromagnetic resonance	旋磁谐振	Xuáncí xiézhèn	
Gyromagnetic resonator	旋磁谐振器	Xuáncí xiézhènqì	
Gyro-peniotron	回旋潘尼管	Huíxuán pān-ní-guǎn	
Gyro-peniotron	回旋佩尼管	Huíxuán pèi-ní-guǎn	
Gyroresonant accelerator	回旋谐振加速器	Huíxuán xiézhèn jiāsùqì	
Gyroscoper	回旋器	Huíxuánqì	
Gyrotron	回旋管	Huíxuán guǎn	

H

H plane T-junction	H 面 T 形接头	H-miàn T-xing jiētóu	
H plane waveguide bend	H 面弯波导	H-miàn wān bōdǎo	
Haar transform	哈尔变换	Hā-ěr biànhuàn	HrT

Hacker	骇客	Hài-kè	
Hacker	黑客	Hēi-kè	
Hacker intrusion	黑客侵入	Hēi-kè qīnrù	
Hagelbarger code	黑格巴哥码	Hēi-gé-bā-gē mǎ	
Half adder	半加器	Bànjiāqì	HA
Half angle character (single byte character)	半角字符	Bànjiǎo zìfú	
Half dipole, half doublet	半偶极子	Bàn ǒujízi	
Half duplex	半双工	Bànshuānggōng	HDX
Half duplex channel	半双工通道	Bànshuānggōng tōngdào	HDC
Half duplex transmission module	半双工传输模块	Bànshuānggōng chuánshū mókuài	HDTM
Half duplex transmission system	半双工传输系统	Bànshuānggōng chuánshū xìtǒng	HDTS
Half rate	半速率	Bàn sùlǜ	HR
Half rate data traffic channel	半速率数据业务信道	Bàn sùlǜ shùjù yèwù xìndào	TCH/H
Half rate speech traffic channel	半速率话音业务信道	Bàn sùlǜ huàyīn yèwù xìndào	TCH/HS
Half rate traffic channel	半速率业务信道	Bàn sùlǜ yèwù xìndào	TCH/H
Half-cycle	半占空	Bànzhànkōng	
Half-duplex transmission	半双工传输	Bàn shuānggōng chuánshū	
Half-power bandwidth	半功率波束	Bàngōnglǜ bōshù	HPBW
Half-power beamwidth (3 dB beamwidth)	半功率点波瓣宽度	Bàn gōnglǜdiǎn bōbàn kuāndù	
Half-rate	半速	Bànsù	HR
Half-rate traffic channel	半速率信道	Bànsùlǜ xìndào	Lm
Half-silvered mirror	半涂银面镜	Bàn túyín miànjìng	
Halftone	半色调	Bànsèdiào	
Half-wave bridge rectifier	半波桥式整流器	Bànbō qiáoshì zhěngliúqì	HWBR
Half-wave dipole	半波偶极子	Bànbō ǒujízi	HWD
Half-wave plate (in a waveguide)	半波板	Bànbō bǎn	
Halides (in SMT)	卤化物	Lǔhuàwù	
Halogen light source	卤素灯	Lǔsù dēng	
Halogen-free, flame retardant jacket (FOC)	无卤阻燃护套	Wúlǔ zǔrán hùtào	HFFR
Hamilton circuit	哈密尔顿环	Hā-mì-ěr-dùn huán	
Hamming code	海明码	Hǎi-míng mǎ	
Hamming code	汉明码	Hàn-míng mǎ	
Hamming distance	汉明间距	Hàn-míng jiānjù	
Hamming distance	汉明距离	Hàn-míng jùlí	
Hamming space	海明空间	Hǎi-míng kōngjiān	
Hamming weight	汉明重量	Hàn-míng zhòngliàng	
Hand hole (for access to buried cable)	手孔	Shǒu kǒng	
Hand input	手写输入	Shǒuxiě shūrù	
Hand portable unit	手提单元	Shǒutí dānyuán	HPU
Hand-held color image scanner	手持式影像扫描器	Shǒuchí-shì yǐngxiàng sǎomiáoqì	
Hand-held laser bar code scanner	手持式激光条码扫描器	Shǒuchí-shì jīguāng tiáomǎ sǎomiáoqì	
Hand-held PC	手持式电脑	Shǒuchí-shì diànnǎo	HPC
Handle	句柄	Jùbǐng	
Handler	处理器	Chǔlǐqì	
Handover access	切换接入	Qiēhuàn jiērù	
Handover access burst	越区切换接入突发	Yuèqū qiēhuàn jiērù tūfā	

Handover call arrival rate	切换呼叫到达率	Qiēhuàn hūjiào dàodá lǜ	
Handover candidate inquiry	切换候选者讯问	Qiēhuàn hòuxuǎnzhě xùnwèn	
Handover candidate response	切换候选者响应	Qiēhuàn hòuxuǎnzhě xiǎngyìng	
Handover command	切换命令	Qiēhuàn mìnglìng	
Handover complete	切换完成	Qiēhuàn wánchéng	
Handover control	切换控制	Qiēhuàn kòngzhì	
Handover detect	切换检测到	Qiēhuàn jiǎncè dào	
Handover execution	越区切换执行	Yuèqū qiēhuàn zhíxíng	
Handover failure	切换故障	Qiēhuàn gùzhàng	
Handover margin	越区切换界限	Yuèqū qiēhuàn jièxiàn	
Handover path switching	切换路径开关	Qiēhuàn lùjìng kāiguān	HPS
Handover reference	切换参考	Qiēhuàn cānkǎo	
Handover request	切换请求	Qiēhuàn qǐngqiú	
Handover request acknowledge	切换请求证实	Qiēhuàn qǐngqiú zhèngshí	
Handover required	切换要求	Qiēhuàn yāoqiú	
Handover resource reservation	切换资源预留	Qiēhuàn zīyuán yùliú	HRR
Handover strategy	越区切换策略	Yuèqū qiēhuàn cèlüè	
Handover test	移交测试	Yíjiāo cèshì	
Handover, handoff	切换	Qiēhuàn	HO
Handover, handoff (inter-cell)	越区切换	Yuèqū qiēhuàn	HO
Handset	手柄	Shǒubǐng	
Handset, handheld device	手持机	Shǒuchíjī	
Handshake	握手	Wòshǒu	
Handshake	信号握手	Xìnhào wòshǒu	
Handshake failure message (IPsec TLS)	握手失败消息	Wòshǒu shībài xiāoxi	
Handshake protocol (IPsec)	握手协议	Wòshǒu xiéyì	
Handshaking procedure (IPsec)	握手规程	Wòshǒu guīchéng	
Handwriting recognition	手写辨识	Shǒuxiě biànshí	
Handwriting recognition	手写识别	Shǒuxiě shíbié	
Hang (computer program malfunction)	当机	Dāngjī	
Hang up	挂机	Guàjī	
Hang up	中止	Zhōngzhǐ	
Hanging wall	上盘	Shàngpán	
Hang-up signal	挂机信号	Guàjī xìnhào	
Harbor management system	港口管理系统	Gǎngkǒu guǎnlǐ xìtǒng	
Harbor traffic control system	港口交通管理系统	Gǎngkǒu jiāotōng guǎnlǐ xìtǒng	
Hard copy	硬拷贝	Yìngkǎobèi	
Hard decision decoding	硬判决译码	Yìng pànjué yìmǎ	
Hard disk	硬盘	Yìngpán	
Hard disk – floppy disk controller card	软硬盘监控卡	Ruǎn/yìngpán jiānkòng qiǎ	
Hard disk controller	硬盘控制器	Yìngpán kòngzhìqì	HDC
Hard handover	硬切换	Yìng qiēhuàn	HHO
Hard limiter	硬限幅器	Yìng xiànfúqì	
Hard line terminator	硬行终止符	Yìng háng zhōngzhǐ fú	
Hard tube pulse modulator	刚管脉冲调制器	Gāngguǎn màichōng tiáozhìqì	
Hard water	硬水	Yìngshuǐ	

Hard-coded	硬编码的	Yìng biānmǎde	
Hard-copy	截屏图	Jiépíng tú	
Hardener (in SMT)	硬化剂	Yìnghuàjì	
Hardening rule	硬化规则	Yìnghuà guīzé	
Hardware	硬件	Yìngjiàn	
Hardware abstraction layer	硬件抽象层	Yìngjiàn chōuxiàng céng	HAL
Hardware abstraction layer	硬件抽像化层	Yìngjiàn chōuxiànghuà céng	HAL
Hardware address	硬件地址	Yìngjiàn dìzhǐ	
Hardware address control	机器地址控制	Jīqì dìzhǐ kòngzhì	HAC
Hardware compatibility list	硬件兼容性列表	Yìngjiàn jiānróngxìng lièbiǎo	HCL
Hardware compatibility test	硬件兼容性测试	Yìngjiàn jiānróngxìng cèshì	HCT
Hardware description language	硬件描述语言	Yìngjiàn miáoshù yǔyán	HDL
Hardware emulation layer	硬件仿真层	Yìngjiàn fǎngzhēn céng	HEL
Hardware emulation layer	硬件模拟层	Yìngjiàn mónǐ céng	HEL
Hardware environment	硬件环境	Yìngjiàn huánjìng	
Hardware failure-oriented group blocking acknowledgement message	面向硬件故障的群闭塞证实消息	Miànxiàng yìngjiàn gùzhàngde qún bìsè zhèngshí xiāoxi	HBA
Hardware failure-oriented group blocking message	面向硬件故障的群闭塞消息	Miànxiàng yìngjiàn gùzhàngde qún bìsè xiāoxi	HGB
Hardware failure-oriented group unblocking message	面向硬件故障的群闭塞解除消息	Miànxiàng yìngjiàn gùzhàngde qún bìsè jiěchú xiāoxi	HGU
Hardware failure-oriented group unblocking-acknowledgement message	面向硬件故障的群闭塞解除证实消息	Miànxiàng yìngjiàn gùzhàngde qún bìsè jiěchú zhèngshí xiāoxi	HUA
Hardware insert press (in SMT)	压接机	Yājiējī	
Hardware motion compensation	硬件运动补偿	Yìngjiàn yùndòng bǔcháng	
Hardware priority level	硬件优先级	Yìngjiàn yōuxiān jí	
Hardware timer	硬件时钟	Yìngjiàn shízhōng	
Hardware virtualizer	硬件虚拟器	Yìngjiàn xūnǐqì	HV
Harmful interference	有害干扰	Yǒuhài gānrǎo	
Harmonic	谐波	Xiébō	
Harmonic and noise suppression	谐波和杂波抑制	Xiébō hé zábō yìzhì	
Harmonic component	谐波分量	Xiébō fènliàng	
Harmonic conjugate signal	谐波共轭信号	Xiébō gòng'è xìnhào	
Harmonic content	谐波含量	Xiébō hánliàng	
Harmonic distortion	谐波失真	Xiébō shīzhēn	HD
Harmonic distortion factor	谐波失真系数	Xiébō shīzhēn xìshù	
Harmonic drive gearing	谐波传动	Xiébō chuándòng	
Harmonic emission	谐波发射	Xiébō fāshè	
Harmonic filter	谐波滤波器	Xiébō lǜbōqì	
Harmonic number	谐波次数	Xiébō cìshù	
Harmonic output power	谐波输出功率	Xiébō shūchū gōnglǜ	
Harmonic radar	谐波雷达	Xiébō léidá	
Harness	光缆捆束	Guānglǎn kǔnshù	
Harness assembly	光缆捆束组件	Guānglǎn kǔnshù zǔjiàn	
Harris Corporation (US company)	哈里斯公司	Hā-lǐ-sī gōngsī	
Harsh condition-resistant fiber	抗恶环境光纤	Kàng'èhuánjìng guāngxiān	

Hartley	哈脱莱	Hā-tuō-lái	
Hash (in encryption)	信息摘要	Xìnxī zhāiyào	
Hash algorithm (IPsec)	散列算法	Sànliè suànfǎ	
Hash function (cryptography)	散列函数	Sànliè hánshù	
Hash join (in SQL Server)	散列连接	Sànliè liánjiē	
Hash search	散列查找	Sànliè cházhǎo	
Hash table	哈希表	Hā-xī biǎo	
Hash table	散列表	Sànliè biǎo	
Hash-based message authentication code	基于散列的消息验证代码	Jīyú sànliède xiāoxi yànzhèng dàimǎ	HMAC
Hashed message authentication code	哈希消息认证代码	Hā-xī xiāoxi rènzhèng dàimǎ	HMAC
Hashing	散列法	Sànliè fǎ	
Hashing (in cryptography)	散列	Sànliè	
Hayes compatible modem	海斯调制解调器	Hǎi-sī tiáozhì jiětiáoqì	
Head	弧头	Hútóu	
Head disk assembly	磁头集合	Cítóu jíhé	HDA
Head disk assembly	头盘部件	Tóu pán bùjiàn	I
Head end	端头	Duāntou	
Head end	头端	Tóuduān	
Head mounted display	头戴式显示器	Tóudài-shì xiǎnshìqì	HMD
Head node	头结点	Tóu jiédiǎn	
Head of line blocking	队头阻塞	Duìtóu zǔsè	
Head pointer	头指针	Tóu zhǐzhēn	
Head related transfer function	头部关联传输功能	Tóubù guānlián chuánshū gōngnéng	HRTF
Head-down indicator	下视显示器	Xiàshì xiǎnshìqì	
Header (WP command)	首页标	Shǒuyè biāo	
Header error check	头校验码	Tóu jiàoyàn mǎ	HEC
Header error check	信头差错校验	Xìntóu chācuò jiàoyàn	HEC
Header error control	报头错误控制	Bàotóu cuòwù kòngzhì	HEC
Header error control	头部差错控制	Tóubù chācuò kòngzhì	HEC
Header error control	信头差错控制码	Xìntóu chācuò kòngzhì mǎ	HEC
Header error control	信头差错控制域	Xìntóu chācuò kòngzhì yù	HEC
Header error control	信头误码控制	Xìntóu wùmǎ kòngzhì	HEC
Header extension length	扩展头部长度	Kuòzhǎn tóubù chángdù	HEL
Header file	头文件	Tóu wénjiàn	
Header record	头记录	Tóu jìlù	
Header segment	电文头段	Diànwén tóuduàn	
Header vertical redundancy check error	头标垂向冗余校验错	Tóubiāo chuíxiàng rǒngyú jiàoyàn cuò	HRC
Header; heading (of a data block)	信头	Xìntóu	
Heading of station	电台航向	Diàntái hángxiàng	
Headset	戴在头上的耳机或听筒	Dài zài tóushàngde ěrjī huò tīngtǒng	HS
Head-up display	抬头显示器	Táitóu xiǎnshìqì	HUD
Head-up indicator	平视显示器	Píngshì xiǎnshìqì	
Heap sort	堆排序	Duī páixù	
Heap structure (in SQL Server)	堆存储方式	Duīcúnchǔ fāngshì	
Heap, stack	堆	Duī	
Hearing survey	访问调查	Fǎngwèn diàochá	

Heat detector	感温探测器	Gǎnwēn tàncèqì	HD
Heat dissipation	散热	Sànrè	
Heat distortion	热老化	Rè lǎohuà	
Heat exchanger	热交换器	Rè jiāohuànqì	
Heat exchanger (semiconductor mfg)	恒温热传导器机	Héngwēn rè chuándǎoqìjī	
Heat flow cryptography	热流密码学	Rèliú mìmǎxué	
Heat pipe	热管	Règuǎn	
Heat resistant fiber	耐热光纤	Nàirè guāngxiān	
Heat sink	散热器	Sànrèqì	
Heat stripping tool (FOC)	热剥离工具	Rè bōlí gōngjù	
Heat temperature sensor	热温度传感器	Rè wēndù chuángǎnqì	HTS
Heat transfer fluid (semiconductor mfg)	热传导液	Rèchuándǎo yè	
Heating ventilation air conditioning	暖通空调	Nuǎn tōng kōngtiáo	HVAC
Height-finding radar	测高雷达	Cègāo léidá	
Heisenberg uncertainty principle (physics, math/crypto.)	海森伯格测不准原理	Hǎi-sēn-bó-gé cèbuzhǔn yuánlǐ	
Helical antenna	螺线天线	Luóxiàn tiānxiàn	
Helical antenna	螺旋型天线	Luóxuán-xíng tiānxiàn	HA
Helium-cadmium (He-Cd) laser	氦镉激光	Hài-gé jīguāng	
Helium-neon (He-Ne) laser	氦氖激光	Hài-nǎi jīguāng	
Hell system (for teleprinting)	海尔系统	Hǎi'ěr xìtǒng	
Hello packet	呼叫数据包	Hūjiào shùjù bāo	
Hello protocol	呼叫协议	Hūjiào xiéyì	
Help desk software	帮助台软件	Bāngzhùtái ruǎnjiàn	
Help file	帮助文件	Bāngzhù wénjiàn	
Helper address	辅助地址	Fǔzhù dìzhǐ	
Henkel Chemical Products Corp. (German company)	汉高化学物品公司	Hàn-gāo huàxué wùpǐn gōngsī	
Henry (unit of inductance)	亨利	Hēnglì	H
Hercules graphic adapter	大力士监控卡	Dàlìshì jiānkòng kǎ	
Herd effect	群聚	Qúnjù	
Hermetic seal	密封接头	Mìfēng jiētóu	
Hermetic window	密封窗	Mìfēng chuāng	
Hertzian electric dipole	赫兹电偶极子	Hè-zī diàn'ǒujízǐ	
Hertzian magnetic dipole	赫兹磁偶极子	Hè-zī cí'ǒujízi	
Hertzian waves	赫兹波	Hè-zī bō	
Heterochronous	异步的	Yìbùde	
Heterodyne amplifier	外差放大器	Wàichāi fàngdàqì	HA
Heterodyne reception	外差式接收	Wàichāishì jiēshōu	
Heterodyne tracking	外差跟踪	Wàichāi gēnzōng	
Heterogeneity	异构性	Yìgòuxìng	
Heterogeneous	异构	Yìgòu	
Heterogeneous data	异类数据	Yìlèi shùjù	
Heterogeneous frequency diplex	异波长双工	Yìbōcháng shuānggōng	
Heterogeneous multiplex	异类复用	Yìlèi fùyòng	
Heterogeneous nucleating thermochemical reaction (FOC mfg)	非均匀成核热化学反应	Fēijūnyún chénghé rèhuàxué fǎnyìng	HNTD
Heterogenous environment	异构环境	Yìgòu huánjìng	

Heterogenous network	异构网络	Yìgòu wǎngluò	
Heuristic repetitive reasoning	启发式反复的推理	Qǐfā-shì fǎnfùde tuīlǐ	
Heuristic search procedure	启发式搜索过程	Qǐfā-shì sōusuǒ guòchéng	
Heuristics	启发	Qǐfā	
Hewlett-Packard Corp. (US company)	惠普有限公司	Huì-pǔ yǒuxiàn gōngsī	HP
Hexadecimal	十六进制	Shíliùjìnzhì	
Hexadecimal	十六进制的	Shíliùjìnzhìde	H
Hexadecimal notation	十六进制记数法	Shíliùjìnzhì jìshù fǎ	
Hexadecimal symbolic loader	十六进制符号装入程序	Shíliùjìnzhì fúhào zhuāngrù chéngxù	HDLR
Hextree	六叉树	Liùchā shù	
Hidden file	隐含文件	Yǐnhán wénjiàn	
Hidden file attributes	隐含文件属性	Yǐnhán wénjiàn shǔxìng	
Hidden line	隐蔽线	Yǐnbì xiàn	
Hidden line removal	隐蔽线消除	Yǐnbì xiàn xiāochú	
Hidden Markovian model	隐马尔科夫模型	Yǐn mǎ-ěr-kē-fū móxíng	HMM
Hidden neuron	隐层神经元	Yǐncéng shénjīngyuán	
Hidden surface removal	隐蔽面消除	Yǐnbì miàn xiāochú	
Hidden text (WP command)	隐藏文字	Yǐncáng wénzì	
Hide conical-scan	隐蔽锥扫	Yǐnbì zhuī sǎo	
Hierarchical abstract computer	分级抽象计算机	Fēnjí chōuxiàng jìsuànjī	HAC
Hierarchical cell structure	分层小区结构	Fēncéng xiǎoqū jiégòu	HCS
Hierarchical cell structure	分层小区技术	Fēncéng xiǎoqū jìshù	HCS
Hierarchical classification	分层分类	Fēncéng fēnlèi	
Hierarchical communications architecture	分层通信结构	Fēncéng tōngxìn jiégòu	
Hierarchical control	分级控制	Fēnjí kòngzhì	
Hierarchical data	层次式数据	Céngcì shì shùjù	
Hierarchical data	阶层式数据	Jiēcéng-shì shùjù	
Hierarchical data structure	层次数据结构	Céngcì shùjù jiégòu	
Hierarchical database	层次数据库	Céngcì shùjùkù	
Hierarchical direct access method	分级直接存取法	Fēnjí zhíjiē cúnqǔ fǎ	HDAM
Hierarchical fair service curve	优先级的公平服务曲线	Yōuxiān jíde gōngping fúwù qūxiàn	H-FSC
Hierarchical indexed sequential access method	分级编址按序存取法	Fēnjí biānzhǐ ànxù cúnqǔ fǎ	HISAM
Hierarchical network	分级递阶网路	Fēnjí dìjiē wǎnglù	
Hierarchical network architecture	分级网络结构	Fēnjí wǎngluò jiégòu	HNA
Hierarchical patch dynamics	等级嵌块动态	Děngjí qiànkuài dòngtài	
Hierarchical restart	分级再启动	Fēnjí zàiqǐdòng	
Hierarchical scalable reliable multicast	层次化可扩展可靠组播	Céngcìhuà kěkuòzhǎn kěkào zǔbō	HSRM
Hierarchical star topology	分层星形拓扑	Fēncéng xīngxíng tuòpū	
Hierarchical structure	分级结构	Fēnjí jiégòu	
Hierarchically synchronized network	分级同步网络	Fēnjí tóngbù wǎngluò	HSN
Hierarchy	层次结构	Céngcì jiégòu	
Hierarchy	继承体系	Jìchéng tǐxì	
Hierarchy fault tree analysis	层次故障树分析	Céngcì gùzhàng shù fēnxī	
Hierarchy system	分级系统	Fēnjí xìtǒng	
High altitude large optics	极高大型光学计划	Jígāo dà-xíng guāngxué jìhuà	HALO
High altitude platform station	平流层高空气艇平台	Píngliúcéng gāokōng qìtǐng píngtái	HAPS

High availability cluster multi-processor	高可用集群多处理机	Gāokěyòng jíqún duō chǔlǐjī	HACMP
High bit rate DSL	高比特率数字订阅线路	Gāobǐtèlǜ shùzì dìngyuè xiànlù	HDSL
High bit-rate digital subscriber line	高比特率数字用户线	Gāobǐtèlǜ shùzì yònghù xiàn	HDSL
High bit-rate digital subscriber line	高速数字用户回路	Gāosù shùzì yònghù huílù	HDSL
High capacity IPC back panel	高容量 IPC 后面板	Gāoróngliàng IPC hòumian bǎn	HIBP
High capacity IPC processor	高容量 IPC 处理器	Gāoróngliàng IPC chǔlǐqì	BHIP
High capacity mobile telephone system (Japan)	大容量移动电话系统	Dàróngliàng yídòng diànhuà xìtǒng	HCMTS
High capacity trunk radio	高容量干线无线电	Gāoróngliàng gànxiàn wúxiàndiàn	HCTR
High capacity trunk radio	高容量中继无线电	Gāoróngliàng zhōngjì wúxiàndiàn	HCTR
High data-rate digital subscriber line	高速数字用户线	Gāosù shùzì yònghù xiàn	HDSL
High definition compatible digital	高密兼容数码	Gāomì jiānróng shùmǎ	HDCD
High definition television	高密电视	Gāomì diànshì	HDTV
High definition television	高清晰度电视	Gāoqīngxīdù diànshì	HDTV
High definition TV	高分辦率电视	Gāofēnbànlǜ diànshì	HDTV
High density	高密	Gāomì	HD
High density	高密度	Gāomìdù	HD
High density binary-3	高密度二进制 3 型码	Gāomìdù èrjìnzhì san xíng mǎ	HDB3
High density bipolar coding	高密度双极性码	Gāomìdù shuāngjíxìng mǎ	HDB
High density complementary metal oxide semiconductor (CMOS)	高密度互补金属氧化物半导体	Gāomìdù hùbǔ jīnshǔ yǎnghuàwù bàndǎotǐ	HCMOS
High density data	高密度数据	Gāomìdù shuju	HDD
High density data system	高密度数据系统	Gāomìdù shujù xìtǒng	HDDS
High density fixed service	高密度固定业务	Gāomìdù gùdìng yèwù	HDFS
High density polyethylene	高密聚乙烯	Gāomì jùyǐxī	HDPE
High earth orbit	高地球轨道	Gāo dìqiú guǐdào	HEO
High electron mobility transistor	高电子迁移率晶体管	Gāo diànzǐ qiānyílǜ jīngtǐguǎn	HEMT
High end	高端	Gāoduān	
High fiber count cable	大芯数光缆	Dàxīnshù guānglǎn	
High fidelity	高保真度	Gāobǎozhēndù	HIFI
High fidelity amplitude modulation	高保真度调幅	Gāobǎozhēndù tiáofú	HIFAM
High frequency	高频	Gāopín	HF
High frequency amplifier	高频放大器	Gāopín fàngdàqì	HFA
High frequency boost	高频提升	Gāopín tíshēng	
High frequency data link	高频数据链	Gāopín shùjù liàn	HFDL
High frequency gain control	高频增益控制	Gāopín zēngyì kòngzhì	
High frequency repeater distribution frame	高频中继配线架	Gāopín zhōngjì pèixiànjià	HFRDF
High frequency transmitting frequency deviation	高频制频率时的发射频偏	Gāopínzhì pínlǜshíde fāshè pínpiān	
High gain amplifier	高增益放大器	Gāozēngyì fàngdàqì	HGA
High gain power amplifier board	高增益功放板	Gāozēngyì gōngfàng bǎn	HPA
High Ge-doped optical fiber	高掺锗光纤	Gāo chānzhě guāngxiān	
High integrated bus	高集成总线	Gāojíchéng zǒngxiàn	HIB
High layer compatibility	高层兼容性	Gāocéng jiānróngxìng	HLC
High layer function	高层功能	Gāocéng gōngnéng	HLF
High layer uniformity	高层一致性	Gāocéng yīzhìxìng	
High level data control	高级数据控制	Gāojí shùjù kòngzhì	HLDC
High level data link channel	高级数据链路通道	Gāojí shùjù liànlù tōngdào	HDLC

English	Chinese	Pinyin	Abbreviation
High level data link control	高阶数据链路（连接）控制	Gāojiē shùjù liànlù (liánjiē) kòngzhì	HDLC
High level data link control (HDLC) procedure	高级数据链路控制规程	Gāojí shùjù liànlù kòngzhì guīchéng	
High level interface request	高级接口请求	Gāojí jiēkǒu qǐngqiú	HLIR
High mass soldering (semiconductor mfg)	大量焊	Dàliàng hàn	
High Mobility Multi-purpose Wheeled Vehicle (US military vehicle popularly called Humvee)	高机动多用途轮试车	Gāojīdòng duōyòngtú lúnshìchē	HMMWV
High modulus glass fiber	高模数玻璃纤维	Gāomóshù bōli xiānwéi	HMGF
High order, higher order	高阶	Gāojiē	HO
High pass filter	高通滤波器	Gāotōng lǜbōqì	HPF
High performance communications adapter	高性能通信适配器	Gāoxìngnéng tōngxìn shìpèiqì	HPCA
High performance computing and communication	高性能计算和通信	Gāoxìngnéng jìsuàn hé tōngxìn	HPCC
High performance European radio LAN	欧洲高性能无线 LAN	Oūzhōu gāoxìngnéng wúxiàn LAN	HIPERLAN
High performance optical cable connector	高性能光缆连接器	Gāoxìngnéng guānglǎn liánjiēqì	
High performance optical fiber connector	高性能光纤连接器	Gāoxìngnéng guāngxiān liánjiēqì	
High performance parallel interface	高性能并行接口	Gāoxìngnéng bìngxíng jiēkǒu	HIPPI
High performance server	高性能服务器	Gāoxìngnéng fúwùqì	HPS
High power amplifier block	高功率放大器	Gāogōnglǜ fàngdàqì	HPAB
High power amplifier unit	高功率放大单元	Gāogōnglǜ fàngdà dānyuán	HPAU
High power duplexer unit	高功率耦合器	Gāogōnglǜ ǒuhéqì	HPDU
High power klystron	大功率速调管	Dàgōnglǜ sùtiáoguǎn	HPK
High power microwave assembly	大功率微波部件	Dàgōnglǜ wēibō bùjiàn	HPMA
High quality voice	高保真语音	Gāobǎozhēn yǔyīn	HV
High resolution (semiconductor mfg)	高准确性	Gāozhǔnquèxìng	
High resolution graphics	高解像	Gāojiě xiàng	
High resolution graphics	高解析图像	Gāojiěxī túxiàng	
High resolution visible image system	高分辨率可见光影像系统	Gāofēnbiànlǜ kějiàn guāng yǐngxiàng xìtǒng	HRVIS
High resolution X-ray inspection system (semiconductor mfg)	高解析 X 射线检测系统	Gāojiěxī X shèxiàn jiǎncè xìtǒng	
High speed downlink packet access	高速下行链路分组接入	Gāosù xiàxíng liànlù fēnzǔ jiērù	HSDPA
High speed international packet switching	国际通信网络的高速分组交换	Guójì tōngxìn wǎngluòde gāosù fēnzǔ jiāohuàn	HIPS
High temperature high humidity biased testing	高温高湿偏置试验	Gāowēn gāoshī piānzhì shìyàn	HHBT
High temperature nitrogen soldering (semiconductor mfg)	高温氮焊	Gāowēn dàn hàn	
High temperature power burn-in	高温功率老化	Gāowēn gōnglǜ lǎohuà	
High temperature soldering (semiconductor mfg)	高温焊	Gāowēn hàn	
High temperature superconductor filter	高温超导过滤波器	Gāowēn chāodǎoguò lǜbōqì	
High temperature test	高温试验	Gāowēn shìyàn	
High terrain	山区	Shānqū	HT
High thermal, low profile, plastic ball grid array	高耐热、轻薄型塑胶球状矩阵封装	Gāonàirè、qīngbó-xíng sùjiāo qiúzhuàng jǔzhèn fēngzhuāng	HL-PBGA
High threshold logic	高阈值逻辑电路	Gāo yù zhí luójidiànlù	HTL
High triangle count (video)	复杂三角形计数	Fùzá sānjiǎoxíng jìshù	
High usage inter-toll trunk	高利用率长途台间中继线	Gāolìyòng lǜ chángtútái-jiān zhōngjìxiàn	HUT
High voltage delay-time protection circuit	高压延时保护电路	Gāoyā yánshí bǎohù diànlù	
High voltage electric power equipment	高压电力设备	Gāoyā diànlì shèbèi	
High voltage technique	高电压技术	Gāodiànyā jìshù	

High-angle ray	高波	Gāobō	
High-bit-rate digital subscriber link	高比特数字用户链路	Gāobǐtè shùzì yònghù liànlù	HDSL
High-capacity floppy disk	高容量软盘	Gāoróngliàng ruǎnpán	HiFD
High-data-rate digital subscriber line	高数据速率数字用户线	Gāoshùjùsùlǜ shùzì yònghù xiàn	HDSL
Higher mode	高次型	Gāocì xíng	
Higher order assembler	高阶组装器	Gāojiē zǔzhuāngqì	HOA
Higher order connection supervision	高阶连接监控	Gāojiē liánjiē jiānkòng	HCS
Higher order connection supervision	高阶连接监视	Gāojiē liánjiē jiānshì	HCS
Higher order interface	高阶接口	Gāojiē jiēkǒu	HOI
Higher order path	高阶通道	Gāojiē tōngdào	HP
Higher order path access point identifier	高阶通道接入点标识符	Gāojiē tōngdào jiērùdiǎn biāozhì fú	HOAPID
Higher order path adaptation	高阶通道适配	Gāojiē tōngdào shìpèi	HPA
Higher order path connection	高阶通道连接	Gāojiē tōngdào liánjiē	HPC
Higher order path layer	高阶通道层	Gāojiē tōngdào céng	HOPL
Higher order path network connection	高阶通道网络连接	Gāojiē tōngdào wǎngluò liánjiē	HOP NC
Higher order path overhead	高阶通道开销	Gāojiē tōngdào kāixiao	HPOH
Higher order path overhead monitor	高阶通道开销监视	Gāojiē tōngdào kāixiao jiānshì	HPOM
Higher order path payload label mismatch	高阶通道净荷标记失配	Gāojiē tōngdào jìnghé biāojì shīpèi	HP-PLM
Higher order path protection	高阶通道保护	Gāojiē tōngdào bǎohù	HPP
Higher order path remote defect indication	高阶通道远端缺陷指示	Gāojiē tōngdào yuǎnduān quēxiàn zhǐshì	HP-RDI
Higher order path remote error indication	高阶通道远端误码指示	Gāojiē tōngdào yuǎnduān wùmǎ zhǐshì	HP-REI
Higher order path supervision unequipped termination	高阶通道监控未装装载终	Gāojiē tōngdào jiānkòng wèizhuāng zhuāngzài zhōng	HSUT
Higher order path supervisory unequipped termination	高阶通道监控未装载终端	Gāojiē tōngdào jiānkòng wèizhuāngzài zhōngduān	HSUT
Higher order path tandem connection adaptation	高阶通道串联连接适配	Gāojiē tōngdào chuànlián liánjiē shìpèi	HTCA
Higher order path tandem connection monitor	高阶通道串联连接监视	Gāojiē tōngdào chuànlián liánjiē jiānshì	HTCM
Higher order path tandem connection termination	高阶通道串联连接终端	Gāojiē tōngdào chuànlián liánjiē zhōngduān	HTCT
Higher order path termination	高阶通道终端	Gāojiē tōngdào zhōngduān	HPT
Higher order path trace identification mismatch	高阶通道路踪识别失配	Gāojiē tōngdào lùzōng shíbié shīpèi	HP-TIM
Higher order path unequipped	高阶通道未装载	Gāojiē tōngdào wèizhuāngzài	HP-UNEQ
Higher order path-remote error indication	高阶通道远端错误指示	Gāojiē tōngdào yuǎnduān cuòwù zhǐshì	HP-REI
Higher order tandem connection monitor	高阶通道串联连接监控	Gāojiē tōngdào chuànlián liánjiē jiānkòng	HO-TCM
Higher order virtual container	高阶虚容器	Gāojiē xūróngqì	HOVC
Higher-order mode	高次模	Gāocì mó	
Highest voltage for equipment	设备最高电压	Shèbèi zuìgāo diànyā	
High-level architecture	高级体系结构	Gāojí tǐxì jiégòu	HLA
High-level data link control	高层数据链路控制	Gāocéng shùjù liànlù kòngzhì	HDLC
High-level data link control	高级数据链脚控制规程	Gāojí shùjù liànchí kòngzhì guīchéng	HDLC
High-level data link control	高级数据链路控制	Gāojí shùjù liànlù kòngzhì	HDLC
High-level data link control	高级数据链路控制规程	Gāojí shùjù liànlù kòngzhì guīchéng	HDLC
High-level data link control protocol	高级数据链路控制协议	Gāojí shùjù liànlù kòngzhì xiéyì	HDLC
High-level entity management system	高级实体管理系统	Gāojí shítǐ guǎnlǐ xìtǒng	HEMS
High-level language	高级语言	Gāojí yǔyán	
High-level link control	高层链路控制	Gāocéng liànlù kòngzhì	HDLC
High-level modulation	高电平调制	Gāodiànpíng tiáozhì	
High-level output current	高电平输出电流	Gāodiànpíng shūchū diànliú	

High-level output voltage	高电平输出电压	Gāodiànpíng shūchū diànyā	
High-level path receive defect indicator	高阶通道接收缺陷指示	Gāojiē tōngdào jiēshōu quēxiàn zhǐshì	HP-RDI
High-level service control point	高等级业务控制点	Gāoděngjí yèwù kòngzhìdiǎn	HSCP
High-level signal transfer point	高级信令转换点	Gāojí xìnlìng zhuǎnhuàn diǎn	HSTP
High-level signaling transfer point	高级信令转接点	Gāojí xìnlìng zhuǎnjiēdiǎn	HSTP
Highlight	突出显示	Tūchū xiǎnshì	
Highly efficient router operating system	高性能路由器操作系统	Gāoxìngnéng lùyóuqì cāozuò xìtǒng	HEROS
Highly elliptical orbit	高椭圆轨道（高轨）	Gāotuǒyuán guǐdào (gāo guǐ)	HEO
Highly elliptical orbit	椭圆轨道	Tuǒyuán guǐdào	HEO
High-performance common channel signaling module	高性能公共信道模块	Gāoxìngnéng gōnggòng xìndào mókuài	
High-performance workstation	高性能工作站	Gāoxìngnéng gōngzuòzhàn	HPW
High-power modulation	高功率调制	Gāogōnglǜ tiáozhì	
High-speed C bus service unit	高速 C 总线服务单元	Gāosù C zǒngxiàn fúwù dānyuán	HCBS
High-speed cache	高速缓存器	Gāosù huǎncúnqì	
High-speed cache aging	高速缓存老化数据清除	Gāosù huǎncún lǎohuà shùjù qīngchú	
High-speed cache controller	高速缓冲存储控制器	Gāosù huǎnchōng cúnchǔ kòngzhìqì	
High-speed cache controller	高速缓存控制器	Gāosù huǎncún kòngzhìqì	
High-speed cache memory	高速缓冲存储器	Gāosù huǎnchōng cúnchǔqì	
High-speed circuit switched data	高速电路交换数据	Gāosù diànlù jiāohuàn shùjù	HSCSD
High-speed circuit switched data	高速率电路交换数据	Gāosùlǜ diànlù jiāohuàn shùjù	HCSD
High-speed data	高速数据	Gāosù shùjù	HSD
High-speed data link control	高速数据链路规程	Gāosù shùjù liànlù guīchéng	HDLC
High-speed data link control	高速数据链路控制	Gāosù shùjù liànlù kòngzhì	HDLC
High-speed digital switch	高速数字交换机	Gāosù shùzì jiāohuànjī	HDS
High-speed downlink packet access	高速下行包数据接入	Gāosù xiàxíng bāo shùjù jiērù	HSPDA
High-speed downlink packet access	高速下行分组接入	Gāosù xiàxíng fēnzǔ jiērù	HSDPA
High-speed IPC node board assembly	高速 IPC 节点集成板	Gāosù IPC jiédiǎn jíchéngbǎn	HINA
High-speed IPC processor assembly	高速 IPC 处理器集成板	Gāosù IPC chǔlǐqì jíchéngbǎn	HIPA
High-speed local area network	高速局域网	Gāosù júyùwǎng	HSLAN
High-speed multi-layer protocol	高速多层协议	Gāosù duō céng xiéyì	H-MLP
High-speed pager coding standard (in the PRC)	高速寻呼编码体制	Gāosù xúnhū biānmǎ tǐzhì	FLEX
High-speed serial backplane	高速背板	Gāosù bèibǎn	
High-speed serial data connection	高速串行数据连接	Gāosù chuànháng shùjù liánjiē	HSSDC
High-speed serial interface	高速串行接口	Gāosù chuànháng jiēkǒu	HSSI
High-speed-rate data interface board	超速率数据接口板	Chāosùlǜ shùjù jiēkǒu bǎn	HSL
High-video pass circuit	极窄视频脉冲通过电路	Jízhǎi shìpín màichōng tōngguò diànlù	HVP
Highway	高速公路	Gāosù gōnglù	HW
Highway addressable remote transducer	可寻址远程传感器高速通道	Kěxúnzhǐ yuǎnchéng chuángǎnqì gāosù tōngdào	HART
Highway addressable remote transducer (used in process controls)	可寻址远程传感器数据公路	Kěxúnzhǐ yuǎnchéng chuángǎnqì shùjù gōnglù	HART
Highway traffic control system	公路交通管制系统	Gōnglù jiāotōng guǎnzhì xìtǒng	
Hilbert array	希尔伯特数组	Xī-ěr-bó-tè shùzǔ	
Hilbert curve	希尔伯特曲线	Xī-ěr-bó-tè qūxiàn	
Hilbert transform	希尔伯特变换	Xī-ěr-bó-tè biànhuàn	
Hiss	嘘音	Xūyīn	

Histogram	直方图	Zhífāngtú	
Histogram adjust	直方图调整	Zhífāngtú tiáozhěng	
Histogram equalization	直方图均衡化	Zhífāngtú jūnhénghuà	
Histogram normalization	直方图正态化	Zhífāngtú zhèngtàihuà	
Histogram specification	直方图规定化	Zhífāngtú guīdìnghuà	
Hitachi (Japanese company)	日立	Rìlì	
Hits (number of)	点击数	Diǎnjī shù	
Hits, visits (on a web page)	阅读次数	Yuèdú cìshù	
Hodograph curve	速端曲线	Sùduān qūxiàn	
Hogg horn antenna	喇叭型天线	Lǎba-xíng tiānxiàn	HA
Hoghorn antenna	帚形喇叭天线	Zhǒuxíng lǎba tiānxiàn	
Hold	保持	Bǎochí	
Hold acknowledge	保证证实	Bǎozhèng zhèngshí	
Hold off time	挂起时间	Guàqǐ shíjiān	HO
Hold off time	拖延时间	Tuōyán shíjiān	
Holddown	阻持	Zǔchí	
Hold-in range	同步带	Tóngbù dài	
Hold-off time (SDH)	保护等候时间	Bǎohù děnghòu shíjiān	
Holdover mode	保持模式	Bǎochí móshì	Ho
Holdover mode	保持状态	Bǎochí zhuàngtài	Ho
Hole	洞	Dòng	
Hole-type directional coupler	孔型定向耦合器	Kǒngxíng dìngxiàng ǒuhéq	
Hollerith code	何勒内斯代码	Hé-lè-nèi-sī dàimǎ	
Hollow fiber	空心光纤	Kōngxīn guāngxiān	
Hologram	浮影图	Fúyǐngtú	
Hologram	全息图	Quánxītú	
Holographic display	全像显示器	Quánxiàng xiǎnshìqì	
Holographic film	全像底片	Quánxiàng dǐpiàn	
Holographic filter	全像滤光镜	Quánxiàng lǜguāngjìng	
Holographic mechanical optical scanner	全像方式机械光扫瞄器	Quánxiàng fāngshì jīxiè guāng sǎomiáoqì	
Holographic plate	全像感光板	Quánxiàng gǎnguāng bǎn	
Holographic storage	全息存储	Quánxī cúnchǔ	
Holography	全息	Quánxī	
Home address	归属地址	Guīshǔ dìzhǐ	HA
Home agent	本地代理	Běndì dàilǐ	HA
Home agent	归属代理	Guīshǔ dàilǐ	HA
Home agent	住地代理	Zhùdì dàilǐ	
Home area	归属区	Guīshǔqū	
Home automation	家用电器智能化	Jiāyòng diànqì zhìnénghuà	HA
Home directory	宿主目录	Sùzhǔ mùlù	
Home environment	归属环境	Guīshǔ huánjìng	HE
Home environment value added service provider	归属环境附加值业务提供者	Guīshǔ huánjìng fùjiāzhí yèwù tígòngzhě	HE-VASP
Home key	本位键	Běnwèi jiàn	
Home location register	归属寄存位置寄存器	Guīshǔ jìcún wèizhì jìcúnqì	HLR
Home location register	归属位置寄存器	Guīshǔ wèizhì jìcúnqì	HLR

Home location register	归属用户位置寄存器	Guīshǔ yònghù wèizhì jìcúnqì	HLR
Home location register	原籍位置登记器	Yuánjí wèizhì dēngjìqì	HLR
Home location register	原籍位置注册处	Yuánjí wèizhì zhùcèchù	HLR
Home mobile services switching center	原籍移动无线局	Yuánjí yídòng wúxiàn jú	HMSC
Home mobile subscriber	原籍移动用户	Yuánjí yídòng yònghù	
Home page	主页	Zhǔ yè	
Home page	主页	Zhǔyè	
Home Phoneline Networking Alliance	家庭电话线网络集团	Jiātíng diànhuà xiàn wǎngluò jítuán	HPNA
Home Phoneline Networking Alliance	家用电话线网络联盟	Jiāyòng diànhuà xiàn wǎngluò liánméng	HPNA
Home PLMN	归属 PLMN	Guīshǔ PLMN	HPLMN
Home position	初始位置	Chūshǐ wèizhì	
Home position	返回位置	Fǎnhuí wèizhì	
Home public land mobile network	归属公用陆地移动通信网	Guīshǔ gōngyòng lùdì yídòng tōngxìnwǎng	HPLMN
Home Radio Frequency Working Group	家用射频工作组	Jiāyòng shèpín gōngzuòzǔ	HRFWG
Home rule	地方自治	Dìfāng zìzhì	
Home subscriber server	本地用户服务器	Běndì yònghù fúwùqì	HSS
Home subscriber server	归属用户服务器	Guīshǔ yònghù fúwùqì	HSS
Home subscriber server	家庭用户服务器	Jiātíng yònghù fúwùqì	HSS
Home unit	归属单元	Guīshǔ dānyuán	HU
Home unit	家庭单元	Jiātíng dānyuán	HU
Homenet	家庭网络	Jiātíng wǎngluò	HN
Homing	返回	Fǎnhuí	
Homochronous	恒步的	Héngbùde	
Homochronous	类同步的	Lèi tóngbùde	
Homochronous	类同步的	Lèitóngbùde	
Homodyne	零差检测	Língchà jiǎncè	
Homodyne reception	零差式接收	Língchàshì jiēshōu	
Homogeneity analysis	同齐性分析	Tóngqíxìng fēnxī	
Homogeneous	同构	Tónggòu	
Homogeneous data	同类数据	Tónglèi shùjù	
Homogeneous multiplex	同类复用	Tónglèi fùyòng	
Homologation	一致化	Yīzhì huà	
Homolosine map project (GIS)	等积地图投影	Děngjī dìtú tóuyǐng	
Homomorphic signal processing	同态信号处理	Tóngtài xìnhào chǔlǐ	
Homomorphism	同质	Tóngzhì	
Honeynet (computer security slang)	蜜网	Mìwǎng	
Honeypot (computer security slang)	蜜罐	Mìguàn	
Hong Kong Internet Exchange	香港因特网交换中心	Xiānggǎng Yīntèwǎng jiāohuàn zhōngxīn	HKIX
Hong Kong Star Internet Service	香港星光国际网络服务公司	Xiānggǎng xīngguāng guójì wǎngluò fúwù gōngsī	
Hook	钩子	Gōuzi	
Hook-up wire	安装线	Ānzhuāng xiàn	
Hop	步跳	Bùtiào	
Hop (noun)	跃点	Yuèdiǎn	
Hop count	跳计数	Tiào jìshù	
Hop count	跳数	Tiào shù	

Hop counter (in SS7)	跳计数器	Tiào jìshùqì	
Hop distance	跳距	Tiàojù	
Hop-by-hop	逐跳式	Zhútiàoshì	
Hop-by-hop route	逐跳路由	Zhútiào lùyóu	
Hopping sequence number	跳频序列号码	Tiàopín xùliè hàomǎ	HSN
Horizontal and vertical parity check code	二维奇偶验码	Èrwéi jī'ǒu yàn mǎ	
Horizontal cabling	水平电缆	Shuǐpíng diànlǎn	
Horizontal control network	水平控制网	Shuǐpíng kòngzhì wǎng	
Horizontal cross connect	水平交叉连接	Shuǐpíng jiāochā liánjiē	HCC
Horizontal deflection	水平偏转	Shuǐpíng piānzhuǎn	HD
Horizontal directivity pattern	水平方向性图	Shuǐpíng fāngxiàngxìng tú	
Horizontal length	水平长度	Shuǐpíng chángdù	HL
Horizontal magnetic dipole	水平磁偶极子	Shuǐpíng cí ǒujízi	HMD
Horizontal optical cabling	水平光缆	Shuǐpíng guānglǎn	
Horizontal partitioning	水平分区	Shuǐpíng fēnqū	
Horizontal plane	水平面	Shuǐpíngmiàn	
Horizontal plane bandWidth	水平面波束宽度	Shuǐpíngmiàn bōshù kuāndù	HPBW
Horizontal redundancy check	横向冗余检验	Héngxiàng rǒngyú jiǎnyàn	HRC
Horizontal scan frequency	水平扫描频率	Shuǐpíng sǎomiáo pínlǜ	
Horizontal scrollbar	横卷动干	Héng juǎndòng gān	
Horizontal tabulation	横向制表	Héngxiàng zhìbiǎo	HT
Horizontal tabulation	纵向制表	Zòngxiàng zhìbiǎo	
Horizontally polarized field vector	水平极化场矢量	Shuǐpíng jíhuà cháng shǐliàng	
Horn antenna	喇叭天线	Lǎba tiānxiàn	
Horn parabolic reflector antenna	喇叭抛物反射面天线	Lǎba pāowù fǎnshèmiàn tiānxiàn	
Horn reflector antenna	喇叭反射器天线	Lǎba fǎnshè qì tiānxiàn	
Host (application program)	宿主(应用程序)	Sùzhǔ (yìngyòng chéngxù)	
Host bus adapter	主机总线适配器	Zhǔjī zǒngxiàn shìpèiqì	HBA
Host controller interface	主控制器接口	Zhǔ kòngzhìqì jiēkǒu	HCI
Host controller interface	主机控制接口	Zhǔjī kòngzhì jiēkǒu	HCI
Host digital terminal	局用数字终端	Jú-yòng shùzì zhōngduān	HDT
Host element	宿主单元	Sùzhǔ dānyuán	
Host exchange	母局	Mǔjú	
Host exchange	主交换机	Zhǔ jiāohuànjī	
Host machine	宿主机	Sùzhǔ jī	
Host monitoring protocol	宿主机监视协议	Sùzhǔ jī jiānshì xiéyì	HMP
Host service provider	宿主业务提供商	Sùzhǔ yèwù tígōng shāng	HSP
Host signal	主信号	Zhǔ xìnhào	
Host station	主站	Zhǔ zhàn	HST
Host vulnerability scanner	主机漏洞扫描器	Zhǔjī lòudòng sǎomiáoqì	
Host, master (of networked computers)	主机	Zhǔjī	
Host-based IDS	基于主机的 IDS	Jīyú zhǔjīde IDS	
Hosting	托管	Tuōguǎn	
Hot air leveller (PCB manufacturing)	热风整平机	Rèfēng zhěng píng jī	HAL
Hot data replication	热数据复制	Rè shùjù fùzhì	
Hot interconnect	热互连	Rè hùlián	

Hot key	热键	Rè jiàn	
Hot line service	热线服务	Rèxiàn fúwù	
Hot mirror	热镜	Rè jìng	
Hot news	热闻	Rè wén	
Hot spare	热备份	Rè bèifèn	
Hot standby	热备用	Rè bèiyòng	
Hot standby routing protocol	热备份路由协议	Rè bèifèn lùyóu xiéyì	HSRP
Hot standby routing protocol	热备份路由器协议	Rè bèifèn lùyóuqì xiéyì	HSRP
Hot swappable	热替换	Rè tìhuan	
Hot swapping	热存储交换	Rè cúnchǔ jiāohuàn	
Hot water supply	热水供应系统	Rèshuǐ gōngyìng xìtǒng	HWS
Hot wire	火线	Huǒxiàn	
HotJava © (Sun Microsystems)	热爪哇	Rè Zhǎo-wā	
Hotsite	热门网站	Rèmén wǎngzhàn	
Hot-swapping	热交换	Rè jiāohuàn	
Hotwired (Web magazine)	热连线	Rè liánxiàn	
Hourly rate	小时率	Xiǎoshí lǜ	
Howler	嗥鸣器	Háomíngqì	
H-plane corner	H-面弯头	H-miàn wāntóu	
H-plane lens	H 面透镜	H-miàn tòujìng	
H-plane sectoral horn antenna	H 面扇形喇叭天线	H-miàn shànxíng lǎba tiānxiàn	
H-plane T circulator	H 面 T 形环行器	H-miàn T-xíng huánxíngqì	
H-plane Y circulator	H 面 Y 形环行器	H-miàn Y-xíng huánxíngqì	
H-plane Y junction	H-面 Y 形接头	H-miàn Y-xíng jiētóu	
Huawei Integrated Services Optical access Network (trademark)	华为综合业务接入网商标	Huáwéi zōnghé yèwù jiērù wǎng shāngbiāo	HONET
Hub	集线器	Jíxiànqì	HUB
Hub	中转站	Zhōngzhuǎnzhàn	
Hub (station)	中枢站	Zhōngshū zhàn	
Hubbed mode	集中模式	Jízhōng móshì	
Hue	色调	Sèdiào	
Huffman code	霍夫曼编码	Huò-fū-màn biānmǎ	
Huffman run-length encoding	霍夫曼行程编码	Huò-fū-màn xíngchéng biānmǎ	
Huffman tree	哈夫曼树	Hā-fū-màn shù	
Hughes Corp.	休斯公司	Xiū-sī gōngsī	
Hum	哼声	Hēngshēng	
Hum	交流声	Jiāoliúshēng	
Human computer interaction	人机对话	Rén jī duìhuà	HCI
Human factors	人为因素	Rénwéi yīnsù	HF
Human interface device	人机接口设备	Rén jī jiēkǒu shèbèi	HID
Human-machine adaption	人机适配	Rén jī shìpèi	HMA
Humid heat test	湿热试验	Shīrè shìyàn	
Humidty test	湿度试验	Shīdù shìyàn	
Hung system	挂起系统	Guàqǐ xìtǒng	
Hunt group	搜寻组	Sōuxún zǔ	HG
Hunt group	寻找组	Xúnzhǎo zǔ	
Hutchison (HK company)	和记	Hé-jì	

Hutchison Optel Telecom Technology Co. Ltd.	和记奥普泰通信技术有限公司	Hé-jì ào-pǔ-tài tōngxìn jìshù yǒuxiàn gōngsī	
Hutchison Telecom (Hong Kong GSM network operator)	香港和记电讯	Xiānggǎng hé-jì diànxùn	
Hutchison Whampoa (Hong Kong cellular provider)	和记黄埔	Hé-jì Huángpǔ	
Hybird channel assignment	混合信道指配	Hùnhé xìndào zhǐpèi	
Hybrid	混合式	Hùnhé-shì	
Hybrid (2/4-wire conversion -the H in BORSCHT)	混合（2/4 线转换电路）	Hùnhé (2/4-xiàn zhuǎnhuàn diànlù)	
Hybrid analog and digital modulation	混合模拟和数字调制	Hùnhé mónǐ hé shùzì tiáozhì	HADM
Hybrid association rule	混合关联规则	Hùnhé guānlián guīzé	
Hybrid automatic repeat request	混合自动重传	Hùnhé zìdòng chóngchuán	HARQ
Hybrid automatic repeat request	混合自动请求重传	Hùnhé zìdòng qǐngqiú chóngchuán	HARQ
Hybrid automatic test system	混合自动测试系统	Hùnhé zìdòng cèshì xìtǒng	HATS
Hybrid cable	混合电缆	Hùnhé diànlǎn	
Hybrid cable	混合缆	Hùnhé lǎn	
Hybrid cable	综合电缆、光缆	Zōnghé diànlǎn、guānglǎn	
Hybrid cable	综合光缆	Zōnghé guānglǎn	
Hybrid channel assignment	混合信道指配方式	Hùnhé xìndào zhǐpèi fāngshì	HCA
Hybrid coil	混合线圈	Hùnhé xiànquān	
Hybrid combiner	混合瞧型合路器	Hùnhé qiáo-xíng hélùqì	HC/HY-COM
Hybrid combiner board	合路器板	Hélùqì bǎn	HYCOM
Hybrid communication routing	混合通行路由选择	Hùnhé tōngxíng lùyóu xuǎnzé	HCR
Hybrid companding delta modulation	混合压扩增量调制	Hùnhé yākuò zēngliàng tiáozhì	HCDM
Hybrid computer	并合电脑	Bìnghé diànnǎo	
Hybrid coupler	混合耦合器	Hùnhé ǒuhéqì	
Hybrid data structure	混合数据结构	Hùnhé shùjù jiégòu	
Hybrid differential pulse code modulation	混合差动脉码调制	Hùnhé chādòng màimǎ tiáozhì	HDPCM
Hybrid diversity	混合分集	Hùnhé fēnjí	
Hybrid error control	混合差错控制	Hùnhé chācuò kòngzhì	HEC
Hybrid error correction	混合纠错	Hùnhé jiūcuò	HEC
Hybrid error-correcting method	混合救错方式	Hùnhé jiùcuò fāngshì	
Hybrid fiber coax	光纤-同轴电缆混合系统	Guāngxiān –tóngzhóu diànlǎn hùnhé xìtǒng	HFC
Hybrid fiber wireless system	混合光纤无线系统	Hùnhé guāngxiān wúxiàn xìtǒng	HFW
Hybrid fiber/coaxial cable	混合光纤/同轴电缆	Hùnhé guāngxiān/tóngzhóu diànlǎn	HFC
Hybrid fiber-coaxial network	光纤铜轴混合网	Guāngxiān tóngzhóu hùnhé wǎng	HFC
Hybrid integrated circuit	混合集成电路	Hùnhé jíchéng diànlù	
Hybrid interface structure	混合接口结构	Hùnhé jiēkǒu jiégòu	
Hybrid junction	电桥	Diànqiáo	
Hybrid junction	混合接头	Hùnhé jiētóu	
Hybrid load balancing algorithm	混合负载均衡算法	Hùnhé fùzài jūnhéng suànfǎ	HLB
Hybrid mode (in a waveguide)	混合模	Hùnhé mó	
Hybrid mode horn antenna	混合模喇叭天线	Hùnhé mó lǎba tiānxiàn	
Hybrid multiplexed synchronous digital converter	混合多路复用同步数字转换器	Hùnhé duōlù fùyòng tóngbù shùzì zhuǎnhuànqì	HMSDC
Hybrid network	混合网络	Hùnhé wǎngluò	
Hybrid online analytical processing	混合联机分析处理	Hùnhé liánjī fēnxī chǔlǐ	HOLAP

Hybrid optical cable	混合光缆	Hùnhé guānglǎn	
Hybrid optical cable connector	综合式光缆连接器	Zōnghé-shì guānglǎn liánjiēqì	
Hybrid phase locked loop	混合锁相环	Hùnhé suǒxiàng huán	HPLL
Hybrid phase modulation	混合调相	Hùnhé tiáoxiàng	HPM
Hybrid receiver circuit	混合接收电路	Hùnhé jiēshōu diànlù	HRC
Hybrid ring	环行电桥	Huánxíng diànqiáo	
Hybrid ring	混合环	Hùnhé huán	
Hybrid scalability	混合可伸缩性	Hùnhé kě shēnsuōxìng	
Hybrid spread spectrum	混合扩频	Hùnhé kuòpín	
Hybrid T-juntion	混合 T 型接头	Hùnhé T-xíng jiētóu	
Hybrid transformer	混合变量器	Hùnhé biànliàngqì	
Hybrid uni-digit pulse code modulation	混合单数字脉码调制	Hùnhé dānshùzì màimǎ tiáozhì	HU-PCM
Hydraulic amplifier	液压放大器	Yèyā fàngdàqì	
Hydraulic buffer	液压缓冲器	Yèyā huǎnchōngqì	
Hydraulic follow-up unit	液压随动装置	Yèyā suídòng zhuāngzhì	
Hydraulic loading and unloading foot walk	液压式装卸过桥	Yèyā-shì zhuāngxiè guòqiáo	
Hydraulic motor	液压马达	Yèyā mǎdá	
Hydraulic pump	液压泵	Yèyā bèng	
Hydro-acoustic communication system	水声通信系统	Shuǐshēng tōngxìn xìtǒng	
Hydrogen sulfide	硫化氢	Liúhuàqīng	
Hyper terminal (application in Microsoft Windows)	超级终端	Chāojí zhōngduān	
Hyperband	超频道	Chāopíndào	
Hyperbolic radionavigation	双曲线无线电导航	Shuāng qūxiàn wúxiàndiàn dǎoháng	
Hypercard software	超卡软件	Chāokǎ ruǎnjiàn	
Hypercube	超立方体	Chāolìfāngtǐ	
Hyperelliptic curve (cryptology)	超椭圆曲线	Chāotuǒyuán qūxiàn	
Hyperframe	超高帧	Chāogāozhèng	
Hypergraph	超图	Chāotú	
Hypergraph data model	超图数据模型	Chāotú shùjù móxíng	
Hypergraph model	超图模型	Chāotú móxíng	
Hypergraph-based outlier test	基于超图模型的离群点检测方法	Jīyú chāo tú móxíngde líqún diǎn jiǎncè fāngfǎ	HOT
Hyperlink	超级链接	Chāojí liànjiē	
Hyperlink	超联	Chāolián	
Hyperlink	超联结	Chāoliánjié	
Hyperlink	超连接	Chāoliánjiē	
Hypermedia	超媒体	Chāoméitǐ	
Hypermedia intelligent computer-based instruction	基于超媒体的职能计算机辅助教学	Jīyú chāoméitǐde zhínéng jìsuànjī fǔzhù jiàoxué	HICAI
Hypermedia management protocol (in common information model)	超媒体管理协议	Chāoméitǐ guǎnlǐ xiéyì	HMMP
Hypermedia management schema (in common information model)	超媒体管理模式	Chāoméitǐ guǎnlǐ móshì	HMMS
Hypermedia model	超媒体模型	Chāoméitǐ móxíng	
Hypermedia object management (in common information model)	超媒体对象管理	Chāoméitǐ duìxiàng guǎnlǐ	HMOM
Hyperspace	超空间	Chāokōngjiān	
Hyperstable adaptive recursive filter	超稳定自适应递归滤波器	Chāowěndìng zìshìyìng dìguī lǜbōqì	HARF

Hypertext	超文本	Chāowénběn	
Hypertext application	超文本应用程序	Chāowénběn yìngyòng chéngxù	HTA
Hypertext cache protocol	超文本缓存协议	Chāowénběn huǎncún xiéyì	HTCP
Hypertext cursor (WP command)	文字连接光标	Wénzì liánjiē guāngbiāo	
Hypertext markup language	超文本标记语言	Chāowénběn biāojì yǔyán	HTML
Hypertext markup language	超文本标识语言	Chāowénběn biāozhì yǔyán	HTML
Hypertext markup language	超文本组合语言	Chāowénběn zǔhé yǔyán	HTML
Hypertext markup language (in SQL Server)	超文本链接标示语	Chāowénběn liànjiē biāoshì yǔ	HTML
Hypertext transfer protocol	超文本传输协议	Chāowénběn chuánshū xiéyì	HTTP
Hypertext transfer protocol	超文本传送协议	Chāowénběn chuánsòng xiéyì	http
Hypertext transfer protocol server	超文本传送协议服务器	Chāowénběn chuánsòng xiéyì fúwùqì	HTTPS
Hyphen (-)	连字符	Liánzìfú	
Hypothesis testing	假设检验	Jiǎshè jiǎnyàn	
Hypothetical digital reference connection	假设数字参考连接	Jiǎshè shùzì cānkǎo liánjiē	HDRC
Hypothetical reference circuit	假设参考电路	Jiǎshè cānkǎo diànlù	
Hypothetical reference connection	假设参考连接	Jiǎshè cānkǎo liánjiē	HRX
Hypothetical reference digital link	假设参考数字链路	Jiǎshè cānkǎo shùzì liànlù	HRDL
Hypothetical reference digital path	假设参考数字通道	Jiǎshè cānkǎo shùzì tōngdào	HDRP
Hypothetical reference digital section	假设参考数字段	Jiǎshè cānkǎo shùzì duàn	HRDS
Hypothetical reference endpoint	假想参考点	Jiǎxiǎng cānkǎodiǎn	HRE
Hypothetical reference path	假设参考通道	Jiǎshè cānkǎo tōngdào	HRP
Hypsography	测高学	Cègāoxué	
Hypsometric map	地势图	Dìshì tú	
Hypsometric map	分层设色图	Fēncéng shèsè tú	
Hypsometric tending method (GIS)	分层设色法	Fēncéng shèsè fǎ	
Hypsometry	测高法	Cègāofǎ	
HZ code (computer code for Chinese characters)	汉字码	Hànzì mǎ	

I

I column	工字柱	Gōng-zì zhù	
I interface subscriber module	I 接口用户模块	I jiēkǒu yònghù mókuài	
I seek you	网络呼叫器	Wǎngluò hūjiàoqì	ICQ
IBM Corporation	万国商业机器	Wànguó shāngyè jīqì	
ICMP router discovery protocol	ICMP 路由发现协议	ICMP lùyóu fāxiàn xiéyì	IRDP
ICMP router discovery protocol (IETF usage)	ICMP 路由器发现协议	ICMP lùyóuqì fāxiàn xiéyì	IRDP
Icon	图标	Túbiāo	
Icon	图签	Túqiān	
Ideal busy tone multiple access	理想忙音信好多路存取	Lǐxiǎng mángyīn xìnhǎo duōlù cúnqǔ	I-BTMA
Ideal instant	理想瞬时	Lǐxiǎng shùnshí	
Identical synchronization	恒等同步	Héngděng tóngbù	
Identification code	识别码	Shíbié mǎ	
Identification sequence field	识别序列字段	Shíbié xùliè zìduàn	ID SEQ
Identification/Identity	身份标识	Shēnfen biāozhì	ID
Identification/identity, recognition	识别	Shíbié	ID
Identifier	标识	Biāozhì	ID
Identifier	识别器	Shíbiéqì	ID

Identifier (in software)	标识符	Biāozhìfú	
Identifier friend or foe	敌我识别雷达	Díwǒ shíbié léidá	IFF
Identity	标识	Biāozhì	ID
Identity	鉴别号码	Jiànbié hàomǎ	ID
Identity column	标识列	Biāozhì liè	
Identity interception	身分窃取	Shēnfen qièqǔ	
Identity link	标识连接	Biāozhì liánjiē	
Identity property	标识属性	Biāozhì shǔxìng	
Identity request	识别请求	Shíbié qǐngqiú	
Identity-based security policy (IPsec)	基于身份的安全策略	Jīyú shēnfende ānquán cèlüè	
Idle	空闲	Kòngxián	
Idle	闲置	Xiánzhì	
Idle cell	空闲信元	Kòngxián xìnyuán	
Idle channel	空闲信道	Kòngxián xìndào	
Idle channel detection	空闲信道检测	Kòngxián xìndào jiǎncè	
Idle circuit condition	空占电路状态	Kōngzhàn diànlù zhuàngtài	
Idle mode	空闲模式	Kòngxián móshì	
Idle signal identification	空闲信号识别	Kòngxián xìnhào shíbié	ISID
Idle signal multiple access	空线信号多路存取	Kōng xiàn xìnhào duōlù cúnqǔ	ISMA
Idle signal unit	空闲信号系统	Kòngxián xìnhào xìtǒng	IDU
Idle signal unit	闲置信号单元	Xiánzhì xìnhào dānyuán	IDU
Idle state; free state	空闲状态	Kòngxián zhuàngtài	
Idle time	空闲时间	Kòngxián shíjiān	
Idling circuit	空载电路	Kōngzài diànlù	IC
If and only if	当且仅当	Dāng qiě jǐn dāng	
I-LACS Technology Co. Ltd, Chinese maker of milspec laptop computers	艾雷斯科技有限公司	Àiléisī kējì yǒuxiàn gōngsī	
Illegal address error	非法地址错误	Fēifǎ dìzhǐ cuòwù	
Illegal code	非法代码	Fēifǎ dàimǎ	
Illegal parameter message (IPsec TLS)	非法参数消息	Fēifǎ cānshù xiāoxi	
Illumination pattern, illumination diagram	照射图形	Zhàoshè túxíng	
Image analysis	图像分析	Túxiàng fēnxī	
Image antenna	镜像天线	Jìngxiàng tiānxiàn	
Image area	图文区	Túwén qū	
Image area	图像区	Túxiàng qū	
Image catalog	图像目录	Túxiàng mùlù	
Image classification	影像分类	Yǐngxiàng fēnlèi	
Image coding	图像编码	Túxiàng biānmǎ	
Image compression	图像压缩	Túxiàng yāsuō	
Image compression encoding	图像压缩编码	Túxiàng yāsuō biānmǎ	
Image data	影像数据	Yǐngxiàng shùjù	
Image division	影像分割	Yǐngxiàng fēngē	
Image enhancement	影像增强	Yǐngxiàng zēngqiáng	
Image frequency (in superheterodyne reception)	镜像频率	Jìngxiàng pínlǜ	
Image frequency rejection mixer	镜频抑制混频器	Jìngpín yìzhì hùnpínqì	
Image frequency rejection ratio	像频抑制比	Xiàngpín yìzhì bǐ	
Image information	影像信息	Yǐngxiàng xìnxī	

Image integration	影像集成	Yǐngxiàng jíchéng	
Image integrator	影像集成器	Yǐngxiàng jíchéngqì	
Image interpretation	影像判读	Yǐngxiàng pàndú	
Image management	图像管理	Túxiàng guǎnlǐ	
Image matching	影像匹配	Yǐngxiàng pǐpèi	
Image morphology	图像形态学	Túxiàng xíngtàixué	
Image processing	图像处理	Túxiàng chǔlǐ	
Image processing	影像处理	Yǐngxiàng chǔlǐ	
Image processing and pattern recognition	图像处理和模式识别	Túxiàng chǔlǐ hé móshì shíbié	IPPR
Image processing facility	影像处理设备	Yǐngxiàng chǔlǐ shèbèi	
Image recovery	镜频回收	Jìngpín huíshōu	
Image recovery mixer	镜像回收混频器	Jìngxiàng huíshōu hùnpínqì	
Image reflection	镜频反射	Jìngpín fǎnshè	
Image registration	影像配准	Yǐngxiàng pèizhǔn	
Image rejection	镜频抑制	Jìngpín yìzhì	
Image rejection	镜像抑制	Jìngxiàng yìzhì	
Image rejection ratio	镜频抑制比	Jìngpín yìzhì bǐ	
Image rejection ratio	镜像抑制比	Jìngxiàng yìzhì bǐ	
Image restoration	图像恢复	Túxiàng huīfù	
Image restoration	影像复原	Yǐngxiàng fùyuán	
Image restoration (GIS)	图像复原	Túxiàng fùyuán	
Image scanner	影像扫描器	Yǐngxiàng sǎomiáoqì	
Image search	图像检索	Túxiàng jiǎnsuǒ	
Image search engine	图像搜索引擎	Túxiàng sōusuǒ yǐnqíng	
Image segmentation	图像分割	Túxiàng fēngē	
Image sharpening	图像锐化	Túxiàng ruìhuà	
Image smoothing	图像平滑	Túxiàng pínghuá	
Image texture	影像纹理	Yǐngxiàng wénlǐ	
Image watermarking	图像水印	Túxiàng shuǐyìn	
Image, graphic	图像	Túxiàng	
Imagery	图像	Túxiàng	
Imagery	影像	Yǐngxiàng	
Imaginary frequency characteristic	虚频特性	Xū pín tèxing	
Imaging order	成像次序	Chéngxiàng cìxù	
Imaging order	成形次序	Chéngxíng cìxù	
Imaging process	成像处理	Chéngxiàng chǔlǐ	
Imaging process	成形处理	Chéngxíng chǔlǐ	
IMedia (US company)	艾媒体	Ài-méitǐ	
Immediate assignment	立即分配	Lìjí fēnpèi	
Immediate assignment	立即指配	Lìjí zhǐpèi	
Immediate base	直接基类	Zhíjiē jī lèi	
Immediate connection message	立即指配消息	Lìjí zhǐpèi xiāoxi	
Immediate data	立即数据	Lìjí shùjù	
Immediate derived	直接派生类	Zhíjiē pàishēng lèi	
Immediate mode	即时模式	Jíshí móshì	
Immediate mode	直接模式	Zhíjiē móshì	

Immediate predecessor	直接前趋	Zhíjiē qiánqū	
Immediate recipient	直接接收者	Zhíjiē jiēshōuzhě	
Immediate successor	直接后继	Zhíjiē hòujì	
Immediate superior	直接上级	Zhíjiē shàngjí	
Immediate transactional consistency (in SQL Server)	立即事务一致性	Lìjí shìwù yīzhìxìng	
Immediate transmission	立即传输	Lìjí chuánshū	IT
Immediate updating subscription server	即时更新订阅服务器	Jíshí gēngxīn dìngyuè fúwùqì	
Immediate updating subscriptions	即时更新订阅	Jíshí gēngxīn dìngyuè	
Immediate updating (for database)	即时更新	Jíshí gēngxīn	
Immediately allocating method	直接定址法	Zhíjiē dìngzhǐ fǎ	
Immunity (to a disturbance)	抗扰度	Kàngrǎodù	
Immunity (to a disturbance)	抗扰性	Kàngrǎoxìng	
Immunity (to a disturbance)	抗骚扰性	Kàngsāorǎoxìng	
Immunity (to interference)	抗干扰性	Kànggānrǎoxìng	
Immunity level	抗扰性电平	Kàngrǎoxìng diànpíng	
Immunity limit	抗扰性限值	Kàngrǎoxìng xiànzhí	
Immunity margin	抗扰性裕量	Kàngrǎoxìng yùliàng	
Immunity test level	抗扰试验电平	Kàngrǎo shìyàn diànpíng	
Impact printer	撞击式打印机	Zhuàngjīshì dǎyìnjī	
Impact test	跌落试验	Diēluò shìyàn	
Impedance	阻抗	Zǔkàng	
Impedance converter	阻抗变换器	Zǔkàng biànhuànqì	
Impedance coupling	阻抗耦合	Zǔkàng ǒuhé	IC
Impedance matching	阻抗匹配	Zǔkàng pǐpèi	IM
Impedance ratio	阻抗比	Zǔkàng bǐ	
Impedance transformer	阻抗变换器	Zǔkàng biànhuànqì	
Imperceptibility	不可感知性	Bùkěgǎnzhī xìng	
Impersonation attack (IPsec)	伪装攻击	Wěizhuāng gōngjī	
Implementation	实现	Shíxiàn	
Implementation conformance statement	操作适合性宣言	Cāozuò shìhé xìng xuānyán	
Implementation conformance statement	实现一致性声明	Shíxiàn yīzhìxìng shēngmíng	ICS
Implementation corresponds to the documentation; done as written	文实相符	Wén shí xiàngfú	
Implementation extra information	执行额外信息	Zhíxíng éwài xìnxī	IXIT
Implementation under test	测试中的实现	Cèshì zhōngdì shíxiàn	IUT
Implementation under test	测试下的实现	Cèshì-xiàde shíxiàn	IUT
Implementation under test	经测试实现	Jīng cèshì shíxiàn	IUT
Implementation under test	在测试实现	Zài cèshì shíxiàn	IUT
Implication under test	被测实现	Bèicè shíxiàn	IUT
Implicit	隐式	Yǐnshì	
Implicit addressing	隐式地址	Yǐnshì dìzhǐ	
Implicit conversion	隐式转换	Yǐnshì zhuǎnhuàn	
Implicit invocation	隐式调用	Yǐnshì diàoyòng	
Implicit token register	隐含令牌寄存器	Yǐnhán lìngpái jìcúnqì	ITR
Implicit topological description	隐式拓扑记述	Yǐnshì tuòpū jìshù	
Implicit transaction	隐性事务	Yǐnxìng shìwù	

Implicit transaction (for database)	隐式事务	Yǐnshì shìwù	
Implied permission	暗示性权限	Ànshì xìng quánxiàn	
Import	导入	Dǎorù	
Import media pool	导入媒体池	Dǎorù méitǐ chí	
Importance factor	重要性系数	Zhòngyàoxìng xìshù	
Improved in-phase quadrature modulation	改进同相正交调制	Gǎijìn tóngxiàng zhèngjiāo tiáozhì	IIQ
Improved Land Radio Phone (Japan)	改进的陆地无线电话系统	Gǎijìnde lùdì wúxiàn diànhuà xìtǒng	ILRP
Improved multi-band excitation	改进多频带激励	Gǎijìn duō píndài jīlì	IMBE
Improved multi-band excitation	改进的多带激励编码	Gǎijìnde duōdài jīlì biānmǎ	IMBE
Improved packet radio network	改进的分组交换无线电网络	Gǎijìnde fēnzǔ jiāohuàn wúxiàndiàn wǎngluò	IPR
Improved sidelobe suppression	改进的旁瓣抑制	Gǎijìnde pángbàn yìzhì	ISLS
Improved spectral subtraction	改进谱减法	Gǎijìn pǔ jiǎnfǎ	ISS
Improvement	改善	Gǎishàn	
Improving restoration works	改善修复	Gǎishàn xiūfù	
Impulse	冲激脉冲	Chōngjī màichōng	
Impulse response	冲击响应	Chōngjī xiǎngyìng	
Impulsive disturbance	脉冲骚扰	Màichōng sāorǎo	
Impulsive disturbance	脉动骚扰	Màidòng sāorǎo	
Impulsive noise	脉冲噪声	Màichōng zàoshēng	
Impulsive noise	脉动噪声	Màidòng zàoshēng	
Impulsive noise tolerance	脉冲噪声容限	Màichōng zàoshēng róngxiàn	
In hollow spaces of ceiling	吊顶内敷设	Diào dǐng-nèi fūshè	
In my humble opinion (computer chat)	我的浅见	Wǒde qiǎnjiàn	IMHO
In my humble opinion (computer chat)	依比人之见	Yī bǐ rén zhī jiàn	IMHO
Inactive character	无效字符	Wúxiào zìfú	
Inactive part of timeslot	时隙的非活动部分	Shíxìde fēihuódòng bùfen	
Inactive sharing mechanism (in CSCW)	非活动共享机制	Fēihuódòng gòngxiǎng jīzhì	
In-band	带内	Dài-nèi	
In-band harmonic	带内谐波	Dài-nèi xiébō	
In-band noise	带内噪声	Dài-nèi zàoshēng	
In-band signaling	带内信令	Dài-nèi xìnlìng	
Inbound	呼入	Hūrù	
Inbound control channel	入境控制信道	Rùjìng kòngzhì xìndào	ICC
Inbound packet processing (IPsec)	入界包处理	Rùjiè bāo chǔlǐ	
In-call modification	呼叫变更	Hūjiào biàngēng	IM
Incident current	入射电流	Rùshè diànliú	
Incident edge	关联边	Guānlián biān	
Incident handling	事件处理	Shìjiàn chǔlǐ	
Incident response	事件响应	Shìjiàn xiǎngyìng	
Incident wave	入射波	Rùshè bō	
Incidental phase modulation	附带的相位调制	Fùdàide xiàngwèi tiáozhì	IPM
In-circuit test (in SMT)	在线测试	Zàixiàn cèshì	
Inclination (of a satellite orbit)	倾角	Qīngjiǎo	
Inclined orbit (of a satellite)	倾斜轨道	Qīngxié guǐdào	
Inclined slot array for antenna	斜缝隙天线阵	Xié fèngxì tiānxiàn zhèn	

Inclined-V antenna	斜 V 形天线	Xié V-xíng tiānxiàn	
Incoming	来话	Láihuà	
Incoming	入局	Rùjú	
Incoming answer	来话应答	Láihuà yìngdá	
Incoming call barred	阻止入呼叫	Zǔzhǐ rù hūjiào	
Incoming call gateway	来话呼叫网关	Láihuà hūjiào wǎngguān	ICGW
Incoming call modification	入呼叫变更	Rù hūjiào biàngēng	ICM
Incoming call option	入局呼叫选项	Rùjú hūjiào xuǎnxiàng	IOPT
Incoming call screening service	来话呼叫筛选业务	Láihuà hūjiào shāixuǎn yèwù	ICS
Incoming calls barred	来话呼叫限制	Láihuà hūjiào xiànzhì	ICB
Incoming calls barred (within the CUG)	入局呼叫禁止（限于闭合用户群）	Rùjú hūjiào jìnzhǐ (xiànyú bìhé yònghù qún)	ICB
Incoming echo suppressor	输入回波抑制器	Shūrù huíbō yìzhìqì	IES
Incoming error count	输入误码计数	Shūrù wùma jìshù	IEC
Incoming frame	入帧	Rù zhèng	ICF
Incoming inspection test	入厂校验	Rùchǎng jiàoyàn	
Incoming interface	入接口	Rù jiēkǒu	iif
Incoming label map	入标记映射	Rù biāojì yìngshè	ILM
Incoming register link	入局记发链路	Rùjú jìfā liànlù	IRL
Incoming signal failure	输入信号失效	Shūrù xìnhào shīxiào	ISF
Incoming traffic	入局业务量	Rùjú yèwùliàng	
Incoming trunk	入局中继	Rùjú zhōngjì	ICT
Incoming/outgoing switched virtual circuit setup request	入呼叫,出呼叫交换虚电路请求	Rù hūjiào, chū hūjiào jiāohuàn xū diànlù qǐngqiú	
Incompatibility	不兼容	Bùjiānróng	
Incomplete dialing	不完全的拔号	Bùwánquánde bōhào	
Incomplete parameter checking	不完全参数校验	Bùwánquán cānshù jiàoyàn	
Incompressibility	非压缩性	Fēiyāsuōxìng	
Inconclusive verdict	无结论判定	Wújiélùn pàndìng	
Incorporated sweep	插入扫描	Chārù sǎomiáo	
Incorrect signal	不正确信号	Bùzhèngquè xìnhào	
Increment operator	增加操作符	Zēngjiā cāozuò fú	
Incremental backup	增量备份	Zēngliàng bèifèn	
Incremental duplex	增压式双工	Zēngyāshì shuānggōng	
Incremental loading analysis	负载增量分析	Fùzài zēngliàng fēnxī	
Incremental phase modulation	增量相位调制	Zēngliàng xiàngwèi tiáozhì	IPM
Incremental redundancy	逐步增加冗余	Zhúbù zēngjiā rǒngyú	
Incremental update (for database)	增量更新	Zēngliàng gēngxīn	
Incremental zone transfer	增量区域传送	Zēngliàng qūyù chuánsòng	IXFR
Indegree	入度	Rùdù	
Indentation	缩进	Suōjìn	
Independent coordinate system	独立坐标系	Dúlì zuòbiāo xì	
Independent fault	独立故障	Dúlì gùzhàng	
Independent frequency shift keying/frequency hopping	独立频移键控/跳频	Dúlì pínyí jiànkòng/tiàopín	I-FSK/FH
Independent hardware vendor	独立硬件购买者	Dúlì yìngjiàn gòumǎizhě	IHV
Independent set	独立集	Dúlì jí	

Independent sideband	独立边带	Dúlì biāndài	ISB
Independent software vendor	独立软件提供者	Dúlì ruǎnjiàn tígòngzhě	ISV
Independent software vendors	独立软件供应商	Dúlì ruǎnjiàn gōngyìngshāng	ISVs
Independent software vendors	独立软件购买者	Dúlì ruǎnjiàn gòumǎizhě	ISV
Independent telephone company	独立电话公司	Dúlì diànhuà gōngsī	ITC
Independent waveband file	独立波段文件	Dúlì bōduàn wénjiàn	
Index	索引	Suǒyǐn	
Index coverage	索引图层	Suǒyǐn tú céng	
Index matching material	折射率匹配材料	Zhéshèlǜ pǐpèi cáiliào	
Index of cooperation	合作指数	Hézuò zhǐshù	
Index of refraction	折射率	Zhéshèlǜ	
Index OR operation	索引或运算	Suǒyǐn huò yùnsuàn	
Index page	索引页	Suǒyǐn yè	
Index register	变址寄存器	Biànzhǐ jìcúnqì	IXR
Index server	索引服务器	Suǒyǐn fúwùqì	
Index tuning wizard (in SQL Server)	索引调整向导	Suǒyǐn tiáozhěng xiàngdǎo	
Indexed file	索引文件	Suǒyǐn wénjiàn	
Indexed non-sequential file	索引非顺序文件	Suǒyǐn fēishùnxù wénjiàn	
Indexed sequential access method	索引顺序访问方法	Suǒyǐn shùnxù fǎngwèn fāngfǎ	ISAM
Indexed sequential file	索引顺序文件	Suǒyǐn shùnxù wénjiàn	
Indexed views (in SQL Server)	索引化视图	Suǒyǐnhuà shìtú	
Indexing	变址	Biànzhǐ	
Indication, indicator	指示	Zhǐshì	
Indicator bit	指示比特	Zhǐshì bǐtè	IB
Indicator lamp panel	指示灯盘	Zhǐshì dēngpán	
Indirect address	间接地址	Jiànjiē dìzhǐ	
Indirect contact	间接接触	Jiànjiē jiēchù	
Indirect control	间接控制	Jiànjiē kòngzhì	
Indirect distribution	间接分配	Jiànjiē fēnpèi	
Indirect evaluation method	间接评估法	Jiànjiē pínggū fǎ	
Indirect frequency modulation	间接调频	Jiànjiē tiáopín	
Indirect location	间接定位	Jiànjiē dìngwèi	
Indirect submission	间接提交	Jiànjiē tíjiāo	
Indirect user	间接用户	Jiànjiē yònghù	
Indium phosphide	磷化铟	Línhuàyīn	InP
Indium-tin-oxide	氧化铟锡	Yǎnghuàyīnxī	ITO
Individual reception (in satellite broadcasting)	个体接收	Gètǐ jiēshōu	
Individual store and forward readout	单独存储与正向读出	Dāndú cúnchǔ yǔ zhèngxiàng dúchū	ISF
Individual subscriber authentication key	单个用户的鉴别钥匙	Dāngè yònghùde jiànbié yàoshi	Ki
Individual subscriber authentication key	个人身份鉴权键	Gèrén shēnfen jiànquán jiàn	Ki
Individual tone sequential system	顺序单音制	Shùnxù dānyīn zhì	
Individual tone sequential system	顺序列单音制	Shùnxùliè dānyīn zhì	
Individual tone system	单音制	Dānyīnzhì	
Individuality service	个性化服务	Gèxìnghuà fúwù	
Indonesian Satellite Corp.	印尼卫星公司	Yìnní wèixīng gōngsī	Indosat
Indoor optical cable	室内光缆	Shìnèi guānglǎn	

Indoor pan and tilt unit	室内水平俯仰云台	Shìnèi shuǐpíng fǔyǎng yúntái	IPTU
Indoor unit	室内单元	Shìnèi dānyuán	IDU
Induced voltage	感生电压	Gǎnshēng diànyā	
Induction field	感应场	Gǎnyìng cháng	
Induction field (region)	感应场区	Gǎnyìng cháng qū	
Induction phase shifter	感应移相器	Gǎnyìng yíxiàngqì	
Industrial computer backplane	工业计算机背板	Gōngyè jìsuànjī bèibǎn	
Industrial distribution system	工业布线系统	Gōngyè bùxiàn xìtǒng	IDS
Industrial interference	工业干扰	Gōngyè gānrǎo	
Industrial power supply	工业级电源供应器	Gōngyè jí diànyuán gōngyìngqì	
Industrial, scientific and medical	工科医	Gōng kē yī	ISM
Industrial, scientific and medical apparatus	工业，科学，医疗设备	Gōngyè, kēxué, yīliáo shèbèi	ISM
Industrial, scientific and medical applications (of radio frequency energy)	工业,科学和医疗应用	Gōngyè, kēxué hé yīliáo yìngyòng	ISM
Industry standard architecture	工业标准架构	Gōngyè biāozhǔn jiàgòu	ISA
Industry/Government Open System Specification	工业,政府部门开放系统技术规范	Gōngyè, zhèngfǔ bùmén kāifàng xìtǒng jìshù guīfàn	IGOSS
Inertia element (aperiodic element)	惯性环节（非周期环节）	Guànxìng huánjié (fēizhōuqī huánjié)	
Inertia force	惯性力	Guànxìnglì	
Inertial navigation	惯性导航	Guànxìng dǎoháng	
Inertial navigation (short form)	惯导	Guàndǎo	
Inertial navigation system	惯性导航系统	Guànxìng dǎoháng xìtǒng	
Inertial positioning system	惯性定位系统	Guànxìng dìngwèi xìtǒng	
Inferior, subordinate	低级	Dījí	
Infineon Technologies AG	英飞凌科技	Yīng-fēi-líng kējì	
Infinite duration impulse response	无限区间脉冲响应	Wúxiàn qūjiān màichōng xiǎngyìng	IIR
Infinite loop	无限循环	Wúxiàn xúnhuán	
Infinite recursive	无限递归	Wúxiàn dìguī	
Inflation radome	充气天线罩	Chōngqì tiānxiàn zhào	
Inflow	流入量	Liúrùliàng	
Infobahn	信息巴恩	Xìnxī bā-ēn	
Infocosm	资讯化空间	Zīxùnhuà kōngjiān	
Infomercial	资讯商业	Zīxùn shāngyè	
Infomix Software Corp. (China)	英孚美软件有限公司	Yīng-fú-měi ruǎnjiàn yǒuxiàn gōngsī	
Informatics	信息学	Xìnxīxué	
Informatics	资讯科技展	Zīxùn kējì zhǎn	
Informatics Computer School (Singapore)	英华美电脑学校	Yīng-huá-měi diànnǎo xuéxiào	
Information (ISUP message)	信息	Xìnxī	INF
Information acquisition	信息获取	Xìnxī huòqǔ	
Information and communications technology	信息与通信技术	Xìnxī yǔ tōngxìn jìshù	ICT
Information assurance	信息保障	Xìnxī bǎozhàng	IA
Information assurance technical framework	信息保障技术框架	Xìnxī bǎozhàng jìshù kuàngjià	IATF
Information attribute	信息属性	Xìnxī shǔxìng	
Information bit	信息比特	Xìnxī bǐtè	
Information bit	信息位	Xìnxī wèi	
Information block	信息块	Xìnxī kuài	
Information block	信息码组	Xìnxī mǎzǔ	I-Block

Information concealment, steganography	信息隐匿技术	Xìnxī yǐnnì jìshù	
Information consultant	信息咨询	Xìnxī zīxún	
Information content	信息内容	Xìnxī nèiróng	
Information conversion function	信息转换功能	Xìnxī zhuǎnhuàn gōngnéng	ICF
Information descriptor record	信息描述符记录	Xìnxī miáoshù fú jìlù	IDR
Information desk	查号台	Cháhàotái	
Information element	信息单元	Xìnxī dānyuán	IE
Information element	信息元素	Xìnxī yuánsù	IE
Information element identifier	信息单元标识符	Xìnxī dānyuán biāozhìfú	IEI
Information element identity	信息单元识别	Xìnxī dānyuán shíbié	IEI
Information engineering	信息工程	Xìnxī gōngchéng	
Information entropy	信息熵	Xìnxī shāng	
Information extraction	信息提取	Xìnxī tíqǔ	
Information field	信息字段	Xìnxī zìduàn	INF
Information field sizes	信息字段大小	Xìnxī zìduàn dàxiǎo	IFS
Information field sizes for the terminal	终端信息字段大小	Zhōngduān xìnxī zìduàn dàxiǎo	IFST
Information field sizes for the UICC	UICC 信息字段大小	UICC xìnxī zìduàn dàxiǎo	IFSC
Information file	信息文件	Xìnxī wénjiàn	INF File
Information flow	信息流	Xìnxī liú	IF
Information flow chart	信息流程图	Xìnxī liúchéngtú	
Information frame	信息帧	Xìnxī zhèng	I
Information fusion	信息融合	Xìnxī rónghé	
Information group	信息组	Xìnxī zǔ	IG
Information hiding	信息隐藏	Xìnxī yǐncáng	
Information highway	信息高速公路	Xìnxī gāosù gōnglù	
Information infrastructure	信息基础设施	Xìnxī jīchǔ shèshī	
Information management	信息管理	Xìnxī guǎnlǐ	
Information message (ISUP)	信息消息	Xìnxī xiāoxi	INF
Information model	信息模型	Xìnxī móxíng	IM
Information modeling	信息建模	Xìnxī jiànmó	
Information network	信息通信网	Xìnxī tōngxìn wǎng	
Information network	信息网	Xìnxīwǎng	IN
Information network system	信息通信系统	Xìnxī tōngxìn xìtǒng	INS
Information outlet	信息插座	Xìnxī chāzuò	IO
Information payload	信息净负荷	Xìnxī jìngfùhè	
Information payload capacity	信息负荷能力	Xìnxī fùhè nénglì	
Information payload capacity	信息净荷能力	Xìnxī jìnghé nénglì	
Information payload capacity	信息净荷容量	Xìnxī jìnghé róngliàng	
Information payload capacity	信息有效负荷能力	Xìnxī yǒuxiào fùhè nénglì	
Information processing	信息处理	Xìnxī chǔlǐ	
Information processing standard for computer	计算机信息处理标准	Jìsuànjī xìnxī chǔlǐ biāozhǔn	IPSC
Information protocol identifier	信息协议识别符	Xìnxī xiéyì shíbiéfú	IPI
Information rate	信息速率	Xìnxī sùlǜ	
Information request	信息查询	Xìnxī cháxún	IRQ
Information request (computer term)	信息请求	Xìnxī qǐngqiú	IRQ
Information request (ISUP message)	信息请求	Xìnxī qǐngqiú	INR

Information request acknowledge	信息查询确认	Xìnxī cháxún quèrèn	IACK
Information request acknowledged	信息请求证实	Xìnxī qǐngqiú zhèngshí	IACK
Information request message (ISUP)	信息请求消息	Xìnxī qǐngqiú xiāoxi	INR
Information request negative acknowledge	信息查询否认	Xìnxī cháxún fǒurèn	INAK
Information request negative acknowledge	信息请求否认	Xìnxī qǐngqiú fǒurèn	INAK
Information request reason	信息请求原因	Xìnxī qǐngqiú yuányīn	IRR
Information request response	信息查询响应	Xìnxī cháxún xiǎngyìng	IRR
Information request response	信息请求响应	Xìnxī qǐngqiú xiǎngyìng	IRR
Information resource dictionary system	信息资源词典系统	Xìnxī zīyuán cídiǎn xìtǒng	
Information resource management	信息资源管理	Xìnxī zīyuán guǎnlǐ	
Information retrieval system	信息检索系统	Xìnxī jiǎnsuǒ xìtǒng	
Information science	信息科学	Xìnxī kēxué	
Information security	信息安全	Xìnxī ānquán	INFOSEC
Information security	信息加密	Xìnxī jiāmì	
Information Security Sub-Committee (of CIITA)	西安全产业分会	Xī'ān quán chǎnyè fēnhuì	ISSC
Information service trades	信息服务业	Xìnxī fúwùyè	
Information set	信息集	Xìnxī jí	
Information sink	信宿	Xìnsù	
Information source	信源	Xìnyuán	
Information superhighway	资讯超速公路	Zīxùn chāosù gōnglù	
Information superhighway; data highway	数据高速通路	Shùjù gāosù tōnglù	
Information system	信息系统	Xìnxī xìtǒng	
Information system engineering	信息系统工程	Xìnxī xìtǒng gōngchéng	
Information system security	信息系统安全	Xìnxī xìtǒng ānquán	
Information systems security engineering	信息系统安全工程	Xìnxī xìtǒng ānquán gōngchéng	ISSE
Information technology	信息技术	Xìnxī jìshù	IT
Information Technology Association of America	美国信息技术协会	Měiguó xìnxī jìshù xiéhuì	ITAA
Information technology equipment	信息技术设备	Xìnxī jìshù shèbèi	ITE
Information technology security evaluation criteria	信息技术安全评级准则	Xìnxī jìshù ānquán píngjí zhǔnzé	
Information theoretic cryptography	信息理论密码学	Xìnxī lǐlùn mìmǎxué	
Information theory	信息论	Xìnxīlùn	
Information tone	信息音	Xìnxī yīn	
Information transfer	信息传递	Xìnxī chuándì	
Information transfer capability	信息传送容量	Xìnxī chuánsòng róngliàng	ITC
Information transfer channel	信息传送通道	Xìnxī chuánsòng tōngdào	ITC
Information transfer gain	转信增益	Zhuǎnxìn zēngyì	
Information transmission system	信息传输系统	Xìnxī chuánshū xìtǒng	
Information unit	信息单位	Xìnxī dānwèi	
Information utilization	信息施用	Xìnxī shīyòng	
Information-oriented society	信息社会	Xìnxī shèhuì	
Informix (IBM software)	英孚美	Yīng-fú-měi	
Infoseek	资讯查找	Zīxùn cházhǎo	
Infotainment	信息娱乐	Xìnxī yúlè	
Infradyne receiver	低外差式接收机	Dīwàichāi-shì jiēshōujī	
In-frame (SDH)	定帧	Dìngzhèng	IF
Infrared	红外线	Hóngwàixiàn	IR

Infrared absorbing filter	红外吸收射滤光镜	Hóngwài xīshōu shè lǜguāngjìng	
Infrared communications	红外通信	Hóngwài tōngxìn	IrCOMM
Infrared communications system	红外线通信系统	Hóngwàixiàn tōngxìn xìtǒng	ICS
Infrared crystal	红外线晶体	Hóngwàixiàn jīngtǐ	
Infrared curing oven	红外线固化炉	Hóngwàixiàn gùhuà lú	
Infrared Data Association	红外数据联合会	Hóngwài shùjù liánhéhuì	IrDA
Infrared Data Association	红外数据联盟	Hóngwài shùjù liánméng	IrDA
Infrared Data Association	红外数据协会	Hóngwài shùjù xiéhuì	IrDA
Infrared Data Association	红外线数据标准协会	Hóngwàixiàn shùjù biāozhǔn xiéhuì	IrDA
Infrared detector	红外线检测器	Hóngwàixiàn jiǎncèqì	
Infrared film	红外线底片	Hóngwàixiàn dǐpiàn	
Infrared glass	红外线玻璃	Hóngwàixiàn bōli	
Infrared light source	红外线光源	Hóngwàixiàn guāngyuán	
Infrared material	红外线材料	Hóngwàixiàn cáiliào	
Infrared mobile communications	红外移动通信	Hóngwài yídòng tōngxìn	IrMC
Infrared object exchange	红外对象交换协议	Hóngwài duìxiàng jiāohuàn xiéyì	IrOBEX
Infrared optical fiber	红外光纤	Hóngwài guāngxiān	
Infrared plate	红外线感光板	Hóngwàixiàn gǎnguāng bǎn	
Infrared port	红外端口	Hóngwài duānkǒu	
Infrared radar tracking transfer test	红外雷达跟踪转换试验	Hóngwài léidá gēnzōng zhuǎnhuàn shìyàn	
Infrared reflecting filter	红外反射滤光镜	Hóngwài fǎnshè lǜguāngjìng	
Infrared scanner, thermal mapper	红外线扫描仪	Hóngwàixiàn sǎomiáoyí	
Infrared tracker	红外跟踪器	Hóngwài gēnzōngqì	
Infrared tracking test	红外跟踪试验	Hóngwài gēnzōng shìyàn	
Infrared transmitting filter	红外透过滤光镜	Hóngwài tòuguò lǜguāngjìng	
Infrastructure	底层结构	Dǐcéng jiégòu	IF
Infrastructure	基础设施	Jīchǔ shèshī	
Infrastructure lifecycle management	架构生命周期管理	Jiàgòu shēngmìng zhōuqī guǎnlǐ	
Ingress label switch router	不同边缘入节点	Bùtóng biānyuán rù jiédiǎn	
Inherent distortion (of a transmission channel)	固有畸变	Gùyǒu jībiàn	
Inherent frequency error	固有频差	Gùyǒu pínchà	
Inherent monitoring	固有监视	Gùyǒu jiānshì	
Inherent reliability	固有可靠性	Gùyǒu kěkàoxìng	
Inheritance	继承	Jìchéng	
Inheritance	继承机制	Jìchéng jīzhì	
Inheritance	继承性	Jìchéng-xìng	
Inheritance hierarchy	继承等级	Jìchéng děngjí	
Inherited rights filter	继承权限过滤器	Jìchéng quánxiàn guòlǜqì	
In-house call center	自用呼叫中心	Zìyòng hūjiào zhōngxīn	
Initial address information	初始地址信息	Chūshǐ dìzhǐ xìnxī	
Initial address information	起始地址信息	Qǐshǐ dìzhǐ xìnxī	IAI
Initial address message	初始地址消息	Chūshǐ dìzhǐ xiāoxi	IAM
Initial address message with additional information	带有附加信息的初始地址消息	Dàiyǒu fùjiā xìnxīde chūshǐ dìzhǐ xiāoxi	IAI
Initial address with additional information	带附加信息的初始地址消息	Dài fùjiā xìnxīde chūshǐ dìzhǐ xiāoxi	IAI

Initial charge (of a battery)	初充电	Chūchōngdiàn	
Initial condition	初始条件	Chūshǐ tiáojiàn	
Initial detection point	启动检出点	Qǐdòng jiǎnchū diǎn	IDP
Initial domain identifier	初始域标识	Chūshǐ yù biāozhì	IDI
Initial domain part	初始域部分	Chūshǐ yù bùfen	IDP
Initial graphics exchange specification	初始化图形交换规程	Chūshǐhuà túxíng jiāohuàn guīchéng	IGES
Initial node	初始结点	Chūshǐ jiédiǎn	
Initial point	初始点	Chūshǐ diǎn	
Initial program loader	初始程序输入器	Chūshǐ chéngxù shūrùqì	IPL
Initial program loader	初始程序装入程序	Chūshǐ chéngxù zhuāngrù chéngxù	IPL
Initial public offering	上市	Shàngshì	IPO
Initial signal unit	初始信号单元	Chūshǐ xìnhào dānyuán	ISU
Initial value managed object	管理目标初始值	Guǎnlǐ mùbiāo chūshǐ zhí	IVMO
Initial vector	初始向量	Chūshǐ xiàngliàng	IV
Initialization	初始化	Chūshǐhuà	
Initialization	启始化	Qǐshǐhuà	
Initialization and maintenance	初始化和维护	Chūshǐhuà hé wéihù	BIM
Initialization file; .INI file	初始化文件	Chūshǐhuà wénjiàn	
Initialization list	初始值列表	Chūshǐ zhí lièbiǎo	
Initialization list	初始化列表	Chūshǐhuà lièbiǎo	
Initialization media	初始化媒体	Chūshǐhuà méitǐ	
Initialization power	初始功率	Chūshǐ gōnglǜ	INIT_PWR
Initialization snapshot	初始化快照	Chūshǐhuà kuàizhào	
Initialize	初始化	Chūshǐhuà	INIT
Initialize address message	初始化地址消息	Chūshǐhuà dìzhǐ xiāoxi	
Initiate call attempt	启动试呼	Qǐdòng shìhū	ICA
Initiation control	起动控制	Qǐdòng kòngzhì	
Initiator	初始者	Chūshǐzhě	
Initiator	启动设备	Qǐdòng shèbèi	
Inject light diode	注入式激光二极管	Zhùrùshì jīguāng èrjíguǎn	ILD
Injection	注入	Zhùrù	
Injection equipment	注入装置	Zhùrù zhuāngzhì	
Injection locked local oscillator	注入锁定本地振荡器	Zhùrù suǒdìng běndì zhèndàngqì	
Injection molding equipment	射出成形机	Shèchū chéngxíngjī	
Injection molding equipment	注射成形机	Zhùshè chéngxíngjī	
Injection well	注入井	Zhùrù jǐng	
Injection-molded (FOC mfg)	注入模	Zhùrù mó	
Injector angle	注入角	Zhùrù jiǎo	
Ink jet printer head (semiconductor mfg)	打印喷墨头	Dǎyìn pēn mò tóu	
Inkjet plain paper facsimile	喷墨普通纸传真机	Pēnmò pǔtōng zhǐ chuánzhēnjī	
Inkjet plotter	喷墨绘图仪	Pēnmò huìtúyí	
Inkjet printer	喷墨打印机	Pēnmò dǎyìnjī	
Inland Revenue Integrated System	艾丽斯	Ài-lì-sī	IRIS
Inland Revenue integrated system	综合税务系统	Zōnghé shuìwù xìtǒng	IRIS
Inlet	入口	Rùkǒu	
Inline	内联	Nèilián	

English	Chinese	Pinyin	Abbreviation
Inline expansion	内联展开	Nèilián zhǎnkāi	
Inline table-valued functions (in SQL Server)	内联表值型函数	Nèilián biǎozhíxíng hánshù	
In-line tester	在线测试仪	Zàixiàn cèshìyí	
In-local	本机操作	Běnjī cāozuò	
Inner join (for database)	内联接	Nèi liánjiē	
Inoperable	不可操作	Bùkěcāozuò	INOP
In-order traversal	中序遍历	Zhōngxù biànlì	
In-phase + quadrature	同相+正交	Tóngxiàng+zhèngjiāo	IQ
In-phase + quadrature channel loop	同相+正交信道环路	Tóngxiàng+zhèngjiāo xìndào huánlù	IQL
In-phase + quadrature direct sequence spread spectrum	同相+正交直接序列扩展频谱	Tóngxiàng+zhèngjiāo zhíjiē xùliè kuòzhǎn pínpǔ	IQ-DS-SS
In-place active	现场激活	Xiànchǎng jīhuó	
In-plane shearing mode	平面内剪切模式	Píngmiàn-nèi jiǎnqiē móshì	
Input access control register	输入访问控制寄存器	Shūrù fǎngwèn kòngzhì jìcúnqì	IACR
Input acknowledge	输入认可	Shūrù rènkě	IA
Input characteristics	输入特性	Shūrù tèxìng	
Input impedance	输入阻抗	Shūrù zǔkàng	
Input jitter	输入抖动	Shūrù dǒudòng	
Input jitter tolerance	输入抖动容限	Shūrù dǒudòng róngxiàn	
Input level	输入电平	Shūrù diànpíng	
Input member	输入成员	Shūrù chéngyuán	
Input method editor	输入法编辑器	Shūrù fǎ biānjíqì	IME
Input method window (WP command)	输入法窗口	Shūrù fǎ chuāngkǒu	
Input offset current	输入补偿电流	Shūrù bǔcháng diànliú	
Input optical power	输入光功率	Shūrù guāng gōnglǜ	IOP
Input power	输入功率	Shūrù gōnglǜ	
Input power control	输入电源控制	Shūrù diànyuán kòngzhì	
Input power control	输入功率控制	Shūrù gōnglǜ kòngzhì	
Input reference plane	输入参考面	Shūrù cānkǎo miàn	
Input set	输入集	Shūrù jí	
Input simulation network	输入模拟网络	Shūrù mónǐ wǎngluò	
Input source	输入源	Shūrù yuán	
Input speech domain	输入语音域	Shūrù yǔyīn yù	
Input voltage range	输入电压范围	Shūrù diànyā fànwéi	
Input wander tolerance	输入漂移容限	Shūrù piāoyí róngxiàn	
Input/output	输入/输出	Shūrù/shūchū	I/O
Input/output cell	输入/输出单元	Shūrù/shūchū dānyuán	
Input/output channel	输入/输出通道	Shūrù/shūchū tōngdào	
Input/output controller hub	输入/输出控制中心	Shūrù/shūchū kòngzhì zhōngxīn	ICH
Input/output device	输入/输出设备	Shūrù/shūchū shèbèi	I/O
Input/output instruction	输入/输出指令	Shūrù/shūchū zhǐlìng	
Input/output list	输入/输出表	Shūrù/shūchū biǎo	
Input/output processor	输入/输出处理机	Shūrù/shūchū chǔlǐjī	IOP
Input/output statement	输入/输出语句	Shūrù/shūchū yǔjù	
Input; import	输入	Shūrù	
Input-output block	输出输入模块	Shūchū shūrù mókuài	IOB

English	Chinese	Pinyin	Abbreviation
Input-signal source	输入信号源	Shūrù xìnhào yuán	
Input-signal voltage	输入信号电压	Shūrù xìnhào diànyā	
Inquiry (noun), poll (verb)	查询	Cháxún	
Inquiry access code	查询访问码	Cháxún fǎngwèn mǎ	IAC
Inquiry message exchange	询问信息交换	Xúnwèn xìnxī jiāohuàn	IMX
Insensitive cursor	不感知游标	Bùgǎnzhī yóubiāo	
Insert	插入	Chārù	
Insert key	加插键	Jiāchā jiàn	Ins
Insert menu (WP command)	插入菜单	Chārù càidān	
Insert mode (WP command)	插入状态	Chārù zhuàngtài	
Insert new table (WP command)	插入新表格	Chārù xīn biǎogé	
Insert query	插入查询	Chārù cháxún	
Insert row (WP command)	插入一行	Chārù yīháng	
Insert subscriber data	插入用户数据	Chārù yònghù shùjù	
Insert values query	插入值查询	Chārù zhí cháxún	
Insertion error	插入错误	Chārù cuòwù	
Insertion gain	插入增益	Chārù zēngyì	
Insertion gain (of two-port-network)	介入增益	Jièrù zēngyì	
Insertion loss	插入损耗	Chārù sǔnhào	IL
Insertion loss (FOC)	介入损耗	Jièrù sǔnhào	IL
Insertion optical fiber (cable) connector	插入式光纤(缆)连接器	Chārù shì guāngxiān (lǎn) liánjiē qì	
Insertion phase shift	插入相移	Chārù xiāngyí	
Insertion sort	插入排序	Chārù páixù	
Insertion-frame	插框	Chākuàng	
Insertion-frame component	插框组件	Chākuàng zǔjiàn	
Inside vapor phase deposition (FOC mfg)	内汽相沉积法	Nèi qìxiàng chénjī fǎ	IVPD
In-slot signaling	隙内信令	Xì-nèi xìnlìng	
Inspecting afterwards	事后检查	Shìhòu jiǎnchá	
Inspection grounding	检修接地	Jiǎnxiū jiēdì	
Inspection, examination	检查	Jiǎnchá	
Install (verb)	安装	Ānzhuāng	
Installable client driver	可安装客户端驱动程序	Kě'ānzhuāng kèhù duān qūdòng chéngxù	ICD
Installation test	实装测试	Shízhuāng cèshì	
Installation wiring impedance	设备接线阻抗	Shèbèi jiēxiàn zǔkàng	
Installation wiring impedance	装置连线阻抗	Zhuāngzhì liánxiàn zǔkàng	
Installed in cable tray	电缆桥架敷设	Diànlǎn qiáojià fūshè	CT
Instance	实例	Shílì	
Instance level	实例级	Shílì jí	
Instance model	即时模型	Jíshí móxíng	
Instant	时刻	Shíkè	
Instantaneous automatic gain control	瞬时自动增益控制	Shùnshí zìdòng zēngyì kòngzhì	IAGC
Instantaneous availability	瞬时可用性	Shùnshí kěyòngxìng	A(t)
Instantaneous deviation control	瞬时频偏控制	Shùnshí pínpiān kòngzhì	IDC
Instantaneous deviation controller	瞬时频偏控制器	Shùnshí pínpiān kòngzhìqì	IDC
Instantaneous failure intensity	瞬时失效频度	Shùnshí shīxiào píndù	Z(t)
Instantaneous failure rate	瞬时失效率	Shùnshí shīxiào lǜ	

Instantaneous frequency (of a signal)	瞬时频率	Shùnshí pínlǜ	
Instantaneous frequency deviation	瞬时频率偏移	Shùnshí pínlǜ piānyí	
Instantaneous frequency measurement receiver	瞬时测频接收机	Shùnshí cèpín jiēshōujī	
Instantaneous peak power (in a transmission line)	瞬时峰值功率	Shùnshí fēngzhí gōnglǜ	
Instantaneous phase deviation	瞬时相位偏移	Shùnshí xiàngwèi piānyí	
Instantaneous repair rate	瞬时修复率	Shùnshí xiūfù lǜ	
Instantaneous state	瞬态	Shùntài	
Instantaneous unavailability	瞬时不可用性	Shùnshí bùkěyòngxìng	U(t)
Instantiated (usually for a template)	具现化	Jùxiànhuà	
Instantiated (usually for a template)	实体化	Shítǐhuà	
Instantiation (usually for a template)	具现化实体	Jùxiànhuà shítǐ	
Instantiation (usually for a template)	具现体	Jùxiàntǐ	
Institute for International Research	国际会议机构	Guójì huìyì jīgòu	IIR
Institute of Electrical and Electronic Engineers	电气与电子工程师协会	Diànqì yǔ diànzǐ gōngchéngshī xiéhuì	IEEE
Institute of Electrical and Electronics Engineers	电子电气工程学会	Diànzǐ diànqì gōngchéng xuéhuì	IEEE
Institute of Electrical and Electronics Engineers	美国电气及电子工程师协会	Měiguó diànqì jí diànzǐ gōngchéngshī xiéhuì	IEEE
Institute of Software (under the China Academy of Sciences)	软件研究所	Ruǎnjiàn yánjiūsuǒ	
Institution of Electrical Engineers (UK)	电气工程师协会	Diànqì gōngchéngshī xiéhuì	IEE
Instruction address A-register	指令地址 A 寄存器	Zhǐlìng dìzhǐ A jìcúnqì	IAA
Instruction cache	指令存储单元	Zhǐlìng cúnchǔ dānyuán	
Instruction coloring	指令分类	Zhǐlìng fēnlèi	
Instruction control unit	指令控制单元	Zhǐlìng kòngzhì dānyuán	ICU
Instruction issue	指令发送	Zhǐlìng fāsòng	
Instruction set architecture	指令集架构	Zhǐlìng jí jiàgòu	ISA
Instruction set processor language	指令集处理机语言	Zhǐlìng jí chǔlǐjī yǔyán	ISPL
Instruction storage unit	指令存储器	Zhǐlìng cúnchǔqì	ISU
Instructions cache	指令缓存	Zhǐlìng huǎncún	
Instructions per clock cycle	指令/时钟周期	Zhǐlìng/shízhōng zhōuqī	IPC
Instrument BASIC language	仪器 BASIC 语言	Yíqì BASIC yǔyán	IBASIC
Instrument landing system	仪表着陆系统	Yíbiǎo zhuólù xìtǒng	ILS
Instrument landing system glide path	仪表着陆系统下滑信标	Yíbiǎo zhuólù xìtǒng xiàhuá xìnbiāo	
Instrument landing system localizer	仪表着陆系统航向信标	Yíbiǎo zhuólù xìtǒng hángxiàng xìnbiāo	
Instrument Society of America	美国仪表协会	Měiguó yíbiǎo xiéhuì	ISA
Instrument under test	被测试实现体	Bèi cèshì shíxiàn tǐ	IUT
Instrument under test	被测对象	Bèicè duìxiàng	IUT
Instrumented bend test	采用仪表的弯曲实验	Cǎiyòng yíbiǎode wānqū shíyàn	IBT
Insufficient security message (IPsec TLS)	不够安全消息	Bùgòu ānquán xiāoxi	
Insulated gate bipolar transistor	绝缘栅双极型晶体管	Juéyuán zhà shuāngjíxíng jīngtǐguǎn	IGBT
Insulated gate field effect transistor	绝缘栅场效应晶体管	Juéyuán zhà chǎng xiàoyìng jīngtǐguǎn	IGFET
Insulation	绝缘	Juéyuán	
Insulation displacement connection	绝缘层信移连接件	Juéyuán céng xìnyí liánjiē jiàn	IDC
Insulation fault	绝缘故障	Juéyuán gùzhàng	
Insulation monitoring and warning device	绝缘监视和报警装置	Juéyuán jiānshì hé bàojǐng zhuāngzhì	
Insulation resistance	绝缘电阻	Juéyuán diànzǔ	
Insulation system	绝缘结构	Juéyuán jiégòu	

Insulator	绝缘体	Juéyuántǐ	
Insurance charge for correspondence	保价函件保价费	Bǎojià hánjiàn bǎojiàfèi	
Insured burst	安全突发量	Ānquán tūfāliàng	
Insured correspondence	保价函件	Bǎojià hánjiàn	
Insured letter	保价信函	Bǎojià xìnhán	
Insured parcel commission fee	保价包裹手续费	Bǎojià bāoguǒ shǒuxùfèi	
Insured rate	安全速率	Ānquán sùlǜ	
Insured traffic	安全业务量	Ānquán yèwùliàng	
Intake pipe	取水管	Qǔshuǐguǎn	
Integer	整型	Zhěngxíng	
Integer execution unit	整数执行单元	Zhěngshù zhíxíng dānyuán	IEU
Integral antenna equipment	一体化天线的设备	Yītǐhuà tiānxiànde shèbèi	
Integral element	积分环节	Jīfēn huánjié	
Integral pulse frequency modulation	积分脉冲调制	Jīfēn màichōng iáozhì	IPFM
Integral refractive index meter	积分折射率仪	Jīfēn zhéshèlǜyí	
Integral square linear error	积累平房线性误差	Jīlěi píngfáng xiànxìng wùchā	ISLE
Integrate	整合	Zhěnghé	
Integrate-and-dump	积分冲洗	Jīfēn chōngxǐ	I&D
Integrated access device	综合接入设备	Zōnghé jiērù shèbèi	IAD
Integrated automated office system	综合办公室自动化系统	Zōnghé bàngōngshì zìdònghuà xìtǒng	
Integrated broadband access system	综合宽带接入系统	Zōnghé kuāndài jiērù xìtǒng	IBAS
Integrated building distribution network	建筑物综合分布网络	Jiànzhùwù zōnghé fēnbù wǎngluò	IBDN
Integrated circuit	集成电路	Jíchéng diànlù	IC
Integrated circuit identity	集成电路识别码	Jíchéng diànlù shíbié mǎ	ICCID
Integrated circuit test sockets (semiconductor mfg)	半导体成测插座	Bàndǎotǐ chéngcè chāzuò	
Integrated communication, navigation and identification avionics	综合化通信导航识别航空电子系统	Zōnghéhuà tōngxìn dǎoháng shíbié hángkōng diànzǐ xìtǒng	ICNIA
Integrated communications control panel	综合通信控制板	Zōnghé tōngxìn kòngzhì bǎn	ICCP
Integrated communications controller	集成通信控制器	Jíchéng tōngxìn kòngzhìqì	
Integrated data	集成数据	Jíchéng shùjù	
Integrated data network	综合数据网	Zōnghé shùjù wǎng	IDN
Integrated database management system	集成数据库管理系统	Jíchéng shùjùkù guǎnlǐ xìtǒng	
Integrated development environment	集成开发环境	Jíchéng kāifā huánjìng	IDE
Integrated devices electronics	综合电器介面	Zōnghé diànqì jièmiàn	IDE
Integrated digital communication system	综合数字通信系统	Zōnghé shùzì tōngxìn xìtǒng	IDCS
Integrated digital enhanced network	数字集群调度专网	Shùzì jíqún diàodù zhuānwǎng	iDEN
Integrated digital loop carrier	综合数字环路载波	Zōnghé shùzì huánlù zàibō	IDLC
Integrated digital network	数字综合网	Shùzì zōnghé wǎng	IDN
Integrated digital network	综合数字网	Zōnghé shùzì wǎng	IDN
Integrated digital transmission and switching	综合数字传输和交换	Zōnghé shùzì chuánshū hé jiāohuàn	
Integrated distribution network system	综合布线网络系统	Zōnghé bùxiàn wǎngluò xìtǒng	IDNS
Integrated drive electronics	电子集成驱动器	Diànzǐ jíchéng qūdòngqì	IDE
Integrated electronic signal processor	综合电子信号处理机	Zōnghé diànzi xìnhào chǔlǐjī	IESP
Integrated electronic warfare system	综合电子战系统	Zōnghé diànzǐzhàn xìtǒng	
Integrated equipment	一体化型设备	Yītǐhuàxíng shèbèi	
Integrated framing	集成帧	Jíchéng zhèng	

Integrated gateway	综合接口局	Zōnghé jiēkǒujú	
Integrated gateway boards	综合网关模块	Zōnghé wǎng guān mókuài	IGW
Integrated ground	综合接地	Zōnghé jiēdì	
Integrated information system	综合信息系统	Zōnghé xìnxī xìtǒng	
Integrated link information	综合链信息	Zōnghé liàn xìnxī	
Integrated local management interface	集成本地管理接口	Jíchéng běndì guǎnlǐ jiēkǒu	ILMI
Integrated model	集成模式	Jíchéng móshì	IM
Integrated modem	集成调制解调器	Jíchéng tiáozhì jiětiáoqì	
Integrated network management	综合网络管理	Zōnghé wǎngluò guǎnlǐ	INM
Integrated network management system	综合网络管理系统	Zōnghé wǎngluò guǎnlǐ xìtǒng	INMS
Integrated node information	综合结点信息	Zōnghé jiédiǎn xìnxī	
Integrated on-demand network	按需要集成的网络	Àn xūyào jíchéngde wǎngluò	ION
Integrated on-demand network	一体化按需网络	Yītǐhuà ànxū wǎngluò	ION
Integrated optical device	积体光元件	Jītǐ guāng yuánjiàn	
Integrated optical hybrid circuit	混合光集成电路	Hùnhé guāng jíchéng diànlù	INOHYC
Integrated opto-electronic circuit	光电子集成电路	Guāng diànzǐ jíchéng diànlù	IOEC
Integrated phase control	综合相位控制	Zōnghé xiàngwèi kòngzhì	
Integrated positioning system	综合定位系统	Zōnghé dìngwèi xìtǒng	
Integrated reference point	集成参考点	Jíchéng cānkǎo diǎn	IRP
Integrated reference point	综合参考点	Zōnghé cānkǎo diǎn	IRP
Integrated security	集成安全性	Jíchéng ānquánxìng	
Integrated service	综合服务	Zōnghé fúwù	
Integrated service access network	综合业务接入网	Zōnghé yèwù jiērù wǎng	ISAN
Integrated service control function	综合业务控制功能	Zōnghé yèwù kòngzhì gōngnéng	ISCF
Integrated service creation environment point	综合业务生成环境点	Zōnghé yèwù shēngchéng huánjìng diǎn	ISCEP
Integrated service data network	综合业务数据网络	Zōnghé yèwù shùjù wǎngluò	ISDN
Integrated service data point	综合业务数据点	Zōnghé yèwù shùjù diǎn	ISDN
Integrated service management access point	综合业务管理接入点	Zōnghé yèwù guǎnlǐ jiērù diǎn	ISMAP
Integrated service management function	综合业务管理功能	Zōnghé yèwù guǎnlǐ gōngnéng	ISMF
Integrated service management point	综合业务管理点	Zōnghé yèwù guǎnlǐ diǎn	ISMP
Integrated service model	集成服务模型	Jíchéng fúwù móxíng	IntServ
Integrated services business exchange	综合业务企业交换	Zōnghé yèwù qǐyè jiāohuàn	ISBX
Integrated services control point	综合业务控制点	Zōnghé yèwù kòngzhì diǎn	ISCP
Integrated services digital network	一体化服务数字网络	Yītǐhuà fúwù shùzì wǎngluò	ISDN
Integrated services digital network	一线通	Yīxiàn tōng	ISDN
Integrated services digital network	综合服务数字网络	Zōnghé fúwù shùzì wǎngluò	ISDN
Integrated services digital network	综合业务数字网	Zōnghé yèwù shùzì wǎng	ISDN
Integrated services digital network user part	综合业务数字网用户部分	Zōnghé yèwù shùzì wǎng yònghù bùfen	ISUP
Integrated services digital terminal	综合服务数字终端	Zōnghé fúwù shùzì zhōngduān	ISDT
Integrated services network	综合业务网	Zōnghé yèwù wǎng	
Integrated services private branch exchange	综合业务用户交换机	Zōnghé yèwù yònghù jiāohuànjī	ISPBX
Integrated services unit	综合业务单元	Zōnghé yèwù dānyuán	ISU
Integrated switching and transmission network	综合交换和传输网络	Zōnghé jiāohuàn hé chuánshū wǎngluò	ISTN
Integrated switching element	集成交换单元	Jíchéng jiāohuàn dānyuán	ISE
Integrated symbolic debugger	综合符号调式程序	Zōnghé fúhào diàoshì chéngxù	ISD
Integrated terminal plan or program	综合终端计划	Zōnghé zhōngduān jìhuà	ITP

Integrated terrain unit mapping	综合地形单元制图	Zōnghé dìxíng dānyuán zhìtú	ITUM
Integrated test and checkout procedures	综合测试和检查程序	Zōnghé cèshì hé jiǎnchá chéngxù	ITCP
Integrated traffic handling	多元业务量处理	Duōyuán yèwùliàng chǔlǐ	
Integrated voice/data transmission system	话音/数据综合传输系统	Huàyīn/shùjù zōnghé chuánshū xìtǒng	
Integrated voice-messaging system	综合声音信息系统	Zōnghé shēngyīn xìnxī xìtǒng	IVMS
Integrated wideband communication system	综合宽带通信系统	Zōnghé kuāndài tōngxìn xìtǒng	IWCS
Integrating circuit	积分电路	Jīfēndiànlù	
Integrating delta modulation	积分增量调制	Jīfēn zēngliàng tiáozhì	IDM
Integrating-type A/D converter	积分式模/数转换器	Jīfēn-shì mó/shù zhuǎnhuànqì	
Integration	集成	Jíchéng	
Integration detector	指向累计检测器	Zhǐxiàng lěijì jiǎncèqì	
Integration loss	积累损耗	Jīlěi sǔnhào	
Integrator	积分器	Jīfēnqì	
Integrity (IPsec) ; completeness	完整性	Wánzhěngxìng	
Integrity authentication	完整性鉴定	Wánzhěngxìng jiàndìng	
Integrity check value	集成校验值	Jíchéng jiàoyàn zhí	ICV
Integrity check value	完整性检测值	Wánzhěngxìng jiǎncè zhí	ICV
Integrity check value	完整性检查值	Wánzhěngxìng jiǎnchá zhí	ICV
Integrity check value	完整性效验值	Wánzhěngxìng xiàoyàn zhí	
Integrity check vector	完整性检测向量	Wánzhěngxìng jiǎncè xiàngliàng	ICV
Integrity constraint (for database)	完整性约束	Wánzhěngxìng yuēshù	
Integrity protected command (in FTP)	完整性保护命令	Wánzhěngxìng bǎohù mìnglìng	MIC
Integrity sequencing	序列完整性	Xùliè wánzhěngxìng	
Intel ® (US company)	英特尔	Yīng-tè-ěr	
Intel ® architecture	英特尔架构	Yīng-tè-ěr jiàgòu	IA
Intel ® mobile module	英特尔移动模块	Yīng-tè-ěr yídòng mókuài	IMM
Intel Developer forum	英特尔开发者论坛	Yīng-tè-ěr kāifāzhě lùntán	IDF
Intel® Architecture Labs	Intel 公司构架实验室	Intel gōngsī gòujià shíyànshì	IAL
Intelligence	脑能	Nǎonéng	
Intelligent access function	智能接入功能	Zhìnéng jiērù gōngnéng	IAF
Intelligent agent	智能代理	Zhìnéng dàilǐ	
Intelligent building	智能大楼	Zhìnéng dàlóu	ZNL
Intelligent building	智能大厦	Zhìnéng dàshà	IB
Intelligent building	智能建筑	Zhìnéng jiànzhù	IB
Intelligent building management system	智能建筑管理系统	Zhìnéng jiànzhù guǎnlǐ xìtǒng	IBMS
Intelligent building system	智能大楼布线系统	Zhìnéng dàlóu bùxiàn xìtǒng	IBS
Intelligent content distribution	智能化内容配送	Zhìnénghuà nèiróng pèisòng	
Intelligent control	智能控制	Zhìnéng kòngzhì	
Intelligent decision support system	智能决策支持系统	Zhìnéng juécè zhīchí xìtǒng	IDSS
Intelligent document processing	智能文档处理	Zhìnéng wéndàng chǔlǐ	
Intelligent drive electronics	智能驱动电子仪器	Zhìnéng qūdòng diànzǐyíqì	IDE
Intelligent filtering	智能化滤波	Zhìnénghuà lǜbō	
Intelligent fire controller	照明智能控制器	Zhàomíng zhìnéng kòngzhìqì	IFC
Intelligent frequency hopping	智能跳频	Zhìnéng tiàopín	
Intelligent local search algorithm	智能本地搜索算法	Zhìnéng běndì sōusuǒ suànfǎ	ILSA
Intelligent multi-service transport platform	智能多业务光传送平台	Zhìnéng duō yèwù guāng chuánsòng píngtái	IMTP

Intelligent network	智能网	Zhìnéng wǎng	IN
Intelligent network	智能网络	Zhìnéng wǎngluò	IN
Intelligent network application part	职能网应用部分	Zhínéng wǎng yìngyòng bùfen	INAP
Intelligent network application procedure	职能网应用规程	Zhínéng wǎng yìngyòng guīchéng	INAP
Intelligent network application protocol	职能网应用协议	Zhínéng wǎng yìngyòng xiéyì	INAP
Intelligent network service node	智能网业务节点	Zhìnéng wǎng yèwù jiédiǎn	
Intelligent optical network	智能光网络	Zhìnéng guāng wǎngluò	OIN
Intelligent optical switching	智能光交换	Zhìnéng guāng jiāohuàn	IOS
Intelligent out station	智能外围站	Zhìnéng wàiwéizhàn	IOS
Intelligent peripheral	智能外设	Zhìnéng wàishè	IP
Intelligent peripheral	智能外围设备	Zhìnéng wàiwéi shèbèi	IP
Intelligent peripheral interface	智能外设接口	Zhìnéng wàishè jiēkǒu	IPI
Intelligent printer data stream (IBM use)	智能打印机数据流	Zhìnéng dǎyìnjī shùjùliú	IPDS
Intelligent queuing system	智能排队系统	Zhìnéng páiduì xìtǒng	
Intelligent railway system	智能铁路系统	Zhìnéng tiělù xìtǒng	IRS
Intelligent raster	智能栅格	Zhìnéng zhàgé	
Intelligent terminal	智能终端	Zhìnéng hōngduān	
Intelligent time division multiplexer	智能时分多路复用器	Zhìnéng shífèn duōlù fùyòngqì	ITDM
Intelligent transportation system	智能运输系统	Zhìnéng yùnshū xìtǒng	ITS
Intelligent underlay overlay	智能分层覆盖	Zhìnéng fēncéng fùgài	IUO
Intelligent underlay-overlay (network)	智能双层网	Zhìnéng shuāngcéng wǎng	IUO
Intelligent workstation	智能工作台	Zhìnéng gōngzuòtái	IWS
Intelligent workstation	智能工作站	Zhìnéng gōngzuòzhàn	IWS
Intelligibility	可懂度	Kědǒngdù	
Intensity control	辉亮控制	Huīliàng kòngzhì	
Intensity correction	辉亮校正	Huīliàng jiàozhèng	
Intensity modulation	辉亮调制	Huīliàng tiáozhì	
Intensity modulation-direction modulation	直接强度调制	Zhíjiē qiángdù tiáozhì	IM-DM
Intent lock	意向锁	Yìxiàng suǒ	
Inter Media Asia	亚洲多媒体展	Yàzhōu duōméitǐ zhǎn	
Interact, interactive	交互	Jiāohù	
Interaction	交互作用	Jiāohù zuòyòng	
Interaction matrix	交互矩阵	Jiāohù jǔzhèn	
Interactive	互动式	Hùdòngshì	
Interactive	交互式	Jiāohù-shì	
Interactive	交流式	Jiāoliú-shì	
Interactive application communication	交互式应用程序通讯	Jiāohù-shì yìngyòng chéngxù tōngxùn	IAC
Interactive around-sound	交互式环绕声	Jiāohù-shì huánrào shēng	IAS
Interactive computer graphics	交互计算机制图	Jiāohù jìsuànjī zhìtú	
Interactive debug	交互调式	Jiāohù diàoshì	IAD
Interactive dialog box	交互式对话框	Jiāohù-shì duìhuà kuàng	
Interactive digitizing	交互式数字化	Jiāohù-shì shùzìhuà	
Interactive graphics design software	交互式图形设计软件	Jiāohù-shì túxíng shèjì ruǎnjiàn	IDGS
Interactive logon	交互式登录	Jiāohù-shì dēnglù	
Interactive mode	交互方式	Jiāohù fāngshì	
Interactive Multimedia Association	交互式多媒体协议	Jiāohù-shì duōméitǐ xiéyì	IMA

Interactive processing	交互过程	Jiāohù guòchéng	
Interactive programming system	会话形式程序设计系统	Huìhuà xíngshì chéngxù shèjì xìtǒng	IPS
Interactive service	交互型业务	Jiāohù-xíng yèwù	
Interactive simulation library	交互仿真库	Jiāohù fǎngzhēn kù	
Interactive structured query language	交互式结构化查询语言	Jiāohù-shì jiégòuhuà cháxún yǔyán	ISQL
Interactive surface modeling	交互式表面模拟	Jiāohù-shì biǎomiàn mónǐ	
Interactive teleVision	互动电视	Hùdòng diànshì	ITV
Interactive terminal protocol	交互终端规约	Jiāohù zhōngduān guīyuē	ITP
Interactive tevevision	交互式电视	Jiāohù-shì diànshì	ITV
Interactive transaction	交互式事务	Jiāohù-shì shìwù	
Interactive video on demand with delayed access	延时交互式视频点播	Yánshí jiāohùshì shìpín diǎnbō	IVOD-d
Interactive videography	双向图文视传	Shuāngxiàng túwén shìchuán	
Interactive visualization	交互可视化	Jiāohù kěshìhuà	
Interactive visualization	交互式可视化	Jiāohù-shì kěshìhuà	
Interactive voice over data with instantaneous access	即时交互式视频点播	Jíshí jiāohùshì shìpín diǎnbō	IVOD-i
Interactive voice response	互动式语音应答	Hùdòngshì yǔyīn yìngdá	
Interactive voice response	交互语音响应	Jiāohù yǔyīn xiǎngyìng	IVR
Interactive voice response	交互语音应答	Jiāohù yǔyīn yìngdá	IVR
Interactive voice response	交互式语音应答	Jiāohù-shì yǔyīn yìngdá	
Interactive voice response (equipment)	语音交互设备	Yǔyīn jiāohù shèbèi	IVR
Interactive voice response system	交互语音应答系统	Jiāohù yǔyīn yìngdá xìtǒng	IVR
Inter-application communication	内部应用程序通讯	Nèibù yìngyòng chéngxù tōngxùn	IAC
Inter-area cell transfer	区域之间小区转移	Qūyù zhījiān xiǎoqū zhuǎnyí	
Inter-aural intensity difference	两侧声音强度差别	Liǎngcè shēngyīn qiángdù chābié	IID
Interband transmission	带间传输	Dài-jiān chuánshū	
Intercast	数据广播	Shùjù guǎngbō	
Inter-cell hand-off (cellular telephony)	过区切换	Guòqū qiēhuàn	
Inter-cell handover	小区间的越区切换	Xiǎoqū jiānde yuèqū qiēhuàn	
Inter-cell handover; intercell hand-off	小区间切换	Xiǎoqū-jiān qiēhuàn	
Intercept probability of frequency	频率截获概率	Pínlǜ jiéhuò gàilǜ	
Intercepted power	截取功率	Jiéqǔ gōnglǜ	
Interception of call service (by the switch, to route call to an automatic recording)	截接服务	Jiéjiē fúwù	
Interceptor flight tool (software)	拦截飞行工具	Lánjié fēixíng gōngjù	IFT
Interchange	互换	Hùhuàn	
Interchange data element	互换数据元素	Hùhuàn shùjù yuánsù	
Interchange format	互换格式	Hùhuàn géshi	
Interchange format	交换格式	Jiāohuàn géshi	
Interchange format class	互换格式类别	Hùhuàn géshi lèibié	
Inter-channel cross-color	信道间串色	Xìndào-jiān chuànsè	
Inter-channel cross-talk	信道间串话	Xìndào-jiān chuànhuà, chuàn sè	
Inter-channel gain difference	相互波道间增益差	Xiānghù bōdào-jiān zēngyì chà	
Inter-channel gain-change difference	相互波道间增益变化差	Xiānghù bōdào-jiān zēngyì biànhuà chà	
Inter-channel gain-change ratio	相互波道间增益变化率	Xiānghù bōdào-jiān zēngyì biànhuà lǜ	
Inter-channel interference	路际串扰	Lùjì chuànrǎo	ICI
Inter-channel interference	信道间干扰	Xìndào-jiān gānrǎo	ICI

Inter-channel time base error	通道间时基误差	Tōngdào-jiān shíjī wùchā	ITBE
Inter-character rest condition	字符间休止状态	Zìfú-jiān xiūzhǐ zhuàngtài	
Inter-character space	字符间隙	Zìfú jiànxì	
Inter-clutter visibility	杂波间可见度	Zábō-jiān kějiàndù	
Intercom telephone set	对讲电话机	Duìjiǎngdiànhuàjī	
Inter-communication	相互通信	Xiānghù tōngxìn	
Inter-computer communication link	计算机间通信链路	Jìsuànjī-jiān tōngxìn liànlù	ICL
Interconnect backboard	互联后面板	Hùlián hòumian bǎn	BIBB
Interconnect panel	互联面板	Hùlián miànbǎn	XICP
Interconnection	互连	Hùlián	
Interconnection charge	互连费	Hùlián fèi	
Interconnection network control sub-system	互联网控制子系统	Hùliánwǎng kòngzhì zixìtǒng	INCS
Interconnection network maintenance sub-system	互联网维护子系统	Hùliánwǎng wéihù zìxìtǒng	INMS
Inter-departmental net	部门联网	Bùmén liánwǎng	IDNet
Interdiction (IPsec)	禁止	Jìnzhǐ	
Inter-domain policy routing	域际策略路由选择	Yùjì cèlüè lùyóu xuǎnzé	IDPR
Inter-domain policy routing	域间策略路由选择	Yùjiān cèlüè lùyóu xuǎnzé	IDPR
Inter-domain routing protocol	域间路由协议	Yùjiān lùyóu xiéyì	IDRP
Inter-domain routing protocol	域间选路协议	Yùjiān xuǎnlù xiéyì	IDRP
Inter-domain routing protocol (ISO use)	域间路由选择协议	Yùjiān lùyóu xuǎnzé xiéyì	IDRP
Interface	接口	Jiēkǒu	
Interface bit rate	接口比特率	Jiēkǒu bǐtè lǜ	
Interface control	接口控制	Jiēkǒu kòngzhì	
Interface data unit	接口数据单元	Jiēkǒu shùjù dānyuán	IDU
Interface definition language	接口定义语言	Jiēkǒu dìngyì yǔyán	IDL
Interface description language	接口描述语言	Jiēkǒu miáoshù yǔyán	IDL
Interface gateway	接口网关	Jiēkǒu wǎngguān	IGW
Interface implication	接口含义	Jiēkǒu hányì	
Interface integrated circuit	接口集成电路	Jiēkǒu jíchéng diànlù	
Interface overhead	接口开销	Jiēkǒu kāixiao	
Interface overhead bit	接口附加位	Jiēkǒu fùjiā wèi	
Interface payload	接口负荷	Jiēkǒu fùhè	
Interface payload	接口净荷	Jiēkǒu jìnghé	
Interface payload	接口有效负荷	Jiēkǒu yǒuxiào fùhè	
Interface rate	接口速率	Jiēkǒu sùlǜ	
Interface service node	接口服务节点	Jiēkǒu fúwù jiédiǎn	ISN
Interface specification	接口规范	Jiēkǒu guīfàn	
Interface specification	协议书	Xiéyì shū	
Interface structure	接口结构	Jiēkǒu jiégòu	
Interface subscriber module	接口用户模块	Jiēkǒu yònghù mókuài	ISM
Interface translation	接口翻译	Jiēkǒu fānyì	
Interface (for GUI)	界面	Jièmiàn	
Interference	串扰	Chuànrǎo	
Interference cancellation system	干扰消除系统	Gānrǎo xiāochú xìtǒng	ICS
Interference compliance test	干扰顺从度测试	Gānrǎo shùncóngdù cèshì	ICT
Interference current	干扰电流	Gānrǎo diànliú	

Interference field strength	干扰场强	Gānrǎo chǎngqiáng	
Interference filter (optical)	干涉滤光镜	Gānshè lǜguāngjìng	
Interference overlay (coverage)	干涉性复盖层	Gānshè-xìng fùgài céng	
Interference power	干扰功率	Gānrǎo gōnglǜ	
Interference protection ratio	干扰保护比	Gānrǎo bǎohù bǐ	
Interference resistance or jamming resistance	抗扰度	Kàngrǎodù	
Interference signal code power	干扰信号码功率	Gānrǎo xìnhào mǎ gōnglǜ	ISCP
Interference source	干扰源	Gānrǎo yuán	
Interference suppression	干扰抑制	Gānrǎo yìzhì	
Interference suppression ignition cable	干扰抑制点火电缆	Gānrǎo yìzhì diǎnhuǒ diànlǎn	
Interference suppressor	干扰抑制器	Gānrǎo yìzhìqì	
Interference voltage	干扰电压	Gānrǎo diànyā	
Interfering signal	干扰信号	Gānrǎo xìnhào	
Interferometer (noun) , interferometric (adj)	干涉仪	Gānshèyí	IF
Interferometric synthetic aperture radar	干涉合成孔径雷达	Gānshè héchéng kǒngjìng léidá	
Interflow	层间流	Céngjiānliú	
Inter-frame transform	帧间变换	Zhèng-jiān biànhuàn	
Inter-governmental agreement	政府间协议	Zhèngfǔ-jiān xiéyì	
Interim coordination group	中间协调组	Zhōngjiān xiétiáo zǔ	ICG
Interim European Telecommunications Standard	欧洲通信临时（中间）标准	Oūzhōu tōngxìn línshí (zhōngjiān) biāozhǔn	I-ETS
Interim inter-switch signaling protocol	中期交换机间的信令协议	Zhōngqī jiāohuànjī jiānde xìnlìng xiéyì	iisp
Interim local management interface	过度期本地管理接口	Guòdùqī běndì guǎnlǐ jiēkǒu	ILMI
Interim local management interface	临时的局部管理接口	Línshíde júbù guǎnlǐ jiēkǒu	ILMI
Interim type approval	中间型号批准	Zhōngjiān xínghào pīzhǔn	ITA
Interim-interswitch signaling protocol	交换机间临时信令系统	Jiāohuànjī-jiān línshí xìnlìng xìtǒng	IISP
Interior gateway protocol	内部路由协议	Nèibù lùyóu xiéyì	IGP
Interior gateway routing protocol	内部网关路由选择协议	Nèibù wǎngguān lùyóu xuǎnzé xiéyì	IGRP
Interior gateway routing protocol (Cisco use)	内部网关路由协议	Nèibù wǎngguān lùyóu xiéyì	IGRP
Interlace (video term)	隔行	Géháng	
Interleave delay	交织延时	Jiāozhī yánshí	
Interleaved (adjective)	内插的	Nèichāde	
Interleaver	间插分复用器	Jiānchā fēn fùyòngqì	
Interleaving	交错	Jiāocuò	
Interleaving	交织	Jiāozhī	
Interleaving semantics	交织语义	Jiāozhī yǔyì	
Interlock	互锁	Hùsuǒ	
Interlock code (CUG SS)	闭锁码	Bìsuǒ mǎ	IC
Interlock code (CUG SS)	连锁码	Liánsuǒ mǎ	IC
Interlock code of the preferential CUG (closed user group)	优先的 CUG 连锁码	Yōuxiānde CUG liánsuǒ mǎ	IC(pref)
Interlocking device	联锁机构	Liánsuǒ jīgòu	
Intermediate altitude communication satellite	中高空通信卫星	Zhōng gāokōng tōngxìn wèixīng	IACS
Intermediate carrier	中间载波	Zhōngjiān zàibō	
Intermediate character	中间字符	Zhōngjiān zìfú	
Intermediate cross connect	中介交叉联接	Zhōngjiè jiāochā liánjiē	ICC
Intermediate data rate	中速率	Zhōng sùlǜ	IDR

Intermediate data rate (between 64kbps and 44.763Mbps)	中等数据率	Zhōngděng shùjù lǜ	IDR
Intermediate distributing frame	中级配线架	Zhōngjí pèixiànjià	IDF
Intermediate distribution facility	中介分布设备	Zhōngjiè fēnbù shèbèi	IDF
Intermediate distribution frame	中间配线架	Zhōngjiān pèixiànjià	IDF
Intermediate equipment	中间设备	Zhōngjiān shèbèi	
Intermediate feed antenna	中馈天线	Zhōngkuì tiānxiàn	
Intermediate frame bit	中间帧比特	Zhōngjiān zhèng bǐtè	I
Intermediate frequency	中频	Zhōngpín	IF
Intermediate frequency amplifier	中频放大器	Zhōngpín fàngdàqì	
Intermediate frequency amplifier center frequency	中频放大器的中心频率	Zhōngpín fàngdàqìde zhōngxīn pínlǜ	
Intermediate frequency amplifier gain	中频放大器增益	Zhōngpín fàngdàqì zēngyì	
Intermediate frequency canceller	中频对消器	Zhōngpín duìxiāoqì	
Intermediate frequency integration	中频积累	Zhōngpín jīlěi	
Intermediate frequency jamming (interference)	中频干扰	Zhōngpín gānrǎo	
Intermediate frequency limiting amplifier	限幅中频放大器	Xiànfú zhōngpín fàngdàqì	
Intermediate frequency preamplifier	前置中频放大器	Qiánzhì zhōngpín fàngdàqì	
Intermediate frequency rejection ratio	中频抑制比	Zhōngpín yìzhì bǐ	
Intermediate frequency switching matrix	中频交换矩阵	Zhōngpín jiāohuàn jǔzhèn	IF-SM
Intermediate language	中间语言	Zhōngjiān yǔyán	IL
Intermediate language	中介语言	Zhōngjiè yǔyán	IL
Intermediate network node	中间网络节点	Zhōngjiān wǎngluò jiédiǎn	INN
Intermediate node	中间节点	Zhōngjiān jiédiǎn	
Intermediate routing node	中介路由选择节点	Zhōngjiè lùyóu xuǎnzé jiédiǎn	IRN
Intermediate services part	中间业务部分	Zhōngjiān yèwù bùfen	ISP
Intermediate session routing	中介会话路由选择	Zhōngjiè huìhuà lùyóu xuǎnzé	ISR
Intermediate system	中间系统	Zhōngjiān xìtǒng	IS
Intermediate system	中介系统	Zhōngjiè xìtǒng	IS
Intermediate system to intermediate system protocol (ISO, IETF usage)	中间系统到中间系统协议	Zhōngjiān xìtǒng dào zhōngjiān xìtǒng xiéyì	IS-IS
Intermediate system to intermediate system routing exchange protocol	中间系统到中间系统路由交换协议	Zhōngjiān xìtǒng dào zhōngjiān xìtǒng lùyóu jiāohuàn xiéyì	IS-IS
Intermediate system-to-intermediate system	中介系统到中介系统	Zhōngjiè xìtǒng dào zhōngjiè xìtǒng	IS-IS
Intermittent fault	断续故障	Duànxù gùzhàng	
Intermittent line	间断线	Jiànduàn xiàn	
Intermittent ringing	断续振铃	Duànxù zhènlíng	
Intermodulation	互调	Hùtiáo	IM
Intermodulation	互相调制	Hùxiāng tiáozhì	IM
Intermodulation component	互调分量	Hùtiáo fēnliàng	
Intermodulation distortion	互调失真	Hùtiáo shīzhēn	IMD
Intermodulation fade	互调衰减	Hùtiáo shuāijiǎn	
Intermodulation immunity	互调抗扰性	Hùtiáo kàngrǎoxìng	
Intermodulation noise	互调噪声	Hùtiáo zàoshēng	
Intermodulation product	互调产物	Hùtiáo chǎnwù	
Intermodulation product order	互调产物阶次	Hùtiáo chǎnwù jiēcì	
Intermodulation suppression	互调抑制	Hùtiáo yìzhì	
Inter-module communication	模块间通信	Mókuài-jiān tōngxìn	

Internal boundary layer	内部边界层	Nèibù biānjiècéng	
Internal chassis management bus	内部管理总线	Nèibù guǎnlǐ zǒngxiàn	ICMB
Internal damping	内部阻尼	Nèibù zǔní	
Internal data	内部数据	Nèibù shùjù	
Internal data structure	内部数据结构	Nèibù shùjù jiégòu	
Internal data transfer rate	内部数据传输率	Nèibù shùjù chuánshū lǜ	
Internal disabled state	内因不能工作状态	Nèiyīn bùnéng gōngzuò zhuàngtài	
Internal error (IPsec TLS)	内部错误消息	Nèibù cuòwù xiāoxi	
Internal flag	内部标识码	Nèibù biāozhì mǎ	
Internal gateway protocol	内部网关协议	Nèibù wǎngguān xiéyì	IGP
Internal hard disk	内置硬盘	Nèizhì yìngpán	
Internal host	内部主机	Nèibù zhǔjī	
Internal identifier	内部标识符	Nèibù biāozhì fú	
Internal immunity	内部抗扰性	Nèibù kàngrǎo xìng	
Internal immunity	内部抗扰性	Nèibù kàngrǎoxìng	
Internal impedance	内阻	Nèizǔ	
Internal interrupt	内部中断	Nèibù zhōngduàn	
Internal memory	内存储器	Nèi cúnchǔqì	
Internal network	内部网络	Nèibù wǎngluò	
Internal network-node interface	内部网络节点接口	Nèibù wǎngluò jiédiǎn jiēkǒu	I-NNI
Internal noise	内部噪声	Nèibù zàoshēng	
Internal reference point	内部参考点	Nèibù cānkǎo diǎn	IRP
Internal ring pliers, snap ring pliers	挡圈钳	Dǎngquānqián	
Internal security audit (IPsec)	内部安全审计	Nèibù ānquán shěnjì	
Internal service broker (in VPN)	内部服务代理	Nèibù fúwù dàilǐ	ISB
Internal sort	内部排序	Nèibù páixù	
Internal spot extraction equipment	内光点录取设备	Nèi guāng diǎn lùqǔ shèbèi	
Internal stack	内置堆栈	Nèizhì duīzhàn	IS
Internal sub-layer service	内部子层服务	Nèibù zicéng fúwù	ISS
Internal videotex application provider	可视图文应用内部提供者	Kěshì túwén yìngyòng nèibù tígòngzhě	
Internal wave	内波	Nèibō	
Internal wave generator	内波发生器	Nèibō fāshēngqì	
International alphabet no. 5	国际 5 号电码表	Guójì wǔhào diànmǎ biǎo	IA5
International alphabet no.5 (ISO 7-bit code)	国际五号电码	Guójì wǔhào diànmǎ	IA5
International alphabet set	国际字母	Guójì zìmǔ	IAS
International alternative billing service	国际可选记帐业务	Guójì kěxuǎn jìzhàng yèwù	IABS
International atomic time	国际原子时	Guójì yuánzǐshí	TAI
International automatic circuit	国际自动电路	Guójì zìdòng diànlù	
International automatic time	国际原子时间	Guójì yuánzǐ shíjiān	TAI
International both way trunk	国际双向中继线	Guójì shuāngxiàng zhōngjìxiàn	INTBWT
International Business Machines (US company)	国际商业机器公司	Guójì shāngyè jīqì gōngsī	IBM
International Civil Aviation Organization	国际民航组织	Guójì mínháng zǔzhī	ICAO
International code designator	国际编码设计	Guójì biānmǎ shèjì	ICD
International Committee on Radio Interference	国际无线电干扰委员会	Guójì wúxiàndiàn gānrǎo wěiyuánhuì	CCIR
International communications satellite organization	国际通信卫星组织	Guójì tōngxìn wèixīng zǔzhī	INTERSAT
International Computer Security Association	国际计算机安全协会	Guójì jìsuànjī ānquán xiéhuì	ICSA

International connection	国际连接	Guójì liánjiē	
International Data Corporation	国际数据机构	Guójì shùjù jīgòu	IDC
International data encryption algorithm	国际数据加密算法	Guójì shùjù jiāmì suànfǎ	IDEA
International Data Group	国际数据集团	Guójì shùjù jítuán	IDG
International Data Group	国际数据组织	Guójì shùjù zǔzhī	IDG
International data transmission link	国际数据传输链路	Guójì shùjù chuánshū liànlù	
International data transmission system	国际数据传输系统	Guójì shùjù chuánshū xìtǒng	
International direct dialing	国际直拨	Guójì zhíbō	IDD
International direct distance dialing	国际长途自动电话	Guójì chángtú zìdòngdiànhuà	IDDD
International Electromagnetic Interference Commission	国际电磁干扰委员会	Guójì diàncí gānrǎo wěiyuánhuì	CISPR
International Electrotechnical Commission	国际电工技术委员会	Guójì diàngōng jìshù wěiyuánhuì	IEC
International Electrotechnical Commission	国际电工委员会	Guójì diàngōng wěiyuánhuì	IEC
International Electrotechnical Commission	国际电子技术委员会	Guójì diànzǐ jìshù wěiyuánhuì	IEC
International Federation for Information Processing	国际信息处理联合会	Guójì xìnxī chǔlǐ liánhéhuì	IFIP
International forum white paper	国际白皮书论坛	Guójì báipíshū lùntán	IFWP
International gateway	国际接口局	Guójì jiēkǒu jú	IG
International Graphics Exchange System (US company)	国际图形交换系统	Guójì túxíng jiāohuàn xìtǒng	IGES
International leased circuit	国际租用电路	Guójì zūyòng diànlù	
International line	国际线路	Guójì xiànlù	
International link	国际链路	Guójì liànlù	
International main section	国际主段	Guójì zhǔduàn	
International Maritime Satellite Organization	国际海事卫星组织	Guójì hǎishì wèixīng zǔzhī	INMARSAT
International Maritime Satellite Telecommunications Organization	国际海事卫星通信组织	Guójì hǎishì wèixīng tōngxìn zǔzhī	INMARSAT
International mobile equipment identity	国际移动设备识别码	Guójì yídòng shèbèi shíbié mǎ	IMEI
International mobile equipment identity software version	国际移动设备识别软件版本	Guójì yídòng shèbèi shíbié ruǎnjiàn bǎnběn	IMEISV
International mobile equipment identity software version	国际移动台识别软件版本号	Guójì yídòngtái shíbié ruǎnjiàn bǎnběn hào	IMEISV
International mobile group identity	国际移动群识别	Guójì yídòngqún shíbié	IMGI
International mobile station equipment identity	国际移动设备识别号码	Guójì yídòng shèbèi shíbié hàomǎ	IMEI
International mobile station identity	国际移动台标识符	Guójì yídòngtái biāozhìfú	IMSI
International mobile station identity	国际移动台识别号码	Guójì yídòngtái shíbié hàomǎ	IMSI
International mobile subscriber ID code	国际移动用户识别码	Guójì yídòng yònghù shíbié mǎ	IMSI
International mobile subscriber identity	国际移动用户标识	Guójì yídòng yònghù biāozhì	IMSI
International mobile subscriber identity	国际移动用户识别号码	Guójì yídòng yònghù shíbié hàomǎ	IMSI
International mobile telecommnications 2000	国际移动通信 2000	Guójì yídòng tōngxìn 2000	IMT-2000
International mobile telecommunications	国际移动通信	Guójì yídòng tōngxìn	IMT
International mobile terminal equipment identity	国际移动终端设备标识	Guójì yídòng zhōngduān shèbèi biāozhì	IMEI
International mobile user number	国际移动用户号码	Guójì yídòng yònghù hàomǎ	IMUN
International Multimedia Teleconferencing Consortium	国际多媒体电子会议协会	Guójì duōméitǐ diànzǐ huìyì xiéhuì	IMTC
International Organization for Standardization	国际标准化组织	Guójì Biāozhǔnhuà Zǔzhī	ISO
International Packet Switching Service (BPO)	国际信息包交换业务	Guójì xìnxī bāojiāohuàn yèwù	IPSS
International portable equipment identifier	国际移动设备标识号	Guójì yídòng shèbèi biāozhì hào	IPEI
International portable user identity	国际移动用户标识号	Guójì yídòng yònghù biāozhì hào	IPUI

International public facsimile service	国际公用传真业务	Guójì gōngyòng chuánzhēn yèwù	
International Radio Consultative Committee	国际无线电咨询委员会	Guójì wúxiàndiàn zīxún wěiyuánhuì	CCIR
International Roaming Experts Group (GSM MoU)	国际漫游组	Guójì mànyóu zǔ	IREG
International routing plan	国际线路选定计划	Guójì xiànlù xuǎndìng jìhuà	IRP
International Science Committee	国际科学委员会	Guójì kēxué wěiyuánhuì	ISC
International section	国际段	Guójì duàn	
International service control point	国际业务控制点	Guójì yèwù kòngzhìdiǎn	ISCP
International service switching point	国际业务交换点	Guójì yèwù jiāohuàndiǎn	ISSP
International signal transfer point	国际信令转接点	Guójì xìnlìng zhuǎnjiē diǎn	ISTP
International signaling point	国际信令点	Guójì xìnlìng diǎn	ISP
International Softswitch Consortium	国际软交换协会	Guójì ruǎn jiāohuàn xiéhuì	ISC
International Solid-State Circuits Conference	国际晶体管电路讨论会	Guójì jīngtǐguǎn diànlù tǎolùnhuì	ISSCC
International Special Committee on Radio Interference	国际无线电干扰专门委员会	Guójì wúxiàndiàn gānrǎo zhuānmén wěiyuánhuì	CISPR
International Standard Code for Information Interchange	信息交换用国际标准代码	Xìnxī jiāohuàn-yòng guójì biāozhǔn dàimǎ	ISCII
International Standard Organization's Moving Picture Expert group	国际标准化组织的活动图片专家组	Guójì Biāozhǔnhuà Zǔzhīde huódòng túpiàn zhuānjiāzǔ	ISO/MPEG
International Standardization Organization	国际标准化组织	Guójì Biāozhǔnhuà Zǔzhī	ISO
International standardized profile	国际标准规格	Guójì biāozhǔn guīgé	
International subscriber dialing	国际用户拨号	Guójì yònghù bōhào	ISD
International switching center	国际交换中心	Guójì jiāohuàn zhōngxīn	ISC
International switching center	国际局	Guójì jú	ISC
International switching center	国际软交换中心	Guójì ruǎnjiāohuàn zhōngxīn	ISC
International Switching Maintenance Center	国际电话交换维护中心	Guójì diànhuà jiāohuàn wéihù zhōngxīn	ISMC
International Symposium on Computer and Information Service	国际计算机与信息学论专题讨论会	Guójì jìsuànjī yǔ xìnxīxué lùn zhuāntí tǎolùn huì	COINS
International system of units	国际单位制	Guójì dānwèizhì	
International Telecommunication Union – Radiocommunication Sector	国际电信联盟 - 无线通讯分册	Guójì Diànxìn Liánméng - wúxiàn tōngxùn fēncè	ITU-R
International Telecommunication Union-Telecommunication Standardization Sector	国际电信联盟-电信标准部门	Guójì Diànxìn Liánméng-- Diànxìn biāozhǔn bùmén	ITU-T
International Telecommunications satellite	国际电信卫星组织	Guójì diànxìn wèixīng zǔzhī	INTELSAT
International Telecommunications Satellite Organization	国际远程通信卫星组织	Guójì yuǎnchéng tōngxìn wèixīng zǔzhī	ITSO
International Telecommunications Union - Telecommunications Standardization Sector	国际电信联盟-电信标准化部门	Guójì Diànxìn Liánméng—diànxìn biāozhǔnhua bùmén	ITU-T
International Telecommunications Union (UN)	国际电信联盟	Guójì Diànxìn Liánméng	ITU
International telegraph alphabet no.1	国际一号电码	Guójì yīhào diànmǎ	
International telegraph alphabet no.2	国际二号电码	Guójì èrhào diànmǎ	
International telegraph alphabet no.4	国际四号电码	Guójì sìhào diànmǎ	
International Telegraph and Telephone Consultative Committee	国际电报电话咨询委员会	Guójì diànbào diànhuà zīxún wěiyuánhuì	CCITT
International Telegraph and Telephone Consultative Committee	国际电话电报咨询委员会	Guójì diànhuà diànbào zīxún wěiyuánhuì	CCITT
International Telegraph and Telephone Consultative Committee's high-level language	国际电话电报咨询委员会高级语言	Guójì diànhuà diànbào zīxún wěiyuánhuì gāojí yǔyán	CHILL
International Telephone and Telegraph Co. ITT (UK)	国际电话电报公司	Guójì diànhuà diànbào gōngsī	ITT

English	Chinese	Pinyin	Abbr.
International telephone connection	国际电话连接	Guójì diànhuà liánjiē	
International transit part	国际转接部分	Guójì zhuǎnjiē bùfen	ITP
International transit switch	国际转接交换局	Guójì zhuǎnjiē jiāohuànjú	INTS
International transit switching center	国际转换中心	Guójì zhuǎnhuàn zhōngxīn	ITSC
International user identification module identifier	国际 USIM 标识符	Guójì USIM biāozhìfú	IUI
International videotex gateway	国际可视图文网关	Guójì kěshì túwén wǎngguān	
International virtual private network service	国际虚拟专网业务	Guójì xūnǐ zhuān wǎng yèwù	IVPN
Internet	国际互连网	Guójì hùliánwǎng	
Internet	互联网	Hùliánwǎng	
Internet	联网	Liánwǎng	
Internet	英特网	Yīng-tè-wǎng	
Internet	因特网	Yīntèwǎng	
Internet access provider	因特网接入提供者	Yīntèwǎng jiērù tígòngzhě	IAP
Internet Activities Board	因特网工作委员会	Yīntèwǎng gōngzuò wěiyuánhuì	IAB
Internet activities board	因特网活动委员会	Yīntèwǎng huódòng wěiyuánhuì	IAB
Internet adapter	因特网适配器	Yīntèwǎng shìpèiqì	IA
Internet address	因特网网络地址	Yīntèwǎng wǎngluò dìzhǐ	IA
Internet Architecture Board	国际互联网体系结构委员会	Guójì hùliánwǎng tǐxì jiégòu wěiyuánhuì	IAB
Internet Architecture Board	国际互联网网络体系技术委员会	Guójì hùliánwǎng wǎngluò tǐxì jìshù wěiyuánhuì	IAB
Internet Architecture Board	因特网结构委员会	Yīntèwǎng jiégòu wěiyuánhuì	IAB
Internet Architecture Board	因特网体系结构委员会	Yīntèwǎng tǐxì jiégòu wěiyuánhuì	IAB
Internet Assigned Numbers Authority	因特网编号分配委员会	Yīntèwǎng biānhào fēnpèi wěiyuánhuì	IANA
Internet Assigned Numbers Authority	因特网编号管理局	Yīntèwǎng biānhào guǎnlǐjú	IANA
Internet Assigned Numbers Authority	因特网编号收授权委员会	Yīntèwǎng biānhào shōu shòuquán wěiyuánhuì	IANA
Internet Assigned Numbers Authority	因特网号码分配部门	Yīntèwǎng hàomǎ fēnpèi bùmén	IANA
Internet aware fax	能直接连在 IP 网上的传真机	Néng zhíjiē liánzài IP wǎngshàngde chuánzhēnjī	IAF
Internet business center	因特网商业中心	Yīntèwǎng shāngyè zhōngxīn	IBC
Internet cache protocol	英特网缓存协议	Yīng-tè-wǎng huǎncún xiéyì	ICP
Internet café	网吧	Wǎngbā	
Internet call center	因特网呼叫中心	Yīntèwǎng hūjiào zhōngxīn	ICC
Internet call screening	因特网呼叫筛选	Yīntèwǎng hūjiào shāixuǎn	
Internet call waiting	因特网呼叫等待	Yīntèwǎng hūjiào děngdài	
Internet connection server	因特网连接服务器	Yīntèwǎng liánjiē fúwùqì	ICS
Internet content provider	互联网内容提供商	Hùliánwǎng nèiróng tígōng shāng	ICP
Internet content provider	因特网内容提供商	Yīntèwǎng nèiróng tígōngshāng	ICP
Internet content provider	因特网内容提供者	Yīntèwǎng nèiróng tígòngzhě	ICP
Internet control message protocol	互联网控制消息协议	Hùliánwǎng kòngzhì xiāoxi xiéyì	ICMP
Internet control message protocol	互联网消息协议	Hùliánwǎng xiāoxi xiéyì	ICMP
Internet control message protocol	网际控制消息协议	Wǎngjì kòngzhì xiāoxi xiéyì	ICMP
Internet control message protocol	因特网控制报文协议	Yīntèwǎng kòngzhì bàowén xiéyì	ICMP
Internet control message protocol	因特网控制信息协议	Yīntèwǎng kòngzhì xìnxī xiéyì	ICMP
Internet control message protocol	因特网信息控制协议	Yīntèwǎng xìnxī kòngzhì xiéyì	ICMP

Internet control message protocol router discovery	因特网控制报文协议发现路由器	Yīntèwǎng kòngzhì bàowén xiéyì fāxiàn lùyóuqì	IRD
Internet controller	互相网控制器	Hùxiāngwǎng kòngzhìqì	INC
Internet data center	互联网数据中心	Hùliánwǎng shùjù zhōngxīn	IDC
Internet data center	因特网数据中心	Yīntèwǎng shùjù zhōngxīn	IDC
Internet draft	因特网草案	Yīntèwǎng cǎo'àn	ID
Internet Engineering Note	因特网工程备忘录	Yīntèwǎng gōngchéng bèiwànglù	IEN
Internet Engineering Steering group	因特网工程管理组	Yīntèwǎng gōngchéng guǎnlǐ zǔ	IESG
Internet Engineering Task Force	互联网工程任务组	Hùliánwǎng gōngchéng rènwu zǔ	IETF
Internet Engineering Task Force	Internet 工程任务组	Internet gōngchéng rènwu zǔ	IETF
Internet Engineering Task Force	英特网工程任务阻	Yīng-tè-wǎng gōngchéng rènwu zǔ	IETF
Internet Engineering Task Force	因特网工程部	Yīntèwǎng gōngchéng bù	IETF
Internet Engineering Task Force	因特网工程任务组	Yīntèwǎng gōngchéng rènwu zǔ	IETF
Internet Engineering Task Force	因特网工程作业推动	Yīntèwǎng gōngchéng zuòyè tuīdòng	IETF
Internet experiment note	因特网实验备忘录	Yīntèwǎng shíyàn bèiwànglù	IEN
Internet explorer	因特网测试员	Yīntèwǎng cèshìyuán	IE
Internet fiber channel protocol (IETF use)	Internet 光纤信道协议	Internet guāngxiān xìndào xiéyì	iFCP
Internet group management protocol	互联网组管理协议	Hùliánwǎng zǔ guǎnlǐ xiéyì	IGMP
Internet group management protocol (IPsec)	网际群组管理协议	Wǎngjì qúnzǔ guǎnlǐ xiéyì	IGMP
Internet group membership protocol	因特网组成员协议	Yīntèwǎng zǔchéngyuán xiéyì	IGMP
Internet group message protocol	互联网组消息协议	Hùliánwǎng zǔ xiāoxi xiéyì	IGMP
Internet group message protocol	互联网组播成员管理协议	Hùliánwǎng zǔbō chéngyuán guǎnlǐ xiéyì	IGMP
Internet hosted octet stream service	因特网提供的八比特组流量业务	Yīntèwǎng tígōngde bābǐtèzǔ liúliàng yèwù	IHOSS
Internet imaging protocol	因特网图像协议	Yīntèwǎng túxiàng xiéyì	IIP
Internet information server	互联网信息服务器	Hùliánwǎng xìnxī fúwùqì	IIS
Internet information server	因特网信息服务器	Yīntèwǎng xìnxī fúwùqì	IIS
Internet information services (in SQL Server)	因特网信息服务	Yīntèwǎng xìnxī fúwù	IIS
Internet inter-ORB protocol	互联网 ORB 间通信协议	Hùliánwǎng ORB-jiān tōngxìn xiéyì	IIOP
Internet inter-ORB protocol (CORBA term)	因特网 ORB 间协议	Yīntèwǎng ORB-jiān xiéyì	IIOP
Internet key exchange	网络钥匙交换	Wǎngluò yàoshi jiāohuàn	IKE
Internet key exchange	因特网密钥交换	Yīntèwǎng mìyào jiāohuàn	IKE
Internet key exchange protocol	因特网密钥交换协议	Yīntèwǎng mìyào jiāohuàn xiéyì	IKE
Internet mail consortium	因特网邮件组织	Yīntèwǎng yóujiàn zǔzhī	IMC
Internet message access protocol	因特网信息访问协议	Yīntèwǎng xìnxī fǎngwèn xiéyì	IMAP
Internet message access protocol version 4	第四版因特网信息存取协议	Dìsìbǎn Yīntèwǎng xìnxī cúnqǔ xiéyì	IMAP4
Internet mobile/multimedia telecommunication	因特网移动/多媒体通信	Yīntèwǎng yídòng/duōméitǐ tōngxìn	IMT-2000
Internet monthly report	因特网月度报告	Yīntèwǎng yuèdù bàogào	IMR
Internet multiedia sub-system	因特网多媒体子网	Yīntèwǎng duōméitǐ ziwǎng	IMS
Internet navigation	因特网导航	Yīntèwǎng dǎoháng	
Internet network information center	国际互联网网络信息中心	Guójì hùliánwǎng wǎngluò xìnxī zhōngxīn	InterNIC
Internet network information center	网际网络信息中心	Wǎngjì wǎngluò xìnxī zhōngxīn	InterNIC
Internet open trading protocol	互联网开放贸易协议	Hùliánwǎng kāifàng màoyì xiéyì	IOTP
Internet payment provider	因特网支付提供商	Yīntèwǎng zhīfù tígōng shāng	IPP
Internet phone	网际电话	Wǎngjì diànhuà	

Internet presence provider	因特网平台提供者	Yīntèwǎng píngtái tígòngzhě	IPP
Internet printing protocol	因特网打印协议	Yīntèwǎng dǎyìn xiéyì	IPP
Internet protocol	互联网规程	Hùliánwǎng guīchéng	IP
Internet protocol	互联网协议	Hùliánwǎng xiéyì	IP
Internet protocol	联网协议	Liánwǎng xiéyì	IP
Internet protocol	网际互联协议	Wǎngjì hùlián xiéyì	IP
Internet protocol	网际协议	Wǎngjì xiéyì	IP
Internet protocol	因特网协议	Yīntèwǎng xiéyì	IP
Internet protocol (IP) over synchronous digital hierarchy (SDH)	SDH 上传送 IP	SDH-shàng chuansòng IP	POS
Internet protocol address	数字地址	Shùzì dìzhǐ	
Internet protocol device control	IP 设备控制	IP shèbèi kòngzhì	IPDC
Internet protocol mobility support protocol	IP 活动支持协议	IP huódòng zhīchí xiéyì	
Internet protocol navigator	IP 导航器	IP dǎohángqì	
Internet protocol over synchronous digital hierarchy	同步数字系列上的因特网协议	Tóngbù shùzì xìliè shàngde Yīntèwǎng xiéyì	IP over SDH
Internet protocol packet spoofing (hacker term)	欺骗 IP 包	Qīpiàn IP bāo	
Internet protocol security	网际协议安全	Wǎngjì xiéyì ānquán	IPSec
Internet protocol security protocol	IP 网络安全协议	IP wǎngluò ānquán xiéyì	IPSEC
Internet protocol switching	IP 交换	IP jiāohuàn	
Internet protocol version 4	因特网协议版本 4	Yīntèwǎng xiéyì bǎnběn 4	Ipv4
Internet protocol version 6	互联网协议-第 6 版	Hùliánwǎng xiéyì--dì 6 bǎn	IPv6
Internet protocol version 6	因特网协议版本 6	Yīntèwǎng xiéyì bǎnběn 6	IPv6
Internet protovol version 4	互联网协议-第 4 版	Hùliánwǎng xiéyì--dì 4 bǎn	Ipv4
Internet relay chat	联网中继聊天	Liánwǎng zhōngjì liáotiān	
Internet relay chat	网际清淡	Wǎngjì qīngdàn	IRC
Internet relay chat	网络聊天	Wǎngluò liáotiān	IRC
Internet relay chat	网络中继聊天	Wǎngluò zhōngjì liáotiān	IRC
Internet relay chat	因特网接力闲谈	Yīntèwǎng jiēlì xiántán	IRC
Internet relay chat	因特网中继闲谈	Yīntèwǎng zhōngjì xiántán	IRC
Internet relay chat protocol (IETF usage)	网际转发闲聊协议	Wǎngjì zhuǎnfā xiánliáo xiéyì	IRCP
Internet Research Steering group	因特网研究管理组	Yīntèwǎng yánjiū guǎnlǐ zǔ	IRSG
Internet Research Steering group	因特网研究指导组	Yīntèwǎng yánjiū zhǐdǎo zǔ	IRSG
Internet Research Task Force	因特网研究部	Yīntèwǎng yánjiū bù	IRTF
Internet security association and key management protocol	因特网安全连接和密钥管理协议	Yīntèwǎng ānquán liánjiē hé miyào guǎnlǐ xiéyì	ISAKMP
Internet service provider	互联网业务提供商	Hùliánwǎng yèwù tígōng shāng	ISP
Internet service provider	Internet 服务提供商	Internet fúwù tígōngshāng	ISP
Internet service provider	英特网业务提供者	Yīng-tè-wǎng yèwù tígòngzhě	ISP
Internet service provider	因特网服务提供商	Yīntèwǎng fúwù tígōngshāng	ISP
Internet service provider	因特网服务提供者	Yīntèwǎng fúwù tígòngzhě	ISP
Internet service provider	因特网业务提供商	Yīntèwǎng yèwù tígōng shāng	ISP
Internet service provider	因特网业务提供者	Yīntèwǎng yèwù tígòngzhě	ISP
Internet short message gateway	互联网短信网关	Hùliánwǎng duǎnxin wǎngguān	ISMG
Internet short message gateway	因特网短消息网关	Yīntèwǎng duǎn xiāoxi wǎngguān	ISMG
Internet small computer system interface (IETF usage)	Internet 小型计算机系统接口	Internet xiǎoxíng jìsuànjī xìtǒng jiēkǒu	iSCSI

Internet Society	因特网协会	Yīntèwǎng xiéhuì	ISOC
Internet Society	因特网学会	Yīntèwǎng xuéhuì	ISOC
Internet storage name service (IETF usage)	Internet 存储名称服务	Internet cúnchǔ míngchēng fúwù	iSNS
Internet Streaming Media Alliance (created by Apple, Cisco, Lasenna, and Philips)	互联网流媒体联盟	Hùliánwǎng liú méitǐ liánméng	
Internet talk radio	网际广播	Wǎngjì guǎngbō	ITR
Internet telephone gateway	因特网电话网关	Yīntèwǎng diànhuà wǎngguān	ITG
Internet videoconference	因特网电视会议	Yīntèwǎng diànshì huìyì	
Internet videoconference	因特网会议电视	Yīntèwǎng huìyì diànshì	
Internet videoconference	因特网视频会议	Yīntèwǎng shìpín huìyì	
Inter-network circuit section	网间电路段	Wǎngjiān diànlù duàn	ICS
Inter-network datagram protocol	网间互通数据报协议	Wǎngjiān hùtōng shùjùbào xiéyì	IDP
Inter-network packet exchange	包交换协议	Bāo jiāohuàn xiéyì	IPX
Inter-network packet exchange	交互网络信息包交换	Jiāohù wǎngluò xìnxī bāo jiāohuàn	IPX
Inter-network packet exchange	网际数据包(分组)交换	Wǎngjì shùjù bāo (fēnzǔ) jiāohuàn	IPX
Inter-network packet exchange control protocol	网间数据包交换控制协议	Wǎngjiān shùjù bāo jiāohuàn kòngzhì xiéyì	IPXCP
Internetwork packet exchange protocol (Novell usage)	网络分组交换协议	Wǎngluò fēnzǔ jiāohuàn xiéyì	IPX
Inter-network protocol data unit	互联网协议数据单元	Hùliánwǎng xiéyì shùjù dānyuán	IPDU
Internetworking data switching exchange	网络互连数据交换机	Wǎngluò hùlián shùjù jiāohuànjī	IDSE
Internetworking protocol	组网协议	Zǔwǎng xiéyì	IP
Inter-office communication	室内通信	Shìnèi tōngxìn	IOC
Interoffice line	局间线路	Jú-jiān xiànlù	
Interoperability	互操作能力	Hùcāozuò nénglì	
Interoperability	互操作性	Hùcāozuòxìng	
Interoperability	互通性	Hùtōngxìng	
Interoperability	齐套性	Qítàoxìng	
Interoperable interface	可互操作接口	Kěhùcāozuò jiēkǒu	
Interoperable object reference	可互操作的对象引用	Kěhùcāozuòde duìxiàng yǐnyòng	IOR
Inter-operation, inter-operability	互操作	Hùcāozuò	
Inter-paging networking protocol	高速寻呼联网协议	Gāosù xúnhū liánwǎng xiéyì	IPNP
Interpersonal	人际	Rénjì	IP
Interpersonal message	人际消息	Rénjì xiāoxi	IPM
Interpersonal messaging - message store	个人间通信-消息存储	Gèrén-jiān tōngxìn- xiāoxi cúnchǔ	IPM-MS
Interpersonal messaging service	人际消息传递业务	Rénjì xiāoxi chuándì yèwù	IPM
Interpersonal messaging service	人际消息通信服务	Rénjì xiāoxi tōngxìn fúwù	
Interpersonal messaging system	人际消息通信系统	Rénjì xiāoxi tōngxìn xìtǒng	IPMS
Interpolation	内插	Nèichā	
Interpolation (in digital photography)	插值	Chāzhí	
Interpretation	解译	Jiěyì	
Interpreter	解释器	Jiěshìqì	
Interprocess communication	进程间通信	Jìnchéng-jiān tōngxìn	IPC
Interprocess communication	进程间通讯	Jìnchéng-jiān tōngxùn	IPC
Inter-processor common bus	处理机间共用总线	Chǔlǐjī-jiān gòngyòng zǒngxiàn	IPBUS
Inter-processor communication	处理器间通信	Chǔlǐqì-jiān tōngxìn	IPC
Inter-pulse frequency shifting	脉间跳频	Mài-jiān tiàopín	
Inter-record gap	记录间间隔	Jìlù-jiān jiàngé	IRG

Interrogating node	咨询节点	Zīxún jiédiǎn	IN
Interrogating node (GSM term)	询问节点	Xúnwèn jiédiǎn	
Interrogator	询问机	Xúnwèn jī	
Interrupt (computer term)	中断	Zhōngduàn	
Interrupt channel control block	中断通道控制块	Zhōngduàn tōngdào kòngzhì kuài	INTCCB
Interrupt control register	中断控制寄存器	Zhōngduàn kòngzhì jìcúnqì	INCR
Interrupt control unit	中断控制器	Zhōngduàn kòngzhìqì	ICU
Interrupt descriptor table base address	中断描述符表基地址	Zhōngduàn miáoshùfú biǎo jī dìzhǐ	IDT Base Address
Interrupt enable	中断启动	Zhōngduàn qǐdòng	INTE
Interrupt level (computer term)	中断级	Zhōngduàn jí	
Interrupt level status table	中断级状态表	Zhōngduàn jí zhuàngtài biǎo	ILST
Interrupt mask register	中断屏弊寄存器	Zhōngduàn píngbì jìcúnqì	IMR
Interrupt processing or handling	中断处理	Zhōngduàn chùlǐ	
Interrupt request	中断请求	Zhōngduàn qǐngqiú	IRQ
Interrupt request vector	中断请求向量	Zhōngduàn qǐngqiú xiàngliàng	IRV
Interrupt service routine	中断服务程序	Zhōngduàn fúwù chéngxù	ISR
Interrupt signal	中断信号	Zhōngduàn xìnhào	
Interrupt status word	中断状态字	Zhōngduàn zhuàngtài zì	ISW
Interruption	瞬断	Shùnduàn	
Interruption duration	中断持续时间	Zhōngduàn chíxù shíjiān	
Inter-satellite link	卫星间链路	Wèixīng-jiān liànlù	
Inter-satellite service	卫星间业务	Wèixīng-jiān yèwù	
Intersect	交叉	Jiāochā	
Intersection	交集	Jiāojí	
Intersection	相交区	Xiāngjiāoqū	
Inter-service provider interface	业务提供者之间的接口	Yèwù tígòngzhě-zhījiānde jiēkǒu	
Inter-site messaging service	站间消息传递服务	Zhàn-jiān xiāoxi chuándì fúwù	ISM
Inter-station muting	台间静噪	Tái-jiān jìngzào	
Inter-station noise suppression	台间噪声抑制	Tái-jiān zàoshēng yìzhì	
Inter-stream synchronization	流间同步	Liú-jiān tóngbù	
Inter-switch link	交换机间连接	Jiāohuànjī-jiān liánjiē	ISL
Inter-switch link	级间链路	Jí-jiān liànlù	
Intersymbol interference	符号间干扰	Fúhào-jiān gānrǎo	ISI
Inter-symbol interference	码间干扰	Mǎ-jiān gānrǎo	ISI
Inter-system electromagnetic compatibility	系统间电磁兼容性	Xìtǒng-jiān diàncí jiānróngxìng	
Inter-system interference	系统间干扰	Xìtǒng-jiān gānrǎo	
Intertoll trunk	长途电话中继线	Chángtú diànhuà zhōngjìxiàn	ITT
Inter-transmitter intermodulation	发射机之间的互调	Fāshèjī-zhījiānde hùtiáo	
Inter-type optical fiber (cable) connector adapter	不同型号光纤（缆）连接器转接座	Bùtóng xínghào guāngxiān (lǎn) liánjiēqì zhuǎnjiēzuò	
Interval scale	间隔刻度	Jiàngé kèdù	
Interval time scale	间隔时间标度	Jiàngé shíjiān biāodù	
Interval usage coding	间隔使用编码	Jiàngé shǐyòng biānmǎ	IUC
Intervisibility	内部可视性	Nèibù kěshìxìng	
Interworking	互连	Hùlián	
Interworking	互通	Hùtōng	

Interworking agent function	互联代理功能	Hùlián dàilǐ gōngnéng	IAF
Interworking between networks	网间互通	Wǎng-jiān hùtōng	
Interworking by call control mapping	通过呼叫控制映射的互通	Tōngguò hūjiào kòngzhì yìngshède hùtōng	
Interworking by port access	通过端口接入的互通	Tōngguò duānkǒu jiērùde hùtōng	
Interworking equipment	互联设备	Hùlián shèbèi	IWE
Interworking function	互连功能	Hùlián gōngnéng	IWF
Interworking function	互配功能	Hùpèi gōngnéng	IWF
Interworking function	互通功能	Hùtōng gōngnéng	IWF
Interworking function	互通功能模块	Hùtōng gōngnéng mókuài	IWF
Interworking function unit	互通功能单元	Hùtōng gōngnéng dānyuán	IFU
Interworking gateway	互联网关	Hùlián wǎngguān	IWGW
Interworking module	互通模块	Hùtōng mókuài	IWM
Interworking MSC	互通功能装备的 MSC	Hùtōng gōngnéng zhuāngbèide MSC	IWMSC
Interworking protocol	互通协议	Hùtōng xiéyì	IP
Interworking unit	互通单元	Hùtōng dānyuán	IWU
Intraband clustering	带内聚簇	Dài-nèi jùcù	
Intraband transmission	带内传输	Dài-nèi zhuànshū	
Intra-cell handover；intra-cell hand-off	小区内切换	Xiǎoqū-nèi qiēhuàn	
Intra-exchange signaling	局内信令	Jú-nèi xìnlìng	
Intra-file seek time	文件内布寻找时间	Wénjiàn nèibù xúnzhǎo shíjiān	
Intra-frame transform	帧内变换	Zhèng-nèi biànhuàn	
Intranet	内联网	Nèiliánwǎng	
Intranet	企业网	Qǐyèwǎng	
Intra-pulse frequency shifting	脉内跳频	Mài-nèi tiàopín	
Intra-stream synchronization	流内同步	Liú-nèi tóngbù	
Intra-system electromagnetic compatibility	系统内电磁兼容性	Xìtǒng-nèi diàncí jiānróngxìng	
Intra-system interference	系统内干扰	Xìtǒng-nèi gānrǎo	
Intra-system noise	系统内噪声	Xìtǒng-nèi zàoshēng	
Intrinsic attenuation	固有衰减	Gùyǒu shuāijiǎn	
Intrinsic burst tolerance	固有突发容限	Gùyǒu tūfā róngxiàn	IBT
Intrinsic noise	固有噪声	Gùyǒu zàoshēng	
Intrinsic sensitivity	固有灵敏度	Gùyǒu língmǐndù	
Introspection	自省	Zìxǐng	
Intruder alarm	防盗报警	Fángdào bàojǐng	IA
Intrusion	插入	Chārù	
Intrusion detection	入侵监测	Rùqīn jiāncè	
Intrusion detection system	入侵监测系统	Rùqīn jiāncè xìtǒng	IDS
Intrusion detection system exchange format	入侵检测系统交换格式	Rùqīn jiǎncè xìtǒng jiāohuàn géshi	IDEF
Intrusion detection working group	入侵检测工作组	Rùqīn jiǎncè gōngzuòzǔ	IDWG
Intrusion detection working group	入侵检测任务组	Rùqīn jiǎncè rènwuzǔ	IDWG
Intrusion event generator	入侵事件产生器	Rùqīn shìjiàn chǎnshēngqì	
Intrusion tolerance	入侵容忍	Rùqīn róngrěn	
Intrusion tone	插入音	Chārù yīn	
Intrusive monitoring	介入监视	Jièrù jiānshì	
Inundation	泛滥	Fànlàn	
Invalid cell	无效信元	Wúxiào xìnyuán	

Invalid instruction	无效指令	Wúxiào zhǐlìng	
Invalid interrupt	无效中断	Wúxiào zhōngduàn	
Invalid target BS	不适置的目标 BS	Bùshìzhìde mùbiāo BS	
Invariant (noun)	不变性	Bùbiànxìng	
Inventory control system	库存管理系统	Kùcún guǎnlǐ xìtǒng	
Inverse clipper circuit	去反峰电路	Qù fǎnfēng diànlù	
Inverse conical scan jamming	倒相干扰	Dǎoxiāng gānrǎo	
Inverse damping circuit	反峰阻尼电路	Fǎnfēng zǔní diànlù	
Inverse discrete cosine transform	反转离散余弦变换	Fǎnzhuǎn lísàn yúxián biànhuàn	IDCT
Inverse discrete cosine transform	非连续反余弦变换	Fēiliánxù fǎnyúxián biànhuàn	IDCT
Inverse discrete fourier transform	离散傅里叶反变换	Lísàn fù-lǐ-yè fǎnbiànhuàn	IDFT
Inverse dispersion	逆扩散	Nì kuòsàn	
Inverse fast Fourier transform	逆快速傅立叶变换	Nì kuàisù fù-lì-yè biànhuàn	IFFT
Inverse filter	逆滤波器	Nì lǜbōqì	
Inverse gain jamming	逆增益干扰	Nì zēngyì gānrǎo	
Inverse multiplexing access	反向复用板	Fǎnxiàng fùyòng bǎn	IMA
Inverse multiplexing on ATM	在 ATM 上逆多路复用	Zài ATM-shàng nì duōlù fùyòng	IMA
Inverse probability criterion	反概率准则	Fǎn gàilǜ zhǔnzé	
Inverse probability receiver	反概率接收机	Fǎn gàilǜ jiēshōujī	
Inverse pulse	反转脉冲	Fǎnzhuǎn màichōng	
Inversion analysis	逆解析	Nì jiěxī	
Inversion layer	逆转层	Nìzhuǎn céng	
Inverted file	倒排文件	Dàopái wénjiàn	
Inverted-L antenna	倒 L 形天线	Dǎo L-xíng tiānxiàn	
Inverted-V antenna	倒 V 形天线	Dǎo V-xíng tiānxiàn	
Investigation of land form	地形调查	Dìxíng diàochá	
Invisible line	不可见线	Bùkějiàn xiàn	
Invocation	诱发	Yòufā	
Invoice rule	发票制	Fāpiào zhì	
Invoke	调用	Diàoyòng	
Invoke ID	调用识别码	Diàoyòng shíbiémǎ	
Invoke SS	请求 SS	Qǐngqiú SS	
Invoke trace	调用跟踪	Diàoyòng gēnzōng	
Invoked application	调用的应用	Diàoyòngde yìngyòng	
Ion beam	离子束	Lízǐshù	
Ion exchange works	离子交换设施	Lízǐ jiāohuàn shèshī	
Ion implantation equipment	离子植入机	Lízǐ zhírùjī	
Ion implanter (semiconductor mfg)	离子注入机	Lízǐ zhùrùjī	
Ionization smoke detector	离子感烟探测器	Lízǐ gǎnyān tàncèqì	ISD
Ionosphere	电离层	Diànlícéng	
Ionosphere absorption	电离层吸收	Diànlícéng xīshōu	
Ionosphere disturbance	电离层骚扰	Diànlícéng sāorǎo	
Ionosphere reflection propagation	电离层反射传播	Diànlícéng fǎnshè chuánbō	
Ionosphere refraction	电离层折射	Diànlícéng zhéshè	
Ionosphere scatter propagation	电离层散射传播	Diànlícéng sǎnshè chuánbō	
Ionospheric propagation	电离层传播	Diànlícéng chuánbō	

English	Chinese	Pinyin	Abbreviation
Ionospheric reflection	电离层反射	Diànlícéng fǎnshè	
Ionospheric scatter	电离层散射	Diànlícéng sǎnshè	
Ionospheric wave	电离层波	Diànlícéng bō	
IP control protocol	IP 控制协议	IP kòngzhì xiéyì	IPCP
IP multicast	IP 多播	IP duōbō	IP-M
IP over ATM	ATM 上的网际协议	ATM-shàngde wǎngjì xiéyì	IPoA
IP phone	IP 电话	IP diànhuà	Iphone
IP security	IP 安全协议	IP ānquán xiéyì	IPSec
IP security option	IP 安全选项	IP ānquán xuǎnxiàng	IPSO
IP-multicast	IP 组播业务	IP zǔbō yèwù	IP-M
Iridium Star System (satellite telephony)	铱星系统	Yīxīng xìtǒng	
Iridium system	铱系统	Yī xìtǒng	
Iris (in a waveguide)	膜片	Mópiàn	
Iron-core deflection coil	铁芯偏转线圈	Tiěxīn piānzhuǎn xiànquān	
Irregular form	不规则形式	Bùguīzé xíngshì	
Irregular tessellation	不规则分割法	Bùguīzé fēngē fǎ	
Irrelevancy	不相干度	Bùxiānggān dù	
Isarithm	等值线	Děngzhíxiàn	
Isarithmic flow control	恒信息流控制	Héng xìnxīliú kòngzhì	
Isarithmic map	等值线图	Děngzhíxiàn tú	
ISDN digital subscriber line	ISDN 数字用户线路	ISDN shùzì yònghù xiànlù	IDSL
ISDN protocol reference mode	ISDN 协议参考模型	ISDN xiéyì cānkǎo móxíng	ISDN-PRM
ISDN subscriber module	ISDN 用户模块	ISDN yònghù mókuài	ISM
ISDN subscriber number	ISDN 用户号码	ISDN yònghù hàomǎ	ISDN-SN
ISDN user part	ISDN 用户部分	ISDN yònghù bùfen	ISUP
Islanding	孤岛	Gūdǎo	
ISO country code	ISO 国家代码	ISO guójiā dàimǎ	
ISO data and country code	ISO 数据和国家代码	ISO shùjù hé guójiā dàimǎ	ISO DCC
ISO transport protocol class 4	ISO 运输层协议 4 级	ISO yùnshū céng xiéyì 4 jí	TP4
Isobar	等压线	Děngyāxiàn	
Isochronism, isochronous	等时	Děngshí	
Isochronous	等步的	Děngbùde	
Isochronous modulation	等时调制	Děngshí tiàozhì	
Isochronous signal	等时信号	Děngshí xìnhào	
Isochronous transmission	等时传输	Děngshí chuánshū	
Isoethernet	等时以太网	Děngshí yǐtàiwǎng	
Isogonic chart (GIS)	等偏角图表	Děngpiānjiǎo túbiǎo	
Isogonic line	等偏角线	Děngpiānjiǎo xiàn	
Isogram	等值线图	Děngzhíxiàn tú	
Isolate	隔离	Gélí	
Isolated ground	分开接地	Fēnkāi jiēdì	
Isolated port	隔离端口	Gélí duānkǒu	
Isolation	隔离比	Gélí bǐ	
Isolation	隔离度	Gélí dù	
Isolation amplifier	隔离放大器	Gélí fàngdàqì	
Isolation between antennae	天线间的隔离度	Tiānxiàn-jiānde gélídù	

English	Chinese	Pinyin	Abbr.
Isolation level (for database)	隔离级别	Gélí jíbié	
Isolation ratio (of a multi-port antenna)	隔离比	Gélí bǐ	
Isolator	隔离器	Gélíqì	
Isolator/tap coupler/wavelength division multiplexer	隔离器/分路器/滤波型波分复用器	Gélíqì/fēnlùqì/lǜbō-xíng bōfēn fùyòngqì	ITMX
Isoline	等值线	Děngzhíxiàn	
Isoline map	等值线图	Děngzhíxiàn tú	
Isoline method	等值线法	Děngzhíxiàn fǎ	
Isometric map	等测图	Děngcè tú	
Isomorphic mapping	同构图	Tónggòu tú	
Isomorphism	同型性	Tóngxíngxìng	
Isopleth map	等值线图	Děngzhíxiàn tú	
Isosurface	等值面	Děngzhí miàn	
Isotropic gain (of an antenna)	各向同性增益	Gèxiàng tóngxìng zēngyì	
Isotropic identification	各向同性识别	Gèxiàng tóngxìng shíbié	ISOID
Isotropic material	各向同性材料	Gèxiàng tóngxìng cáiliào	
Isotropic radiator	各向同性辐射器	Gèxiàng tóngxìng fúshèqì	
Isotropic radiator	各向同性辐射体	Gèxiàng tóngxìng fúshètǐ	IR
Isotropy	等向性	Děngxiàngxìng	
Issue	收汇	Shōuhuì	
Issue overrun	汇超	Huìchāo	
IT outsourcing	IT 托管	IT tuōguǎn	
Italic (WP command)	解体	Jiětǐ	
ITC Corp. (US-China JV with MIT)	爱特信有限公司	Ài-tè-xìn yǒuxiàn gōngsī	
Item identifier	项标识符	Xiàng biāozhìfú	
Item indexing	字段索引	Zìduàn suǒyǐn	
Item, subject	项	Xiàng	
Iterate, iteration	迭代	Diédài	
Iteration function system	迭代函数系统	Diédài hánshù xìtǒng	IFS
Iterative	迭代的	Diédàide	
Iterative	反复的	Fǎnfùde	
Iterative block cipher	迭代分组密码	Diédài fēnzǔ mìmǎ	
Iterative ground	重复接地	Chóngfù jiēdì	
Iterative matching scheduling algorithm	迭代匹配调度算法	Diédài pǐpèi diàodù suànfǎ	
Iterative operation	迭代运算	Diédài yùnsuàn	IO
Iterative tunneling	迭代隧道	Diédài suìdào	
Iterator	迭代器	Diédàiqì	
ITU-T Software Tools Library, release 2000	ITU-T 软件工具库 2000 年版	ITU-T ruǎnjiàn gōngjùkù 2000 nián bǎn	STL-2000

J

English	Chinese	Pinyin	Abbr.
Jack	塞孔	Sāikǒng	
Jade Bird short Message platform	青鸟短消息平台	Qīngniǎo duǎn xiāoxi píngtái	
Jammer	干扰机	Gānrǎojī	
Jamming blanket factor	干扰压制系数	Gānrǎo yāzhì xìshù	
Jamming blanketed zone	干扰压制区	Gānrǎo yāzhì qū	

Jamming modulation type	干扰调制样式	Gānrǎo tiáozhì yàngshì	
Jamming parameter	干扰参数	Gānrǎo cānshù	
Jamming power density	干扰功率密度	Gānrǎo gōnglǜ mìdù	
Jamming signal bandwidth	干扰信号带宽	Gānrǎo xìnhào dàikuān	
Jamming strength	干扰强度	Gānrǎo qiángdù	
Jamming test of duct	进气道干扰试验	Jìnqìdào gānrǎo shìyàn	
Jamming, interference	干扰	Gānrǎo	
Japan digital cellular system	日本数字蜂窝系统	Rìběn shùzì fēngwō xìtǒng	JDC
Japan Unix Network	日本 UNIX 网络	Rìběn UNIX wǎngluò	JUNET
Japanese earth resources satellite	日本地球资源卫星	Rìběn dìqiú zīyuán wèixīng	JERS
Java APIs for integrated networks	综合网络的 Java API	Zōnghé wǎngluòde Java API	JAIN
Java archive file	Java 归档文件	Java guīdàng wénjiàn	JAR file
Java automatic paralleling system	Java 自动并行化系统	Java zìdòng bìngxínghuà xìtǒng	JAPS
Java chip operating system	Java 芯片操作系统	Java xìnpiàn cāozuò xìtǒng	JCOS
Java cryptographic architecture	Java 密码体系结构	Java mìmǎ tǐxì jiégòu	JCA
Java cryptographic extension	Java 密码扩展	Java mìmǎ kuòzhǎn	JCE
Java development kit	Java 开发包	Java kāifā bāo	JDK
Java language ©	爪哇语言	Zhǎo-wā yǔyán	
Java naming directory interface	Java 命名索引薄接口	Java mìngmíng suǒyǐn báo jiēkǒu	JNDI
Java secure socket extension	Java 安全套接字扩展	Java ānquán tàojiēzì kuòzhǎn	JSSE
Java telephony application programming interface	Java 电话应用程序设计接口	Java diànhuà yìngyòng chéngxù shèjì jiēkǒu	JTAPI
Java virtual machine	Java 虚拟机	Java xūnǐjī	JVM
Jet Propulsion Laboratory (US)	喷气推进实验室	Pēnqì tuījìn shíyànshì	JPL
Jig	筛选机	Shāixuǎnjī	
Jitter	抖动	Dǒudòng	
Jitter	跳动	Tiàodòng	
Jitter and wander	抖动和漂移	Dǒudòng hé piāoyí	FW
Jitter attribute	抖动特性	Dǒudòng tèxìng	
Jitter gain	抖动增益	Dǒudòng zēngyì	
Jitter generator	抖动发生器	Dǒudòng fāshēngqì	
Jitter measurement filter	抖动测量滤波器	Dǒudòng cèliáng lǜbōqì	
Jitter receiver	抖动接收器	Dǒudòng jiēshōuqì	
Jitter tolerance	抖动容限	Dǒudòng róngxiàn	
Job	作业	Zuòyè	
Job scheduling	工程安排	Gōngchéng ānpái	
Join	联接	Liánjiē	
Join column	联接列	Liánjiē liè	
Join condition	联接条件	Liánjiē tiáojiàn	
Join field	联接字段	Liánjiē zìduàn	
Join filter	联接筛选	Liánjiē shāixuǎn	
Join group request message (in multicast)	加入组请求消息	Jiārù zǔ qǐngqiú xiāoxi	
Join operator	联接运算符	Liánjiē yùnsuàn fú	
Join path	联接路径	Liánjiē lùjìng	
Join table	联接表	Liánjiē biǎo	
Joining (using a laser)	焊接加工	Hànjiē jiāgōng	

Joint	节理	Jiélǐ	
Joint academic network	联合科研网	Liánhé kēyán wǎng	JANET
Joint bi-level Image Experts Group	联合两级图象专家组	Liánhé liǎngjí túxiàng zhuānjiāzǔ	JBIG
Joint bi-level Imaging Group	联合双态成像组	Liánhé shuāngtài chéngxiàngzǔ	JBIG
Joint detection	联合检波	Liánhé jiǎnbō	JD
Joint detection	联合检测	Liánhé jiǎncè	
Joint Electronic Device Engineering Council	联合电子设备工程委员会	Liánhé diànzǐ shèbèi gōngchéng wěiyuánhuì	JEDEC
Joint Electronic payment initiative	联合电子支付联盟	Liánhé diànzǐ zhīfù liánméng	JEPI
Joint filter (in SQL Server)	联合过滤	Liánhé guòlǜ	
Joint intrusion detection system	捷普入侵检测系统	Jiépǔ rùqīn jiǎncè xìtǒng	JIDS
Joint management model	联合管理模型	Liánhé guǎnlǐ móxíng	
Joint Maritime Communications Strategy	联合海上通信系统策略	Liánhé hǎishàng tōngxìn xìtǒng cèlüè	JMCOMS
Joint Photographic Experts Group	联合摄影专家组	Liánhé shèyǐng zhuānjiāzǔ	JPEG
Joint Photographic Experts Group	联合图象专家组	Liánhé túxiàng zhuānjiāzǔ	JPEG
Joint Photographic Experts Group	联合照相专家组	Liánhé zhàoxiàng zhuānjiāzǔ	JPEG
Joint pre-distortion	接头预失真	Jiētóu yùshīzhēn	JP
Joint space time processing	联合时空处理	Liánhé shíkōng chǔlǐ	
Joint Surveillance and Target Attack Radar System (US military)	联合监视和目标攻击雷达系统	Liánhé jiānshì hé mùbiāo gōngjī léidá xìtǒng	JSTARS
Joint Tactical Information Distribution System (U.S.)	联合战术信息分发系统	Liánhé zhànshù xìnxī fēnfā xìtǒng	JTIDS
Joint Tactical Information Distribution System (US)	联合战术信息分布系统	Liánhé zhànshù xìnxī fēnbù xìtǒng	JTIDS
Joint Tactical Radio System (US military usage)	联合战术无线电系统	Liánhé zhànshù wúxiàndiàn xìtǒng	JTRS
Joint translation angle	节理走向	Jiélǐ zǒuxiàng	
Joint-equity cooperative enterprise	股份合作企业	Gǔfèn hézuò qǐyè	
Joint-equity enterprise	股份制企业	Gǔfènzhì qǐyè	
Jones matrix eigenanalysis	琼斯矩阵本征分析	Qióng-sī jǔzhèn běnzhēng fēnxī	JME
Joule (unit of electrical energy)	焦耳	Jiāo'ěr	
Joystick	操纵杆	Cāozònggǎn	
Joystick	摇杆	Yáogǎn	
Jughead search (Internet tool)	盲目搜寻	Mángmù sōuxún	
Jump transition	跳跃转换	Tiàoyuè zhuǎnhuàn	
Jumper wire	跨接线	Kuàjiēxiàn	
Jumper wire	跳线	Tiàoxiàn	
Junction	汇接点	Huìjiē diǎn	
Junction	结	Jié	
Junction barrier	交叉点障碍	Jiāochādiǎn zhàng'ài	
Junction box	分线盒	Fēnxiàn hé	
Junction box	接线盒	Jiēxiànhé	
Junction circulator	结式环行器	Jiéshì huánxíngqì	
Junction element	交叉点元素	Jiāochādiǎn yuánsù	
Junction feature class	交叉点特征类	Jiāochādiǎn tèzhēng lèi	
Junction field effect transistor	结型场效应晶体管	Jiéxíng cháng xiàoyìng jīngtǐguǎn	JFET
Junction flag	交叉点标志	Jiāochādiǎn biāozhì	
Junction point	交叉点	Jiāochādiǎn	
Junction table	连接表	Liánjiē biǎo	

Just a bunch of disks	磁盘束	Cípán shù	JBOD
Just in time	准时制生产	Zhǔnshí zhì shēngchǎn	JIT
Just in time (JIT) object activation	及时对象激活	Jíshí duìxiàng jīhuó	
Just in time compilation	即时编译	Jíshí biānyì	
Justification	码速调整	Mǎsù tiáozhěng	
Justification	正确性证明	Zhèngquèxìng zhèngmíng	
Justification (WP command)	对齐	Duìqí	
Justification ratio	码速调整比	Mǎsù tiáozhěng bǐ	
Justification service digits	调整指示码位	Tiáozhěng zhǐshì mǎwèi	
Justified (in word processing)	整版	Zhěngbǎn	
Justifying digit	调整码位	Tiáozhěng mǎwèi	
Just-in-time	刚好准时	Gānghǎo zhǔnshí	JIT

K

K desktop environment (in UNIX)	K 桌面环境	K zhuōmiàn huánjìng	KDE
Kalman filter	卡尔曼滤波	Kǎ-ěr-màn lǜbō	
Karaoke on demand	随选伴唱服务	Suíxuǎn bànchàng fúwù	
Karhunen Loeve transform	KL 变换	KL Biànhuàn	KLT
Kassmi code	卡沙米码	Kǎ-shā-mǐ mǎ	
Katmai new instructions	Katmai 新指令集	Katmai xīn zhǐlìng jí	KNI
Keep alive interval	保留间隔	Bǎoliú jiàngé	
Kenwood Communications Corp. (US company)	健伍通信有限公司	Jiàn-wǔ tōngxìn yǒuxiàn gōngsī	
Kerberos application library	Kerberos 应用程序库	Kerberos yìngyòng chéngxù kù	
Kermit	柯密	Kē-mì	
Kern	字凸	Zìtū	
Kernel	核心	Héxīn	
Kernel	内核	Nèihé	
Kernel function	核函数	Hé hánshù	
Kernel transport network	核心传送网络	Héxīn chuánsòng wǎngluò	KTN
Kevlar	芳纶	Fānglún	
Key (in switching)	电键	Diànjiàn	
Key (on a keyboard, also used in databases)	键	Jiàn	
Key column (for database)	键列	Jiàn liè	
Key distribution cryptosystem	公钥分配密码体制	Gōngyào fēnpèi mìmǎ tǐzhì	
Key enciphering key	密钥加密密钥	Mìyào jiāmì mìyào	KK
Key entry	键盘输入	Jiànpán shūrù	
Key injector	密码注入器	Mìmǎ zhùrùqì	
Key management algorithm	密钥管理算法	Mìyào guǎnlǐ suànfǎ	K-ALG
Key protection	键保护	Jiàn bǎohù	KEY
Key range lock	键范围锁	Jiàn fànwéi suǒ	
Key telephone system	按键电话系统	Ànjiàn diànhuà xìtǒng	KTS
Keyboard	电键盘	Diànjiànpán	
Keyboard	键盘	Jiànpán	KB
Keyboard controller	键盘控制器	Jiànpán kòngzhìqì	KBC
Keyboard layout	键盘布局	Jiànpán bùjú	
Keycap	键帽	Jiànmào	

Keying	键控	Jiànkòng	
Keypad facility	键盘设施	Jiànpán shèshī	
Keypad facility	键盘性能	Jiànpán xìngnéng	
Keyring	钥匙环	Yàoshi huán	
Keyset-driven cursor	键集驱动游标	Jiànjí qūdòng yóubiāo	
Keyword	关键词	Guānjiàn cí	KW
Keyword	检索词	Jiǎnsuǒ cí	
Keyword (IPsec)	关键字	Guānjiàn zì	
Kilobits per second	每秒千比特	Měi miǎo qiānbǐtè	Kbps
Kilobyte (1024 bytes)	千字节	Qiānzìjié	KB
Kilo-symbols per second	每秒千符号（码元）	Měi miǎo qiānfúhào (mǎ yuán)	Ksps
Kilovolt ampere-hour	千伏安小时	Qiānfú'ān xiǎoshí	KVAH
Kilowatt hour	千瓦小时	Qiānwǎ xiǎoshí	KWh
Kinematic model	运动力学	Yùndòng lìxué	
Kinetic energy intercept	动能拦截	Dòngnéng lánjié	
Klystron	速调管	Sùtiáoguǎn	
Klystron amplifier	速调管放大器	Sùtiáoguǎn fàngdàqì	KLA
Knapsack problem	背包问题	Bēibāo wèntí	
Knowledge acquisition	知识获取	Zhīshi huòqǔ	
Knowledge base	知识库	Zhīshikù	
Knowledge discovery	知识发现	Zhīshi fāxiàn	
Knowledge discovery in databases	数据库中的知识发现	Shùjùkù-zhōngde zhīshi fāxiàn	KDD
Knowledge engineer	知识工程师	Zhīshi gōngchéngshī	
Knowledge expression	知识表示	Zhīshi biǎoshì	
Knowledge query management language	知识查询管理语言	Zhīshi cháxún guǎnlǐ yǔyán	KQML
Knowledge reduction	知识约简	Zhīshi yuējiǎn	
Knowledge-based system	知识系统	Zhīshi xìtǒng	
Known plaintext attack (in cryptography)	已知密文攻击	Yǐzhī mìwén gōngjī	
Knurled plate gasket	波纹边片状垫片	Bōwén biān piànzhuàng diànpiàn	
Kokusai Denshin Denwa Co. Ltd. (Japan)	国际电信电话有限公司	Guójì diànxìn diànhuà yǒuxiàn gōngsī	KDD
Konica (Japanese company)	科尼卡	Kē-ní-kǎ	
Korea Mobile Telecom	韩国移动通信	Hánguó yídòng tōngxìn	KMT
Korn shell	康氏外壳	Kāng-shì wàiké	
Kriging	克里格法	Kè-lǐ-gé fǎ	
Krypton laser	氪离子激光	Kè lízǐ jīguāng	
Krypton light source	氪灯	Kè dēng	
KTN computing configuration management	KTN 计算组成管理	KTN jìsuàn zǔchéng guǎnlǐ	KTN-Com.CM
KTN configuration management	KTN 组成管理	KTN zǔchéng guǎnlǐ	KTN.CM
KTN connection configuration management	KTN 连接组成管理	KTN liánjiē zǔchéng guǎnlǐ	KTN-Con.CM
KTN protocol configuration management	KTN 协议组成管理	KTN xiéyì zǔchéng guǎnlǐ	KTN-Pro.CM
KTN topology configuration management	KTN 拓扑组成管理	KTN tuòpū zǔchéng guǎnlǐ	KTN-TCM
Kutter's formula	库特公式	Kù-tè gōngshì	

L

L2R bit-oriented protocol	L2R 比特定向协议	L2R bǐtè dìngxiàng xiéyì	
L2R function-oriented protocol	L2R 性能定向协议	L2R xìngnéng dìngxiàng xiéyì	

L2TP access concentrator	L2TP 接入聚合器	L2TP jiērù jùhéqì	LAC
L2TP network server	L2TP 网络服务器	L2TP wǎngluò fúwùqì	
Label	标号	Biāohào	
Label	标记	Biāojì	
Label	标志	Biāozhì	
Label a disk (verb)	标注磁盘	Biāozhù cípán	
Label distribution protocol	标记分发协议	Biāojì fēnfā xiéyì	LDP
Label distribution protocol	标签分配协议	Biāoqiān fēnpèi xiéyì	LDP
Label distribution protocol	标志分配协议	Biāozhì fēnpèi xiéyì	LDP
Label distribution protocol (IETF usage)	标记分配协议	Biāojì fēnpèi xiéyì	LDP
Label edge router	标签边缘路由器	Biāoqiān biānyuán lùyóuqì	LER
Label edge router	标签交换边沿路由器	Biāoqiān jiāohuàn biānyán lùyóuqì	LER
Label field	标号字段	Biāohào zìduàn	
Label information base	标记信息库	Biāojì xìnxīkù	LIB
Label management (system)	标记管理	Biāojì guǎnlǐ	LMS
Label merge	标签合并	Biāoqiān hébìng	
Label point	标记点	Biāojì diǎn	
Label printer	标签打印机	Biāoqiān dǎyìnjī	
Label stack	标记堆栈	Biāojì duīzhàn	LS
Label switch path	标签交换路径	Biāoqiān jiāohuàn lùjìng	LSP
Label switch router	标记交换路由器	Biāojì jiāohuàn lùyóuqì	LSR
Label switch router	标签交换路由器	Biāoqiān jiāohuàn lùyóuqì	LSR
Label switching	标签交换	Biāoqiān jiāohuàn	LS
Label switching path	标记交换路径	Biāojì jiāohuàn lùjìng	LSP
Label switching path	标志交换路径	Biāozhì jiāohuàn lùjìng	LSP
Label switching router	标志交换路由器	Biāozhì jiāohuàn lùyóuqì	LSR
Labeled channel	带标号的信道	Dài biāohàode xìndào	
Labeled channel	有标号通路	Yǒu biāohào tōnglù	
Labeled deterministic channel	带标号的确定性信道	Dài biāohàode quèdìngxìng xìndào	
Labeled deterministic channel	有标号确定性通路	Yǒu biāohào quèdìngxìng tōnglù	
Labeled interface structure	带标号的接口结构	Dài biāohàode jiēkǒu jiégòu	
Labeled interface structure	有标号的接口结构	Yǒu biāohàode jiēkǒu jiégòu	
Labeled multiplexing	带标号的复用	Dài biāohàode fùyòng	
Labeled multiplexing	有标号复用	Yǒu biāohào fùyòng	
Labeled statistical channel	带标号的统计信道	Dài biāohàode tǒngjì xìndào	
Labeled statistical channel	有标号的统计性通路	Yǒu biāohàode tǒngjìxìng tōnglù	
Laboratory test	实验室试验	Shíyànshì shìyàn	
Ladder filter	梯型滤波器	Tī-xíng lǜbōqì	
Laddered siloxane polymer (FOC mfg)	梯型硅氧烷聚合物	Tī-xíng guīyǎng wán jùhéwù	LSP
Lagrange multipliers method	拉格朗日乘积因子法	Lā-gé-lǎng-rì chéngjī yīnzǐ fǎ	
Laid in floor or under floor	地板或地板下敷设	Dìbǎn huò dìbǎn-xià fūshè	
Lambda router	波长路由器	Bōcháng lùyóuqì	
Lambertian distribution	朗伯分布	Lǎng-bó fēnbù	
Lambertian source	朗伯辐射体	Lǎng-bó fúshètǐ	
Laminar flow	层流	Céngliú	
Laminated flat cable	层状绝缘扁平电缆	Céngzhuàng juéyuán biǎnpíng diànlǎn	LFC

Laminated object manufacturing	叠层工艺法	Diécéng gōngyì fǎ	LOM
LAN emulation - network to network interface	LAN 仿真-网间接口	LAN fǎngzhēn- wǎngjiān jiēkǒu	LANE-NNI
LAN emulation address resolution protocol	局域网仿真地址解析协议	Júyùwǎng fǎngzhēn dìzhǐ jiěxī xiéyì	LE-ARP
Land classification system	土地分类系统	Tǔdì fēnlèi xìtǒng	
Land conservation	国土保护	Guótǔ bǎohù	
Land form classification	地形分类	Dìxíng fēnlèi	
Land form, topography	地形	Dìxíng	
Land information system	土地信息系统	Tǔdì xìnxī xìtǒng	LIS
Land mobile radio	陆地移动无线电	Lùdì yídòng wúxiàndiàn	LMR
Land mobile service	陆地移动业务	Lùdì yídòng yèwù	
Land mobile station	陆地移动电台	Lùdì yídòng diàntái	
Land mobile-satellite service	卫星陆地移动业务	Wèixīng lùdì yídòng yèwù	
Land parcel	地块	Dìkuài	
Land station	陆地电台	Lùdì diàntái	
Landline frequency modulation	陆线调频	Lùxiàn tiáopín	LLFM
Landline subscriber	地面连线用户	Dìmiàn liánxiàn yònghù	
Landline trunk controller	有线线路分配器	Yǒuxiàn xiànlù fēnpèiqì	LTC
Landsat	陆地卫星	Lùdì wèixīng	
Landscape date mark	风景日戳	Fēngjǐng rìchuō	
Language of temporal ordering specification	时序描述语言	Shíxù miáoshù yǔyán	LOTOS
Language processor (device)	语言处理器	Yǔyán chǔlǐqì	LP
Language processor (program)	语言加工程序	Yǔyán jiāgōng chéngxù	
LAPOSH® single mode optical fiber	大保实®单模光纤	Dàbǎoshí® dānmó guāngxiān	LAPOSH®
Laptop computer	膝上型电脑	Xīshàngxíng diànnǎo	
Large area synchronous code division multiple access	大区域同步码分多址接入	Dàqūyù tóngbù mǎfēn duōzhǐ jiērù	LAS-CDMA
Large complicated systems	大型复杂系统	Dàxíng fùzá xìtǒng	LCS
Large dynamic range linear receiver	大动态线形接收机	Dàdòngtài xiànxíng jiēshōujī	
Large effective area non-zero dispersion-shifted optical fiber	大容量正色散位移单模光纤	Dàróngliàng zhèng sèsàn wèiyí dānmó guāngxiān	
Large effective area optical fiber	大有效面积光纤	Dàyǒuxiào miànjī guāngxiān	
Large enterprises	大型企业	Dàxíng qǐyè	LE
Large scale	大比例尺	Dàbǐlìchǐ	
Large scale integrated circuit	大规模集成电路	Dàguīmó jíchéng diànlù	LSI
Large screen display	大屏幕显示	Dàpíngmù xiǎnshì	
Large texture (video)	大型纹理	Dàxíng wénlǐ	
Large traffic simulation test	大话务量模拟测试	Dàhuàwùliàng mónǐ cèshì	
Large-signal output stability	大信号增益输出稳定性	Dàxìnhào zēngyì shūchū wěndìngxìng	
Larmor frequency	拉莫尔频率	Lā-mò-ěr pínlǜ	
Laser absorber	激光光吸收体	Jīguāng guāng xīshōu tǐ	
Laser amplifier chain	激光放大器电路	Jīguāng fàngdàqì diànlù	LAC
Laser annealing equipment	激光退火装置	Jīguāng tuìhuǒ zhuāngzhì	
Laser attenuator assembly	激光衰减控制器	Jīguāng shuāijiǎn kòngzhìqì	LAA
Laser backface optical power	激光器背光功率	Jīguāngqì bèiguāng gōnglǜ	LBOP
Laser base current monitor	激光器偏流监视	Jīguāngqì piānliú jiānshì	LSBCM
Laser beam printer, laser printer	激光打印机	Jīguāng dǎyìnjī	LBP
Laser bias current	激光器偏置电流	Jīguāngqì piānzhì diànliú	LB

Laser cell	激光用盒	Jīguāng-yòng hé	
Laser chirp	激光啁啾	Jīguāng zhōujiū	
Laser color printer	彩色激光印表机	Cǎisè jīguāng yìn biǎojī	
Laser control equipment	激光控制设备	Jīguāng kòngzhì shèbèi	
Laser control field	激光器控制域	Jīguāngqì kòngzhì yù	LCF
Laser device	激光器	Jīguāngqì	LD
Laser digital color copy machine	彩色激光数位影印机	Cǎisè jīguāng shùwèi yǐngyìnjī	
Laser diode	激发二极管	Jīfā èrjíguǎn	
Laser diode	激发管	Jīfāguǎn	
Laser diode	激光二极管	Jīguāng èrjíguǎn	LD
Laser display	激光显示器	Jīguāng xiǎnshìqì	
Laser dye	激光用染料	Jīguāng-yòng rǎnliào	
Laser facsimile	激光传真机	Jīguāng chuánzhēnjī	
Laser glass	激光玻璃	Jīguāng bōli	
Laser holography	激光全息	Jīguāng quánxī	
Laser interconnection unit	激光互连装置	Jīguāng hùlián zhuāngzhì	LIU
Laser mirror	激光面镜	Jīguāng miànjìng	
Laser module	激光器组	Jīguāngqì zǔ	
Laser offset control	激光器偏置控制	Jīguāngqì piānzhì kòngzhì	
Laser plotter	激光光绘仪	Jīguāng guānghuìyí	
Laser plotting	激光光绘	Jīguāng guāng huì	
Laser positioning equipment	激光定位设备	Jīguāng dìngwèi shèbèi	
Laser processing equipment	激光加工机	Jīguāng jiāgōngjī	
Laser protective glasses	激光护眼镜	Jīguāng hù yǎnjìng	
Laser pumped dye laser	激光激发染料激光	Jīguāng jīfā rǎnliào jīguāng	
Laser radar	激光雷达	Jīguāng léidá	
Laser ranging unit	激光测距仪	Jīguāng cèjùyí	
Laser resonator cavity	激光共振腔	Jīguāng gòngzhènqiāng	
Laser rod	激光棒	Jīguāng bàng	
Laser slab	激光板	Jīguāng bǎn	
Laser source	激光源	Jīguāng yuán	
Laser space communication	空间激光通信	Kōngjiān jīguāng tōngxìn	
Laser temperature	激光器温度	Jīguāngqì wēndù	LT
Laser tube or bore	激光管	Jīguāng guǎn	
Last frame address register	最后帧地址寄存器	Zuìhòu zhèng dìzhǐ jìcúnqì	LFAR
Last known good configuration	上次已知的正确配置	Shàngcì yǐzhīde zhèngquè pèizhì	
Last level register	末级寄存器	Mòjí jìcúnqì	LLR
Last number dialed	拨最后的号码	Bō zuìhòude hàomǎ	LND
Last number dialed	最后拨号存储	Zuìhòu bōhào cúnchǔ	LND
Last-in first-out list	后进先出表（队列）	Hòu jìn xiān chū biǎo (duìliè)	
Latching	自锁	Zìsuǒ	
Latching stability	锁定稳定性	Suǒdìng wěndìngxìng	
Late binding	迟绑定	Chí bǎngdìng	
Latency	存储转发时间	Cúnchǔ zhuǎnfā shíjiān	
Latency	等待时间	Děngdài shíjiān	
Latency	滞后时间	Zhìhòu shíjiān	

Latency	潜伏期	Qiánfúqī	
Latency	时延	Shíyán	
Latent fault	潜伏故障	Qiánfú gùzhàng	
Latent jitter	延时抖动	Yánshí dǒudòng	
Latent transactional consistency (in SQL Server)	潜在事务一致性	Qiánzài shìwù yīzhìxìng	
Lateral beam angle	侧波束角	Cè bōshù jiǎo	
Lateral flow	侧向流动	Cèxiàng liúdòng	
Lateral offset	横向偏移	Héngxiàng piānyí	
Lateral offset-Focus	横向偏焦	Héngxiàng piānjiāo	
Lateral pressure	侧压	Cèyā	
Latin hypercube sampling	拉丁超立方体抽样	Lā-dīng chāolìfāngtǐ chōuyàng	
Latitude / longitude	纬度/经度	Wěidù/jīngdù	LL
Lattice basis reduction algorithm	格基归约算法	Gé jī guīyuē suànfǎ	
Lattice diffraction graph fabrication	点阵衍射图制作技术	Diǎnzhèn yǎnshètú zhìzuò jìshù	
Lattice reflector	栅状反射器	Zhàzhuàng fǎnshèqì	
Launching fiber	注入光纤	Zhùrù guāngxiān	
LawsNet ©	法律网络	Fǎlǜ wǎngluò	
Lay, install (pipe, cable, etc.)	敷设	Fūshè	
Layer	层	Céng	
Layer 1	层 1	Céng yī	L1
Layer 1 (physical layer)	第一层（物理层）	Dìyīcéng (wùlǐ céng)	L1
Layer 2 (data link later)	第二层（数据链路层）	Dì'èrcéng (shùjù liànlù céng)	L2
Layer 2 forwarding protocol (Cisco usage)	第二层转发协议	Dì'èrcéng zhuǎnfā xiéyì	L2F
Layer 2 management link	层 2 管理连接	Céng èr guǎnlǐ liánjiē	L2ML
Layer 2 management link	第二层链路管理	Dì'èrcéng liànlù guǎnlǐ	L2ML
Layer 2 management link (OSI data link layer)	第二层管理链路	Dì'èrcéng guǎnlǐ liànlù	L2ML
Layer 2 relay	层 2 中继	Céng èr zhōngjì	L2R
Layer 2 relay	层2转发	Céng èr zhuǎnfā	L2R
Layer 2 relay	第二层中继	Dì'èrcéng zhōngjì	L2R
Layer 2 transport protocol	二层传送协议	Èrcéng chuánsòng xiéyì	L2TP
Layer 2 tunneling protocol	层二隧道协议	Céng èr suìdào xiéyì	L2TP
Layer 2 tunneling protocol	二级通道协议	Èrjí tōngdào xiéyì	L2TP
Layer 2 tunneling protocol (Cisco usage)	第二层隧道协议	Dì'èrcéng suìdào xiéyì	L2TP
Layer 3	第三层	Dìsāncéng	L3
Layer clock	等级钟	Děngjí zhōng	LC
Layer header	层标题	Céng biāotí	
Layer interface	层接口	Céng jiēkǒu	
Layer link (for ATM)	层链路	Céng liànlù	
Layer management	层管理	Céng guǎnlǐ	
Layer management entity	层管理实体	Céng guǎnlǐ shítǐ	LME
Layer management entity identifier	层的管理实体标识符	Céngde guǎnlǐ shítǐ biāozhìfú	LMEI
Layer network	层网络	Céng wǎngluò	
Layer service	层的服务	Céngde fúwù	
Layer service provider	层的服务提供者	Céngde fúwù tígòngzhě	
Layer system	分层系统	Fēncéng xìtǒng	
Layered video multicast	层次视频组播	Céngcì shìpín zǔbō	

Layering	分层	Fēncéng	
Layout category	布局分类	Bùjú fēnlèi	
Layout object	布局客体	Bùjú kètǐ	
Layout object class	布局客体类别	Bùjú kètǐ lèibié	
Layout process	布局处理	Bùjú chǔlǐ	
Layout stream	布局流	Bùjú liú	
Layout structure	布局结构	Bùjú jiégòu	
Layout style	布局式样	Bùjú shìyàng	
Layout view	图面配置视图	Túmiàn pèizhì shìtú	
Lead code	前导码	Qiándǎo mǎ	
Lead configuration (in SMT)	引脚外形	Yǐnjiǎo wàixíng	
Lead soldering temperature	引线焊接温度	Yǐnxiàn hànjiē wēndù	
Lead, Pigtail	尾纤	Wěixiān	
Lead-in line	引入线	Yǐnrùxiàn	
Leading edge	前边缘	Qián bianyuán	
Leading edge clipping	前沿切割	Qiányán qiēgē	
Leading-edge broadening	前沿展宽	Qiányán zhǎnkuān	
Lead-out line	引出线	Yǐnchū xiàn	
Lead-zirconium titanate wafer	钛酸锆酸铅晶圆	Tàisuān gàosuān qiān jīngyuán	PLZT
Leaf	叶	Yè	
Leaf area index	叶面积指数	Yèmiàn jī zhǐshù	
Leaf internetwork	叶互联网络	Yè hùlián wǎngluò	
Leaf level	叶级	Yè jí	
Leaf member	叶成员	Yè chéngyuán	
Leakage current	泄漏电流	Xièlòu diànliú	
Leaky cable system	漏泄电缆系统	Lòuxiè diànlǎn xìtǒng	
Leaky-wave antenna	漏波天线	Lòubō tiānxiàn	
Lean production (Japanese concept)	精良生产	Jīngliáng shēngchǎn	LP
Learning Bridge	自学网桥	Zìxué wǎngqiáo	
Learning process (for reliability)	认识过程	Rènshi guòchéng	
Learning station	教学点	Jiàoxué diǎn	
Leased circuit data transmission service	租用电路数据传输业务	Zūyòng diànlù shùjù chuánshū yèwù	
Leased line	租用线路	Zūyòng xiànlù	
Leased line adapter	租用线路转换器	Zūyòng xiànlù zhuǎnhuànqì	LLA
Leased line service	租用线路业务	Zūyòng xiànlù yèwù	
Least connection first algorithm	链接最小优先算法	Liànjiē zuìxiǎo yōuxiān suànfǎ	LCF
Least load first algorithm	负载最小优先算法	Fùzài zuìxiǎo yōuxiān suànfǎ	LLF
Least mean square	最小均芳	Zuìxiǎo jūn fāng	LMS
Least mean square (algorithm)	最小均方（算法）	Zuìxiǎo jūn fāng (suànfǎ)	LMS
Least mean squares	最小均方根	Zuìxiǎo jūn fānggēn	LMS
Least median square	最小中值法	Zuìxiǎo zhōng zhí fǎ	LMS
Least privilege (IPsec)	最小特权	Zuìxiǎo tèquán	
Least significant bit	最低位	Zuìdī wèi	LSB
Least significant bit	最低有效比特	Zuìdī yǒuxiào bǐtè	LSB
Least significant bit	最低有效位	Zuìdī yǒuxiào wèi	LSB
Least significant digit	最低有效位	Zuìdī yǒuxiào wèi	LSD

Least square method	最小二乘法	Zuìxiǎo èrchéngfǎ	
Least-cost path	最少花费路径	Zuìshǎo huāfèi lùjìng	
Leave group request message (in multicast)	退出组请求消息	Tuìchū zǔ qǐngqiú xiāoxi	
Lecroy Corp. (US maker of test instruments)	力科有限公司	Lì-kē yǒuxiàn gōngsī	
Left hand circular polarization	左漩圆极化	Zuǒxuán yuán jíhuà	LHCP
Left hand edge	左边缘	Zuǒ bianyuán	
Left hand polarization	左旋转化	Zuǒxuán zhuǎnhuà	
Left margin	左边界	Zuǒ bianjiè	
Left outer join (for database)	左向外联接	Zuǒ xiàngwài liánjiē	
Left outer join (in SQL Server)	左外部连接	Zuǒ wàibù liánjiē	
Left value (lvalue)	左值	Zuǒzhí	
Left-hand polarized wave	左旋极化波	Zuǒxuán jíhuà bō	
Left-handed	左手习惯	Zuǒshǒu xíguàn	
Legal and Regulatory Group (GSM MoU)	政策法规组	Zhèngcè fǎguī zǔ	L&G
Legend	图例	Túlì	
Legend (PRC computer company)	联想	Liánxiǎng	
Legitimacy	合法性	Héfǎ-xìng	
Length bit	长度比特	Chángdù bǐtè	LTH
Length indicator	长度指示	Chángdù zhǐshì	LI
Lens antenna	透镜天线	Tòujìng tiānxiàn	LA
Lens design consultant	镜头设计顾问	Jìngtóu shèjì gùwèn	
Lens tissue	拭镜纸	Shìjìng zhǐ	
Lens-corrected horn antenna	透镜校正的喇叭天线	Tòujìng jiàozhèngde lǎba tiānxiàn	
Letter	信函	Xìnhán	
Letter box	邮政信箱	Yóuzhèng xìnxiāng	
Letter case	字母键位	Zìmǔ jiànwèi	
Letter for reporting mineral deposits	报矿信函	Bàokuàng xìnhán	
Letter shift	字母转移	Zìmǔ zhuǎnyí	
Lettering annotation	地图注记	Dìtú zhùjì	
Letter-shift signal	字母转移信号	Zìmǔ zhuǎnyí xìnhào	
Level	层次	Céngcì	
Level	层例	Cénglì	
Level	级别	Jíbié	
Level	阶	Jiē	
Level (the instrument)	水准仪	Shuǐzhǔnyí	
Level change	水准变动	Shuǐzhǔn biàndòng	
Level hierarchy	级别层次结构	Jíbié céngcì jiégòu	
Level modulation	电平调节	Diànpíng tiáojié	LM
Level of a time variable	时间变量电平	Shíjiān biànliàng diànpíng	
Level of maintenance	维护程度	Wéihù chéngdù	
Level surface	水准面	Shuǐzhǔn miàn	
Level, class	级	Jí	
Leveling	水准测量	Shuǐzhǔn cèliáng	
Leveling origin	水准原点	Shuǐzhǔn yuándiǎn	
Leveling route	水准路线	Shuǐzhǔn lùxiàn	
Levels of truncation	级截断环节	Jí jiéduàn huánjié	

Lexical language	词典语言	Cídiǎn yǔyán	
Lexical space	词法空间	Cífǎ kōngjiān	
Lexmark (US company)	利盟	Lì-méng	
Liability for data and information	数据与信息责任	Shùjù yǔ xìnxī zérèn	
Librarian	图库管理系统	Túkù guǎnlǐ xìtǒng	
Library	库	Kù	
Library (for imagery)	图库	Túkù	
Library InfoGate	图书馆资讯门	Túshūguǎn zīxùn mén	
License	许可证	Xǔkězhèng	
Liebert China Headquarters, subsidiary of Liebert Corp.	力博特中国总部	Lì-bó-tè Zhōngguó zǒngbù	
Life cycle	寿命周期	Shòumìng zhōuqī	
Life test	寿命试验	Shòumìng shìyàn	
Lifecycle	生命周期	Shēngmìng zhōuqī	
Lifeguard station	救生台	Jiùshēngtái	
Lifetime	生命期	Shēngmìng qī	
Lifetime	寿命	Shòumìng	
Lifetime; service life	使用寿命	Shǐyòng shòumìng	
Lift	抬升	Táishēng	
Light activated silicon controlled switch	光控可控硅开关	Guāng kòng kěkòngguī kāiguān	LASCS
Light amplification by stimulated emission of radiation	辐射激发的光线放大	Fúshè jīfāde guāngxiàn fàngdà	LASER
Light armored cable	轻铠缆	Qīng kǎi lǎn	
Light dependent resistor	光敏电阻	Guāng mǐndiànzǔ	LDR
Light emitting diode	发光二极管	Fāguāng èrjíguǎn	LED
Light emitting diode	发光二极体	Fāguāng èrjítǐ	LED
Light emitting diode	发光管	Fāguāng guǎn	LED
Light emitting diode display	发光二极体显示器	Fāguāng èrjítǐ xiǎnshìqì	
Light emitting diode display system	发光二极体显示系统	Fāguāng èrjítǐ xiǎnshì xìtǒng	
Light emitting diode facsimile	发光二极体传真机	Fāguāng èrjítǐ chuánzhēnjī	
Light emitting diode wafer	发光二极体晶圆	Fāguāng èrjítǐ jīngyuán	
Light interface technology	光接口计数	Guāng jiēkǒu jìshù	LIT
Light pen	光笔	Guāngbǐ	
Light source	光源	Guāngyuán	
Light source	光源设备	Guāngyuán shèbèi	
Light-guide board	光导板	Guāngdǎobǎn	
Lightguide interconnection unit	光纤互连装置	Guāngxiān hùlián zhuāngzhì	LIU
Lightning arrester	避雷计	Bì léi jì	LA
Lightning arrester	避雷器	Bìléiqì	
Lightning data transport	闪电数据传输总线	Shǎndiàn shùjù chuánshū zǒngxiàn	LDT
Lightning electromagnetic pulse	闪电电磁脉冲	Shǎndiàn diàncí màichōng	LEMP
Lightning protection	防雷	Fángléi	
Lightning surge	雷电冲击	Léidiàn chōngjī	
Light-pen extraction equipment	光学录取设备	Guāngxué lùqǔ shèbèi	
LightPointe Company (U.K. company)	亮点公司	Liàngdiǎn gōngsī	
Lightstream ATM switch	光流 ATM 交换机	Guāngliú ATM jiāohuànjī	
Lightweight directory access protocol	轻量目录访问协议	Qīngliàng mùlù fǎngwèn xiéyì	LDAP

English	Chinese	Pinyin	Abbr.
Lightweight directory access protocol	轻量级目录访问协议	Qīngliàngjí mùlù fǎngwèn xiéyì	LDAP
Lightweight directory access protocol	轻权目录访问协议	Qīngquán mùlù fǎngwèn xiéyì	LDAP
Lightweight directory access protocol	轻型目录存取协议	Qīngxíng mùlù cúnqǔ xiéyì	LDAP
Lightweight presentation protocol (IETF usage)	轻量级表示协议	Qīngliàngjí biǎoshì xiéyì	LPP
Likelihood ratio	似然比	Sìrán bǐ	
Limit of disturbance	骚扰限值	Sāorǎo xiànzhí	
Limit of interference	干扰允许值	Gānrǎo yǔnxǔ zhí	
Limit of interference (permissible value)	干扰限值（允许值）	Gānrǎo xiànzhí (yǔnxǔ zhí)	
Limit test	限值测试	Xiànzhí cèshì	
Limit value	限值	Xiànzhí	
Limited access (IPsec)	受限访问	Shòuxiàn fǎngwèn	
Limited bandwidth white noise	有限带宽的白噪声	Yǒuxiàn dàikuānde bái zàoshēng	
Limited current circuit	限流电路	Xiànliú diànlù	
Limited inquiry access code	有限查询访问码	Yǒuxiàn cháxún fǎngwèn mǎ	LIAC
Limited resource link	有限资源链接	Yǒuxiàn zīyuán liànjiē	
Limited time message	限时消息	Xiànshí xiāoxi	
Limited-route explorer packet	有限路由探测器数据分组	Yǒuxiàn lùyóu tàncèqì shùjù fēnzǔ	
Limiter of moment	力矩限制器	Lìjǔ xiànzhìqì	
Limiting	限幅	Xiànfú	
Limiting intermediate frequency amplifier	限幅式中频放大器	Xiànfú-shì zhōngpín fàngdàqì	
Lincompex, line compressor/expander	链路压扩器	Liànlù yākuòqì	
Line access point	线路接入点	Xiànlù jiērùdiǎn	
Line activation	线路激活	Xiànlù jīhuó	
Line amplifier	线路放大器	Xiànlù fàngdàqì	LA
Line and circuit test interface	线性电路测试接口	Xiànxìng diànlù cèshì jiēkǒu	LCTI
Line and trunk access	线路和中继通路	Xiànlù hé zhōngjì tōnglù	LTA
Line and trunk access sub-system	线路和中继通路子系统	Xiànlù hé zhōngjì tōnglù zixìtǒng	LTAS
Line attenuation	线路衰减	Xiànlù shuāijiǎn	
Line attribute	线属性	Xiàn shǔxìng	
Line box	行框	Háng kuàng	
Line card control	线路卡控制	Xiànlù kǎ kòngzhì	LCC
Line card processor	用户板处理机	Yònghù bǎn chǔlǐjī	LCP
Line card to switch	线卡到交换机	Xiànkǎ dào jiāohuànjī	LCS
Line certification	生产线确认	Shēngchǎnxiàn quèrèn	
Line circuit	用户电路	Yònghù diànlù	
Line code	线路码	Xiànlù mǎ	
Line code type	线路编码类型	Xiànlù biānmǎ lèixíng	
Line coding	线型码	Xiànxíng mǎ	
Line concentrator	线路集中器	Xiànlù jízhōngqì	
Line concentrator module	线路集线器模块	Xiànlù jíxiànqì mókuài	LCM
Line conditioning	线路调整	Xiànlù tiáozhěng	
Line continuity	线连续性	Xiàn liánxùxìng	
Line detection	直线检测	Zhíxiàn jiǎncè	
Line digital rate	线路数字速率	Xiànlù shùzì sùlǜ	
Line drawing	线拷贝	Xiàn kǎobèi	
Line driver	线路驱动器	Xiànlù qūdòngqì	

Line enhancement	线划增强	Xiànhuà zēngqiáng	
Line entity	线实体	Xiàn shítǐ	
Line expansion module	线路扩展模块	Xiànlù kuòzhǎn mókuài	LEM
Line fault	线路故障	Xiànlù gùzhàng	
Line feature	线要素	Xiàn yàosù	
Line feed	换行	Huànháng	LF
Line feed	馈电	Kuìdiàn	
Line finding	寻线组	Xúnxiànzǔ	
Line generalization	线综合	Xiàn zōnghé	
Line graph	折线图	Zhéxiàntú	
Line home position	行初始位置	Háng chūshǐ wèizhì	
Line hunting	连续寻线	Liánxù xúnxiàn	LH
Line hunting	寻线	Xúnxiàn	LH
Line identity	线路识别	Xiànlù shíbié	LI
Line impedance stability network	线路阻抗稳定网络	Xiànlù zǔkàng wěndìng wǎngluò	LISN
Line interface circuit	线路接口电路	Xiànlù jiēkǒu diànlù	LIC
Line interface coupler	线路接口耦合器	Xiànlù jiēkǒu ǒuhéqì	LIC
Line interface E1 link assembly	线路 E1 接口链路集成件	Xiànlù E1 jiēkǒu liànlù jíchéngjiàn	LIEA
Line interface module	线路接口模块	Xiànlù jiēkǒu mókuài	LIM
Line interface T1 link assembly	线路 T1 接口链路集成件	Xiànlù T1 jiēkǒu liànlù jíchéngjiàn	LITA-A/D
Line lengthener	线路电长度变换器	Xiànlù diànchángdù biànhuànqì	
Line link	线路链路	Xiànlù liànlù	
Line map	线状图	Xiànzhuàng tú	
Line modulator	线型调制器	Xiànxíng tiáozhìqì	
Line of sight	视距	Shìjù	LoS
Line of sites	站点线路	Zhàndiǎn xiànlù	LOS
Line printer	行式打印机	Hángshì dǎyìnjī	L/P
Line printer daemon	行式打印机程序	Hángshì dǎyìnjī chéngxù	LPD
Line printer daemon	线路打印机监控	Xiànlù dǎyìnjī jiānkòng	
Line printer handler	行式打印机处理器	Hángshì dǎyìnjī chǔlǐ qì	LPH
Line progression	行行进方向	Háng hángjìn fāngxiàng	
Line regulation	电源电压调整率	Diànyuán diànyā tiáozhěnglǜ	
Line release message	线路释放消息	Xiànlù shìfàng xiāoxi	REL
Line searching	线索	Xiànsuǒ	
Line segment	线段	Xiànduàn	
Line signal	线路信号	Xiànlù xìnhào	
Line signaling	线路信令	Xiànlù xìnlìng	
Line smoothing	线划平滑	Xiànhuà pínghuá	
Line smoothing (GIS)	曲线光滑	Qūxiàn guānghuá	
Line snapping	线划拼接	Xiànhuà pīnjiē	
Line spacing	行间距	Háng jiānjù	
Line spectrum	线谱	Xiànpǔ	
Line status signaling	线路状态信号	Xiànlù zhuàngtài xìnhào	
Line stretcher	线路拉伸器	Xiànlù lāshēnqì	
Line symbol	线状符号	Xiànzhuàng fúhào	
Line symbol rate	线路符号速率	Xiànlù fúhào sùlǜ	

Line terminal	线路终端	Xiànlù zhōngduān	LT
Line termination	线路终端	Xiànlù zhōngduān	LT
Line termination	线路终接	Xiànlù zhōngjiē	LT
Line termination equipment	线路终端设备	Xiànlù zhōngduān shèbèi	LT
Line terminator	行终止符	Háng zhōngzhǐfú	
Line test block	线路测试模块	Xiànlù cèshì mókuài	LTB
Line thinning	线划细划	Xiànhuà xìhuà	
Line transient suppression	线路瞬时抑制	Xiànlù shùnshí yìzhì	LTS
Line type	线型	Xiàn xíng	
Line unit	线路单元	Xiànlù dānyuán	LU
Line, wire	线	Xiàn	
Line/trunk group	用户中继群	Yònghù zhōngjì qún	LTG
Lineage	数据志	Shùjù zhì	
Linear actuator	线性激动器	Xiànxìng jīdòngqì	
Linear actuator	线性致动器	Xiànxìng zhìdòngqì	
Linear add/drop multiplexer	线性分叉复用器	Xiànxìng fēnchā fùyòngqì	LADM
Linear amplifier	线性放大器	Xiànxìng fàngdàqì	
Linear analog control	线性模拟控制	Xiànxìng mónǐ kòngzhì	
Linear approximation	线性近似	Xiànxìng jìnsì	
Linear array (antenna)	直线阵	Zhíxiàn zhèn	
Linear array antenna	线性天线阵	Xiànxìng tiānxiàn zhèn	LAA
Linear array antenna	线性阵列天线	Xiànxìng zhènliè tiānxiàn	LAA
Linear array antenna	线阵天线	Xiànzhèn tiānxiàn	
Linear array test	线阵试验	Xiànzhèn shìyàn	
Linear block code	线性分组码	Xiànxìng fēnzǔ mǎ	
Linear burst	线性突发	Xiànxìng tūfā	
Linear charging	线性充电	Xiànxìng chōngdiàn	
Linear circuit	线性电路	Xiànxìng diànlù	
Linear complexity profile	线性复杂度曲线	Xiànxìng fùzádù qǔxiàn	
Linear control system	线形控制系统	Xiànxíng kòngzhì xìtǒng	
Linear cryptanalysis	线性密码分析	Xiànxìng mìmǎ fēnxī	
Linear deflection speed	线形偏转速度	Xiànxíng piānzhuǎn sùdù	
Linear delta modulation	线性增量调制	Xiànxìng zēngliàng tiáozhì	LDM
Linear demodulation	线性解调	Xiànxìng jiětiáo	
Linear detection	线性检波	Xiànxìng jiǎnbō	
Linear detector array	线型检光元件	Xiànxíng jiǎnguāng yuánjiàn	
Linear digital modulation	线性数字调制	Xiànxìng shùzì tiáozhì	
Linear distortion	线性失真	Xiànxìng shīzhēn	
Linear distortion correction	线性失真校正	Xiànxìng shīzhēn jiàozhèng	
Linear equation	线性方程组	Xiànxìng fāngchéngzǔ	
Linear error correcting code	线性误差校正码	Xiànxìng wùchā jiàozhèng mǎ	LECC
Linear feature	线要素	Xiàn yàosù	
Linear feedback shift register	现行反馈移位寄存器	Xiànxíng fǎnkuì yíwèi jìcúnqì	LFSR
Linear filter	线性滤波器	Xiànxìng lǜbōqì	
Linear filtering	线性过滤	Xiànxìng guòlǜ	LF
Linear frequency modulation	线性频率调制	Xiànxìng pínlǜ tiáozhì	LFM

Linear frequency modulation	线性调频	Xiànxìng tiáopín	
Linear frequency modulation (FM)	线性调频	Xiànxìng tiáopín	
Linear frequency modulation (FM) pulse compression	线性调频脉冲压缩	Xiànxìng tiáopín màichōng yāsuō	
Linear integrated circuit	线性集成电路	Xiànxìng jíchéng diànlù	
Linear interpolation	线性插值	Xiànxìng chāzhí	
Linear interpretation	线状解译	Xiànzhuàng jiěyì	
Linear linked list	线性链表	Xiànxìng liàn biǎo	
Linear list	线性表	Xiànxìng biǎo	
Linear low density polyethylene	线性低密聚乙烯	Xiànxìng dīmì jùyǐxī	LLDPE
Linear minimum variance estimation	线性最小方差估计	Xiànxìng zuìxiǎo fāngchà gūjì	
Linear modulated signal	线性调制信号	Xiànxìng tiáozhì xìnhào	
Linear modulation	线性调制	Xiànxìng tiáozhì	
Linear network	线性网络	Xiànxìng wǎngluò	
Linear phase code modulation	线性相码调制	Xiànxìng xiàngmǎ tiáozhì	LPCM
Linear polarization	线极化	Xiàn jíhuà	
Linear positioning system	线形定位系统	Xiànxíng dìngwèi xìtǒng	
Linear power amplifier rack	线性功率放大器机架	Xiànxìng gōnglǜ fàngdàqì jījià	LPAR
Linear power amplifier shelf	线性功率放大器架子	Xiànxìng gōnglǜ fàngdàqì jiàzi	LPAS
Linear prediction	线性预测	Xiànxìng yùcè	
Linear prediction coefficient	线性预测系数	Xiànxìng yùcè xìshù	LP
Linear prediction vocoder	线性预测声码器	Xiànxìng yùcè shēngmǎqì	
Linear predictive code	线性预测编码	Xiànxìng yùcè biānmǎ	LPC
Linear predictive coding	线性预测编码	Xiànxìng yùcè biānmǎ	LPC
Linear predictive residual - pitch-cycle waveform	线性预测残差-基音周期波形	Xiànxìng yùcè cánchā—jīyīn zhōuqī bōxíng	LPR-PCW
Linear programming	线性规划	Xiànxìng guīhuà	
Linear referencing system	线性参照系统	Xiànxìng cānzhào xìtǒng	
Linear regression	线性回归	Xiànxìng huíguī	
Linear search	线性查找	Xiànxìng cházhǎo	
Linear stage positioning equipment	直线台定位设备	Zhíxiàntái dìngwèi shèbèi	
Linear structure	线性结构	Xiànxìng jiégòu	
Linear temporal logic	线性时序逻辑	Xiànxìng shíxù luóji	LTL
Linear temporal logic with clocks	带有时钟变量的线性时序逻辑	Dàiyǒu shízhōng biànliàngde xiànxìng shíxù luóji	LTLC
Linear transform	线性变换	Xiànxìng biànhuàn	
Linear transponder	线性转发器	Xiànxìng zhuǎnfāqì	
Linear vibration	线性振动	Xiànxìng zhèndòng	
Linear voltage regulator	线性稳压器	Xiànxìng wěnyāqì	
Linear-based correlation method	基于线性关联技术	Jīyú xiànxìng guānlián jìshù	
Linearity of tuning	调谐线性	Tiáoxié xiànxìng	
Linearly polarized field vector	线极化场矢量	Xiàn jíhuàcháng shǐliàng	
Linearly polarized plane wave	线极化场平面波	Xiàn jíhuàcháng píngmiànbō	
Linearly polarized wave	线极化波	Xiàn jíhuà bō	
Line-load control	线路负荷控制	Xiànlù fùhè kòngzhì	
Linemans pliers	钢丝钳	Gāngsīqián	
Line-of-sight propagation	视距传播	Shìjù chuánbō	

Line-of-sight radio-relay link	视距无线电中继链路	Shìjù wúxiàndiàn zhōngjì liànlù	LOSRRL
Line-of-sight radio-relay system	视距无线电中继系统	Shìjù wúxiàndiàn zhōngjì xìtǒng	LOSRRL
Line-only activation	仅线路激活	Jǐn xiànlù jīhuó	
Line-out-of-service signal	线路不工作信号	Xiànlù bùgōngzuò xìnhào	LOS
Line-spectrum pair	线谱对	Xiàn pǔ duì	
Line-speed switch router	线速交换路由器	Xiànsù jiāohuàn lùyóuqì	
Link	链路	Liànlù	
Link (in software)	链接	Liànjiē	
Link access control	链路接入控制	Liànlù jiērù kòngzhì	LAC
Link access procedure	链路接入规程	Liànlù jiērù guīchéng	LAP
Link access procedure - balanced	链路接入规程 - 平衡	Liànlù jiērù guīchéng –pínghéng	LAPB
Link access procedure balanced (ISO usage)	链路访问过程平衡	Liànlù fǎngwèn guòchéng pínghéng	LAPB
Link access procedure D-channel	链路接入过程 D-信道	Liànlù jiērù guòchéng D-xìndào	LAP-D
Link access procedure for modem	调制解调器的链路接入规程	Tiáozhì jiětiáoqìde liànlù jiērù guīchéng	LAPM
Link access procedure- half-duplex	半双工链路接入规程	Bànshuānggōng liànlù jiērù guīchéng	LAPX
Link access procedure on D channel	D 信道链路接入规程	D xìndào liànlù jiērù guīchéng	LAPD
Link access procedure on the D-channel	D 通路上的链路接入规程	D-tōnglù-shàngde liànlù jiērù guīchéng	LAPD
Link access procedure to frame mode bearer service	帧模式承载业务链路接入规程	Zhèng móshì chéngzài yèwù liànlù jiērù guīchéng	LAPF
Link access procedure, balanced	平衡链路接入规程	Pínghéng liànlù jiērù guīchéng	LAPB
Link access procedure-balanced	平衡型链路接入规程	Pínghéng-xíng liànlù jiērù guīchéng	LAPB
Link access procedures on the D-channel	D 通路上的链路接入程序	D-tōnglù shàngde liànlù jiērù chéngxù	LAPD
Link access procedure-SDH	链路接入规程-SDH	Liànlù jiērù guīchéng-SDH	LAPS
Link access protocol	链路访问协议	Liànlù fǎngwèn xiéyì	LAP
Link access protocol	链路接入协议	Liànlù jiērù xiéyì	LAP
Link access protocol balanced	链路接入平衡协议	Liànlù jiērù pínghéng xiéyì	LAPB
Link access protocol balanced	平衡链路接入协议	Pínghéng liànlù jiērù xiéyì	LAPB
Link access protocol channel D	链路访问协议 D 信道	Liànlù fǎngwèn xiéyì D xìndào	LAP-D
Link access protocol D	链路接入规程 D	Liànlù jiērù guīchéng D	LAP-D
Link access protocol frame	链路接入协议帧	Liànlù jiērù xiéyì zhèng	LAPF
Link access protocol on D channel	D 信道上的链路接入协议	D-xìndào shàngde liànlù jiērù xiéyì	LAPD
Link access protocol on Dm channel	Dm 信道上链路接入协议	Dm xìndàoshàng liànlù jiērù xiéyì	LAPDm
Link access protocol on the D channel	D 信道上的链路访问协议	D-xìndào-shàngde liànlù fǎngwèn xiéyì	LAP-D
Link access protocol on the Dm channel	Dm 信道上的链路访问协议	Dm-xìndào-shàngde liànlù fǎngwèn xiéyì	LAP-Dm
Link access protocol on the Dm channel	在 Dm 信道上链路接入协议	Zài Dm xìndàoshàng liànlù jiērù xiéyì	LAPDm
Link access protocol-SDH	链路接入协议-SDH	Liànlù jiērù xiéyì-SDH	LAPS
Link adaptation	链路自适应	Liànlù zìshìyìng	
Link aggregration	链路聚合	Liànlù jùhé	
Link and node structure	连线--节点结构	Liánxiàn—jiédiǎn jiégòu	
Link attenuation value	链路衰减值	Liànlù shuāijiǎn zhí	
Link bit error rate test board assembly	链路误码率测试集成板	Liànlù wùmǎlǜ cèshì jíchéngbǎn	LBTA
Link board (2Mb/s)	链路板	Liànlù bǎn	LK2M
Link by link	逐段转接	Zhúduàn zhuǎnjiē	LXL
Link by link	逐条链路	Zhútiáo liànlù	
Link by link encipherment (IPsec)	逐条链路加密	Zhútiáo liànlù jiāmì	
Link capacity adjusting scheme	链路容量调整方案	Liànlù róngliàng tiáozhěng fāng'àn	LCAS

Link capacity adjustment scheme	链路容量调节方案	Liànlù róngliàng tiáojié fāng'àn	LCAS
Link connected switching stage	链路连接的交换级	Liànlù liánjiēde jiāohuànjí	
Link connection	链路连接	Liànlù liánjiē	LC
Link control procedure	链路控制规程	Liànlù kòngzhì guīchéng	
Link control protocol	链路控制协议	Liànlù kòngzhì xiéyì	LCP
Link controller	链路控制器	Liànlù kòngzhìqì	LC
Link controller service signaling	链路控制器服务信令	Liànlù kòngzhìqì fúwù xìnlìng	LCSP
Link disconnect	链路断开	Liànlù duànkāi	LD
Link encryption (IPsec)	链路加密	Liànlù jiāmì	
Link establishment indication	链路建立指示	Liànlù jiànlì zhǐshì	
Link field (in software)	链域	Liàn yù	
Link identification code	链路标识符	Liànlù biāozhì fú	LIC
Link interface E1 board assembly	链路 E1 接口集成板	Liànlù E1 jiēkǒu jíchéngbǎn	LIEA
Link interface IPC processor assembly	链路接口 IPC 处理器集成件	Liànlù jiēkǒu IPC chǔlǐqì jíchéng jiàn	LIPA
Link interface T1 board assembly	链路 T1 接口集成板	Liànlù T1 jiēkǒu jíchéngbǎn	LITA
Link layer	链路层	Liànlù céng	LL
Link layer protocol	链路层协议	Liànlù céng xiéyì	
Link layer service unit	链路层服务单元	Liànlù céng fúwù dānyuán	LLSU
Link lockout	链路锁定	Liànlù suǒdìng	
Link management protocol	链路管理协议	Liànlù guǎnlǐ xiéyì	LMP
Link manager	链路管理	Liànlù guǎnlǐ	LM
Link monitor	链路监视	Liànlù jiānshì	
Link power budget	链路功率预算	Liànlù gōnglǜ yùsuàn	
Link protocol data unit	链路协议数据单元	Liànlù xiéyì shùjù dānyuán	LPDU
Link quality monitor	链路质量监视	Liànlù zhìliàng jiānshì	LQM
Link quality report	链路质量报告	Liànlù zhìliàng bàogào	LQR
Link reset	链路重启	Liànlù chóngqǐ	LR
Link reset response	链路重启应答	Liànlù chóngqǐ yìngdá	LRR
Link resource manager	链路资源管理器	Liànlù zīyuán guǎnlǐqì	LRM
Link selector parameter	链路选择器参数	Liànlù xuǎnzéqì cānshù	LSP
Link state	链路状态	Liànlù zhuàngtài	
Link state advertisement	链路状态通告	Liànlù zhuàngtài tōnggào	LSA
Link state database	链接状态数据库	Liànjiē zhuàngtài shùjùkù	
Link state packet	链路状态包	Liànlù zhuàngtài bāo	LSP
Link status signal unit	链路状态信号单元	Liànlù zhuàngtài xìnhào dānyuán	LSSU
Link status Signaling unit	链路状态信令单元	Liànlù zhuàngtài xìnlìng dānyuán	LSSU
Linkage editor	连接编辑程序	Liánjiē biānjí chéngxù	LEDT
Linkage learning	链接学习	Liànjiē xuéxí	
Link-by-link signaling	链路到链路信令	Liànlù dào liànlù xìnlìng	
Link-by-link signaling	逐段转发信令	Zhúduàn zhuǎnfā xìnlìng	
Linked companding	链接压扩	Liànjiē yākuò	
Linked compression and expansion	链路压扩	Liànlù yākuò	
Linked compressor and expander	链接的压扩器	Liànjiēde yākuòqì	
Linked datacube	链接多维数据集	Liànjiē duōwéi shùjùjí	
Linked ID	连接识别码	Liánjiē shíbié mǎ	
Linked list	链表	Liàn biǎo	

Linked server	链接服务器	Liànjiē fúwùqì	
Linked table	链接表	Liànjiē biǎo	
Linker (in software)	连接器	Liánjiēqì	
Linker (in software)	链接器	Liànjiēqì	
Linux (Taiwan term)	李尼克斯	Lǐ-ní-kè-sī	
Lip microphone	唇式传声器	Chúnshì chuánshēngqì	
Liquid cooling	液体冷却	Yètǐ lěngquè	
Liquid crystal	液晶	Yèjīng	
Liquid crystal (LCD) monitor	液晶监视器	Yèjīng jiānshìqì	
Liquid crystal (LCD) projector	液晶投影机	Yèjīng tóuyǐngjī	
Liquid crystal (LCD) TV	液晶电视	Yèjīng diànshì	
Liquid crystal adjustable (tunable) filter	液晶可调滤波器	Yèjīng kětiáo lǜbōqì	
Liquid crystal display	液晶显示屏	Yèjīng xiǎnshì píng	LCD
Liquid crystal display	液晶显示器	Yèjīng xiǎnshìqì	LCD
Liquid crystal injection equipment	液晶注入装置	Yèjīng zhùrù zhuāngzhì	
Liquid crystal on silicon	硅上液晶	Guī-shàng yèjīng	LCOS
Liquid phase epitaxy	液相外延	Yèxiàng wàiyán	LPE
List	列表	Lièbiǎo	
List	清单	Qīngdān	
List box	列表框	Lièbiǎo kuàng	
List of publishing in detail	报刊出版详情登记表	Bàokān chūbǎn xiángqíng dēngjìbiǎo	
Listserv (computer term)	邮电服务系统	Yóudiàn fúwù xìtǒng	
Literal constant	字面常数	Zìmiàn chángshù	
Lithium ion battery	锂离子电池	Lǐ lízǐ diànchí	
Lithium niobate	铌酸锂	Nísuānlǐ	$LiNbO_3$
Little-endian (data storage format)	低地址低字节	Dīdìzhǐ dīzìjié	
Live part	带电部分	Dàidiàn bùfen	
Live synchronization	现场同步	Xiànchǎng tóngbù	
Live-Link ©	动态连接	Dòngtài liánjiē	
Livelock (for database)	活锁	Huósuǒ	
Liveware	人力资源	Rénlì zīyuán	
Load	负载	Fùzài	
Load (verb)	加载	Jiāzài	
Load and resistance factor design method	负载耐力系数设计法	Fùzài nàilì xìshù shèjì fǎ	
Load balancing	负载平衡	Fùzài pínghéng	
Load capacity	负荷容量	Fùhè róngliàng	
Load coil	加感线圈	Jiāgǎn xiànquān	
Load disconnect control panel	负载断路控制板	Fùzài duànlù kòngzhì bǎn	
Load effect	负载效应	Fùzài xiàoyìng	
Load factor	负载系数	Fùzài xìshù	
Load factor	负载因子	Fùzài yīnzǐ	LF
Load index	负载指数	Fùzài zhǐshù	
Load indication	负载指示	Fùzài zhǐshì	
Load module	装入模块	Zhuāngrù mókuài	
Load moment	负载力矩	Fùzài lìjǔ	
Load regulation	负载调整率	Fùzài tiáozhěnglǜ	

Load sharing	负载分配	Fùzài fēnpèi	
Load sharing (in common channel signaling)	负荷分担	Fùhè fēndān	
Load shedding	减载	Jiǎnzài	
Load shedding	泄荷	Xiè hé	
Load transfer	负荷转移	Fùhè zhuǎnyí	
Load-carrying channel	承载通路	Chéngzài tōnglù	
Loaded folded dipole	加载折合偶极子	Jiāzài zhéhé ǒujízi	
Loader	载入器	Zǎirùqì	
Loader	装入程序	Zhuāngrù chéngxù	
Loader	装载器	Zhuāngzàiqì	
Loader (in component assembly process)	进料器	Jìnliàoqì	
Loader language	装入程序语言	Zhuāngrù chéngxù yǔyán	
Loading	装载	Zhuāngzài	LD
Loading, to load (software)	装入	Zhuāngrù	
Lobe distortion	波瓣畸变	Bōbàn jībiàn	
Local	局部的	Júbùde	
Local access and transport area	本地访问和传输区域	Běndì fǎngwèn hé chuánshū qūyù	LATA
Local access and transport area	本地接入及传动区	Běndì jiērù jí chuánsòng qū	LATA
Local area augmentation system	局域加强系统	Júyù jiāqiáng xìtǒng	LAAS
Local area communications network	局部通信网络	Júbù tōngxìn wǎngluò	LACN
Local area network	本地网	Běndì wǎng	LAN
Local area network	局域网络	Júyù wǎngluò	LAN
Local area network	局域网	Júyùwǎng	LAN
Local area network	区域网络	Qūyù wǎngluò	LAN
Local area network (LAN) emulation - user to network interface	LAN 仿真–用户与网络间接口	LAN fǎngzhēn– yònghù yǔ wǎngluòjiān jiēkǒu	LANE-UNI
Local area network access point	局域网接入点	Júyùwǎng jiērù diǎn	LAP
Local area network drivers	局域网驱动	Júyùwǎng qūdòng	
Local area network emulation	局域网仿真	Júyùwǎng fǎngzhēn	LANE
Local area network emulation client	局域网仿真客户机	Júyùwǎng fǎngzhēn kèhùjī	LEC
Local area network emulation server	局域网仿真服务器	Júyùwǎng fǎngzhēn fúwùqì	LES
Local area protocol (IEEE usage)	局域网协议	Júyùwǎng xiéyì	
Local automatic circuit exchange	市内自动线路交换机	Shìnèi zìdòng xiànlù jiāohuànjī	LACE
Local automatic message accounting	本端自动消息记帐	Běnduān zìdòng xiāoxi jìzhàng	LAMA
Local bearing	局部方位	Júbù fāngwèi	
Local bus	局部总线	Júbù zǒngxiàn	LB
Local bus	区汇流排	Qū huìliú pái	
Local cable	市话电缆	Shìhuà diànlǎn	
Local caching	局部磁盘缓存	Júbù cípán huǎncún	
Local carrier demodulation	本地载波解调	Běndì zàibō jiětiáo	
Local carrier reception	本地载波接收	Běndì zàibō jiēshōu	
Local cell identifier	本地小区标识符	Běndì xiǎoqū biāozhì fú	LCI
Local central office	本地交换局	Běndì jiāohuàn jú	LCO
Local charging generator software	本地计费生成软件	Běndì jìfèi shēngchéng ruǎnjiàn	LCG
Local communication interconnection network	本地通信互联网	Běndì tōngxìn hùliánwǎng	LCIN
Local communication network	本地通信网络	Běndì tōngxìn wǎngluò	LCN

Local communications network	本地通信网	Běndì tōngxìnwǎng	LCN
Local conductor	本地主持者	Běndì zhǔchízhě	
Local control	本地控制	Běndì kòngzhì	LC
Local coordinate system	地方坐标系	Dìfang zuòbiāo xì	
Local correspondence	本埠函件	Běnbù hánjiàn	
Local craft terminal	本地维护终端	Běndì wéihù zhōngduān	LCT
Local data cube	本地多维数据集	Běndì duōwéi shùjùjí	
Local digital message exchange	局部数字信息交换	Júbù shùzì xìnxī jiāohuàn	LDME
Local distinguished name	本地识别名	Běndì shíbié míng	LDN
Local distributor	本地分发服务器	Běndì fēnfā fúwùqì	
Local error	局地的错误	Júdìde cuòwù	
Local exchange	本地交换网	Běndì jiāohuàn wǎng	LE
Local exchange	本地交换机	Běndì jiāohuànjī	LE
Local exchange	本地交换局	Běndì jiāohuànjú	LE
Local exchange carrier	本地交换公司	Běndì jiāohuàn gōngsī	LEC
Local exchange carrier	本地交换运营商	Běndì jiāohuàn yùnyíng shāng	LEC
Local exchange center	本地交换中心	Běndì jiāohuàn zhōngxīn	
Local exchange operation system	本地交换运行系统	Běndì jiāohuàn yùnxíng xìtǒng	LE-OpS
Local explorer packet	局部探测器数据分组	Júbù tàncèqì shùjù fēnzǔ	
Local flow	局部流	Júbù liú	
Local function capabilities	本地功能能力	Běndì gōngnéng nénglì	LFC
Local group	本地组	Běndì zǔ	
Local high capacity IPC processor	本地高容量 IPC 处理器	Běndì gāo róngliàng IPC chǔlǐqì	LHIP
Local injection and detection (FOC)	局部通光检测	Júbù tōngguāng jiǎncè	LID
Local interconnect	局域互连	Júyù hùlián	
Local interoffice optical communication system	局间中继光通讯系统	Jú-jiān zhōngjì guāng tōngxùn xìtǒng	
Local inter-office trunking	市内局间中继线	Shìnèi jú-jiān zhōngjìxiàn	LIT
Local line automatic (testing) routine	本地线路自动检验列行程序	Běndì xiànlù zìdòng jiǎnyàn lièxíng chéngxù	LLAR
Local line clock distribution	本地线路时钟分配	Běndì xiànlù shízhōng fēnpèi	LLCK
Local login identification	本地登录标识	Běndì dēnglù biāozhì	
Local loop	局部回路	Júbù huílù	
Local maintenance terminal	本地维护终端	Běndì wéihù zhōngduān	LMT
Local management service point	本地管理业务点	Běndì guǎnlǐ yèwù diǎn	LMSP
Local message metering system	局部信息计费	Júbù xìnxī jìfèi	LMM
Local mobile station identity	本地移动用户身份	Běndì yídòng yònghù shēnfen	LMSI
Local mobile station identity	本地移动台识别	Běndì yídòngtái shíbié	LMSI
Local mobile station identity	本地移动台识别码	Běndì yídòngtái shíbié mǎ	LMSI
Local mobile subscriber identity	本地移动用户识别号	Běndì yídòng yònghù shíbié hào	LMSI
Local mode	本地方式	Běndì fāngshì	
Local multipoint communication system (Canadian term for LMDS)	本地多点通信系统	Běndì duōdiǎn tōngxìn xìtǒng	LMCS
Local multipoint distributed system	局域多点分布式系统	Júyù duōdiǎn Fēnbùshì xìtǒng	LMDS
Local multipoint distribution service	本地多点分配业务	Běndì duōdiǎn fēnpèi yèwù	LMDS
Local network management center	本地网络管理中心	Běndì wǎngluò guǎnlǐ zhōngxīn	LNMC
Local network server	本地网络服务器	Běndì wǎngluò fúwùqì	
Local node clock	本地节点时钟	Běndì jiédiǎn shízhōng	LNC

Local object	局部对象	Júbù duìxiàng	
Local operations control station	本地操作控制台	Běndì cāozuò kòngzhìtái	LOC
Local oscillator	本地振荡器	Běndì zhèndàngqì	
Local path index (in XML)	局部路径索引	Júbù lùjìng suǒyǐn	LPI
Local peripheral bus	局域边缘总线	Júyù biānyuán zǒngxiàn	
Local postal attributes	本地邮政属性	Běndì yóuzhèng shǔxìng	
Local primary reference	本地基准参考	Běndì jīzhǔn cānkǎo	LPR
Local primary reference	区域基准时钟	Qūyù jīzhǔn shízhōng	LPR
Local primary reference	区域基准钟	Qūyù jīzhǔn zhōng	LPR
Local primary reference source	本地主基准源	Běndì zhǔ jīzhǔn yuán	LPR
Local public land mobile communications network	本地公用陆地移动通信网络	Běndì gōngyòng lùdì yídòng tōngxìnwǎng luò	LPLMN
Local record	本机记录	Běnjī jìlù	
Local server	本地服务器	Běndì fúwùqì	
Local significance	局部意义	Júbù yìyì	
Local subscription	本地订阅	Běndì dìngyuè	
Local switch	本地端局	Běndì duānjú	LS
Local switch	本地交换机	Běndì jiāohuànjī	LS
Local switch	本地交换局	Běndì jiāohuànjú	LS
Local switch	端局交换机	Duān jú jiāohuànjī	LS
Local switch, end office	端局	Duānjú	
Local switching sub-system	本地交换子系统	Běndì jiāohuàn zìxìtǒng	LSS
Local system environment	本地系统环境	Běndì xìtǒng huánjìng	LSE
Local terminal	局侧终端	Júcè zhōngduān	LT
Local terminal emulator	本地终端仿真器	Běndì zhōngduān fǎngzhēnqì	LTE
Local terminal emulator	本地终端模拟器	Běndì zhōngduān mónǐqì	
Local termination	局部终止	Júbù zhōngzhǐ	
Local time reference	本地时钟参考	Běndì shízhōng cānkǎo	LTR
Local time zone	本地时区	Běndì shíqū	LTZ
Local traffic filtering	局部业务量过滤	Júbù yèwùliàng guòlǜ	
Local unit	本地单元	Běndì dānyuán	LU
Local variable	局部变量	Júbù biànliàng	
Locale	区域设置	Qūyù shèzhì	
Locale identifier	区域设置标识符	Qūyù shèzhì biāozhì fú	LCID
Localization service	定位业务	Dìngwèi yèwù	LCS
Localize software	本土化软件	Běntǔhuà ruǎnjiàn	
Localized service area	局部业务区域	Júbù yèwù qūyù	LSA
Locally active	本地在用	Běndì zàiyòng	
LocalTalk link access protocol (Apple use)	AppleTalk 链路访问协议	AppleTalk liànlù fǎngwèn xiéyì	LLAP
Location and allocation model	选址-配置模型	Xuǎnzhǐ—pèizhì móxíng	
Location area	位置区	Wèizhì qū	LA
Location area	位置区域	Wèizhì qūyù	LA
Location area code	位置区码	Wèizhì qū mǎ	LAC
Location area code	位置区域码	Wèizhì qūyù mǎ	LAC
Location area identification	位置区识别	Wèizhì qū shíbié	LAI
Location area identification	位置区域识别	Wèizhì qūyù shíbié	LAI
Location area identity	位置区号	Wèizhì qū hào	LAI

Location area information	位置区信息	Wèizhì qū xìnxī	LAI
Location area update	位置区域更新	Wèizhì qūyù gēngxīn	LAU
Location cancellation procedure	位置取消规程	Wèizhì qǔxiāo guīchéng	
Location cancellation procedure	位置删除程序	Wèizhì shānchú chéngxù	
Location confirm	定位确认	Dìngwèi quèrèn	LCF
Location confirm	地址解析回答	Dìzhǐ jiěxī huídá	LCF
Location confirm	地址解析确认	Dìzhǐ jiěxī quèrèn	LCF
Location correlation	位置相关	Wèizhì xiāngguān	
Location counter	指令计数器	Zhǐlìng jìshùqì	
Location deregistration	位置撤消登记	Wèizhì chèxiāo dēngjì	
Location directory	位置目録	Wèizhì mùlù	LD
Location division multiple access	位置划分多路存取	Wèizhì huàfēn duōlù cúnqǔ	LDMA
Location information	位置信息	Wèizhì xìnxī	
Location information requested procedure	位置信息请求规程	Wèizhì xìnxī qǐngqiú guīchéng	
Location information retrieval procedure	位置信息恢复规程	Wèizhì xìnxī huīfù guīchéng	
Location measurement unit	定位测量单元	Dìngwèi cèliáng dānyuán	LMU
Location PLMN	本地 PLMN	Běndì PLMN	LPLMN
Location reference	位置参照	Wèizhì cānzhào	
Location reference code	位置参照代码	Wèizhì cānzhào dàimǎ	
Location reference type	位置参照类型	Wèizhì cānzhào lèixíng	
Location register	位置登记器	Wèizhì dēngjìqì	LR
Location register	位置寄存器	Wèizhì jìcúnqì	LR
Location register system ACE	位置寄存器系统 ACE	Wèizhì jìcúnqì xìtǒng ACE	LRSACE
Location registration	位置登记	Wèizhì dēngjì	
Location registration sub-system	位置登记子系统	Wèizhì dēngjì zixìtǒng	LRS
Location reject	定位拒绝	Dìngwèi jùjué	LRJ
Location reject (packet protocol)	地址解析拒绝	Dìzhǐ jiěxī jùjué	LRJ
Location reject message	拒绝地址解析	Jùjué dìzhǐ jiěxī	LRJ
Location request	定位请求	Dìngwèi qǐngqiú	LRQ
Location request	地址解析请求	Dìzhǐ jiěxī qǐngqiú	LRQ
Location sensitive billing system	用户位置的灵活计账系统	Yònghù wèizhìde línghuó jìzhàng xìtǒng	LSBS
Location server	位置服务器	Wèizhì fúwùqì	
Location server, position server	定位服务器	Dìngwèi fúwùqì	
Location services	定位业务	Dìngwèi yèwù	LCS
Location services client	定位业务客户	Dìngwèi yèwù kèhù	LCSC
Location services server	定位业务服务器	Dìngwèi yèwù fúwùqì	LCSS
Location tracking	位置跟踪	Wèizhì gēnzōng	
Location update	位置更新	Wèizhì gēngxīn	LU
Location update accept	位置更新接受	Wèizhì gēngxīn jiēshòu	
Location updating procedure	位置更新程序	Wèizhì gēngxīn chéngxù	
Location updating procedure	位置更新规程	Wèizhì gēngxīn guīchéng	
Location updating type	位置更新类型	Wèizhì gēngxīn lèixíng	
Locational reference	定位参照系	Dìngwèi cānzhàoxì	
Locator	定位仪	Dìngwèiyí	
Lock	锁	Suǒ	
Lock out (used for computer login or malfunction)	暂停	Zàntíng	LO

Lock-and-key protection system (IPsec)	锁和密钥保护系统	Suŏ hé mìyào băohù xìtŏng	
Locked mode	锁定状态	Suŏdìng zhuàngtài	Lo
Locked set-up time	锁定建立时间	Suŏdìng jiànlì shíjiān	
Lockheed Martin Corp. (US company)	洛克希德马丁公司	Luò-kè-xī-dé Mă-dīng gōngsī	
Lock-in amplifier	锁定放大器	Suŏdìng fàngdàqì	
Locking time	锁定时间	Suŏdìng shíjiān	
Log	日志	Rìzhì	
Log file	日志文件	Rìzhì wénjiàn	
Log page (in Sybase)	日志页	Rìzhì yè	
Log periodic antenna	对数周期天线	Duìshù zhōuqī tiānxiàn	LPA
Log periodic dipole array	对数周期偶极子天线阵	Duìshù zhōuqī ŏujízi tiānxiàn zhèn	LPDA
Log periodic dipole array antenna	对数偶极子阵列天线	Duìshù ŏujízi zhènliè tiānxiàn	
Log reader agent (in SQL Server)	日志阅读代理	Rìzhì yuèdú dàilĭ	
Logarithm, logarithmic	对数	Duìshù	
Logarithmic amplifier	对数放大器	Duìshù fàngdàqì	
Logarithmic detector	对数检波器	Duìshù jiănbōqì	
Logarithmic frequency characteristic	对数频率特性	Duìshù pínlǜ tèxìng	
Logarithmic intermediate frequency amplifier	对数中频放大器	Duìshù zhōngpín fàngdàqì	
Logarithmic receiver	对数接收机	Duìshù jiēshōujī	
Logarithmic transfer matrix	对数传输矩阵	Duìshù chuánshū jŭzhèn	
Logarithmic video amplifier	对数视频放大器	Duìshù shìpín fàngdàqì	
Logatom articulation	试音音节清晰度	Shìyīn yīnjié qīngxīdù	
Log-FTC (fast time constant) circuit	对数-快时间常数电路	Duìshù-kuài shíjiān chángshù diànlù	
Logger, logging instrument	测井仪	Cèjĭngyí	
Logging	纪录测井	Jìlù cèjĭng	
Logging	日志	Rìzhì	
Logic analyzer	逻辑分析仪	Luójì fēnxīyí	
Logic bomb (hacker attack)	逻辑炸弹	Luójì zhàdàn	
Logic bomb virus	逻辑炸弹病毒	Luójì zhàdàn bìngdú	
Logic cell array (FPGA term)	逻辑单元阵列	Luójì dānyuán zhènliè	LCA
Logic circuit	逻辑电路	Luójì diànlù	
Logic design	逻辑设计	Luójì shèjì	
Logic element	逻辑元件	Luójì yuánjiàn	
Logic gate, logic element	逻辑门	Luójì mén	
Logic link control layer	逻辑链路控制层	Luójì liànlù kòngzhì céng	LLC
Logic module	逻辑模块	Luójì mókuài	LM
Logic port	逻辑端口	Luójì duānkŏu	LP
Logic units (ITU-T usage)	逻辑单元	Luójì dānyuán	LU
Logical anti-jamming processing	逻辑抗干扰处理	Luójì kàng gānrăo chŭlĭ	
Logical assignment statement	逻辑赋值语句	Luójì fùzhí yŭjù	
Logical block addressing	逻辑块寻址	Luójì kuài xúnzhĭ	LBA
Logical channel	逻辑信道	Luójì xìndào	LC
Logical channel command word	逻辑通道命令字	Luójì tōngdào mìnglìng zì	LCCW
Logical channel identifier	逻辑通路标识符	Luójì tōnglù biāozhìfú	LCI
Logical connector	逻辑连接符	Luójì liánjiēfú	
Logical consistency	逻辑一致性	Luójì yīzhìxìng	

Logical constant	逻辑常数	Luóji chángshù	
Logical data structures	逻辑数据结构	Luóji shùjù jiégòu	
Logical database	逻辑数据库	Luóji shùjùkù	
Logical database design	数据库逻辑设计	Shùjùkù luóji shèjì	
Logical drive	逻辑驱动器	Luóji qūdòngqì	
Logical expression	逻辑式	Luóji shì	
Logical function	逻辑函数	Luóji hánshù	
Logical group node	逻辑群节点	Luóji qún jiédiǎn	LGN
Logical group node	逻辑组节点	Luóji zǔ jiédiǎn	
Logical IF statement	逻辑条件语句	Luóji tiáojiàn yǔjù	
Logical Internet protocol (IP) sub-network	逻辑因特网协议子网	Luóji Yīntèwǎng xiéyì zìwǎng	LIS
Logical IP sub-network	逻辑 IP 子网	Luóji IP zìwǎng	LIS
Logical line code	逻辑线路组	Luóji xiànlù zǔ	LLG
Logical link control (sub-layer) (IEEE 802.2)	逻辑链路控制（子层）	Luóji liànlù kòngzhì (zǐcéng)	LLC
Logical link control and adaptation protocol	逻辑链路控制和适配协议	Luóji liànlù kòngzhì hé shìpèi xiéyì	L2CAP
Logical link control, type 2	第二类逻辑链路控制	Dì'èrlèi luóji liànlù kòngzhì	LLC2
Logical loopback	逻辑环回	Luóji huánhuí	
Logical name	逻辑名	Luóji míng	LN
Logical name	逻辑名称	Luóji míngchēng	
Logical object	逻辑客体	Luóji kètǐ	
Logical object class	逻辑客体类别	Luóji kètǐ lèibié	
Logical operation	逻辑运算	Luóji yùnsuàn	
Logical operator	逻辑操作符	Luóji cāozuòfú	
Logical operators	逻辑运算符	Luóji yùnsuànfú	
Logical overlay (in computers)	逻辑覆盖	Luóji fùgài	
Logical page	逻辑页	Luóji yè	
Logical product	逻辑乘积	Luóji chéngjī	
Logical query	逻辑查询	Luóji cháxún	
Logical record	逻辑记录	Luóji jìlù	
Logical relationship	逻辑关系	Luóji guānxi	
Logical selection	逻辑选择	Luóji xuǎnzé	
Logical signaling channel	逻辑信令信道	Luóji xìnlìng xìndào	
Logical signaling channel	信令逻辑通路	Xìnlìng luóji tōnglù	
Logical space	逻辑空间	Luóji kōngjiān	
Logical structure	逻辑结构	Luóji jiégòu	
Logical structure editing process	逻辑结构编辑处理	Luóji jiégòu biānjí chǔlǐ	
Logical sub-fiber protection	逻辑子光纤保护	Luóji zìguāngxiān bǎohù	LSP
Logical sum	逻辑和	Luóji hé	
Logical terminal profile	逻辑终端轮廓	Luóji zhōngduān lúnkuò	LTP
Logical user port	逻辑用户端口	Luóji yònghù duānkǒu	LUP
Logical_join	逻辑联接	Luóji liánjiē	
Login	注册	Zhùcè	
Login	上机	Shàngjī	
Login security mode (for database)	登录安全模式	Dēnglù ānquán móshì	
Login server	登录服务器	Dēnglù fúwùqì	
Login, load	载入	Zǎirù	

English	Chinese	Pinyin	Abbr.
Login, logon	登录	Dēnglù	
Login, register (verb)	登记	Dēngjì	
Login; on-line	连线	Liánxiàn	
Logistic delay	后勤迟延	Hòuqín chíyán	
Logistic delay	后勤耽误	Hòuqín dānwù	
Logistics management	物流管理	Wùliú guǎnlǐ	
Logistics resource planning	物流资源计划	Wùliú zīyuán jìhuà	LRP
Logitech (US company)	罗技公司	Luó-jì gongsī	
Log-normal	对数正态	Duìshù zhèngtài	
Log-normal distribution	对数正态分布	Duìshù zhèngtài fēnbù	
Log-odds ratio	对数几率比	Duìshù jīlǜ bǐ	
Logon rights	登录权限	Dēnglù quánxiàn	
Logon script	登录脚本	Dēnglù jiǎoběn	
Logon script path	登录脚本路径	Dēnglù jiǎoběn lùjìng	
Logout	载出	Zàichū	
Logout	注销	Zhùxiāo	
Logout	退出连线	Tuìchū liánxiàn	
Lone signal unit	单一信号单元	Dānyī xìnhào dānyuán	LSU
Long Bridge	长桥	Cháng qiáo	
Long distance cable line	长途电缆线路	Chángtú diànlǎn xiànlù	CXD
Long distance console	长途台	Chángtútái	CT
Long distance open line	长途明线线路	Chángtú míngxiàn xiànlù	CXM
Long distance optical cable line	长途光缆线路	Chángtú guānglǎn xiànlù	CXG
Long distance unmanned cable station	长途电缆无人站	Chángtú diànlǎn wúrénzhàn	CLW
Long life ceramic emitters (semiconductor mfg)	寿命长的陶瓷发射器	Shòumìng chángde táocí fāshèqì	
Long unit data (in SS7)	长单位数据	Cháng dānwèi shùjù	LUDT
Long unit data transmission	长单位数据传输	Cháng dānwèi shùjù chuánshū	LUDT
Long unit data transmission service	长单位数据传输业务	Cháng dānwèi shùjù chuánshū yèwù	LUDTS
Long wave	长波	Chángbō	
Long wave infrared (semiconductor mfg)	长波红外	Chángbō hóngwài	
Long wavelength optical fiber	长波光纤	Chángbō guāngxiān	LWL
Long wavelength semiconductor laser module	长波长半导体激光模组	Cháng bōcháng bàndǎotǐ jīguāng mózǔ	
Longest common sub-string	最长公共子串	Zuìcháng gōnggòng zichuàn	
Longest prefix matching	最长前缀匹配	Zuìcháng qiánzhuì pǐpèi	
Long-haul optical transmission set	远程光传输设备	Yuǎnchéng guāng chuánshū shèbèi	LHOTS
Long-haul terrestrial optical communication system	长途干线中继光通讯系统	Chángtú gànxiàn zhōngjì guāng tōngxùn xìtǒng	
Longitude	经度	Jīngdù	
Longitudinal conversion loss	纵模变换损耗	Zòngmó biànhuàn sǔnhào	LCL
Longitudinal conversion loss	纵向变换损耗	Zòngxiàng biànhuàn sǔnhào	LCL
Longitudinal conversion loss	纵向转换衰减	Zòngxiàng zhuǎnhuàn shuāijiǎn	LCL
Longitudinal conversion loss	纵向转换损耗	Zòngxiàng zhuǎnhuàn sǔnhào	LCL
Longitudinal conversion transfer loss	纵向变换转移损耗	Zòngxiàng biànhuàn zhuǎnyí sǔnhào	LCTL
Longitudinal electromotive force	纵电动势	Zòng diàndòngshì	
Longitudinal judder	纵向抖动	Zòngxiàng dǒudòng	
Longitudinal over-voltage	纵向过电压	Zòngxiàng guòdiànyā	
Longitudinal redundancy check	纵向冗余(码)校验	Zòngxiàng rǒngyú (mǎ) jiàoyàn	LRC

English	Chinese	Pinyin	Abbreviation
Longitudinal shunt slot non-resonance array	纵向并联缝隙非谐振式天线阵	Zòngxiàng bìnglián fèngxì fēixiézhèn-shì tiānxiàn zhèn	
Longitudinal shunt slot resonance array	纵向并联缝隙谐振式天线阵	Zòngxiàng bìnglián fèngxì xiézhèn-shì tiānxiàn zhèn	
Longitudinal wave	纵波	Zòngbō	
Long-line oscillator	长线型振荡器	Chángxiàn-xíng zhèndàngqì	
Long-period observation	长期观测	Chángqī guāncè	
Long-range forecasting	长期预报	Chángqī yùbào	
Long-term flicker indicator	长期抖动指示器	Chángqī dǒudòng zhǐshìqì	
Long-term frequency stability	长期频率稳定度	Chángqī pínlǜ wěndìngdù	
Long-wavelength detector for communication	通信用长波长检光元件	Tōngxìn-yòng cháng bōcháng jiǎn guāng yuánjiàn	
Long-wire antenna	长线天线	Chángxiàn tiānxiàn	
Long-word instruction	长字指令	Cháng zì zhǐlìng	
Look up table	查询表	Cháxúnbiǎo	LUT
Lookup table (for database)	查找表	Cházhǎo biǎo	
Loop antenna	环形天线	Huánxíng tiānxiàn	
Loop checking	环路检验	Huánlù jiǎnyàn	
Loop DC overall gain	环路直流总增益	Huánlù zhíliú zǒngzēngyì	
Loop filter proportion coefficient	环路滤波器比例系数	Huánlù lǜbōqì bǐlì xìshù	
Loop gain	环路增益	Huánlù zēngyì	
Loop initialization fabric assigned frame	环路初始化架构分配帧	Huánlù chūshǐhuà jiàgòu fēnpèi zhèng	LIFA
Loop initialization hard assigned frame	环路初始化硬分配帧	Huánlù chūshǐhuà yìng fēnpèi zhèng	LIHA
Loop initialization previously assigned	环路初始化预分配	Huánlù chūshǐhuà yùfēnpèi	LIPA
Loop initialization primitive sequence	环路初始化进程	Huánlù chūshǐhuà jìnchéng	LIP
Loop initialization report position frame	环路初始化位置报告帧	Huánlù chūshǐhuà wèizhì bàogào zhèng	LIRP
Loop initialization select master frame	环路初始化主控制器选择帧	Huánlù chūshǐhuà zhǔ kòngzhìqì xuǎnzé zhèng	LISM
Loop initialization soft assigned frame	环路初始化软分配帧	Huánlù chūshǐhuà ruǎn fēnpèi zhèng	LISA
Loop interface-central office end	局端环路接口	Júduān huánlù jiēkǒu	U-C
Loop interface-remote terminal end	远端环路接口	Yuǎnduān huánlù jiēkǒu	U-R
Loop join (in SQL Server)	循环连接	Xúnhuán liánjiē	
Loop lockable maximum margin angular frequency	环路可锁定最高界限角频率	Huánlù kěsuǒdìng zuìgāo jièxiàn jiǎopínlǜ	
Loop lockable minimum margin angular frequency	环路可锁定最底界限角频率	Huánlù kěsuǒdìng zuìdǐ jièxiàn jiǎopínlǜ	
Loop multiplexer	环路复用器	Huánlù fùyòngqì	LM
Loop natural resonant angular frequency	环路自然谐振角频率	Huánlù zìrán xiézhèn jiǎopínlǜ	
Loop noise bandwidth	环路噪声带宽	Huánlù zàoshēng dàikuān	
Loop port bypass	环路端口旁路	Huánlù duānkǒu pánglù	LPB
Loop port enable	环路端口启用	Huánlù duānkǒu qǐyòng	LPE
Loop port state machine	环路端口状态机	Huánlù duānkǒu zhuàngtài jī	LPSM
Loop radio frequency overall gain	环路高频总增益	Huánlù gāopín zǒngzēngyì	
Loop stick antenna	环棒天线	Huánbàng tiānxiàn	LSA
Loop system	环路系统	Huánlù xìtǒng	
Loop transmission	环路传输	Huánlù chuánshū	
Loop trunk board	环路中继板	Huánlù zhōngjì bǎn	
Loop, cycle, circular	循环	Xúnhuán	
Loop/disconnect signaling	环路环路断续信令	Huánlù duànxù xìnlìng	
Loopback	环回	Huánhuí	

Loop-back acknowledgement (ISUP message)	环路已接通	Huánlù yǐ jiētōng	LPA
Loopback alias	回送别名	Huísòng biémíng	
Loopback application	环回应用	Huánhuí yìngyòng	
Loopback control mechanism	环回控制机制	Huánhuí kòngzhì jīzhì	
Loopback control point	环回控制点	Huánhuí kòngzhìdiǎn	
Loopback interface	回送接口	Huísòng jiēkǒu	
Loopback point	环回点	Huánhuídiǎn	
Loopback requesting point	环回请求点	Huánhuí qǐngqiúdiǎn	
Loopback test pattern	环回测试码型	Huánhuí cèshì mǎxíng	
Loop-back testing	环测	Huáncè	
Loophole (IPsec)	漏洞	Lòudòng	
Looplet	小环路	Xiǎo huánlù	
Loose coupling	松散耦合	Sōngsǎn ǒuhé	
Loose jacket (of fiber optic cable)	松套层	Sōng tàocéng	
Loose name checking	宽限名称检查	Kuānxiàn míngchēng jiǎnchá	
Loose tube (of fiber optic cable)	松套	Sōng tào	
Loosely buffered fiber optic cable	松包式光缆	Sōngbāo-shì guānglǎn	
Loose-tube layer stranded optical fiber ribbon cable	松套层绞式光纤带光缆	Sōng tàocéng jiǎo-shì guāngxiāndài guānglǎn	
Loose-tube stranded optical cable	松套层绞光缆	Sōng tàocéng jiǎo guānglǎn	
Loss angle	损耗角	Sǔnhào jiǎo	
Loss of alignment	帧失位	Zhèng shīwèi	LOA
Loss of cell delineation	信元定界丢失	Xìnyuán dìngjiè diūshī	LCD
Loss of continuity	连续性丢失	Liánxùxìng diūshī	LOC
Loss of continuity on optical transmission section	光传送段连续性丢失	Guāng chuánsòng duàn liánxùxìng diūshī	LOC-OTS
Loss of frame	帧丢失	Zhèng diūshī	LOF
Loss of frame alarm	帧丢失告警	Zhèng diūshī gàojǐng	LOF
Loss of information	信息丢失	Xìnxī diūshī	
Loss of link	链路丢失	Liànlù diūshī	
Loss of maintenance flow	维护流丢失	Wéihù liú diūshī	LMF
Loss of multi-frame	复帧丢失	Fùzhèng diūshī	LOM
Loss of pointer	指针丢失	Zhǐzhēn diūshī	LOP
Loss of power	电源丢失	Diànyuán diūshī	
Loss of signal	信号丢失	Xìnhào diūshī	LOS
Loss of signal	失去信号	Shīqù xìnhào	LOS
Loss of signal (optical)	光信号丢失	Guāng xìnhào diūshī	LOS
Loss of signal alarm	信号丢失告警	Xìnhào diūshī gàojǐng	LOS
Loss of signal defect	信号丢失缺陷	Xìnhào diūshī quēxiàn	dLOS
Loss of sync word	同步字丢失	Tóngbù zì diūshī	LOSW
Loss of timing information	失去定时信息	Shīqù dìngshí xìnxī	LTI
Loss ratio	损耗比	Sǔnhào bǐ	
Loss relative to free space	相对于自由空间的损耗	Xiāngduìyú zìyóu kōngjiānde sǔnhào	
Losses between stages	级间损耗	Jí-jiān sǔnhào	
Lossy	有损耗的	Yǒu sǔnhàode	
Lost call cleared	丢失呼叫清除	Diūshī hūjiào qīngchú	LCC
Lost call hold	丢失呼叫保持	Diūshī hūjiào bǎochí	LCH
Lost error bit	丢失错误位	Diūshī cuòwù wèi	LEB

Lost frame	丢失帧	Diūshī zhèng	
Lost frames	丢失帧	Diūshī zhèng	
Lost synchronization coefficient	失步系数	Shībù xìshù	
Lost time	损失时间	Sǔnshī shíjiān	
Lotus Development Corp. (US company)	莲花发展集团	Liánhuā fāzhǎn jítuán	
Lotus Smartsuite ©	莲花智慧配套	Liánhuā zhìhui pèitào	
Loudness rating	响度评定值	Xiǎngdù píngdìngzhí	LR
Love wave	拉夫波	Lā-fū bō	
Low address part	低地址段	Dīdìzhǐ duàn	LAP
Low atmospheric pressure test	低气压实验	Dīqìyā shíyàn	
Low battery alarm	电池低压报警	Diànchí dīyā bàojǐng	
Low battery cut-off	电池低压关机	Diànchí dīyā guānjī	
Low bit rate	低比特率	Dībǐtè lǜ	
Low constrained delay	低约束时延	Dīyuēshù shíyán	LCD
Low cycle fatigue	低循环疲劳	Dīxúnhuán píláo	
Low data rate transmission	低数据率传输	Dīshùjùlǜ chuánshū	LDRT
Low density polyethylene	低密聚乙烯	Dīmì jùyǐxī	LDPE
Low dispersion slope optical fiber	低色散斜率光纤	Dīsèsàn xiélǜ guāngxiān	
Low earth orbit	低地球轨道	Dīdìqiú guǐdào	LEO
Low earth orbit	低轨道	Dīguǐdào	LEO
Low earth orbit satellite mobile communication system	低轨道卫星系统	Dīguǐdào wèixīng xìtǒng	
Low earth orbit satellites	地球低轨卫星	Dìqiú dīguǐ wèixīng	LEO
Low emissivity	低辐射	Dīfúshè	
Low exponent attack	地指数攻击	Dìzhǐshù gōngjī	
Low frequency	低频	Dīpín	LF
Low frequency amplifier	低频放大器	Dīpín fàngdàqì	LFA
Low frequency load shedding	低频减载	Dīpín jiǎnzài	
Low frequency slip ring	低频滑环	Dīpín huáhuán	
Low insertion force	小插接力	Xiǎo chājiēlì	LIF
Low layer compatibility	低层兼容性	Dīcéng jiānróngxìng	LLC
Low layer function	低层功能	Dīcéng gōngnéng	LLF
Low layer management entity	低层管理实体	Dīcéng guǎnlǐ shítǐ	LLME
Low layer uniformity	底层一致性	Dǐcéng yīzhìxìng	
Low level interrupt request	低级中断请求	Dījí zhōngduàn qǐngqiú	LLIR
Low level language	低级语言	Dījí yǔyán	
Low level signal transfer point	低级信令转换点	Dījí xìnlìng zhuǎnhuàn diǎn	LSTP
Low level signal transfer point	低级信令转接点	Dījí xìnlìng zhuǎnjiē diǎn	LSTP
Low order service control point	低等级业务控制点	Dīděngjí yèwù kòngzhìdiǎn	LSCP
Low pass filter	低通滤波器	Dītōng lǜbōqì	LPF
Low pass function	低通功能	Dītōng gōngnéng	LPF
Low power oscillator	低功率振荡器	Dīgōnglǜ zhèndàngqì	LOP
Low pressure	低压	Dīyā	
Low probability of detection	低检测概率	Dījiǎncè gàilǜ	LPD
Low probability of intercept	低截获概率	Dījiéhuò gàilǜ	LPI
Low probability of position fix	低定位概率	Dīdìngwèi gàilǜ	LPPF
Low probability of signal exploitation	低溯源概率	Dīsùyuán gàilǜ	LPSE

Low smoke zero halogen (FOC)	低烟无卤阻燃	Dīyān wúlǔ zǔrán	LSZH
Low speed-rate asynchronous digital subscriber line without voice splitter	无话音分离器的低速不对称数字用户线	Wúhuàyīn fēnlíqìde dīsù bùduìchèn shùzì yònghù xiàn	ADSL.lite
Low temperature antenna	低温度天线	Dīwēndù tiānxiàn	
Low temperature test	低温试验	Dīwēn shìyàn	
Low velocity zone	低速度带	Dīsùdù dài	
Low voltage differential signal	低电压差动信号	Dīdiànyā chādòng xìnhào	LVDS
Low voltage load shedding	低压减载	Dīyā jiǎnzài	
Low voltage small aperture grid with impregnated cathode	低电压光圈阴极管	Dīdiànyā guāngquān yīnjíguǎn	L-SAGIC
Low-altitude surveillance radar	低空搜索雷达	Dīkōng sōusuǒ léidá	
Low-delay - code excited linear prediction coding	低时延码激励线性预测编码	Dīshíyán mǎ jīlì xiànxìng yùcè biānmǎ	LD-CELP
Low-delay - code excited linear prediction	低时延码激励线性预测	Dīshíyán mǎ jīlì xiànxìng yùcè	LD-CELP
Low-entry networking node	低输入网络连接节点	Dīshūrù wǎngluò liánjiē jiédiǎn	LEN node
Lower address latch	低位址锁定	Dīwèizhǐ suǒdìng	
Lower call attempt threshold	试呼下界	Shìhū xiàjiè	
Lower case	小写字母	Xiǎoxiě zìmǔ	
Lower command packet address	命令包地区地址	Mìnglìng bāo dìqū dìzhǐ	LCPA
Lower layer compatibility	低层兼容	Dīcéng jiānróng	LLC
Lower order	低阶	Dījiē	LO
Lower order connection supervision	低阶连接监控	Dījiē liánjiē jiānkòng	LCS
Lower order connection supervision	低阶连接监视	Dījiē liánjiē jiānshì	LCS
Lower order interface	低阶接口	Dījiē jiēkǒu	LOI
Lower order path	低阶通道	Dījiē tōngdào	LP
Lower order path adaptation	低阶通道适配	Dījiē tōngdào shìpèi	LPA
Lower order path connection	低阶通道连接	Dījiē tōngdào liánjiē	LPC
Lower order path layer	低阶通道层	Dījiē tōngdào céng	LOPL
Lower order path network connection	低阶通道网络连接	Dījiē tōngdào wǎngluò liánjiē	LOP NC
Lower order path overhead	低阶通道开销	Dījiē tōngdào kāixiao	LPOH
Lower order path overhead monitor	低阶通道开销监视器	Dījiē tōngdào kāixiao jiānshìqì	LPOM
Lower order path overhead monitoring	低阶通道开销监视	Dījiē tōngdào kāixiao jiānshì	LPOM
Lower order path protection	低阶通道保护	Dījiē tōngdào bǎohù	LPP
Lower order path receive defect indicator	低阶通道接收缺陷指示	Dījiē tōngdào jiēshōu quēxiàn zhǐshì	LP-RDI
Lower order path remote defect indication	低阶通道远端缺陷指示	Dījiē tōngdào yuǎnduān quēxiàn zhǐshì	LP-RDI
Lower order path supervisory unequipped termination	低阶通道监控未装载终端	Dījiē tōngdào jiānkòng wèizhuāngzài zhōngduān	LSUT
Lower order path tandem connection adaptation	低阶通道串联连接适配	Dījiē tōngdào chuànlián liánjiē shìpèi	LTCA
Lower order path tandem connection monitor	低阶通道串联连接监视	Dījiē tōngdào chuànlián liánjiē jiānshì	LTCM
Lower order path tandem connection termination	低阶通道串联连接终端	Dījiē tōngdào chuànlián liánjiē zhōngduān	LTCT
Lower order path termination	低阶通道终端	Dījiē tōngdào zhōngduān	LPT
Lower order path trace identification mismatch	低阶通道路踪识别失配	Dījiē tōngdào lùzōng shíbié shīpèi	LP-TIM
Lower order path unequipped	低阶通道未装载	Dījiē tōngdào wèizhuāngzài	LP-UNEQ
Lower order tandem connection monitor	低阶通道串联连接监视器	Dījiē tōngdào chuànlián liánjiē jiānshìqì	LO-TCM
Lower order virtual container	低阶虚容器	Dījiē xūróngqì	LOVC
Lower sideband	下边带	Xiàbiandài	LSB
Lowest required radiated power	所需最小辐射功率	Suǒxū zuìxiǎo fúshè gōnglǜ	LRRP
Lowest useful frequency	最低可用频率	Zuìdī kěyòng pínlǜ	LUF

Low-level message function	低层消息函数	Dīcéng xiāoxi hánshù	
Low-level output current	低电平输出电流	Dīdiànpíng shūchūdiànliú	
Low-level output voltage	低电平输出电压	Dīdiànpíng shūchū diànyā	
Low-loss coaxial cable	低损耗同轴电缆	Dīsǔnhào tóngzhóu diànlǎn	
Low-noise amplifier	低噪声放大器	Dīzàoshēng fàngdàqì	LNA
Low-noise amplifier	低噪音放大器	Dīzàoyīn fàngdàqì	LNA
Low-noise antenna	低噪声天线	Dīzàoshēng tiānxiàn	
Low-noise cable	低噪声电缆	Dīzàoshēng diànlǎn	LNC
Low-noise microwave amplifier	低噪音微波放大器	Dīzàoyīn wēibō fàngdàqì	
Low-power beacon	低功率信标	Dīgōnglǜ xìnbiāo	
Low-power modulation	低电平调制	Dīdiànpíng tiáozhì	
Low-smoke	低烟	Dīyān	
Low-speed data	低速数据	Dīsù shùjù	LSD
Low-speed data channel	低速数据通道	Dīsù shùjù tōngdào	LDC
Low-speed line card	低速线路卡	Dīsù xiànlù qiǎ	LSC
Lucent Technologies Corp. (US company)	朗讯科技公司	Lǎng-xùn kējì gōngsī	
Lumen (unit of measure for the flow of light)	流明	Liúmíng	Lm
Luminance	辉度	Huīdù	
Luminance (video term)	亮度	Liàngdù	
Luminescent fiber	发光光纤	Fāguāng guāngxiān	
Luminosity	发光度	Fāguāngdù	
Luminous phenomenon	发光现象	Fāguāng xiànxiàng	
Lumpability	汇集性	Huìjíxìng	
Lumped mass system	集中质量体系	Jízhōng zhìliàng tǐxì	
Lumped-element circulator	集总元件环行器	Jízǒng yuánjiàn huánxíngqì	
Lumped-element isolator	集总元件隔离器	Jízǒng yuánjiàn gélíqì	
Luneberg lens antenna	龙伯透镜天线	Lóng-bó tòujìng tiānxiàn	
Luneburg lens antenna	楞勃透镜天线	Léng-bó tòujìng tiānxiàn	LLA
Lux (unit of illumination)	勒克司	Lè-kè-sī	

M

MAC protocol data unit	MAC 协议数据单元	MAC xiéyì shùjù dānyuán	MPDU
MAC service access point	MAC 服务访问点	MAC fúwù fǎngwèn diǎn	MSAP
MAC service data unit	MAC 服务数据单元	MAC fúwù shùjù dānyuán	MSDU
Machine address	机器地址	Jīqì dìzhǐ	MA
Machine code	机器代码	Jīqì dàimǎ	
Machine code	机器码	Jīqì mǎ	
Machine code	机械码	Jīxiè mǎ	
Machine cycle	机器周期	Jīqì zhōuqī	
Machine encoding	机器编码	Jīqì biānmǎ	
Machine instruction	机器指令	Jīqì zhǐlìng	
Machine instruction code	机器指令码	Jīqì zhǐlìng mǎ	MIC
Machine language	机器语言	Jīqì yǔyán	
Machine language	机械语言	Jīxiè yǔyán	
Machine language program	机器语言程序	Jīqì yǔyán chéngxù	MLP
Machine learning	机器学习	Jīqì xuéxí	

Machine motion noise	机械传动噪声	Jīxiè chuándòng zàoshēng	
Machine protection unit	机械隔离装置	Jīxiè gélí zhuāngzhì	
Machine translation	机器翻译	Jīqì fānyì	MT
Machine vision (in SMT)	机器视觉	Jīqì shìjué	
Machine-centric	机器中心的	Jīqì zhōngxīnde	
Mach-Zehnder interferometer	马赫-曾泽尔干涉仪	Mǎ-hè—céng-zé-ěr gānshèyí	
Mach-Zehnder modulator	马赫-曾德尔调制器	Mǎ-hè—céng-dé-ěr tiáozhìqì	
Macintosh; Mac (US company)	麦金塔	Mài-jīn-tǎ	
Macro analysis	常量分析	Chángliàng fēnxī	
Macro assembler	宏功能汇编语言	Hóng gōngnéng huìbiān yǔyán	MAC
Macro assembler instruction	宏汇编程序指令	Hóng huìbiān chéngxù zhǐlìng	MAI
Macro assembly language	宏汇编语言	Hóng huìbiān yǔyán	
Macro instruction	宏指令	Hóng zhǐlìng	
Macro name	宏名字	Hóng míngzì	
Macro programming	宏编程	Hóng biānchéng	
Macro virus	宏病毒	Hóng bìngdú	
Macro, large	宏	Hóng	
Macro-bending loss	宏弯损耗	Hóng wān sǔnhào	
Macro-block	宏块	Hóng kuài	MB
Macro-flow	宏流	Hóng liú	
Macro-instruction	宏指令	Hóngzhǐlìng	
Macro-zoning	大区划	Dàqūhuà	
Macula	斑点	Bāndiǎn	
Magazine (in component assembly)	下扳机	Xiàbānjī	
Magic-T	魔 T	Mó-T	
Magic-T hybrid network	魔 T 混合网络	Mó-T hùnhé wǎngluò	
Magnet	磁铁	Cítiě	
Magnetic anomaly	磁异常	Cí yìcháng	
Magnetic bearing of station	电台磁方位	Diàntái cí fāngwèi	
Magnetic card reader	磁卡阅读机	Cíkǎ yuèdújī	
Magnetic changes	磁力变化	Cílì biànhuà	
Magnetic conductor	导磁体	Dǎocí tǐ	
Magnetic core	磁心	Cíxīn	
Magnetic core antenna	磁芯天线	Cíxīn tiānxiàn	
Magnetic declination	磁针偏差	Cízhēn piānchā	
Magnetic deflection	磁偏转	Cí piānzhuǎn	
Magnetic deflection CRT	磁偏转管	Cí piānzhuǎn guǎn	
Magnetic disk	磁盘	Cípán	
Magnetic drum	磁鼓	Cígǔ	M/D
Magnetic field meter	磁场计	Cíchǎngjì	
Magnetic field radiated emissions (Mil-Std-461E, RE101)	磁场辐射发射	Cíchǎng fúshè fāshè	
Magnetic field radiated susceptibility (Mil-Std-461E, RS101)	磁场辐射敏感度	Cíchǎng fúshè mǐngǎndù	
Magnetic flux transducer/sensor	磁通传感器	Cítōng chuángǎnqì	
Magnetic focus	磁聚焦	Cí jùjiāo	
Magnetic head	磁头	Cítóu	

Magnetic hysteresis	磁滞	Cízhì	
Magnetic induced polarization instrument	磁激电仪	Cí jī diàn yí	
Magnetic logger	磁测井仪	Cí cèjǐngyí	
Magnetic modulating switch	磁调制开关	Cí tiáozhì kāiguān	
Magnetic moment	磁矩	Cíjǔ	M
Magnetic pulse modulator	磁脉冲调制器	Cí màichōng tiáozhìqì	
Magnetic sensors	磁场感应器	Cíchǎng gǎnyìngqì	MS
Magnetic shield	磁屏蔽	Cí píngbì	
Magnetic stripes	磁条	Cítiáo	
Magnetic tape	磁带	Cídài	
Magnetic tuning filter	磁调滤波器	Cí tiáo lǜbōqì	
Magnetically shielded room	磁场屏蔽室	Cíchǎng píngbìshì	MSR
Magnetization vector	磁化矢量	Cíhuà shǐliàng	
Magneto-optic modulator	磁光调变器	Cí guāng tiáobiànqì	
Magneto-optical (MO) disk drive	光磁碟机	Guāng cídiéjī	
Magneto-resistive head	磁阻磁头	Cízǔ cítóu	
Magnetron filament voltage controlling circuit	磁控管灯丝电压控制电路	Cíkòngguǎn dēngsī diànyā kòngzhì diànlù	
Magnification rate	放大率	Fàngdàlǜ	
Magnitude	量级	Liàngjí	
Magnitude of a voltage fluctuation	电压波动幅度	Diànyā bōdòng fúdù	
Magnitude refinement	幅值细化	Fúzhí xìhuà	
Magnitude spectrum	密度谱	Mìdù pǔ	
Mail	邮件	Yóujiàn	
Mail box	邮箱	Yóuxiāng	
Mail box	邮政信箱	Yóuzhèng xìnxiāng	
Mail loop	邮件循环	Yóujiàn xúnhuán	
Mail transfer agent	邮件传输代理	Yóujiàn chuánshū dàilǐ	MTA
Mailing list	邮单	Yóudān	
Mailing list	邮递名单	Yóudì míngdān	
Mail-safe transfer format	邮件安全传输格式	Yóujiàn ānquán chuánshū géshi	MSTF
Main beam (of an antenna)	主射束	Zhǔ shèshù	
Main beam clutter	主波束杂波	Zhǔ bōshù zábō	MBC
Main carrier	主载波	Zhǔ zàibō	
Main clock board	主时钟板	Zhǔ shízhōng bǎn	MCK
Main control board assembly	主控制集成板	Zhǔ kòngzhì jíchéngbǎn	MCPA
Main control station	主控站	Zhǔkòngzhàn	
Main control unit rack	主控制单元机架	Zhǔ kòngzhì dānyuán jījià	MCUR
Main cross connect	主交叉连接	Zhǔ jiāochā liánjiē	MCC
Main distributing frame	总配线架	Zǒng pèixiànjià	
Main grounding bar	主接地排	Zhǔ jiēdì pái	
Main grounding terminal	主接地端子	Zhǔ jiēdì duānzi	
Main memory	主存储器	Zhǔ cúnchǔqì	
Main menu	主菜单	Zhǔ càidān	
Main menu	主选单	Zhǔ xuǎndān	
Main path interface	主通道接口	Zhǔ tōngdào jiēkǒu	MPI
Main path interface	主通路接口	Zhǔ tōnglù jiēkǒu	MPI

Main path interface at the receiver	主通道接收参考点	Zhǔ tōngdào jiēshōu cānkǎo diǎn	MPI-R
Main path interface at the receiver	主通道接收端	Zhǔ tōngdào jiēshōu duān	MPI-R
Main path interface at the transmitter	主通道发送参考点	Zhǔ tōngdào fāsòng cānkǎo diǎn	MPI-S
Main path interface at the transmitter	主通道发送端	Zhǔ tōngdào fāsòng duān	MPI-S
Main processor back panel	主处理器后面板	Zhǔ chǔlǐqì hòumianbǎn	MPBP
Main processor duplication manager	主处理器复制管理器	Zhǔ chǔlǐqì fùzhì guǎnlǐqì	MPDM
Main processor SCSI BUS interface	主处理器 SCSI BUS 接口	Zhǔ chǔlǐqì SCSI Bus jiēkǒu	MSBI
Main processor unit	主处理单元	Zhǔ chǔlǐ dānyuán	MPU
Main reflector	主反射器	Zhǔ fǎnshèqì	
Main reflector	主反射体	Zhǔ fǎnshètǐ	
Main routine	主程序	Zhǔ chéngxù	
Main section	主段	Zhǔ duàn	
Main storage data register	主存储器数据寄存器	Zhǔ cúnchǔqì shùjù jìcúnqì	MSDR
Main switching center	主要的交换中心	Zhǔyàode jiāohuàn zhōngxīn	MSC
Main vector identifier	主向量标示	Zhǔ xiàngliàng biāoshì	MVID
Mains antenna	电源线天线	Diànyuánxiàn tiānxiàn	
Mains decoupling factor	电网去耦系数	Diànwǎng qù'ǒu xìshù	
Mains decoupling factor	电源去耦系数	Diànyuán qù'ǒu xìshù	
Mains immunity	电源抗扰性	Diànyuán kàngrǎoxìng	
Mains supply	市电电源	Shìdiàn diànyuán	
Mains-borne disturbance	电源骚扰	Diànyuán sāorǎo	
Mains-interference immunity factor	抗电网干扰系数	Kàng diànwǎng gānrǎo xìshù	
Maintain	维护	Wéihù	
Maintainability	可维修性	Kěwéixiūxìng	
Maintainability	维修性	Wéixiūxìng	
Maintainability (performance)	可维护性（性能）	Kěwéihùxìng (xìngnéng)	
Maintainability allocation	可维护性分配	Kěwéihùxìng fēnpèi	
Maintainability demonstration	观察数据	Guānchá shùjù	
Maintainability model	可维护性模型	Kěwéihùxìng móxíng	
Maintainability prediction	可维护性预测	Kěwéihùxìng yùcè	
Maintainability verification	可维护性检验	Kěwéihùxìng jiǎnyàn	
Maintaining line arrangements	平面分割	Píngmiàn fēngē	
Maintenance	维修	Wéixiū	
Maintenance action; maintenance task	维护工作	Wéihù gōngzuò	
Maintenance and adaptation	维护和适配	Wéihù hé shìpèi	MA
Maintenance and administration personal computer	维护和管理 PC 机	Wéihù hé guǎnlǐ PC-jī	MAP
Maintenance and fault back panel	维护和故障后面板	Wéihù hé gùzhàng hòumianbǎn	MFBP
Maintenance and supply center	维护和供应中心	Wéihù hé gōngyìng zhōngxīn	MSC
Maintenance and test console	维测台	Wéicè tái	
Maintenance bus	维护总线	Wéihù zǒngxiàn	M-BUS
Maintenance cell description	维护信元描述	Wéihù xìnyuán miáoshù	MCD
Maintenance center	维护中心	Wéihù zhōngxīn	
Maintenance channel buffer register	维护通道缓冲寄存器	Wéihù tōngdào huǎnchōng jìcúnqì	MCHB
Maintenance channel command register	维护通道指令寄存器	Wéihù tōngdào zhǐlìng jìcúnqì	MCHC
Maintenance control sub-system	维护控制子系统	Wéihù kòngzhì zixìtǒng	MCS
Maintenance echelon; line of maintenance	维护等级	Wéihù děngjí	

Maintenance entity	维护实体	Wéihù shítǐ	ME
Maintenance entity assembly	维护实体组	Wéihù shítǐ zǔ	MEA
Maintenance entity function	维护实体功能	Wéihù shítǐ gōngnéng	MEF
Maintenance event	维护事件	Wéihù shìjiàn	
Maintenance event information	维护事件信息	Wéihù shìjiàn xìnxī	MEI
Maintenance management	维护管理	Wéihù guǎnlǐ	
Maintenance man-hours	维护工时	Wéihù gōngshí	MMH
Maintenance operation protocol	维护操作协议	Wéihù cāozuò xiéyì	MOP
Maintenance philosophy	维护准则	Wéihù zhǔnzé	
Maintenance policy	维护策略	Wéihù cèlüè	
Maintenance policy	维护方针	Wéihù fāngzhēn	
Maintenance service provider	维护业务提供者	Wéihù yèwù tígòngzhě	MSP
Maintenance sub-entity	维护子实体	Wéihù zǐshítǐ	MSE
Maintenance support performance	维护支持性能	Wéihù zhīchí xìngnéng	
Maintenance tree	维护树	Wéihù shù	
Maintenance-free (semiconductor mfg)	免维护	Miǎnwéihù	
Maintenance-oriented group blocking acknowledgement message	面向维护的群闭塞证实消息	Miànxiàng wéihùde qún bìsè zhèngshí xiāoxi	MBA
Maintenance-oriented group blocking message	面向维护的群闭塞消息	Miànxiàng wéihùde qún bìsè xiāoxi	MGB
Maintenance-oriented group unblocking acknowledgement message	面向维护的群解除闭塞证实消息	Miànxiàng wéihùde qún jiěchú bìsè zhèngshí xiāoxi	MUA
Maintenance-oriented group unblocking message	面向维护的群闭塞解除消息	Miànxiàng wéihùde qún bìsè jiěchú xiāoxi	MGU
Major alarm	严重告警	Yánzhòng gàojǐng	
Major fault	严重故障	Yánzhòng gùzhàng	
Major lobe, main lobe	主瓣	Zhǔ bàn	
Major node earth terminal	主要结点地面终端	Zhǔyào jiédiǎn dìmiàn zhōngduān	MNT
Major portion of the earth's atmosphere	地球大气层的主要部分	Dìqiú dàqìcéngde zhǔyào bùfen	
Majority voting (SDH term)	多数表决判定	Duōshù biǎojué pàndìng	
Make table query	生成表查询	Shēngchéng biǎo cháxún	
Make up a deficiency of payment	补兑	Bǔ duì	
Malata Electronics Co. Ltd., Fujian	万利达电子有限公司	Wàn-lì-dá diànzǐ yǒuxiàn gōngsī	
Malaysian Institute of Microelectronic Systems	马来西亚微电子学院	Mǎ-lái-xī-yà wēidiànzǐ xuéyuàn	MIMOS
Malfunction (electric power term)	误动	Wùdòng	
Malicious call identification	捣乱呼叫识别	Dǎoluàn hūjiào shíbié	MCI
Malicious call identification	恶意呼叫识别	Èyì hūjiào shíbié	MCI
Malicious call identification supplementary service	恶意呼叫检验补充业务	Èyì hūjiào jiǎnyàn bǔchōng yèwù	MCI
Malicious call tracing	查找恶意呼叫	Cházhǎo èyì hūjiào	
Managed code	受控代码	Shòukòng dàimǎ	
Managed code	托管代码	Tuōguǎn dàimǎ	
Managed domain	被管理域	Bèiguǎnlǐ yù	
Managed element	被管单元	Bèiguǎn dānyuán	
Managed element (network management term)	被管元素	Bèiguǎn yuánsù	
Managed entity	被管实体	Bèiguǎn shítǐ	
Managed extensions	受控扩充件	Shòukòng kuòchōng jiàn	
Managed extensions	托管扩展	Tuōguǎn kuòzhǎn	
Managed group (in multicast)	托管组	Tuōguǎn zǔ	
Managed network service	受管网络服务	Shòuguǎn wǎngluò fúwù	

Managed node	受管节点	Shòuguǎn jiédiǎn	
Managed object	被管对象	Bèiguǎn duìxiàng	
Managed object	管理对象	Guǎnlǐ duìxiàng	MO
Managed object	管理目标	Guǎnlǐ mùbiāo	MO
Managed object	受控对象	Shòukòng duìxiàng	
Managed object	托管对象	Tuōguǎn duìxiàng	
Managed object attribute	被管对象的属性	Bèiguǎn duìxiàngde shǔxìng	
Managed object class	被管对象类别	Bèiguǎn duìxiàng lèibié	
Managed object class	管理对象类	Guǎnlǐ duìxiàng lèi	MOC
Managed object conformance statement	管理目标一致性句法	Guǎnlǐ mùbiāo yīzhìxìng jùfǎ	MOCS
Managed object instance	被管对象实例	Bèiguǎn duìxiàng shílì	
Managed object instance	管理对象实例	Guǎnlǐ duìxiàng shílì	MOI
Managed solution	管理方案	Guǎnlǐ fāng'àn	MS
Managed system	被管（开放）系统	Bèiguǎn xìtǒng	
Managed-object agent	被管目标代理	Bèiguǎn mùbiāo dàilǐ	MOA
Managed-object class	被管对象类	Bèiguǎn duìxiàng lèi	MOC
Management application function	管理应用功能	Guǎnlǐ yìngyòng gōngnéng	MAF
Management database	管理数据库	Guǎnlǐ shùjùkù	
Management domain	管理域	Guǎnlǐ yù	MD
Management domain name	管理域名	Guǎnlǐ yùmíng	
Management domains	管理区域	Guǎnlǐ qūyù	MD
Management entity	管理实体	Guǎnlǐ shítǐ	
Management entity – physical layer (primitive)	管理实体 - 物理层原语	Guǎnlǐ shítǐ-wùlǐ céng yuányǔ	MPH
Management gateway function	管理网关功能	Guǎnlǐ wǎngguān gōngnéng	MGF
Management information	管理信息	Guǎnlǐ xìnxī	MI
Management information base	管理信息基	Guǎnlǐ xìnxījī	MIB
Management information base	管理信息库	Guǎnlǐ xìnxīkù	MIB
Management information catalogue	管理信息目录	Guǎnlǐ xìnxī mùlù	MIC
Management information library	管理信息定义库	Guǎnlǐ xìnxī dìngyìkù	MIL
Management information model	管理信息模式	Guǎnlǐ xìnxī móshì	MIM
Management information model	管理信息模型	Guǎnlǐ xìnxī móxíng	MIM
Management information service	管理信息业务	Guǎnlǐ xìnxī yèwù	MIS
Management information system	管理信息系统	Guǎnlǐ xìnxī xìtǒng	MIS
Management information tree	管理信息树	Guǎnlǐ xìnxīshù	MIT
Management layer	管理层	Guǎnlǐ céng	
Management plane	管理面	Guǎnlǐ miàn	
Management plane	管理平面	Guǎnlǐ píngmiàn	MP
Management point	管理点	Guǎnlǐ diǎn	MP
Management service provider	管理业务提供者	Guǎnlǐ yèwù tígòngzhě	MSP
Management sub-domain	管理子域	Guǎnlǐ ziyù	
Management support object	管理支持目标	Guǎnlǐ zhīchí mùbiāo	MSO
Management system	管理系统	Guǎnlǐ xìtǒng	
Manager	管理器	Guǎnlǐqì	
Manager	管理者	Guǎnlǐzhě	M
Manager role	管理者角色	Guǎnlǐzhě juésè	
Manchester auto-code	曼彻斯特自动带码	Màn-chè-sī-tè zìdòng dàimǎ	MAC

Manchester encoding	曼彻斯特编码	Màn-chè-sī-tè biānmǎ	
Mandatory	强制	Qiángzhì	
Mandatory	强制性的	Qiángzhìxìngde	M
Mandatory access control (IPsec)	强制访问控制	Qiángzhì fǎngwèn kòngzhì	MAC
Mandatory access control (Linux)	强制存取控制	Qiángzhì cúnqǔ kòngzhì	MAC
Mandatory attribute	必备属性	Bìbèi shǔxìng	
Mandatory news service station	报刊发行站	Bàokān fāxíng zhàn	
Mandatory user profile	强制用户配置文件	Qiángzhì yònghù pèizhì wénjiàn	
Mandatory, forced updating	强制更新	Qiángzhì gēngxīn	
Manhole	人孔	Rénkǒng	
Manifest	清单	Qīngdān	
Man-in-the-middle attack (cryptology term)	中间人攻击	Zhōngjiānrén gōngjī	
Manipulated variable	操纵变量	Cāozòng biànliàng	
Manipulation detection (IPsec)	操作检测	Cāozuò jiǎncè	
Manipulator (part of C++ iostream)	操纵器	Cāozòngqì	
Man-machine command	人机命令	Rén jī mìnglìng	MMC
Man-machine communication	人机通信	Rén jī tōngxìn	
Man-machine interface	人机接口	Rén jī jiēkǒu	MMI
Man-machine interface back panel	人机接口后面板	Rén jī jiēkǒu hòumian bǎn	MMBP
Man-machine language	人机语言	Rén jī yǔyán	MML
Man-made interference	人为干扰	Rénwéi gānrǎo	
Man-made jamming	人为干扰	Rénwéi gānrǎo	
Man-made noise	人为噪声	Rénwéi zàoshēng	
Manning formula	曼宁公式	Màn-níng gōngshì	
Manometer	压力计	Yālìjì	
Mantissa	尾数	Wěishù	
Manual access multiple channel cordless telephone	人工接入多信道无绳电话机	Réngōng jiērù duōxìndào wúshéng diànhuàjī	
Manual digitizing	手工数字化	Shǒugōng shùzìhuà	
Manual extraction	人工录取	Réngōng lùqǔ	
Manual frequency control	手动频率控制	Shǒudòng pínlǜ kòngzhì	
Manual gain control	手动增益控制	Shǒudòng zēngyì kòngzhì	
Manual interpretation	人工判读	Réngōng pàndú	
Manual intervention	人工干预	Réngōng gānyù	
Manual office	人工局	Réngōng jú	
Manual pick and place workstation (semiconductor mfg)	手动拾放工作站	Shǒudòng shífàng gōngzuòzhàn	
Manual pick and place workstation (semiconductor mfg)	手动拾放机	Shǒudòng shífàngjī	
Manual position	人工坐席	Réngōng zuòxí	
Manual screen printer (semiconductor mfg)	手动屏印制机	Shǒudòng píng yìnzhìjī	
Manual screen printer (semiconductor mfg)	手动丝网印刷机	Shǒudòng sīwǎng yìnshuājī	
Manual switch	人工切换	Réngōng qiēhuàn	MSw
Manual switching	人工交换	Réngōng jiāohuàn	
Manual telephone	人工电话	Réngōng diànhuà	
Manual toll switch	人工长话交换	Réngōng chánghuà jiāohuàn	CHR
Manual transmission rerouting	人工传输再选路	Réngōng chuánshū zàixuǎnlù	
Manually routed call	人工接通的呼叫	Réngōng jiētōngde hūjiào	

Manual-toll switch office	人工长途局	Réngōng chángtújú	M-TS
Manufacturing automation protocol	制造自动化协议	Zhìzào zìdònghuà xiéyì	MAP
Manufacturing automation protocol	生产自动化协议	Shēngchǎn zìdònghuà xiéyì	MAP
Manufacturing failure	制造失效	Zhìzào shīxiào	
Manufacturing fault	制造故障	Zhìzào gùzhàng	
Manufacturing resource planning	制造资源规划系统	Zhìzào zīyuán guīhuà xìtǒng	MRP
Manufacturing resource planning	制造资源计划	Zhìzào zīyuán jìhuà	MRP
Many-to-many relationship	多对多关系	Duō duì duō guānxi	
Many-to-one relationship	多对一关系	Duō duì yī guānxi	
Map accuracy	地图精度	Dìtú jīngdù	
Map adjustment	地图接边	Dìtú jiēbiān	
Map algebra	地图代数	Dìtú dàishù	
Map animation	地图动画	Dìtú dònghuà	
Map border	图廓	Túkuò	
Map conflation	地图合并	Dìtú hébìng	
Map coordinate origin	地图坐标原点	Dìtú zuòbiāo yuándiǎn	
Map coverage	地图层	Dìtú céng	
Map cultural feature	地图人文要素	Dìtú rénwén yàosù	
Map data	地图数据	Dìtú shùjù	
Map design	地图设计	Dìtú shèjì	
Map digitization	地图数字化	Dìtú shùzìhuà	
Map distortion	地图变形	Dìtú biànxíng	
Map document	地图文献	Dìtú wénxiàn	
Map element	地图元素	Dìtú yuánsù	
Map extent	图幅	Túfú	
Map hypsographic	地图标高	Dìtú biāogāo	
Map integration	地图集成	Dìtújí chéng	
Map library	地图库	Dìtúkù	
Map limits	图幅范围	Túfú fànwéi	
Map matching	地图匹配	Dìtú pǐpèi	
Map nadir	图面天底点	Túmiàn tiāndǐ diǎn	
Map name	图名	Túmíng	
Map projection	地图投影	Dìtú tóuyǐng	
Map query	地图查询	Dìtú cháxún	
Map registration (in GIS)	地图配准	Dìtú pèizhǔn	
Map scale	地图比例尺	Dìtú bǐlìchǐ	
Map section	地图组	Dìtú zǔ	
Map series	地图系列	Dìtú xìliè	
Map specification	地图规范	Dìtú guīfàn	
Map symbol base	地图符号库	Dìtú fúhàokù	
Map units	地图单位	Dìtú dānwèi	
Mapping	映射	Yìngshè	
Mapping	映象	Yìngxiàng	
Mapping jitter	映射抖动	Yìngshè dǒudòng	
Mapping multiplexing	映射复用	Yìngshè fùyòng	
Mapping radar	地形测绘雷达	Dìxíng cèhuì léidá	

English	Chinese	Pinyin	Abbr.
Map-to-page transformation	地图页面转换	Dìtú yèmiàn zhuǎnhuàn	
Marconi Corp. (UK company)	马可尼公司	Mǎ-kě-ní gōngsī	
Margin	备余量	Bèiyúliàng	
Margin	图廓	Túkuò	
Margin (of a receiver or terminal)	改正力	Gǎizhènglì	
Margin of a synchronous receiver	同步收报机的改正力	Tóngbù shōubàojīde gǎizhèng lì	
Marine radar	航海雷达	Hánghǎi léidá	
Maritime digital selective-calling system	水上数字选呼系统	Shuǐshàng shùzì xuǎnhū xìtǒng	
Maritime mobile satellite service	卫星水上移动业务	Wèixīng shuǐshàng yídòng yèwù	
Maritime mobile service	海事移动业务	Hǎishì yídòng yèwù	
Maritime mobile service	水上移动业务	Shuǐshàng yídòng yèwù	
Maritime mobile-satellite service	海事卫星移动业务	Hǎishì wèixīng yídòng yèwù	
Maritime radio navigation satellite service	卫星水上无线电导航业务	Wèixīng shuǐshàng wúxiàndiàn dǎoháng yèwù	
Maritime radio navigation service	水上无线电导航业务	Shuǐshàng wúxiàndiàn dǎoháng yèwù	
Maritime satellite communications	海事卫星通信	Hǎishì wèixīng tōngxìn	
Mark condition (in Morse code)	传号状态	Chuánhào zhuàngtài	
Mark down	标记关闭	Biāojì guānbì	
Mark up	标记打开	Biāojì dǎkāi	
Mark up (in price) (verb and noun)	标高	Biāogāo	MU
Mark up (in price) (verb and noun)	记账	Jìzhàng	MU
Mark up (in price) (verb and noun)	涨价	Zhǎngjià	MU
Mark, label (verb); nominal (adjective)	标称	Biāochēng	
Marker	标记	Biāojì	
Marker	标志器	Biāozhìqì	MKR
Marker beacon	指点信标	Zhǐdiǎn xìnbiāo	
Marker stack control word	标记栈控制字	Biāojì zhàn kòngzhì zì	MSCW
Market penetration	市场普及率	Shìchǎng pǔjílǜ	PM
Marketing Planning group (GSM MoU)	市场规划组	Shìchǎng guīhuà zǔ	MP
Marking	标志	Biāozhì	
Markov process	马尔可夫过程	Mǎ-ěr-kě-fū guòchéng	
Markov vector method	马尔可夫向量方法	Mǎ-ěr-kě-fū xiàngliàng fāngfǎ	
Markovian observational congruence	马尔科夫观察一致性	Mǎ-ěr-kē-fū guānchá yīzhìxìng	
Markup language	标记语言	Biāojì yǔyán	
Marshal	列集	Lièjí	
Mask	模框	Mókuàng	
Mask	掩码	Yǎnmǎ	
Mask making equipment (semiconductor mfg)	光罩制造设备	Guāng zhào zhìzào shèbèi	
Masking-pattern universal sub-band integrated coding and multiplexing	掩蔽模型通用子带综合编码和复用	Yǎnbì móxíng tōngyòng zidài zōnghé biānmǎ hé fùyòng	MUSICAM
Masquerade (IPsec)	冒充	Màochōng	
Masquerade (IPsec)	伪装	Wěizhuāng	
Masquerade, impersonation (IPsec)	假冒	Jiǎmào	
Mass	质量	Zhìliàng	
Mass call	大众呼叫	Dàzhòng hūjiào	MAS
Mass calling service	大众呼叫业务	Dàzhòng hūjiào yèwù	MAS
Mass communication	大众传媒	Dàzhòng chuánméi	

Mass flow-rate	质量流量	Zhìliàng liúliàng	
Mass point	取样点	Qǔyàng diǎn	
Mass storage	海存	Hǎi cún	
Mass storage controller	大容量存储控制器	Dàróngliàng cúnchǔ kòngzhìqì	MSC
Mass transport	质量输送	Zhìliàng shūsòng	
Massive parallel processing	巨量平行处理架构	Jùliàng píngxíng chǔlǐ jiàgòu	MPP
Master boot record	主引导记录	Zhǔ yǐndǎo jìlù	MBR
Master clock	主时钟	Zhǔ shízhōng	
Master clock	主钟	Zhǔ zhōng	
Master clock generator	主时钟发生器	Zhǔ shízhōng fāshēngqì	MCG
Master configuration table	主配置表	Zhǔ pèizhì biǎo	MCT
Master definition site	主定义位置	Zhǔ dìngyì wèizhì	
Master file	主文件	Zhǔ wénjiàn	
Master file	主文件	Zhǔ wénjiàn	MF
Master file	主要文件	Zhǔyào wénjiàn	MF
Master file table	主文件表	Zhǔ wénjiàn biǎo	MFT
Master headend	主前端	Zhǔ qiánduān	
Master index	主索引	Zhǔ suǒyǐn	
Master international frequency register	国际频率登记总表	Guójì pínlǜ dēngjì zǒngbiǎo	MIFR
Master key enciphering key	主密钥	Zhǔ mìyào	KKM
Master management agent	主管理代理	Zhǔ guǎnlǐ dàilǐ	MMA
Master oscillator	主振荡器	Zhǔ zhèndàngqì	
Master oscillator power amplifier transmitter	主振放大式发射机	Zhǔ zhèn fàngdàshì fāshèjī	MOPA
Master plan	总体规划	Zǒngtǐ guīhuà	
Master processor	主处理机	Zhǔ chǔlǐjī	
Master secret (IPsec)	主机密	Zhǔ jīmì	
Master site	主位置	Zhǔ wèizhì	
MasterCard International Inc.	万事达公司	Wàn-shì-dá gōngsī	
Mastergroup	主群	Zhǔ qún	
Mastergroup link	主群链路	Zhǔ qún liànlù	
Mastergroup section	主群段	Zhǔ qún duàn	
Master-slave flip-flop	主从触发器	Zhǔ cóng chùfāqì	MSFF
Master-slave synchronization	主从同步	Zhǔ cóng tóngbù	
Match (noun. when searching for a term)	匹配项	Pǐpèixiàng	
Matched coaxial single mode optical fiber	匹配包层单模光纤	Pǐpèi bāo céng dānmó guāngxiān	MCSM
Matched filter	匹配滤波器	Pǐpèi lǜbōqì	
Matched filter receiver	匹配滤波器接收机	Pǐpèi lǜbōqì jiēshōujī	
Matched filtering	匹配滤波	Pǐpèi lǜbō	
Matched load	匹配负载	Pǐpèi fùzài	
Matched termination	匹配终端	Pǐpèi zhōngduān	
Matched-load voltage	匹配负载电压	Pǐpèi fùzài diànyā	
Matching (between a load and a source)	匹配	Pǐpèi	
Matching network	匹配网络	Pǐpèi wǎngluò	
Matching section	匹配段	Pǐpèi duàn	
Matching stub	匹配短线	Pǐpèi duǎnxiàn	
Material dispersion	材料色散	Cáiliào sèsàn	

Material requirement planning	物料需求计划	Wùliào xūqiú jìhuà	MRP
Math coprocessor	数学附处理器	Shùxué fùchǔlǐqì	
Mathematical morphology (in GIS)	数学形态学	Shùxué xíngtàixué	
Mating face seal	配合面密封	Pèihémiàn mìfēng	
Matrix	矩阵	Jǔzhèn	
Matrix clustering	矩阵聚类	Jǔzhèn jùlèi	
Matrix decomposition	矩阵分解	Jǔzhèn fēnjiě	
Matrix multiplication	矩阵乘法	Jǔzhèn chéngfǎ	
Matroid structure	拟阵结构	Nǐzhèn jiégòu	
Matsushita (sometimes used for Panasonic, a trade name of Matsushita, Japanese electronics company)	松下	Sōngxià	
Matsushita Electric Research and Development (China) Corp. (subsidiary of Matsushita Japan)	松下电器研究发展(中国)有限公司	Sōngxià diànqì yánjiū fāzhǎn (Zhōngguó) yǒuxiàn gōngsī	CMRD
Maximal ratio combining	最大比值合并	Zuìdà bǐzhí hébìng	MRC
Maximization of total utility	总效用最大化	Zǒng xiàoyòng zuìdàhuà	
Maximize	最大化	Zuìdàhuà	
Maximum *a posteriori* probability	最大后验概率	Zuìdà hòuyàn gàilǜ	MAP
Maximum allowable tension	最大充许使用张力	Zuìdà chōngxǔ shǐyòng zhānglì	MAT
Maximum allowed tension	最大充许拉力	Zuìdà chōngxǔ lālì	MAT
Maximum amplitude	最大振幅	Zuìdà zhènfú	
Maximum attainable rate	最大可行速率	Zuìdà kěxíng sùlǜ	
Maximum bit forwarding rate	最大位转发率	Zuìdà wèi zhuǎnfā lǜ	MBFR
Maximum burst size	最大突发量	Zuìdà tūfāliàng	MBS
Maximum cell rate	最大的信元率	Zuìdàde xìnyuán lǜ	maxCR
Maximum detection range (of radar)	最大探测距离	Zuìdà tàncè jùlí	
Maximum discharge	最大流量	Zuìdà liúliàng	
Maximum downlook detection range (of radar)	下视最大探测距离	Xiàshì zuìdà tàncè jùlí	
Maximum envelope method	最大包络法	Zuìdà bāoluò fǎ	MEM
Maximum frequency of oscillation	最高振荡频率	Zuìgāo zhèndàng pínlǜ	
Maximum justification rate	最大调整率	Zuìdà tiáozhěnglǜ	
Maximum likelihood	最大似然	Zuìdà sìrán	ML
Maximum likelihood decoding	最大似然译码	Zuìdà sìrán yìmǎ	
Maximum likelihood sequence estimation	最大似然序列估计	Zuìdà sìrán xùliè gūjì	MLSE
Maximum likelihood sequence estimation	最大似然序列估值	Zuìdà sìrán xùliè gūzhí	MLSE
Maximum loop resistance	最大环路阻抗	Zuìdà huánlù zǔkàng	
Maximum matching	最大匹配	Zuìdà pǐpèi	
Maximum number of re-tries	最大重发次数	Zuìdà chóngfā cìshù	
Maximum packet lifetime	最大包寿命时间	Zuìdà bāo shòumìng shíjiān	MPL
Maximum permissible frequency deviation	最大允许频偏	Zuìdà yǔnxǔ pínpiān	
Maximum permissible phase deviation	最大允许相偏	Zuìdà yǔnxǔ xiāngpiān	
Maximum phase deviation	最大相位偏移	Zuìdà xiàngwèi piānyí	MPD
Maximum ratio consolidation	最大比合并	Zuìdà bǐ hébìng	MRC
Maximum receive unit	最大接收单元	Zuìdà jiēshōu dānyuán	MRU
Maximum relative side lobe level	最大副/主瓣比	Zuìdà fù/zhǔ bàn bǐ	
Maximum relative side lobe level	最大相对旁瓣电平	Zuìdà xiāngduì pángbàn diànpíng	MRSLL
Maximum relative time interval error	最大相对时间间隔误差	Zuìdà xiāngduì shíjiān jiàngé wùchā	MRTIE

Maximum response displacement	最大反应位移	Zuìdà fǎnyìng wèiyí	
Maximum segment lifetime	最大段寿命	Zuìdà duàn shòumìng	MSL
Maximum sensitivity	最大灵敏度	Zuìdà língmǐndù	
Maximum small-signal gain	最大小信号增益	Zuìdà xiǎo xìnhào zēngyì	
Maximum small-signal gain wavelength	最大小信号增益波长	Zuìdà xiǎo xìnhào zēngyì bōcháng	
Maximum stuffing rate	最大塞入率	Zuìdà sāirùlǜ	
Maximum theoretical bandwidth	最大理论带宽	Zuìdà lǐlùn dàikuān	MTB
Maximum theoretical numerical aperture	最大理论数值孔径	Zuìdà lǐlùn shùzhí kǒngjìng	NAMAX.TH
Maximum timing interval error	最大时间间隔误差	Zuìdà shíjiān jiàngé wùchā	MTIE
Maximum transmission unit	最大传输单元	Zuìdà chuánshū dānyuán	MTU
Maximum transmission unit	最大的传输单元	Zuìdàde chuánshū dānyuán	MTU
Maximum transmission unit	最大的传送单元	Zuìdàde chuánsòng dānyuán	MTU
Maximum uplook detection range (of radar)	上视最大探测距离	Shàngshì zuìdà tàncè jùlí	
Maximum usable amplitude deviation	最大可用幅偏	Zuìdà kěyòng fúpiān	
Maximum usable frequency	最高可用频率	Zuìgāo kěyòng pínlǜ	MUF
Maximum useful power	最大有用功率	Zuìdà yǒuyòng gōnglǜ	
Maximum waiting delay	最大等待时延	Zuìdà děngdài shíyán	MWD
Maximum wave pressure	最大波压	Zuìdà bōyā	
Maximum-length shift register	最长移位寄存器	Zuìcháng yíwèi jìcúnqì	MLSR
Maximum-length shift register	最大长度移位寄存器	Zuìdà chángdù yíwèi jìcúnqì	MLSR
Maxtor (US company)	美达	Měi-dá	
Maxtor Corporation (US company)	迈拓公司	Mài-tuò gōngsī	
Maxwell model	麦克斯威而模型	Mài-kè-sī-wēi-ér móxíng	
Mean access delay (in telecommunication)	平均接入迟延（电信中）	Píngjūn jiērù chíyán (diànxìn zhōng)	
Mean accumulated down time	平均累积不可用时间	Píngjūn lěijī bùkěyòng shíjiān	MADT
Mean active corrective maintenance time	平均有效修复性维护时间	Píngjūn yǒuxiào xiūfùxìng wéihù shíjiān	
Mean administrative delay	平均管理耽误	Píngjūn guǎnlǐ dānwù	MAD
Mean availability	平均可用性	Píngjūn kěyòngxìng	
Mean down time	平均不可用时间	Píngjūn bùkěyòng shíjiān	MDT
Mean down time	平均停机时间	Píngjūn tíngjī shíjiān	MDT
Mean equivalent noise temperature (of a linear two-port network)	平均等效噪声温度	Píngjūn děngxiào zàoshēng wēndù	
Mean fading reserve	平衰落储备	Píng shuāiluò chǔbèi	
Mean failure intensity	平均失效频度	Píngjūn shīxiào píndù	
Mean failure rate	平均失效率	Píngjūn shīxiào lǜ	
Mean interruption duration	平均中断持续时间	Píngjūn zhōngduàn chíxù shíjiān	
Mean launched power	平均发射光功率	Píngjūn fāshè guāng gōnglǜ	
Mean logistic delay	平均后勤耽误	Píngjūn hòuqín dānwù	MLD
Mean maintenance manhours	平均维护工时	Píngjūn wéihù gōngshí	
Mean noise factor (of a linear two-port net-work)	平均噪声系数	Píngjūn zàoshēng xìshù	
Mean noise temperature	平均噪声温度	Píngjūn zàoshēng wēndù	
Mean operating time between failures	平均失效间工作时间	Píngjūn shīxiào-jiān gōngzuò shíjiān	MTBF
Mean operating time between failures	平均无故障工作时间	Píngjūn wúgùzhàng gōngzuò shíjiān	MTBF
Mean opinion score	主观平均得分	Zhǔguān píngjūn défēn	MOS
Mean opinion score	平均鉴定分数	Píngjūn jiàndìng fēnshù	MOS
Mean opinion score	平均评价得分	Píngjūn píngjià défēn	MOS
Mean opinion score	平均主管得分	Píngjūn zhǔguǎn défēn	MOS

Mean packet delay	平均包延迟	Píngjūn bāo yánchí	MPD
Mean polarization mode dispersion differential group delay	平均偏振模色散差分群时延	Píngjūn piānzhèn mó sèsàn chāfēn qún shíyán	
Mean power (of a radio transmitter)	平均功率	Píngjūn gōnglǜ	PY
Mean received signal strength indication	平均接收信号强度指示	Píngjūn jiēshōu xìnhào qiángdù zhǐshì	
Mean repair rate	平均修复率	Píngjūn xiūfù lǜ	
Mean repair time	平均修理时间	Píngjūn xiūlǐ shíjiān	MRT
Mean service access delay	平均业务接入迟延	Píngjūn yèwù jiērù chíyán	
Mean service preparation time	平均业务准备时间	Píngjūn yèwù zhǔnbèi shíjiān	
Mean sidelobe level	平均旁瓣电平	Píngjūn pángbàn diànpíng	MSLL
Mean slip velocity	平均变异速度	Píngjūn biànyì sùdù	
Mean slowdown	平均减速	Píngjūn jiǎnsù	
Mean square signal-to-noise	均方信噪比	Jūn fāng xìn zào bǐ	MSSN
Mean square value	平均平方值	Píngjūn píngfāng zhí	
Mean time between failure	平均无故障时间	Píngjūn wúgùzhàng shíjiān	MTBF
Mean time between failures	连续无故障时间	Liánxù wúgùzhàng shíjiān	MTBF
Mean time between failures	平均故障间隔时间	Píngjūn gùzhàng jiàngé shíjiān	MTBF
Mean time between failures	平均故障时间	Píngjūn gùzhàng shíjiān	MTBF
Mean time between failures	平均失效间隔时间	Píngjūn shīxiào jiàngé shíjiān	MTBF
Mean time between interrupts	平均中断（间隔）时间	Píngjūn zhōngduàn (jiàngé) shíjiān	MTBI
Mean time between maintenance	平均维护（间隔）时间	Píngjūn wéihù (jiàngé) shíjiān	MTBM
Mean time between service outages	平均业务运行中断间隔时间	Píngjūn yèwù yùnxíng zhōngduàn jiàngé shíjiān	MTBSO
Mean time to failure	平均失效前时间	Píngjūn shīxiào qián shíjiān	MTTF
Mean time to failure	平均无故障时间	Píngjūn wúgùzhàng shíjiān	MTTF
Mean time to first failure	平均首次失效前时间	Píngjūn shǒucì shīxiào qián shíjiān	MTTFF
Mean time to recovery	平均恢复时间	Píngjūn huīfù shíjiān	MTTR
Mean time to repair	平均故障修理时间	Píngjūn gùzhàng xiūlǐ shíjiān	MTTR
Mean time to repair	平均恢复时间	Píngjūn huīfù shíjiān	
Mean time to repair	平均修复时间	Píngjūn xiūfù shíjiān	MTTR
Mean time to restoration	平均恢复时间	Píngjūn huīfù shíjiān	MTTR
Mean time to restore service	恢复业务平均时间	Huīfù yèwù píngjūn shíjiān	MTRS
Mean time to service restoration	平均业务恢复时间	Píngjūn yèwù huīfù shíjiān	MTTSR
Mean unavailability	平均不可用性	Píngjūn bùkěyòngxing	
Mean up time	平均可用时间	Píngjūn kěyòng shíjiān	MUT
Means of test	测试方式	Cèshì fāngshì	MOT
Measure	度量值	Dùliàng zhí	
Measure (as applied in the probabilistic treatment of reliability and related areas)	量度	Liángdù	
Measurement	测量	Cèliáng	MEA
Measurement	度量	Dùliàng	
Measurement	量测	Liángcè	
Measurement and control (telecom) ; tracking and control (satellites)	测控	Cèkòng	
Measurement equipment	测量设备	Cèliáng shèbèi	
Measurement point	测量点	Cèliáng diǎn	MP
Measurement report	测量报告	Cèliáng bàogào	MR
Measurement result	测量结果	Cèliáng jiéguǒ	
Measurements and statistics data I/O block	测量和统计数据 I/O 模块	Cèliáng hé tǒngjì shùjù I/O mókuài	MSDIO

Measuring line	测量线	Cèliáng xiàn	
Measuring normalizing block	标准化段测量	Biāozhǔnhuà duàn cèliáng	
Mechanical abrasion resistance	机械耐磨性	Jīxiè nàimóxìng	
Mechanical attenuator	机械式衰减器	Jīxiè-shì shuāijiǎnqì	
Mechanical axis	机械轴	Jīxiè zhóu	
Mechanical crosspoint	机械交叉点	Jīxiè jiāochādiǎn	
Mechanical extrusion forming (FOC mfg)	机械挤压法	Jīxiè jǐyā fǎ	MSP
Mechanical loading and unloading foot walk	机械式装卸过桥	Jīxiè-shì zhuāngxiè guòqiáo	
Mechanical nesting	机械嵌套	Jīxiè qiàntào	
Mechanical optical deflector	机械式光偏折器	Jīxiè-shì guāng piānzhéqì	
Mechanical optical modulator	机械式光调变器	Jīxiè-shì guāng tiáobiànqì	
Mechanical optical scanner	机械式光扫描器	Jīxiè-shì guāng sǎomiáoqì	
Mechanical optical switch	机械式光开关	Jīxiè-shì guāng kāiguān	
Mechanical reference surface	机械基准面	Jīxiè jīzhǔnmiàn	
Mechanical stripping tool (FOC)	机械剥离工具	Jīxiè bōlí gōngjù	
Mechanical switch	机械转换开关	Jīxiè zhuǎnhuàn kāiguān	
Mechanical time constant (of an indicating instrument)	机械时间常数	Jīxiè shíjiān chángshù	
Mechanically intermateable optical fiber (cable) connector	机械互配光纤（缆）连接器	Jīxiè hùpèi guāngxiān (lǎn) liánjiē qì	
Media access control	介质访问控制	Jièzhì fǎngwèn kòngzhì	MAC
Media access control	媒介访问控制	Méijiè fǎngwèn kòngzhì	MAC
Media access control	媒介接入控制	Méijiè jiērù kòngzhì	MAC
Media access control	媒体访问控制	Méitǐ fǎngwèn kòngzhì	MAC
Media access control	媒体接入控制	Méitǐ jiērù kòngzhì	MAC
Media access control	媒体控制访问	Méitǐ kòngzhì fǎngwèn	MAC
Media access control	媒质接入控制	Méizhì jiērù kòngzhì	MAC
Media access control layer	媒体访问控制层	Méitǐ fǎngwèn kòngzhì céng	MAC
Media access control sub-layer	媒体访问控制子层	Méitǐ fǎngwèn kòngzhì zicéng	MAC
Media access control sub-layer	媒体接入控制子层	Méitǐ jiērù kòngzhì zicéng	MAC
Media adapter	媒体适配器	Méitǐ shìpèiqì	MA
Media attachment unit	介质链接单元	Jièzhì liànjiē dānyuán	MAU
Media attachment unit	媒体附加接口	Méitǐ fùjiā jiēkǒu	MAU
Media bay	介质槽	Jièzhì cáo	
Media control interface	媒体控制介面	Méitǐ kòngzhì jièmiàn	MCI
Media control unit	媒体控制单元	Méitǐ kòngzhì dānyuán	MCU
Media dependent interface	媒体相关接口	Méitǐ xiāngguān jiēkǒu	MDI
Media dependent interface	媒体依赖接口	Méitǐ yīlài jiēkǒu	MDI
Media description	媒体描述	Méitǐ miáoshù	
Media family	媒体家族	Méitǐ jiāzú	
Media gateway	媒体网关	Méitǐ wǎngguān	MG
Media gateway control	媒体网关控制	Méitǐ wǎngguān kòngzhì	MEGACO
Media gateway control function	媒体网关控制功能	Méitǐ wǎngguān kòngzhì gōngnéng	MGCF
Media gateway control part	媒体网关控制部分	Méitǐ wǎngguān kòngzhì bùfen	MGCP
Media gateway control protocol	媒体网关控制协议	Méitǐ wǎngguān kòngzhì xiéyì	Megaco
Media gateway control protocol	媒体网关控制协议	Méitǐ wǎngguān kòngzhì xiéyì	MGCP
Media gateway control protocol	媒体网关控制器协议	Méitǐ wǎngguān kòngzhìqì xiéyì	MGCP

Media gateway control unit	媒体网关控制单元	Méitǐ wǎngguān kòngzhì dānyuán	MGCU
Media gateway controller	媒体网关控制器	Méitǐ wǎngguān kòngzhìqì	MGC
Media gateway function	媒体网关功能	Méitǐ wǎngguān gōngnéng	MGF
Media gateway unit	媒体网关单元	Méitǐ wǎngguān dānyuán	MGU
Media header	媒体首部	Méitǐ shǒubù	
Media independent interface	媒体无关接口	Méitǐ wúguān jiēkǒu	MII
Media interface adapter	介质接口适配器	Jièzhì jiēkǒu shìpèiqì	MIA
Media interface connector	介质接口连接器	Jièzhì jiēkǒu liánjiēqì	MIC
Media interface connector	媒体接口连接器	Méitǐ jiēkǒu liánjiēqì	MIC
Media layer	媒体层	Méitǐ céng	
Media manager	媒体管理	Méitǐ guǎnlǐ	MM
Media name	媒体名称	Méitǐ míngchēng	
Media pool	媒体池	Méitǐ chí	
Media record	媒体记录	Méitǐ jìlù	
Media record specifications	媒体记录规范	Méitǐ jìlù guīfàn	
Media resource function	媒体资源功能	Méitǐ zīyuán gōngnéng	MRF
Media resources function control	媒体资源功能控制	Méitǐ zīyuán gōngnéng kòngzhì	MRFC
Media resources function processing	媒体资源功能处理	Méitǐ zīyuán gōngnéng chǔlǐ	MRFP
Media set	媒体集	Méitǐ jí	
Media stream processor	媒体流处理器	Méitǐ liú chǔlǐqì	MSP
Media stream provider	媒体流提供程序	Méitǐ liú tígōng chéngxù	MSP
Media streaming broadcast and distribution	媒体流广播和分发	Méitǐ liú guǎngbō hé fēnfā	MSBD
Media switching function	媒体交换模块	Méitǐ jiāohuàn mókuài	MSF
Media units	媒介单位	Méijiè dānwèi	
Medial-axis transformation	中轴变换	Zhōngzhóu biànhuàn	
Median	中位数	Zhōngwèishù	
Median filter	中值滤波器	Zhōngzhí lǜbōqì	
Median of signal level	信号电平中值	Xìnhào diànpíng zhōng zhí	
Mediation device	协调设备	Xiétiáo shèbèi	MD
Mediation device	协调装置	Xiétiáo zhuāngzhì	
Mediation device	中介设备	Zhōngjiè shèbèi	MD
Mediation device	中介装置	Zhōngjiè zhuāngzhì	MD
Mediation device	调停手段	Tiáoting shǒuduàn	MD
Mediation function	协调功能	Xiétiáo gōngnéng	
Mediation function block	中介功能块	Zhōngjiè gōngnéng kuài	MF
MediNet	医药网络	Yīyào wǎngluò	
Medium access control	媒质接入控制层	Méizhì jiērù kòngzhì céng	MAC
Medium access control layer	介质访问控制层	Jièzhì fǎngwèn kòngzhì céng	MAC
Medium altitude communication satellite	中高空通信卫星	Zhōng gāokōng tōngxìn wèixīng	MACS
Medium density polyethylene	中密集聚乙烯	Zhōng mìjí jùyǐxī	MDPE
Medium earth orbit	中地球轨道	Zhōng dìqiú guǐdào	MEO
Medium earth orbit	中轨	Zhōngguǐ	MEO
Medium frequency	中频	Zhōngpín	MF
Medium frequency slip ring	中频滑环	Zhōngpín huá huán	
Medium rate data	中速率数据	Zhōng sùlǜ shùjù	DM
Medium wave propagation	中波传输	Zhōngbō chuánshū	

Medium, media	媒体	Méitǐ	
Medium-scale integrated circuit	中规模集成电路	Zhōng guīmó jíchéng diànlù	MSI
Medium-term prediction	中期预测	Zhōngqī yùcè	
Mega- (prefix meaning 10^6)	兆	Zhào	
Megabit (10^6 bit)	兆位	Zhàowèi	MB
Megabits per second	兆比特每秒	Zhàobǐtè měi miǎo	Mb/s
Megabyte (10^6 bytes)	兆字节	Zhàozìjié	MB, mb
MegaHertz	兆赫	Zhàohè	MHZ
MegaHertz	兆赫兹	Zhàohè-zī	MHz
Megamedia	巨媒体	Jùméitǐ	
Melissa (computer virus)	梅利沙	Méi-lì-shā	
Member	成员	Chéngyuán	
Member access operator	成员取用运算子	Chéngyuán qǔyòng yùnsuàn zi	
Member delegation	成员委派	Chéngyuán wěipài	
Member ductility factor	部件延性系数	Bùjiàn yánxìng xìshù	
Member function	成员函数	Chéngyuán hánshù	
Member group	成员组	Chéngyuán zǔ	
Member initialization list	成员初始值列表	Chéngyuán chūshǐ zhí lièbiǎo	
Member key column	成员键列	Chéngyuán jiàn liè	
Member name column	成员名列	Chéngyuán míngliè	
Member object (GIS term)	成员对象	Chéngyuán duìxiàng	
Member property	成员属性	Chéngyuán shǔxìng	
Member variable	成员变量	Chéngyuán biànliàng	
Memo	备注	Bèizhù	
Memorandum of understanding	备忘录	Bèiwànglù	MoU
Memorandum of understanding	谅解备忘录	Liàngjiě bèiwànglù	MoU
Memory	存储器	Cúnchǔqì	
Memory	内存	Nèicún	
Memory access controller	存储器存取控制器	Cúnchǔqì cúnqǔ kòngzhìqì	MAC
Memory address allocation	存储地址分配	Cúnchǔ dìzhǐ fēnpèi	
Memory address register	存储地址寄存器	Cúnchǔ dìzhǐ jìcúnqì	MAR
Memory allocation	存储分配	Cúnchǔ fēnpèi	
Memory allocation	内存分配	Nèicún fēnpèi	
Memory allocation manager	存储分配管理程序	Cúnchǔ fēnpèi guǎnlǐ chéngxù	MAM
Memory and I/O bridge controller (chip)	内存和 I/O 桥控制器	Nèicún hé I/O qiáo kòngzhìqì	MIOC
Memory backup	存储备份	Cúnchǔ bèifèn	
Memory buffer register	存储器缓冲寄存器	Cúnchǔqì huǎnchōng jìcúnqì	MBR
Memory control unit	存储控制装置	Cúnchǔ kòngzhì zhuāngzhì	MCU
Memory interface	存储器接口	Cúnchǔqì jiēkǒu	
Memory interleave	存储器交替	Cúnchǔqì jiāotì	
Memory leak	内存泄漏	Nèicún xièlòu	
Memory module	内存模块	Nèicún mókuài	
Memory protect violation error	存储保护侵犯错误	Cúnchǔ bǎohù qīnfàn cuòwù	
Memory protection	存储保护	Cúnchǔ bǎohù	
Memory register	存储寄存器	Cúnchǔ jìcúnqì	MR
Memory register exponent	存储器寄存器指数	Cúnchǔqì jìcúnqì zhǐshù	MRE

Memory repeater hub	内存数据处理中心	Nèicún shùjù chǔlǐ zhōngxīn	MRH
Memory resident software	记忆驻留软件	Jìyì zhùliú ruǎnjiàn	
Memory transfer hub	内存转换中心	Nèicún zhuǎnhuàn zhōngxīn	MTH
Mental rotation	心理旋转	Xīnlǐ xuánzhuǎn	
Menu	菜单	Càidān	
Menu	选单	Xuǎndān	
Menu bar	菜单条	Càidān tiáo	
Menu button	菜单按钮	Càidān ànniǔ	
Merchandise counterfeit authentication solution	商品防伪认证解决方案	Shāngpǐn fángwěi rènzhèng jiějué fāng'àn	MCAS
Merge	合并	Hébìng	
Merge agent (in SQL Server)	合并代理	Hébìng dàilǐ	
Merge cells (WP command)	方格合并	Fānggé hébìng	
Merge join (in SQL Server)	合并连接	Hébìng liánjiē	
Merge replication	合并复制	Hébìng fùzhì	
Merge sort	归并排序	Guībìng páixù	
Meridian plane	子午面	Zìwǔ miàn	
Meridian ray	子午光线	Zìwǔ guāngxiàn	
Mesh point	网格点	Wǎnggé diǎn	
Mesh simplification	网格简化	Wǎnggé jiǎnhuà	
Mesh-connected	网格互连	Wǎnggé hùlián	
Meso-analysis	中尺变分析	Zhōng chǐbiàn fēnxī	
Mesochronous	均步的	Jūnbùde	
Mesochronous	同步的	Tóngbùde	
Message	消息	Xiāoxi	
Message (in telegraph and data communication)	报文	Bàowén	
Message administration service element	消息管理服务要素	Xiāoxi guǎnlǐ fúwù yàosù	MASE
Message alignment indicator	消息定位表示语	Xiāoxi dìngwèi biǎoshìyǔ	
Message authentication code	报文鉴别代码	Bàowén jiànbié dàimǎ	MAC
Message authentication code	报文认证码	Bàowén rènzhèng mǎ	MAC
Message authentication code	消息鉴权码	Xiāoxi jiànquán mǎ	MAC
Message authentication code	消息校验码	Xiāoxi jiàoyàn mǎ	MAC
Message authentication code	消息认证码	Xiāoxi rènzhèng mǎ	MAC
Message authentication code	消息验证码	Xiāoxi yànzhèng mǎ	MAC
Message authentication code	认证消息码	Rènzhèng xiāoxi mǎ	MAC
Message center	消息中心	Xiāoxi zhōngxīn	MC
Message clearinghouse	信息交换站	Xìnxī jiāohuànzhàn	
Message communications function	消息通信功能	Xiāoxi tōngxìn gōngnéng	MCF
Message delivery service element	消息投递服务要素	Xiāoxi tóudì fúwù yàosù	MDSE
Message digest	报文摘要	Bàowén zhāiyào	
Message digest	消息摘要	Xiāoxi zhāiyào	
Message digest 5	第 5 类报文摘要	Dìwǔlèi bàowén zhāiyào	MD5
Message digest algorithm	报文摘要算法	Bàowén zhāiyào suànfǎ	MDA
Message digest version 5	消息摘要版本 5	Xiāoxi zhāiyào bǎnběn 5	MD5
Message discrimination	消息鉴别	Xiāoxi jiànbié	
Message distribution	消息分配	Xiāoxi fēnpèi	
Message entry device	消息输入设备	Xiāoxi shūrù shèbèi	MED

Message error rate	消息差错率	Xiāoxi chācuò lǜ	MER
Message flooding	报文泛滥	Bàowén fànlàn	
Message format	电文格式	Diànwén géshi	
Message format	消息格式	Xiāoxi géshi	
Message handling	消息处理	Xiāoxi chǔlǐ	
Message handling environment	消息处理环境	Xiāoxi chǔlǐ huánjìng	
Message handling service	消息处理服务	Xiāoxi chǔlǐ fúwù	
Message handling service	消息处理业务	Xiāoxi chǔlǐ yèwù	
Message handling system	消息处理系统	Xiāoxi chǔlǐ xìtǒng	MHS
Message header	消息报头	Xiāoxi bàotóu	HEADER
Message identifier	消息标识符	Xiāoxi biāozhìfú	MID
Message identifier	消息识别码	Xiāoxi shíbié mǎ	MID
Message indication service	信息指示业务	Xìnxī zhǐshì yèwù	
Message integrity code	消息完整性编码	Xiāoxi wánzhěngxìng biānmǎ	MIC
Message integrity code	信息完整性编码	Xìnxī wánzhěngxìng biānmǎ	MIC
Message loop	消息环	Xiāoxi huán	
Message mode	消息方式	Xiāoxi fāngshì	
Message mode	消息模式	Xiāoxi móshì	
Message number	消息编号	Xiāoxi biānhào	
Message numbering	电文编号	Diànwén biānhào	
Message on demand	点播消息	Diǎnbō xiāoxi	MOD
Message origination	上传消息	Shàngchuán xiāoxi	MO
Message output descriptor	报文输出描述符	Bàowén shūchū miáoshùfú	MOD
Message passage interface	消息传递接口	Xiāoxi chuándì jiēkǒu	
Message priority	报文优先等级	Bàowén yōuxiān děngjí	
Message processing procedure specification	报文处理过程说明	Bàowén chǔlǐ guòchéng shuōmíng	MPPS
Message push	推信息	Tuī xìnxī	MP
Message queue	电文队列	Diànwén duìliè	
Message queuing	消息队列	Xiāoxi duìliè	
Message queuing interface	报文排队接口	Bàowén páiduì jiēkǒu	MQI
Message recovery	消息恢复	Xiāoxi huīfù	
Message retrieval service element	消息检索服务要素	Xiāoxi jiǎnsuǒ fúwù yàosù	MRSE
Message router	消息路由器	Xiāoxi lùyóuqì	BMR
Message routing	电文路由选择	Diànwén lùyóu xuǎnzé	
Message routing control	消息路由控制	Xiāoxi lùyóu kòngzhì	
Message security mode	消息资源保护模式	Xiāoxi zīyuán bǎohù móshì	
Message security protocol	信息安全协议	Xìnxī ānquán xiéyì	MSP
Message sequence chart	消息顺序表	Xiāoxi shùnxù biǎo	MSC
Message sequence chart	消息序列表	Xiāoxi xùliè biǎo	MSC
Message sequence chart	信息顺序图	Xìnxī shùnxù tú	MSC
Message signal unit	消息信号单元	Xiāoxi xìnhào dānyuán	MSU
Message signaling unit	消息信令单元	Xiāoxi xìnlìng dānyuán	MSU
Message store	消息存储	Xiāoxi cúnchǔ	MS
Message submission service element	消息提文服务要素	Xiāoxi tíwén fúwù yàosù	MSSE
Message switching	报文交换	Bàowén jiāohuàn	
Message switching	电文交换	Diànwén jiāohuàn	

Message switching	消息交换	Xiāoxi jiāohuàn	
Message switching center	信息交换中心	Xìnxī jiāohuàn zhōngxīn	MSC
Message switching data service	报文交换数据服务	Bàowén jiāohuàn shùjù fúwù	MSDS
Message switching multiplexer	报文转发多路复用器	Bàowén zhuǎnfā duōlù fù yòngqì	MSM
Message switching network	电文交换网络	Diànwén jiāohuàn wǎngluò	
Message syntax	消息句法	Xiāoxi jùfǎ	
Message termination	下传消息	Xiàchuán xiāoxi	MT
Message transfer	消息传送	Xiāoxi chuánsòng	MT
Message transfer agent	文电传递代理	Wéndiàn chuándì dàilǐ	MTA
Message transfer agent	消息传送代理	Xiāoxi chuánsòng dàilǐ	MTA
Message transfer part	消息传递部分	Xiāoxi chuándì bùfen	MTP
Message transfer part	消息传输部分	Xiāoxi chuánshū bùfen	MTP
Message transfer part	消息传送部分	Xiāoxi chuánsòng bùfen	MTP
Message transfer part	信息传输部分	Xìnxī chuánshū bùfen	MTP
Message transfer part level 2 (in SS7)	消息传递部二层	Xiāoxi chuándìbù èrcéng	MTPL2
Message transfer protocol 2 (MTP2) peer-to-peer adaptation layer	消息传递部分第二级对等适配层	Xiāoxi chuándì bùfen dì'èrjí duìděng shìpèi céng	M2PA
Message transfer service	消息传送服务	Xiāoxi chuánsòng fúwù	
Message transfer service	消息传送业务	Xiāoxi chuánsòng yèwù	
Message transfer service element	消息传送服务要素	Xiāoxi chuánsòng fúwù yàosù	MTSE
Message transfer system	消息传送系统	Xiāoxi chuánsòng xìtǒng	MTS
Message transport part	信息传递部分	Xìnxī chuándì bùfen	MTP
Message transport protocol 3 (MTP3) user adaptation layer	消息传递部分第三级用户适配层	Xiāoxi chuándì bùfen dìsānjí yònghù shìpèi céng	M3UA
Message trunking	消息集群	Xiāoxi jíqún	
Message type	消息类型	Xiāoxi lèixíng	
Message waiting data	消息等待数据	Xiāoxi děngdài shùjù	MWD
Message waiting indication	消息等待指示	Xiāoxi děngdài zhǐshì	MWI
Message-based	基于消息的	Jīyú xiāoxide	
Message-oriented middleware	定向信息中间件	Dìngxiàng xìnxī zhōngjiān jiàn	MOM
Message-oriented middleware	面向消息的中间件	Miànxiàng xiāoxide zhōngjiān jiàn	MOM
Message-waiting indication	报文等待指示	Bàowén děngdài zhǐshì	MWI
Messaging application procedure interface	信息应用过程接口	Xìnxī yìngyòng guòchéng jiēkǒu	MAPI
Messaging application programming interface	消息应用程序接口	Xiāoxi yìngyòng chéngxù jiēkǒu	MAPI
Messaging application programming interface	信报传递应用程序接口	Xìnbào chuándì yìngyòng chéngxù jiēkǒu	MAPI
Messaging service	电子信函业务	Diànzi xìnhán yèwù	
Messaging service	消息型业务	Xiāoxixíng yèwù	
Messaging system	消息传递系统	Xiāoxi chuándì xìtǒng	
Messaging system	消息通信系统	Xiāoxi tōngxìn xìtǒng	
Messaging system	消息通信系统	Xiāoxi tōngxìn xìtǒng	
Meta data services (in SQL Server)	元数据服务	Yuán shùjù fúwù	
Meta introducer	中间介绍人	Zhōngjiān jièshàorén	
Meta-anaphora	元指代	Yuánzhǐdài	
Meta-computing	元计算	Yuánjìsuàn	
Metadata	元数据	Yuánshùjù	
Metadata catalogue	元数据目录	Yuánshùjù mùlù	

Metadata dataset	元数据集	Yuánshùjùjí	
Metadata element	元数据元素	Yuánshùjù yuánsù	
Metadata element dictionary	元数据元素字典	Yuánshùjù yuánsù zìdiǎn	
Metadata entity	元数据实体	Yuánshùjù shítǐ	
Metadata entity type	元数据实体类型	Yuánshùjù shítǐ lèixíng	
Metadata package	元数据包	Yuánshùjù bāo	
Metadata schema	元数据模式	Yuánshùjù móshì	
Metadata type	元数据型	Yuánshùjù xíng	
Metal coated fiber	金属涂层光纤	Jīnshǔ túcéng guāngxiān	
Metal delay lens antenna	金属延迟透镜天线	Jīnshǔ yánchí tòujìng tiānxiàn	
Metal ferrule	金属箍	Jīnshǔ gū	
Metal mirror	金属面镜	Jīnshǔ miànjìng	
Metal organic vapor phase epitaxy	金属有机化学汽相沉积	Jīnshǔ yǒujī huàxué qìxiāng chénjī	MOVPE
Metal oxide semiconductor	金属氧化物半导体	Jīnshǔ yǎnghuàwù bàndǎotǐ	MOS
Metal oxide semiconductor field effect transistor	金属氧化物半导体场效应晶体管	Jīnshǔ yǎnghuàwù bàndǎotǐ cháng xiàoyìng jīngtǐguǎn	MOSFET
Metal oxide varister	金属氧化物变阻器	Jīnshǔ yǎnghuàwù biànzǔqì	MOV
Metal plate air seal gasket	气密性金属封垫片	Qìmìxìng jīnshǔ fēngdiànpiàn	
Metal vapor laser	金属蒸气激光	Jīnshǔ zhēngqì jīguāng	
Meta-language	元语言	Yuányǔyán	
Metallic aerial self-supporting (FOC)	金属自承光缆	Jīnshǔ zì chéng guānglǎn	MASS
Metallo-organic chemical vapor deposition	金属有机化学汽相沉积法	Jīnshǔ yǒujī huàxué qìxiàng chénjī fǎ	MOCVD
Metal-plate lenses antenna	金属板透镜天线	Jīnshǔ bǎn tòujìng tiānxiàn	
Meta-model	元模型	Yuánmóxíng	
Metaprogramming	元编程	Yuánbiānchéng	
Meta-signaling	元信令	Yuánxìnlìng	
Meta-signaling cell	元信令信元	Yuánxìnlìng xìnyuán	
Meteor scattering communication	流星散射通信	Liúxīng sǎnshè tōngxìn	
Meteor trail	流星余迹	Liúxīng yújì	
Meteor trail communications	流星余迹通信	Liúxīng yújì tōngxìn	
Meteorological aids service	气象辅助业务	Qìxiàng fǔzhù yèwù	
Meteorological pulse-Doppler radar	气象脉冲多普勒雷达	Qìxiàng màichōng duō-pǔ-lè léidá	
Meteorological satellite	气象卫星	Qìxiàng wèixīng	
Meteorological satellite service	卫星气象业务	Wèixīng qìxiàng yèwù	
Meter counts collector	计费汇总计数收集器	Jìfèi huìzǒng jìshù shōujíqì	MCC
Meter pulse message	计次脉冲消息	Jìcì màichōng xiāoxi	MPM
Metes bounds (GIS)	边界测量法定义组件	Biānjiè cèliángfǎ dìngyì zǔjiàn	
Method of state variable	状态变量法	Zhuàngtài biànliàng fǎ	
Metonic cycle	默冬周期	Mòdōng zhōuqī	
Metric	步长	Bùcháng	
Metric	度量	Dùliàng	
Metric representation	度量值表达	Dùliàng zhí biǎodá	
Metric server	度量服务器	Dùliàng fúwùqì	
Metric space	度量空间	Dùliàng kōngjiān	
Metric system	公制	Gōngzhì	
Metropolitan area network	城域网	Chéngyù wǎng	MAN

MexE service environment	MExE 业务环境	MexE yèwù huánjìng	MSE
Mianyang Kilopass Microelectronics Inc.	绵阳凯路微电子有限公司	Miányáng kǎilù wēidiànzǐ yǒuxiàn gōngsī	
Michelson interferometer	迈克尔逊型干涉仪	Mài-kè-ěr xùn-xíng gānshèyí	
Micro- (prefix meaning 10^{-6})	微	Wēi	
Micro channel architecture	微渠道架构	Wēiqúdào jiàgòu	MCA
Micro channel architecture	微通道体系结构	Wēitōngdào tǐxì jiégòu	MCA
Micro channel architecture	微信道结构	Wēixìndào jiégòu	MCA
Micro electronic mechanical system	微电 - 机系统	Wēidiànjī xìtǒng	MEMS
Micro instruction	微指令	Wēizhǐlìng	
Micro interference filter (optical)	微小干涉滤光镜	Wēixiǎo gānshè lǜguāngjìng	
Micro payment transfer protocol	小额支付传输协议	Xiǎo'é zhīfù chuánshū xiéyì	MPTP
Micro prism	微小棱镜	Wēixiǎo léngjìng	
Micro stepping closed loop control	微步闭环回路控制	Wēibù bìhuán huílù kòngzhì	
Microampere	微安	Wēi'ān	μ A
Microbar	微巴	Wēibā	
Microbending loss	微弯损耗	Wēiwān sǔnhào	
Microcell	微区	Wēiqū	
Microcell	微小组	Wēixiǎo zǔ	MC
Microcell (cellular telephony)	微小区	Wēixiǎo qū	
Microcell controller	微小组控制器	Wēixiǎo zǔ kòngzhìqì	MCC
Microcellular system	微蜂窝系统	Wēifēngwō xìtǒng	MCS
Microchannel plate	微道板	Wēidàobǎn	
Microchip	微晶片	Wēijīngpiàn	
Microcode	微代码	Wēidàimǎ	
Microcode	微码	Wēimǎ	
Microcomputer	微计算机	Wēijìsuànjī	
Microcomputer communications	微机通信	Wēijī tōngxìn	
Microcosm	微化空间	Wēihuà kōngjiān	
Microelectromechanical mirror arrays	微电机镜阵列	Wēidiànjī jìng zhènliè	MEMMA
MicroElectroMechanical switch	微电子机械开关	Wēidiànzǐ jīxiè kāiguān	MEMS
Micro-electromechanical system	微机电系统	Wēijī diàn xìtǒng	MEMS
Microelectronic mechanical system	微电子机械系统	Wēidiànzǐ jīxiè xìtǒng	MEMS
Microelectronic packaging	微电子组装	Wēidiànzǐ zǔzhuāng	
Microfiche	缩微胶片	Suōwēi jiāopiàn	
Micro-kernel	微内核	Wēinèihé	
Microlab (US company)	麦蓝	Mài-lán	
Micro-machining	微机电技术	Wēijī diàn jìshù	
Micron	微米	Wēimǐ	
Micro-optics	微光子学	Wēiguāngzixué	
Micro-packaging (electronics mfg)	微封装	Wēifēngzhuāng	
Micro-payment	微支付	Wēizhīfù	
Micro-payment transport protocol	微支付传输协议	Wēizhīfù chuánshū xiéyì	MPTP
Microphone	传声器	Chuánshēngqì	
Microphone	麦克风	Màikèfēng	MIC
Microphone	微音器	Wēiyīnqì	MIC
Microphone effect of variable capacitor	可变电容器微音效应	Kěbiàn diànróngqì wēiyīn xiàoyìng	

English	Chinese	Pinyin	Abbreviation
Microphone noise	传声器噪声	Chuánshēngqì zàoshēng	
Microphone noise	话筒噪声	Huàtǒng zàoshēng	
Microphone socket (on radio)	话筒插座	Huàtǒng chāzuò	MIC
Microprocessor	微处理机	Wēichǔlǐjī	
Microprocessor	微处理器	Wēichǔlǐqì	
Microprocessor development system	微处理机开发系统	Wēichǔlǐjī kāifā xìtǒng	
Microprocessor-controlled automatic positioning equipment	含微处理机控制式自动定位装置	Hán wēichǔlǐjī kòngzhì-shì zìdòng dìngwèi zhuāngzhì	
Microprogram	微程序	Wēichéngxù	
Microscope imbedding media	显微镜埋置用材料	Xiǎnwēijìng máizhìyòng cáiliào	
Microscope immersion liquid	显微镜浸液	Xiǎnwēijìng jìnyè	
Microsecond	微妙	Wēimiào	μs
Micro-segmentation	微分段	Wēifēnduàn	
Microsoft (US company)	微软公司	Wēiruǎn gōngsī	MS
Microsoft Certified Solution Providers	微软认证解决方案供应商	Wēiruǎn rènzhèng jiějué fāng'àn gōngyìngshāng	MCSP
Microsoft Corporation; MS ©	微软集团	Wēiruǎn jítuán	
Microsoft diagnostics	微软诊断程序	Wēiruǎn zhěnduàn chéngxù	MSD
Microsoft Encarta ©	微软百科全书	Wēiruǎn bǎikē quánshū	
Microsoft Excel ©	微软优越试算表	Wēiruǎn yōuyuè shìsuànbiǎo	
Microsoft Exchange ©	微软交流群组软件	Wēiruǎn jiāoliú qúnzǔ ruǎnjiàn	
Microsoft foundation classes	微软基础类库	Wēiruǎn jīchǔ lèi kù	MFC
Microsoft Front/Backoffice ©	微软办公前 / 后室	Wēiruǎn bàngōng qián/hòushì	
Microsoft Home ©	微软家用软件	Wēiruǎn jiāyòng ruǎnjiàn	
Microsoft Learning and Entertainment	微软教学与娱乐公司	Wēiruǎn jiàoxué yǔ yúlè gōngsī	MLE
Microsoft Millionaire ©	微软富豪	Wēiruǎn fùháo	
Microsoft Network ©	微软网络	Wēiruǎn wǎngluò	MSN
Microsoft Office ©	微软办公室配套软件	Wēiruǎn bàngōngshì pèitào ruǎnjiàn	
Microsoft PowerPoint ©	微软电力站简报软件	Wēiruǎn diànlìzhàn jiǎnbào ruǎnjiàn	
Microsoft TV Platform adaptation kit	微软 TV 平台适配套件	Wēiruǎn TV píngtái-shì pèitào jiàn	MTVPAK
Microsoft Windows Hardware Quality lab	微软公司视窗硬件质量实验室	Wēiruǎn gōngsī shìchuāng yìngjiàn zhìliàng shíyànshì	WHQL
Microsoft Word ©	微软文书软件	Wēiruǎn wénshū ruǎnjiàn	
Microsoft Works ©	微软工作软件	Wēiruǎn gōngzuò ruǎnjiàn	
Microsoft® media server	微软媒体服务器	Wēiruǎn méitǐ fúwùqì	MMS
Microstrip	微带	Wēidài	
Microstrip	微带线	Wēidàixiàn	
Microstrip antenna	微带天线	Wēidài tiānxiàn	MA, MSA
Microstrip array	微带阵列	Wēidài zhènliè	MA
Microstrip linear antenna	微带线性天线	Wēidài xiànxìng tiānxiàn	MLA
Micro-structured polymer optical fiber	聚合物微结构光纤	Jùhéwù wēi jiégòu guāngxiān	MPOF
Micro-switch	微型开关	Wēixíng kāiguān	MSW
Microwave	微波	Wēibō	
Microwave band-stop filter	微波带阻滤波器	Wēibō dàizǔ lǜbōqì	
Microwave carrier	微波载波	Wēibō zàibō	WZ
Microwave circuit	微波电路	Wēibō diànlù	
Microwave communications	微波通信	Wēibō tōngxìn	

Microwave detector	微波检波器	Wēibō jiǎnbōqì	
Microwave duplexer	微波双工器	Wēibō shuānggōngqì	
Microwave field effect transistor amplifier	微波场效应晶体管放大器	Wēibō cháng xiàoyìng jīngtǐguǎn fàngdàqì	
Microwave high-pass filter	微波高通滤波器	Wēibō gāotōng lǜbōqì	
Microwave hologram radar	微波全息雷达	Wēibō quánxī léidá	
Microwave hybrid integrated circuit	微波混合集成电路	Wēibō hùnhé jíchéng diànlù	
Microwave integrated circuit	微波集成电路	Wēibō jíchéng diànlù	
Microwave integrated high frequency amplifier	微波集成高频放大器	Wēibō jíchéng gāopín fàngdàqì	
Microwave interference protection	微波干扰防护	Wēibō gānrǎo fánghù	MIP
Microwave landing system	微波着陆系统	Wēibō zhuólù xìtǒng	MLS
Microwave link	微波链路	Wēibō liànlù	
Microwave low noise amplifier	微波低躁声放大器	Wēibō dīzàoshēng fàngdàqì	
Microwave low noise transistor amplifier	微波低噪声晶体管放大器	Wēibō dīzàoshēng jīngtǐguǎn fàngdàqì	
Microwave low-pass filter	微波低通滤波器	Wēibō dītōng lǜbōqì	
Microwave monolithic integrated circuit	微波单片集成电路	Wēibō dānpiàn jíchéng diànlù	MMIC
Microwave multiplexer	微波多工器	Wēibō duōgōngqì	
Microwave multipoint distribution system	微波多点分配系统	Wēibō duōdiǎn fēnpèi xìtǒng	MMDS
Microwave power amplifier	微波功率放大器	Wēibō gōnglǜ fàngdàqì	
Microwave power meter	微波功率计	Wēibō gōnglǜjì	
Microwave pulse shaping network	微波脉冲整形网络	Wēibō màichōng zhěngxíng wǎngluò	MPSN
Microwave radio link	微波无线电链接	Wēibō wúxiàndiàn liànjiē	
Microwave relay station	微波中继站	Wēibō zhōngjìzhàn	
Microwave relay unit	微波中继装置	Wēibō zhōngjì zhuāngzhì	MRU
Microwave terminal station	微波终端站	Wēibō zhōngduān zhàn	
Microwave tower	微波铁塔	Wēibō tiětǎ	WT
Microwave transport equipment	微波传输设备	Wēibō chuánshū shèbèi	MTE
Microwave unreflected chamber	微波暗室	Wēibō ànshì	
Microwave unreflected chamber	微波暗室	Wēibō ànshì	
Microwave video distribution system (European term for LMDS)	微波视像分配系统	Wēibō shìxiàng fēnpèi xìtǒng	MVDS
Microwave/millimeter wave monolithic integrated circuit	微波/毫米波单片集成电路	Wēibō/háomībō dānpiàn jíchéng diànlù	
Micro-zoning	小区划	Xiǎoqū huà	
Midamble (center section of a frame)	帧中中间码	Zhèng-zhōng zhōngjiān mǎ	
Middle tier	中间层	Zhōngjiān céng	
Middleman (in business)	中间商	Zhōngjiānshāng	
Middleware	中间件	Zhōngjiān jiàn	
Middleware	中间设备	Zhōngjiān shèbèi	
Middleware	中介软件	Zhōngjiè ruǎnjiàn	
Midrange server	中型服务器	Zhōngxíng fúwùqì	MRS
Midrange workstation	中型工作站	Zhōngxíng gōngzuòzhàn	MRW
Midsplit	频带中分	Píndài zhōngfēn	
Mid-square method	平方取中法	Píngfāng qǔzhòng fǎ	
Migrate	转移	Zhuǎnyí	
Migration	迁移	Qiānyí	
Mildew-proof spray coating	防霉喷涂层	Fángméi pēntú céng	
Military Industrial Product Design Finalization Commission	军工产品定型委员会	Jūngōng chǎnpǐn dìngxíng wěiyuánhuì	

Milli- (prefix meaning 10^{-3})	毫	Háo	
Millimeter wave	毫米波	Háomǐbō	
Millimeter wave monolithic integrated circuit	毫米波单片集成电路	Háomǐbō dānpiàn jíchéng diànlù	MIMIC
Million floating point operations per second	百万次浮点运算/秒	Bǎiwàncì fúdiǎn yùnsuàn/miǎo	MEGAFLOP
Million floating point operations per second	每秒百万次浮点运算	Měi miǎo bǎiwàncì fúdiǎn yùnsuàn	MFLOPS
Million floating point operations per second	每秒百万个浮点操作	Měi miǎo bǎiwàngè fúdiǎn cāozuò	MFLOPS
Million instructions per second	百万条指令/秒	Bǎiwàn tiáo zhǐlìng/miǎo	MIPS
Million instructions per second	每秒百万次指令	Měi miǎo bǎiwàncì zhǐlìng	MIPS
Million instructions per second	每秒百万条指令	Měi miǎo bǎiwàntiáo zhǐlìng	MIPS
Million pixels per second	百万个像素/秒	Bǎiwàn gè xiàngsù/miǎo	MPPS
Millions of instructions per second	每秒多少百万个指令	Měi miǎo duōshao bǎiwàngè zhǐlìng	MIPS
Millisecond	毫秒	Háomiǎo	ms
Millitron	密力管	Mìlìguǎn	
Mimicking (IPsec)	仿制	Fǎngzhì	
Mineral-insulated cable	无机物绝缘电缆	Wújīwù juéyuán diànlǎn	MIC
Mini disk	微型唱盘	Wēixíng chàngpán	
Miniature free space optical isolator	微型自由空间光隔离器	Wēixíng zìyóu kōngjiān guāng gélíqì	MOFI
Miniature light source	小型光源	Xiǎoxíng guāngyuán	
Miniature unit-coupling (FOC term)	小型单元耦合型	Xiǎoxíng dānyuán ǒuhéxíng	MU
Minicomputer	微型电脑	Wēixíng diànnǎo	
Minicomputer	小型计算机	Xiǎoxíng jìsuànjī	
Minimal charging of postal circulation	报刊发行起点费	Bàokān fāxíng qǐdiǎn fèi	
Minimal shift keying	最小频移键控	Zuìxiǎo pínyí jiànkòng	MSK
Minimize	最小化	Zuìxiǎohuà	
Minimum (cost) spanning tree	最小（代价）生成树	Zuìxiǎo (dàijià) shēngchéng shù	
Minimum (frequency) shift keying	最小移频键控	Zuìxiǎo yípín jiànkòng	MSK
Minimum (root) mean square error	最小均方根差	Zuìxiǎo jūn fānggēn chà	MMSE
Minimum access time	最快存取时间	Zuìkuài cúnqǔ shíjiān	
Minimum bounding rectangle	最小矩形	Zuìxiǎo jǔxíng	MBR
Minimum cell rate	最小信元速率	Zuìxiǎo xìnyuán sùlǜ	MCR
Minimum delay protocol for unicast	基于单播的最小延时	Jīyú dānbōde zuìxiǎo yánshí	MDPU
Minimum description length	最小描述长度	Zuìxiǎo miáoshù chángdù	MDL
Minimum detectable signal	最小可探测信号	Zuìxiǎo kětàncè xìnhào	MDS
Minimum detectable signal-to-noise ratio	最小可检测信噪比	Zuìxiǎo kějiǎncè xìnzào bǐ	
Minimum detection range	最小作用距离	Zuìxiǎo zuòyòng jùlí	
Minimum distance (for coding)	最小码距	Zuìxiǎo mǎjù	
Minimum installation (of software)	最小安装	Zuìxiǎo ānzhuāng	
Minimum jamming range	最小干扰距离	Zuìxiǎo gānrǎo jùlí	
Minimum mapping units	最小制图单元	Zuìxiǎo zhìtú dānyuán	
Minimum mean square error	最小均方误差	Zuìxiǎo jūn fāng wùchā	MMSE
Minimum measure distance	最小测试距离	Zuìxiǎo cèshì jùlí	
Minimum password length	最小密码长度	Zuìxiǎo mìmǎ chángdù	
Minimum picture interval	最小画面间隔	Zuìxiǎo huàmiàn jiàngé	MPI
Minimum spanning tree	最小生成树	Zuìxiǎo shēngchéng shù	
Minimum usable field-strength	最小可用场强	Zuìxiǎo kěyòng chǎngqiáng	Emin
Minimum usable power flux density	最小可用功率通量密度	Zuìxiǎo kěyòng gōnglǜ tōngliàng mìdù	Pmin

Minimum-conflict heuristic repair	最小冲突启发式修补	Zuìxiǎo chōngtū qǐfāshì xiūbǔ	MCHR
Minimum-conflict weight learning algorithm	最小冲突权值学习算法	Zuìxiǎo chōngtū quán zhí xuéxí suànfǎ	MCWLA
Minimum-phase frequency shift keying	最小相位频移键控	Zuìxiǎo xiàngwèi pínyí jiànkòng	MSK
Minimum-phase harmonics	最小相位谐波	Zuìxiǎo xiàngwèi xiébō	
Mining model	挖掘模型	Wājué móxíng	
Mining model training	挖掘模型培训	Wājué móxíng péixùn	
Mini-satellite earth station	小卫星地球站	Xiǎo wèixīng dìqiúzhàn	XWD
Ministry of Information Industry (China)	信息产业部	Xìnxī chǎnyè bù	MII
Ministry of Post and Telecommunications (PRC)	邮政与电信部	Yóuzhèng yǔ diànxìn bù	MPT
Ministry of science and technology	科学技术部	Kēxué jìshù bù	MST
Minolta (Japanese company)	美能达	Měi-néng-dá	
Minor alarm	次要告警	Cìyào gàojǐng	
Minor alarm	一般告警	Yībān gàojǐng	
Minor fault	轻度故障	Qīngdù gùzhàng	
Minor lobe level	副瓣电平	Fùbàn diànpíng	
Minor road	便道	Biàndào	
Miratech (IT company)	奇宝高科	Qí-bǎo gāokē	
Mirror ball	镜面球	Jìngmiàn qiú	
Mirror set	镜像集	Jìngxiàng jí	
Mirror site	对映站	Duìyìng zhàn	
Mirror site	镜像站点	Jìngxiàng zhàndiǎn	
Mirrored volume	镜像卷	Jìngxiàng juàn	
Mirroring	镜像	Jìngxiàng	
Misalignment	形位偏差	Xíngwèi piānchā	
Miscellaneous	杂项	Záxiàng	
Miscellaneous message	其它消息	Qítā xiāoxi	
Mishandling failure	误操作失效	Wùcāozuò shīxiào	
Mishandling fault	误操作故障	Wùcāozuò gùzhàng	
Mismatched termination	失配终端	Shīpèi zhōngduān	
Mis-routed frames	误传帧	Wùchuán zhèng	
Mis-routing	错误路由	Cuòwù lùyóu	
Mis-routing	误传	Wùchuán	
Missed synchronization	漏同步	Lòutóngbù	
Missile battery data link (US military)	导弹连数据链	Dǎodàn lián shùjù liàn	MBDL
Missile flight tool (software)	导弹飞行工具	Dǎodàn fēixíng gōngjù	MFT
Missile-range-instrumentation radar	靶场测量雷达	Bǎchǎng cèliáng léidá	
Missing command	漏指令	Lòuzhǐlìng	
Missing data problem	丢失数据问题	Diūshī shùjù wèntí	
Missing pulse	漏脉冲	Lòu màichōng	
Misuse detection	误用检测	Wùyòng jiǎncè	
Mis-use detection	滥用检测	Lànyòng jiǎncè	
Misuse failure	误用失效	Wùyòng shīxiào	
Misuse fault	误用故障	Wùyòng gùzhàng	
Mitsubishi (Japanese company)	三菱	Sān-líng	
Mitsubishi Heavy Industries (Japan)	三菱重工	Sān-líng zhònggōng	MHI
Mix column	列混合	Liè hùnhé	

English	Chinese	Pinyin	Abbr.
Mixed analog/digital channel	模拟数字混合通路	Mónǐ shùzì hùnhé tōnglù	
Mixed character string type	混合字符串型	Hùnhé zìfú chuànxíng	MC
Mixed display	混合显示	Hùnhé xiǎnshì	
Mixed document	混合文件	Hùnhé wénjiàn	
Mixed document	混合型文件	Hùnhé-xíng wénjiàn	
Mixed excitation linear prediction	混合激励线性预测	Hùnhé jīlì xiànxìng yùcè	MELP
Mixed excitation linear predictive coder	混合激励线性预测编码器	Hùnhé jīlì xiànxìng yùcè biānmǎqì	MELP
Mixed mode	混合方式	Hùnhé fāngshì	
Mixed mode	混合模式	Hùnhé móshì	
Mixed mode of operation	混合式操作	Hùnhé-shì cāozuò	
Mixed reality	混合实境	Hùnhé shíjìng	
Mixed signal applications	混合信号应用	Hùnhé xìnhào yìngyòng	
Mixed tunnel and avalanche transit-time diode	混合型隧道和雪崩度起时间二极管	Hùnhé-xíng suìdào hé xuěbēng dùqǐ shíjiān èrjíguǎn	MITATT
Mixed use	混合用途	Hùnhé yòngtú	
Mixed-path propagation	混合路径传播	Hùnhé lùjìng chuánbō	
Mixer	合路器	Hélùqì	
Mixer amplification by variable reactance	脉伐，可变电抗混频放大	Mài fá, kěbiàn diànkàng hùnpín fàngdà	MAVAR
Mixer spurious response	混频器的寄生响应	Hùnpínqìde jìshēng xiǎngyìng	
Mixer transmission coefficient	混频器传输系数	Hùnpínqì chuánshū xìshù	
Mixing (in switching)	混合	Hùnhé	
Mnemonic	助记符	Zhùjìfú	
Mnemonic code	助记忆码	Zhù jìyì mǎ	
Mobile (frequency) allocation	移动台（频率）分配	Yídòngtái (pínlǜ) fēnpèi	MA
Mobile (satellite) earth station	移动地球站	Yídòng dìqiúzhàn	MES
Mobile (station) terminating	移动台被叫	Yídòngtái bèijiào	MT
Mobile access	移动接入	Yídòng jiērù	MA
Mobile access hunting	移动访问捕获	Yídòng fǎngwèn bǔhuò	MAH
Mobile access hunting	移动台接入寻找	Yídòngtái jiērù xúnzhǎo	MAH
Mobile access hunting supplementary service	移动地址搜索附加业务	Yídòng dìzhǐ sōusuǒ fùjiā yèwù	MAH
Mobile ad hoc network	移动特设网络	Yídòng tèshè wǎngluò	MANET
Mobile additional function	移动通信附加功能	Yídòng tōngxìn fùjiā gōngnéng	MAF
Mobile address allocation	移动通信地址分配	Yídòng tōngxìn dìzhǐ fēnpèi	MA
Mobile agent	移动代理	Yídòng dàilǐ	MA
Mobile agent system	移动代理系统	Yídòng dàilǐ xìtǒng	MOGENT
Mobile allocation	移动分配	Yídòng fēnpèi	MA
Mobile allocation	移动台划分	Yídòngtái huàfēn	
Mobile allocation channel number	移动分配信道号	Yídòng fēnpèi xìndàohào	MACN
Mobile allocation channel number	移动通信指配信道号码	Yídòng tōngxìn zhǐpèi xìndào hàomǎ	MACN
Mobile allocation index	移动分配索引	Yídòng fēnpèi suǒyǐn	MAI
Mobile allocation index offset	移动分配索引偏移	Yídòng fēnpèi suǒyǐn piānyí	MAIO
Mobile application part	移动通信应用部分	Yídòng tōngxìn yìngyòng bùfen	MAP
Mobile application part	移动应用部分	Yídòng yìngyòng bùfen	MAP
Mobile application part	移动应用单元	Yídòng yìngyòng dānyuán	MAP
Mobile application sub-system	移动应用子系统	Yídòng yìngyòng zixìtǒng	MAS
Mobile assisted handover	移动台辅助切换	Yídòngtái fǔzhù qiēhuàn	MAHO

Mobile attenuation code	移动衰减码	Yídòng shuāijiǎn mǎ	MAC
Mobile broadband service	移动宽带业务	Yídòng kuāndài yèwù	MBS
Mobile broadband system	移动宽带系统	Yídòng kuāndài xìtǒng	MBS
Mobile cellular telephony	移动蜂窝电话	Yídòng fēngwō diànhuà	
Mobile commerce	移动商务	Yídòng shāngwù	MC
Mobile communication system	移动通信系统	Yídòng tōngxìn xìtǒng	
Mobile computing device	移动计算设备	Yídòng jìsuàn shèbèi	MCD
Mobile connectivity product	移动连接产品	Yídòng liánjiē chǎnpǐn	
Mobile control station	移动控制站	Yídòng kòngzhìzhàn	MCS
Mobile country code	国家移动代码	Guójiā yídòng dàimǎ	MCC
Mobile country code	移动国家号码	Yídòng guójiā hàomǎ	MCC
Mobile country code	移动国家码	Yídòng guójiā mǎ	MCC
Mobile country code	移动通信国家码	Yídòng tōngxìn guójiā mǎ	MCC
Mobile data base station	移动数据基站	Yídòng shùjù jīzhàn	MDBS
Mobile data intermediate system	移动数据中介系统	Yídòng shùjù zhōngjiè xìtǒng	MD-IS
Mobile data link connection	移动数据链路连接	Yídòng shùjù liànlù liánjiē	MDLC
Mobile data link connection identifier	移动数据链路连接标识符	Yídòng shùjù liànlù liánjiē biāozhìfú	MDLCI
Mobile data link protocol	移动数据链路协议	Yídòng shùjù liànlù xiéyì	MDLP
Mobile data transmission	移动数据传输	Yídòng shùjù chuánshū	
Mobile daughter card	移动式子卡	Yídòng-shì zikǎ	MDC
Mobile dial telephone system	移动拨号电话系统	Yídòng bōhào diànhuà xìtǒng	MDTS
Mobile directory number	移动目录号码	Yídòng mùlù hàomǎ	MDN
Mobile echo control	移动回音控制	Yídòng huíyīn kòngzhì	MEC
Mobile end system	移动端系统	Yídòng duān xìtǒng	M-ES
Mobile equipment	移动设备	Yídòng shèbèi	ME
Mobile equipment identity register	移动设备识别寄存器	Yídòng shèbèi shíbié jìcúnqì	EIR
Mobile evaluated handover	移动切换估算	Yídòng qiēhuàn gūsuàn	MEHO
Mobile execution environment	移动运行环境	Yídòng yùnxíng huánjìng	MexE
Mobile global title	全球移动通信名称	Quánqiú yídòng tōngxìn míngchēng	MGT
Mobile global title	全球移动通信图标	Quánqiú yídòng tōngxìn túbiāo	MGT
Mobile home	移动住宅	Yídòng zhùzhái	
Mobile home function	移动归属功能	Yídòng guīshǔ gōngnéng	MHF
Mobile identification number	移动标识号码	Yídòng biāozhì hàomǎ	MIN
Mobile identification number	移动识别码	Yídòng shíbié mǎ	MIN
Mobile identification number	移动台标志号码	Yídòngtái biāozhì hàomǎ	MIN
Mobile interface controller	移动接口控制器	Yídòng jiēkǒu kòngzhìqì	MIC
Mobile internet technical architecture	移动因特网技术的体系结构	Yídòng Yīntèwǎng jìshùde tǐxì jiégòu	MITA
Mobile interwork control element	移动互通控制单元	Yídòng hùtōng kòngzhì dānyuán	MICE
Mobile interwork module	移动互通模块	Yídòng hùtōng mókuài	MIM
Mobile management entity	移动管理实体	Yídòng guǎnlǐ shítǐ	MME
Mobile management entity - data link layer	移动管理实体-数据链路层	Yídòng guǎnlǐ shítǐ - shùjù liànlù céng	MDL
Mobile management entity - physical layer	移动管理实体-物理层	Yídòng guǎnlǐ shítǐ - wùlǐ céng	MPH
Mobile network code	移动电话网号码	Yídòng diànhuà wǎng hàomǎ	MNC
Mobile network code	移动网编号	Yídòng wǎng biānhào	MNC
Mobile network code	移动网号	Yídòng wǎng hào	MNC
Mobile network code	移动网络码	Yídòng wǎngluò mǎ	MNC

Mobile network location protocol	移动网位置协议	Yídòng wǎng wèizhì xiéyì	MNLP
Mobile network registration protocol	移动网登记协议	Yídòng wǎng dēngjì xiéyì	MNRP
Mobile node	移动节点	Yídòng jiédiǎn	MN
Mobile number portability	移动号码可携	Yídòng hàomǎ kěxié	MNP
Mobile number portability	移动号码可携带性	Yídòng hàomǎ kěxiédàixìng	MNP
Mobile optical communication system	光移动通讯系统	Guāng yídòng tōngxùn xìtǒng	
Mobile originated	移动发起	Yídòng fāqǐ	MO
Mobile originated	移动台发起的	Yídòngtái fāqǐde	MO
Mobile originated	移动台始呼	Yídòngtái shǐhū	MO
Mobile originated handover	开始移动切换	Kāishǐ yídòng qiēhuàn	MOHO
Mobile originating	移动始发呼叫	Yídòng shǐfā hūjiào	MO
Mobile originating call	移动发端呼叫	Yídòng fāduān hūjiào	MOC
Mobile originating call	移动主叫	Yídòng zhǔjiào	MOC
Mobile originating call	移动台主叫	Yídòngtái zhǔ jiào	MOC
Mobile originating location request	移动发起定位请求	Yídòng fāqǐ dìngwèi qǐngqiú	MO-LR
Mobile packet radio network	移动式信包无线电通信网	Yídòng-shì xìnbāo wúxiàndiàn tōngxìn wǎng	MPRN
Mobile radio system ACE	移动无线系统 ACE	Yídòng wúxiàn xìtǒng ACE	MRSACE
Mobile satellite communications	移动卫星通讯	Yídòng wèixīng tōngxùn	MSC
Mobile satellite service	卫星移动业务	Wèixīng yídòng yèwù	
Mobile satellite service	移动卫星业务	Yídòng wèixīng yèwù	MSS
Mobile service	移动业务	Yídòng yèwù	
Mobile service switching center	移动业务交换中心	Yídòng yèwù jiāohuàn zhōngxīn	MSC, MSSC
Mobile serving function	移动业务功能	Yídòng yèwù gōngnéng	MSF
Mobile station	移动电台	Yídòng diàntái	MS
Mobile station	移动台	Yídòngtái	MS
Mobile station	移动站	Yídòngzhàn	MS
Mobile station class mark	移动台等级标	Yídòngtái děngjí biāo	MSCM
Mobile station control unit	移动台控制单元	Yídòngtái kòngzhì dānyuán	MSCU
Mobile station feature	移动台特性	Yídòngtái tèxìng	
Mobile station identification number	移动台识别号码	Yídòngtái shíbié hàomǎ	MSIN
Mobile station identification number	移动站识别号	Yídòngzhàn shíbié hào	MSIN
Mobile station identifier	移动台标识符	Yídòngtái biāozhìfú	MSID
Mobile station International ISDN number	移动台国际 ISDN 号码	Yídòngtái guójì ISDN hàomǎ	MSISDN
Mobile station international ISDN number	移动站国际 ISDN 号	Yídòngzhàn guójì ISDN hào	MSISDN
Mobile station ISDN number	移动台 ISDN 号码	Yídòngtái ISDN hàomǎ	MSISDN
Mobile station memory capacity exceeded flag	移动台存储能力溢出标志	Yídòngtái cúnchǔ nénglì yìchū biāozhì	MCEF
Mobile station power level	移动台功率电平	Yídòngtái gōnglǜ diànpíng	PL
Mobile station roaming number	移动台漫游号码	Yídòngtái mànyóu hàomǎ	MSRN
Mobile subscriber	移动用户	Yídòng yònghù	MS
Mobile subscriber directory number	移动用户电话码	Yídòng yònghù diànhuà mǎ	DN
Mobile subscriber ISDN number	移动用户 ISDN 号码	Yídòng yònghù ISDN hàomǎ	MSISDN
Mobile subscriber roaming number	移动用户漫游号码	Yídòng yònghù mànyóu hàomǎ	MSRN
Mobile subscriber temporary local directory number	移动用户临时本地电话号码	Yídòng yònghù línshí běndì diànhuà hàomǎ	TLDN
Mobile subscriber unit	移动用户单元	Yídòng yònghù dānyuán	MSU
Mobile switching center	移动交换中心	Yídòng jiāohuàn zhōngxīn	MSC

Mobile switching center	移动交换机	Yídòng jiāohuànjī	MSC
Mobile switching center	移动交换局	Yídòng jiāohuànjú	MSC
Mobile switching center	移动无线局	Yídòng wúxiàn jú	MSC
Mobile telecommunication	移动通信	Yídòng tōngxìn	YD
Mobile telephone switching office	移动电话交换局	Yídòng diànhuà jiāohuànjú	MTSO
Mobile Telephone System (Canada)	移动电话系统	Yídòng diànhuà xìtǒng	MTS
Mobile terminal	移动终端	Yídòng zhōngduān	MT
Mobile terminal locating center	移动终端定位中心	Yídòng zhōngduān dìngwèi zhōngxīn	MLC
Mobile terminal location request	移动终端定位请求	Yídòng zhōngduān dìngwèi qǐngqiú	MT-LR
Mobile terminated	移动终接	Yídòng zhōngjiē	MT
Mobile terminated	移动终止	Yídòng zhōngzhǐ	MT
Mobile terminated	移动台终止的	Yídòngtái zhōngzhǐde	MT
Mobile terminated call	移动终止呼叫	Yídòng zhōngzhǐ hūjiào	MT
Mobile terminating call	移动被叫	Yídòng bèijiào	MTC
Mobile terminating call	移动台被叫	Yídòngtái bèijiào	MTC
Mobile termination call	移动终端呼叫	Yídòng zhōngduān hūjiào	MTC
Mobile traffic control sub-system	移动业务控制子系统	Yídòng yèwù kòngzhì zixìtǒng	MTCS
Mobile user directory number	移动用户号码簿号码	Yídòng yònghù hàomǎbù hàomǎ	DN
Mobile user identification number	移动用户识别码	Yídòng yònghù shíbié mǎ	MIN
Mobile user identifier	移动用户标识符	Yídòng yònghù biāozhìfú	MUI
Mobile virtual network operator	移动虚拟网络运营商	Yídòng xūnǐ wǎngluò yùnyíngshāng	MVNO
Mobile virtual private network	移动虚拟专用网	Yídòng xūnǐ zhuānyòng wǎng	MVPN
Mobile wireless access	移动无线接入	Yídòng wúxiàn jiērù	MWA
Mobile-controlled handoff	移动台控制切换	Yídòngtái kòngzhì qiēhuàn	MCHO
Mobile-to-mobile (call)	移动到移动（呼叫）	Yídòng dào yídòng (hūjiào)	MTM
Mobility application part	移动性应用部分	Yídòngxìng yìngyòng bùfen	MAP
Mobility binding	移动绑定	Yídòng bǎngdìng	
Mobility management	移动性管理	Yídòngxìng guǎnlǐ	MM
Mobility security association (in mobile IP)	移动安全关联	Yídòng ānquán guānlián	
Mobitex	流动电文	Liúdòng diànwén	
Mock-up	实物模型	Shíwù móxíng	
Modal analysis	型分析法	Xíng fēnxī fǎ	
Modal noise	模式噪声	Móshì zàoshēng	
Mode	模式	Móshì	
Mode conversion (in waveguide)	模变换	Mó biànhuàn	
Mode conversion gain	模变换增益	Mó biànhuàn zēngyì	
Mode conversion loss	模变换损耗	Mó biànhuàn sǔnhào	
Mode converter	模变换器	Mó biànhuànqì	
Mode coupling	模式耦合	Móshì ǒuhé	
Mode designation (in a waveguide or cavity resonator)	模标志	Mó biāozhì	
Mode dispersion	模式色散	Móshì sèsàn	
Mode field	模场	Móchǎng	FAT
Mode field concentricity deviation (FOC mfg)	模场同心度偏差	Móchǎng tóngxīndù piānchā	
Mode field concentricity error (FOC)	模场同心度误差	Móchǎng tóngxīndù wùchā	
Mode field diameter (of FOC)	模场直径	Móchǎng zhíjìng	MFD
Mode filter	模滤波器	Mó lǜbōqì	

Mode hopping	跳模	Tiàomó	
Mode of propagation (in a transmission line)	传播模	Chuánbō mó	
Mode partition noise	模分配噪声	Mó fēnpèi zàoshēng	MPN
Mode scrambler	混模器	Hùnmóqì	
Mode scrambler	搅模器	Jiǎomóqì	
Mode status register	方式状态寄存器	Fāngshì zhuàngtài jìcúnqì	MSR
Mode superposition method	型叠置法	Xíng diézhì fǎ	
Mode switch (on radio)	工种开关	Gōngzhǒng kāiguān	
Mode switching	替换模	Tìhuan mó	
Mode transformer	模式变换器	Móshì biànhuànqì	
Mode, status, state	状态	Zhuàngtài	
Model	模型	Móxíng	
Model aggregation	模型聚集技术	Móxíng jùjí jìshù	
Model database	模型数据库	Móxíng shùjùkù	
Model dependency	模型相关性	Móxíng xiāngguānxìng	
Model of the load-deflection relation	负荷-偏差关系模型	Fùhè—piānchā guānxi móxíng	
Model project	示范工程	Shìfàn gōngchéng	
Model simplification	模型简化	Móxíng jiǎnhuà	
Model testing	模型验证	Móxíng yànzhèng	
Modeling and Simulation Master Plan (US)	建模与仿真主计划	Jiànmó yǔ fǎngzhēn zhǔ jìhuà	MSMP
Modeling language	建模语言	Jiànmó yǔyán	
Modelling, model building	建模	Jiànmó	
Model-specific register	模型特定寄存器	Móxíng tèdìng jìcúnqì	MSR
Modem, modulator/demodulator	调制/解调器	Tiáozhì/jiětiáoqì	MODEM
Modification of wrong account	错账冲正	Cuòzhàng chōngzhèng	
Modified Allan deviation	修正艾伦偏差	Xiūzhèng ài-lún piānchā	MADEV
Modified alternate mark inversion	变形交替传号反转	Biànxíng jiāotì chuánhào fǎnzhuǎn	
Modified chemical vapor deposition	改进化学汽相沉积法	Gǎijìn huàxué qìxiàng chénjī fǎ	MCVD
Modified Hadama variance	修正哈达玛方差	Xiūzhèng hǎ-dá-mǎ fāngchà	MHV
Modified Huffman code	变形赫夫门码	Biànxíng hè-fū-mén mǎ	MHC
Modified phase modification synchronization (in CORBA)	改进的相位修改协议	Gǎijìnde xiàngwèi xiūgǎi xiéyì	MPM
Modified quadrature overlapped raised-cosine modulation	修正的正交重叠基座余弦调制	Xiūzhèngde zhèngjiāo chóngdié jīzuò yúxián tiáozhì	MQORC
Modified relative element address designator code	修正的相对元素位置指示编码	Xiūzhèngde xiāngduì yuánsù wèizhì zhǐshì biānmǎ	MR
Modified vapor phase deposition (FOC mfg)	改良式汽相沉积法	Gǎiliáng-shì qìxiàng chénjī fǎ	MVPD
Modified, exclusive, shared, invalid	修改，排除，共享，废弃	Xiūgǎi, páichú, gòngxiǎng, fèiqì	MESI
Modifier	修改量	Xiūgǎi liàng	
Modifier	修饰符	Xiūshì fú	
Modifier	修饰字	Xiūshì zì	
Modify complete	修改完成	Xiūgǎi wánchéng	
Modular exponentiation	方幂模	Fāng mìmó	
Modular exponentiation	模幂乘	Mómìchéng	
Modular multiplication	模乘	Mó chéng	
Modular router	中档路由器	Zhōngdàng lùyóuqì	
Modular visualization environment	模块化可视化环境	Mókuàihuà kěshìhuà huánjìng	

Modularize	模块化	Mókuàihuà	
Modulated oscillation	已调振荡	Yǐtiáo zhèndàng	
Modulated signal	已调信号	Yǐtiáo xìnhào	
Modulated wave	已调波	Yǐtiáo bō	
Modulating pulse amplitude	调制脉冲幅度	Tiáozhì màichōng fúdù	
Modulating pulse amplitude stability	调制脉冲幅度稳定度	Tiáozhì màichōng fúdù wěndìngdù	
Modulating pulse front edge	调制脉冲前沿	Tiáozhì màichōng qiányán	
Modulating pulse lagging edge	调制脉冲后沿	Tiáozhì màichōng hòuyán	
Modulating pulse length	调制脉冲宽度	Tiáozhì màichōng kuāndù	
Modulating pulse overshoot (spike)	调制脉冲上冲（波尖）	Tiáozhì màichōng shàngchōng (bōjiān)	
Modulating pulse top unevenness	调制脉冲顶部不平度	Tiáozhì màichōng dǐngbù bùpíngdù	
Modulating pulse undershoot (negative spike)	调制脉冲下冲（反峰）	Tiáozhì màichōng xiàchōng (fǎn fēng)	
Modulating signal	调制信号	Tiáozhì xìnhào	
Modulating wave	调制波	Tiáozhì bō	
Modulation	调制	Tiáozhì	
Modulation by pulse	用脉冲进行调制	Yòng màichōng jìnxíng tiáozhì	
Modulation characteristic	调制特性	Tiáozhì tèxìng	
Modulation code	调制编码	Tiáozhì biānmǎ	
Modulation depth	调制深度	Tiáozhì shēndù	
Modulation factor	调制系数	Tiáozhì xìshù	
Modulation gain	调制增益	Tiáozhì zēngyì	
Modulation hum	调制交流声	Tiáozhì jiāoliúshēng	
Modulation index	调制指数	Tiáozhì zhǐshù	
Modulation instability	调制不稳定性	Tiáozhì bùwěndìngxìng	MI
Modulation limiting	调制限制	Tiáozhì xiànzhì	
Modulation rate	调制速率	Tiáozhì sùlǜ	
Modulation sensitivity	调制灵敏度	Tiáozhì língmǐndù	
Modulator	调制器	Tiáozhìqì	
Modulator demodulator	调制解调器	Tiáozhì jiětiáoqì	MODEM
Module	模块	Mókuài	
Module	模组	Mózǔ	
Module interconnection language	模块互连语言	Mókuài hùlián yǔyán	MIL
Module test system	模块试验系统	Mókuài shìyàn xìtǒng	MTS
Modulo ...	以...为模	Yǐ ...wéi mó	
Modulo 2 add	模 2 加	Mó èr jiā	
Modulus conversion	模数转换	Móshù zhuǎnhuàn	
Mogel-Dellinger fade-out	莫吉尔 - 戴林格信号消逝	Mò-jí-ěr dài-lín-gé xìnhào xiāoshì	
Moisture protection; protect against moisture (one of the “Six protects”)	防潮	Fángcháo	
Moisture-proof packaging	防湿保存箱	Fángshī bǎocún xiāng	
Mold proof	防霉	Fángméi	
Mold test	霉菌试验	Méijùn shìyàn	
Molecular beam epitaxy	分子束外延	Fènzi shù wàiyán	MBE
Moment	瞬时	Shùnshí	
Moment of friction	摩擦力矩	Mócā lìjǔ	
Moment of inertia	惯性矩	Guànxìngjǔ	
Moment of inertia	转动惯量	Zhuàndòng guànliàng	

Monitor (noun)	监视器	Jiānshìqì	
Monitor bit	监视器比特	Jiānshìqì bǐtè	M
Monitor electromagnetic screening	显示器电磁屏蔽	Xiǎnshìqì diàncí píngbì	
Monitor terminal	监视终端	Jiānshì zhōngduān	
Monitored	被检测的	Bèijiǎncède	MON
Monitored parameter	受监视参数	Shòujiānshì cānshù	
Monitoring and control panel	监控维护盘	Jiānkòng wéihù pán	MCP
Monitoring and system support facilities	监控和系统支持设施	Jiānkòng hé xìtǒng zhīchí shèshī	MSSF
Monitoring cell	监视信元	Jiānshì xìnyuán	
Monitoring center	监测中心	Jiāncè zhōngxīn	MC
Monitoring, supervisory control	监控	Jiānkòng	
Monochrome	单色	Dānsè	
Monochrome adapter (video term)	单色适配器	Dānsè shìpèiqì	MDA
Monochrome display adapter	单色显示监控器	Dānsè xiǎnshì jiānkòngqì	MDA
Monochrome laser printer	单色激光印表机	Dānsè jīguāng yìnbiǎojī	
Monolithic integrated circuit	单片集成电路	Dānpiàn jíchéng diànlù	
Monopole antenna, unipole antenna	单极子天线	Dānjízi tiānxiàn	
Monopulse antenna	单脉冲天线	Dānmàichōng tiānxiàn	
Monopulse radar	单脉冲雷达	Dānmàichōng léidá	
Monopulse radar receiver	单脉冲雷达接收机	Dānmàichōng léidá jiēshōujī	
Monospace	等宽	Děngkuān	
Monospace	划一字距	Huàyī zì jù	
Monostable circuit	单稳态电路	Dānwěntài diànlù	
Monostable trigger circuit	单稳态触发电路	Dānwěntài chùfā diànlù	
Monostatic radar	单基地雷达	Dānjīdì léidá	
Monte Carlo simulation	蒙特卡洛模拟	Méng-tè-kǎ-luò mónǐ	MCS
Moore's law	摩尔定律	Mó-ěr dìnglǜ	
Moratorium	延期支付	Yánqī zhīfù	
More data	后续数据	Hòuxù shùjù	
More segments	多程序段	Duōchéngxù duàn	MS
Morphing (in image processing)	变形	Biànxíng	
Morphological representation of wavelet data	小波数据的形态学表示	Xiǎobo shùjùde xíngtàixué biǎoshì	MRWD
Morse code	莫尔斯电码	Mò-ěr-sī diànmǎ	
Morse telegraphy	莫尔斯电报	Mò-ěr-sī diànbào	
Morton order	莫顿序	Mò-dùn xù	
Mosaic browser © (Internet tool)	马赛克浏览器	Mǎ-sài-kè liúlǎnqì	
Mosaic telegraphy	镶嵌电报	Xiāngqiàn diànbào	
Most derived class	最底层的派生类	Zuìdǐcéngde pàishēng lèi	
Most redundant bandwidth adaptive route selecting	最大冗余带宽适应路由选择	Zuìdà rǒngyú dàikuān shìyìng lùyóu xuǎnzé	RBAR
Most significant bit	最高位	Zuìgāo wèi	MSB
Most significant bit	最高有效比特	Zuìgāo yǒuxiào bǐtè	MSB
Most significant bit	最高有效位	Zuìgāo yǒuxiào wèi	MSB
Most significant byte	最高有效字节	Zuìgāo yǒuxiào zìjié	MSB
Motherboard	母板	Mǔbǎn	MMB
Motherboard; system board	主机板	Zhǔjī bǎn	
Mothproof	防蛀性	Fángzhùxìng	

Motion blur (video term)	动态模糊	Dòngtài móhu	
Motion compensation (video term)	动态补偿	Dòngtài bǔcháng	
Motion compensation (video term)	运动补偿	Yùndòng bǔcháng	MC
Motion estimation (video term)	运动估值	Yùndòng gūzhí	
Motion Joint Photographic Experts Group	移动式连续图像专家组	Yídòng-shì liánxù túxiàng zhuānjiāzǔ	MJPEG
Motion Picture Experts Group	动画专家组	Dònghuà zhuānjiāzǔ	MPEG
Motion Picture Experts Group	活动图像专家组	Huódòng túxiàng zhuānjiāzǔ	MPEG
Motion Picture Experts Group	运动图像专家组	Yùndòng túxiàng zhuānjiāzǔ	MPEG
Motion planning	运动规划	Yùndòng guīhuà	
Motion tracking	运动跟踪	Yùndòng gēnzōng	
Motion, mobile	移动	Yídòng	
Motor uniselector	电动单行程选择器	Diàndòng dānxíngchéng xuǎnzéqì	
Motorola (US company)	摩托罗拉	Mó-tuō-luó-lā	
Motor-stator deflection coil	马达定子式偏转线圈	Mǎdá dìngzi-shì piānzhuǎn xiànquān	
Mount (hardware)	装入	Zhuāngrù	
Mouse	电子鼠	Diànzǐ shǔ	
Mouse	滑鼠	Huáshǔ	
Mouse	鼠标器	Shǔbiāoqì	
Mouse pad	鼠标垫	Shǔbiāo diàn	
Mouth reference point	口参考点	Kǒu cānkǎo diǎn	MRP
Mouth reference point	嘴参考点	Zuǐ cānkǎo diǎn	MRP
Movable part	活动部分	Huódòng bùfen	
Movable radar	机动雷达	Jīdòng léidá	
Movable-slot time-division multiplexing	活动槽口时分多路复用	Huódòng cáokǒu shífēn duōlù fùyòng	MSTDM
Movement	运动	Yùndòng	
Movie on demand	点播电影	Diǎnbō diànyǐng	MOD
Moving average filter	滑动平均滤波器	Huádòng píngjūn lǜbōqì	
Moving Picture Coding Experts Group	活动图像编码专家组	Huódòng túxiàng biānmǎ zhuānjiāzǔ	MPEG
Moving Pictures Experts Group	移动图象专家组	Yídòng túxiàng zhuānjiāzǔ	MPEG
Moving target detector	动目标检测器	Dòng mùbiāo jiǎncèqì	MTD
Moving target indicator	动目标显示	Dòng mùbiāo xiǎnshì	MTI
Moving targets indication radar	动目标显示雷达	Dòng mùbiāo xiǎnshì léidá	MTI
Moving-coil type transducer	可动线圈式变换器	Kědòng xiànquān-shì biànhuànqì	
MPEG transmission stream	MPEG 传输流	MPEG chuánshū liú	MPEG TS
MPEG transmission stream	MPEG 传送流	MPEG chuánsòng liú	MPEG-TS
MPLS forum	MPLS 论坛	MPLS lùntán	MPLSF
M-scope	M 型显示器	M-xíng xiǎnshìqì	
MSP management function	MSP 管理功能	MSP guǎnlǐ gōngnéng	MSP-MF
MSP operation system	MSP 运行系统	MSP yùnxíng xìtǒng	MSP-OpS
MTP2-user adaptation layer	MTP 第二级用户适配层	MTP dì'èrjí yònghù shìpèi céng	M2UA
MTP3-user adaptation layer	MTP 第三级用户适配层	MTP dìsānjí yònghù shìpèi céng	M3UA
M-type device	M 型器件	M-xíng qìjiàn	
Mud pumping	喷泥	Pēn ní	
Multi function device	多功能设备	Duōgōngnéng shèbèi	MFD
Multi-address call	多址呼叫	Duōzhǐ hūjiào	
Multi-agent system	多代理系统	Duōdàilǐ xìtǒng	MAS

Multi-amplitude minimum shift keying	多振幅最小移位键控	Duōzhènfú zuìxiǎo yíwèi jiànkòng	MAMSK
Multi-astigmatism lens system (video term)	多重散光聚焦系统	Duōzhòng sǎnguāng jùjiāo xìtǒng	MALS
Multi-axial stress condition	多轴应力状态	Duōzhóu yìnglì zhuàngtài	
Multi-band cell reporting	多频小区报告	Duōpín xiǎoqū bàogào	MBCR
Multiband excitation	多频带激励	Duōpíndài jīlì	MBE
Multi-band excitation	多带激励	Duōdài jīlì	MBE
Multi-band excitation	多带激励编码	Duōdài jīlì biānmǎ	MBE
Multiband multimode radio (a US system)	多频段多模式无线电台	Duōpínduàn duōmóshì wúxiàndiàntái	MBMMR
Multi-beam antenna	多波束天线	Duōbōshù tiānxiàn	MBA
Multi-beam antenna, multi-pattern antenna	多射束天线	Duōshèshù tiānxiàn	
Multi-beam forming network	多波束合成网络	Duōbōshù héchéng wǎngluò	
Multi-beam klystron	多束速调管	Duōshù sùtiáoguǎn	MBK
Multi-business group	多种商业组群	Duōzhǒng shāngyè zǔqún	MBG
Multi-byte expansion	多字节扩展	Duōzìjié kuòzhǎn	MBE
Multi-call agent	多项呼叫代理	Duōxiàng hūjiào dàilǐ	
Multi-carrier modulation	多载波调制	Duōzàibō tiáozhì	MCM
Multi-carrier pulse position modulation	多载波脉冲位置调制	Duōzàibō màichōng wèizhì tiáozhì	MPPM
Multicast	多播	Duōbō	
Multicast	多点播发	Duōdiǎn bōfā	
Multicast	多目广播	Duōmù guǎngbō	
Multicast	组播	Zǔbō	
Multicast adaptation protocol	组播适配协议	Zǔbō shìpèi xiéyì	MAP
Multicast adaptation protocol/protocol data unit	组播适配协议-协议数据单元	Zǔbō shìpèi xiéyì/xiéyì shùjù dānyuán	MAPPDU
Multicast adaptation protocol/service access point	组播适配协议--服务接入点	Zǔbō shìpèi xiéyì/fúwù jiērù diǎn	MAPSAP
Multicast address dynamic client allocation protocol	多播地址动态客户端分配协议	Duōbō dìzhǐ dòngtài kèhùduān fēnpèi xiéyì	MADCAP
Multicast address resolution server (IETF usage)	组播地址解析服务	Zǔbō dìzhǐ jiěxī fúwù	MARS
Multicast address resolution service	多播地址解析服务	Duōbō dìzhǐ jiěxī fúwù	MARS
Multicast addressing	多播地址	Duōbō dìzhǐ	MA
Multicast aware level 2 switch	组播敏感的第二层交换机	Zǔbō mǐngǎnde dì'èrcéng jiāohuànjī	MAS
Multicast backbone	多播主干网	Duōbō zhǔgàn wǎng	MBONE
Multicast backbone network	组播主干网	Zǔbō zhǔgàn wǎng	MBONE
Multicast border gateway protocol	多目广播边界网关协议	Duōmù guǎngbō biānjiè wǎngguān xiéyì	MBGP
Multicast border gateway protocol	组播边界网关协议	Zǔbō biānjiè wǎngguān xiéyì	MBGP
Multicast call	多播呼叫	Duōbō hūjiào	
Multicast call	组播呼叫	Zǔbō hūjiào	
Multicast conference name	组播会议名称	Zǔbō huìyì míngchēng	
Multicast conferencing media stream provider	组播会议媒体流提供程序	Zǔbō huìyì méitǐ liú tígōng chéngxù	
Multicast conferencing model	组播会议模型	Zǔbō huìyì móxíng	
Multicast datagram	多播数据报	Duōbō shùjù bào	
Multicast delegate	多点委托	Duōdiǎn wěituō	
Multicast delegate	组播委托	Zǔbō wěituō	
Multicast group	多播群	Duōbō qún	
Multicast group	组播群	Zǔbō qún	
Multicast internet protocol	组播互联网协议	Zǔbō hùliánwǎng xiéyì	MIP

Multicast key management protocol	多播密钥管理协议	Duōbō mìyào guǎnlǐ xiéyì	MKMP
Multicast media access control address	多播媒体访问控制地址	Duobō méitǐ fǎngwèn kòngzhì dìzhǐ	
Multicast open shortest path first protocol	开最短路径优先组播路由协议	Kāi zuìduǎn lùjìng yōuxiān zǔbō lùyóu xiéyì	MOSPF
Multicast routing	多点广播路由	Duōdiǎn guǎngbō lùyóu	
Multicast scope zone announcement protocol (IETF usage)	组播区域范围公告协议	Zǔbō qūyù fànwéi gōnggào xiéyì	MZAP
Multicast server	多播服务器	Duōbō fúwùqì	
Multicast service	多播业务	Duōbō yèwù	
Multicast service	组播业务	Zǔbō yèwù	
Multicast service policy server	组播策略服务器	Zǔbō cèlüè fúwùqì	MuPS
Multicast source discovery protocol	组播源发现协议	Zǔbō yuán fāxiàn xiéyì	MSDP
Multicast transmission protocol/self-ordering	组播传送协议/自组织	Zǔbō chuánsòng xiéyì/zìzǔzhī	MTP/SO
Multi-cellular lens	窗格式透镜	Chuānggé-shì tòujìng	
Multi-channel	多通道	Duōtōngdào	MCH
Multi-channel	多信道	Duōxìndào	MCH
Multi-channel access	多信道选取	Duōxìndào xuǎnqǔ	MCA
Multi-channel access system without central control	无中心多信道选址系统	Wúzhōngxīn duōxìndào xuǎnzhǐ xìtǒng	
Multi-channel carrier telephone system	多信道载波电话系统	Duōxìndào zàibō diànhuà xìtǒng	MCCTS
Multi-channel fiber optic connector	多心光纤连接器	Duōxīn guāngxiān liánjiēqì	
Multi-channel gain tilt	多波道增益斜率	Duōbōdào zēngyì xiélǜ	
Multi-channel gain variation	多波道增益变化	Duōbōdào zēngyì biànhuà	
Multi-channel gain-change difference	多波道增益变化差	Duōbōdào zēngyì biànhuà chà	
Multi-channel gain-change ratio	多波道增益变化比	Duōbōdào zēngyì biànhuà bǐ	
Multi-channel local area network	多通道局域网	Duōtōngdào júyùwǎng	MLAN
Multi-channel microwave distribution system	多路微波分配系统	Duōlù wēibō fēnpèi xìtǒng	MMDS
Multi-channel microwave distribution system	多信道微波分配系统	Duōxìndào wēibō fēnpèi xìtǒng	MMDS
Multi-channel multipoint distribution service	多波段多点分发服务	Duōbōduàn duōdiǎn fēnfā fúwù	MMDS
Multi-channel multipoint distribution service	多路多点分配业务	Duōlù duōdiǎn fēnpèi yèwù	MMDS
Multi-channel multipoint distribution service	多信道多点分配业务	Duōxìndào duōdiǎn fēnpèi yèwù	MMDS
Multi-channel per carrier	每载波多信道	Měi zàibō duō xìndào	MCPC
Multi-channel programming	多道程序设计	Duōdào chéngxù shèjì	
Multi-channel rotary joint	多路旋转关节	Duōlù xuánzhuǎn guānjié	
Multi-channel system (optical)	多波长系统	Duōbōcháng xìtǒng	MCS
Multi-channel voice frequency	多路语音频率	Duōlù yǔyīn pínlǜ	MCVF
Multi-channel voice-frequency telegraphy	多路音频电报	Duōlù yīnpín diànbào	MCVFT
Multi-charge rate	复费率	Fùfèi lǜ	
Multi-chip module (electronics mfg)	多芯片模块	Duōxìnpiàn mókuài	MCM
Multi-class multi-link point to point protocol	多级多链路 ppp	Duōjí duōliànlù PPP	MCML
Multi-code	多码	Duōmǎ	
Multi-color graphics array	多色图像阵列	Duōsè túxiàng zhènliè	MCGA
Multi-color laser	多色激光	Duōsè jīguāng	
Multi-component signal (in ac signaling)	多成分信号（交流信令中）	Duō chéngfèn xìnhào (jiāoliú xìnlìng zhōng)	
Multi-computer system	多计算机系统	Duōjìsuànjī xìtǒng	
Multi-conductor element	多导线单元	Duō dǎoxiàn dānyuán	
Multi-connection endpoint identifier	多连接端点标识符	Duōliánjiē duāndiǎn biāozhì fú	

Multi-core fiber	多芯光纤	Duōxīn guāngxiān	
Multi-coupler (of an antenna)	多路耦合器	Duōlù ǒuhéqì	
Multi-cycle control (by half-cycles)	按半周的多周控制	An bànzhōude duōzhōu kòngzhì	
Multicycle controlled by half-cycle	按半周进行的多周期控制	Àn bànzhōu jìnxíngde duōzhōuqī kòngzhì	
Multi-dimensional array	多维数组	Duōwéishù zǔ	
Multi-dimensional data	多维数据	Duōwéi shùjù	
Multi-dimensional expressions	多维表达式	Duōwéi biǎodá shì	MDX
Multi-dimensional online analytical processing	多维联机分析处理	Duōwéi liánjī fēnxī chǔlǐ	MOLAP
Multi-dimensional scaling	多维尺度	Duōwéi chǐdù	
Multi-dimensional scaling analysis	多维等级分析	Duōwéi děngjí fēnxī	
Multi-dimensional structure	多维结构	Duōwéi jiégòu	
Multi-disciplinary database	多领域数据库	Duōlǐngyù shùjùkù	
Multi-documentation interface	多文档界面	Duōwéndàng jièmiàn	MDI
Multi-drop line	多点线路	Duōdiǎn xiànlù	
Multidrop network	多分转站网	Duōfēn zhuǎnzhàn wǎng	
Multi-feed antenna	多馈线天线	Duōkuìxiàn tiānxiàn	MFA
Multi-fiber cable	多芯光缆	Duōxīn guānglǎn	
Multi-fiber cable connector	多芯光缆连接器	Duōxīn guānglǎn liánjiēqì	
Multi-fiber fiber optic cable	多心式光缆	Duōxīnshì guānglǎn	
Multi-frame	多帧	Duōzhèng	MF
Multi-frame	复帧	Fùzhèng	
Multi-frame mode	多帧模式	Duōzhèng móshì	
Multi-frequency control board	多频互控板	Duōpín hùkòngbǎn	MFC
Multi-frequency dial register sender	多频拨号记存发送器	Duōpín bōhào jìcún fāsòngqì	MDRS
Multi-frequency dialing	多频拨号	Duōpín bōhào	MFD
Multi-frequency output sender	多频输出发送器	Duōpín shūchū fāsòngqì	MFOS
Multi-frequency press button	多频按键	Duōpín ànjiàn	MFPB
Multi-frequency signaling	多频信令	Duōpín xìnlìng	
Multi-function broadband communication system	多功能宽带通信系统	Duōgōngnéng kuāndài tōngxìn xìtǒng	MBCS
Multi-function digital signaling service	多功能数字信号服务	Duōgōngnéng shùzì xìnhào fúwù	MDSS
Multi-function peripheral	多功能外围设备	Duōgōngnéng wàiwéi shèbèi	MFP
Multi-function product	多功能复合事务机	Duōgōngnéng fùhé shìwùjī	MFP
Multi-function terminal adapter	多功能终端适配器	Duōgōngnéng zhōngduān shìpèiqì	MTA
Multi-gun cathode ray tube (CRT)	多枪管	Duōqiāngguǎn	
Multi-homed host	多宿主机	Duōsù zhǔjī	
Multihop path	多跳路径	Duōtiào lùjìng	
Multi-hop satellite link	多跳卫星链路	Duōtiào wèixīng liànlù	
Multi-horn feed	多喇叭馈电器	Duōlǎba kuìdiànqì	
Multi-input multi-output	多输入多输出	Duōshūrù duō shūchū	MIMO
Multi-input multi-output	多输入输出	Duōshūrù shūchū	MIMO
Multi-join expression	多连接表达式	Duōliánjiē biǎodá shì	
Multi-layer ceramic capacitor	陶瓷多层电容器	Táocí duōcéng diànróngqì	MLC
Multi-layer mirror	多层面镜	Duōcéng miànjìng	
Multi-layer protocol	多层协议	Duōcéng xiéyì	MLP
Multi-layer switch	多层交换机	Duōcéng jiāohuànjī	
Multi-leaving telecommunications access method	多点传送远程通信存取方法	Duōdiǎn chuánsòng yuǎnchéng tōngxìn cúnqǔ fāngfǎ	MTAM

Multi-level coded modulation	多电平编码调制	Duōdiànpíng biānmǎ tiáozhì	MLCM
Multi-level device	多级设备	Duōjí shèbèi	
Multi-level modulation	多电平调制	Duōdiànpíng tiáozhì	
Multi-level phase shift keying	多级相移键控	Duōjí xiāngyí jiànkòng	MPSK
Multi-level precedence and preemption	多等级优先占用	Duō děngjí yōuxiān zhànyòng	MLPP
Multilevel processing	多级处理	Duōjí chǔlǐ	
Multi-level pulse code modulation, polarization modulated (pulse source)	多级脉码调制,极化 调制(脉冲源)	Duōjí màimǎ tiáozhì, jíhuà tiáozhì (màichōng yuán)	M-PCM-PM(PS)
Multi-level pulse code modulation, intensity modulated (pulse source)	多级脉码调制,强度 调制(脉冲源)	Duōjí màimǎ tiáozhì, qiángdù tiáozhì (màichōng yuán)	M-PCM-IM(PS)
Multi-level quadrature amplitude modulation (QAM)	多电平正交调幅	Duōdiànpíng zhèngjiāo tiáofú	
Multi-level security (IPsec)	多级安全	Duōjí ānquán	
Multi-line automatic calling system	复式线路自动呼叫系统	Fùshì xiànlù zìdòng hūjiào xìtǒng	MACS
Multi-link dialing	多链路拨号	Duōliànlù bōhào	
Multi-link point-to-point protocol	多链接点到点协议	Duōliànjiē diǎn dào diǎn xiéyì	PPP
Multilink PPP	PPP 多链路协议	PPP duō liànlù xiéyì	MP
Multi-link procedure	多链路规程	Duōliànlù guīchéng	MLP
Multi-linked list	多重链表	Duōchóng liàn biǎo	
Multi-list file	多重链表文件	Duōchóng liàn biǎo wénjiàn	
Multi-longitude mode	多纵模	Duōzòngmó	MLM
Multi-longitudinal mode laser	多纵模激光器	Duōzòngmó jīguāngqì	MLM
Multi-loop control system	多回路控制系统	Duōhuílù kòngzhì xìtǒng	
Multi-master system	多主系统	Duōzhǔ xìtǒng	
Multimedia	多媒体	Duōméitǐ	
Multimedia action	多媒体操作	Duōméitǐ cāozuò	
Multimedia and hypermedia information coding expert group	多媒体和超媒体信息编码专家组	Duōméitǐ hé chāoméitǐ xìnxī biānmǎ zhuānjiāzǔ	MHEG
Multimedia communications	多媒体通信	Duōméitǐ tōngxìn	
Multimedia communications	多媒体通讯	Duōméitǐ tōngxùn	
Multimedia description	多媒体描述	Duōméitǐ miáoshù	
Multimedia digital surveillance system	多媒体数字监控系统	Duōméitǐ shùzì jiānkòng xìtǒng	
Multimedia distribution service	多媒体业务分布	Duōméitǐ yèwù fēnbù	MDS
Multimedia enabling tool	多媒体启动工具	Duōméitǐ qǐdòng gōngjù	
Multimedia extensions	多媒体扩展指令集	Duōméitǐ kuòzhǎn zhǐlìng jí	MMX
Multimedia interactive group	多媒体交流团	Duōméitǐ jiāoliú tuán	
Multimedia local network	多媒体本地网	Duōméitǐ běndì wǎng	
Multimedia mail transfer protocol	多媒体邮件传送协议	Duōméitǐ yóujiàn chuánsòng xiéyì	MMTP
Multimedia mailing	多媒体邮件	Duōméitǐ yóujiàn	MMM
Multimedia message gateway	多媒体信息网关	Duōméitǐ xìnxī wǎngguān	MMG
Multimedia messaging service	多媒体信息服务	Duōméitǐ xìnxī fúwù	MMS
Multimedia on demand	随选多媒体服务	Suíxuǎn duōméitǐ fúwù	
Multimedia outlet	多媒体插座	Duōméitǐ chāzuò	MMO
Multimedia periphery router	多媒体外设路由器	Duōméitǐ wàishè lùyóuqì	MPRouter
Multimedia service	多媒体业务	Duōméitǐ yèwù	
Multimedia signal processing equipment	多媒体信号处理装置	Duōméitǐ xìnhào chǔlǐ zhuāngzhì	MPE
Multimedia synchronization specification	多媒体同步规范	Duōméitǐ tóngbù guīfàn	

Multimedia unit	多媒体单元	Duōméitǐ dānyuán	MMU
Multimedia video file	多媒体视频文件	Duōméitǐ shìpín wénjiàn	MMVF
Multimode - multi-horn feed	多模多喇叭馈电器	Duōmó duōlǎba kuìdiànqì	
Multimode antenna	多模天线	Duōmó tiānxiàn	
Multimode feed	多模馈电器	Duōmó kuìdiànqì	
Multimode graded index optical fiber	多模渐变型光纤	Duōmó jiànbiànxíng guāngxiān	
Multimode horn antenna	多模喇叭天线	Duōmó lǎba tiānxiàn	
Multimode network	多模网络	Duōmó wǎngluò	
Multimode optical fiber	多模光纤	Duōmó guāngxiān	MMF
Multimode silica fiber optic cable	多模态石英系光缆	Duōmótài shíyīng xì guānglǎn	
Multimode stepped index optical fiber	多模突变型光纤	Duōmó tūbiànxíng guāngxiān	
Multimode vulnerability	多点漏洞	Duōdiǎn lòudòng	
Multimode waveguide	多模波导	Duōmó bōdǎo	
Multimode, multi-channel fiber optic connector	多模态多心光纤连接器	Duōmótài duōxīn guāngxiān liánjiēqì	
Multinary quadrature amplitude modulation	多进制正交幅度调制	Duōjìnzhì zhèngjiāo fúdù tiáozhì	MQAM
Multinary spread spectrum	多进制扩频	Duōjìnzhì kuòpín	
Multinomial logic regression	多项逻辑回归	Duōxiàng luóji huíguī	
Multi-objective genetic programming	多目标遗传规划	Duōmùbiāo yíchuán guīhuà	MOGP
Multi-objective optimization	多目标优化	Duōmùbiāo yōuhuà	
Multi-objective proportional selection scheme	多目标并列选择机制	Duōmùbiāo bìngliè xuǎnzéjī zhì	
Multi-party	多方会话	Duōfāng huìhuà	MPTy
Multi-party	多用户	Duōyònghù	MPTY
Multi-party call	多方呼叫	Duōfāng hūjiào	MPTY
Multi-party multimedia session control	多方多媒体会话控制	Duōfāng duōméitǐ huìhuà kòngzhì	MMUSIC
Multi-party supplementary services	多方通信附加业务	Duōfāng tōngxìn fùjiā yèwù	
Multi-party telecommunication	多方通话	Duōfāng tōnghuà	MPTY
Multipath	多径	Duōjìng	
Multipath delay	多径时延	Duōjìng shíyán	
Multipath diversity	多径分集	Duōjìng fēnjí	
Multipath effect	多径效应	Duōjìng xiàoyìng	
Multi-path error	多路径误差	Duōlùjìng wùchā	
Multipath fading	多径衰落	Duōjìng shuāiluò	
Multi-path fading distortion	多路径衰落失真	Duōlùjìng shuāiluò shīzhēn	MPF
Multi-path fading simulator	多路衰减模拟器	Duōlù shuāijiǎn mónǐqì	
Multi-path interference	多径干扰	Duōjìng gānrǎo	
Multi-path multicast	多路径多播	Duōlùjìng duōbō	
Multipath propagation	多径传播	Duōjìng chuánbō	
Multipath propagation function	多径传播函数	Duōjìng chuánbō hánshù	
Multi-path Rayleigh fading channels	多径 Rayleigh 衰落 信道	Duōjìng Rayleigh shuāiluò xìndào	
Multi-path self-routing	多路径自选路由	Duōlùjìng zìxuǎn lùyóu	MPSR
Multi-phase flow	多相流	Duōxiàng liú	
Multiple	复接	Fùjiē	
Multiple access	多路接入	Duōlù jiērù	MA
Multiple access	多址联接	Duōzhǐ liánjiē	
Multiple access interference	多址干扰	Duōzhǐ gānrǎo	MAI
Multiple access rights terminal	多访问权终端	Duōfǎngwènquán zhōngduān	

Multiple access switching system	多路进入交换系统	Duōlù jìnrù jiāohuàn xìtǒng	MASS
Multiple address translation	多重地址转换	Duōchóng dìzhǐ zhuǎnhuàn	
Multiple amplitude shift keying	多幅移键控	Duōfúyí jiànkòng	MASK
Multiple association control function	多偶联控制功能	Duō'ǒulián kòngzhì gōngnéng	MACF
Multiple association control function	多相关控制功能	Duōxiàngguān kòngzhì gōngnéng	MACF
Multiple band antenna	多频带天线	Duōpíndài tiānxiàn	
Multiple boot	多重启动	Duōchóng qǐdòng	
Multiple bundle cable	多束光缆	Duōshù guānglǎn	
Multiple burst mode controller	多突发模式控制器	Duōtūfā móshì kòngzhìqì	MBMC
Multiple call processing unit	多呼叫处理装置	Duōhūjiào chǔlǐ zhuāngzhì	MCPU
Multiple channel per carrier	每载波多路	Měi zàibō duōlù	MCPC
Multiple connection system	复接制	Fùjiēzhì	
Multiple data link controller	多路数据链接控制器	Duōlù shùjù liànjiē kòngzhìqì	MDLC
Multiple data message format	复合数据消息格式	Fùhé shùjù xiāoxi géshi	MDMF
Multiple domain network	多域网络	Duōyù wǎngluò	
Multiple folded dipole	多折合偶极子	Duōzhéhé ǒujízi	
Multiple frame operation	多帧操作	Duōzhèng cāozuò	
Multiple frame transmission	多帧传输	Duōzhèng chuánshū	
Multiple frequency reuse pattern	多重复用方式	Duōchóng fùyòng fāngshì	MRP
Multiple frequency shift keying	多路移频键控	Duōlù yípín jiànkòng	MFSK
Multiple frequency shift keying	多频移频键控	Duōpín yípín jiànkòng	MFSK
Multiple image lens	多影像透镜	Duōyǐngxiàng tòujìng	
Multiple inheritance	多重继承	Duōchóng jìchéng	
Multiple inheritance	多重继承	Duōzhòng jìchéng	
Multiple input	多重输入	Duōchóng shūrù	
Multiple instances	多实例	Duōshílì	
Multiple modulations	多次调制	Duōcì tiáozhì	
Multiple phase shift keying	多相移相键控	Duōxiàng yíxiāng jiànkòng	MPSK
Multiple phase shift keying	多值相移键控	Duōzhí xiāngyí jiànkòng	MPSK
Multiple priority levels	多优先级	Duōyōuxiān jí	
Multiple priority queue	多优先队列	Duōyōuxiān duìliè	MPQ
Multiple quadrature amplitude modulation	多重星座调制	Duōzhòng xīngzuò tiáozhì	MQAM
Multiple quantum well device	多量子阱器件	Duōliàngzǐ jǐng qìjiàn	MQW
Multiple quantum well distributed feedback laser device	多量子阱分布反馈激光器	Duōliàngzǐ jǐng fēnbù fǎnkuì jīguāngqì	MQW-DFB-LD
Multiple quantum well laser device	多量子阱激光器	Duōliàngzǐ jǐng jīguāngqì	MQW-LD
Multiple reflection	多重反射	Duōchóng fǎnshè	
Multiple regression	多元回归	Duōyuán huíguī	
Multiple regression analysis	多重回归分析	Duōchóng huíguī fēnxī	
Multiple representations	多重表达	Duōchóng biǎodá	
Multiple service provisioning platform	多业务配置平台	Duōyèwù pèizhì píngtái	MSPP
Multiple sidelobe cancellation system	多旁瓣抑制系统	Duōpángbàn yìzhì xìtǒng	MSLC
Multiple signal classification	多信号类级	Duōxìnhào lèijí	MUSIC
Multiple sub-Nyquist sampling encoding	多重子奈奎斯特抽样编码	Duōchóng zi nài-kuí-sī-tè chōuyàng biānmǎ	MUSE
Multiple sub-Nyquist sampling encoding	多重子奈奎斯特抽样编码	Duōzhòng ziNài-kuí-sī-tè chōuyàng biānmǎ	MUSE
Multiple subscriber number	多重用户号码	Duōchóng yònghù hàomǎ	MSN
Multiple subscriber profile	多用户分布	Duōyònghù fēnbù	MSP

English	Chinese	Pinyin	Abbreviation
Multiple timeframe	多重时帧	Duōchòngshí zhèng	
Multiple user dimension	多用户	Duōyònghù	MUD
Multiple virtual storage distribution library	多虚拟存储器分布库	Duōxūnǐ cúnchǔqì fēnbù kù	MVSDLIB
Multiple wavelength solution	多波长解决方案	Duōbōcháng jiějué fāng'àn	MWS
Multiple-channel mobile communication system with automatic dialing	多信道自动拨号移动通信系统	Duōxìndào zìdòng bōhào yídòng tōngxìn xìtǒng	
Multiple-tuned antenna	复调谐天线	Fù tiáoxié tiānxiàn	MTA
Multiple-unit steerable array (antenna)	多元可控阵	Duōyuán kěkòng zhèn	MUSA
Multiplex	多路传输	Duōlù chuánshū	
Multiplex	多路复用	Duōlù fùyòng	MUX
Multiplex aggregate bit rate	复用集合比特率	Fùyòng jíhé bǐtè lǜ	
Multiplex and demultiplex	多路复用和多路分用	Duōlù fùyòng hé duōlù fēnyòng	MULDEX
Multiplex interface	多路复用接口	Duōlù fùyòng jiēkǒu	
Multiplex interface adapter	多路转换接口适配器	Duōlù zhuǎnhuàn jiēkǒu shìpèiqì	MIA
Multiplex link	多路复用链路	Duōlù fùyòng liànlù	
Multiplex modulation system	多路复用调制系统	Duōlù fùyòng tiáozhì xìtǒng	MMS
Multiplex section	复接段	Fùjiē duàn	MS
Multiplex section	复用段	Fùyòng duàn	MS
Multiplex section adaptation	复用段适配	Fùyòng duàn shìpèi	MSA
Multiplex section alarm indication signal	复用段告警指示	Fùyòng duàn gàojǐng zhǐshì	MS-AIS
Multiplex section alarm indication signal	复用段告警指示信号	Fùyòng duàn gàojǐng zhǐshì xìnhào	MS-AIS
Multiplex section automatic protection switching	复用段自动保护倒换	Fùyòng duàn zìdòng bǎohù dǎohuàn	MS-APS
Multiplex section data communications channel	复用段数据通信通道	Fùyòng duàn shùjù tōngxìn tōngdào	MS-DCC
Multiplex section network connection	复用段网络连接	Fùyòng duàn wǎngluò liánjiē	MS-NC
Multiplex section overhead	复接段开销	Fùjiē duàn kāixiao	MSOH
Multiplex section overhead	复用段开销	Fùyòng duàn kāixiao	MSOH
Multiplex section protection	复用段保护	Fùyòng duàn bǎohù	MSP
Multiplex section remote defect indication	复用段远端缺陷指示	Fùyòng duàn yuǎnduān quēxiàn zhǐshì	MS-RDI
Multiplex section remote error indication	复用段远端差错指示	Fùyòng duàn yuǎnduān chācuò zhǐshì	MS-REI
Multiplex section remote error indication	复用段远端误码指示	Fùyòng duàn yuǎnduān wùmǎ zhǐshì	MS-REI
Multiplex section remote error indicator	复用段远端差错指针	Fùyòng duàn yuǎnduān chācuò zhǐzhēn	MS-REI
Multiplex section terminating element	复用段终端元	Fùyòng duàn zhōngduān yuán	MSTE
Multiplex section termination	复用段终端	Fùyòng duàn zhōngduān	MST
Multiplex section termination	复用段终结	Fùyòng duàn zhōngjié	MST
Multiplex section termination function	复用段终端功能	Fùyòng duàn zhōngduān gōngnéng	MST
Multiplex section-shared protection ring	复用段共享保护环	Fùyòng duàn gòngxiǎng bǎohù huán	MS-SPRing
Multiplex segment far-end receive expiration	复用段远端接收失效	Fùyòng duàn yuǎnduān jiēshōu shīxiào	MS-FERE
Multiplex segment receive defect indicator	复用段接收缺陷指示	Fùyòng duàn jiēshōu quēxiàn zhǐshì	MS-RDI
Multiplex segment shared protection ring	复用段保护环	Fùyòng duàn bǎohù huán	MSPring
Multiplex signal, multiplexed signal	复用信号	Fùyòng xìnhào	
Multiplex stage protection	复用段保护	Fùyòng duàn bǎohù	MSP
Multiplexed packet network	多路传输包网络	Duōlù chuánshū bāo wǎngluò	MPN
Multiplexed packet network	多路复用分组网络	Duōlù fùyòng fēnzǔ wǎngluò	MPN
Multiplexer	多工器	Duōgōngqì	
Multiplexer	多路复用器	Duōlù fùyòngqì	MUX
Multiplexer	多路转换器	Duōlù zhuǎnhuànqì	MPX

Multiplexer	分流器	Fēnliúqì	
Multiplexer	复接设备	Fùjiē shèbèi	MUX
Multiplexer	复接器	Fùjiēqì	
Multiplexer	复用器	Fùyòngqì	MUX
Multiplexer channel	多路信道	Duōlù xìndào	
Multiplexer/demultiplexer	复接器 / 分接器	Fùjiēqì/fēnjiēqì	MUX/DEMUX
Multiplexer-demultiplexer	复用分用器	Fùyòng fēnyòngqì	Muldex
Multiplexing	多工	Duōgōng	
Multiplexing	多工化	Duōgōng huà	
Multiplexing	多工器分流	Duōgōngqì fēnliú	
Multiplexing	多路复接	Duōlù fùjiē	
Multiplexing	复用	Fùyòng	
Multiplexing gain	多路增益	Duōlù zēngyì	
Multiplexing identification	复用标志	Fùyòng biāozhì	MID
Multiplexing identification	复用标识	Fùyòng biāozhì	MID
Multiplicative array antenna system	乘积阵天线系统	Chéngjī zhèn tiānxiàn xìtǒng	MAAS
Multiplier	多倍仪	Duōbèiyí	
Multipoint	多点	Duōdiǎn	
Multipoint access	多点接入	Duōdiǎn jiērù	
Multipoint command conference	多点命令会议	Duōdiǎn mìnglìng huìyì	MCC
Multipoint command negotiation	多点命令协商	Duōdiǎn mìnglìng xiéshāng	MCN
Multipoint command service	多点命令服务	Duōdiǎn mìnglìng fúwù	MCS
Multipoint command symmetrical data transmission	多点命令相称性数据传输	Duōdiǎn mìnglìng xiāngchènxìng shùjù chuánshū	MCS
Multipoint communication service	多点通信服务	Duōdiǎn tōngxìn fúwù	MCS
Multipoint communication service access point	多点通信服务接入点	Duōdiǎn tōngxìn fúwù jiērùdiǎn	MCSAP
Multipoint conferencing unit	多点会议单元	Duōdiǎn huìyì dānyuán	MCU
Multipoint control unit	多点控制单元	Duōdiǎn kòngzhì dānyuán	MCU
Multipoint controller	多点控制器	Duōdiǎn kòngzhìqì	MC
Multipoint jamming	多点干扰	Duōdiǎn gānrǎo	
Multipoint processor	多点处理器	Duōdiǎn chǔlǐqì	MP
Multipoint to point tree	多点到点树	Duōdiǎn dào diǎn shù	MPT
Multipoint video distribution service	多点视频分配业务	Duōdiǎn shìpín fēnpèi yèwù	MVDS
Multipoint video distribution system	多点视频分配系统	Duōdiǎn shìpín fēnpèi xìtǒng	MVDS
Multi-port	多串口	Duōchuànkǒu	
Multi-port antenna	多端口天线	Duōduānkǒu tiānxiàn	
Multi-port network	多端网络	Duōduān wǎngluò	
Multi-port programmable communications interface	多端口可编程序通信接口	Duōduānkǒu kěbiān chéngxù tōngxìn jiēkǒu	MPCI
Multi-processor and multi-control unit	多点处理器及多点控制单元	Duōdiǎn chǔlǐqì jí duōdiǎn kòngzhì dānyuán	MP&MCU
Multi-processor architecture	多重处理器架构	Duōzhòng chǔlǐqì jiàgòu	MPA
Multi-processor specification	多处理器规范	Duōchǔlǐqì guīfàn	MPS
Multi-processor specification	多重处理器规范	Duōzhòng chǔlǐqì guīfàn	MPS
Multi-processor task	多处理机任务	Duōchǔlǐjī rènwu	
Multi-protocol	多协议	Duōxiéyì	
Multiprotocol border gateway protocol	多协议边缘网关协议	Duōxiéyì biānyuán wǎngguān xiéyì	MBGP
Multi-protocol communications controller	多协议通信控制器	Duōxiéyì tōngxìn kòngzhìqì	MPCC

Multi-protocol extension for BGP-4	多协议扩展的 BGP 协议	Duōxiéyì kuòzhǎnde BGP xiéyì	BGP-MP
Multi-protocol label switching	多协议标答交换	Duōxiéyì biāodá jiāohuàn	MPLS
Multi-protocol label switching	多协议标号交换	Duōxiéyì biāohào jiāohuàn	MPLS
Multi-protocol label switching	多协议标记交换	Duōxiéyì biāojì jiāohuàn	MPLS
Multi-protocol label switching	多协议标签交换	Duōxiéyì biāoqiān jiāohuàn	MPLS
Multi-protocol label switching	多协议标签协议	Duōxiéyì biāoqiān xiéyì	MPLS
Multi-protocol label switching	多协议标志交换	Duōxiéyì biāozhì jiāohuàn	MPLS
Multi-protocol over asynchronous transfer mode	ATM 上的多协议	ATM-shàngde duō xiéyì	MPOA
Multi-protocol over ATM	ATM 上的多协议规范	ATM-shàngde duō xiéyì guīfàn	MPOA
Multi-protocol over ATM (technology)	ATM 上的多协议(技术)	ATM-shàngde duō xiéyì (jìshù)	MPoA
Multi-protocol wavelength switching	多协议波长交换	Duōxiéyì bōcháng jiāohuàn	MPIS
Multi-protocol wavelength switching	多协议 λ 交换	Duōxiéyì λ jiāohuàn	MPLambdaS
Multi-pulse excitation linear predictive coding	多脉冲激励线性预测编码	Duōmàichōng jīlì xiànxìng yùcè biānmǎ	MPE-LPC
Multi-pulse jamming	多脉冲干扰	Duōmàichōng gānrǎo	
Multi-pulse linear prediction code	多脉冲线性预测编码	Duōmàichōng xiànxìng yùcè biānmǎ	MPLPC
Multi-purpose cadastre	多用途地籍簿	Duōyòngtú dìjíbù	
Multi-purpose internet mail extension	多用途因特网邮件扩展	Duōyòngtú Yīntèwǎng yóujiàn kuòzhǎn	MIME
Multipurpose Internet mail extensions	多用途的网际邮件扩充协议	Duōyòngtúde wǎngjì yóujiàn kuòchōng xiéyì	MIME
Multi-quantum well	多量子阱	Duōliàngzǐ jǐng	MQW
Multirate circuit switching	多速率电路交换	Duōsùlǜ diànlù jiāohuàn	
Multirate single pair digital subscriber loop	多速率单一线对数字用户环路	Duōsùlǜ dānyī xiànduì shùzì yònghù huánlù	MSDSL
Multirate symmetrical digital subscriber line	多速率对称数字用户线	Duōsùlǜ duìchèn shùzì yònghù xiàn	MSDSL
Multirate symmetrical digital subscriber loop	多速率对称数字用户环路	Duōsùlǜ duìchèn shùzì yònghù huánlù	MSDSL
Multi-resolution mesh (video term)	多重分辨率组合	Duōzhòng fēnbiànlǜ zǔhé	
Multi-reuse patterns	多复用模式	Duōfùyòng móshì	MRP
Multi-satellite link	多级卫星链路	Duōjí wèixīng liànlù	
Multi-satellite link	多卫星链路	Duōwèixīng liànlù	
Multi-scale database	多尺度数据库	Duōchǐdù shùjùkù	
Multiserver queue	多服务器队列	Duōfúwùqì duìliè	
Multi-service access module	多业务接入模块	Duōyèwù jiērù mókuài	MSA
Multi-service access network	多业务接入网	Duōyèwù jiērù wǎng	MSAN
Multi-service access nodes	多业务接入节点	Duōyèwù jiērù jiédiǎn	MAN
Multi-service access platform	多业务接入平台	Duōyèwù jiērù píngtái	MSAP
Multi-service access point	多业务接入点	Duōyèwù jiērùdiǎn	MSAP
Multi-service confluence point	多业务汇接点	Duōyèwù huìjiēdiǎn	MSCP
Multi-service fiber access platform	多服务光纤接入平台	Duōfúwù guāngxiān jiērù píngtái	
Multi-service gateway	多业务网关	Duōyèwù wǎngguān	MSG
Multi-service link layer	多业务链路层	Duōyèwù liànlùcéng	
Multi-service packet ring	多业务分组环	Duōyèwù fēnzǔ huán	MPR
Multi-service packet transmission platform	多业务分组传输平台	Duōyèwù fēnzǔ chuánshū píngtái	MXP
Multi-service platform	多业务平台	Duōyèwù píngtái	MP
Multi-service provider platform	多业务提供平台	Duōyèwù tígōng píngtái	MSPP
Multi-service provisioning platform	多业务供应平台	Duōyèwù gōngyìng píngtái	
Multi-service switching forum	多业务交换论坛	Duōyèwù jiāohuàn lùntán	MSF
Multi-service transmission platform	多业务传输节点	Duōyèwù chuánshū jiédiǎn	MSTP

English	Chinese	Pinyin	Abbreviation
Multi-service transport platform	多业务传输平台	Duōyèwù chuánshū píngtái	MSTP
Multi-slot operation	多时隙操作	Duōshíxì cāozuò	
Multi-spectral composite imagery	多光谱合成图像	Duōguāngpǔ héchéng túxiàng	
Multi-spectral remote sensing (GIS)	多波段遥感	Duōbōduàn yáogǎn	
Multi-spectral scanner	多光谱扫描仪	Duōguāngpǔ sǎomiáo yí	
Multi-speed-rate data (type of interface board)	多速率同步数据	Duōsùlǜ tóngbù shùjù	MSRD
Multi-stage interconnection network	多级互连网络	Duōjí hùlián wǎngluò	MIN
Multi-state modulation	多状态调制	Duōzhuàngtài tiáozhì	
Multi-statement table-valued functions (in SQL Server)	多声明表值型函数	Duō shēngmíng biǎozhíxíng hánshù	
Multi-static radar	多基地雷达	Duōjīdì léidá	
Multi-station access unit	多站访问单元	Duōzhàn fǎngwèn dānyuán	MAU
Multi-station teletex installation	多站智能用户电报装置	Duōzhàn zhìnéng yònghù diànbào zhuāngzhì	
Multi-step forming	多工步成形	Duōgōngbù chéngxíng	
Multi-stream data transmission interface	多路数据传输接口	Duōlù shùjù chuánshū jiēkǒu	MDTI
Multi-subscriber number	多用户号码	Duōyònghù hàomǎ	MSN
Multi-subscriber profile	多用户线路	Duōyònghù xiànlù	MSP
Multi-subscriber time shared (computer system)	多用户分时（计算机系统）	Duōyònghù fēnshí (jìsuànjī xìtǒng)	MSTS
Multi-subscriber unit	多用户单元	Duōyònghù dānyuán	
Multi-tasking	多工作业	Duōgōngzuò yè	
Multi-tasking	多任务	Duōrènwu	
Multi-temporal image	多时相图像	Duōshíxiàng túxiàng	
Multi-terminal service circuit	多终端公务电路	Duōzhōngduān gōngwù diànlù	
Multi-texture (video term)	多重纹理	Duōzhòng wénlǐ	
Multi-thread server	多线路服务器	Duōxiànlù fúwùqì	MTS
Multi-threaded server application	多线程服务器应用程序	Duōxiànchéng fúwùqì yìngyòng chéngxù	
Multi-threading	多工运作	Duōgōngyùn zuò	
Multi-threading	多线程	Duōxiànchéng	
Multi-tier architecture	多级体系	Duōjí tǐxì	
Multi-tool integration	多工具集成	Duōgōngjù jíchéng	
Multi-unit message	多单元消息	Duōdānyuán xiāoxi	MUM
Multi-unit steerable antenna	多单元可控天线	Duōdānyuán kěkòng tiānxiàn	MUSA
Multi-user	多用户	Duōyònghù	
Multi-user channel	多用户信道	Duōyònghù xìndào	
Multi-user detection	多用户检测	Duōyònghù jiǎncè	MUD
Multi-user information outlet	多用户信息插座	Duōyònghù xìnxī chāzuò	MIO
Multi-user mobile station	多用户移动台	Duōyònghù yídòngtái	MUMS
Multi-variate analysis	多元变量分析	Duōyuán biànliàng fēnxī	
Multi-variate spatial database	多元空间数据库	Duōyuán kōngjiān shùjùkù	
Multi-vendor network	多厂商网络	Duōchǎngshāng wǎngluò	
Multi-vibrator	多谐发生器	Duōxié fāshēngqì	
Multi-wavelength laser diode	多波长激光器	Duōbōcháng jīguāngqì	
Multi-wavelength laser source	多波长光源	Duōbōcháng guāngyuán	
Multi-wavelength optical network	多波长光网络	Duōbōcháng guāng wǎngluò	
Multi-wavelength transmission network	多波长传送网	Duōbōcháng chuánsòng wǎng	
Multi-window graphical interface	多窗口图文界面	Duōchuāngkǒu túwén jièmiàn	

Multi-wire element	多导线单元	Duō dǎoxiàn dānyuán	
Mult-link point-to-point protocol	多重链路点对点协议	Duōzhòng liànlù diǎn duì diǎn xiéyì	MultiPPP
Municipal service area	城域服务区	Chéngyù fúwùqū	
Mushroom database	蘑菇数据库	Mógu shùjùkù	
Musical instrument digital interface	乐器数位介面	Yuèqì shùwèi jièmiàn	MIDI
Musical instrument digital interface	乐器数字接口	Yuèqì shùzì jiēkǒu	MIDI
Mutable	可变的	Kěbiànde	
Mutation engine	变体引擎	Biàntǐ yǐnqíng	
Mutation operator	变异算子	Biànyì suànzǐ	
Mute tuning	静噪调谐	Jìngzào tiáoxié	
Mutex, mutual exclusion object	互斥元	Hùchì yuán	
Mutex, mutual exclusion object	互斥体	Hùchìtǐ	
Mutilation	损伤	Sǔnshāng	
Muting	噪声抑制	Zàoshēng yìzhì	
Mutual assistance control signal	互助控制信号	Hùzhù kòngzhì xìnhào	
Mutual assistance logic	互助逻辑	Hùzhù luóji	
Mutual control logic	互控逻辑	Hùkòng luóji	
Mutual exclusion object, mutex	互斥元	Hùchì yuán	
Mutual exclusion object, mutex	互斥体	Hùchìtǐ	
Mutual impedance	互相抗	Hùxiāng kàng	
Mutual impedance (of antenna elements)	互阻抗	Hùzǔkàng	
Mutual recognition agreements	相互认可协议	Xiānghù rènkě xiéyì	MRA
Mutually suspicious (IPsec)	互疑	Hùyí	
Mutually synchronized network	互同步网	Hùtóngbù wǎng	
MU-type connecter	MU 型连接器	MU-xíng liánjiēqì	
MU-type connector series	MU 型连接器系列	MU-xíng liánjiēqì xìliè	
Myriametric wave communication	超长波通信	Chāochángbō tōngxìn	

N

N scope	N 型显示器	N-xíng xiǎnshìqì	
N value	N 值	N-zhí	
Nak attack (Ipsec, attack based on 'negative acknowledge' or NAK message)	无防备攻击	Wúfángbèi gōngjī	
Name binding	名结合	Míng jiéhé	
Name binding protocol	名字绑定协议	Míngzì bǎngdìng xiéyì	NBP
Name binding protocol (Apple usage)	名称绑定协议	Míngchēng bǎngdìng xiéyì	NBP
Name caching	名字高速缓存	Míngzì gāosù huǎncún	
Name phrasing	名称句式	Míngchēng jùshì	
Named instance	命名实例	Mìngmíng shílì	
Named parameter	命名参数	Mìngmíng cānshù	
Named pipe	命名管道	Mìngmíng guǎndào	
Named set	命名集	Mìngmíng jí	
Namespace	命名空间	Mìngmíng kōngjiān	
Namespace	名字空间	Míngzì kōngjiān	
Naming domain	命名域	Mìngmíng yù	
Naming relationship	命名关系	Mìngmíng guānxi	
Naming tree	命名树	Mìngmíng shù	

N-AND gate	“与非”门	Yǔfēi mén	
Nanjing Walsin Fujikura Optical Communications Co. Ltd.	南京华新藤仓光通信有限公司	Nánjīng huá-xīn téngcāng guāng tōngxìn yǒuxiàn gōngsī	
Nano- (prefix meaning 10^{-9})	毫微	Háowēi	N
Nano- (prefix meaning 10^{-9})	纳	Nà	
Nanometer	纳米	Nàmǐ	
Nanosecond	毫微秒	Háowēimiǎo	NS
Nanotechnology	纳米技术	Nàmǐ jìshù	
Nanotechnology (Singapore usage)	那诺科技	Nà-nuò kējì	
Narrowband	窄带	Zhǎidài	
Narrowband data link (line)	窄带数据链(线路)	Zhǎidài shùjù liàn (xiànlù)	NBDL
Narrowband device	窄带器件	Zhǎidài qìjiàn	
Narrowband device	窄带设备	Zhǎidài shèbèi	
Narrowband emission	窄带发射	Zhǎidài fāshè	
Narrowband frequency modulation	窄带调频	Zhǎidài tiáopín	NFM
Narrowband frequency modulation	窄带调制	Zhǎidài tiáozhì	NBFM
Narrowband integrated services digital network	窄带综合业务数字网	Zhǎidài zōnghé yèwù shùzì wǎng	N-ISDN
Narrowband integrated services digital network	窄带综合业务网	Zhǎidài zōnghé yèwù wǎng	N-ISDN
Narrowband interference	窄带干扰	Zhǎidài gānrǎo	
Narrowband ISDN user part	窄带 ISDN 用户部分	Zhǎidài ISDN yònghù bùfen	N-ISUP
Narrowband passive optical network	窄带无源光网络	Zhǎidài wúyuán guāng wǎngluò	NPON
Narrowband phase modulation	窄带调相	Zhǎidài tiáoxiàng	NBPM
Narrowband process	窄带(频)过程	Zhǎidài (pin) guòchéng	
Narrowband quadrature frequency shift keying	窄带正交移频键控	Zhǎidài zhèngjiāo yípín jiànkòng	N-QFSK
Narrowband quadrature phase shift keying	窄带正交移相键控	Zhǎidài zhèngjiāo yíxiàng jiànkòng	N-QPSK
Narrowband time division multiple access	窄频带时分多路存取	Zhǎipíndài shífēn duōlù cúnqǔ	NBTDMA
Narrowcast; narrowcasting	窄带广播	Zhǎidài guǎngbō	
N-ary digit	n 进制数字	n-jìnzhì shùzì	
N-ary digit	n 进制位	n-jìnzhì wèi	
n-ary digital group	数字 *n* 次群	Shùzì *n*-cì qún	
N-ary digital signal	n 进制数字信号	n-jìnzhì shùzì xìnhào	
n-ary digital signaling	*n* 进制数字信令	*n*-jìnzhì shùzì xìnlìng	
NASDAQ	美国第二级股市	Měiguó dì'èrjí gǔshì	
NASDAQ	那斯达克	Nà-sī-dá-kè	
National (Mobile Communications) Network Management Center	全国(移动通信)操作维护中心	Quánguó (yídòng tōngxìn) cāozuò wéihù zhōngxīn	NNMC
National Aeronautics and Space Administration (US)	国家航空航天局	Guójiā hángkōng hángtiān jú	NASA
National area message	国内地区使用消息	Guónèi dìqū shǐyòng xiāoxi	NAM
National Board for Industrial and Technical Development (Sweden)	瑞典国立工业和技术发展委员会制订	Ruìdiǎn guólì gōngyè hé jìshù fāzhǎn wěiyuánhuì zhìdìng	NBITD
National Bureau of Standards (US)	国家标准局	Guójiā Biāozhǔnjú	NBS
National Cable Television Association (US)	美国电缆电视协会	Měiguó diànlǎn diànshì xiéhuì	NCTA
National call supervision message	国内呼叫监视消息	Guónèi hūjiào jiānshì xiāoxi	NCB
National Center for Geographic Information and Analysis	国家地理信息与分析中心	Guójiā dìlǐ xìnxī yǔ fēnxī zhōngxīn	NCGIA

National Center for Intelligent Computing	国家智能计算机研究开发中心	Guójiā zhìnéng jìsuànjī yánjiū kāifā zhōngxīn	NCIC
National Center for Supercomputing Applications (US)	国家超级计算应用中心	Guójiā chāojí jìsuàn yìngyòng zhōngxīn	NCSA
National Committee for Digital Cartographic Data Standards	数字制图数据标准国家委员会	Shùzì zhìtú shùjù biāozhǔn guójiā wěiyuánhuì	NCDCDS
National compensation	国家赔偿	Guójiā péicháng	
National Computer Board	国家电脑局	Guójiā diànnǎo jú	NCB
National Computer Security Association	国家计算机安全协会	Guójiā jìsuànjī ānquán xiéhuì	NCSA
National Computer Security Center (US)	国家计算机安全中心	Guójiā jìsuànjī ānquán zhōngxīn	NCSC
National destination code	本国目的代码	Běnguó mùdì dàimǎ	
National destination code	国家目的码	Guójiā mùdì mǎ	NDC
National destination code	国家终点局代码	Guójiā zhōngdiǎnjú dàimǎ	NDC
National destination code	国内目的地码	Guónèi mùdìdì mǎ	NDC
National destination code	国内终点号码	Guónèi zhōngdiǎn hàomǎ	NDC
National Digital Cartographic Data Base	国家数字制图数据库	Guójiā shùzì zhìtú shùjùkù	NDCDB
National Geodetic Reference System (US)	国家测量参照系	Guójiā cèliáng cānzhàoxì	NGRS
National Geographic Directorate	国家地理管理局	Guójiā dìlǐ guǎnlǐjú	NGD
National Geological Library (China)	国家地质图书馆	Guójiā dìzhì túshūguǎn	NGL
National Geospatial Database	国家地理空间数据库	Guójiā dìlǐ kōngjiān shùjùkù	NGD
National grid	国家格网	Guójiā géwǎng	NG
National information infrastructure	国家信息基础结构	Guójiā xìnxī jīchǔ jiégòu	NII
National Information Infrastructure	国家信息基础设施	Guójiā xìnxī jīchǔ shèshī	NII
National Information Infrastructure	全国资讯体系	Quánguó zīxùn tǐxì	NII
National Information Security Assessment and Authentication Center	国家信息安全测评认证中心	Guójiā xìnxī ānquán cèpíng rènzhèng zhōngxīn	
National Institute of Standards and Technology (US)	国家标准技术研究所	Guójiā biāozhǔn jìshù yánjiūsuǒ	NIST
National land policy	国土政策	Guótǔ zhèngcè	
National language support	国家语言支持	Guójiā yǔyán zhīchí	NLS
National main section	国内主段	Guónèi zhǔduàn	
National Map Accuracy Standards (US)	国家地图精度标准	Guójiā dìtú jīngdù biāozhǔn	NMAS
National map grid	国家地图方里网	Guójiā dìtú fānglǐ wǎng	
National mobile station identification number	国家移动台识别号	Guójiā yídòngtái shíbiéhào	NMSI
National mobile station identifier	国家移动台标识符	Guójiā yídòngtái biāozhìfú	NMSI
National mobile station identity	国内移动台识别号码	Guónèi yídòngtái shíbié hàomǎ	NMSI
National Network Management Center	全国网络管理中心	Quánguó wǎngluò guǎnlǐ zhōngxīn	NNMC
National number	国内号码	Guónèi hàomǎ	NN
National Oceanic and Atmospheric Administration (US)	国家海洋与大气署	Guójiā hǎiyáng yǔ dàqì shǔ	NOAA
National Packet-Switched Data Transmission System	全国包交换数据传输系统	Quánguó bāo jiāohuàn shùjù chuánshū xìtǒng	NPSS
National processing Center	国家处理中心	Guójiā chǔlǐ zhōngxīn	NPC
National processing center (in the finance network)	国家处理中心	Guójiā chǔlǐ zhōngxīn	NPC
National Public Switched Telecommunications Network	国家公共交换电信网	Guójiā gōnggòng jiāohuàn diànxìn wǎng	NPSIN
National Research and Education Network	国家科研教育网络	Guójiā kēyán jiàoyù wǎngluò	NREN
National road class	国道等级	Guódào děngjí	
National Science Foundation (US)	国家科学基金会	Guójiā Kēxué Jījīnhuì	NSF
National Science Foundation Network (US)	国家科学基金会网络	Guójiā Kēxué Jījīnhuì wǎngluò	NSFnet

National Security Agency (US)	国家安全局	Guójiā ānquán jú	NSA
National Semiconductor (US company)	国家半导体	Guójiā bàndǎotǐ	
National signaling point	国内信令点	Guónèi xìnlìng diǎn	NSP
National successful backward set-up message	国内后向建立成功消息	Guónèi hòuxiàng jiànlì chénggōng xiāoxi	NSB
National Television Standard Committee	国家电视标准委员会	Guójiā diànshì biāozhǔn wěiyuánhuì	NTSC
National Television Systems Committee (US television broadcast standard)	全国电视系统委员会制式	Quánguó diànshì xìtǒng wěiyuánhuì zhìshì	NTSC
National transfer format	国家传输格式	Guójiā chuánshū géshi	NTF
National unsuccessful backward set-up message	国内后向建立不成功消息	Guónèi hòuxiàng jiànlì bùchénggōng xiāoxi	NUB
National use	国内使用	Guónèi shǐyòng	NU
National user/user identification module identifier	国家用户/普通用户识别模块标识符	Guójiā yònghù/pǔtōng yònghù shíbié mókuài biāozhì fú	NUI
National-network-congestion signal	国内网拥塞信号	Guónèi wǎng yōngsè xìnhào	NNC
Nation-wide Technical Standardization Committee of geographic Information	全国地理信息标准化技术委员会	Quánguó dìlǐ xìnxī biāozhǔnhuà jìshù wěiyuánhuì	
Native	本地的	Běndìde	
Native	原生的	Yuánshēngde	
Native client interface architecture	本地客户接口结构	Běndì kèhù jiēkǒu jiégòu	NCIA
Native code	本地码	Běndì mǎ	
Native code	本机码	Běnjī mǎ	
Native format	本机格式	Běnjī géshi	
Native image generator	本地映像生成器	Běndì yìngxiàng shēngchéngqì	NGEN
Native mode	本机模式	Běnjī móshì	
Native mode usage	本机操作模式	Běnjī cāozuò móshì	NMU
Natural binary-coded decimal	自然二进制编码的十进制	Zìrán èrjìnzhì biānmǎde shíjìnzhì	NBCD
Natural binary-coded hexadecimal	自然二进制编码的十六进制	Zìrán èrjìnzhì biānmǎde shíliùjìnzhì	NBCH
Natural bit (nat)	奈特	Nàitè	
Natural climate test	天然气候试验	Tiānrán qìhòu shìyàn	
Natural convection	自然对流	Zìrán duìliú	
Natural cooling	自然冷却	Zìrán lěngquè	
Natural frequency	自然频率	Zìrán pínlǜ	
Natural frequency (in a cavity resonator)	固有频率	Gùyǒu pínlǜ	
Natural interference	自然干扰	Zìrán gānrǎo	
Natural keyboard	工学键盘	Gōngxué jiànpán	
Natural language Chinese query interface	自然语言汉语查询界面	Zìrán yǔyán hànyǔ cháxún jièmiàn	NLCQI
Natural language processing	自然语言处理	Zìrán yǔyán chǔlǐ	
Natural language processing	自然语言理解	Zìrán yǔyán lǐjiě	NLP
Natural noise	自然噪声	Zìrán zàoshēng	
Natural period	固有周期	Gùyǒu zhōuqī	
Natural radiator	自然辐射源	Zìrán fúshèyuán	
Natural resonance frequency	自然谐振频率	Zìrán xiézhèn pínlǜ	
Natural space radiation	自然空间辐射	Zìrán kōngjiān fúshè	
Naturalness of speech	语言自然度	Yǔyán zìrándù	
Nature of address indicator	地址性质表示语	Dìzhǐ xìngzhì biǎoshì yǔ	NAI
Nature of address indicator	地址指示器的特性	Dìzhǐ zhǐshìqìde tèxìng	NAI
Nature of connection indicators	连接特性	Liánjiē tèxìng	
Naval electronic warfare system	舰载电子战系统	Jiànzài diànzǐzhàn xìtǒng	

Navigation	导航	Dǎoháng	
Navigation model	导航模型	Dǎoháng móxíng	
Navigator	导览器	Dǎolǎnqì	
Navigator ® (Netscape software product)	引航者	Yǐnhángzhě	
Navy technological forecast	海军技术预测	Hǎijūn jìshù yùcè	NTF
N-bit byte	n 比特字节	n-bǐtè zìjié	
N-bit byte	n 位字节	n-wèi zìjié	
NBMA address resolution protocol (IETF use)	NBMA 地址解析协议	NBMA dìzhǐ jiěxī xiéyì	NARP
N-condition frequency shift keying	n 态频移键控	n-tài pínyí jiànkòng	n-FSK
Near letter quality	近打字效果	Jìn dǎzì xiàoguǒ	NLQ
Near video on demand	准点播电视	Zhǔn diǎnbō diànshì	NVOD
Near video on demand	准影视点播	Zhǔn yǐngshì diǎnbō	NVOD
Near-end background block error	近端背景误块	Jìnduān bèijǐng wùkuài	NBBE
Near-end cross talk	近端串音	Jìnduān chuànyīn	NEXT
Near-end crosstalk	近端串话	Jìnduān chuànhuà	NEC
Near-end crosstalk	近端串扰	Jìnduān chuànrǎo	NEXT
Near-end crosstalk attenuation power sum	近端串音衰减功率和	Jìnduān chuànyīn shuāijiǎn gōnglǜ hé	PSNEXT
Near-end crosstalk power sum	近端串音功率和	Jìnduān chuànyīn gōnglǜ hé	PSNEXT
Near-end defective second	近端缺陷秒	Jìnduān quēxiàn miǎo	NDS
Near-end echo suppressor	近端回波抑制器	Jìnduān huíbō yìzhìqì	NES
Near-end error block counter	近端误块计数	Jìnduān wùkuài jìshù	NEBC
Near-end errored second	近端误块秒	Jìnduān wùkuài miǎo	NES
Near-end severely errored second	近端严重误块秒	Jìnduān yánzhòng wùkuài miǎo	NSES
Near-end subscriber access	近端用户接入	Jìnduān yònghù jiērù	SA-N
Near-end subscriber installation	近端用户设备	Jìnduān yònghù shèbèi	SI-N
Nearest active upstream neighbor	最近的,运行着的上行邻居	Zuìjìnde, yùnxíngzhede shàngxíng línjū	NAUM
Nearest feature line (CAD/CAM)	最近特征线	Zuìjìn tèzhēng xiàn	NFL
Nearest Mipmap (video term)	邻近 MIP 映射	Línjìn MIP yìngshè	
Nearest neighbor	最近邻域	Zuìjìn línyù	
Nearest neighbor (CAD/CAM)	最近邻	Zuìjìn lín	NN
Nearest neighbor search	最近点对查询	Zuìjìn diǎn duì cháxún	
Near-field pattern	近场图	Jìnchǎng tú	NFP
Near-field region	近场区	Jìnchǎng qū	
Near-infrared photodiode	近红外光光二极体	Jìn hóngwàiguāng guāng èrjítǐ	
Necessary and sufficient condition	充分必要条件	Chōngfèn bìyào tiáojiàn	
Necessary bandwidth	必要带宽	Bìyào dàikuān	
Negative acknowledge	否认字符	Fǒurèn zìfú	NAK
Negative acknowledge	消极确认	Xiāojí quèrèn	NAK
Negative acknowledgement	错误应答	Cuòwù yìngdá	NACK
Negative association rule	负关联规则	Fùguānlián guīzé	
Negative caching	相反缓存	Xiāngfǎn huǎncún	
Negative electrode	负极	Fùjí	
Negative feedback	负反馈	Fùfǎnkuì	
Negative friction	负摩擦	Fùmócā	
Negative functional feature (CAD/CAM)	负功能特征	Fùgōngnéng tèzhēng	
Negative ion	负离子	Fùlízǐ	

Negative justification	负码速调整	Fùmăsù tiáozhěng	
Negative logic	负逻辑	Fùluóji	
Negative mismatching	负失配	Fùshīpèi	
Negative password check	否定的口令检验	Fǒudìngde kǒulìng jiǎnyàn	
Negative printing amount percent	负印量差	Fùyìnliáng chà	
Negative pulse stuffing	负脉冲塞入	Fùmàichōng sāirù	
Negative resistance amplifier	负阻放大器	Fùzǔ fàngdàqì	
Negative resistance effect	负阻效应	Fùzǔ xiàoyìng	
Negative resistance oscillation	负阻振荡	Fùzǔ zhèndàng	
Negative temperature coefficient	负温度系数	Fùwēndù xìshù	NTC
Negative-pressure head	负压水头	Fùyā shuǐtóu	
Neighbor acquisition	邻机探测	Línjī tàncè	
Neighbor cell	邻小区	Línxiǎoqū	
Neighbor cell definition table	邻小区列表	Línxiǎoqū lièbiǎo	
Neighbor discovery protocol	邻机发现协议	Línjī fāxiàn xiéyì	NDP
Neighbor information frame	相邻站点信息帧	Xiānglín zhàndiǎn xìnxī zhèng	NIF
Neighbor reachability	邻机可达性	Línjī kědáxìng	
Neighbor station advice	邻站通知	Línzhàn tōngzhī	NN
Neighborhood analysis	邻域分析	Línyù fēnxī	
Neighborhood discovery	寻找邻居	Xúnzhǎo línjū	ND
Neighborhood discovery daemon	寻找邻居守护程序	Xúnzhǎo línjū shǒuhù chéngxù	
Neighborhood query	邻域查询	Línyù cháxún	
Neighboring cell	相邻小区	Xiānglín xiǎoqū	NCELL
Neighboring channel interference protection ratio	邻频干扰保护比	Línpín gānrǎo bǎohùbǐ	
Neighboring mobile access point	相邻移动接入点	Xiānglín yídòng jiērù diǎn	NMAP
Neighboring router	邻近路由器	Línjìn lùyóuqì	
Neighboring service area	相邻业务区	Xiānglín yèwù qū	
Neotechnology	新技术	Xīn jìshù	
Neper (unit of attenuation, =8.686 dB)	奈培	Nài-péi	NP
Nerd, technonerd	电脑迷	Diànnǎo mí	
Nested class	巢状类别	Cháozhuàng lèibié	
Nested class	嵌套类	Qiàntào lèi	
Nested dynamic fault-tolerant protocol	嵌套动态容错协议	Qiàntào dòngtài róngcuò xiéyì	
Nested query (for database)	嵌套查询	Qiàntào cháxún	
Nested table (for database)	嵌套表	Qiàntào biǎo	
Nesting	嵌套	Qiàntào	
Net etiquette; netiquette	网络礼仪	Wǎngluò lǐyí	
NetBIOS extended user interface	网络基本输入/输出系统扩展用户接口	Wǎngluò jīběn shūrù/shūchū xìtǒng kuòzhǎn yònghù jiēkǒu	NetBEUI
NetBIOS extended user interface (IBM usage)	NetBIOS 扩展用户接口	NetBIOS kuòzhǎn yònghù jiēkǒu	NetBEUI
Netiquette	网规	Wǎngguī	
Net-library (in SQL Server)	网络库	Wǎngluò kù	
NetMonkey (website software)	往猴	Wǎnghóu	
Netscape ® browser	网景浏览器	Wǎngjǐng liúlǎnqì	
Netscape Corporation	网景公司	Wǎngjǐng gōngsī	
Netscape Navigator ©	网景导览器	Wǎngjǐng dǎolǎnqì	

Net-shaped reflecting surface	网状反射面	Wǎngzhuàng fǎnshè miàn	
Netted radar system	雷达网系统	Léidá wǎng xìtǒng	
Netware	网件	Wǎngjiàn	
NetWare link services protocol	NetWare 链路服务协议	NetWare liànlù fúwù xiéyì	NLSP
NetWare link state protocol (Novell usage)	NetWare 链路服务协议	NetWare liànlù fúwù xiéyì	NLSP
NetWare loadable module	NetWare 可装入模块	NetWare kězhuāngrù mókuài	NLM
Network	网络	Wǎngluò	
Network (mainly Taiwan usage)	网路	Wǎnglù	
Network access controller	网络接入控制器	Wǎngluò jiērù kòngzhìqì	NAC
Network access identifier	网络接入标识符	Wǎngluò jiērù biāozhì fú	NAI
Network access point	网络访问点	Wǎngluò fǎngwèn diǎn	NAP
Network access point	网络接入点	Wǎngluò jiērù diǎn	
Network access server	网络访问服务器	Wǎngluò fǎngwèn fúwùqì	NAS
Network access server	网络接入服务器	Wǎngluò jiērù fúwùqì	NAS
Network adapter	网络适配器	Wǎngluò shìpèiqì	NA
Network addess transform	网址变换	Wǎngzhǐ biànhuàn	NAT
Network address	网络地址	Wǎngluò dìzhǐ	
Network address block	网络地址块	Wǎngluò dìzhǐ kuài	NAB
Network address port translation	网络地址端口转换	Wǎngluò dìzhǐ duānkǒu zhuǎnhuàn	NAPT
Network address port translation	网络地址及端口转换	Wǎngluò dìzhǐ jí duānkǒu zhuǎnhuàn	NAPT
Network address translation	网络地址解析	Wǎngluò dìzhǐ jiěxī	NAT
Network address translation	网络地址转换	Wǎngluò dìzhǐ zhuǎnhuàn	NAT
Network address translation/protocol translation (in IPv6)	网络地址转换/协议转换技术	Wǎngluò dìzhǐ zhuǎnhuàn/ xiéyì zhuǎnhuàn jìshù	NAT-PT
Network address translator	网络地址翻译器	Wǎngluò dìzhǐ fānyìqì	NAT
Network address translator	网络地址转换器	Wǎngluò dìzhǐ zhuǎnhuànqì	NAT
Network addressable unit (IBM usage)	网络可寻址单元	Wǎngluò kěxúnzhǐ dānyuán	NAU
Network addressing domain	网络编址域	Wǎngluò biānzhǐ yù	
Network administration	网络行政管理	Wǎngluò xíngzhèng guǎnlǐ	
Network analysis	网络分析	Wǎngluò fēnxī	
Network analysis point	网络分析点	Wǎngluò fēnxī diǎn	
Network analysis system	网络分析系统	Wǎngluò fēnxī xìtǒng	
Network and switch management	网络与交换管理	Wǎngluò yǔ jiāohuàn guǎnlǐ	NSM
Network and trunk control	网络及总线控制	Wǎngluò jí zǒngxiàn kòngzhì	NTC
Network appearance	网络外貌	Wǎngluò wàimào	
Network application service	网络应用业务	Wǎngluò yìngyòng yèwù	
Network application software	网络应用软件	Wǎngluò yìngyòng ruǎnjiàn	
Network architecture	网络体系结构	Wǎngluò tǐxì jiégòu	
Network architecture 7-layer model (the OSI reference model)	网络结构的七层模型	Wǎngluò jiégòude qī céng móxíng	
Network Associates (US company)	网络联盟	Wǎngluò liánméng	
Network attached storage	附网存储	Fùwǎng cúnchǔ	NAS
Network attached storage	网络存储设备	Wǎngluò cúnchǔ shèbèi	NAS
Network attached storage	网络附加存储	Wǎngluò fùjiā cúnchǔ	NAS
Network attached storage	网络连接存储	Wǎngluò liánjiē cúnchǔ	NAS
Network basic input output system (IBM usage)	网络基本输入输出系统	Wǎngluò jīběn shūrù shūchū xìtǒng	NetBIOS
Network basic input/output system	网络基本输入/输出系统	Wǎngluò jīběn shūrù/shūchū xìtǒng	NetBIOS

Network call controller	网络呼叫控制器	Wǎngluò hūjiào kòngzhìqì	NCC
Network capability gateway	网络能力网关	Wǎngluò nénglì wǎngguān	
Network card	网卡	Wǎngkǎ	
Network centric computing	网络中心计算	Wǎngluò zhōngxīn jìsuàn	
Network chain; network link	网络链	Wǎngluò liàn	
Network color code	网络色码	Wǎngluò sèmǎ	NCC
Network communication access method	网络通信访问法	Wǎngluò tōngxìn fǎngwèn fǎ	NCAM
Network compiler simulation program	网络编译程序的仿真程序	Wǎngluò biānyì chéngxùde fǎngzhēn chéngxù	NCSP
Network computer	网络计算机	Wǎngluò jìsuànjī	NC
Network computing	网络计算	Wǎngluò jìsuàn	
Network configuration management	网络配置管理	Wǎngluò pèizhì guǎnlǐ	
Network configuration management	网络组成管理	Wǎngluò zǔchéng guǎnlǐ	NCM
Network congestion	网络拥挤	Wǎngluò yōngjǐ	
Network connect block	网络连接块	Wǎngluò liánjiē kuài	NCB
Network connection	网络连接	Wǎngluò liánjiē	NC
Network control center	网络控制中心	Wǎngluò kòngzhì zhōngxīn	NCC
Network control hand-off	网络控制切换	Wǎngluò kòngzhì qiēhuàn	NCHO
Network control key	网络控制键	Wǎngluò kòngzhì jiàn	NCK
Network control protocol	网络控制协议	Wǎngluò kòngzhì xiéyì	NCP
Network control unit	网络控制单元	Wǎngluò kòngzhì dānyuán	NCU
Network core protocol (Novell usage)	网络核心协议	Wǎngluò héxīn xiéyì	NCP
Network coverage	网络图层	Wǎngluò túcéng	
Network data link control	网络数据链控制	Wǎngluò shùjù liàn kòngzhì	NDLC
Network data management protocol	网络数据管理协议	Wǎngluò shùjù guǎnlǐ xiéyì	NDMP
Network data model	网状数据模型	Wǎngzhuàng shùjù móxíng	
Network default	网络默认值	Wǎngluò mòrèn zhí	ND
Network defense	网络防卫	Wǎngluò fángwèi	ND
Network design and management system	网络设计和管理系统	Wǎngluò shèjì hé guǎnlǐ xìtǒng	NDMS
Network determined user busy	网络决定用户忙	Wǎngluò juédìng yònghù máng	NDUB
Network determined user busy	网络确定用户忙	Wǎngluò quèdìng yònghù máng	NDUB
Network determited user busy	确定网络用户忙	Quèdìng wǎngluò yònghù máng	NDUP
Network digit	网络数字	Wǎngluò shùzì	ND
Network directed criteria	网络指定判据	Wǎngluò zhǐdìng pànjù	
Network directed system selection	网络指示的系统选择	Wǎngluò zhǐshìde xìtǒng xuǎnzé	NDSS
Network driver interface specification	网络驱动程序接口规范	Wǎngluò qūdòng chéngxù jiēkǒu guīfàn	NDIS
Network driver interface specification	网络驱动器接口规范	Wǎngluò qūdòngqì jiēkǒu guīfàn	NDIS
Network dynamic data exchange	网络动态数据交换	Wǎngluò dòngtài shùjù jiāohuàn	NetDDE
Network echo cancellation	网络回音消除	Wǎngluò huíyīn xiāochú	ECAN
Network element	网络单元	Wǎngluò dānyuán	NE
Network element	网络元素	Wǎngluò yuánsù	
Network element	网元	Wǎngyuán	NE
Network element function	网络单元功能	Wǎngluò dānyuán gōngnéng	NEF
Network element function	网元功能	Wǎngyuán gōngnéng	NEF
Network element function block	网络单元功能块	Wǎngluò dānyuán gōngnéng kuài	NEF
Network element layer	网元层	Wǎngyuán céng	NEL
Network element level	网元层	Wǎngyuán céng	NEL

Network element log	网络单元登录	Wǎngluò dānyuán dēnglù	
Network element management system	网元管理系统	Wǎngyuán guǎnlǐ xìtǒng	NEMS
Network element resources control	网络单元资源控制	Wǎngluò dānyuán zīyuán kòngzhì	RCne
Network element transit delay	网元转接延时	Wǎngyuán zhuǎnjiē yánshí	
Network entity identifier	网络实体标识符	Wǎngluò shítǐ biāozhìfú	NEI
Network entity title	网络实体名称	Wǎngluò shítǐ míngchēng	NET
Network equipment	网络设备	Wǎngluò shèbèi	NE
Network error management facilities	网络错误管理设施	Wǎngluò cuòwù guǎnlǐ shèshī	NEMF
Network evaluated handover	判断网络切换	Pànduàn wǎngluò qiēhuàn	NEHO
Network facility extensions	网络设施扩展	Wǎngluò shèshī kuòzhǎn	NFE
Network fault management	网络故障管理	Wǎngluò gùzhàng guǎnlǐ	
Network file access protocol	网络文件访问存取协议	Wǎngluò wénjiàn fǎngwèn cúnqǔ xiéyì	NFAP
Network file system	网络文件系统	Wǎngluò wénjiàn xìtǒng	NFS
Network flow	网络流	Wǎngluò liú	
Network function	网络功能	Wǎngluò gōngnéng	NF
Network graphics protocol	网络图解协议	Wǎngluò tújiě xiéyì	NGP
Network hosting	网络托管	Wǎngluò tuōguǎn	
Network identification	网络标识	Wǎngluò biāozhì	NID
Network identity	网络识别码	Wǎngluò shíbié mǎ	NID
Network identity and time zone	网络识别和时域	Wǎngluò shíbié hé shíyù	NITZ
Network image	网络图	Wǎngluò túxiàng	
Network independent clocking	网络独立同步	Wǎngluò dúlì tóngbù	NIC
Network indicator	网络表示语	Wǎngluò biǎoshì yǔ	NI
Network induced location request	导致网络定位请求	Dǎozhì wǎngluò dìngwèi qǐngqiú	NI-LR
Network information and control exchange protocol (in DECnet)	网络信息和控制交换协议	Wǎngluò xìnxī hé kòngzhì jiāohuàn xiéyì	NICE
Network information center	网络信息中心	Wǎngluò xìnxī zhōngxīn	NIC
Network information files	网络信息文件	Wǎngluò xìnxī wénjiàn	NIF
Network information system	网络信息服务	Wǎngluò xìnxī fúwù	NIS
Network integration	网络集成	Wǎngluò jíchéng	
Network integrator	网络综合器	Wǎngluò zōnghéqì	NI
Network integrity control system	网络统一控制系统	Wǎngluò tǒngyī kòngzhì xìtǒng	NICS
Network interconnect function	网络互连功能	Wǎngluò hùlián gōngnéng	NIF
Network interface	网络接口	Wǎngluò jiēkǒu	NI
Network interface adapter	网络接口传接器	Wǎngluò jiēkǒu chuánjiēqì	NIA
Network interface card	网络接口卡	Wǎngluò jiēkǒu kǎ	NIC
Network interface controller	网络接口控制器	Wǎngluò jiēkǒu kòngzhìqì	NIC
Network interface element	网络接口单元	Wǎngluò jiēkǒu dānyuán	NIE
Network interface unit	网络接口单元	Wǎngluò jiēkǒu dānyuán	NIU
Network interworking	网络互连	Wǎngluò hùlián	
Network interworking	网络互通	Wǎngluò hùtōng	
Network intrusion detection system	网络入侵检测系统	Wǎngluò rùqīn jiǎncè xìtǒng	
Network layer	网络层	Wǎngluò céng	
Network layer control protocol	网络层控制协议	Wǎngluò céng kòngzhì xiéyì	NCP
Network layer protocol identifier	网络层协议标识符	Wǎngluò céng xiéyì biāozhì fú	NLPI
Network layer service access point identifier	网络层业务接入点标识符	Wǎngluò céng yèwù jiērùdiǎn biāozhìfú	NSAPI
Network layer topology configurator	网络层拓扑结构	Wǎngluò céng tuòpū jiégòu	NLTC

Network level aggregation identifer	网络级聚集标识符	Wǎngluò jí jùjí biāozhìfú	NLAID
Network management	网管	Wǎngguǎn	NM
Network management	网络管理	Wǎngluò guǎnlǐ	NM
Network management center	网管中心	Wǎngguǎn zhōngxīn	NMC
Network management center	网络管理中心	Wǎngluò guǎnlǐ zhōngxīn	NMC
Network management forum	网络管理论坛	Wǎngluò guǎnlǐ lùntán	NMF
Network management interface	网管接口	Wǎngguǎn jiēkǒu	NMI
Network management layer	网络管理层	Wǎngluò guǎnlǐ céng	NML
Network management layer topology configurator	网络管理层拓扑结构	Wǎngluò guǎnlǐ céng tuò pū jiégòu	NMLTC
Network management sub-system	网络管理子系统	Wǎngluò guǎnlǐ zixìtǒng	NMS
Network management system	网管系统	Wǎngguǎn xìtǒng	NMS
Network management system	网络管理系统	Wǎngluò guǎnlǐ xìtǒng	NMS
Network management terminal	网管终端	Wǎngguǎn zhōngduān	NMT
Network management vector transport	网络管理相量传输	Wǎngluò guǎnlǐ xiāngliáng chuánshū	NMVT
Network management work station	网管工作站	Wǎngguǎn gōngzuòzhàn	NAWS
Network manager	网络管理者	Wǎngluò guǎnlǐzhě	NM
Network mapper	网络映射器	Wǎngluò yìngshèqì	
Network mapping	网络映像	Wǎngluò yìngxiàng	
Network maximum segment size	网络最大段长度	Wǎngluò zuìdà duàn chángdù	NMSS
Network measurement results	网络测量结果	Wǎngluò cèliáng jiéguǒ	NMR
Network monitor and control	网络监控	Wǎngluò jiānkòng	NMAC
Network news transfer protocol	网络新闻传输协议	Wǎngluò xīnwén chuánshū xiéyì	NNTP
Network news transfer protocol	网络新闻传送协议	Wǎngluò xīnwén chuánsòng xiéyì	NNTP
Network node	网络节点	Wǎngluò jiédiǎn	
Network node interface	网路节点接口	Wǎnglù jiédiǎn jiēkǒu	NNI
Network node interface	网络节点接口	Wǎngluò jiédiǎn jiēkǒu	NNI
Network operating center	网络运行中心	Wǎngluò yùnxíng zhōngxīn	NOC
Network operation and maintenance center	网络操作和维护中心	Wǎngluò cāozuò hé wéihù zhōngxīn	NOMC
Network operation system	网络操作系统	Wǎngluò cāozuò xìtǒng	NOS
Network operations center	网络操作中心	Wǎngluò cāozuò zhōngxīn	NOC
Network operator	网络运营商	Wǎngluò yùnyíngshāng	NO
Network optimization	网络优化	Wǎngluò yōuhuà	
Network packet sniffing software	网络数据嗅探器软件	Wǎngluò shùjù xiùtànqì ruǎnjiàn	
Network parameter control	网络参数控制	Wǎngluò cānshù kòngzhì	NPC
Network partition	网络分区	Wǎngluò fēnqū	
Network path	网络通路	Wǎngluò tōnglù	
Network performance	网络性能	Wǎngluò xìngnéng	NP
Network performance analyzer	网络性能分析程序	Wǎngluò xìngnéng fēnxī chéngxù	NPA
Network performance management	网络性能管理	Wǎngluò xìngnéng guǎnlǐ	
Network planning	网络规划	Wǎngluò guīhuà	
Network port	网络口	Wǎngluò kǒu	
Network protection equipment	网络保护设备	Wǎngluò bǎohù shèbèi	NPE
Network protocol	网络协议	Wǎngluò xiéyì	
Network protocol address information	网络协议地址信息	Wǎngluò xiéyì dìzhǐ xìnxī	NPAI
Network protocol data unit	网络协议数据单元	Wǎngluò xiéyì shùjù dānyuán	NPDU
Network provider	网络提供商	Wǎngluò tígōngshāng	NP

English	Chinese	Pinyin	Abbr.
Network reachability	网络可达性	Wǎngluò kědáxìng	
Network resource	网络资源	Wǎngluò zīyuán	NR
Network resource architecture	网络资源结构	Wǎngluò zīyuán jiégòu	NRA
Network resource information model	网络资源信息模型	Wǎngluò zīyuán xìnxī móxíng	NRIM
Network resource management	网络资源管理	Wǎngluò zīyuán guǎnlǐ	NRM
Network resource model	网络资源模型	Wǎngluò zīyuán móxíng	NRM
Network resources control	网络资源控制	Wǎngluò zīyuán kòngzhì	NRC
Network scanner	网络扫描器	Wǎngluò sǎomiáoqì	
Network section	网络段	Wǎngluò duàn	
Network section ensemble	网络段集合	Wǎngluò duàn jíhé	NSE
Network security	网络保安	Wǎngluò bǎo'ān	
Network security	网络保密	Wǎngluò bǎomì	
Network security management and access control	网络安全管理和访问控制	Wǎngluò ānquán guǎnlǐ hé fǎngwèn kòngzhì	
Network server	网络服务器	Wǎngluò fúwùqì	
Network service	网络服务	Wǎngluò fúwù	NS
Network service	网络业务	Wǎngluò yèwù	NS
Network service access point	网络服务访问点	Wǎngluò fúwù fǎngwèn diǎn	NSAP
Network service access point	网络服务接入点	Wǎngluò fúwù jiērù diǎn	NSAP
Network service access point	网络业务接入点	Wǎngluò yèwù jiērù diǎn	NSAP
Network service access point identifier	网络业务接入点标识符	Wǎngluò yèwù jiērù diǎn biāozhìfú	NSAPI
Network service center	网络服务中心	Wǎngluò fúwù zhōngxīn	NSC
Network service data unit	网络服务数据单元	Wǎngluò fúwù shùjù dānyuán	NSDU
Network service data unit	网络业务数据单元	Wǎngluò yèwù shùjù dānyuán	NSDU
Network service entity	网络业务实体	Wǎngluò yèwù shítǐ	NSE
Network service entity identifier	网络业务实体标识符	Wǎngluò yèwù shítǐ biāozhìfú	NSEI
Network service layer	网络业务层	Wǎngluò yèwù céng	
Network service part	网络服务部分	Wǎngluò fúwù bùfen	NSP
Network service protocol (in DECnet)	网络服务协议	Wǎngluò fúwù xiéyì	NSP
Network service provider	网络服务提供商	Wǎngluò fúwù tígōngshāng	NSP
Network service provider	网络业务提供者	Wǎngluò yèwù tígòngzhě	NSP
Network service virtual connection	网络业务虚连接	Wǎngluò yèwù xū liánjiē	NS-VC
Network service virtual connection identifier	网络业务虚连接标识符	Wǎngluò yèwù xū liánjiē biāozhìfú	NS-VCI
Network service virtual link	网络业务虚链路	Wǎngluò yèwù xū liànlù	NS-VL
Network service virtual link identifier	网络业务虚链路标识符	Wǎngluò yèwù xū liànlù biāozhìfú	NS-VLI
Network sniffer	网络嗅探器	Wǎngluò xiùtànqì	
Network specification	网络规范	Wǎngluò guīfàn	
Network storage	网络存储	Wǎngluò cúnchǔ	
Network subset control key	网络用户电话机控制键	Wǎngluò yònghù diànhuàjī kòngzhì jiàn	NSCK
Network sub-system	网络子系统	Wǎngluò zixitǒng	NSS
Network switching sub-system	网络交换子系统	Wǎngluò jiāohuàn zixitǒng	NSS
Network synchronization	网同步	Wǎng tóngbù	NS
Network synchronization back panel	网络同步后面板	Wǎngluò tóngbù hòumianbǎn	NSBP
Network synchronization clock generation	网络同步时钟发生器	Wǎngluò tóngbù shízhōng fāshēngqì	NSCG
Network synchronization clock maintenance	网络同步时钟维护	Wǎngluò tóngbù shízhōng wéihù	NSCM
Network synchronization clock repeater	网络同步时钟中继器	Wǎngluò tóngbù shízhōng zhōngjìqì	NSCR

Network synchronization connection function module	网同步连接功能模块	Wăng tóngbù liánjiē gōngnéng mókuài	NS-C
Network synchronization control processor board assembly	网络同步控制处理器集成板	Wăngluò tóngbù kòngzhì chŭlĭqì jíchéngbăn	NCPA
Network synchronization distributor back panel	网络同步分配器后面板	Wăngluò tóngbù fēnpèiqì hòumianbăn	NDBP
Network terminal number	网络终端号码	Wăngluò zhōngduān hàomă	NTN
Network terminal type 1	第一类网络终端	Dìyīlèi wăngluò zhōngduān	NT1
Network terminal unit	网络终端单元	Wăngluò zhōngduān dānyuán	NTU
Network terminal, termination	网络终端	Wăngluò zhōngduān	NT
Network termination	网络终接	Wăngluò zhōngjiē	NT
Network termination 1	网络终端设备 1	Wăngluò zhōngduān shèbèi 1	NT-1
Network termination for B-ISDN	B-ISDN 网络终端	B-ISDN wăngluò zhōngduān	B-NT
Network termination point	网络终端端点	Wăngluò zhōngduān duāndiăn	NTP
Network test equipment	网络测试设备	Wăngluò cèshì shèbèi	
Network time protocol	网络时间同步协议	Wăngluò shíjiān tóngbù xiéyì	NTP
Network time protocol	网络时间协议	Wăngluò shíjiān xiéyì	NTP
Network time reference	网络时钟参考	Wăngluò shízhōng cānkăo	NTR
Network timing protocol	网络定时协议	Wăngluò dìngshí xiéyì	NTP
Network to network interface	网络间接口	Wăngluò-jiān jiēkŏu	NNI
Network topology	网络拓扑	Wăngluò tuòpū	
Network topology	网络拓扑结构	Wăngluò tuòpū jiégòu	
Network topology configuration management	网络拓扑组成管理	Wăngluò tuòpū zŭchéng guănlĭ	NTCM
Network topology management	网络拓扑管理	Wăngluò tuòpū guănlĭ	
Network traffic management system	网络话务管理系统	Wăngluò huàwù guănlĭ xìtŏng	NTMS
Network transfer delay	网络传输时延	Wăngluò chuánshū shíyán	
Network transfer delay	网络传送延迟	Wăngluò chuánsòng yánchí	
Network under test	被测网络	Bèicè wăngluò	
Network user access	网络用户地址	Wăngluò yònghù dìzhĭ	NUA
Network user identification	网络用户标示	Wăngluò yònghù biāoshì	NUI
Network user identification	网络用户识别	Wăngluò yònghù shíbié	NUI
Network user part	网络用户部分	Wăngluò yònghù bùfen	NUP
Network vulnerability scanner	网络漏洞扫描器	Wăngluò lòudòng săomiáoqì	
Network-attached storage	直接挂网的存储器	Zhíjiē guàwăngde cúnchŭqì	NAS
Network-based VPN (virtual private network)	基于网络的 VPN	Jīyú wăngluòde VPN	
Networking Interoperability Alliance	网络互操作联盟	Wăngluò hùcāozuò liánméng	NIA
Networking software	网络软件	Wăngluò ruănjiàn	
Network-specific facilities	网络特有性能	Wăngluò tèyŏu xìngnéng	
Network-to-network interface	网络-网络接口	Wăngluò—wăngluò jiēkŏu	NNI
Neural network	神经网络	Shénjīng wăngluò	
Neutral conductor	中性导体	Zhōngxìng dăotĭ	
Neutral density filter (optical)	中性密度滤光镜	Zhōngxìng mìdù lǜguāngjìng	
Neutral message language	中性消息语言	Zhōngxìng xiāoxi yŭyán	NML
Neutral wire	中线	Zhōngxiàn	
Neutral wire	中性线	Zhōngxìng xiàn	
Neutral, neutralization	中和	Zhōnghé	
Neutrodyne	中和元件	Zhōnghé yuánjiàn	
New data flag	新数据标帜	Xīn shùjù biāozhì	NDF

New data flag	新数据标识	Xīn shùjù biāozhì	NDF
New data flag (in SDH)	新数据标志	Xīn shùjù biāozhì	NDF
New data type	新数据型	Xīn shùjù xíng	
New deal	新协议	Xīn xiéyì	
New Internet knowledge system	新因特网智能系统	Xīn Yīntèwǎng zhìnéng xìtǒng	NIKOS
New type approval advisory board	新定型咨询台	Xīn dìngxíng zīxún tái	NTAAB
Newbie (Internet novice)	新手	Xīnshǒu	
Newsgroup	新闻栏	Xīnwén lán	
Newsgroup	新闻组	Xīnwén zǔ	
Newspaper and periodical distribution office	发报刊局	Fā bàokān jú	
Newspapers and periodicals of special distribution	特发报刊	Tèfā bàokān	
Newspapers and periodicals of special price	特价报刊	Tèjià bàokān	
Newspapers pasted on public bulletin boards	贴报	Tiēbào	
Newton channel	牛顿信道	Niú-dùn xìndào	
Next (WP command)	下一步	Xiàyībù	
Next generation input/output	新一代输入/输出标准	Xīn yīdài shūrù/shūchū biāozhǔn	NGIO
Next generation Internet	下一代因特网	Xiàyīdài Yīntèwǎng	NGI
Next generation local switch	下一代本地交换系统	Xiàyīdài běndì jiāohuàn xìtǒng	
Next generation network	下一代网络	Xiàyīdài wǎngluò	NGN
Next generation operating system and software	下一代电信运营系统和软件	Xiàyīdài diànxìn yùnyíng xìtǒng hé ruǎnjiàn	NGOSS
Next hop client	下一跳客户	Xiàyītiào kèhù	NHC
Next hop label forwarding entry	下一跳标记转发条目	Xiàyītiào biāojì zhuǎnfā tiáomù	NHLFE
Next hop routing protocol	下一跳路由协议	Xiàyītiào lùyóu xiéyì	NHRP
Next-hop	下一跳级	Xiàyītiào jí	
Next-hop (address) resolution protocol	下一跳地址解析协议	Xiàyītiào dìzhǐ jiěxī xiéyì	NHRP
Next-hop resolution protocol	下一跳解析协议	Xiàyītiào jiěxī xiéyì	NHRP
Next-hop server	下一跳服务器	Xiàyītiào fúwùqì	NHS
Nibble (half a byte)	半字节	Bànzìjié	
Nibble (half of a byte)	四位元	Sìwèi yuán	
Nidroff (Netherlands company)	利多福	Lì-duō-fú	
Nikon (Japanese company)	尼康	Ní-kāng	
Nintendo	任天堂	Rèn-tiān-táng	
Nintendo 64 (computer game)	任天堂 64 位游戏机	Rèntiāntáng 64 wèi yóuxìjī	N64
Nintendo Super Famicom (computer game)	超级任天堂 16 位游戏机	Chāojí rèntiāntáng 16 wèi yóuxìjī	SFC
Niobium-doped fiber amplifier	掺铌光纤放大器	Chānní guāngxiān fàngdàqì	NDFA
Nippon Electric Company Advanced Mobile Telephone System	日本电气公司先进移动电话系统	Rìběn Diànqì Gōngsī xiānjìn yídòng diànhuà xìtǒng	NAMTS
Nippon Electronics Corporation	日电	Rì diàn	NEC
Nippon Telegraph & Telephone	日本电报电话	Rìběn Diànbào Diànhuà	NTT
Nitrogen laser	氮分子激光	Dàn fènzi jīguāng	
Nitrogen soldering	氮锡焊接	Dàn xī hàn jiē	
Nixie light	数码管	Shùmǎ guǎn	
N-layer managed object	n-层被管对象	n-céng bèiguǎn duìxiàng	
No answer	无答应	Wúdáying	NA
No cell defined	无信元定界	Wúxìnyuán dìngjiè	NCD
No dialing after off-hook for a long time	摘机后久不拨号	Zhāijī hòu jiǔ bù bōhào	

No handover number available	没有可用的切换号码	Méiyǒu kěyòngde qiēhuàn hàomǎ	
No radio channel available	没有可用的无线信道	Méiyǒu kěyòngde wúxiàn xìndào	
No radio resource available	没有可用的无线资源	Méiyǒu kěyòngde wúxiàn zīyuán	
No re-negotiation message (IPsec TLS)	不重新协商消息	Bù chóngxīn xiéshāng xiāoxi	
No roaming number available	无可用漫游号码	Wúkěyòng mànyóu hàomǎ	
No-account overclock	无效超频	Wúxiào chāopín	NAOC
Nodal period	交点周期	Jiāodiǎn zhōuqī	
Nodal throughput	节点吞吐	Jiédiǎn tūntǔ	
Node	结点	Jiédiǎn	
Node	节点	Jiédiǎn	
Node address byte	节点地址字节	Jiédiǎn dìzhǐ zìjié	NAD
Node B application part	节点 B 应用部分	Jiédiǎn B yìngyòng bùfen	NBAP
Node control	节点控制	Jiédiǎn kòngzhì	NC
Node interworking function	节点互通功能	Jiédiǎn hùtōng gōngnéng	NIF
Node loop port	节点环端口	Jiédiǎn huán duānkǒu	NLPort
Node match tolerance	节点匹配容差	Jiédiǎn pǐpèi róngchā	
Node record	节点记录	Jiédiǎn jìlù	
Node resource unit	节点资源单位	Jiédiǎn zīyuán dānwèi	NRU
Node-by-node selecting	逐点选择	Zhúdiǎn xuǎnzé	
Noise	噪声	Zàoshēng	
Noise	噪音	Zàoyīn	
Noise amplitude modulation (AM) jamming	噪声调幅干扰	Zàoshēng tiáofú gānrǎo	
Noise amplitude modulation-phase modulation jamming	噪声调幅调相干扰	Zàoshēng tiáofú tiáoxiàng gānrǎo	
Noise bandwidth	躁声带宽	Zàoshēng dàikuān	
Noise current	噪声电流	Zàoshēng diànliú	
Noise electromotive force	噪声电动势	Zàoshēng diàndòngshì	
Noise equivalent bandwidth	噪声等效带宽	Zàoshēng děngxiào dàikuān	NEB
Noise equivalent flux	噪声等效通量	Zàoshēng děngxiào tōngliàng	NEF
Noise equivalent flux density	噪声等效流密度	Zàoshēng děngxiào liú mìdù	NEFD
Noise equivalent input signal	噪声等效输入信号	Zàoshēng děngxiào shūrù xìnhào	NES
Noise equivalent intensity	噪声等效强度	Zàoshēng děngxiào qiángdù	NEI
Noise equivalent power	噪声等效功率	Zàoshēng děngxiào gōnglǜ	NEP
Noise equivalent power density	噪声等效功率密度	Zàoshēng děngxiào gōnglǜ mìdù	NEPD
Noise equivalent radiance	噪声等效辐射率	Zàoshēng děngxiào fúshè lǜ	NER
Noise equivalent temperature	噪声等效温度	Zàoshēng děngxiào wēndù	NET
Noise equivalent temperature difference	噪声等效温差	Zàoshēng děngxiào wēnchā	NETD
Noise feedback control	噪声反馈控制	Zàoshēng fǎnkuì kòngzhì	NFC
Noise field strength	噪声场强	Zàoshēng chǎngqiáng	
Noise figure	噪声系数	Zàoshēng xìshù	NF
Noise frequency modulation (FM) jamming	噪声调频干扰	Zàoshēng tiáopín gānrǎo	
Noise frequency modulation effective frequency shift	噪声调频有效频移	Zàoshēng tiáopín yǒuxiào pínyí	
Noise limited sensitivity	噪声限制灵敏度	Zàoshēng xiànzhì língmǐndù	
Noise margin	噪声余度	Zàoshēng yúdù	
Noise phase modulation (PM) jamming	噪声调相干扰	Zàoshēng tiáoxiàng gānrǎo	
Noise power	噪声功率	Zàoshēng gōnglǜ	

Noise power ratio	噪声功率比	Zàoshēng gōnglǜ bǐ	NPR
Noise source	噪声源	Zàoshēng yuán	
Noise suppression	噪声抑制	Zàoshēng yìzhì	
Noise suppression circuit	噪声抑制电路	Zàoshēng yìzhì diànlù	NSC
Noise temperature (of a receiving antenna)	噪声温度	Zàoshēng wēndù	
Noise temperature of antenna	天线噪声温度	Tiānxiàn zàoshēng wēndù	NTA
Noise to masking ratio	噪声掩蔽比	Zàoshēng yǎnbì bǐ	NMR
Noise transfer	噪声传递	Zàoshēng chuándì	
Noise voltage	噪声电压	Zàoshēng diànyā	
Noise word	干扰词	Gānrǎo cí	
Noise-modulated jamming	噪声调制干扰	Zàoshēng tiáozhì gānrǎo	
Noise-quieting input-signal level	抑噪输入信号电平	Yìzào shūrù xìnhào diànpíng	
Noise-quieting input-signal level	抑躁输入信号电平	Yìzào shūrù xìnhào diànpíng	
Noise-temperature ratio	噪声温度比	Zàoshēng wēndù bǐ	NTR
Nokia (Finnish company)	诺基亚	Nuò-jī-yà	
Nokia Measurement System for X-Windows	诺基亚基于 X-Windows 平台的测量系统	Nuò-jī-yà jīyú X-Windows píngtáide cèliáng xìtǒng	NMS/X
Nokia Planning System for X-Windows	诺基亚基于 X-Windows 平台的规划系统	Nuò-jī-yà jīyú X-Windows píngtáide guīhuà xìtǒng	NPS/X
Nomadic wireless access	游牧式无线接入	Yóumù shì wúxiàn jiērù	
Nominal black (white)	标称黑（白）	Biāochēng hēi (bái)	
Nominal calling probability	标称呼通概率	Biāochēng hūtōng gàilǜ	
Nominal center frequency	标称中心频率	Biāochēng zhōngxīn pínlǜ	
Nominal characteristic impedance	标称特性阻抗	Biāochēng tèxìng zǔkàng	
Nominal data	名称数据	Míngchēng shùjù	
Nominal data	名义数据	Míngyì shùjù	
Nominal justification rate	标称调整率	Biāochēng tiáozhěnglǜ	
Nominal margin (of a type of apparatus)	标称改正力	Biāochēng gǎizhènglì	
Nominal page	标称页	Biāochēng yè	
Nominal power	标称功率	Biāochēng gōnglǜ	NOM_PWR
Nominal power	名义功率	Míngyì gōnglǜ	
Nominal root-mean square	标称均方根	Biāochēng jūn fānggēn	NRMS
Nominal service	正常服务	Zhèngcháng fúwù	
Nominal stuffing rate	标称塞入率	Biāochēng sāirùlǜ	
Nominal value	标称值	Biāochēng zhí	
Nominal value	票面价值	Piàomiàn jiàzhí	
Nominal voltage	标称电压	Biāochēng diànyā	
Nominal zero dispersion wavelength (FOC term)	标称零色散波长	Biāochēng líng sèsàn bōcháng	
Non-access stage	非接入层	Fēijiērù céng	NAS
Non-adaptive motion compensation algorithm	非自适应运动补偿算法	Fēizìshìyìng yùndòng bǔcháng suànfǎ	NAMC
Non-algorithmic digital record systems	非规则数字记录系统	Fēiguīzé shùzì jìlù xìtǒng	NDRS
Non-associated signaling	非直联信令方式	Fēizhílián xìnlìng fāngshì	
Non-assured operations	非确保工作过程	Fēiquèbǎo gōngzuò guòchéng	
Non-authoritative restore	非强制性还原	Fēiqiángzhìxìng huányuán	
Non-blind retrieval	非盲提取	Fēimáng tíqǔ	
Non-blocking cross-connect connection	无堵塞交叉连接	Wúdǔsè jiāochā liánjiē	

Non-blocking interconnection network	非阻塞互连网络	Fēizǔsè hùlián wǎngluò	
Non-broadcast multi-access	非广播式多路访问	Fēiguǎngbō-shì duōlù fǎngwèn	NBMA
Non-broadcast multiple access	非广播多接入	Fēiguǎngbō duōjiērù	NBMA
Non-canonical format indication	非规范的格式标识符	Fēiguīfànde géshi biāozhì fú	NCFI
Non-canonical format indication	新规范的格式表示	Xīn guīfànde géshi biǎoshì	NCFI
Nonce (in IP)	随机数	Suíjī shù	
Non-circularity	不圆度	Bùyuándù	
Non-clustered index	非聚集索引	Fēijùjí suǒyǐn	
Non-clustered index (in SQL Server)	非簇索引	Fēicù suǒyǐn	
Non-coherent carrier keying	非相干载波键控	Fēixiānggān zàibō jiànkòng	NCCK
Non-coherent frequency shift keyed modulation	非相干频移键控调制	Fēixiānggān pínyí jiànkòng tiáozhì	NCFSK
Non-coherent jamming/Interference	非相关干扰	Fēixiāngguān gānrǎo	
Non-coherent moving target indicator (MTI)	非相干动目标显示	Fēixiānggān dòng mùbiāo xiǎnshì	
Non-commuting	不对易	Bùduìyì	
Non-conducted conference	不受控会议	Bù shòukòng huìyì	
Non-conformance	不一致	Bùyīzhì	
Non-conformant traffic	非顺从流	Fēishùncóng liú	
Non-critical failure	非危险失效	Fēiwēixiǎn shīxiào	
Non-critical fault	非危险故障	Fēiwēixiǎn gùzhàng	
Non-data-set clocking	非数据集时钟	Fēishùjùjí shízhōng	NDSC
Non-dedicated control channel	非专用控制信道	Fēizhuānyòng kòngzhì xìndào	
Non-dedicated control channel	非专作控制信道	Fēizhuānzuò kòngzhì xìndào	
Non-delivery	不投递	Bùtóudì	
Non-delivery remittance	无法兑付汇款	Wúfǎ duìfù huìkuǎn	
Non-destructive read-only	非破坏只读	Fēipòhuài zhǐ dú	NDRO
Non-destructive read-only	无损只读	Wúsǔn zhǐdú	NDRO
Non-destructive read-out	非破坏读出	Fēipòhuài dúchū	
Non-determinate fault	非确定性故障	Fēiquèdìngxìng gùzhàng	
Non-deterministic functions (in SQL Server)	不确定性函数	Bùquèdìngxìng hánshù	
Non-developmental item	非发展项目	Fēifāzhǎn xiàngmù	NDI
Non-dispersion shifted optical fiber	非色散位移光纤	Fēisèsàn wèiyí guāngxiān	
Non-driven element	非受激单元	Fēishòujī dānyuán	
Non-DWORD-aligned (audio term)	非 DWORD 排列	Fēi DWORD páiliè	NDA
Non-executive director	非执行董事	Fēizhíxíng dǒngshì	
Non-forwarding address	非转发地址	Fēizhuǎnfā dìzhǐ	NFA
Non-GPRS alert flag	非 GPRS 提示标志	Fēi GPRS tíshì biāozhì	NGAF
Non-graphic data	非图形数据	Fēitúxíng shùjù	
Non-identified DTE service	菲识别型 DTE 业务	Fēishíbiéxíng DTE yèwù	
Non-impact printer	非撞击式打印机	Fēizhuàngjī-shì dǎyìnjī	
Non-inferior solution	非劣解	Fēiliè jiě	
Non-Intel ®	非英特尔架构	Fēi Yīng-tè-ěr jiàgòu	NI
Non-intrusive monitoring	非介入监视	Fēijièrù jiānshì	
Non-leaf	非叶	Fēiyè	
Non-leaf member	非叶成员	Fēiyè chéngyuán	
Nonlinear circuit	非线性电路	Fēixiànxìng diànlù	
Non-linear control system	非线形控制系统	Fēixiànxíng kòngzhì xìtǒng	

English	Chinese	Pinyin	Abbreviation
Non-linear correction	非线性校正	Fēixiànxìng jiàozhèng	
Non-linear crystal	非线性光学晶体	Fēixiànxìng guāngxué jīngtǐ	
Non-linear differential equation	非线性微分方程	Fēixiànxìng wēifēn fāngchéng	NDE
Non-linear digital modulation	非线性数字调制	Fēixiànxìng shùzì tiáozhì	
Non-linear distortion	非线性失真	Fēixiànxìng shīzhēn	NLD
Non-linear finite element method	非线性有限元方法	Fēixiànxìng yǒuxiàn yuán fāngfǎ	
Non-linear frequency modulated pulse compression	非线性调频脉冲压缩	Fēixiànxìng tiáopín màichōng yāsuō	
Non-linear frequency modulation	非线性调频	Fēixiànxìng tiáopín	NLFM
Non-linear optical fiber loop mirror	非线性光纤环路镜	Fēixiànxìng guāngxiān huánlù jìng	NOLM
Non-linear optical loop	非线性光纤环	Fēixiànxìng guāngxiān huán	
Non-linear optical loop mirroring	非线性光纤环行镜	Fēixiànxìng guāngxiān huánxíng jìng	NOLM
Non-linear processor	非线性处理器	Fēixiànxìng chǔlǐqì	NLP
Non-linear programming	非线性规划	Fēixiànxìng guīhuà	NP
Non-linear recurrence algorithm	非线性送代算法	Fēixiànxìng sòngdài suànfǎ	
Non-linear structure	非线性结构	Fēixiànxìng jiégòu	
Non-linear time series prediction	非线性时间序列预测	Fēixiànxìng shíjiān xùliè yùcè	
Non-linear vibration	非线形振动	Fēixiànxíng zhèndòng	
Non-linearity	非线性	Fēixiànxìng	
Non-linearity distortion	非线性失真	Fēixiànxìng shīzhēn	
Non-linearity effect	非线性效应	Fēixiànxìng xiàoyìng	
Non-line-of-site	非站点线路	Fēizhàndiǎn xiànlù	NLOS
Non-mandatory attribute	非必备属性	Fēibìbèi shǔxìng	
Non-mechanical optical switch	非机械式光开关	Fēijīxiè-shì guāng kāiguān	
Non-metallic cable	非金属缆	Fēijīnshǔ lǎn	
Non-multiplexed address bus mode	非复用寻址总线模式	Fēifùyòng xúnzhǐ zǒngxiàn móshì	
Non-operating state	非工作状态	Fēigōngzuò zhuàngtài	
Non-operating time	非工作时间	Fēigōngzuò shíjiān	
Non-packet digital terminal equipment	非包式数字终端设备	Fēibāo-shì shùzì zhōngduān shèbèi	NPDTE
Non-packet Terminal	非分组终端	Fēifēnzǔ zhōngduān	NPT
Non-parameter detector	非参量检测器	Fēicānliàng jiǎncèqì	
Non-parametric test	非参数检验	Fēicānshù jiǎnyàn	
Non-participating mode	多加入模式	Duōjiārù móshì	
Non-periodic signal	非周期信号	Fēizhōuqī xìnhào	
Non-periodic, aperiodic	非周期	Fēizhōuqī	
Non-persistent carrier sensing multiple access	非持续载波传感多路存取	Fēichíxù zàibō chuángǎn duōlù cúnqǔ	NCSMA
Non-persistent carrier sensing multiple access with collision detection	碰撞检测非持续载波传感多路存取	Pèngzhuàng jiǎncè fēichíxù zàibō chuángǎn duōlù cúnqǔ	NCSMA-CD
Non-preemptive	非抢占式	Fēiqiǎngzhàn-shì	
Non-preemptive priority queuing discipline	非强占优先规则	Fēiqiángzhàn yōuxiān guīzé	
Non-print cycle	非打印周期	Fēidǎyìn zhōuqī	
Non-process monitor system	非过程监督系统	Fēiguòchéng jiāndū xìtǒng	NPMS
Non-promiscuous	非混杂模式	Fēihùnzá móshì	
Non-real time	非实时	Fēishíshí	NRT
Non-real time polling service	非实时查询业务	Fēishíshí cháxún yèwù	NrtPS
Non-real time variable bit rate	非实时可变比特率	Fēishíshí kěbiàn bǐtè lǜ	nrt-VBR
Non-reciprocal circular polarized phase shifter	非互易圆极化移相器	Fēihùyì yuán jíhuà yíxiàngqì	

Non-reciprocal phase shifter	非互易移相器	Fēihùyì yíxiàngqì	
Non-reciprocal polarization rotator	非互易极化旋转器	Fēihùyì jíhuà xuánzhuǎnqì	
Non-recursive filtering	非递归滤波器	Fēidìguī lǜbōqì	
Non-regenerative repeater	无再生中继器	Wúzàishēng zhōngjìqì	NrREP
Non-registered access	非登记的访问	Fēidēngjìde fǎngwèn	
Non-registered access	未登记的访问	Wèidēngjìde fǎngwèn	
Non-relevant failure	非关联失效	Fēiguānlián shīxiào	
Non-repaired item	非修理产品(装备)	Fēixiūlǐ chǎnpǐn (zhuāngbèi)	
Non-repeatable read	不可重复读取	Bùkěchóngfù dúqǔ	
Non-repudiation	不可否认	Bùkěfǒurèn	
Non-repudiation	非否认协议	Fēifǒurèn xiéyì	
Non-required time	无要求的时间	Wúyāoqiúde shíjiān	
Non-resident area	非常驻区	Fēichángzhù qū	
Non-resident task	非常驻任务	Fēichángzhù rènwu	
Non-return to zero	不归零制	Bùguīlíng zhì	NRZ
Non-return to zero (inverted)	不归零反相	Bùguīlíng (fǎnxiāng)	NRZI
Non-return to zero (NRZ) coding	不归零码	Bùguīlíng mǎ	
Non-return to zero coding	非归零码	Fēiguīlíng mǎ	NRZ
Non-return to zero-level	不归零电平	Bùguīlíng diànpíng	NRZL
Non-revertive (protection) operation	非回复（保护）运行	Fēihuífù (bǎohù) yùnxíng	
Non-saving system	非退避方式	Fēituìbì fāngshì	
Non-SDH network element	非 SDH 网元	Fēi SDH wǎng yuán	NNE
Non-seed router	非种子路由器	Fēizhǒngzǐ lùyóuqì	
Non-significant address part	不重要的地址部分	Bùzhòngyàode dìzhǐ bùfen	NAP
Non-silica imaging fiber optic bundle	多成分影像光纤	Duōchéngfèn yǐngxiàng guāngxiān	
Non-standard	非标准	Fēibiāozhǔn	NS
Non-standard data	非标准数据	Fēibiāozhǔn shùjù	
Non-stationary nature	非平稳性	Fēipíngwěn xìng	
Non-stationary random process	非稳态随机过程	Fēiwěntài suíjī guòchéng	
Non-structural element	非结构元素	Fēijiégòu yuánsù	
Non-stub area	非存根区	Fēicúngēn qū	
Non-switched connection	非交换连接	Fēijiāohuàn liánjiē	
Non-switched connection element	非交换连接单元	Fēijiāohuàn liánjiē dānyuán	
Non-switched ISDN connection element	非交换 IDSN 连接单元	Fēijiāohuàn ISDN liánjiē dānyuán	
Nonsynchronized network	异步网	Yìbù wǎng	
Non-synchronized network	非同步网	Fēitóngbù wǎng	
Non-synchronous pulse jamming	非同步脉冲干扰	Fēitóngbù màichōng gānrǎo	
Non-tangible	不可触摸	Bùkěchùmō	
Non-transformer power supply	无变压器电源	Wúbiànyāqì diànyuán	
Non-transparent loop back	不透时环回	Bùtòu shíhuánhuí	
Non-transparent support of services	业务的非透明支持	Yèwùde fēitòumíng zhīchí	
Non-trigger protection circuit	无触发保护电路	Wúchùfā bǎohù diànlù	
Non-underlay coverage	非重叠覆盖	Fēichóngdié fùgài	
Non-uniform encoding	非均匀编码	Fēijūnyún biānmǎ	
Non-uniform quantizing	非均匀量化	Fēijūnyún liànghuà	
Non-uniform rational B-splines	非均匀有理 B 样条	Fēijūnyún yǒulǐ B-yàng tiáo	NURBS

Non-vectored interrupt	非向量中断	Fēixiàngliàng zhōngduàn	NVI
Non-voice service call	非话业务呼叫	Fēihuàyèwù hūjiào	
Non-volatile electrically alterable memory	永久性电可变存储器	Yǒngjiǔxìng diàn kěbiàn cúnchǔqì	NEAM
Non-volatile memory	不挥发存储器	Bùhuīfā cúnchǔqì	
Non-volatile memory	不挥发存储器	Bùhuīfā cúnchǔqì	NVM
Non-volatile memory	非挥发性存储器	Fēihuīfāxìng cúnchǔqì	
Non-volatile random access memory	非易失随机存取存储器	Fēiyìshī suíjī cúnqǔ cúnchǔqì	NVRAM
Non-volatile storage or memory	非易失存储器	Fēiyìshī cúnchǔqì	
Nonwetting (in SMT)	不熔湿的	Bùróngshīde	
Non-zero dispersion fiber	非零色散光纤	Fēilíng sèsàn guāngxiān	NZDF
Non-zero dispersion-shifted optical fiber	非零色散位移光纤	Fēilíng sèsàn wèiyí guāngxiān	NZDSF
Non-zero dispersion-shifted single mode optical fiber	正色散位移单模光纤	Zhèng sèsàn wèiyí dān ó guāngxiān	
Non-zero-dispersion shift fiber	非零散位移光纤	Fēiíngsǎn wèiyí guāngxiān	NZ-DSF
NOR gate	"或非"门	Huòfēi mén	
Nordic Mobile Telephone System	北欧移动电话系统	Běi'ōu yídòng diànhuà xìtǒng	NMT
Normal access control level	普通接入控制级别	Pǔtōng jiērù kòngzhì jíbié	
Normal burst	常规突发脉冲序列	Chángguī tūfā màichōng xùliè	NB
Normal burst	正常突发	Zhèngcháng tūfā	
Normal burst	普通信息分组	Pǔtōng xìnxī fēnzǔ	NB
Normal charging	正常充电	Zhèngcháng chōngdiàn	
Normal condition	正常状态	Zhèngcháng zhuàngtài	
Normal consolidation	正常固结	Zhèngcháng gùjié	
Normal coupling torque	正常耦合转矩	Zhèngcháng ǒuhé zhuànjǔ	
Normal disconnected mode	正常断开方式	Zhèngcháng duànkāi fāngshì	NDM
Normal dispersion	正规散射	Zhèngguī sǎnshè	
Normal distribution	正规分布	Zhèngguī fēnbù	
Normal distribution	正态分布	Zhèngtài fēnbù	
Normal inspection	正常检查	Zhèngcháng jiǎnchá	
Normal load	额定负载	Édìng fùzài	
Normal load	正常负载	Zhèngcháng fùzài	
Normal mode (in a waveguide)	简正模	Jiǎnzhèngmó	
Normal operation with successful outcome	带成功结果的常规操作	Dài chénggōng jiéguǒde chángguī cāozuò	
Normal primary sampling plan (in quality standards)	一次正常抽样方案	Yīcì zhèngcháng chōuyàng fāng'àn	
Normal response mode	正常响应方式	Zhèngcháng xiǎngyìng fāngshì	NRM
Normal signal	正常信号	Zhèngcháng xìnhào	
Normal stress	法向应力	Fǎxiàng yìnglì	
Normalization rules	规范化规则	Guīfànhuà guīzé	
Normalization type	标准型	Biāozhǔn xíng	NZ
Normalization, standardize	标准化	Biāozhǔnhuà	
Normalize	规格化	Guīgéhuà	
Normalized admittance	归一化导纳	Guīyīhuà dǎonà	
Normalized complex wave amplitude	归一化复数波振幅	Guīyīhuà fùshùbō zhènfú	
Normalized difference slope	归一化差斜率	Guīyīhuà chā xiélǜ	
Normalized impedance	归一化阻抗	Guīyīhuà zǔkàng	
Normalized least mean square	归一最小均方	Guī yī zuìxiǎo jūn fāng	NLMS

Normalized least mean squares	归一化最小均方误差	Guīyīhuà zuìxiǎo jūnfāng wùchā	NLMS
Normalized offset	归一化的偏置	Guīyīhuàde piānzhì	
Normalized pattern	归一化方向图	Guīyīhuà fāngxiàng tú	
Norme Francaise (French standards organization)	法国标准	Fǎguó biāozhǔn	NF
Nortel networks	北电网络	Běidiàn wǎngluò	
Nortel, Northern Telecom (Canada company)	北方电讯有限公司	Běifāng Diànxùn yǒuxiàn gōngsī	
North America Digital cellular System	北美数字蜂窝系统	Běiměi shùzì fēngwō xìtǒng	ADC；DAMPS
North American Datum (GIS)	北美大地基准面	Běiměi dàdì jīzhǔnmiàn	NAD
North American equal access	北美平等接入	Běiměi píngděng jiērù	NAEA
North Bridge chip	北桥芯片	Běiqiáo xìnpiàn	NBC
North China Institute of Computing Technology	华北计算技术研究所	Huáběi Jìsuàn Jìshù Yánjiūsuǒ	NCI
Northern Eagle Technology Corp. (US company)	北鹰科技有限公司	Běiyīng kējì yǒuxiàn gōngsī	NET
Norton Disk Doctor ©	诺顿磁盘医生	Nuò-dùn cípán yīshēng	NDD
Norton Utilities ©	诺顿工具软件	Nuò-dùn gōngjù ruǎnjiàn	
Not	非	Fēi	NOT
Not AND (a logical operator)	与非	Yǔ fēi	NAND
Not equal	不等于	Bùděngyú	NE
NOT gate	"非"门	Fēi mén	
Not or	"或非"	Huò fēi	NOR
Not transparent	不透明的	Bùtòumíngde	NT
Not used, not applicable	不适用	Bùshìyòng	N/A
Notarization (IPsec)	公证	Gōngzhèng	
Notch	下凹	Xià'āo	
Note internal handover	标注局内切换	Biāozhù júnèi qiēhuàn	
Notebook computer	笔记本电脑	Bǐjìběn diànnǎo	
Notebook computer	笔记型电脑	Bǐjìxíng diànnǎo	
Notification channel	通知信道	Tōngzhī xìndào	NCH
Notification indicator	通知指示	Tōngzhī zhǐshì	
Notify	通知	Tōngzhī	
Nozzle	吸嘴	Xīzuǐ	
N-phase pulse-shift-keying	N 相脉冲移位链控	N-xiàng màichōng yíwèi liànkòng	N-PSK
N--protocol-control-information	n-协议控制信息	n-xiéyì kòngzhì xìnxī	
N--protocol-data-unit	n-协议数据单元	n-xiéyì shùjù dānyuán	
N--service-access-point-address	n-服务访问点地址	n-fúwù fǎngwèn diǎn dìzhǐ	
N-state amplitude phase shift keying	n 状态幅度相移键控	n-zhuàngtài fúdù xiāngyí jiànkòng	
N-state quadrature amplitude modulation	N 态正交调幅	N-tài zhèngjiāo tiáofú	N-QAM
N-state quadrature amplitude modulation	n 状态正交幅度调制	n-zhuàngtài zhèngjiāo fúdù tiáozhì	n-QAM
N-state quadrature amplitude modulation	N 状态正交调幅	N-zhuàngtài zhèngjiāo tiáofú	N-QAM
Nth harmonic ratio	第 n 次谐波比	Dì n-cì xiébō bǐ	
N-th order valley	N 次谷	N-cì gǔ	
NTT DoCoMo	日本电报电话多科莫	Rìběn Diànbào Diànhuà duō-kē-mò	
Nuclear electromagnetic pulse	核电磁脉冲	Hédiàncí màichōng	
Null	空白	Kòngbái	NUL
Null modem	空调制解调器	Kōng tiáozhì jiětiáoqì	
Null modem cable	零调制解调器电缆	Líng tiáozhì jiětiáoqì diànlǎn	
Null point identification	无效指针指示	Wúxiào zhǐzhēn zhǐshì	NPI

English	Chinese	Pinyin	Abbr.
Null state	零状态	Líng zhuàngtài	
Null string	空串	Kōng chuàn	
Null string	零串	Líng chuàn	
Null value	空值	Kōngzhí	
Nullability	为空性	Wéi kōngxing	
Null-steering antenna	零转向天线	Líng zhuǎnxiàng tiānxiàn	NSAN
Null-steering antenna	零点可控天线	Língdiǎn kěkòng tiānxiàn	
Null-steering antenna	零控天线	Língkòng tiānxiàn	
Number assignment module	号码分配模块	Hàomǎ fēnpèi mókuài	NAM
Number crunching	数字运算	Shùzì yùnsuàn	
Number handling sub-system	编号处理子系统	Biānhào chǔlǐ zixitǒng	NHS
Number identification supplementary service	号码识别附加业务	Hàomǎ shíbié fùjiā yèwù	
Number lock key	数字键位	Shùzì jiàn wèi	NumLock
Number of access permission blocks	接入允许块数	Jiērù yǔnxǔ kuài shù	
Number of bits	比特数	Bǐtè shù	
Number of calculation rounds	运算轮数	Yùnsuàn lúnshù	
Number of frames between Similar pages	相同寻呼间帧数	Xiāngtóng xúnhū-jiān zhèng shù	
Number of significant conditions	特征状态数	Tèzhēng zhuàngtài shù	
Number portability	号码可携带	Hàomǎ kěxiédài	NP
Number portability	号码流动	Hàomǎ liúdòng	NP
Numbering plan	编号计划	Biānhào jihuà	NP
Numbering plan	编号制度	Biānhào zhìdù	
Numbering plan	号码规划	Hàomǎ guīhuà	NP
Numbering plan area	编号计划范围	Biānhào jihuà fànwéi	NPA
Numbering plan identifier	编号计划标识符	Biānhào jihuà biāozhì fú	NPI
Numbering plan indicator	编号计划指示符	Biānhào jihuà zhǐshì fú	NPI
Number-unobtainable tone	空号音	Kōnghàoyīn	
Numeric coding	数字编码	Shùzì biānmǎ	
Numeric coprocessor	数字附处理器	Shùzì fùchǔlǐqì	
Numeric expression	数值表达式	Shùzhí biǎodá shì	
Numeric keypad	数字小键盘	Shùzì xiǎojiànpán	
Numeric O/R address	数字式 O/R 地址	Shùzì-shì O/R dìzhǐ	
Numeric O/R address	数字式 O/R 地址	Shùzì-shì O/R dìzhǐ	
Numerical analysis	数值解析	Shùzhí jiěxī	
Numerical aperture (of FOC)	数值孔径	Shùzhí kǒngjìng	NA
Numerical classification	数值分类	Shùzhí fēnlèi	
Numerical experiments	数值实验	Shùzhí shíyàn	
Numerical model	数值模型	Shùzhí móxíng	
Numerical problem	数值问题	Shùzhí wèntí	
Numerical simulation	数值模拟	Shùzhí mónǐ	
Numerically controlled oscillator	数控振荡器	Shùkòng zhèndàngqì	NCO
NumLock key	数字锁定键	Shùzì suǒdìng jiàn	
N-unit code	n 单位代码	n-dānwèi dàimǎ	
N-unit code alphabet	n 单位电码表	n-dānwèi diànmǎ biǎo	
Nylon	尼龙	Ní-lóng	
Nyquist rate	奈奎斯特率	Nài-kuí-sī-tè lǜ	

O

OADM common control channel	OADM 公共控制信道	OADM gōnggòng kòngzhì xìndào	OCCCH
OAMC management function	OAMC 管理功能	OAMC guǎnlǐ gōngnéng	OAMC-MF
OAMC operation system	OAMC 运行系统	OAMC yùnxíng xìtǒng	OAMC-OpS
Object	对象	Duìxiàng	
Object	客体	Kètǐ	
Object activation	对象激活	Duìxiàng jīhuó	
Object class	对象类	Duìxiàng lèi	
Object class	对象类别	Duìxiàng lèibié	
Object class	客体类别	Kètǐ lèibié	
Object class description	客体类别描述	Kètǐ lèibié miáoshù	
Object code	目标代码	Mùbiāo dàimǎ	
Object computer	目标计算机	Mùbiāo jìsuànjī	
Object dataflow graph	对象数据流图	Duìxiàng shùjùliú tú	ODG
Object definition language	对象定义语言	Duìxiàng dìngyì yǔyán	ODL
Object dependencies	对象相关性	Duìxiàng xiāngguānxìng	
Object description	客体描述	Kètǐ miáoshù	
Object entry	客体登录项	Kètǐ dēnglù xiàng	
Object exchange	对象交换	Duìxiàng jiāohuàn	OBEX
Object exchange model	对象交换模型	Duìxiàng jiāohuàn móxíng	OEM
Object exchange protocol (in Bluetooth)	对象交换协议	Duìxiàng jiāohuàn xiéyì	OBEX
Object file	目标文件	Mùbiāo wénjiàn	
Object file area	目标文件区	Mùbiāo wénjiàn qū	OFA
Object generalization	对象复合	Duìxiàng fùhé	
Object geometry	对象几何	Duìxiàng jǐhé	
Object group	对象组	Duìxiàng zǔ	OG
Object identifier	对象标识符	Duìxiàng biāozhìfú	
Object instance	对象实例	Duìxiàng shílì	
Object linking and embedding	对象的连接与嵌入	Duìxiàng liánjiē yǔ qiànrù	OLE
Object linking and embedding	目标连接与嵌入	Mùbiāo liánjiē yǔ qiànrù	OLE
Object management architecture	对象管理结构	Duìxiàng guǎnlǐ jiégòu	OMA
Object management architecture	对象管理体系结构	Duìxiàng guǎnlǐ tǐxì jiégòu	OMA
Object management group	对象管理组	Duìxiàng guǎnlǐ zǔ	OMG
Object management group	对象管理组织	Duìxiàng guǎnlǐ zǔzhī	OMG
Object management group-common data representation	客体管理组 - 通用数据表示	Kètǐ guǎnlǐ zǔ-tōng yòng shùjù biǎoshì	OMG-CDR
Object management group-general internal object request broker (ORB) protocol	客体管理组 - 一般内部 ORB 协议	Kètǐ guǎnlǐ zǔ-yībān nèibù ORB xiéyì	OMG-GIOP
Object management-oriented modeling tools	面向管理对象建模工具	Miànxiàng guǎnlǐ duìxiàng jiànmo gōngjù	OOMT
Object model	对象模型	Duìxiàng móxíng	
Object model development tool	对象模型开发工具	Duìxiàng móxíng kāifā gōngjù	OMDT
Object model template	对象模型模板	Duìxiàng móxíng múbǎn	OMT
Object modeling technique	对象模型技术	Duìxiàng móxíng jìshù	OMT
Object module assembly program	目标模块汇编程序	Mùbiāo mókuài huìbiān chéngxù	OMAP
Object module library	目标模块库	Mùbiāo mókuài kù	OML
Object module library update	目标模块库修改	Mùbiāo mókuài kù xiūgǎi	OMLU

Object owner	对象所有者	Duìxiàng suǒyǒuzhě	
Object permission	对象权限	Duìxiàng quánxiàn	
Object pooling	对象池化	Duìxiàng chíhuà	
Object program	目标程序	Mùbiāo chéngxù	
Object program loader	目标程序装入器	Mùbiāo chéngxù zhuāngrùqì	OPL
Object push profile	对象推操作	Duìxiàng tuī cāozuò	
Object references	对象参照	Duìxiàng cānzhào	
Object registration	对象注册	Duìxiàng zhùcè	
Object relationship model	对象关系模型	Duìxiàng guānxi móxíng	
Object relationship model	对象联系模型	Duìxiàng liánxì móxíng	
Object rendering	对象表达	Duìxiàng biǎodá	
Object request broker	对象请求代理	Duìxiàng qǐngqiú dàilǐ	ORB
Object request broker	对象请求代理器	Duìxiàng qǐngqiú dàilǐqì	ORB
Object request broker	目标请求掮客	Mùbiāo qǐngqiú qiánkè	ORB
Object reuse (IPsec)	客体重用	Kètǐ chóngyòng	
Object supports	对象支持	Duìxiàng zhīchí	OS
Object type	客体类型	Kètǐ lèixíng	
Object variable	对象变量	Duìxiàng biànliàng	
Object, destination, target	目标	Mùbiāo	
Object-based	基于对象的	Jīyú duìxiàngde	
Object-based analysis-synthesis coding	基于对象分析合成编码	Jīyú duìxiàng fēnxī héchéng biānmǎ	OBASC
Objective estimation or evaluation	客观评价	Kèguān píngjià	
Objective reference equivalent meter	客观参考当量表	Kèguān cānkǎo dāngliàng biǎo	
Object-oriented	面向对象	Miànxiàng duìxiàng	
Object-oriented	面向对象的	Miànxiàng duìxiàngde	
Object-oriented analysis	面向对象分析	Miànxiàng duìxiàng fēnxī	OOA
Object-oriented compiler	面向对象编译	Miànxiàng duìxiàng biānyì	
Object-oriented database	面向对象数据库	Miànxiàng duìxiàng shùjùkù	OODB
Object-oriented database system	面向对象数据库系统	Miànxiàng duìxiàng shùjùkù xìtǒng	OODS
Object-oriented design	面向对象设计	Miànxiàng duìxiàng shèjì	OOD
Object-oriented design	面向目标的设计	Miànxiàng mùbiāode shèjì	OOD
Object-oriented programming	面向对象编程	Miànxiàng duìxiàng biānchéng	OOP
Object-oriented programming	面向对象程序设计	Miànxiàng duìxiàng chéngxù shèjì	OOP
Object-oriented programming	面向对象的程序设计	Miànxiàng duìxiàngde chéngxù shèjì	OOP
Object-process diagram	对象过程图	Duìxiàng guòchéng tú	OPD
Object-process methodology	对象过程方法	Duìxiàng guòchéng fāngfǎ	OPM
Objects-by-reference	对象引用	Duìxiàng yǐnyòng	
Observability	可观测性	Kěguāncèxìng	
Observation during and after construction	施工监测	Shīgōng jiāncè	
Observed time difference	观察时间差异	Guānchá shíjiān chāyì	OTD
Obstacle	阻挡物	Zǔdǎngwù	
Obstacle detection	障碍物检测	Zhàng'àiwù jiǎncè	
Occupancy rate	占有率	Zhànyǒu lǜ	
Occupied band	占用频带	Zhànyòng píndài	
Occupied bandwidth	占用带宽	Zhànyòng dàikuān	
Occupied bandwidth	占有带宽	Zhànyǒu dàikuān	OBW

Occupied bandwidth	射频占有带宽	Shèpín zhànyǒu dàikuān	OBW
Occupied, busy	占线	Zhànxiàn	
Octal	八进制的	Bājìnzhìde	
Octal phase shift keying	八进制移相键控	Bājìnzhì yíxiāng jiànkòng	8PSK
Octave	倍频程	Bèipínchéng	
Octave filter	倍频程滤波器	Bèipínchéng lǜbōqì	
Octet	八比特组	Bā bǐtè zǔ	
Octet	八位组	Bā wèizǔ	
Octet	字节	Zìjié	
Octet (in digital data)	八位位组	Bā wèi wèizǔ	
Octet byte	八位字节	Bā wèi zìjié	
Octet counting	八位位组计数	Bā wèi wèizǔ jìshù	
Octet stream protocol	八比特组数据流协议	Bā bǐtè zǔ shùjùliú xiéyì	OSP
Octet stream protocol for Internet-hosted octet stream service	字节流协议用于因特网的主机字节流业务	Zìjié liú xiéyì yòng yú Yīntèwǎngde zhǔjī zìjié liú yèwù	OSP:IHOSS
Octet string type	八比特组串类型	Bā bǐtè zǔ chuàn lèixíng	
Octet-based IP packet throughput	基于字节的 IP 包吞吐量	Jīyú zìjiéde IP bāo tūntǔliàng	IPOT
Octtree	八叉树	Bā chā shù	
Odd parity check	奇检验	Qí jiǎnyàn	
Odd-parity check	奇数奇偶校验	Jīshù jī'ǒu jiàoyàn	OPC
ODMA dedicated control channel	ODMA 专用控制信道	ODMA zhuānyòng kòngzhì xìndào	ODCCH
ODMA dedicated traffic channel	ODMA 专用业务信道	ODMA zhuānyòng yèwù xìndào	ODTCH
ODMA random access channel	ODMA 随机接入信道	ODMA suíjī jiērù xìndào	ORACH
Off deck	断开板	Duànkāi bǎn	
Off-air call set up	停播建立呼叫	Tíngbō jiànlì hūjiào	
Off-air call setup	不占用空中通道的呼叫启动	Bùzhànyòng kōngzhōng tōngdàode hūjiào qǐdòng	OACSU
Off-air call setup	非占空呼叫建立	Fēizhànkōng hūjiào jiànlì	OACSU
Off-boresight angle	脱离瞄视角	Tuōlí miáo shìjiǎo	OBA
Off-centering	偏心数值	Piānxīn shùzhí	
Off-centering deflection coil	偏心偏转线圈	Piānxīn piānzhuǎn xiànquān	
Off-hook signal	摘机信号	Zhāijī xìnhào	
Off-hook waiting	摘机等候	Zhāijī děnghòu	
Off-hook, pick up a telephone	摘机	Zhāijī	
Office automation	办公自动化	Bàngōng zìdònghuà	OA
Office document architecture	办公文档结构	Bàngōng wéndàng jiégòu	ODA
Office of issue	收汇局	Shōuhuì jú	
Office of Telecommunications Policy (US)	电信政策办公室	Diànxìn zhèngcè bàngōngshì	OTP
Offices exchanging international remittances	通汇局	Tōnghuì jú	
Official code	正式代码	Zhèngshì dàimǎ	
Official comment (in groupware document handling; originally a term in official circles meaning 'to write an official reply to a petition')	批示	Pīshì	
Official language	官方语言	Guānfāng yǔyán	
Official name	正式名称	Zhèngshì míngchēng	
Official name body	正式名称本体	Zhèngshì míngchēng běntǐ	
Official name text	正式名称文字	Zhèngshì míngchēng wénzì	
Official street name	正式街道名称	Zhèngshì jiēdào míngchēng	

Official street name body	正式街道名称本体	Zhèngshì jiēdào míngchēng běntǐ	
Official street name text	正式街道名称文字	Zhèngshì jiēdào míngchēng wénzì	
Off-line	离线	Líxiàn	
Off-line	脱机	Tuōjī	
Off-line crypto operation	脱机加密操作	Tuōjī jiāmì cāozuò	
Off-line primitive sequence	离线原语序列	Líxiàn yuányǔ xùliè	OLS
Off-line remittance service counter	非联网汇兑网点	Fēiliánwǎng huìduì wǎngdiǎn	
Off-line test	离线测试	Líxiàn cèshì	
Off-line test	脱机测试	Tuōjī cèshì	
Off-screen surface	屏外表面	Píng-wài biǎomiàn	
Offset	偏差	Piānchā	
Offset	偏置	Piānzhì	
Offset (adjective)	偏置的	Piānzhìde	
Offset amplitude-phase shift keying	补偿幅-相偏移键控	Bǔcháng fú—xiāng piānyí jiànkòng	OAPSK
Offset feed	偏置馈源	Piānzhì kuìyuán	
Offset parabolic antenna	偏置抛物面天线	Piānzhì pāowùmiàn tiānxiàn	
Offset paraboloidal reflector antenna	偏置抛物面反射器天线	Piānzhì pāowùmiàn fǎnshèqì tiānxiàn	
Offset quadrature amplitude shift keying	偏移正交幅移键控	Piānyí zhèngjiāo fúyí jiànkòng	OQASK
Offset quadrature phase shift keying	偏移四相移相键控	Piānyí sìxiāng yíxiāng jiànkòng	OQPSK
Offset quadrature phase shift keying	偏移正交相移键控	Piānyí zhèngjiāo xiàngyí jiànkòng	OQPSK
Offset quadriphase phase shift keying	偏移四相相移键控	Piānyí sìxiàng xiàngyí jiànkòng	OQPSK
Offset quadriphase shift keying	偏置四相相移键控	Piānzhì sìxiāng xiāngyí jiànkòng	OQPSK
Offset-keyed quadriphase phase shift keying	参差四相相移键控	Cēncī sìxiāng xiāngyí jiànkòng	OQPSK
Offset-keying quadrature phase shift keying	偏移键控正交相移键控	Piānyí jiànkòng zhèngjiāo xiàngyí jiànkòng	OM-QPSK
Off-site maintenance	非现场维护	Fēixiànchǎng wéihù	
Oh, I see (computer chat)	哦,我明白了	Ó, wǒ míngbai le	OIC
Ohm (unit of resistance)	欧姆	Oū-mǔ	Ω
Oil pump carriage	油泵车	Yóubèng chē	
Oil-filled cable	充油电缆	Chōng yóu diànlǎn	OFC
Okumura model (to calculate RF path loss in urban area)	奥村计算法	Ào-cūn jìsuàn fǎ	
Olympus	奥林巴斯	Ào-lín-bā-sī	
Omegameter (in SMT)	奥米加表	Àomǐjiā biǎo	
Omnibus service circuit	站间联络公务电路	Zhàn-jiān liánluò gōngwù diànlù	
Omni-directional antenna	全向天线	Quánxiàng tiānxiàn	OA, ODA
Omni-directional antenna	全向天线	Quánxiàng tiānxiàn	
Omni-directional antenna (in a given plane)	全向辐射天线	Quánxiàng fúshè tiānxiàn	
Omni-directional radiator	无方向性辐射器	Wúfāng xiàngxìng fúshèqì	
Omron (Japan optical instrument mfr.)	欧姆龙	Oū-mǔ-lóng	
On deck (switching on exciter)	接通板（接通激励器）	Jiētōng bǎn (jiētōng jīlìqì)	
On wall surface (telecom installation)	沿墙面敷设	Yán qiángmiàn fūshè	WS
On-air-call-set-up	占空建立呼叫	Zhànkōng jiànlì hūjiào	
On-board communication station (on a ship)	船上通信电台	Chuánshàng tōngxìn diàntái	
On-board controller	板上控制器	Bǎn-shàng kòngzhìqì	OBC
Onboard debugger	板载调试器	Bǎnzài tiáoshìqì	
On-chip memory	片上存储器	Piàn-shàng cúnchǔqì	OCM
One pulse per second	秒脉冲	Miǎo màichōng	1PPS

One to one marketing	一对一行销	Yī duì yī xíngxiāo	OOM
One week forecast	一周预报	Yīzhōu yùbào	
One-dimensional datum	一维数据	Yīwéi shùjù	
One-dimensional linear array	一维线阵	Yīwéi xiàn zhèn	
One-dimensional phase-sweep active phase-controlled array antenna	一维相扫有源相控阵天线	Yīwéi xiàngsǎo yǒuyuán xiàngkòngzhèn tiānxiàn	
Oneness	单一化	Dānyīhuà	
One-point multiple access communications	一点多址通信	Yīdiǎn duōzhǐ tōngxìn	DZ
One-port	单端口	Dānduānkǒu	
One-port network	单端网络	Dānduān wǎngluò	
One-port network	单端口网络	Dānduānkǒu wǎngluò	
One-shot multi-vibrator	单稳线路	Dānwěn xiànlù	
One-step activation	一步激活	Yībù jīhuó	
One-step deactivation	一步去激活	Yībù qù jīhuó	
One-stop shopping	一站购齐	Yīzhàn gòuqí	
One-time password (crypto)	一次性口令	Yīcìxìng kǒulìng	OTP
One-time programmable	一次性编程	Yīcìxìng biānchéng	
One-time signature scheme	一次性签名方案	Yīcìxìng qiānmíng fāng'àn	
One-to-many relationship	一对多联系	Yī duì duō liánxì	
One-to-many relationship (for database)	一对多关系	Yī duì duō guānxi	
One-to-one relationship (for database)	一对一关系	Yī duì yī guānxi	
One-way communication	单向通信	Dānxiàng tōngxìn	OWC
One-way function algorithm	单向功能算法	Dānxiàng gōngnéng suànfǎ	O-ALG
One-way logical channel incoming	单向逻辑信道入	Dānxiàng luójì xìndào rù	
One-way logical channel outgoing	单向逻辑信道出	Dānxiàng luójì xìndào chū	
One-way trust	单向信任	Dānxiàng xìnrèn	
On-hook waiting	挂机等候	Guàjī děnghòu	
Online	联机	Liánjī	
On-line	网上	Wǎngshàng	
On-line	线上	Xiànshàng	
Online access	联机访问	Liánjī fǎngwèn	OA
Online analog output	在线模拟量输出	Zàixiàn mónǐliàng shūchū	OAO
Online analysis and processing	在线分析与处理	Zàixiàn fēnxī yǔ chǔlǐ	OAP
Online analytical processing	联机分析处理	Liánjī fēnxī chǔlǐ	OLAP
Online automatic testing function	在线自动测试功能	Zàixiàn zìdòng cèshì gōngnéng	
Online billing server	在线计费服务器	Zàixiàn jìfèi fúwùqì	OBS
Online crypto-operation (IPsec)	联机加密操作	Liánjī jiāmì cāozuò	
On-line diagnostics	联线诊断	Liánxiàn zhěnduàn	OLD
Online grid control	在线格网控制	Zàixiàn géwǎng kòngzhì	OGC
On-line handwriting signature verification	在线手写签名认证	Zàixiàn shǒuxiě qiānmíng rènzhèng	
Online help	在线帮助	Zàixiàn bāngzhù	
Online insertion and removal	在线插入和拆卸	Zàixiàn chārù hé chāixiè	OIR
On-line payment	通兑	Tōngduì	
On-line philatelic service	网上集邮业务	Wǎngshàng jíyóu yèwù	
Online query	在线查询	Zàixiàn cháxún	
On-line real-time control	线上实时控制	Xiànshàng shíshí kòngzhì	
Online redo log (for database)	联机重做日志	Liánjī chóngzuò rìzhì	

English	Chinese	Pinyin	Abbr.
On-line remittance	网上汇款	Wǎngshàng huìkuǎn	
On-line remittance service counter	联网汇兑网点	Liánwǎng huìduì wǎngdiǎn	
Online service provider	在线服务提供者	Zàixiàn fúwù tígōngzhě	OSP
On-line test (short for 联机测试)	联试	Liánshì	
On-line testing	在线测试	Zàixiàn cèshì	
Online transaction processing	在线事务进程	Zàixiàn shìwù jìnchéng	OLTP
Online transaction processing (for database)	联机事务处理	Liánjī shìwù chǔlǐ	OLTP
Online transformation	在线变换	Zàixiàn biànhuàn	
On-off keying	开关键控	Kāiguān jiànkòng	OOK
On-off keying	通断键控	Tōng duàn jiànkòng	OOK
On-off keying	通断键控	Tōngduàn jiànkòng	OOK
On-off transmission	启闭传输	Qǐbì chuánshū	
On-site data processing	现场数据处理	Xiànchǎng shùjù chǔlǐ	OSDP
On-site maintenance; in situ maintenance	现场维护	Xiàncháng wéihù	
On-site test, in-situ test	现场试验	Xiànchǎng shìyàn	
On-the-fly packet switching	高速包交换	Gāosù bāo jiāohuàn	
On-the-fly packet switching	就近分组交换	Jiùjìn fēnzǔ jiāohuàn	
Open (system) distributed management architecture	开放分布管理体系	Kāifàng fēnbù guǎnlǐ tǐxì	ODMA
Open (system) distributed processing	开放分布处理	Kāifàng fēnbù chǔlǐ	ODP
Open applications architecture	开放应用体系结构	Kāifàng yìngyòng tǐxì jiégòu	OAA
Open Arcade Architecture Forum	开放式 Arcade 体系论坛	Kāifàngshì Arcade tǐxì lùntán	OAAF
Open Architecture Developers Group	开放结构开发组织	Kāifàng jiégòu kāifā zǔzhī	OADG
Open channel	明渠	Míngqú	
Open circuit	开路	Kāilù	
Open circuit termination	开路终端	Kāilù zhōngduān	
Open connection port dialog	打开连接端口对话	Dǎkāi liánjiē duānkǒu duìhuà	OCPD
Open cooperative computing architecture	开放式协作运算体系	Kāifàng-shì xiézuò yùnsuàn tǐxì	OCCA
Open data link interface	开放数据链路接口	Kāifàng shùjù liànlù jiēkǒu	ODI
Open data services (for database)	开放式数据服务	Kāifàng-shì shùjù fúwù	ODS
Open database communication	开放式数据库互连	Kāifàng-shì shùjùkù hùlián	ODBC
Open database connectivity	开放数据库互连	Kāifàng shùjùkù hùlián	ODBC
Open database connectivity	开放数据库连通性	Kāifàng shùjùkù liántōngxìng	ODBC
Open database connectivity	开放式数据库链接	Kāifàng-shì shùjùkù liànjiē	ODBC
Open distribution telecom architecture	分布式开放的电信结构	Fēnbùshì kāifàngde diànxìn jiégòu	ODTA
Open document management architecture	开放式文件管理结构	Kāifàng-shì wénjiàn guǎnlǐ jiégòu	ODMA
Open geodata interoperability specification	开放式地学数据互操作规范	Kāifàng-shì dìxué shùjù hùcāozuò guīfàn	OGIS
Open GIS consortium	开放式 GIS 协会	Kāifàng-shì GIS xiéhuì	OGC
Open information model	开放信息模型	Kāifàng xìnxī móxíng	OIM
Open Java virtual machine interface	开放 JAVA 虚拟机接口	Kāifàng JAVA xūnǐ jī jiēkǒu	OJI
Open line carrier	明线载波	Míngxiàn zàibō	MZ
Open logical channel	打开逻辑通道	Dǎkāi luóji tōngdào	OLC
Open logical channel acknowledge	打开逻辑通道确认	Dǎkāi luóji tōngdào quèrèn	OLCA
Open logical channel reject	打开逻辑通道拒绝	Dǎkāi luóji tōngdào jùjué	OLCR
Open primitive signal	连接建立原语信号	Liánjiē jiànlì yuányǔ xìnhào	OPN
Open service access	开放业务接入	Kāifàng yèwù jiērù	OSA
Open service architecture	开放的业务结构	Kāifàngde yèwù jiégòu	OSA

Open shortest path first	开放最短路径优先	Kāifàng zuìduǎn lùjìng yōuxiān	OSPF
Open shortest path first [Protocol]	最短路径先开协议	Zuìduǎn lùjìng xiān kāi xiéyì	OSPF
Open shortest path first protocol	开放最短路经优先协议	Kāifàng zuìduǎn lùjīng yōuxiān xiéyì	OSPF
Open shortest path first protocol	开放式最短路径优先协议	Kāifàngshì zuìduǎn lùjìng yōuxiān xiéyì	OSPF
Open slot, gapped	开隙	Kāixì	
Open Software Foundation	开放软件基金会	Kāifàng ruǎnjiàn jījīnhuì	OSF
Open system	开放系统	Kāifàng xìtǒng	
Open system environment	开放系统环境	Kāifàng xìtǒng huánjìng	
Open system interchange	开放系统互联	Kāifàng xìtǒng hùlián	OSI
Open system interconnection	开放系统互连	Kāifàng xìtǒng hùlián	OSI
Open system interconnection environment	开放系统互连环境	Kāifàng xìtǒng hùlián huánjìng	
Open system interconnection model	开放式系统互连模型	Kāifàng-shì xìtǒng hùlián móxíng	OSIM
Open system interconnection plan	开放型系统互连计划	Kāifàng-xíng xìtǒng hùlián jìhuà	OSIP
Open systems architecture	开放系统体系结构	Kāifàng xìtǒng tǐxì jiégòu	OSA
Open systems interconnect (OSI) management-based interface realization for customer cetwork management service	用户网络管理业务的基于开放式系统互连参考模型管理的接口实现	Yònghù wǎngluò guǎnlǐ yèwùde jīyú kāifàngshì xìtǒng hùlián cānkǎo móxíng guǎnlǐde jiēkǒu shíxiàn	CNMc
Open systems interconnection (reference model)	开放系统互连(参考模型)	Kāifàng xìtǒng hùlián (cānkǎo móxíng)	OSI
Open trench shallow burial	明槽浅埋	Míng cáo qiǎn mái	
Open-circuit voltage	开路电压	Kāilù diànyā	
Opening code	开门码	Kāimén mǎ	
Opening period	开放期间	Kāifàng qījiān	
Open-loop control system	开环控制系统	Kāihuán kòngzhì xìtǒng	
Open-loop gain	开环增益	Kāihuán zēngyì	
Open-loop voltage gain	开环电压增益	Kāihuán diànyā zēngyì	
Open-phase protection	断相保护	Duànxiāng bǎohù	
Operand	操作数	Cāozuòshù	
Operand	运算数	Yùnsuàn shù	
Operand address register	操作数据地址寄存器	Cāozuò shùjù dìzhǐ jìcúnqì	OAR
Operand field	操作数字段	Cāozuòshù zìduàn	
Operating and maintenance back panel	操作维护后面板	Cāozuò wéihù hòumian bǎn	OMBP
Operating bandwidth	工作带宽	Gōngzuò dàikuān	
Operating capacitance	工作电容	Gōngzuò diànróng	
Operating class (of an amplifying stage)	工作类别	Gōngzuò lèibié	
Operating conditions	工作条件	Gōngzuò tiáojiàn	
Operating conditions	运行条件	Yùnxíng tiáojiàn	
Operating expenses	运营成本	Yùnyíng chéngběn	OPEX
Operating frequency	工作频率	Gōngzuò pínlǜ	
Operating frequency range	工作频率范围	Gōngzuò pínlǜ fànwéi	
Operating life	工作寿命	Gōngzuò shòumìng	
Operating state	工作状态	Gōngzuò zhuàngtài	
Operating support system	运行支持系统	Yùnxíng zhīchí xìtǒng	OSS
Operating system	操作系统	Cāozuò xìtǒng	OS
Operating system command languages	操作系统命令语言	Cāozuò xìtǒng mìnglìng yǔyán	OSCL
Operating system for distributed switching	分散交换的操作系统	Fēnsàn jiāohuànde cāozuò xìtǒng	OSDS
Operating system function	操作系统功能	Cāozuò xìtǒng gōngnéng	OSF

Operating time	工作时间	Gōngzuò shíjiān	
Operating time between failures	失效间工作时间	Shīxiào-jiān gōngzuò shíjiān	
Operating wavelength	工作波长	Gōngzuò bōcháng	
Operating wavelength range	工作波长范围	Gōngzuò bōcháng fànwéi	
Operation	运行	Yùnxíng	
Operation and maintenance	运行和维护	Yùnxíng hé wéihù	OAM
Operation and maintenance	运行与维护	Yùnxíng yǔ wéihù	O&M
Operation and maintenance center	操作维护中心	Cāozuò wéihù zhōngxīn	OMC
Operation and maintenance link	操作维护链路	Cāozuò wéihù liànlù	OML
Operation and management	操作与管理	Cāozuò yǔ guǎnlǐ	OAM
Operation code	操作码	Cāozuòmǎ	OP
Operation field	操作码字段	Cāozuòmǎ zìduàn	
Operation indicator	运算指示符	Yùnsuàn zhǐshìfú	
Operation parameter	运算参数	Yùnsuàn cānshù	
Operation sub-system	操作子系统	Cāozuò zixìtǒng	OSS
Operation support system	操作支援系统	Cāozuò zhīyuán xìtǒng	OSS
Operation support system	运营支撑系统	Yùnyíng zhīchēng xìtǒng	OSS
Operation support system	运营支持系统	Yùnyíng zhīchí xìtǒng	OSS
Operation support system/business support system	业务运营支撑系统	Yèwù yùnyíng zhīchēng xìtǒng	OSS/BSS, BOSS
Operation system	运行系统	Yùnxíng xìtǒng	OS
Operation system function	运行系统功能	Yùnxíng xìtǒng gōngnéng	OSF
Operation system function block	运行系统功能块	Yùnxíng xìtǒng gōngnéng kuài	OSF
Operation system function or mediation function	操作系统功能或协调功能	Cāozuò xìtǒng gōngnéng huò xiétiáo gōngnéng	OSF/MF
Operation system or mediation device	操作系统或协调装置	Cāozuò xìtǒng huò xiétiáo zhuāngzhì	OS/MD
Operation, administration and maintenance	运行，管理和维护	Yùnxíng, guǎnlǐ hé wéihù	OAM
Operation, administration and maintenance center	运行、管理和维护中心	Yùnxíng、guǎnlǐ hé wéihù zhōngxīn	OAMC
Operation, administration, maintenance, and provisioning	运行管理维护和预置	Yùnxíng guǎnlǐ wéihù hé yùzhì	OAM&P
Operational amplifier	运算放大器	Yùnsuàn fàngdàqì	
Operational analysis	操作分析	Cāozuò fēnxī	OA
Operational control center	操作控制中心	Cāozuò kòngzhì zhōngxīn	
Operational design and analysis	操作设计与分析	Cāozuò shèjì yǔ fēnxī	ODA
Operational maximum usable frequency	工作最高可用频率	Gōngzuò zuìgāo kěyòng pínlǜ	
Operational parameter	工作参数	Gōngzuò cānshù	
Operational phase (of product life cycle)	使用阶段	Shǐyòng jiēduàn	
Operational status bit	操作状态位	Cāozuò zhuàngtài wèi	OSB
Operational-address instruction	运算地址指令	Yùnsuàn dìzhǐ zhǐlìng	OAI
Operations and maintenance	操作和维护	Cāozuò hé wéihù	O&M; OM
Operations and maintenance application part	操作维护应用部分	Cāozuò wéihù yìngyòng bùfen	OMAP
Operations and maintenance center	操作与维护中心	Cāozuò yǔ wéihù zhōngxīn	OMC
Operations and maintenance link	操作与维护链路	Cāozuò yǔ wéihù liànlù	OML
Operations and maintenance sub-system	操作维护分系统	Cāozuò wéihù fēn xìtǒng	OMS
Operations and maintenance unit (board)	操作维护单元（板）	Cāozuò wéihù dānyuán (bǎn)	OMU
Operations management center	操作管理中心	Cāozuò guǎnlǐ zhōngxīn	OMC
Operations support system	操作支持系统	Cāozuò zhīchí xìtǒng	OSS
Operations, administration and maintenance	操作管理和维护	Cāozuò guǎnlǐ hé wéihù	OAM

English	Chinese	Pinyin	Abbreviation
Operations, administration and maintenance	操作、维护和管理	Cāozuò, wéihù hé guǎnlǐ	OA&M
Operations, administration and maintenance center	操作,管理和维护中心	Cāozuò, guǎnlǐ hé wéihù zhōngxīn	OAMC
Operations, administration, maintenance and provisioning	操作管理维护和指配	Cāozuò guǎnlǐ wéihù hé zhǐpèi	OAM&P
Operator (computational)	操作符	Cāozuò fú	
Operator (computational)	运算符	Yùnsuàn fú	
Operator call-in signal	呼叫话务员信号	Hūjiào huàwùyuán xìnhào	
Operator determined barring	操作员确定闭锁	Cāozuòyuán quèdìng bìsuǒ	ODB
Operator determined barring	运营者决定的闭锁业务	Yùnyíngzhě juédìngde bìsuǒ yèwù	Odb
Operator distance dialing	操作员远程拨号	Cāozuòyuán yuǎnchéng bōhào	ODD
Operator signal	话务员信号	Huàwùyuán xìnhào	OPR
Operator specific service	运营者特定业务	Yùnyíngzhě tèdìng yèwù	OSS
Operator's console	操作台	Cāozuòtái	
Operator-oriented language	面向操作员的语言	Miànxiàng cāozuòyuánde yǔyán	OOL
Operators harmonization group	运营者融合组	Yùnyíngzhě rónghé zǔ	OHG
Oplock (in SAMBA)	机会锁	Jīhuì suǒ	
Opportunity driven multiple access	驱动多接入机会	Qūdòng duō jiērù jīhuì	ODMA
Opposition duplex	反压式双工	Fǎnyāshì shuānggōng	
Optel	奥普泰	Ào-pǔ-tài	
Optic line back panel	光线路后面板	Guāng xiànlù hòumian bǎn	OLBP
Optic link switch interface	光链路交换接口	Guāng liànlù jiāohuàn jiēkǒu	OLSI
Optical access network	光接入网	Guāng jiērù wǎng	OAN
Optical access network	光纤接入网	Guāngxiān jiērùwǎng	OAN
Optical add and drop multiplexer	光分插复用器	Guāng fēnchā fùyòngqì	OADM
Optical add drop multiplexer	光波分插复用器	Guāngbō fēn chā fùyòngqì	OADM
Optical add/drop multiplexer	光分插复用设备	Guāng fēn/chā fùyòng shèbèi	OADM
Optical add/drop multiplexer	光上/下路复用器	Guāng shàng/xià lù fùyòngqì	OADM
Optical adhesive	光学用接著剂	Guāngxué-yòng jiēzhejì	
Optical amplifer section adapter	光放大段适配	Guāng fàngdà duàn shìpèi	OASA
Optical amplifier	光放大器	Guāng fàngdàqì	OA
Optical amplifier section	光放大段	Guāng fàngdà duàn	OAS
Optical amplifier section overhead handling	光放大段开销处理	Guāng fàngdà duàn kāixiao chǔlǐ	OASOH
Optical amplifier section termination	光放大段终结	Guāng fàngdà duàn zhōngjié	OAST
Optical amplifier span	光放段	Guāng fàng duàn	OAS
Optical attached aerial cable	附属式架空光缆	Fùshǔ-shì jiàkōng guānglǎn	OPAC
Optical attenuator	光衰减器	Guāng shuāijiǎnqì	
Optical axis	光轴	Guāngzhóu	
Optical backbone network	光纤骨干网	Guāngxiān gǔgàn wǎng	
Optical barcode reader	光条形码阅读器	Guāng tiáoxíng mǎ yuèdúqì	OBR
Optical barcode recognition	光学条码识读	Guāngxué tiáomǎ shídú	OBR
Optical beam flame detector	线型光速火焰探测器	Xiànxíng guāngsù huǒyàn tàncèqì	OBFD
Optical bench	光具座	Guāng jùzuò	
Optical booster amplifier	功率光放大器	Gōnglǜ guāng fàngdàqì	BA
Optical booster amplifier	光功放	Guāng gōng fàng	OBA
Optical branching device	光分路器	Guāng fēnlùqì	OBD
Optical burst switching	光突发交换	Guāng tūfā jiāohuàn	

Optical bypass switch	光旁路开关	Guāng pánglù kāiguān	
Optical cable connector	光缆连接器	Guānglǎn liánjiēqì	
Optical cable connector interface	光缆连接器界面	Guānglǎn liánjiēqì jièmiàn	
Optical cable jacketing	光缆护套	Guānglǎn hùtào	
Optical cable remote on-line supervision system	光缆远程在线监控系统	Guānglǎn yuǎnchéng zàixiàn jiānkòng xìtǒng	
Optical cable resources management system	光缆资源管理系统	Guānglǎn zīyuán guǎnlǐ xìtǒng	
Optical cable splice	光缆固定接头	Guānglǎn gùdìng jiētóu	
Optical cables along electrical power lines	电力线架空光缆	Diànlìxiàn jiàkōng guānglǎn	OCEPL
Optical carrier	光载波	Guāng zàibō	OC
Optical carrier level 1	光运载第 1 级	Guāng yùnzài dì yī jí	OC-1
Optical carrier level-N	光载波级 N	Guāng zàibō jí N	OC-N
Optical cement	光学用胶合剂	Guāngxué-yòng jiāohéjì	
Optical channel	光通道	Guāng tōngdào	OC
Optical channel	光通路	Guāng tōnglù	OCh
Optical channel	光信道	Guāng xìndào	Och
Optical channel adapter	光通道适配器	Guāng tōngdào shìpèiqì	OCA
Optical channel adapter	光通道转接器	Guāng tōngdào zhuǎnjiēqì	OCA
Optical channel cost	光通道代价	Guāng tōngdào dàijià	
Optical channel layer	光通道层	Guāng tōngdào céng	OCH
Optical channel overhead handling	光通路开销处理	Guāng tōnglù kāixiao chǔlǐ	OCOH
Optical channel power penalty	光通道功率代价	Guāng tōngdào gōnglǜ dàijià	
Optical channel termination	光通道终结	Guāng tōngdào zhōngjié	OCT
Optical channel termination	光通路终结	Guāng tōnglù zhōngjié	OCT
Optical character recognition	光学字符识别	Guāngxué zìfú shíbié	OCR
Optical character recognition	光学字符识读	Guāngxué zìfú shídú	OCR
Optical character recognition equipment	光学字元阅读机	Guāngxué zìyuán yuèdújī	OCR
Optical chopper	光截波器	Guāng jiébōqì	
Optical circulator	光环流器	Guāng huánliúqì	
Optical code division multiple access	光码分多址	Guāng mǎfēn duōzhǐ	
Optical communication system	光通讯系统	Guāng tōngxùn xìtǒng	OCS
Optical conductor	光导体	Guāngdǎotǐ	
Optical connection	光学连接	Guāngxué liánjiē	
Optical connection controller	光连接控制器	Guāng liánjiē kòngzhìqì	OCC
Optical connector	光连接器	Guāng liánjiēqì	
Optical control device	光控制元件	Guāng kòngzhì yuánjiàn	
Optical core device	光核心设备	Guāng héxīn shèbèi	OCD
Optical core switch	光核心交换	Guāng héxīn jiāohuàn	
Optical coupler	光耦合器	Guāng ǒuhéqì	
Optical coupler, tap/splitter	光纤耦合器	Guāngxiān ǒuhéqì	
Optical cross-connect	光交叉连接器	Guāng jiāochā liánjiēqì	OXC
Optical cross-connect node	光交叉连接节点	Guāng jiāochā liánjiē jiédiǎn	OXCN
Optical cross-connection	光交叉连接	Guāng jiāochā liánjiē	OXC
Optical data disk	数据记录光盘	Shùjù jìlù guāngpán	ODD
Optical data unit	光数据单元	Guāng shùjù dānyuán	ODU
Optical demultiplexer	光分波器	Guāng fēnbōqì	OD
Optical design and engineering services	光学设计及技术服务	Guāngxué shèjì jí jìshù fúwù	

Optical design consultant	光学设计顾问	Guāngxué shèjì gùwèn	
Optical design software and equipment	光学设计软件及设备	Guāngxué shèjì ruǎnjiàn jí shèbèi	
Optical device polishing machine	光学元件研磨加工设备	Guāngxué yuánjiàn yánmó jiāgōng shèbèi	
Optical device vacuum evaporation equipment	光学元件真空蒸镀设备	Guāngxué yuánjiàn zhēnkōng zhēng dù shèbèi	
Optical digital voice processor	光学数字音频信息处理机	Guāngxué shùzì yīnpín xìnxī chǔlǐjī	ODVP
Optical disk	光碟	Guāngdié	
Optical disk	光盘	Guāngpán	
Optical disk data storage material	光碟数据记录材料	Guāngdié shùjù jìlù cáiliào	
Optical disk substrate	光碟基板	Guāngdié jībǎn	
Optical disk substrate material	光碟基板材料	Guāngdié jībǎn cáiliào	
Optical disk technology	光盘技术	Guāngpán jìshù	
Optical distance measurement	光学测距	Guāngxué cèjù	
Optical distance measuring device	光学测距仪	Guāngxué cèjùyí	
Optical distributed network	光分配网络	Guāng fēnpèi wǎngluò	ODN
Optical distribution frame	光配线架	Guāng pèixiànjià	ODF
Optical distribution frame	光纤分配架	Guāngxiān fēnpèijià	ODF
Optical distribution network	光配线网	Guāng pèixiànwǎng	ODN
Optical domain service interconnect	光域业务互连	Guāngyù yèwù hùlián	ODSI
Optical domain service interconnect	光域业务内部连接	Guāngyù yèwù nèibù liánjiē	ODSI
Optical domain service interworking	光域业务互联	Guāngyù yèwù hùlián	ODSI
Optical Domain Services Internetworking Federation	光域业务互连联盟	Guāngyù yèwù hùlián liánméng	ODSI
Optical etching machine	光刻机	Guāng qún jiégòu	
Optical feed system	光学馈电系统	Guāngxué kuìdiàn xìtǒng	
Optical fiber	光导纤维	Guāngdǎo xiānwéi	
Optical fiber	光导纤维	Guāngdǎo xiānwéi	
Optical fiber	光纤	Guāngxiān	
Optical fiber	光纤	Guāngxiān	
Optical fiber (cable) composite connector	组合式光纤（缆）连接器	Zǔhé-shì guāngxiān (lǎn) liánjiēqì	
Optical fiber (cable) connector with focusing junction	有聚焦结的光纤（缆）连接器	Yǒu jùjiāojiéde guāngxiān (lǎn) liánjiē qì	
Optical fiber (cable) connector without focusing junction	无聚焦结的光纤（缆）连接器	Wújù jiāojiéde guāngxiān (lǎn) liánjiē qì	
Optical fiber amplifer	光纤放大器	Guāngxiān fàngdàqì	OFA
Optical fiber broadband coupler	光纤宽带耦合器	Guāngxiān kuāndài ǒuhéqì	
Optical fiber bundle	光纤束	Guāngxiān shù	
Optical fiber cable	光缆	Guānglǎn	
Optical fiber cable	光纤电缆	Guāngxiān diànlǎn	OFC
Optical fiber cable with no riser	无导体竖井光缆	Wúdǎotǐ shùjǐng guānglǎn	OFNR
Optical fiber coating machine	光纤着色机	Guāngxiān zhuosèjī	
Optical fiber communication conference	光纤通信国际会议	Guāngxiān tōngxìn guójì huìyì	OFC
Optical fiber communications	光纤通信	Guāngxiān tōngxìn	OFC
Optical fiber composite ground wire	复合地线光缆	Fùhé dìxiàn guānglǎn	OPGW
Optical fiber composite ground wire	光纤复合接地线	Guāngxiān fùhé jiēdìxiàn	OPGW
Optical fiber composite ground wire	接地线复合光缆	Jiēdìxiàn fùhé guānglǎn	OPGW
Optical fiber connector	光纤连接器	Guāngxiān liánjiēqì	

Optical fiber connector interface	光纤连接器界面	Guāngxiān liánjiēqì jièmiàn	
Optical fiber cord	光纤软线	Guāngxiān ruǎnxiàn	
Optical fiber cord	软光缆	Ruǎn guānglǎn	
Optical fiber display	光纤显示器	Guāngxiān xiǎnshìqì	
Optical fiber duplex adapter	光纤双芯适配器	Guāngxiān shuāngxīn shìpèiqì	
Optical fiber duplex connector	光纤双芯连接器	Guāngxiān shuāngxīn liánjiēqì	
Optical fiber fusion splicer	单芯融接机	Dānxīn róngjiējī	
Optical fiber fusion splicer	光纤熔接机	Guāngxiān róngjiējī	
Optical fiber loop converter	光纤环路转换器	Guāngxiān huánlù zhuǎnhuànqì	
Optical fiber pole-mounted composite ground wire	光纤复合架空地线	Guāngxiān fùhé jiàkōng dìxiàn	OPGW
Optical fiber preform	光纤预制棒	Guāngxiān yùzhì bàng	
Optical fiber pressure sensor	光纤压力传感器	Guāngxiān yālì chuángǎnqì	
Optical fiber ribbon cable	光线带光缆	Guāngxiàn dài guānglǎn	
Optical fiber sensor	光纤传感器	Guāngxiān chuángǎnqì	OFS
Optical fiber splice	光纤固定接头	Guāngxiān gùdìng jiētóu	
Optical fiber transfer function	光导纤维传送功能	Guāngdǎo xiānwéi chuánsòng gōngnéng	OFTF
Optical fiber transmission line	光纤传输线	Guāngxiān chuánshūxiàn	OFTL
Optical fiber transmission system	光纤传输系统	Guāngxiān chuánshū xìtǒng	OFTS
Optical fiber two-window bandwidth coupler	光纤双窗口带宽耦合器	Guāngxiān shuāngchuāngkǒu dàikuān ǒuhéqì	
Optical fiber wave division multiplexing coupler	光纤波分复用耦合器	Guāngxiān bōfēn fùyòng ǒuhéqì	
Optical fiber with no plenum layer	无导体天花板隔层光缆	Wúdǎotǐ tiānhuābǎn gécéng guānglǎn	OFNP
Optical filter	光滤波器	Guāng lǜbōqì	
Optical flow switching	光流交换	Guāngliú jiāohuàn	
Optical frequency division multiplexing	光频分复用	Guāng pínfēn fùyòng	OFDM
Optical frequency hopping	光跳	Guāng tiào	
Optical full service network	光纤全业务网	Guāngxiān quán yèwù wǎng	
Optical glass	光学玻璃	Guāngxué bōli	
Optical guided wave	光导波	Guāngdǎobō	OGW
Optical injector	光注入器	Guāng zhùrùqì	
Optical input and output device	光输入输出装置	Guāng shūrù shūchū zhuāngzhì	
Optical interface adapter	光接口适配器	Guāng jiēkǒu shìpèiqì	OIA
Optical Internetworking Forum	光互联网络论坛	Guāng hùlián wǎngluò lùntán	OIF
Optical internetworking Forum	光联网论坛	Guāng liánwǎng lùntán	OIF
Optical internetworking Forum	光因特网论坛	Guāng Yīntèwǎng lùntán	OIF
Optical internetworking forum	光纤互连网络论坛	Guāngxiān hùlián wǎngluò lùntán	OIF
Optical isolation (FOC)	光隔离度	Guāng gélídù	
Optical jumper	光纤跳线插头	Guāngxiān tiàoxiàn chātóu	
Optical label switch	光标记交换	Guāng biāojì jiāohuàn	OLS
Optical layer cross connection	光层交叉连接	Guāng céng jiāochā liánjiē	OLXC
Optical line amplifier	光线路放大器	Guāng xiànlù fàngdàqì	OLA
Optical line amplifier	线路光放大器	Xiànlù guāng fàngdàqì	OLA
Optical line terminal	光线路终端	Guāng xiànlù zhōngduān	OLT
Optical line terminal	光纤线路终端	Guāngxiān xiànlù zhōngduān	OLT
Optical line transmission coding	光线路传输码型	Guāng xiànlù chuánshū mǎxíng	
Optical local area network system	光区域网络系统	Guāng qūyù wǎngluò xìtǒng	
Optical loop subscriber carrier system	光用户环路载波系统	Guāng yònghù huánlù zàibō xìtǒng	

Optical material	光学材料	Guāngxué cáiliào	
Optical material machining service	光学材料机械加工	Guāngxué cáiliào jīxiè jiāgōng	
Optical micro-photo-engraving encryption	光学缩微光刻加密技术	Guāngxué suōwēi guāngkè jiāmì jìshù	
Optical mouse	光标	Guāngbiāo	
Optical mouse	光学滑鼠	Guāngxué huáshǔ	
Optical multiplex section adapter	光复用段适配	Guāng fùyòng duàn shì pèi	OMSA
Optical multiplex section overhead handling	光复用段开销处理	Guāng fùyòng duàn kāixiao chǔlǐ	OMSOH
Optical multiplex section termination	光复用段终结	Guāng fùyòng duàn zhōngjié	OMST
Optical multiplex segment layer	光复用段层	Guāng fùyòng duàn céng	OMS
Optical multiplex stage	光复用段	Guāng fùyòng duàn	OMS
Optical multiplex stage protection	光复用段保护	Guāng fùyòng duàn bǎohù	OMSP
Optical multiplexer	光复用器	Guāng fùyòngqì	OM
Optical multiplexer	光合波器	Guāng hébōqì	OM
Optical multiplexer/demultiplexer	光复用器/解复用器	Guāng fùyòngqì/jiě fùyòngqì	OM/DM
Optical multiplexer/demultiplexer	光解复用器	Guāng jiě/fùyòngqì	OD
Optical multiplexing	光复用	Guāng fùyòng	OM
Optical multiplexing terminal	光复用终端	Guāng fùyòng zhōngduān	OMT
Optical multi-service node	光多业务节点设备	Guāng duō yèwù jiédiǎn shèbèi	OMSN
Optical network termination	光网络终端	Guāng wǎngluò zhōngduān	ONT
Optical network unit	光网络单元	Guāng wǎngluò dānyuán	ONU
Optical network unit	光纤网络单元	Guāngxiān wǎngluò dānyuán	ONU
Optical orthogonal code	光正交码	Guāng zhèngjiāo mǎ	OOC
Optical packet data unit	光分组数据单元	Guāng fēnzǔ shùjù dānyuán	OPDU
Optical packet switch	光包交换	Guāng bāo jiāohuàn	OPS
Optical packet switching	光分组交换	Guāng fēnzǔ jiāohuàn	OPS
Optical passive device	光被动元件	Guāng bèidòng yuánjiàn	
Optical path	光路	Guāng lù	
Optical path length	光程长度	Guāngchéng chángdù	
Optical performance monitor	光性能监测器	Guāng xìngnéng jiāncèqì	OPM
Optical performance monitoring	光性能监控	Guāng xìngnéng jiānkòng	OPM
Optical phase conductor (FOC)	光纤复合相导线	Guāngxiān fùhé xiāng dǎoxiàn	OPPC
Optical phase shifter	光移相器	Guāng yíxiàngqì	
Optical positioning system	光学定位系统	Guāngxué dìngwèi xìtǒng	OPS
Optical power budget	光功率预算	Guāng gōnglǜ yùsuàn	
Optical power control	光功率控制	Guāng gōnglǜ kòngzhì	
Optical power grounded waveguide optical fiber	地线复合光缆	Dìxiàn fùhéguāng lǎn	OPGW
Optical power grounded waveguide optical fiber	光纤架空地线	Guāngxiān jiàkōng dìxiàn	OPGW
Optical power without optical alarm	无光告警光功率	Wú guāng gàojǐng guāng gōnglǜ	
Optical pre-amplifier	光前置放大器	Guāng qiánzhì fàngdàqì	
Optical printer	光学印表机	Guāngxué yìnbiǎojī	
Optical probe	光学探头	Guāngxué tàntóu	OP
Optical pulse generator	光脉冲产生设备	Guāng màichōng chǎnshēng shèbèi	
Optical receiver	光接收机	Guāng jiēshōujī	Rx
Optical repeater equipment	光学中继设备	Guāngxué zhōngjì shèbèi	ORE
Optical resonators	光共振器	Guāng gòngzhènqì	
Optical retun loss	光回波损耗	Guāng huíbō sǔnhào	ORL

Optical return loss	光回呼损耗	Guāng huíhū sǔnhào	ORL
Optical return loss	光回损	Guāng huísǔn	
Optical ribbon cable	光纤带	Guāngxiān dài	
Optical ribbon cable	光纤带	Guāngxiān dài	
Optical section	光信号段	Guāng xìnhào duàn	OS
Optical section	光纤段	Guāngxiān duàn	OS
Optical signal processing	光学信号处理	Guāngxué xìnhào chǔlǐ	OSP
Optical signal to noise ratio	光信噪比	Guāng xìn zào bǐ	OSNR
Optical signaling and routing protocol	光信令路由协议	Guāng xìnlìng lùyóu xiéyì	OSRP
Optical signal-to-noise ratio	光信号-噪声比	Guāng xìnhào-zàoshēng bǐ	OSNR
Optical space-division multiplexing	光空分多路复用	Guāng kōngfēn duōlù fùyòng	OSDM
Optical space-division multiplexing	光空分复用	Guāng kōngfēn fùyòng	OSDM
Optical spectrum analyzer	光频谱分析单元	Guāng pínpǔ fēnxī dānyuán	OSA
Optical sub-network connection protection	光子网连接保护	Guāng zǐwǎng liánjiē bǎohù	O-SNCP
Optical sub-network connection protection	光子网连接保护	Guāngzǐ wǎng liánjiē bǎohù	O-SNCP
Optical supervisory channel	光监控通道	Guāng jiānkòng tōngdào	OSC
Optical supervisory channel	光监控通路	Guāng jiānkòng tōnglù	OSC
Optical supervisory channel	光监控信道	Guāng jiānkòng xìndào	OSC
Optical supervisory channel adapter	光监控通路适配	Guāng jiānkòng tōnglù shìpèi	OSCA
Optical surge protection	光浪涌保护	Guāng làngyǒng bǎohù	OSP
Optical surveillance channel	光监控信道	Guāng jiānkòng xìndào	OSC
Optical switch	光开关	Guāng kāiguān	
Optical table top	光学桌平台	Guāngxué zhuō píngtái	
Optical technology for Internet with multi-wavelength environment (Chinese term based on English abbreviation)	光时代	Guāng shídài	O-TIME
Optical terminal	光端机	Guāng duānjī	
Optical terminal module	光纤终端模块	Guāngxiān zhōngduān mókuài	
Optical terminal multiplexer	光终端复用单元	Guāng zhōngduān fùyòng dānyuán	OTM
Optical terminal multiplexer	光终端复用器	Guāng zhōngduān fùyòngqì	OTM
Optical time domain reflectometer	光时域反射计	Guāng shíyù fǎnshèjì	OTDR
Optical time domain reflectometer	光时域反射器	Guāng shíyù fǎnshèqì	OTDR
Optical time domain reflectometer	光时域反射仪	Guāng shíyù fǎnshèyí	OTDR
Optical time domain reflectometry	光时域反射测量法	Guāng shíyù fǎnshè cèliángfǎ	OTDR
Optical time domain reflectometry	光时域反射法	Guāng shíyù fǎnshèfǎ	OTDR
Optical time-division multiplexing	光时分复用	Guāng shífèn fùyòng	OTDM
Optical transform unit	光转化单元	Guāng zhuǎnhuà dānyuán	OTU
Optical transmission equipment	光传输设备	Guāng chuánshū shèbèi	
Optical transmission network	光传输网	Guāng chuánshū wǎng	OTN
Optical transmission protection	光信道监控保护	Guāng xìndào jiānkòng bǎohù	OTP
Optical transmission section	光传送段	Guāng chuánsòng duàn	OTS
Optical transmission section layer	光传输段层	Guāng chuánshū duàn céng	
Optical transmission stage	光传输段	Guāng chuánshū duàn	
Optical transmitter	光发射机	Guāng fāshèjī	Tx
Optical transmitter	光发送机	Guāng fāsòngjī	Tx
Optical transponder	光转换器	Guāng zhuǎnhuànqì	OT
Optical transponder unit	波长转换器	Bōcháng zhuǎnhuànqì	OTU

Optical transponder unit	光转发器	Guāng zhuǎnfāqì	OTU
Optical transponder unit	光转换单元	Guāng zhuǎnhuàn dānyuán	OTU
Optical transponder unit	光转换器单元	Guāng zhuǎnhuànqì dānyuán	OTU
Optical transponder unit-add	上路波长转换器	Shànglù bōcháng zhuǎnhuànqì	OTU-A
Optical transponder unit-drop	下路波长转换器	Xiàlù bōcháng zhuǎnhuànqì	OTU-D
Optical transport hierarchy	光传送体制	Guāng chuánsòng tǐzhì	OTH
Optical transport management network	光传送网管理网	Guāng chuánsòng wǎng guǎnlǐ wǎng	OMN
Optical transport module	光传送模块	Guāng chuánsòng mókuài	OTM
Optical transport network	光传送网络	Guāng chuánsòng wǎngluò	OTN
Optical transport segment layer	光传送段层	Guāng chuánsòng duàn céng	OTS
Optical virtual private network	光虚拟专网	Guāng xūnǐ zhuān wǎng	OVPN
Optical virtual private network	光虚拟专用网	Guāng xūnǐ zhuānyòng wǎng	OVPN
Optical waveguide modulator	光波导形调变器	Guāng bōdǎo-xíng tiáobiànqì	
Optical wavelength division multiplexing	光波分复用	Guāng bōfēn fùyòng	
Optical wavelength interleaver	光波长交错器	Guāng bōcháng jiāocuòqì	
Optical/electronic converter	光/电转换器	Guāng/diàn zhuǎnhuànqì	O/E
Optical-coated abrasive	光学研磨材料	Guāngxué yánmó cáiliào	
Optical-electrical-optical converter	光/电/光转换器	Guāng/diàn/guāng zhuǎnhuànqì	OEO
Optically active device	光有源器件	Guāng yǒuyuán qìjiàn	OAD
Optically addressed light modulator	光选址光调制器	Guāng xuǎnzhǐ guāng tiáozhìqì	OALM
Optically amplified receiver	带光放大器的接收机	Dài guāng fàngdàqìde jiēshōujī	OAR
Optically amplified receiver	光放大接收机	Guāng fàngdà jiēshōujī	OAR
Optically amplified transmitter	带光放大器的发送机	Dài guāng fàngdàqìde fāsòngjī	OAT
Optically amplified transmitter	光放大发射机	Guāng fàngdà fāshèjī	OAT
Optically passive device	光无源器件	Guāng wúyuán qìjiàn	OPD
Optical-powder or grit abrasive	光学砥粒研磨材料	Guāngxué dǐlì yánmó cáiliào	
Optical-wheel abrasive	光学砥石研磨材料	Guāngxué dǐshí yánmó cáiliào	
Optics coupling display unit	光纤耦合显示器	Guāngxiān ǒuhé xiǎnshìqì	OCDU
Optics custom fabrication	光学元件订制	Guāngxué yuánjiàn dìngzhì	
Optimal amplitude and phase modulation	最佳调幅和调相	Zuìjiā tiáofú hétiáo xiāng	OAPM
Optimal information rate	最优信息率	Zuìyōu xìnxī lǜ	
Optimal interpolation	最优内插	Zuìyōu nèichā	OI
Optimal location	最优区位	Zuìyōu qūwèi	OL
Optimal routing	最佳路由选择	Zuìjiā lùyóu xuǎnzé	OR
Optimal routing for late call forwarding	对滞后呼叫前转的最佳路由选择	Duì zhìhòu hūjiào qiánzhuǎnde zuìjiā lùyóu xuǎnzé	ORLCF
Optimization	最优化	Zuìyōuhuà	
Optimization method	最优化方法	Zuìyōuhuà fāngfǎ	
Optimization model	优化模型	Yōuhuà móxíng	
Optimize synchronization	优化同步	Yōuhuà tóngbù	
Optimized production technology	优化生产技术	Yōuhuà shēngchǎn jìshù	OPT
Optimizer (device)	优化器	Yōuhuàqì	
Optimizer (program)	优化程序	Yōuhuà chéngxù	
Optimum jamming type	最佳干扰样式	Zuìjiā gānrǎo yàngshì	
Optimum stagger ratio	最佳参差比	Zuìjiā cēncī bǐ	
Optimum threshold	最佳门限	Zuìjiā ménxiàn	

Optimum usable frequency	最佳可用频率	Zuìjiā kěyòng pínlǜ	OUF
Optimum working frequency	最佳工作频率	Zuìjiā gōngzuò pínlǜ	OWF
Option	选项	Xuǎnxiàng	
Option pack	功能补丁	Gōngnéng bǔdìng	
Optional forward call indicator	可选前向呼叫指示	Kěxuǎn qiánxiàng hūjiào zhǐshì	
Optional parameter	任选参数	Rènxuǎn cānshù	
Optional response poll (bit protocol control)	任选响应轮询(位协议控制)	Rènxuǎn xiǎngyìng lúnxún (wèi xiéyì kòngzhì)	ORP
Optional service sub-system	任选服务子系统	Rènxuǎn fúwù zìxìtǒng	OSS
Optional user facility	任选用户设施	Rènxuǎn yònghù shèshī	OUF
Opto[-electronic] terminal lead	光[电]端机尾纤	Guāng [diàn] duānjī wěixiān	
Opto-electronic combiner	光电合架	Guāngdiàn héjià	
Opto-electronic integrated circuit	光电子集成	Guāng diànzǐ jíchéng	OEIC
Opto-electronic integrated circuit	光电集成电路	Guāngdiàn jíchéng diànlù	OEIC
Opto-electronic multiplex switch	光电多路复用开关	Guāngdiàn duōlù fùyòng kāiguān	OMS
Opto-electronic responsivity	光电灵敏度	Guāngdiàn língmǐndù	
Opto-electronic scanner	光电扫描仪	Guāngdiàn sǎomiáoyí	
Opto-electronic terminal	光电端机	Guāngdiàn duānjī	
OR function	“或”功能	Huò gōngnéng	OR
OR gate	“或”门	Huò mén	OG, OR
OR logic circuit	或逻辑电路	Huò luójídiànlù	OR
Orbit	轨道	Guǐdào	
Orbital elements	轨道要素	Guǐdào yàosù	
Orbital inclination (of an earth satellite)	轨道倾角	Guǐdào qīngjiǎo	
Orbital period (of a satellite)	轨道周期	Guǐdào zhōuqī	
Orbital plane (of a satellite)	轨道平面	Guǐdào píngmiàn	
Orbitron (mm wave device)	轨道管	Guǐdào guǎn	
Orchestration	和谐安排	Héxié ānpái	
Order of diversity	分集度	Fēnjí dù	
Order of sub-records	子记录的顺序	Zìjìlùde shùnxù	
Order wire unit	公务单元	Gōngwù dānyuán	OWU
Ordered pair	有序对	Yǒuxù duì	
Ordered set	有序集	Yǒuxù jí	
Ordered tree	有序数	Yǒuxù shù	
Orderwire	公务电话	Gōngwù diànhuà	OW
Orderwire	公务联络	Gōngwù liánluò	
Orderwire	公务线	Gōngwù xiàn	
Ordinal data	序数数据	Xùshù shùjù	
Ordinal logistic regression	序数逻辑回归	Xùshù luójì huíguī	
Ordinal reference system	有序参照系	Yǒuxù cānzhào xì	
Ordinal scale	顺序刻度	Shùnxù kèdù	
Ordinal temporal reference system	标准时间参照系	Biāozhǔn shíjiān cānzhàoxì	
Ordinal time scale	有序时间标度	Yǒuxù shíjiān biāodù	OTS
Ordinary correspondence	平常函件	Píngcháng hánjiàn	
Ordnance Survey Transfer Format (UK)	陆地测量部传输格式	Lùdì cèliángbù chuánshū géshi	OSTF
Organic activated (in SMT)	有机活性的	Yǒujī huóxìngde	OA
Organic land grid array	基板栅格阵列	Jībǎn zhàgé zhènliè	OLGA

English	Chinese	Pinyin	Abbr.
Organic light-emitting diode	有机发光二极管	Yǒujī fāguāng èrjíguǎn	OLED
Organic optical materials	有机光学材料	Yǒujī guāngxué cáiliào	
Organic photo conductor drum	有机感光鼓	Yǒujī gǎnguāng gǔ	
Organic thin-film field effect transistor	有机薄膜场效晶体管	Yǒujī bómó chǎng xiào jīngtǐguǎn	OTFT
Organization authority (CMM)	组织主管	Zǔzhī zhǔguǎn	OA
Organization name	组织名	Zǔzhī míng	
Organizational unique identifier	组织性唯一标示符	Zǔzhīxìng wéiyī biāoshìfú	OUI
Orientation	定方位	Dìng fāngwèi	
Orientation	定位	Dìngwèi	
Orientation range	定位范围	Dìngwèi fànwéi	
Orifice reflecting surface	有孔反射面	Yǒukǒng fǎnshè miàn	
Origin	起始点	Qǐshǐ diǎn	
Origin address field	源地址段	Yuán dìzhǐ duàn	OAF
Origin object	起始对象	Qǐshǐ duìxiàng	
Origin port address	始点端口地址	Shǐdiǎn duānkǒu dìzhǐ	OPA
Origin server	起源服务器	Qǐyuán fúwùqì	
Original called number	原始被叫号码	Yuánshǐ bèijiào hàomǎ	
Original equipment manufacturer	初始设备制造厂	Chūshǐ shèbèi zhìzàochǎng	OEM
Original equipment manufacturer	原始设备制造厂家	Yuánshǐ shèbèi zhìzào chǎngjiā	OEM
Original equipment manufacturer	原始设备制造商	Yuánshǐ shèbèi zhìzàoshāng	OEM
Original point code	起始信令点编码	Qǐshǐ xìnlìngdiǎn biānmǎ	OPC
Original topography	原地形	Yuán dìxíng	
Originating	发端	Fāduān	
Originating basic call state model	始发基本呼叫状态模型	Shǐfā jīběn hūjiào zhuàngtài móxíng	O-BCSM
Originating call	主叫	Zhǔjiào	OC
Originating CAMEL subscription information	发端 CAMEL 签约信息	Fāduān CAMEL qiānyuē xìnxī	O - CSI
Originating camel subscription information	始发 CAMEL 签约信息	Shǐfā CAMEL qiānyuē xìnxī	O-CSI
Originating local exchange	发端端局交换机	Fāduān duānjú jiāohuànjī	OLE
Originating number register	发端(信息)编号寄存器	Fāduān (xìnxī) biānhào jìcúnqì	ONR
Originating number sender	发端(信息)编号发送器	Fāduān (xìnxī) biānhào fāsòngqì	ONS
Originating point code	起源点编码	Qǐyuándiǎn biānmǎ	OPC
Originating point code	始点码	Shǐdiǎn mǎ	OPC
Originating subscriber	始发用户	Shǐfā yònghù	OS
Originating toll center	去话长途电话中心局	Qù huà chángtú diànhuà zhōngxīnjú	OTC
Originating traffic	发话话务	Fāhuà huàwù	
Origination indicator	主叫标识	Zhǔjiào biāozhì	OI
Origination point code	发源点编码	Fāyuándiǎn biānmǎ	OPC
Origination point code	源信令点	Yuán xìnlìng diǎn	OPC
Origination point code	源信令点编码	Yuán xìnlìng diǎn biānmǎ	OPC
Origination/termination-CAMEL subscription information	始发 / 终接 CAMEL 用户签约信息	Shǐfā/zhōngjiē CAMEL yònghù qiānyuē xìnxī	O/T-CSI
Originator	发起方	Fāqǐ fāng	
Originator	始发者	Shǐfāzhě	
Originator/recipient	始发者/接收者	Shǐfāzhě/jiēshōuzhě	O/R
Origin-destination survey	起终点调查(测量)	Qǐ-zhōngdiǎn diàochá (cèliáng)	
Orotron (mm wave device)	奥罗管	Ào luó guǎn	

Orphan	孤儿	Gū'ér	
Orphan (in word processing)	孤行	Gūxíng	
Orphan file	孤立文件	Gūlì wénjiàn	
Orthogonal array processor	正交数组处理程序	Zhèngjiāo shùzǔ chǔlǐ chéngxù	OAP
Orthogonal channel noise simulator	正交信道噪声仿真器	Zhèngjiāo xìndào zàoshēng fǎngzhēnqì	OCNS
Orthogonal channels	正交信道	Zhèngjiāo xìndào	
Orthogonal code	正交编码	Zhèngjiāo biānmǎ	
Orthogonal code-shift keying	正交码偏移键控	Zhèngjiāo mǎ piānyí jiànkòng	OCSK
Orthogonal co-frequency (adjective)	正交同频率的	Zhèngjiāo tóng pínlǜde	
Orthogonal coordinate axes	直角坐标轴	Zhíjiǎo zuòbiāozhóu	
Orthogonal dual linear polarization	正交双线极化	Zhèngjiāo shuāngxiàn jíhuà	
Orthogonal frequency division modulation	正交频分调制	Zhèngjiāo pínfēn tiáozhì	OFDM
Orthogonal frequency division multiplexing	正交频分复用	Zhèngjiāo pínfēn fùyòng	OFDM
Orthogonal frequency division multiplexing	直角频率部分多路复用	Zhíjiǎo pínlǜ bùfen duōlù fùyòng	OFDM
Orthogonal frequency division multiplexing forum	正交频分复用论坛	Zhèngjiāo pínfēn fùyòng lùntán	OFDMF
Orthogonal frequency spread	正交扩频	Zhèngjiāo kuòpín	
Orthogonal list	十字链表	Shízì liàn biǎo	
Orthogonal mode coupler	正交模耦合器	Zhèngjiāo mó ǒuhéqì	
Orthogonal modes	正交模	Zhèngjiāo mó	
Orthogonal polarization	正交极化	Zhèngjiāo jíhuà	OP
Orthogonal quaternary phase shift keying	正交四相相移键控	Zhèngjiāo sìxiàng xiàngyí jiànkòng	OQPSK
Orthogonal transmission diversity	正交发送分集	Zhèngjiāo fāsòng fēnjí	OTD
Orthogonal variable spread factor codes	正交可变扩频系数码	Zhèngjiāo kěbiàn kuòpín xìshù mǎ	OVSF
Orthogonal variable spreading factor	正交可变扩频因子	Zhèngjiāo kěbiàn kuòpín yīnzǐ	OVSF
Orthogonality	正交性	Zhèngjiāoxìng	
Orthographic view	正投影视图	Zhèngtóuyǐng shìtú	
Orthomode transducer	正交模耦合器	Zhèngjiāo mó ǒuhéqì	OMT
Orthomode transducer	正交模转换器	Zhèngjiāo mó zhuǎnhuànqì	
Ortho-photo map	正射影像地图	Zhèngshè yǐngxiàng dìtú	
Ortho-photography	正射投影像片	Zhèngshè tóuyǐng xiàngpiàn	
Ortho-photoquad	正方形正射图片	Zhèngfāngxíng zhèngshè túpiàn	
Ortho-photoscope	正射投影仪	Zhèngshè tóuyǐngyí	
Ortho-rectification	正射投影图像	Zhèngshè tóuyǐng túxiàng	
Oscillating element	振荡环节	Zhèndàng huánjié	
Oscillation	振荡	Zhèndàng	
Oscillation mode	振荡模式	Zhèndàng móshì	
Oscillator	振荡器	Zhèndàngqì	O, OSC
OSI reference model	OSI 参考模型	OSI cānkǎo móxíng	OSI RM
Other teletex character repertoires	其他智能用户电报字符总表	Qítā zhìnéng yònghù diànbào zìfú zǒng biǎo	
Other than telecommunication centers	非电信中心	Fēidiànxìn zhōngxīn	
Out of cell delineation	信元定界失同步	Xìnyuán dìngjiè shī tóngbù	OCD
Out of cell delineation	信元定界失步	Xìnyuán dìngjiè shībù	OCD
Out of order	乱序执行	Luànxù zhíxíng	OoO
Outbound	呼出	Hūchū	
Outbound control channel	出境控制信道	Chūjìng kòngzhì xìndào	OCC
Outbound packet processing (IPsec)	出界包处理	Chūjiè bāo chǔlǐ	

Out-channel call related user interaction	与呼叫相关的通路外的用户交互作用	Yǔ hūjiào xiāngguānde tōnglù wàide yònghù jiāohù zuòyòng	OCCRUI
Outdegree	出度	Chūdù	
Outdoor unit	室外单元	Shìwài dānyuán	ODU
Outer join (for database)	外联接	Wài liánjiē	
Outgoing access	向外访问	Xiàngwài fǎngwèn	OA
Outgoing call	去话	Qùhuà	
Outgoing call barred	阻止出呼叫	Zǔzhǐ chū hūjiào	
Outgoing call barred within the closed user group	在闭锁用户群中禁止出局呼叫	Zài bìsuǒ yònghù qún zhōng jìnzhǐ chūjú hūjiào	OCB
Outgoing call barring	呼出限制	Hūchū xiànzhì	
Outgoing circuit group	出局电路群	Chūjú diànlù qún	
Outgoing defect indication	输出缺陷指示	Shūchū quēxiàn zhǐshì	ODI
Outgoing error indication	输出误码指示	Shūchū wùmǎ zhǐshì	OEI
Outgoing interface	出接口	Chū jiēkǒu	oif
Outgoing interface list	输出接口列表	Shūchū jiēkǒu lièbiǎo	OIL
Outgoing primary switch frame	出局初级接线器架	Chūjú chūjí jiēxiànqì jià	OGPSWF
Outgoing repeater	输出转换器	Shūchū zhuǎnhuànqì	OGR
Outgoing repeater or relay	输出中继器	Shūchū zhōngjìqì	OGR
Outgoing rural line	农村去话电话线	Nóngcūn qùhuà diànhuà xiàn	OGRL
Outgoing sender	出局发码器	Chūjú fāmǎqì	OS
Outgoing sending link	出局发送链路	Chūjú fāsòng liànlù	OSL
Outgoing trunk	出中继	Chūzhōngjì	OGT
Outgoing trunk call circuit	打出去的长途电话电路	Dǎchūqùde chángtú diànhuà diànlù	OGTC
Outgoing trunk transmission system	去中继传输系统	Qù zhōngjì chuánshū xìtǒng	OTTS
Outlet	出口	Chūkǒu	
Outlet line terminal	引出线端子	Yǐnchū xiàn duānzi	
Outlier	离群点	Líqúndiǎn	
Outlier	异常值	Yìcháng zhí	
Outline	外形线	Wàixíng xiàn	
Out-of plane shear mode	平面外剪切模式	Píngmiàn-wài jiǎnqiē móshì	
Out-of-allocated band emission	划分频带外发射	Huàfēn píndài-wài fāshè	
Out-of-band	带外	Dài-wài	
Out-of-band attack (IPsec)	带外攻击	Dài-wài gōngjī	
Out-of-band emission	带外发射	Dài-wài fāshè	
Out-of-band emission	带外辐射	Dài-wài fúshè	OBE
Out-of-band emission	频带外发射	Píndài-wài fāshè	
Out-of-band power	带外功率	Dài-wài gōnglǜ	
Out-of-band signaling	带外信令	Dài-wài xìnlìng	
Out-of-band spectrum	带外频谱	Dài-wài pínpǔ	
Out-of-frame	帧失步	Zhèng shībù	OOF
Out-of-frame alignment time	帧失位时间	Zhèng shīwèi shíjiān	
Out-of-frame second	帧失步秒	Zhèng shībù miǎo	OFS
Output	输出	Shūchū	
Output acknowledged	输出认可	Shūchū rènkě	OA
Output buffer register	输出缓冲寄存器	Shūchū huǎnchōng jìcúnqì	OBR

English	Chinese	Pinyin	Abbr.
Output bus driver	输出总线驱动器	Shūchū zǒngxiàn qūdòngqì	OBD
Output characteristics	输出特性	Shūchū tèxìng	
Output command data set	输出指令数据装置	Shūchū zhǐlìng shùjù zhuāngzhì	OCDS
Output control shift register	输出控制移位寄存器	Shūchū kòngzhì yíwèi jìcúnqì	OCSR
Output data buffer	输出数据缓冲器	Shūchū shùjù huǎnchōngqì	ODBR
Output feedback	输出反馈	Shūchū fǎnkuì	OFB
Output filter	输出滤波器	Shūchū lǜbōqì	
Output format handler	输出格式处理器	Shūchū géshi chǔlǐqì	OFH
Output handler	输出处理器	Shūchū chǔlǐqì	OPH
Output impedance	输出阻抗	Shūchū zǔkàng	
Output jitter	输出抖动	Shūchū dǒudòng	
Output level	输出电平	Shūchū diànpíng	
Output limited message (IPsec TLS)	输出限制消息	Shūchū xiànzhì xiāoxi	
Output logic macrocell	输出逻辑宏单元	Shūchū luóji hóngdānyuán	
Output multiplex synchronizer	输出多路复用同步装置	Shūchū duōlù fùyòng tóngbù zhuāngzhì	OMS
Output optical power	输出光功率	Shūchū guāng gōnglǜ	
Output power control	输出电源控制	Shūchū diànyuán kòngzhì	
Output printer	输出打印机	Shūchū dǎyìnjī	OP
Output reference plane	输出参考面	Shūchū cānkǎo miàn	
Output register	输出寄存器	Shūchū jìcúnqì	OR
Output ripple voltage	输出绞波电压	Shūchū jiǎobō diànyā	
Output routing pool	输出布线池	Shūchū bùxiàn chí	
Output signal balance	输出口信号平衡	Shūchūkǒu xìnhào pínghéng	OSB
Output torque	输出转矩	Shūchū zhuànjǔ	
Outside diameter; exradius; outer diameter; external diameter; major diameter	外径	Wàijìng	
Outside director	外部董事	Wàibù dǒngshì	
Outside plant equipment	外部工厂设备	Wàibù gōngchǎng shèbèi	
Outside vapor deposition (FOC mfg)	外部汽相沉积法	Wàibù qìxiàng chénjī fǎ	OVD
Outside vapor phase deposition (FOC mfg)	外汽相沉积法	Wài qìxiàng chénjī fǎ	OVPD
Outside-tube [chemical] vapor deposition (for FOC)	外部化学气相沉积法	Wàibù huàxué qìxiàng chénjī fǎ	OVD
Outside-tube vapor deposition (for FOC)	管外气相沉积法	Guǎn-wài qìxiàng chénjī fǎ	OVD
Out-slot signaling	隙外信令	Xì-wài xìnlìng	
Outsourcing	外包	Wàibāo	
Outsourcing institute	外包研究所	Wàibāo yánjiūsuǒ	
Oval oscillation	椭圆振荡	Tuǒyuán zhèndàng	
Over consolidation ratio	超固结比	Chāogùjié bǐ	OCR
Over edge	界外	Jièwài	
Overall development	全面开发	Quánmiàn kāifā	
Overall loudness rating	总额定响度	Zǒng'é dìngxiǎngdù	OLR
Overall noise	总噪声	Zǒng zàoshēng	
Overbuild	过度建设	Guòdù jiànshè	
Overcharge (a battery)	过充电	Guòchōngdiàn	
Overclock	超频	Chāopín	
Overcrowding	过度拥挤	Guòdù yōngjǐ	
Overcurrent	过电流	Guòdiànliú	

English	Chinese	Pinyin	Abbr.
Overcurrent protection	过流保护	Guòliú bǎohù	
Over-current protection	过电流保护	Guòdiànliú bǎohù	
Overcurrent protection circuit	过流保护电路	Guòliú bǎohù diànlù	
Over-current protective device	过电流保护装置	Guòdiànliú bǎohù zhuāngzhì	
Over-damping	过度阻尼	Guòdù zǔní	
Over-discharge (run down a battery)	过放电	Guòfàngdiàn	
Overdraw (video term)	透支	Tòuzhī	
Overfitting	过适	Guòshì	
Overflow	溢出	Yìchū	OVF
Overflow	上溢	Shàng yì	OVF
Overflow	上限溢位	Shàngxiàn yìwèi	
Overflow meter	溢呼表	Yìhū biǎo	
Overflow route	溢呼路由	Yìhū lùyóu	
Overhead	额外开销	Éwài kāixiao	
Overhead (SDH term)	开销	Kāixiao	
Overhead access	开销接入	Kāixiao jiērù	OHA
Overhead and adaptation trail	开销和适配路径	Kāixiao hé shìpèi lùjìng	
Overhead processing	开销处理	Kāixiao chǔlǐ	OHP
Overhead processor (unit)	开销处理单元	Kāixiao chǔlǐ dānyuán	OHP
Overheat protection circuit	过温保护电路	Guòwēn bǎohù diànlù	
Overlap (in facsimile)	重叠	Chóngdié	
Overlap sending	重叠发送	Chóngdié fāsòng	
Overlap signaling	重叠信令	Chóngdié xìnlìng	
Overlapped PAM transmission with interlocking spectra	频谱互锁重叠的 PAM 传输	Pínpǔ hùsuǒ chóngdiéde PAM chuánshū	OPTIS
Overlay (GIS)	重叠	Chóngdié	
Overlay (GIS)	叠加	Diéjiā	
Overlay coverage	重叠覆盖	Chóngdié fùgài	
Overlay description language	覆盖描述语言	Fùgài miáoshù yǔyán	ODL
Overlay model	重叠模式	Chóngdié móshì	OM
Overlay structure program	覆盖结构程序	Fùgài jiégòu chéngxù	
Overload	过负载	Guòfùzài	
Overload	过载	Guòzài	
Overload	重载	Zhòngzài	
Overload circuit breaker	过载断路器	Guòzài duànlùqì	OCB
Overload control	过荷控制	Guòhè kòngzhì	
Overload control category	过荷分级控制	Guòhè fēnjí kòngzhì	
Overload current (of a circuit)	过载电流	Guòzài diànliú	
Overload factor (of a receiver)	过载系数	Guòzài xìshù	
Overload factor of receiver	接收机的过载系数	Jiēshōujīde guòzài xìshù	
Overload message	过载信息	Guòzài xìnxī	OLM
Overload point	过荷点	Guòhè diǎn	
Overload power	过载功率	Guòzài gōnglǜ	
Overload protecting circuit	过荷保护电路	Guòhè bǎohù diànlù	
Overload resolution	重载决议	Zhòngzài juéyì	
Overloaded function	重载的函数	Zhòngzàide hánshù	
Overloaded operator	被重载的操作符	Bèizhòngzàide cāozuò fú	

English	Chinese	Pinyin	Abbreviation
Over-moded waveguide	过模波导	Guòmó bōdǎo	
Over-modulation	过调制	Guòtiáozhì	
Overprint	叠印	Diéyìn	
Overreach interference	越站干扰	Yuèzhàn gānrǎo	
Override	重新定义	Chóngxīn dìngyì	
Override	覆写	Fùxiě	
Override	重载	Zhòngzài	
Overrun bit	超(负荷)运行位	Chāo (fùhè) yùnxíng wèi	OR
Over-sampling	过采样技术	Guòcǎiyàng jìshù	
Overshoot	过冲	Guòchōng	
Over-the-air parameter administration	空中下载业务准备	Kōngzhōng xiàzài yèwù zhǔnbèi	OTASP
Over-the-air service provisioning function	空中下载业务准备操作	Kōngzhōng xiàzài yèwù zhǔnbèi cāozuò	OTAF
Over-the-horizon radar	超视距雷达	Chāoshìjù léidá	
Over-voltage	过电压	Guòdiànyā	
Over-voltage protection	过电压保护	Guòdiànyā bǎohù	
Over-voltage protection (the O in BORSCHT)	过压保护	Guòyā bǎohù	
Over-voltage protection circuit	过压保护电路	Guòyā bǎohù diànlù	
Over-voltage to earth	对地过电压	Duìdì guòdiànyā	
Ownership	所有权	Suǒyǒuquán	
Oxidation furnace	氧化设备	Yǎnghuà shèbèi	
Oxide aligned transistor (product of TRW)	氧化物对准晶体管	Yǎnghuàwù duìzhǔn jīngtǐguǎn	OAT
Oxide-coated	敷氧化层的	Fūyǎnghuà céngde	O
Oxygen-free high conductivity copper	无氧高电导铜	Wúyǎng gāodiàndǎo tóng	OFHC

P

English	Chinese	Pinyin	Abbreviation
P delta effects	P-Δ 效应	P-Δ xiàoyìng	
P scope (plane position indicator)	P 型显示器(平面位置显示器)	P-xíng xiǎnshìqì (píngmiàn wèizhì xiǎnshìqì)	
P wave	P 波	P-bō	
p/4 shifted, differentially encoded quadrature phase-shift keying	p/4 相移的差分编码正交移相键控	p/4 xiàngyíde chāfēn biānmǎ zhèngjiāo yíxiàng jiànkòng	p/4DQPSK
Pacific Internet	太平洋网际网络	Tàipíngyáng wǎngjì wǎngluò	
Pacing	调步	Tiáobù	
Pack (verb)	紧缩	Jǐnsuō	
Package	程序包	Chéngxù bāo	
Package weight	包装重量	Bāozhuāng zhòngliàng	
Packages (in generic network information model)	特征包	Tèzhēng bāo	
Packaging density	装配密度	Zhuāngpèi mìdù	
Packaging efficiency	组装效率	Zǔzhuāng xiàolǜ	
Packet	包	Bāo	
Packet	报文分组	Bàowén fēnzǔ	
Packet	分组	Fēnzǔ	
Packet	信息包	Xìnxī bāo	
Packet access grant channel	分组接入应答信道	Fēnzǔ jiērù yìngdá xìndào	PACCH
Packet access grant channel	分组接入允许信道	Fēnzǔ jiērù yǔnxǔ xìndào	PAGCH
Packet access grant channel	分组接入准许信道	Fēnzǔ jiērù zhǔnxǔ xìndào	PAGCH
Packet accompanying control channel	分组伴随控制信道	Fēnzǔ bànsuí kòngzhì xìndào	PACCH

Packet adaptive routing	包自适应路径选择	Bāo zìshìyìng lùjìng xuǎnzé	PAR
Packet assembler/disassembler	报文分组组装器/拆卸器	Bàowén fēnzǔ zǔzhuāngqì/chāixièqì	PAD
Packet assembler/disassembler	分组装/卸	Fēnzǔ zhuāng/xiè	PAD
Packet assembler/disassembler	分组组装/分解设备	Fēnzǔ zǔzhuāng/fēnjiě shèbèi	PAD
Packet assembly	组装	Zǔzhuāng	PA
Packet assembly (data communications)	包装	Bāozhuāng	PA
Packet assembly and disassembly	包装配与拆卸	Bāo zhuāngpèi yǔ chāixiè	PAD
Packet assembly and disassembly	打包和拆包	Dǎbāo hé chāibāo	PAD
Packet assembly and disassembly	分组组装与拆卸	Fēnzǔ zǔzhuāng yǔ chāixiè	
Packet assembly/disassembly	分组拆装	Fēnzǔ chāizhuāng	PAD
Packet assembly/disassembly	分组装拆包	Fēnzǔ zhuāngchāi bāo	PAD
Packet assembly/disassembly equipment	分组装拆设备	Fēnzǔ zhuāngchāi shèbèi	PAD
Packet assembly/disassembly facility	分组装拆设施	Fēnzǔ zhuāngchāi shèshī	
Packet associated control channel	分组随路控制信道	Fēnzǔ suílù kòngzhì xìndào	PACCH
Packet broadcast control channel	分组广播控制信道	Fēnzǔ guǎngbō kòngzhì xìndào	PBCCH
Packet bus management interface	包总线管理接口	Bāo zǒngxiàn guǎnlǐ jiēkǒu	PBMI
Packet centralization equipment	分组集中器	Fēnzǔ jízhōngqì	PCE
Packet chaining	报文链	Bàowén liàn	
Packet check code (IPsec)	分组校检码	Fēnzǔ jiàojiǎn mǎ	
Packet circuit multiplication equipment	分组电路倍增设备	Fēnzǔ diànlù bèizēng shèbèi	PCME
Packet common control channel	分组公共控制信道	Fēnzǔ gōnggòng kòngzhì xìndào	PCCCH
Packet communication I/F card assembly	分组通信 I/F 集成卡	Fēnzǔ tōngxìn I/F jíchéng kǎ	PCIA
Packet control unit	分组控制单元	Fēnzǔ kòngzhì dānyuán	PCU
Packet controlled function	分组控制功能	Fēnzǔ kòngzhì gōngnéng	PCF
Packet data channel	分组数据信道	Fēnzǔ shùjù xìndào	PDCH
Packet data control function	分组数据控制功能	Fēnzǔ shùjù kòngzhì gōngnéng	PCF
Packet data convergence protocol	分组数据会聚协议	Fēnzǔ shùjù huìjù xiéyì	PDCP
Packet data network	分组数据网	Fēnzǔ shùjù wǎng	
Packet data network	分组数据网络	Fēnzǔ shùjù wǎngluò	PDN
Packet data protocol	分组数据协议	Fēnzǔ shùjù xiéyì	PDP
Packet data service network	分组数据业务网络	Fēnzǔ shùjù yèwù wǎngluò	PDSN
Packet data serving node	分组数据服务节点	Fēnzǔ shùjù fúwù jiédiǎn	PDSN
Packet data traffic channel	分组数据传输信道	Fēnzǔ shùjù chuánshū xìndào	PDTCH
Packet data traffic channel	分组数据业务信道	Fēnzǔ shùjù yèwù xìndào	PDTCH
Packet data transfer channel	分组数据传递信道	Fēnzǔ shùjù chuándì xìndào	PDTCH
Packet data unit	分组数据单元	Fēnzǔ shùjù dānyuán	PCU
Packet dropout measurement	丢包测量	Diūbāo cèliáng	
Packet encoding rules	分组编码规则	Fēnzǔ biānmǎ guīzé	PER
Packet entry event	分组进入事件	Fēnzǔ jìnrù shìjiàn	
Packet error rate	包出错率	Bāo chūcuò lǜ	PER
Packet error rate	分组差错率	Fēnzǔ chācuò lǜ	PER
Packet error rate	分组错误率	Fēnzǔ cuòwù lǜ	PER
Packet exit event	分组离开事件	Fēnzǔ líkāi shìjiàn	
Packet fair queuing	分组公平排队算法	Fēnzǔ gōngping páiduì suànfǎ	PFQ
Packet filtering	包过滤	Bāo guòlǜ	
Packet filtering	分组过滤	Fēnzǔ guòlǜ	

Packet format description language	报文格式描述语言	Bàowén géshi miáoshù yǔyán	PFDL
Packet grabber (hacker tool)	抓包器	Zhuābāoqì	
Packet handler	分组处理器	Fēnzǔ chǔlǐqì	PH
Packet handler for voice	语音分组处理程序（器）	Yǔyīn fēnzǔ chǔlǐ chéngxù (qì)	PHV
Packet handler function	分组处理器功能	Fēnzǔ chǔlǐqì gōngnéng	PHF
Packet handler interface	分组处理器接口	Fēnzǔ chǔlǐqì jiēkǒu	PHI
Packet handler module	分组处理模块	Fēnzǔ chǔlǐ mókuài	PHM
Packet handling	分组处理	Fēnzǔ chǔlǐ	
Packet handling interface	分组处理接口	Fēnzǔ chǔlǐ jiēkǒu	PHI
Packet header	包标题	Bāo biāotí	PH
Packet header (IPsec)	包头	Bāotóu	
Packet identification	分组包识别	Fēnzǔbāo shíbié	PID
Packet idle mode	分组空闲模式	Fēnzǔ kòngxián móshì	
Packet insertion rate	分组插入率	Fēnzǔ chārù lǜ	PIR
Packet Internet groper	分组因特网查询进程	Fēnzǔ Yīntèwǎng cháxún jìnchéng	PING
Packet Internet groper	分组因特网探索程序	Fēnzǔ Yīntèwǎng tànsuǒ chéngxù	PING
Packet Internet groper	网际包探测器	Wǎngjì bāo tàncèqì	PING
Packet layer control processor	分组层控制处理器	Fēnzǔ céng kòngzhì chǔlǐqì	PLCP
Packet layer protocol	分组层协议	Fēnzǔ céng xiéyì	PLP
Packet layer reference event	分组层参考事件	Fēnzǔ céng cānkǎo shìjiàn	PE
Packet line card	分组线路板	Fēnzǔ xiànlù bǎn	PLC
Packet local access	分组本地介入	Fēnzǔ běndì jièrù	
Packet loss rate	分组丢失率	Fēnzǔ diūshī lǜ	PLR
Packet mobile management	分组移动管理	Fēnzǔ yídòng guǎnlǐ	PMM
Packet mode	包方式	Bāo fāngshì	PM
Packet mode bearer service	分组承载业务	Fēnzǔ chéngzài yèwù	PMBS
Packet mode bearer service	分组模式承载业务	Fēnzǔ móshì chéngzài yèwù	PMBS
Packet multiplexer	包多路复用器	Bāo duōlù fùyòngqì	PMX
Packet notification channel	分组通知信道	Fēnzǔ tōngzhī xìndào	PNCH
Packet over SDH	承载分组信号的 SDH	Chéngzài fēnzǔ xìnhàode SDH	POS
Packet over synchronous digital hierarchy	在同步数字系统上传输分组	Zài tóngbù shùzì xìtǒng-shàng chuánshū fēnzǔ	PoS
Packet over synchronous digital hierarchy (SDH)	分组按同步数字体系传送	Fēnzǔ àn tóngbù shùzì tǐxì chuánsòng	POS
Packet paging channel	分组寻呼信道	Fēnzǔ xúnhū xìndào	PPCH
Packet radio	包无线电	Bāo wúxiàndiàn	
Packet radio network	分组无线网	Fēnzǔ wúxiàn wǎng	
Packet random access channel	分组随机接入信道	Fēnzǔ suíjī jiērù xìndào	PRACH
Packet reservation multiple access	分组预约多址	Fēnzǔ yùyuē duō zhǐ	PRMA
Packet routing address	分组路由选择地址	Fēnzǔ lùyóu xuǎnzé dìzhǐ	PRA
Packet scheduling algorithm	数据包调度算法	Shùjù bāo diàodù suànfǎ	
Packet statistical multiplexing	数字包统计多路复用	Shùzì bāo tǒngjì duōlù fùyòng	
Packet switch	分组交换机	Fēnzǔ jiāohuànjī	PAC
Packet switched data	包交换数据	Bāo jiāohuàn shùjù	PSD
Packet switched data network	分组交换数据网	Fēnzǔ jiāohuàn shùjù wǎng	PSDN
Packet switched data transmission service	分组交换数据传输业务	Fēnzǔ jiāohuàn shùjù chuánshū yèwù	
Packet switched digital data network	分组交换数字数据网	Fēnzǔ jiāohuàn shùzì shùjù wǎng	DATAPAC
Packet switched media gateway	分组域媒体网关	Fēnzǔ yù méitǐ wǎngguān	PS-MGW

Packet switched network	分组交换网络	Fēnzǔ jiāohuàn wǎngluò	PSN
Packet switched or switching	分组交换	Fēnzǔ jiāohuàn	PS
Packet switched public data network	包交换公共数据网	Bāo jiāohuàn gōnggòng shùjù wǎng	PSPDN
Packet switched public data network	包交换公众数据网	Bāo jiāohuàn gōngzhòng shùjù wǎng	PSPDN
Packet switched public data network	分组交换公共数据网	Fēnzǔ jiāohuàn gōnggòng shùjù wǎng	PSPDN
Packet switched public data network	分组交换共用数据网	Fēnzǔ jiāohuàn gòngyòng shùjù wǎng	PSPDN
Packet switched public data network	公众分组交换数据网	Gōngzhòng fēnzǔ jiāohuàn shùjù wǎng	PSPDN
Packet switched public data network	公众分组交换网	Gōngzhòng fēnzǔ jiāohuàn wǎng	PSPDN
Packet switching protocol	分组交换协议	Fēnzǔ jiāohuàn xiéyì	PSP
Packet temporary mobile station identity	分组移动台临时识别号	Fēnzǔ yídòngtái línshí shíbié hào	P-TMSI
Packet temporary mobile subscription identity	分组临时移动用户识别码	Fēnzǔ línshí yídòng yònghù shíbié mǎ	P-TMSI
Packet terminal	分组终端	Fēnzǔ zhōngduān	PT
Packet time advance control channel	分组时间提前量控制信道	Fēnzǔ shíjiān tíqiánliàng kòngzhì xìn dào	PTCCH
Packet timing advance control channel	分组时间提前信道	Fēnzǔ shíjiān tíqián xìndào	PTCCH
Packet timing control channel/downlink	分组定时控制信道一下行	Fēnzǔ dìngshí kòngzhì xìndào yīxià xíng	PTCCH/D
Packet timing control channel/uplink	分组定时控制信道一上行	Fēnzǔ dìngshí kòngzhì xìndào yī shàngxíng	PTCCH/U
Packet traffic channel	分组业务信道	Fēnzǔ yèwù xìndào	PTCH
Packet transfer mode	分组传递方式	Fēnzǔ chuándì fāngshì	
Packet transfer mode	分组传输模式	Fēnzǔ chuánshū móshì	
Packet transfer mode	分组传送模式	Fēnzǔ chuánsòng móshì	
Packet transfer protocol	包传输协议	Bāo chuánshū xiéyì	PTP
Packet transmission channel	包传输通道	Bāo chuánshū tōngdào	PTC
Packet trunking	分组中继	Fēnzǔ zhōngjì	
Packet voice terminal	报文语言终端	Bàowén yǔyán zhōngduān	PVT
Packet-filter firewall	包过滤式防火墙	Bāo guòlǜshì fánghuǒqiáng	
Packetized virtual circuit	包式虚拟电路	Bāo shì xūnǐ diànlù	PVC
Packet-level filtering	包级过滤	Bāo jí guòlǜ	
Packet-level protocol	包级协议	Bāo jí xiéyì	PLP
Packet-mode terminal	包方式终端	Bāo fāngshì zhōngduān	PMT
Packet-mode terminal	分组方式终端	Fēnzǔ fāngshì zhōngduān	PMT
Packet-switching node	分组交换节点	Fēnzǔ jiāohuàn jiédiǎn	PSN
Packing	包装	Bāozhuāng	
Packing boxes for half folding	半叠盖式包装箱	Bàndiégàishì bāozhuāngxiāng	
Packing fraction	敛集率	Liǎnjí lǜ	
Packing fraction loss	敛集率损耗	Liǎnjí lǜ sǔnhào	
Packing list	明细表	Míngxìbiǎo	P/L
Packing list	装箱单	Zhuāngxiāng dān	P/L
Pad attenuator	缓冲衰减器	Huǎnchōng shuāijiǎnqì	
Paddle card	插卡	Chākǎ	
p-adic vector expression	p 进制向量表示	p-jìnzhì xiàngliàng biǎoshì	
Page	页	Yè	
Page (verb)	寻呼	Xúnhū	
Page break (WP command)	页分界线	Yè fēnjièxiàn	
Page break (WP term)	分页符	Fēn yè fú	
Page coordinate system	页坐标系统	Yè zuòbiāo xìtǒng	
Page down key	下页键	Xiàyè jiàn	

Page extent	页面范围	Yèmiàn fànwéi	
Page flipping	页翻转	Yè fānzhuǎn	
Page indicator	寻呼指示器	Xúnhū zhǐshìqì	PI
Page length	页长	Yè cháng	
Page mode RAM	页面方式 RAM	Yèmiàn fāngshì RAM	
Page set	页集	Yè jí	
Page setup (WP command)	页面设置	Yèmiàn shèzhì	
Page size extension	页面尺寸扩展模式	Yèmiàn chǐcùn kuòzhǎn móshì	PSE
Page size extension 36-bit (chip)	页面尺寸扩展模式, 36 位	Yèmiàn chǐcùn kuòzhǎn móshì, 36 wèi	PSE36
Page split	页拆分	Yè chāifēn	
Page up key	上页	Shàng yè	
Page wait	页面等待	Yèmiàn děngdài	
Pager mode	寻呼模式	Xúnhū móshì	
Pages per minute	每分钟多少页	Měi fēnzhōng duōshao yè	PPM
Pages per minute (printer term)	页/分	Yè/ fēn	ppm
Paging block periodicity	寻呼闭塞周期性	Xúnhū bìsè zhōuqīxìng	PBP
Paging channel	寻呼信道	Xúnhū xìndào	PC, PCH
Paging control channel	寻呼控制信道	Xúnhū kòngzhì xìndào	PCCH
Paging indicator channel	寻呼指示信道	Xúnhū zhǐshì xìndào	PICH
Paging packet calculation	寻呼分组计算	Xúnhū fēnzǔ jìsuàn	
Paging procedure	寻呼规程	Xúnhū guīchéng	
Paging proceed flag	进行寻呼标志	Jìnxíng xúnhū biāozhì	PPF
Paging receiver	寻呼接收机	Xúnhū jiēshōujī	
Paging request	寻呼请求	Xúnhū qǐngqiú	PR
Paging request type	寻呼请求类型	Xúnhū qǐngqiú lèixíng	
Paging response	寻呼响应	Xúnhū xiǎngying	
Paging system	寻呼系统	Xúnhū xìtǒng	
Painter (radar term)	靶板	Bǎ bǎn	
Pair gain	线对增容	Xiànduì zēngróng	
Pair high bit-rate digital subscriber line	双线制高比特率数字用户线	Shuāngxiàn zhìgāo bǐtèlǜ shùzì yònghù xiàn	PHDSL
Paired-disparity code	成对不等性码	Chéngduì bùděngxìng mǎ	
Pairwise kerning	成对字符组间距	Chéngduì zìfú zǔ jiānjù	
Palette	调色板	Tiáosèbǎn	
Palette of functions	功能栏	Gōngnéng lán	
Pallet	货盘	Huòpán	
Palmtop	顶置盒	Dǐngzhìhé	
Palmtop computer	掌上型电脑	Zhǎngshàngxíng diànnǎo	
Pan (video term)	漫游	Mànyóu	
Pan American Satellite Corp. (US)	泛美卫星公司	Fànměi wèixīng gōngsī	PanAmSat
Pan unit and controller	云台及云台控制器	Yúntái jí yúntái kòngzhìqì	PAC
Panda Electronics (PRC company)	熊猫电子	Xióngmāo diànzǐ	
Panel (of radiating element)	盘	Pán	
Panel antenna	板状天线	Bǎnzhuàng tiānxiàn	
Panel of radiating dipoles	辐射偶极子盘	Fúshè ǒujízi pán	
Panel seal	面板密封	Miànbǎn mìfēng	
Pan-European digital cellular land mobile telecommunication system	泛欧数字蜂窝移动通信系统	Fàn'ōu shùzì fēngwō yídòng tōngxìn xìtǒng	

Panoramic receiver	全景接收机	Quánjǐng jiēshōujī	
Panoramic receiver	扫描接收机	Sǎomiáo jiēshōujī	
Paper map	纸质地图	Zhǐzhì dìtú	
Paper tape punch	纸带穿孔机	Zhǐdài chuānkǒngjī	PTP
Paper tape reader	纸带阅读机	Zhǐdài yuèdújī	PTR
Parabolic antenna	抛物面天线	Pāowùmiàn tiānxiàn	
Parabolic corner reflector	抛物面角型反射器	Pāowùmiàn jiǎo-xíng fǎnshèqì	PACORE
Parabolic cylindrical antenna	抛物柱面天线	Pāowù zhùmiàn tiānxiàn	
Parabolic reflector	抛物反射面	Pāowù fǎnshè miàn	
Parabolic reflector	抛物面反射器	Pāowùmiàn fǎnshèqì	
Parabolic reflector antenna	抛物反射面天线	Pāowù fǎnshè miàn tiānxiàn	
Parabolic torus antenna	抛物环面天线	Pāowù huánmiàn tiānxiàn	
Paraboloid mirror	抛物面镜	Pāowùmiàn jìng	
Paraboloidal reflector antenna	抛物面反射器天线	Pāowùmiàn fǎnshèqì tiānxiàn	
Paragraph (WP command)	段落	Duànluò	
Paragraph mark (WP command)	段落结束标志	Duànluò jiéshù biāozhì	
Parallax	视差	Shìchā	
Parallel	并行	Bìngxíng	
Parallel algorithm	并行算法	Bìngxíng suànfǎ	
Parallel annotation	并行注释	Bìngxíng zhùshì	
Parallel automatic calling	并行自动呼叫	Bìngxíng zìdòng hūjiào	
Parallel channel	并行信道	Bìngxíng xìndào	
Parallel communication interface	并行通信接口	Bìngxíng tōngxìn jiēkǒu	PCI
Parallel communications	并行通信	Bìngxíng tōngxìn	
Parallel compiler	并行编译器	Bìngxíng biānyìqì	
Parallel compiling	并行编译	Bìngxíng biānyì	
Parallel computing	并行计算	Bìngxíng jìsuàn	
Parallel concatenated convolutional code	并联链接卷积码	Bìnglián liànjiē juànjīmǎ	PCCC
Parallel feed	并馈	Bìng kuì	
Parallel feedback compensation network	并联校正网络	Bìnglián jiàozhèng wǎngluò	
Parallel frequency hopping	并行频率跳变	Bìngxíng pínlǜ tiàobiàn	PFH
Parallel genetic algorithm	并行遗传算法	Bìngxíng yíchuán suànfǎ	
Parallel graphics configuration	并行图像配置	Bìngxíng túxiàng pèizhì	PGC
Parallel input output	并行输入输出	Bìngxíng shūrù shūchū	PIO
Parallel instruction code	并行指令代码	Bìngxíng zhǐlìng dàimǎ	PIC
Parallel interface	并行接口	Bìngxíng jiēkǒu	
Parallel interference cancellation	并行干扰消除	Bìngxíng gānrǎo xiāochú	PIC
Parallel iterative matching	并行迭代匹配	Bìngxíng diédài pǐpèi	PIM
Parallel port	并行接口	Bìngxíng jiēkǒu	
Parallel processing	并行处理	Bìngxíng chǔlǐ	
Parallel processing perspective engine	平行处理透视引擎	Píngxíng chǔlǐ tòushì yǐnqíng	
Parallel resonant frequency	并联谐振频率	Bìnglián xiézhèn pínlǜ	PRF
Parallel scheduling	并行调度	Bìngxíng diàodù	
Parallel terminal	并行终端	Bìngxíng zhōngduān	
Parallel to serial converter	并串变换器	Bìng chuàn biànhuànqì	
Parallel transmission	并行传输	Bìngxíng chuánshū	

English	Chinese	Pinyin	Abbr.
Parallel video server	并行视频服务器	Bìngxíng shìpín fúwùqì	
Parallel virtual machine	并行虚拟计算机	Bìngxíng xūnǐ jìsuànjī	PVM
Parallel wire	平行线	Píngxíng xiàn	
Parallelism	并行性	Bìngxíngxìng	
Parallel-plate lens	平行板透镜	Píngxíng bǎn tòujìng	
Parameter	参量	Cānliàng	
Parameter	参数	Cānshù	
Parameter amplifier	参量放大器	Cānliàng fàngdàqì	
Parameter detector	参量检测器	Cānliàng jiǎncèqì	
Parameter estimation	参量估计	Cānliàng gūjì	
Parameter group identifier	参数组标识符	Cānshù zǔ biāozhì fú	PGI
Parameter identifier	参数标识符	Cānshù biāozhì fú	PI
Parameter list	参数列表	Cānshù lièbiǎo	
Parameter management frame	参数管理帧	Cānshù guǎnlǐ zhèng	PMF
Parameter validity check (CAD/CAM)	参数有效性检查	Cānshù yǒuxiàoxìng jiǎnchá	PVC
Parameter validity condition (CAD/CAM)	参数有效性条件	Cānshù yǒuxiàoxìng tiáojiàn	PVC
Parameter value	参数值	Cānshù zhí	PV
Parameterize	参数化	Cānshù huà	
Parametric down-converter	参量下变频器	Cānliàng xià biànpínqì	
Parametric drawing	参数化绘图	Cānshùhuà huìtú	
Parametric oscillator	参数振汤器	Cānshù zhèndàngqì	
Parametric up-converter	参量上变频器	Cānliàng shàng biànpínqì	
Parasitic element	寄生单元	Jìshēng dānyuán	
Parasitic feedback	寄生反馈	Jìshēng fǎnkuì	
Parasitic modulation	寄生调制	Jìshēng tiáozhì	
Parasitic oscillation	寄生振荡	Jìshēng zhèndàng	
Paraxial ray	傍轴光线	Bàngzhóu guāngxiàn	
Parcel coordinate system	局部坐标系	Júbù zuòbiāo xì	
Parcel identification numbers	地块标识号	Dìkuài biāozhìhào	
Pardon my jumping in (computer chat)	原谅我的参与	Yuánliàng wǒde cānyù	PMJI
Parent	父代	Fù dài	
Parent	母体	Mǔtǐ	
Parent class	父类	Fù lèi	
Parent domain	父域	Fù yù	
Parent object	父对象	Fù duìxiàng	
Parent-child linkage	父子类连接	Fùzǐ lèi liánjiē	
Parentheses ( )	圆括号	Yuán kuòhào	
Parentheses ( )	圆括弧	Yuán kuòhú	
Parenting	父处理	Fù chǔlǐ	
Parity bit	奇偶检验位	Jīǒu jiǎnyàn wèi	
Parity check	寄偶校验	Jì’ǒu jiàoyàn	PAR
Parity check	奇偶校验	Jīǒu jiàoyàn	
Parity check code	奇偶检验码	Jīǒu jiǎnyàn mǎ	
Parity check code	奇偶校验码	Jīǒu jiàoyàn mǎ	
Parity check function	奇偶检验功能	Jīǒu jiǎnyàn gōngnéng	
Parity error	寄偶错误	Jì’ǒu cuòwù	

English	Chinese	Pinyin	Abbreviation
Park (verb) (used for computer hard disk)	暂停	Zàntíng	
Parked	待复原	Dàifùyuán	
Parse	解析	Jiěxī	
Parser	解析器	Jiěxīqì	
Partial array test	小面阵试验	Xiǎomiàn zhèn shìyàn	
Partial constant angular velocity	部分恒定角速度	Bùfen héngdìng jiǎosùdù	PCAV
Partial effective area (of an antenna for a given polarization and direction)	部分有效面积	Bùfen yǒuxiào miànjī	
Partial failure	部分失效	Bùfen shīxiào	
Partial gain (of an antenna)	部分增益	Bùfen zēngyì	
Partial generator set	部分生成符集	Bùfen shēngchéngfú jí	
Partial ID number type	局部 ID 号码类型	Júbù ID hàomǎ lèixíng	PID
Partial information feedback	部分信息反馈	Bùfen xìnxī fǎnkuì	PIF
Partial loop back	部分环回	Bùfen huánhuí	
Partial mesh	部分网格	Bùfen wǎnggé	
Partial optical splitter	部分光分路器	Bùfen guāng fēnlùqì	
Partial parsing	部分句法分析	Bùfen jùfǎ fēnxī	
Partial path index (in XML)	部分路径索引	Bùfen lùjìng suǒyǐn	PPI
Partial period correlation	部分相关	Bùfen xiāngguān	PPC
Partial response frequency modulation	部分响应频率调制	Bùfen xiǎngyìng pínlǜ tiáozhì	PRFM
Partial response inter-symbol-interference and jitter free offset quadrature phase shift keying	部分响应符号间干扰和无跳动编移正交相移键控	Bùfen xiǎngyìng fúhào jiān gānrǎo hé wú tiàodòng biānyí zhèngjiāo xiāngyí jiànkòng	PR-IJF-OQPSK
Partial response maximum likelihood	最大可能部分反应	Zuìdà kěnéng bùfen fǎnyìng	PRML
Partial sequence numbers protocol data unit	部分序列号协议数据单元	Bùfen xùlièhào xiéyì shùjù dānyuán	PSNP
Partial specialization	局部特化	Júbù tèhuà	
Partial texture download	部分纹理下载	Bùfen wénlǐ xiàzài	
Partial transfer function	部分传递函数	Bùfen chuándì hánshù	PTF
Partiality test (circuit test to determine if one component receives more voltage than another, usually within permissible range of fluctuation leading to fault on either extreme.)	拉偏测试	Lāpiān cèshì	
Partially stabilized zirconia	部分稳定氧化锆	Bùfen wěndìng yǎnghuà gào	
Participating mode	加入模式	Jiārù móshì	
Participation factor	参与系数	Cānyù xìshù	
Participation vector	参与矢量	Cānyù shǐliàng	
Particle size, grain size	粒度	Lìdù	
Particle swarm optimization	粒子群优化	Lìzi qún yōuhuà	PSO
Particular mobile communication system	特种移动通信系统	Tèzhǒng yídòng tōngxìn xìtǒng	
Partition	分区	Fēnqū	
Partition boot sector	分区启动扇区	Fēnqū qǐdòng shànqū	
Partition information table	分区信息表	Fēnqū xìnxī biǎo	PIT
Partition refinement	分解精化	Fēnjiě jīnghuà	
Partitionable frequency expansion	可分频率展开	Kěfēn pínlǜ zhǎnkāi	
Partitioning, separation	分割	Fēngē	
Partner	配对	Pèiduì	
Partner list	配对表	Pèiduì biǎo	
Parts mounter (SMT)	贴片机	Tiēpiànjī	
Parts per million	百万分之几	Bǎiwàn fēn zhī jǐ	PPM

Parts per million	百万分率	Bǎiwàn fēnlǜ	PPm
Pass by reference	按引用传递	Àn yǐnyòng chuándì	
Pass by reference	传地址	Chuán dìzhǐ	
Pass by value	按值传递	Àn zhí chuándì	
Pass order	传递顺序	Chuándì shùnxù	
Pass port (FOC)	透射端口	Tòushè duānkǒu	
Pass through, cut across	穿越	Chuānyuè	
Pass verdict	通过判定	Tōngguò pàndìng	
Pass-along message (ISUP message)	传送信息	Chuánsòng xìnxī	PAM
Pass-along method	信号路由法	Xìnhào lùyóu fǎ	
Passband	通带	Tōngdài	
Passband	通频带	Tōngpíndài	
Passband flatness	通带平坦度	Tōngdài píngtǎndù	
Passing restrictions	限制通行	Xiànzhì tōngxíng	
Passive address auto configuration, stateful address auto-configuration	被动地址自动配置	Bèidòng dìzhǐ zìdòng pèizhì	
Passive component	无源元件	Wúyuán yuánjiàn	
Passive corrective network	无源校正网络	Wúyuán jiàozhèng wǎngluò	
Passive detection	无源探测	Wúyuán tàncè	
Passive dispersion compensator	无源色散补偿器	Wúyuán sèsàn bǔchángqì	PDC
Passive filter	无源滤波器	Wúyuán lǜbōqì	
Passive infrared detector	被动式红外传感器	Bèidòngshì hóngwài chuángǎnqì	PID
Passive jamming	无源干扰	Wúyuán gānrǎo	
Passive location	无源定位	Wúyuán dìngwèi	
Passive network	无源网络	Wúyuán wǎngluò	
Passive optical network	无源光网络	Wúyuán guāng wǎngluò	PON
Passive optical network	无源光纤网	Wúyuán guāngxiān wǎng	PON
Passive optical network based on ATM	基于 ATM 的无源光网络	Jīyú ATM de wúyuán guāng wǎngluò	A-PON
Passive reflector	无源反射器	Wúyuán fǎnshèqì	
Passive relay station	无源中继站	Wúyuán zhōngjìzhàn	
Passive sensor	无源遥感器	Wúyuán yáogǎnqì	
Passive threat	被动威胁	Bèidòng wēixié	
Passive tracking	无源跟踪	Wúyuán gēnzōng	
Passive wiretapping	被动窃听	Bèidòng qiètīng	
Passive wiretapping (IPsec)	被动搭线窃听	Bèidòng dāxiàn qiètīng	
Passphrase	通行码	Tōngxíng mǎ	
Pass-through query	直接传递查询	Zhíjiē chuándì cháxún	
Pass-through statement	直接传递语句	Zhíjiē chuándì yǔjù	
Password	口令	Kǒulìng	PW
Password	密码	Mìmǎ	PS
Password	通过字	Tōngguò zì	PW
Password	通行字	Tōngxíng zì	
Password authentication protocol	口令认证协议	Kǒulìng rènzhèng xiéyì	PAP
Password authentication protocol	密码认证协议	Mìmǎ rènzhèng xiéyì	PAP
Password authentication protocol	密码验证协议	Mìmǎ yànzhèng xiéyì	PAP
Password cracking (hacker attack)	口令字猜测	Kǒulìng zì cāicè	
Password dialog (IPsec)	口令对话	Kǒulìng duìhuà	

Password registration failure	口令登记故障	Kǒulìng dēngjì gùzhàng	
Paste (WP command)	粘贴	Zhāntiē	
Paste special (WP command)	粘贴为	Zhāntiē wéi	
Patch	补丁	Bǔding	
Patch	修补	Xiūbǔ	
Patch (verb)	插入	Chārù	
Patch analysis	嵌块分析	Qiànkuài fēnxī	
Patch antenna	微块天线	Wēikuài tiānxiàn	
Patch cord	接插软线	Jiēchā ruǎnxiàn	
Patch cord, jumper	跳线尾纤	Tiàoxiàn wěixiān	
Patch panel	插线板	Chāxiànbǎn	
Patch panel	配线盘	Pèixiàn pán	
Path (in a computer directory)	路径	Lùjìng	
Path (in communications networks and SDH)	通道	Tōngdào	
Path allocation	通道分配	Tōngdào fēnpèi	
Path control layer	路径控制层	Lùjìng kòngzhì céng	
Path control network	路径控制网	Lùjìng kòngzhì wǎng	
Path cost	路径代价	Lùjìng dàijià	
Path diversity	路径分集	Lùjìng fēnjí	
Path end point	通道端点	Tōngdào duāndiǎn	PEP
Path index	路径索引	Lùjìng suǒyǐn	
Path layer network	通道层网络	Tōngdào céng wǎngluò	
Path name	路径名	Lùjìng míng	
Path overhead	通道附加值	Tōngdào fùjiā zhí	
Path overhead	通道开销	Tōngdào kāixiao	POH
Path overhead	通路开销	Tōnglù kāixiao	POH
Path protection ring	通道保护环	Tōngdào bǎohù huán	
Path selector (SDH)	通道选择器	Tōngdào xuǎnzéqì	
Path setting	通道设定	Tōngdào shèdìng	
Path terminating element	通道终端设备	Tōngdào zhōngduān shèbèi	PTE
Path termination	通道终端	Tōngdào zhōngduān	PT
Path termination	通道终结	Tōngdào zhōngjié	PT
Path trace identifier	通道踪迹标识	Tōngdào zōngjī biāozhì	
Path-based aggregation	基于路径的汇集	Jīyú lùjìngde huìjí	
Pathfinding	路径查询	Lùjìng cháxún	
Pathfinding	探路	Tànlù	
Pathfinding algorithm	路径寻找算法	Lùjìng xúnzhǎo suànfǎ	
Pathfinding algorithm	探路算法	Tànlù suànfǎ	
Pathloss	路径损耗	Lùjìng sǔnhào	
Pathloss	路径损失	Lùjìng sǔnshī	
Path-switched ring	通道倒换环	Tōngdào dǎohuàn huán	
Patriot (US anti-missile missile)	爱国者	Àiguózhě	
Patriot digital information link (US military)	爱国者数字信息链	Àiguózhě shùzì xìnxī liàn	PADIL
Pattern	模式	Móshì	
Pattern detection	模式探测	Móshì tàncè	
Pattern generalization	模式概化	Móshì gàihuà	

Pattern recognition	模式识别	Móshì shíbié	
Pattern recognition	形式辨识	Xíngshì biànshí	
Pattern recognition	形式识别	Xíngshì shíbié	
Pattern recogniton method	模式识别法	Móshì shíbié fǎ	PRM
Pause key	停止键	Tíngzhǐ jiàn	
Pawsey stub (device to connect an unbalanced coaxial feeder to a balanced antenna)	不平衡同轴馈线/平衡天线变换器	Bùpínghéng tóngzhóu kuìxiàn/ pínghéng tiānxiàn biànhuànqì	
Pay tone (in a pay telephone)	付费音	Fùfèi yīn	
Payee	收款人	Shōukuǎnrén	
Payee's authorized representative	代领人	Dàilǐng rén	
Payload	有效报文	Yǒuxiào bàowén	
Payload	有效负荷	Yǒuxiào fùhè	
Payload	载荷	Zàihè	
Payload (SDH term)	负荷	Fùhè	
Payload (SDH term)	净负荷	Jìngfùhè	
Payload header suppression	净荷包头抑制	Jìnghé bāotóu yìzhì	PHS
Payload header suppression field	净荷包头抑制域	Jìnghé bāotóu yìzhì yù	PHSF
Payload header suppression index	净荷包头抑制索引	Jìnghé bāotóu yìzhì suǒyǐn	PHSI
Payload header suppression marker	净荷包头抑制校验	Jìnghé bāotóu yìzhì jiàoyàn	PHSM
Payload header suppression rule	净荷包头抑制规则	Jìnghé bāotóu yìzhì guīzé	PHS Rule
Payload header suppression size	净荷包头抑制长度	Jìnghé bāotóu yìzhì chángdù	PHSS
Payload header suppression valid	净荷包头抑制校验	Jìnghé bāotóu yìzhì jiàoyàn	PHSV
Payload length	净荷长度	Jìnghé chángdù	
Payload mismatch	净荷失配	Jìnghé shīpèi	PLM
Payload module	符荷模块	Fúhé mókuài	
Payload module	净荷模块	Jìnghé mókuài	
Payload module	有效负荷模块	Yǒuxiào fùhè mókuài	
Payload type	净荷类型	Jìnghé lèixíng	PT
Payload type indication	净荷类型指示	Jìnghé lèixíng zhǐshì	PTI
Payload unit	有效负载单元	Yǒuxiào fùzài dānyuán	PU
Payload unit start indicator	净负荷起始标识符	Jìnghè qǐshǐ biāozhì fú	PUSI
Payload-only encryption (IPsec)	净荷加密	Jìnghé jiāmì	
Payment	兑付	Duìfù	
Payment notification	取款通知单	Qǔkuǎn tōngzhīdān	
Payment office	兑付局	Duìfù jú	
Payment overrun	兑超	Duìchāo	
PCI expander bridge	PCI 增强桥	PCI zēngqiáng qiáo	PXB
PCI Industry Computer Manufacturers group	PCI 工业计算机制造商协会	PCI gōngyè jìsuànjī zhìzàoshāng xiéhuì	PCIMG
P-Com Inc (US company)	立康普公司	Lì-kāng-pǔ gōngsī	
P-doped optical fiber	硫系光纤	Liúxì guāngxiān	
Peak acceleration	最大加速度	Zuìdà jiāsùdù	
Peak cell rate	峰值信元速率	Fēngzhí xìnyuán sùlǜ	PCR
Peak code domain error	峰值码域误差	Fēngzhí mǎyù wùchā	PCDE
Peak detector	峰值检波器	Fēngzhí jiǎnbōqì	
Peak discharge	洪峰流量	Hóngfēng liúliàng	
Peak envelope detection	峰值包络检波	Fēngzhí bāoluò jiǎnbō	

Peak envelope power (of a radio transmitter)	峰包功率	Fēng bāo gōnglǜ	PX
Peak envelope power (of a transmitter)	峰值包络功率	Fēngzhí bāoluò gōnglǜ	
Peak factor	峰值因子	Fēngzhí yīnzǐ	
Peak isolation	峰值隔离度	Fēngzhí gélídù	
Peak limiting	峰值限制	Fēngzhí xiànzhì	
Peak loudness rating	峰值音量比率	Fēngzhí yīnliàng bǐlǜ	
Peak memory usage	高峰内存使用	Gāofēng nèicún shǐyòng	
Peak phase deviation	峰值相位偏移	Fēngzhí xiàngwèi piānyí	
Peak power	峰值功率	Fēngzhí gōnglǜ	
Peak power class (of a mobile station)	峰值功率等级	Fēngzhí gōnglǜ děngjí	
Peak ripple factor	纹波峰值系数	Wénbō fēngzhí xìshù	
Peak sideband power	边带峰值功率	Biāndài fēngzhí gōnglǜ	PSP
Peak signal-to-noise ratio	峰值信噪比	Fēngzhí xìn zào bǐ	PSNR
Peak to average ratio	峰值对平均值比率	Fēngzhí duì píngjūnzhí bǐlǜ	PAR
Peak to peak	峰峰值	Fēng-fēng zhí	Pk-Pk
Peak value	峰值	Fēngzhí	
Peak voltage	峰值电压	Fēngzhí diànyā	
Peaking inductor	峰化电感	Fēnghuà diàngǎn	
Peak-ripple factor	峰值-波纹系数	Fēngzhí-bōwén xìshù	
Peak-to-peak	峰-峰	Fēng—Fēng	
Peak-to-peak (frequency) deviation	峰-峰值频率偏移。	Fēng/fēngzhí pínlǜ piānyí.	
Peak-to-peak detector circuit	峰-峰检波电路	Fēng—Fēng jiǎnbō diànlù	
Peano curve	皮诺曲线	Pí-nuò qūxiàn	
Peano relation	皮诺关系	Pí-nuò guānxi	
Peano tuple algebra	皮诺元组代数	Pí-nuò yuán zǔ dàishù	
Pearson *chi*-square	皮尔逊卡方	Pí-ĕr-xùn kǎ fāng	
Pedestrian way	人行道	Rénxíngdào	
Peeling	剥落	Bōluò	
Peer	对等	Duìděng	
Peer entities	对等实体	Duìděng shítǐ	
Peer entity authentication (IPsec)	对等实体认证	Duìděng shítǐ rènzhèng	
Peer relationships	对等关系	Duìděng guānxi	
Peering	对等操作	Duìděng cāozuò	
Peer-to-peer communication	对等通信	Duìděng tōngxìn	
Peer-to-peer computing	对等计算	Duìděng jìsuàn	
Peer-to-peer network	并行联机	Bìngxíng liánjī	
Peer-to-peer protocol	端对端协议	Duān duì duān xiéyì	PPP
Peltier effect	帕尔贴效应	Pà-ĕr-tiē xiàoyìng	
Pen plotter	笔式绘图仪	Bǐshì huìtúyí	
Penalty time	惩罚时间	Chéngfá shíjiān	PT
Pen-based-input computer	笔输式电脑	Bǐshū-shì diànnǎo	
Pencil beam antenna	笔形波束天线	Bǐxíng bōshù tiānxiàn	PBA
Pencil-beam antenna	笔表射束天线	Bǐbiǎo shèshù tiānxiàn	
Pending operating state (IPsec)	即将操作状态	Jíjiāng cāozuò zhuàngtài	
Pending read state (IPsec)	即将读状态	Jíjiāng dú zhuàngtài	
Pending write state (IPsec)	即将写状态	Jíjiāng xiě zhuàngtài	

Penetration (IPsec)	渗透	Shèntòu	
Penetration loss	穿透损耗	Chuāntòu sǔnhào	
Penetration profile (IPsec)	渗透概述	Shèntòu gàishù	
Penetration rate	渗透率	Shèntòu lǜ	
Penetration signature (IPsec)	渗透印迹	Shèntòu yìnjī	
Penetration testing (IPsec)	渗透测试	Shèntòu cèshì	
Peniotron	潘尼管	Pān-ní-guǎn	
Peniotron	佩尼管	Pèi-ní-guǎn	
Pentagonal prism	五面棱镜	Wǔmiàn léngjìng	
Pentium Pro ©	后奔腾	Hòu bēnténg	
Pentium® chip	奔腾芯片	Bēn-téng xìnpiàn	
People, price and product	人员,价格和产品	Rényuán, jiàgé hé chǎnpǐn	P3
Peoples Air Defense telephone post	人防电话站	Rénfáng diànhuàzhàn	PAD
Per domain behavior	每域行为	Měi yù xíngwéi	PDB
Perceived speech	感知语音	Gǎnzhī yǔyīn	
Percent of calls completed	呼叫接通率	Hūjiào jiētōnglǜ	
Percentage point[s]	百分点	Bǎifēndiǎn	
Perception	感知	Gǎnzhī	
Perception	理解	Lǐjiě	
Perceptual speech quality measure	知觉话音质量度量	Zhījué huàyīn zhìliàng dùliàng	PSQM
Perceptual speech quality measure	知觉语言质量度量	Zhījué yǔyán zhìliàng dùliàng	PSQM
Perfect linear complexity sequence	完备线性复杂度序列	Wánbèi xiànxìng fùzádù xùliè	
Perfect signal	完好信号	Wánhǎo xìnhào	
Perforated lens	多孔透镜	Duōkǒng tòujìng	
Perforation	齿孔度数	Chǐkǒng dùshu	
Perform handover	进行切换	Jìnxíng qiēhuàn	
Perform subsequent handover	进行后续切换	Jìnxíng hòuxù qiēhuàn	
Performance analysis display system	性能分析显示系统	Xìngnéng fēnxī xiǎnshì xìtǒng	PADS
Performance availability	性能可用性	Xìngnéng kěyòngxìng	
Performance criteria for continuous phenomena applied to repeaters and ancillary RF amplifiers	中继器和辅助射频放大器的连续骚扰性能判据	Zhōngjìqì hé fǔzhù shèpín fàngdàqìde liánxù sāorǎo xìngnéng pànjù	CRptr
Performance criteria for transient phenomena applied to repeaters and ancillary RF amplifiers	中继器和辅助射频放大器的瞬态骚扰性能判据	Zhōngjìqì hé fǔzhù shèpín fàngdàqìde shùntài sāorǎo xìngnéng pànjù	TRptr
Performance criterion	性能判据	Xìngnéng pànjù	
Performance degradation	性能降低	Xìngnéng jiàngdī	
Performance degradation	性能下降	Xìngnéng xiàjiàng	
Performance evaluation	性能评价	Xìngnéng píngjià	
Performance indicator	性能表示	Xìngnéng biǎoshì	
Performance management	性能管理	Xìngnéng guǎnlǐ	
Performance management cell	性能管理信元	Xìngnéng guǎnlǐ xìnyuán	
Performance monitoring	性能监测	Xìngnéng jiāncè	
Performance monitoring	性能监视	Xìngnéng jiānshì	
Performance rate	性能比率	Xìngnéng bǐlǜ	PR
Performance, capability, property, facility	性能	Xìngnéng	
Performing CMISE-service-user	执行方 CMISE 服务用户	Zhíxíng fāng CMISE fúwù yònghù	
Per-hop behavior	每跳行为	Měi tiào xíngwéi	PHB

Per-hop behavior	每站行为	Měi zhàn xíngwéi	
Per-hop behavior	逐跳转发行为	Zhútiào zhuǎnfā xíngwéi	PHB
Periapsis	近拱点	Jìngǒngdiǎn	
Perigee	近地点	Jìndìdiǎn	
Period (of a satellite)	卫星周期	Wèixīng zhōuqī	
Period (of a satellite)	周期	Zhōuqī	
Period-frequency spectrum	周期-频率谱	Zhōuqī—pínlǜ pǔ	
Periodic frame	周期帧	Zhōuqī zhèng	
Periodic frame	周期性帧	Zhōuqīxìng zhèng	
Periodic location re-timer (timing refresher)	周期位置更新定时器	Zhōuqī wèizhì gēngxīn dìngshíqì	
Periodic resource distribution	周期资源分配	Zhōuqī zīyuán fēnpèi	PRD
Periodic signal	周期信号	Zhōuqī xìnhào	
Periodic test	周期试验	Zhōuqī shìyàn	
Periodic time	周期时间	Zhōuqī shíjiān	
Periodic verification	周期检定	Zhōuqī jiǎndìng	
Periodical frequency forecast	定期频率预报	Dìngqī pínlǜ yùbào	
Periodically loaded waveguide	周期性加载波导	Zhōuqīxìng jiāzài bōdǎo	
Periodicity	周期性	Zhōuqīxìng	
Peripheral	周边器材	Zhōubiān qìcái	
Peripheral board controller	外设板控制器	Wàishèbǎn kòngzhìqì	PBC
Peripheral component interconnect	互连外围设备	Hùlián wàiwéi shèbèi	PCI
Peripheral component interconnect	外部部件互连	Wàibù bùjiàn hùlián	PCI
Peripheral component interconnect	外围设备互联	Wàiwéi shèbèi hùlián	PCI
Peripheral component interconnect	周边器材互联	Zhōubiān qìcái hùlián	PCI
Peripheral component interconnect special interest group	互连外围设备专业组	Hùlián wàiwéi shèbèi zhuānyè zǔ	PCI SIG
Peripheral component interface	外围设备接口	Wàiwéi shèbèi jiēkǒu	PCI
Peripheral exchange synchronization	外围交换同步化	Wàiwéi jiāohuàn tóngbùhuà	PESY
Periscope antenna	潜望镜天线	Qiánwàngjìng tiānxiàn	
Permanent activation	永久激活	Yǒngjiǔ jīhuó	
Permanent circuit service	常设电路业务	Chángshè diànlù yèwù	
Permanent circuit service	永久电路业务	Yǒngjiǔ diànlù yèwù	
Permanent circuit telecommunication service	永久电路电信业务	Yǒngjiǔ diànlù diànxìn yèwù	
Permanent link	永久链路	Yǒngjiǔ liànlù	
Permanent link layer	永久链路层	Yǒngjiǔ liànlù céng	PLL
Permanent logical link	永久逻辑链路	Yǒngjiǔ luóji liànlù	PLL
Permanent nucleus (the European GSM standards setting group)	核心小组	Héxīn xiǎozǔ	PN
Permanent storage	永久存储器	Yǒngjiǔ cúnchǔqì	
Permanent virtual channel	永久虚信道	Yǒngjiǔ xū xìndào	PVC
Permanent virtual channel connection	永久虚信道连接	Yǒngjiǔ xū xìndào liánjiē	PVCC
Permanent virtual circuit	永久虚电路	Yǒngjiǔ xū diànlù	PVC
Permanent virtual connection	永久虚连接	Yǒngjiǔ xū liánjiē	PVC
Permanent virtual connection	永久虚拟连接	Yǒngjiǔ xūnǐ liánjiē	PVC
Permanent virtual path	永久虚电路	Yǒngjiǔ xū diànlù	PVP
Permanent virtual path	永久虚通道	Yǒngjiǔ xū tōngdào	PVP
Permanent virtual path connection	永久虚通路连接	Yǒngjiǔ xū tōnglù liánjiē	PVPC

English	Chinese	Pinyin	Abbreviation
Permissible code block	许用码组	Xǔyòng mǎzǔ	
Permissible deviation	允许偏差	Yǔnxǔ piānchā	
Permissible interference	允许干扰	Yǔnxǔ gānrǎo	
Permissible maximum transmit power	允许最大发射功率	Yǔnxǔ zuìdà fāshè gōnglǜ	
Permissible minimum receive power	允许最小接收功率	Yǔnxǔ zuìxiǎo jiēshōu gōnglǜ	
Permissible out-of-band power	允许带外功率	Yǔnxǔ dàiwài gōnglǜ	
Permissible out-of-band spectrum	允许带外频谱	Yǔnxǔ dàiwài pínpǔ	
Permit processing	允许处理	Yǔnxǔ chǔlǐ	
Permutation frequency shift keying	置换频移键控	Zhìhuàn pínyí jiànkòng	PFSK
Permutation group theory	置换群理论	Zhìhuàn qún lǐlùn	
Per-seat licensing	每客户授权	Měi kèhù shòuquán	
Per-server licensing	每服务器授权	Měi fúwùqì shòuquán	
Persistence	持久性	Chíjiǔxìng	
Persistence	持续性	Chíxùxìng	
Persistence	余辉时间	Yúhuī shíjiān	
Persistent fault	持续故障	Chíxù gùzhàng	
Persistent lock	永久性锁	Yǒngjiǔxìng suǒ	
Personal (handset system) Internet access forum standard	个人手机系统因特网接入论坛标准	Gèrén shǒujī xìtǒng Yīntèwǎng jiērù lùntán biāozhǔn	PIAFS
Personal (radio) station	个人电台	Gèrén diàntái	PS
Personal access system	个人接入系统	Gèrén jiērù xìtǒng	PAS
Personal area network	个人域网	Gèrén yù wǎng	PAN
Personal communication network	个人通信网	Gèrén tōngxìnwǎng	PCN
Personal communication service	个人通讯服务	Gèrén tōngxùn fúwù	PCS
Personal communication services	个人通信	Gèrén tōngxìn	PCS
Personal communication system – mobile switching center	个人通信系统-移动交换中心	Gèrén tōngxìn xìtǒng—yídòng jiāohuàn zhōngxīn	PCS-MSC
Personal communications service	个人通信业务	Gèrén tōngxìn yèwù	PCS
Personal communications systems	个人通信系统	Gèrén tōngxìn xìtǒng	PCS
Personal computer	个人电脑	Gèrén diànnǎo	PC
Personal computer	个人计算机	Gèrén jìsuànjī	PC
Personal computer extended technology bus	个人计算机扩充技术总线	Gèrén jìsuànjī kuòchōng jìshù zǒngxiàn	PCET
Personal computer memory card international	国际个人计算机存储卡协会	Guójì gèrén jìsuànjī cúnchǔ qiǎ xiéhuì	PCMCIA
Personal Computer Memory Card International Association	个人计算机存储卡国际联合会	Gèrén jìsuànjī cúnchǔkǎ Guójì liánhéhuì	PCMCIA
Personal Computer Memory Card International Association	个人计算机内存卡国际标准协会	Gèrén jìsuànjī nèicúnkǎ guójì biāozhǔn xiéhuì	PCMCIA
Personal computer-based private branch exchange	基于电脑的小型用户交换机	Jīyú diànnǎode xiǎoxíng yònghù jiāohuànjī	PC-based PBX
Personal computer-disk operating system	个人计算机磁盘操作系统	Gèrén jìsuànjī cípán cāozuò xìtǒng	PC-DOS
Personal digital assistant	个人数字辅助器	Gèrén shùzì fǔzhùqì	PDA
Personal digital assistant	个人数字助理	Gèrén shùzì zhùlǐ	PDA
Personal digital cellular system (Japan)	个人数字蜂窝系统	Gèrén shùzì fēngwō xìtǒng	PDC
Personal digital cellular telecommunications system (Japan)	个人数字蜂窝通信系统	Gèrén shùzì fēngwō tōngxìn xìtǒng	PDC
Personal equity plan	个人股东投资计划	Gèrén gǔdōng tóuzī jìhuà	PEP
Personal handy phone	个人携带电话	Gèrén xiédài diànhuà	PHP
Personal handyphone system	个人便携电话系统	Gèrén biànxié diànhuà xìtǒng	

Personal handy-phone system	个人手持电话系统	Gèrén shǒuchí diànhuà xìtǒng	PHS
Personal handy-phone system	个人无绳电话系统	Gèrén wúshéng diànhuà xìtǒng	PHS
Personal identification number	个人身份识别号	Gèrén shēnfen shíbié hào	PIN
Personal identification number	个人识别号码	Gèrén shíbié hàomǎ	PIN
Personal identification number	个人识别码	Gèrén shíbié mǎ	PIN
Personal identification number	用户个人资料识别码	Yònghù gèrén zīliào shíbié mǎ	PIN
Personal identification number	身份识别码	Shēnfen shíbié mǎ	PIN
Personal identification number (PIN) unblocking key	个人识别码解锁密码	Gèrén shíbié mǎ jiěsuǒ mìmǎ	PUK
Personal information assistant	个人信息助理	Gèrén xìnxī zhùlǐ	PIA
Personal information management	个人信息管理系统	Gèrén xìnxī guǎnlǐ xìtǒng	PIM
Personal mobile radio	个人移动无线电	Gèrén yídòng wúxiàndiàn	PMR
Personal mobility	个人移动性	Gèrén yídòngxìng	
Personal name	个人名	Gèrén míng	
Personal service environment	个人服务环境	Gèrén fúwù huánjìng	PSE
Personal system 2	个人系统二型	Gèrén xìtǒng èr xíng	PS2
Personal telecommunication number	个人通信号码	Gèrén tōngxìn hàomǎ	PTN
Personal telephone number	个人电话号码	Gèrén diànhuà hàomǎ	PTN
Personalization center	个人化中心	Gèrénhuà zhōngxīn	PCS
Personalization control key	个性化控制键	Gèxìnghuà kòngzhì jiàn	PCK
Personnel security	人事安全	Rénshì ānquán	
Person-to-number call	叫号呼叫	Jiàohào hūjiào	
Person-to-person call	叫人呼叫	Jiào rén hūjiào	
Perspective correction	透视纠正	Tòushì jiūzhèng	PC
Perturbation method	扰动法	Rǎodòng fǎ	
Petabit (10^{15} bits)	拍比特	Pāibǐtè	
Petabyte	批比特	Pībǐtè	
P-fractile access delay (in telecommunication)	p 分位接入迟延	p-fènwèi jiērù chíyán	
P-fractile administrative delay	p 分位管理耽误	p-fènwèi guǎnlǐ dānwù	
P-fractile logistic delay	p 分位后勤耽误	p-fènwèi hòuqín dānwù	
P-fractile repair time	p 分位修理时间	p-fènwèi xiūlǐ shíjiān	
Phantom	幻像	Huànxiàng	
Phantom circuit	幻线电路	Huànxiàn diànlù	
Phase (of a signal)	相位	Xiàngwèi	γ, φ
Phase alternating line (European television broadcast standard)	逐行倒相制式	Zhúháng dǎoxiāng zhìshì	PAL
Phase canceller	相位对消器	Xiàngwèi duìxiāoqì	
Phase center	相位中心	Xiàngwèi zhōngxīn	
Phase changer (in a transmission line)	相位变换器	Xiàngwèi biànhuànqì	
Phase characteristics	相位特征	Xiàngwèi tèzhēng	
Phase coefficient	相位系数	Xiàngwèi xìshù	
Phase coherence	相位相干	Xiàngwèi xiānggān	PC
Phase coherent carrier band	相位相干载波带	Xiàngwèi xiānggān zàibō dài	
Phase comparison sinusoidal frequency shift keying	相位比较正弦移频键控	Xiàngwèi bǐjiào zhèngxián yípín jiànkòng	PCSFSK
Phase continuous carrier band	相位连续载波带	Xiàngwèi liánxù zàibō dài	
Phase control	相位控制	Xiàngwèi kòngzhì	
Phase demodulation	相位解调	Xiàngwèi jiětiáo	

Phase detection discriminator	鉴相鉴频器	Jiànxiāng jiànpínqì	
Phase detector	鉴相器	Jiànxiāngqì	
Phase detector	相位检波器	Xiàngwèi jiǎnbōqì	
Phase deviation	相位偏移	Xiàngwèi piānyí	
Phase discontinuity	相位不连续性	Xiàngwèi bùliánxùxìng	
Phase discrimination	相位鉴别	Xiàngwèi jiànbié	
Phase discriminator	鉴相器	Jiànxiāngqì	
Phase discriminator output error voltage	鉴相器输出误差电压	Jiànxiāngqì shūchū wùchā diànyā	
Phase distortion	相位失真	Xiàngwèi shīzhēn	
Phase distortion correction	相位失真校正	Xiàngwèi shīzhēn jiàozhèng	
Phase division multiplexing	相分多路复用	Xiàngfēn duōlù fùyòng	PDM
Phase encoding	相位编码	Xiàngwèi biānmǎ	PE
Phase equalization	相位均衡	Xiàngwèi jūnhéng	
Phase equalization	相位一致性	Xiàngwèi yīzhìxìng	
Phase error in aperture	口面相差	Kǒumiàn xiàngchà	
Phase interference	相位干涉	Xiàngwèi gānshè	
Phase inversion modulation	倒相调制	Dǎoxiāng tiáozhì	
Phase jitter	相位抖动	Xiàngwèi dǒudòng	
Phase locked loop	锁相环	Suǒxiàng huán	PLL
Phase locked loop	锁相环路	Suǒxiàng huánlù	PLL
Phase locking circuit	锁相电路	Suǒxiàng diànlù	
Phase modification synchronization (in CORBA)	相位修改同步协议	Xiàngwèi xiūgǎi tóngbù xiéyì	PM
Phase modulated sensitivity	相位调制灵敏度	Xiàngwèi tiáozhì língmǐndù	
Phase modulation	相位调制	Xiàngwèi tiáozhì	PM
Phase modulation	调相	Tiáoxiàng	PM
Phase noise	相位噪声	Xiàngwèi zàoshēng	
Phase noise power spectrum density	相位噪声功率谱密度	Xiàngwèi zàoshēng gōnglǜ pǔ mìdù	
Phase pattern	相位方向图	Xiāngwèi fāngxiàng tú	
Phase pattern (graphical representation)	相位方向图的图示法	Xiàngwèi fāngxiàng túde túshìfǎ	
Phase pattern (mathematical representation)	相位方向图的数学表达式	Xiàngwèi fāngxiàng túde shùxué biǎodá shì	
Phase quantization	相位量化	Xiàngwèi liànghuà	
Phase relationship	相位关系	Xiàngwèi guānxi	
Phase reversal modulation	倒相调制	Dǎoxiàng tiáozhì	PRM
Phase separated glass (FOC mfg)	玻璃分相法	Bōli fēnxiàng fǎ	PSG
Phase shift	相移	Xiāngyí	
Phase shift keying	移相键控	Yíxiāng jiànkòng	PSK
Phase shift layer	相位差板	Xiàngwèi chà bǎn	
Phase shift network	移相网络	Yíxiàng wǎngluò	
Phase shifter, phase changer	移相器	Yíxiàngqì	
Phase spectrum	相位谱	Xiàngwèi pǔ	
Phase transient response	相位瞬变响应	Xiàngwèi shùnbiàn xiǎngyìng	
Phase transition	相变	Xiàngbiàn	
Phase truncation	相位舍位	Xiàngwèi shèwèi	
Phase truncation error signal	相位舍位误差信号	Xiàngwèi shèwèi wùchā xìnhào	
Phase velocity	相速	Xiàngsù	
Phase velocity	相位速度	Xiàngwèi sùdù	

Phase/amplitude distortion	相位幅度失真	Xiāngwèi fúdù shīzhēn	
Phase/frequency characteristic	相频特性	Xiāng/pín tèxìng	
Phase/frequency characteristic	相位频率特性	Xiāngwèi pínlǜ tèxìng	
Phase/frequency distortion	相位频率失真	Xiàngwèi pínlǜ shīzhēn	
Phase-coded pulse compression	相位编码脉冲压缩	Xiàngwèi biānmǎ màichōng yāsuō	
Phase-coded spread-spectrum modulation	相位编码扩展频谱调制	Xiàngwèi biānmǎ kuòzhǎn pínpǔ tiáozhì	PCSSM
Phase-coded spread-spectrum signal	相位编码扩展频谱信号	Xiàngwèi biānmǎ kuòzhǎn pínpǔ xìnhào	PCSS
Phase-comparison monopulse radar	比相单脉冲雷达	Bǐxiāng dān màichōngléidá	
Phase-controlled array	相控阵	Xiàngkòng zhèn	
Phase-controlled array antenna	相控阵天线	Xiàngkòng zhèn tiānxiàn	
Phased array antenna	相控阵天线	Xiàngkòng zhèn tiānxiàn	
Phased array control electronics	相位阵控制电子设备	Xiàngwèi zhèn kòngzhì diànzǐ shèbèi	PACE
Phased array jammer	相控阵干扰机	Xiàngkòng zhèn gānrǎojī	
Phased array radar	相控阵雷达	Xiàngkòng zhèn léidá	
Phased array radar	相位阵列雷达	Xiàngwèi zhènliè léidá	
Phased-locked loop quadrature phase shift keying	锁相环四相相移键控	Suǒxiānghuán sìxiāng xiāngyí jiànkòng	PLL-QPSK
Phase-frequency characteristic	相频特性	Xiàngpín tèxìng	
Phase-frequency equalization	相频一致性	Xiàngpín yīzhìxìng	
Phase-lock acquisition	锁相捕获	Suǒxiāng bǔhuò	
Phase-locked detector	同相检波	Tóngxiāng jiǎnbō	PLD
Phase-locked local oscillator	相位锁定本地振荡器	Xiàngwèi suǒdìng běndì zhèndàngqì	
Phase-locked loop quadrature phase shift keying	锁相环四相相移键控	Suǒxiāng huán sìxiāng xiāngyí jiànkòng	PLL-QPSK
Phase-locked receiver	锁相接收机	Suǒxiàng jiēshōujī	
Phase-scanned radar	相位扫描雷达	Xiàngwèi sǎomiáo léidá	
Phase-shift coherent oscillator	相移相干振荡器	Xiàngyí xiānggān zhèndàngqì	
Phase-shift constant	相移常数	Xiāngyí chángshù	
Phase-shift keying	相移键控	Xiàngyí jiànkòng	PSK
Phase-shifting circulator	移相式环行器	Yíxiàng-shì huánxíngqì	
Phase-state low electron (hole)-number drive memory	相位态低电子驱动存储器	Xiàngwèi tài dīdiànzǐ qūdòng cúnchǔqì	PLEDM
Phase-sweep	相扫	Xiàngsǎo	
Phasing (in facsimile)	对相	Duìxiāng	
Phasing signal	对相信号	Duìxiāng xìnhào	
Phenomenon fluctuation	现象波动	Xiànxiàng bōdòng	
Phenomenon generalization	现象综合	Xiànxiàng zōnghé	
Philippine Communications Satellite Corp.	菲律宾卫星公司	Fēi-lǜ-bīn wèixīng gōngsī	Philcomsat
Philips (Netherlands company)	飞利浦	Fēi-lì-pǔ	
Phone query	电话语音识别	Diànhuà yǔyīn shíbié	
Phoneline network transceiver	电话线网络收发器	Diànhuàxiàn wǎngluò shōufāqì	PNT
Phonetically balanced word list	语音平衡单词表	Yǔyīn pínghéng dāncí biǎo	
Phosphorous oxychloride	三氯化氧磷	Sānlǜhuàyǎnglín	$POCl_3$
Photo compact disk	相片光碟	Xiàngpiàn guāngdié	
Photo detector	光电探测器	Guāngdiàn tàncèqì	PD
Photo facsimile	相片传真	Xiàngpiàn chuánzhēn	
Photo interrupter	光断续器	Guāng duànxùqì	
Photo reflector	光反射器	Guāng fǎnshèqì	
Photoceramic	光学陶瓷	Guāngxué táocí	

English	Chinese	Pinyin	Abbr.
Photochromic material	光色材料	Guāngsè cáiliào	
Photoconductive cell	光导电池	Guāngdǎo diànchí	
Photocoupler	光电耦合器	Guāngdiàn ǒuhéqì	
Photodiode	光二极体	Guāng èrjítǐ	
Photoelastic modulator	光弹性调变器	Guāng tánxìng tiáobiànqì	
Photoelectric diode	光电二极管	Guāngdiàn èrjíguǎn	
Photoelectric smoke detector	光电感烟探测器	Guāngdiàn gǎnyān tàncèqì	PSD
Photogrammetric calibration	摄影测度定标	Shèyǐng cèdù dìngbiāo	
Photogrammetric digitizing	摄影测量数字化	Shèyǐng cèliáng shùzìhuà	
Photogrammetric mapping	摄影测量制图	Shèyǐng cèliáng zhìtú	
Photogrammetry	摄影测量学	Shèyǐng cèliángxué	
Photographic chemical	相片用化学药品	Xiàngpiàn-yòng huàxué yàopǐn	
Photographic filter	照像用滤光镜	Zhàoxiàng-yòng lǜguāngjìng	
Photographic map; photomap	影像地图	Yǐngxiàng dìtú	
Photo-intrinsic diode	光电二极管	Guāngdiàn èrjíguǎn	PIN
Photolithography simulation software (semiconductor mfg)	光刻模拟软件	Guāngkè mónǐ ruǎnjiàn	
Photomask material	光罩材料	Guāng zhào cáiliào	
Photomultiplier	光电子增倍管	Guāngdiànzǐ zēngbèiguǎn	PMT
Photon integrated multi-quantum well fast switching light source	光子集成多量子阱快速交换光源	Guāngzǐ jíchéng duō liàngzǐ jǐng kuàisù jiāohuàn guāngyuán	
Photonic band gap	光子带隙	Guāngzǐ dàixì	PBG
Photonic band gap	光子禁带	Guāngzǐ jìndài	PBG
Photonic Bridges Inc., (US company)	美国光桥网络有限公司	Měiguó guāng qiáo wǎngluò yǒuxiàn gōngsī	
Photonic crystal fiber	光子晶体光纤	Guāngzǐ jīngtǐ guāngxiān	PCF
Photonic integrated circuit	光子集成电路	Guāngzǐ jíchéng diànlù	PIC
Photonic switching method	光交换方式	Guāng jiāohuàn fāngshì	
Photoplotter (in SMT)	相片绘图仪	Xiàngpiàn huìtúyí	
Photosensing unit	光感测元件	Guāng gǎncè yuánjiàn	
PhotoShop ©	相馆	Xiàngguǎn	
Photothyristor	光闸流晶体管	Guāng zháliú jīngtǐguǎn	
Phototransistor	光电晶体	Guāngdiàn jīngtǐ	
Phototube	光电管	Guāngdiànguǎn	
Phrase	短语	Duǎnyǔ	
Phrasing	句式	Jùshì	
Physical architecture	物理体系结构	Wùlǐ tǐxì jiégòu	
Physical channel	物理信道	Wùlǐ xìndào	
Physical circuit	物理线路	Wùlǐ xiànlù	
Physical coding sub-layer	物理编码子层	Wùlǐ biānmǎ zicéng	PCS
Physical common packet channel	物理公共分组信道	Wùlǐ gōnggòng fēnzǔ xìndào	PCPCH
Physical configuration	物理配置	Wùlǐ pèizhì	
Physical connection	物理连接	Wùlǐ liánjiē	PHC
Physical database design	数据库物理设计	Shùjùkù wùlǐ shèjì	
Physical dedicated channel	专用物理信道	Zhuānyòng wùlǐ xìndào	PDCH
Physical delivery	物理投递	Wùlǐ tóudì	PD
Physical delivery access unit	物理投递访问单元	Wùlǐ tóudì fǎngwèn dānyuán	PDAU
Physical delivery address components	物理投递地址的组成成份	Wùlǐ tóudì dìzhǐde zǔchéng chéngfèn	

Physical delivery country name	物理投递国家名	Wùlǐ tóudì guójiā míng	
Physical delivery message	物理投递消息	Wùlǐ tóudì xiāoxi	PDM
Physical delivery office address components	物理投递局地址组成成份	Wùlǐ tóudìjú dìzhǐ zǔchéng chéngfèn	
Physical delivery office name	物理投递局名	Wùlǐ tóudìjú míng	
Physical delivery office number	物理投递局号	Wùlǐ tóudìjú hào	
Physical delivery organization name	物理投递组织名	Wùlǐ tóudì zǔzhī míng	
Physical delivery personal name	物理投递个人名	Wùlǐ tóudì gèrén míng	
Physical delivery service	物理投递服务	Wùlǐ tóudì fúwù	
Physical delivery service name	物理投递服务名	Wùlǐ tóudì fúwù míng	
Physical delivery system	物理投递系统	Wùlǐ tóudì xìtǒng	PDS
Physical design exchange format	物理设计交换格式	Wùlǐ shèjì jiāohuàn géshi	PDEF
Physical downlink shared channel	物理下行共享信道	Wùlǐ xiàxíng gòngxiǎng xìndào	PDSCH
Physical downlink shared channel	下行链路共享物理信道	Xiàxíng liànlù gòngxiǎng wùlǐ xìndào	PDSCH
Physical entity	物理实体	Wùlǐ shítǐ	PE
Physical frame	物理帧	Wùlǐ zhèng	
Physical information	物理信息	Wùlǐ xìnxī	
Physical interface	物理接口	Wùlǐ jiēkǒu	
Physical interface specification	物理接口规范	Wùlǐ jiēkǒu guīfàn	
Physical layer	物理层	Wùlǐ céng	PH, PHY
Physical layer device	物理层设备	Wùlǐ céng shèbèi	PHY
Physical layer signaling	物理层信令	Wùlǐ céng xìnlìng	PLS
Physical layer-operation and maintenance (cell)	物理层-操作和维护(信元)	Wùlǐ céng—cāozuò hé wéihù (xìnyuán)	PL-OAM
Physical line	实线电路	Shíxiàn diànlù	
Physical line transmission	实线传输	Shíxiàn chuánshū	
Physical map (GIS term)	自然地图	Zìrán dìtú	
Physical media	物理媒体	Wùlǐ méitǐ	PM
Physical media access	物理介质接入	Wùlǐ jièzhì jiērù	PMA
Physical media dependent	物理媒体相关	Wùlǐ méitǐ xiāngguān	PMD
Physical media dependent	物理媒体有关	Wùlǐ méitǐ yǒuguān	PMC
Physical media dependent	物理媒质相关	Wùlǐ méizhì xiāngguān	PMD
Physical media independent	物理媒体无关	Wùlǐ méitǐ wúguān	PMI
Physical media sub-layer	物理媒介子层	Wùlǐ méijiè zicéng	
Physical media sub-layer	物理媒质子层	Wùlǐ méizhì zicéng	
Physical media-specific transmission channel layer	物理媒质特定传输汇聚层	Wùlǐ méizhì tèdìng chuánshū huìjù céng	PMS-TC
Physical medium dependent	物理介质相关	Wùlǐ jièzhì xiāngguān	PMD
Physical medium dependent sub-layer	物理介质相关子层	Wùlǐ jièzhì xiāngguān zicéng	PMD
Physical medium dependent/transmission channel	物理媒体相关/传输会聚	Wùlǐ méitǐ xiāngguān/chuánshū huìjù	PMD/TC
Physical medium sub-layer	物理媒体子层	Wùlǐ méitǐ zicéng	PM
Physical message	物理消息	Wùlǐ xiāoxi	
Physical model	物理模型	Wùlǐ móxíng	
Physical name	物理名称	Wùlǐ míngchēng	
Physical page	物理页	Wùlǐ yè	
Physical protocol data unit	物理协议数据单元	Wùlǐ xiéyì shùjù dānyuán	PHPDU
Physical random access channel	随机接入物理信道	Suíjī jiērù wùlǐ xìndào	PRACH
Physical random access channels	物理随机接入信道	Wùlǐ suíjī jiērù xìndào	PRACH
Physical reads	物理读取	Wùlǐ dúqǔ	

Physical rendition	物理复现	Wùlǐ fùxiàn	
Physical security (IPsec)	物理安全	Wùlǐ ānquán	
Physical service	物理服务	Wùlǐ fúwù	PhS
Physical service access point	物理业务访问点	Wùlǐ yèwù fǎngwèn diǎn	PhSAP
Physical service data unit	物理服务数据单元	Wùlǐ fúwù shùjù dānyuán	PhSDU
Physical service port	物理业务端口	Wùlǐ yèwù duānkǒu	PSP
Physical shared channel	物理共享信道	Wùlǐ gòngxiǎng xìndào	PSCH
Physical signaling channel	物理信令通路	Wùlǐ xìnlìng tōnglù	
Physical signaling channel	物理信令信道	Wùlǐ xìnlìng xìndào	
Physical space	物理空间	Wùlǐ kōngjiān	
Physical structure	物理结构	Wùlǐ jiégòu	
Physical uplink shared channel	上行共用物理信道	Shàngxíng gòngyòng wùlǐ xìndào	PUSCH
Physical uplink shared channel	上行链路共享物理信道	Shàngxíng liànlù gòngxiǎng wùlǐ xìndào	PUSCH
Physical user port	物理用户端口	Wùlǐ yònghù duān kǒu	PUP
Physically foaming	物理发泡	Wùlǐ fāpāo	
Pick and place machine (semiconductor mfg)	拾放机	Shí fàng jī	
Pick and place workstation (semiconductor mfg)	拾放工作站	Shífàng gōngzuòzhàn	
Pick-and-place (in SMT)	拾取-贴装设备	Shíqǔ-tiēzhuāng shèbèi	
Pickup (audio)	拾音器	Shíyīnqì	PU
Pico- (prefix meaning 10^{-12})	微微	Wēiwēi	P
Picocell	微微蜂窝	Wēiwēi fēngwō	
Picocell	微微区	Wēiwēi qū	
Pico-net	微微网	Wēiwēi wǎng	
Picosecond	微微秒	Wēiwēi miǎo	
Picosecond	皮可秒	Píkěmiǎo	
Picosecond	皮秒	Pímiǎo	
Picture (WP command)	图片	Túpiàn	
Picture access unit	图像接入单元	Túxiàng jiērù dānyuán	PAU
Picture element	图象要素	Túxiàng yàosù	
Picture facsimile	图片传真	Túpiàn chuánzhēn	
Picture messaging service	图像短信息传送服务	Túxiàng duǎn xìnxī chuánsòng fúwù	PMS
Pie chart	饼状图	Bǐngzhuàng tú	
Pie graph	饼图	Bǐng tú	
Piezoelectric effect	压电效应	Yādiàn xiàoyìng	
Piezoelectric positioning equipment	压电定位设备	Yādiàn dìngwèi shèbèi	
Piggy back entry	非法进入	Fēifǎ jìnrù	
Piggybacked acknowledge	捎带确认	Shāodài quèrèn	
Pillbox antenna	抛物盒天线	Pāowùhé tiānxiàn	
Pill-box antenna	窄盒形天线	Zhǎihéxíng tiānxiàn	
Pilot balloon	导向气球	Dǎoxiàng qìqiú	
Pilot beacon	导频引导	Dǎopín yǐndǎo	
Pilot channel	导频信道	Dǎopín xìndào	
Pilot fall-down	导频跌落	Dǎopín diēluò	
Pilot frequency	导频	Dǎopín	
Pilot synchronization/access channel	导频同步/接入信道	Dǎopín tóngbù/jiērù xìndào	PAC
Pilot tone in-band single sideband	带内导频单边带	Dài-nèi dǎopín dānbiāndài	

English	Chinese	Pinyin	Abbr.
Pin (on a connector)	引脚	Yǐnjiǎo	
Pin (on a plug or insertion chip)	插脚	Chājiǎo	
PIN diode antenna duplexer (lit. Rx/Tx switch)	PIN 二极管天线收发开关	PIN erjíguǎn tiānxiàn shōufā kāiguān	
PIN diode phase shifter	PIN 二极管移相器	PIN erjíguǎn yíxiàngqì	
PIN diode switch	PIN 二极管开关	PIN erjíguǎn kāiguān	
Pin grid array	引脚网格阵列	Yǐnjiǎo wǎnggé zhènliè	PGA
Pin grid array (electronics mfg)	针栅阵列	Zhēn zhà zhènliè	PGA
Pin location	管脚位置	Guǎnjiǎo wèizhì	
PIN modulator	PIN 调制器	PIN tiáozhìqì	
Pin, inserted pin, connector pin	插针	Chāzhēn	
Ping-pong method	乒乓法	Pīngpāng fǎ	
Pinhole automatic light compensation (ALC) lens	针孔型自动亮度补偿镜头	Zhēnkǒng-xíng zìdòng liàngdù bǔcháng jìngtóu	PAL
Pinhole filter (optical)	针孔滤光镜	Zhēnkǒng lǜguāngjìng	
Pink noise	粉红噪声	Fěnhóng zàoshēng	
Pioneer (US company)	先锋	Xiānfēng	
Pipe symbol (|)	转向符	Zhuǎnxiàng fú	
Pipe utilities	管道设施	Guǎndào shèshī	
Pipeline	管路	Guǎnlù	
Pipeline computer	流水线计算机	Liúshuǐxiàn jìsuànjī	
Pipelining	管道传送	Guǎndào chuánsòng	
Piping	管道系统	Guǎndào xìtǒng	
Pirated (software)	翻版	Fānbǎn	
Pirelli (FOC manufacturer)	比瑞利	Bǐ-ruì-lì	
Piston	活塞	Huósāi	
Piston attenuator	活塞式衰减器	Huósāi-shì shuāijiǎnqì	
Pitch angle	俯仰角	Fǔyǎngjiǎo	
Pitch excited linear productive coding	高度激励线性生产编码	Gāodù jīlì xiànxìng shēngchǎn biānmǎ	PELPC
Pitch synchronous innovation-code excited linear prediction	基音同步更新码激励线性预测	Jīyīn tóngbù gēngxīn mǎ jīlì xiànxìng yùcè	PSI-CELP
Pitch-cycle waveform	基音周期波形	Jīyīn zhōuqī bōxíng	PCW
Pivot	数据透视	Shùjù tòushì	
Pixel	像素	Xiàngsù	
Pixel address	象素地址	Xiàngsù dìzhǐ	PA
Pixel array	像素阵列	Xiàngsù zhènliè	
Pixel fill rate (measured in Mpix/sec)	像素填充率	Xiàngsù tiánchōng lǜ	
Pixel path	像素走向	Xiàngsù zǒuxiàng	
Pixel spacing	像素间距	Xiàngsù jiānjù	
Place (in Petri net)	位置	Wèizhì	
Placeholder	占位符	Zhànwèifú	
Placement equipment (in SMT)	贴装设备	Tiēzhuāng shèbèi	
Plain old telephone service	老式普通电话业务	Lǎoshì pǔtōng diànhuà yèwù	POTS
Plain old telephone service	普通电话业务	Pǔtōng diànhuà yèwù	POTS
Plain old telephone service	普通老式电话业务	Pǔtōng lǎoshì diànhuà yèwù	POTS
Plain old telephone system	简易老式电话系统	Jiǎnyì lǎoshì diànhuà xìtǒng	POTS
Plain text (IPsec)	明文	Míngwén	
Plan value	计划值	Jìhuà zhí	

Planar array	平面阵	Píngmiàn zhèn	
Planar array	平面阵列	Píngmiàn zhènliè	PA
Planar array antenna	平面阵天线	Píngmiàn zhèn tiānxiàn	
Planar array waveguide grating	平面阵列波导光栅	Píngmiàn zhènliè bōdǎo guāngshān	
Planar coordinate systems	平面坐标系统	Píngmiàn zuòbiāo xìtǒng	
Planar coordinates	平面坐标	Píngmiàn zuòbiāo	
Planar graph	平面图	Píngmiàn tú	
Planar lightwave circuit	平面波导线路	Píngmiàn bōdǎo xiànlù	PLC
Planar lightwave circuit	平面光波电路	Píngmiàn guāngbō diànlù	PLC
Planar optical waveguide device	平面光波导器件	Píngmiàn guāng bōdǎo qìjiàn	
Planar topological complex	平面拓扑复合体	Píngmiàn tuòpū fùhétǐ	
Planarity detection and embedding	平面性检测和嵌入	Píngmiàn-xìng jiǎncè hé qiànrù	
Plane Archimedes spiral antenna	阿基米德平面螺旋天线	Ājīmǐdé píngmiàn luóxuán tiānxiàn	
Plane connection	平面连接	Píngmiàn liánjiē	PC
Plane connection	平面连接	Píngmiàn liánjiē	PC
Plane equiangular spiral antenna	等角平面螺旋天线	Děngjiǎo píngmiàn luóxuán tiānxiàn	
Plane joint	平面接头	Píngmiàn jiētóu	
Plane management	面管理	Miàn guǎnlǐ	
Plane of polarization	极化面	Jíhuà miàn	
Plane position indicator	平面位置显示器	Píngmiàn wèizhì xiǎnshìqì	
Plane radome	平板天线罩	Píngbǎn tiānxiàn zhào	
Planetable	平板仪	Píngbǎnyí	
Planetary gear reductor	行星轮减速器	Xíngxīng lún jiǎnsùqì	
Planetary wave	行星波	Xíngxīng bō	
Planimetric feature	平面地物	Píngmiàn dìwù	
Planimetric map	平面测量地图	Píngmiàn cèliáng dìtú	
Planimetry	测面法	Cèmiànfǎ	
Planting works	种植工程	Zhòngzhí gōngchéng	
Plasma chemical vapor deposition (FOC mfg)	等离子体化学汽相沉积法	Děnglízǐtǐ huàxué qìxiāng chénjīfǎ	PCVD
Plasma display panel	等离子显示板	Děnglízǐ xiǎnshì bǎn	
Plasma display panel	电浆显示器	Diànjiāng xiǎnshìqì	PDP
Plasma display panel (PDP) television	电浆电视	Diànjiāng diànshì	
Plasma enhanced chemical vapor deposition	等离子体增强化学汽相沉积	Děnglízǐtǐ zēngqiáng huàxué qìxiāng chénjī	PECVD
Plasma etcher (semiconductor mfg)	等离子刻蚀机	Děnglízi kèshíjī	
Plasma etcher (semiconductor mfg)	等离子蚀刻机	Děnglízǐ shíkèjī	
Plasma modified chemical vapor deposition	等离子改良的化学汽相沉积法	Děnglízǐ gǎiliángde huàxué qìxiāng chénjīfǎ	PMCVD
Plasma photoresist stripper (semiconductor mfg)	等离子光阻去除机	Děnglízǐ guāngzǔ qùchújī	
Plasma surface modification machine (semiconductor mfg)	等离子表面改质机	Děnglízǐ biǎomiàn gǎizhìjī	
Plasma-activated chemical vapor deposition (for FOC)	等离子体激活化学气相沉积	Děnglízǐtǐ jīhuó huàxué qìxiāng chénjī	PCVD
Plastic analysis	塑性解析	Sùxìng jiěxī	
Plastic clad fiber	塑包光纤	Sùbāo guāngxiān	
Plastic clad silica fiber	塑包石英光纤	Sùbāo shíyīng guāngxiān	PCS
Plastic conditioning (semiconductor mfg)	塑性调节	Sùxìng tiáojié	
Plastic ferrule	塑胶箍	Sùjiāo gū	

English	Chinese	Pinyin	Abbreviation
Plastic fiber optic cable	塑胶光缆	Sùjiāo guānglǎn	
Plastic filter	塑胶滤光镜	Sùjiāo lǜguāngjìng	
Plastic index	塑性指数	Sùxìng zhǐshù	
Plastic limit	塑性界限	Sùxìng jièxiàn	
Plastic optical fiber	塑胶光纤	Sùjiāo guāngxiān	
Plastic optical fiber	塑料光纤	Sùliào guāngxiān	
Plastic pin grid array	塑胶针状矩阵封装	Sùjiāo zhēnzhuàng jǔzhèn fēngzhuāng	PPGA
Plastic quad flat package	塑料方块平面封装	Sùliào fāngkuài píngmiàn fēngzhuāng	PQFP
Plastic-clad silica fiber optic cable	石英系塑胶包覆光缆	Shíyīng xì sùjiāo bāofù guānglǎn	
Plastic-clad silica optical fiber	石英系塑胶包覆光纤	Shíyīng xì sùjiāo bāofù guāngxiān	
Plasticity	塑性	Sùxìng	
Plasticity chart	塑性图	Sùxìng tú	
Plat	平面地图	Píngmiàn dìtú	
Plate gasket	板状垫片	Bǎnzhuàng diànpiàn	
Plate module	板金模块	Bǎnjīn mókuài	
Plate number	版号	Bǎn hào	
Platform	平台	Píngtái	
Platform for Internet content selection	因特网内容选择平台	Yīntèwǎng nèiróng xuǎnzé píngtái	PICS
Platform invoke service	平台调用服务	Píngtái diàoyòng fúwù	PInvoke
Platform loader (in component assembly process)	平台式上扳机	Píngtái-shì shàngbānjī	
Platform security division	平台安全部分	Píngtái ānquán bùfēn	PSD
Platform specification	平台规范	Píngtái guīfàn	
Plating and coating testing	镀涂层测试	Dù túcéng cèshì	
Platinotron	泊管	Póguǎn	
Platinum resistance thermometer	铂电阻温度计	Bó diànzǔ wēndùjì	PRT
Platy joint	板状节理	Bǎnzhuàng jiélǐ	
Play announcement	播送通知	Bōsòng tōngzhī	PA
Plenum	天花板	Tiānhuābǎn	
Plenum cable	天花板隔层电缆	Tiānhuābǎn gécéng diànlǎn	
Plesiochronous	准同步的	Zhǔn tóngbùde	
Plesiochronous connection supervision	准同步连接管理	Zhǔn tóngbù liánjiē guǎnlǐ	PCS
Plesiochronous connection supervision	准同步连接监督	Zhǔn tóngbù liánjiē jiāndū	PCS
Plesiochronous digital hierarchy	准同步数字体系	Zhǔn tóngbù shùzì tǐxì	PDH
Plesiochronous digital hierarchy	准同步数字系列	Zhǔn tóngbù shùzì xìliè	PDH
Plessey (UK company)	菲利斯	Fēi-lì-sī	
Plot (verb)	点迹	Diǎnjì	
Plot filter	点迹过滤	Diǎnjì guòlǜ	
Plotter	绘图仪	Huìtúyí	
Plug	插头	Chātóu	
Plug and play	即插即用	Jíchā jíyòng	PnP
Plug body	插头外壳	Chātóu wàiké	
Plug seat	插孔	Chākǒng	
Plug-and-play	即装即用	Jízhuāng jíyòng	PNP
Plugged box	插箱	Chāxiāng	
Plugged unit	插入单元	Chārù dānyuán	
Plug-in board	插件	Chājiàn	

Plurality voting	多数投票	Duōshù tóupiào	
Pneumatic loading and unloading foot walk	气囊式装卸过桥	Qìnángshì zhuāngxiè guòqiáo	
Pocket (personal) equipment	袖珍设备	Xiùzhēn shèbèi	
Pocket bell	袖珍铃	Xiù zhēnlíng	
Poincare sphere	邦加球	Bāng-jiā qiú	PS
Point and click	点击方式	Diǎnjī fāngshì	
Point directive character string	点指向字符串	Diǎn zhǐxiàng zìfúchuàn	
Point in association	相关点	Xiāngguān diǎn	PIA
Point in call	呼叫点	Hūjiào diǎn	
Point light	一般点光源	Yībān diǎn guāngyuán	
Point location query	位置查询	Wèizhì cháxún	
Point of control and observation	控制观察点	Kòngzhì guānchádiǎn	PCO
Point of control and observation	控制和观测点	Kòngzhì hé guāncèdiǎn	PCO
Point of control and observation	控制和观察点	Kòngzhì hé guānchá diǎn	PCO
Point of interconnection	互连点	Hùliándiǎn	POI
Point of presence	存在点	Cúnzài diǎn	POP
Point of presence	服务呈现点	Fúwù chéngxiàn diǎn	
Point of presence	业务提供点	Yèwù tígōng diǎn	PoP
Point of sale	销售点	Xiāoshòu diǎn	POS
Point of sale machine	销售终端机	Xiāoshòu zhōngduānjī	
Point of sale system	销售点系统	Xiāoshòu diǎn xìtǒng	POS
Point of sales	销售点终端	Xiāoshòu diǎn zhōngduān	POS
Point sampling	点采样技术	Diǎn cǎiyàng jìshù	
Point spread function	点扩散函数	Diǎn kuòsàn hánshù	
Point symbol, marker	点状符号	Diǎnzhuàng fúhào	
Point target	点目标	Diǎn mùbiāo	
Point-and-click	指点	Zhǐdiǎn	
Point-area communication	点对地区通信	Diǎn duì dìqū tōngxìn	
Pointer	指标	Zhǐbiāo	
Pointer	指标字	Zhǐbiāo zì	
Pointer	指向点	Zhǐxiàng diǎn	
Pointer	指针	Zhǐzhēn	PTR
Pointer field (in software)	指针域	Zhǐzhēn yù	
Pointer justification count	指针调整记数	Zhǐzhēn tiáozhěng jìshù	PJC
Pointer justification event	指针调整事件	Zhǐzhēn tiáozhěng shìjiàn	PJE
Pointer processing (SDH term)	指针处理	Zhǐzhēn chǔlǐ	
Pointer processor (SDH)	指针处理器	Zhǐzhēn chǔlǐqì	
Pointer synchronization	指针同步	Zhǐzhēn tóngbù	
Pointer variable	指标字变量	Zhǐbiāo zì biànliàng	
Point-generating algorithm	点生成算法	Diǎn shēngchéng suànfǎ	
Point-in-polygon operation	多边形内点识别	Duōbiānxíng-nèi diǎn shíbié	
Point-to-area communication	点对区域通信	Diǎn duì qūyù tōngxìn	
Point-to-multipoint	点到多点	Diǎn dào duōdiǎn	
Point-to-multipoint communication	点对多点通信	Diǎn duì duōdiǎn tōngxìn	
Point-to-multipoint connection	点对多点连接	Diǎn duì duōdiǎn liánjiē	
Point-to-multipoint group call	点对多点群呼业务	Diǎn duì duōdiǎn qúnhū yèwù	PTM-G

English	Chinese	Pinyin	Abbreviation
Point-to-multipoint multicast	点对多点组播业务	Diǎn duì duōdiǎn zǔbō yèwù	DAC
Point-to-multipoint multicasting	点对多点广播业务	Diǎn duì duōdiǎn guǎngbō yèwù	PTM-M
Point-to-multipoint service	点对多点业务	Diǎn duì duōdiǎn yèwù	PTM
Point-to-point	点到点	Diǎn dào diǎn	PP, P2P
Point-to-point communication	点对点通信	Diǎn duì diǎn tōngxìn	
Point-to-point connection	点对点连接	Diǎn duì diǎn liánjiē	
Point-to-point connectionless-mode network service	点对点无连接网络业务	Diǎn duì diǎn wúliánjiē wǎngluò yèwù	PTP-CLNS
Point-to-point protocol	点到点协议	Diǎn dào diǎn xiéyì	PPP
Point-to-point protocol	点对点传输协议	Diǎn duì diǎn chuánshū xiéyì	PPP
Point-to-point protocol	点对点通信协议	Diǎn duì diǎn tōngxìn xiéyì	PPP
Point-to-point protocol	点对点协议	Diǎn duì diǎn xiéyì	PPP
Point-to-point protocol in frame relay	帧中继中的点到点协议	Zhèng zhōngjì zhòngde diǎn dàodiǎn xiéyì	PPPIFR
Point-to-point protocol over AAL5	AAL5 上的点到点协议	AAL5-shàngde diǎn dàodiǎn xiéyì	PPPOA
Point-to-point protocol over asynchronous transfer mode	ATM 上的 PPP	ATM-shàngde PPP	PPPoA
Point-to-point protocol over Ethernet	以太网上传送 PPP 协议	Yǐtàiwǎng-shàng chuánsòng PPP xiéyì	PPPOE
Point-to-point protocol over Ethernet	以太网上点到点链路协议	Yǐtàiwǎng-shàng diǎn dàodiǎn liànlù xiéyì	PPPOE
Point-to-point protocol over Ethernet	以太网上点到点协议	Yǐtàiwǎng-shàng diǎn dàodiǎn xiéyì	PPPoE
Point-to-point protocol over Ethernet	以太网上 PPP 协议	Yǐtàiwǎng-shàng PPP xiéyì	PPPoE
Point-to-point service	点对点业务	Diǎn duì diǎn yèwù	PTP
Point-to-point tunneling protocol	点到点隧道协议	Diǎn dào diǎn suìdào xiéyì	PPTP
Point-to-point tunneling protocol	点对点隧道协议	Diǎn duì diǎn suìdào xiéyì	PPTP
Point-to-point tunneling protocol	点对点通道协议	Diǎn duì diǎn tōngdào xiéyì	PPTP
Point-to-point-connection network service	点对点面向连接网络业务	Diǎn duì diǎn miànxiàng liánjiē wǎngluò yèwù	PTP-CONS
Poisson distribution	泊松分布	Pó-sōng fēnbù	
Poisson process	泊送过程	Bó-sòng guòchéng	
Poisson process	泊松过程	Pó-sōng guòchéng	
Poisson ratio	泊松比	Pó-sōng bǐ	
Polar coordinate kernel	极坐标核	Jí zuòbiāo hé	
Polar impedance diagram; Smith chart (polar admittance diagram)	导纳圆图	Dǎonà yuántú	
Polar impedance diagram; Smith chart (polar admittance diagram)	阻抗圆图（导纳圆图）	Zǔkàng yuán tú (dǎonà yuán tú)	
Polar orbit (of a satellite)	极轨道	Jí guǐdào	
Polarity	极性	Jíxìng	
Polarity decorrelation	极化去相关	Jíhuà qùxiāngguān	
Polarity diversity	极化分集	Jíhuà fēnjí	
Polarity modulator	极性调制器	Jíxìng tiáozhìqì	
Polarization (of a degenerate mode in a waveguide)	极化	Jíhuà	
Polarization (referring to light, FOC)	偏振	Piānzhèn	
Polarization decoupling ratio (of an antenna),	极化去耦比	Jíhuà qù'ǒu bǐ	
Polarization division multiple access	极化分割多路存取	Jíhuà fēngē duōlù cúnqǔ	PDMA
Polarization ellipse	极化椭圆	Jíhuà tuǒyuán	
Polarization extinction ratio (FOC)	偏振消光比	Piānzhèn xiāoguāng bǐ	
Polarization loss	极化损耗	Jíhuà sǔnhào	
Polarization maintaining and absorption reducing (fiber)	偏振保持和吸收衰减(纤维)	Piānzhèn bǎochí hé xīshōu shuāijiǎn (xiānwéi)	PANDA
Polarization maintaining fiber	保偏光纤	Bǎo piān guāngxiàn	

Polarization maintaining fiber	偏振保持光纤	Piānzhèn bǎochí guāngxiān	PMF
Polarization match	极化匹配	Jíhuà pǐpèi	
Polarization mode (FOC)	偏振模式	Piānzhèn mōshì	
Polarization mode dispersion	极化模色散	Jíhuà mó sèsàn	PMD
Polarization mode dispersion	偏振模式色散	Piānzhèn móshì sèsàn	PMD
Polarization mode dispersion (FOC)	偏振模色散	Piānzhèn mó sèsàn	PMD
Polarization mode dispersion (PMD) coefficient	偏振模色散系数	Piānzhèn mó sèsàn xìshù	
Polarization mode dispersion (PMD) differential group delay	偏振模色散差分群时延	Piānzhèn mó sèsàn chāfēn qún shíyán	PMD-DGD
Polarization mode dispersion compensator (FOC)	偏振模色散补偿器	Piānzhèn mó sèsàn bǔchángqì	PMDC
Polarization mode laser	极化模激光器	Jíhuà mó jīguāngqì	
Polarization plane	极化平面	Jíhuà píngmiàn	
Polarization ratio (of a field vector)	极化比	Jíhuà bǐ	
Polarization resolver	极化分离器	Jíhuà fēnlíqì	
Polarization selection anti-jamming technique	极化选择抗干扰技术	Jíhuà xuǎnzé kàng gānrǎo jìshù	
Polarization selector	极化选择器	Jíhuà xuǎnzéqì	
Polarization-dependent fiber isolator (FOC)	偏振相关光隔离器	Piānzhèn xiāngguān guāng gélíqì	PDFI
Polarization-dependent gain	偏振相关增益	Piānzhèn xiāngguān zēngyì	PDG
Polarization-dependent gain variation	偏振相关增益变化	Piānzhèn xiāngguān zēngyì biànhuà	
Polarization-dependent loss (FOC)	偏振相关损耗	Piānzhèn xiāngguān sǔnhào	PDL
Polarization-insensitive fiber isolator (FOC)	偏振无关光隔离器	Piānzhèn wúguān guāng gélíqì	PIFI
Polarization-insensitive phase shifter	极化不灵敏移相器	Jíhuà bùlíngmǐn yíxiàngqì	
Polarization-maintaining fiber optic cable	偏振恒持光缆	Piānzhèn héngchí guānglǎn	
Polarization-maintaining optical fiber	偏振恒持光纤	Piānzhèn héngchí guāngxiān	
Polarized light	光偏振	Guāng piānzhèn	
Polarizer layer (referring to light)	偏光板	Piānguāng bǎn	
Polarizing crystal	偏光晶体	Piānguāng jīngtǐ	
Polarizing filter	偏光滤光镜	Piānguāng lǜguāngjìng	
Policy database (for QoS)	策略服务器	Cèlüè fúwùqì	
Policy decision point	策略决定点	Cèlüè juédìng diǎn	PDP
Policy enhancement point	策略强加点	Cèlüè qiángjiā diǎn	PEP
Policy, protection, detection, response	策略,保护,检测,响应	Cèlüè, bǎohù, jiǎncè, xiǎngyìng	P2DR
Policy-based network management	基于政策的网络管理	Jīyú zhèngcède wǎngluò guǎnlǐ	PBNM
Policy-based routing	基于策略路由	Jīyú cèlüè lùyóu	
Polishing (optical device processing)	研磨	Yánmó	
Polishing compound	研磨化合物	Yánmó huàhéwù	
Poll	轮询	Lúnxún	
Poll/final	探询,终止	Tànxún, zhōngzhǐ	P/F
Polling	查询	Cháxún	
Polling interval	轮询间隔	Lúnxún jiàngé	
Polling system	查询系统	Cháxún xìtǒng	
Polling system	探询系统	Tànxún xìtǒng	
Polyamide	聚酰胺	Jùxiān'àn	
Polybutylene terephthalate	聚对苯二甲酸丁二醇酯	Jùduìběn èrjiǎsuān dīng'èrchúnzhǐ	PBT
Polycarbonate	聚碳酸酯	Jùtànsuānzhǐ	PC
Polyethylene	聚乙烯	Jùyǐxī	PE
Polygon	多边形	Duōbiānxíng	

Polygon attribute table	多边形属性表	Duōbiānxíng shǔxìng biǎo	
Polygon line	多边形线	Duōbiānxíng xiàn	
Polygon overlay	多边形叠加	Duōbiānxíng diéjiā	
Polygon partitioning	多边形分割	Duōbiānxíng fēngē	
Polygon structure	多边形结构	Duōbiānxíng jiégòu	
Polygon transformation and lighting (video term)	多边形转换与光源处理	Duōbiānxíng zhuǎnhuàn yǔ guāngyuán chǔlǐ	T&L
Polygonal fusion	多边形融合	Duōbiānxíng rónghé	
Polygonal mirror	多面镜	Duōmiànjìng	
Polygon-arc topology	多边形-弧段拓扑数据结构	Duōbiānxíng—húduàn tuòpū shùjù jiégòu	
Polymer optical fiber	聚合体光纤	Jùhétǐ guāngxiān	POF
Polymer optical fiber	聚合物光纤	Jùhéwù guāngxiān	POF
Polymer optical fiber	塑料光纤	Sùliào guāngxiān	
Polymer photonic band gap fiber	聚合物光子禁带光纤	Jùhéwù guāngzǐ jìn dài guāngxiān	
Polymer photonic crystal optical fiber	聚合物光子晶体光纤	Jùhéwù guāngzǐ jīngtǐ guāngxiān	PPCF
Polymethyl methacrylate	聚甲基丙烯酸甲酯	Jùjiǎjī bǐngxīsuān jiǎzhǐ	PMMA
Polymorphism	多态性	Duōtàixìng	
Polynomial	多项式	Duōxiàngshì	
Polynomial transformation	多项式变换	Duōxiàngshì biànhuàn	
Polyphase merging sort	多步归并排序	Duōbù guībìng páixù	
Polypropylene	聚丙烯	Jùbǐngxī	
Polystyrene	聚苯乙烯	Jùběnyǐxī	PS
Polyvinyl chloride	聚氯乙烯	Jùlǜyǐxī	PVC
Polyvinylidene fluoride	聚偏二氟乙烯	Jùpiān èrfúyǐxī	PVDF
Pooling	池化	Chíhuà	
Pooling	缓冲池	Huǎnchōng chí	
Pooling point operation	共用节点操作	Gòngyòng jiédiǎn cāozuò	
Poor contact	接触不良	Jiēchùbùliáng	
Pop up	弹出式	Tánchū-shì	
Pop-up menu	跳出式菜单	Tiàochū-shì càidān	
Pop-up window	弹出式窗口	Tánchū-shì chuāngkǒu	
Porous tungsten	活性钨	Huóxìng wū	
Port access entity	端口访问实体	Duānkǒu fǎngwèn shítǐ	PAE
Port and core function	端口及核心功能	Duānkǒu jí héxīn gōngnéng	PCF
Port and core function-operating system	端口及核心功能-运行系统	Duānkǒu jí héxīn gōngnéng--yùnxíng xìtǒng	PCF-OS
Port and core function-operating system function	端口及核心功能-运行系统功能	Duānkǒu jí héxīn gōngnéng--yùnxíng xìtǒng gōngnéng	PCF-OSF
Port bundling	端口捆绑	Duānkǒu kǔnbǎng	
Port bypass circuit	端口旁路电路	Duānkǒu pánglù diànlù	PBC
Port level manager	端口级管理程序	Duānkǒu-jí guǎnlǐ chéngxù	PLM
Port log	端口日志	Duānkǒu rìzhì	
Port log dump	端口日志查看	Duānkǒu rìzhì chákàn	
Port mapping	端口映射	Duānkǒu yìngshè	
Port mirroring	端口镜像	Duānkǒu jìngxiàng	
Port name	端口名	Duānkǒu míng	
Port operations service (seaport)	港口操作业务	Gǎngkǒu cāozuò yèwù	
Port scanning	端口扫描	Duānkǒu sǎomiáo	

English	Chinese	Pinyin	Abbreviation
Port station (seaport)	港口电台	Gǎngkǒu diàntái	
Port, terminal	端口	Duānkǒu	
Portability	可移植性	Kěyízhíxìng	
Portability (of software)	可携性	Kěxiéxìng	
Portable	便携	Biànxié	
Portable access rights key	移动用户接入权限识别码	Yídòng yònghù jiērù quánxiàn shíbié mǎ	PARK
Portable computer	手提电脑	Shǒutí diànnǎo	
Portable document format	轻便文档格式	Qīngbiàn wéndàng géshi	PDF
Portable document format (Adobe format)	可移植资料格式	Kěyízhí zīliào géshi	.pdf
Portable document format (Adobe)	移植资料格式	Yízhí zīliào géshi	.pdf
Portable equipment	便携设备	Biànxié shèbèi	
Portable executable file	可移植可执行文件	Kěyízhí kě zhíxíng wénjiàn	PE
Portable mobile station (walkie-talkie)	步谈机	Bùtánjī	
Portable operating system interface for UNIX	轻便操作系统界面	Qīngbiàn cāozuò xìtǒng jièmiàn	POSIX
Portable station	便携电台	Biànxié diàntái	
Portable telephone	便携电话	Biànxié diànhuà	
Portable telephone set	携带式电话机	Xiédàishì diànhuàjī	
Portable vehicle equipment	便携式载体设备	Biànxiéshì zàitǐ shèbèi	
Portal	门户	Ménhù	
Portal	入口	Rùkǒu	
Portal server	门户服务器	Ménhù fúwùqì	
Portal site	门户站点	Ménhù zhàndiǎn	
Portnet	港务网	Gǎngwù wǎng	
Portrayal	描绘	Miáohuì	
Portrayal catalogue	描述目录	Miáoshù mùlù	
Portrayal element	描绘元素	Miáohuì yuánsù	
Portrayal rule	描绘规则	Miáohuì guīzé	
Portrayal service	描绘服务	Miáohuì fúwù	
Portrayal specification	描绘规范	Miáohuì guīfàn	
Ports in telecommunications buildings	电信建筑中的端口	Diànxìn jiànzhù-zhòngde duānkǒu	
POSH® single mode optical fiber	保实®单模光纤	Bǎo-shí ® dānmó guāngxiān	POSH®
Position	位置	Wèizhì	
Position determining entity	位置确定实体	Wèizhì quèdìng shítǐ	PDE
Position field descriptor	位置字段描述符	Wèizhì zìduàn miáoshù fú	
Position keying	定位销	Dìngwèi xiāo	
Position manipulation	位操作	Wèi cāozuò	
Position point	定位点	Dìngwèi diǎn	
Position register	坐席记发器	Zuòxí jìfāqì	
Position resolution	位置分辨率	Wèizhì fēnbiànlǜ	
Position sleeve	定位套	Dìngwèi tào	
Positional accuracy	位置准确性	Wèizhì zhǔnquèxìng	
Positional accuracy, locational accuracy	定位精度	Dìngwèi jīngdù	
Positional precision	位置精度	Wèizhì jīngdù	
Positional reference frame	位置参考框架	Wèizhì cānkǎo kuàngjià	
Positioned channel	定位信道	Dìngwèi xìndào	
Positioned channel	有固定位置的通路	Yǒu gùdìng wèizhìde tōnglù	

English	Chinese	Pinyin	Abbreviation
Positioned interface structure	定位接口结构	Dìngwèi jiēkǒu jiégòu	
Positioned interface structure	有固定位置的接口结构	Yǒu gùdìng wèizhìde jiēkǒu jiégòu	
Positioned update	定位更新	Dìngwèi gèngxīn	
Positioning area	定位区	Dìngwèi qū	
Positioning system	定位系统	Dìngwèi xìtǒng	
Position-limiting switch	行程限制开关	Xíngchéng xiànzhì kāiguān	
Positive acknowledgment with retransmission	用于重发的肯定应答	Yòng yú chóngfāde kěndìng yìngdá	PAR
Positive and inverse code	正反码	Zhèng-fǎn mǎ	
Positive association rule	正关联规则	Zhèng guānlián guīzé	
Positive feedback	正反馈	Zhèng fǎnkuì	
Positive justification	正码速调整	Zhèng mǎsù tiáozhěng	
Positive logic	正逻辑	Zhèng luóji	
Positive mismatching	正失配	Zhèng shīpèi	
Positive printing amount percent	征印量差	Zhēng yìn liáng chà	
Positive pulse stuffing	正脉冲塞入	Zhèng màichōng sāirù	
Post and telecommunications	邮政	Yóuzhèng	PTT
Post and telecoms electrical control	由政电控	Yóuzhèng diànkòng	YDK
Post and telecoms machinery	邮政电机械	Yóuzhèng diànjīxiè	YJX
Post box (to send letters)	信筒	Xìntǒng	
Post office box address (P.O. box address)	邮局信箱地址	Yóujú xìnxiāng dìzhǐ	
Post Office Code Standardization Advisory Group (UK)	邮政总局寻码标准化咨询组	Yóuzhèng zǒngjú xúnmǎ biāozhǔnhuà zīxúnzǔ	POCSAG
Post office protocol	邮局协议	Yóujú xiéyì	POP
Post office protocol 3	第三号邮局协议	Dìsānhào yóujú xiéyì	POP3
Post office protocol 3	邮局协议的第 3 个版本	Yóujú xiéyìde dìsangè bǎnběn	POP3
Post office protocol version 3	第三版电子邮局协议	Dìsānbǎn diànzǐ yóujú xiéyì	POP3
Postage certificate	邮资凭证	Yóuzī píngzhèng	
Postage item	邮资票品	Yóuzī piàopǐn	
Postage item for communication	通信用邮资票品	Tōngxìn-yòng yóuzī piàopǐn	
Postal code	邮政编码	Yóuzhèng biānmǎ	
Postal code	邮政编码	Yóuzhèng biānmǎ	
Postal O/R address	邮政 O/R 地址	Yóuzhèng O/R dìzhǐ	
Postal O/R address components	邮政 O/R 地址组成成份	Yóuzhèng O/R dìzhǐ zǔchéng chéngfèn	
Post-dialing delay	拨号后延迟	Bōhào hòu yánchí	
Posting	传载	Chuánzài	
Postorder traversal	后序遍历	Hòuxù biànlì	
Post-production processing	后期制作处理	Hòuqī zhìzuò chǔlǐ	
Post-production processing	生产后处理	Shēngchǎn hòuchǔlǐ	
Potential browser	潜在浏览器	Qiánzài liúlǎnqì	
Potential event report	潜在事件报告	Qiánzài shìjiàn bàogào	
Potential recipient	潜在接收者	Qiánzài jiēshōuzhě	
Potential round robin	势轮转算法	Shì lúnzhuàn suànfǎ	PRR
Potter horn antenna	普特喇叭天线	Pǔ-tè lǎba tiānxiàn	
Powder coat cure (semiconductor mfg)	粉涂层硫化	Fěntúcéng liúhuà	
Powder coated external frame (semiconductor mfg)	粉末涂层外部结构	Fěnmò túcéng wàibù jiégòu	
Power	功率	Gōnglǜ	POW

English	Chinese	Pinyin	Abbr.
Power amplifier	功率放大器	Gōnglǜ fàngdàqì	
Power amplifier interconnection panel	功率放大器互联面板	Gōnglǜ fàngdàqì hùlián miànbǎn	PICP
Power attack (computer hacking)	能量攻击	Néngliàng gōngjī	
Power cable and power lead damped sinusoidal transient conducted susceptibility (Mil-Std-461E, CS116)	电缆和电源线阻尼正弦瞬变传导敏感度	Diànlǎn hé diànyuánxiàn zǔní zhèngxián shùnbiàn chuándǎo mǐngǎndù	
Power carriage	电源车	Diànyuán chē	
Power conditioning	电源调节	Diànyuán tiáojié	
Power conditioning equipment	电力调节设备	Diànlì tiáojié shèbèi	
Power control	功率控制	Gōnglǜ kòngzhì	PC
Power control circuit	电源控制电路	Diànyuán kòngzhì diànlù	
Power control level	功率控制电平	Gōnglǜ kòngzhì diànpíng	
Power control message	功率控制报文	Gōnglǜ kòngzhì bàowén	
Power control unit	功率控制单元	Gōnglǜ kòngzhì dānyuán	PCU
Power divider	功率分配器	Gōnglǜ fēnpèiqì	
Power factor	功率因数	Gōnglǜ yīnshù	PF
Power factor	功率因素	Gōnglǜ yīnsù	
Power factor	功率因子	Gōnglǜ yīnzǐ	
Power generation set	发电机组	Fādiàn jīzǔ	
Power lead conducted emissions (Mil-Std-461E, CE101)	电源线传导发射	Diànyuánxiàn chuándǎo fāshè	
Power lead conducted susceptibility (Mil-Std-461E, CS101)	电源线传导敏感度	Diànyuánxiàn chuándǎo mǐngǎndù	
Power lead peak signal (time domain) conducted emissions (Mil-Std-461E, CE107)	电源线尖峰信号(时域)传导发射	Diànyuánxiàn jiānfēng xìnhào (shí yù) chuándǎo fāshè	
Power lead peak signal conducted susceptibility (Mil-Std-461E, CS106)	电源线尖峰信号传导敏感度	Diànyuánxiàn jiānfēng xìnhào chuándǎo mǐngǎndù	
Power level	功率电平	Gōnglǜ diànpíng	PL
Power loss	功率损耗	Gōnglǜ sǔnhào	
Power loss, outage	掉电	Diàodiàn	LPR
Power Mac ©	威力麦金塔	Wēilì mài-jīn-tǎ	
Power management system	电源管理系统	Diànyuán guǎnlǐ xìtǒng	PMS
Power matching	功率匹配	Gōnglǜ pǐpèi	PM
Power of loudspeaker	扬声器功率	Yángshēngqì gōnglǜ	
Power offset	功率偏移	Gōnglǜ piānyí	
Power output	输出电平	Shūchū diànpíng	
Power PC	威力电脑	Wēilì diànnǎo	
Power penalty	功率代价	Gōnglǜ dàijià	
Power product	功率生成	Gōnglǜ shēngchéng	
Power product	功率生成	Gōnglǜ shēngchéng	
Power recovery processing	复电处理	Fùdiàn chǔlǐ	
Power reflection factor (in a transmission line)	功率反射系数	Gōnglǜ fǎnshè xìshù	
Power requirement	电源要求	Diànyuán yāoqiú	
Power spectrum	功率谱	Gōnglǜ pǔ	
Power spectrum density	功率谱密度	Gōnglǜ pǔ mìdù	PSD
Power spectrum density mask	功率谱密度模板	Gōnglǜ pǔ mìdù múbǎn	PSDMASK
Power standing-wave ratio	功率驻波比	Gōnglǜ zhùbōbǐ	PSWR
Power step	功率步长	Gōnglǜ bùcháng	PWR_STEP
Power sum near-end crosstalk	综合近端串扰	Zōnghé jìnduān chuànrǎo	PS-NEXT

Power supply	电源	Diànyuán	DY
Power supply	供电电源	Gōngdiàn diànyuán	
Power supply bias test	电源拉偏测试	Diànyuán lāpiān cèshì	
Power supply distribution frame	电原配电架	Diànyuán pèidiànjià	PDF
Power supply motherboard	电源母	Diànyuán mǔ	PWB
Power switch (on electronic equipment)	电源开关	Diànyuán kāiguān	
Power synthesis	功率合成	Gōnglǜ héchéng	
Power system	电源系统	Diànyuán xìtǒng	PWS
Power transmission factor (in a transmission line)	功率传输系数	Gōnglǜ chuánshū xìshù	
Power tray	电源支架	Diànyuán zhījià	
Power user	高档用户	Gāodàng yònghù	
Power, exertion (power grid term)	出力	Chūlì	
Power-handling capacity	功率容量	Gōnglǜ róngliàng	
Powerline access	电力线接入	Diànlìxiàn jiērù	PLA
Powerline broadband	电力线宽带	Diànlìxiàn kuāndài	PLB
Powerline carrier	电力线载波	Diànlìxiàn zàibō	PLC
Powerline carrier forum	电力线载波论坛	Diànlìxiàn zàibō lùntán	PLCF
Powerline telecommunications	电力线通信	Diànlìxiàn tōngxìn	PLT
Power-managed jammer	功率管理干扰机	Gōnglǜ guǎnlǐ gānrǎojī	
Power-on restore	上电修复	Shàngdiàn xiūfù	
Power-on self test	加电自测试	Jiādiàn zìcèshì	POST
Power-on self test	加电自检	Jiādiàn zìjiǎn	POST
Power-on self test	开机自动测试	Kāijī zìdòng cèshì	POST
Power-on self test	上电自检	Shàngdiàn zì jiǎn	POST
Power-on self-test	通电自检	Tōngdiàn zì jiǎn	POST
Poynting vector	玻印迁矢量	Bō-yìn-qiān shǐliàng	
Practical extraction and report language	实用摘录与报告语言	Shíyòng zhāilù yǔ bàogào yǔyán	PERL
Pragmatic general multicast protocol (IETF usage)	实用通用组播协议	Shíyòng tōngyòng zǔbō xiéyì	PGM
Praseodymium-doped fiber amplifier	掺镨光纤放大器	Chān pǔ guāngxiān fàngdàqì	PDFA
Preamble	前导字节	Qiándǎo zìjié	
Preamplification	前置放大	Qiánzhì fàngdà	
Preamplifier	前级放大器	Qiánjí fàngdàqì	
Pre-amplifier	预放	Yùfàng	PA
Pre-amplifier	预放大器	Yùfàngdàqì	PA
Pre-amplifier	前置放大器	Qiánzhì fàngdàqì	PA
Preassigned multiple access	预分配多址	Yùfēnpèi duōzhǐ	PMA
Preassigned time division multiple access	预分配分时多路存取	Yùfēnpèi fēnshí duōlù cúnqǔ	PA-TDMA
Pre-assignment	预分配	Yùfēnpèi	
Precedence	优先序	Yōuxiānxù	
Precession	进动	Jìndòng	
Pre-chirp	预啁啾	Yùzhōujiū	PCH
Precipitation compensation	降雨补偿	Jiàngyǔ bǔcháng	
Precipitation degradation	降雨衰落	Jiàngyǔ shuāiluò	
Precipitation scatter propagation	降落物散射传播	Jiàngluòwù sǎnshè chuánbō	
Precise pixel interpolation	精确像素插值	Jīngquè xiàngsù chāzhí	
Precise serialization	精确串行化	Jīngquè chuànhánghuà	PS

English	Chinese	Pinyin	Abbr.
Precision	精度	Jīngdù	
Precision	紧密度	Jǐnmìdù	
Precision fine pitch	精细间距	Jīngxì jiānjù	
Precision guided weapon	精确制导的武器	Jīngquè zhìdǎode wǔqì	
Precision optical fiber (cable) connector	精密光纤（缆）连接器	Jīngmì guāngxiān (lǎn) liánjiēqì	
Precision orbit determination system	经确定轨系统	Jīngquè dìngguǐ xìtǒng	PODS
Precision positioning service	精密定位业务	Jīngmì dìngwèi yèwù	PPS
Precision positioning service (in GPS)	精密定位服务	Jīngmì dìngwèi fúwù	PPS
Pre-connect	预连接	Yùliánjiē	
Pre-correction	预校正	Yùjiàozhèng	
Precursor	前兆	Qiánzhào	
Predecessor	前趋	Qiánqū	
Pre-dialing time supervision	拨号前时间监视	Bōhào-qián shíjiān jiānshì	
Predicted distortion	预畸变	Yùjībiàn	
Prediction	预测	Yùcè	
Prediction error	预测误差	Yùcè wùchā	
Predictive differential quantizer	预测差分量化器	Yùcè chāfēn liànghuàqì	PDQ
Predistortion	预失真	Yùshīzhēn	
Predominant period	显著周期	Xiǎnzhe zhōuqī	
Pre-emphasis (radio term)	预加重	Yùjiāzhòng	
Pre-emption	强占	Qiángzhàn	
Preemptive-resume priority scheme	抢先 - 恢复优先规则	Qiǎngxiān-huīfù yōuxiān guīzé	
Pre-equalization	预均衡	Yùjūnhéng	
Preferred recipient	优先接收者	Yōuxiān jiēshōuzhě	
Pre-fetch	预获取	Yùhuòqǔ	
Prefix	字冠	Zìguān	
Prefix	前缀	Qiánzhuì	
Prefix characters	前缀字符	Qiánzhuì zìfú	
Prefix information options	前缀信息可选项	Qiánzhuì xìnxī kěxuǎnxiàng	
Prefix length	前缀长度	Qiánzhuì chángdù	
Prefix search	前缀搜索	Qiánzhuì sōusuǒ	
Prefix sum method	前缀和算法	Qiánzhuì hé suànfǎ	
Preform (noun)	预型体	Yùxíngtǐ	
Preform (noun) (of FOC)	预制棒	Yùzhìbàng	
Preform rod (FOC mfg)	预型体	Yùxíngtǐ	
Preform rod manufacturing equipment (FOC)	预型体制造设备	Yùxíngtǐ zhìzào shèbèi	
Preform rod polishing equipment (FOC)	预型体研磨加工设备	Yùxíngtǐ yánmó jiāgōng shèbèi	
Pre-image (in hash signature technology)	预映射	Yùyìngshè	
Preliminary topology	初级拓扑	Chūjí tuòpū	
Pre-master secret (IPsec)	预住机密	Yùzhù jīmì	
Premature convergence	早熟收敛	Zǎoshú shōuliǎn	
Premature disconnection	提前释放	Tíqián shìfàng	
Premature release	过早释放	Guòzǎo shìfàng	
Premises distribution system	建筑综合布线系统	Jiànzhù zōnghé bùxiàn xìtǒng	PDS
Premises distribution system	建筑物布线系统	Jiànzhùwù bùxiàn xìtǒng	PDS
Premises distribution system	建筑物结构化综合布线系统	Jiànzhùwù jiégòuhuà zōnghé bùxiàn xìtǒng	PDS

Premises distribution system	综合布线系统	Zōnghé bùxiàn xìtǒng	PDS
Premodulation Gaussian filtered MSK	调前高斯滤波的 MSK	Tiáoqián gāo-sī lǜbōde MSK	GMSK
Preorder traversal	先序遍历	Xiānxù biànlì	
Prepaid billing platform	预付费平台	Yùfùfèi píngtái	
Prepaid charging	预付费业务	Yùfùfèi yèwù	PPC
Prepaid wireless service	预缴无线服务	Yùjiǎo wúxiàn fúwù	
Prepare handover	准备切换	Zhǔnbèi qiēhuàn	
Prepare subsequent handover	准备后续切换	Zhǔnbèi hòuxù qiēhuàn	
Prepay	预支付	Yùzhīfù	
Pre-payment billing service	预付费业务	Yùfùfèi yèwù	
Pre-payment rule	预付票底制	Yùfùpiào dǐzhì	
Pre-processor	预处理器	Yùchǔlǐqì	
Pre-scalar	前置分频器	Qiánzhì fēnpínqì	
Prescalar divider division ratio	可预置分频器分频比	Kě yùzhì fēnpínqì fènpín bǐ	
Pre-selected channel	预选信道	Yùxuǎn xìndào	
Pre-selector	选组器	Xuǎnzǔqì	
Pre-selector	预选器	Yùxuǎnqì	
Presence	在席	Zàixí	
Presentation	显现	Xiǎnxiàn	
Presentation connection end point	表示连接端点	Biǎoshì liánjiē duāndiǎn	PCEP
Presentation context	表示上下文	Biǎoshì shàngxiàwén	
Presentation control functions	显示控制功能	Xiǎnshì kòngzhì gōngnéng	
Presentation element	显现元素	Xiǎnxiàn yuánsù	
Presentation function	表示功能	Biǎoshì gōngnéng	PF
Presentation indicator	展示指示器	Zhǎnshì zhǐshìqì	PI
Presentation layer	表示层	Biǎoshì céng	
Presentation layer protocol (in ISO's OSI)	表示层协议	Biǎoshì céng xiéyì	PP
Presentation medium	显现媒体	Xiǎnxiàn méitǐ	
Presentation protocol control information	表示协议控制信息	Biǎoshì xiéyì kòngzhì xìnxī	PPCI
Presentation protocol data unit	表示协议数据单元	Biǎoshì xiéyì shùjù dānyuán	PPDU
Presentation protocol machine	表示协议机	Biǎoshì xiéyì jī	PPM
Presentation service	表示服务	Biǎoshì fúwù	PS
Presentation service access point	表示服务访问点	Biǎoshì fúwù fǎngwèn diǎn	PSAP
Presentation service data unit	表示服务数据单元	Biǎoshì fúwù shùjù dānyuán	PSDU
Presentation services layer	会话服务层	Huìhuà fúwù céng	
Presentation software	简报软件	Jiǎnbào ruǎnjiàn	
Presentation style	显现式样	Xiǎnxiàn shìyàng	
Presentation surface	显现面	Xiǎnxiàn miàn	
Preset	预置	Yùzhì	
Preset jammer	预调干扰机	Yùdiào gànrǎojī	
Pressure	压力	Yālì	
Pressure control valve	压力控制阀	Yālì kòngzhì fá	
Pressure fastener	压接机	Yājiējī	
Pressure gradient	压差式	Yāchā-shì	PG
Pressure gradient	压力梯度	Yālì tīdù	
Pressure operated	压强式	Yāqiáng-shì	PO

Pressurization fan	加压风机	Jiāyā fēngjī	PF
Pre-translator	预译码器	Yùyìmǎqì	PX
Pretty good privacy	优良保密协议	Yōuliáng bǎomì xiéyì	PGP
Preventive cyclic retransmission	预防性的循环重发	Yùfángxìngde xúnhuán chóngfā	
Preventive maintenance	预防性维护	Yùfángxìng wéihù	PM
Preventive maintenance	预防性维修	Yùfángxìng wéixiū	
Preventive maintenance time	预防性维护时间	Yùfángxìng wéihù shíjiān	
Preview	预览	Yùlǎn	
Previous function state	前函数状态	Qián hánshù zhuàngtài	
Previous rate	先前速率	Xiānqián sùlǜ	
Price band	价格带	Jiàgé dài	
Price per unit currency table	每单位市场价格表	Měi dānwèi shìchǎng jiàgé biǎo	PUCT
Primary address code	原址代码	Yuánzhǐ dàimǎ	PAC
Primary body (in relation to a satellite)	主星体	Zhǔ xīngtǐ	
Primary cable access	主干电缆接入	Zhǔgàn diànlǎn jiērù	
Primary cause	主因	Zhǔ yīn	
Primary cell	原电池	Yuándiànchí	
Primary circuit	一次电路	Yīcì diànlù	
Primary clock pulse generator	主时钟脉冲发生器	Zhǔ shízhōng màichōng fāshēngqì	PCPG
Primary coating (procoated)	一次被覆层(预涂层)	Yīcì bèifù céng (yù túcéng)	
Primary coating fiber	一次被覆光纤	Yīcì bèifù guāngxiān	
Primary common control physical channel	基本公共控制物理信道	Jīběn gōnggòng kòngzhì wùlǐ xìndào	P-CCPCH
Primary common pilot channel	基本公共导频信道	Jīběn gōnggòng dǎopín xìndào	P-CPIH
Primary data source	主要数据源	Zhǔyào shùjù yuán	
Primary design	主要设计	Zhǔyào shèjì	
Primary digital group	数字基群	Shùzì jīqún	PDG
Primary digital group	数字一次群	Shùzì yīcì qún	
Primary dimension table	主维度表	Zhǔ wéidù biǎo	
Primary distribution link	初级分布线路	Chūjí fēnbù xiànlù	
Primary domain controller	主域控制器	Zhǔ yù kòngzhìqì	PDC
Primary failure	独立失效	Dúlì shīxiào	
Primary graphic element	基本图形要素	Jīběn túxíng yàosù	
Primary key (cryptography)	初始密钥	Chūshǐ mìyào	
Primary key constraint (in SQL Server)	主关键字约束	Zhǔ guānjiàn zì yuēshù	
Primary keyword	主关键字	Zhǔ guānjiàn zì	
Primary keyword (for database)	主键	Zhǔ jiàn	PK
Primary link	基群链路	Jīqún liànlù	PLK
Primary link for interactive services	交互型业务的基群链路	Jiāohù-xíng yèwùde jīqún liànlù	IPL
Primary multiplexer	一次复用器	Yīcì fùyòngqì	
Primary node	主节点	Zhǔ jiédiǎn	
Primary partition	主分区	Zhǔ fēnqū	
Primary pattern	初级方向图	Chūjí fāngxiàngtú	
Primary pulse code modulation (PCM) group	脉冲编码调制基群	Màichōng biānmǎ tiáozhì jīqún	
Primary radar	一次雷达	Yīcì léidá	
Primary radiator	初级辐射器	Chūjí fúshèqì	
Primary rate access	基群速率接入	Jīqún sùlǜ jiērù	PRA

Primary rate access	一次群速率接入	Yīcì qún sùlǜ jiērù	PRA
Primary rate access	一次群速率入口	Yīcì qún sùlǜ rùkǒu	PRA
Primary rate access	主群速率	Zhǔ qún sùlǜ	PRA
Primary rate interface	基群速率接口	Jīqún sùlǜ jiēkǒu	PRI
Primary rate interface	一次群接口	Yīcì qún jiēkǒu	PRI
Primary rate interface	原级速率界面	Yuánjí sùlǜ jièmiàn	PRI
Primary rate interface (North America and Japan)	主群速率接口	Zhǔ qún sùlǜ jiēkǒu	PRI
Primary rate interface structure	一次群速率接口结构	Yīcì qún sùlǜ jiēkǒu jiégòu	
Primary rate of access	次群速率接入	Cì qún sùlǜ jiērù	
Primary rate user-network interface	基群速率用户-网络接口	Jīqún sùlǜ yònghù—wǎngluò jiēkǒu	PRUNI
Primary reference clock	基准参考时钟	Jīzhǔn cānkǎo shízhōng	PRC
Primary reference clock	基准时钟	Jīzhǔn shízhōng	PRC
Primary reference clock	基准钟	Jīzhǔn zhōng	PRC
Primary reference clock	主参考时钟	Zhǔ cānkǎo shízhōng	PRC
Primary reference clock	主基准时钟	Zhǔ jīzhǔn shízhōng	PRC
Primary reference clock	全网基准钟	Quán wǎng jīzhǔn zhōng	PRC
Primary reference clock	全国基准时钟	Quánguó jīzhǔn shízhōng	PRC
Primary reference source	基准参考源	Jīzhǔn cānkǎoyuán	PRS
Primary reference source (timing)	时间基准	Shíjiān jīzhǔn	PRS
Primary resource clock	基准主时钟	Jīzhǔn zhǔ shízhōng	PRC
Primary supply	主供电	Zhǔ gōngdiàn	
Primary synchronization code	主同步码	Zhǔ tóngbù mǎ	PSC
Primary table (for database)	主表	Zhǔ biǎo	
Primary template	原始模板	Yuánshǐ múbǎn	
Prime code	素数码	Sùshù mǎ	
Primitive	基元	Jīyuán	
Primitive (in OSI reference model)	原语	Yuányǔ	
Primitive (noun)	原素	Yuánsù	
Primitive entitiy	原素实体	Yuánsù shítǐ	
Primitive sequence	原语序列	Yuányǔ xùliè	
Primitive signal	原语信号	Yuányǔ xìnhào	
Primitive type	原始类型	Yuánshǐ lèixíng	
Principal axis	主轴	Zhǔ zhóu	
Principal axis of pressure	主压力轴	Zhǔ yālì zhóu	
Principal axis of tension	主张力轴	Zhǔ zhānglì zhóu	
Principal state of polarization	主偏振态	Zhǔ piānzhèn tài	PSP
Principle component analysis	主成分分析	Zhǔ chéngfèn fēnxī	
Principle half-power beamwidths	主波束宽度	Zhǔ bōshù kuāndù	
Print (WP command)	打印	Dǎyìn	
Print preview	打印预览	Dǎyìn yùlǎn	
Print preview	打印预视	Dǎyìn yùshì	
Print setup	打印设置	Dǎyìn shèzhì	
Print suppress (IPsec)	打印隐蔽	Dǎyìn yǐnbì	
Printable area	可打印区	Kědǎyìn qū	
PrintBrush ©	画笔软件	Huàbǐ ruǎnjiàn	
Printed circuit	印制电路	Yìnzhì diànlù	

Printed circuit antenna	印制电路天线	Yìnzhì diànlù tiānxiàn	PCA
Printed circuit board	印刷电路板	Yìnshuā diànlù bǎn	PCB
Printed circuit board	印制板	Yìnzhì bǎn	PCB
Printed circuit board assembly	印刷电路板装配	Yìnshuā diànlù bǎn zhuāngpèi	PCBA
Printed circuit board assembly	印制电路板组件	Yìnzhì diànlù bǎn zǔjiàn	PCBA
Printed circuit board assembly	印制电路集成板	Yìnzhì diànlù jíchéngbǎn	PBA
Printed circuit board diverter (in component assembly process)	电路板回流器	Diànlù bǎn huíliúqì	
Printed circuit board slot	印刷板式插座	Yìnshuābǎn-shi chāzuò	
Printed oscillator	印刷振子	Yìnshuā zhènzǐ	
Printer	打印机	Dǎyìnjī	
Printer access protocol (Apple usage)	打印机访问协议	Dǎyìnjī fǎngwèn xiéyì	PAP
Printer control language	打印机控制语言	Dǎyìnjī kòngzhì yǔyán	PCL
Printer driver	打印机驱动程式	Dǎyìnjī qūdòng chéngshì	
Printer emulation	模拟打印机	Mónǐ dǎyìnjī	
Printer font	打印机字型	Dǎyìnjī zìxíng	
Printer job language	打印机作业语言	Dǎyìnjī zuòyè yǔyán	PJL
Printer port	打印机接口	Dǎyìnjī jiēkǒu	
Printing and distribution in other cities	分地印刷发行	Fēndì yìnshuā fāxíng	
Printing code	印码	Yìnmǎ	
Printing list	报刊印数通知单	Bàokān yìnshù tōngzhīdān	
Printing reports	打印报表	Dǎyìn bàobiǎo	
Printing sort	版别	Bǎn bié	
Printing telegraphy	印字电报	Yìnzì diànbào	
PrintScreen key	屏面打印键	Píngmiàn dǎyìn jiàn	
PrintShop © (graphics software)	印务馆	Yìnwùguǎn	
Prioritized carrier-sense multiple access with collision detection	带有碰撞检测的优先载波读出多路存取	Dàiyǒu pèngzhuàng jiǎncède yōuxiān zàibō dúchū duōlù cúnqǔ	PCSMA/CD
Priority	优先级	Yōuxiān jí	
Priority access and channel assignment	优先接入及信道指配	Yōuxiān jiērù jí xìndào zhǐpèi	PACA
Priority call	优先（权）呼叫	Yōuxiān (quán) hūjiào	
Priority control	优先级控制	Yōuxiān jí kòngzhì	PC
Priority for called subscriber	被呼用户优先	Bèihū yònghù yōuxiān	
Priority interrupt	优先中断	Yōuxiān zhōngduàn	
Priority maneuver	优先机动	Yōuxiān jīdòng	
Priority queuing	优先队列	Yōuxiān duìliè	PQ
Priority queuing	优先权排队	Yōuxiānquán páiduì	PQ
Priority-based block and inheritance	基于优先级封锁-继承	Jīyú yōuxiānjí fēngsuǒ—jìchéng	PBBI
Priority-based transaction restart	基于优先级的事务重启	Jīyú yōuxiānjíde shìwù chóngqǐ	PBTS
Prism	棱镜	Léngjìng	
Privacy (?) authentication protocol	密码鉴权协议	Mìmǎ jiànquán xiéyì	PAP
Privacy amplification (in quantum cryptography)	保密增强	Bǎomì zēngqiáng	
Privacy enhanced mail	私有加强邮件	Sīyǒu jiāqiáng yóujiàn	PEM
Privacy preference project	个人私隐安全平台	Gèrén sīyǐn ānquán píngtái	P3P
Privacy protected command (in FTP)	保密保护命令	Bǎomì bǎohù mìnglìng	
Privacy transformation	保密变换	Bǎomì biànhuàn	
Privacy transformation (IPsec)	保密换算	Bǎomì huànsuàn	

English	Chinese	Pinyin	Abbreviation
Privacy, confidentiality	私密性	Sīmìxìng	
Private automatic branch exchange	用户自动交换机	Yònghù zìdòng jiāohuànjī	PABX
Private automatic branch exchange	用户自动小交换机	Yònghù zìdòng xiǎo jiāohuànjī	PABX
Private automatic branch exchange	专用自动交换分机	Zhuānyòng zìdòng jiāohuàn fēnjī	PABX
Private automatic branch exchange	专用自动小交换机	Zhuānyòng zìdòng xiǎo jiāohuànjī	PABX
Private automatic branch exchange	专用自动用户交换机	Zhuānyòng zìdòng yònghù jiāohuànjī	PABX
Private automatic branch eXchange access for GSM extension	全球移动通信系统分机用专用自动小交换机接入	Quánqiú yídòng tōngxìn xìtǒng fēnjī yòng zhuānyòng zìdòng xiǎo jiāohuànjī jiērù	PAGC
Private branch exchange	用户交换机	Yònghù jiāohuànjī	PBX
Private branch exchange	用户小交换机	Yònghù xiǎo jiāohuànjī	PBX
Private branch exchange	专用交换机	Zhuānyòng jiāohuànjī	PBX
Private branch exchange	专用小交换机	Zhuānyòng xiǎo jiāohuànjī	PBX
Private branch exchange for B-ISDN	B-ISDN 专用小交换机	B-ISDN zhuānyòng xiǎo jiāohuànjī	B-ISDN PBX
Private circuit digital data service	专用电路数字数据业务	Zhuānyòng diànlù shùzì shùjù yèwù	PCDDS
Private conversation	私人通话（选呼）	Sīrén tōnghuà (xuǎn hū)	
Private data network	专用数据网络	Zhuānyòng shùjù wǎngluò	
Private device	专用设备	Zhuānyòng shèbèi	
Private dimension	专用维度	Zhuānyòng wéidù	
Private directory management domain	专用号码簿管理域	Zhuānyòng hàomǎbù guǎnlǐ yù	PRDMD
Private domain name	专用域名	Zhuānyòng yùmíng	
Private intelligent peripheral	专用智能外设	Zhuānyòng zhìnéng wài shè	PIP
Private key	私有密钥	Sīyǒu mìyào	
Private letter box	用户信报箱	Yònghù xìnbàoxiāng	
Private line	专用线路	Zhuānyòng xiànlù	PL
Private loop	专用环路	Zhuānyòng huánlù	
Private loop device	专用环路设备	Zhuānyòng huánlù shèbèi	
Private loop direct attached	私有环路直接连接	Sīyǒu huánlù zhíjiē liánjiē	PLDA
Private management domain	专用管理域	Zhuānyòng guǎnlǐ yù	PRMD
Private memory	专用存储器	Zhuānyòng cúnchǔqì	PM
Private mobile communication system	专用移动通信系统	Zhuānyòng yídòng tōngxìn xìtǒng	
Private mobile radio	集群移动通信	Jíqún yídòng tōngxìn	PMR
Private mobile radio	专用调度集群移动通信网	Zhuānyòng diàodù jíqún yídòng tōngxìnwǎng	PMR
Private mobile radio	专用集群移动通信网	Zhuānyòng jíqún yídòng tōngxìnwǎng	PMR
Private mobile radio	专用移动无线电	Zhuānyòng yídòng wúxiàndiàn	PMR
Private network access point	私人网路接入节点	Sīrén wǎnglù jiērù jiédiǎn	PNAP
Private network Q reference point signaling system	专用网络 Q 参考点信令系统	Zhuānyòng wǎngluò Q cānkǎodiǎn xìnlìng xìtǒng	PSS
Private network-network interface	专用网络-网络接口	Zhuānyòng wǎngluò—wǎngluò jiēkǒu	PNNI
Private network-to-network interface	专用网间接口	Zhuānyòng wǎngjiān jiēkǒu	PNNI
Private numbering plan	用户编号计划	Yònghù biānhào jìhuà	PNP
Private numbering plan	专用编号计划	Zhuānyòng biānhào jìhuà	PNP
Private numbering plan	专用网编号计划	Zhuānyòng wǎng biānhào jìhuà	PNP
Private operating agencies	私人运营机构	Sīrén yùnyíng jīgòu	
Private telecommunication network	专用通信网	Zhuānyòng tōngxìnwǎng	PTN
Private use option	专用选项	Zhuānyòng xuǎnxiàng	
Private user network interface	专用网接口	Zhuānyòng wǎng jiēkǒu	PUNI

English	Chinese	Pinyin	Abbr.
Privilege management infrastructure	特权管理基础设施	Tèquán guǎnlǐ jīchǔ shèshī	PMI
Privileged access control (in Linux)	特权存取控制	Tèquán cúnqǔ kòngzhì	PAC
Privileged instruction	特权指令	Tèquán zhǐlìng	
Privileged mode	特权模式	Tèquán móshì	
Probabalistic decoding (crypt.)	概率译码	Gàilǜ yìmǎ	
Probabalistic process algebra	概率进程代数	Gàilǜ jìnchéng dàishù	
Probabilistic information	概率信息	Gàilǜ xìnxī	
Probabilistic method	概率论方法	Gàilǜ lùn fāngfǎ	
Probabilistic theory	概率论	Gàilǜ lùn	
Probability	概率	Gàilǜ	
Probability bisimulation	概率相似	Gàilǜ xiāngsì	
Probability density function	概率密度函数	Gàilǜ mìdù hánshù	
Probability distribution	概率分布	Gàilǜ fēnbù	
Probability distribution function	概率分布函数	Gàilǜ fēnbù hánshù	
Probability map	概率图	Gàilǜ tú	
Probability of error	差错（误码）概率	Chācuò (wù mǎ) gàilǜ	PE
Probability of exceedance	超越概率	Chāoyuè gàilǜ	
Probability of false report	虚报概率	Xūbào gàilǜ	
Probability of safety	安全概率	Ānquán gàilǜ	
Probability of slip report	漏报概率	Lòubào gàilǜ	
Probability of timeout	超时概率	Chāoshí gàilǜ	
Probable error	概率误差	Gàilǜ wùchā	
Probe	探查	Tànchá	
Problem-oriented language	面向问题的语言	Miànxiàng wèntíde yǔyán	
Procedural	过程化的	Guòchénghuàde	
Procedural	过程式的	Guòchéng-shìde	
Procedural language	过程型语言	Guòchéng-xíng yǔyán	
Procedural security	规程安全	Guīchéng ānquán	
Procedural texture (video term)	规程纹理	Guīchéng wénlǐ	
Procedure	过程	Guòchéng	
Procedure cache	过程缓存	Guòchéng huǎncún	
Procedure, program	程序	Chéngxù	
Procedures fee for newspapers and periodicals changing	报刊变动手续费	Bàokān biàndòng shǒuxùfèi	
Procedures fee for return payments	退款手续费	Tuìkuǎn shǒuxùfèi	
Procedures fee of breaking off or changing address	报刊退订、改寄手续费	Bàokān tuìdìng、gǎijì shǒuxùfèi	
Procedures fee of presentation or exchanging newspapers and periodicals	报刊赠阅、交换手续费	Bàokān zèngyuè、jiāohuàn shǒuxùfèi	
Proceed-to-send signal	请发送信号	Qǐng fāsòng xìnhào	
Process	过程	Guòchéng	
Process	进程	Jìnchéng	
Process (verb), processing (noun)	处理	Chǔlǐ	
Process access signaling	处理接入信令	Chǔlǐ jiērù xìnlìng	
Process blueprint (in Visual Basic)	过程蓝图	Guòchéng lántú	
Process control computer	过程控制计算机	Guòchéng kòngzhì jìsuànjī	
Process control language	过程控制语言	Guòchéng kòngzhì yǔyán	PCL
Process display	过程显示装置	Guòchéng xiǎnshì zhuāngzhì	

Process ID (Unix)	进程标识	Jìnchéng biāozhì	pid
Process identifier	进程标识符	Jìnchéng biāozhìfú	PID
Process input/output device	过程输入/输出装置	Guòchéng shūrù/shūchū zhuāngzhì	PI/O
Process knowledge	过程知识	Guòchéng zhīshi	
Process label	进程标签	Jìnchéng biāoqiān	
Process migration	进程迁移	Jìnchéng qiānyí	
Process model simulating environment	过程模型模拟环境	Guòchéng móxíng mónǐ huánjìng	PMSE
Process module	处理模块	Chǔlǐ mōkuài	
Process monitor system	过程监督系统	Guòchéng jiāndū xìtǒng	PMS
Process unstructured SS data request	处理 USSD 请求	Chǔlǐ USSD qǐngqiú	PSSR
Process unstructured supplementary services data	过程非结构化补充服务数据	Guòchéng fēijiégòuhuà bǔchōng fúwù shùjù	PSSD
Process unstructured supplementary services request	过程非结构化补充服务请求	Guòchéng fēijiégòuhuà bǔchōng fúwù qǐngqiú	PSSR
Process, procedure, (and sometimes protocol)	规程	Guīchéng	
Processable form	可处理形式	Kěchǔlǐ xíngshì	
Processable mode number one	一号可处理方式	Yīhào kěchǔlǐ fāngshì	PM1
Processing gain	处理增益	Chǔlǐ zēngyì	PG
Processing unit	处理单元	Chǔlǐ dānyuán	
Processor	处理机	Chǔlǐjī	
Processor and test equipment interface	处理器和测试设备接口	Chǔlǐqì hé cèshì shèbèi jiēkǒu	PTEI
Processor communication control board assembly	处理器通信控制集成板	Chǔlǐqì tōngxìn kòngzhì jíchéngbǎn	PCCA
Processor controlled memory access	处理机控制存储存取	Chǔlǐjī kòngzhì cúnchǔ cúnqǔ	PCMA
Processor information ROM	处理器信息 ROM	Chǔlǐqì xìnxī ROM	PIROM
Processor inter-communication interface	处理器内部通信接口	Chǔlǐqì nèibù tōngxìn jiēkǒu	PICI
Processor load data	处理器装载数据	Chǔlǐqì zhuāngzài shùjù	PLD
Processor loader	处理器承载器	Chǔlǐqì chéngzàiqì	PL
Processor serial number	处理器序列号	Chǔlǐqì xù lièhào	PSN
Processor-controlled digital exchange	处理机控制的数字交换机	Chǔlǐjī kòngzhìde shùzì jiāohuànjī	PDX
Processor-in-a-box	盒装处理器	Hézhuāng chǔlǐqì	PIB
Prodigy (ISP)	天才	Tiāncái	
Producer	发生器	Fāshēngqì	
Product Assurance Confidence Evaluator (TRW Inc.)	产品保证可信度评估程序	Chǎnpǐn bǎozhèng kěxìndù pínggū chéngxù	PACE
Product baseline	产品基线	Chǎnpǐn jīxiàn	
Product codeform state gain vector quantization	乘积码形状增益矢量量化	Chéngjī mǎxíng zhuàng zēngyì shǐliàng liànghuà	PSGVQ
Product data management	产品数据管理	Chǎnpǐn shùjù guǎnlǐ	PDM
Product form solution	乘积形式解	Chéngjī xíngshì jiě	PFS
Product information management	产品信息管理	Chǎnpǐn xìnxī guǎnlǐ	PIM
Product interoperability	产品齐套性	Chǎnpǐn qítàoxing	
Product lifecycle management	产品生命周期管理	Chǎnpǐn shēngmìng zhōuqī guǎnlǐ	
Product specification	产品规范	Chǎnpǐn guīfàn	
Product thermal field application (semiconductor mfg)	产品热领域应用	Chǎnpǐn rè lǐngyù yìngyòng	
Production phase (of product life cycle)	生产阶段	Shēngchǎn jiēduàn	
Product-term	乘积项	Chéngjī xiàng	
Professional graphics adapter	专用图形适配器	Zhuānyòng túxíng shìpèiqì	PGA
Profile	评测	Píngcè	

English	Chinese	Pinyin	Abbr.
Profiler	效能评测器	Xiàonéng píngcè qì	
Profiler	性能评测器	Xìngnéng píngcèqì	
Profiling capability (semiconductor mfg)	靠模性能	Kàomú xìngnéng	
Profit margin	利润率	Lìrùnlǜ	
Program	程序	Chéngxù	P
Program block	程序块	Chéngxù kuài	
Program command	程序指令	Chéngxù zhǐlìng	
Program controlled city switch	程控市话交换	Chéngkòng shìhuà jiāohuàn	CSJ
Program controlled combined city/toll office	程控长市合一	Chéngkòng cháng shì héyī	CCS
Program controlled digital automatic branch exchange	程控数字自动交换机	Chéngkòng shùzì zìdòng jiāohuànjī	
Program controlled toll switch	程控长话交换	Chéngkòng chánghuà jiāohuàn	CCJ
Program counter	程序记数器	Chéngxù jìshùqì	P
Program counter save register	程序记数器保存积存器	Chéngxù jìshùqì bǎocún jīcúnqì	PCS
Program crash	程序瘫痪	Chéngxù tānhuàn	
Program debugging system	程序调试系统	Chéngxù tiáoshì xìtǒng	PDS
Program entry point	程序入口点	Chéngxù rùkǒu diǎn	
Program fingerprint	程序指纹	Chéngxù zhǐwén	
Program generator	程序产生器	Chéngxù chǎnshēngqì	
Program memory sweep	程序存贮器扫描	Chéngxù cúnzhùqì sǎomiáo	
Program optimization	程序优化	Chéngxù yōuhuà	
Program status word	程序状态字	Chéngxù zhuàngtài zì	PSW
Programmable asynchronous dual line adapter	可编程序异步双线适配器	Kěbiān chéngxù yìbù shuāngxiàn shìpèiqì	PADLA
Programmable asynchronous line adapter	可编程序异步线路转换器	Kěbiān chéngxù yìbù xiànlù zhuǎnhuànqì	PASLA
Programmable cellular automata (crypt,)	可编程细胞自动机	Kěbiānchéng xìbāo zìdòngjī	PCA
Programmable digital radio	可编程数字无线电	Kěbiānchéng shùzì wúxiàndiàn	PDR
Programmable front end processor	可编程前端处理机	Kěbiānchéng qiánduān chǔlǐjī	PFEP
Programmable input output	可编程输入输出模式	Kěbiānchéng shūrù shūchū móshì	PIO
Programmable interrupt controller	可编程中断控制器	Kěbiānchéng zhōngduàn kòngzhìqì	PIC
Programmable logic array	可编程序的逻辑阵列	Kěbiān chéngxùde luóji zhènliè	PLA
Programmable logic controller	可编程逻辑控制器	Kěbiānchéng luóji kòngzhìqì	PLC
Programmable logic device	可变程逻辑器件	Kěbiànchéng luóji qìjiàn	PLD
Programmable network	可编程网	Kěbiānchéng wǎng	
Programmable priority encoder	可编程优选译码器	Kěbiānchéng yōuxuǎn yìmǎqì	PPE
Programmable read-only memory	可编只读存储器	Kěbiān zhǐ dú cúnchǔqì	PROM
Programmable terminal	可编程终端	Kěbiānchéng zhōngduān	
Programmable unijunction transistor	可编程单结晶体管	Kěbiānchéng dānjié jīngtǐguǎn	PUT
Programmable unit	可编程单元	Kěbiānchéng dānyuán	PU
Programmed multi-line controller	程序多线控制器	Chéngxù duōxiàn kòngzhìqì	PMLC
Programmer	程序员	Chéngxù yuán	
Programmer's hierarchical interactive graphics standard	程序员用分极较糊图形标准	Chéngxùyuán-yòng fēnjí jiàohú túxíng biāozhǔn	PHIGS
Programming	编程	Biānchéng	
Programming	程序编写	Chéngxù biānxiě	
Programming	程序设计	Chéngxù shèjì	
Programming environment	程序设计环境	Chéngxù shèjì huánjìng	
Programming system	程序设计系统	Chéngxù shèji xìtǒng	

Program-sensitive fault	程序敏感性故障	Chéngxù mǐngǎnxìng gùzhàng	
Progress bar	进度指示器	Jìndù zhǐshìqì	
Progress indicator	进展指示	Jìnzhǎn zhǐshì	
Progressive (video term)	逐行	Zhúxíng	
Progressive network audio	渐进网络音频	Jiànjìn wǎngluò yīnpín	PNA
Progressive streaming	顺序流式传输	Shùnxù liú-shì chuánshū	
Project	项目	Xiàngmù	
Project	事业	Shìyè	
Project authority (CMM)	项目主管	Xiàngmù zhǔguǎn	PA
Project coordination group	项目协调组	Xiàngmù xiétiáo zǔ	PCG
Project delivery (CMM term)	项目交付	Xiàngmù jiāofù	PD
Project for advancement of coding technique	改进编码技术的研究计划	Gǎijìn biānmǎ jìshùde yánjiū jìhuà	PACT
Project initiation request (CMM)	项目启动申请	Xiàngmù qǐdòng shēnqǐng	PIR
Project undertaking organization	项目承办单位	Xiàngmù chéngbàn dānwèi	
Project; engineering	工程	Gōngchéng	
Projected coordinate system	投影坐标系统	Tóuyǐng zuòbiāo xìtǒng	
Projection	投影	Tóuyǐng	
Projection file	投影文件	Tóuyǐng wénjiàn	
Projection method	投影法	Tóuyǐng fǎ	
Projection transformation	投影变换	Tóuyǐng biànhuàn	
Promiscuous	混杂模式	Hùnzá móshì	
Prompt (noun)	提示符	Tíshì fú	
Prompt and collect user information	提示并收集用户信息	Tíshì bìng shōují yònghù xìnxī	P&C
Prompt maintenance alarm	即时维护告警	Jíshí wéihù gàojǐng	PMA
Pronunciation	发音	Fāyīn	
Pronunciation system	发音系统	Fāyīn xìtǒng	
Proof coupling torque	试验耦合转矩	Shìyàn ǒuhé zhuànjǔ	
Proof of concept	方案论证	Fāng'àn lùnzhèng	
Proof of delivery (IPsec)	交付证据	Jiāofù zhèngjù	
Proof of origin (IPsec)	源端证据	Yuánduān zhèngjù	
Proof plot	校样图	Jiàoyàng tú	
Proof polygon	校对多边形	Jiàoduì duōbiānxíng	
Proof-of-concept (for hardware)	概念验证	Gàiniàn yànzhèng	POC
Propagation channel	传播信道	Chuánbō xìndào	
Propagation coefficient	传播系数	Chuánbō xìshù	
Propagation constant	传播常数	Chuánbō chángshù	
Propagation delay	传播时延	Chuánbō shíyán	
Propagation delay	传播延迟	Chuánbō yánchí	
Propagation error	传播误差	Chuánbō wùchā	
Propagation of switching (SDH)	倒换的传播	Dǎohuànde chuánbō	
Propagation performance	传播性能	Chuánbō xìngnéng	
Propagation property	扩散准则	Kuòsàn zhǔnzé	
Propagation time	传播时间	Chuánbō shíjiān	
Proper area	固有领域	Gùyǒu lǐngyù	
Properties management building block	性能管理构件	Xìngnéng guǎnlǐ gòujiàn	PMBB
Property	属性	Shǔxìng	

Property management system	资源管理系统	Zīyuán guǎnlǐ xìtǒng	PMS
Property pages	属性页	Shǔxìng yè	
Proportional element (amplification element)	比例环节（放大环节）	Bǐlì huánjié (fàngdà huánjié)	
Proportional-integral (controller)	比例积分(控制器)	Bǐlì jīfēn (kòngzhìqì)	PI
Proportional-integral-differential (controller)	比例积分微分(控制器)	Bǐlì jīfēn wēifēn (kòngzhìqì)	PID
Protect against electromagnetic leakage (TEMPEST)	防电磁泄漏	Fáng diàncí xièlòu	
Protect against emissions (one of the Three protects)	防辐射	Fángfúshè	
Protect against interference or jamming (one of the Three protects)	防干扰	Fánggānrǎo	
Protect against lightning (one of the “Six protects”)	防雷	Fángléi	
Protect against rats (one of the “Six protects”)	防鼠	Fángshǔ	
Protect against salt (one of the “Six protects”)	防盐	Fángyán	
Protect against static (one of the “Six protects”)	防静	Fángjìng	
Protect against static (one of the Three protects)	防静电	Fángjìngdiàn	
Protect against viruses (one of the “Six protects”)	防毒	Fángdú	
Protected against dropping water	防滴	Fángdī	
Protected against splashing	防溅	Fángjiàn	
Protected against submersion	防潜水	Fángqiánshuǐ	
Protected against the effects of immersion	防漫水	Fángmànshuǐ	
Protected monitoring point	保护监测点	Bǎohù jiāncèdiǎn	
Protected network	受保护网洛	Shòubǎohù wǎngluò	
Protection against direct contact	直接接触防护	Zhíjiē jiēchù fánghù	
Protection against indirect contact	间接接触保护	Jiànjiē jiēchù bǎohù	
Protection against message falsification (IPsec)	防消息伪造	Fáng xiāoxi wěizào	
Protection against shock in normal service	正常工作时触电防护	Zhèngcháng gōngzuò shí chùdiàn fánghù	
Protection against shock in the case of a fault	故障时触电保护	Gùzhàng shí chùdiàn bǎohù	
Protection buffer size	保护缓冲容量	Bǎohù huǎnchōng róngliàng	PBSZ
Protection earth and neutral	保护和中性公用线	Bǎohù hé zhōngxìng gōngyòng xiàn	PEN
Protection earth wire	保护线	Bǎohù xiàn	PE
Protection link switching	保护链路转换	Bǎohù liànlù zhuǎnhuàn	
Protection margin	保护裕量	Bǎohù yùliàng	
Protection network connection	保护网络连接	Bǎohù wǎngluò liánjiē	
Protection path	保护通道	Bǎohù tōngdào	
Protection ratio	保护比	Bǎohù bǐ	
Protection ratio	保护率	Bǎohù lǜ	
Protection register	保护寄存器	Bǎohù jìcúnqì	PRT
Protection ring	保护环	Bǎohù huán	
Protection section	保护段	Bǎohù duàn	
Protection sub-network connection	保护子网连接	Bǎohù ziwǎng liánjiē	
Protection switching	保护倒换	Bǎohù dǎohuàn	
Protection switching	保护转换	Bǎohù zhuǎnhuàn	
Protection switching count	保护倒换计数	Bǎohù dǎohuàn jìshù	PSC
Protection switching duration	保护倒换持续时间	Bǎohù dǎohuàn chíxù shíjiān	PSD
Protection switching duration	保护倒换间隔时间	Bǎohù dǎohuàn jiàngé shíjiān	PSD
Protection switching event	保护倒换事件	Bǎohù dǎohuàn shìjiàn	PSE
Protection trail	保护路径	Bǎohù lùjìng	

Protective circuit	保护电路	Bǎohù diànlù	
Protective conductor	保护导体	Bǎohù dǎotǐ	
Protective cover	防护罩	Fánghùzhào	
Protective current transformer	保护用电流互感器	Bǎohù-yòng diànliú hùgǎnqì	
Protective gap	保护间隙	Bǎohù jiànxì	
Protective ground	保护接地	Bǎohù jiēdì	PG
Protective relay	保护继电器	Bǎohù jìdiànqì	
Protective tube for fiber optic fiber	光纤保护管	Guāngxiān bǎohù guǎn	
Protective voltage transformer	保护用电压互感器	Bǎohù-yòng diànyā hùgǎnqì	
Protector	保安器	Bǎo'ānqì	
Protocol	协议	Xiéyì	
Protocol analysis	协议分析	Xiéyì fēnxī	
Protocol analyzer	协议分析器	Xiéyì fēnxīqì	
Protocol and parameter select	协议和参数选择	Xiéyì hé cānshù xuǎnzé	PPS
Protocol attack (crypto)	协议攻击	Xiéyì gōngjī	
Protocol binding	协议捆绑	Xiéyì kǔnbǎng	
Protocol conformance test report	协议一致性测试报告	Xiéyì yīzhìxìng cèshì bàogào	PCTR
Protocol control byte	协议控制字节	Xiéyì kòngzhì zìjié	PCB
Protocol control information	协议控制信息	Xiéyì kòngzhì xìnxī	PCI
Protocol controller	协议控制器	Xiéyì kòngzhìqì	PC
Protocol conversion	协议转换	Xiéyì zhuǎnhuàn	
Protocol converter	协议转换器	Xiéyì zhuǎnhuànqì	
Protocol data unit	协商数据单元	Xiéshāng shùjù dānyuán	PDU
Protocol data unit	协议数据单元	Xiéyì shùjù dānyuán	PDU,PDY
Protocol discriminator	协议标识符	Xiéyì biāozhì fú	PD
Protocol discriminator	协议鉴别器	Xiéyì jiànbiéqì	PD
Protocol encoder/decoder	协议编译码器	Xiéyì biānyìmǎqì	PED
Protocol entity	协议实体	Xiéyì shítǐ	PE
Protocol event	协议事件	Xiéyì shìjiàn	PE
Protocol for sessions traversal across firewall securely (IETF usage)	防火墙安全会话转换协议	Fánghuǒqiáng ānquán huìhuà zhuǎnhuàn xiéyì	Socks
Protocol identifier	协议标识符	Xiéyì biāozhì fú	PI
Protocol implementation conformance statement	协议实现一致性声明	Xiéyì shíxiàn yīzhìxìng shēngmíng	PICS
Protocol implementation conformance statement	协议实现的一致性陈述	Xiéyì shíxiànde yīzhìxìng chénshù	PICS
Protocol implementation conformity statement	协议实现一致性说明	Xiéyì shíxiàn yīzhìxìng shuōmíng	PICS
Protocol implementation extra information for testing	协议实现附加测试信息	Xiéyì shíxiàn fùjiā cèshì xìnxī	PIXIT
Protocol implementation extra information for testing	协议实现的测试补充材料	Xiéyì shíxiànde cèshì bǔchōng cáiliào	PIXIT
Protocol integrated test system	协议集成测试系统	Xiéyì jíchéng cèshì xìtǒng	PITS
Protocol profile	协议轮廓	Xiéyì lúnkuò	
Protocol reference model	协议参考模型	Xiéyì cānkǎo móxíng	PRM
Protocol reference model of broadband ISDN	宽带 ISDN 协议参考模型	Kuāndài ISDN xiéyì cānkǎo móxíng	B-ISDN PRM
Protocol stack	协议栈	Xiéyì zhàn	
Protocol sub-tree identification	协议子树标识	Xiéyì zishù biāozhì	PI
Protocol suite	协议套	Xiéyì tào	
Protocol tunneling (in IP)	协议隧道	Xiéyì suìdào	
Protocol type	协议类型	Xiéyì lèixíng	PT

Protocol type select	协议类型选择	Xiéyì lèixíng xuǎnzé	PTS
Protocol version message (IPsec TLS)	协议版本消息	Xiéyì bǎnběn xiāoxi	
Protocol-independent multicast	独立于协议的组播协议	Dúlì yú xiéyìde zǔbō xiéyì	PIM
Protocol-independent multicast	协议无关多点广播	Xiéyì wúguān duōdiǎn guǎngbō	PIM
Protocol-independent multicast (PIM) multicast border router	协议无关组播协议组播边界路由器	Xiéyì wúguān zǔbō xiéyì zǔbō biānjiè lùyóuqì	PMBR
Protocol-independent multicast dense mode	独立组播协议密集模式	Dúlì zǔbō xiéyì mìjí móshì	PIM DM
Protocol-independent multicast dense mode	协议独立稠密模式组播	Xiéyì dúlì chóumì móshì zǔbō	PIM-DM
Protocol-independent multicast sparse mode	独立组播协议稀疏模式	Dúlì zǔbō xiéyì xīshū móshì	PIM SM
Protocol-independent multicast sparse mode	协议独立稀疏模式组播	Xiéyì dúlì xīshū móshì zǔbō	PIM-SM
Protocol-independent multicast--dense mode	协议无关组播-密集模式	Xiéyì wúguān zǔbō--mìjí móshì	PIM-DM
Protocol-independent multicast--sparse mode	协议无关组播-稀疏模式	Xiéyì wúguān zǔbō--xīshū móshì	PIM-SM
Protocol-independent muticast	独立组播协议	Dúlì zǔbō xiéyì	PIM
Proton exchange	质子交换	Zhìzǐ jiāohuàn	PE
Prototype	原型	Yuánxíng	
Prototype experiment	原型实验	Yuánxíng shíyàn	
Prototype waveform interpolation	典型波形内插	Diǎnxíng bōxíng nèichā	PWI
Provide roaming number	提供漫游号码	Tígōng mànyóu hàomǎ	
Provider edge	提供商边缘	Tígōng shāng biānyuán	PE
Provider edge router	运营商边缘路由器	Yùnyíngshāng biānyuán lùyóuqì	PE
Provider program	提供程序	Tígōng chéngxù	
Provider router	运营商路由器	Yùnyíngshāng lùyóuqì	P
Provider-initiated service	提供者起始型服务	Tígòngzhě qǐshǐxíng fúwù	
Provider-initiated-service	提供者发起型业务	Tígòngzhě fāqǐ-xíng yèwù	
Provincial (mobile communications net) network management center	省移动通信网网络管理中心	Shěng yídòng tōngxìnwǎng wǎngluò guǎnlǐ zhōngxīn	PNMC
Provincial management center	省级管理中心	Shěngjí guǎnlǐ zhōngxīn	P-PMS
Provincial monitoring center	省监测中心	Shěng jiāncè zhōngxīn	PMC
Provision variant	指配变量	Zhǐpèi biànliàng	
Provisioning	供给	Gōngjǐ	
Proximal polygon	接近多边形	Jiējìn duōbiānxíng	
Proximal tolerance	最小容差	Zuìxiǎo róngchā	
Proximity	亲近性	Qīnjìnxìng	
Proximity analysis	邻近分析	Línjìn fēnxī	
Proximity beacon detection	接近信标探测	Jiējìn xìnbiāo tàncè	
Proximity card	接近卡	Jiējìn kǎ	PC
Proximity search	近似搜索	Jìnsì sōusuǒ	
Proxy explorer	代理探索器	Dàilǐ tànsuǒqì	
Proxy polling	代理轮询	Dàilǐ lúnxún	
Proxy server	代理服务器	Dàilǐ fúwùqì	
Pruning (database term)	可剪裁性	Kějiǎncáixìng	
Pseudo code	伪码	Wěimǎ	
Pseudo code	虚拟码	Xūnǐ mǎ	
Pseudo instruction	伪指令	Wěizhǐlìng	PSEUDO
Pseudo node	伪节点	Wěijiédiǎn	
Pseudo range (GPS term)	伪距	Wěijù	
Pseudo response spectrum	拟反应谱	Nǐfǎnyìng pǔ	

Pseudo variable	伪变量	Wěibiànliàng	
Pseudo velocity response spectrum	伪速度反应谱	Wěisùdù fǎnyìng pǔ	
Pseudo wire emulation edge to edge	伪线仿真边缘到边缘	Wěixiàn fǎngzhēn biānyuán dào biānyuán	PWE3
Pseudo wires edge-to-edge emulation	边缘到边缘伪线路仿真	Biānyuán dào biānyuán wěixiànlù fǎngzhēn	PWE3
Pseudocode algorithm	伪代码算法	Wěidàimǎ suànfǎ	
Pseudo-flaw (IPsec)	伪缺陷	Wěiquēxiàn	
Pseudo-noise	伪噪声	Wěizàoshēng	PN
Pseudo-random binary sequence	伪随机二进制序列	Wěisuíjī èrjìnzhì xùliè	PRBS
Pseudo-random binary sequence	伪随机二元序列	Wěisuíjī èryuán xùliè	PRBS
Pseudo-random binary sequence	伪随机码序列	Wěisuíjī mǎ xùliè	PRBS
Pseudo-random bit sequence	伪随机比特序列	Wěisuíjī bǐtè xùliè	PRBS
Pseudo-random code	伪随机码	Wěisuíjī mǎ	
Pseudo-random downlink sequence	下行伪随机序列	Xiàxíng wěi suíjī xùliè	PRD
Pseudo-random noise	伪随机噪声	Wěisuíjī zàoshēng	PN
Pseudo-random noise generation	伪随机噪声生成	Wěisuíjī zàoshēng shēngchéng	PRNG
Pseudo-random number	伪随机数	Wěisuíjīshù	RAND
Pseudo-random sequence	伪随机序列	Wěisuíjī xùliè	
Pseudo-synchronous digital hierarchy	伪同步数字网	Wěitóngbù shùzì wǎng	PDH
Pseudo-synchronous digital hierarchy	准同步数字分级	Zhǔn tóngbù shùzì fēnjí	PDH
Pseudo-synchronous digital hierarchy	准同步数字体系	Zhǔn tóngbù shùzì tǐxì	PDH
Pseudo-ternary code	伪三进制码	Wěisān jìnzhì mǎ	
Pseudo-ternary signal	伪三进制信号	Wěisānjìnzhì xìnhào	
Psophometrically weighted noise	噪声计加权噪声	Zàoshēng jì jiāquán zàoshēng	
PTM groupcall	PTM 组呼叫	PTM zǔ hūjiào	PTM-G
PTM multicast	PTM 多播	PTM duōbō	PTM-M
Public access mobile radio	公用调度集群通信网	Gōngyòng diàodù jíqún tōngxìnwǎng	PAMR
Public access mobile radio	共用调度集群移动通信网	Gòngyòng diàodù jíqún yídòng tōngxìnwǎng	
Public address system	公共广播音响系统	Gōnggòng guǎngbō yīnxiǎng xìtǒng	PAS
Public correspondence	公众通信	Gōngzhòng tōngxìn	
Public data	公用数据	Gōngyòng shùjù	PD
Public data network	共用数据网	Gòngyòng shùjù wǎng	PDN
Public data network	公用数据网	Gōngyòng shùjù wǎng	PDN
Public data transmission service	公用数据传输业务	Gōngyòng shùjù chuánshū yèwù	
Public device	公共设备	Gōnggòng shèbèi	
Public directory support	公众目录支持	Gōngzhòng mùlù zhīchí	PDS
Public domain	共有地域	Gòngyǒu dìyù	
Public domain software	公用软件	Gōngyòng ruǎnjiàn	
Public facsimile bureau	公用传真局	Gōngyòng chuánzhēnjú	
Public facsimile station	公用传真站	Gōngyòng chuánzhēnzhàn	
Public hot-spot	公众热点	Gōngzhòng rèdiǎn	
Public information system	公众信息系统	Gōngzhòng xìnxī xìtǒng	
Public initialization node	公共发起节点	Gōnggòng fāqǐ jiédiǎn	PIN
Public key	公开密钥	Gōngkāi mìyào	
Public key algorithm	公用密钥算法	Gōngyòng mìyào suànfǎ	PKA
Public key certificate	公钥证明	Gōngyào zhèngmíng	
Public key encryption algorithm (IPsec)	公钥密码算法	Gōngyào mìmǎ suànfǎ	

Public key infrastructure	公共键构	Gōnggòng jiàn gòu	PKI
Public key infrastructure	公共密钥基础设施	Gōnggòng mìyào jīchǔ shèshī	PKI
Public key infrastructure	公钥基础结构	Gōngyào jīchǔ jiégòu	PKI
Public key infrastructure	公钥基础设施	Gōngyào jīchǔ shèshī	PKI
Public key infrastructure	公钥机制	Gōngyào jīzhì	PKI
Public key infrastructure	公用关键基础设施	Gōngyòng guānjiàn jīchǔ shèshī	PKI
Public key system	公开密匙体制	Gōngkāi mìyào tǐzhì	
Public key system	公钥体制	Gōngyào tǐzhì	
Public land cellular mobile network	公用陆地蜂窝移动通信网	Gōngyòng lùdì fēngwō yídòng tōngxìnwǎng	PLMN
Public land mobile communications network	公用陆地移动通信网	Gōngyòng lùdì yídòng tōngxìnwǎng	PLMN
Public land mobile network	公共陆地移动通信网	Gōnggòng lùdì yídòng tōngxìnwǎng	PLMN
Public land mobile network	公共陆地移动网络	Gōnggòng lùdì yídòng wǎngluò	PLMN
Public land mobile network	公共陆基移动网	Gōnggòng lùjī yídòngwǎng	PLMN
Public land mobile network	公用陆地移动网络	Gōngyòng lùdì yídòng wǎngluò	PLMN
Public land mobile network	公众陆地移动电话网	Gōngzhòng lùdì yídòng diànhuà wǎng	PLMN
Public land mobile telecommunications system	共用陆地移动通信系统	Gòngyòng lùdì yídòng tōngxìn xìtǒng	PLMTS
Public Land Survey System (US)	国家土地调查体系	Guójiā tǔdì diàochá tǐxì	PLSS
Public Land System (US)	国家土地系统	Guójiā tǔdì xìtǒng	PLS
Public loop	公共环路	Gōnggòng huánlù	
Public loop device	公共环路设备	Gōnggòng huánlù shèbèi	
Public network interface	公共网接口	Gōnggòng wǎng jiēkǒu	
Public network interface	公用网接口	Gōngyòng wǎng jiēkǒu	
Public packet data network	公用分组数据网	Gōngyòng fēnzǔ shùjù wǎng	X.25
Public packet network interface	公用包网络接口	Gōngyòng bāo wǎngluò jiēkǒu	PPNI
Public packet switched network	公共分组交换网	Gōnggòng fēnzǔ jiāohuàn wǎng	
Public packet switched network	公用分租接转网络	Gōngyòng fēnzū jiēzhuǎn wǎngluò	PPSN
Public power source board	公共电源板	Gōnggòng diànyuán bǎn	PWC
Public secure answer point	公众安全应答服务机构	Gōngzhòng ānquán yìngdá fúwù jīgòu	PSAP
Public switched data network	共用数据交换网	Gòngyòng shùjù jiāohuàn wǎng	PSDN
Public switched network	公用交换网	Gōngyòng jiāohuàn wǎng	PSN
Public switched packet data network	公用交换分组数据网	Gōngyòng jiāohuàn fēnzǔ shùjù wǎng	PSPDN
Public switched telecommunication network	公共交换电信网	Gōnggòng jiāohuàn diànxìn wǎng	PSTN
Public switched telephone network	公共电话交换网	Gōnggòng diànhuà jiāohuàn wǎng	PSTN
Public switched telephone network	公共交换电话网	Gōnggòng jiāohuàn diànhuà wǎng	PSTN
Public switched telephone network	公共交换式电话网络	Gōnggòng jiāohuànshì diànhuà wǎngluò	PSTN
Public switched telephone network	公用电话交换网	Gōngyòng diànhuà jiāohuàn wǎng	PSTN
Public switched telephone network	公用交换电话网	Gōngyòng jiāohuàn diànhuà wǎng	PSTN
Public switched telephone network	公用交换式电话网	Gōngyòng jiāohuàn-shì diànhuà wǎng	PSTN
Public switched telephone network	公众电话交换网	Gōngzhòng diànhuà jiāohuàn wǎng	PSTN
Public switched telephone network	公众交换电话网	Gōngzhòng jiāohuàn diànhuà wǎng	PSTN
Public switching packet data network	公共交换分组数据网	Gōnggòng jiāohuàn fēnzǔ shùjù wǎng	PSPDN
Public telecom operator	公众电信运营者	Gōngzhòng diànxìn yùnyíngzhě	PTO
Public telephone booth	公用电话亭	Gōngyòng diànhuà tíng	
Public utility works	公益事业	Gōngyì shìyè	
Public video conferencing system	公用型会议电视系统	Gōngyòng-xíng huìyì diànshì xìtǒng	PVCS
Publication	发布	Fābù	

Publication database	发布数据库	Fābù shùjùkù	
Publication retention period	发布保持期	Fābù bǎochí qī	
Publicly accessed node	公共被寻址节点	Gōnggòng bèi xúnzhǐ jiédiǎn	PAN
Published data	已发布数据	Yǐfābù shùjù	
Publisher	发布服务器	Fābù fúwùqì	
Publishing subscriber (in SQL Server)	出版订购者	Chūbǎn dìnggòuzhě	
Publishing table	发布表	Fābù biǎo	
Pull partner	拉伙伴	Lā huǒbàn	
Pull string	拉线	Lāxiàn	
Pull subscription	请求订阅	Qǐngqiú dìngyuè	
Pull-down	下拉	Xiàlā	
Pull-down menu	拉下式菜单	Lāxià-shì càidān	
Pull-down menu	下拉式选单	Xiàlā-shì xuǎndān	
Pull-down resistance	下拉电阻	Xiàlā diànzǔ	
Pull-in	牵引入	Qiānyǐn rù	
Pull-in banwidth	捕捉带宽	Bǔzhuō dàikuān	
Pull-in range	捕捉带	Bǔzhuō dài	
Pull-in range	牵引范围	Qiānyǐn fànwéi	
Pull-in time	捕捉时间	Bǔzhuō shíjiān	
Pull-out	牵引出	Qiānyǐn chū	
Pull-up resistance	上拉电阻	Shànglā diànzǔ	
Pulsating	脉动	Màidòng	
Pulse	脉冲	Màichōng	P
Pulse	脉冲	Màichōng	
Pulse amplitude and phase modulation	脉冲调幅调相	Màichōng tiáofú tiáoxiàng	PAPM
Pulse amplitude modulation	脉冲幅度	Màichōng fúdù	PAM
Pulse amplitude modulation	脉冲幅度调制	Màichōng fúdù tiáozhì	PAM
Pulse amplitude modulation	脉冲振幅调制	Màichōng zhènfú tiáozhì	PAM
Pulse break/make ratio	脉冲断续比	Màichōng duànxù bǐ	
Pulse code equipment	脉码设备	Màimǎ shèbèi	MM
Pulse code generator	脉冲发码	Màichōng fā mǎ	
Pulse code modulation	脉冲编码调制	Màichōng biānmǎ tiáozhì	PCM
Pulse code modulation	脉冲码调制	Màichōng mǎ tiáozhì	PCM
Pulse code modulation	脉码调制	Màimǎ tiáozhì	PCM
Pulse code modulation (PCM) multiplex equipment	脉码调制复用设备	Màimǎ tiáozhì fùyòng shèbèi	
Pulse code modulation intensity modulated (pulse source)	强调制的脉码调制(脉冲源)	Qiáng tiáozhìde màimǎ tiáozhì (màichōng yuán)	PCM-IM (PS)
Pulse code modulation-linear	线性脉码调制	Xiànxìng màimǎ tiáozhì	PCM-LIN
Pulse code modulation-logarithmic companded	对数压缩扩展脉码调制	Duìshù yāsuō kuòzhǎn màimǎ tiáozhì	PCM-LOG
Pulse code modulation-polarization modulation (pulse source)	极化调制脉码调制(脉冲源)	Jíhuà tiáozhì màimǎ tiáozhì (màichōng yuán)	PCM-PM (PS)
Pulse compressive reconnaissance receiver	脉冲压缩侦察接收机	Màichōng yāsuō zhēnchá jiēshōujī	
Pulse corrector	脉冲校正器	Màichōng jiàozhèngqì	
Pulse counting system	脉冲计数制	Màichōng jìshù zhì	
Pulse counting system	脉数制	Màishùzhì	
Pulse decay time	脉冲下降时间	Màichōng xiàjiàng shíjiān	
Pulse delay binary modulation	脉冲延迟二进制调制	Màichōng yánchí èrjìnzhì tiáozhì	PDBM

Pulse delta modulation	脉冲增量调制	Màichōng zēngliàng tiáozhì	PDM
Pulse density	脉冲密度	Màichōng mìdù	
Pulse detector	脉冲检波器	Màichōng jiǎnbōqì	
Pulse dialing	脉冲拨号	Màichōng bōhào	
Pulse disturbance	脉冲骚扰	Màichōng sāorǎo	
Pulse duration	脉冲持续时间	Màichōng chíxù shíjiān	
Pulse duration modulation	脉冲宽度调制	Màichōng kuāndù tiáozhì	PDM
Pulse duration modulation, pulse width modulation	脉冲持续时间调制	Màichōng chíxù shíjiān tiáozhì	PDM
Pulse duration system	脉冲宽度制	Màichōng kuāndù zhì	
Pulse duration system	脉宽制	Màikuānzhì	
Pulse duty factor	脉冲占空系数	Màichōng zhànkōng xìshù	
Pulse encoded modulation	脉冲编码调制	Màichōng biānmǎ tiáozhì	PEM
Pulse excitation linear predictive coding	脉冲激励线性预测编码	Màichōng jīlì xiànxìng yùcè biānmǎ	
Pulse forming network (radar term)	脉冲形成网络	Màichōng xíngchéng wǎngluò	
Pulse frequency modulation	脉冲频率调制	Màichōng pínlǜ tiáozhì	PFM
Pulse front edge jitter	脉冲前沿抖动	Màichōng qiányán dǒudòng	
Pulse interlacing	脉冲交织	Màichōng jiāozhī	
Pulse interval modulation	脉冲区间调制	Màichōng qūjiān tiáozhì	PIM
Pulse jamming	脉冲干扰	Màichōng gānrǎo	
Pulse length discrimination	脉冲长度鉴别	Màichōng chángdù jiànbié	
Pulse mask	脉冲模框	Màichōng mókuàng	
Pulse modulation	脉冲调制	Màichōng tiáozhì	
Pulse motor	脉冲马达	Màichōng mǎdá	
Pulse noise	脉冲噪声	Màichōng zàoshēng	
Pulse per second	脉冲/秒	Màichōng/miǎo	PPS
Pulse phase modulation	脉冲相位洲制	Màichōng xiàngwèi zhōuzhì	PPM
Pulse position modulation	脉冲位调制	Màichōng wèi tiáozhì	PPM
Pulse position modulation	脉冲位置调制	Màichōng wèizhì tiáozhì	PPM
Pulse position modulation	脉位调制	Màiwèi tiáozhì	PPM
Pulse position system	脉冲位置制	Màichōng wèizhì zhì	
Pulse position system	脉位制	Màiwèizhì	
Pulse power	脉冲功率	Màichōng gōnglǜ	
Pulse recurrent time	脉冲周期时间	Màichōng zhōuqī shíjiān	PRT
Pulse regenerator	脉冲再生器	Màichōng zàishēngqì	
Pulse repetition cycle	脉冲重复周期	Màichōng chóngfù zhōuqī	
Pulse repetition frequency	脉冲重复频率	Màichōng chóngfù pínlǜ	
Pulse repetition rate modulation	脉冲重复频率调制	Màichōng chóngfù pínlǜ tiáozhì	
Pulse response characteristics	脉冲响应特性	Màichōng xiǎngyìng tèxìng	
Pulse response curve	脉冲响应曲线	Màichōng xiǎngyìng qūxiàn	
Pulse rise time	脉冲上升时间	Màichōng shàngshēng shíjiān	
Pulse series	脉冲串	Màichōng chuàn	
Pulse signal	脉冲信号	Màichōng xìnhào	
Pulse signal generator	脉冲信号发生器	Màichōng xìnhào fāshēngqì	
Pulse spacing	脉冲间隔	Màichōng jiàngé	
Pulse stuffing	脉冲塞入	Màichōng sāirù	
Pulse time modulation	脉冲时间调制	Màichōng shíjiān tiáozhì	PTM

Pulse top clipper circuit	脉冲顶部限幅电路	Màichōng dǐngbù xiàn fú diànlù	
Pulse top compensation circuit	脉冲顶部补偿电路	Màichōng dǐngbù bǔcháng diànlù	
Pulse train	脉冲列	Màichōng liè	
Pulse transformer	脉冲变压器	Màichōng biànyāqì	
Pulse waveform discrimination	脉冲波形鉴别	Màichōng bōxíng jiànbié	
Pulse width	脉冲宽度	Màichōng kuāndù	
Pulse width discrimination	脉冲宽度鉴别	Màichōng kuāndù jiànbié	
Pulse width discrimination	脉宽鉴别	Màikuān jiànbié	
Pulse width modulation	脉宽调制	Mài kuān tiáozhì	PWM
Pulse width modulation	脉冲宽度调制	Màichōng kuāndù tiáozhì	PDM
Pulse width with carrier modulation	带载波调制的脉冲宽度	Dài zàibō tiáozhìde màichōng kuāndù	PWCM
Pulse-amplitude-code modulation	脉冲幅度编码调制	Màichōng fúdù biānmǎ tiáozhì	PACM
Pulsed carrier	脉冲载波	Màichōng zàibō	
Pulsed carrier modulation	脉冲载波调制	Màichōng zàibō tiáozhì	
Pulsed CO_2 laser	脉冲二氧化碳激光	Màichōng èryǎnghuàtàn jīguāng	
Pulsed Fourier transform	脉冲傅氏转换	Màichōng fù-shì zhuǎnhuàn	PFT
Pulsed individual tone sequential system	顺序脉冲单音制	Shùnxù màichōng dānyīn zhì	
Pulsed individual tone sequential system	顺序脉冲单音制	Shùnxù màichōng dānyīn zhì	
Pulsed laser	脉冲式激光	Màichōng-shì jīguāng	
Pulsed-individual tone system	脉冲单音制	Màichōng dānyīn zhì	
Pulse-duration modulation frequency modulation	脉宽调制-调制	Màikuān tiáozhì—tiáozhì	PDM-FM
Pulse-response function	脉冲响应函数	Màichōng xiǎngyìng hánshù	
Pulses per second	每秒脉冲数	Měi miǎo màichōng shù	PPS
Pump source	泵浦源	Bèngpǔ yuán	
Pump unit	泵组	Bèng zǔ	
Pumped fiber optic amplifier	泵浦光纤放大器	Bèngpǔ guāngxiān fàngdàqì	
Pumped laser	泵浦激光器	Bèngpǔ jīguāngqì	
Pumping light source	激发光源	Jīfā guāngyuán	
Punch card	打卡	Dǎkǎ	
Punch tool	穿孔工具	Chuānkǒng gōngjù	
Punch-through factor	穿通因数	Chuāntōng yīnshù	PTF
Punch-through modulation	穿通调制	Chuāntōng tiáozhì	PTM
Pure-noise jamming	纯噪声干扰	Chún zàoshēng gānrǎo	
Purge	舍弃	Shěqì	
Purge (IPsec), erasure	消除	Xiāochú	
Purge operation	撤消操作	Chèxiāo cāozuò	
Push	压入	Yārù	
Push and pull media	推送和拉取方式	Tuīsòng hé lāqǔ fāngshì	
Push partner	推伙伴	Tuī huǒbàn	
Push subscription	强制订阅	Qiángzhì dìngyuè	
Push technology	推送技术	Tuīsòng jìshù	
Push-button telephone set	按键电话机	Ànjiàn diànhuàjī	
Push-button telephone set	按钮话机	Ànniǔ huàjī	
Push-pull amplifier	推挽放大器	Tuīwǎn fàngdàqì	
Push-pull type	推换式	Tuī huàn shì	
Push-push type (switch or smart card reader)	推推型	Tuī tuī xíng	

Put a project into practice	实转	Shízhuǎn	
Pyramidal horn antenna	角锥形喇叭天线	Jiǎozhuī-xíng lǎba tiānxiàn	
Pyroelectric detector	热电检测器	Rèdiàn jiǎncèqì	
Pyroelectric radiation detector	热电辐射控测器	Rèdiàn fúshè kòngcèqì	PRD

Q

Q-adapter function block	Q 适配器功能块	Q-shìpèiqì gōngnéng kuài	QAF
Quad flat pack (electronics mfg)	方平包装	Fāngpíng bāozhuāng	QFP
Quad flat package	四列扁平封装	Siliè biǎnpíng fēngzhuāng	QFP
Quad-band memory	四倍边带内存	Sibèi biāndài nèicún	QBM
Quad-centered photograph	中心四边形像片	Zhōngxīn sìbiānxíng xiàngpiàn	
Quad-port acceleration	四接口加速	Sì jiēkǒu jiāsù	QPA
Quadrangle	四边形	Sìbiānxíng	
Quadrant antenna	正方形天线	Zhèngfāngxíng tiānxiàn	
Quadrat	样方	Yàngfāng	
Quadrat frame	样方框	Yàngfāng kuàng	
Quadratic phase error	平方相差	Píngfāng xiàngchà	
Quadrature amplitude modulation	正交幅度调制	Zhèngjiāo fúdù tiáozhì	QAM
Quadrature amplitude modulation	正交调幅	Zhèngjiāo tiáofú	QAM
Quadrature channel	正交通道	Zhèngjiāo tōngdào	
Quadrature coherent demodulator	正交相干解调器	Zhèngjiāo xiānggān jiětiáoqì	
Quadrature differential phase shift keying	四相差分相移键控	Sìxiāng chàfēn xiàngyí jiànkòng	QDPSK
Quadrature frequency hopping	正交跳频	Zhèngjiāo tiàopín	
Quadrature mirror filter	正交镜象滤波器	Zhèngjiāo jìngxiàng lǜbōqì	QMF
Quadrature modulation	正交调制	Zhèngjiāo tiáozhì	QM
Quadrature modulator	正交调幅器	Zhèngjiāo tiáofúqì	
Quadrature partial response keying	正交部分响应键控	Zhèngjiāo bùfen xiǎngyìng jiànkòng	QPRK
Quadrature phase shift keying	正交相移键控	Zhèngjiāo xiāngyí jiànkòng	QPSK
Quadrature phase shift keying	正交移相键控	Zhèngjiāo yíxiàng jiànkòng	QPSK
Quadrature phase-shift keying	四相相移键控	Sìxiāng xiāngyí jiànkòng	QPSK
Quadrature signal	正交信号	Zhèngjiāo xìnhào	
Quadriphase shift keying	四相相移键控	Sìxiāng xiāngyí jiànkòng	QPSK
Quadtree	四叉树	Sìchā shù	
Qualcomm (US company)	高通	Gāo-tōng	
Qualcomm code excited linear prediction	码激励线性预测编码	Mǎjīlì xiànxìng yùcè biānmǎ	QCELP
Qualcomm code excited linear prediction	Qualcomm 码激励线性预测编码	Qualcomm mǎjīlì xiànxìng yùcè biānmǎ	QCELP
Qualification level (IPsec)	资格级别	Zīge jíbié	
Qualified (in C++)	经过资格修饰	Jīngguò zīge xiūshì	
Qualified logic link control (for SNA over X.25)	限定式逻辑链路控制	Xiàndìngshì luójì liànlù kòngzhì	QLLC
Qualifier	修饰符	Xiūshì fú	
Qualitative	定性的	Dìngxìngde	
Quality	质量	Zhìliàng	
Quality assurance	质量保证	Zhìliàng bǎozhèng	QA
Quality control	质量控制	Zhìliàng kòngzhì	QC
Quality factor	质量因子	Zhìliàng yīnzǐ	

Quality factor	Q因数	Q-yīnshù	
Quality function deployment	质量功能配置	Zhìliàng gōngnéng pèizhì	QFD
Quality level	质量等级	Zhìliàng děngjí	QL
Quality management	质量管理	Zhìliàng guǎnlǐ	
Quality minimum	质量等级下限	Zhìliàng děngjí xiàxiàn	
Quality monitoring	质量监督	Zhìliàng jiāndū	
Quality of access	接入质量	Jiērù zhìliàng	QoA
Quality of service	服务质量	Fúwù zhìliàng	QOS
Quality of service	业务质量	Yèwù zhìliàng	QoS
Quality of technical service	软质量	Ruǎn zhìliàng	
Quality protection	保护质量	Bǎohù zhìliàng	QOP
Quality schema	质量模式	Zhìliàng móshì	
Quality test	质量测试	Zhìliàng cèshì	
Quantile	分位数	Fènwèi shù	
Quantitative	定量的	Dìngliàngde	
Quantization loss in gain	量化增益损失	Liànghuà zēngyì sǔnshī	
Quantization matrix (video term)	量化矩阵	Liànghuà jǔzhèn	
Quantization, quantizing	量化	Liànghuà	
Quantized amplitude modulation	量化调幅	Liànghuà tiáofú	QAM
Quantized amplitude modulation	量化振幅调制	Liànghuà zhènfú tiáozhì	QAM
Quantizer	量化器	Liànghuàqì	
Quantizing distortion	量化失真	Liànghuà shīzhēn	
Quantizing distortion efficiency	量化失真效率	Liànghuà shīzhēn xiàolǜ	
Quantizing interval	量化区间	Liànghuà qūjiān	
Quantizing noise	量化噪声	Liànghuà zàoshēng	
Quantum amplifier	量子放大器	Liàngzǐ fàngdàqì	
Quantum complementarity	量子互补	Liàngzǐ hùbǔ	
Quantum cryptography	量子密码学	Liàngzǐ mìmǎxué	
Quantum efficiency	量子效率	Liàngzǐ xiàolǜ	
Quantum key distribution	量子密钥分布	Liàngzǐ mìyào fēnbù	QKD
Quantum key distribution	量子密钥分配	Liàngzǐ mìyào fēnpèi	QKD
Quantum noise	量子噪声	Liàngzǐ zàoshēng	
Quantum physics	量子物理学	Liàngzǐ wùlǐxué	
Quantum well	量子阱	Liàngzǐ jǐng	
Quantum well distributed feedback laser	量子阱分布反馈激光器	Liàngzǐ jǐng fēnbù fǎnkuì jīguāngqì	QW-DFB-LD
Quantum well semiconductor laser	量子阱半导体激光器	Liàngzǐ jǐng bàndǎotǐ jīguāngqì	QWSL
Quarter circle	四分圆	Sìfēn yuán	
Quarter-common intermediate format	四分之一公共中介格式	Sì fēn zhī yī gōnggòng zhōngjiè géshi	QCIF
Quarterion	四元数	Sìyuánshù	
Quarter-wave contact piston	四分之一波长接触式活塞	Sìfēnzhīyī bōcháng jiēchù-shì huósāi	
Quarter-wave plate (in a waveguide)	四分之一波长板	Sìfēnzhīyī bōcháng bǎn	
Quarter-wave stop filter	四分之一波长阻塞滤波器	Sìfēnzhīyī bōcháng zǔsè lǜbōqì	
Quarter-wave transformer	四分之一波长变换器	Sìfēnzhīyī bōcháng biànhuànqì	
Quartet byte	四位字节	Sìwèi zìjié	
Quartz crystal oscillator	石英晶体振荡器	Shíyīng jīngtǐ zhèndàngqì	
Quasi-associated signaling	准直联信令方式	Zhǔn zhílián xìnlìng fāngshì	

Quasi-impulsive disturbance (noise)	准脉冲骚扰	Zhǔn màichōng sāorǎo	
Quasi-impulsive noise	准脉冲噪声	Zhǔn màichōng zàoshēng	
Quasi-nearby terminal	准近端	Zhǔn jìnduān	
Quasi-optical	准光	Zhǔn guāng	
Quasi-peak	准峰值	Zhǔn fēngzhí	QP
Quasi-peak detector	准峰值检波器	Zhǔn fēngzhí jiǎnbōqì	
Quasi-peak voltmeter	准峰值电压表	Zhǔn fēngzhí diànyābiǎo	
Quasi-remote terminal	准远端	Zhǔn yuǎnduān	
Quasi-reversability	准可逆行	Zhǔn kěnìxíng	
Quasi-transmission trunking	准传输集群	Zhǔn chuánshū jíqún	
Quaternary phase-shift keying	四相移相键控	Sìxiàng yíxiàng jiànkòng	QPSK
Query builder	查询生成器	Cháxún shēngchéngqì	
Query expansion	查询扩充	Cháxún kuòchōng	
Query function	查询函数	Cháxún hánshù	
Query graph model	查询图模型	Cháxúntú móxíng	QGM
Query language	查询语言	Cháxún yǔyán	
Query optimization	查询优化	Cháxún yōuhuà	
Query optimizer	查询优化器	Cháxún yōuhuà qì	
Query point (CAD/CAM)	查询点	Cháxúndiǎn	
Query window	查询窗口	Cháxún chuāngkǒu	
Question builder	问题生成器	Wèntí shēngchéng qì	
Question file (.eqq)	问题文件	Wèntí wénjiàn	
Question mark (?)	问号	Wènhào	
Question template	问题模板	Wèntí múbǎn	
Questionnaire	问卷调查	Wènjuàn diàochá	
Questionnaire by mail	通信调查	Tōngxìn diàochá	
Queue	队列	Duìliè	
Queue scheduling	队列调度	Duìliè diàodù	
Queued updating (in SQL Server)	排队更新	Páiduì gēngxīn	
Queuing	排队	Páiduì	
Queuing delay	排队时延	Páiduì shíyán	
Queuing delay	排队延时	Páiduì yánshí	
Queuing discipline	排队规则	Páiduì guīzé	
Queuing indication	排队指示	Páiduì zhǐshì	
Queuing model	排队模型	Páiduì móxíng	
Queuing network	排队网络	Páiduì wǎngluò	QN
Queuing theory	排队论	Páiduì lùn	
Quick mail transfer protocol	快速邮件传输协议	Kuàisù yóujiàn chuánshū xiéyì	QMTP
Quick response	快速反应	Kuàisù fǎnyìng	QR
Quick shear test	快剪试验	Kuàijiǎn shìyàn	
Quick sort	快速排序	Kuàisù páixù	
Quiesce	停顿	Tíngdùn	
Quiescent, standby	待用	Dàiyòng	
Quintet byte	五位字节	Wǔwèi zìjié	
Quotient operator	除操作	Chú cāozuò	
Quotient register	扩展累加器	Kuòzhǎn lěijiāqì	Q

Qwest video services for business	Qwest 企业视像业务	Qwest qǐyè shìxiàng yèwù	QVSB

R

Race condition	竞争条件	Jìngzhēng tiáojiàn	
Racing game (computer game)	赛车类游戏	Sàichē lèi yóuxì	RAC
Rackmount	机架式	Jījià-shì	
Radar	雷达	Léidá	
Radar astronomy	雷达天文学	Léidá tiānwénxué	
Radar beacon	雷达信标	Léidá xìnbiāo	Racon
Radar cabin	雷达方舱	Léidá fāngcāng	
Radar camouflage	雷达伪装	Léidá wěizhuāng	
Radar echo	雷达回波	Léidá huíbō	
Radar equation	雷达方程	Léidá fāngchéng	
Radar fuse	雷达信管	Léidá xìnguǎn	
Radar jammer	雷达干扰机	Léidá gānrǎojī	
Radar jamming shell	雷达干扰弹	Léidá gānrǎo dàn	
Radar performance-to-cost ratio	雷达性能价格比	Léidá xìngnéng jiàgé bǐ	
Radar platform movement compensation	雷达平台运动补偿	Léidá píngtái yùndòng bǔcháng	
Radar reflective balloon	雷达反射气球	Léidá fǎnshè qìqiú	
Radar resolution	雷达分辨力	Léidá fēnbiànlì	
Radar self-screening range	雷达自卫距离	Léidá zìwèi jùlí	
Radar shelter	雷达车厢	Léidá chēxiāng	
Radar signals simulator	雷达信号模拟器	Léidá xìnhào mónǐqì	
Radar silence	雷达沉默	Léidá chénmò	
Radar target	雷达目标	Léidá mùbiāo	
Radar target identification	雷达目标识别	Léidá mùbiāo shíbié	
Radar trap	雷达陷阱	Léidá xiànjǐng	
Radar vectoring coverage	雷达引导范围	Léidá yǐndǎo fànwéi	
Radar warning coverage	雷达警戒范围	Léidá jǐngjiè fànwéi	
Radarsat	雷达卫星	Léidá wèixīng	
Radial 0-line plotting	辐射 0-线绘图法	Fúshè 0-xiàn huìtú fǎ	
Radial distance	辐射距	Fúshè jù	
Radial sweep (radar term)	径向扫描	Jìngxiàng sǎomiáo	
Radial transmission line	径向传输线	Jìngxiàng chuánshūxiàn	
Radian	弧度	Húdù	
Radiance	辐射亮度	Fúshè liàngdù	
Radiance map	辐射度图	Fúshè dù tú	
Radiant energy	辐射能	Fúshènéng	
Radiant protection unit	辐射隔离装置	Fúshè gélí zhuāngzhì	
Radiated area	辐射区	Fúshè qū	
Radiated emission	辐射发射	Fúshè fāshè	
Radiated interference	辐射干扰	Fúshè gānrǎo	
Radiated spurious emission	辐射杂散发射	Fúshè zásǎn fāshè	
Radiated susceptibility	辐射敏感度	Fúshè mǐngǎndù	
Radiating cable	泄漏电缆	Xièlòu diànlǎn	
Radiating element	辐射单元	Fúshè dānyuán	

English	Chinese	Pinyin	Abbr.
Radiating near field region	辐射近场区	Fúshè jìncháng qū	
Radiation	辐射	Fúshè	
Radiation characteristic pattern	辐射特性图	Fúshè tèxìngtú	
Radiation damping	辐射衰减	Fúshè shuāijiǎn	
Radiation efficiency (of an antenna)	辐射效率	Fúshè xiàolǜ	
Radiation fog	辐射雾	Fúshè wù	
Radiation imaging	辐射成象	Fúshè chéngxiàng	
Radiation impedance	辐射阻抗	Fúshè zǔkàng	
Radiation intensity, radiant intensity	辐射强度	Fúshè qiángdù	
Radiation lobe	辐射瓣	Fúshè bàn	
Radiation pattern	辐射方向图	Fúshè fāngxiàngtú	
Radiation pattern (graphical representation)	辐射方向图的图示法	Fúshè fāngxiàngtúde túshìfǎ	
Radiation pattern (mathematical representation)	辐射方向图的数学表达式	Fúshè fāngxiàngtúde shùxué biǎodá shì	
Radiation pattern envelope	辐射图包络	Fúshè tú bāoluò	RPE
Radiation resistance (of an antenna)	辐射电阻	Fúshè diànzǔ	
Radiation resistant fiber	抗辐射光纤	Kàngfúshè guāngxiān	
Radiation resolution (GIS)	辐射分辨力	Fúshè fēnbiànlì	
Radiation test site	辐射测试场地	Fúshè cèshì chǎngdì	
Radiation test site	辐射实验场地	Fúshè shíyàn chǎngdì	
Radiative cooling	辐射冷却	Fúshè lěngquè	
Radical lookup (WP command)	部首查字	Bùshǒu chá zì	
Radical mean square	均方根	Jūn fānggēn	Rms
Radio	无线电	Wúxiàndiàn	
Radio (frequency) noise	射频噪声	Shèpín zàoshēng	
Radio access bearer	无线接入承载	Wúxiàn jiērù chéngzài	RAB
Radio access bearer service	无线接入承载业务	Wúxiàn jiērù chéngzài yèwù	RAB
Radio access network	无线接入网	Wúxiàn jiērù wǎng	RAN
Radio access network	无线接入网络	Wúxiàn jiērù wǎngluò	RAN
Radio access network application part	无线接入网应用部分	Wúxiàn jiērù wǎng yìngyòng bùfen	RANAP
Radio access network application part	无线接入网络应用部分	Wúxiàn jiērù wǎngluò yìngyòng bùfen	RANAP
Radio access network system	无线接入网系统	Wúxiàn jiērù wǎng xìtǒng	RNS
Radio access point	无线电接入点	Wúxiàndiàn jiērù diǎn	RAP
Radio adapter port	电台接口	Diàntái jiēkǒu	RAP
Radio air interface	无线电空中接口	Wúxiàndiàn kōngzhōng jiēkǒu	
Radio altimeter	无线电高度表	Wúxiàndiàn gāodùbiǎo	
Radio amateur, ham	无线电业余爱好者	Wúxiàndiàn yèyú àihàozhě	
Radio astronomy	射电天文	Shèdiàn tiānwén	
Radio astronomy	射电天文学	Shèdiàn tiānwénxué	
Radio astronomy service	射电天文业务	Shèdiàn tiānwén yèwù	
Radio astronomy service	射频天文业务	Shèpín tiānwén yèwù	
Radio astronomy station	射电天文电台	Shèdiàn tiānwén diàntái	
Radio astronomy station	射频天文电台	Shèpín tiānwén diàntái	
Radio base station	无线基站	Wúxiàn jīzhàn	RBS
Radio beacon	无线电信标	Wúxiàndiàn xìnbiāo	
Radio beacon station	无线电信标电台	Wúxiàndiàn xìnbiāo diàntái	
Radio bearer	无线承载电路	Wúxiàn chéngzài diànlù	RB

Radio bearer common functionality	无线承载共用功能	Wúxiàn chéngzài gòngyòng gōngnéng	RBCF
Radio broadcasting	无线电广播	Wúxiàndiàn guǎngbō	
Radio button	单选按钮	Dānxuǎn ànniǔ	
Radio cell	无线小区	Wúxiàn xiǎoqū	RC
Radio channel	无线电波道	Wúxiàndiàn bōdào	RC
Radio channel	无线电信道	Wúxiàndiàn xìndào	RC
Radio channel group	无线信道群	Wúxiàn xìndào qún	RCG
Radio communication	无线电通信	Wúxiàndiàn tōngxìn	
Radio communication service	无线通信业务	Wúxiàn tōngxìn yèwù	
Radio control terminal	无线电控制终端	Wúxiàndiàn kòngzhì zhōngduān	RCT
Radio data system transmission	无线数据广播	Wúxiàn shùjù guǎngbō	RDS
Radio determination	无线电测定	Wúxiàndiàn cèdìng	
Radio determination service	无线电测定业务	Wúxiàndiàn cèdìng yèwù	
Radio determination station	无线电测定电台	Wúxiàndiàn cèdìng diàntái	
Radio direction-finding	无线电测向	Wúxiàndiàn cèxiàng	
Radio direction-finding	无线电定向	Wúxiàndiàn dìngxiàng	
Radio direction-finding station	无线电测向电台	Wúxiàndiàn cèxiàng diàntái	
Radio display paging	无线电显示寻呼	Wúxiàndiàn xiǎnshì xúnhū	
Radio disturbance	无线电骚扰	Wúxiàndiàn sāorǎo	
Radio environment	无线电环境	Wúxiàndiàn huánjìng	
Radio equipment	无线设备	Wúxiàn shèbèi	REP
Radio frequency	无线电频率	Wúxiàndiàn pínlǜ	RF
Radio frequency	无线电射频	Wúxiàndiàn shèpín	
Radio frequency	射频	Shèpín	RF
Radio frequency amplifier	射频放大器	Shèpín fàngdàqì	
Radio frequency channel	无线电频道	Wúxiàndiàn píndào	
Radio frequency filter	射频滤波器	Shèpín lǜbōqì	
Radio frequency heating apparatus	射频加热装置	Shèpín jiārè zhuāngzhì	
Radio frequency interference	射频干扰	Shèpín gānrǎo	RFI
Radio frequency leakage	射频泄漏	Shèpín xièlòu	
Radio frequency protection ratio	射频保护比	Shèpín bǎohù bǐ	
Radio frequency pulse spectrum	射频脉冲频谱	Shèpín màichōng pínpǔ	
Radio frequency terminal	射频终端	Shèpín zhōngduān	RFT
Radio frequency test equipment	无线频率测试设备	Wúxiàn pínlǜ cèshì shèbèi	RFTE
Radio frequency unit	无线频率单元	Wúxiàn pínlǜ dānyuán	RFU
Radio frequency unit rack	无线频率单元机架	Wúxiàn pínlǜ dānyuán jījià	RFUR
Radio guidance	无线电制导	Wúxiàndiàn zhìdǎo	
Radio homing	无线电寻的	Wúxiàndiàn xúndì	
Radio horizon	无线电地平线	Wúxiàndiàn dìpíngxiàn	
Radio in the local loop	本地环路无线电	Běndì huánlù wúxiàndiàn	RLL
Radio interface layer	无线接口层	Wúxiàn jiēkǒu céng	RIL
Radio interference	无线电干扰	Wúxiàndiàn gānrǎo	
Radio interference error code	无线干扰误码	Wúxiàn gānrǎo wùmǎ	
Radio interference meter	无线电干扰测量仪	Wúxiàndiàn gānrǎo cèliángyí	
Radio jamming	无线电干扰	Wúxiàndiàn gānrǎo	
Radio line protocol	无线电线路规约	Wúxiàndiàn xiànlù guīyuē	RLP

Radio link	无线线路	Wúxiàn xiànlù	
Radio link	无线电链路	Wúxiàndiàn liànlù	
Radio link control	无线链路控制	Wúxiàn liànlù kòngzhì	RLC
Radio link control protocol	无线链路控制协议	Wúxiàn liànlù kòngzhì xiéyì	RLCP
Radio link control sub-layer	无线链路控制子层	Wúxiàn liànlù kòngzhì zicéng	RLC
Radio link management	无线链路管理	Wúxiàn liànlù guǎnlǐ	RLM
Radio link protocol	无线链路规约	Wúxiàn liànlù guīyuē	RLP
Radio link protocol	无线链路协议	Wúxiàn liànlù xiéyì	RLP
Radio link setup	无线链路建立	Wúxiàn liànlù jiànlì	RLS
Radio location	无线电定位	Wúxiàndiàn dìngwèi	
Radio location land station	无线电定位陆地电台	Wúxiàndiàn dìngwèi lùdì diàntái	
Radio location mobile station	无线电定位移动电台	Wúxiàndiàn dìngwèi yídòng diàntái	
Radio location service	无线电定位业务	Wúxiàndiàn dìngwèi yèwù	
Radio microwave link	无线电微波线路	Wúxiàndiàn wēibō xiànlù	RML
Radio navigation	无线电导航	Wúxiàndiàn dǎoháng	
Radio navigation land station	无线电导航陆地电台	Wúxiàndiàn dǎoháng lùdì diàntái	
Radio navigation mobile station	无线电导航移动电台	Wúxiàndiàn dǎoháng yídòng diàntái	
Radio navigation service	无线电导航业务	Wúxiàndiàn dǎoháng yèwù	
Radio network controller	无线电网络控制器	Wúxiàndiàn wǎngluò kòngzhìqì	RNC
Radio network controller	无选网络控制器	Wúxuǎn wǎngluò kòngzhìqì	RNC
Radio network sub-system	无线网络子系统	Wúxiàn wǎngluò zixìtǒng	RNS
Radio network sub-system	无线电网络子系统	Wúxiàndiàn wǎngluò zixìtǒng	RNS
Radio network sub-system application part	无线网络子系统应用部分	Wúxiàn wǎngluò zixìtǒng yìngyòng bùfen	RNSAP
Radio network sub-system application part	无线电网络子系统应用部分	Wúxiàndiàn wǎngluò zixìtǒng yìngyòng bùfen	RNSAP
Radio network temporary identity	无线电网络临时识别	Wúxiàndiàn wǎngluò línshí shíbié	RNTI
Radio noise	无线电噪声	Wúxiàndiàn zàoshēng	
Radio over fiber	光纤无线电	Guāngxiān wúxiàndiàn	ROF
Radio pager	无线电寻呼机	Wúxiàndiàn xúnhūjī	
Radio pager identity code	寻呼机标识码	Xúnhūjī biāozhì mǎ	RIC
Radio paging	无线电寻呼	Wúxiàndiàn xúnhū	
Radio paging system	无线寻呼系统	Wúxiàn xúnhū xìtǒng	
Radio receiver	无线电接收机	Wúxiàndiàn jiēshōujī	
Radio reception	无线电接收	Wúxiàndiàn jiēshōu	
Radio relay communication	无线电接力通信	Wúxiàndiàn jiēlì tōngxìn	
Radio relay equipment interface (microwave)	微波接力设备接口	Wēibō jiēlì shèbèi jiēkǒu	RR-EI
Radio relay link	无线电中继链路	Wúxiàndiàn zhōngjì liànlù	RRL
Radio relay system	无线电中继系统	Wúxiàndiàn zhōngjì xìtǒng	RRL
Radio relay system reference point	微波接力系统的参考点	Wēibō jiēlì xìtǒngde cānkǎo diǎn	RR-RP
Radio repeater	无线电中继器	Wúxiàndiàn zhōngjìqì	
Radio resource	无线资源	Wúxiàn zīyuán	RR
Radio resource control	无线资源控制	Wúxiàn zīyuán kòngzhì	RRC
Radio resource control layer	无线资源控制层	Wúxiàn zīyuán kòngzhì céng	RRC
Radio resource management	无线资源管理	Wúxiàn zīyuán guǎnlǐ	RRM
Radio resource management entity	无线资源管理实体	Wúxiàn zīyuán guǎnlǐ shítǐ	RRME
Radio resource management protocol	无线资源管理协议	Wúxiàn zīyuán guǎnlǐ xiéyì	RRMP
Radio resources	无线电资源	Wúxiàndiàn zīyuán	RR

Radio resources control	无线电资源控制	Wúxiàndiàn zīyuán kòngzhì	RRC
Radio resources management	无线电资源管理	Wúxiàndiàn zīyuán guǎnlǐ	RRM
Radio signaling link	无线信令链路	Wúxiàn xìnlìng liànlù	RSL
Radio signaling link	无线电信令链路	Wúxiàndiàn xìnlìng liànlù	RSL
Radio silence	无线电寂静	Wúxiàndiàn jìjìng	
Radio source	射频源	Shèpín yuán	
Radio standard	无线电规范	Wúxiàndiàn guīfàn	RS
Radio station	无线电台	Wúxiàndiàntái	
Radio subscriber	无线用户	Wúxiàn yònghù	RS
Radio sub-system criteria	无线分系统准则	Wúxiàn fēnxìtǒng zhǔnzé	
Radio sub-system directed handover	无线分系统指定越区切换	Wúxiàn fēnxìtǒng zhǐdìng yuèqū qiēhuàn	
Radio sub-system management	无线子系统管理	Wúxiàn zixìtǒng guǎnlǐ	RSM
Radio system entity	无线电系统实体	Wúxiàndiàn xìtǒng shítǐ	RSE
Radio system management	无线系统管理	Wúxiàn xìtǒng guǎnlǐ	RSM
Radio Technology Committee, Marine	海事无线电技术委员会	Hǎishì wúxiàndiàn jìshù wěiyuánhuì	RTCM
Radio telegram	无线电报	Wúxiàndiàn bào	
Radio telegraphy	无线电报技术	Wúxiàndiànbào jìshù	
Radio telemetry	无线电遥测技术	Wúxiàndiàn yáocè jìshù	
Radio telephone	无线电话	Wúxiàn diànhuà	
Radio telephony	无线电话技术	Wúxiàn diànhuà jìshù	
Radio teletype	无线电传打字电报	Wúxiàndiàn chuándǎzì diànbào	RTTY
Radio terminal function	无线电终端功能	Wúxiàndiàn zhōngduān gōngnéng	RTF
Radio test equipment (board)	无线测试设备(板)	Wúxiàn cèshì shèbèi (bǎn)	RTE
Radio transmission specific functionality	无线传输特定功能	Wúxiàn chuánshū tèdìng gōngnéng	RTSF
Radio transmission technology	无线电传输技术	Wúxiàndiàn chuánshū jìshù	RTT
Radio transmitter	无线电发射机	Wúxiàndiàn fāshèjī	
Radio transponder	无线电转发器	Wúxiàndiàn zhuǎnfāqì	
Radio wave	无线电波	Wúxiàndiànbō	
Radio wave fading	电波衰落	Diànbō shuāiluò	
Radio wave propagation	无线电波传播	Wúxiàndiànbō chuánbō	
Radio waves	无线电波	Wúxiàndiàn bō	
Radiodetection Corp. (US company)	雷迪有限公司	Léi-dí yǒuxiàn gōngsī	
Radio-determination satellite service	卫星无线电测定业务	Wèixīng wúxiàndiàn cèdìng yèwù	
Radio-frequency channel	无线电频率信道	Wúxiàndiàn pínlǜ xìndào	RFC
Radio-frequency channel	射频信道	Shèpín xìndào	
Radio-frequency disturbance	无线电频率骚扰	Wúxiàndiàn pínlǜ sāorǎo	
Radio-frequency disturbance	射频骚扰	Shèpín sāorǎo	
Radio-frequency heating apparatus	无线电频率加热装置	Wúxiàndiàn pínlǜ jiārè zhuāngzhì	
Radio-frequency interference	无线电频率干扰	Wúxiàndiàn pínlǜ gānrǎo	RFI
Radio-frequency noise	无线电频率噪声	Wúxiàndiàn pínlǜ zàoshēng	
Radio-frequency power amplifier	射频功率放大器	Shèpín gōnglǜ fàngdàqì	
Radio-frequency radiation	射频辐射	Shèpín fúshè	
Radio-frequency signal-to-interference ratio	射频信号干扰比	Shèpín xìnhào gānrǎo bǐ	
Radio-frequency test equipment	射频测试设备	Shèpín cèshì shèbèi	RFTE
Radiometric correction (GIS)	辐射校正	Fúshè jiàozhèng	
Radio-navigation satellite service	卫星无线电导航业务	Wèixīng wúxiàndiàn dǎoháng yèwù	

English	Chinese	Pinyin	Abbr.
Radio-paging code no.1	无线寻呼 1 号码	Wúxiàn xúnhū yihàomǎ	
Radiosonde	无线电高空测候器	Wúxiàndiàn gāokōng cèhòuqì	
Radiotelegram	无线电报	Wúxiàndiànbào	
Radiotelephone call	无线电话呼叫	Wúxiàn diànhuà hūjiào	
Radiotelex call	无线电用户电报呼叫	Wúxiàndiàn yònghù diànbào hūjiào	
Radio-wave lens	无线电波透镜	Wúxiàndiàn bō tòujìng	
Radius	半径	Bànjìng	
Radius of gyration	回转半径	Huízhuǎn bànjìng	
Radius server	认证服务器	Rènzhèng fúwùqì	RS
Radix sort	基数排序	Jīshù páixù	
Radome	天线罩	Tiānxiàn zhào	
Radome beam pointing error	天线罩波束指向误差	Tiānxiàn zhào bōshù zhǐxiàng wùchā	
Radome insertion	天线罩插入相移	Tiānxiàn zhào chārù xiāngyí	
Radon concentration	氡浓度	Dōng nóngdù	
Ragged hierarchy	不齐整层次结构	Bùqízhěng céngcì jiégòu	
Railcom (Railway Telecommunications Information Co. Ltd.)	铁通公司（铁路通信有限公司）	Tiě tōng gōngsī (tiělù tōngxìn yǒuxiàn gōngsī)	
Railgun	导轨炮	Dǎoguǐ páo	
Railway Telecommunications Information Co. Ltd. (Railcom) (China company)	铁路通信有限公司（铁通公司）	Tiělù tōngxìn yǒuxiàn gōngsī (tiě tōng gōngsī)	
Railway traffic control automation	铁路行车指挥自动化系统	Tiělù xíngchē zhǐhuī zìdònghuà xìtǒng	
Railway train dispatch system	铁路列车调度系统	Tiělù lièchē diàodù xìtǒng	
Railway yard automation	铁路编组站自动化	Tiělù biānzǔzhàn zìdònghuà	
Rainfall test (radar term)	淋雨试验	Línyǔ shìyàn	
Raise (as 'to raise an exception')	引发	Yǐnfā	
Raman effect	喇曼效应	Lǎ-màn xiàoyìng	
Raman fiber	喇曼光纤	Lǎ-màn guāngxiān	
Raman optical time-domain reflectometry	拉曼光学时域反射测量术	Lā-màn guāngxué shíyù fǎnshè cèliáng shù	ROTDR
Rambus application specific integrated circuit cell	Rambus 集成电路单元	Rambus jíchéng diànlù dānyuán	RAC
Rambus direct random access memory	直接型 RambusRAM	Zhíjiē-xíng Rambus RAM	RDRAM
RAMBUS in-line memory module	RAMBUS 内嵌式内存模块	RAMBUS nèiqiàn-shì nèicún mókuài	RIMM
Random	随机	Suíjī	
Random access	随机访问	Suíjī fǎngwèn	
Random access burst	随机接入分组	Suíjī jiērù fēnzǔ	RAB
Random access channel	随机接入信道	Suíjī jiērù xìndào	RACH
Random access control address	离散用户的随机接入	Lísàn yònghùde suíjī jiērù	RADA
Random access instant assignment	随机接入立即分配	Suíjī jiērù lìjí fēnpèi	
Random access memory	随机存取存储器	Suíjī cúnqǔ cúnchǔqì	RAM
Random access memory	随机存取记存器	Suíjī cúnqǔ jìcúnqì	RAM
Random access memory digital to analog converter	随机存储器数/模转换器	Suíjī cúnchǔqì shù/mó zhuǎnhuànqì	RAMDAC
Random and burst error correcting code	同时纠随机与突发错误码	Tóngshí jiū suíjī yǔ tūfā cuòwù mǎ	
Random assignment multiple access	随机分配多址	Suíjī fēnpèi duōzhǐ	
Random disturbance	随机骚扰	Suíjī sāorǎo	
Random dot	随机点	Suíjī diǎn	
Random early detection	随机早期检测	Suíjī zǎoqī jiǎncè	RED
Random early detection	随机早期侦测	Suíjī zǎoqī zhēncè	RED

English	Chinese	Pinyin	Abbreviation
Random error	随机差错	Suíjī chācuò	
Random error	随机误差	Suíjī wùchā	
Random failure rate	随机失效率	Suíjī shīxiào lǜ	
Random frequency hopping	随机跳频	Suíjī tiàopín	
Random frequency shift keying/frequency hopping	随机频移键控/频率跳变	Suíjī pínyí jiànkòng/pínlǜ tiàobiàn	RFSK/FH
Random mode request information field	请求信息字段随机模式	Qǐngqiú xìnxī zìduàn suíjī móshì	RA
Random noise	随机噪声	Suíjī zàoshēng	
Random number	随机号码	Suíjī hàomǎ	RAND
Random number (used for authentication)	随机数	Suíjī shù	RAND
Random number generation	随机数生成	Suíjī shù shēngchéng	
Random number generator	随机数字发生器	Suíjī shùzì fāshēngqì	RNG
Random number method	随机数法	Suíjī shùfǎ	
Random phase feed	随机馈相	Suíjī kuìxiàng	
Random phase modulation	随机相位调制	Suíjī xiàngwèi tiáozhì	RPM
Random pulse jamming	杂乱脉冲干扰	Záluàn màichōng gānrǎo	
Random search	随机搜寻	Suíjī sōuxún	
Random slow frequency hopping multiple access	随机缓慢跳频变多路存取	Suíjī huǎnmàn tiàopín biàn duōlù cúnqǔ	RSFHMA
Random sweep	随机扫描	Suíjī sǎomiáo	
Random time division multiple access	随机分时多路存取	Suíjī fēnshí duōlù cúnqǔ	RTDMA
Random vibration	随机振动	Suíjī zhèndòng	
Randomized non-return to zero	随机不归零制	Suíjī bù guī líng zhì	RNZR
Range	范围	Fànwéi	
Range	区间	Qūjiān	
Range calibration	距离标校	Jùlí biāojiào	
Range encoder (radar term)	距离编码器	Jùlí biānmǎqì	
Range gate walk-off jamming	距离波门拖引干扰	Jùlí bōmén tuōyǐn gānrǎo	
Range marker	距离标志	Jùlí biāozhì	
Range noise	距离噪声	Jùlí zàoshēng	
Range of influence	影响范围	Yǐngxiǎng fànwéi	
Range query	范围查询	Fànwéi cháxún	
Range resolution	距离分辨率	Jùlí fēnbiànlǜ	
Range-azimuth indicator	距离-方位显示器	Jùlí—fāngwèi xiǎnshìqì	
Ranging	测距	Cèjù	
Ranging response message	测距响应消息	Cèjù xiǎngyìng xiāoxi	RNG-RSP
Rank	等级	Děngjí	
Rank quantity detector	量化秩值检测器	Liànghuà zhìzhí jiǎncèqì	
Rank sum slide-window detector	秩和滑窗检测器	Zhì hé huáchuāng jiǎncèqì	
Rapid acquisition by sequential estimation	序贯估计快速捕获	Xùguàn gūjì kuàisù bǔhuò	RASE
Rapid prototyping platform	快速样机平台	Kuàisù yàngjī píngtái	
Rapid thermal processing	快速热处理	Kuàisù rèchǔlǐ	RTP
Rapid transport protocol	快速传输协议	Kuàisù chuánshū xiéyì	RTP
Rapid transport protocol	快速传送协议	Kuàisù chuánsòng xiéyì	RTP
Rare earth material	稀土族材料	Xītǔ zú cáiliào	
Rare earth optical amplifier	掺稀土光纤放大器	Chān xītǔ guāngxiān fàngdàqì	
RAS/CAS generator	RAS/CAS 发生器	RAS/CAS fāshēngqì	RCG
Raster	栅格	Zhàgé	

Raster data	栅格数据	Zhàgé shùjù	
Raster data model	栅格数据模型	Zhàgé shùjù móxíng	
Raster data structure	栅格数据结构	Zhàgé shùjù jiégòu	
Raster fonts	光栅字体	Guāngshān zìtǐ	
Raster graphics element	光栅图形元素	Guāngshān túxíng yuánsù	
Raster map	栅格地图	Zhàgé dìtú	
Raster object	栅格对象	Zhàgé duìxiàng	
Raster structure	栅格结构	Zhàgé jiégòu	
Raster sweep	光栅扫描	Guāngshān sǎomiáo	
Raster to vector conversion	栅格矢量转换	Zhàgé shǐliàng zhuǎnhuàn	
Rasterization	矢量数据栅格化	Shǐliàng shùjù zhàgéhuà	
Rate adaptation	速率适配	Sùlǜ shìpèi	RA
Rate adapter	速率适配器	Sùlǜ shìpèiqì	RA
Rate adaptive digital subscriber line	速率自适应数字订阅线路	Sùlǜ zìshìyìng shùzì dìngyuè xiànlù	RADSL
Rate adaptive digital subscriber line	速率自适应数字用户线	Sùlǜ zìshìyìng shùzì yònghù xiàn	RADSL
Rate bridge	速率电桥	Sùlǜ diànqiáo	
Rate change	速率改变	Sùlǜ gǎibiàn	
Rate compatible puncturing Turbo code	速率适配凿孔 Turbo 码	Sùlǜ shìpèi záokǒng Turbo mǎ	RCPT
Rate enforcement	速率控制	Sùlǜ kòngzhì	
Rate monotonic analysis (in CORBA)	比率单调分析	Bǐlǜ dāndiào fēnxī	RMA
Rate of occurrence of voltage change	电压变化发生率	Diànyā biànhuà fāshēng lǜ	
Rate of rise thermal detector	差温探测器	Chà wēn tàncèqì	RORTD
Rate queue	速率队列	Sùlǜ duìliè	
Rate scalable	码率可分级	Mǎlǜ kěfēnjí	
Rate-adjustable digital subscriber line	可调速率数字用户线	Kětiáo sùlǜ shùzì yònghù xiàn	RADSL
Rated audio-frequency output power	额定音频输出功率	Édìng yīnpín shūchū gōnglǜ	
Rated bandwidth	额定带宽	Édìng dàikuān	
Rated impedance of earphone	耳机额定阻抗	Ěrjī édìng zǔkàng	
Rated impedance of loudspeaker	扬声器额定阻抗	Yángshēngqì édìng zǔkàng	
Rated operating range	额定使用范围	Édìng shǐyòng fànwéi	
Rated optical output power	额定输光功率	Édìng shūguāng gōnglǜ	
Rated output power (of a transmitter)	额定输出功率	Édìng shūchū gōnglǜ	
Rated output power of transmitter	发射机额定输出功率	Fāshèjī édìng shūchū gōnglǜ	
Rated radio-frequency output power	额定射频输出功率	Édìng shèpín shūchū gōnglǜ	
Rated tensile strength	额定抗拉强度	Édìng kànglā qiángdù	RTS
Rated tensile strength	额定拉断力	Édìng lāduànlì	RTS
Rated value	额定值	Édìngzhí	
Rated voltage for equipment	设备额定电压	Shèbèi édìng diànyā	
Rate-distortion coding cost function	速率失真编码代价函数	Sùlǜ shīzhēn biānmǎ dàijià hánshù	
Rating	额定值	Édìngzhí	
Ratio of energy per modulating bit to noise spectral density	每调制比特的射频能量对噪声频谱密度比	Měi tiáozhì bǐtède shèpín néngliàng duì zàoshēng pínpǔ mìdùbǐ	Ec/No
Ratioing	求比率法	Qiú bǐlǜ fǎ	
Rationality	合理性	Hélǐxìng	
Rationalizing engineering (German concept)	合理化工程	Hélǐhuà gōngchéng	RE
Raw	未经处理的	Wèijīng chǔlǐde	

Raw pulse code modulated	元脉码调制	Yuánmàimă tiáozhì	Raw PCM
Ray path transmission loss	射手系统射线路径传输损耗	Shèshǒu xìtǒng shèxiàn lùjìng chuánshū sǔnhào	
Ray theory	波线理论	Bōxiàn lǐlùn	
Ray tracing	光线跟踪	Guāngxiàn gēnzōng	
Raychem (US company)	瑞侃公司	Ruì-kǎn gōngsī	
Rayleigh fading	瑞利衰减	Ruì-lì shuāijiǎn	
Rayleigh fading	瑞利衰落	Ruì-lì shuāiluò	
Rayleigh scattering	瑞利散射	Ruì-lì sǎnshè	
Rayleigh wave	瑞利波	Ruì-lì bō	
Raytheon Corp. (US company)	雷声公司	Léi-shēng gōngsī	
Reachability	可到达性	Kědàodá-xìng	
Reachability graph (in stochastic process algebra)	可达图	Kědá tú	
Reactive attenuator	电抗式衰减器	Diànkàng-shì shuāijiǎnqì	
Reactive ion etch	反应式离子蚀刻法	Fǎnyingshì lízǐ shíkè fǎ	RIE
Reactive loading phase shifter	电抗加载移相器	Diànkàng jiāzài yíxiāngqì	
Reactive near field (region)	无功近场区	Wúgōng jìncháng qū	
Reactive near-field region	感应近场区	Gǎnyìng jìncháng qū	
Read after write	写后读	Xiě hòu dú	RAW
Read only	只读	Zhǐ dú	RO
Read only memory	只读内储	Zhǐ dú nèichǔ	ROM
Readable format	可读格式	Kědú géshi	
Read-ahead (in SAMBA)	向前读	Xiàngqián dú	
Read-only memory	唯读记忆体	Wéidú jìyìtǐ	ROM
Read-only memory	只读存储器	Zhǐ dú cúnchǔqì	ROM
Ready	就绪	Jiùxù	
Real end system	实端系统	Shíduān xìtǒng	
Real frequency characteristic	实频特性	Shípín tèxìng	
Real media file format	真实媒体文件格式	Zhēnshí méitǐ wénjiàn géshi	RMFF
Real numbers	实型数据	Shíxíng shùjù	
Real open system	开放实系统	Kāifàng shí xìtǒng	
Real sub-network	实子网	Shí zǐwǎng	
Real system	实系统	Shí xìtǒng	
Real time	即时	Jíshí	
Real time	实时	Shíshí	
Real time strategy (computer game)	实时战略	Shíshí zhànlüè	RTS
Real world computing	真实世界电脑	Zhēnshí shìjiè diànnǎo	RWC
Reality	实境	Shíjìng	
Reallocation command	再分配命令	Zàifēnpèi mìnglìng	
Really simple syndication	真正简单的整合	Zhēnzhèng jiǎndānde zhěnghé	RSS
RealMedia architecture ©	实媒体架构	Shí méitǐ jiàgòu	RMA
Real-time adaptive control	实时自适应控制	Shíshí zìshìyìng kòngzhì	RTAC
Real-time and dynamic management and control support	实时动态管控支持	Shíshí dòngtài guǎnkòng zhīchí	RDMCS
Real-time billing	实时计费	Shíshí jìfèi	RTB
Real-time channel estimation	实时信道估算	Shíshí xìndào gūsuàn	
Real-time clock	实时时钟	Shíshí shízhōng	RTC

Real-time communication	实时通信	Shíshí tōngxìn	RTC
Real-time conferencing	实时会议	Shíshí huìyì	
Real-time control protocol	实时控制协议	Shíshí kòngzhì xiéyì	RTCP
Real-time database management system	实时数据库管理系统	Shíshí shùjùkù guǎnlǐ xìtǒng	RTDMS
Real-time difference	实际时钟差异	Shíjì shízhōng chāyì	RTD
Realtime exclusive mode applications	实时高级应用	Shíshí gāojí yìngyòng	REMA
Real-time executive	实时执行	Shíshí zhíxíng	RTE
Real-time input/output scan	即时 I/O 扫描	Jíshí I/O sǎomiáo	
Real-time inter-ORB (object request broker) protocol	对象请求代理间的实时协议	Duìxiàng qǐngqiú dàilǐ jiānde shíshí xiéyì	RTIOP
Real-time management and control support fragment	实时管控支持段	Shíshí guǎnkòng zhīchí duàn	RMCSF
Real-time management control function	实时管理协调功能	Shíshí guǎnlǐ xiétiáo gōngnéng	RTMC
Real-time multi-tasking operating system	实时多任务操作系统	Shíshí duō rènwu cāozuò xìtǒng	RMOS
Real-time operating system	实时操作系统	Shíshí cāozuò xìtǒng	RTOS
Real-time polling service	实时查询业务	Shíshí cháxún yèwù	rtPS
Real-time protocol	实时协议	Shíshí xiéyì	RTP
Real-time security management	实时安全管理	Shíshí ānquán guǎnlǐ	RTSec.M
Real-time security management fragment	实时安全管理段	Shíshí ānquán guǎnlǐ duàn	RSMF
Real-time streaming	实时流式传输	Shíshí liú-shì chuánshū	
Real-time streaming media protocol	实时流媒体协议	Shíshí liúméitǐ xiéyì	RTSP
Real-time streaming protocol	实时流协议	Shíshí liú xiéyì	RTSP
Real-time transmission control protocol	实时传输控制协议	Shíshí chuánshū kòngzhì xiéyì	RTCP
Real-time transport production	实时传送流	Shíshí chuánsòng liú	RTP
Real-time transport protocol	实时传输协议	Shíshí chuánshū xiéyì	RTP
Real-time transport protocol	实时传送协议	Shíshí chuánsòng xiéyì	RTP
Real-time variable bit rate	实时可变比特率	Shíshí kěbiàn bǐtè lǜ	RT-VBR
Reanswer signal	再应答信号	Zàiyìngdá xìnhào	RAN
Reanswer time supervision	再应答时间监视	Zàiyìngdá shíjiān jiānshì	
Rear (of a queue)	队尾	Duìwěi	
Rear port	后窗管	Hòu chuāngguǎn	
Reasonableness check	合理性检查	Hélǐxìng jiǎnchá	
Reassembling	拼段	Pīnduàn	
Reassembly	重新组装	Chóngxīn zǔzhuāng	
Reassembly	组装	Zǔzhuāng	
Rebated rate for handling subscription and delivery	报刊代订、代投折扣率	Bàokān dàidìng、dàitóu zhékòulǜ	
Rebinding state	重新绑定状态	Chóngxīn bǎngdìng zhuàngtài	
Reboot	重新启动	Chóngxīn qǐdòng	
Rebound	回弹	Huítán	
Re-broadcast transmitter	转播发射机	Zhuǎnbō fāshèjī	
Recall signal	再呼叫信号	Zàihūjiào xìnhào	
Receipt for recorded correspondence	给据函件收据	Gěijù hánjiàn shōujù	
Receipt, receive	接收	Jiēshōu	
Receive amplifier/divider assembly	接收放大/分集集成件	Jiēshōu fàngdà/ fēnjí jíchéng jiàn	RADA
Receive block	接收块	Jiēshōu kuài	
Receive buffer	收缓存	Shōu huǎncún	
Receive defect indicator	接收缺陷指示	Jiēshōu quēxiàn zhǐshì	RDI

Receive front end shelf	接收前端架	Jiēshōu qiánduān jià	RFES
Receive level	收信电平值	Shōuxìn diànpíng zhí	RXLE
Receive main path interface reference point	接收主通道接口参考点	Jiēshōu zhǔtōngdào jiēkǒu cānkǎodiǎn	MPI-R
Receive not ready	接收未准备好	Jiēshōu wèizhǔnbèi hǎo	RNR
Receive objective loudness result	接收客观响度评定值	Jiēshōu kèguān xiǎngdù píngdìng zhí	ROLR
Receive quality	收信质量级	Shōuxìn zhìliàng jí	RXQUA
Receive ready	接收准备好	Jiēshōu zhǔnbèi hǎo	RR
Receive to transmit echo loss	接收至发射的回波耗损	Jiēshōu zhì fāshède huíbō hàosǔn	RTEL
Receive to transmit stability loss	接收至发射的稳定耗损	Jiēshōu zhì fāshède wěndìng hàosǔn	RTSL
Received isotropic power	各向同性接收功率	Gèxiàng tóngxìng jiēshōu gōnglǜ	RIP
Received signal code power	接收信号码功率	Jiēshōu xìnhào mǎ gōnglǜ	RSCP
Received signal level	接收信号等级	Jiēshōu xìnhào děngjí	RXLEV
Received signal level	接收信号电平	Jiēshōu xìnhào diànpíng	EXLEV
Received signal quality	接收信号质量	Jiēshōu xìnhào zhìliàng	RXQUAL
Received signal quality indicator	接收信号质量指示	Jiēshōu xìnhào zhìliàng zhǐshì	RSQI
Received signal strength indication	接收信号强度指示	Jiēshōu xìnhào qiángdù zhǐshì	RSSI
Received upstream neighbor station address	收到的上游邻站地址	Shōudàode shàngyóu línzhàn dìzhǐ	RUA
Receiver	接收机	Jiēshōujī	Rx
Receiver (in signaling)	接收器	Jiēshōuqì	
Receiver antenna module	接收天线模块	Jiēshōu tiānxiàn mókuài	RXMOD
Receiver attenuation	接收机衰减	Jiēshōujī shuāijiǎn	RA
Receiver band pass filter	接收机带宽滤波器	Jiēshōujī dàikuān lǜbōqì	RBPF
Receiver blocking	接收机阻塞	Jiēshōujī zǔsè	
Receiver continuous disturbance	收信机的连续骚扰	Shōuxìnjīde liánxù sāorǎo	CR
Receiver control field	接收机控制域	Jiēshōujī kòngzhì yù	RXCF
Receiver dynamic range	接收机动态范围	Jiēshōujī dòngtài fànwéi	
Receiver front end	接收机前端	Jiēshōujī qiánduān	
Receiver multi-coupler	接收多路藕合器	Jiēshōu duōlù ǒuhéqì	RXMUCO
Receiver multi-coupler	接收机分路器	Jiēshōujī fēnlùqì	
Receiver off-hook	接收机脱钩	Jiēshōujī tuōgōu	ROH
Receiver overload power	接收机过载功率	Jiēshōujī guòzài gōnglǜ	
Receiver protector	接收机保护装置	Jiēshōujī bǎohù zhuāngzhì	
Receiver saturation	接收机饱和	Jiēshōujī bǎohé	
Receiver space diversity	接收机空间分集	Jiēshōujī kōngjiān fēnjí	
Receiver threshold-signal level	接收机门限电平	Jiēshōujī ménxiàn diànpíng	
Receiver transient disturbance	收信机的瞬态骚扰	Shōuxìnjīde shùntài sāorǎo	TR
Receiver/reception	收音机/接收	Shōuyīnjī/ jiēshōu	
Receive-ready block	接收准备部件	Jiēshōu zhǔnbèi bùjiàn	R-Block
Receiving antenna	接收天线	Jiēshōu tiānxiàn	
Receiving loudness rating	接收响度评定值	Jiēshōu xiǎngdù píngdìng zhí	RLR
Receiving reference equivalent	接收参考当量	Jiēshōu cānkǎo dāngliàng	
Receiving station	接收台	Jiēshōutái	
Receptacle	插座	Chāzuò	
Recessed	嵌入式	Qiànrù-shì	
Rechecking	复核	Fùhé	
Recipient	接收者	Jiēshōuzhě	

Reciprocal phase shifter	互易移相器	Hùyì yíxiàngqì	
Recirculating chiller (semiconductor mfg)	循环冷却机	Xúnhuán lěngquèjī	
Recognised private operating agency	认可的专用运行代理	Rènkěde zhuānyòng yùnxíng dàilǐ	RPOA
Recognition time	识别时间	Shíbié shíjiān	
Recognized operating authority	经认可的运营机构	Jīng rènkěde yùnyíng jīgòu	ROA
Recognized source	已知信息源	Yǐzhī xìnxī yuán	
RECommendation	建议	Jiànyì	REC
Recommendation	建议	Jiànyì	REC
Recommendation	推荐	Tuījiàn	REC
Recommendation system	推荐系统	Tuījiàn xìtǒng	
Recommended Standard 232	第 232 号推荐标准	Dì 232 hào tuījiàn biāozhǔn	RS-232
Reconditioned carrier demodulation	恢复载波解调	Huīfù zàibō jiětiáo	
Reconditioned carrier reception	恢复载波接收	Huīfù zàibō jiēshōu	
Reconfigurable	可重构	Kěchónggòu	
Reconfigurable	可重组	Kěchóngzǔ	
Reconfigurable key	可设置键	Kěshèzhì jiàn	
Reconstructed frame (video term)	重建帧	Chóngjiàn zhèng	
Reconstructed picture (video term)	重建图像	Chóngjiàn túxiàng	
Reconstructed sample	重建样值	Chóngjiàn yàngzhí	
Reconstruction, restoration	重建	Chóngjiàn	
Record	记录	Jìlù	
Record control fields	记录控制字段	Jìlù kòngzhì zìduàn	
Record definition	记录定义	Jìlù dìngyì	
Record format for spatial data	空间数据记录格式	Kōngjiān shùjù jìlù géshi	
Record locator	记录定位	Jìlù dìngwèi	
Record overflow message (IPsec TLS)	记录液出消息	Jìlù yèchū xiāoxi	
Record protocol (IPsec)	纪录协议	Jìlù xiéyì	
Record separator	记录分隔	Jìlù fēngé	RS
Record sequence	记录顺序	Jìlù shùnxù	
Recordable compact disk	可录写光碟	Kělùxiě guāngdié	
Recorded correspondence	给据函件	Gěijù hánjiàn	
Recorded delivery charge	确认投递费	Quèrèn tóudì fèi	
Recorder-warning tone	记录器告警音	Jìlùqì gàojǐng yīn	
Recording density	记录密度	Jìlù mìdù	
Recording Industry Association of America	美国唱片工业协会	Měiguó chàngpiàn gōngyè xiéhuì	RIAA
Recording optical spectrum analyzer	记录光谱分析仪	Jìlù guāngpǔ fēnxīyí	ROSA
Recording tone	记录音	Jìlù yīn	
Recordset (for database)	记录集	Jìlù jí	
Recovery interval	恢复间歇	Huīfù jiànxiē	
Recovery procedure (IPsec)	恢复规程	Huīfù guīchéng	
Rectangular array	矩形阵	Jǔxíng zhèn	
Rectangular coordinate indicator	直角坐标显示器	Zhíjiǎo zuòbiāo xiǎnshìqì	
Rectangular density model	矩形密度模型	Jǔxíng mìdù móxíng	
Rectangular flexible waveguide	矩形软波导	Jǔxíng ruǎn bōdǎo	
Rectangular grid	直角坐标网	Zhíjiǎo zuòbiāo wǎng	
Rectangular prism	直角棱镜	Zhíjiǎo léngjìng	

Rectangular waveguide	矩形波导	Jǔxíng bōdǎo	
Rectangular-elliptical waveguide transformer	矩形椭圆波导变换器	Jǔxíng tuǒyuán bōdǎo biànhuànqì	
Rectangular-elliptical waveguide transformer	矩圆波导变换器	Jǔyuán bōdǎo biànhuànqì	
Rectangular-wave modulation	矩形波调制	Jǔxíng bō tiáozhì	RWM
Rectification	整流	Zhěngliú	
Rectified alternating current	被整流的直流	Bèizhěngliúde zhíliú	RAC
Recurrence curve	循环曲线	Xúnhuán qūxiàn	
Recursive	递归	Dìguī	
Recursive function	递归函数	Dìguī hánshù	
Recursive least square	递归最小二乘	Dìguī zuìxiǎo èrshèng	RLS
Recursive least square	递归最小平方	Dìguī zuìxiǎo píngfāng	RLS
Recursive partitioning	递归分区	Dìguī fēnqū	
Recursive systematic convolutional code	递归系统卷积码	Dìguī xìtǒng juànjīmǎ	RSC
Recycle bin © (MS Windows)	回收站	Huíshōuzhàn	
Redevelopment	再开发	Zàikāifā	
Redial	重拨	Chóng bō	
Redirect confirm packet	重定向确认分组	Chóngdìngxiàng quèrèn fēnzǔ	RDC
Redirect request packet	重定向请求分组	Chóngdìngxiàng qǐngqiú fēnzǔ	RDR
Redirect server	重定向服务器	Chóngdìngxiàng fúwùqì	RDS
Redirect, re-direction	重定向	Chóngdìngxiàng	
Redirecting name display	改向名字显示	Gǎixiàng míngzì xiǎnshì	RND
Redirection	改投	Gǎitóu	
Redirection of remittance	改汇	Gǎihuì	
Redistribution	重新分配	Chóngxīn fēnpèi	
Redo (WP command)	重做	Chóngzuò	
Reduced bandwidth quadrature phase shift keying	减小带宽正交相移键控	Jiǎnxiǎo dàikuān zhèngjiāo xiāngyí jiànkòng	RBQPSK
Reduced carrier	减幅载波	Jiǎnfú zàibō	
Reduced carrier emission	减载波发射	Jiǎnzàibō fāshè	
Reduced carrier single sideband emission	减载波单边带发射	Jiǎnzàibō dānbiāndài fāshè	
Reduced carrier single-sideband emission	减载波单边带发射	Jiǎn zàibō dānbiāndài fāshè	
Reduced instruction set computer	精简指令计算机	Jīngjiǎn zhǐlìng jìsuànjī	RISC
Reduced instruction set computing	精简指令集计算	Jīngjiǎn zhǐlìng jí jìsuàn	RISC
Reduced instruction set computing	精简指令集计算机	Jīngjiǎn zhǐlìng jí jìsuànjī	RISC
Reduced instruction-set computer	简约指令集计算机	Jiǎnyuē zhǐlìngjí jìsuànjī	RISC
Reduced latency	低延迟	Dīyánchí	
Reduced latency dynamic random access memory	低延迟动态随机存取存储器	Dīyánchí dòngtài suíjī cúnqǔ cúnchǔqì	RLDRAM
Reduced rate	减价费率	Jiǎnjià fèilǜ	
Reduced swing differential signal	小幅度摆动差动信号	Xiǎo fúdù bǎidòng chādòng xìnhào	RSDS
Reduced TDMA frame number	简化 TDMA 帧号	Jiǎnhuà TDMA zhènghào	RFN
Reducing valve	减压阀	Jiǎnyāfá	
Reduction algorithm	归约算法	Guīyuē suànfǎ	
Redundancy	多余度	Duōyúdù	
Redundancy	冗余	Rǒngyú	
Redundancy memory unit	冗余存贮器	Rǒngshé cúnzhùqì	RMU
Redundant array of inexpensive disks	独立磁盘冗余阵列	Dúlì cípán rǒngyú zhènliè	RAID
Redundant array of inexpensive disks	经济磁盘冗余阵列	Jīngjì cípán rǒngyú zhènliè	RAID

Redundant array of inexpensive disks	廉价冗余硬磁盘阵列	Liánjià rǒngyú yìngcípán zhènliè	RAID
Redundant arrays of inexpensive disks	冗余廉价磁盘阵列	Rǒngyú liánjià cípán zhènliè	RAID
Redundant backup	冗余备分	Rǒngyú bèifēn	
Redundant code	冗余码	Rǒngyú mǎ	
Redundant digital signal	冗余数字信号	Rǒngyú shùzì xìnhào	
Redundant line code	冗余线路码	Rǒngyú xiànlù mǎ	
Redundant n-ary signal	冗余 n进制信号	Rǒng yú n-jìnzhì xìnhào	
Redundant space and frequency tree	冗余的空间和频率树	Rǒngyúde kōngjiān hé pínlǜ shù	RSFT
Reed-Solomon code	里德-所罗门码	Lǐ-dé—suǒ-luó-mén mǎ	RSC
Reed-Solomon code	里德-索洛蒙码	Lǐ-dé—suǒ-luò-méng mǎ	RS
Re-engineering	重组工程	Chóngzǔ gōngchéng	
Reenterable program	可再入程序	Kězàirù chéngxù	
Reenterable routine	可再入例行程序	Kězàirù lìxíng chéngxù	
Reenterable sub-routine	可再入子程序	Kězàirù zǐchéngxù	
Re-entrant trunking	中继再进入	Zhōngjì zàijìnrù	
Re-factoring	重构	Chónggòu	
Refer	引用	Yǐnyòng	
Refer, reference	参考	Cānkǎo	
Reference	引用	Yǐnyòng	
Reference antenna	参考天线	Cānkǎo tiānxiàn	
Reference area	参考区	Cānkǎo qū	
Reference bandwidth	参考带宽	Cānkǎo dàikuān	BWr
Reference boresight (axis)	基准轴	Jīzhǔn zhóu	
Reference borseight (of an antenna)	参考视轴	Cānkǎo shìzhóu	
Reference broadband	参考宽带	Cānkǎo kuāndài	BWr
Reference clock	参考时钟	Cānkǎo shízhōng	
Reference clock	参考钟	Cānkǎo zhōng	
Reference clock	基准时钟	Jīzhǔn shízhōng	
Reference condition	基准条件	Jīzhǔn tiáojiàn	
Reference configuration	参考结构	Cānkǎo jiégòu	
Reference configuration	参考配置	Cānkǎo pèizhì	
Reference counting	引用计数	Yǐnyòng jìshù	
Reference data	基准数据	Jīzhǔn shùjù	
Reference ellipsoid	参考椭球体	Cānkǎo tuǒqiútǐ	
Reference equivalent	参考当量	Cānkǎo dāngliàng	
Reference error ratio	参考差错率	Cānkǎo chācuò lǜ	
Reference event	参考事件	Cānkǎo shìjiàn	RE
Reference example	参考实例	Cānkǎo shílì	
Reference field (video term)	参考场	Cānkǎo cháng	
Reference frame (video term)	参考帧	Cānkǎo zhèng	
Reference frequency	参考频率	Cānkǎo pínlǜ	
Reference impedance	参考阻抗	Cānkǎo zǔkàng	
Reference impedance	基准阻抗	Jīzhǔn zǔkàng	
Reference implementation	参考实现	Cānkǎo shíxiàn	
Reference line	参考行	Cānkǎo háng	
Reference load	参考负荷	Cānkǎo fùhè	

Reference model	参考模型	Cānkǎo móxíng	
Reference model of open distributed processing	开放分布式处理的参考模型	Kāifàng fēnbùshì chǔlǐde cānkǎo móxíng	RM-ODP
Reference monitor concept	基准监控概念	Jīzhǔn jiānkòng gàiniàn	
Reference output power	参考输出功率	Cānkǎo shūchū gōnglǜ	
Reference point	参考点	Cānkǎo diǎn	
Reference sensitivity	参考灵敏度	Cānkǎo língmǐndù	
Reference sideband power	参考边带功率	Cānkǎo biāndài gōnglǜ	
Reference space	参照空间	Cānzhào kōngjiān	
Reference studs	基准桩	Jīzhǔn zhuāng	
Reference surface center	基准面中心	Jīzhǔn miànzhōngxīn	
Reference surface diameter	基准面直径	Jīzhǔn miànzhíjìng	
Reference test method	基准试验方法	Jīzhǔn shìyàn fāngfǎ	RTM
Reference usable field-strength	参考可用场强	Cānkǎo kěyòng chǎngqiáng	
Reference voltage	参考电压	Cānkǎo diànyā	
Reference voltage	基准电压	Jīzhǔn diànyā	
Referenced key	引用键	Yǐnyòng jiàn	
Referencing key	参照键	Cānzhào jiàn	
Referential integrity	引用完整性	Yǐnyòng wánzhěngxìng	
Referential integrity (in SQL Server)	参照完整性	Cānzhào wánzhěngxìng	
Reflected current	反射电流	Fǎnshè diànliú	
Reflected sound	反射场	Fǎnshè cháng	RS
Reflected wave	反射波	Fǎnshè bō	
Reflecting satellite	反射卫星	Fǎnshè wèixīng	
Reflection	反射	Fǎnshè	
Reflection coefficient, reflectance	反射系数	Fǎnshè xìshù	
Reflection grating	反射光栅	Fǎnshè guāngshān	
Reflection loss	反射损耗	Fǎnshè sǔnhào	
Reflection mapping (video term)	反射贴图	Fǎnshè tiētú	
Reflection mode filter	反射滤模器	Fǎnshè lǜmóqì	
Reflection of electromagnetic wave	电磁波反射	Diàncíbō fǎnshè	
Reflection port (FOC)	反射端口	Fǎnshè duānkǒu	
Reflection power	反射功率	Fǎnshè gōnglǜ	
Reflection-type star optical coupler	反射形星状光纤耦合器	Fǎnshè-xíng xīngzhuàng guāngxiān ǒuhéqì	
Reflective array antenna; reactive reflector antenna	反射阵天线	Fǎnshèzhèn tiānxiàn	
Reflectometer	反射计	Fǎnshèjì	
Reflector (of an antenna)	反射器	Fǎnshèqì	
Reflector antenna	反射器天线	Fǎnshèqì tiānxiàn	
Reflector element (of an antenna)	反射单元	Fǎnshè dānyuán	
Reflexive relationship	反身关系	Fǎnshēn guānxi	
Reflow convection oven (PCB manufacture)	全热风回流炉	Quán rèfēng huíliú lú	
Reflow oven	热风回流焊机	Rèfēng huíliú hànjī	
Reflow oven (semiconductor mfg)	回流炉	Huíliú lú	
Reflow oven (SMT)	回流户	Huíliú hù	
Reflow soldering (in SMT)	回流焊接	Huíliú hànjiē	
Reformatting	重新格式化	Chóngxīn géshihuà	
Refracted near field	折射近场	Zhéshè jìncháng	

Refracted wave	折射波	Zhéshèbō	
Refraction	折射	Zhéshè	
Refraction	绕射	Ràoshè	
Refraction of electromagnetic wave	电磁波折射	Diàncíbō zhéshè	
Refractive index	折射指数	Zhéshè zhǐshù	
Refractive index liquid	折射率液	Zhéshèlǜ yè	
Refractive index meter	折射率仪	Zhéshèlǜ yí	
Refractive index profile	折射率分布	Zhéshèlǜ fēnbù	
Refresh data (for database)	刷新数据	Shuāxīn shùjù	
Refresh graphics	图象刷新	Túxiàng shuāxīn	
Refresh rate	刷新频率	Shuāxīn pínlǜ	
Refund	退缴	Tuìjiǎo	
Refurbish (semiconductor mfg)	翻新	Fānxīn	
Regenerating transponder	再生转发器	Zàishēng zhuǎnfāqì	
Regeneration	再生	Zàishēng	
Regeneration, reshaping, retiming	再生、重整形和重定时	Zàishēng、chóngzhěngxíng hé chóngdìngshí	3R
Regenerative feedback	再生反馈	Zàishēng fǎnkuì	
Regenerative receiver	再生接收机	Zàishēng jiēshōujī	
Regenerative relay station	再生中继站	Zàishēng zhōngjìzhàn	
Regenerative repeater	再生中继器	Zàishēng zhōngjìqì	REG
Regenerator	再生设备	Zàishēng shèbèi	RG
Regenerator	再生器	Zàishēngqì	REG
Regenerator relay section	再生中继段	Zàishēng zhōngjì duàn	
Regenerator relay section level	再生中继段级	Zàishēng zhōngjì duàn jí	
Regenerator section	再生段	Zàishēng duàn	RS
Regenerator section network connection	再生段网络连接	Zàishēng duàn wǎngluò liánjiē	RS NC
Regenerator section overhead	再生段开销	Zàishēng duàn kāixiao	RSOH
Regenerator section termination	再生段终端	Zàishēng duàn zhōngduān	RST
Regenerator section trace identification mismatch	再生段路踪识别失配	Zàishēng duànlù zōng shíbié shīpèi	RS-TIM
Regenerator timing generator	再生器定时发生器	Zàishēngqì dìngshí fāshēngqì	RTG
Region	区域	Qūyù	
Region automaton	域自动机	Yù zìdòngjī	
Region code	区域码	Qūyù mǎ	
Regional analysis	区域分析	Qūyù fēnxī	
Regional automatic circuit exchange	地区自动电路交换机	Dìqū zìdòng diànlù jiāohuànjī	RACE
Regional Bell operating company	地方贝尔运营公司	Dìfang Bèi-ěr yùnyíng gōngsī	RBOC
Regional coefficient	区域系数	Qūyù xìshù	
Regional management system	区域管理系统	Qūyù guǎnlǐ xìtǒng	RMS
Regional planning	区域规划	Qūyù guīhuà	
Regional subscription zone identity	地方的预约信息段识别	Dìfangde yùyuē xìnxī duàn shíbié	RSZI
Regional subscription zone identity	区域使用识别码	Qūyù shǐyòng shíbié mǎ	RSZI
Regional subscription zone identity	区域性签约区域识别号码	Qūyùxìng qiānyuē qūyù shíbié hàomǎ	RSZI
Regional subscription zone identity	区域性预约区标示	Qūyùxìng yùyuēqū biāoshì	RSZI
Regionality	区域性	Qūyùxìng	
Regionalized variable	区域化变量	Qūyù-huà biànliàng	

English	Chinese	Pinyin	Abbreviation
Register	寄存器	Jìcúnqì	
Register acknowledge message	登记确认消息	Dēngjì quèrèn xiāoxi	REG-ACK
Register call	登记呼叫	Dēngjì hūjiào	
Register contention	寄存器冲突	Jìcúnqì chōngtū	
Register contention	抢占寄存器	Qiǎngzhàn jìcúnqì	
Register dump	套打	Tào dǎ	
Register file	寄存器文件	Jìcúnqì wénjiàn	
Register function	记发器功能	Jìfāqì gōngnéng	
Register password	登记口令	Dēngjì kǒulìng	
Register pressure	寄存器不足	Jìcúnqì bùzú	
Register renaming	寄存器重命名	Jìcúnqì chóng mìngmíng	
Register request message	登记请求消息	Dēngjì qǐngqiú xiāoxi	REG-REQ
Register response message	登记响应消息	Dēngjì xiǎngyìng xiāoxi	REG-RSP
Register signal, signaling	记发器信号	Jìfāqì xìnhào	
Register signaling	记发器信令	Jìfāqì xìnlìng	
Register SS	登记 SS	Dēngjì SS	
Register stack	寄存器栈	Jìcúnqì zhàn	
Registered access	已登记访问	Yǐdēngjì fǎngwèn	
Registered call	遇忙寄存呼叫	Yùmáng jìcún hūjiào	
Registered correspondence	挂号函件	Guàhào hánjiàn	
Registered jack connector	注册的插座连接器	Zhùcède chāzuò liánjiēqì	RJ Connector
Registered public land mobile network	登记的公用陆地移动通信网	Dēngjìde gōngyòng lùdì yídòng tōngxìnwǎng	RPLMN
Registered table	注册表	Zhùcè biǎo	
Register-translator	寄存择码器	Jìcún zémǎqì	
Registrar server	注册服务器	Zhùcè fúwùqì	
Registration	配准	Pèizhǔn	
Registration accuracy	配准精度	Pèizhǔn jīngdù	
Registration confirm (packet protocol)	注册确认	Zhùcè quèrèn	RCF
Registration interval	登记周期	Dēngjì zhōuqī	REGINT
Registration reject (packet protocol)	注册拒绝	Zhùcè jùjué	RRJ
Registration reject message	拒绝注册	Jùjué zhùcè	RRJ
Registration reply	注册应答	Zhùcè yìngdá	RR
Registration reply message (in IP)	注册回应消息	Zhùcè huíyìng xiāoxi	
Registration request (packet protocol)	注册请求	Zhùcè qǐngqiú	RRQ
Registration request message (in IP)	注册请求消息	Zhùcè qǐngqiú xiāoxi	
Registration task request	登记任务请求	Dēngjì rènwu qǐngqiú	
Registration, admission and status	注册，接入和状态	Zhùcè, jiērù hé zhuàngtài	RAS
Registration, admission, status	注册,认证,状态	Zhùcè, rènzhèng, zhuàngtài	RAS
Registry (in Windows)	注册表	Zhùcè biǎo	
Registry boot	注册表启动	Zhùcè biǎo qǐdòng	
Registry size limit	注册表大小限制	Zhùcè biǎo dàxiǎo xiànzhì	RSL
Regression analysis	回归分析	Huíguī fēnxī	
Regression line	回归线	Huíguī xiàn	
Regression model	回归模型	Huíguī móxíng	
Regressive equation	回归方程	Huíguī fāngchéng	
Regular data cube	常规多维数据集	Chángguī duōwéi shùjùjí	

Regular dimension	常规维度	Chángguī wéidù	
Regular expression	正则表达式	Zhèngzé biǎodá shì	
Regular pulse excitation	规则脉冲激励编码	Guīzé màichōng jīlì biānmǎ	RPE
Regular pulse excitation - long-term prediction - linear predictive coding	规则脉冲激励-长期预测-线性预测编码	Guīzé màichōng jīlì--chángqī yùcè—xiànxìng yùcè biānmǎ	RPE-LTP-LPC
Regular pulse excitation linear predictive coding	规则脉冲激励线性预测编码	Guīzé màichōng jīlì xiànxìng yùcè biānmǎ	
Regular pulse excitation linear predictive coding with long-term prediction	带有长期预测的规则脉冲激励线性预测编码	Dàiyǒu chángqī yùcède guīzé màichōng jīlì xiànxìng yùcè biānmǎ	RPE-LTP
Regular pulse excitation long-term predictive coding	规则脉冲激励长时预测编码	Guīzé màichōng jīlì--chángshí yùcè biānmǎ	REP-LPC
Regular pulse excited-long term predition-linear predictive coding	规则脉冲激励—长时预测—线性预测编码	Guīzé màichōng jīlì— chángshí yùcè—xiànxìng yùcè biānmǎ	RPE-LTP-LPC
Regular signal	规则信号	Guīzé xìnhào	
Regular signaling link	常用信令链路	Chángyòng xìnlìng liànlù	
Regulated line section	调节线路段	Tiáojié xiànlù duàn	
Regulated voltage supply	稳压电源	Wěnyā diànyuán	
Regulating stand	调试架	Tiáoshì jià	
Regulating transformer	调节变压器	Tiáojié biànyāqì	
Regulation factor	稳压系数	Wěnyā xìshù	
Regulator performance parameter	稳压器的性能参数	Wěnyāqìde xìngnéng cānshù	
Regulator reference voltage	稳压器的基准电压	Wěnyāqìde jīzhǔn diànyā	
Rehabilitation	复原	Fùyuán	
Reinforced insulation	加强绝缘	Jiāqiáng juéyuán	
Reinforcement	增强	Zēngqiáng	
Reject power down	拒绝掉电	Jùjué diàodiàn	REJPDN
Reject reason	拒绝原因	Jùjué yuányīn	
Reject(ion)	拒绝	Jùjué	REJ
Reject, rejection	阻止	Zǔzhǐ	REJ
Rejection band filter (optical)	排除频带滤光镜	Páichú píndài lǜguāngjìng	
Relational algebra	关系代数	Guānxi dàishù	
Relational database	关系数据库	Guānxì shùjùkù	RDB
Relational database	关系型数据库	Guānxi-xíng shùjùkù	
Relational database management system	关联式数据库管理系统	Guānlián-shì shùjùkù guǎnlǐ xìtǒng	RDBMS
Relational database management system	关系数据库管理系统	Guānxì shùjùkù guǎnlǐ xìtǒng	RDBMS
Relational database management system	关系型数据库管理系统	Guānxi-xíng shùjùkù guǎnlǐ xìtǒng	RDBMS
Relational expression	关系表达式	Guānxi biǎodá shì	
Relational join	关系合并	Guānxi hébìng	
Relational matching	关系匹配	Guānxi pǐpèi	
Relational model (in SQL Server)	关系模型	Guānxi móxíng	RM
Relational online analytical processing	关系联机分析处理	Guānxi liánjī fēnxī chǔlǐ	ROLAP
Relational operator	关系算子	Guānxi suànzǐ	
Relational operator (in FORTRAN)	关系操作符	Guānxi cāozuò fú	
Relationship	关系	Guānxi	
Relationship catalogue	关系目录	Guānxi mùlù	
Relationship class	关系类型	Guānxi lèixíng	
Relationship definition	关系定义	Guānxi dìngyì	
Relationship list	关系表	Guānxi biǎo	

English	Chinese	Pinyin	Abbreviation
Relationship object	关系对象	Guānxi duìxiàng	
Relationship type codes	关系类型代码	Guānxi lèixíng dàimǎ	
Relative accuracy	相对准确性	Xiāngduì zhǔnquèxìng	
Relative address	相对地址	Xiāngduì dìzhǐ	
Relative audio frequency intermodulation distortion	相对音频互调失真	Xiāngduì yīnpín hùtiáo shīzhēn	
Relative audio frequency intermodulation product level	相对音频互调产物电平	Xiāngduì yīnpín hùtiáo chǎnwù diànpíng	
Relative coordinate	相对坐标	Xiāngduì zuòbiāo	
Relative cross entropy	相对交叉熵	Xiāngduì jiāochā shāng	
Relative density	相对密度	Xiāngduì mìdù	
Relative distinguished name	相对辨别名	Xiāngduì biàn biémíng	RDN
Relative distinguished name	相对可识别名	Xiāngduì kěshíbié míng	RDN
Relative distinguished name	相对识别名	Xiāngduì shíbié míng	RDN
Relative element address designator code	相对元素位置指示编码	Xiāngduì yuánsù wèizhì zhǐshì biānmǎ	
Relative equivalent	相对当量	Xiāngduì dāngliàng	
Relative equivalent for receiving	接收相对当量	Jiēshōu xiāngduì dāngliàng	
Relative equivalent for sending	发送相对当量	Fāsòng xiāngduì dāngliáng	
Relative error	相对误差	Xiāngduì wùchā	
Relative gain (of an antenna with respect to that of a reference antenna)	相对增益	Xiāngduì zēngyì	
Relative intermodulation product level	相对互调产物电平	Xiāngduì hùtiáo chǎnwù diànpíng	
Relative ionosphere transparency meter	电离层相对透明度仪	Diànlícéng xiāngduì tòumíngdùyí	
Relative level	相对电平	Xiāngduì diànpíng	
Relative line number	相对线路号	Xiāngduì xiànlù hào	
Relative position	相对位置	Xiāngduì wèizhì	
Relative positional accuracy	相对位置精度	Xiāngduì wèizhì jīngdù	
Relative power level	相对功率电平	Xiāngduì gōnglǜ diànpíng	
Relative voltage change	相对电压变化	Xiāngduì diànyā biànhuà	
Relative-motion indicator	相对运动显示器	Xiāngduì yùndòng xiǎnshìqì	
Relaxation oscillator	张弛振荡器	Zhāngchí zhèndàngqì	
Relaxation time	松弛时间	Sōngchí shíjiān	
Relay	中继器	Zhōngjìqì	
Relay control system	继电控制系统	Jìdiàn kòngzhì xìtǒng	
Relay lens	替续透镜	Tìxù tòujìng	
Relay output	继电器输出	Jìdiànqì shūchū	
Relay set	继电器组	Jìdiànqì zǔ	
Relay station	接力站	Jiēlì zhàn	RS
Relay station	中继站	Zhōngjìzhàn	
Relay switch	继电器接线器	Jìdiànqì jiēxiànqì	
Release	释放	Shìfàng	REL
Release (of a mechanical switching device)	脱扣器	Tuōkòuqì	
Release acknowledged (SCCP message)	释放确认	Shìfàng quèrèn	RELAK
Release call	释放呼叫	Shìfàng hūjiào	RC
Release complete	线路释放完成	Xiànlù shìfàng wánchéng	RLC
Release complete (ISUP message)	释放完成	Shìfàng wánchéng	RLC
Release complete message (ISUP)	释放完成消息	Shìfàng wánchéng xiāoxi	RLC
Release confirm (SS7)	释放确认	Shìfàng quèrèn	

English	Chinese	Pinyin	Abbreviation
Release guard	释放监护	Shìfàng jiānhù	
Release guard (in CORBA)	启动保护协议	Qǐdòng bǎohù xiéyì	RG
Release guard signal	释放监护信号	Shìfàng jiānhù xìnhào	RLG
Release indication (SS7)	释放指示	Shìfàng zhǐshì	
Release message (ISUP)	释放消息	Shìfàng xiāoxi	REL(ISUP)
Release query	释放查询	Shìfàng cháxún	QoR
Release request (SS7, SCCP message)	释放请求	Shìfàng qǐngqiú	RELRE
Release time	释放时间	Shìfàng shíjiān	
Release-guard signal	释放保护信号	Shìfàng bǎohù xìnhào	
Relevant failure	关联失效	Guānlián shīxiào	
Reliability	可靠度	Kěkàodù	
Reliability (performance)	可靠性（性能）	Kěkàoxìng (xìngnéng)	
Reliability allocation	可靠性分配	Kěkàoxìng fēnpèi	
Reliability and maintainability assurance	可靠性和可维护性保证	Kěkàoxìng hé kěwéihùxìng bǎozhèng	
Reliability and maintainability audit	可靠性和可维护性审核	Kěkàoxìng hé kěwéihùxìng shěnhé	
Reliability and maintainability control	可靠性和可维护性控制	Kěkàoxìng hé kěwéihùxìng kòngzhì	
Reliability and maintainability management	可靠性和可维护性管理	Kěkàoxìng hé kěwéihùxìng guǎnlǐ	
Reliability and maintainability plan	可靠性和可维护性计划	Kěkàoxìng hé kěwéihùxìng jìhuà	
Reliability and maintainability program	可靠性和可维护性程序	Kěkàoxìng hé kěwéihùxìng chéngxù	
Reliability and maintainability surveillance	可靠性和可维护性监督	Kěkàoxìng hé kěwéihùxìng jiāndū	
Reliability block diagram	可靠性框图	Kěkàoxìng kuàngtú	
Reliability design	可靠性设计	Kěkàoxìng shèjì	
Reliability growth	可靠性增长	Kěkàoxìng zēngzhǎng	
Reliability improvement	可靠性改进	Kěkàoxìng gǎijìn	
Reliability model	可靠性模型	Kěkàoxìng móxíng	
Reliability prediction	可靠性预计	Kěkàoxìng yùjì	
Reliability test	可靠性试验	Kěkàoxìng shìyàn	
Reliability testing	可靠性测试	Kěkàoxìng cèshì	
Reliability testing	信赖度测试	Xìnlàidù cèshì	
Reliability, maintainability and safety	可靠性、维修性和安全性	Kěkàoxìng、wéixiūxìng hé ānquánxìng	RMS
Reliable data protocol	可靠数据协议	Kěkào shùjù xiéyì	RDP
Reliable multicast protocol	可靠多播协议	Kěkào duōbō xiéyì	
Reliable multicast protocol	可靠组播协议	Kěkào zǔbō xiéyì	RMP
Reliable multicast transport protocol	可靠组播传输协议	Kěkào zǔbō chuánshū xiéyì	RMTP
Reliable transfer	可靠传送	Kěkào chuánsòng	
Reliable transfer service element	可靠传送服务要素	Kěkào chuánsòng fúwù yàosù	RTSE
Reliable transfer service element	可靠的传送业务单元	Kěkàode chuánsòng yèwù dānyuán	RTSE
Reliable transfer service element protocol	可靠传输服务元素协议	Kěkào chuánshū fúwù yuánsù xiéyì	RTSE
Reliable user datagram protocol	可靠用户数据报协议	Kěkào yònghù shùjùbào xiéyì	RUDP
Relief	地势	Dìshì	
Relief map	立体地图	Lìtǐ dìtú	
Relief shading	立体阴影处理技术	Lìtǐ yīnyǐng chǔlǐ jìshù	
Relocatable	可再定位	Kězàidìngwèi	
Relocatable address	可再定位地址	Kězàidìngwèi dìzhǐ	
Re-locate	再定位	Zàidìngwèi	
Remailer	重邮器	Chóngyóuqì	

Remittance document	汇兑单据	Huìduì dānjù	
Remittance fee	汇费	Huìfèi	
Remittance service center	汇兑中心	Huìduì zhōngxīn	
Remittance service where sender informs the payee	自行通知汇款业务	Zìxíng tōngzhī huìkuǎn yèwù	
Remitting in account	财户汇款	Cáihù huìkuǎn	
Remitting in cash	现金汇款	Xiànjīn huìkuǎn	
Remote	远程	Yuǎnchéng	
Remote access	遥接	Yáojiē	
Remote access	远端接入	Yuǎnduān jiērù	
Remote access connection element	远程接入连接单元	Yuǎnchéng jiērù liánjiē dānyuán	
Remote access connection element	远端接入连接单元	Yuǎnduān jiērù liánjiē dānyuán	
Remote access dial-in user service	拨号用户远程认证服务	Bōhào yònghù yuǎnchéng rènzhèng fúwù	RADIUS
Remote access dial-in user service	远程接入/拨号用户业务	Yuǎnchéng jiērù/bōhào yònghù yèwù	RADIUS
Remote access server	远程接入服务器	Yuǎnchéng jiērù fúwùqì	RAS
Remote access server	远端访问服务器	Yuǎnduān fǎngwèn fúwùqì	RAS
Remote access service	远程访问服务	Yuǎnchéng fǎngwèn fúwù	
Remote access service	远程接入服务	Yuǎnchéng jiērù fúwù	RAS
Remote access terminal	远端接入终端	Yuǎnduān jiērù zhōngduān	RET
Remote access VPN (virtual private network)	远端接入虚拟专用网	Yuǎnduān jiērù xūnǐ zhuānyòng wǎng	RAVPN
Remote alarm	遥警	Yáojǐng	
Remote alarm indication	远端告警指示	Yuǎnduān gàojǐng zhǐshì	RAI
Remote authentication dial-in user service	远程拨号用户认证服务	Yuǎnchéng bōhào yònghù rènzhèng fúwù	Radius
Remote authentication dial-in user service	远程认证拨入用户服务	Yuǎnchéng rènzhèng bōrù yònghù fúwù	RADIUS
Remote authentication dial-in user service	远程身份验证拨入用户服务	Yuǎnchéng shēnfen yànzhèng bōrù yònghù fúwù	RADIUS
Remote authentication dial-in user service	远程用户拨号认证系统	Yuǎnchéng yònghù bōhào rènzhèng xìtǒng	RADIUS
Remote authentication dial-in user service	远端拨入用户验证服务	Yuǎnduān bōrù yònghù yànzhèng fúwù	RADIUS
Remote authentication dial-in user service	远端鉴权拨号接入用户业务	Yuǎnduān jiànquán bōhào jiērù yònghù yèwù	RADIUS
Remote authentication dial--in user service	远程认证拨号用户服务	Yuǎnchéng rènzhèng bōhào yònghù fúwù	RADIUS
Remote authentication dial-in user service (IPsec)	远端认证拨入用户业务	Yuǎnduān rènzhèng bōrù yònghù yèwù	RADIUS
Remote authorization dial in user service	远程授权拨入用户服务	Yuǎnchéng shòuquán bōrù yònghù fúwù	RADIUS
Remote bit and gain information	远端比特和增益信息	Yuǎnduān bǐtè hé zēngyì xìnxī	R-B&G
Remote boot	远程引导	Yuǎnchéng yǐndǎo	
Remote bridge	远程桥连接	Yuǎnchéng qiáo liánjiē	
Remote bridge	远端网桥	Yuǎnduān wǎngqiáo	
Remote bridging	远程桥接	Yuǎnchéng qiáojiē	
Remote call forwarding	远程呼叫转移	Yuǎnchéng hūjiào zhuǎnyí	RCF
Remote circuit U reference point	远端线路 U 参考点	Yuǎnduān xiànlù U cānkǎo diǎn	U-R
Remote circuit U reference point 2	远端线路 U 参考点 2	Yuǎnduān xiànlù U cānkǎo diǎn 2	U-R2
Remote computing service	远程计算业务	Yuǎnchéng jìsuàn yèwù	RCS
Remote concentrator	远端集线器	Yuǎnduān jíxiànqì	
Remote control line	遥控线	Yáokòng xiàn	YX
Remote control radio	遥控台	Yáokòng tái	
Remote control unit	终端控制器	Zhōngduān kòngzhìqì	RCU
Remote copy program	远端复制程序	Yuǎnduān fùzhì chéngxù	RCP
Remote copy protocol	远程拷贝协议	Yuǎnchéng kǎobèi xiéyì	RCP

English	Chinese	Pinyin	Abbreviation
Remote copy protocol	远端复制协议	Yuǎnduān fùzhì xiéyì	rcp
Remote data	远程数据	Yuǎnchéng shùjù	
Remote data object	远程数据对象	Yuǎnchéng shùjù duìxiàng	RDO
Remote database access	远端数据库访问	Yuǎnduān shùjùkù fǎngwèn	RDA
Remote database management system	远端数据库管理系统	Yuǎnduān shùjùkù guǎnlǐ xìtǒng	RDBMS
Remote defect indication	远端缺陷指示	Yuǎnduān quēxiàn zhǐshì	RDI
Remote defect indication	远端失效指示	Yuǎnduān shīxiào zhǐshì	RDI
Remote defect indication	远端限质指示	Yuǎnduān xiànzhì zhǐshì	RDI
Remote defect indicator	远端故障指示	Yuǎnduān gùzhàng zhǐshì	RDI
Remote degradation indicator	远端降质指示	Yuǎnduān jiàng zhì zhǐshì	RDI
Remote digital loopback	远程数字回送	Yuǎnchéng shùzì huísòng	RDL
Remote distribution server	远程分发服务器	Yuǎnchéng fēnfā fúwùqì	
Remote document access	远程文件访问	Yuǎnchéng wénjiàn fǎngwèn	
Remote document management	远程文件管理	Yuǎnchéng wénjiàn guǎnlǐ	
Remote electrical tilt	远程电调	Yuǎnchéng diàntiáo	RET
Remote error indication	远端差错指示	Yuǎnduān chācuò zhǐshì	REI
Remote error indication	远端误码指示	Yuǎnduān wùmǎ zhǐshì	REI
Remote error indication of lower order path	低阶通道远端误码指示	Dījiē tōngdào yuǎnduān wùmǎ zhǐshì	LP-REI
Remote failure indication	远端失效指示	Yuǎnduān shīxiào zhǐshì	RFI
Remote failure indication of lower order path	低阶通道远端失效指示	Dījiē tōngdào yuǎnduān shīxiào zhǐshì	LP-RFI
Remote fiber test system	远程光缆监测系统	Yuǎnchéng guānglǎn jiāncè xìtǒng	RFTS
Remote file browser	远程文件浏览器	Yuǎnchéng wénjiàn liúlǎnqì	RFB
Remote file transfer	远程文件传送	Yuǎnchéng wénjiàn chuánsòng	RFT
Remote frame handler	远端帧处理器	Yuǎnduān zhèng chǔlǐqì	RFH
Remote frame handler interface	远端帧处理器接口	Yuǎnduān zhèng chǔlǐqì jiēkǒu	RFHI
Remote head end	远地前端	Yuǎndì qiánduān	RHE
Remote information	远程信息	Yuǎnchéng xìnxī	RI
Remote information	远端信息	Yuǎnduān xìnxī	RI
Remote job entry	远端任务入口	Yuǎnduān rènwu rùkǒu	RJE
Remote line concentrator	远程线路集线器	Yuǎnchéng xiànlù jíxiànqì	RLC
Remote login	远端联机	Yuǎnduān liánjī	
Remote login (in Unix)	远程登录命令	Yuǎnchéng dēnglù mìnglìng	RLOGIN
Remote login identification	远程登录标识	Yuǎnchéng dēnglù biāozhì	
Remote maintenance	遥控维护	Yáokòng wéihù	
Remote method interface	远程调用接口	Yuǎnchéng diàoyòng jiēkǒu	RMI
Remote method invocation	远程方法调度	Yuǎnchéng fāngfǎ diàodù	RMI
Remote monitoring	远端监控	Yuǎnduān jiānkòng	RMON
Remote monitoring (in SNMP)	远程监控	Yuǎnchéng jiānkòng	RMON
Remote operation	远程操作	Yuǎnchéng cāozuò	
Remote operation service element	遥控操作业务单元	Yáokòng cāozuò yèwù dānyuán	ROSE
Remote operation service element	远程操作服务元素	Yuǎnchéng cāozuò fúwù yuánsù	ROSE
Remote operation service element	远端操作服务要素	Yuǎnduān cāozuò fúwù yàosù	ROSE
Remote operation service element	远端操作业务单元	Yuǎnduān cāozuò yèwù dānyuán	ROSE
Remote operations service element	远程操作业务单元	Yuǎnchéng cāozuò yèwù dānyuán	ROSE
Remote operations service element	远端操作业务元素	Yuǎnduān cāozuò yèwù yuánsù	ROSE
Remote operations stub generator	远操作规范数结构生成器	Yuǎn cāozuò guīfàn shù jiégòu shēngchéngqì	ROSY

Remote packet concentrator	远程数组集中器	Yuǎnchéng shùzǔ jízhōngqì	RPC
Remote partition	远程分区	Yuǎnchéng fēnqū	
Remote point	远端点	Yuǎnduān diǎn	RP
Remote power-feeding	远距离供电	Yuǎnjùlí gōngdiàn	
Remote procedure call	远程过程调用	Yuǎnchéng guòchéng diàoyòng	RPC
Remote procedure call	远端程序调度	Yuǎnduān chéngxù diàodù	RPC
Remote procedure call	远端程序调用	Yuǎnduān chéngxù diàoyòng	RPC
Remote procedure call protocol (IETF use)	远程过程调用协议	Yuǎnchéng guòchéng diàoyòng xiéyì	RPC
Remote redirection attack (in IPsec)	远程重定向攻击	Yuǎnchéng chóngdìngxiàng gōngjī	
Remote request	远程请求	Yuǎnchéng qǐngqiú	
Remote S reference point	远端 S 参考点	Yuǎnduān S cānkǎo diǎn	T/S
Remote sensing	遥感	Yáogǎn	
Remote server	远程服务器	Yuǎnchéng fúwùqì	
Remote shell protocol	远端外壳协议	Yuǎnduān wàiké xiéyì	rsh
Remote source-route bridging	远端信源路由网桥	Yuǎnduān xìnyuán lùyóu wǎngqiáo	RSRB
Remote spooling communication system	远程假脱机通信系统	Yuǎnchéng jiǎtuōjī tōngxìn xìtǒng	RSCS
Remote station	远程站	Yuǎnchéng zhàn	RST
Remote station data terminal	远程站数据终端	Yuǎnchéng zhàn shùjù zhōngduān	RSDT
Remote stored procedure	远程存储过程	Yuǎnchéng cúnchǔ guòchéng	
Remote subscriber access	远端用户接入	Yuǎnduān yònghù jiērù	RSA
Remote subscriber module	远端用户模块	Yuǎnduān yònghù mókuài	RSM
Remote subscriber processing	远端用户处理	Yuǎnduān yònghù chǔlǐ	RSP
Remote subscriber unit	远端用户单元	Yuǎnduān yònghù dānyuán	RSU
Remote supervision system	远程监控系统	Yuǎnchéng jiānkòng xìtǒng	
Remote switch	远程交换机	Yuǎnchéng jiāohuànjī	
Remote switch unit	远端交换模块	Yuǎnduān jiāohuàn mókuài	RSU
Remote switch unit	远端模块局	Yuǎnduān mókuài jú	RSU
Remote switching unit	远端交换单元	Yuǎnduān jiāohuàn dānyuán	RSU
Remote synchronous terminal control program	远程同步终端控制程序	Yuǎnchéng tóngbù zhōngduān kòngzhì chéngxù	RSTCP
Remote T reference point	远端 T 参考点	Yuǎnduān T cānkǎo diǎn	T/R
Remote table	远程表	Yuǎnchéng biǎo	
Remote terminal	远端机	Yuǎnduān jī	RT
Remote terminal emulator	远程终端仿真器	Yuǎnchéng zhōngduān fǎngzhēnqì	RTE
Remote terminal identification	远程终端识别	Yuǎnchéng zhōngduān shíbié	RTI
Remote transmission unit	远程传输单元	Yuǎnchéng chuánshū dānyuán	RTU
Remote unit	远端单元	Yuǎnduān dānyuán	RU
Remote video surveillance	远程视频监视	Yuǎnchéng shìpín jiānshì	RVS
Remote whois protocol	远程目录访问协议	Yuǎnchéng mùlù fǎngwèn xiéyì	
Remote workstation	远端工作站	Yuǎnduān gōngzuòzhàn	RWS
Remote, far end	远端	Yuǎnduān	
Remote-procedure call	远端过程调用	Yuǎnduān guòchéng diàoyòng	RPC
Removable storage device	移动式存储设备	Yídòng-shì cúnchǔ shèbèi	RSD
Removable storage device	装卸式器材	Zhuāngxièshì qìcái	
Render (video term)	渲染	Xuànrǎn	
Render (video term)	着色	Zhuósè	
Rendering	绘制	Huìzhì	

Rendering	涂色描绘	Túsè miáohuì	
Rendezvous point	汇集点	Huìjídiǎn	RP
Rendezvous point	汇聚点	Huìjù diǎn	RP
Rendezvous point	聚合点	Jùhé diǎn	RP
Rendezvous radar	交会雷达	Jiāohuì léidá	RVR
Rendezvous server	聚集服务器	Jùjí fúwùqì	
Renormalization	重新规范化	Chóngxīn guīfànhuà	
Re-paginate (WP command)	重新分页	Chóngxīn fēnyè	
Repair	修理	Xiūlǐ	
Repair center	修理中心	Xiūlǐ zhōngxīn	RC
Repair coverage	修复范围	Xiūfù fànwéi	
Repair time	修理时间	Xiūlǐ shíjiān	
Repaired item	修理产品(装备)	Xiūlǐ chǎnpǐn (zhuāngbèi)	
Repeat indicator	重复指示	Chóngfù zhǐshì	
Repeat statement	重复语句	Chóngfù yǔjù	
Repeat test	重发测试	Chóngfā cèshì	
Repeat timeout	重发超时	Chóngfā chāoshí	RTO
Repeatability	重复性	Chóngfù-xìng	
Repeatability	可重复性	Kěchóngfù-xìng	
Repeated clear forward signal	重复拆线信号	Chóngfù chāixiàn xìnhào	
Repeated signal	重复信号	Chóngfù xìnhào	
Repeater	中继器	Zhōngjìqì	
Repeater	转发台	Zhuǎnfā tái	
Repeater	转发器	Zhuǎnfāqì	
Repeater jamming	回答式干扰	Huídá-shì gānrǎo	
Repeater section	中继段	Zhōngjì duàn	
Repeater station	直放站	Zhífàngzhàn	
Repeater station	中继站	Zhōngjìzhàn	Rep
Repeating attack rejection	转发启动抗扰性	Zhuǎnfā qǐdòng kàngrǎoxìng	
Repeating attack sensitivity	转发启动灵敏度	Zhuǎnfā qǐdòng língmǐndù	
Repeating distortion	转发音频失真	Zhuǎnfā yīnpín shīzhēn	
Repeating field groups	重复字段组	Chóngfù zìduàn zǔ	
Repeating fields	重复字段	Chóngfù zìduàn	
Repeating modulation sensitivity	转发调制灵敏度	Zhuǎnfā tiáozhì língmǐndù	
Repertoire of signals	信号清单	Xìnhào qīngdān	
Repetition code	重复码	Chóngfù mǎ	
Repetition cycle	重发周期	Chóngfā zhōuqī	
Repetitive strain injury	重复动作损伤	Chóngfù dòngzuò sǔnshāng	RSI
Repetitively pulsed Q-switching	重复脉冲 Q 开关	Chóngfù màichōng Q kāiguān	
Replace	取代	Qǔdài	
Replace (WP command)	替换	Tihuan	
Replacement selection sort	置换选择排序	Zhìhuàn xuǎnzé páixù	
Replay attack (IPsec)	重放攻击	Chóngfàng gōngjī	
Replicated data	已复制数据	Yǐfùzhì shùjù	
Replication	复制	Fùzhì	
Replication conflict viewer	复制冲突查看器	Fùzhì chōngtū chákàn qì	

Replication conflict viewer (in SQL Server)	复制冲突观察器	Fùzhì chōngtū guāncháqì	
Replication monitor	复制监视器	Fùzhì jiānshìqì	
Replication scripting	编写复制脚本	Biānxiě fùzhì jiǎoběn	
Replication topology	复制拓扑	Fùzhì tuòpū	
Report	报告	Bàogào	
Reporting group	报表栏	Bàobiǎo lán	
Reporting office	报室	Bào shì	BF
Repository	知识库	Zhīshikù	
Repository engine	知识库引擎	Zhīshikù yǐnqíng	
Repository object	知识库对象	Zhīshikù duìxiàng	
Repository structured query language (SQL) schema	知识库结构化查询语言架构	Zhīshikù jiégòuhuà cháxún yǔyán jiàgòu	
Repository type information model	知识库类型信息模型	Zhīshikù lèixíng xìnxī móxíng	RTIM
Represent	表述	Biǎoshù	
Represent	表现	Biǎoxiàn	
Represent (verb)	表示	Biǎoshì	
Representation	对象描述	Duìxiàng miáoshù	
Representative point	代表点	Dàibiǎo diǎn	
Reproducibility	再现性	Zàixiànxìng	
Reproducible failure	可再现失效	Kězàixiàn shīxiào	
Reproduction	复制	Fùzhì	
Reproduction ratio	复制比	Fùzhì bǐ	
Republish	再次发布	Zàicì fābù	
Republisher	再次发布者	Zàicì fābùzhě	
Repudiation (IPsec)	抵赖性	Dǐlàixìng	
Repudiation (IPsec)	否认	Fǒurèn	
Request	请求	Qǐngqiú	REQ, RQ
Request (primitive)	请求（原语）	Qǐngqiú (yuányǔ)	
Request acess unit	请求接入单元	Qǐngqiú jiērù dānyuán	RAU
Request agent	请求代理	Qǐngqiú dàilǐ	RA
Request cycle	响应周期	Xiǎngyìng zhōuqī	
Request cycle	请求周期	Qǐngqiú zhōuqī	
Request disconnect	请求断开	Qǐngqiú duànkāi	RD
Request for comment	征求意见	Zhēngqiú yìjiàn	RFC
Request for comment	请求评论文档	Qǐngqiú pínglùn wéndàng	RFC
Request for comment	请求评议	Qǐngqiú píngyì	RFC
Request for comments	注释请求	Zhùshì qǐngqiú	RFC
Request for connection	要求连接	Yāoqiú liánjiē	RFC
Request for initialization	初始化请求	Chūshǐhuà qǐngqiú	RQI
Request for proposal	建议请求	Jiànyì qǐngqiú	RFP
Request frame	请求帧	Qǐngqiú zhèng	REQ
Request in process	请求处理中	Qǐngqiú chǔlǐ zhōng	RIP
Request in progress	进展请求	Jìnzhǎn qǐngqiú	RIP
Request interrupt	请求中断	Qǐngqiú zhōngduàn	RQI
Request management (CMM)	需求管理	Xūqiú guǎnlǐ	RM
Request packet	请求包	Qǐngqiú bāo	RP
Request reference	请求参考	Qǐngqiú cānkǎo	

Request report BCSM event	请求报告 BCSM 事件	Qǐngqiú bàogào BCSM shìjiàn	RRBE
Request sequence number	请求序列编号	Qǐngqiú xùliè biānhào	
Request to power down	掉电请求	Diàodiàn qǐngqiú	REQPDN
Request to send	需求发送	Xūqiú fāsòng	RTS
Request to send	请求发送	Qǐngqiú fāsòng	RTS
Request to send/ clear to send	请求发送/允许发送协议	Qǐngqiú fāsòng/yǔnxǔ fāsòng xiéyì	RTS/CTS
Required callback	必需回叫	Bìxū huíjiào	
Required function	所需功能	Suǒxū gōngnéng	
Required time	有要求时间	Yǒu yāoqiú shíjiān	
Requirements engineering	需求工程	Xūqiú gōngchéng	
Re-radiation	再辐射	Zàifúshè	
Reringing	再振铃	Zàizhènlíng	
Re-routing	路由再选定	Lùyóu zàixuǎndìng	
Rerouting wavelength	回路由波长	Huílùyóu bōcháng	
Re-routing wavelength	迂回路由波长	Yūhuí lùyóu bōcháng	
Resampling	重采样	Chóng cǎiyàng	
Rescue	救助	Jiùzhù	
Rescue handoff	挽救切换	Wǎnjiù qiēhuàn	
Research and Development Center for Radio System (Japan)	无线系统研究开发中心	Wúxiàn xìtǒng yánjiū kāifā zhōngxīn	RCR
Research and Development Program on Advanced communications technologies for Europe	欧洲选进通信技术研究和发展规划	Oūzhōu xuǎnjìn tōngxìn jìshù yánjiū hé fāzhǎn guīhuà	RACE
Research in Advanced communication for Europe	欧洲先进通信研究	Oūzhōu xiānjìn tōngxìn yánjiū	RACE
Research Institute of Telecommunications Transmission (MII)	电信传输研究所	Diànxìn chuánshū yánjiūsuǒ	
Research on Advanced Communications in Europe	欧洲高级通信研究计划	Ōuzhōu gāojí tōngxìn yánjiū jìhuà	RACE
Réseaux Associés pour la Recherche Européenne	欧洲大学和研究中心协会	Oūzhōu dàxué hé yánjiū zhōngxīn xiéhuì	RARE
Réseaux IP Européennes	欧洲 IP 网络	Oūzhōu IP wǎngluò	RIPE
Reserve for future use	保留未用	Bǎoliú wèi yòng	RFU
Reserve signaling link	备用信令链路	Bèiyòng xìnlìng liànlù	
Reserved	预定	Yùdìng	RES
Reserved circuit service	预订电路业务	Yùdìng diànlù yèwù	
Reserved circuit telecommunication service	预约电路电信业务	Yùyuē diànlù diànxìn yèwù	
Reserved for future use	留作将来使用	Liúzuò jiānglái shǐyòng	RFU
Reserved word	保留字	Bǎoliúzì	
Reserved word	预定字	Yùdìng zì	
Reserved word	预约字	Yùyuē zì	
Reset	复位	Fùwèi	
Reset	置闲	Zhìxián	
Reset	设置	Shèzhì	RST
Reset button/key	重新启动键	Chóngxīn qǐdòng jiàn	
Reset circuit signal	电路复原信号	Diànlù fùyuán xìnhào	RSC
Reset procedure	重置规程	Chóngzhì guīchéng	
Reset procedure	复位程序	Fùwèi chéngxù	
Reset signal	复位信号	Fùwèi xìnhào	RST
Resettability	重置性	Chóngzhìxìng	
Resetting	重置	Chóngzhì	

Reshaping	重整形	Chóngzhěngxíng	
Resident program area	常驻程序区域	Chángzhù chéngxù qūyù	
Resident task	常驻任务	Chángzhù rènwu	
Residential broadband network	社区宽带网络	Shèqū kuāndài wǎngluò	RBB
Residential gateway	驻地网关	Zhùdì wǎngguān	RG
Residential gateway	住户网关	Zhùhù wǎngguān	RGW
Residential gateway	社区网关	Shèqū wǎngguān	RG
Residential program	记忆驻留程序	Jìyì zhùliú chéngxù	
Residual amplitude modulation	剩余调幅	Shèngyú tiáofú	
Residual attenuation	残余衰减	Cányú shuāijiǎn	
Residual attenuation	残余衰减量	Cányú shuāijiǎn liàng	
Residual bit error rate	残余比特差错率	Cányú bǐtè chācuò lǜ	RBER
Residual bit error rate	残余误码率	Cányú wùmǎ lǜ	RBER
Residual current	残余电流	Cányú diànliú	
Residual current circuit-breaker	漏电断路器	Lòudiàn duànlùqì	
Residual error rate	残留差错率	Cánliú chācuò lǜ	
Residual error rate	差错漏检率	Chācuò lòujiǎnlǜ	
Residual error rate	乘除差错率	Chéngchú chācuò lǜ	
Residual error-rate	剩余差错率	Shèngyú chācuòlǜ	
Residual excitation linear prediction coding	残差激励线性预测编码	Cánchā jīlì xiànxìng yùcè biānmǎ	RELP
Residual excitation linear predictive coding	残余激励线性预测编码	Cányú jīlì xiànxìng yùcè biānmǎ	RELP
Residual frame error rate	残留错帧率	Cánliú cuòzhèng lǜ	RFER
Residual frame error rate	残余错帧率	Cányú cuòzhèng lǜ	RFER
Residual frequency deviation	剩余频偏	Shèngyú pínpiān	
Residual frequency modulation	剩余调频	Shèngyú tiáopín	
Residual intelligibility	剩余可懂度	Shèngyú kědǒngdù	
Residual margin amplitude modulation	残余边带振幅调制	Cányú biāndài zhènfú tiáozhì	
Residual margin modulation	残余边带调制	Cányú biāndài tiáozhì	
Residual speech domain	残差语音域	Cánchā yǔyīn yù	
Residual strength	残余强度	Cányú qiángdù	
Residual time stamp	剩余时间标志法	Shèngyú shíjiān biāozhì fǎ	RTS
Resilient chaff	弹性干扰物	Tánxìng gānrǎowù	
Resilient packet ring	弹性分组环	Tánxìng fēnzǔ huán	RPR
Resistance factor	抗力系数	Kànglì xìshù	
Resistance temperature detector	电阻温度传感器	Diànzǔ wēndù chuángǎnqì	RTD
Resistance thermometer	电阻温度计	Diànzǔ wēndùjì	
Resistance, resistor	电阻	Diànzǔ	
Resistibility	耐受性	Nàishòuxìng	
Resistive (adj.)	电阻性	Diànzǔxìng	
Resistive attenuator	电阻式衰减器	Diànzǔ-shì shuāijiǎnqì	
Resistive distributor brush	电阻性点火分配器电刷	Diànzǔxìng diǎnhuǒ fēnpèiqì diànshuā	
Resistor transistor logic circuit	电阻晶体管逻辑电路	Diànzǔ jīngtǐguǎn luójì diànlù	RTL
Resolution	分辨力	Fēnbiànlì	
Resolution	分辨力	Fēnbiànlì	
Resolution	分辨率	Fēnbiànlǜ	
Resolution	解析过程	Jiěxī guòchéng	

English	Chinese	Pinyin	Abbr.
Resolution	解析度	Jiěxīdù	
Resolution bandwidth	分辨带宽	Fēnbiàn dàikuān	RWB
Resolution bandwidth	分辨率带宽	Fēnbiànlǜ dàikuān	RBW
Resolution, definition (video)	清晰度	Qīngxīdù	
Resolve	解析	Jiěxī	
Resolve	决议	Juéyì	
Resonance frequency (in a cavity resonator)	谐振频率	Xiézhèn pínlǜ	
Resonance isolator	谐振式隔离器	Xiézhèn-shì gélíqì	
Resonance mode (in a cavity resonator)	谐振模	Xiézhèn mó	
Resonant impedance	谐振阻抗	Xiézhèn zǔkàng	
Resonant iris	谐振膜片	Xiézhèn mópiàn	
Resonant isolator	共振式隔离器	Gòngzhèn-shì gélíqì	
Resonant mode filter	谐振滤模器	Xiézhèn lǜmóqì	
Resonant window	谐振窗	Xiézhèn chuāng	
Resource availability confirm	可用资源确认	Kěyòng zīyuán quèrèn	RAC
Resource availability indication	可用资源指示	Kěyòng zīyuán zhǐshì	RAI
Resource availability indication	资源可用性指示	Zīyuán kěyòngxìng zhǐshì	RAI
Resource configuration fragment	资源组成段	Zīyuán zǔchéng duàn	RCF
Resource constraint	资源限制	Zīyuán xiànzhì	
Resource contention	资源冲突	Zīyuán chōngtū	
Resource control object	资源控制对象	Zīyuán kòngzhì duìxiàng	RCO
Resource description format	资源描述方式	Zīyuán miáoshù fāngshì	RDF
Resource description framework	资源描述框架	Zīyuán miáoshù kuàngjià	RDF
Resource document	资源文件	Zīyuán wénjiàn	
Resource domain	资源域	Zīyuán yù	
Resource fork	资源派生	Zīyuán pàishēng	
Resource management	资源管理	Zīyuán guǎnlǐ	RM
Resource management and operations	资源管理和运营	Zīyuán guǎnlǐ hé yùnyíng	
Resource management building block	资源管理构件	Zīyuán guǎnlǐ gòujiàn	RMBB
Resource management cell	资源管理信元	Zīyuán guǎnlǐ xìnyuán	
Resource manager	资源管理器	Zīyuán guǎnlǐqì	RM
Resource monitor	资源监视器	Zīyuán jiānshìqì	
Resource record	资源记录	Zīyuán jìlù	RR
Resource request table	资源请求表	Zīyuán qǐngqiú biǎo	RRT
Resource reserVation protocol	资源保留协议	Zīyuán bǎoliú xiéyì	RRVP
Resource reservation protocol	资源预留协议	Zīyuán yùliú xiéyì	RSVP
Resource reservation protocol-traffic engineering (IETF usage)	基于流量工程扩展的资源预留协议	Jīyú liúliàng gōngchéng kuòzhǎnde zīyuán yùliú xiéyì	RSVP-TE
Resource unit	资源单位	Zīyuán dānwèi	RU
Resources	资源	Zīyuán	
Resources available confirmation	资源可用性确认	Zīyuán kěyòngxìng quèrèn	RAC
Response (primitive)	响应(原语)	Xiǎngyìng (yuányǔ)	
Response analysis	响应分析	Xiǎngyìng fēnxī	
Response analysis for call evaluation	通话鉴定的响应分析	Tōnghuà jiàndìngde xiǎngyìng fēnxī	RACE
Response center	响应中心	Xiǎngyìng zhōngxīn	
Response identifier	响应标识符	Xiǎngyìng biāozhìfú	RI

Response modification factor	响应修正系数	Xiǎngyìng xiūzhèng xìshù	
Response request	响应请求	Xiǎngyìng qǐngqiú	
Response spectrum	响应频谱	Xiǎngyìng pínpǔ	
Response time approximation	响应时间近似变换	Xiǎngyìng shíjiān jìnsì biànhuàn	RTA
Response unit (in IDS)	响应单元	Xiǎngyìng dānyuán	
Responsiveness	应答性	Yìngdáxìng	
Restart procedure	再起动规程	Zàiqǐdòng guīchéng	
Restatement	复述	Fùshù	
Restitution sequence of conditions	状态恢复序列	Zhuàngtài huīfù xùliè	
Restoration algorithm	恢复算法	Huīfù suànfǎ	
Restoration control center	恢复控制中心	Huīfù kòngzhì zhōngxīn	
Restoration control point	恢复控制点	Huīfù kòngzhì diǎn	RCP
Restoration control point	恢复控制点	Huīfù kòngzhì diǎn	RCP
Restoration network	恢复网络	Huīfù wǎngluò	
Restoration time	恢复时间	Huīfù shíjiān	Tr
Restoration transfer time	恢复转移时间	Huīfù zhuǎnyí shíjiān	T4
Restoration unit	恢复单位	Huīfù dānwèi	
Restoration; recovery	恢复	Huīfù	
Restorationy procedure	恢复规程	Huīfù guīchéng	
Restore	修复	Xiūfù	
Restore confirm	复原证实	Fùyuán zhèngshí	RESCO
Restore log file	恢复日志文件	Huīfù rìzhì wénjiàn	
Restore request	复原请求	Fùyuán qǐngqiú	RESRE
Restore threshold report	门限复位报告	Ménxiàn fùwèi bàogào	RTR
Restore, restoration, recover	恢复	Huīfù	
Restoring force characteristics	恢复力特征	Huīfù lì tèzhēng	
Restricted area	限制区	Xiànzhì qū	
Restricted digital information	禁止的数字信息	Jìnzhǐde shùzì xìnxī	RDI
Restricted digital information	限制的数字信息	Xiànzhìde shùzì xìnxī	RDI
Restricted service	有限服务	Yǒuxiàn fúwù	
Restricted-radiation frequency (for ISM apparatus)	有限辐射频率	Yǒuxiàn fúshè pínlǜ	
Restriction level (in SS7)	限制等级	Xiànzhì děngjí	RL
Restriction sub-level (in SS7)	限制子等级	Xiànzhì ziděngjí	RSL
Result set (for database)	结果集	Jiéguǒ jí	
Resume	重新开始	Chóngxīn kāishǐ	
Resume	恢复	Huīfù	RES
Resume acknowledge	重新开始证实	Chóngxīn kāishǐ zhèngshí	
Resume acknowledge	恢复认可	Huīfù rènkě	
Resume message (ISUP)	恢复消息	Huīfù xiāoxi	RES
Resume reject	重新开始拒绝	Chóngxīn kāishǐ jùjué	
Resume reject	恢复拒绝	Huīfù jùjué	
Resume request (ISUP message)	呼叫恢复请求	Hūjiào huīfù qǐngqiú	RES
Retained mode	保留模式	Bǎoliú móshì	
Reticle inspection manager (semiconductor mfg)	光掩膜检测管理	Guāngyǎnmó jiǎncè guǎnlǐ	RIM
Retimer	重定时器	Chóngdìngshíqì	
Retiming	重定时	Chóngdìngshí	

English	Chinese	Pinyin	Abbreviation
Retiming	再定时	Zàidìngshí	
Retirement	指令引退	Zhǐlìng yǐntuì	
Retirement phase (of product life cycle)	退役阶段	Tuìyì jiēduàn	
Retrieval	检索	Jiǎnsuǒ	
Retrieval (in common channel signaling)	恢复	Huīfù	
Retrieval service	检索(型)业务	Jiǎnsuǒ (xíng) yèwù	
Retrieval service	检索业务	Jiǎnsuǒ yèwù	
Retrieval system	检索系统	Jiǎnsuǒ xìtǒng	
Retrieve	复原	Fùyuán	
Retrieve (verb)	转收	Zhuǎnshōu	
Retrieve data	检索数据	Jiǎnsuǒ shùjù	
Retrograde orbit (of a satellite)	逆行轨道	Nìxíng guǐdào	
Retry interval	重试间隔	Chóngshì jiàngé	
Return	返回	Fǎnhuí	
Return address	返回地址	Fǎnhuí dìzhǐ	
Return code	返回码	Fǎnhuí mǎ	
Return loss	反射衰减	Fǎnshè shuāijiǎn	RL
Return loss	反射损耗	Fǎnshè sǔnhào	RL
Return loss	回路损耗	Huílù sǔnhào	RL
Return loss	回输损耗	Huíshū sǔnhào	RL
Return loss	回损	Huísǔn	
Return loss (radio term)	回波损耗	Huíbō sǔnhào	RL
Return of remittance	退汇	Tuìhuì	
Return on investment	投资回报	Tóuzī huíbào	ROI
Return parameters	返回参数	Fǎnhuí cānshù	
Return path	返回路径	Fǎnhuí lùjìng	
Return payments of newspapers and periodicals	报刊退款	Bàokān tuìkuǎn	
Return period	再现期间	Zàixiàn qījiān	
Return result of prompt and collect user information	提示并收集用户信息的返回结果	Tíshì bìng shōují yònghù xìnxīde fǎnhuí jiéguǒ	RR-P&C
Return to N automatic repeat request	回到 N 自动重发请求	Huídào N zìdòng chóngfā qǐngqiú	
Return to zero	归零制	Guīlíng zhì	RZ
Return to zero coding	归零码	Guīlíng mǎ	
Return type	返回类型	Fǎnhuí lèixíng	
Return value	返回值	Fǎnhuí zhí	
Return voice channel	反响话音信道	Fǎnxiǎng huàyīn xìndào	RVC
Reusability	可重用性	Kěchóngyòng-xìng	
Reusable bookmark	可再次使用的书签	Kězàicì shǐyòngde shūqiān	
Reusable program	可再用程序	Kězàiyòng chéngxù	
Reusable routine	可再用例行程序	Kězàiyòng lìxíng chéngxù	
Revenue model	收入模式	Shōurù móshì	
Reverberation radius	混响半径	Hùnxiǎng bànjìng	RR
Reverberation time	混响时间	Hùnxiǎng shíjiān	RT
Reverberator	混响器	Hùnxiǎngqì	
Reversal loss	反向损耗	Fǎnxiàng sǔnhào	
Reverse address resolution protocol	反向地址解析协议	Fǎnxiàng dìzhǐ jiěxī xiéyì	RARP

Reverse address resolution protocol	反向地址判别协议	Fǎnxiàng dìzhǐ pànbié xiéyì	RARP
Reverse address resolution protocol	逆地址解析协议	Nì dìzhǐ jiěxī xiéyì	RARP
Reverse address resolution protocol	逆向地址解析协议	Nìxiàng dìzhǐ jiěxī xiéyì	RARP
Reverse bend, reverse bending	反复弯曲	Fǎnfù wānqū	
Reverse channel	反向信道	Fǎnxiàng xìndào	
Reverse charging	被叫计费	Bèijiào jìfèi	REV
Reverse charging	对方计费	Duìfāng jìfèi	REV
Reverse code division multiple access channel	反向码分多址信道	Fǎnxiàng mǎfēn duōzhǐ xìndào	
Reverse conducting thyristor	逆导晶闸管	Nìdǎo jīngzháguǎn	RCT
Reverse control channel	反向控制信道	Fǎnxiàng kòngzhì xìndào	RECC
Reverse direction (in a circulator or isolator)	反向	fǎnxiàng	
Reverse dispersion fiber	反色散光纤	Fǎnsèsàn guāngxiān	
Reverse engineering	反向工程	Fǎnxiàng gōngchéng	
Reverse engineering	逆向工程	Nìxiàng gōngchéng	
Reverse error control	反响误差控制	Fǎnxiǎng wùchā kòngzhì	REC
Reverse isolation	反向隔离	Fǎnxiàng gélí	
Reverse link	反向链路	Fǎnxiàng liànlù	
Reverse link power control	反向链路功率控制	Fǎnxiàng liànlù gōnglǜ kòngzhì	
Reverse lookup	反向搜索	Fǎnxiàng sōusuǒ	
Reverse loss (in a circulator or isolator)	反向损耗	fǎnxiàng sǔnhào	
Reverse oscillation lay (FOC)	反向振荡节距	Fǎnxiàng zhèndàng jiéjù	ROL
Reverse path forwarding	反向路径转发	Fǎnxiàng lùjìng zhuǎnfā	RPF
Reverse path forwarding	反向路径转换	Fǎnxiàng lùjìng zhuǎnhuàn	RPF
Reverse path forwarding	反转路径转发	Fǎnzhuǎn lùjìng zhuǎnfā	RPF
Reverse path forwarding	逆向路径转发	Nìxiàng lùjìng zhuǎnfā	RPF
Reverse path multicasting	反向路径组播	Fǎnxiàng lùjìng zǔbō	RPM
Reverse photocurrent	反向光电	Fǎnxiàng guāngdiàn	
Reverse post-order	逆后序	Nì hòuxù	
Reverse proxy	逆向代理	Nìxiàng dàilǐ	
Reverse signal	反极信号	Fǎnjí xìnhào	REV
Reverse voice channel	反向话音信道	Fǎnxiàng huàyīn xìndào	RVC
Reversible antenna	可逆天线	Kěnì tiānxiàn	
Revertive protection operation	回复保护运行	Huífù bǎohù yùnxíng	
Revetment	护岸	Hù'àn	
Revoke	撤销	Chèxiāo	
Revoke	废除	Fèichú	
Rework (in SMT)	返工	Fǎngōng	
Rewritable optical disk	可重写光盘	Kěchóngxiě guāngpán	
Reynolds number	雷诺数	Léi-nuò shù	
RF protection ratio	RF 保护比	RF bǎohù bǐ	
RF signal-to-interference ratio	RF 信号干扰比	RF xìnhào gānrǎo bǐ	
Rheology (in SMT)	流变学	Liúbiànxué	
Rhombic antenna	菱形天线	Língxíng tiānxiàn	
Ribbon	墨带	Mòdài	
Ribbon cable	扁萍带缆	Biǎnpíng dàilǎn	
Ribbon fiber cable	带状光缆	Dàizhuàng guānglǎn	

Ribbon fiber optic cable	光纤带光缆	Guāngxiān dài guānglǎn	
Richardson number	理查森数	Lǐ-chá-sēn shù	
Ricoh (Japanese company)	理光	Lǐ-guāng	
Ridge waveguide	脊波导	Jǐ bōdǎo	RWG
Ridge waveguide	脊形波导	Jǐxíng bōdǎo	
Ridged horn antenna	脊形喇叭天线	Jǐxíng lǎba tiānxiàn	
Right click (computer mouse command)	右击	Yòujī	
Right hand circular polarized (wave, signal)	右旋圆极化(波,信号)	Yòuxuán yuán jíhuà (bō, xìnhào)	RHCP
Right hand polarization	右旋极化	Yòuxuán jíhuà	RHP
Right outer join (in SQL Server)	右外部连接	Yòu wàibù liánjiē	
Right outer join (for database)	右向外联接	Yòu xiàngwài liánjiē	
Right value (rvalue)	右值	Yòuzhí	
Right-angle prism	直角棱镜	Zhíjiǎo léngjìng	
Right-hand circular polarization	右旋圆极化	Yòuxuán yuán jíhuà	RCP
Right-hand edge	右边缘	Yòu bianyuán	
Right-hand polarization	右旋转化	Yòuxuán zhuǎnhuà	
Right-hand polarized wave	右旋极化波	Yòuxuán jíhuà bō	
Right-handed	右手习惯	Yòushǒu xíguàn	
Right-of-way	通行权	Tōngxíng quán	
Right-sizing	正移	Zhèngyí	
Rigid coaxial line	硬同轴线	Yìng tóngzhóu xiàn	
Rigid feedback	硬反馈	Yìng fǎnkuì	
Rigid frame	刚性架构	Gāngxìng jiàgòu	
Rigidity	硬度率	Yìngdù lǜ	
Ring array	环形阵	Huánxíng zhèn	
Ring array	圆形阵	Yuánxíng zhèn	
Ring counter	环形计数器	Huánxíng jìshùqì	
Ring error monitor	环差错监视器	Huán chācuò jiānshìqì	REM
Ring generator back panel	震铃产生器后面板	Zhènlíng chǎnshēngqì hòumianbǎn	RGBP
Ring group	环组	Huánzǔ	
Ring group	铃群组	Líng qún zǔ	RG
Ring in, ring out	环入/环出	Huán rù/ huán chū	RI/RO
Ring interconnection (SDH)	环的互连	Huánde hùlián	
Ring interworking	环的互通	Huánde hùtōng	
Ring laser gyroscope	圆环激光陀螺仪	Yuánhuán jīguāng tuóluóyí	
Ring latency	环等待时间	Huán děngdài shíjiān	
Ring latency	环路延迟	Huánlù yánchí	
Ring mixer	环形混频器	Huánxíng hùnpínqì	
Ring monitor	环监视器	Huán jiānshìqì	
Ring monitor	环路监视器	Huánlù jiānshìqì	
Ring network	环网	Huán wǎng	
Ring oscillator	振铃振荡器	Zhènlíng zhèndàngqì	RO
Ring parameter server	环参数服务器	Huán cānshù fúwùqì	RPS
Ring protection	环保护	Huán bǎohù	
Ring signal generate unit	震铃信号产生单元	Zhènlíng xìnhào chǎnshēng dānyuán	RSGU
Ring topology	环形拓扑	Huánxíng tuòpū	

Ring voltage	振铃电压	Zhènlíng diànyā	
Ring wave	环形波	Huánxíng bō	
Ring, ringing, alerting	振铃	Zhènlíng	
Ring-back	回叫	Huíjiào	
Ring-back	回铃	Huílíng	
Ring-back signal	回叫信号	Huíjiào xìnhào	
Ring-back signal	回铃信号	Huílíng xìnhào	
Ring-back tone	回铃音	Huílíng yīn	
Ringing current	铃流	Líng liú	
Ringing current supply (the R in BORSCHT)	振铃电流	Zhènlíng diànliú	
Ringing tone	振铃音	Zhènlíng yīn	
Ring-switch	环形开关	Huánxíng kāiguān	
Ripple	纹波	Wénbō	
Rise rate	上升率	Shàngshēng lǜ	
Rise time	上升时向	Shàngshēng shí xiàng	
Rise time (of a pulse)	上升时间	Shàngshēng shíjiān	
Riser (FOC)	竖井	Shùjǐng	
Riser backbone sub-system	垂直子系统	Chuízhí zi xìtǒng	RBS
Riser backbone sub-system	主干子系统	Zhǔgàn zixìtǒng	RBS
Rise-time broadening	上升时间展宽	Shàngshēng shíjiān zhǎnkuān	
Risk	风险	Fēngxiǎn	
Risk analysis	风险分析	Fēngxiǎn fēnxī	
Risk assessment	风险评价	Fēngxiǎn píngjià	
Risk information criterion	风险信息准则	Fēngxiǎn xìnxī zhǔnzé	
Risk management	风险管理	Fēngxiǎn guǎnlǐ	
Riverstone Networks Inc. (US company)	瑞通公司	Ruì-tōng gōngsī	
Rivest-Shamir-Adelman coding	通用关键子密码方法	Tōngyòng guānjiàn zi mìmǎ fāngfǎ	RSA
Roadside improvement project	路边改良项目	Lùbiān gǎiliáng xiàngmù	
Roamer (cellular telephony)	漫游者	Mànyóuzhě	
Roaming (cellular telephony)	漫游	Mànyóu	
Roaming not allowed	不允许漫游	Bùyǔnxǔ mànyóu	
Roaming signaling gateway	漫游信令网关	Mànyóu xìnlìng wǎngguān	R-SGW
Roaming subscriber	漫游用户	Mànyóu yònghù	
Roaming user profile	漫游用户配置文件	Mànyóu yònghù pèizhì wénjiàn	
Robotic vision	机器人视觉	Jīqìrén shìjué	
Robust	健壮	Jiànzhuàng	
Robust estimation	韧性估计	Rènxìng gūjì	
Robust watermark	鲁棒型水印	Lǔbàngxíng shuǐyìn	
Robustness	健壮性	Jiànzhuàngxìng	
Robustness	鲁棒性	Lǔbàngxìng	
Rockwell hardness test	洛氏硬度试验	Luò-shì yìngdù shìyàn	
Rod line	棒状线	Bàngzhuàng xiàn	
Rod making (FOC mfg)	制棒	Zhì bàng	
Rogue agent	伪代理	Wěidàilǐ	
Role	角色	Juésè	
Role hierarchy	角色层次	Juésè céngcì	

Role playing game (computer game)	角色扮演游戏	Juésè bànyǎn yóuxì	RPG
Role set	角色集	Juésè jí	
Role-based access control	基于角色访问控制	Jīyú juésè fǎngwèn kòngzhì	RBAC
Role-based workflow model	基于角色工作流模型	Jīyú juésè gōngzuòliú móxíng	
Role-task assignment	角色任务指派	Juésè rènwu zhǐpài	
Roll back	回滚	Huígǔn	
Roll forward (for database)	前滚	Qiángǔn	
Roll in	转入	Zhuǎnrù	
Roll out	转出	Zhuǎnchū	
Rollback current table	回滚本表	Huígǔn běnbiǎo	
Rollback segment (in ORACLE)	回滚段	Huígǔn duàn	
Roll-call polling	论叫轮询	Lùnjiào lúnxún	
Roll-off	滚降	Gǔnjiàng	
Roll-off	频率响应下降	Pínlǜ xiǎngyìng xiàjiàng	
Roll-off (short for 频率响应下降)	频响	Pínxiǎng	
Room coefficient	房间系数	Fángjiān xìshù	RC
Root bridge	根网桥	Gēn wǎngqiáo	
Root certificate	根证书	Gēn zhèngshū	
Root directory	根目录	Gēn mùlù	
Root form	原形	Yuánxíng	
Root mean square	均方根	Jūn fānggēn	RMS
Root mean square (rms) value	均方根值	Jūn fānggēn zhí	
Root mean square (rms)-ripple factor	均方根-波纹系数	Jūn fānggēn-bōwén xìshù	
Root mean square detector	均方根值检波器	Jūn fānggēn zhí jiǎnbōqì	RMS
Root mean square error	均方根误差	Jūn fānggēn wùchā	RMSE
Root mean square ripple factor	纹波均方根系数	Wénbō jūnfānggēn xìshù	
Root raised cosine	升余弦	Shēng yúxián	
Root segment	常驻段	Chángzhù duàn	
Root segment	根基段	Gēnjī duàn	
Root user, super user	超级用户	Chāojí yònghù	
Root-mean square detector	均方根检波器	Jūn fānggēn jiǎnbōqì	
Root-sum square	平方和的根	Píngfānghéde gēn	RSS
Rossby wave	罗斯比波	Luó-sī-bǐ bō	
Rotary acceleration feed forward (Western Digital Corp. hard drive technology)	旋转加速伺服系统	Xuánzhuǎn jiāsù sìfú xìtǒng	RAFF
Rotary deflection coil	旋转式偏转线圈	Xuánzhuǎn-shì piānzhuǎn xiànquān	
Rotary joint	旋转关节	Xuánzhuǎn guānjié	
Rotary phase changer	旋转式相位变换器	Xuánzhuǎnshì xiàngwèi biànhuànqì	
Rotary selector	旋转式选择器	Xuánzhuǎnshì xuǎnzéqì	
Rotary transformer	旋转变压器	Xuánzhuǎn biànyāqì	
Rotary vane attenuator	旋转式翼形衰减器	Xuánzhuǎnshì yìxíng shuāijiǎnqì	
Rotating polygonal mirror mechanical optical scanner	回转多面镜方式机械式扫描器	Huízhuǎn duō miànjìng fāngshì jīxiè-shì sǎomiáoqì	
Rotating-field antenna	旋转场天线	Xuánzhuǎn cháng tiānxiàn	
Rotation anomaly	旋转异常	Xuánzhuǎn yìcháng	
Rotation dynamics theory	旋转动力学理论	Xuánzhuǎn dònglìxué lǐlùn	

Rotation stage positioning equipment (semiconductor mfg)	回转台定位设备	Huízhuǎntái dìngwèi shèbèi	
Rotational speed	转速	Zhuànsù	
Rotations per minute	转/分	Zhuǎn/fēn	RPM
Rough set	粗糙集	Cūcāo jí	
Rough sets theory	粗糙集理论	Cūcāo jí lǐlùn	
Round function (crypt.)	轮函数	Lún hánshù	
Round robin matching	轮循匹配	Lúnxún pǐpèi	RRM
Round robin method	时间轮循方式	Shíjiān lúnxún fāngshì	
Round trip delay	回路延迟	Huílù yánchí	
Round trip delay	往返行程时延	Wǎngfǎn xíngchéng shíyán	
Rounding relay	环行延迟	Huánxíng yánchí	
Round-trip time	来往传输时间	Láiwǎng chuánshū shíjiān	RTT
Round-trip time	往返时间	Wǎngfǎn shíjiān	RTT
Round-trip transmission time	双向传播时间	Shuāngxiàng chuánbō shíjiān	RTT
Round-trip transmission time variation	双向传播时间变化	Shuāngxiàng chuánbō shíjiān biànhuà	RTTVAR
Route	路线	Lùxiàn	
Route	路由	Lùyóu	
Route analysis	路由分析	Lùyóu fēnxī	
Route attribute table	路线属性表	Lùxiàn shǔxìng biǎo	RAT
Route clock	线路时钟	Xiànlù shízhōng	RCLK
Route direction	路径方向	Lùjìng fāngxiàng	
Route extension	路由扩展	Lùyóu kuòzhǎn	
Route information	路径信息	Lùjìng xìnxī	
Route intrusion detection	路由入侵检测	Lùyóu rùqīn jiǎncè	RID
Route link	路由链路	Lùyóu liànlù	
Route map	路由映射	Lùyóu yìngshè	
Route mapping	路由映像	Lùyóu yìngxiàng	
Route measure	路线测量	Lùxiàn cèliáng	
Route number	路线编号	Lùxiàn biānhào	
Route processor	路由处理器	Lùyóu chǔlǐqì	RP
Route redistribution	路由重新分配	Lùyóu chóngxīn fēnpèi	
Route selector	路由选择器	Lùyóu xuǎnzéqì	
Route set-up packet	路由设置表	Lùyóu shèzhì biǎo	RSUP
Route summarization	路由摘要	Lùyóu zhāiyào	
Route system	路线系统	Lùxiàn xìtǒng	
Route verify test	选路验证测试	Xuǎnlù yànzhèng cèshì	RVT
Router	路由器	Lùyóuqì	
Router advertisements	路由器广播	Lùyóuqì guǎngbō	
Router and BIN back panel	路由器和 BIN 后面板	Lùyóuqì hé BIN hòumianbǎn	RBBP
Router and GCIN rack	路由器和 GCIN 机架	Lùyóuqì hé GCIN jījià	RAGR
Router discovery	路由器搜索	Lùyóuqì sōusuǒ	
Router solicitations	路由器请求	Lùyóuqì qǐngqiú	
Routine	例程	Lìchéng	
Routine	例行程序	Lìxíng chéngxù	
Routine or periodic testing	例行或定期测试	Lìxíng huò dìngqī cèshì	
Routing	路由选定	Lùyóu xuǎndìng	

Routing	路由选择	Lùyóu xuǎnzé	
Routing and assignment of wavelength	路由及波长分配	Lùyóu jí bōcháng fēnpèi	RAW
Routing and control processor	路由和控制处理机	Lùyóu hé kòngzhì chǔlǐjī	RCP
Routing area	路由区	Lùyóu qū	RA
Routing area	路由区域	Lùyóu qūyù	RA
Routing area	路由选择范围	Lùyóu xuǎnzé fànwéi	RA
Routing area code	路由区域码	Lùyóu qūyù mǎ	RAC
Routing area code	路由选择区域码	Lùyóu xuǎnzé qūyù mǎ	RAC
Routing area identity	路由区识别号	Lùyóu qū shíbiéhào	RAI
Routing area identity	路由选择区域识别	Lùyóu xuǎnzé qūyù shíbié	RAI
Routing area update	路由选择区域更新	Lùyóu xuǎnzé qūyù gēngxīn	RAU
Routing context	选路上下文	Xuǎnlù shangxiàwén	
Routing control	路由控制	Lùyóu kòngzhì	
Routing control function	路由选择控制功能	Lùyóu xuǎnzé kòngzhì gōngnéng	
Routing controller	路由控制器	Lùyóu kòngzhìqì	RC
Routing domain	路由区域	Lùyóu qūyù	RD
Routing domain	路由选择域	Lùyóu xuǎnzé yù	RD
Routing identifier	路径选择标识符	Lùjing xuǎnzé biāozhìfú	
Routing information	路由选择信息	Lùyóu xuǎnzé xìnxī	RI
Routing information field	路由信息域	Lùyóu xìnxī yù	RIF
Routing information field	路由选择信息字段	Lùyóu xuǎnzé xìnxī zìduàn	RIF
Routing information indicator	路由选择信息指示符	Lùyóu xuǎnzé xìnxī zhǐshìfú	RII
Routing information protocol	路由信息协议	Lùyóu xìnxī xiéyì	RIP
Routing information protocol for IPv6	IPv6 的路由信息协议	IPv6-de lùyóu xìnxī xiéyì	RIPng
Routing information protocol over Internet packet exchange	在 IPX 上的路由信息协议	Zài IPX-shàngde lùyóu xìnxī xiéyì	RIPX
Routing keyword	选路关键字	Xuǎnlù guānjiàn zì	
Routing lookup	路由查找	Lùyóu cházhǎo	
Routing metric	路由量度	Lùyóu liángdù	
Routing metric	路由选择矩阵	Lùyóu xuǎnzé jǔzhèn	
Routing policy	选路策略	Xuǎnlù cèlüè	
Routing selection information	路由选择信息	Lùyóu xuǎnzé xìnxī	
Routing sequence number	路径选择序号	Lùjing xuǎnzé xùhào	
Routing table	路由表	Lùyóu biǎo	
Routing table maintenance protocol	路由表维护协议	Lùyóu biǎo wéihù xiéyì	RTMP
Routing table maintenance protocol	路由选择表维护协议	Lùyóu xuǎnzé biǎo wéihù xiéyì	RTMP
Routing table protocol	路由表协议	Lùyóu biǎo xiéyì	RTP
Routing table protocol	路由选择表协议	Lùyóu xuǎnzé biǎo xiéyì	RTP
Routing tag	路由标签	Lùyóu biāoqiān	
Routing type	路径选择类型	Lùjing xuǎnzé lèixíng	
Routing type	路由选择类型	Lùyóu xuǎnzé lèixíng	RT
Routing update	路由更新	Lùyóu gēngxīn	
Routing verification test	路由证实测试	Lùyóu zhèngshí cèshì	RVT
Row address selection	行地址选定	Háng dìzhǐ xuǎndìng	RAS
Row addressable strobe	行地址控制器	Háng dìzhǐ kòngzhìqì	RAS
Row aggregate function	行聚合函数	Háng jùhé hánshù	
Row filter	行筛选	Háng shāixuǎn	

Row filter (in SQL Server)	行过滤	Háng guòlǜ	
Row lock (for database)	行锁	Háng suǒ	
Row major order	以行为主的顺序分配	Yǐ háng wéi zhǔde shùnxù fēnpèi	
Row position (WP command)	行位置	Háng wèizhì	
Row, line (for database or table)	行	Háng	
Rowset (for database)	行集	Háng jí	
RP-rooted share tree	以 RP 为树跟的共享树	Yǐ RP wéi shùgēnde gòngxiǎng shù	RPT
Rrestoration control program	恢复控制程序	Huīfù kòngzhì chéngxù	
R-tree	R-树	R-shù	
Rubber	橡皮	Xiàngpí	
Rubber sheeting	橡皮拉伸	Xiàngpí lāshēn	
Ruby laser	红宝石激光	Hóngbǎoshí jīguāng	
Rule (IPsec)	规则	Guīzé	
Rule extraction	规则抽取	Guīzé chōuqǔ	
Rule option	规则选项	Guīzé xuǎnxiàng	
Rule set	规则集	Guīzé jí	
Rule-based colored Petri net	基于规则约束着色 Petri 网	Jīyú guīzé yuēshù zhuosè Petri wǎng	RCPN
Rule-based security policy (IPsec)	基于规则的安全策略	Jīyú guīzéde ānquán cèlüè	
Ruler	尺标	Chǐbiāo	
Run	执行	Zhíxíng	
Run in flame-retardant semi-rigid PVC conduit	穿阻燃半硬聚乙烯管敷设	Chuān zǔrán bànyìng jùyǐxī guǎn fūshè	FPC
Run in flexible metal conduit	穿蛇皮管敷设	Chuān shépíguǎn fūshè	FMC
Run in metallic raceway	金属线槽敷设	Jīnshǔ xiàncáo fūshè	
Run in metallic tubing	穿金属管敷设	Chuān jīnshǔguǎn fūshè	MT
Run in PVC raceway (telecom installation)	塑料线槽敷设	Sùliào xiàncáo fūshè	
Run in rigid PVC conduit	穿硬聚乙烯管敷设	Chuān yìng jùyǐxī guǎn fūshè	PC
Run length encoding	行程编码	Xíngchéng biānmǎ	RLE
Run length encoding	游程编码	Yóuchéng biānmǎ	RLE
Run path	游程	Yóuchéng	
Runge	龙格	Lóng-gé	
Run-length coding	游程长度编码	Yóuchéng chángdù biānmǎ	RLC
Runtime	执行期	Zhíxíng qī	
Runtime	执行时	Zhíxíng shí	
Run-time	运行程序	Yùnxíng chéngxù	
Run-time	运行期	Yùnxíng qī	
Run-time	运行时	Yùnxíng shí	
Run-time infrastructure	运行时间支撑系统	Yùnxíng shíjiān zhīchēng xìtǒng	RTI
Run-time repository (in CORBA)	运行库	Yùnxíng kù	
Rural telephony	农村电话	Nóngcūn diànhuà	

S

S wave velocity	S 波速度	S-bō sùdù	
S3 texture compression (video term)	S3 纹理压缩	S3 wénlǐ yāsuō	S3TC
S3 transformation and lighting (video term)	S3 多边形转换和光源处理	S3 duōbiānxíng zhuǎnhuàn hé guāngyuán chǔlǐ	S3TL
Safe distance	安全距离	Ānquán jùlí	
Safe mode (in computers)	安全模式	Ānquán móshì	

Safety automation	安全自动化	Ānquán zìdònghuà	
Safety automation system	保安自动化系统	Bǎo'ān zìdònghuà xìtǒng	SAS
Safety circuit and device	安全电路和装置	Ānquán diànlù hé zhuāngzhì	
Safety color	安全色	Ānquán sè	
Safety control switch	安全控制开关	Ānquán kòngzhì kāiguān	SCS
Safety extra-low voltage	安全特低电压	Ānquán tèdī diànyā	SELV
Safety factor	安全因子	Ānquán yīnzǐ	
Safety fuse	保险丝	Bǎoxiǎnsī	SF
Safety ground wire	安全地线	Ānquán dìxiàn	
Safety impedance	安全阻抗	Ānquán zǔkàng	
Safety index	安全指数	Ānquán zhǐshù	
Safety isolating transformer	安全隔离变压器	Ānquán gélí biànyāqì	
Safety marking	安全标志	Ānquán biāozhì	
Safety service	安全业务	Ānquán yèwù	
Safety switch	安全开关	Ānquán kāiguān	
Sag	电垂	Diànchuí	
Sagem Ltd. (French company)	萨基姆有限公司	Sà-jī-mǔ yǒuxiàn gōngsī	
Sale entrusted by publishing house	代销	Dàixiāo	
Sale of non-return surplus	寄售	Jìshòu	
Sales automation	销售自动化	Xiāoshòu zìdònghuà	
Sales available market	可发售市场	Kěfāshòu shìchǎng	SAM
Sales contract	销售确认书	Xiāoshòu quèrènshū	S/C
Salt fog test	盐雾试验	Yánwù shìyàn	
Same-edge aggregation (CAD/CAM)	同边聚合	Tóngbiān jùhé	
Sample	样值	Yàngzhí	
Sample bias	样本偏差	Yàngběn piānchā	
Sample data	示例数据	Shìlì shùjù	
Sample rate, sampling rate	采样速率	Cǎiyàng sùlǜ	
Sample relay	取样继电器	Qǔyàng jìdiànqì	SR
Sample, specimen	抽样	Chōuyàng	
Sampled data phase-locked loop	取样数据锁相环	Qǔyàng shùjù suǒxiàng huán	SDPLL
Sampling	采样	Cǎiyàng	
Sampling adaptive algorithm	采样字适应算法	Cǎiyàng zìshìyìng suànfǎ	SAA
Sampling frequency	采样频率	Cǎiyàng pínlǜ	
Sampling period	采样周期	Cǎiyàng zhōuqī	
Sampling rate	抽样率	Chōuyàng lǜ	
Sampling resolution	采样间隔	Cǎiyàng jiàngé	
Sampling resolution	取样分辨率	Qǔyàng fēnbiànlǜ	
Sampling theorem	采样定理	Cǎiyàng dìnglǐ	
Sampo (Taiwan company)	新宝	Xīnbǎo	
Samsung Electronics Ltd (Korean company)	三星电子株式会社	Sān-xīng diànzǐ zhūshì huìshè	
Sand-and-dust test	沙尘试验	Shāchén shìyàn	
Sanity loader	正常运行承载器	Zhèngcháng yùnxíng chéngzàiqì	
Sanity manager	正常运行管理器	Zhèngcháng yùnxíng guǎnlǐqì	
Sanity manager	正常化管理器	Zhèngchánghuà guǎnlǐqì	SM
Sanyo (Japanese company)	三洋	Sān-yáng	

Saponifier (in SMT)	皂化剂	Zàohuàjì	
Satellite	卫星	Wèixīng	
Satellite access	卫星接入	Wèixīng jiērù	SA
Satellite broadcasting	卫星广播	Wèixīng guǎngbō	
Satellite capacity	卫星容量	Wèixīng róngliàng	
Satellite city	卫星城市	Wèixīng chéngshì	
Satellite communications	卫星通信	Wèixīng tōngxìn	
Satellite control network	卫星控制网	Wèixīng kòngzhìwǎng	SCN
Satellite data transmission	卫星数据传输	Wèixīng shùjù chuánshū	
Satellite delay compensation unit	卫星延迟补偿器	Wèixīng yánchí bǔchángqì	SDCU
Satellite digital communications system	卫星数字通信系统	Wèixīng shùzì tōngxìn xìtǒng	SDCS
Satellite disk	卫星天碟	Wèixīng tiāndié	
Satellite earth station	卫星地球站	Wèixīng dìqiúzhàn	WD
Satellite fixed wireless access	卫星固定无线接入	Wèixīng gùdìng wúxiàn jiērù	SFWA
Satellite geodesy	卫星测地学	Wèixīng cèdìxué	
Satellite image	卫星像片	Wèixīng xiàngpiàn	
Satellite laser ranging	人造卫星激光测距	Rénzào wèixīng jīguāng cèjù	
Satellite link	卫星链路	Wèixīng liànlù	
Satellite link	卫星线路	Wèixīng xiànlù	
Satellite master antenna television /master antenna television	卫星共用天线电视/共用天线电视	Wèixīng gòngyòng tiānxiàn diànshì/Gòngyòng tiānxiàn diànshì	SMATV/MATV
Satellite master antenna television /master antenna television	主卫星天线电视/主天线电视	Zhǔ wèixīng tiānxiàn diànshì/zhǔ tiānxiàn diànshì	SMATV/MATV
Satellite mobile access	卫星移动接入	Wèixīng yídòng jiērù	SMA
Satellite mobile communication system	卫星移动通信系统	Wèixīng yídòng tōngxìn xìtǒng	
Satellite mobile service switching center	卫星移动业务交换中心	Wèixīng yídòng yèwù jiāohuàn zhōngxīn	SMSC
Satellite multi-service system	卫星多业务系统	Wèixīng duō yèwù xìtǒng	SMS
Satellite network	卫星网络	Wèixīng wǎngluò	
Satellite positioning systems	卫星定位系统	Wèixīng dìngwèi xìtǒng	
Satellite radio location systems	卫星无线电定位系统	Wèixīng wúxiàndiàn dìngwèi xìtǒng	
Satellite radio-determination	卫星无线电测定	Wèixīng wúxiàndiàn cèdìng	
Satellite radio-navigation	卫星无线电导航	Wèixīng wúxiàndiàn dǎoháng	
Satellite station	卫星观测点	Wèixīng guāncèdiǎn	
Satellite switched multiple access	卫星交换多址	Wèixīng jiāohuàn duōzhǐ	SSMA
Satellite switched time-division multiple access	卫星转接十分多路存取	Wèixīng zhuǎnjiē shífēn duōlù cúnqǔ	SSTDMA
Satellite system	卫星系统	Wèixīng xìtǒng	
Satellite Tactical Data Information Link (US military)	卫星战术数据信息链	Wèixīng zhànshù shùjù xìnxī liàn	STADIL
Satellite telephone switching center	卫星电话交换中心	Wèixīng diànhuà jiāohuàn zhōngxīn	STC
Satellite telephony	卫星电话	Wèixīng diànhuà	
Satellite television	卫星电视	Wèixīng diànshì	SATV
Satellite transponder	卫星转发器	Wèixīng zhuǎnfāqì	
Satisfiability	可满足性	Kěmǎnzúxìng	
Saturable reactor	饱和电抗器	Bǎohé diànkàngqì	SR
Saturated flux density	饱和通量密度	Bǎohé tōngliàng mìdù	
Saturated model	饱和模型	Bǎohé móxíng	
Saturation	饱和度	Bǎohédù	

Save (computer command)	保存	Bǎocún	
Save all (computer command)	保存全部	Bǎocún quánbù	
Save all (WP command)	全部保存	Quánbù bǎocún	
Save as (WP command)	保存为	Bǎocún wéi	
Save point (for database)	保存点	Bǎocún diǎn	
Scalability	可扩展性	Kěkuòzhǎnxìng	
Scalability	可升级性	Kěshēngjíxìng	
Scalability	可伸缩性	Kěshēnsuōxìng	
Scalability	融通性	Róngtōngxìng	
Scalable	可扩展的	Kěkuòzhǎnde	
Scalable	可伸缩的	Kěshēnsuōde	
Scalable multicast key distribution	可伸缩多播密钥分配	Kěshēnsuō duōbō mìyào fēnpèi	SKMD
Scalable reliable multicast	可扩展可靠组播	Kěkuòzhǎn kěkào zǔbō	SRM
Scalar aggregate	标量聚合	Biāoliàng jùhé	
Scalar functions (in SQL Server)	标量型函数	Biāoliàngxíng hánshù	
Scale	比例尺	Bǐlìchǐ	
Scale bar	线状比例尺	Xiànzhuàng bǐlìchǐ	
Scale conversion	标度变换	Biāodù biànhuàn	
Scaled measurement unit	标尺测量单位	Biāochǐ cèliáng dānwèi	SMU
Scaling law	相似形法则	Xiāngsìxíng fǎzé	
Scan and signal unit	扫描及信号单元	Sǎomiáo jí xìnhào dānyuán	SSU
Scan channel	信道扫描	Xìndào sǎomiáo	
Scan control block	浏览控制模块	Liúlǎn kòngzhì mókuài	SCB
Scan conversion	扫描转换	Sǎomiáo zhuǎnhuàn	
Scan, sweep	扫描	Sǎomiáo	
Scanline interleave	扫描线间插	Sǎomiáo xiànjiān chā	SLI
Scanner	扫描器	Sǎomiáoqì	SCN
Scanner	扫描仪	Sǎomiáoyí	
Scanner control unit	扫描器控制部件	Sǎomiáoqì kòngzhì bùjiàn	SCU
Scanning antenna	扫描天线	Sǎomiáo tiānxiàn	
Scanning density	扫描密度	Sǎomiáo mìdù	
Scanning line	扫描线	Sǎomiáo xiàn	
Scanning pitch	扫描行距	Sǎomiáo hángjù	
Scatter communication	散射通信	Sǎnshè tōngxìn	
Scatter graph	散点图	Sàndiǎntú	
Scatter search	分散搜索	Fēnsàn sōusuǒ	
Scattering cross section, scattering area (of an antenna)	散射截面	Sǎnshè jiémiàn	
Scattering matrix	散射矩阵	Sǎnshè jǔzhèn	
Scattering of electromagnetic wave	电磁波散射	Diàncíbō sǎnshè	
Scattering parameter	散射参数	Sǎnshè cānshù	Sij
Scatternet	分布式网络	Fēnbùshì wǎngluò	
Scatternet	分散网	Fēnsàn wǎng	
Scatternet	松散网	Sōngsǎn wǎng	
Scavenging (IPsec)	搜寻	Sōuxún	
SCCP routing verification test	SCCP 路由证实测试	SCCP lùyóu zhèngshí cèshì	SRVT
SCCP user adaptation layer	SCCP 用户适配层	SCCP yònghù shìpèi céng	SUA

English	Chinese	Pinyin	Abbreviation
Scene analysis	景观分析	Jǐngguān fēnxī	
Schedulability analysis (in CORBA)	可调度分析	Kědiàodù fēnxī	
Scheduled backup	已调度备份	Yǐdiàodù bèifèn	
Scheduled maintenance	定期维护	Dìngqī wéihù	
Scheduler	调度程序	Diàodù chéngxù	
Scheduler (for QoS)	调度器	Diàodùqì	
Scheduling	调度	Diàodù	
Scheduling algorithm	调度算法	Diàodù suànfǎ	
Schema	纲目结构	Gāngmù jiégòu	
Schema	架构	Jiàgòu	
Schema	模式	Móshì	
Schema	数据模式	Shùjù móshì	
Schema model	数据模式模型	Shùjù móshì móxíng	
Schema rowset	架构行集	Jiàgòu hángjí	
Schematic capture	原理图输入器	Yuánlǐ tú shūrùqì	
Schmid Corp. (Swiss company)	施密德公司	Shī-mì-dé gōngsī	
Schmitt trigger	施密特触发器	Shī-mì-tè chùfāqì	
Scintillation fiber	闪光光纤	Shǎnguāng guāngxiān	
Scope	生存空间	Shēngcún kōngjiān	
Scope	作用域	Zuòyòng yù	
Scope operator	生存空间操作符	Shēngcún kōngjiān cāozuò fú	
Scope resolution operator	生存空间解析操作符	Shēngcún kōngjiān jiěxī cāozuò fú	
Scoping	划定范围	Huàdìng fànwéi	
Scramble	置乱	Zhìluàn	
Scramble, scrambling	扰码	Rǎomǎ	
Scrambler	扰码器	Rǎomǎqì	
Scratchpad memory	暂时存储器	Zànshí cúnchǔqì	SPM
Screen	屏蔽	Píngbì	
Screen	屏幕	Píngmù	
Screen buffer	屏幕缓冲	Píngmù huǎnchōng	
Screen copy device	屏幕拷贝设备	Píngmù kǎobèi shèbèi	
Screen filter	护目镜	Hùmùjìng	
Screen pop	屏幕计事本	Píngmù jìshìběn	
Screen printer (in printed circuit board manufacture)	丝网印刷及	Sīwǎng yìnshuājí	
Screen printer (PCB manufacture)	带视览丝印机	Dài shì lǎn sīyìnjī	
Screen saver	屏幕保护程序	Píngmù bǎohù chéngxù	
Screened circuit	屏蔽电路	Píngbì diànlù	
Screened host gateway	被屏蔽主机网关	Bèipíngbì zhǔjī wǎngguān	
Screened sub-network	被屏蔽子网	Bèipíngbì ziwǎng	
Screened sub-network	屏蔽子网	Píngbì ziwǎng	
Screening	筛选	Shāixuǎn	
Screening indicator	屏蔽指示器	Píngbì zhǐshìqì	SI
Screening router	屏蔽路由器	Píngbì lùyóuqì	
Screening router	筛选路由器	Shāixuǎn lùyóuqì	
Screening tensile strength (FOC)	筛选张力	Shāixuǎn zhānglì	
Screening test	筛选试验	Shāixuǎn shìyàn	

Screw filter	螺旋滤波器	Luóxuán lǜbōqì	
Scribing (semiconductor mfg process)	铭刻	Míngkè	
Script	脚本	Jiǎoběn	
Script kiddies	脚本小子	Jiǎoběn xiǎozǐ	
Script program	脚本程序	Jiǎoběn chéngxù	
Scroll	滚动	Gǔndòng	
Scroll (verb)	卷动	Juǎndòng	
Scroll bar	滚动条	Gǔndòng tiáo	
Scroll lock key	停止卷动键	Tíngzhǐ juǎndòng jiàn	
SCSI over IP	IP 网络上的 SCSI 接口	IP wǎngluò-shàngde SCS jiēkǒu	SoIP
SCSI Trade Association	SCSI 同业公会	SCSI tóngyè gōnghuì	STA
SDH cross-connection	SDH 交叉连接	SDH jiāochā liánjiē	SDXC
SDH equipment clock	SDH 设备时钟	SDH shèbèi shízhōng	SEC
SDH link termination board	SDH 链路终端板	SDH liànlù zhōngduān bǎn	SLK
SDH management network	SDH 管理网	SDH guǎnlǐ wǎng	SMN
SDH management sub-network	SDH 管理子网	SDH guǎnlǐ ziwǎng	SMS
SDH mapping	SDH 映射	SDH yìngshè	
SDH physical interface	SDH 物理接口	SDH wùlǐ jiēkǒu	SPI
SDL development tool	SDL 开发工具	SDL kāifā gōngjù	SDT
SeaGate (US hard drive maker)	希捷公司	Xījié gōngsī	
Sealed class	密封类	Mìfēng lèi	
Sealed tube CO_2 laser	密封型二氧化碳激光	Mìfēng-xíng èryǎnghuàtàn jīguāng	
Seamless database	无缝数据库	Wúféng shùjùkù	
Seamless handover	无缝越区切换	Wúféng yuèqū qiēhuàn	
Seamless steel pipe	无缝钢管	Wúfèng gāngguǎn	
Search	检索	Jiǎnsuǒ	
Search	搜寻	Sōuxún	
Search agent (in Java)	搜索代理	Sōusuǒ dàilǐ	
Search and replace	搜寻取代	Sōuxún qǔdài	
Search and rescue	搜索救援	Sōusuǒ jiùyuán	SAR
Search bar (WP command)	查寻工具	Cháxún gōngjù	
Search condition	搜索条件	Sōusuǒ tiáojiàn	
Search engine	查询器	Cháxúnqì	
Search engine	搜索引警	Sōusuǒ yǐnjǐng	
Search engine	搜索引擎	Sōusuǒ yǐnqíng	
Search engine	搜寻引擎	Sōuxún yǐnqíng	
Search for extra-terrestrial intelligence	地外文明探索	Dìwài wénmíng tànsuǒ	SETI
Search region	搜索区	Sōusuǒ qū	
Search tool	搜索工具	Sōusuǒ gōngjù	
Search, searching	查找	Cházhǎo	
Searching carrier	搜索载波	Sōusuǒ zàibō	
SeaShield (Seagate's static shielding, trademark)	希捷公司的静电防撞击外壳	Xījié gōngsīde jìngdiàn fáng zhuàngjī wàiké	
Second adjacent channel	第二相邻信道	Dì'èr xiānglín xìndào	
Second coating	二次被覆层	Èrcì bèifù céng	
Second coating optical fiber	二次被覆光纤	Èrcì bèifù guāngxiān	
Second data multiplexer	第二级数据复用器	Dì'èrjí shùjù fùyòngqì	

Second generation	第二代	Dì'èrdài	2G
Second moment polarization mode dispersion differential group delay	二阶矩偏振模色散差分群时延	Èrjiē jǔ piānzhèn mó sèsàn chāfēn qún shíyán	
Second normal form	第 2 范式	Dì'èr fànshì	2NF
Second order coherent multiple access	二阶相关多路存取	Èrjiē xiāngguān duōlù cúnqǔ	SOCMA
Second order distortion	二阶失真	Èrjiē shīzhēn	
Second order effect	二阶效应	Èrjiē xiàoyìng	
Second reflection	二次反射	Èrcì fǎnshè	
Second Wiener filter solution	第二维纳滤波器解	Dì'èr wéinà lǜbōqì jiě	SWFS
Secondary circuit	辅助电路	Fǔzhù diànlù	
Secondary common control physical channel	第二公共控制物理信道	Dì'èr gōnggòng kòngzhì wùlǐ xìndào	S-CCPCH
Secondary common pilot channel	第二公共导频信道	Dì'èr gōnggòng dǎopín xìndào	S-CPICH
Secondary data capture	辅助数据获取	Fǔzhù shùjù huòqǔ	
Secondary design	二次设计	Èrcì shèjì	
Secondary development interface (similar in function to API)	二次开发接口	Èrcì kāifā jiēkǒu	
Secondary digital carrier	二次数字载波	Èrcì shùzì zàibō	SDC
Secondary digital multiplexer	二次数字复用器	Èrcì shùzì fùyòngqì	
Secondary distribution link	次级分布线路	Cìjí fēnbù xiànlù	
Secondary distribution network	二次配线网	Èrcì pèixiànwǎng	SDN
Secondary failure	从属失效	Cóngshǔ shīxiào	
Secondary flow	二次流	Èrcì liú	
Secondary lobe, minor lobe	副瓣	Fùbàn	
Secondary logical unit	辅助逻辑设备单元	Fǔzhù luójì shèbèi dānyuán	SLU
Secondary node	辅节点	Fǔ jiédiǎn	
Secondary power supply	二次供电	Èrcì gōngdiàn	
Secondary power switchover (to secondary battery)	二次下电	Èrcì xiàdiàn	
Secondary radar	二次雷达	Èrcì léidá	
Secondary radiation	二次辐射	Èrcì fúshè	
Secondary ring	二级环	Èrjí huán	
Secondary station	辅站	Fǔzhàn	
Secondary surveillance radar	二次监视雷达	Èrcì jiānshì léidá	SSR
Secondary synchronization code	第二同步码	Dì'èr tóngbùmǎ	SSC
Secret cipher key tree	密钥树	Mìyào shù	
Secretary telephone set	秘书电话机	Mìshū diànhuàjī	
Section	路线段	Lùxiàn duàn	
Section (in SDH)	段	Duàn	
Section boundary	段的边界	Duànde biānjiè	
Section break (WP command)	章节分界线	Zhāngjié fēnjièxiàn	
Section overhead	段开销	Duàn kāixiao	SOH
Section termination	段终端	Duàn zhōngduān	
Sectional loaded antenna	分段加载天线	Fēnduàn jiāzài tiānxiàn	
Sector (of a digital signal)	区段	Qūduàn	
Sector (of a hard drive or mobile telephone cell)	扇区	Shànqū	
Sector address	区段地址	Qūduàn dìzhǐ	SA
Sector address type	扇形地址类型	Shànxíng dìzhǐ lèixíng	SA

Sector interface block	扇区接口模块	Shànqū jiēkǒu mókuài	SIB
Sector interface card assembly	扇区接口卡集成件	Shànqū jiēkǒu kǎ jíchéng jiàn	SICA
Sector interface card processor	扇区接口卡处理器	Shànqū jiēkǒu kǎ chǔlǐqì	SICP
Sector interface processor	扇区接口处理器	Shànqū jiēkǒu chǔlǐqì	SIP
Sector member (for ITU)	部门成员	Bùmén chéngyuán	
Sector sharing	扇区共享	Shànqū gòngxiǎng	
Sectoral horn antenna	扇形喇叭天线	Shànxíng lǎba tiānxiàn	
Sectored cell	扇型小区	Shàn-xíng xiǎoqū	
Sectorized transmission path	分区传输路径	Fēnqū chuánshū lùjìng	
Secular variation	长期变化	Chángqī biànhuà	
Secure communication	保密通信	Bǎomì tōngxìn	
Secure configuration management	安全配置管理	Ānquán pèizhì guǎnlǐ	
Secure electronic payment process	安全电子支付过程	Ānquán diànzǐ zhīfù guòchéng	SEPP
Secure electronic payment protocol	安全电子结算协议	Ānquán diànzǐ jiésuàn xiéyì	SEPP
Secure electronic transaction	安全电子事务处理	Ānquán diànzǐ shìwù chǔlǐ	SET
Secure electronic transfer	安全电子交易	Ānquán diànzi jiāoyì	SET
Secure exchange protocol	安全交换协议	Ānquán jiāohuàn xiéyì	
Secure hash algorithm	安全散列算法	Ānquán sànliè suànfǎ	SHA
Secure hypertext transfer protocol	安全超文本传输协议	Ānquán chāowénběn chuánshū xiéyì	HTTPS
Secure hypertext transfer protocol (IETF use)	加密的 HTTP 协议	Jiāmìde HTTP xiéyì	S-HTTP
Secure interaction policy	安全交互策略	Ānquán jiāohù cèlüè	
Secure middleware	安全中间件	Ānquán zhōngjiān jiàn	
Secure multi-purpose Internet mail extension	安全多用途因特网邮件扩展协议	Ānquán duōyòngtú Yīntèwǎng yóujiàn kuòzhǎn xiéyì	S/MIME
Secure multi-purpose Internet mail extensions	安全多用途网际邮件扩展协议	Ānquán duōyòngtú wǎngjì yóujiàn kuòzhǎn xiéyì	S/MIME
Secure operating system	安全操作系统	Ānquán cāozuò xìtǒng	
Secure path (IPsec)	安全通路	Ānquán tōnglù	
Secure shell protocol (ITU-T usage)	安装配置	Ānzhuāng pèizhì	SSH
Secure socket layer	安全插座层	Ānquán chāzuò céng	SSL
Secure socket layer	安全套接层	Ānquán tàojiē céng	SSL
Secure socket layer	加密套接字安全层	Jiāmì tàojiēzì ānquán céng	SSL
Secure socket layer (CORBA term)	安全套接字层	Ānquán tàojiē zìcéng	SSL
Secure state (IPsec)	安全状态	Ānquán zhuàngtài	
Secure transaction technology	交易保安技术	Jiāoyì bǎo'ān jìshù	STT
Secure voice system	保密音频系统	Bǎomì yīnpín xìtǒng	SVS
Secure wireless access	安全的无线接入	Ānquánde wúxiàn jiērù	
Secured by porcelain clip	瓷夹敷设	Cíjiā fūshè	PL
Secured by PVC clip	塑料夹敷设	Sùliào jiā fūshè	PCL
Security	安全	Ānquán	
Security account manager	安全帐户管理器	Ānquán zhànghù guǎnlǐqì	SAM
Security administrator tool for analyzing networks	网络安全分析器	Wǎngluò ānquán fēnxīqì	SATAN
Security architecture for IP network	IP 层协议安全结构	IP céng xiéyì ānquán jiégòu	IPsec
Security arrangements (in common channel signaling)	安全措施（公共信道信令中）	Ānquán cuòshī (gōnggòng xìndào xìnlìng zhōng)	
Security assertion markup language	安全性断言标记语言	Ānquánxìng duànyán biāojì yǔyán	SAML

Security association	安全关联	Ānquán guānlián	SA
Security association	安全联盟	Ānquán liánméng	SA
Security association bundle	安全关联捆绑	Ānquán guānlián kǔnbǎng	
Security association database	安全关联数据库	Ānquán guānlián shùjùkù	SAD
Security audit (IPsec)	安全审计	Ānquán shěnjì	
Security audit event (IPsec)	安全审计事件	Ānquán shěnjì shìjiàn	
Security audit trail (IPsec)	安全审计路踪	Ānquán shěnjì lùzōng	
Security boundary	安全周界	Ānquán zhōujiè	
Security class (IPsec)	安全级别	Ānquán jíbié	
Security context (IPsec)	安全文字	Ānquán wénzì	
Security delegation (in SQL Server)	安全授权	Ānquán shòuquán	
Security environment	安全保密环境	Ānquán bǎomì huánjìng	SE
Security evaluation	安全评估	Ānquán pínggū	
Security evaluation (IPsec)	安全评估	Ānquán pínggū	
Security exchange service element	安全交易业务单元	Ānquán jiāoyì yèwù dānyuán	SESE
Security fault management	安全故障管理	Ānquán gùzhàng guǎnlǐ	
Security feature	安全特性	Ānquán tèxìng	
Security features	安全特征	Ānquán tèzhēng	
Security filter	安全过滤器	Ānquán guòlǜqì	
Security gateway	安全网关	Ānquán wǎngguān	SG
Security group (GSM MoU)	安全保密组	Ānquán bǎomì zǔ	SG
Security hash algorithm	安全 Hash 算法	Ānquán hash suànfǎ	SHA
Security identifier	安全标识号	Ānquán biāozhì hào	SID
Security kernel	安全内核	Ānquán nèihé	
Security label (IPsec)	安全标签	Ānquán biāoqiān	
Security management	安全管理	Ānquán guǎnlǐ	SM
Security management	安全性管理	Ānquánxìng guǎnlǐ	SM
Security management center	安全管理中心	Ānquán guǎnlǐ zhōngxīn	SMC
Security management entity	安全管理实体	Ānquán guǎnlǐ shítǐ	SME
Security management information base	安全管理信息库	Ānquán guǎnlǐ xìnxīkù	SMIB
Security management system, security administration system	安全管理系统	Ānquán guǎnlǐ xìtǒng	SMS
Security mode (telecom usage)	安全模式	Ānquán móshì	
Security parameter index (IPsec)	安全参数索引	Ānquán cānshù suǒyǐn	SPI
Security perimeter	安全周边	Ānquán zhōubiān	
Security policy	安全保密政策	Ānquán bǎomì zhèngcè	
Security policy (IPsec)	安全策略	Ānquán cèlüè	
Security policy database	安全策略数据库	Ānquán cèlüè shùjùkù	SPD
Security requirements	安全需求	Ānquán xūqiú	
Security service (IPsec)	安全服务	Ānquán fúwù	
Security specifications	安全规范	Ānquán guīfàn	
Security system	保安系统	Bǎo'ān xìtǒng	
Security testing	安全测试	Ānquán cèshì	
Security work station	安全工作站	Ānquán gōngzuòzhàn	SWS
Security, safety	安全性	Ānquánxìng	
Sedimentation	沉砂	Chénshā	
See you later (computer chat)	以后见	Yǐhòu jiàn	CUL

English	Chinese	Pinyin	Abbreviation
Seed	种子点	Zhǒngzǐ diǎn	
Seed function	种子函数	Zhǒngzǐ hánshù	
Seed router	源路由器	Yuán lùyóuqì	
Seed router	种子路由器	Zhǒngzǐ lùyóuqì	
Sega (Japanese company)	世嘉	Shì-jiā	
Sega Saturn (computer game)	世嘉土星 32 位游戏机	Shì-jiā tǔxīng 32- wèi yóuxìjī	
Segment	片段	Piànduàn	
Segment	网段	Wǎngduàn	
Segment (of a network)	区段	Qūduàn	
Segment control bits	段控制位	Duàn kòngzhì wèi	SCB
Segment deflection	段偏移	Duàn piānyí	
Segment descriptor	段描述符	Duàn miáoshùfú	SDT
Segment descriptor block	段描述子块	Duàn miáoshù zikuài	SDB
Segment identifier	段识别符	Duàn shíbiéfú	SID
Segment interface protocol	段接口协议	Duàn jiēkǒu xiéyì	SIP
Segment register	段寄存器	Duàn jìcúnqì	SR
Segment type	段类型	Duàn lèixíng	ST
Segment, segmenting, segmentation (of packet data)	分段	Fēnduàn	
Segmentation and reassembly	程序分段和重编	Chéngxù fēnduàn hé chóngbiān	SAR
Segmentation and reassembly	分段和重装	Fēnduàn hé chóngzhuāng	SAR
Segmentation and reassembly	分段和重组	Fēnduàn hé chóngzǔ	SAR
Segmentation and reassembly	分段与组装	Fēnduàn yǔ zǔzhuāng	SAR
Segmentation and reassembly	分装段和重组	Fēnzhuāng duàn hé chóngzǔ	SAR
Segmentation and reassembly sub-layer	拆装子层	Chāizhuāng zicéng	SAR
Segmentation and reassembly sub-layer	分段和重装子层	Fēnduàn hé chóngzhuāng zicéng	SARS
Segmentation error	分割错误	Fēngē cuòwù	
Segmentation message (ISUP)	分段消息	Fēnduàn xiāoxi	SGM
Segmentation/reassembly	分割/组装	Fēngē/Zǔzhuāng	
Segmented encoding law	折线编码律	Zhéxiàn biānmǎ lǜ	
Segmenting	分组	Fēnzǔ	
Segments left	剩余段	Shèngyú duàn	SL
Seize, seizure	占用	Zhànyòng	
Seizing signal	占机信号	Zhànjī xìnhào	
Seizing signal	占用信号	Zhànyòng xìnhào	
Seizing-acknowledgement signal	占机证实信号	Zhànjī zhèngshí xìnhào	
Seizure acknowledged signal time supervision	占用证实信号时间监视	Zhànyòng zhèngshí xìnhào shíjiān jiānshì	
Seizure precursor	占线前标	Zhànxiàn qiánbiāo	
Select all (WP command)	全选	Quán xuǎn	
Select all (WP command)	选择全部	Xuǎnzé quánbù	
Select list	选择列表	Xuǎnzé lièbiǎo	
Select query	选择查询	Xuǎnzé cháxún	
Select, selection, selective	选择	Xuǎnzé	
Selected communications mode	选择通信模式	Xuǎnzé tōngxìn móshì	SCM
Selection coverage	选择图层	Xuǎnzé tú céng	
Selection sort	选择排序	Xuǎnzé páixù	
Selection transmission diversity	选择发送分集	Xuǎnzé fāsòng fēn jí	STD

Selective availability	选择可用性	Xuǎnzé kěyòngxìng	SA
Selective availability	选择性供给	Xuǎnzéxìng gōngjǐ	SA
Selective broadcast signaling virtual channel	选择性广播信令虚通路	Xuǎnzéxìng guǎngbō xìnlìng xū tōnglù	
Selective broadcast signaling virtual channel	选择性广播信令虚信道	Xuǎnzéxìng guǎngbō xìnlìng xū xìndào	SBSVC
Selective broadcast signaling virtual path	选择性广播信令虚通路	Xuǎnzéxìng guǎngbō xìnlìng xū tōnglù	
Selective calling	选择性呼叫	Xuǎnzéxìng hūjiào	
Selective field confidentiality (IPsec)	选择域机密性	Xuǎnzé yù jīmìxìng	
Selective field connection integrity (IPsec)	选择域连接完整性	Xuǎnzé yù liánjiē wánzhěngxìng	
Selective field connectionless integrity (IPsec)	选择域无连接完整性	Xuǎnzé yù wúliánjiē wánzhěngxìng	
Selective field protection (IPsec)	选择域保护	Xuǎnzé yù bǎohù	
Selective frequency repeater	选频直防站	Xuǎnpín zhífángzhàn	
Selective incoming load control	选择输入装载控制	Xuǎnzé shūrù zhuāngzài kòngzhì	SILC
Selective laser sintering	激光选区烧结法	Jīguāng xuǎnqū shāojiéfǎ	SLS
Selective reject	选择拒绝	Xuǎnzé jùjué	SREJ
Selective repeat ARQ	选择重发ARQ	Xuǎnzé chóngfā ARQ	
Selective statement	选择语句	Xuǎnzé yǔjù	
Selective-calling equipment	选择呼叫设备	Xuǎnzé hūjiào shèbèi	
Selective-calling system	选择呼叫系统	Xuǎnzé hūjiào xìtǒng	
Selectivity	选择性	Xuǎnzéxìng	
Selector	选配器	Xuǎnpèiqì	
Selector	选择器	Xuǎnzéqì	
Selector bank sub-system	选择器子系统	Xuǎnzéqì zixìtǒng	SBS
Selector bank sub-system rack	选择器子系统机架	Xuǎnzéqì zixìtǒng jījià	SBSR
Selector interface card manager	选择器接口卡管理器	Xuǎnzéqì jiēkǒu kǎ guǎnlǐqì	SCM
Selector transcoder assembly	选择易码集成件	Xuǎnzé yìmǎ jíchéng jiàn	SXOA
Selector transcoder interface assembly	选择易码接口集成件	Xuǎnzé yìmǎ jiēkǒu jíchéng jiàn	SXIA
Selector vocoder processor	选择声码处理器	Xuǎnzé shēngmǎ chǔlǐqì	SVP
Selector/vocoder	选择器/声码器	Xuǎnzéqì/shēngmǎqì	S/V
Self impedance (of antenna elements)	自阻抗	Zìzǔkàng	
Self routing tag	自选路由标签	Zìxuǎn lùyóu biāoqiān	SRTR
Self-adaptive bandwidth	自适应带宽	Zìshìyìng dàikuān	
Self-balancing power bridge	自平衡桥式功率计	Zìpínghéng qiáoshì gōnglǜjì	
Self-calibrating	自校准	Zì jiàozhǔn	
Self-compensating network	自补偿网络	Zìbǔcháng wǎngluò	SCN
Self-delineating block	自定界块	Zìdìngjiè kuài	
Self-delineating labeled interface	自定界带标号的接口	Zìdìngjiè dài biāohàode jiēkǒu	
Self-discharge	自放电	Zìfàngdiàn	
Self-excited oscillation	自激荡器	Zìjī dàngqì	
Self-excited oscillation	自激振荡	Zìjī zhèndàng	
Self-expanding file	自解文件	Zìjiě wénjiàn	
Self-healing	自愈	Zìyù	
Self-healing hybrid ring (SDH term)	自愈环	Zìyù huán	SHR
Self-healing network	自愈网	Zìyù wǎng	
Self-join	自联接	Zì liánjiē	
Self-learning system	自学习系统	Zìxuéxí xìtǒng	
Self-monitoring analysis and report technology	自动检测分析及报告技术	Zìdòng jiǎncè fēnxī jí bàogào jìshù	SMART

Self-organizing radio communication network	自组织无线电通信网	Zìzǔzhī wúxiàndiàn tōngxìn wǎng	
Self-phase modulation	自相位调制	Zìxiàngwèi tiáozhì	SPM
Self-service remitting	自助汇款	Zìzhù huìkuǎn	
Self-supporting (FOC mfg)	自承式	Zìchéngshì	
Self-sustained (optical fiber cable)	自持(光纤电缆)	Zìchí (guāngxiān diànlǎn)	SS
Self-synchronous scrambler	自同步扰码器	Zìtóngbù rǎomǎqì	
Self-test	自测试	Zìcèshì	
Semantic content	语义学内容	Yǔyìxué nèiróng	
Semantic data modeling	语义数据建模	Yǔyì shùjù jiànmó	
Semantic information	语义信息	Yǔyì xìnxī	
Semantic knowledge	语义知识	Yǔyì zhīshi	
Semantic object	语义对象	Yǔyì duìxiàng	
Semantic relationship	语义关系	Yǔyì guānxi	
Semantic serializability	语义可串行性	Yǔyì kěchuànhángxìng	
Semantic serialization graph	语义串行化图	Yǔyì chuànhánghuà tú	SeSG
Semantic transparency	语义透明	Yǔyì tòumíng	
Semantic unit	语义单元	Yǔyì dānyuán	
Semantics	语义	Yǔyì	
Semantics-oriented component model	面向语义构件模型	Miànxiàng yǔyì gòujiàn móxíng	
Semaphore	信号量	Xìnhào liàng	
Semaphore	信号灯	Xìnhàodēng	
Sembawang Telecommunications Pvt.Ltd. (Singapore company)	胜宝旺通讯私人有限公司	Shèng-bǎo-wàng tōngxùn sīrén yǒuxiàn gōngsī	
Semi-additive measure	半加法度量	Bànjiāfǎ dùliàng	
Semi-aqueous cleaning (in SMT)	不完全水清洗	Bùwánquán shuǐ qīngxǐ	
Semi-automated digitizing	半自动化数字化	Bànzìdònghuà shùzìhuà	
Semi-automatic call connection	半自动呼叫接续	Bànzìdòng hūjiào jiēxù	
Semi-automatic screen printer with visual	半自动代视觉丝印机	Bànzìdòng dài shìjué sīyìnjī	
Semi-automatic switching	半自动交换	Bàn zìdòng jiāohuàn	
Semiautomatic toll offering	长途半自动插入	Chángtú bànzìdòng chārù	
Semiconductor Industry Association	半导体工业协会	Bàndǎotǐ gōngyè xiéhuì	SIA
Semiconductor integrated circuit	半导体集成电路	Bàndǎotǐ jíchéng diànlù	
Semiconductor laser	半导体激光器	Bàndǎotǐ jīguāngqì	
Semiconductor laser amplifier	半导体光放大器	Bàndǎotǐ guāng fàngdàqì	SLA
Semiconductor lithography	半导体图案处理曝光	Bàndǎotǐ tú'àn chǔlǐ bàoguāng	
Semiconductor memory	半导体存储器	Bàndǎotǐ cúnchǔqì	
Semiconductor optical amplifier	半导体光放大器	Bàndǎotǐ guāng fàngdàqì	SOA
Semiconductor polishing machine	半导体研磨加工设备	Bàndǎotǐ yánmó jiāgōng shèbèi	
Semiconductor trimming	半导体整修	Bàndǎotǐ zhěngxiū	
Semiconductor vacuum evaporation equipment	半导体真空蒸镀设备	Bàndǎotǐ zhēnkōng zhēngdù shèbèi	
Semiconductor visible laser module	半导体可见光激光模组	Bàndǎotǐ kějiànguāng jīguāng mózǔ	
Semi-duplex operation	半双工操作	Bànshuānggōng cāozuò	
Semigroup structure	半群结构	Bànqún jiégòu	
Semi-insulated buried heterostructure (laser)	半绝缘隐埋式异质结（激光器）	Bàn juéyuán yǐnmáishì yìzhìjié (jīguāngqì)	SIBH
Semi-major axis	长半径	Cháng bànjìng	
Semi-minor axis	短半径	Duǎn bànjìng	

Semi-permanent link layer	半永久链路层	Bàn yǒngjiǔ liànlù céng	SPLL
Semi-public environment	半公共环境	Bàngōnggòng huánjìng	SPE
Semi-rigid cable	半刚电缆	Bàngāng diànlǎn	
Semi-rigid coaxial line	半刚性同轴线	Bàn gāngxìng tóngzhóu xiàn	
Semi-variogram	半变异函数	Bànbiànyì hánshù	
Send authentication information	发鉴权信息	Fā jiànquán xìnxī	
Send data	发送数据	Fāsòng shùjù	SD
Send data condition	发送数据条件	Fāsòng shùjù tiáojiàn	SDC
Send data request message (in multicast)	发送数据请求消息	Fāsòng shùjù qǐngqiú xiāoxi	
Send e-mail (WP command)	传送邮件	Chuánsòng yóujiàn	
Send end signal	发结束信号	Fā jiéshù xìnhào	
Send message	发送消息	Fāsòng xiāoxi	SM
Send parameters	发参数	Fā cānshù	
Send routing information	发路由信息	Fā lùyóu xìnxī	
Send routing information	发送路由信息	Fāsòng lùyóu xìnxī	SRI
Send routing information acknowledgment	发送路由信息证实	Fāsòng lùyóu xìnxī zhèngshí	SRIack
Send sequence number	发送序列号	Fāsòng xùlièhào	SSN
Send special-information tone signal	发送专用信息音信号	Fāsòng zhuānyòng xìnxī yīnxìnhào	SST
Send-digits signal	请发码信号	Qǐng fāmǎ xìnhào	
Sender (in signaling)	发送器（信令中）	Fāsòngqì (xìnlìng zhōng)	
Sender-initiated	送者初始	Sòngzhě chūshǐ	
Sending complete	发送完全	Fāsòng wánquán	
Sending loudness rating	发送响度评定值	Fāsòng xiǎngdù píngdìngzhí	
Sending reference equivalent	发送参考当量	Fāsòng cānkǎo dāngliàng	
Sensed heat	显热	Xiǎn rè	
Sensitive cursor	感知游标	Gǎnzhī yóubiāo	
Sensitive information	敏感信息	Mǐngǎn xìnxī	
Sensitivity (of a receiver)	灵敏度	Língmǐndù	
Sensitivity analysis	敏感性分析	Mǐngǎn-xìng fēnxī	
Sensitivity threshold of automatic frequency control	自动频率控制的灵敏度门限	Zìdòng pínlǜ kòngzhìde língmǐndù ménxiàn	
Sensitivity threshold of automatic gain control	自动增益控制的[灵敏度]门限	Zìdòng zēngyì kòngzhìde língmǐndù ménxiàn	
Sensitizer (chemical)	感光剂	Gǎnguāngjì	
Sensor	传感器	Chuángǎnqì	
Sensor calibration	传感器定标	Chuángǎnqì dìngbiāo	
Sensor glove	感应手套	Gǎnyìng shǒutào	
Sensor resolution	传感器分辨率	Chuángǎnqì fēnbiànlǜ	
Sentence articulation	语句清晰度	Yǔjù qīngxīdù	
Sentence intelligibility	句子可懂度	Jùzi kědǒngdù	
Separate message approach	独立信息处理	Dúlì xìnxī chǔlǐ	
Separation	分割	Fēngē	
Septate waveguide	隔膜波导	Gémó bōdǎo	
Septet byte	七位字节	Qīwèi zìjié	
Sequence	序列	Xùliè	
Sequence division multiple access	顺序分配多路存取	Shùnxù fēnpèi duōlù cúnqǔ	SDMA
Sequence initiator	序列发起方	Xùliè fāqǐ fāng	

Sequence number	顺序号	Shùnxù hào	SN
Sequence number	序列号码	Xùliè hàomǎ	SN
Sequence number attack (cryptology)	序号攻击	Xùhào gōngjī	
Sequence number protection	顺序号码保护	Shùnxù hàomǎ bǎohù	SNP
Sequence number protection	序号保护	Xùhào bǎohù	SNP
Sequence numbers protocol data unit	序列号协议数据单元	Xùlièhào xiéyì shùjù dānyuán	SNP
Sequence recipient	序列接收方	Xùliè jiēshōu fāng	
Sequence shift keying-direct sequence spread spectrum	顺序位移键控-直接序列扩展频谱	Shùnxù wèiyí jiànkòng—zhíjiē xùliè kuòzhǎn pínpǔ	SSK-DS-SS
Sequenced collection	顺序集合	Shùnxù jíhé	
Sequenced packet exchange	顺序分组交换	Shùnxù fēnzǔ jiāohuàn	SPX
Sequenced packet exchange protocol (Novell usage)	序列分组交换协议	Xùliè fēnzǔ jiāohuàn xiéyì	SPX
Sequenced packet protocol	顺序分组协议	Shùnxù fēnzǔ xiéyì	SPP
Sequenced packet protocol	顺序信息包协议	Shùnxù xìnxī bāo xiéyì	SPP
Sequenced relationship	顺序关系	Shùnxù guānxi	
Sequenced routing update protocol	顺序路由更新协议	Shùnxù lùyóu gēngxīn xiéyì	SRTP
Sequenced routing update protocol	序列路由更新协议	Xùliè lùyóu gēngxīn xiéyì	SRTP
Sequencing	排序	Páixù	
Sequential access method	按序存取方式	Ànxù cúnqǔ fāngshì	SAM
Sequential cellular automata (cryptology)	串行细胞自动机	Chuànháng xìbāo zìdòngjī	SCA
Sequential computing	串行计算	Chuànháng jìsuàn	
Sequential container	序列式容器	Xùlièshì róngqì	
Sequential control logic	顺序控制逻辑	Shùnxù kòngzhì luóji	SCL
SEquential Couleur avec memoire (French television broadcast standard)	顺序与存储彩色电视系统	Shùnxù yǔ cúnchǔ cǎisè diànshì xìtǒng	SECAM
Sequential Couleur avec Memoire (Middle East television standard)	顺序彩色和存储视频制式	Shùnxù cǎisè hé cúnchǔ shìpín zhìshì	SECAM
Sequential disk processor	顺序磁盘处理机	Shùnxù cípán chǔlǐjī	SDP
Sequential file	顺序文件	Shùnxù wénjiàn	
Sequential fuzzy language	时序模糊语言	Shíxù móhu yǔyán	SFL
Sequential hunting	顺序搜寻	Shùnxù sōuxún	
Sequential layout order	顺序布局次序	Shùnxù bùjú cìxù	
Sequential logical order	顺序逻辑次序	Shùnxù luóji cìxù	
Sequential numbering scheme	序列号码机制	Xùliè hàomǎ jīzhì	SEQN
Sequential order	顺序次序	Shùnxù cìxù	
Sequential search	顺序查找	Shùnxù cházhǎo	
Sequential thinning	序列细化	Xùliè xìhuà	
Serial	串行	Chuànháng	
Serial arithmetic	串行运算	Chuànháng yùnsuàn	
Serial ATA (asynchronous terminal adapter)	串行 ATA	Chuànháng ATA	SATA
Serial automatic calling	串行自动呼叫	Chuànháng zìdòng hūjiào	
Serial clock transmit	串行时标发送	Chuànháng shíbiāo fāsòng	SCT
Serial clock transmit external	串行时钟外部传输	Chuànháng shízhōng wàibù chuánshū	SCTE
Serial code	串行码	Chuànháng mǎ	
Serial communication controller	串行通信控制器	Chuànháng tōngxìn kòngzhìqì	SCC
Serial data transmission	串行数据传输	Chuànháng shùjù chuánshū	SDT
Serial data trunk	串行数据总线	Chuànháng shùjù zǒngxiàn	

Serial infrared port	红外线串列接口	Hóngwàixiàn chuànliè jiēkǒu	
Serial input output handler	串行输入输出处理器	Chuànháng shūrù shūchū chǔlǐqì	SIOH
Serial input/output	串行输入输出	Chuànháng shūrù shūchū	SIO
Serial line interface protocol	串行线路接口协议	Chuànháng xiànlù jiēkǒu xiéyì	SLIP
Serial line interface protocol (IETF usage)	串形线路接口协议	Chuànxíng xiànlù jiēkǒu xiéyì	SLIP
Serial line Internet protocol	串行线路网际协议	Chuànháng xiànlù wǎngjì xiéyì	SLIP
Serial line internet protocol	互联网串行线协议	Hùliánwǎng chuànxíng xiàn xiéyì	SLIP
Serial number	串联号码	Chuànlián hàomǎ	SNR
Serial number	序号	Xùhào	SNR
Serial number	序号码	Xùhào mǎ	
Serial peripheral interface	串行外围接口	Chuànháng wàiwéi jiēkǒu	SPI
Serial port logic	串口逻辑	Chuànkǒu luójì	
Serial presence detect	串行存在检查	Chuànháng cúnzài jiǎnchá	SPD
Serial presence detect	内存内部序号检测装置	Nèicún nèibù xùhào jiǎncè zhuāngzhì	SPD
Serial presence detect	序号检测装置	Xùhào jiǎncè zhuāngzhì	SPD
Serial telecommunications Bus	串行通信总线	Chuànháng tōngxìn zǒngxiàn	ST-BUS
Serial to parallel converter	串并变换器	Chuàn-bìng biànhuànqì	
Serial tunnel	串行隧道	Chuànháng suìdào	STUN
Serial Viterbi decoder	串行维特比解码器	Chuànháng wéi-tè-bǐ jiěmǎqì	SVD
Serial/parallel conversion	穿/并变换	Chuān/bìng biànhuàn	S/P
Serializability	可串行性	Kěchuànháng-xìng	
Serializable	可串行	Kěchuànháng	
Serialization graph	串行化图	Chuànhánghuà tú	SG
Serialization/serialize	序列化	Xùlièhuà	
SERializing/DESerializing circuitry	串行并行转换电路	Chuànháng bìngxíng zhuǎnhuàn diànlù	SERDES
Serial-parallel conversion	串并行变换	Chuàn bìngxíng biànhuàn	
Serial-to-parallel converter, deserializer	串并行转换器	Chuàn bìngxíng zhuǎnhuànqì	
Series circuit, sequential circuit	时序电路	Shíxù diànlù	
Series-loaded antenna	串联加载天线	Chuànlián jiāzài tiānxiàn	
Seriously errored cell block ratio	严重误信元块比例	Yánzhòng wùxìn yuán kuài bǐlì	SECBR
Server	服务端	Fúwù duān	
Server	服务器	Fúwùqì	
Server	服务者	Fúwùzhě	
Server cluster	服务器群集	Fúwùqì qúnjí	
Server cursor (for database)	服务端游标	Fúwù duān yóubiāo	
Server cursor (for database)	服务器游标	Fúwùqì yóubiāo	
Server layer network	服务层网	Fúwù céng wǎng	
Server message block	服务器消息块	Fúwùqì xiāoxi kuài	SMB
Server message block	服务器信息块	Fúwùqì xìnxī kuài	SMB
Server message block protocol (IBM use)	服务器信息块协议	Fúwùqì xìnxī kuài xiéyì	SMB
Server name	服务器名称	Fúwùqì míngchēng	
Server operating system	服务器操作系统	Fúwùqì cāozuò xìtǒng	SOS
Server query analyzer (in SQL Server)	查询分析器	Cháxún fēnxīqì	
Server side include	服务器方包含	Fúwùqì fāng bāohán	SSI
Server signal degrade	服务层信号劣化	Fúwù céng xìnhào lièhuà	SSD
Server signal degrade	服务器信号劣化	Fúwùqì xìnhào lièhuà	SSD

Server signal fail	服务层信号失效	Fúwù céng xìnhào shīxiào	SSF
Server signal fail	服务器信号失效	Fúwùqì xìnhào shīxiào	SFF
Service	服务	Fúwù	
Service [quality] level agreement	服务品质协议	Fúwù pǐnzhì xiéyì	SLA
Service ability limit state	功能极限状态	Gōngnéng jíxiàn zhuàngtài	
Service access multiplexer	业务接入复用器	Yèwù jiērù fùyòngqì	SAM
Service access multiplexer interface	业务接入复用器接口	Yèwù jiērù fùyòngqì jiēkǒu	SAMI
Service access point	服务访问点	Fúwù fǎngwèn diǎn	SAP
Service access point	服务接入点	Fúwù jiērù diǎn	SAP
Service access point	业务接入点	Yèwù jiērù diǎn	SAP
Service access point identifier	服务访问电识别符	Fúwù fǎngwèn diàn shíbiéfú	SAPI
Service access point identifier	服务接入点识别符	Fúwù jiērù diǎn shíbiéfú	SAPI
Service access point identifier	服务接入点识别器	Fúwù jiērù diǎn shíbiéqì	SAPI
Service access point identifier	业务接入点标志	Yèwù jiērù diǎn biāozhì	SAPI
Service access point identifier	业务接入点识符	Yèwù jiērù diǎn shífú	SAPI
Service access point identity	业务接入识别码	Yèwù jiērù shíbié mǎ	SAPI
Service access point indicator	服务访问点标识符	Fúwù fǎngwèn diǎn biāozhì fú	SAPI
Service access point indicator	服务接入点标识	Fúwù jiērù diǎn biāozhì	SAPI
Service access probability	业务接概率	Yèwù jiē gàilǜ	
Service accessibility	服务可得到性	Fúwù kědédàoxìng	
Service accessibility	业务可接入性	Yèwù kějiērùxìng	
Service accessibility performance	业务可接入性性能	Yèwù kějiērùxìng xìngnéng	
Service activator	服务启动	Fúwù qǐdòng	
Service alarm	业务告警	Yèwù gàojǐng	SA
Service allowance control	业务容许控制	Yèwù róngxǔ kòngzhì	SAC
Service application gateway function	业务应用网关功能	Yèwù yìngyòng wǎngguān gōngnéng	SAGF
Service arc	服务弧	Fúwù hú	
Service area	服务区	Fúwùqū	
Service assurance	业务保障	Yèwù bǎozhàng	SA
Service attribute	业务属性	Yèwù shǔxìng	
Service availability	业务可用性	Yèwù kěyòngxìng	
Service bit rate	业务比特率	Yèwù bǐtè lǜ	
Service broker (in VPN)	服务代理	Fúwù dàilǐ	
Service capability feature	业务能力特征	Yèwù nénglì tèzhēng	SCF
Service capability server	业务能力服务器	Yèwù nénglì fúwùqì	SCS
Service center	业务中心	Yèwù zhōngxīn	SC
Service channel	服务信道	Fúwù xìndào	SC
Service channel	勤务信道	Qínwù xìndào	
Service circuit	业务电路	Yèwù diànlù	
Service circuit module	服务电路模块	Fúwù diànlù mókuài	SCM
Service class of incoming trunk	入中继业务类别	Rù zhōngjì yèwù lèibié	
Service code	业务码	Yèwù mǎ	SC
Service code	业务码	Yèwù mǎ	SC
Service communication system	勤务通信系统	Qínwù tōngxìn xìtǒng	
Service computer (in telecommunication)	业务计算机	Yèwù jìsuànjī	
Service configuration management	服务组成管理	Fúwù zǔchéng guǎnlǐ	Ser.CM

Service confirmation	业务确认	Yèwù quèrèn	SCF
Service connection impedance	供电连接阻抗	Gōngdiàn liánjiē zǔkàng	
Service connection impedance	业务连线阻抗	Yèwù liánxiàn zǔkàng	
Service consumer system	业务使用者系统	Yèwù shǐyòngzhě xìtǒng	SCS
Service control function	业务控制功能	Yèwù kòngzhì gōngnéng	SCF
Service control function - call unrelated service function	业务控制功能-不相干呼叫业务功能	Yèwù kòngzhì gōngnéng-bùxiānggān hūjiào yèwù gōngnéng	SCF-CUSF
Service control function - service control function	业务控制功能 -业务控制功能	Yèwù kòngzhì gōngnéng - yèwù kòngzhì gōngnéng	SCF-SCF
Service control function - service data function	业务控制功能 – 业务数据功能	Yèwù kòngzhì gōngnéng – yèwù shùjù gōngnéng	SCF-SDF
Service control function - service switching function	业务控制功能 – 业务交换功能	Yèwù kòngzhì gōngnéng – yèwù jiāohuàn gōngnéng	SCF-SSF
Service control function - specialized resource function	业务控制功能 专用资源功能	Yèwù kòngzhì gōngnéng-zhuānyòng zīyuán gōngnéng	SCF-SRF
Service control gateway function	业务控制网关功能	Yèwù kòngzhì wǎngguān gōngnéng	SCGF
Service control point	业务控制点	Yèwù kòngzhì diǎn	SCP
Service control user agent function	业务控制用户代理功能	Yèwù kòngzhì yònghù dàilǐ gōngnéng	SCUAF
Service creation engineering environment	业务生成工程环境	Yèwù shēngchéng gōngchéng huánjìng	SCREEN
Service creation environment	业务创造环境	Yèwù chuàngzào huánjìng	SCE
Service creation environment	业务生成环境	Yèwù shēngchéng huánjìng	SCE
Service creation environment function	业务创建环境功能	Yèwù chuàngjiàn huánjìng gōngnéng	SCEF
Service creation environment function	业务生成环境功能	Yèwù shēngchéng huánjìng gōngnéng	SCEF
Service creation environment point	业务生成环境点	Yèwù shēngchéng huánjìng diǎn	SCEP
Service data function	业务数据功能	Yèwù shùjù gōngnéng	SDF
Service data point	业务数据点	Yèwù shùjù diǎn	SDP
Service data unit	服务数据单元	Fúwù shùjù dānyuán	SDU
Service data unit	业务数据单元	Yèwù shùjù dānyuán	SDU
Service digit	勤务数位	Qínwù shùwèi	
Service digit	业务位	Yèwù wèi	
Service discovery	服务搜索	Fúwù sōusuǒ	SD
Service discovery and application profile	服务发现和应用配置	Fúwù fāxiàn hé yìngyòng pèizhì	SDAP
Service discovery database	服务搜索数据库	Fúwù sōusuǒ shùjùkù	SDDB
Service discovery protocol	业务搜索协议	Yèwù sōusuǒ xiéyì	SDP
Service element	服务元素	Fúwù yuánsù	
Service feature	业务特征	Yèwù tèzhēng	SF
Service flow identifier	业务流标识符	Yèwùliú biāoshífú	SFID
Service fulfillment	业务开通	Yèwù kāitōng	SF
Service gateway control protocol	业务网关控制协议	Yèwù wǎngguān kòngzhì xiéyì	SGCP
Service GPRS support node	服务 GPRS 支持节点	Fúwù GPRS zhīchí jiédiǎn	SGSN
Service identifier	业务标识符	Yèwù biāozhì fú	SID
Service implementation capabilities	实现业务容量	Shíxiàn yèwù róngliàng	SIC
Service in random order	随机服务	Suíjī fúwù	
Service indicator	业务指示	Yèwù zhǐshì	
Service indicator	业务指示表示语	Yèwù zhǐshì biǎoshì yǔ	
Service industry	服务产业	Fúwù chǎnyè	

Service information byte	业务信息字节	Yèwù xìnxī zìjié	
Service information octet	业务消息八位位组	Yèwù xiāoxi bāwèi wèizǔ	SIO
Service information octet	业务信息八位位组	Yèwù xìnxī bāwèi wèizǔ	SIO
Service integrity	服务完善性	Fúwù wánshànxìng	
Service integrity	业务完善性	Yèwù wánshànxìng	
Service interaction manager	业务相互作用管理	Yèwù xiānghù zuòyòng guǎnlǐ	SIM
Service interface and protocol processing unit	业务接口和协议处理单元	Yèwù jiēkǒu hé xiéyì chǔlǐ dānyuán	SIPP
Service interface V.11	服务接口 V.11	Fúwù jiēkǒu V.11	Q.1
Service interworking	业务互通	Yèwù hùtōng	SI
Service interworking	业务协调	Yèwù xiétiáo	
Service level agreement	业务等级协商	Yèwù děngjí xiéshāng	SLA
Service level agreement	业务级别协议	Yèwù jíbié xiéyì	SLA
Service location protocol	服务定位协议	Fúwù dìngwèi xiéyì	SLP
Service logic	业务逻辑	Yèwù luóji	SL
Service logic execution environment	业务逻辑执行环境	Yèwù luóji zhíxíng huánjìng	SLEE
Service logic processing instance	业务逻辑处理实例	Yèwù luóji chǔlǐ shílì	SLPI
Service logic program	业务逻辑程序	Yèwù luóji chéngxù	SLP
Service logic program	业务逻辑进程	Yèwù luóji jìnchéng	SLP
Service logic program instance	业务逻辑进程实例	Yèwù luóji jìnchéng shílì	SLPI
Service management	服务管理	Fúwù guǎnlǐ	SM
Service management access function	业务管理接入功能	Yèwù guǎnlǐ jiērù gōngnéng	SMAF
Service management access point	业务管理接入点	Yèwù guǎnlǐ jiērù diǎn	SMAP
Service management and operations	服务管理和运营	Fúwù guǎnlǐ hé yùnyíng	
Service management control platform	业务管理控制平台	Yèwù guǎnlǐ kòngzhì píngtái	SMCP
Service management function	业务管理功能	Yèwù guǎnlǐ gōngnéng	SMF
Service management layer	业务管理层	Yèwù guǎnlǐ céng	SML
Service management platform	业务管理平台	Yèwù guǎnlǐ píngtái	SMP
Service management point	业务管理点	Yèwù guǎnlǐ diǎn	SMP
Service management system	业务管理系统	Yèwù guǎnlǐ xìtǒng	SMS
Service mix	业务组合	Yèwù zǔhé	
Service network interface	业务网络接口	Yèwù wǎngluò jiēkǒu	SNI
Service node	服务节点	Fúwù jiédiǎn	SN
Service node	业务节点	Yèwù jiédiǎn	SN
Service node interface	业务节点接口	Yèwù jiédiǎn jiēkǒu	SNI
Service node/intelligent peripheral	服务节点 / 智能外围设备	Fúwù jiédiǎn/zhìnéng wàiwéi shèbèi	SN / IP
Service operability	服务易行性	Fúwù yìxíngxìng	
Service operability	业务可操作性	Yèwù kěcāozuòxìng	
Service operability performance	业务可操作性性能	Yèwù kěcāozuòxìng xìngnéng	
Service pack	服务补丁	Fúwù bǔdìng	
Service port	业务端口	Yèwù duānkǒu	
Service port function	业务端口功能	Yèwù duānkǒu gōngnéng	SPF
Service port function	业务口功能	Yèwù kǒu gōngnéng	SPF
Service primitive	服务原语	Fúwù yuányǔ	
Service processing module	业务处理模块	Yèwù chǔlǐ mókuài	SPM
Service profile	业务轮廓	Yèwù lúnkuò	
Service profile identifier	服务类型标识	Fúwù lèixíng biāozhì	SPID

Service profile management	业务轮廓管理	Yèwù lúnkuò guǎnlǐ	
Service programming code	业务编程代码	Yèwù biānchéng dàimǎ	SPC
Service provider	服务提供部门	Fúwù tígōng bùmén	
Service provider	服务提供商	Fúwù tígōng shāng	SP
Service provider	服务提供者	Fúwù tígòngzhě	
Service provider	业务提供商	Yèwù tígōngshāng	SP
Service provider	业务提供者	Yèwù tígòngzhě	SP
Service provider control key	业务提供者控制键	Yèwù tígòngzhě kòngzhì jiàn	SPCK
Service provider identifier	业务提供者标识符	Yèwù tígòngzhě biāozhìfú	SPI
Service provider interface	业务提供者接口	Yèwù tígòngzhě jiēkǒu	SPI
Service provider link	业务提供者链路	Yèwù tígòngzhě liànlù	SPL
Service provider network	业务提供者网络	Yèwù tígòngzhě wǎngluò	SPN
Service provider network identifier	业务提供者网络标识符	Yèwù tígòngzhě wǎngluò biāozhìfú	SPNI
Service provisioning time	服务准备时间	Fúwù zhǔnbèi shíjiān	
Service reject	业务拒绝	Yèwù jùjué	SRJ
Service relationships	服务关系	Fúwù guānxi	
Service request	业务请求	Yèwù qǐngqiú	SRQ
Service request not honored	不能对应传送请求	Bùnéng duìyìng chuánsòng qǐngqiú	SNH
Service request report	业务请求报告	Yèwù qǐngqiú bàogào	SRQR
Service requirement	使用要求	Shǐyòng yāoqiú	
Service retainability	服务可保持性	Fúwù kěbǎochíxìng	
Service retainability	业务可保持性	Yèwù kěbǎochíxìng	
Service retainability performance	业务可保持性性能	Yèwù kěbǎochíxìng xìngnéng	
Service scheduler (in CORBA)	服务调度器	Fúwù diàodùqì	
Service selection server	服务选择服务器	Fúwù xuǎnzé fúwùqì	SSS
Service selection server	业务选择服务器	Yèwù xuǎnzé fúwùqì	SSS
Service selector (in SDH)	业务选择器	Yèwù xuǎnzéqì	
Service set identity	业务组标识符	Yèwù zǔ biāozhì fú	SSID
Service signal failure	业务信号失效	Yèwù xìnhào shīxiào	SSF
Service specific coordination function supporting user-to-network interface	支持用户网络接口的业务特定协调功能	Zhīchí yònghù wǎngluò jiēkǒude yèwù tèdìng xiétiáo gōngnéng	SSCF-UNI
Service status	服务状况	Fúwù zhuàngkuàng	
Service support performance	业务支持性能	Yèwù zhīchí xìngnéng	
Service support transmission protocol	业务支撑传输协议	Yèwù zhīchēng chuánshū xiéyì	SSTP
Service supportability	服务支持性	Fúwù zhīchíxìng	
Service switching center	业务交换中心	Yèwù jiāohuàn zhōngxīn	SSC
Service switching function	业务交换功能	Yèwù jiāohuàn gōngnéng	SSF
Service switching point	业务交换点	Yèwù jiāohuàn diǎn	SSP
Service switching point	业务交换眯	Yèwù jiāohuàn mí	SSP
Service ticket	服务票据	Fúwù piàojù	ST
Service to user information	业务到用户信息	Yèwù dào yònghù xìnxī	STUI
Service usage	业务使用率	Yèwù shǐyònglǜ	SU
Service user abandonment probability	业务用户弃用概率	Yèwù yònghù qìyòng gàilǜ	
Service user mistake probability	业务用户差错概率	Yèwù yònghù chācuò gàilǜ	
Serviceability	可服务性	Kěfúwùxìng	
Serviceability performance	业务能力性能	Yèwù nénglì xìngnéng	

Service-independent building blocks	业务独立构件	Yèwù dúlì gòujiàn	SIB
Service-level agreement	服务等级协议	Fúwù děngjí xiéyì	SLA
Service-level agreement	服务级别协定	Fúwù jíbié xiédìng	SLA
Service-level agreement	服务水平协议	Fúwù shuǐpíng xiéyì	SLA
Service-level agreement	业务等级协议	Yèwù děngjí xiéyì	SLA
Service-level management	服务级管理	Fúwù jí guǎnlǐ	SLM
Service-level objective	服务等级目标	Fúwù děngjí mùbiāo	SLO
Service-oriented part	面向业务部分	Miànxiàng yèwù bùfen	
Services Experts Rapporteurs Group (GSM MoU)	业务专家组	Yèwù zhuānjiāzǔ	SERG
Services interface and protocol processing	业务接口和协议处理	Yèwù jiēkǒu hé xiéyì chǔlǐ	SIPP
Service-specific connection oriented protocol in a multi-link and connectionless environment	在一个多连接和无连接环境中业务特定面向连接协议	Zài yīgè duō liánjiē hé wú liánjiē huánjìng zhōng yèwù tèdìng miànxiàng liánjiē xiéyì	SSCOPMCE
Service-specific connection-oriented function	业务特定面向连接功能	Yèwù tèdìng miànxiàng liánjiē gōngnéng	SSCOF
Service-specific connection-oriented protocol	面向业务专用连接的协议	Miànxiàng yèwù zhuānyòng liánjiēde xiéyì	SSCOP
Service-specific connection-oriented protocol	特定服务的面向连接协议	Tèdìng fúwùde miànxiàng liánjiē xiéyì	SSCOP
Service-specific connection-oriented protocol	业务特定面向连接协议	Yèwù tèdìng miànxiàng liánjiē xiéyì	SSCOP
Service-specific convergence layer	业务特有会聚层	Yèwù tèyǒu huìjù céng	SSCS
Service-specific convergence sub-layer	特定服务的汇聚子层	Tèdìng fúwùde huìjù zicéng	SSCS
Service-specific convergence sub-layer	特殊业务会聚子层	Tèshū yèwù huìjù zicéng	SSCS
Service-specific convergence sub-layer	业务特定会聚子层	Yèwù tèdìng huìjù zicéng	SSCS
Service-specific coordination function	特殊业务协调功能	Tèshū yèwù xiétiáo gōngnéng	SSCF
Service-specific coordination function	业务特定的协调功能	Yèwù tèdìngde xiétiáo gōngnéng	SSCF
Service-specific coordination function-network node interface	特殊业务协调功能-网络节点接口	Tèshū yèwù xiétiáo gōngnéng- wǎngluò jiédiǎn jiēkǒu	SSCF-NNI
Service-specific segmentation and re-assembly sub-layer	特殊业务分段和重新装配子层	Tèshū yèwù fēnduàn hé chóngxīn zhuāngpèi zicéng	SSSAR
Service-user	服务用户	Fúwù yònghù	
Serviceware revolution	服务件革命	Fúwù jiàn gémìng	
Serving base station	服务基站	Fúwù jīzhàn	
Serving cell	服务小区	Fúwù xiǎoqū	
Serving GPRS supporting node	GPRS 服务支持节点	GPRS fúwù zhīchí jiédiǎn	SGSN
Serving mobile data intermediate system	服务移动数据中介系统	Fúwù yídòng shùjù zhōngjiè xìtǒng	
Serving network	服务网络	Fúwù wǎngluò	SN
Serving radio network controller	服务无线电网络控制器	Fúwù wúxiàndiàn wǎngluò kòngzhìqì	SRNC
Serving radio network sub-system	服务无线网络分系统	Fúwù wúxiàn wǎngluò fēnxìtǒng	SRNS
Servlet	小服务程序	Xiǎo fúwù chéngxù	
Servo drive system	伺服驱动系统	Sì-fú qūdòng xìtǒng	SDS
Session	对话	Duìhuà	
Session announcement protocol	会话通知协议	Huìhuà tōngzhī xiéyì	SAP
Session announcement protocol (IETF use)	会话通告协议	Huìhuà tōnggào xiéyì	SAP
Session control protocol (in DECnet)	会话控制协议	Huìhuà kòngzhì xiéyì	SCP
Session description protocol	会话描述协议	Huìhuà miáoshù xiéyì	SDP
Session initiation protocol	会话初始协议	Huìhuà chūshǐ xiéyì	SIP
Session initiation protocol	会话发起协议	Huìhuà fāqǐ xiéyì	SIP
Session initiation protocol	会话启动协议	Huìhuà qǐdòng xiéyì	SIP
Session initiation protocol	会话起始协议	Huìhuà qǐshǐ xiéyì	SIP

Session key	对话密钥	Duìhuà mìyào	
Session layer	会话层	Huìhuà céng	
Session layer protocol (in ISO's OSI)	会话层协议	Huìhuà céng xiéyì	SP
Session manager	会话管理	Huìhuà guǎnlǐ	SM
Session protocol data unit	会话协议数据单元	Huìhuà xiéyì shùjù dānyuán	SPDU
Session protocol machine	会话协议机	Huìhuà xiéyìjī	SPM
Session service	会话服务	Huìhuà fúwù	SS
Session service access point	话路服务接入点	Huàlù fúwù jiērù diǎn	SSAP
Session service access point	会话服务访问点	Huìhuà fúwù fǎngwèn diǎn	SSAP
Session service data unit	会话服务数据单元	Huìhuà fúwù shùjù dānyuán	SSDU
Session (for database)	会话	Huìhuà	
Session-initiated protocol	起始会话协议	Qǐshǐ huìhuà xiéyì	SIP
Set	集合	Jíhé	
Set (in switching)	置位	Zhìwèi	
Set (verb, in switching)	置忙	Zhìmáng	
Set and string problems	集合与串的问题	Jíhé yǔ chuànde wèntí	
Set asynchronous balanced mode	设立异步均衡模式	Shèlì yìbù jūnhéng móshì	SABM
Set asynchronous balanced mode	设置异步平衡模式	Shèzhì yìbù pínghéng móshì	SABM
Set asynchronous balanced mode	置异步平衡方式	Zhì yìbù pínghéng fāngshì	SABM
Set asynchronous balanced mode extended	置扩展的异步平衡方式	Zhì kuòzhǎnde yìbù pínghéng fāngshì	SABME
Set asynchronous balanced mode extended	置异步平衡扩展模式	Zhì yìbù pínghéng kuòzhǎn móshì	SABME
Set cover	集合覆盖	Jíhé fùgài	
Set function	集合函数	Jíhé hánshù	
Set initialization mode	设置初始化模式	Shèzhì chūshǐhuà móshì	SIM
Set initialization mode	置初始化方式	Zhì chūshǐhuà fāngshì	SIM
Set normal response	设置正常应答	Shèzhì zhèngcháng yìngdá	SNR
Set normal response mode	置正常响应方式	Zhì zhèngcháng xiǎngyìng fāngshì	SNRM
Set packing	集合配置	Jíhé pèizhì	
Set top box	顶置盒	Dǐngzhìhé	STB
Setter (in software)	设值函数	Shèzhí hánshù	
Setting	版式	Bǎnshì	
Settling time	设置时间	Shèzhì shíjiān	
Set-top-box	机顶盒	Jīdǐnghé	STB
Setup	建立	Jiànlì	
Setup acknowledge	建立认可	Jiànlì rènkě	
Setup entire table	设定整表	Shèdìng zhěngbiǎo	
Setup initialization file	安装程序初始化文件	Ānzhuāng chéngxù chūshǐhuà wénjiàn	
Setup record	设定记录	Shèdìng jìlù	
Severely disturbed period	严重扰动期	Yánzhòng rǎodòng qī	SDP
Severely errored cell block	严重误信元块	Yánzhòng wù xìnyuán kuài	SECB
Severely errored cell block ratio	严重差错信元块比	Yánzhòng chācuò xìnyuán kuài bǐ	SECBR
Severely errored cell block ratio	严重误信元块比例	Yánzhòng wùxìn yuán kuài bǐlì	SECBR
Severely errored frame	严重错误帧	Yánzhòng cuòwù zhèng	SEF
Severely errored second	严重差错秒	Yánzhòng chācuò miǎo	SES
Severely errored second	严重误块秒	Yánzhòng wùkuài miǎo	SES
Severely errored second	严重误码秒	Yánzhòng wùmǎ miǎo	SES

English	Chinese	Pinyin	Abbreviation
Severely errored second ratio	严重差错秒比	Yánzhòng chācuò miǎo bǐ	SESR
Severely errored second ratio	严重误块秒比	Yánzhòng wùkuài miǎo bǐ	SESR
Severely errored second ratio	严重误码秒比	Yánzhòng wùmǎ miǎo bǐ	SESR
Severity level	严重级别	Yánzhòng jíbié	
Sextet byte	六位字节	Liùwèi zìjié	
Shading	形态描影	Xíngtài miáoyǐng	
Shading (video term)	描影	Miáoyǐng	
Shadow mask (video term)	阴罩式	Yīnzhàoshì	
Shadowing (in SMT)	阴影	Yīnyǐng	
Shallow parsing	浅层句法分析	Qiǎncéng jùfǎ fēnxī	
Shallow-trench isolation	浅槽隔离	Qiǎncáo gélí	
Shanghai Bell Corp.	上海贝尔	Shànghǎi bèi-ěr	
Shanghai Raychem (China subsidiary of Raychem US)	上海瑞侃电缆附件有限公司	Shànghǎi ruì-kǎn diànlǎn fùjiàn yǒuxiàn gōngsī	
Shanghai Research Institute of Optics and Fine Mechanics	上海光学精密机械研究所	Shànghǎi guāngxué jīngmìjīxiè yánjiūsuǒ	
Shannon (Claude Shannon, a pioneer of digital communications)	香农	Xiāng-nóng	
Shannon, Claude	山农	Shān-nóng	
Shape analysis	形状分析	Xíngzhuàng fēnxī	
Shape similarity	形相似多边	Xíngxiàngsì duōbiān	
Shaped-beam antenna	赋形射束天线	Fùxíng shèshù tiānxiàn	
Share disk	共享磁盘	Gòngxiǎng cípán	SD
Share everything	完全共享	Wánquán gòngxiǎng	SE
Share of expenses	费用分担	Fèiyòng fēndān	
Shared area	共用领域	Gòngyòng lǐngyù	
Shared band	共用频带	Gòngyòng píndài	
Shared boundary	公共边界	Gōnggòng biānjiè	
Shared buffer memory	共享存储器	Gòngxiǎng cúnchǔqì	SBM
Shared channel control channel	共享信道控制信道	Gòngxiǎng xìndào kòngzhì xìndào	SHCCH
Shared dimension	共享维度	Gòngxiǎng wéidù	
Shared feature	共享特征	Gòngxiǎng tèzhēng	
Shared interworking function system	共享互通功能	Gòngxiǎng hùtōng gōngnéng	SIWFS
Shared lock (for database)	共享锁	Gòngxiǎng suǒ	
Shared memory architecture	共享内存结构	Gòngxiǎng nèicún jiégòu	SMA
Shared memory mapping	共享内存映射	Gòngxiǎng nèicún yìngshè	
Shared protection ring	分享保护环	Fēnxiǎng bǎohù huán	
Shared protection ring	共享保护环	Gòngxiǎng bǎohù huán	
Shared protection ring	共用保护环	Gòngyòng bǎohù huán	
Shared resources module	共享资源模块	Gòngxiǎng zīyuán mókuài	SRM
Shared risk link group	共享风险链路组	Gòngxiǎng fēngxiǎn liànlù zǔ	SRLG
Shared secret data	共享保密数据	Gòngxiǎng bǎomì shùjù	SSD
Shared secret data	共用保密数据	Gòngyòng bǎomì shùjù	SSD
Shared system key	共享密钥	Gòngxiǎng mìyào	
Shared tree	共享树	Gòngxiǎng shù	
Shared unlicenced personal radio network	共用无执照个人无线电网络	Gòngyòng wúzhízhào gèrén wúxiàndiàn wǎngluò	SUPERNET
Shared vertex	公共顶节点	Gōnggòng dǐng jiédiǎn	
Shared wireless access protocol	共享无线访问协议	Gòngxiǎng wúxiàn fǎngwèn xiéyì	SWAP

Sharp (Japanese company)	夏普	Xià-pǔ	
Sharp cutoff filter (optical)	尖锐滤光镜	Jiānruì lǜguāngjìng	
Shear	剪切	Jiǎnqiē	
Shear failure	剪切破坏	Jiǎnqiē pòhuài	
Shear strain	剪切应变	Jiǎnqiē yìngbiàn	
Shear stress	剪切应力	Jiǎnqiē yìnglì	
Shear wave	剪切波	Jiǎnqiē bō	
Shear wave velocity	剪切波速度	Jiǎnqiē bō sùdù	
Shearing strength	剪切强度	Jiǎnqiē qiángdù	
Shearing test	剪切实验	Jiǎnqiē shíyàn	
Sheath, jacket	护套	Hùtào	
Sheet-fed color image scanner	馈纸式影像扫描器	Kuìzh-shì yǐngxiàng sǎomiáoqì	
Shelf	子架	Zijià	
Shell, case	壳	Ké	
Shelter	方舱	Fāngcāng	
Shianfu (abbreviation for the Shianfu Optical Fiber and Cables Co. Ltd.)	西古	Xī gǔ	
Shield	屏蔽体	Píngbìtǐ	
Shielded cable	屏蔽电缆	Píngbì diànlǎn	
Shielded enclosure	屏蔽壳体	Píngbì kétǐ	
Shielded enclosure (radio frequency)	屏蔽室	Píngbìshì	
Shielded foil twisted pair	屏蔽金融箔对线	Píngbì jīnróng bó duìxiàn	SFTP
Shielded twisted pair	屏幕双绞线	Píngmù shuāngjiǎoxiàn	STP
Shielded twisted pair cable	屏蔽对线电缆	Píngbì duìxiàn diànlǎn	
Shielded twisted pair cables	屏蔽对绞电缆	Píngbì duìjiǎo diànlǎn	
Shielded-loop antenna	屏蔽环形天线	Píngbì huánxíng tiānxiàn	
Shielding	屏蔽	Píngbì	
Shielding effectiveness	屏蔽效能	Píngbì xiàonéng	
Shielding factor	屏蔽系数	Píngbì xìshù	
Shift	移位	Yíwèi	
Shift in	移入	Yírù	SI
Shift key	换档键	Huàn dàng jiàn	
Shift key	移位键	Yíwèi jiàn	
Shift out	移出	Yíchū	SO
Shift pulse	移位脉冲	Yíwèi màichōng	SP
Shift register	移位寄存器	Yíwèi jìcúnqì	
Shift row	行移位	Háng yíwèi	
Shift, offset	偏移	Piānyí	
Shim program (used between two interface programs)	垫片程序	Diànpiàn chéngxù	
Ship earth station	船舶地球站	Chuánbó dìqiúzhàn	
Ship movement service	船舶移动业务	Chuánbó yídòng yèwù	
Ship radio	船用收音机	Chuányòng shōuyīnjī	
Ship station	船舶电台	Chuánbó diàntái	
Ship's emergency transmitter	船舶应急发信机	Chuánbó yìngjí fāxìnjī	
Shock current	触电电流	Chùdiàn diànliú	
Shock protection system	抗震保护系统	Kàngzhèn bǎohù xìtǒng	SPS

Shock sensor	震动传感器	Zhèndòng chuángǎnqì	SS
Shock toughness	冲击切性	Chōngjī qiēxìng	
Shooting game (computer game)	射击类游戏	Shèjī lèi yóuxì	STG
Short	短接	Duǎnjiē	
Short column	短柱	Duǎn zhù	
Short interruption (of supply voltage)	短时间中断	Duǎnshíjiān zhōngduàn	
Short message	短消息	Duǎn xiāoxi	SM
Short message application layer	短消息应用层	Duǎn xiāoxi yìngyòng céng	SM-AL
Short message center	短消息中心	Duǎn xiāoxi zhōngxīn	SMC, SC
Short message center acceptance console	短消息中心受理台	Duǎn xiāoxi zhōngxīn shòulǐ tái	
Short message control entity	短消息控制实体	Duǎn xiāoxi kòngzhì shítǐ	SMC
Short message data link layer	短消息数据链路层	Duǎn xiāoxi shùjù liànlù céng	SM - DLL
Short message entity	段消息实体	Duàn xiāoxi shítǐ	SME
Short message gateway	短消息网关	Duǎn xiāoxi wǎng guān	SMG
Short message mobile-originated point-to-point	移动发起的点对点短消息	Yídòng fāqǐde diǎn duì diǎn duǎn xiāoxi	SM MO
Short message mobile-terminated point-to-point	移动终止的点对点短消息	Yídòng zhōngzhǐde diǎn duì diǎn duǎn xiāoxi	SM MT
Short message peer to peer protocol	短消息点对点协议	Duǎn xiāoxi diǎn duì diǎn xiéyì	SMPP
Short message point to point protocol	短消息点对点协议	Duǎn xiāoxi diǎn duì diǎn xiéyì	SMPP
Short message relay entity	短消息中继实体	Duǎn xiāoxi zhōngjì shítǐ	SMR
Short message relay layer	短消息中继层	Duǎn xiāoxi zhōngjì céng	SM-RL
Short message relay protocol	短消息中继协议	Duǎn xiāoxi zhōngjì xiéyì	SM-RP
Short message service	短消息业务	Duǎn xiāoxi yèwù	SMS
Short message service	短信业务	Duǎnxìn yèwù	SMS
Short message service cell broadcast	短消息小区广播	Duǎn xiāoxi xiǎoqū guǎngbō	SMSCB
Short message service cell broadcast	短消息业务小区广播	Duǎn xiāoxi yèwù xiǎoqū guǎngbō	SMS-CB
Short message service center	短消息业务中心	Duǎn xiāoxi yèwù zhōngxīn	SMSC
Short message service point to point	点对点短消息业务	Diǎn duì diǎn duǎn xiāoxi yèwù	SMS PP
Short message service/point-to-point	短消息业务/点到点	Duǎn xiāoxi yèwù/diǎn dàodiǎn	SMS/PP
Short message service-cell broadcast service center	短消息小区广播业务中心	Duǎn xiāoxi xiǎoqū guǎngbō yèwù zhōngxīn	SMS-CBSC
Short message service-mobile originating/point-to-point	移动台起始点对点短消息业务	Yídòngtái qǐshǐ diǎn duì diǎn duǎn xiāoxi yèwù	SMS-MO/PP
Short message service-mobile terminating/point-to-point	移动台终接点对点短消息业务	Yídòngtái zhōngjiēdiǎn duì diǎn duǎn xiāoxi yèwù	SMS-MT/PP
Short message switching center	短消息交换中心	Duǎn xiāoxi jiāohuàn zhōngxīn	SMSC
Short message system	短消息系统	Duǎn xiāoxi xìtǒng	
Short message terminal equipment	短消息终端	Duǎn xiāoxi zhōngduān	SMTE
Short message termination	短消息终端	Duǎn xiāoxi zhōngduān	SMTE
Short message transfer layer	短消息传递层	Duǎn xiāoxi chuándì céng	SM-TL
Short message transfer layer	短消息传送层	Duǎn xiāoxi chuánsòng céng	SM - TL
Short message transport layer	短消息传送层	Duǎn xiāoxi chuánsòng céng	SM-TL
Short name server/service	简单名字服务器/服务	Jiǎndān míngzì fúwùqì/fúwù	SNS
Short number dialing	简缩拨号	Jiǎnsuō bōhào	SND
Short number dialing	缩位拨号	Suōwèi bōhào	SND
Short signal	短信号	Duǎn xìnhào	
Short slot coupler	短开槽耦合器	Duǎn kāicáo ǒuhéqì	

English	Chinese	Pinyin	Abbr.
Short wave antenna	短波天线	Duǎnbō tiānxiàn	TX
Short wave communication	短波通信	Duǎnbō tōngxìn	
Short wave propagation	短波传播	Duǎnbō chuánbō	
Short wavelength optical fiber	短波光纤	Duǎnbō guāngxiān	SWL
Short wavelength semiconductor laser module	短波长半导体激光模组	Duǎn bōcháng bàndǎotǐ jīguāng mózǔ	
Short word size type	短句尺寸型	Duǎnjù chǐcùnxíng	SWS
Short-circuit	短路	Duǎnlù	
Short-circuit current	短路电流	Duǎnlù diànliú	
Short-circuit protection	短路保护	Duǎnlù bǎohù	
Short-circuit termination	短路终端	Duǎnlù zhōngduān	
Shortcut	快捷方式	Kuàijié fāngshì	
Shortcut key	快捷键	Kuàijié jiàn	
Shortened cyclic codes	缩短循环码	Suōduǎn xúnhuán mǎ	
Shortest common superstring	最短公共父串	Zuìduǎn gōnggòng fùchuàn	
Shortest path	最短路径	Zuìduǎn lùjìng	
Shortest path first	最短路径优先	Zuìduǎn lùjìng yōuxiān	SPF
Shortest path first algorithm	最短路径优先算法	Zuìduǎn lùjìng yōuxiān suànfǎ	SPF
Shortest path tree	源最短路径树	Yuán zuìduǎn lùjìng shù	STP
Shortest path tree	最短路径树	Zuìduǎn lùjìng shù	SPT
Shortest searching time first	最短寻道时间优先	Zuìduǎn xúndào shíjiān yōuxiān	SSTF
Shortest-path routing	最短路由选择	Zuìduǎn lùyóu xuǎnzé	
Shorthand	词组简码输入	Cízǔ jiǎnmǎ shūrù	
Short-hold (ISDN term)	线路保持	Xiànlù bǎochí	
Short-range forecast	短期预报	Duǎnqī yùbào	
Short-term card	计时票	Jìshí piào	
Short-term flicker indicator	短期抖动指示器	Duǎnqī dǒudòng zhǐshìqì	
Short-term frequency stability	短期频率稳定度	Duǎnqī pínlǜ wěndìngdù	
Short-term prediction	短期预报	Duǎnqī yùbào	
Shortwave fade-out	短波信号消逝	Duǎnbō xìnhào xiāoshì	SWF
Short-word instruction	短字指令	Duǎn zì zhǐlìng	
Shot noise	散弹噪声	Sàndàn zàoshēng	
Show plan	显示计划	Xiǎnshì jìhuà	
Show table grid (WP command)	显示表格线	Xiǎnshì biǎogé xiàn	
Shredder	粉碎机	Fěnsuìjī	
Shuffle (from mahjong slang)	洗牌	Xǐpái	
Shunning, evasion	躲避	Duǒbì	
Shunt-fed vertical antenna	并馈垂直天线	Bìngkuì chuízhí tiānxiàn	
Sibling	同级	Tóngjí	
Sichuan Unilink Microwave Communications Equipment and Engineering Co. Ltd.	四川省优立微波通讯设备工程公司	Sìchuān-shěng yōulì wēibō tōngxùn shèbèi gōngchéng gōngsī	
Side effect	副作用	Fùzuòyòng	
Side information (video term)	边信息	Biān xìnxī	
Side lobe suppression	边瓣抑制	Biānbàn yìzhì	
Side mode suppression ratio	边摸抑制比	Biānmō yìzhìbǐ	SMSR
Side tone masking rating	侧音屏蔽平定值	Cèyīn píngbì píngdìng zhí	STMR
Side tone reference equivalent	侧音参考当量	Cèyīn cānkǎo dāngliàng	

Sideband	边带	Biāndài	
Sideband address port	边带寻址端口	Biāndài xúnzhǐ duānkǒu	SAP
Sideband addressing	边带寻址	Biāndài xúnzhǐ	SBA
Sideband interference	边带干扰	Biāndài gānrǎo	
Sideband linear crosstalk	边带线性串扰	Biāndài xiànxìng chuànrǎo	
Sideband non-linear crosstalk	边带非线性串扰	Biāndài fēixiànxìng chuànrǎo	
Sideband suppression	边带抑制度	Biāndài yìzhìdù	
Sidelobe	旁瓣	Pángbàn	
Sidelobe cancellation	旁瓣消除	Pángbàn xiāochú	SLC
Sidelobe level	旁瓣电平	Pángbàn diànpíng	
Sidelobe suppression	旁瓣抑制	Pángbàn yìzhì	SLS
Side-looking radar	侧视雷达	Cèshì léidá	SLR
Sidereal period of rotation (of an object in space)	自转周期	Zìzhuàn zhōuqī	
Sidereal period revolution (of a satellite)	公转周期	Gōngzhuàn zhōuqī	
Sidetone loss	侧音消耗	Cèyīn xiāohào	
Siecor (JV between Siemens and Corning)	西康	Xī-kāng	
Siemens (German company)	西门子	Xī-mén-zǐ	
Sight, sound, speed	视频、音频、速度	Shìpín、yīnpín、sùdù	S3
Sign bit	符号位	Fúhào wèi	
Signal	信号	Xìnhào	
Signal analysis	信号分析	Xìnhào fēnxī	
Signal arithmetic unit	信号运算器	Xìnhào yùnsuànqì	
Signal byte expansion	信号字节扩展	Xìnhào zìjié kuòzhǎn	SBE
Signal combining equipment	信号组合设备	Xìnhào zǔhé shèbèi	SCE
Signal compander	信号压扩器	Xìnhào yākuòqì	
Signal component (in AC signaling)	信号成分	Xìnhào chéngfèn	
Signal conditioner	信号整形回路	Xìnhào zhěngxíng huílù	SGC
Signal constellation (in digital modulation)	信号星座	Xìnhào xīngzuò	
Signal conversion equipment	信号变换装置	Xìnhào biànhuàn zhuāngzhì	SCE
Signal conversion equipment	信号转换设备	Xìnhào zhuǎnhuàn shèbèi	
Signal degrade	信号劣化	Xìnhào lièhuà	SD
Signal degrade threshold	信号劣化门限	Xìnhào lièhuà ménxiàn	SDT
Signal detector	信号检测器	Xìnhào jiǎncèqì	
Signal distribution	信号分配	Xìnhào fēnpèi	
Signal element	信号码元	Xìnhào mǎyuán	
Signal element	信号元	Xìnhào yuán	
Signal fail	信号失效	Xìnhào shīxiào	SF
Signal failure threshold	信号失败门限	Xìnhào shībài ménxiàn	SFT
Signal function	信号功能	Xìnhào gōngnéng	
Signal gain	信号增益	Xìnhào zēngyì	
Signal gateway	信号网关	Xìnhào wǎngguān	SG
Signal gateway unit	信号网关单元	Xìnhào wǎngguān dānyuán	SGU
Signal generator	信号发生器	Xìnhào fāshēngqì	
Signal imitation (in VF signaling)	虚假信号	Xūjiǎ xìnhào	
Signal label	信号标签	Xìnhào biāoqiān	SL
Signal label mismatch	信号标记失配	Xìnhào biāojì shīpèi	SLM

Signal level	信号电平	Xìnhào diànpíng	
Signal limit length	信号极限长度	Xìnhào jíxiàn chángdù	
Signal message	信号消息	Xìnhào xiāoxi	
Signal operations platforms-provisioning (operating system)	信号操作平台服务提供(操作系统)	Xìnhào cāozuò píngtái fúwù tígōng (cāozuò xìtǒng)	SOP
Signal power-to-noise power density ratio	信号功率噪声功率密度比	Xìnhào gōnglǜ zàoshēng gōnglǜ mìdù bǐ	SNDR
Signal processing antenna	信号处理天线	Xìnhào chǔlǐ tiānxiàn	
Signal processor card common	信号处理器公用卡	Xìnhào chǔlǐqì gōngyòng kǎ	SPCC
Signal quality detection	信号质量检测	Xìnhào zhìliàng jiǎncè	
Signal quality detector	信号质量检测器	Xìnhào zhìliàng jiǎncèqì	SQD
Signal quality error	信号特性错误	Xìnhào tèxìng cuòwù	SQE
Signal quality error	信号质量错误	Xìnhào zhìliàng cuòwù	SQE
Signal reference grid	信号基准网	Xìnhào jīzhǔn wǎng	
Signal reference ground	信号参考地	Xìnhào cānkǎo dì	
Signal repetition	重发信号	Chóngfā xìnhào	
Signal source, annunciator	信号源	Xìnhào yuán	
Signal spill-over (in VF signaling)	信号泄漏	Xìnhào xièlòu	
Signal split	信号分割	Xìnhào fēngē	
Signal splitter	信号分路器	Xìnhào fēnlùqì	
Signal stability routing	信号稳定度的路由算法	Xìnhào wěndìngdùde lùyóu suànfǎ	SSR
Signal strength	信号场强	Xìnhào chǎngqiáng	
Signal strength	信号强度	Xìnhào qiángdù	
Signal strength on center frequency	中心频率信号强度	Zhōngxīn pínlǜ xìnhào qiángdù	SS/CF
Signal structure beamforming	信号结构波束成型	Xìnhào jiégòu bōshù chéngxíng	SSBF
Signal to interference ratio	信号干扰比	Xìnhào gānrǎo bǐ	
Signal to noise ratio	信纳比	Xìn nà bǐ	S/N
Signal tone	信号音	Xìnhào yīn	
Signal tone receiver	信号音接收器	Xìnhào yīn jiēshōuqì	
Signal trail	信号路径	Xìnhào lùjìng	
Signal transfer	信号传送	Xìnhào chuánsòng	SIGTRAN
Signal transfer point	信号传送点	Xìnhào chuánsòng diǎn	STP
Signal transfer point	信号转接点	Xìnhào zhuǎnjiē diǎn	
Signal unit	信号单元	Xìnhào dānyuán	
Signal unit error rate monitor	信号单元差错率监视	Xìnhào dānyuán chācuò lǜ jiānshì	SUERM
Signal unit indicator	信号单元表示语	Xìnhào dānyuán biǎoshìyǔ	
Signaling	信令	Xìnlìng	
Signaling asynchronous transfer mode adaptation layer	信令 ATM 适配层	Xìnlìng ATM shìpèi céng	SAAL
Signaling ATM adaptation layer	ATM 信令适配层	ATM xìnlìng shìpèi céng	SAAL
Signaling channel	信令信道	Xìnlìng xìndào	
Signaling channel controller	信令信道控制器	Xìnlìng xìndào kòngzhìqì	SCC
Signaling code transition	信令码转换	Xìnlìng mǎ zhuǎnhuàn	
Signaling connection control part	信令连接控制部分	Xìnlìng liánjiē kòngzhì bùfen	SCCP
Signaling connection control part user adaptation layer	信令连接控制部分用户适配层	Xìnlìng liánjiē kòngzhì bùfen yònghù shìpèi céng	SUA
Signaling controller	信令控制器	Xìnlìng kòngzhìqì	SC
Signaling converter	信令转换器	Xìnlìng zhuǎnhuànqì	

English	Chinese	Pinyin	Abbreviation
Signaling data link level	信令数据链路级	Xìnlìng shùjù liànlù jí	
Signaling end point	信令端点	Xìnlìng duāndiǎn	SEP
Signaling end point	信令终结点	Xìnlìng zhōngjié diǎn	SEP
Signaling equipment	信号设备	Xìnhào shèbèi	
Signaling extraction	信令的提取	Xìnlìngde tíqǔ	
Signaling gateway	信令网关	Xìnlìng wǎngguān	SG
Signaling gateway function	信令网关功能	Xìnlìng wǎngguān gōngnéng	SGF
Signaling gateway process	信令网关进程	Xìnlìng wǎngguān jìnchéng	SGP
Signaling gateway unit	信令网关单元	Xìnlìng wǎngguān dānyuán	SGU
Signaling information	信令信息	Xìnlìng xìnxī	
Signaling information element	信令信息元素	Xìnlìng xìnxī yuánsù	IE
Signaling information field	令信息字段	Lìngxìnxī zìduàn	SIF
Signaling information field	信令信息段	Xìnlìng xìnxī duàn	SIF
Signaling insertion	信令的插入	Xìnlìngde chārù	
Signaling interworking	信令互通	Xìnlìng hùtōng	
Signaling link	信令链路	Xìnlìng liànlù	
Signaling link code	信令链路码	Xìnlìng liànlù mǎ	SLC
Signaling link level	信令链路级	Xìnlìng liànlù jí	
Signaling link selection	信令链路选择	Xìnlìng liànlù xuǎnzé	SLS
Signaling link terminal	信令链路终端	Xìnlìng liànlù zhōngduān	SLT
Signaling link terminal board A	信令链路终端板 A	Xìnlìng liànlù zhōngduān bǎn A	SLTA
Signaling link terminal control	信令链路终端控制	Xìnlìng liànlù zhōngduān kòngzhì	SILTC
Signaling link test message	信令链路测试消息	Xìnlìng liànlù cèshì xiāoxi	SLTM
Signaling management equipment	信令管理设备	Xìnlìng guǎnlǐ shèbèi	SME
Signaling message	信令消息	Xìnlìng xiāoxi	
Signaling message handling sub-system	信号消息处理子系统	Xìnhào xiāoxi chǔlǐ zixìtǒng	SMHS
Signaling module	信令模块	Xìnlìng mókuài	
Signaling network	信令网	Xìnlìng wǎng	XLW
Signaling network	信令网络	Xìnlìng wǎngluò	
Signaling network layer	信号网络层	Xìnhào wǎngluò céng	SNL
Signaling network level	信令网络级	Xìnlìng wǎngluò jí	
Signaling network management	信令网管理	Xìnlìng wǎng guǎnlǐ	
Signaling path (in common channel signaling)	信令通道	Xìnlìng tōngdào	
Signaling point	信令点	Xìnlìng diǎn	SP
Signaling point code	信令点编码	Xìnlìng diǎn biānmǎ	SPC
Signaling point management cluster	信令点管理簇	Xìnlìng diǎn guǎnlǐ cù	SPMC
Signaling route	信令路由	Xìnlìng lùyóu	
Signaling routing	信令路由选定	Xìnlìng lùyóu xuǎndìng	
Signaling security (in common channel signaling)	信令安全性	Xìnlìng ānquánxìng	
Signaling service sub-system	信令服务子系统	Xìnlìng fúwù zi xìtǒng	SSS
Signaling system	信令系统	Xìnlìng xìtǒng	
Signaling system multi-frequency	多频信令系统	Duōpín xìnlìng xìtǒng	SSMF
Signaling system no.7	七号信令系统	Qīhào xìnlìng xìtǒng	SS7
Signaling terminal	信令终端	Xìnlìng zhōng duān	STE
Signaling terminal control board assembly	信令终端控制集成板	Xìnlìng zhōngduān kòngzhì jíchéngbǎn	STCA
Signaling terminal network interface board assembly	信令终端网络接口集成板	Xìnlìng zhōngduān wǎngluò jiēkǒu jíchéngbǎn	STNI

Signaling time slot	信令时隙	Xìnlìng shíxì	
Signaling tone	信令音	Xìnlìng yīn	ST
Signaling tone peak frequency deviation	信令音峰值频偏	Xìnlìng yīn fēngzhí pínpiān	
Signaling transfer end point	信令转接终结点	Xìnlìng zhuǎnjiē zhōngjié diǎn	STEP
Signaling transfer equipment	信令转换设备	Xìnlìng zhuǎnhuàn shèbèi	STE
Signaling transfer point	信令传送点	Xìnlìng chuánsòng diǎn	STP
Signaling transfer point	信令转接点	Xìnlìng zhuǎnjiē diǎn	STP
Signaling transfer processor	信令转换处理器	Xìnlìng zhuǎnhuàn chǔlǐqì	STP
Signaling transmission gain	信令发送增益	Xìnlìng fāsòng zēngyì	
Signaling transport	信令传送	Xìnlìng chuánsòng	SIGTRAN
Signaling transport converter	信令传送转换器	Xìnlìng chuánsòng zhuǎnhuànqì	STC
Signaling transport layer	信令传送层	Xìnlìng chuánsòng céng	STL
Signaling unit	信令单元	Xìnlìng dānyuán	
Signaling virtual channel	信令虚通路	Xìnlìng xū tōnglù	SVC
Signaling virtual channel	信令虚信道	Xìnlìng xū xìndào	SVC
Signal-satellite network	卫星信号网络	Wèixīng xìnhào wǎngluò	SSN
Signal-to-clutter ratio	信号杂波比	Xìnhào zábō bǐ	SCR
Signal-to-complexity ratio	信杂比	Xìn zá bǐ	SCR
Signal-to-disturbance ratio	信骚比	Xìn sāo bǐ	
Signal-to-interference noise ratio	信干噪比	Xìn gānzào bǐ	SINR
Signal-to-interference ratio	信干比	Xìn gān bǐ	
Signal-to-interference ratio	信号对干扰比（信干比）	Xìnhào duì gānrǎo bǐ (xìn gān bǐ)	SIR
Signal-to-masking ratio	信号掩蔽比	Xìnhào yǎnbì bǐ	SMR
Signal-to-noise density ratio	信号噪声密度比	Xìnhào zàoshēng mìdù bǐ	SNDR
Signal-to-noise ratio	信噪比	Xìn zào bǐ	SNR
Signal-to-noise ratio	信号与噪声之比	Xìnhào yǔ zàoshēng zhī bǐ	
Signal-to-noise ratio	信号噪声比	Xìnhào zàoshēng bǐ	SNR
Signal-to-noise ratio of strong signal	信号信躁比	Xìnhào xìn zào bǐ	
Signal-to-residual output-power ratio	信号对剩余输出电平比	Xìnhào duì shèngyú shūchū diànpíng bǐ	
Signal-to-residual output-power ratio	信号对剩余输出功率比	Xìnhào duì shèngyú shūchū gōnglǜ bǐ	
Signature	签名	Qiānmíng	
Signature element	签名要素	Qiānmíng yàosù	SIG
Signature signal	签字信号	Qiānzì xìnhào	
Signed response	符号响应	Fúhào xiǎngyìng	SRES
Signed response	签署响应	Qiānshǔ xiǎngyìng	SRES
Significant condition	特征状态	Tèzhēng zhuàngtài	
Significant digit	有效位	Yǒuxiào wèi	
Significant figure	有效数字	Yǒuxiào shùzì	
Significant instant	特征瞬时	Tèzhēng shùnshí	
Significant instants of a digital signal	数字信号的有效瞬时	Shùzì xìnhàode yǒuxiào shùnshí	
Significant interval	特征间隔	Tèzhēng jiàngé	
Significant wave	有效波	Yǒuxiào bō	
Silence descriptor	静寂帧	Jìngjì zhèng	SID
Silence descriptor	静音描述	Jìngyīn miáoshù	SID
Silence descriptor	静音指示	Jìngyīn zhǐshì	SID
Silent period (in signaling)	无声阶段	Wúshēng jiēduàn	

Silica imaging fiber optic bundle	石英系影像光纤	Shíyīng xì yǐngxiàng guāngxiān	
Silica multimode graded index [of refraction] optical fiber	石英系多模态渐近式折射率型光纤	Shíyīng xì duōmótài jiànjìn-shì zhéshèlǜ-xíng guāngxiān	
Silica multimode stepped index [of refraction] optical fiber	石英系多模态步阶式折射率型光纤	Shíyīng xì duōmótài bùjiēshì zhéshèlǜ-xíng guāngxiān	
Silica optical fiber	石英光纤	Shíyīng guāngxiān	
Silicon bi-directional switch	硅双向开关	Guī shuāngxiàng kāiguān	SBS
Silicon bi-directional switch	双向硅开关	Shuāngxiàng guī kāiguān	SBS
Silicon chlorate (used in FOC manufacture)	四氯化硅	Sìlǜhuàguī	$SiCl_4$
Silicon controlled rectifier	可控硅整流器	Kěkòngguī zhěngliúqì	SCR
Silicon controlled switch	可控硅开关	Kěkòng guī kāiguān	SCS
Silicon core tubing	硅芯管	Guī xīn guǎn	
Silicon germanium	锗硅	Zhěguī	SiGe
Silicon Graphics (US company)	矽图	Xī tú	
Silicon hydrochloride (used in FOC manufacture)	三氯氢硅	Sānlǜqīngguī	$SiHCl_3$
Silicon Integrated Systems Inc.	硅片综合系统公司	Guī piàn zōnghé xìtǒng gōngsī	SiS
Silicon readout cell	硅读出单元	Guī dúchū dānyuán	
Silicon rectifier	硅整流器	Guī zhěngliúqì	SR
Silicon semiconductor material	矽半导体材料	Xī bàndǎotǐ cáiliào	
Silicon switch	硅交换机	Guī jiāohuànjī	
Silicon switch engine	硅交换机引擎	Guī jiāohuànjī yǐnqíng	SSE
Silicon switch processor	硅交换机处理器	Guī jiāohuànjī chǔlǐqì	SSP
Silicon switching	硅交换	Guī jiāohuàn	
Silicon switching engine	硅交换引擎	Guī jiāohuàn yǐnqíng	SSE
Silicon symmetrical switch	硅对称开关	Guī duìchèn kāiguān	SSS
Silicon symmetrical switch	双向可控硅	Shuāngxiàng kěkòng guī	SSS
Silicon Valley	矽谷	Xī gǔ	
Silicon Valley Chinese Engineer Association	硅谷中国工程师协会	Guīgǔ Zhōngguó gōngchéngshī xiéhuì	SCEA
Silicon Valley Chinese Overseas Business Association	硅谷留美博士企业家协会	Guīgǔ liúměi bóshì qǐyèjiā xiéhuì	SCOBA
Silicon-on-insulator	绝缘体硅片	Juéyuántǐ guīpiàn	SOI
Silver chromate test (in SMT)	铬酸银测试	Gèsuānyín cèshì	
Similar curve	近似曲线	Jìnsì qūxiàn	
Similarity analysis	相似性分析	Xiāngsìxìng fenxī	
Similarity retrieval	相似性检索	Xiāngsìxìng jiǎnsuǒ	
Similarity transformation	相似性变换	Xiāngsìxìng biànhuàn	
Simple (single) lens	单透镜	Dāntòujing	
Simple and efficient AAL	简单和有效的 AAL	Jiǎndān hé yǒuxiàode AAL	SEAL
Simple and efficient adaptation layer	简单有效的适配层	Jiǎndān yǒuxiàode shìpèi céng	SEAL
Simple authentication	简单鉴别	Jiǎndān jiànbié	
Simple authentication	简单验证	Jiǎndān yànzhèng	
Simple Boolean expression	简单布尔表示式	Jiǎndān Bù-ěr biǎoshì shì	SBE
Simple boot flag specification	简单引导标记规范	Jiǎndān yǐndǎo biāojì guīfàn	SBFS
Simple cycle	简单回路	Jiǎndān huílù	
Simple data link	简单数据通路	Jiǎndān shùjù tōnglù	SDL
Simple data link	简易数据链路	Jiǎnyì shùjù liànlù	SDL
Simple digital modulation	简单数字调制	Jiǎndān shùzì tiáozhì	

English	Chinese	Pinyin	Abbreviation
Simple feature	简单特征	Jiǎndān tèzhēng	
Simple gateway control protocol	简单网关控制协议	Jiǎndān wǎngguān kòngzhì xiéyì	SGCP
Simple gateway monitoring protocol	简单网关监视协议	Jiǎndān wǎngguān jiānshì xiéyì	SGMP
Simple internet protocol	简单因特网协议	Jiǎndān Yīntèwǎng xiéyì	SIP
Simple key exchange Internet protocol	因特网简单密钥交换协议	Yīntèwǎng jiǎndān mìyào jiāohuàn xiéyì	SKIP
Simple mail transfer protocol	简单邮件传输协议	Jiǎndān yóujiàn chuánshū xiéyì	SMTP
Simple mail transfer protocol	简单邮件传送协议	Jiǎndān yóujiàn chuánsòng xiéyì	SMTP
Simple mail transfer protocol	简单的邮件传送协议	Jiǎndānde yóujiàn chuánsòng xiéyì	SMTP
Simple message function	简单消息函数	Jiǎndān xiāoxi hánshù	
Simple multipoint circuit	简单的多点电路	Jiǎndānde duōdiǎn diànlù	
Simple network management protocol	简单网络管理协议	Jiǎndān wǎngluò guǎnlǐ xiéyì	SNMP
Simple network time protocol	简单网络定时协议	Jiǎndān wǎngluò dìngshí xiéyì	SNTP
Simple network time protocol (IETF use)	简单网络时间协议	Jiǎndān wǎngluò shíjiān xiéyì	SNTP
Simple object	简单对象	Jiǎndān duìxiàng	
Simple object access protocol	简单对象访问协议	Jiǎndān duìxiàng fǎngwèn xiéyì	SOAP
Simple path	简单路径	Jiǎndān lùjìng	
Simple programmable logic device	简单可编程逻辑器件	Jiǎndān kě biānchéng luóji qìjiàn	
Simple public key GSS-API mechanism	简单公共密匙 GSS - API 机制	Jiǎndān gōnggòng mìchí GSS-API jīzhì	SPKM
Simple rectification	简单校正	Jiǎndān jiàozhèng	
Simple server redundancy protocol	简单服务器冗余协议	Jiǎndān fúwùqì rǒngyú xiéyì	SSRP
Simple signal (in AC signaling)	单频信号	Dānpín xìnhào	
Simple type	简单类型	Jiǎndān lèixíng	
Simplex	单工	Dāngōng	
Simplex circuit	单工线路	Dāngōng xiànlù	SPX
Simplex operation	单工操作	Dāngōng cāozuò	
Simplex radio telephone	单工无线电话机	Dāngōng wúxiàn diànhuàjī	
Simplification	简化	Jiǎnhuà	
Simplified data link	简单数据链路	Jiǎndān shùjù liànlù	SDL
Simplified data link	简化数据链路	Jiǎnhuà shùjù liànlù	SDL
Simplifying polygons	多边形化简	Duōbiānxíng huà jiǎn	
SimToolKit	用户识别应用发展工具	Yònghù shíbié yìngyòng fāzhǎn gōngjù	STK
Simulated video	模拟视频	Mónǐ shìpín	
Simulation	模拟	Mónǐ	
Simulation attack (cryptography)	模仿攻击	Mófǎng gōngjī	
Simulation game (computer game)	模拟类游戏	Mónǐ lèi yóuxì	SLG
Simulation program with integrated circuit emphasis	用集成电路加强的仿真程序	Yòng jíchéng diànlù jiāqiángde fǎngzhēn chéngxù	SPIC
Simulation-based design	基于仿真设计	Jīyú fǎngzhēn shèjì	SBD
Simulator	模拟器	Mónǐqì	
Simultaneous interpretation conference system	同声传译系统	Tóngshēng chuányì xìtǒng	SICS
Simultaneous line downtime	同时用户中断	Tóngshí yònghù zhōngduàn	
Simultaneous tone sequential system	同时单音顺序制	Tóngshí dānyīn shùnxù zhì	
Simultaneous tone system	同时单音制	Tóngshí dānyīn zhì	
Simultaneous trunk downtime	同时中继中断	Tóngshí zhōngjì zhōngduàn	
Simultaneously accessible parts	同时可触及部分	Tóngshí kěchùjí bùfen	
Sine	正弦	Zhèngxián	

English	Chinese	Pinyin	Abbreviation
Sine transform coding	正弦变换编码	Zhèngxián biànhuàn biānmǎ	STC
Sine wave	正弦波	Zhèngxiánbō	
Sine wave generator	正弦波发生器	Zhèngxiánbō fāshēngqì	
Sine wave test signal	正弦波测试信号	Zhèngxiánbō cèshì xìnhào	
Singapore MobileOne Asia (GSM network operator)	新加坡亚洲第一通信	Xīnjiāpō Yàzhōu dìyī tōngxìn	
Singapore Telecom	新加坡电信	Xīnjiāpō diànxìn	
Singing	振鸣	Zhènmíng	
Single address code	单地址编码	Dāndìzhǐ biānmǎ	SAC
Single association control function	单偶联控制功能	Dān'ǒulián kòngzhì gōngnéng	SACF
Single association control function	单相关控制功能	Dānxiàng guān kòngzhì gōngnéng	SACF
Single association object	单偶联对象	Dān'ǒulián duìxiàng	SAO
Single association object	单偶联体	Dānǒuliántǐ	SAO
Single association object	单相关对象	Dānxiàng guān duìxiàng	SAO
Single attachment concentrator	单点接触集中器	Dāndiǎn jiēchù jízhōngqì	
Single bit	单位	Dānwèi	
Single bit error	一位出错	Yīwèi chūcuò	SBE
Single board	单板	Dānbǎn	
Single board computer	单板计算机	Dānbǎn jìsuànjī	SBC
Single board design	单板设计	Dānbǎn shèjì	
Single bundle cable	单束光缆	Dānshù guānglǎn	
Single byte expansion	单字节扩展	Dānzìjié kuòzhǎn	SBE
Single call	单呼	Dānhū	
Single cell	一单元	Yī dānyuán	
Single channel cordless telephone	单信道无绳电话机	Dānxìndào wúshéng diànhuàjī	
Single channel ground and airborne radio system (US military)	单信道地面和机载无线电分系统	Dānxìndào dìmiàn hé jīzài wúxiàndiàn fēnxìtǒng	SINCGARS
Single channel modem	单路调制解调器	Dānlù tiáozhì jiětiáoqì	SCM
Single channel monopulse radar	单通道单脉冲雷达	Dāntōngdào dānmàichōng léidá	
Single channel per burst	单路单突发	Dānlù dāntūfā	SCPB
Single channel per carrier	单路单载波	Dānlù dānzàibō	SCPC
Single channel per carrier	单载波单路	Dānzàibō dānlù	SCPC
Single channel per carrier	每载波单路	Měi zàibō dānlù	SCPC
Single channel per carrier- pulse code modulation- multiple access- demand assignment	每载波单路-脉码调制-多址联接-按申请分配	Měi zàibō dānlù-mài mǎ tiáozhì- Duō zhǐ liánjiē- Àn shēnqǐng fēnpèi	SPADE
Single channel per transponder	每转发器单路	Měi zhuǎnfāqì dānlù	SCPT
Single channel radio access (an Alcatel-Telletra system)	单信道无线电接入	Dānxìndào wúxiàndiàn jiērù	SCRA
Single channel system (optical)	单波长系统	Dānbōcháng xìtǒng	SCS
Single channel transponder	单路转发器	Dānlù zhuǎnfāqì	SCT
Single channel voice frequency telegraphy	单路音频电报	Dānlù yīnpín diànbào	SCVFT
Single click (of a computer mouse)	单击	Dānjī	
Single crystal growing equipment	单结晶制造设备	Dānjiéjīng zhìzào shèbèi	
Single current transmission	单流传输	Dānliú chuánshū	
Single data message format	单数据消息格式	Dānshùjù xiāoxī géshi	SDMF
Single data-rate SDRAM	单数据率 SDRAM	Dānshùjù lǜ SDRAM	SDR SDRAM
Single digital subscriber line	单线制数字用户线	Dānxiànzhì shùzì yònghù xiàn	SDSL

Single edge connector	单边连接器	Dānbiān liánjiēqì	SEC
Single error	单个差错	Dāngè chācuò	
Single error correcting (codes)	单错校正(码)	Dāncuò jiàozhèng (mǎ)	SEC
Single fiber cable	单芯光缆	Dānxīn guānglǎn	
Single fiber cable connector	单芯光缆连接器	Dānxīn guānglǎn liánjiēqì	
Single frequency duplex	单频双工	Dānpín shuānggōng	
Single frequency network	单频网	Dānpín wǎng	
Single frequency noise	单频噪声	Dānpín zàoshēng	
Single frequency receiving level	单频接收电平	Dānpín jiēshōu diànpíng	
Single frequency signaling	单频信令	Dānpín xìnlìng	
Single inline memory module	单边接触内存模组	Dānbiān jiēchù nèicún mózǔ	SIMM
Single instruction multiple data	单指令多数据流	Dānzhǐlìng duō shùjùliú	SIMD
Single layer ceramic capacitor	陶瓷单层电容器	Táocí dāncéng diànróngqì	SLC
Single link procedure	单链路规程	Dānliànlù guīchéng	SLP
Single linked list	单链表	Dānliàn biǎo	
Single longitudinal mode laser	单纵模激光器	Dānzòngmó jīguāngqì	SLM
Single message rate timing	单信号率定时	Dānxinhào lǜ dìngshí	SMRT
Single metering	单式计次	Dānshì jìcì	
Single mode fiber	单模纤维	Dānmó xiānwéi	SMF
Single mode fiber coupler	单模分光器	Dānmó fēnguāngqì	SMFC
Single mode fiber optic connector	单模态光纤连接器	Dānmótài guāngxiān liánjiēqì	
Single mode optical fiber	单模光纤	Dānmó guāngxiān	
Single mode single window broadband coupler	单模单窗宽带分光器	Dānmó dānchuāng kuāndài fēnguāngqì	SWBC
Single mode single window broadband star coupler	单模单窗宽带星型分光器	Dānmó dānchuāng kuāndài xīngxíng fēnguāng qì	SWSC
Single mode single window broadband tree coupler	单模单窗宽带树型分光器	Dānmó dānchuāng kuāndài shùxíng fēnguāngqì	SWTC
Single mode star coupler	单模星型分光器	Dānmó xīngxíng fēnguāngqì	SMSC
Single mode stepped index optical fiber	单模突变型光纤	Dānmó tūbiànxíng guāngxiān	
Single mode tree coupler	单模树型分光器	Dānmó shùxíng fēnguāngqì	SMTC
Single mode two window broadband coupler	单模双窗宽带分光器	Dānmó shuāngchuāng kuāndài fēnguāngqì	TWBC
Single mode two window broadband star coupler	单模双窗宽带星型分光器	Dānmó shuāngchuāng kuāndài xīngxíng fēnguāngqì	TWSC
Single mode two window broadband tree coupler	单模双窗宽带树型分光器	Dānmó shuāngchuāng kuāndài shùxíng fēnguāngqì	TWTC
Single mode wavelength division multiplexer	单模波分复用器	Dānmó bōfēn fùyòngqì	SWDM
Single node interconnection (in SDH)	单节点互连	Dānjiédiǎn hùlián	
Single operation test	单独操作试验	Dāndú cāozuò shìyàn	SOT
Single pair high-speed digital subscriber line	单线对高速数据用户线	Dānxiànduì gāosù shùjù yònghù xiàn	SHDSL
Single pass multi-texturing (video term)	单通道多纹理	Dāntōngdào duōwénlǐ	
Single phase	单相	Dānxiàng	
Single phase asymmetrical control	单相不对称控制	Dānxiàng bùduìchèn kòngzhì	
Single phase symmetrical control	单机对称控制	Dānjī duìchèn kòngzhì	
Single phase symmetrical control	单相对称控制	Dānxiàng duìchèn kòngzhì	
Single point of failure	单点故障源	Dāndiǎn gùzhàng yuán	SPOF
Single point positioning	单点定位	Dāndiǎn dìngwèi	
Single polarization fiber isolator	单偏振隔离器	Dānpiānzhèn gélíqì	SPFI
Single pole	单极点	Dānjí diǎn	
Single precision	单精度	Dānjīngdù	

English	Chinese	Pinyin	Abbreviation
Single segment message	单段消息	Dānduàn xiāoxi	SSM
Single sheet density	单层紧度	Dāncéng jǐndù	
Single sideband	单边带	Dānbiāndài	SSB
Single sideband (SSB) transmitter	单边带发射机	Dānbiāndài fāshèjī	
Single sideband amplitude modulation	单边带调幅	Dānbiāndài tiáofú	SSBAM
Single sideband demodulation	单边带解调	Dānbiāndài jiětiáo	
Single sideband emission	单边带发射	Dānbiāndài fāshè	
Single sideband frequency modulation	单边带调频	Dānbiāndài tiáopín	SSFM, SSBFM
Single sideband modulation	单边带调制	Dānbiāndài tiáozhì	SSB
Single sideband phase modulation	单边带调相	Dānbiāndài tiáoxiàng	SSPM
Single sideband signal generator	单边带信号发生器	Dānbiāndài xìnhào fāshēngqì	
Single sign-on	单一登录	Dānyī dēnglù	
Single sign-on	统一权限	Tǒngyī quánxiàn	
Single sign-on	一次性登录	Yīcìxìng dēnglù	SSO
Single stream	单码流	Dānmǎliú	
Single track seek time	单磁道时间	Dāncídào shíjiān	
Single track seek time	道至道时间	Dào zhì dào shíjiān	
Single user account	单用户帐号	Dānyònghù zhànghào	SUA
Single wavelength solution	单波长解决方案	Dānbōcháng jiějué fāng'àn	SWS
Single-attached concentrator	单连集线器	Dānlián jíxiànqì	SAC
Single-attached concentrator	单连接集中器	Dānliánjiē jízhōngqì	SAC
Single-component signal (in AC signaling)	单成分信号	Dānchéngfèn xìnhào	
Single-ended input	单端输入	Dānduān shūrù	
Single-ended synchronization	单端同步	Dānduān tóngbù	
Single-level device	单级设备	Dānjí shèbèi	
Single-line digital subscriber line	单线数字用户线路	Dānxiàn shùzì yònghù xiànlù	SDSL
Single-longitudinal mode	单纵模	Dānzòngmó	SLM
Single-pair high bit-rate digital subscriber line	单线对高比特率数字用户线	Dānxiànduì gāobǐtèlǜ shùzì yònghù xiàn	SHDSL
Single-phase neutral grounding reactor	单相中性点接地电抗器	Dānxiàng zhōngxìngdiǎn jiēdì diànkàngqì	
Single-polarization fiber	单极化纤维	Dānjíhuà xiānwéi	SPF
Single-polarized antenna	单极化天线	Dānjíhuà tiānxiàn	
Single-route explorer packet	单路由探测包	Dānlùyóu tàncè bāo	
Single-save system	一重保存方式	Yīchóng bǎocún fāngshì	
Single-signal method	单信号法	Dānxìnhào fǎ	
Single-threaded	单线程	Dānxiànchéng	
Single-unit message	一单元消息	Yī dānyuán xiāoxi	
Single-user mode	单用户模式	Dānyònghù móshì	
Single-vendor network	单厂商网络	Dānchǎngshāng wǎngluò	
Single-wire line	单导线传输线	Dāndǎoxiàn chuánshūxiàn	
SingTel Mobile (Singapore GSM network operator)	新加坡电信移动通信	Xīnjiāpō diànxìn yídòng tōngxìn	
Singular value decomposition	单一值分解技术	Dānyī zhí fēnjiě jìshù	
Sink	汇点	Huìdiǎn	
Sink	宿	Sù	
Sintering (FOC manufacture)	烧结	Shāojié	
Sinusoidal distribution (of a current in an antenna)	正弦波形分布	Zhèngxián bōxíng fēnbù	
Sinusoidal frequency shift keying	正弦曲线频移键控	Zhèngxián qūxiàn pínyí jiànkòng	SFSK

Sinusoidal phase variation	正弦相位变化	Zhèngxián xiàngwèi biànhuà	
Sinusoidal transfer	正弦变换	Zhèngxián biànhuàn	
Sinusoidal transfer coder	正弦变换编码奇	Zhèngxián biànhuàn biānmǎqí	STC
Site alarm block	位置告警模块	Wèizhì gàojǐng mókuài	SAB
Site database	现场数据库	Xiànchǎng shùjùkù	SDB
Site diversity reception	位置分集接收	Wèizhì fēnjí jiēshōu	
Site selection diversity transmission	选择位置分集发射	Xuǎnzé wèizhì fēnjí fāshè	SSDT
Site-level aggregation identifier	站点层次聚集标识符	Zhàndiǎn céngcì jùjí biāozhìfú	SLAID
Six degrees of separation	六度分离	Liù dù fēnlí	
Six protects (for computers: protect against self-induction, static, magnetic field, heat, dampness, vibration)	六防	Liù fáng	
Six protects, or six protections (in telecom construction: against salt, moisture, viruses, rats, lightning and static)	六防	Liù fáng	
Skeleton curve	构架曲线	Gòujià qūxiàn	
Skew	歪斜	Wāixié	
Skew ray	不交轴光线	Bùjiāozhóu guāngxiàn	
Skin depth	趋肤深度	Qūfū shēndù	
Skin effect	趋肤效应	Qūfū xiàoyìng	
Skinny client control protocol (Cisco use)	小客户控制协议	Xiǎokèhù kòngzhì xiéyì	SCCP
Sky wave	天波	Tiānbō	
Skynet	天网	Tiānwǎng	
Sky-wave delay	天波时延	Tiānbō shíyán	
Sky-wave path loss	天波路径损耗	Tiānbō lùjìng sǔnhào	
Slab laser	平板激光	Píngbǎn jīguāng	
Slab line	板状线	Bǎnzhuàng xiàn	
Slave clock	从时钟	Cóngshízhōng	
Slave clock	从钟	Cóngzhōng	
Slave machine	从机	Cóngjī	
Slave processor	从处理机	Cóngchǔlǐjī	
Sleep mode	睡眠方式	Shuìmián fāngshì	
Sleeve	套筒	Tàotǒng	
Sleeve dipole (antenna)	套筒偶极子	Tàotǒng ǒujízi	
Sleeve monopole, sleeve stub (antenna)	套筒单极子	Tàotǒng dānjízi	
Sleeve type suppressor	套管型抑制器	Tàoguǎn-xíng yìzhìqì	
Slew rate (video term)	转换速度	Zhuǎnhuàn sùdù	
Slewing array antenna	回转阵天线	Huízhuǎn zhèn tiānxiàn	
Slice	切片	Qiēpiàn	
Slice (format of digital modularized radio)	插板集成	Chābǎn jíchéng	
Slice (video term)	片	Piàn	
Slicer	双削波器	Shuāng xiāo bōqì	
Slicing	双削波	Shuāng xiāo bō	
Slide screw tuner	滑动螺钉调节器	Huádòng luódīng tiáojiéqì	
Slide surface	滑动面	Huádòng miàn	
Slider	滑块	Huákuài	
Sliding load	滑动负载	Huádòng fùzài	
Sliding mode	滑动模式	Huádòng móshì	

Sliding shutter	滑动阀门	Huádòng fámén	
Sliding window	滑动窗口	Huádòng chuāngkǒu	
Sliding window flow control	滑窗流控	Huáchuāng liú kòng	
Sliding window flow control	滑动窗流量控制	Huádòng chuāng liúliàng kòngzhì	
Slip	滑动	Huádòng	
Slip control hysteresis	滑动控制滞后	Huádòng kòngzhì zhìhòu	
Slip objective (SDH timing)	滑动指标	Huádòng zhǐbiāo	
Slit-barrier	截槽障	Jiécáo zhàng	
Sliver polygon (GIS)	碎多边形	Suì duōbiānxíng	
Slope	斜率	Xiélǜ	
Slope efficiency (FOC)	斜效率	Xié xiàolǜ	
Slope works	护坡工程	Hùpō gōngchéng	
Slot	插槽	Chācáo	
Slot (on computer chassis)	槽位	Cáowèi	
Slot antenna	缝隙天线	Fèngxì tiānxiàn	
Slot antenna	隙缝天线	Xìfèng tiānxiàn	
Slot array (antenna)	隙缝阵	Xìfèng zhèn	
Slot radiator	隙缝辐射器	Xìfèng fúshèqì	
Slotted ALOHA system	时隙 ALOHA 系统	Shíxì ALOHA xìtǒng	
Slotted coaxial balun (balanced/unbalanced device)	开槽同轴平衡/不平衡变换器	Kāicáo tóngzhóu pínghéng/bùpínghéng biànhuànqì	
Slotted core (optical fiber type)	骨架	Gǔjià	
Slotted cylinder antenna	圆筒隙缝天线	Yuántǒng xìfèng tiānxiàn	
Slotted cylinder panel	圆筒隙缝盘	Yuántǒng xìfèng pán	
Slotted line	开槽线	Kāicáoxiàn	
Slotted line carriage	开槽线架	Kāicáoxiàn jià	
Slotted panel	开槽盘天线	Kāicáopán tiānxiàn	
Slotted ring	分槽环	Fēncáo huán	
Slotted ring	时隙环	Shíxì huán	
Slotted ring	时隙振铃	Shíxì zhènlíng	
Slotted waveguide (antenna)	波导隙缝天线	Bōdǎo xìfèng tiānxiàn	
Slotted-core optical ribbon	骨架式光纤带	Gǔjià-shì guāngxiān dài	
Slotted-core ribbon optical cable	骨架式光纤带光缆	Gǔjià-shì guāngxiān dài guānglǎn	
Slow assisted control channel	慢速辅助控制信道	Mànsù fǔzhù kòngzhì xìndào	SACCH
Slow assisted control channel/traffic channel	慢速辅助控制信道/业务信道	Mànsù fǔzhù kòngzhì xìndào/yèwù xìndào	SACCH/T
Slow assisted control channel/traffic channel full rate	慢速辅助控制信道/全速率业务信道	Mànsù fǔzhù kòngzhì xìndào/quánsùlǜ yèwù xìndào	SACCH/TF
Slow assisted control channel/traffic channel half rate	慢速辅助控制信道/半速率业务信道	Mànsù fǔzhù kòngzhì xìndào/bàn sùlǜ yèwù xìndào	SACCHTH
Slow associated control channel	慢速随路控制信道	Mànsù suílù kòngzhì xìndào	SACCH
Slow associated control channel/traffic channel	慢速随路控制信道/业务信道	Mànsù suílù kòngzhì xìndào/yèwù xìndào	SACCH/T
Slow associated control channel/traffic channel full rate	慢速随路控制信道/全速率业务信道	Mànsù suílù kòngzhì xìndào/quán sùlǜ yèwù xìndào	SACCH/TF
Slow frequency hopping	慢跳频	Màntiàopín	SFH

Slow frequency hopping multiple access	慢频率跳编多路存取	Màn pínlǜ tiàobiān duōlù cúnqǔ	SFHMA
Slow Switching	低速交换	Dīsù jiāohuàn	
Slow wave	慢波	Mànbō	
Slow wave structure	慢波结构	Mànbō jiégòu	
Slug tuner	条状调节器	Tiáozhuàng tiáojiéqì	
Sluggish stream	缓流	Huǎnliú	
Slump (in SMT)	坍落	Tānluò	
Small and medium-sized enterprises	中小型企业	Zhōngxiǎoxíng qǐyè	SME
Small communication terminal	小型通信终端设备	Xiǎoxíng tōngxìn zhōngduān shèbèi	SCOT
Small computer system interface	小型电脑系统介面	Xiǎoxíng diànnǎo xìtǒng jièmiàn	SCSI
Small computer system interface	小型计算机系统接口	Xiǎoxíng jìsuànjī xìtǒng jiēkǒu	SCSI
Small office home office	小型家庭办公室	Xiǎoxíng jiātíng bàngōngshì	SOHO
Small office/home office	小办公室/家庭办公室	Xiǎo bàngōngshì/Jiātíng bàngōngshì	SOHO
Small outline dual-inline memory module	小型双重内嵌式内存模块	Xiǎoxíng shuāngchóng nèiqiàn-shì nèicún mókuài	SO-DIMM
Small outline integrated circuit	小型塑封集成电路	Xiǎoxíng sùfēng jíchéng diànlù	SOIC
Small outline transistor	小型塑封晶体管	Xiǎoxíng sùfēng jīngtǐguǎn	SOT
Small scale integrated circuit	小规模集成	Xiǎoguīmó jíchéng	SSIC
Small topographies	微地形	Wēidìxíng	
Small World Networks	小世界网络	Xiǎo shìjiè wǎngluò	
Small-signal gain	小信号增益	Xiǎo xìnhào zēngyì	
Small-signal gain stability	小信号增益稳定性	Xiǎo xìnhào zēngyì wěndìngxìng	
Small-signal gain wavelength bandwidth	小信号增益波长带宽	Xiǎo xìnhào zēngyì bōcháng dàikuān	
Small-signal gain wavelength variation	小信号增益波长变化	Xiǎo xìnhào zēngyì bōcháng biànhuà	
Smart antenna	智能天线	Zhìnéng tiānxiàn	SA
Smart card	智能卡	Zhìnéng kǎ	
Smart card reader	智能卡读取器	Zhìnéng kǎ dúqǔqì	
Smart filter	智能过滤	Zhìnéng guòlǜ	
Smart home	智能家园	Zhìnéng jiāyuán	
Smart pointer	智能指针	Zhìnéng zhǐzhēn	
Smiley ☺, :-)	笑脸符号	Xiàoliǎn fúhào	
Smiley ☺, :-)	表情符	Biǎoqíng fú	
Smith chart	史密斯圆图	Shǐ-mì-sī yuántú	
Smog-proof (one of the "three proofings")	防烟雾	Fáng yānwù	
Smoke damper	排烟阀	Páiyān fá	SD
Smoke detector	感烟探测器	Gǎnyān tàncèqì	SD
Smoke extractor exhaust fan	排烟风机	Páiyān fēngjī	SEEF
Smoke vent	排烟器	Páiyānqì	SV
Smoothed round-trip transmission time	平滑的双向传输时间	Pínghuáde shuāngxiàng chuánshū shíjiān	SRTT
Smoothing	平滑	Pínghuá	
Snail mail	普通邮件	Pǔtōng yóujiàn	
Snap (ARCView term)	吸引	Xīyǐn	
SNAP-encoded tag protocol identifier	SNAP 编码标记协议标识符	SNAP biānmǎ biāojì xiéyì biāozhìfú	STPID
SNAP-encoded tag protocol identifier snap	编码标记协议标识符	Biānmǎ biāojì xiéyì biāozhìfú	STPID
Snapshot	截屏图	Jiépíng tú	
Snapshot	快照	Kuàizhào	
Snapshot agent	快照代理程序	Kuàizhào dàilǐ chéngxù	

English	Chinese	Pinyin	Abbreviation
Snapshot agent utility	快照代理程序实用工具	Kuàizhào dàilǐ chéngxù shíyòng gōngjù	
Snapshot cursor	快照游标	Kuàizhào yóubiāo	
Snapshot replication	快照复制	Kuàizhào fùzhì	
SNI bearer capability	SNI 承载能力	SNI chéngzài nénglì	
Sniff (verb)	呼吸	Hūxī	
Sniffer (computer web application)	探测	Tàncè	
Sniffer (hacker program)	嗅探器	Xiùtànqì	
Snowflake model	雪花模型	Xuěhuā móxíng	
Snowflake schema	雪花架构	Xuěhuā jiàgòu	
Society for Worldwide Interbank Financial Telecommunications	世界银行间金融电信协会	Shìjiè yínháng-jiān jīnróng diànxìn xiéhuì	SWIFT
Socket	插口	Chākǒu	SO
Socket	插座	Chāzuò	SK
Socket	套接字	Tàojiēzì	
Socket connector	接插件	Jiēchājiàn	
Socket flange	自对准法兰	Zìduìzhǔn fǎlán	
Soft copper wire	软圆铜线	Ruǎn yuán tóngxiàn	
Soft decision decoding	软判决解码	Ruǎn pànjué jiěmǎ	
Soft decision decoding	软判决译码	Ruǎn pànjué yìmǎ	
Soft device	软设备	Ruǎn shèbèi	
Soft ground	软质地基	Ruǎn zhìdì jī	
Soft handoff	软切换	Ruǎn qiēhuàn	
Soft input soft output (algorithm)	软输入软输出（算法）	Ruǎn shūrù ruǎn shūchū (suànfǎ)	SISO
Soft line terminator	软行终止符	Ruǎn háng zhōngzhǐ fú	
Soft output Viterbi algorithm	软输出维特比算法	Ruǎn shūchū wéi-tè-bǐ suànfǎ	SOVA
Soft permanent circuit mode	软永久电路模式	Ruǎn yǒngjiǔ diànlù móshì	SPC
Soft permanent circuit model	软永久电路模型	Ruǎn yǒngjiǔ diànlù móxíng	SPC Model
Soft permanent virtual channel	软永久虚信道	Ruǎn yǒngjiǔ xū xìndào	SPVC
Soft permanent virtual path	软永久虚电路	Ruǎn yǒngjiǔ xū diànlù	SPVP
Soft reflections (video term)	柔和反射	Róuhe fǎnshè	
Soft shadows (video term)	柔和阴影	Róuhe yīnyǐng	
Softcopy	软拷贝	Ruǎn kǎobèi	
SoftSwitch	软交换	Ruǎn jiāohuàn	
Softswitch	软交换机	Ruǎn jiāohuànjī	
Softswitch control device	软交换控制设备	Ruǎn jiāohuàn kòngzhì shèbèi	SCD
Software	软件	Ruǎnjiàn	
Software architectural description language	软件构架描述语言	Ruǎnjiàn gòujià miáoshù yǔyán	SADL
Software automation (semiconductor mfg)	软件自动化	Ruǎnjiàn zìdònghuà	
Software call-up hook (to invoke a sub-routine)	软件运行支口	Ruǎnjiàn yùnxíng zhīkǒu	
Software center	软件中心	Ruǎnjiàn zhōngxīn	SC
Software compatibility test	软件兼容性测试	Ruǎnjiàn jiānróngxìng cèshì	SCT
Software compiler for user programmable arrays	用户可编程阵列综合编译器	Yònghù kěbiānchéng zhènliè zōnghé biānyìqì	
Software configuration	软件配置	Ruǎnjiàn pèizhì	
Software controlled library (configuration management)	软件受控库	Ruǎnjiàn shòukòng kù	
Software decoder	软件解码器	Ruǎnjiàn jiěmǎqì	
Software defined radio	软件定义的无线电	Ruǎnjiàn dìngyìde wúxiàndiàn	SDR

Software development kit	软件开发包	Ruǎnjiàn kāifā bāo	SDK
Software development kit	软件开发工具包	Ruǎnjiàn kāifā gōngjù bāo	SDK
Software development library	软件开发库	Ruǎnjiàn kāifā kù	
Software development organization	软件开发单位	Ruǎnjiàn kāifā dānwèi	
Software development tool	软件开发工具	Ruǎnjiàn kāifā gōngjù	
Software development toolkit	软件开发套件	Ruǎnjiàn kāifā tàojiàn	SDK
Software engineering	软件工程	Ruǎnjiàn gōngchéng	
Software Engineering Group (CMM)	软件工程组	Ruǎnjiàn gōngchéng zǔ	SWEG
Software environment	软件环境	Ruǎnjiàn huánjìng	
Software interrupt request register	软件中断请求寄存器	Ruǎnjiàn zhōngduàn qǐngqiú jìcúnqì	SIRR
Software license	软件使用权	Ruǎnjiàn shǐyòngquán	
Software life cycle	软件生存周期	Ruǎnjiàn shēngcún zhōuqī	
Software package	软件包	Ruǎnjiàn bāo	
Software piracy	软件盗版	Ruǎnjiàn dàobǎn	
Software priority level	软件优选段	Ruǎnjiàn yōuxuǎn duàn	
Software product library	软件产品库	Ruǎnjiàn chǎnpǐn kù	
Software production language	软件生产语言	Ruǎnjiàn shēngchǎn yǔyán	SPL
Software project plan (CMM)	软件项目计划	Ruǎnjiàn xiàngmù jìhuà	SPP
Software project tracking and oversight (CMM term)	软件项目跟踪和监控	Ruǎnjiàn xiàngmù gēnzōng hé jiānkòng	SPTO
Software Publishers Association	软件出版商协会	Ruǎnjiàn chūbǎnshāng xiéhuì	SPA
Software radio	软件无线电	Ruǎnjiàn wúxiàndiàn	
Software radio, software station	软件电台	Ruǎnjiàn diàntái	
Software Relational Group (CMM)	软件相关组	Ruǎnjiàn xiāngguān zǔ	SRG
Software timer	软件时钟	Ruǎnjiàn shízhōng	
Software version number	软件版号	Ruǎnjiàn bǎn hào	SVN
Soft-wired lookup table	软连接查找表	Ruǎn liánjiē cházhǎo biǎo	
Sohu.com	搜狐网站	Sōuhú wǎngzhàn	
Sohu.com (Web magazine)	搜狐	Sōuhú	
Solar cell	太阳电池	Tàiyáng diànchí	
Solaris © (Sun Microsystems software)	太阳系	Tàiyángxì	
Solarizing test	日晒试验	Rìshài shìyàn	
Solder bump (in SMT)	焊锡球	Hànxī qiú	
Solderability	可焊性	Kěhànxìng	
Solderability test	可焊性试验	Kěhànxìng shìyàn	
Soldermask (in SMT)	阻焊	Zǔhàn	
Sol-gel method (FOC mfg)	溶胶-凝胶法	Róngjiāo—níngjiāo fǎ	SOL-GEL
Solid	立体	Lìtǐ	
Solid fault	硬故障	Yìng gùzhàng	
Solid state transmitter	固态发射机	Gùtài fāshèjī	
Solid-state array spectroradiometer	固体列阵式光谱辐射计	Gùtǐ lièzhèn-shì guāngpǔ fúshèjì	SAS
Solid-state disk	固态盘	Gùtài pán	
Solid-state laser	固态激光	Gùtài jīguāng	
Solid-state power amplifier	固体功率放大器	Gùtǐ gōnglǜ fàngdàqì	SSPA
Solid-state relay	固体继电器	Gùtǐ jìdiànqì	SSR
Solidus (in SMT)	固相线	Gùxiàng xiàn	
Soliton	光孤子	Guāng gūzǐ	

Solution	解	Jiě	
Solve order	求解次序	Qiújiě cìxù	
Sonic	声音	Shēngyīn	
Sonic wave	声波	Shēngbō	
Sony (Japan company)	索尼	Suǒ-ní	
Sony Computer Entertainment (company)	索尼计算机娱乐部	Suǒní jìsuànjī yúlè bù	SCE
Sony Play Station (computer game)	索尼 32 位游戏机	Suǒní 32 wèi yóuxìjī	PS
Sony Pocket Station (computer game)	索尼手提游戏机	Suǒní shǒutí yóuxìjī	PS
Sony/Phillips digital interface	索尼/飞利普数字接口	Suǒ-ní—fēi-lì-pǔ shùzì jiēkǒu	S/PDIF
Sort (verb)	排序	Páixù	
Sort key	排序关键字	Páixù guānjiàn zì	
Sort order	排序次序	Páixù cìxù	
Sort table	排序本表	Páixù běn biǎo	
Sound absorption ability	吸声能力	Xīshēng nénglì	SAA
Sound articulation	语音清晰度	Yǔyīn qīngxīdù	
Sound broadcasting (by radio)	声音广播	Shēngyīn guǎngbō	
Sound detection and ranging	声雷达	Shēng léidá	SODAR
Sound energy	声能	Shēngnéng	SE
Sound energy density	声能密度	Shēngnéng mìdù	SED
Sound field non-uniformity	声场不均匀度	Shēngchǎng bùjūnyún dù	SFN
Sound field processor	声场处进器	Shēngchǎng chùjìnqì	SFP
Sound Galaxy © card	宇音卡	Yǔyīn kǎ	
Sound installation	音响设备	Yīnxiǎng shèbèi	SI
Sound insulation	隔音	Géyīn	SI
Sound navigation and ranging	声纳	Shēngnà	SONAR
Sound pressure level	声压级	Shēngyājí	SPL
Sound reinforcement system	扩声系统	Kuòshēng xìtǒng	SRS
Sound retrieval service	声音检索业务	Shēngyīn jiǎnsuǒ yèwù	
Sound retrieval system	声音修复系统	Shēngyīn xiūfù xìtǒng	SRS
Sound source	音源	Yīnyuán	SS
Soundex	语音拼写法	Yǔyīn pīnxiěfǎ	
Sounding	探测	Tàncè	
Sounding datum	深度基准	Shēndù jīzhǔn	
Source	源	Yuán	
Source	源点	Yuándiǎn	
Source address	源地址	Yuán dìzhǐ	SA
Source and target	源和目标	Yuán hé mùbiāo	
Source call signal address	源呼叫信令地址	Yuán hūjiào xìnlìng dìzhǐ	
Source category	源类	Yuán lèi	SC
Source code	源程序	Yuán chéngxù	
Source code	源代码	Yuán dàimǎ	
Source code	源码	Yuánmǎ	
Source coding	信源编码	Xìnyuán biānmǎ	
Source computer	源计算机	Yuán jìsuànjī	
Source coupler	光源耦合器	Guāngyuán ǒuhéqì	
Source database	源数据库	Yuán shùjùkù	

Source datacube	源多维数据集	Yuán duōwéi shùjùjí	
Source disk	源盘	Yuán pán	
Source host	源主机	Yuán zhǔjī	SRC
Source Internet protocol (IP) address	源因特网协议地址	Yuán Yīntèwǎng xiéyì dìzhǐ	
Source language	源语言	Yuán yǔyán	
Source library	源程序库	Yuán chéngxù kù	
Source library update	源程序库更新	Yuán chéngxù kù gēngxīn	SLU
Source main path interface reference point	发射主通道接口参考点	Fāshè zhǔtōngdào jiēkǒu cānkǎodiǎn	MPI-S
Source material	原始资料	Yuánshǐ zīliào	
Source media access control	源媒体接入控制	Yuán méitǐ jiērù kòngzhì	SMAC
Source object	源对象	Yuán duìxiàng	
Source of ringing current	铃流源	Líng liú yuán	
Source partition	源分区	Yuán fēnqū	
Source port	源端口	Yuán duānkǒu	
Source program	源程序	Yuán chéngxù	
Source routing (computer attack)	源路由	Yuán lùyóu	
Source routing and transparency	源路由选择并透明	Yuán lùyóu xuǎnzé bìng tòumíng	SRT
Source routing selection	源路由选择	Yuán lùyóu xuǎnzé	
Source traffic descriptor	源业务量描述语	Yuán yèwùliàng miáoshù yǔ	
Source traffic descriptor	源业务量描述语	Yuán yèwùliáng miáoshùyǔ	
Source/sink relationship	源宿关系	Yuán sù guānxi	
Source-concealed user intrusion	伪装成源的用户入侵	Wěizhuāng chéng yuánde yònghù rùqīn	
Source-route bridging	源路由桥接	Yuán lùyóu qiáojiē	SRB
Source-route translational bridging	源路由平移桥接	Yuán lùyóu píngyí qiáojiē	SR/TLB
Source-route translational bridging	源路由转换桥接	Yuán lùyóu zhuǎnhuàn qiáojiē	SRTLB
Source-route transparent bridging	源路由透明桥接	Yuán lùyóu tòumíng qiáojiē	SRT
South African Council for Automation and Computation	南非自动化和计算委员会	Nánfēi zìdònghuà hé jìsuàn wěiyuánhuì	SACAC
South Bridge chip	南桥芯片	Nánqiáo xìnpiàn	SBC
South Korea Telecom (GSM network operator)	南朝鲜京电信	Nán Cháoxiān jīng diànxìn	SK Telecom
Space (between characters and words in Morse code)	间隔	Jiàngé	
Space and time resource	时空资源	Shíkōng zīyuán	STR
Space connector	空中接口	Kōngzhōng jiēkǒu	UM
Space diversity	空间分集	Kōngjiān fēnjí	
Space diversity doublet	空间分集偶极天线	Kōngjiān fēnjí ǒují tiānxiàn	SD
Space division	空分	Kōngfēn	
Space division multiple access	空分多址	Kōngfēn duōzhǐ	SDMA
Space division multiple access	空间分割多路存取	Kōngjiān fēngē duōlù cúnqǔ	SDMA
Space division multiplexing	空分复用	Kōngfēn fùyòng	SDM
Space division multiplexing	空间分割多种复用	Kōngjiān fēngē duōzhǒng fùyòng	SDM
Space division switching	空分交换	Kōngfēn jiāohuàn	
Space division switching method	空分交换方式	Kōngfēn jiāohuàn fāngshì	
Space frequency modulation	空间频率调制	Kōngjiān pínlǜ tiáozhì	SFM
Space operation service	空间操作业务	Kōngjiān cāozuò yèwù	
Space probe	空间探测器	Kōngjiān tàncèqì	
Space radio communication	空间电通信	Kōngjiān diàn tōngxìn	

Space radio communication	空间无线电通信	Kōngjiān wúxiàndiàn tōngxìn	
Space recycle protocol	空间再利用协议	Kōngjiān zàilìyòng xiéyì	SRP
Space research service	空间研究业务	Kōngjiān yánjiū yèwù	
Space station	空间站	Kōngjiānzhàn	
Space switch back panel	空分交换后面板	Kōngfēn jiāohuàn hòumian bǎn	SSBP
Space switch clock distribution board assembly	空分交换时钟分配集成板	Kōngfēn jiāohuàn shízhōng fēnpèi jíchéngbǎn	SSCA
Space switch clock distributor	空分交换时钟分配器	Kōngfēn jiāohuàn shízhōng fēnpèiqì	SSCK
Space switch control and maintenance	空分交换控制和维护	Kōngfēn jiāohuàn kòngzhì hé wéihù	SSCM
Space switch input and output	空分交换输入输出	Kōngfēn jiāohuàn shūrù shūchū	SSIO
Space switch matrix	空分交换矩阵	Kōngfēn jiāohuàn jǔzhèn	SSMX
Space system	空间系统	Kōngjiān xìtǒng	
Space telecommand	空间谣令	Kōngjiān yáolìng	
Space telemetry	空间遥测技术	Kōngjiān yáocè jìshù	
Space time transmit diversity	空时发射分集	Kōngshí fāshè fēnjí	STTD
Space time transmit diversity (space time block coding based on transmit antenna diversity)	基于发射天线分集的空间时间分组编码分集	Jīyú fāshè tiānxiàn fēnjíde kōngjiān shíjiān fēnzǔ biānmǎ fēnjí	STTD
Space tracking	空间跟踪	Kōngjiān gēnzōng	
Space transmit diversity	空间发分集	Kōngjiān fāfēnjí	STD
Space-based infrared surveillance	空基红外监视	Kōngjī hóngwài jiānshì	SBIRS
Space-code division multiple access	空间码分多址	Kōngjiān mǎfēn duōzhǐ	SCDMA
Spacecraft	航天器	Hángtiānqì	
Spacecraft	空间飞行器	Kōngjiān fēixíngqì	
Spacecraft	宇宙飞船	Yǔzhòu fēichuán	
Spacer	间隔物	Jiàngéwù	
Spacer dispersion equipment	间隔物散布装置	Jiàngéwù sànbù zhuāngzhì	
Space-time transmission diversity	空时发送分集	Kōngshí fāsòng fēnjí	STTD
Spacing ratio	间距比	Jiānjù bǐ	
Spam	垃圾邮件	Lājī yóujiàn	
Span	跨距	Kuàjù	
Span	跨越	Kuàyuè	
Span (of cable)	档距	Dàngjù	
Spanned volume	跨区卷	Kuà qū juàn	
Spanning explorer packet	生成探测包	Shēngchéng tàncè bāo	
Spanning explorer packet	展开式探测包	Zhǎnkāishì tàncè bāo	
Spanning forest	生成森林	Shēngchéng sēnlín	
Spanning tree	生成树	Shēngchéng shù	
Spanning tree algorithm	生成树算法	Shēngchéng shù suànfǎ	STA
Spanning tree protocol (IEEE 802.1D)	生成树协议	Shēngchéng shù xiéyì	STP
Spare	备用	Bèiyòng	SP
Spare mode	备用工作方式	Bèiyòng gōngzuò fāngshì	
Spare point	备用点	Bèiyòng diǎn	
Spark plug suppressor	火花塞抑制器	Huǒhuāsāi yìzhìqì	
Sparse binary matrix	稀疏二元矩阵	Xīshū èryuán jǔzhèn	
Sparse graph	稀疏图	Xīshū tú	
Sparse matrix	稀疏矩阵	Xīshū jǔzhèn	
Sparse mode	稀疏模式	Xīshū móshì	SM

English	Chinese	Pinyin	Abbreviation
Sparse mode PIM	稀疏型 PIM	Xīshū-xíng PIM	
Sparse rule base	稀疏规则库	Xīshū guīzé kù	
Sparsity	稀疏度	Xīshū dù	
Spatial access methods	空间逼近发	Kōngjiān bījìn fā	SAMS
Spatial analysis	空间分析	Kōngjiān fēnxī	
Spatial attribute	空间属性	Kōngjiān shǔxìng	
Spatial autocorrelation	空间自相关	Kōngjiān zìxiāngguān	
Spatial complexity	空间复杂型	Kōngjiān fùzáxíng	
Spatial data	空间数据	Kōngjiān shùjù	
Spatial data infrastructure	空间数据基础设施	Kōngjiān shùjù jīchǔ shèshī	
Spatial data manipulation language	空间数据操作语言	Kōngjiān shùjù cāozuò yǔyán	SDML
Spatial data model	空间数据模型	Kōngjiān shùjù móxíng	
Spatial data modeling	空间数据建模	Kōngjiān shùjù jiànmó	
Spatial data structure	空间数据结构	Kōngjiān shùjù jiégòu	
Spatial data transfer	空间数据转换	Kōngjiān shùjù zhuǎnhuàn	
Spatial data transfer standard / topologic vector product	空间数据交换标准/拓扑矢量产品	Kōngjiān shùjù jiāohuàn biāozhǔn/ tuòpū shīliàng chǎnpǐn	SDTS/TVP
Spatial data transform standard	空间数据转换标准	Kōngjiān shùjù zhuǎnhuàn biāozhǔn	SDTS
Spatial database engine	空间数据库引擎	Kōngjiān shùjùkù yǐnqíng	SDE
Spatial database management system	空间数据库管理系统	Kōngjiān shùjùkù guǎnlǐ xìtǒng	SDBMS
Spatial datum	空间基准	Kōngjiān jīzhǔn	
Spatial dependency	空间依赖性	Kōngjiān yīlàixìng	
Spatial domain	空间域	Kōngjiān yù	
Spatial domain	空域	Kōngyù	
Spatial entity	空间实体	Kōngjiān shítǐ	
Spatial feature	空间特征	Kōngjiān tèzhēng	
Spatial filter	空间滤波器	Kōngjiān lǜbōqì	
Spatial indexing	空间索引	Kōngjiān suǒyǐn	
Spatial information	空间信息	Kōngjiān xìnxī	
Spatial information enquiry service	空间信息查询服务	Kōngjiān xìnxī cháxún fúwù	SINES
Spatial intensity distribution (FOC)	空间强度分布	Kōngjiān qiángdù fēnbù	
Spatial interaction	空间相互作用	Kōngjiān xiānghù zuòyòng	
Spatial interaction model	空间相互作用模型	Kōngjiān xiānghù zuòyòng móxíng	
Spatial interpolation	空间插值	Kōngjiān chāzhí	
Spatial join	空间合并	Kōngjiān hébìng	
Spatial join	空间连接	Kōngjiān liánjiē	
Spatial light modulator	空间调变元件	Kōngjiān tiáobiàn yuánjiàn	
Spatial modeling	空间建模	Kōngjiān jiànmó	
Spatial object	空间对象	Kōngjiān duìxiàng	
Spatial operator	空间算符	Kōngjiān suànfú	
Spatial optical transmission system	光空间传输系统	Guāng kōngjiān chuánshū xìtǒng	
Spatial order	空间顺序	Kōngjiān shùnxù	
Spatial overlay	空间叠加	Kōngjiān diéjiā	
Spatial pattern	空间模式	Kōngjiān móshì	
Spatial phenomena	空间现象	Kōngjiān xiànxiàng	
Spatial primitive	空间原素	Kōngjiān yuánsù	

Spatial projection	空间投影	Kōngjiān tóuyǐng	
Spatial proximity	空间接近性	Kōngjiān jiējìnxìng	
Spatial query	空间查询	Kōngjiān cháxún	
Spatial query language	空间查询语言	Kōngjiān cháxún yǔyán	
Spatial reference	空间参照	Kōngjiān cānzhào	
Spatial reference system (coordinate)	空间参照系(坐标)	Kōngjiān cānzhàoxì (zuòbiāo)	
Spatial relationship	空间关系	Kōngjiān guānxi	
Spatial resolution	空间分辨率	Kōngjiān fēnbiànlǜ	
Spatial reuse protocol	空间复用协议	Kōngjiān fùyòng xiéyì	SRP
Spatial reuse protocol	空间再用协议	Kōngjiān zàiyòng xiéyì	SRP
Spatial sampling	空间采样	Kōngjiān cǎiyàng	
Spatial scalability coding	空间可分级编码	Kōngjiān kěfēnjí biānmǎ	
Spatial simulation modeling	空间仿真建模	Kōngjiān fǎngzhēn jiànmó	
Spatial smoothing	空间平滑	Kōngjiān pínghuá	
Spatial syntax	空间句法	Kōngjiān jùfǎ	
Spatial unit	空间单元	Kōngjiān dānyuán	
Spatial/optical matched filter	空间/光学匹配滤光镜	Kōngjiān/guāngxué pǐpèi lǜguāngjìng	
Spatio-temporal database	时空数据库	Shíkōng shùjùkù	
Spatio-temporal key	时空索引	Shíkōng suǒyǐn	
Spatio-temporal object relationship model	时空对象关系模型	Shíkōng duìxiàng guānxi móxíng	STORM
Spatio-temporal topology	时空拓扑	Shíkōng tuòpū	
SPEAKeasy (software radio developed by US military and Hazeltine Corporation)	易通话	Yìtōnghuà	
Speaker recognition	人声识别技术	Rénshēng shíbié jìshù	SR
Speaker telephone set	扬声电话机	Yángshēng diànhuàjī	
Special access control level	特殊接入控制级别	Tèshū jiērù kòngzhì jíbié	
Special coinbox discriminating tone	专用投币电话鉴别音	Zhuānyòng tóubì diànhuà jiànbié yīn	
Special connection	特种接续	Tèzhǒng jiēxù	
Special dial tone	特殊拨号音	Tèshū bōhàoyīn	
Special function (WP command)	特殊功能	Tèshū gōngnéng	
Special interest group	特别兴趣小组	Tèbié xìngqu xiǎozǔ	SIG
Special interest group	特殊利益集团	Tèshū lìyì jítuán	SIG
Special management application element	特定管理应用元素	Tèdìng guǎnlǐ yìngyòng yuánsù	SMASE
Special management information service element	专用管理信息业务单元	Zhuānyòng guǎnlǐ xìnxī yèwù dānyuán	SMISE
Special mobile group	特别移动通信组	Tèbié yídòng tōngxìn zǔ	SMG
Special mobile radio	专用移动无线电	Zhuānyòng yídòng wúxiàndiàn	SMR
Special number for receiving	接收专号	Jiēshōu zhuānhào	
Special purpose electronic warfare aircraft	专用电子战飞机	Zhuānyòng diànzǐzhàn fēijī	
Special radio station	特种电台	Tèzhǒng diàntái	
Special resource function	专用资源功能	Zhuānyòng zīyuán gōngnéng	SRF
Special resources function	特殊资源功能	Tèshū zīyuán gōngnéng	SRF
Special restrictions	特殊限制	Tèshū xiànzhì	
Special routing	特殊路由选择	Tèshū lùyóu xuǎnzé	
Special service	特别业务	Tèbié yèwù	
Special service device	特业台	Tèyètái	SSD
Special service number (such as 411 for information, 117 for fire)	特服号	Tèfúhào	

Specialization	特化	Tèhuà	
Specialization	专门化	Zhuānménhuà	
Specialized application service	特定应用服务要素	Tèdìng yìngyòng fúwù yàosù	SASE
Specialized mobile radio system	集群移动通信	Jíqún yídòng tōngxìn	SMR
Specialized mobile radio system	专用移动无线电系统	Zhuānyòng yídòng wúxiàndiàn xìtǒng	SMRS
Specialized resource function	专用的资源处理函数	Zhuānyòngde zīyuán chǔlǐ hánshù	SRF
Specialized resource report	专用资源报告	Zhuānyòng zīyuán bàogào	SRR
Specialized-communication common carrier	专用通信公共载波	Zhuānyòng tōngxìn gōnggòng zàibō	SCCC
Specific access function	特定接入功能	Tèdìng jiērù gōngnéng	SAF
Specific cymomotive force	特定的场强-距离乘积	Tèdìngde chǎngqiáng-jùlí chéngjī	
Specific field strength-distance product	特定的场强-距离乘积	Tèdìngde chǎngqiáng-jùlí chéngjī	SCMF
Specific general packet radio service node	特定的通用分组无线电业务节点	Tèdìngde tōngyòng fēnzǔ wúxiàndiàn yèwù jiédiǎn	SGSN
Specific inspection level (in quality standards)	特殊检查水平	Tèshū jiǎnchá shuǐpíng	
Specific layout structure	特定布局结构	Tèdìng bùjú jiégòu	
Specific logical structure	特定逻辑结构	Tèdìng luóji jiégòu	
Specification	规范	Guīfàn	
Specification	规格	Guīgé	
Specification and description language	规范和描述语言	Guīfàn hé miáoshù yǔyán	SDL
Specification description language	规范描述语言	Guīfàn miáoshù yǔyán	SDL
Specification description language	说明与描述语言	Shuōmíng yǔ miáoshù yǔyán	SDL
Specificity	专指度	Zhuānzhǐdù	
Spectral characteristic	光谱特性	Guāngpǔ tèxìng	
Spectral coherence	普相关	Pǔ xiāngguān	
Spectral component	频谱分量	Pínpǔ fènliàng	
Spectral domain technique	谱域法	Pǔyùfǎ	
Spectral expansion	频谱扩展	Pínpǔ kuòzhǎn	
Spectral line	谱线	Pǔxiàn	
Spectral line width	光谱线宽度	Guāngpǔxiàn kuāndù	
Spectral linewidth	谱线宽度	Pǔxiàn kuāndù	
Spectral power density	谱功率密度	Pǔ gōnglǜ mìdù	
Spectral representation	频谱表示法	Pínpǔ biǎoshìfǎ	
Spectral resolution (GIS)	波谱分辨力	Bōpǔ fēnbiàn lì	
Spectral response range	光谱响应范围	Guāngpǔ xiǎngyìng fànwéi	
Spectral signature	光谱信号	Guāngpǔ xìnhào	
Spectral width	谱宽	Pǔkuān	
Spectrophotometry (semiconductor mfg)	分光光度计	Fēnguāng guāngdùjì	
Spectrum analyzer	频谱分析仪	Pínpǔ fēnxīyí	
Spectrum effectiveness	频谱效率	Pínpǔ xiàolǜ	
Spectrum purity	频谱纯度	Pínpǔ chúndù	
Spectrum saving	频谱节约	Pínpǔ jiéyuē	
Spectrum-sliced	光谱分割	Guāngpǔ fēngē	
Speculative execution	预测执行	Yùcè zhíxíng	
Speech activity	话音激活率	Huàyīn jīhuólǜ	
Speech analog input to digitizer	数字转换器的语言模拟输入	Shùzì zhuǎnhuànqìde yǔyán mónǐ shūrù	SAID
Speech bandwidth	语音带宽	Yǔyīn dàikuān	

Speech channel	话路	Huàlù	
Speech coding	语音编码	Yǔyīn biānmǎ	
Speech compiler	语音采编器	Yǔyīn cǎibiānqì	
Speech compiler console	语音采编台	Yǔyīn cǎibiāntái	
Speech current	话音电流	Huàyīn diànliú	
Speech decoder	语音解码器	Yǔyīn jiěmǎqì	SPD
Speech digit signaling	话音数位信令	Huàyīn shùwèi xìnlìng	
Speech digit signaling	话音数字信令	Huàyīn shùzì xìnlìng	
Speech digit signaling	语音数位信令	Yǔyīn shùwèi xìnlìng	
Speech digit signaling	语音位信令	Yǔyīn wèi xìnlìng	
Speech encoder	语音编码器	Yǔyīn biānmǎqì	SPE
Speech predictive encoded communication	话音预测编码通信	Huàyīn yùcè biānmǎ tōngxìn	SPEC
Speech processing	语声处理	Yǔshēng chǔlǐ	
Speech recognition	语音识别	Yǔyīn shíbié	
Speech recognition processor	语言识别处理器	Yǔyán shíbié chǔlǐqì	SRP
Speech scrambling	语音置乱	Yǔyīn zhìluàn	
Speech security	语音保密	Yǔyīn bǎomì	
Speech segmentation algorithm	语音分割算法	Yǔyīn fēngē suànfǎ	
Speech spurt	话音突发	Huàyīn tūfā	
Speech synthesis	语音合成	Yǔyīn héchéng	
Speech vs silence discrimination	有无话鉴别	Yǒu wú huà jiànbié	
Speech wire	通话线	Tōnghuà xiàn	
Speech+duplex equipment	语音+双工设备	Yǔyīn+shuānggōng shèbèi	
Speech+simplex equipment	语音+单工设备	Yǔyīn+dāngōng shèbèi	
Speech-predictive coding	语言预测编码	Yǔyán yùcè biānmǎ	SPEC
Speed control system	速度控制系统	Sùdù kòngzhì xìtǒng	SCS
Speed dialing	略位拨号	Lüèwèi bōhào	
Speed matching	快速匹配	Kuàisù pǐpèi	
Speed matching	速度匹配	Sùdù pǐpèi	
Speed restrictions	限速	Xiànsù	
Speedrate conversion	速率变换	Sùlǜ biànhuàn	
Spew	过度发送	Guòdù fāsòng	
Sphere coordinate kernel	球面坐标核	Qiúmiàn zuòbiāo hé	
Spherical array	球形阵	Qiúxíng zhèn	
Spherical array (antenna)	球星天线阵	Qiúxīng tiānxiàn zhèn	SA
Spherical center deflection	球心偏移度	Qiúxīn piānyídù	
Spherical concave mirror	球面凹面镜	Qiúmiàn āomiànjìng	
Spherical convex mirror	球面凸面镜	Qiúmiàn tūmiànjìng	
Spherical reflector	球面反射器	Qiúmiàn fǎnshèqì	
Spherical reflector antenna	球面反射器天线	Qiúmiàn fǎnshèqì tiānxiàn	
Spheroid	大地椭球体	Dàdì tuǒqiú tǐ	
Spike	尖峰脉冲	Jiānfēng màichōng	
Spike	尖峰信号	Jiānfēng xìnhào	
Spike	脉冲	Màichōng	
Spill-over factor	溢失因数	Yìshī yīnshù	
Spill-over power	溢失功率	Yìshī gōnglǜ	

Spiral antenna	螺旋天线	Luóxuán tiānxiàn	SA
Splice	接头	Jiētóu	
Splice and distribution unit	熔接配线单元	Róngjiē pèixiàn dānyuán	
Splice point	熔接点	Róngjiē diǎn	
Spline	样条插值曲线	Yàngtiáo chāzhí qūxiàn	
Spline smoothing	样条平滑	Yàngtiáo pínghuá	
Splining	样条方法	Yàngtiáo fāngfǎ	
Split access and flexible egress routing	分开存取和灵活发送的路由选择	Fēnkāi cúnqǔ hé línghuó fāsòngde lùyóu xuǎnzé	SAFER
Split antenna	对分天线	Duìfēn tiānxiàn	
Split cell (WP command)	方格划分	Fānggé huàfēn	
Split domain name server	隔离域名服务器	Gélí yùmíng fúwùqì	
Split horizon	水平拆分	Shuǐpíng chāifēn	
Split phase code	裂相码	Lièxiāng mǎ	
Split prism	分离棱镜	Fēnlí léngjìng	
Split-horizon update	分区更新	Fēnqū gēngxīn	
Split-horizon updates	水平分割更新	Shuǐpíng fēngē gēngxīn	
Splitter	分离器	Fēnlíqì	
Splitter board	分路器板	Fēnlùqì bǎn	SPL
Splitter power supply board	分路器电源板	Fēnlùqì diànyuán bǎn	PWF
Splitter unit motherboard	分路器框背板	Fēnlùqì kuàng bèibǎn	SUB
Splitter (in software)	切分窗口	Qiēfēn chuāngkǒu	
Splitter, tap coupler (FOC)	分路器	Fēnlùqì	
Splitting of the incoming line (in voice frequency signaling)	接收分割	Jiēshōu fēngē	
Splitting of the outgoing line (in voice frequency signaling)	发送分割（音频信令中）	Fāsòng fēngē (yīnpín xìnlìng zhōng)	
Spontaneous noise figure	自发辐射噪声系数	Zìfā fúshè zàoshēng xìshù	
Spoofing	欺骗	Qīpiàn	
Spooler program	假脱机程序	Jiǎtuōjī chéngxù	
Spooler system	假脱机系统	Jiǎtuōjī xìtǒng	
Spooling device	段脱机设备	Duàntuōjī shèbèi	SP
Sports games (computer game)	运动类游戏	Yùndòng lèi yóuxì	SPG
Spot beam antenna	点波束天线	Diǎn bōshù tiānxiàn	
Spot noise factor (of a linear two-port device)	点噪声因数（线性双端口装置的）	Diǎn zàoshēng yīnshù (xiànxìng shuāng duān kǒu zhuāngzhìde)	
Spot noise factor (of a linear two-port network)	点噪声系数（线性双端口网络的）	Diǎn zàoshēng xìshù (xiànxìng shuāng duānkǒu wǎngluòde)	F(f)
Spot noise figure (of a linear two-port device)	点噪声系数（线性双端口装置的）	Diǎn zàoshēng xìshù (xiànxìng shuāng duān kǒu zhuāngzhìde)	
Spot noise temperature (of a one-port network)	点噪声温度（单端口网络的）	Diǎn zàoshēng wēndù (dān duānkǒu wǎngluòde)	
Spotlight	小型点光源	Xiǎoxíng diǎn guāngyuán	
Spread spectrum	扩展频谱	Kuòzhǎn pínpǔ	SS
Spread spectrum (short for 扩展频谱)	扩频	Kuòpín	
Spread spectrum coefficient	扩谱系数	Kuòpǔ xìshù	
Spread spectrum communication	扩频通信	Kuòpín tōngxìn	SSC

Spread spectrum communication	扩展频谱通信	Kuòzhǎn pínpǔ tōngxìn	
Spread spectrum frequency hopping	扩展频谱频率跳变	Kuòzhǎn pínpǔ pínlǜ tiàobiàn	SSFH
Spread spectrum modulation	扩频调制	Kuòpín tiáozhì	
Spread spectrum modulation	扩展频谱调制	Kuòzhǎn pínpǔ tiáozhì	SSM
Spread spectrum multiple access	扩频多址	Kuòpín duōzhǐ	SSMA
Spread spectrum multiple access	扩展频谱多址	Kuòzhǎn pínpǔ duōzhǐ	SSMA
Spread spectrum random access	扩频随机接入	Kuòpín suíjī jiērù	SSRA
Spreading factor	扩频因子	Kuòpín yīnzǐ	SF
Spreading gain	扩频增益	Kuòpín zēngyì	SG
Spreading loss	扩展耗损	Kuòzhǎn hàosǔn	
Spreading rate	扩张速率	Kuòzhāng sùlǜ	
Spring jig	弹性类	Tánxìng lèi	
Sprinkler system	自动喷水灭火系统	Zìdòng pēnshuǐ mièhuǒ xìtǒng	SS
Sprint (US company)	斯普林特	Sī-pǔ-lín-tè	
Spur feeder	分支线	Fēnzhī xiàn	
Spurious emission	杂散发射	Zásǎn fāshè	
Spurious emissions	杂散骚扰	Zásǎn sāorǎo	
Spurious in-band signal	带内寄生信号	Dài-nèi jìshēng xìnhào	
Spurious narrow-band (RF) components	杂散窄带（射频）分量	Zásǎn zhǎidài (shèpín) fènliàng	
Spurious packet ratio	虚假包比例	Xūjiǎ bāo bǐlì	SPR
Spurious polygon	伪多边形	Wěiduōbiānxíng	
Spurious radiation	寄生辐射	Jìshēng fúshè	
Spurious response frequency	杂散响应频率	Zásǎn xiǎngyìng pínlǜ	
Spurious response immunity	杂散响应抗扰性	Zásǎn xiǎngyìng kàngrǎoxìng	
Spurious response rejection ratio	杂散响应抑制比	Zásǎn xiǎngyìng yìzhì bǐ	
Spurious transmitter noise	发射机杂散噪声	Fāshèjī zásǎn zàoshēng	
Spurious-wave output power	杂散输出功率	Zásǎn shūchū gōnglǜ	
Sputtering equipment (semiconductor mfg)	溅镀设备	Jiàndù shèbèi	
Square law detection	平方律检波	Píngfāng lǜ jiǎnbō	
Square root calculation	平方根计算	Píngfānggēn jìsuàn	SQRT
Square root of the sum of the squares method	平方和平方根法	Píngfānghé píngfānggēn fǎ	
Squeeze section (of a waveguide)	压缩波导段	Yāsuō bōdǎo duàn	
Squelch	静音	Jìngyīn	
Squelch	静噪	Jìngzào	
Squelch	屏蔽	Píngbì	SQLCH
Squelch blocking threshold	静噪阻塞门限	Jìngzào zǔsè ménxiàn	
Squelch detuning threshold	静噪失谐门限	Jìngzào shīxié ménxiàn	
Squelch opening delay and closing delay	静噪开启时延和闭锁时延	Jìngzào kāiqǐ shíyán hé bìsuǒ shíyán	
Squelch opening level and closing level	静噪开启电平和闭锁电平	Jìngzào kāiqǐ diànpíng hé bìsuǒ diànpíng	
Squelching (on SDH)	压制	Yāzhì	
Squint	偏斜	Piānxié	
Squint angle	偏斜角	Piānxié jiǎo	
Squirrel-cage	鼠笼型	Shǔlóng xíng	
SRNC radio network temporary identity	SRNC 无线网络临时识别	SRNC wúxiàn wǎngluò línshí shíbié	S-RNTI
Stability	稳定度	Wěndìngdù	
Stability analysis	稳定分析	Wěndìng fēnxī	

English	Chinese	Pinyin	Abbr.
Stability coefficient	稳定系数	Wěndìng xìshù	
Stabilized light source	安定化光源	Āndìnghuà guāngyuán	
Stable channel	稳定河道	Wěndìng hédào	
Stack	堆栈	Duīzhàn	
Stack	栈	Zhàn	
Stack full	栈满	Zhàn mǎn	SF
Stack overflow	栈溢出	Zhàn yìchū	
Stack pointer	栈指示字	Zhàn zhǐshìzì	SP
Stack unwinding	叠辗转开解	Dié zhǎnzhuǎn kāijiě	
Stacker control instruction	栈控制指令	Zhàn kòngzhì zhǐlìng	SCI
Stacking	迭层	Diécéng	
Stacking	叠加	Diéjiā	
Stage-by-stage selecting	逐级选择	Zhújí xuǎnzé	
Staggered quadrature overlapped raised cosine (modulation)	参差正交重叠上升余弦(调制)	Cēncī zhèngjiāo chóngdié shàngshēng yúxián (tiáozhì)	SQORC
Staggered quadrature partial response (modulation)	参差正交部分响应调制	Cēncī zhèngjiāo bùfen xiǎngyìng tiáozhì	SQPR
Staggered quadriphase pseudo-noise modulation	参差四相伪噪声调制	Cēncī sìxiāng wěizàoshēng tiáozhì	SQPNM
Staggered quadriphase shift keying	交错四相相移键控	Jiāocuò sìxiāng xiāngyí jiànkòng	SQPSK
Staggered quadriphase shift keying	交错四相移键控	Jiāocuò sìxiāngyí jiànkòng	SQPSK
Stainless steel internal oven, with venturi apertures (semiconductor mfg)	不锈钢内炉, 带文氏孔	Bùxiùgāng nèi lú, dài wén-shì kǒng	
Stainless steel ladder mesh belt (semiconductor mfg)	不锈钢阶梯网状带	Bùxiùgāng jiētī wǎngzhuàng dài	
Stall; stalled	停顿	Tíngdùn	
Stamped envelope	邮资信封	Yóuzī xìnfēng	
Stamped letter card	邮资信卡	Yóuzī xìnkǎ	
Stamped postcard	邮资明信片	Yóuzī míngxìnpiàn	
Stand alone synchronization equipment	独立型同步设备	Dúlì-xíng tóngbù shèbèi	SASE
Stand-alone	独立的	Dúlìde	
Stand-alone dedicated control channel	独立专用控制信道	Dúlì zhuānyòng kòngzhì xìndào	SDCCH
Standalone home location register	独立的标识位置寄存器	Dúlìde biāozhì wèizhì jìcúnqì	SHLR
Standalone home location register	独立的原始位置寄存器	Dúlìde yuánshǐ wèizhì jìcúnqì	SHLR
Stand-alone server	独立服务器	Dúlì fúwùqì	
Stand-alone synchronization equipment	独立型同步设备	Dúlì-xíng tóngbù shèbèi	SASE
Standalone synchronization supply equipment	独立同步供给设备	Dúlì tóngbù gōngjǐ shèbèi	SASE
Standard adaptor	标准适配器	Biāozhǔn shìpèiqì	
Standard artificial antenna	标准模拟天线	Biāozhǔn mónǐ tiānxiàn	
Standard attribute	标准属性	Biāozhǔn shǔxìng	
Standard calling probability	标准呼通概率	Biāozhǔn hūtōng gàilǜ	
Standard code test signal	标准码试验信号	Biāozhǔn mǎ shìyàn xìnhào	SCTS
Standard communications platform	标准通信平台	Biāozhǔn tōngxìn píngtái	SCP
Standard definition television	标准清晰度电视	Biāozhǔn qīngxīdù diànshì	SDTV
Standard description protocol	标准描述协议	Biāozhǔn miáoshù xiéyì	SDP
Standard design response spectrum	标准反应谱	Biāozhǔn fǎnyìng pǔ	
Standard deviation	标准差	Biāozhǔn chā	
Standard for the exchange of product model data	产品模型数据交换标准	Chǎnpǐn móxíng shùjù jiāohuàn biāozhǔn	STEP
Standard for the exchange of product model data	产品模型数据转换标准	Chǎnpǐn móxíng shùjù zhuǎnhuàn biāozhǔn	STEP

Standard frequency	标准频率	Biāozhǔn pínlǜ	
Standard frequency and time signal service	标准频率和时间信号业务	Biāozhǔn pínlǜ hé shíjiān xìnhào yèwù	
Standard frequency and time signal station	标准频率和时间信号电台	Biāozhǔn pínlǜ hé shíjiān xìnhào diàntái	
Standard frequency and time signals	标准频率和时间信号	Biāozhǔn pínlǜ hé shíjiān xìnhào	SFTS
Standard frequency and time signal-satellite service	卫星标准频率和时间信号业务	Wèixīng biāozhǔn pínlǜ hé shíjiān xìnhào yèwù	
Standard general markup language (in SQL Server)	标准通用标示语言	Biāozhǔn tōngyòng biāoshì yǔyán	SGML
Standard generalized markup language	标准规范化标记语言	Biāozhǔn guīfànhuà biāojì yǔyán	SGML
Standard generalized markup language	标准普及标记语言	Biāozhǔn pǔjí biāojì yǔyán	SGML
Standard generalized markup language	标准通用标记语言	Biāozhǔn tōngyòng biāojì yǔyán	SGML
Standard header	标准头	Biāozhǔn tóu	
Standard input signal	标准输入信号	Biāozhǔn shūrù xìnhào	
Standard input-signal frequency	标准输入信号频率	Biāozhǔn shūrù xìnhào pínlǜ	
Standard input-signal level	标准输入信号电平	Biāozhǔn shūrù xìnhào diànpíng	
Standard interchange format	标准交换格式	Biāozhǔn jiāohuàn géshi	SIF
Standard interface	标准界面	Biāozhǔn jièmiàn	
Standard interval	标准间隔	Biāozhǔn jiàngé	
Standard label	标准标记	Biāozhǔn biāojì	
Standard library	标准库	Biāozhǔn kù	
Standard light source	标准光源	Biāozhǔn guāngyuán	
Standard modulation	标准调制	Biāozhǔn tiáozhì	
Standard network access protocol	标准网络连接协议	Biāozhǔn wǎngluò liánjiē xiéyì	SNAP
Standard optical fiber connector	光纤标准连接器	Guāngxiān biāozhǔn liánjiēqì	
Standard optical fiber coupler	光纤标准耦合器	Guāngxiān biāozhǔn ǒuhéqì	
Standard pack	标准包	Biāozhǔn bāo	
Standard page description language	标准页面描述语言	Biāozhǔn yèmiàn miáoshù yǔyán	SPDL
Standard parallel (GIS)	标准纬线	Biāozhǔn wěixiàn	
Standard parallel port	标准并行口	Biāozhǔn bìngxíng kǒu	SPP
Standard Performance Evaluation Corporation	标准性能评估测试有限公司	Biāozhǔn xìngnéng pínggū cèshì yǒuxiàn gōngsī	SPEC
Standard plug	标准插头	Biāozhǔn chātóu	
Standard positioning service	标准定位业务	Biāozhǔn dìngwèi yèwù	SPS
Standard positioning service (in GPS)	标准定位服务	Biāozhǔn dìngwèi fúwù	SPS
Standard power output	标准输出功率	Biāozhǔn shūchū gōnglǜ	
Standard resource record format	标准资源记率格式	Biāozhǔn zīyuán jìlǜ géshi	SRRF
Standard signal to noise	标准信躁比	Biāozhǔn xìn zào bǐ	
Standard single mode fiber	标准单模光纤	Biāozhǔn dānmó guāngxiān	SSMF
Standard source	标准辐射源	Biāozhǔn fúshèyuán	
Standard template library	标准模板库	Biāozhǔn múbǎn kù	
Standard test modulation	标准试验调制	Biāozhǔn shìyàn tiáozhì	
Standard wire gauge (UK)	标准线规	Biāozhǔn xiànguī	SWG
Standardized option	标准化选项	Biāozhǔnhuà xuǎnxiàng	
Standardized raster graphic	标准化栅格图形	Biāozhǔnhuà zhàgé túxíng	SRG
Standards Adherence Section (an office responsible for assuring conformance to overall operating standards such as ISO:9001, and to QHSE (Quality, Health, Safety and Environment) standards.)	贯标办	Guàn biāo bàn	

English	Chinese	Pinyin	Abbreviation
Standard-time-signal emission	标准时间信号发射	Biāozhǔn shíjiān xìnhào fāshè	
Standby (verb, command)	待命	Dàimìng	
Stand-by communication channel	备用 C 通路	Bèiyòng C tōnglù	
Standby fiber	备纤	Bèixiàn	
Standby mode	专用模式	Zhuānyòng móshì	
Standby monitor presence	备用监视器存在	Bèiyòng jiānshìqì cúnzài	SMP
Stand-by redundancy	备用冗余	Bèiyòng rǒngyú	
Stand-by state	备用状态	Bèiyòng zhuàngtài	
Stand-by time	备用时间	Bèiyòng shíjiān	
Standing wave	驻波	Zhùbō	
Standing wave protection ciruit	驻波保护电路	Zhùbō bǎohù diànlù	
Standing wave voltage-ratio	驻波电压比	Zhùbō diànyā bǐ	SWVR
Standing-wave acousto-optical modulation	驻波声光调制	Zhùbō shēngguāng tiáozhì	SWAOM
Standing-wave antenna	驻波天线	Zhùbō tiānxiàn	SWA
Standing-wave detector	驻波检波器	Zhùbō jiǎnbōqì	
Standing-wave maximum	驻波最大点	Zhùbō zuìdà diǎn	
Standing-wave meter	驻波测量计	Zhùbō cèliángjì	
Standing-wave minimum	驻波最小点	Zhùbō zuìxiǎo diǎn	
Standing-wave ratio	驻波比	Zhùbōbǐ	SWR
Standing-wave ratio dynamometer	驻波比功率计	Zhùbōbǐ gōnglǜjì	
Standing-wave ratio trip	驻波比切断器	Zhùbōbǐ qiēduànqì	
Stanford Telecom (US company)	斯坦富电信公司	Sī-tǎn-fù diànxìn gōngsī	
Star coupler	星型耦合器	Xīngxíng ǒuhéqì	
Star interface	星形接口	Xīngxíng jiēkǒu	
Star join	星型联接	Xīngxíng liánjiē	
Star optical coupler	星状光纤耦合器	Xīngzhuàng guāngxiān ǒuhéqì	
Star schema	星型架构	Xīngxíng jiàgòu	
Star topology	星形拓扑	Xīngxíng tuòpū	
Stargate satellite network access point	星关卫星网路接入节点	Xīngguān wèixīng wǎnglù jiērù jiédiǎn	SSNAP
Start	启动	Qǐdòng	ST
Start bit	起始位	Qǐshǐ wèi	
Start code	始点码	Shǐdiǎn mǎ	
Start delimiter	起始定界符	Qǐshǐ dìngjièfú	SD
Start edge	起始边缘	Qǐshǐ biānyuán	
Start element	起码元	Qǐmǎyuán	
Start element	起始码元	Qǐshǐ mǎyuán	
Start field	起始字段	Qǐshǐ zìduàn	SF
Start frame sequence	帧起始序列	Zhèng qǐshǐ xùliè	SFS
Start of frame	帧起始符	Zhèng qǐshǐfú	SOF
Start of header	标题开始	Biāotí kāishǐ	SOH
Start of message	报文开始	Bàowén kāishǐ	SOM
Start of text	正文开始	Zhèngwén kāishǐ	STX
Start of text	正文开头	Zhèngwén kāitóu	STX
Start point	始点	Shǐdiǎn	
Start signal	起始信号	Qǐshǐ xìnhào	
Start transmission	起始传输	Qǐshǐ chuánshū	

Start-aligned	起始对准	Qǐshǐ duìzhǔn	
Starter	启动器	Qǐdòngqì	ST
Start-of-block signal	码组起始信号	Mǎzǔ qǐshǐ xìnhào	
Start-of-pulsing signal	脉冲开始信号	Màichōng kāishǐ xìnhào	
Start-stop apparatus	起止设备	Qǐzhǐ shèbèi	
Start-stop signal	起止信号	Qǐzhǐ xìnhào	
Start-stop system	起止系统	Qǐzhǐ xìtǒng	
Start-stop transmission	起止传输	Qǐzhǐ chuánshū	
Start-stop transmission	起止式传输	Qǐ-zhǐ-shì chuánshū	
State	态	Tài	
State Administration of Radio, Film and Television	国家广播电影和电视总局	Guójiā guǎngbō diànyǐng hé diànshì zǒngjú	SARFT
State confirm (SS7)	状态确认	Zhuàngtài quèrèn	
State control register	状态控制寄存器	Zhuàngtài kòngzhì jìcúnqì	SCR
State indication (SS7)	状态指示	Zhuàngtài zhǐshì	
State machine	状态机	Zhuàngtài jī	
State machine object	状态机对象	Zhuàngtài jī duìxiàng	SMO
State merging technique	状态合并环节	Zhuàngtài hébìng huánjié	
State of polarization	偏振态	Piānzhèn tài	SOP
State owned land	国有土地	Guóyǒu tǔdì	
State plane coordinate system	国家平面坐标系	Guójiā píngmiàn zuòbiāo xì	SPCS
State request (SS7)	状态请求	Zhuàngtài qǐngqiú	
State space truncation	状态截断环节	Zhuàngtài jiéduàn huánjié	
Stateful inspection (IPsec)	状态检查	Zhuàngtài jiǎnchá	
Stateless	无状态的	Wúzhuàngtàide	
Stateless address auto-configuration	主动地址自动配置	Zhǔdòng dìzhǐ zìdòng pèizhì	
Statement	声明	Shēngmíng	
Statement	语句	Yǔjù	
Statement block	语句块	Yǔjù kuài	
Statement function	语句函数	Yǔjù hánshù	
Statement number	语句编号	Yǔjù biānhào	
Statement permission	语句权限	Yǔjù quánxiàn	
State-transition diagram	状态转移图	Zhuàngtài zhuǎnyí tú	
Static allocation	固定分配方式	Gùdìng fēnpèi fāngshì	
Static analysis	静态分析	Jìngtài fēnxī	
Static conformance requirement	静态一致性要求	Jìngtài yīzhìxìng yāoqiú	
Static core	静态内核	Jìngtài nèihé	
Static cursor (for database)	静态游标	Jìngtài yóubiāo	
Static data authentication	静态数据鉴别	Jìngtài shùjù jiànbié	
Static dialog box	静态对话框	Jìngtài duìhuà kuàng	
Static fatigue (FOC)	静态疲劳	Jìngtài píláo	
Static induction thyristor	静电感应晶闸管	Jìngdiàn gǎnyìng jīngzháguǎn	SITH
Static induction transistor	静电感应晶体管	Jìngdiàn gǎnyìng jīngtǐguǎn	SIT
Static instability	静不稳定	Jìng bùwěndìng	
Static load balancing	静态负载平衡	Jìngtài fùzài pínghéng	
Static memory allocation	固定存储分配	Gùdìng cúnchǔ fēnpèi	
Static phase offset	静态相位偏差	Jìngtài xiàngwèi piānchā	

Static positioning	静态定位	Jìngtài dìngwèi	
Static random access memory	静态随机存储器	Jìngtài suíjī cúnchǔqì	SRAM
Static random access memory	静态随机存取存储器	Jìngtài suíjī cúnqǔ cúnchǔqì	SRAM
Static repository (in CORBA)	静态库	Jìngtài kù	
Static separation of duties	静态取责分离	Jìngtài qǔzé fènlí	SSD
Static structured query language (SQL) statements (for database)	静态结构化查询语言语句	Jìngtài jiégòuhuà cháxún yǔyán yǔjù	
Static stub (CORBA term)	静态存根	Jìngtài cúngēn	
Statically assigned socket	静态指定套接字	Jìngtài zhǐdìng tàojiēzì	
Statically determinate structure	静定结构	Jìngdìng jiégòu	
Static-column RAM	静态列 RAM	Jìngtài liè RAM	
Station (a radio station)	电台	Diàntái	
Station class mark	移动台级别标志	Yídòngtái jíbié biāozhì	SCM
Station clock	站钟	Zhàn zhōng	
Station management	站管理	Zhàn guǎnlǐ	SMT
Stationary random process	平稳随机过程	Píngwěn suíjī guòchéng	
Stationary satellite	静止卫星	Jìngzhǐ wèixīng	
Station-keeping (of a satellite)	指向精度	Zhǐxiàng jīngdù	
Station-keeping satellite	控位卫星	Kòngwèi wèixīng	
Station-keeping satellite	位置保持卫星	Wèizhì bǎochí wèixīng	
Statistic	统计量	Tǒngjì liàng	
Statistical	统计性	Tǒngjìxìng	
Statistical analysis	统计分析	Tǒngjì fēnxī	
Statistical bit rate	统计比特率	Tǒngjì bǐtè lǜ	SBR
Statistical communication	统计通信理论	Tǒngjì tōngxìn lǐlùn	
Statistical correlation	统计相关	Tǒngjì xiāngguān	
Statistical method	统计方法	Tǒngjì fāngfǎ	
Statistical multiplex	统计复用	Tǒngjì fùyòng	
Statistical pattern recognition	统计模式识别	Tǒngjì móshì shíbié	
Statistical process control	统计过程控制	Tǒngjì guòchéng kòngzhì	SPC
Statistical standard deviation for the population (in SQL Server)	函数返回总体标准差	Hánshù fǎnhuí zǒngtǐ biāozhǔn chà	STDEVP
Statistical surface	统计面	Tǒngjì miàn	
Statistical time-division multiplexer	统计时分复用器	Tǒngjì shífēn fùyòngqì	STMPX
Statistical time-division multiplexing	统计时分复用	Tǒngjì shífēn fùyòng	STDM
Statistical transfer mode	统计型传递方式	Tǒngjìxíng chuándì fāngshì	
Statistical variance (in SQL Server)	统计变异数	Tǒngjì biànyì shù	
Statistical variance for the population (in SQL Server)	函数返回总体变异数	Hánshù fǎnhuí zǒngtǐ biànyì shù	VARP
Statistics	统计	Tǒngjì	
Statistics maintenance manager	统计维护管理器	Tǒngjì wéihù guǎnlǐqì	SMM
Statistics of extremes	极值统计	Jízhí tǒngjì	
Status	状况	Zhuàngkuàng	
Status bar	状态栏	Zhuàngtài lán	
Status bar	状态条	Zhuàngtài tiáo	
Status bar (WP command)	状态窗口	Zhuàngtài chuāngkǒu	
Status change registration	状态改变注册	Zhuàngtài gǎibiàn zhùcè	SCR
Status field	状态段	Zhuàngtài duàn	SF

English	Chinese	Pinyin	Abbr.
Status field	状态字段	Zhuàngtài zìduàn	SF
Status handling	状态处理	Zhuàngtài chǔlǐ	
Status information frame	状态信息帧	Zhuàngtài xìnxī zhèng	SIF
Status inquiry	状态查询	Zhuàngtài cháxún	
Status inquiry	状态询问	Zhuàngtài xúnwèn	
Status manager	状态管理	Zhuàngtài guǎnlǐ	STM
Status transition system	状态转换系统	Zhuàngtài zhuǎnhuàn xìtǒng	
Status word	状态字	Zhuàngtài zì	SW
Steady flow	定流	Dìngliú	
Steady point	稳定点	Wěndìng diǎn	
Steady state	稳态的	Wěntàide	
Steady state gain response	稳态增益响应	Wěntài zēngyì xiǎngyìng	
Steady-state availability	稳态可用性	Wěntài kěyòngxìng	
Steady-state unavailability	稳态不可用性	Wěntài bùkěyòngxìng	
Stealth mode	窃用模式	Qièyòng móshì	
Stealth technology	隐身技术	Yǐnshēn jìshù	
Steel sheath	钢护套	Gāng hùtào	
Steel-pipe pile	钢管桩	Gāngguǎn zhuāng	
Steerable-beam antenna	可控射束天线	Kěkòng shèshù tiānxiàn	
Steerable-beam antenna system	波束可控天线系统	Bōshù kěkòng tiānxiàn xìtǒng	SBAS
Steering	绕开	Ràokāi	
Steganography	匿形术	Nìxíngshù	
Stegano-media	伪装媒体	Wěizhuāng méitǐ	
Stencil buffers	模板缓冲	Múbǎn huǎnchōng	
Step by step	步进制	Bùjìnzhì	SXS
Step by step switch	步进制交换机	Bùjìnzhì jiāohuànjī	SXS
Step by step switch local exchange	步进制市话局	Bùjìnzhì shìhuà jú	
Step index fiber	突变型多模光纤	Tūbiànxíng duōmó guāngxiān	SIF
Step index fiber	突变型光纤	Tūbiànxíng guāngxiān	
Step index profile	突变折射率分布	Tūbiàn zhéshèlǜ fēnbù	
Step object	步骤对象	Bùzhòu duìxiàng	
Step stress test	步进应力试验	Bùjìn yìnglì shìyàn	
Step twist	阶梯扭波导	Jiētī niǔ bōdǎo	
Step voltage	跨步电压	Kuà bù diànyā	
Step-by-step selector	步进选择器	Bùjìn xuǎnzéqì	
Stepped index plastic optical fiber	阶跃型塑胶光纤	Jiēyuèxíng sùjiāo guāngxiān	SI-POF
Stepped overlay function	分级叠加功能	Fēnjí diéjiā gōngnéng	
Stepped start-stop system (of data transmission)	步进起止系统	Bùjìn qǐzhǐ xìtǒng	
Stepped-impedance transformer	阶梯阻抗变换器	Jiētī zǔkàng biànhuànqì	
Stepping motor	步进式马达	Bùjìnshì mǎdá	
Stepwise maximum interference removal algorithm	分布最大干扰移去算法	Fēnbù zuìdà gānrǎo yíqù suànfǎ	SMIRA
Stepwise removal algorithm	分布移去算法	Fēnbù yíqù suànfǎ	SRA
Stereo	双声道	Shuāng shēngdào	
Stereolithography	光固化法	Guāng gùhuà fǎ	SL
Stereoplotter	立体绘图仪	Lìtǐ huìtú yí	
Stiffness	硬度	Yìngdù	

Still image conference entity	静止图像会议实体	Jìngzhǐ túxiàng huìyì shítǐ	SICE
Still image protocol data unit	静止图像协商数据单元	Jìngzhǐ túxiàng xiéshāng shùjù dānyuán	SIPDU
Still picture interchange file format	静止图象交换文件格式	Jìngzhǐ túxiàng jiāohuàn wénjiàn géshi	SPIFF
Still picture video-television	静止图象电视电话	Jìngzhǐ túxiàng diànshì diànhuà	
Still-picture television	静止图像电视	Jìngzhǐ túxiàng diànshì	SPTV
Stimulated Brillouin scattering	受激布里渊散射	Shòujī bù-lǐ-yuān sǎnshè	SBS
Stimulated Raman scattering	受激拉曼散射	Shòujī lā-màn sǎnshè	SRS
Stimulus terminal	激励型终端	Jīlì-xíng zhōngduān	
Stochastic	随机	Suíjī	
Stochastic automata network	随机自动机网络	Suíjī zìdòngjī wǎngluò	
Stochastic fair sharing	随机公平共享	Suíjī gōngping gòngxiǎng	SFS
Stochastic graph model	随机图刑模型	Suíjī túxíng móxíng	
Stochastic phenomena	随机现象	Suíjī xiànxiàng	
Stochastic process algebra	随机进程代数	Suíjī jìnchéng dàishù	SPA
Stochastic resonance theory	随机共振理论	Suíjī gòngzhèn lǐlùn	
Stochastic uncertainty	随机不确定性	Suíjī bùquèdìngxìng	
Stochastic uncertainty	随机误差	Suíjī wùchā	
Stokes line	斯托克斯线	Sī-tuō-kè-sī xiàn	
Stokes parameter evaluation	斯托克斯参数测定	Sī-tuō-kè-sī cānshù cèdìng	SPE
Stokes parameter evaluation technique	斯托克斯参数测定法	Sī-tuō-kè-sī cānshù cèdìng fǎ	
Stop bit	停止位	Tíngzhǐ wèi	
Stop element	停止码元	Tíngzhǐ mǎyuán	
Stop filter	阻塞滤波器	Zǔsè lǜbōqì	
Stop ringing	截铃	Jiélíng	
Stop signal	停止信号	Tíngzhǐ xìnhào	
Stop timer	停止定时器	Tíngzhǐ dìngshíqì	
Stopword	禁用词	Jīnyòng cí	
Storage area network	存储局域网络	Cúnchǔ júyù wǎngluò	SAN
Storage area network	存储区域网络	Cúnchǔ qūyù wǎngluò	SAN
Storage area network and SAN protocols (IETF, ANSI and ISO usage)	存储区域网络及其协议	Cúnchǔ qūyù wǎngluò jíqí xiéyì	SAN
Storage data register	存储器数据寄存器	Cúnchǔqì shùjù jìcúnqì	SDR
Storage director	存储器导向器	Cúnchǔqì dǎoxiàngqì	
Storage error	存储器错误	Cúnchǔqì cuòwù	SE
Storage function method	储留函数法	Chǔliú hánshù fǎ	
Storage key	存取键	Cúnqǔ jiàn	SKEY
Storage life	储存寿命	Chǔcún shòumìng	
Storage life	贮存寿命	Zhùcún shòumìng	
Storage network, storage area network	存储器网	Cúnchǔqì wǎng	SAN
Storage Networking Industry Association	存储连网行业协会	Cúnchǔ liánwǎng hángyè xiéhuì	SNIA
Storage price	库存核算价	Kùcún hésuàn jià	
Storage quota management	库存定额管理	Kùcún dìng'é guǎnlǐ	
Storage resource management	存储资源管理	Cúnchǔ zīyuán guǎnlǐ	SRM
Storage service agent	存储服务代理	Cúnchǔ fúwù dàilǐ	
Storage space	存贮器空间	Cúnzhùqì kōngjiān	
Storage virtualization	存储虚拟化	Cúnchǔ xūnǐhuà	
Storage within the network	网络内存储	Wǎngluò nèicúnchǔ	

Storage-area network	存储域网	Cúnchǔ yù wǎng	SAN
Storage-class resource	存储类资源	Cúnchǔ lèi zīyuán	
Storage-only	只存	Zhǐ cún	
Store and forward	存储转发	Cúnchǔ zhuǎnfā	
Store and forward service	存贮转发式服务	Cúnzhù zhuǎnfāshì fúwù	
Store and forward video transfer	存储转发式图像传输	Cúnchǔ zhuǎnfā-shì túxiàng chuánshū	
Store-and-forward	存储并转发	Cúnchǔ bìng zhuǎnfā	
Store-and-forward database	保存与转发数据库	Bǎocún yǔ zhuǎnfā shùjùkù	
Stored procedure (for database)	存储过程	Cúnchǔ guòchéng	
Stored procedure invocation (in SQL Server)	存储过程的调用	Cúnchǔ guòchéngde diàoyòng	
Stored program control	存储程序控制	Cúnchǔ chéngxù kòngzhì	SPC
Stored program controlled local exchange	程控市话局	Chéngkòng shìhuàjú	
Stored program controlled switching system	存储程序控制交换机	Cúnchǔ chéngxù kòngzhì jiāohuànjī	
Stored program system	存储程序	Cúnchǔ chéngxù	
Stored response FIR digital filter	存贮响应 FIR 数字滤波器	Cúnzhù xiǎngyìng FIR shùzì lǜbōqì	FIR-SRDF
Stored upstream neighbor station address	存储的上游邻站地址	Cúnchǔde shàngyóu línzhàn dìzhǐ	SUA
Straight pulse-code modulation	直接脉码调制	Zhíjiē màimǎ tiáozhì	SPCM
Straight tip (optical fiber connector)	直通式光纤连接器	Zhítōng-shì guāngxiān liánjiēqì	ST
Straight-through cross-connection	直通交叉连接	Zhítōng jiāochā liánjiē	
Strain	应变	Yìngbiàn	
Strain energy	应变能	Yìngbiàn néng	
Strain margin	应变限量	Yìngbiàn xiànliàng	
Strain meter	应变计	Yìngbiànjì	
Strain range	应变范围	Yìngbiàn fànwéi	
Strain tensor	应变张量	Yìngbiàn zhāngliàng	
Strained layer multiple quantum well	应变层多量子阱	Yìngbiàn céng duō liàngzǐ jiē	SLMQW
Stranded (optical fiber type)	层绞	Céngjiǎo	
Strap	搭接片	Dājiēpiàn	
Strategic cipher system	战略密码体制	Zhànlüè mìmǎ tǐzhì	
Strategic Defense Initiative (US)	战略防御计划	Zhànlüè fángyù jìhuà	SDI
Strategic enterprise management	企业战略管理	Qǐyè zhànlüè guǎnlǐ	SEM
Strategies group	政策集团	Zhèngcè jítuán	
Strategy role play games (computer game)	战略角色扮演游戏	Zhànlüè juésè bànyǎn yóuxì	SRPG
Stratum 2 clock	二级时钟	Èrjí shízhōng	
Stream	流	Liú	
Stream cipher	流密码	Liú mìmǎ	
Stream cipher	序列密码	Xùliè mìmǎ	
Stream compressing	流压缩	Liú yāsuō	
Stream control transmission protocol	流控传输协议	Liú kòng chuánshū xiéyì	SCTP
Stream control transmission protocol	流控制传输协议	Liú kòngzhì chuánshū xiéyì	SCTP
Stream control transport protocol	流控制传送协议	Liú kòngzhì chuánsòng xiéyì	SCTP
Stream label (in IPv6)	流标记	Liú biāojì	
Stream mode	流水线模式	Liúshuǐxiàn móshì	
Stream processor	流线处理	Liúxiàn chǔlǐ	
Stream sequence number	流顺序号码	Liú shùnxù hàomǎ	SSN
Streaming	串流	Chuànliú	

English	Chinese	Pinyin	Abbr.
Streaming	流式	Liú-shì	
Streaming audio	流音频	Liú yīnpín	
Streaming cipher algorithm	流密码算法	Liú mìmă suànfă	
Streaming media server	流媒体服务器	Liú méitǐ fúwùqì	
Streaming mode	串型	Chuànxíng	
Streaming mode	流方式	Liú fāngshì	
Streaming mode	流模式	Liú móshì	
Streaming SIMD extensions	单一指令多数据流扩展	Dānyī zhǐlìng duō shùjùliú kuòzhǎn	SSE
Streaming video	流视象	Liú shìxiàng	
Strength	强度	Qiángdù	
Stress	应力	Yìnglì	
Stress analysis	应力分析	Yìnglì fēnxī	
Stress concentration	应力集中	Yìnglì jízhōng	
Stress corrosion	应力腐蚀	Yìnglì fǔshí	
Stress drop	应力下降	Yìnglì xiàjiàng	
Stress field	应力场	Yìnglì cháng	
Stress intensity factor	应力强度系数	Yìnglì qiángdù xìshù	
Stress measurement	应力测定	Yìnglì cèdìng	
Stress model	应力模型	Yìnglì móxíng	
Stress relaxation model	应力松弛模型	Yìnglì sōngchí móxíng	
Stress relief method	应力释放法	Yìnglì shìfàng fă	
Stress tensor	应力张量	Yìnglì zhāngliàng	
Stress-induced birefringence fiber	应力感应双折射纤维	Yìnglì gănyìng shuāngzhéshè xiānwéi	SIF
Stress-strain curve	应力应变曲线	Yìnglì yìngbiàn qūxiàn	
Stretch system	延伸系统	Yánshēn xìtǒng	
Strike	走向	Zǒuxiàng	
Strikeout	走向线	Zǒuxiàng xiàn	
Strikethrough (WP command)	删除线	Shānchú xiàn	
String matching	模式匹配	Móshì pǐpèi	
Striping (RAID technology)	磁盘条纹	Cípán tiáowén	
Stripline	带状线	Dàizhuàngxiàn	
Stroboscopic light source	闪光光源	Shǎnguāng guāngyuán	
Strong authentication	强鉴别	Qiáng jiànbié	
Strong authentication	强验证	Qiáng yànzhèng	
Strong Markovian bisimulation	强马尔科夫相似	Qiáng mă-ĕr-kē-fū xiāngsì	
Strongly connected graph	强连通图	Qiáng liántōng tú	
Strowger selector	史端乔选择器	Shǐ duānqiáo xuănzéqì	
Structural calculation standard	结构计算标准	Jiégòu jìsuàn biāozhǔn	
Structural coefficient	结构系数	Jiégòu xìshù	
Structural element	结构部件	Jiégòu bùjiàn	
Structural engineering	结构工程	Jiégòu gōngchéng	
Structural equation modeling	结构化方程模型	Jiégòuhuà fāngchéng móxíng	SEM
Structural factor	结构要素	Jiégòu yàosù	
Structural mechanics	结构力学	Jiégòu lìxué	
Structural planning	结构设计	Jiégòu shèjì	
Structural return loss	结构器波损耗	Jiégòuqì bō sǔnhào	SRL

Structural type factor	结构类型系数	Jiégòu lèixíng xìshù	
Structure	结构	Jiégòu	
Structure category	结构分类	Jiégòu fēnlèi	
Structure element	结构元素	Jiégòu yuánsù	
Structure of management information	管理信息结构	Guǎnlǐ xìnxī jiégòu	SMI
Structure optimization	结构优化	Jiégòu yōuhuà	
Structured analysis and design technique	结构化分析与设计技术	Jiégòuhuà fēnxī yǔ shèjì jìshù	SADT
Structured cabling system	结构化布线系统	Jiégòuhuà bùxiàn xìtǒng	SCS
Structured data transfer	结构数据传送	Jiégòu shùjù chuánsòng	SDT
Structured programming	结构程序设计	Jiégòu chéngxù shèjì	
Structured query language	结构化查询语言	Jiégòuhuà cháxún yǔyán	SQL
Structured query language	结构式询问语言	Jiégòushì xúnwèn yǔyán	SQL
Structured query language / multimedia	多媒体结构化查询语言	Duōméitǐ jiégòuhuà cháxún yǔyán	SQL/MM
Structured storage file	结构化存储文件	Jiégòuhuà cúnchǔ wénjiàn	
Structured type	结构类型	Jiégòu lèixíng	
Stub (CORBA term)	存根	Cúngēn	
Stub area	存根区域	Cúngēn qūyù	
Stub network	存根网络	Cúngēn wǎngluò	
Stub tuner	调节短线	Tiáojié duǎnxiàn	
Stuffable digit time slot	可塞入数位时隙	Kěsāirù shùwèi shíxì	
Stuffing (video term)	填充	Tiánchōng	
Stuffing digit	塞入码位	Sāirù mǎ wèi	
Stuffing ratio	塞入比	Sāirù bǐ	
Sub-address	子地址	Zidìzhǐ	
Sub-addressing	子地址寻址	Zidìzhǐ xúnzhǐ	SUB
Sub-addressing service	子地址业务	Zidìzhǐ yèwù	
Sub-area	子域	Ziyù	
Sub-area node	子域节点	Ziyù jiédiǎn	
Sub-assembly	分机结构	Fēnjī jiégòu	
Sub-band coding	分波段编码	Fēnbōduàn biānmǎ	SBC
Sub-band coding	子带编码	Zidài biānmǎ	SBC
Sub-band coding for adaptive differential pulse-code modulation	自适应微分脉码调制的部分波段编码	Zìshìyìng wēifēn màimǎ tiáozhìde bùfen bōduàn biānmǎ	SBC-ADPCM
Sub-base station	子基地台	Zijīdìtái	
Sub-carrier	副载波	Fùzàibō	
Sub-carrier frequency modulation	副载波调制	Fùzàibō tiáozhì	SCM
Sub-carrier multiple access	副载波多址接入	Fùzàibō duōzhǐ jiērù	SCMA
Sub-carrier multiplex	子载波复用	Zizàibō fùyòng	SCM
Sub-carrier multiplexing	副载波复用	Fùzàibō fùyòng	SCM
Sub-carrier oscillator	负载波振荡器	Fùzàibō zhèndàngqì	SCO
Sub-channel	子信道	Zixìndào	
Sub-channel number	子信道号码	Zixìndào hàomǎ	SCN
Sub-channel phase transmission	子信道同相传输	Zixìndào tóngxiāng chuánshū	
Sub-class	子类	Zǐlèi	
Sub-class	子类别	Zǐlèibié	
Sub-complex	子复合型	Zifùhéxíng	

Sub-configuration mode	子配置模式	Zipèizhì móshì	
Sub-control station	副控制站	Fùkòngzhìzhàn	
Sub-critical flow	亚临界流	Yà línjiè liú	
Sub-directory	子目录	Zimùlù	
Sub-frame	子帧	Zizhèng	
Sub-frequency	分谐频	Fēnxiépín	
Sub-graph	子图	Zitú	
Sub-group security controller	子组安全控制器	Zizǔ ānquán kòngzhìqì	SGSC
Subharmonic	分谐波	Fēnxiébō	
Sub-highway multiplexer and demultiplexer	子公共信道多路复用和多路分解器	Zigōnggòng xìndào duōlù fùyòng hé duōlù fēnjiěqì	SMDX
Subject	主题	Zhǔtí	
Subject	主体	Zhǔtǐ	
Subject message	主题消息	Zhǔtí xiāoxi	
Subject probe	主题探查	Zhǔtí tànchá	
Sub-layer	子层	Zicéng	
Sub-layer monitoring	子层监视	Zicéng jiānshì	
Subliminal channel	阈下信道	Yùxià xìndào	
Sub-loop	子环	Zihuán	
Submarine cable	海底电缆	Hǎidǐ diànlǎn	HL
Submarine cable line termination equipment	海缆线路终端设备	Hǎilǎn xiànlù zhōngduān shèbèi	SLTE
Submarine optical cable	海底光缆	Hǎidǐ guānglǎn	HGL
Submarine optical fiber cable	水下光缆	Shuǐxià guānglǎn	SOFC
Submerged cable	水底电缆	Shuǐdǐ diànlǎn	SL
Submerged optical cable	水底光缆	Shuǐdǐ guānglǎn	SG
Submerged tunnel	沉埋隧道	Chénmái suìdào	
Submillimeter wavelength	亚毫米波长	Yàháomǐ bōcháng	
Sub-miniature integrated antenna	超小型机成天线	Chāoxiǎoxíng jīchéng tiānxiàn	SIA
Submission information rate	提交信息率	Tíjiāo xìnxī lǜ	SIR
Submit current table	提交本表	Tíjiāo běn biǎo	
Sub-multiplexer	子复用器	Zifùyòngqì	SMUX,SM
Sub-multiplexer for base station interface	用于 BS 接口的子复用器	Yòng yú BS jiēkǒude zifùyòngqì	SMBS
Sub-multiplexer highway board	干线子复用器板	Gànxiàn zifùyòngqì bǎn	SMHW
Sub-multiplexer interface	子复用板	Zifùyòng bǎn	SMI
Sub-multiplexer unit	子多路复用器	Ziduōlù fùyòngqì	SMX
Sub-net address	子网地址	Ziwǎng dìzhǐ	
Sub-net bandwidth management	子网带宽管理	Ziwǎng dàikuān guǎnlǐ	SBM
Sub-net mask	子网掩码	Ziwǎng yǎnmǎ	
Sub-net-directed broadcast address (in IP)	子网导向广播地址	Ziwǎng dǎoxiàng guǎngbō dìzhǐ	
Sub-network access protocol	子网访问协议	Ziwǎng fǎngwèn xiéyì	SNAP
Sub-network access protocol	子网接入协议	Ziwǎng jiērù xiéyì	SNAP
Sub-network connection	子网连接	Ziwǎng liánjiē	SNC
Sub-network connection protection	子网连接保护	Ziwǎng liánjiē bǎohù	SNCP
Sub-network connection protection with non-intrusive monitoring	带非介入监视的子网连接保护	Dài fēijièrù jiānshìde ziwǎng liánjiē bǎohù	SNC/N
Sub-network connection with inherent monitoring	带固有监视的子网连接保护	Dài gùyǒu jiānshìde zi wǎng liánjiē bǎohù	SNC/I

Sub-network convergence	子网收敛	Ziwǎng shōuliǎn	
Sub-network dependent convergence	子网依赖汇聚	Ziwǎng yīlài huìjù	SNDC
Sub-network dependent convergence function	子网从属会聚功能	Ziwǎng cóngshǔ huìjù gōngnéng	SNDCF
Sub-network dependent convergence layer	子网依赖结合层	Ziwǎng yīlài jiéhé céng	SNDC
Sub-network dependent convergence protocol	子网相关收敛协议	Ziwǎng xiāngguān shōuliǎn xiéyì	SNDCP
Sub-network dependent convergence protocol	子网依赖汇聚协议	Ziwǎng yīlài huìjù xiéyì	SNDCP
Sub-network dependent convergence protocol data unit	子网依赖汇聚协议分组数据单元	Ziwǎng yīlài huìjù xiéyì fēnzǔ shùjù dānyuán	SN-PDU
Sub-network management system	子网管理系统	Ziwǎng guǎnlǐ xìtǒng	SNM
Sub-network point of access	子网接入点	Ziwǎng jiērù diǎn	SNPA
Sub-network point of attachment	子网连接点	Ziwǎng liánjiē diǎn	SNPA
Sub-network point of attachment address	子网连接点地址	Ziwǎng liánjiē diǎn dìzhǐ	
Sub-network protocol data unit	子网协议数据单元	Ziwǎng xiéyì shùjù dānyuán	SNPDU
Sub-network service data unit	子网服务数据单元	Ziwǎng fúwù shùjù dānyuán	SNSDU
Sub-network, sub-net	子网	Ziwǎng	
Sub-object	子对象	Ziduìxiàng	
Subordinate managed object	下级被管理对象	Xiàjí bèiguǎnlǐ duìxiàng	
Subordinate, inferior	下级	Xiàjí	
Sub-program, sub-routine	子程序	Zǐchéngxù	
Sub-query (for database)	子查询	Zicháxún	
Sub-reflector	副反射器	Fùfǎnshèqì	
Sub-routine	子例程	Zilìchéng	
Sub-routine call table	子程序调用表	Zǐchéngxù diàoyòng biǎo	SCT
Subscriber access management function	用户接入管理功能	Yònghù jiērù guǎnlǐ gōngnéng	SAMF
Subscriber alerting signal	用户提示音	Yònghù tíshì yīn	SAS
Subscriber application	用户应用	Yònghù yìngyòng	SA
Subscriber authentication key	用户鉴权密码	Yònghù jiànquán mìmǎ	Ki
Subscriber authentication key	用户鉴权密钥	Yònghù jiànquán mìyào	Ki
Subscriber busy (electrical)	用户忙信号(电的)	Yònghù máng xìnhào (diànde)	SSB
Subscriber call attempts on busy hour	用户线忙时试呼	Yònghù xiàn mángshí shì hū	
Subscriber concentrator	用户集中器	Yònghù jízhōngqì	
Subscriber connection network	用户连接网络	Yònghù liánjiē wǎngluò	SCN
Subscriber connector	用户连接器	Yònghù liánjiēqì	SC
Subscriber facsimile station	用户传真站	Yònghù chuánzhēnzhàn	
Subscriber feeder	用户线	Yònghù xiàn	SF
Subscriber identification module	用户识别模块	Yònghù shíbié mókuài	SIM
Subscriber identity authentication	用户身份鉴权	Yònghù shēnfen jiànquán	
Subscriber identity confidentiality	用户身份保密	Yònghù shēnfen bǎomì	
Subscriber identity module	用户标识模块	Yònghù biāozhì mókuài	SIM
Subscriber identity module	用户身份模块	Yònghù shēnfen mókuài	SIM
Subscriber identity module	用户身份模组	Yònghù shēnfen mózǔ	SIM
Subscriber identity module	用户识别模组	Yònghù shíbié mózǔ	SIM
Subscriber identity module	用户识别卡	Yònghù shíbiékǎ	SIM
Subscriber identity module interface	用户标识模块接口	Yònghù biāozhì mókuài jiēkǒu	SIMI
Subscriber installation	用户装备	Yònghù zhuāngbèi	
Subscriber installation	用户装置	Yònghù zhuāngzhì	SI

Subscriber installation management function	用户装置管理功能	Yònghù zhuāngzhì guǎnlǐ gōngnéng	SIMF
Subscriber installation operation system	用户装置运行系统	Yònghù zhuāngzhì yùnxíng xìtǒng	SI-OpS
Subscriber interface back panel	用户接口后面板	Yònghù jiēkǒu hòumian bǎn	SIBP
Subscriber LCS privacy profile	LCS 用户保密指南	LCS yònghù bǎomì zhǐnán	SLPP
Subscriber line	用户线	Yònghù xiàn	
Subscriber line	用户线路	Yònghù xiànlù	
Subscriber line access protocol	用户线接入协议	Yònghù xiàn jiērù xiéyì	SLAP
Subscriber line audio processing circuit	用户线路声频信息处理电路	Yònghù xiànlù shēngpín xìnxī chǔlǐ diànlù	SLAC
Subscriber line concentration ratio	用户集线比	Yònghù jíxiàn bǐ	
Subscriber line concentration switch	用户线集中交换机	Yònghù xiàn jízhōng jiāohuànjī	SLCS
Subscriber line concentrator	程控市话用户集中器	Chéngkòng shìhuà yònghù jízhōngqì	
Subscriber line concentrator	用户集线器	Yònghù jíxiànqì	
Subscriber line interface circuit	用户线接口电路	Yònghù xiàn jiēkǒu diànlù	SLIC
Subscriber line interface circuit	用户线路接口电路	Yònghù xiànlù jiēkǒu diànlù	
Subscriber line interface controller	用户线接口控制器	Yònghù xiàn jiēkǒu kòngzhìqì	SLIC
Subscriber line measurement equipment	用户线测试设备	Yònghù xiàn cèshì shèbèi	SLME
Subscriber line module, analog	模拟用户线模块	Mónǐ yònghùxiàn mókuài	SLMA
Subscriber line module, digital	数字用户线模块	Shùzì yònghù xiàn mókuài	SLMD
Subscriber line signaling	用户信令	Yònghù xìnlìng	
Subscriber line traffic	用户线话务量	Yònghù xiàn huàwùliàng	
Subscriber local busy signal	用户本地忙信号	Yònghù běndì máng xìnhào	SLB
Subscriber local busy signal	用户市忙信号	Yònghù shì máng xìnhào	SLB
Subscriber location server	用户位置服务器	Yònghù wèizhì fúwùqì	
Subscriber loop	用户环路	Yònghù huánlù	
Subscriber loop carrier system	用户环路载波系统	Yònghù huánlù zàibō xìtǒng	SLC
Subscriber loop optical communication system	用户回路光通讯系统	Yònghù huílù guāng tōngxùn xìtǒng	
Subscriber loop termination unit	用户环路终端单元	Yònghù huánlù zhōngduān dānyuán	SLTU
Subscriber management system	注册用户管理系统	Zhùcè yònghù guǎnlǐ xìtǒng	SMS
Subscriber management systtem	用户管理系统	Yònghù guǎnlǐ xìtǒng	SMS
Subscriber media gateway	用户媒体网关	Yònghù méitǐ wǎngguān	SMG
Subscriber meter	用户计数器	Yònghù jìshùqì	
Subscriber network interface	用户网络接口	Yònghù wǎngluò jiēkǒu	SNI
Subscriber network interface	用户-网络接口	Yònghù—wǎngluò jiēkǒu	SNI
Subscriber number	用户号	Yònghù hào	SN
Subscriber number	用户号码	Yònghù hàomǎ	SN
Subscriber optical network	用户光纤网	Yònghù guāngxiān wǎng	YGQ
Subscriber premises network	用户室内网	Yònghù shìnèi wǎng	SPN
Subscriber premises network	用户住宅网	Yònghù zhùzhái wǎng	SPN
Subscriber register	用户寄存器	Yònghù jìcúnqì	SR
Subscriber service control block	用户服务控制模块	Yònghù fúwù kòngzhì mókuài	SSCO
Subscriber signal	用户信号	Yònghù xìnhào	
Subscriber storage	用户存储器	Yònghù cúnchǔqì	
Subscriber terminal equipment	用户终端设备	Yònghù zhōngduān shèbèi	STE
Subscriber test back panel	用户测试后面板	Yònghù cèshì hòumian bǎn	STBP
Subscriber timeout request message (in multicast)	用户超时请求消息	Yònghù chāoshí qǐngqiú xiāoxi	
Subscriber toll busy signal	用户长忙信号	Yònghù cháng máng xìnhào	STB

Subscriber toll busy signal	用户长途忙信号	Yònghù chángtú máng xìnhào	STB
Subscriber trunk dialing	用户干线拨号	Yònghù gànxiàn bōhào	STD
Subscriber unit	用户单元	Yònghù dānyuán	SU
Subscriber, customer	用户	Yònghù	
Subscriber's digital interface unit	用户数字接口设备	Yònghù shùzì jiēkǒu shèbèi	SDIU
Subscriber's line equipment	用户线路设备	Yònghù xiànlù shèbèi	SLE
Subscriber's premises	用户端	Yònghù duān	
Subscriber's tap	用户分支器	Yònghù fēnzhīqì	ST
Subscribers call processing	用户呼叫处理	Yònghù hūjiào chǔlǐ	SCP
Subscriber-side CRF	用户侧的 CRF	Yònghù cede CRF	CRF-S
Subscript (WP command)	下标	Xiàbiāo	
Subscript operator	下标操作符	Xiàbiāo cāozuò fú	
Subscription	订阅	Dìngyuè	
Subscription	开户入网	Kāihù rùwǎng	
Subscription by permit	凭证订阅	Píngzhèng dìngyuè	
Subscription database	订阅数据库	Dìngyuè shùjùkù	
Subscription form	报刊续订通知单	Bàokān xùdìng tōngzhīdān	
Subscription in the distribution branch station	报刊发行站收订	Bàokān fāxíng zhàn shōu dìng	
Subscription server	订阅服务器	Dìngyuè fúwùqì	
Subscription violation	签约违例	Qiānyuē wéilì	
Subsequent address message	后继地址消息	Hòujì dìzhǐ xiāoxi	SAM
Subsequent address message	后续地址消息	Hòuxù dìzhǐ xiāoxi	SAM
Subsequent address message with one signal	带有一信号的后续地址消息	Dàiyǒu yī xìnhàode hòuxù dìzhǐ xiāoxi	SAO
Subsequent flow	后续流	Hòuxù liú	
Subsequent handover failure	后续切换故障	Hòuxù qiēhuàn gùzhàng	
Subsequent handover procedure	后续切换程序	Hòuxù qiēhuàn chéngxù	
Subsequent handover procedure	子序列越区规程	Zixùliè yuèqū guīchéng	
Subsequent signal unit	后续信号单元	Hòuxù xìnhào dānyuán	SSU
Sub-service field	业务子段	Yèwù ziduàn	
Sub-service field	子业务字段	Ziyèwù zìduàn	SSF
Subset	子集	Zǐjí	
Subset phrasing	子集句式	Zǐjí jùshì	
Subset-division-based zerotree wavelet coding algorithm	基于自集分割的零树小波编码算法	Jīyú zìjí fēngēde língshù xiǎobō biānmǎ suànfǎ	SDZW
Subsidy	资助	Zīzhù	
Sub-space	子空间	Zikōngjiān	
Substitute recipient	取代接收者	Qǔdài jiēshōuzhě	
Substitution	取代	Qǔdài	SUB
Substitution attack (cryptography)	代换攻击	Dàihuàn gōngjī	
Substitution cipher	置换密码	Zhìhuàn mìmǎ	
Sub-STM (synchronous transfer mode)	子类同步传输模式	Zǐlèi tóngbù chuánshū móshì	sSTM
Substrate	基板	Jībǎn	
Substrate (semiconductor mfg)	衬底	Chèndǐ	
Sub-string	子串	Zichuàn	
Sub-synchronous satellite	分同步卫星	Fēntóngbù wèixīng	
Sub-system congestion	子系统拥塞	Zixìtǒng yōngsè	SSC

Sub-system multiplicity indicator (in SS7)	子系统复合表示语	Zìxìtǒng fùhé biǎoshì yǔ	
Sub-system number	子系统号码	Zìxìtǒng hàomǎ	SSN
Sub-telephone transmission	话下传输	Huà-xià chuánshū	
Subtraction	差	Chà	
Subtractive process (in SMT)	负过程	Fù guòchéng	
Sub-tree	子树	Zishù	
Sub-type	子类型	Zǐlèixíng	
Suburb connection	郊区电话接续	Jiāoqū diànhuà jiēxù	
Sub-vector	子矢量	Zishǐliàng	
Sub-vector	子向量	Zixiàngliàng	SV
Sub-vector indicator	子向量标识符	Zixiàngliàng biāozhìfú	SVI
Sub-vector length	子向量长度	Zixiàngliàng chángdù	SVL
Successful backward set-up information message	后向建立成功信息消息	Hòuxiàng jiànlì chénggōng xìnxī xiāoxi	SBM
Successful call	呼叫到达	Hūjiào dàodá	
Successive comparison A/D converter	逐级比较模/数转换器	Zhújí bǐjiào mó/shù zhuǎnhuànqì	
Successor	后继	Hòujì	
Sudden cosmic noise absorption	突发宇宙噪声吸收	Tūfā yǔzhòu zàoshēng xīshōu	SCNA
Sudden failure	突然失效	Tūrán shīxiào	
Sudden ionospheric disturbance	突发电离层骚扰	Tūfā diànlícéng sāorǎo	SID
Suffix	后缀	Hòuzhuì	
Suffix digit	后缀数字	Hòuzhuì shùzì	
Suitability model	适宜性模型	Shìyíxìng móxíng	
Suitability ranking	适宜性分级	Shìyíxìng fenjí	
Sulfuric acid gas	亚硫酸气	Yàliúsuān qì	
Sumcheck (telecom billing)	和校验	Hé jiàoyàn	
Summary authentication protocol (IPsec)	摘要认证协议	Zhāiyào rènzhèng xiéyì	
Sun Microsystems (US company)	华胜	Huáshèng	
Sun Microsystems, Inc. (US company)	太阳微系统公司	Tàiyáng wēi xìtǒng gōngsī	
Sunrise and sunset transition	日出日落过渡期	Rìchū rìluò guòdùqī	
Super absorbent	高能吸水剂	Gāonéng xīshuǐjì	
Super audio CD	超级音乐 CD	Chāojí yīnyuè CD	SACD
Super bandwidth infrastructure	超级带宽架构	Chāojí dàikuān jiàgòu	SBI
Super density	超密度	Chāomìdù	SD
Super high frequency	超高频	Chāogāopín	SHF
Super Hornet (U.S. F/A-18 aircraft)	大黄蜂	Dàhuángfēng	
Super intelligent sound ASIC	超级智能音频集成电路	Chāojí zhìnéng yīnpín jíchéng diànlù	
Super Jet (cable blower)	超级喷射器	Chāojí pēnshèqì	
Super light emitting diode	超辐射发光管	Chāofúshè fāguāng guǎn	SLED
Super mastergroup	超主群	Chāozhǔqún	
Super mastergroup link	超主群链路	Chāozhǔqún liànlù	
Super mastergroup section	超主群段	Chāozhǔqún duàn	
Super permanent memory	超级永久性存储器	Chāojí yǒngjiǔxìng cúnchǔqì	XPM
Super plane connection	超级平面连接	Chāojí píngmiàn liánjiē	SPC
Super South Bridge chip	超级南桥芯片	Chāojí nánqiáo xìnpiàn	SSB
Superclass	超级类别	Chāojí lèibié	
Superclass	上级类别	Shàngjí lèibié	

Super-cluster	超类	Chāolèi	
Superdirectivity	超方向性	Chāofāngxiàngxìng	
Superdistribution	超级分发	Chāojí fēnfā	
Superframe	超帧	Chāozhèng	
Supergroup	超群	Chāoqún	
Supergroup assembly link	超群组链路	Chāoqún zǔ liànlù	
Supergroup link	超群链路	Chāoqún liànlù	
Superheterodyne reception	超外差式接收	Chāowàichā-shì jiēshōu	
Superior	上级	Shàngjí	
Super-luminescence diode	超辐射发光管	Chāofúshè fāguāng guǎn	
Super-regeneration	超再生	Chāozàishēng	
Super-regenerator receiver	超再生接收机	Chāozàishēng jiēshōujī	
Superscalar	超标量体系结构	Chāobiāoliàng tǐxì jiégòu	
SuperScaler rendering (video term)	超标量渲染	Chāobiāoliàng xuànrǎn	
Superscript (WP command)	上标	Shàngbiāo	
Supersede	替换	Tìhuan	
Super-singular elliptic curve (cryptology)	超奇异椭圆曲线	Chāoqíyì tuǒyuán qūxiàn	
Superstructure	上部结构	Shàngbù jiégòu	
Super-synchronous satellite	超同步卫星	Chāotóngbù wèixīng	
Supertelex service, high speed telex	高速用户电报业务	Gāosù yònghù diànbào yèwù	
Super-turnstile antenna	超绕杆天线	Chāoràogān tiānxiàn	
Supervision (the S in BORSCHT)	监视	Jiānshì	
Supervision module	监控模块	Jiānkòng mókuài	
Supervisor state	管态	Guǎntài	
Supervisory audio tone	监测单音	Jiāncè dānyīn	SAT
Supervisory audio tone	监测音	Jiāncè yīn	SAT
Supervisory audio tone	监测音频单音	Jiāncè yīnpín dānyīn	SAT
Supervisory audio tone peak deviation	监测音峰频偏	Jiāncè yīnfēng pínpiān	
Supervisory block	监测设备	Jiāncè shèbèi	S-Block
Supervisory channel	监控信道	Jiānkòng xìndào	
Supervisory control and data acquisition	监控和数据采集	Jiānkòng hé shùjù cǎijí	SCADA
Supervisory frame (S-frame)	监帧	Jiān zhèng	
Supervisory lamp	监视灯	Jiānshì dēng	
Supervisory processor	监视处理机	Jiānshì chǔlǐjī	
Supervisory program	管理程序	Guǎnlǐ chéngxù	
Supervisory signal	监视信号	Jiānshì xìnhào	
Supervisory tone	监视音	Jiānshì yīn	
Supervisory unequipped signal	监控的未装载信号	Jiānkòngde wèizhuāngzài xìnhào	
Supervisory-unequipped	监控未装载	Jiānkòng wèizhuāngzài	
Supplement service application protocol data unit	补充业务应用协议数据单元	Bǔchōng yèwù yìngyòng xiéyì shùjù dānyuán	SS APDU
Supplemental logic interconnect cell	补充逻辑相互连接单元	Bǔchōng luóji xiānghù liánjiē dānyuán	
Supplementary information	补充信息	Bǔchōng xìnxī	SI
Supplementary insulation	附加绝缘	Fùjiā juéyuán	
Supplementary marking	补充标志	Bǔchōng biāozhì	
Supplementary protection	附加保护	Fùjiā bǎohù	
Supplementary service	补充业务	Bǔchōng yèwù	SS

English	Chinese	Pinyin	Abbreviation
Supplementary service camel subscription	补充业务 CAMEL 签约信息	Bǔchōng yèwù CAMEL qiānyuē xìnxī	SS-CSI
Supplementary service check	补充业务检查	Bǔchōng yèwù jiǎnchá	SSCHK
Supplementary service control string	补充业务控制串	Bǔchōng yèwù kòngzhì chuàn	SSC
Supplementary service control string	补充业务控制字符串	Bǔchōng yèwù kòngzhì zìfúchuàn	SSC
Supplementary service handling	补充业务处理	Bǔchōng yèwù chǔlǐ	SH
Supplementary service interrogation	补充业务询问	Bǔchōng yèwù xúnwèn	
Supplementary service interworking	补充业务互连	Bǔchōng yèwù hùlián	
Supplementary service registration	补充业务登记	Bǔchōng yèwù dēngjì	
Supplier/partner relationship management	供应商/合作伙关系管理	Gōngyìngshāng/hézuòbàn guānxi guǎnlǐ	
Supplier's declaration of conformity	产品一致性声明	Chǎnpǐn yīzhìxìng shēngmíng	SdoC
Supply chain lifecycle management	供应链生命周期管理	Gōngyìngliàn shēngmìng zhōuqī guǎnlǐ	
Supply chain management	供需链的管理	Gōngxū liànde guǎnlǐ	SCM
Supply chain management	通道资源管理	Tōngdào zīyuán guǎnlǐ	
Supply control system	电源控制系统	Diànyuán kòngzhì xìtǒng	SCS
Supply noise	交流声	Jiāoliúshēng	
Supply system impedance	供电系统阻抗	Gōngdiàn xìtǒng zǔkàng	
Support	支持	Zhīchí	
Support centralized network management	支持中心网络管理	Zhīchí zhōngxīn wǎngluò guǎnlǐ	SCNM
Support communication post	支援通信站	Zhīyuán tōngxìn zhàn	SCP
Support entity	支持实体	Zhīchí shítǐ	SE
Support entity function	支持实体功能	Zhīchí shítǐ gōngnéng	SEF
Support node	支持节点	Zhīchí jiédiǎn	
Support object	支持对象	Zhīchí duìxiàng	
Support of local service area	位置区服务	Wèizhì qū fúwù	SOLSA
Support of localized service area	固定业务区域的支持	Gùdìng yèwù qūyùde zhīchí	SoLSA
Support vector machine	支撑矢量机	Zhīchēng shǐliàngjī	
Supported by messenger wire	钢索敷设	Gāngsuǒ fūshè	M
Supporting network	支撑网	Zhīchēng wǎng	
Suppress outgoing access	压缩出局访问	Yāsuō chūjú fǎngwèn	SOA
Suppress outgoing access	抑制出访	Yìzhì chūfǎng	SOA
Suppressed carrier	抑制载波	Yìzhì zàibō	
Suppressed carrier single-sideband emission	抑制载单边带发射	Yìzhì zài dānbiāndài fāshè	
Suppressed carrier single-sideband emission	抑制载波单边带发射	Yìzhì zàibō dānbiāndài fāshè	
Suppressed spark plug	抑制型火化塞	Yìzhìxíng huǒhuà sāi	
Suppression (e.g. output power suppression)	钳制	Qiánzhì	
Suppression capacitor	抑制电容器	Yìzhì diànróngqì	
Suppression distributor rotor	带抑制器点火分配器转子	Dài yìzhìqì diǎnhuǒ fēnpèiqì zhuànzǐ	
Suppression element	抑制元件	Yìzhì yuánjiàn	
Suppressor	抑制器	Yìzhìqì	
Supradyne receiver	高外差式接收机	Gāowàichāi-shì jiēshōujī	
Surface	表面	Biǎomiàn	
Surface acoustic wave	声表面波	Shēng biǎomiànbō	SAW
Surface acoustic wave (SAW) device	声表面波器件	Shēng biǎomiànbō qìjiàn	
Surface acoustic wave filter	声表面滤波器	Shēng biǎomiàn lǜbōqì	
Surface impedance (of an isotropic material)	表面阻抗	Biǎomiàn zǔkàng	
Surface model	表面模型	Biǎomiàn móxíng	

English	Chinese	Pinyin	Abbr.
Surface mount component (electronics mfg)	表面组装元件	Biǎomiàn zǔzhuāng yuánjiàn	SMC
Surface mount device	表面安装设备	Biǎomiàn ānzhuāng shèbèi	SMD
Surface mount device (electronics mfg)	表面组装器件	Biǎomiàn zǔzhuāng qìjiàn	SMD
Surface mount technology	表面处理技术	Biǎomiàn chǔlǐ jìshù	
Surface mount technology	表面贴装技术	Biǎomiàn tiēzhuāng jìshù	
Surface mounting	表面安装	Biǎomiàn ānzhuāng	
Surface processing technology	表面处理技术	Biǎomiàn chǔlǐ jìshù	
Surface static electricity	表面静电	Biǎomiàn jìngdiàn	
Surface transfer impedance	表面传输阻扰	Biǎomiàn chuánshū zǔrǎo	STI
Surface transfer impedance (of a coaxial line)	表面转移阻抗	Biǎomiàn zhuǎnyí zǔkàng	
Surface transfer impedance of a coaxial line	同轴线表面转移阻抗	Tóngzhóu xiàn biǎomiàn zhuǎnyí zǔkàng	
Surface treatment (semiconductor mfg)	表面处理	Biǎomiàn chǔlǐ	
Surface wave	表面波	Biǎomiàn bō	
Surface wave antenna	表面波天线	Biǎomiàn bō tiānxiàn	SWA
Surface wave magnitude	表面波大小	Biǎomiàn bō dàxiǎo	
Surface-wave waveguide	表面波波导	Biǎomiàn bō bōdǎo	
Surfactant (in SMT)	表面活性剂	Biǎomiàn huóxìngjì	
Surge	电涌	Diànyǒng	
Surge	涌浪	Yǒnglàng	
Surge arrester	避雷器	Bìléiqì	
Surge current	浪涌电流	Làngyǒng diànliú	
Surge protection device	浪涌保护器	Làngyǒng bǎohùqì	
Surge suppressor	浪涌抑制器	Làngyǒng yìzhìqì	
Surge, galloping	浪涌	Làngyǒng	
Surrogate configuration	代理配置	Dàilǐ pèizhì	
Surrogate data	代用数据	Dàiyòng shùjù	
Surrogate data	替代数据	Tìdài shùjù	
Surround sound	环绕立体声	Huánrào lìtǐshēng	
Surveillance and control Data link (US military)	侦察与控制数据链	Zhēnchá yǔ kòngzhì shùjù liàn	SCDL
Surveillance and control of transmission system	传输系统的监视与控制	Chuánshū xìtǒngde jiānshì yǔ kòngzhì	SCOTS
Survey (GIS)	测量	Cèliáng	
Surveying	测量学	Cèliángxué	
Survivability	存活率	Cúnhuólǜ	
Survivability	生存性	Shēngcún-xìng	
Survivability	顽存性	Wáncúnxìng	
Survivable, survivability	抗毁	Kànghuǐ	
Survival craft station	营救器电台	Yíngjiùqì diàntái	
Susceptibility threshold	敏感度门限	Mǐngǎndù ménxiàn	
Susceptible device	敏感器件	Mǐngǎn qìjiàn	
Suspend	挂起	Guàqǐ	
Suspend	暂停	Zàntíng	SUS
Suspend acknowledge	挂起认可	Guàqǐ rènkě	
Suspend message (ISUP)	暂停消息	Zàntíng xiāoxi	SUS
Suspend reject	挂起拒绝	Guàqǐ jùjué	
Suspend request (ISUP message)	呼叫挂器请求	Hūjiào guàqì qǐngqiú	SUS
Suspend to disk	磁盘唤醒	Cípán huànxǐng	STD

Suspend to RAM	内存唤醒	Nèicún huànxǐng	STR
Suspension line	空吊线	Kōngdiàoxiàn	
Suspension of payment	止兑	Zhǐduì	
Sustainable cell rate	持续信元速率	Chíxù xìnyuán sùlǜ	SCR
Sustainable cell rate	可持续信元速率	Kěchíxù xìnyuán sùlǜ	SCR
Sustainable cell rate	可维持信元率	Kěwéichí xìnyuán lǜ	SCR
Sustainable cell rate	可维持信元速率	Kěwéichí xìnyuán sùlǜ	SCR
Sustained data transfer rate	持续数据传输率	Chíxù shùjù chuánshū lǜ	
Swedish Aerospace Corp.	瑞典空间公司	Ruìdiǎn kōngjiān gōngsī	
Sweep driver	扫描驱动器	Sǎomiáo qūdòngqì	SD
Swelling gel	膨胀油膏	Péngzhàng yóugāo	
Swept frequency modulation	扫描频率调制	Sǎomiáo pínlǜ tiáozhì	SFM
Swiss Federal Institute of Technology	瑞士联邦技术研究所	Ruìshì liánbāng jìshù yánjiūsuǒ	
Switch (in a switching network)	接线器	Jiēxiànqì	
Switch (the on-off type)	开关	Kāiguān	
Switch assembly	交换集成件	Jiāohuàn jíchéng jiàn	ISWA
Switch assembly	开关组件	Kāiguān zǔjiàn	SA
Switch card	交换卡	Jiāohuàn kǎ	
Switch control node	交换控制节点	Jiāohuàn kòngzhì jiédiǎn	SCN
Switch hook	摘挂机	Zhāiguàjī	
Switch network sub-system	交换网络子系统	Jiāohuàn wǎngluò zìxìtǒng	SNS
Switch off exciter	断开激励器	Duànkāi jīlìqì	
Switch virtual circuit	交换式虚电路	Jiāohuàn-shì xū diànlù	SVC
Switch, exchange	交换机	Jiāohuànjī	
Switchbaord position	交换台座席	Jiāohuàntái zuòxí	
Switchboard	人工交换台	Réngōng jiāohuàntái	
Switched call	交换呼叫	Jiāohuàn hūjiào	
Switched capacitor network	开关电容网络	Kāiguān diànróng wǎngluò	
Switched circuit network	电路交换网络	Diànlù jiāohuàn wǎngluò	SCN
Switched circuit network	交换电路网	Jiāohuàn diànlù wǎng	SCN
Switched connection	交换连接	Jiāohuàn liánjiē	
Switched connection element	交换连接单元	Jiāohuàn liánjiē dānyuán	
Switched connection element	交换型连接单元	Jiāohuàn-xíng liánjiē dānyuán	
Switched digital video	交换式数字图像	Jiāohuàn-shì shùzì túxiàng	SDV
Switched digital video broadcast	交换式数字电视广播	Jiāohuàn-shì shùzì diànshì guǎngbō	SDVB
Switched inter-networking services	交换式网络互联服务	Jiāohuàn-shì wǎngluò hùlián fúwù	SIS
Switched mode rectifier	开关整流器	Kāiguān zhěngliúqì	
Switched muiti-megabit data service	交换多兆比特数据业务	Jiāohuàn duōzhàobǐtè shùjù yèwù	SMDS
Switched multimegabit data service	交换式多兆比特数据业务	Jiāohuàn-shì duō zhàobǐtè shùjù yèwù	SMDS
Switched multimegabit data service	交换式多兆位数据服务	Jiāohuàn-shì duō zhàowèi shùjù fúwù	SMDS
Switched multimegabit data service	几兆比特数据交换业务	Jǐzhào bǐtè shùjù jiāohuàn yèwù	SMDS
Switched multimegabit digital service	交换型多兆位数字式服务	Jiāohuàn-xíng duō zhàowèi shùzì-shì fúwù	SMDS
Switched network order code	交换网络命令码	Jiāohuàn wǎngluò mìnglìng mǎ	SNOC
Switched permanent virtual circuit	交换型永久虚电路	Jiāohuàn-xíng yǒngjiǔ xū diànlù	SPVC
Switched port analyzer	交换端口分析器	Jiāohuàn duānkǒu fēnxīqì	SPAN
Switched power supply	开关电源	Kāiguān diànyuán	

Switched star network	交换式星形网络	Jiāohuàn-shì xīngxíng wǎngluò	SSN
Switched star system	交换式星形系统	Jiāohuàn-shì xīngxíng xìtǒng	SSS
Switched telephony services	交换话音业务	Jiāohuàn huàyīn yèwù	
Switched virtual channel	交换虚通路	Jiāohuàn xū tōnglù	SVC
Switched virtual channel connection	交换虚信道连接	Jiāohuàn xū xìndào liánjiē	SVCC
Switched virtual circuit	交换虚电路	Jiāohuàn xū diànlù	SVC
Switched virtual circuit	交换虚拟电路	Jiāohuàn xūnǐ diànlù	SVC
Switched virtual circuit	交换型虚电路	Jiāohuàn-xíng xū diànlù	SVC
Switched virtual connection	交换虚连接	Jiāohuàn xū liánjiē	SVC
Switched virtual network	交换虚拟网络	Jiāohuàn xūnǐ wǎngluò	SVN
Switched virtual path	交换式虚通路	Jiāohuàn-shì xū tōnglù	SVP
Switchhook	钩键	Gōujiàn	
Switching	交换	Jiāohuàn	
Switching area	交换区	Jiāohuàn qū	
Switching center	交换中心	Jiāohuàn zhōngxīn	
Switching element	交换单元	Jiāohuàn dānyuán	SE
Switching fabric	交换机构	Jiāohuàn jīgòu	
Switching function	交换功能	Jiāohuàn gōngnéng	SF
Switching matrix	交换矩阵	Jiāohuàn jǔzhèn	
Switching matrix	开关矩阵	Kāiguān jǔzhèn	
Switching module	交换模块	Jiāohuàn mókuài	SM
Switching network	交换网络	Jiāohuàn wǎngluò	SN
Switching node	交换节点	Jiāohuàn jiédiǎn	
Switching noise	切换噪声	Qiēhuàn zàoshēng	
Switching path	交换通道	Jiāohuàn tōngdào	
Switching point	交换点	Jiāohuàn diǎn	SP
Switching processing interface telephone events	交换处理接口电话事件	Jiāohuàn chǔlǐ jiēkǒu diànhuà shìjiàn	SPITEs
Switching select repeater	中断器开关选择器	Zhōngduànqì kāiguān xuǎnzéqì	SSR
Switching stage	交换级	Jiāohuàn jí	
Switching start time	倒换开始时间	Dǎohuàn kāishǐ shíjiān	
Switching sub-system	交换子系统	Jiāohuàn zixìtǒng	SSS
Switching time measurement	倒换时间测试	Dǎohuàn shíjiān cèshì	
Switching tone	交换音	Jiāohuàn yīn	
Switching unit	交换单元	Jiāohuàn dānyuán	
Switching voltage regulator	交换式电压调节	Jiāohuàn-shì diànyā tiáojié	SVR
Switching/signaling node	交换/信令节点	Jiāohuàn/xìnlìng jiédiǎn	SSN
Switching-equipment-congestion signal	交换设备拥塞信号	Jiāohuàn shèbèi yōngsè xìnhào	SEC
Switchover on low voltage (of a battery)	电压低切断	Diànyā dī qiēduàn	
Switch-to-switch protocol	交换机到交换机协议	Jiāohuànjī dào jiāohuànjī xiéyì	SSP
Switch-to-switch protocol	交换机间协议	Jiāohuànjī-jiān xiéyì	SSP
Sybase developer network	Sybase 开发者网络	Sybase kāifāzhě wǎngluò	SDN
Sychronous signaling (in common channel signaling)	同步信令方式	Tóngbù xìnlìng fāngshì	
Syllabic companding	音节压扩	Yīnjié yākuò	
Syllabic companding	音节压缩扩展	Yīnjié yāsuō kuòzhǎn	
Syllable articulation	音节清晰度	Yīnjié qīngxīdù	
Syllable chart	音节表	Yīnjiébiǎo	

Symbol	符号	Fúhào	
Symbol	记号	Jìhào	
Symbol environment	符号环境	Fúhào huánjìng	
Symbol error rate	符号差错率	Fúhào chācuò lǜ	SER
Symbol input (WP command)	符号输入	Fúhào shūrù	
Symbol rate	符号率	Fúhàolǜ	
Symbol table	符号表	Fúhào biǎo	
Symbolic manipulation	符号操作	Fúhào cāozuò	
Symbolic name	符号名	Fúhào míng	
Symbolic reachability graph (in stochastic process algebra)	标识可达图	Biāozhì kědátú	
Symbolic regression	符号回归	Fúhào huíguī	
Symbolization	符号化	Fúhàohuà	
Symbolization identification code (in RTP)	符号化识别码	Fúhàohuà shíbié mǎ	
Symbology	符号表示法	Fúhào biǎoshì fǎ	
Symmetric cryptographic algorithm (IPsec)	对称密码算法	Duìchèn mìmǎ suànfǎ	
Symmetric encryption algorithm (IPsec)	对称加密算法	Duìchèn jiāmì suànfǎ	
Symmetric matrix	对称矩阵	Duìchèn jǔzhèn	
Symmetric multi-processing	对称多重处理	Duìchèn duōchóng chǔlǐ	SMP
Symmetric multi-processing	对称式多重处理架构	Duìchèn-shì duōchóng chǔlǐ jiàgòu	SMP
Symmetric multi-processing	对称式多处理	Duìchèn-shì duōchǔlǐ	SMP
Symmetric quadratic frequency modulation	对称二次调制	Duìchèn èrcì tiáozhì	SQFM
Symmetric rendering architecture	对称渲染架构	Duìchèn xuànrǎn jiàgòu	SRA
Symmetric security protocol (IPsec)	对称保密协议	Duìchèn bǎomì xiéyì	
Symmetric switched broadband	对称交换宽带	Duìchèn jiāohuàn kuāndài	SSB
Symmetrical antenna	对称天线	Duìchèn tiānxiàn	
Symmetrical binary code	对称二元码	Duìchèn èryuán mǎ	
Symmetrical communications	双向对称通信	Shuāngxiàng duìchèn tōngxìn	SC
Symmetrical digital subscriber line	对称数字用户线	Duìchèn shùzì yònghù xiàn	SymDSL
Symmetrical radiating element	对称辐射单元	Duìchèn fúshè dānyuán	
Symmetrical terminal voltage	对称端子电压	Duìchèn duānzi diànyā	
Symmetrical terminal voltage	终端平衡电压	Zhōngduān pínghéng diànyā	
Symmetrical voltage	平衡电压	Pínghéng diànyā	
Synchronization and convergence function	同步和会聚功能	Tóngbù hé huìjù gōngnéng	SCF
Synchronization and convergence function	同步与会聚功能	Tóngbù yú huìjù gōngnéng	SCF
Synchronization bit	同步比特	Tóngbù bǐtè	
Synchronization burst	同步脉冲串	Tóngbù màichōng chuàn	SB
Synchronization burst	同步突发脉冲序列	Tóngbù tūfā màichōng xùliè	SB
Synchronization byte	同步字节	Tóngbù zìjié	SB
Synchronization channel	同步信道	Tóngbù xìndào	SCH
Synchronization channel information	同步信道信息	Tóngbù xìndào xìnxī	
Synchronization clock	同步时钟	Tóngbù shízhōng	
Synchronization code	同步码	Tóngbù mǎ	SC
Synchronization control channel	同步控制信道	Tóngbù kòngzhì xìn dào	SCCH
Synchronization data communications adapter	同步数据通讯适配器	Tóngbù shùjù tōngxùn shìpèiqì	SDCA
Synchronization distribution	同步分配	Tóngbù fēnpèi	SD
Synchronization hold-in time	同步保持时间	Tóngbù bǎochí shíjiān	

Synchronization indication	同步指示	Tóngbù zhǐshì	
Synchronization information	同步信息	Tóngbù xìnxī	
Synchronization link	同步链路	Tóngbù liànlù	
Synchronization link selection	同步链路选择	Tóngbù liànlù xuǎnzé	
Synchronization network local manager	同步网本地管理中心	Tóngbù wǎng běndì guǎnlǐ zhōngxīn	SLM
Synchronization network manager	同步网全网管理中心	Tóngbù wǎng quánwǎng guǎnlǐ zhōngxīn	SNM
Synchronization network regional manager	同步网区域管理中心	Tóngbù wǎng qūyù guǎnlǐ zhōngxīn	SRM
Synchronization node	同步节点	Tóngbù jiédiǎn	
Synchronization signal unit	同步信号单元	Tóngbù xìnhào dānyuán	SYU
Synchronization status message	同步状态信息	Tóngbù zhuàngtài xìnxī	SSM
Synchronization status message byte	同步状态消息字节	Tóngbù zhuàngtài xiāoxi zìjié	SSMB
Synchronization sub-layer	同步子层	Tóngbù zicéng	SSL
Synchronization supervisor module	同步监控模块	Tóngbù jiānkòng mókuài	SSM
Synchronization traceability unknown	同步信息未知	Tóngbù xìnxī wèizhī	STU
Synchronization, synchronous	同步	Tóngbù	
Synchronized compression and expansion	同步压扩	Tóngbù yākuò	Syncompex
Synchronized satellite	同步化卫星	Tóngbùhuà wèixīng	
Synchronizing signal generation	同步信号产生	Tóngbù xìnhào chǎnshēng	SSG
Synchronous (data) transmission	同步数据传输	Tóngbù shùjù chuánshū	
Synchronous backbone system	同步信息骨干系统	Tóngbù xìnxī gǔgàn xitǒng	SBS
Synchronous broadband control element	同步宽带控制器	Tóngbù kuāndài kòngzhìqì	SBCE
Synchronous burst	同步突发	Tóngbù tūfā	SB
Synchronous communication satellite	同步通信卫星	Tóngbù tōngxìn wèixīng	
Synchronous communications	同步通信	Tóngbù tōngxìn	
Synchronous computer	同步计算机	Tóngbù jìsuànjī	
Synchronous connecting link	同步连接链路	Tóngbù liánjiē liànlù	SCO
Synchronous connection-oriented	同步面向连接	Tóngbù miànxiàng liánjiē	SCO
Synchronous correction	同步校正	Tóngbù jiàozhèng	
Synchronous data adapter	同步数据转接器	Tóngbù shùjù zhuǎnjiēqì	SDA
Synchronous data circuit	同步数据电路	Tóngbù shùjù diànlù	CDS
Synchronous data communication control unit	同步数据通信控制器	Tóngbù shùjù tōngxìn kòngzhìqì	SDCCU
Synchronous data link control	同步数据链路控制	Tóngbù shùjù liànlù kòngzhì	SDLC
Synchronous data link control protocol (IBM use)	同步数据链路控制协议	Tóngbù shùjù liànlù kòngzhì xiéyì	SDLC
Synchronous data network	同步数据网	Tóngbù shùjù wǎng	
Synchronous demodulation	同步解调	Tóngbù jiětiáo	
Synchronous digital cross connect equipment	同步数字交叉连接设备	Tóngbù shùzì jiāochā liánjiē shèbèi	SDXC
Synchronous digital cross-connector	同步数字交叉连接器	Tóngbù shùzì jiāochā liánjiēqì	SDXC
Synchronous digital hierarchy	同步数字传输体系	Tóngbù shùzì chuánshū tǐxì	SDH
Synchronous digital hierarchy	同步数字体系	Tóngbù shùzì tǐxì	SDH
Synchronous digital hierarchy	同步数字系列	Tóngbù shùzì xìliè	SDH
Synchronous digital hierarchy	同步数字序列	Tóngbù shùzì xùliè	SDH
Synchronous digital hierarchy equipment clock	同步数字体系设备时钟	Tóngbù shùzì tǐxì shèbèi shízhōng	SEC
Synchronous digital hierarchy management network	同步数字体系管理网络	Tóngbù shùzì tǐxì guǎnlǐ wǎngluò	SMN
Synchronous digital hierarchy management sub-network	同步数字体系管理子网	Tóngbù shùzì tǐxì guǎnlǐ ziwǎng	SMS
Synchronous digital hierarchy physical interface	同步数字体系物理接口	Tóngbù shùzì tǐxì wùlǐ jiēkǒu	SPI

Synchronous dynamic random access memory	同步动态随机存储器	Tóngbù dòngtài suíjī cúnchǔqì	SDRAM
Synchronous equipment management function	同步设备管理功能	Tóngbù shèbèi guǎnlǐ gōngnéng	SEMF
Synchronous equipment timing generator	同步设备定时发生器	Tóngbù shèbèi dìngshí fāshēngqì	SETG
Synchronous equipment timing physical interface	同步设备定时物理接口	Tóngbù shèbèi dìngshí wùlǐ jiēkǒu	SETPI
Synchronous equipment timing source	同步设备定时源	Tóngbù shèbèi dìngshí yuán	SETS
Synchronous frequency encoding technique	同步频率编号技术	Tóngbù pínlǜ biānhào jìshù	SFET
Synchronous graphics random access memory	同步图形随机储存器	Tóngbù túxíng suíjī chǔcúnqì	SGRAM
Synchronous idle	同步空闲	Tóngbù kòngxián	SYN
Synchronous idle character	同步空闲字符	Tóngbù kòngxián zìfú	SYN
Synchronous line adapter	同步线转换器	Tóngbù xiàn zhuǎnhuànqì	SLA
Synchronous line optical interface	同步线路光口板	Tóngbù xiànlù guāng kǒu bǎn	SLI
Synchronous multi-cycle control	同步多周控制	Tóngbù duōzhōu kòngzhì	
Synchronous multi-line controller	同步多路控制器	Tóngbù duōlù kòngzhìqì	SMLC
Synchronous multimedia integrated language	同步多媒体集成语言	Tóngbù duōméitǐ jíchéng yǔyán	SMIL
Synchronous multiplexer	同步复用器	Tóngbù fùyòngqì	SM
Synchronous network	同步网	Tóngbù wǎng	TBW
Synchronous optical network	同步光网络	Tóngbù guāng wǎngluò	SONET
Synchronous optical network	同步光缆网络	Tóngbù guānglǎn wǎngluò	SONET
Synchronous optical network (ANSI/ITU-T)	同步光纤网络和同步数字系列	Tóngbù guāngxiān wǎngluò hé tóngbù shùzì xìliè	SONET/SDH
Synchronous physical interface	同步物理接口	Tóngbù wùlǐ jiēkǒu	SPI
Synchronous residual time stamp	同步剩余时间标志法	Tóngbù shèngyú shíjiān biāozhì fǎ	SRTS
Synchronous satellite	同步卫星	Tóngbù wèixīng	
Synchronous serial data adapter	同步串行数据转换器	Tóngbù chuànháng shùjù zhuǎnhuànqì	SSDA
Synchronous start-stop margin	同步起止改正力	Tóngbù qǐzhǐ gǎizhèng lì	
Synchronous supply unit	同步供给单元	Tóngbù gōngjǐ dānyuán	SSU
Synchronous telegraphy	同步电报	Tóngbù diànbào	
Synchronous time division multiple access	同步时分多路存取	Tóngbù shífèn duōlù cúnqǔ	STDMA
Synchronous time division multiplexing	同步时分复用	Tóngbù shífèn fùyòng	STDM
Synchronous timing generator	同步定时产生器	Tóngbù dìngshí chǎnshēngqì	STG
Synchronous timing generator	同步定时发生器	Tóngbù dìngshí fāshēngqì	STG
Synchronous transfer mode	同步传递方式	Tóngbù chuándì fāngshì	STM
Synchronous transfer mode	同步传递模式	Tóngbù chuándì móshì	STM
Synchronous transfer mode	同步传输模式	Tóngbù chuánshū móshì	STM
Synchronous transfer mode	同步传送模式	Tóngbù chuánsòng móshì	STM
Synchronous transfer mode	同步转移模式	Tóngbù zhuǎnyí móshì	STM
Synchronous transfer module	同步转移模块	Tóngbù zhuǎnyí mókuài	STM
Synchronous transmission	同步传输	Tóngbù chuánshū	
Synchronous transmission mode-N	N 阶同步传送模块	N-jiē tóngbù chuánsòng mókuài	STM-N
Synchronous transport module	同步传输模块	Tóngbù chuánshū mókuài	STM
Synchronous transport module	同步传送模块	Tóngbù chuánsòng mókuài	STM
Synchronous transport module	同步运输模块	Tóngbù yùnshū mókuài	STM
Synchronous transport module level-N	同步传送模块等级 N	Tóngbù chuánsòng mókuài děngjí N	STM-N
Synchronous transport module-N	第 N 级同步传送模块	Dì N-jí tóngbù chuánsòng mókuài	STM-N
Synchronous transport signal level-1	同步运输信号第 1 层	Tóngbù yùnshū xìnhào dìyīcéng	STS-1
Syncompex	同步压扩	Tóngbù yākuò	

Syntax	句法结构	Jùfǎ jiégòu	
Syntax	语法	Yǔfǎ	
Syntax class library	语法类库	Yǔfǎ lèi kù	
Syntax diagram	语法图	Yǔfǎ tú	
Synthesizer	合成器	Héchéngqì	
Synthesizer	综合器	Zōnghéqì	
Synthetic aperture radar	合成孔径雷达	Héchéng kǒngjìng léidá	SAR
Synthetic aperture radar	合成口径雷达	Héchéng kǒujìng léidá	SAR
Synthetic synchronization	合成同步	Héchéng tóngbù	
Syringe (in SMT)	注射器	Zhùshèqì	
System access control list	系统访问控制列表	Xìtǒng fǎngwèn kòngzhì lièbiǎo	SACL
System administrator	系统管理员	Xìtǒng guǎnlǐyuán	
System analysis	系统分析	Xìtǒng fēnxī	SA
System approach	系统方法	Xìtǒng fāngfǎ	
System architecture	系统结构	Xìtǒng jiégòu	
System availability information point	系统可用性信息点	Xìtǒng kěyòngxìng xìnxī diǎn	
System bus interface assembly	系统总线接口集成件	Xìtǒng zǒngxiàn jiēkǒu jíchéng jiàn	SBIA
System catalog	系统目录	Xìtǒng mùlù	
System change number (in ORACLE)	系统变更号码	Xìtǒng biàngēng hàomǎ	SCN
System coding capacity	系统编码容量	Xìtǒng biānmǎ róngliàng	
System coding control	系统编码控制	Xìtǒng biānmǎ kòngzhì	
System communication statement	系统通信语句	Xìtǒng tōngxìn yǔjù	
System conformance statement	系统一致性陈述	Xìtǒng yīzhìxìng chénshù	SCS
System conformance test report	系统一致性测试报告	Xìtǒng yīzhìxìng cèshì bàogào	SCTR
System control	系统控制	Xìtǒng kòngzhì	
System control board	系统控制板	Xìtǒng kòngzhì bǎn	SCB
System control panel	系统控制盘	Xìtǒng kòngzhì pán	SCP
System coordinate system	系统坐标系	Xìtǒng zuòbiāo xì	
System database (for database)	系统数据库	Xìtǒng shùjùkù	
System default profile	系统默认配置文件	Xìtǒng mòrèn pèizhì wénjiàn	
System description language	系统描述语言	Xìtǒng miáoshù yǔyán	SDL
System design review	系统设计评审	Xìtǒng shèjì píngshěn	
System distortion	系统失真	Xìtǒng shīzhēn	SD
System engineer	系统工程师	Xìtǒng gōngchéng hī	SE
System Engineering Group (CMM)	系统工程组	Xìtǒng gōngchéng zǔ	SEG
System evaluation	系统评估	Xìtǒng pínggū	
System failure	系统故障	Xìtǒng gùzhàng	
System feasibility study	系统可行性论证	Xìtǒng kěxíngxìng lùnzhèng	
System for advanced mobile broadband applications	先进的移动宽带应用系统	Xiānjìnde yídòng kuāndài yìngyòng xìtǒng	SAMBA
System frame number	系统帧号码	Xìtǒng zhèng hàomǎ	SFN
System function	系统功能	Xìtǒng gōngnéng	
System function	系统函数	Xìtǒng hánshù	
System gain	系统增益	Xìtǒng zēngyì	SG
System generation	系统生成	Xìtǒng shēngchéng	SYSGEN
System identification	系统标识	Xìtǒng biāozhì	SID
System identification	系统识别码	Xìtǒng shíbié mǎ	SID

English	Chinese	Pinyin	Abbreviation
System information	系统信息	Xìtǒng xìnxī	SI
System information type	系统信息类型	Xìtǒng xìnxī lèixíng	
System information viewer	系统信息观察器	Xìtǒng xìnxī guāncháqì	SIV
System initialization	系统初始化	Xìtǒng chūshǐhuà	
System initiation	系统启动	Xìtǒng qǐdòng	
System integration	系统集成	Xìtǒng jíchéng	
System integration test	系统集成测试	Xìtǒng jíchéng cèshì	SIT
System integrator	系统集成商	Xìtǒng jíchéng shāng	
System integrity	系统完整性	Xìtǒng wánzhěngxìng	
System integrity procedure	系统完整性规程	Xìtǒng wánzhěngxìng guīchéng	
System loader	系统承载器	Xìtǒng chéngzàiqì	
System loading	系统加载	Xìtǒng jiāzài	SL
System loss	系统损耗	Xìtǒng sǔnhào	SL
System management	系统管理	Xìtǒng guǎnlǐ	
System management application entity	系统管理应用实体	Xìtǒng guǎnlǐ yìngyòng shítǐ	SMAE
System management application process	系统管理应用程序	Xìtǒng guǎnlǐ yìngyòng chéngxù	SMAP
System management application protocol machine	系统管理应用协议机	Xìtǒng guǎnlǐ yìngyòng xiéyì jī	SMAPM
System management application service element	系统管理应用服务单元	Xìtǒng guǎnlǐ yìngyòng fúwù dānyuán	SMASE
System management bus	全系统管理总线	Quán xìtǒng guǎnlǐ zǒngxiàn	SMB
System management bus	系统管理总线	Xìtǒng guǎnlǐ zǒngxiàn	SMB
System management function	系统管理功能	Xìtǒng guǎnlǐ gōngnéng	SMF
System management function unit	系统管理功能单位	Xìtǒng guǎnlǐ gōngnéng dānwèi	
System management interrupt	系统管理中断	Xìtǒng guǎnlǐ zhōngduàn	SMI
System management kernel	系统管理内核	Xìtǒng guǎnlǐ nèihé	SMK
System management mode	系统管理模式	Xìtǒng guǎnlǐ móshì	SMM
System management service	系统管理服务	Xìtǒng guǎnlǐ fúwù	
System management service interface	系统管理业务接口	Xìtǒng guǎnlǐ yèwù jiēkǒu	SMSI
System manager terminal	系统管理终端	Xìtǒng guǎnlǐ zhōngduān	
System margin	系统余量	Xìtǒng yúliàng	SM
System memory	系统内存	Xìtǒng nèicún	
System model	系统模型	Xìtǒng móxíng	
System module	系统模块	Xìtǒng mókuài	
System monitoring	系统监视	Xìtǒng jiānshì	
System network architecture	系统网络建筑	Xìtǒng wǎngluò jiànzhù	SNA
System network architecture	系统网络结构	Xìtǒng wǎngluò jiégòu	
System network architecture	系统网络体系结构	Xìtǒng wǎngluò tǐxì jiégòu	SNA
System on a chip	系统集成多功能芯片	Xìtǒng jíchéng duōgōngnéng xìnpiàn	SOAC
System optimization	系统优化	Xìtǒng yōuhuà	
System overall operating time	系统总工作时间	Xìtǒng zǒnggōngzuò shíjiān	
System program	系统程序	Xìtǒng chéngxù	
System protection	系统保护	Xìtǒng bǎohù	
System recovery time	系统恢复时间	Xìtǒng huīfù shíjiān	
System selection for preferred roaming	首选漫游的系统选择	Shǒuxuǎn mànyóude xìtǒng xuǎnzé	SSPR
System self-check	系统自检	Xìtǒng zì jiǎn	
System service layer	系统业务层	Xìtǒng yèwù céng	SSL
System services control point	系统服务控制点	Xìtǒng fúwù kòngzhì diǎn	SSCP

System services control point format	系统服务控制点格式	Xìtǒng fúwù kòngzhì diǎn géshi	SSCPFM
System simulation	系统仿真	Xìtǒng fǎngzhēn	
System simulation	系统模拟	Xìtǒng mónǐ	
System simulator	系统仿真器	Xìtǒng fǎngzhēnqì	SS
System simulator	系统模拟器	Xìtǒng mónǐqì	SS
System specification	系统规范	Xìtǒng guīfàn	
System stored procedures	系统存储过程	Xìtǒng cúnchǔ guòchéng	
System support machine	系统支援机器	Xìtǒng zhīyuán jīqì	SSM
System table	系统表	Xìtǒng biǎo	
System table	系统管理表	Xìtǒng guǎnlǐ biǎo	
System task	系统任务	Xìtǒng rènwu	
System testing	系统测试	Xìtǒng cèshì	
System testing	系统试验	Xìtǒng shìyàn	
System theory	系统论	Xìtǒnglùn	
System time	系统时间	Xìtǒng shíjiān	
System under test	被测系统	Bèicè xìtǒng	
System under test	被测试系统	Bèicèshì xìtǒng	SUT
System under test	测试中的系统	Cèshì zhòngdì xìtǒng	SUT
System under test	测试下的系统	Cèshì-xiàde xìtǒng	SUT
System under test	在测试系统	Zài cèshì xìtǒng	SUT
System utilization monitor	系统利用率监控器	Xìtǒng lìyònglǜ jiānkòngqì	SUM
System with effectively grounded neutral	中性点有效接地系统	Zhōngxìngdiǎn yǒuxiào jiēdì xìtǒng	
System with non-effectively grounded neutral	中性点非有效接地系统	Zhōngxìngdiǎn fēiyǒuxiào jiēdì xìtǒng	
System-aided design	系统辅助设计	Xìtǒng fǔzhù shèjì	SAD
Systematic error	系统误差	Xìtǒng wùchā	
Systematic failure	系统性失效	Xìtǒngxìng shīxiào	
Systematic fault	系统性故障	Xìtǒngxìng gùzhàng	
System-on-a-chip	片上系统	Piàn-shàng xìtǒng	SOC
System-on-a-chip	系统集成芯片	Xìtǒng jíchéng xìnpiàn	SONC
Systems design	系统设计	Xìtǒng shèjì	
Systems development methodology	系统开发方法	Xìtǒng kāifā fāngfǎ	
Systems engineering	系统工程	Xìtǒng gōngchéng	SE
Systems management process	系统管理进程	Xìtǒng guǎnlǐ jìnchéng	
Systems network architecture and protocols (IBM use)	系统网络体系结构及其协议	Xìtǒng wǎngluò tǐxì jiégòu jí qí xiéyì	SNA
Systems planning	系统规划	Xìtǒng guīhuà	
System-wide call	系统全呼	Xìtǒng quánhū	

T

T interface (user interface)	T接口	T jiēkǒu	
T square	丁字尺	Dīngzìchǐ	
Tab (WP command)	间空	Jiānkōng	
Table	表	Biǎo	
Table (WP command)	表格	Biǎogé	
Table area	表格区	Biǎogé qū	
Table chess (computer game)	桌棋类游戏	Zhuō qí lèi yóuxì	TAB
Table constraint (in SQL Server)	表约束	Biǎo yuēshù	

Table lock (for database)	表锁	Biǎo suǒ	
Table scan	表扫描	Biǎo sǎomiáo	
Table-level constraint (for database)	表级约束	Biǎo jí yuēshù	
Tablet coordinate	数字化仪坐标	Shùzìhuàyí zuòbiāo	
Tablet menu	数字化仪菜单	Shùzìhuàyí càidān	
Tabu search algorithm	禁忌搜索算法	Jìnjì sōusuǒ suànfǎ	
Tabular data stream	表格格式数据流	Biǎogé géshi shùjù liú	TDS
Tabulation alignment	制表对准	Zhìbiǎo duìzhǔn	
Tabulation stop	制表点	Zhìbiǎodiǎn	
Tachometer bridge	测速电桥	Cèsù diànqiáo	
Tactical cipher system	战术密码体制	Zhànshù mìmǎ tǐzhì	
Tactical communication electronic warfare system	战术通信电子对抗系统	Zhànshù tōngxìn diànzǐ duìkàng xìtǒng	
Tactical communication system	野战通信系统	Yězhàn tōngxìn xìtǒng	
Tactical Data Information Link (US military)	战术数据信息链	Zhànshù shùjù xìnxī liàn	TADIL
Tactical multi-net gateway	战术多网网间连接器	Zhànshù duōwǎng wǎng jiān liánjiēqì	TMG
Tactical name server	战术名字服务器	Zhànshù míngzì fúwùqì	TNS
Tactical operations center	战术作战中心	Zhànshù zuòzhàn zhōngxīn	TOC
Tactical radio	战术电台	Zhànshù diàntái	
Tag	类号	Lèihào	
Tag control information	标记控制信息	Biāojì kòngzhì xìnxī	TCI
Tag name	标签名	Biāoqiān míng	
Tag protocol identifier	标记协议标识符	Biāojì xiéyì biāozhì fú	TPID
Tag protocol information	标记协议信息	Biāojì xiéyì xìnxī	TPI
Tag switch	标记交换	Biāojì jiāohuàn	
Tag switch router	标记交换路由器	Biāojì jiāohuàn lùyóuqì	TSR
Tag switching	标签交换	Biāoqiān jiāohuàn	
Tag, label	标签	Biāoqiān	
Tagged image file format	标签图像文件格式	Biāoqiān túxiàng wénjiàn géshi	TIFF
Tagged traffic	标记通信	Biāojì tōngxìn	
Tail	弧尾	Húwěi	
Tail bits	尾部比特	Wěibù bǐtè	
Tail optical fiber	引出光纤	Yǐnchū guāngxiān	
Tail pointer	尾指针	Wěi zhǐzhēn	
Tainter gate (in civil engineering)	拉伸门	Lāshēn mén	
Take-off angle	射出角	Shèchū jiǎo	
Talk	交谈	Jiāotán	
Talk program	对谈程序	Duìtán chéngxù	
Talkaround	脱网工作	Tuōwǎng gōngzuò	
Talkgroup call	组呼	Zǔhū	
Tamed frequency modulation	平滑调频	Pínghuá tiáopín	TFM
Tamed frequency oscillator	平滑振荡器	Pínghuá zhèndàngqì	TFO
Tamper resistance	防拆	Fángchāi	
Tamper resistance	抗拆性	Kàngchāixìng	
Tampering (IPsec)	窜改	Cuàngǎi	
Tampering (IW attack)	篡改	Cuàngǎi	
Tandem	汇接	Huìjiē	

Tandem connection monitor	串联连接监视	Chuànlián liánjiē jiānshì	TCM
Tandem connection overhead	串联连接开销	Chuànlián liánjiē kāixiao	TCOH
Tandem connection remote defect indicator	串联连接远端缺陷指示	Chuànlián liánjiē yuǎnduān quēxiàn zhǐshì	TC-RDI
Tandem connection remote error indicator	串联连接远端误差指示	Chuànlián liánjiē yuǎnduān wùchā zhǐshì	TC-REI
Tandem connection terminating element	串联连接终端设备	Chuànlián liánjiē zhōngduān shèbèi	TCTE
Tandem connection trace	串联连接踪迹	Chuànlián liánjiē zōngjī	TCT
Tandem free operation	无二次编解码操作	Wú'èrcì biānjiěmǎ cāozuò	TFO
Tandem free operation	无二次编解码操作	Wú'èrcì biānjiěmǎ cāozuò	TFO
Tandem mobile switching center	移动汇接中心	Yídòng huìjiē zhōngxīn	TMSC
Tandem MSC	汇接 MSC	Huìjiē MSC	TMSC
Tandem office	汇接局	Huìjiē jú	Tm, TO
Tandem switch	汇接交换机	Huìjiē jiāohuànjī	TM
Tap (cryptology)	抽头	Chōutóu	
Tap coupler (FOC)	分光器	Fēnguāngqì	
Tap coupler/filter wavelength division multiplexer	分光器/滤波型波分复用器	Fēnguāngqì/lǜbōxíng bōfēn fùyòngqì	TWDM
Tap port (FOC)	分光端口	Fēnguāng duānkǒu	
Tape backup	磁带备份	Cídài bèifèn	
Tape carrier package	薄膜封装	Báomó fēngzhuāng	TCP
Tape deck equipment	放音设备	Fàngyīn shèbèi	TKEQ
Tape deck trunk	放音中继	Fàngyīn zhōngjì	TKT
Tape drive	磁带驱动器	Cídài qūdòngqì	
Tape-and-reel (in SMT)	带和盘	Dài hé pán	
Tapered distribution	锥削分布	Zhuīxiāo fēnbù	
Tapered distribution of a field over an aperture	口面上场的锥削分布	Kǒumiàn shàngchǎngde zhuīxiāo fēnbù	
Tapered waveguide	渐变波导	Jiànbiàn bōdǎo	
Target	标的	Biāodì	
Target language	目标语言	Mùbiāo yǔyán	
Target object	目标对象	Mùbiāo duìxiàng	
Target partition	目标分区	Mùbiāo fēnqū	
Target program	目标程序	Mùbiāo chéngxù	
Target-based IDS	基于目标的 IDS	Jīyú mùbiāode IDS	
Target-concealed user intrusion	伪装成目的用户入侵	Wěizhuāng chéng mùdì yònghù rùqīn	
Tariff	费率	Fèilǜ	
Task	任务	Rènwu	
Task button	任务按钮	Rènwu ànniǔ	
Task control	任务控制	Rènwu kòngzhì	TC
Task control block	任务控制块	Rènwu kòngzhì kuài	TCB
Task management	任务管理	Rènwu guǎnlǐ	
Task number	任务号	Rènwu hào	
Task number definition block	任务号码定义块	Rènwu hàomǎ dìngyì kuài	TNDB
Task object	任务对象	Rènwu duìxiàng	
Task scheduling	任务调度	Rènwu diàodù	
Task specification language	任务定义语言	Rènwu dìngyì yǔyán	TSL
Task switch	工作切换	Gōngzuò qiēhuàn	
Taskbar	任务栏	Rènwu lán	
Taskbar	任务条	Rènwu tiáo	

Taskbar button	任务栏按钮	Rènwu lán ànniǔ	
Task-oriented procedure	面向任务过程	Miànxiàng rènwu guòchéng	TOP
Taskpad (in SQL Server)	任务板	Rènwu bǎn	
Taylor's chart	泰勒图表	Tài-lè túbiǎo	
T-CAMEL subscription information	终接 CAMEL 签约信息	Zhōngjiē CAMEL qiānyuē xìnxī	T-CSI
TCP/IP packet analysis utility	TCP/IP 数据包分析	TCP/IP shùjùbāo fēnxī	TCPDUMP
TCP/IP packet route tracing tool (Traceroute)	TCP/IP 数据包路由追踪工具	TCP/IP shùjùbāo lùyóu zhuīzōng gōngjù	
Teaching control	教学控制	Jiàoxué kòngzhì	
Teaching management	教学管理	Jiàoxué guǎnlǐ	
Teaching process	教学进程	Jiàoxué jìnchéng	
Tear-off menu	浮动菜单	Fúdòng càidān	
Technical assistance center	技术辅助中心	Jìshù fǔzhù zhōngxīn	TAC
Technical basis for regulation	规章技术基础	Guīzhāng jìshù jīchǔ	TBR
Technical committee	技术委员会	Jìshù wěiyuánhuì	TC
Technical Committee on Computer Communications	计算机通信技术委员会	Jìsuànjī tōngxìn jìshù wěiyuánhuì	TCCC
Technical Committee Special Mobile Group	技术委员会特别移动通信组	Jìshù wěiyuánhuì tèbié yídòng tōngxìn zǔ	TC SMG
Technical committee technical report	技术委员会技术报告	Jìshù wěiyuánhuì jìshù bàogào	TC-TR
Technical data management	技术数据管理	Jìshù shùjù guǎnlǐ	TDM
Technical delay	技术耽误	Jìshù dānwù	
Technical document management	技术文档管理	Jìshù wéndàng guǎnlǐ	TDM
Technical information management	技术信息管理	Jìshù xìnxī guǎnlǐ	TIM
Technical office protocol	技术办公协议	Jìshù bàngōng xiéyì	TOP
Technical report	技术报告	Jìshù bàogào	TR
Technical specification	技术规范	Jìshù guīfàn	TS
Technical specification group	技术规范小组	Jìshù guīfàn xiǎozǔ	TSG
Technical support identification number	技术支持代码	Jìshù zhīchí dàimǎ	TSID
Technological attack	技术攻击	Jìshù gōngjī	
Teflon	聚四氟乙烯	Jùsìfúyǐxī	
Tektronix Electronics (China) Co. Ltd.	泰克电子（中国）有限公司	Tài-kè diànzǐ (Zhōngguó) yǒuxiàn gōngsī	
Teleaction service	遥信业务	Yáoxìn yèwù	
Tele-chat room	电话聊天室	Diànhuà liáotiān shì	
Telecom supporting network	电信支握网	Diànxìn zhīwò wǎng	
Telecommand	谣令	Yáolìng	
Telecommand	遥信	Yáoxìn	
Telecommunication center	电信中心	Diànxìn zhōngxīn	
Telecommunication certification body	通信产品认证机构	Tōngxìn chǎnpǐn rènzhèng jīgòu	TBC
Telecommunication earth station	通信地球站	Tōngxìn dìqiú zhàn	TES
Telecommunication Industries Association (US)	电信工业协会	Diànxìn gōngyè xiéhuì	TIA
Telecommunication maintenance center	远程通信维护中心	Yuǎnchéng tōngxìn wéihù zhōngxīn	TMC
Telecommunication management network	通信管理网络	Tōngxìn guǎnlǐ wǎngluò	TMN
Telecommunication outlet	通信引出端	Tōngxìn yǐnchū duān	TO
Telecommunication outlet (as RS-232, RJ-11)	信息插座	Xìnxī chāzuò	TO
Telecommunication path	电信通道	Diànxìn tōngdào	
Telecommunication socket	通信插座	Tōngxìn chāzuò	
Telecommunication system	通信系统	Tōngxìn xìtǒng	TCS

Telecommunication system	通讯系统	Tōngxùn xìtǒng	TCS
Telecommunication Technology Association	电信技术协会	Diànxìn jìshù xiéhuì	TTA
Telecommunications	电信	Diànxìn	
Telecommunications administration	电信主管部门	Diànxìn zhǔguǎn bùmén	
Telecommunications bus	电信总线	Diànxìn zǒngxiàn	TBUS
Telecommunications cable junction box	通信电缆交接箱	Tōngxìn diànlǎn jiāojiē xiāng	
Telecommunications circuit	电信电路	Diànxìn diànlù	
Telecommunications closet	电信间	Diànxìn jiān	TC
Telecommunications Industry Association	通信工业协会	Tōngxìn gōngyè xiéhuì	TIA
Telecommunications Industry Association (US)	美国电信工业协会	Měiguó diànxìn gōngyè xiéhuì	TIA
Telecommunications information networking architecture	电信信息组网结构	Diànxìn xìnxī zǔwǎng jiégòu	TINA
Telecommunications Management Forum, TeleManagement Forum	电信管理论坛	Diànxìn guǎnlǐ lùntán	TMF
Telecommunications management network	电信管理网	Diànxìn guǎnlǐ wǎng	TMN
Telecommunications Management network	电信管理网络	Diànxìn guǎnlǐ wǎngluò	TMN
Telecommunications Management network-management function	电信管理网管理功能	Diànxìn guǎnlǐ wǎng guǎnlǐ gōngnéng	TMN MF
Telecommunications Management network-management service	电信管理网管理业务	Diànxìn guǎnlǐ wǎng guǎnlǐ yèwù	TMN MS
Telecommunications Management network-management service components	电信管理网管理业务成分	Diànxìn guǎnlǐ wǎng guǎnlǐ yèwù chéngfèn	TMN MSC
Telecommunications network	电信网	Diànxìn wǎng	
Telecommunications network user	电信网用户	Diànxìn wǎng yònghù	
Telecommunications operations map	通信运行地址变换	Tōngxìn yùnxíng dìzhǐ biànhuàn	TO
Telecommunications outlet	电信引出端	Diànxìn yǐnchū duān	TO
Telecommunications outlet	通信插座	Tōngxìn chāzuò	TO
Telecommunications service	电信业务	Diànxìn yèwù	
Telecommunications service attribute	电信业务属性	Diànxìn yèwù shǔxìng	
Telecommunications software	通信软件	Tōngxìn ruǎnjiàn	
Telecommunications supporting networks	电信支撑网	Diànxìn zhīchēng wǎng	TSN
Tele-conference	电话会议	Diànhuà huìyì	
Teleconference service	会议电信业务	Huìyì diànxìn yèwù	
Teleconferencing	电信会议	Diànxìn huìyì	
Telecontrol	遥控	Yáokòng	
Telecooperation	远程协作	Yuǎnchéng xiézuò	
TeleDenmark	丹麦电信	Dān-mài diànxìn	
Teledistortion	远端畸变	Yuǎnduān jībiàn	
Telegram, telegraph	电报	Diànbào	DB
Telegraph alphabet	电报电码表	Diànbào diànmǎ biǎo	
Telegraph code	电报电码	Diànbào diànmǎ	
Telegraph key	手键	Shǒujiàn	
Telegraph key clicks	电键喀呖声	Diànjiàn kā-lì shēng	
Telegraph modulation	电报调制	Diànbào tiáozhì	
Telegraph noise	电报噪声	Diànbào zàoshēng	
Telegraph signal	电报信号	Diànbào xìnhào	
Telegraph terminal	电报终端	Diànbào zhōngduān	
Telegraph transmitter	发报机	Fābàojī	
Telegraphy	电报技术	Diànbào jìshù	

Telegraphy	电报技术	Diànbào jìshù	
Teleguidance	遥导	Yáodǎo	
Tele-imaging	远程传像	Yuǎnchéng chuánxiàng	
Telemarketing	遥控市场推广	Yáokòng shìchǎng tuīguǎng	
Telematic service	远程消息业务	Yuǎnchéng xiāoxi yèwù	
Telematics	远程信息处理	Yuǎnchéng xìnxī chǔlǐ	
Telematics (services)	电传图文（业务）	Diànchuán túwén (yèwù)	
Telematics service	文件图像业务	Wénjiàn túxiàng yèwù	
Telemedia	电讯媒体	Diànxùn méitǐ	
Telemetering	遥测	Yáocè	
Telemetry	遥测技术	Yáocè jìshù	
Telemetry	遥测学	Yáocè xué	
Telemetry service	遥测业务	Yáocè yèwù	
Telemonitoring	遥察	Yáochá	
Telenet access controller	远程通信网存取控制器	Yuǎnchéng tōngxìnwǎng cúnqǔ kòngzhìqì	TAC
Telephone answering	电话答录	Diànhuà dálù	
Telephone answering machine	电话应答机	Diànhuà yìngdájī	TAM
Telephone application programming interface	电话应用程序接口	Diànhuà yìngyòng chéngxù jiēkǒu	TAPI
Telephone booth	电话间	Diànhuà jiān	
Telephone circuit	电话回路	Diànhuà huílù	
Telephone company	电话公司	Diànhuà gōngsī	TELCO
Telephone control protocol	电话控制协议	Diànhuà kòngzhì xiéyì	TCP
Telephone management information system	电话管理信息系统	Diànhuà guǎnlǐ xìnxī xìtǒng	TMIS
Telephone receiver	受话器	Shòuhuàqì	
Telephone repeater station	电话中继局	Diànhuà zhōngjì jú	TRS
Telephone server	电话服务器	Diànhuà fúwùqì	
Telephone set	电话机	Diànhuàjī	
Telephone set resistance	话机电阻	Huàjī diànzǔ	
Telephone terminal	电话终端	Diànhuà zhōngduān	
Telephone traffic	话务量	Huàwù liáng	
Telephone transmitter	送话器	Sònghuàqì	
Telephone type circuit	电话式电路	Diànhuàshì diànlù	
Telephone user part (SS7)	电话用户部分	Diànhuà yònghù bùfen	TUP
Telephone-type channel	电话型信道	Diànhuà-xíng xìndào	
Telephone-type circuit	电话型电路	Diànhuà-xíng diànlù	
Telephonic remittance	电话汇款	Diànhuà huìkuǎn	
Telephony	电话技术	Diànhuà jìshù	
Telephony	电声技术	Diànshēng jìshù	
Telephony control specification	电话控制协议	Diànhuà kòngzhì xiéyì	TCS
Telephony device control bus	电话设备控制总线	Diànhuà shèbèi kòngzhì zǒngxiàn	TD-BUS
Telephony device control master	电话设备控制主机	Diànhuà shèbèi kòngzhì zhǔjī	TDCM
Telephony device master back panel	电话设备主机后面板	Diànhuà shèbèi zhǔjī hòumianbǎn	TMBP
Telephony device system library block	电话设备系统库模块	Diànhuà shèbèi xìtǒngkù mókuài	TDSL
Telephony earth station (Hughes)	话音小站	Huàyīn xiǎozhàn	TES
Telephony routing over IP	IP 电话路由	IP diànhuà lùyóu	TRIP
Telephony routing over IP	IP 网上电话路由选择	IP wǎng-shàng diànhuà lùyóu xuǎnzé	TRIP

Telephony services application programming interface	电话服务应用程序接口	Diànhuà fúwù yìngyòng chéngxù jiēkǒu	TSAPI
Telepoint	无绳电话站	Wúshéng diànhuà zhàn	
Telepoint base station	电信接入点基站	Diànxìn jiērùdiǎn jīzhàn	
Telepoint service	电信接入点业务	Diànxìn jiērùdiǎn yèwù	
Telepresence	远地视在	Yuǎndì shìzài	
Teleprinter	电传机	Diànchuánjī	
Teleprocessing	远程处理	Yuǎnchéng chǔlǐ	
Teleprocessing	远程信息处理	Yuǎnchéng xìnxī chǔlǐ	
Teleprocessing security	远程处理安全	Yuǎnchéng chǔlǐ ānquán	
Telescopic antenna	伸缩天线	Shēnsuō tiānxiàn	
Teleservice	电传业务	Diànchuán yèwù	TS
Teleservice	电信业务	Diànxìn yèwù	TS
Teleservice	用户终端业务	Yònghù zhōngduān yèwù	
Teleservice	终端业务	Zhōngduān yèwù	
Teleservice not provided	不提供电信业务	Bùtígōng diànxìn yèwù	
Teletex	文件用户电报	Wénjiàn yònghù diànbào	
Teletex	智能用户电报	Zhìnéng yònghù diànbào	TTX
Teletex basic control function repertoire	智能用户电报基本控制功能总表	Zhìnéng yònghù diànbào jīběn kòngzhì gōngnéng zǒngbiǎo	
Teletex basic graphic character repertoire	智能用户电报基本图形字符总表	Zhìnéng yònghù diànbào jīběn túxíng zìfú zǒngbiǎo	
Teletex character repertoire	智能用户电报字符总表	Zhìnéng yònghù diànbào zìfú zǒngbiǎo	
Teletex control function repertoire	智能用户电报控制功能总表	Zhìnéng yònghù diànbào kòngzhì gōngnéng zǒngbiǎo	
Teletex document	智能用户电报文件	Zhìnéng yònghù diànbào wénjiàn	
Teletex equipment	智能用户电报设备	Zhìnéng yònghù diànbào shèbèi	
Teletex graphic character repertoire	智能用户电报图形字符总表	Zhìnéng yònghù diànbào túxíng zìfú zǒngbiǎo	
Teletext	电视数据	Diànshì shùjù	TTX
Teletext	电文	Diànwén	
Teletext	可视图文	Kěshì túwén	
Teletext broadcast system	电视文字广播系统	Diànshì wénzì guǎngbō xìtǒng	
Teletext; broadcast videography; videocast	图文电视	Túwén diànshì	
Television	电视	Diànshì	
Television broadcasting	电视广播	Diànshì guǎngbō	
Television receive only ground station	电视接收地面站	Diànshì jiēshōu dìmiànzhàn	TVRO
Television receive only satellite ground station	卫星电视接收地面站	Wèixīng diànshì jiēshōu dìmiànzhàn	
Television-capable personal computer	电视电脑	Diànshì diànnǎo	TVPC
Televoting	电话投票	Diànhuà tóupiào	VOT
Telewriting	电写	Diànxiě	
Telewriting	真迹电报	Zhēnjī diànbào	
Telewriting image	电写图像	Diànxiě túxiàng	
Telewriting telescript	书写电报	Shūxiě diànbào	
Telex	用户电报	Yònghù diànbào	
Telex	用户电报电传	Yònghù diànbào diànchuán	
Tellabs International Inc. (US company)	美国泰乐国际公司	Měiguó tài-lè guójì gōngsī	
Tellurium-doped EDFA	掺碲的 EDFA	Chāndìde EDFA	T-EDFA

Telnet	远程登录	Yuǎnchéng dēnglù	
Telnet	远程载入	Yuǎnchéng zǎirù	
Telstra	澳洲电信	Aòzhōu diànxìn	
Temperature compensated ceramic capacitor	温度补偿瓷介电容器	Wēndù bǔcháng cíjiè diànróngqì	
Temperature compensated power bridge	温度补偿式功率计	Wēndù bǔchángshì gōnglǜjì	
Temperature compensation crystal oscillator	温补晶振	Wēn bǔ jīng zhèn	TCXO
Temperature compensation crystal oscillator	温度补偿晶体振荡器	Wēndù bǔcháng jīngtǐ zhèndàngqì	TCXO
Temperature cycling test	温度循环试验	Wēndù xúnhuán shìyàn	
Temperature probe	温度传感器	Wēndù chuángǎnqì	TP
Temperature-dependent loss	温度相关损耗	Wēndù xiāngguān sǔnhào	TDL
Template	模版	Móbǎn	
Template	模板	Múbǎn	
Template argument deduction	模板参数推导	Múbǎn cānshù tuīdǎo	
Template explicit specialization	模板显式特化	Múbǎn xiǎnshì tèhuà	
Template files (in SQL Server)	模板文件	Múbǎn wénjiàn	
Template parameter	模板参数	Múbǎn cānshù	
Temporal accuracy	时态精度	Shítài jīngdù	
Temporal attribute	时态属性	Shítài shǔxing	
Temporal characteristic	时态特征	Shítài tèzhēng	
Temporal coordinate	时态坐标	Shítài zuòbiāo	
Temporal coordinate system	时态坐标系	Shítài zuòbiāo xì	
Temporal database	时态数据库	Shítài shùjùkù	
Temporal extent	时间范围	Shíjiān fànwéi	
Temporal feature attribute	时间特征属性	Shíjiān tèzhēng shǔxìng	
Temporal feature operation	时间特征操作	Shíjiān tèzhēng cāozuò	
Temporal feature relationship	时间特征关系	Shíjiān tèzhēng guānxi	
Temporal information	时间信息	Shíjiān xìnxī	
Temporal position	时间位置	Shíjiān wèizhì	
Temporal primitive	时间原素	Shíjiān yuánsù	
Temporal reference system	时间参照系	Shíjiān cānzhàoxì	
Temporal resolution	时间分辨力	Shíjiān fēnbiàn lì	
Temporal status transition system	时序状态转换系统	Shíxù zhuàngtài zhuǎnhuàn xìtǒng	TSTS
Temporary block flow	临时块流	Línshí kuàiliú	TBF
Temporary block flow	临时数据块流	Línshí shùjùkuài liú	TBF
Temporary block flow	临时信息组流量	Línshí xìnxīzǔ liúliàng	TBF
Temporary desensitizing suppression	暂时降敏抑制	Zànshí jiàngmǐn yìzhì	
Temporary diversion channel	临时分水道	Línshí fēnshuǐ dào	
Temporary equipment identifier	临时设备标识符	Línshí shèbèi biāozhìfú	TEI
Temporary file, scratch file	临时文件	Línshí wénjiàn	
Temporary flow identity	临时流量识别	Línshí liúliàng shíbié	TFI
Temporary handover number	越局切换号码	Yuèjú qiēhuàn hàomǎ	HOT
Temporary home agent	临时家乡代理	Línshí jiāxiāng dàilǐ	THA
Temporary link level identity	临时链路电平识别	Línshí liànlù diànpíng shíbié	TLLI
Temporary local directory number	临时本地号码	Línshí běndì hàomǎ	TLDN
Temporary local directory number	临时本地号码簿号码	Línshí běndì hàomǎbù hàomǎ	TLDN
Temporary logic link identity	临时逻辑链路识别	Línshí luóji liànlù shíbié	TLLI

Temporary logical link identity	临时逻辑链路标识	Línshí luóji liànlù biāozhì	TLLI
Temporary logical link identity	临时逻辑链路识别	Línshí luóji liànlù shíbié	TLLI
Temporary mobile station identity	临时移动台识别码	Línshí yídòng tái shíbié mǎ	TMSI
Temporary mobile subscriber identity	临时移动用户标识	Línshí yídòng yònghù biāozhì	TMSI
Temporary mobile subscriber identity	临时移动用户识别号码	Línshí yídòng yònghù shíbié hàomǎ	TMSI
Temporary mobile subscriber identity	临时移动用户识别码	Línshí yídòng yònghù shíbié mǎ	TMSI
Temporary object	临时对象	Línshí duìxiàng	
Temporary offset	临时偏移	Línshí piānyí	TO
Temporary offset	暂时偏移	Zànshí piānyí	TO
Temporary ordered routing algorithm	临时按序路由算法	Línshí ànxù lùyóu suànfǎ	TORA
Temporary queuing identity	临时排队识别	Línshí páiduì shíbié	TQI
Temporary stored procedure	临时存储过程	Línshí cúnchǔ guòchéng	
Temporary table (for database)	临时表	Línshí biǎo	
Tenancy	链路租用	Liànlù zūyòng	
Tensile load	拉伸负荷	Lāshēn fùhè	
Tensile strength	抗拉强度	Kànglā qiángdù	
Tensile strength	张力	Zhānglì	
Tensile Stress	拉伸应力	Lāshēn yìnglì	
Tensile testing (FOC)	张力测试	Zhānglì cèshì	
Tension joint	张力节理	Zhānglì jiélǐ	
Tera (prefix meaning 10^{12})	太拉	Tài-lā	
Tera- (prefix meaning 10^{12})	兆兆	Zhàozhào	T, TERA
Terabit (10^{12} bits)	太比特	Tài bǐtè	
Terabit core router	太比特核心路由器	Tài bǐtè héxīn lùyóuqì	
Terabit network router	太比特网络路由器	Tài bǐtè wǎngluò lùyóuqì	TNR
Terabit switch router	太比特交换路由器	Tài bǐtè jiāohuàn lùyóuqì	TSR
Teralight®, an Alcatel optical fiber	特锐光纤	Tè-ruì guāngxiān	
Terminal	终端	Zhōngduān	
Terminal access controller	终端访问控制器	Zhōngduān fǎngwèn kòngzhìqì	TAC
Terminal access controller access control system (Cisco protocol)	终端访问控制器访问控制系统	Zhōngduān fǎngwèn kòngzhìqì fǎngwèn kòngzhì xìtǒng	TACACS
Terminal activated channel test	终端启动通信测试	Zhōngduān qǐdòng tōngxìn cèshì	TACT
Terminal adaptation	终端适配	Zhōngduān shìpèi	TA
Terminal adaptation function	终端适配功能	Zhōngduān shìpèi gōngnéng	TAF
Terminal adapter	终端适配器	Zhōngduān shìpèiqì	TA
Terminal adapter equipment	终端适配设备	Zhōngduān shìpèi shèbèi	TAE
Terminal adapter function	终端适配功能	Zhōngduān shìpèi gōngnéng	TAF
Terminal adaptor for B-ISDN	B-ISDN 终端适配器	B-ISDN zhōngduān shìpèiqì	B-TA
Terminal address register	终端地址寄存器	Zhōngduān dìzhǐ jìcúnqì	TAR
Terminal alias	终端别名	Zhōngduān biémíng	
Terminal balance return loss	终端平衡回波损耗	Zhōngduān pínghéng huíbō sǔnhào	TBRL
Terminal balanced return loss	终端平衡回损	Zhōngduān pínghéng huísǔn	TBRL
Terminal based electronic mail	终端电子邮寄	Zhōngduān diànzǐ yóujì	TBEM
Terminal block	终端块	Zhōngduān kuài	
Terminal body	端接体	Duān jiētǐ	
Terminal body size	端接体尺寸	Duān jiētǐ chǐcùn	

Terminal capacity set	终端能力集	Zhōngduān nénglì jí	TCS
Terminal capacity set acknowledge	终端能力集确认	Zhōngduān nénglì jí quèrèn	TCSA
Terminal capacity set reject	终端能力集拒绝	Zhōngduān nénglì jí jùjué	TCSR
Terminal configuration facilities	终端配置设备	Zhōngduān pèizhì shèbèi	TCF
Terminal emulation protocol	终端仿真协议	Zhōngduān fǎngzhēn xiéyì	
Terminal emulator	终端仿真器	Zhōngduān fǎngzhēnqì	
Terminal end point identifier	终端端点标志	Zhōngduān duāndiǎn biāozhì	TEI
Terminal end point identifier	终端端点标识符	Zhōngduān duāndiǎn biāozhìfú	TEPI
Terminal endpoint identifier	终点端点标志	Zhōngdiǎn duāndiǎn biāozhì	TEI
Terminal endpoint identifier	终端标识	Zhōngduān biāozhì	Tei
Terminal equipment	用户终端	Yònghù zhōngduān	TE
Terminal equipment	终端设备	Zhōngduān shèbèi	TE
Terminal equipment for B-ISDN	B-ISDN 终端设备	B-ISDN zhōngduān shèbèi	B-TE
Terminal equipment/customer premises network	终端设备/用户驻地网	Zhōngduān shèbèi/yònghù zhùdì wǎng	TE/CPN
Terminal guidance radar	末制导雷达	Mòzhìdǎo léidá	
Terminal identification	终端标识	Zhōngduān biāozhì	TID
Terminal identifier	终端标识符	Zhōngduān biāozhìfú	
Terminal identifier	终端识别符	Zhōngduān shíbiéfú	
Terminal interference voltage	端子干扰电压	Duānzi gānrǎo diànyā	
Terminal international center	终端国际中心	Zhōngduān guójì zhōngxīn	TIC
Terminal machine (telecom term)	终端机	Zhōngduānjī	ZD
Terminal mobile services switching center	终端移动无线局	Zhōngduān yídòng wúxiànjú	
Terminal mobility	终端移动性	Zhōngduān yídòngxìng	
Terminal multiplexer	终端多路复用器	Zhōngduān duōlù fùyòngqì	TM
Terminal multiplexer	终端复用器	Zhōngduān fùyòngqì	TM
Terminal multiplexing	终端复用	Zhōngduān fùyòng	TM
Terminal national center	终端国内中心	Zhōngduān guónèi zhōngxīn	TNC
Terminal national section	终端国内段	Zhōngduān guónèi duàn	
Terminal node	终端结点	Zhōngduān jiédiǎn	
Terminal O/R address	终端 O/R 地址	Zhōngduān O/R dìzhǐ	
Terminal operating mode	终端操作方式	Zhōngduān cāozuò fāngshì	
Terminal operation environment	远端运行环境	Yuǎnduān yùnxíng huánjìng	TOE
Terminal portability	终端可携带性	Zhōngduān kěxiédà xìng	TP
Terminal radio station	终端无线电台	Zhōngduān wúxiàndiàntái	RST
Terminal radio-frequency power	末端射频功率	Mòduān shèpín gōnglǜ	
Terminal station	终端站	Zhōngduān zhàn	TS
Terminal token	终端标志	Zhōngduān biāozhì	
Terminal transparency	终端透明度	Zhōngduān tòumíngdù	
Terminal voltage	端子电压	Duānzi diànyā	
Terminal Working Group (GSM MoU)	终端工作组	Zhōngduān gōngzuòzǔ	TWG
Terminate and stay resident	终结并常驻内存	Zhōngjié bìng chángzhù nèicún	TSR
Terminate-and-stay-resident program	终止并驻留内存程序	Zhōngzhǐ bìng zhùliú nèicún chéngxù	TSR
Terminating	收端	Shōuduān	
Terminating basic call state model	终接基本呼叫状态模式	Zhōngjiē jīběn hūjiào zhuàngtài móshì	T-BCSM
Terminating call	被叫	Bèijiào	TC
Terminating camel subscription information	终端 CAMEL 签约信息	Zhōngduān CAMEL qiānyuē xìnxī	T-CSI

Terminating network	终端网络	Zhōngduān wǎngluò	
Terminating toll center	终端长途电话局	Zhōngduān chángtú diànhuàjú	TTC
Terminating toll operator	长途终局话务员	Chángtú zhōngjú huàwùyuán	TX
Termination class	结束类别	Jiéshù lèibié	TC
Termination connection point	终端连接点	Zhōngduān liánjiē diǎn	TCP
Termination connection point	终结连接点	Zhōngjié liánjiē diǎn	TCP
Termination control	结束控制	Jiéshù kòngzhì	
Termination node (SDH)	终结节点	Zhōngjié jiédiǎn	
Termination point fragment	端点段	Duāndiǎn duàn	TPF
Terminator (cap on cable)	端接器	Duānjiēqì	
Terminus	端接体组件	Duān jiētǐ zǔjiàn	
Termite-proof cable	防蚁缆	Fángyǐ lǎn	
Ternary content-addressable memory	三重按内容寻址存储器	Sānchóng àn nèiróng xúnzhǐ cúnchǔqì	TCAM
Ternary content-addressable memory	三元按内容寻址存储器	Sānyuán àn nèiróng xúnzhǐ cúnchǔqì	TCAM
Ternary content-addressable memory	三元内容寻址存储器	Sānyuán nèiróng xúnzhǐ cúnchǔqì	TCAM
Terrain analysis	地形分析	Dìxíng fēnxī	
Terrain contour matching	地形匹配制导	Dìxíng pǐpèi zhìdǎo	TCM
Terrain intervisibility calculation	地形通视分析	Dìxíng tōngshì fēnxī	
Terrain modeling	地形建模	Dìxíng jiànmó	
Terrain representation	地形表达	Dìxíng biǎodá	
Terrain-matching	地形匹配	Dìxíng pǐpèi	
Terrestrial channel	地面通道	Dìmiàn tōngdào	TC
Terrestrial circuit	地面电路	Dìmiàn diànlù	
Terrestrial fixed wireless access	地面固定无线接入	Dìmiàn gùdìng wúxiàn jiērù	TFWA
Terrestrial mobile access	地面移动接入	Dìmiàn yídòng jiērù	TMA
Terrestrial radio communication	地面无线电通信	Dìmiàn wúxiàndiàn tōngxìn	
Terrestrial station	地面电台	Dìmiàn diàntái	
Terrestrial trunked radio	陆上集群无线电	Lùshàng jíqún wúxiàndiàn	TETRA
Terrestrial trunked radio	数码集群流动通讯	Shùmǎ jíqún liúdòng tōngxùn	TETRA
Terrestrial urban	平坦城市	Píngtǎn chéngshì	TU
Terrestrial wireless access	地面无线接入	Dìmiàn wúxiàn jiērù	TWA
Tertiary	第三纪	Dìsānjì	
Tertiary digital multiplexer	三次数字复用器	Sāncì shùzì fùyòngqì	
Tertiary power supply	第三级供电	Dìsānjí gōngdiàn	
Test	试验	Shìyàn	
Test (the T in BORSCHT)	测试	Cèshì	
Test access port	测试存取口	Cèshì cúnqǔ kǒu	TAP
Test and control system	测试和控制系统	Cèshì hé kòngzhì xìtǒng	TCS
Test bed	试验床	Shìyàn chuáng	
Test bus distributor board assembly	测试总线分配集成板	Cèshì zǒngxiàn fēnpèi jíchéngbǎn	TBDA
Test campaign	试验实施过程	Shìyàn shíshī guòchéng	
Test clock input [bus]	测试时钟输入[总线]	Cèshì shízhōng shūrù (zǒngxiàn)	TCK
Test control	测试控制	Cèshì kòngzhì	TC
Test control interface	测试控制接口	Cèshì kòngzhì jiēkǒu	TCI
Test data	试验数据	Shìyàn shùjù	
Test data input [bus]	测试数据输入[总线]	Cèshì shùjù shūrù (zǒngxiàn)	TDI

Test data output [bus]	测试数据输出[总线]	Cèshì shùjù shūchū (zǒngxiàn)	TDO
Test equipment	测试设备	Cèshì shèbèi	
Test load	试验负载	Shìyàn fùzài	
Test management	测试管理	Cèshì guǎnlǐ	TM
Test management protocol	测试管理协议	Cèshì guǎnlǐ xiéyì	TMP
Test manager	测试管理器	Cèshì guǎnlǐqì	TSM
Test mobile	测试移动台	Cèshì yídòngtái	TM
Test mode selector [bus]	测试模式选择[总线]	Cèshì móshì xuǎnzé (zǒngxiàn)	TMS
Test processor	测试处理器	Cèshì chǔlǐqì	
Test program language	试验程序语言	Shìyàn chéngxù yǔyán	TPL
Test purpose	测试目的	Cèshì mùdì	
Test signal identification	测试信号识别	Cèshì xìnhào shíbié	TSID
Test site	试验场地	Shìyàn chǎngdì	
Test suite structure and test purposes	测试组结构和测试目的	Cèshì zǔ jiégòu hé cèshì mùdì	TSS&TP
Test verdict	测试判定	Cèshì pàndìng	
Test with substitution	有替换试验	Yǒu tìhuan shìyàn	
Tested unit	被测单元	Bèicè dānyuán	
Testing point	测试点	Cèshì diǎn	
Testing repetition cycle	检测重发周期	Jiǎncè chóngfā zhōuqī	
Tetrafluoro propyl methyl acrylate (FOC mfg)	四氟丙基丙烯酸甲酸	Sìfúbǐngjī bǐngxīsuān jiǎsuān	TFPMA
Texas Instruments	德州仪器	Dézhōu yíqì	TI
Texel fill rate (measured in Mpix/sec)	材质填充率	Cáizhì tiánchōng lǜ	
Text	文本	Wénběn	
Text area	文本区	Wénběn qū	
Text attribute	文本属性	Wénběn shǔxìng	
Text attribute table	文本属性表	Wénběn shǔxìng biǎo	
Text color (WP command)	字体彩色	Zìtǐ cǎisè	
Text enhanced technology	文本增强技术	Wénběn zēngqiáng jìshù	TET
Text file	文本文件	Wénběn wénjiàn	
Text style	文本样式	Wénběn yàngshì	
Text symbol	文本符号	Wénběn fúhào	
Text unit	文本单元	Wénběn dānyuán	
Text window	文本窗口	Wénběn chuāngkǒu	
Text-to-speech	文语转换	Wén yǔ zhuǎnhuàn	TTS
Text-to-speech	文本语	Wénběn yǔ	
Text-to-speech conversion	文本至语音的转换	Wénběn zhì yǔyīnde zhuǎnhuàn	TTS
Textual database	文本数据库	Wénběn shùjùkù	
Textual fidelity	文本保真度	Wénběn bǎozhēndù	
Texture compression (video term)	纹理压缩	Wénlǐ yāsuō	
Texture element	纹理像素	Wénlǐ xiàngsù	Texel
Texture fidelity (video term)	纹理真实性	Wénlǐ zhēnshíxìng	
Texture memory	纹理内存	Wénlǐ nèicún	
Texture mode	纹理模式	Wénlǐ móshì	
Texture pixels	纹理像素	Wénlǐ xiàngsù	
Texture swapping	纹理交换	Wénlǐ jiāohuàn	
The controlling MSC on which the call was originally established	发起切换的主控 MSC	Fāqǐ qiēhuànde zhǔkòng MSC	MSC-A

The greatest noise power	最大噪声功率	Zuìdà zàoshēng gōnglǜ	TGNP
The MSC to which the MS is handed over in a basic handover	被切换到的 MSC	Bèiqiēhuàndàode MSC	MSC-B
The MSC to which the MS is handed over in a subsequent handover	被切换到的第三方 MSC	Bèiqiēhuàndàode dìsānfāng MSC	MSC-B'
The Open Group	开发组织	Kāifā zǔzhī	TOG
The Open Group	开放组织	Kāifàng zǔzhī	
The TINA trial	TINA 试验	TINA shìyàn	TTT
Theft, pilferage and non-delivery	偷窃提货不着险	Tōuqiè tíhuò bùzháo xiǎn	t.p.n.d
Thematic attribute	专题属性	Zhuāntí shǔxìng	
Thematic data	专题数据	Zhuāntí shùjù	
Thematic map (GIS term)	专题地图	Zhuāntí dìtú	
Thematic mapping	专题绘图	Zhuāntí huìtú	
Theodolite	经纬仪	Jīngwěiyí	
Theoretical duration of a significant interval	特征间隔的理论持续时间	Tèzhēng jiàngéde lǐlùn chíxù shíjiān	
Theoretical margin	理论改正力	Lǐlùn gǎizhèng lì	
Theoretical numerical aperture	理论数值孔径	Lǐlùn shùzhí kǒngjìng	
Thermal noise limited operation	受热噪声限制的工作状态	Shòurè zàoshēng xiànzhìde gōngzuò zhuàngtài	
Thermal noise, Johnson noise	热噪声	Rè zàoshēng	
Thermal paper facsimile	热感纸传真机	Règǎnzhǐ chuánzhēnjī	
Thermal printer	热量打印机	Rèliàng dǎyìnjī	
Thermal shock test	热冲击试验	Rè chōngjī shìyàn	
Thermal switch testing (semiconductor mfg)	热量转换试验	Rèliàng zhuǎnhuàn shìyàn	
Thermal transfer fax	热转写传真机	Rè zhuǎnxiě chuánzhēnjī	
Thermal transfer plotter	热敏绘图仪	Rè mǐn huìtúyí	
Thermal wavelength drift	波长热漂移	Bōcháng rè piāoyí	
Thermistor	电热调解器	Diànrè tiáojiěqì	
Thermistor	热敏电阻	Rèmǐn diànzǔ	
Thermistor power meter	热敏电阻式功率计	Rèmǐn diànzǔshì gōnglǜjì	
Thermochromic material	热色材料	Rèsè cáiliào	
Thermocouple detector	热电偶检测器	Rèdiàn'ǒu jiǎncèqì	
Thermocoupler	热电偶	Rèdiàn'ǒu	
Thermopile detector	热堆检测器	Rèduī jiǎncèqì	
Thermoplastic polyester elastomer (FOC)	热塑性聚酯弹性体	Rèsùxìng jùzhǐ tánxìngtǐ	TPE
Thick-film circuit	厚模电路	Hòumó diànlù	
Thiessen polygon	泰森多边形	Tài-sēn duōbiānxíng	
Thin backside illuminated charge coupled device	薄型背照式电荷耦合器件	Báoxíng bèizhàoshì diànhè ǒuhé qìjiàn	BT-CCD
Thin client	瘦客户端	Shòu kèhù duān	
Thin client	瘦客户机	Shòu kèhùjī	
Thin film	薄膜	Bómó	
Thin film filter	薄膜滤波器	Báomó lǜbōqì	TFF
Thin film hybrid integrated circuit	薄膜混合集成电路	Bómó hùnhé jíchéng diànlù	
Thin film transistor	薄膜晶体管	Báomó jīngtǐguǎn	TFT
Thin quad flat pack	薄四方扁平封装	Báo sìfāng biǎnpíng fēngzhuāng	
Thin small outline package	超小型封装	Chāoxiǎoxíng fēngzhuāng	TSOP
Thin-film integrated circuit	薄膜集成电路	Báomó jíchéng diànlù	
Thin-film metrology system (semiconductor mfg)	薄膜度量系统	Bómó dùliàng xìtǒng	

Thinned array antenna	稀疏天线阵	Xīshū tiānxiàn zhèn	TAA
Thinnet	细电缆网	Xì diànlǎn wǎng	
ThinNet; cheaperNet	细以太网	Xì yǐtàiwǎng	
Thinning	细化	Xìhuà	
Third generation interest group	第三代兴趣小组	Dìsāndài xìngqu xiǎozǔ	3GIG
Third generation mobile telephone	第三代移动通信	Dìsāndài yídòng tōngxìn	3G
Third generation partnership projects	第三代伙伴组织计划	Dìsāndài huǒbàn zǔzhī jìhuà	3GPP
Third normal form	第 3 范式	Dìsān fànshì	3NF
Third order distortion	三阶失真	Sānjiē shīzhēn	
Third order high density bipolar code	三阶高密度双极性码	Sānjiē gāomìdù shuāng jíxìng mǎ	HDB3
Third order intermodulation	三级互调	Sānjí hùtiáo	
Third order intermodulation interference	三阶互调干扰	Sānjiē hùtiáo gànrǎo	
Third party	第三团体	Dìsān tuántǐ	TP
Third party	第三方	Dìsānfāng	
Third party copy	第三方拷贝	Dìsānfāng kǎobèi	TPC
Third party payment/billing	第三方付费	Dìsānfāng fùfèi	
Third party service provider	第三方业务提供者	Dìsānfāng yèwù tígòngzhě	TSP
Thomson Corp (French company)	汤姆逊公司	Tāng-mǔ-xùn gōngsī	
Thread	线程	Xiànchéng	
Thread (computer documents or e-mail messages on one subject)	相关文章	Xiāngguān wénzhāng	
Threaded binary tree	线索二叉树	Xiànsuǒ èrchā shù	
Thread-safe	线程安全的	Xiànchéng ānquánde	
Threat model	威胁模型	Wēixié móxíng	
Threat monitoring	威胁监控	Wēixié jiānkòng	
Three "-izations" (in electronics, 数字化 digitization, 网络化 networked and 知识化 made intelligent)	三化	Sān huà	
Three "-izations" (in telecom, 通用化 or 标准化 standardization, 系列化 serialization and 模块化 modularization)	三化	Sān huà	
Three condition	三态	Sāntài	
Three decibel coupler	三分贝耦合器	Sān fēnbèi ǒuhéqì	
Three dimensional	三维	Sānwéi	3D
Three dimensional (3D) positional audio	三维定位音频	Sānwéi dìngwèi yīnpín	3DPA
Three dimensional sub-system (video)	三维子系统	Sānwéi zixìtǒng	3DS
Three party communications	三方通信	Sānfāng tōngxìn	3PTY
Three party service	三方业务	Sānfāng yèwù	3PTY
Three primary colors (red, green, blue; refers to system for representing colors on a computer display)	三原色	Sānyuánsè	RGB
Three proofings (防潮moisture-proof, 防霉mildew proof, 防烟雾smog-proof)	三防	Sānfáng	
Three protects (protect against interference, emissions and static)	三防	Sān fáng	
Three terminal regulator	三端稳压器	Sānduān wěnyāqì	
Three-dimensional data	三维数据	Sānwéi shùjù	
Three-dimensional entity-constraint graph (CAD/CAM)	三维实体约束图	Sānwéi shítǐ yuēshù tú	

English	Chinese	Pinyin	Abbreviation
Three-dimensional inter-connected warfare (air, sea, land and information technology)	立体交叉战争	Lìtǐ jiāochā zhànzhēng	
Three-dimensional pipeline	三维流水线	Sānwéi liúshuǐxiàn	
Three-dimensional spreadsheet	三维试算表	Sānwéi shìsuànbiǎo	
Three-dimensional vibration	三维振动	Sānwéi zhèndòng	
Three-in-one network (see above)	三网合一	Sānwǎng héyī	
Three-network convergence (telecommunications networks, computer networks, cable TV networks)	三网融合 (通信网,计算机网,有线电视网)	Sānwǎng rónghé (tōngxìnwǎng, jìsuànjī wǎng, yǒuxiàn diànshì wǎng)	
Three-phase	三相	Sānxiàng	
Three-tier architecture	三级体系	Sānjí tǐxì	
Three-way connection	三方接续	Sānfāng jiēxù	
Three-way conversation	三方通话	Sānfāng tōnghuà	
Threshold	门限	Ménxiàn	
Threshold communication secret key sharing system	门限通信密钥分散保管系统	Ménxiàn tōngxìn mìyào fēnsàn bǎoguǎn xìtǒng	TCSSS
Threshold crossing	门限跨越	Ménxiàn kuàyuè	
Threshold crossing alarm	门限超越告警	Ménxiàn chāoyuè gàojǐng	TCA
Threshold crossing alarm	越限告警	Yuèxiàn gàojǐng	TCA
Threshold current	阈值电流	Yùzhí diànliú	
Threshold decoding	门限译码	Ménxiàn yìmǎ	
Threshold extension demodulation	门限扩展解调	Ménxiàn kuòzhǎn jiětiáo	
Threshold level	门限电平	Ménxiàn diànpíng	
Threshold of flicker irritability	闪变应激性门限	Shǎnbiàn yìngjīxìng ménxiàn	
Threshold of flicker irritability	闪烁应激性阈值	Shǎnshuò yìngjīxìng yùzhí	
Threshold of flicker perceptibility	闪变觉察门限	Shǎnbiàn juéchá ménxiàn	
Threshold of flicker perceptibility	闪烁感觉阈值	Shǎnshuò gǎnjué yùzhí	
Threshold of let-go current	摆脱电流阈值	Bǎituō diànliú yùzhí	
Threshold of perception current	感知电流阈值	Gǎnzhī diànliú yùzhí	
Threshold of ventricular fibrillation current	致颤电流阈值	Zhì chàn diànliú yùzhí	
Threshold report	门限报告	Ménxiàn bàogào	TR
Threshold time	阈值时间	Yùzhí shíjiān	
Thresholding	门限判定	Ménxiàn pàndìng	
Throat microphone	喉式传声器	Hóushì chuánshēngqì	
Through flange	直通法兰	Zhítōng fǎlán	
Through-connection delay	直同连接延时	Zhítóng liánjiē yánshí	
Through-group connection point	直通络连接点	Zhítōng luò liánjiē diǎn	
Through-mastergroup connection point	直通主群连接点	Zhítōng zhǔqún liánjiē diǎn	
Throughput (quantity)	吞吐量	Tūntǔliàng	
Throughput (rate)	吞吐率	Tūntǔlǜ	
Through-supergroup assembly connection point	直通超群组连接点	Zhítōng chāoqún zǔ liánjiē diǎn	
Through-supergroup connection point	直通超群连接点	Zhítōng chāoqún liánjiē diǎn	
Through-supermastergroup connection point	直通超主群连接点	Zhítōng chāozhǔqún liánjiē diǎn	
Throw	抛出	Pāochū	
Throw (as causing an exception, in software)	引发	Yǐnfā	
Thulium doped fiber amplifier	参铥光纤放大器	Cān diū guāngxiān fàngdàqì	TDFA
Thumb switch	拨码开关	Bōmǎ kāiguān	
Thumb wheel switch	拇指旋转开关	Mǔzhǐ xuánzhuǎn kāiguān	TWS

English	Chinese	Pinyin	Abbreviation
Thumbnail	缩略图	Suōlüè tú	
Thumbnail view	缩微视图	Suōwēi shìtú	
Tic file	控制点文件	Kòngzhì diǎn wénjiàn	
Tic match tolerance	控制点配准容差	Kòngzhì diǎn pèizhǔn róngchā	
Ticket	话单	Huàdān	
Ticket dispenser	发卡机	Fākǎ jī	TD
Ticket granting ticket	赋予票据的票据	Fùyǔ piàojùde piàojù	TGT
Ticket-based probing	基于标签探测	Jīyú biāoqiān tàncè	TBP
Ticket-granting service	票据授予服务	Piàojù shòuyǔ fúwù	
Tiered	堆叠	Duīdié	
Tight tube (FOC mfg)	紧套	Jǐntào	
Tightly buffered multifiber fiber optic cable	紧包多心式光缆	Jǐnbāo duōxīn-shì guānglǎn	
Tile	瓦片	Wǎpiàn	
Tile horizontally (Windows command)	横向平铺视窗	Héngxiàng píngpū shìchuāng	
Tile vertically (Windows command)	纵向平铺视窗	Zòngxiàng píngpū shìchuāng	
Time acceleration factor	时间加速系数	Shíjiān jiāsù xìshù	
Time advance	提前时间	Tíqián shíjiān	TA
Time assigned speech interpolation	时分话音插空	Shífēn huàyīn chākōng	TAST
Time assignment digit	时间分配数字插入	Shíjiān fēnpèi shùzì chārù	
Time base	时基	Shíjī	
Time between failures	失效间隔时间	Shīxiào jiàngé shíjiān	
Time between interruptions	中断间隔时间	Zhōngduàn jiàngé shíjiān	
Time complexity	时间复杂度	Shíjiān fùzádù	
Time compression	时间压缩法	Shíjiān yāsuō fǎ	
Time compression multiplex	时间压缩多路复用	Shíjiān yāsuō duōlù fùyòng	TCM
Time compression multiplexer	时间压缩复用器	Shíjiān yāsuō fùyòngqì	TCM
Time compression multiplexing	时间压缩复用	Shíjiān yāsuō fùyòng	TCM
Time delay	时间延迟	Shíjiān yánchí	
Time delay spread	时延散布	Shíyán sànbù	
Time dependent constellation	时间决定星座	Shíjiān juédìng xīngzuò	TDC
Time deviation	时间编差	Shíjiān biānchà	TDEV
Time deviation, timing deviation	时间偏差	Shíjiān piānchā	TDEV
Time difference of arrival	到达时差	Dàodá shíchā	TDOA
Time differential phase-shift keying	时间微分相移键控	Shíjiān wēifēn xiàngyí jiànkòng	TDPSK
Time dimension	时间维度	Shíjiān wéidù	
Time distortion	时间畸变	Shíjiān jībiàn	
Time distortion	时间失真	Shíjiān shīzhēn	
Time diversity	时间分集	Shíjiān fēnjí	
Time division	时分	Shífèn	
Time division – code division multiple access	时分码分多址接入	Shífèn mǎfēn duōzhǐ jiērù	TD-CDMA
Time division circuit switching	时分电路交换	Shífèn diànlù jiāohuàn	TDCS
Time division data link	时分数据链	Shífèn shùjù liàn	TDDL
Time division digital network	时分数字网络	Shífèn shùzì wǎngluò	TDDN
Time division duplex	时分双工	Shífèn shuānggōng	TDD
Time division duplex-based ethernet digital subscriber line	基于时分双工的以太数字用户线	Jīyú shífèn shuānggōngde yǐtài shùzì yònghùxiàn	TDD-EDSL

Time division modulation	时分调制	Shífèn tiáozhì	TDM
Time division multiple access	时分多址	Shífèn duōzhǐ	TDMA
Time division multiple access	时分多址访问	Shífèn duōzhǐ fǎngwèn	TDMA
Time division multiple access	时分多址接入	Shífèn duōzhǐ jiērù	TDMA
Time division multiplex	时分多路复用	Shífèn duōlù fùyòng	TDM
Time division multiplex	时分复用	Shífèn fùyòng	TDM
Time division multiplex transmission	时分复用传输	Shífèn fùyòng chuánshū	
Time division multiplexed channel	时分复用信道	Shífèn fùyòng xìndào	TDMC
Time division multiplexed-pulse amplitude modulation	时分多路脉冲调幅	Shífèn duōlù màichōng tiáofú	TDM-PAM
Time division multiplexed-pulse code modulation	时分多路脉码调制	Shífèn duōlù màimǎ tiáozhì	TDM-PCM
Time division multiplexed-variable destination multiple access	时分复用变址多路存取	Shífèn fùyòng biànzhǐ duōlù cúnqǔ	TDM-VDMA
Time division multiplexer	时分多路复用器	Shífèn duōlù fùyòngqì	TDM
Time division multiplexing system	时分复用系统	Shífèn fùyòng xìtǒng	TDMS
Time division switching	时分交换	Shífèn jiāohuàn	
Time division switching	时分交换结构	Shífèn jiāohuàn jiégòu	TDS
Time division synchronous code division multiple access	时分同步码分多址	Shífèn tóngbù mafēn duōzhǐ	TD-SCDMA
Time division-code division multiple access	时分-码分多址	Shífèn-mǎfēn duōzhǐ	TD-CDMA
Time division-time slot interchanger	时分时隙交换器	Shífèn shíxì jiāohuànqì	TDTSI
Time domain	时域	Shíyù	
Time domain coding	时域编码	Shíyù biānmǎ	TDC
Time domain reflectometry	时域反射计量	Shíyù fǎnshèjì liáng	
Time domain reflector	时域反射仪	Shíyù fǎnshèyí	TDR
Time efficiency factor	时间效率系数	Shíjiān xiàolǜ xìshù	
Time factor	时间系数	Shíjiān xìshù	
Time history response analysis method	时程反应分析法	Shíchéng fǎnyìng fēnxīfǎ	
Time hopping	跳时	Tiàoshí	TH
Time interval	时间间隔	Shíjiān jiàngé	
Time interval between pulse series	脉冲串间隔	Màichōng chuàn jiàngé	
Time interval error	时间间隔误差	Shíjiān jiàngé wùchā	TIE
Time limit on periodic location refreshes	周期位置更新时限值	Zhōuqī wèizhì gēngxīn shíxiàn zhí	
Time limited service	时限服务	Shíxiàn fúwù	TLS
Time notify	时间通知	Shíjiān tōngzhī	Tnotify
Time of arrival	到达时间	Dàodá shíjiān	TOA
Time of day	时刻	Shíkè	TOD
Time of switching of date	日切时间	Rì qiē shíjiān	
Time reference beamforming	时间参考波束成型	Shíjiān cānkǎo bōshù chéngxíng	TRB
Time scale decomposition	时间数量级分解	Shíjiān shùliàngjí fēnjiě	TSD
Time series forecasting	时间序列预测	Shíjiān xùliè yùcè	TSF
Time server	时间服务器	Shíjiān fúwùqì	
Time sharing	分时	Fēnshí	
Time shift keying	时移键控	Shíyí jiànkòng	TSK
Time slice	时间片	Shíjiān piàn	
Time slicing	时间分片	Shíjiān fēnpiàn	
Time slot	时隙	Shíxì	TS
Time slot access	时隙访问	Shíxì fǎngwèn	TSA

Time slot assignment circuit	时间片分配电路	Shíjiān piàn fēnpèi diànlù	TSAC
Time slot interchange	时隙变换	Shíxì biànhuàn	
Time slot interchange	时隙交换	Shíxì jiāohuàn	TSI
Time slot interchanging	时隙互换	Shíxì hùhuàn	TSI
Time slot number	时隙号	Shíxì hào	TN
Time slot switching unit	时隙交换单元	Shíxì jiāohuàn dānyuán	TSU
Time stamp	时间戳	Shíjiān chuō	
Time stamp	时间印章	Shíjiān yìnzhāng	
Time stamp (IPsec)	时戳	Shíchuō	
Time supervision	时间监视	Shíjiān jiānshì	
Time switch back panel	时分交换后面板	Shífèn jiāohuàn hòumian bǎn	TSBP
Time switch control and maintenance	时分交换控制和维护	Shífèn jiāohuàn kòngzhì hé wéihù	TSCM
Time switched transmission diversity	时间切换发送分集	Shíjiān qiēhuàn fāsòng fēnjí	TSTD
Time switched transmit diversity	分时发分集	Fēnshí fāfēnjí	TSTD
Time synch	对时	Duìshí	
Time to customer (regarding delivery of goods)	发货至客户	Fāhuò zhì kèhù	
Time to failure	失效前时间	Shīxiào-qián shí jiān	
Time to first failure	首次失效前时间	Shǒucì shīxiào-qián shíjiān	
Time to first fix (in position location)	首次定位时长	Shǒucì dìngwèi shícháng	TTFF
Time to live	存活期	Cúnhuóqī	TTL
Time to live	生存时间	Shēngcún shíjiān	TTL
Time to live (SDH term)	生存期	Shēngcún qī	TTL
Time to restoration; time to recovery	未恢复时间	Wèi huīfù shíjiān	
Time transparency	时间透明	Shíjiān tòumíng	
Time zone	时区	Shíqū	
Time/event processing software	时间/事件处理软件	Shíjiān/shìjiàn chǔlǐ ruǎnjiàn	TEP
Time-assigned speech interpolation	话音插空	Huàyīn chā kōng	TASI
Timebase counters	时基计数器	Shíjī jìshùqì	
Timed automaton	时间自动机	Shíjiān zìdòngjī	
Timed frequency modulation	时控调频	Shíkòng tiáopín	TFM
Timed pre-assigned multiple access	定时预分配多路存取	Dìngshí yù fēnpèi duōlù cúnqǔ	TPMA
Timed process algebra	时间进程代数	Shíjiān jìnchéng dàishù	
Time-dependent password	时间相关口令	Shíjiān xiāngguān kǒulìng	
Time-difference of arrival	到达时间差	Dàodá shíjiān chà	TDOA
Time-divided control	时分控制	Shífèn kòngzhì	
Time-division analog network	分时模拟网络	Fēnshí mónǐ wǎngluò	TDAN
Time-division channel	时分信道	Shífèn xìndào	
Time-division data link	时间分割数据传输器	Shíjiān fēngē shùjù chuánshūqì	TDDL
Time-frame	时帧	Shízhèng	
Time-frequency coded multiple access	时间频率编码多路存取	Shíjiān pínlǜ biānmǎ duōlù cúnqǔ	TFCMA
Time-frequency hopping	时间频率跳变	Shíjiān pínlǜ tiàobiàn	TFH
Time-frequency-shift keying	时频偏移键控	Shípín piānyí jiànkòng	TFSK
Time-out	超时	Chāoshí	TMO
Time-out	时间已过	Shíjiān yǐguò	TMO
Time-out error	过时错误	Guòshí cuòwù	TO
Time-preassigned multiple access	时间预分配多址	Shíjiān yùfēnpèi duōzhǐ	

Timer	定时器	Dìngshíqì	
Timer	记时器	Jìshíqì	T
Timer interrupt request block	时标中断请求块	Shíbiāo zhōngduàn qǐngqiú kuài	TIRB
Timer table	时钟表	Shízhōng biǎo	
Time-scale	时标	Shíbiāo	
Time-sharing	分时共享	Fēnshí gòngxiǎng	
Time-sharing executive system	分时执行系统	Fēnshí zhíxíng xìtǒng	TSES
Time-sharing system	分时系统	Fēnshí xìtǒng	
Time-slot	时槽	Shícáo	
Timeslot number	时隙号码	Shíxì hàomǎ	TN
Timestamp	时标	Shíbiāo	TS
Timestamp interval	时标段	Shíbiāo duàn	TI
Timetabling problem	时间表问题	Shíjiānbiǎo wèntí	
Time-varying quantity	时变量	Shí biànliáng	
Timing advance	定时超前	Dìngshí chāoqián	
Timing advance	定时提前	Dìngshí tíqián	TA
Timing advance	定时提前量	Dìngshí tíqiánliàng	TA
Timing advance	时间提前	Shíjiān tíqián	TA
Timing advance	时间提前量	Shíjiān tíqiánliàng	TA
Timing and frequency block	定时和频率模块	Dìngshí hé pínlǜ mókuài	TFB
Timing attack	定时攻击	Dìngshí gōngjī	
Timing channel	计时通道	Jìshí tōngdào	TC
Timing circuit	定时电路	Dìngshí diànlù	TIM
Timing circuit	时间电路	Shíjiān diànlù	TIM
Timing detection table	定时检测表	Dìngshí jiǎncè biǎo	TDT
Timing deviation	时间方差	Shíjiān fāngchà	TDEV
Timing extraction	定时抽取	Dìngshí chōuqǔ	
Timing information	定时信息	Dìngshí xìnxī	TI
Timing loop	定时环	Dìngshí huán	
Timing period expired	定时器超时	Dìngshíqì chāoshí	
Timing period restarted	定时器重启	Dìngshíqì chóngqǐ	
Timing phase	定时相位	Dìngshí xiàngwèi	
Timing point	定时点	Dìngshí diǎn	TP
Timing pulse	定时脉冲	Dìngshí màichōng	
Timing receiver autonomous integrity monitoring	定时接收机自主完善性监测	Dìngshí jiēshōujī zìzhǔ wánshànxìng jiāncè	TRAIM
Timing recovery	定时恢复	Dìngshí huīfù	
Timing recovery	定时提取	Dìngshí tíqǔ	
Timing signal	定时信号	Dìngshí xìnhào	
Timing stratum	时间等级	Shíjiān děngjí	
Timing synchronization message	定时同步消息	Dìngshí tóngbù xiāoxi	SYNC
TINA open service creation architecture	TINA 开放业务生产结构	TINA kāifàng yèwù shēngchǎn jiégòu	TOSCA
TINA service architecture and intelligent network services	TINA 业务结构和或智能网业务	TINA yèwù jiégòu hé zhìnéng wǎng yèwù	SATIN
To be defined	未定义	Wèidìngyì	TBD
To mobilize, to select people to form groups	抽组	Chōu zǔ	
To switch unit	到交换单元	Dào jiāohuàn dānyuán	TSU

Toggle	反转	Fǎnzhuǎn	
Token	令牌	Lìngpái	TK
Token (in software)	标记	Biāojì	
Token (in software)	符号	Fúhào	
Token bucket marking	令牌桶标记	Lìngpái tǒng biāojì	
Token bus	令牌环总线	Lìngpái huán zǒngxiàn	
Token bus protocol	令牌总线协议	Lìngpái zǒngxiàn xiéyì	TBP
Token granting server (ISO security)	票证许可服务器	Piàozhèng xǔkě fúwùqì	TGS
Token passing	令牌环传递	Lìngpái huán chuándì	
Token passing network	令牌网	Lìngpái wǎng	PLAN
Token ring	令牌环	Lìngpái huán	TR
Token ring	令牌网	Lìngpái wǎng	TR
Token ring	权标环	Quánbiāo huán	TR
Token ring interface coupler	令牌环接口耦合器	Lìngpái huán jiēkǒu ǒuhéqì	TIC
Token ring interface processor	令牌环接口处理器	Lìngpái huán jiēkǒu chǔlǐqì	TRIP
Token ring network	令牌环网	Lìngpái huán wǎng	
Token ring network	令牌环形网	Lìngpái huánxíng wǎng	
Tolerance file	容差文件	Róngchā wénjiàn	
Toll	通行费	Tōngxíng fèi	
Toll center	长途电话交换中心	Chángtú diànhuà jiāohuàn zhōngxīn	TC
Toll offering tone	长途通知音	Chángtú tōngzhīyīn	
Toll point type	收费站类型	Shōufèizhàn lèixíng	
Toll recording and computing equipment	长途电话记录和计算设备	Chángtú diànhuà jìlù hé jìsuàn shèbèi	TRACE
Toll switch	长途交换机	Chángtú jiāohuànjī	TS
Toll switch	长途交换局	Chángtú jiāohuànjú	TS
Toll switch	长途局	Chángtújú	TS
Toll switch office	长话交换局	Chánghuà jiāohuànjú	TS
Toll switch-facsimile equipment	长途交换传真设备	Chángtú jiāohuàn chuánzhēn shèbèi	TS-FX
Tombstoning (in SMT)	元件立起	Yuánjiàn lìqǐ	
Tomcat (U.S. F-14 aircraft)	雄猫	Xióngmāo	
Tone	单音	Dānyīn	
Tone code modulation	音调代码调制	Yīndiào dàimǎ tiáozhì	TCM
Tone control	音质控制	Yīnzhì kòngzhì	
Tone dial receiver	单音拨号的接收机	Dānyīn bōhàode jiēshōujī	TDR
Tone frequency of tone pulse	单音脉冲的单音频率	Dān yīn màichōngde dānyīn pínlǜ	
Tone frequency of tone pulse	单音脉冲的单音频率	Dānyīn màichōngde dānyīn pínlǜ	
Tone modulation	音调调制	Yīndiào tiáozhì	TM
Tone paging	声音寻呼	Shēngyīn xúnhū	
Tone pulse	单音脉冲	Dānyīn màichōng	
Tone pulse decay time	单音脉冲下降时间	Dānyīn màichōng xiàjiàng shíjiān	
Tone pulse duration	单音脉冲持续时间	Dānyīn màichōng chíxù shíjiān	
Tone pulse rise time	单音脉冲上升时间	Dānyīn màichōng shàngshēng shíjiān	
Toner (for a printer)	墨粉	Mòfěn	
Tongguang Nortel Corp. (China-Canada joint venture)	通广北方公司	Tōngguǎng běifāng gōngsī	
To-node	止节点	Zhǐ jiédiǎn	
Toolbar (WP command)	工具箱	Gōngjùxiāng	

English	Chinese	Pinyin	Abbreviation
Toolkit (computer development term)	开发包	Kāifā bāo	
Tools menu (WP command)	工具菜单	Gōngjù càidān	
Top (of a stack)	栈定	Zhàn dìng	
Top edge	上边缘	Shàngbianyuán	
Top left corner	左上角	Zuǒ shàngjiǎo	
Top level aggregation identifier	顶级聚集标识符	Dǐngjí jùjí biāozhìfú	TLAID
Top margin	页面顶栏	Yèmiàn dǐnglán	
Top right corner	右上角	Yòushàngjiǎo	
Top-level domain	顶级域	Dǐngjí yù	
Top-loaded antenna	顶端加载天线	Dǐngduān jiāzài tiānxiàn	
Top-loaded vertical antenna	顶部加载垂直天线	Dǐngbù jiāzài chuízhí tiānxiàn	
Topographic database	地形数据	Dìxíng shùjù	
Topographic feature	地形特征	Dìxíng tèzhēng	
Topographic map	地形图	Dìxíng tú	
Topographic mapping	地形制图	Dìxíng zhìtú	
Topographic visualization	地形可视化	Dìxíng kěshìhuà	
Topographical overlay	地形叠加	Dìxíng diéjiā	
Topologic validity condition (CAD/CAM)	拓扑有效性条件	Tuòpū yǒuxiàoxìng tiáojiàn	TVC
Topological boundary	拓扑边界	Tuòpū biānjiè	
Topological complex	拓扑复合物	Tuòpū fùhéwù	
Topological component	拓扑元件	Tuòpū yuánjiàn	
Topological error	拓扑错误	Tuòpū cuòwù	
Topological expression	拓扑表述	Tuòpū biǎoshù	
Topological function	拓扑函数	Tuòpū hánshù	
Topological object	拓扑对象	Tuòpū duìxiàng	
Topological optimization	拓扑优化	Tuòpū yōuhuà	
Topological order	拓扑有序	Tuòpū yǒu xù	
Topological overlay	拓扑叠加	Tuòpū diéjiā	
Topological primitive	拓扑原素	Tuòpū yuánsù	
Topological relationship	拓扑关系	Tuòpū guānxi	
Topological sorting	拓扑排序	Tuòpū páixù	
Topological structure	拓扑结构	Tuòpū jiégòu	
Topologically integrated geographical encoding and reference	一体化拓扑地理编码和参照	Yītǐhuà tuòpū dìlǐ biānmǎ hé cānzhào	TIGER
Topologically structured data	拓扑结构数据	Tuòpū jiégòu shùjù	
Topology	拓扑	Tuòpū	
Toroidal reflector	环面反射器	Huánmiàn fǎnshèqì	
Torsional deflection	扭转变形	Niǔzhuǎn biànxíng	
Torsional moment	扭矩	Niǔjǔ	
Torsional oscillation	扭振	Niǔzhèn	
Torsional wave	扭振波	Niǔzhèn bō	
Torus	圆环面	Yuánhuán miàn	
Total access communications system	全存取通信系统	Quán cúnqǔ tōngxìn xìtǒng	TACS
Total access communications system	全接入通信系统	Quán jiērù tōngxìn xìtǒng	TACS
Total access communications system	全选址通信系统	Quán xuǎnzhǐ tōngxìn xìtǒng	TACS
Total call connection delay	全部呼叫连接时延	Quánbù hūjiào liánjiē shíyán	TCCD
Total cost of ownership	拥有总成本	Yōngyǒu zǒngchéngběn	TCO

Total distortion factor	总失真系数	Zǒng shīzhēn xìshù	
Total effective area (of an antenna for a given direction)	总有效面积	Zǒng yǒuxiào miànjī	
Total electron content	总电子含量	Zǒng diànzǐ hánliàng	TEC
Total harmonic distortion	总谐波失真	Zǒng xiébō shīzhēn	THD
Total harmonic distortion plus noise	总谐波失真加噪音	Zǒng xiébō shīzhēn jiā zàoyīn	THD+N
Total harmonic factor	总谐波系数	Zǒng xiébō xìshù	
Total impedance of the human body	人体总阻抗	Réntǐ zǒngzǔkàng	
Total internal reflection (type of FOC)	全反射导光型	Quánfǎnshè dǎoguāng xíng	TIR
Total least squares method	总体最小二乘法	Zǒngtǐ zuìxiǎo èrchéngfǎ	
Total loss (of a radio link)	总损耗（无线电链路的）	Zǒng sǔnhào (wúxiàndiàn liànlùde)	
Total noise level	总噪声级	Zǒng zàoshēng jí	TNL
Total output power	总输出功率	Zǒng shūchū gōnglǜ	
Total quality management	全面质量管理	Quánmiàn zhìliàng guǎnlǐ	TQM
Total remote assistance center	远程辅助总中心	Yuǎnchéng fǔzhù zǒng zhōngxīn	TRACE
Total system downtime	系统中断期	Xìtǒng zhōngduàn qī	
Touch-calling multi-frequency	多频键控呼叫	Duōpín jiànkòng hūjiào	TCMF
Touch-calling multi-frequency	链控呼叫多频	Liàn kòng hūjiào duōpín	TCMF
Touch-tone dialing	按键式拨号	Ànjiànshì bō hào	
Tower	铁塔	Tiětǎ	
Tower case	立式机箱	Lìshì jīxiāng	
Tower case	塔式机箱	Tǎ-shì jīxiāng	
T-R cell	T-R 盒	T-R hé	
T-R switch	T-R 开关	T-R kāiguān	
Trace (on an oscilloscope)	踪迹线	Zōngjīxiàn	
Trace (verb)	跟踪	Gēnzōng	
Trace error	路踪误差	Lùzōng wùchā	TE
Trace file	跟踪文件	Gēnzōng wénjiàn	
Trace identifier mismatch	追踪识别符失配	Zhuīzōng shíbiéfú shīpèi	TIM
Trace identifier mismatch	踪迹识别符失配	Zōngjī shíbiéfú shīpèi	TIM
Trace subscriber activity	跟踪用户活动	Gēnzōng yònghù huódòng	
Traceability (IPsec)	可追溯性	Kězhuīsùxìng	
Tracer	跟踪程序	Gēnzōng chéngxù	
Tracing	跟踪	Gēnzōng	
Tracing buffer full	跟踪缓冲器溢出	Gēnzōng huǎnchōngqì yìchū	
Tracing mode	跟踪方式	Gēnzōng fāngshì	
Track and hold circuit	跟踪保持电路	Gēnzōng bǎochí diànlù	
Track, guide	导轨	Dǎoguǐ	
Trackball	轨迹球	Guǐjì qiú	
Tracking and data relay satellite system	跟踪与数据中继卫星系统	Gēnzōng yǔ shùjù zhōngjì wèixīng xìtǒng	TDRSS
Tracking bandwidth	跟踪带宽	Gēnzōng dàikuān	
Tracking error	跟踪误差	Gēnzōng wùchā	
Traction	牵引	Qiānyǐn	
Tractive force	牵引力	Qiānyǐnlì	
Trade-area map	商业区图	Shāngyèqū tú	
Traffic analysis	数据流分析	Shùjù liú fēnxī	
Traffic analysis (IPsec)	通信业务分析	Tōngxìn yèwù fēnxī	

Traffic channel	话务频道	Huàwù píndào	TCH
Traffic channel	话务信道	Huàwù xìndào	TCH
Traffic channel	业务信道	Yèwù xìndào	TCH
Traffic channel with capacity lower than a full rate channel	容量比全速率业务信道低的业务信道	Róngliàng bǐ quánsùlǜ yèwù xìndào dīde yèwù xìndào	Lm
Traffic channel/full rate 4.8kbit/s	业务信道/全速 4.8kbit/s	Yèwù xìndào/quánsù 4.8kbit/s	TCH/H4.8
Traffic channel/full rate 9.6kbit/s	业务信道/全速 9.6kbit/s	Yèwù xìndào/quánsù 9.6kbit/s	TCH/F9.6
Traffic channel/full rate speech	业务信道/全速话音	Yèwù xìndào/quánsù huàyīn	TCH/FS
Traffic channel/half-rate 4.8kbit/s	业务信道/半速 4.8kbit/s	Yèwù xìndào/bànsù 4.8kbit/s	TCH/H4.8
Traffic channel/half-rate speech	业务信道/半速话音	Yèwù xìndào/bànsù huàyīn	TC/HS
Traffic circuit	电信业务电路	Diànxìn yèwù diànlù	
Traffic contract	业务量合约	Yèwùliàng héyuē	
Traffic control	业务量控制	Yèwùliàng kòngzhì	
Traffic control sub-system	业务控制子系统	Yèwù kòngzhì zixìtǒng	TCS
Traffic descriptor	业务量描述语	Yèwùliàng miáoshù yǔ	
Traffic engineering	流量工程	Liúliàng gōngchéng	
Traffic engineering	业务工程	Yèwù gōngchéng	TE
Traffic engineering	业务量工程	Yèwùliàng gōngchéng	TE
Traffic engineering	业务流设计	Yèwùliú shèjì	TE
Traffic flow confidentiality (IPsec)	业务流机密性	Yèwùliú jīmìxìng	
Traffic flow security	通信流安全	Tōngxìn liú ānquán	
Traffic flow template	业务流样板	Yèwùliú yàngbǎn	TFT
Traffic grooming	业务量疏导	Yèwùliàng shūdǎo	
Traffic management	流量管理	Liúliàng guǎnlǐ	
Traffic management	信息量管理	Xìnxīliàng guǎnlǐ	TM
Traffic matrix	通信量矩阵	Tōngxìnliàng jǔzhèn	
Traffic meter (in telecommunication)	业务计数器	Yèwù jìshùqì	
Traffic padding (IPsec)	通信业务填充	Tōngxìn yèwù tiánchōng	
Traffic pattern	业务量模式	Yèwùliàng móshì	
Traffic shaping	流量编整	Liúliàng biānzhěng	
Traffic shaping	通信整形	Tōngxìn zhěngxíng	
Trafficability performance	负荷业务量性能	Fùhè yèwù liáng xìngnéng	
Traffic-carrying device	电信业务运载设备	Diànxìn yèwù yùnzài shèbèi	
Traffic-load control	业务负荷控制	Yèwù fùhè kòngzhì	
Traffic-load divided control	业务负荷分散控制	Yèwù fùhè fēnsàn kòngzhì	
Trail (ATM term)	路径	Lùjìng	
Trail identification mismatch	路径识别符失配	Lùjìng shíbiéfú shīpèi	TIM
Trail signal degrade (ATM term)	路径信号劣化	Lùjìng xìnhào lièhuà	TSD
Trail signal fail	路径信号失效	Lùjìng xìnhào shīxiào	TSF
Trail termination	路径终端	Lùjìng zhōngduān	
Trail termination function	路径终端功能	Lùjìng zhōngduān gōngnéng	TT
Trail termination function	路径终结功能	Lùjìng zhōngjié gōngnéng	TT
Trail termination point	踪迹终结点	Zōngjī zhōngjié diǎn	TTP
Trail termination sink	路径宿端	Lùjìng sù duān	
Trail termination sink	路径终接宿	Lùjìng zhōngjiē sù	
Trail termination source	路径源端	Lùjìng yuánduān	

Trail termination source	路径终接源	Lùjìng zhōngjiē yuán	
Trail trace identifier	路径踪迹识别符	Lùjìng zōngjī shíbiéfú	TTI
Trail trace identifier multi-frame	路径踪迹识别复帧	Lùjìng zōngjī shíbiéfù zhèng	TTI
Trail trace identifier processing	路径踪迹标识处理	Lùjìng zōngjī biāozhì chǔlǐ	TTIP
Trailer	报尾	Bào wěi	
Trailing edge	后边缘	Hòubianyuán	
Trailing edge clipping	后沿切割	Hòuyán qiēgē	
Trailing wire antenna	下垂天线	Xiàchuí tiānxiàn	TWA
Trailing-edge broadening	后沿展宽	Hòuyán zhǎnkuān	
Training	训练	Xùnliàn	
Training dataset	培训数据集	Péixùn shùjù jí	
Training sample	训练样本	Xùnliàn yàngběn	
Training sequence code	训练系列号	Xùnliàn xìliè hào	TSC
Training sequence code	训练序列码	Xùnliàn xùliè mǎ	TSC
Trait phrasing	特征句式	Tèzhēng jùshì	
Transaction	事务	Shìwù	
Transaction between cities within a province	省内异地汇兑交易	Shěngnèi yìdì huìduì jiāoyì	
Transaction between provinces	省际汇兑交易	Shěngjì huìduì jiāoyì	
Transaction capabilities	事务处理能力	Shìwù chǔlǐ nénglì	TC
Transaction capabilities application part	事条能力应用部分	Shìtiáo nénglì yìngyòng bùfen	TCAP
Transaction capabilities application part	事务处理部分	Shìwù chǔlǐ bùfen	TCAP
Transaction capabilities application part	事务处理功能应用部	Shìwù chǔlǐ gōngnéng yìngyòng bù	TCAP
Transaction capabilities application part	事务处理应用部分	Shìwù chǔlǐ yìngyòng bùfen	TCAP
Transaction capabilities part	事务处理能力部分	Shìwù chǔlǐ nénglì bùfen	
Transaction capability and application sub-system	交易能力和应用子系统	Jiāoyì nénglì hé yìngyòng zixìtǒng	TCAS
Transaction capability application part	事务处理能力应用部分	Shìwù chǔlǐ nénglì yìngyòng bùfen	TCAP
Transaction capability application part	事务能力应用部分	Shìwù nénglì yìngyòng bùfen	TCAP
Transaction control	事务控制	Shìwù kòngzhì	
Transaction dependency	事务依赖	Shìwù yīlài	
Transaction identifier	交易标识符	Jiāoyì biāozhìfú	TI
Transaction identifier	事务标识	Shìwù biāozhì	TI
Transaction identifier	事务处理标识符	Shìwù chǔlǐ biāozhìfú	TI
Transaction layer	交易层	Jiāoyì céng	
Transaction log file (in SQL Server)	事务日志文件	Shìwù rìzhì wénjiàn	
Transaction log (for database)	事务日志	Shìwù rìzhì	
Transaction logger	事务记录器	Shìwù jìlùqì	
Transaction manager	事务管理器	Shìwù guǎnlǐqì	TM
Transaction processing	交易处理	Jiāoyì chǔlǐ	
Transaction processing system	事务处理系统	Shìwù chǔlǐ xìtǒng	
Transaction rollback (for database)	事务回滚	Shìwù huígǔn	
Transaction state	事务处理状态	Shìwù chǔlǐ zhuàngtài	
Transaction triggering	事务触发	Shìwù chùfā	
Transaction within a city	同城汇兑交易	Tóngchéng huìduì jiāoyì	
Transactional consistency (in SQL Server)	事务的一致性	Shìwùde yīzhìxìng	
Transactional replication (for database)	事务复制	Shìwù fùzhì	
Transactions per second	每秒处理事项数	Měi miǎo chǔlǐ shìxiàng shù	TPS

Transatlantic Telephone (Cable)	横越大西洋海底电话(电缆)	Héngyuè Dàxīyáng hǎidī diànhuà (diànlǎn)	TAT
Transceiver	收发报机	Shōufābàojī	XCVR
Transceiver (board)	收发信机（板）	Shōufāxìnjī (bǎn)	TRX
Transceiver assembly	收发信机集成板	Shōufāxìnjī jíchéngbǎn	XCVA
Transceiver back plane board	收发信机后面板	Shōufāxìnjī hòumian bǎn	XBPB
Transceiver block	收发信机模块	Shōufāxìnjī mókuài	XCVB
Transceiver control interface	收发信机控制接口	Shōufāxìnjī kòngzhì jiēkǒu	TCI
Transceiver frequency synthesizer board	收发信机频率同步面板	Shōufāxìnjī pínlǜ tóngbù miànbǎn	XFSB
Transceiver interface processor	收发信机接口处理器	Shōufāxìnjī jiēkǒu chǔlǐqì	TIP
Transceiver master control unit	收发信机主机控制单元	Shōufāxìnjī zhǔjī kòngzhì dānyuán	XMCU
Transceiver power supply assembly	收发信机功率供给集成件	Shōufāxìnjī gōnglǜ gōngjǐ jíchéng jiàn	XPSA
Transceiver power supply unit	收发信机功率供给单元	Shōufāxìnjī gōnglǜ gōngjǐ dānyuán	TPSU
Transceiver rack	收发信机机架	Shōufāxìnjī jījià	XCVR
Transceiver shelf	收发信机架	Shōufāxìnjī jià	XCVS
Transceiver slave controller unit	收发信机从属控制单元	Shōufāxìnjī cóngshǔ kòngzhì dānyuán	XSCB
Transceiver speech and data interface	收发信机话音和数据接口	Shōufāxìnjī huàyīn hé shùjù jiēkǒu	TSDI
Transceiver unit	收发信机单元	Shōufāxìnjī dānyuán	XCVU
Transceiver unit processor	收发信机单元处理器	Shōufāxìnjī dānyuán chǔlǐqì	TRUP
Transcode type	译码类型	Yìmǎ lèixíng	TT
Transcode, decode; translate	译码	Yìmǎ	
Transcoder	变码器	Biànmǎqì	
Transcoder	代码转换器	Dàimǎ zhuǎnhuànqì	TC
Transcoder	码变换器	Mǎ biànhuànqì	TC
Transcoder	码型变换器	Mǎ-xíng biànhuànqì	
Transcoder and rate adaptation unit	码型转换和速率适配单元	Mǎ-xíng zhuǎnhuàn hé sùlǜ shìpèi dānyuán	TRAU
Transcoder and rate adapter unit	码变换速率适配单元	Mǎ biànhuàn sùlǜ shìpèi dānyuán	TRAU
Transcoder and selector bank	译码和选择器	Yìmǎ hé xuǎnzéqì	TSB
Transcoder and selector bank rack	译码和选择器机架	Yìmǎ hé xuǎnzéqì jījià	TSBR
Transcoder and sub-multiplex unit	码变换及子复用单元	Mǎ biànhuàn jí zifùyòng dānyuán	TCSM
Transcoder and sub-rate channel multiplexer	码变换器和子复用设备	Mǎ biànhuànqì hé zifùyòng shèbèi	TCSM
Transcoder sub-multiplexer controller	码变换子复用控制器	Mǎ biànhuàn zifùyòng kòngzhìqì	TSC
Transcoding and selector board assembly	译码和选择集成件	Yìmǎ hé xuǎnzé jíchéng jiàn	TASA
Trans-demultiplexer	子速率解复用器	Zisùlǜ jiěfùyòngqì	TDMUX
Transducer	传感器	Chuángǎnqì	
Transducer gain (of a two-port network)	复合损耗	Fùhé sǔnhào	
Transducer loss	转换器损耗	Zhuǎnhuànqì sǔnhào	
Trans-European trunked radio	泛欧洲数字集群标准	Fàn'Oūzhōu shùzì jíqún biāozhǔn	TETRA
Transfer	传送	Chuánsòng	
Transfer	转移	Zhuǎnyí	
Transfer admittance	转移导纳	Zhuǎnyí dǎonà	
Transfer allowed	允许转接	Yǔnxǔ zhuǎnjiē	TFA
Transfer capability	传送能力	Chuánsòng nénglì	
Transfer coefficient	传输系数	Chuánshū xìshù	
Transfer control	传换控制	Chuánhuàn kòngzhì	
Transfer format	转换格式	Zhuǎnhuàn géshi	
Transfer format for spatial data	空间数据交换格式	Kōngjiān shùjù jiāohuàn géshi	

Transfer function	传达系数	Chuándá xìshù	
Transfer function	传递函数	Chuándì hánshù	
Transfer function	传送功能	Chuánsòng gōngnéng	TF
Transfer function-operating system	传送功能-运行系统	Chuánsòng gōngnéng--yùnxíng xìtǒng	TF-OS
Transfer function-operating system function	传送功能-运行系统功能	Chuánsòng gōngnéng--yùnxíng xìtǒng gōngnéng	TF-OSF
Transfer immittance	转移导抗	Zhuǎnyí dǎokàng	
Transfer impedance (of a screened circuit)	屏蔽回路的转移阻抗	Píngbì huílùde zhuǎnyí zǔkàng	
Transfer impedance (of a screened circuit)	转移阻抗	Zhuǎnyí zǔkàng	
Transfer layer protocol	传输层协议	Chuánshū céng xiéyì	TP
Transfer matrix	传输矩阵	Chuánshū jǔzhèn	
Transfer mode	传递方式	Chuándì fāngshì	
Transfer mode	传送模式	Chuánsòng móshì	
Transfer of control	转移控制	Zhuǎnyí kòngzhì	TOC
Transfer prohibited	禁止传输	Jìnzhǐ chuánshū	TFP
Transfer protocol	转让协定书	Zhuǎnràng xiédìng shū	
Transfer protocol data unit	传输协议数据单元	Chuánshū xiéyì shùjù dānyuán	TPDU
Transfer ratio	转移比	Zhuǎnyí bǐ	
Transfer schema	转换计划	Zhuǎnhuàn jìhuà	
Transfer syntax	传送句法	Chuánsòng jùfǎ	
Transfer system	传送系统	Chuánsòng xìtǒng	
Transfer time	传递时间	Chuándì shíjiān	
Transfer time	转移时间	Zhuǎnyí shíjiān	Tt
Transfer-molded (FOC mfg)	转移模	Zhuǎnyí mó	
Transferred account data interchange group (GSM MoU)	数据交换组	Shùjù jiāohuàn zǔ	TADIG
Transferred jitter	传送抖动	Chuánsòng dǒudòng	
Transform	变换	Biànhuàn	
Transformable subscription	可转换订阅	Kězhuǎnhuàn dìngyuè	
Transformable subscriptions (in SQL Server)	可转换订购	Kězhuǎnhuàn dìnggòu	
Transformation	转换	Zhuǎnhuàn	
Transformation	坐标转换	Zuòbiāo zhuǎnhuàn	
Transformation domain	变换域	Biànhuàn yù	
Transformation schema	转换计划	Zhuǎnhuàn jìhuà	
Transformer station	变电站	Biàndiànzhàn	
Trans-horizon radio-relay system	超地平无线接力系统	Chāodìpíng wúxiàn jiēlì xìtǒng	
Trans-horizon radio-relay system	超视距无线电中继系统	Chāoshìjù wúxiàndiàn zhōngjì xìtǒng	
Transhorizon tropospheric transmission	超地平对流层传播	Chāodìpíng duìliúcéng chuánbō	
Transient (adjective and noun)	瞬态	Shùntài	
Transient characteristic	瞬间特性	Shùnjiān tèxìng	TC
Transient communication	瞬时通信	Shùnshí tōngxìn	
Transient cross saturation	瞬态交扰饱和	Shùntài jiāorǎo bǎohé	
Transient distortion	瞬态失真	Shùntài shīzhēn	
Transient electromagnetic field radiated susceptibility (Mil-Std-461E, RCS105)	瞬变电磁场辐射敏感度	Línbiàn diàncíchǎng fúshè mǐngǎndù	
Transient electromagnetic pulse emanation standard	瞬变电磁脉冲发射标准	Shùnbiàn diàncí màichōng fāshè biāozhǔn	TEMPEST
Transient fault	瞬间故障	Shùnjiān gùzhàng	
Transient fault	瞬时故障	Shùnshí gùzhàng	

Transient gain response	瞬时增益响应	Shùnshí zēngyì xiǎngyìng	
Transient overshoot	瞬间过冲	Shùnjiān guòchōng	
Transient process	瞬变过程	Shùnbiàn guòchéng	
Transient response	瞬态响应	Shùntài xiǎngyìng	
Transient response time constant	瞬时响应时间常数	Shùnshí xiǎngyìng shíjiān chángshù	
Transient signal rise time	瞬态信号的上升时间	Shùntài xìnhàode shàngshēng shíjiān	Tr/Th
Transient voltage suppressor	瞬间电压抑制器	Shùnjiān diànyā yìzhìqì	
Transimpedance	跨阻抗型	Kuà zǔkàngxíng	
Trans-inospheric propagation	越电离层传播	Yuè diànlícéng chuánbō	
Transistor-transistor logic circuit	晶体管晶体管逻辑电路	Jīngtǐguǎn jīngtǐguǎn luójidiànlù	TTL
Transit	经纬仪	Jīngwěiyí	
Transit	转接	Zhuǎnjiē	
Transit bridging	过渡桥接	Guòdù qiáojiē	
Transit call	中转呼叫	Zhōngzhuǎn hūjiào	
Transit connection element	转接连接单元	Zhuǎnjiē liánjiē dānyuán	TCE
Transit connection-related function	有关转接连接功能	Yǒuguān zhuǎnjiē liánjiē gōngnéng	TCRF
Transit delay	通过延迟	Tōngguò yánchí	
Transit delay	转接时延	Zhuǎnjiē shíyán	
Transit delay	转接延迟	Zhuǎnjiē yánchí	
Transit exchange	转接交换机	Zhuǎnjiē jiāohuànjī	TE
Transit group	汇接组	Huìjiē zǔ	
Transit label switching router	中间标志交换路由器	Zhōngjiān biāozhì jiāohuàn lùyóuqì	
Transit network	转接网	Zhuǎnjiē wǎng	
Transit network	转移网	Zhuǎnyí wǎng	TN
Transit network segment	转接网络段	Zhuǎnjiē wǎngluò duàn	TNS
Transit network selection	转接网络选择	Zhuǎnjiē wǎngluò xuǎnzé	
Transit node clock	转接节点时钟	Zhuǎnjiē jiédiǎn shízhōng	TNC
Transit point	转接点	Zhuǎnjiē diǎn	
Transit service node	转接服务节点	Zhuǎnjiē fúwù jiédiǎn	TSN
Transition	过渡	Guòdù	
Transition (in Petri net)	变迁	Biànqiān	
Transition band	过滤带	Guòlǜ dài	
Transition condition	迁移条件	Qiānyí tiáojiàn	
Transition point	转接点	Zhuǎnjiēdiǎn	TP
Transition probability density	转移概率密度	Zhuǎnyí gàilǜ mìdù	
Transition time	跃变时刻	Yuèbiàn shíkè	
Transitional variogram	过渡型变异函数	Guòdù-xíng biànyì hánshù	
Transitive closure	传递闭包	Chuándì bìbāo	
Transit-time modulation	渡越时间调制	Dùyuè shíjiān tiáozhì	TTM
Translate look-side buffer	翻译旁视缓冲器	Fānyì pángshì huǎnchōngqì	TLB
Translation unit	翻译单元	Fānyì dānyuán	
Translational bridging	翻译桥接	Fānyì qiáojiē	
Translative mode	转移模式	Zhuǎnyí móshì	
Translator (in switching)	译码器	Yìmǎqì	
Transmission	传达	Chuándá	
Transmission asymmetry	发送非对称性	Fāsòng fēiduìchènxìng	TA

Transmission capability	传输能力	Chuánshū nénglì	
Transmission channel	传输通路	Chuánshū tōnglù	
Transmission channel	传输信道	Chuánshū xìndào	
Transmission contiguity	传输邻接	Chuánshū línjiē	
Transmission control characters	传输控制字符	Chuánshū kòngzhì zìfú	TCC
Transmission control protocol	传输控制规程	Chuánshū kòngzhì guīchéng	TCP
Transmission control protocol	传输控制协议	Chuánshū kòngzhì xiéyì	TCP
Transmission control protocol/Internet protocol	传输控制规约/网间规约	Chuánshū kòngzhì guīyuē/wǎng jiān guīyuē	TCP/IP
Transmission control protocol/Internet protocol	传输控制协议/网际互连协议	Chuánshū kòngzhì xiéyì/wǎngjì hùlián xiéyì	TCP/IP
Transmission control protocol/Internet protocol	传输控制协议/网际协议	Chuánshū kòngzhì xiéyì/wǎngjì xiéyì	TCP/IP
Transmission control protocol/Inter-network protocol	传输控制协议/网间协议	Chuánshū kòngzhì xiéyì/wǎng- jiān xiéyì	TCP/IP
Transmission control protocol/Interwork protocol	传输控制协议/互通协议	Chuánshū kòngzhì xiéyì/hùtōng xiéyì	TCP/IP
Transmission convergence	传输会聚	Chuánshū huìjù	TC
Transmission convergence sub-layer	传输会聚子层	Chuánshū huìjù zicéng	TC
Transmission equipment	传输设备	Chuánshū shèbèi	TE
Transmission frame adaptation	传输帧自适应	Chuánshū zhèng zìshìying	
Transmission frequency characteristic	传输频率特性	Chuánshū pínlǜ tèxing	TFCC
Transmission frequency derivation of a highly modulated frequency	高调制频率时的发射频偏	Gāotiáozhì pínlǜ-shíde fāshè pínpiān	
Transmission frequency meter	通过式频率计	Tōngguò-shì pínlǜjì	
Transmission interface converter	传输接口转换器	Chuánshū jiēkǒu zhuǎnhuànqì	XIC
Transmission layer security protocol	传输层安全协议	Chuánshū céng ānquán xiéyì	TSP
Transmission line	传输线	Chuánshū xiàn	
Transmission line	输电线	Shū diànxiàn	
Transmission line adapter	传输线适配器	Chuánshūxiàn shìpèiqì	
Transmission link	传输链路	Chuánshū liànlù	
Transmission loss	传输损耗	Chuánshū sǔnhào	
Transmission media layer (STM term)	传输媒质层	Chuánshū méizhì céng	
Transmission medium	传输媒体	Chuánshū méitǐ	
Transmission medium requirement	传输媒介请求	Chuánshū méijiè qǐngqiú	TMR
Transmission medium requirement	传输媒体要求	Chuánshū méitǐ yāoqiú	
Transmission network	传输网	Chuánshū wǎng	
Transmission network selection	传输网络选择	Chuánshū wǎngluò xuǎnzé	
Transmission path	传输通道	Chuánshū tōngdào	
Transmission path	传输通路	Chuánshū tōnglù	TP
Transmission path endpoint	传输通路端点	Chuánshū tōnglù duāndiǎn	TPE
Transmission path level	传输通道级	Chuánshū tōngdào jí	
Transmission path level	传输通路级	Chuánshū tōnglù jí	
Transmission performance	传输性能	Chuánshū xìngnéng	
Transmission performance rating	传输性能评定值	Chuánshū xìngnéng píngdìng zhí	
Transmission protocol-specific TC layer	传输协议特定传输汇聚层	Chuánshū xiéyì tèdìng chuánshū huìjù céng	TPS-TC
Transmission restoration	传输恢复	Chuánshū huīfù	
Transmission restoration control function	传输恢复控制功能	Chuánshū huīfù kòngzhì gōngnéng	
Transmission restoration equipment	传输恢复设备	Chuánshū huīfù shèbèi	
Transmission restoration function	传输恢复功能	Chuánshū huīfù gōngnéng	

Transmission restoration system	传输恢复系统	Chuánshū huīfù xìtǒng	
Transmission route	传输路由	Chuánshū lùyóu	
Transmission route diversity	传输路由分集	Chuánshū lùyóu fēnjí	
Transmission security	传输保密	Chuánshū bǎomì	
Transmission service access point	传输服务存取点	Chuánshū fúwù cúnqǔdiǎn	TCAP
Transmission time interval	传输时间间隔	Chuánshū shíjiān jiàngé	TTI
Transmission trunking	传输集群	Chuánshū jíqún	
Transmission, propagation	传播	Chuánbō	
Transmission, transport	传输	Chuánshū	
Transmit	发射	Fāshè	TX
Transmit	发送	Fāsòng	Tx
Transmit band pass filter	传输带宽滤波器	Chuánshū dàikuān lǜbōqì	TBPF
Transmit block	发送块	Fāsòng kuài	
Transmit combiner assembly	传输合并器	Chuánshū hébìngqì	TCOA
Transmit degrade	发送劣化	Fāsòng lièhuà	TD
Transmit fail	发送失效	Fāsòng shīxiào	TF
Transmit front end shelf	传输前端架	Chuánshū qiánduānjià	TFES
Transmit objective loudness result	发送客观响度评定值	Fāsòng kèguān xiǎngdù píngdìngzhí	TOLR
Transmit power control	发射功率控制	Fāshè gōnglǜ kòngzhì	TPC
Transmit up-converter board	传送增频变频器板	Chuánsòng zēngpín biànpínqì bǎn	TUCB
Transmittal	传送进程	Chuánsòng jìnchéng	
Transmitted reference-phase shift keying	发送参考相移键控	Fāsòng cānkǎo xiàngyí jiànkòng	TRPSK
Transmitted wave (in a transmission line)	传输波	Chuánshū bō	
Transmitted waveform amplitude	输出波形幅度	Shūchū bōxíng fúdù	TLA
Transmitter	发射机	Fāshèjī	
Transmitter	发送机	Fāsòngjī	Tx
Transmitter attack time	发射机启动时间	Fāshèjī qǐdòng shíjiān	
Transmitter combiner	发射机合路器	Fāshèjī hélùqì	
Transmitter continuous disturbance	发信机的连续骚扰	Fāxìnjīde liánxù sāorǎo	CT
Transmitter cooling system	发射机冷却系统	Fāshèjī lěngquè xìtǒng	
Transmitter distortion	发报机畸变	Fābàojī jībiàn	
Transmitter duty cycle distortion	工作周期失真	Gōngzuò zhōuqī shīzhēn	TDCD
Transmitter frequency	发射机效率	Fāshèjī xiàolǜ	
Transmitter maximum permissible frequency deviation	发射机最大允许频偏	Fāshèjī zuìdà yǔnxǔ pínpiān	
Transmitter maximum permissible phase deviation	发射机最大允许相偏	Fāshèjī zuìdà yǔnxǔ xiāngpiān	
Transmitter power supply board	发射机电源板	Fāshèjī diànyuán bǎn	PWT
Transmitter sideband spectrum	发射机边带频谱	Fāshèjī biāndài pínpǔ	
Transmitter transient disturbance	发信机的瞬态骚扰	Fāxìnjīde shùntài sāorǎo	TT
Transmitter/transmission	发信机/发射	Fāxìnjī/ Fāshè	Tx
Transmitting station	发射台	Fāshètái	
Transmultiplexer	复用转换器	Fùyòng zhuǎnhuànqì	TMUX
Trans-multiplexer	子速率复用器	Zisùlǜ fùyòngqì	TMUX
Transpacific cable	横渡太平洋的海底电缆	Héngdù Tàipíngyángde hǎidǐ diànlǎn	TPC
Transparency	透明度	Tòumíngdù	
Transparency (video term)	透明状效果	Tòumíng zhuàng xiàoguǒ	
Transparent	简明的	Jiǎnmíngde	T

Transparent blitting	透明位块传输	Tòumíng wèikuài chuánshū	
Transparent bridging	透明桥接	Tòumíng qiáojiē	
Transparent data transfer phase	透明的数据传送阶段	Tòumíngde shùjù chuánsòng jiēduàn	
Transparent field descriptor	透明字段描述符	Tòumíng zìduàn miáoshù fú	
Transparent multiplexing equipment	透明复用设备	Tòumíng fùyòng shèbèi	TMUX
Transparent repeater	透明中继器	Tòumíng zhōngjìqì	
Transparent tone-in-band single sideband	透明带内导频单边带	Tòumíng dàinèi dǎopín dānbiāndài	TTIB
Transparent transponder	透明转发器	Tòumíng zhuǎnfāqì	
Transponder	差转机	Chàzhuǎnjī	
Transponder (in radio communication)	转发器	Zhuǎnfāqì	
Transponder (telecom)	转换器	Zhuǎnhuànqì	
Transport	传送	Chuánsòng	
Transport adapter layer interface	传输适配层接口	Chuánshū shìpèicéng jiēkǒu	TALI
Transport address	传送地址	Chuánsòng dìzhǐ	
Transport channel	传输信道	Chuánshū xìndào	
Transport channel	传送信道	Chuánsòng xìndào	TrCH
Transport connection	运输连接	Yùnshū liánjiē	TC
Transport connection endpoint	运输层联接端点	Yùnshū céng liánjiē duāndiǎn	TCEP
Transport control block	传送控制块	Chuánsòng kòngzhì kuài	TCB
Transport control protocol	传送控制协议	Chuánsòng kòngzhì xiéyì	TCP
Transport control protocol/Internet protocol	传输控制协议/互联网协议	Chuánshū kòngzhì xiéyì/hùliánwǎng xiéyì	TCP/IP
Transport entity	传送实体	Chuánsòng shítǐ	
Transport format	传送格式	Chuánsòng géshi	TF
Transport format combination	传送格式组合	Chuánsòng géshi zǔhé	TFC
Transport format combination indicator	传送格式组合指示器	Chuánsòng géshi zǔhé zhǐshìqì	TFCI
Transport format combination set	传送格式组合集	Chuánsòng géshi zǔhé jí	TFCS
Transport format indicator	传送格式指示器	Chuánsòng géshi zhǐshìqì	TFI
Transport format set	传送格式集	Chuánsòng géshi jí	TFS
Transport function	传送功能	Chuánsòng gōngnéng	TF
Transport layer	传送层	Chuánsòng céng	TL
Transport layer	运输层	Yùnshū céng	
Transport layer protocol	传输层协议	Chuánshū céng xiéyì	
Transport layer protocol (in ISO's OSI)	传输层协议	Chuánshū céng xiéyì	TP
Transport layer security	传输层安全	Chuánshū céng ānquán	TLS
Transport layer security	传输层安全性	Chuánshū céng ānquánxìng	TLS
Transport layer security protocol	安全传输层协议	Ānquán chuánshū céng xiéyì	TLS
Transport media	传送媒体	Chuánsòng méitǐ	TM
Transport network	传送网	Chuánsòng wǎng	
Transport network layer	传送网络层	Chuánsòng wǎngluò céng	
Transport path	传送通道	Chuánsòng tōngdào	TP
Transport plane	传送平面	Chuánsòng píngmiàn	TP
Transport processing function	传送处理功能	Chuánsòng chǔlǐ gōngnéng	
Transport protocol data unit	传送协议数据单元	Chuánsòng xiéyì shùjù dānyuán	TPDU
Transport protocol data unit	运输协议数据单元	Yùnshū xiéyì shùjù dānyuán	TPDU
Transport serial number	传送顺序号	Chuánsòng shùnxù hào	TSN
Transport service	运输服务	Yùnshū fúwù	TS

Transport service access point	传输服务存取点	Chuánshū fúwù cúnqǔdiǎn	TSAP
Transport service access point	传送服务接入点	Chuánsòng fúwù jiērù diǎn	TSAP
Transport service access point	运输服务访问点	Yùnshū fúwù fǎngwèn diǎn	TSAP
Transport service data unit	运输服务数据单元	Yùnshū fúwù shùjù dānyuán	TSDU
Transport signaling gateway	传送信令网关	Chuánsòng xìnlìng wǎngguān	T-SGW
Transport terminal function	传送终端功能	Chuánsòng zhōngduān gōngnéng	TTF
Transport test	运输试验	Yùnshū shìyàn	
Transportable automatic digital switch	可移动式自动数字交换机	Kěyídòng-shì zìdòng shùzì jiāohuànjī	TADS
Transporting zone	输送区	Shūsòng qū	
Transport-level protocol 4	第四类运输层协议	Dìsìlèi yùnshū céng xiéyì	TP4
Transposed matrix	转置矩阵	Zhuǎnzhì jǔzhèn	
Transposition (in switching)	变位	Biànwèi	
Transverse (or lateral) offset loss	横向错位损耗	Héngxiàng cuòwèi sǔnhào	
Transverse electric mode	横电模	Héngdiàn mó	TE
Transverse electromagnetic mode	横电磁模	Héngdiàncí mó	TEM
Transverse electromagnetic wave cell (TEM cell)	恒电磁波小室	Héngdiàncí bō xiǎoshì	
Transverse judder	横向抖动	Héngxiàng dǒudòng	
Transverse magnetic mode	横磁模	Héngcí mó	TM
Transverse wave	横向波	Héngxiàng bō	
Trap	阀门	Fámén	
Trap	陷阱	Xiànjǐng	
Trap door	暗入口	Àn rùkǒu	
Trapdoor (computer hacking)	陷门	Xiànmén	
Trapezoidal modulation	梯调	Tītiáo	
Trapezoidal modulation	梯形调制	Tīxíng tiáozhì	
Trapped mode tropospheric propagation	陷波模式对流层传播	Xiànbō móshì duìliúcéng chuánbō	
Trash	回收站	Huíshōuzhàn	
Traveling salesman problem	旅行商问题	Lǚxíng shāng wèntí	TSP
Traveling wave (in a transmission line)	行波	Xíngbō	
Traveling wave antenna	行波天线	Xíngbō tiānxiàn	TWA
Traveling wave tube	行波管	Xíngbōguǎn	TWT
Traveling wave tube amplifier	行波管放大器	Xíngbōguǎn fàngdàqì	TWTA
Travelling wave coefficient	行波系数	Xíngbō xìshù	
Travelling wave modulator	行波形调变器	Xíngbō-xíng tiáobiànqì	
Travel-time	时间项图	Shíjiān xiàngtú	
Travel-time curve	走时曲线	Zǒushí qūxiàn	
Traverse	遍历	Biànlì	
Traverse	横断线	Héngduàn xiàn	
Traversing binary tree	遍历二叉树	Biànlì èr chā shù	
Traversing graph	遍历图	Biànlì tú	
Tree	树	Shù	
Tree and branch architecture	树型-分支结构	Shù-xíng—fēnzhī jiégòu	
Tree and tabular combined notation	树表结合表示	Shù biǎo jiéhé biǎoshì	TTCN
Tree and tabular combined notation	树形和板状的组合标志	Shùxíng hé bǎnzhuàngde zǔhé biāozhì	TTCN
Tree coupler	树型耦合器	Shù-xíng ǒuhéqì	
Tree index	树型索引	Shù-xíng suǒyǐn	

Tree optical coupler	树状分支光纤耦合器	Shù-zhuàng fēnzhī guāngxiān ǒuhéqì	
Tree tabular combined notation	数表结合的表示法	Shùbiǎo jiéhéde biǎoshì fǎ	TTCN
Tree traversal	树遍历	Shù biànlì	
Tree traversal	树的遍历	Shùde biànlì	
Tree-based multicast	树状多播	Shù-zhuàng duōbō	
Trellis coded modulation	格码调制	Gémǎ tiáozhì	TCM
Trellis coded modulation	格形编码调制	Géxíng biānmǎ tiáozhì	TCM
Trellis coded modulation	格栅编码调制	Gézhà biānmǎ tiáozhì	TCM
Trellis coded modulation	格状编码调制	Gézhuàng biānmǎ tiáozhì	TCM
Trellis coded modulation	网格编码调制	Wǎnggé biānmǎ tiáozhì	TCM
Trellis coded pulse amplitude modulation	格栅编码脉冲幅度调制	Gézhà biānmǎ màichōng fúdù tiáozhì	TCPAM
Trellis encoding	网格编码	Wǎnggé biānmǎ	TE
Trench bank, trench ridge	沟坎	Gōukǎn	
Trenching	挖沟	Wāgōu	
Trial run period	试运行阶段	Shìyùnxíng jiēduàn	
Triangular irregular network	不规则三角网	Bùguīzé sānjiǎo wǎng	TIN
Triangular matrix	三角矩阵	Sānjiǎo jǔzhèn	
Triangular noise	三角噪声	Sānjiǎo zàoshēng	
Triangular routing	三角路由	Sānjiǎo lùyóu	
Triangulation	三角剖分	Sānjiǎo pōufēn	
Triangulation	三角网格化	Sānjiǎo wǎnggéhuà	
Triangulation station	三角点	Sānjiǎo diǎn	
Tributary (SDH term)	支路	Zhīlù	TR
Tributary unit	支路单元	Zhīlù dānyuán	TU
Tributary unit alarm indication signal	支路单元告警指示信号	Zhīlù dānyuán gàojǐng zhǐshì xìnhào	TU-AIS
Tributary unit group	支路单元组	Zhīlù dānyuán zǔ	TUG
Tributary unit loss of pointer	支路单元指针丢失	Zhīlù dānyuán zhǐzhēn diūshī	TU-LOP
Tributary unit payload processing	支路净荷处理	Zhīlù jìnghé chǔlǐ	TUPP
Tributary unit pointer	支路单元指针	Zhīlù dānyuán zhǐzhēn	TU PTR
Tributary unit pointer	支路单元指针	Zhīlù dānyuán zhǐzhēn	TUP
Tributary unit/administrative unit	支路单元/管理单元	Zhīlù dānyuán/guǎnlǐ dānyuán	TU/AU
Tributary unit-loss of multi-frame	支路单元复帧丢失	Zhīlù dānyuán fù zhèng diūshī	TU-LOM
Tridimensional datum	三维基准面	Sānwéi jīzhǔnmiàn	
Trigger (for database)	触发器	Chùfāqì	
Trigger circuit	触发电路	Chùfā diànlù	
Trigger circuit	触发电路	Chùfā diànlù	
Trigger detection point	触发检出点	Chùfā jiǎnchū diǎn	TDP
Trigger detection point-notification	触发检测点 - 通知	Chùfā jiǎncè diǎn-tōngzhī	TDP-N
Trigger detection point-notification	触发检出点——通知	Chùfā jiǎnchū diǎn-tōngzhī	TDP-N
Trigger detection point-request	触发检测点 - 请求	Chùfā jiǎncè diǎn-qǐngqiú	TDP-R
Trigger detection point-request	触发检出点——请求	Chùfā jiǎnchū diǎn-qǐngqiú	TDP-R
Trigger DP-notification	触发 DP 通知	Chùfā DP tōngzhī	TDP-N
Trigger DP-request	触发 DP 请求	Chùfā DP qǐngqiú	TDP-R
Trigger model	触发器模型	Chùfāqì móxíng	
Triggered transaction	被触发事务	Bèichùfā shìwù	
Triggered update	触发更新	Chùfā gēngxīn	

Triggering transaction	触发事务	Chùfā shìwù	
Trihedral corner reflector	三面角形反射器	Sānmiànjiǎoxíng fǎnshèqì	
Trilateration	三角侧面化	Sānjiǎo cèmiànhuà	
Trilinear filtering (video term)	三线性过滤	Sānxiànxing guòlǜ	
Trilinear MIP mapping	三次线性 MIP 材质贴图	Sāncì xiànxìng MIP cáizhì tiē tú	TMIPM
Triode AC switch	三极管交流开关	Sānjíguǎn jiāoliú kāiguān	TRIAC
Triple coated fiber structure	三芯光纤结构	Sānxīn guāngxiān jiégòu	TCFS
Triple code [tentative definition]	三连码	Sān lián mǎ	
Triple data encryption standard	三重数字加密标准	Sānchóng shùzì jiāmì biāozhǔn	Triple-DES
Triple error	三位差错	Sānwèi chācuò	
Triplet byte	三位字节	Sānwèi zìjié	
Triplet harmonics	三次谐波序列	Sāncì xiébō xùliè	
Tri-service Joint Tactical Communications System	三军联合战术通信系统	Sānjūn liánhé zhànshù tōngxìn xìtǒng	TRI-TAC
Tri-technology sensor	三鉴传感器	Sānjiàn chuángǎnqì	TTS
Trivial entertainment news	软新闻	Ruǎn xīnwén	
Trivial file transfer protocol	简单文件传输协议	Jiǎndān wénjiàn chuánshū xiéyì	TFTP
Trivial file transfer protocol	简单文件传送协议	Jiǎndān wénjiàn chuánsòng xiéyì	TFTP
Trivial file transfer protocol	简易文件传输协议	Jiǎnyì wénjiàn chuánshū xiéyì	TFTP
Trivial file transfer protocol	平凡文件传输协议	Píngfán wénjiàn chuánshū xiéyì	TFTP
Trivial file transfer protocol	普通文件传送协议	Pǔtōng wénjiàn chuánsòng xiéyì	TFTP
Trivial file transfer protocol	一般文件传输协议	Yībān wénjiàn chuánshū xiéyì	TFTP
Trojan horse	木马	Mùmǎ	
Trojan horse	特洛伊木马	Tè-luò-yī mùmǎ	
Trojan horse program	木马程式	Mùmǎ chéngshì	
Troposphere	对流层	Duìliúcéng	
Troposphere duct	对流层波道	Duìliúcéng bōdào	
Troposphere scatter propagation	对流层散射传播	Duìliúcéng sǎnshè chuánbō	
Tropospheric propagation	对流层传播	Duìliúcéng chuánbō	
Tropospheric scatter	对流层散射	Duìliúcéng sǎnshè	
Trouble recorder	故障记录器	Gùzhàng jìlùqì	TRR
True Wave fiber © (Lucent product)	真波光纤	Zhēnbō guāngxiān	
Truncate	截断	Jiéduàn	
Truncated differential cryptanalysis	截断差分密码分析	Jiéduàn chāfēn mìmǎ fēnxī	
Truncation	舍位	Shèwèi	
Trunk (TCOM); bus (computer use)	母线	Mǔxiàn	
Trunk access – bus	中继接入-总线	Zhōngjì jiērù—zǒngxiàn	TA-BUS
Trunk amplifier	干线放大器	Gànxiàn fàngdàqì	TA
Trunk amplifier	中继放大器	Zhōngjì fàngdàqì	TA
Trunk block connector	长途中继线接续设备	Chángtú zhōngjìxiàn jiēxù shèbèi	TBC
Trunk cable	干线电缆	Gànxiàn diànlǎn	
Trunk card	干线卡	Gànxiàn kǎ	
Trunk circuit	长途电路	Chángtú diànlù	
Trunk circuit	中继电路	Zhōngjì diànlù	
Trunk circuit network	长途电路网	Chángtú diànlù wǎng	
Trunk code	长途区号	Chángtú qūhào	
Trunk concentrator	中继集线器	Zhōngjì jíxiànqì	

Trunk coupling unit	干线耦合单元	Gànxiàn ǒuhé dānyuán	TCU
Trunk distribution frame	中继线配线架	Zhōngjìxiàn pèixiànjià	TDF
Trunk gateway	中继网关	Zhōngjì wǎngguān	TGW
Trunk group	中继线群	Zhōngjìxiàn qún	
Trunk group (in multicast)	主干组	Zhǔgàn zǔ	
Trunk line	干线	Gànxiàn	
Trunk line	中继线	Zhōngjìxiàn	
Trunk line network	中继线网络	Zhōngjìxiàn wǎngluò	TLN
Trunk line switch	中继链路开关	Zhōngjì liànlù kāiguān	TLSW
Trunk line unmanned re-amplifier	中继线无人赠音站	Zhōngjìxiàn wúrén zèngyīn zhàn	ZW
Trunk media gateway	干线媒体网关	Gànxiàn méitǐ wǎngguān	TMG
Trunk mobile communications	集群移动通信	Jíqún yídòng tōngxìn	
Trunk regenerator	再生中继设备	Zàishēng zhōngjì shèbèi	REG
Trunk test unit	中继测试单元	Zhōngjì cèshì dānyuán	
Trunk up-down	干线升降	Gànxiàn shēngjiàng	TUD
Trunk; relay	中继	Zhōngjì	
Trunked base station	集群基站	Jíqún jīzhàn	
Trunked mobile communication system	集群移动电话系统	Jíqún yídòng diànhuà xìtǒng	
Trunked radio	中继式无线电	Zhōngjìshì wúxiàndiàn	TR
Trunked radio system	集群无线通信系统	Jíqún wúxiàn tōngxìn xìtǒng	
Trunked system	集群系统	Jíqún xìtǒng	
Trunked telephone connect	集群电话互连	Jíqún diànhuà hùlián	
Trunked telephone connector	集群电话互连器	Jíqún diànhuà hùliánqì	
Trunking	集群	Jíqún	
Trunking communications system	集群通信系统	Jíqún tōngxìn xìtǒng	
Trunking efficiency	集群效率	Jíqún xiàolǜ	
Trust	信任	Xìnrèn	
Trust policy	信任策略	Xìnrèn cèlüè	TP
Trusted computer security evaluation criteria	可信计算机安全评级准则	Kěxìn jìsuànjī ānquán píngjí zhǔnzé	TCSEC
Trusted computer system	可信计算机系统	Kěxìn jìsuànjī xìtǒng	
Trusted computing base	可信计算基	Kěxìn jìsuàn jī	TCB
Trusted computing base (ISO security)	可信计算库	Kěxìn jìsuàn kù	TCB
Trusted connection	信任连接	Xìnrèn liánjiē	
Trusted database system	可信数据库系统	Kěxìn shùjùkù xìtǒng	TDBS
Trusted interface unit (ISO security)	可信接入单元	Kěxìn jiērù dānyuán	TIU
Trusted introducer	可信介绍人	Kěxìn jièshàorén	
Trusted network entity	可信网络实体	Kěxìn wǎngluò shítǐ	
Trusted path (IPsec)	可信通路	Kěxìn tōnglù	
Trusted software	可信软件	Kěxìn ruǎnjiàn	
Trusted third party	受托第三方	Shòutuō dìsānfāng	TTP
Trusted third party	中立第三方	Zhōnglì dìsānfāng	TTP
Trusted third party (IPsec)	可信任的第三方	Kěxìnrènde dì sān fāng	TTP
Truth table	真值表	Zhēnzhíbiǎo	
TSB control	TSB 控制	TSB kòngzhì	TCO
TSB interface E1 board assembly	TSB E1 接口集成板	TSB E1 jiēkǒu jíchéngbǎn	TIEA
TSB interface T1 board assembly	TSB T1 接口集成板	TSB T1 jiēkǒu jíchéngbǎn	TITA

Tunable dispersion compensator	可调色散补偿器	Kětiáo sèsàn bǔchángqì	TDC
Tunable filter	可调滤波器	Kětiáo lǜbōqì	
Tunable filter (optical)	可调式滤光镜	Kětiáo-shì lǜguāngjìng	
Tunable wavelength laser diode	波长可调激光源	Bōcháng kětiáo jīguāng yuán	
Tunable-channel multi-access	可调信道多址	Kětiáo xìndào duōzhǐ	TCMA
Tuned amplifier	调谐放大器	Tiáoxié fàngdàqì	
Tuned mass damper	动吸振器	Dòng xīzhènqì	
Tungsten impregnated cathode ray gun (video)	钨传输阴级射线枪	Wū chuánshū yīnjí shèxiàn qiāng	TICRG
Tuning	调谐	Tiáoxié	
Tuning indicator	调谐指示器	Tiáoxié zhǐshìqì	
Tuning knob	调谐旋钮	Tiáoxié xuánniǔ	
Tuning screw	调节螺钉	Tiáojié luódīng	
Tuning slug	调节条	Tiáojié tiáo	
Tunnel broker (in IPv6)	隧道代理	Suìdào dàilǐ	
Tunnel drainage works	隧道排水工程	Suìdào páishuǐ gōngchéng	
Tunnel end point identifier	隧道端点标识符	Suìdào duāndiǎn biāozhìfú	TEID
Tunnel identifier	隧道标识符	Suìdào biāozhìfú	TID
Tunnel transit time diode	隧道渡越时间二极管	Suìdào dùyuè shíjiān èrjíguǎn	TUNNETT
Tunnel; tunneling	隧道	Suìdào	
Tunneling	隧道技术	Suìdào jìshù	
Tunneling mode (IPsec)	隧道模式	Suìdào móshì	
Tunneling protocol (in GPRS)	隧道协议	Suìdào xiéyì	GTP
Tuple	元组	Yuánzǔ	
Tuple space search (for IP packet classification)	元组空间查找算法	Yuánzǔ kōngjiān cházhǎo suànfǎ	
Turbo Internet	高速因特网业务	Gāosù Yīntèwǎng yèwù	
Turbo newscast	高速新闻广播	Gāosù xīnwén guǎngbō	
Turbo webcast	高速网页广播	Gāosù wǎngyè guǎngbō	
Turn impedance	转向阻抗	Zhuǎnxiàng zǔkàng	
Turn rate of sight line	视线转率	Shìxiàn zhuǎn lǜ	
Turn-around time	换向时间	Huànxiàng shíjiān	
Turn-around time	周转时间	Zhōuzhuǎn shíjiān	
Turnkey project	交钥匙项目	Jiāo yàoshi xiàngmù	
Turnkey system	图奇系统	Túqí xìtǒng	
Turnstile antenna	绕杆式天线	Ràogānshì tiānxiàn	
Turntable	转向表	Zhuǎnxiàng biǎo	
Tweaking	补偿配置	Bǔcháng pèizhì	
Twice minimum power points	二倍最小功率点	Èrbèi zuìxiǎo gōnglǜ diǎn	
Twin cache architecture	双缓存结构	Shuāng huǎncún jiégòu	TCA
Twisted pair	对绞线	Duìjiǎo xiàn	TP
Twisted pair distributed data interface	双较线分布式数据接口	Shuāng jiàoxiàn Fēnbùshì shùjù jiēkǒu	TPDDI
Twisted wire pair	双扭线对	Shuāng niǔxiànduì	TWP
Two binary one quaternary	两个二进制一个四进制编码	Liǎnggè èrjìnzhì yīgè sìjìnzhì biānmǎ	2B1Q
Two byte code character	两字节编码字符	Liǎng zìjié biānmǎ zìfú	TBCC
Two dimension (i.e. planar) detector array	面型检光元件	Miàn-xíng jiǎn guāng yuánjiàn	
Two way alternate	双向交替	Shuāngxiàng jiāotì	TWA
Two way simultaneous	双向同时	Shuāngxiàng tóngshí	TWS

Two-address system	二地址系统	Èrdìzhǐ xìtǒng	
Two-cell	二单元	Èrdānyuán	
Two-condition	二态	Èrtài	
Two-dimensional	二维	Èrwéi	2D
Two-dimensional flat surface array	二维平面阵	Èrwéi píngmiàn zhèn	
Two-dimensional manifold	二维副本	Èrwéi fùběn	
Two-dimensional model	二维模型	Èrwéi móxíng	
Two-directional input	双向入力	Shuāngxiàng rùlì	
Two-fiber bi-directional path protection ring	二纤双向通道保护环	Èrxiān shuāngxiàng tōngdào bǎohù huán	
Two-fiber multiplex section shared protection ring	二纤双向复用段共享保护环	Èrxiān shuāngxiàng fùyòng duàn gòngxiǎng bǎohù huán	
Two-fiber unidirectional path protection ring	二纤单向通道保护环	Èrxiān dānxiàng tōngdào bǎohù huán	
Two-frequency system	二频制	Èrpín zhì	
Two-level screening design	两水平筛选设计	Liǎng shuǐpíng shāixuǎn shèjì	
Two-motion selector	双行程选择器	Shuāng xíngchéng xuǎnzéqì	
Two-phase commit	两相提交	Liǎng xiàng tíjiāo	
Two-phase commit (for database)	两阶段提交	Liǎng jiēduàn tíjiāo	
Two-phase lookup (for database)	两阶段查找	Liǎng jiēduàn cházhǎo	
Two-port	双端口	Shuāng duānkǒu	
Two-port network	双端口网络	Shuāng duānkǒu wǎngluò	
Two-signal method	双信号法	Shuāng xìnhào fǎ	
Two-signal method	双信号方法	Shuāngxìnhào fāngfǎ	
Two-stage least squares	二阶最小方乘法	Èrjiē zuìxiǎo fāngchéngfǎ	
Two-step activation	两步激活	Liǎngbù jīhuó	
Two-terminal network	二端网络	Èrduān wǎngluò	
Two-terminal-pair network	双端对网络	Shuāng duānduì wǎngluò	
Two-waveband radio telephone	双波段电台	Shuāng bōduàn diàntái	
Two-way alternate	双向交替	Shuāngxiàng jiāotì	TWA
Two-way paging	双向寻呼	Shuāngxiàng xúnhū	
Two-way power divider	二路功率分配器	Èrlù gōnglǜ fēnpèiqì	2WPD
Two-way simultaneous call	同时双向互发	Tóngshí shuāngxiàng hùfā	TWS
Two-way trust	双向信任	Shuāngxiàng xìnrèn	
Two-way, bilateral, both-ways	双向	Shuāngxiàng	
Two-wire analog interface	二线模拟接口	Èrxiàn mónǐ jiēkǒu	
Two-wire switching	二线交换	Èrxiàn jiāohuàn	
Two-wire system	二线制	Èrxiàn zhì	
Two-word instruction	二字指令	Èrzì zhǐlìng	
Type	类型	Lèixíng	
Type approval code	定型号码	Dìngxíng hàomǎ	TAC
Type approval code	鉴定类型码	Jiàndìng lèixíng mǎ	TAC
Type approval code	型号批准码	Xínghào pīzhǔn mǎ	TAC
Type area	版面	Bǎnmiàn	
Type of address	地址类型	Dìzhǐ lèixíng	TOA
Type of address /numbering plan identifier	地址类型/编号方案标识符	Dìzhǐ lèixíng/ biānhào fāng'àn biāozhì fú	TOA/NPI
Type of number	编号方式	Biānhào fāngshì	TON
Type of number	号码类型	Hàomǎ lèixíng	TON
Type of service	服务类型	Fúwù lèixíng	TOS

Type of service	业务类别	Yèwù lèibié	ToS
Type test	定型试验	Dìngxíng shìyàn	
Type-annotated assembler	带类型注解的汇编器	Dài lèixíng zhùjiěde huìbiānqì	TAAS
Type-length-value	类型长度值	Lèixíng chángdù zhí	TLV
Type-length-value	类型-长度-取值的编码格式	Lèixíng-chángdù-qǔzhíde biānmǎ géshi	TLV
Type-length-value	类型--长度--值	Lèixíng-chángdù-zhí	TLV
Typical installation (of software)	典型安装	Diǎnxíng ānzhuāng	

U

UE service capabilities	UE 业务容量	UE yèwù róngliàng	USC
Ultimate bearing capacity	极限承载力	Jíxiàn chéngzài lì	
Ultimate form	终地形	Zhōng dìxíng	
Ultimate lateral strength	极限水平耐力	Jíxiàn shuǐpíng nàilì	
Ultimate strength	极限强度	Jíxiàn qiángdù	
Ultimate strength design	极限强度设计	Jíxiàn qiángdù shèjì	
Ultra aperture terminal	超小口径卫星地面接收站	Chāoxiǎo kǒujìng wèixīng dìmiàn jiēshōu zhàn	UAT
Ultra direct memory access	超高速直接内存存取	Chāogāosù zhíjiē nèicún cúnqǔ	Ultra DMA
Ultra long-haul fiber	超长光传输	Chāocháng guāng chuánshū	ULH
Ultra long-haul optical transmission technology	超长光传输技术	Chāocháng guāng chuánshū jìshù	ULHOTT
Ultra narrowband filter (optical)	超窄频滤光镜	Chāozhǎi pínlǜ guāngjìng	
Ultra port architecture	超级端口结构	Chāojí duānkǒu jiégòu	UPA
Ultra small terminal mobile satellite communication system	超小型终端移动卫星通信系统	Chāoxiǎoxíng zhōngduān yídòng wèixīng tōngxìn xìtǒng	MSAT
Ultra-dense wavelength division multiplexing	超密集波分复用	Chāomìjí bōfēn fùyòng	UDWDM
Ultra-fine-pitch (in SMT)	超密脚距	Chāomì jiǎojù	
Ultra-high frequency	特高频	Tègāopín	UHF
Ultra-high-speed digital subscriber line	超高速数字用户线	Chāogāosù shùzì yònghù xiàn	UDSL
Ultra-longwave	超长波	Chāochángbō	
Ultra-low frequency	超低频	Chāodīpín	ULF
Ultra-short pulse source	超短脉冲光源	Chāoduǎn màichōng guāngyuán	
Ultra-shortwave	超短波	Chāoduǎnbō	
Ultrasonic wave	超音波	Chāoyīnbō	
Ultraviolet absorbing filter	紫外吸收滤光镜	Zǐwài xīshōu lǜguāngjìng	
Ultraviolet curing equipment	紫外线硬化设备	Zǐwàixiàn yìnghuà shèbèi	
Ultra-violet curing oven (semiconductor mfg)	紫外固化炉	Zǐwài gùhuà lú	
Ultra-violet curing oven (semiconductor mfg)	紫外硫化炉	Zǐwài liúhuà lú	
Ultraviolet light source	紫外线光源	Zǐwàixiàn guāngyuán	
Ultraviolet materials	紫外线材料	Zǐwàixiàn cáiliào	
Ultraviolet photodiode	紫外光二极体	Zǐwài guāng èrjítǐ	
Ultraviolet radiation	紫外辐射	Zǐwài fúshè	UV
Ultraviolet transmitting filter	紫外透过滤光镜	Zǐwài tòuguò lǜguāngjìng	
Ultra-wideband	超宽带	Chāokuāndài	
Ultra-wideband optical fiber amplifier	超宽带光纤放大器	Chāokuāndài guāngxiān fàngdàqì	UWOA
Umbrella antenna	伞形天线	Sǎnxíng tiānxiàn	
Umbrella antenna	伞状天线	Sǎnzhuàng tiānxiàn	
Umbrella reflector antenna	伞形反射器天线	Sǎnxíng fǎnshèqì tiānxiàn	

English	Chinese	Pinyin	Abbr.
UMTS mobile services switching center	UMTS 移动业务交换中心	UMTS yídòng yèwù jiāohuàn zhōngxīn	UMSC
UMTS radio access network	UMTS 无线接入网	UMTS wúxiàn jiērù wǎng	URAN
Unable to comply	无法遵循	Wúfǎ zūnxún	UTC
Unacknowledged information transfer mode	非证实信息传送方式	Fēizhèngshí xìnxī chuánsòng fāngshì	
Unacknowledged information transfer service	不确认式信息传送服务	Bùquèrènshì xìnxī chuánsòng fúwù	UITS
Unacknowledged mode	无应答模式	Wúyìngdá móshì	UM
Unacknowledged operation	无证实操作	Wúzhèngshí cāozuò	
Unallocated-number, vacant number	空号	Kōnghào	UNN
Unary function (in computer programming)	单参函数	Dāncān hánshù	
Unary operator (in computer programming)	一元操作符	Yīyuán cāozuò fú	
Unassigned cell	未分配信元	Wèifēnpèi xìnyuán	
Unattended answering accessory	无人管理应答辅助设备	Wúrén guǎnlǐ yìngdá fǔzhù shèbèi	UNA
Unauthorized access	非授权存取	Fēishòuquán cúnqǔ	
Unauthorized access	未授权的访问	Wèishòuquánde fǎngwèn	
Unavailability	不可用性	Bùkěyòng xìng	
Unavailable second	不可用秒	Bùkěyòng miǎo	UAS
Unavailable time, down time	不可用时间	Bùkěyòng shíjiān	UAT
Unbalanced asynchronous class	不平衡操作的异步响应类别	Bùpínghéng cāozuòde yìbù xiǎngyìng lèibié	UAC
Unbalanced hierarchy	不均衡层次结构	Bùjūnhéng céngcì jiégòu	
Unbalanced impedance about ground	对地不平衡阻抗	Duìdì bùpínghéng zǔkàng	
Unbalanced normal class	不平衡操作的正常响应类别	Bùpínghéng cāozuòde zhèngcháng xiǎngyìng lèibié	UNC
Unbalanced quadrature phase shift keying	不平衡正交相移键控	Bùpínghéng zhèngjiāo xiāngyí jiànkòng	UQPSK
Unblock	解闭	Jiěbì	
Unblocking acknowledge	解闭证实	Jiěbì zhèngshí	
Unblocking acknowledgement signal	解除闭塞信号	Jiěchú bìsè xìnhào	UBA
Unblocking key	解锁密钥	Jiěsuǒ mìyào	
Unblocking procedure	解除阻塞程序	Jiěchú zǔsè chéngxù	
Unblocking request (ISUP message)	解除闭塞请求	Jiěchú bìsè qǐngqiú	UBL
Unblocking signal	解除闭塞信号	Jiěchú bìsèxìnhào	
Unboxing	拆箱	Chāi xiāng	
Unboxing	拆箱转换	Chāi xiāng zhuǎnhuàn	
Uncached speculative write combining	无缓冲思索联合写操作	Wúhuǎnchōng sīsuǒ liánhé xiě cāozuò	USWC
Uncertainty	不确定度	Bùquèdìngdù	
Uncompress, decompress	解压缩	Jiěyāsuō	
Unconfirmed service	非证实服务	Fēizhèngshí fúwù	
Unconfirmed-service	非证实型服务	Fēizhèngshíxíng fúwù	
Unconformity	不整合	Bùzhěng hé	
Unconformity plane	不整合面	Bùzhěng hé miàn	
Unconnected	未连接	Wèiliánjiē	UNC
Unconnected graph	非连通图	Fēiliántōng tú	
Unconnected message manager	非连接报文管理器	Fēiliánjiē bàowén guǎnlǐqì	UCMM
Unconnected signal	未连接信号	Wèiliánjiē xìnhào	
Unconstrained delay data	无约束时延的数据	Wúyuēshù shíyánde shùjù	UDD
Unconstrained non-linear regression	无约束非线性回归	Wúyuēshù fēixiànxìng huíguī	
Uncontrolled DTE not ready	非受控 DTE 未准许好	Fēishòukòng DTE wèi zhǔnxǔ hǎo	
Uncontrolled slip	不受控滑动	Bùshòukòng huádòng	

Uncontrolled slip	非受控滑动	Fēishòukòng huádòng	
Uncorrectable block	不可纠正块	Bùkějiūzhèng kuài	
Uncorrelated jitter	不相关抖动	Bùxiāngguān dǒudòng	
Undefined bit	未定义比特	Wèidìngyì bǐtè	
Undefined bit rate	未指定比特率	Wèizhǐdìng bǐtèlǜ	UBR
Undefined byte	未定义字节	Wèidìngyì zìjié	
Undeliverable remittance	无法退还汇款	Wúfǎ tuìhuán huìkuǎn	
Undeniable signature scheme (IPsec)	不可抵赖签名方案	Bùkědǐlài qiānmíng fāng'àn	
Under modulation	欠调制	Qiàntiáozhì	
Under unit test	被测单元	Bèicè dānyuán	UUT
Underflow	下限溢位	Xiàxiàn yì wèi	
Underflow	下溢	Xiàyì	
Underlap	脱节	Tuōjié	
Underline (WP command)	下划线	Xiàhuàxiàn	
Underlying network	底层网	Dǐcéng wǎng	
Underlying table	基础表	Jīchǔ biǎo	
Underwater laser communication	水下激光通信	Shuǐxià jīguāng tōngxìn	
Underwater telephone	水下电话	Shuǐxià diànhuà	
Underwriters Laboratories Inc. (US)	担保实验室	Dānbǎo shíyànshì	UL
Undetected fault time	未检出故障时间	Wèi jiǎnchū gùzhàng shíjiān	
Undirected graph	无向图	Wúxiàng tú	
Undo (WP command)	撤消	Chèxiāo	
Unenforced relationship	未强制关系	Wèiqiángzhì guānxi	
Unequal	未装载	Wèizhuāngzài	UNEQ
Unequal error protection	非同等错误保护	Fēitóngděng cuòwù bǎohù	UEP
Unequal-arm hybrid coil	不等臂混合线圈	Bùděng bì hùnhé xiànquān	
Unequipped	未装载	Wèizhuāngzài	UNEQ
Unequipped circuit	未装备电路	Wèizhuāngbèi diànlù	
Unequipped circuit identification code (ISUP message)	未装电路标志码	Wèizhuāng diànlù biāozhìmǎ	UCIC
Unexpected data value	非期望的数据值	Fēiqīwàngde shùjù zhí	
Unexpected message (IPsec TLS)	意外消息	Yìwài xiāoxi	
Unguarded interval	无监护间隔	Wújiānhù jiàngé	
UNI bearer capability	UNI 承载能力	UNI chéngzài nénglì	
Unicast	单播	Dānbō	
Unicast	单插	Dānchā	
Unicast	单目广播	Dānmù guǎngbō	
Unicast address	单点广播地址	Dāndiǎn guǎngbō dìzhǐ	
Unicast addressing	单向广播地址	Dānxiàng guǎngbō dìzhǐ	UA
Unicode	联合码	Liánhé mǎ	
Unicode	统一码	Tǒngyī mǎ	
Unidentified subscriber	未标识用户	Wèibiāozhì yònghù	
Unidimensional datum	单维基准	Dānwéi jīzhǔn	
Unidirectional control	单向控制	Dānxiàng kòngzhì	
Unidirectional microphone	单指向性传声器	Dānzhǐxiàng-xìng chuánshēngqì	UM
Uni-directional path switch ring	单向通道倒换环	Dānxiàng tōngdào dǎohuàn huán	UPSR
Uni-directional trail/connection type	单向路径/连接类型	Dānxiàng lùjìng/liánjiē lèixíng	

Uni-directional transmission	单向传输	Dānxiàng chuánshū	
Unifab Electronics Inc. (UK company)	英国联合电子制造公司	Yīngguó liánhé diànzǐ zhìzào gōngsī	
Unified access server	综合接入服务器	Zōnghé jiērù fúwùqì	UAS
Unified communications	统一通信	Tǒngyī tōngxìn	
Unified contact center	统一联络中心	Tǒngyī liánluò zhōngxīn	UCC
Unified memory architecture	统一内存架构	Tǒngyī nèicún jiàgòu	UMA
Unified message service	统一消息	Tǒngyī xiāoxi	UMS
Unified modeling language	标准建模语言	Biāozhǔn jiànmó yǔyán	UML
Unified modeling language	统一建模语言	Tǒngyī jiànmó yǔyán	UML
Unified modeling language	一致性建模语言	Yīzhìxìng jiànmó yǔyán	UML
Unified modelling language	统一模型语言	Tǒngyī móxíng yǔyán	UML
Unified system diagnostic manager	统一系统监测管理器	Tǒngyī xìtǒng jiāncè guǎnlǐqì	USDM
Unified TMN requirement, analysis and design	统一 TMN 需求、分析和设计	Tǒngyī TMN xūqiú、fēnxī hé shèjì	UTRAD
Uniform (universal) resource locator	划一资讯位址	Huàyī zīxùn wèizhǐ	URL
Uniform distribution	均匀分布	Jūnyún fēnbù	
Uniform encoding	均匀编码	Jūnyún biānmǎ	
Uniform flow	均匀流	Jūnyún liú	
Uniform geometric theory of diffraction	一致性几何绕射理论	Yīzhìxìng jǐhé ràoshè lǐlùn	UTD
Uniform numbering	等位编号	Děngwèi biānhào	
Uniform PCM interface	同一标准的 PCM 接口	Tóngyī biāozhǔnde PCM jiēkǒu	UPCMI
Uniform quantizing	均匀量化	Jūnyún liànghuà	
Uniform resource identifier	统一资源标识符	Tǒngyī zīyuán biāozhìfú	URI
Uniform resource locator	统一资源定位地址	Tǒngyī zīyuán dìngwèi dìzhǐ	URL
Uniform resource locator	统一资源定位器(符)	Tǒngyī zīyuán dìngwèiqì (fú)	URL
Uniform resource locator	通用链接定位	Tōngyòng liànjiē dìngwèi	URL
Uniform transmission line	均匀传输线	Jūnyún chuánshūxiàn	
Uniform waveguide	均匀波导	Jūnyún bōdǎo	
Uniform-flow equation	均匀流公式	Jūnyún liú gōngshì	
Uniformity check	一致性检查	Yīzhìxìng jiǎnchá	
Uniformity coefficient	均等系数	Jūnděng xìshù	
Uninstaller	反装置器	Fǎnzhuāngzhìqì	
Uninsured traffic	无保障的通信	Wúbǎozhàngde tōngxìn	
Unintelligible crosstalk	不可懂串音	Bùkědǒng chuànyīn	
Uninterpreted (IPsec)	未解释	Wèijiěshì	
Uninterruptible power supply	不间断电源设备	Bùjiànduàn diànyuán shèbèi	UPS
Union query (for database)	联合查询	Liánhé cháxún	
Unipole antenna	单极天线	Dānjí tiānxiàn	UA
Unique constraint (in SQL Server)	惟一性约束	Wéiyīxìng yuēshù	
Unique index (for database)	唯一索引	Wéiyī suǒyǐn	
Unique values	单值	Dānzhí	
Unisys (US company)	优利	Yōulì	
Unit driver	装置驱动器	Zhuāngzhì qūdòngqì	UD
Unit element	单位码元	Dānwèi mǎyuán	
Unit impulse response	单位冲激响应，	Dānwèi chōngjī xiǎngyìng	
Unit interval	单位间隔	Dānwèi jiàngé	UI

English	Chinese	Pinyin	Abbreviation
Unit interval	单元间隔	Dānyuán jiàngé	UI
Unit of measurement	测量单位	Cèliáng dānwèi	
Unit pulse response	单位脉冲响应	Dānwèi màichōng xiǎngyìng	
Unit scaling	单位标尺	Dānwèi biāochǐ	
Unit separator	单元分隔	Dānyuán fēngé	US
Unit weight	单位体积重量	Dānwèi tǐjī zhònglìang	
Unitary service	统一业务	Tǒngyī yèwù	US
United Microelectronics Corp. (Taiwan semiconductor maker)	联华电子公司	Liánhuá diànzǐ gōngsī	UMC
United Nations Commission on International Trade Law	联合国国际贸易法委员会	Liánhéguó guójì màoyìfǎ wěiyuánhuì	UNCITRAL
United States Geological Survey	美国地质调查所	Měiguó dìzhì diàochá suǒ	
United States National Map Accuracy Standard	美国国家地图精度标准	Měiguó guójiā dìtú jīngdù biāozhǔn	USNMAS
United States Naval Observatory	美国海军天文台	Měiguó hǎijūn tiānwéntái	USNO
United symbol time	组合符号时间	Zǔhé fúhào shíjiān	UST
Unitube optical cable	中心束管光缆	Zhōngxīn shùguǎn guānglǎn	
Unity gain	总体增益	Zǒngtǐ zēngyì	
Univariate analysis	单变量分析	Dānbiànliàng fēnxī	
Universal access	普遍接入	Pǔbiàn jiērù	
Universal access number	通用接入号码	Tōngyòng jiērù hàomǎ	UAN
Universal ADSL Working Group	通用 ADSL 工作组	Tōngyòng ADSL gōngzuòzǔ	UAWG
Universal asynchronous digital subscriber line	通用非对称数字用户线	Tōngyòng fēiduìchèn shùzì yònghù xiàn	UADSL
Universal asynchronous receiver/transmitter	通用异步接收/发送装置	Tōngyòng yìbù jiēshōu/fāsòng zhuāngzhì	UART
Universal asynchronous receiver/transmitter	通用异步收/发器	Tōngyòng yìbù shōu/fāqì	UART
Universal audio server	通用话音服务器	Tōngyòng huàyīn fúwùqì	UAS
Universal character set 2	集合 2 通用符号	Jíhé er tōngyòng fúhào	UCS2
Universal coordinated time	世界协调时	Shìjiè xiétiáo shí	UTC
Universal data access	万能数据访问	Wànnéng shùjù fǎngwèn	UDA
Universal description, discovery and integration protocol	通用描述发现和集成协议	Tōngyòng miáoshù fāxiàn hé jíchéng xiéyì	UDDI
Universal face	完整面	Wánzhěng miàn	
Universal integrated circuit card	通用集成电路卡	Tōngyòng jíchéng diànlù kǎ	UICC
Universal Kriging	泛克里津插值法	Fàn kè-lǐ-jīn chāzhí fǎ	
Universal Memory System (Intel Corp.)	通用存储器系统	Tōngyòng cúnchǔqì xìtǒng	UMS
Universal messaging service	通用信息传送服务	Tōngyòng xìnxī chuánsòng fúwù	UMS
Universal mobile telecommunication system	通用移动通信系统	Tōngyòng yídòng tōngxìn xìtǒng	UMTS
Universal mobile telecommunications system	通用移动电信系统	Tōngyòng yídòng diànxìn xìtǒng	UMTS
Universal mobile telecommunications system subscriber identity module	通用移动通信系统用户识别模块	Tōngyòng yídòng tōngxìn xìtǒng yònghù shíbié mókuài	USIM
Universal mobile telecommunications system-terrestrial radio access	通用移动通信系统地面无线接入	Tōngyòng yídòng tōngxìn xìtǒng dìmiàn wúxiàn jiērù	UTRA
Universal multiple-octet coded character set	通用多 8 位编码字符集	Tōngyòng duō bāwèi biānmǎ zìfú jí	UCS
Universal naming convention (UNC) name	通用命名规则名称	Tōngyòng mìngmíng guīzé míngchēng	
Universal object naming	通用对象命名	Tōngyòng duìxiàng mìngmíng	UON
Universal personal telecommunication number	通用个人电信号码	Tōngyòng gèrén diànxìn hàomǎ	UPTN
Universal personal telecommunications	通用个人通信	Tōngyòng gèrén tōngxìn	UPT
Universal plug and play	通用即插即用	Tōngyòng jí chā jíyòng	UpnP
Universal private telecommunication	通用专线通信	Tōngyòng zhuānxiàn tōngxìn	UPT

Universal product code	通用产品代码	Tōngyòng chǎnpǐn dàimǎ	UPC
Universal resource locator	全球资源位置符	Quánqiú zīyuán wèizhifú	URL
Universal resource locator	通用资源定位符	Tōngyòng zīyuán dìngwèifú	URL
Universal resource locator	通用资源定位器	Tōngyòng zīyuán dìngwèiqì	URL
Universal serial bus	通用串行总线	Tōngyòng chuànháng zǒngxiàn	USB
Universal serial bus	通用串联总线	Tōngyòng chuànlián zǒngxiàn	USB
Universal serial bus device class definition for printing devices	打印设备的通用串行总线级标准	Dǎyìn shèbèide tōngyòng chuànháng zǒngxiàn jí biāozhǔn	USBDCDPD
Universal service	普遍服务	Pǔbiàn fúwù	
Universal Service Fund	普遍服务基金	Pǔbiàn fúwù jījīn	USF
Universal signaling back panel	通用信号后面板	Tōngyòng xìnhào hòumian bǎn	USBP
Universal subscriber identity module	普通用户识别模块	Pǔtōng yònghù shíbié mókuài	USIM
Universal terrestrial radio access	通用地面无线接入	Tōngyòng dìmiàn wúxiàn jiērù	UTRA
Universal terrestrial radio access network	通用陆地无线接入网络	Tōngyòng lùdì wúxiàn jiērù wǎngluò	UTRAN
Universal Time	世界时	Shìjiè shí	UT
Universal time	通用时间	Tōngyòng shíjiān	UT
Universal time	宇宙时	Yǔzhòu shí	UT
Universal time clock	通用时钟	Tōngyòng shízhōng	UTC
Universal time constant	通用世界时	Tōngyòng shìjièshí	UTC
Universal time coordinate	通用时间坐标	Tōngyòng shíjiān zuòbiāo	UTC
Universal Transverse Mercator	通用横轴墨卡托	Tōngyòng héngzhóu mò-kǎ-tuō	UTM
Universal Transverse Mercator grid projection	通用横轴墨卡托投影栅格	Tōngyòng héngzhóu Mò-kǎ-tuō tóuyǐng zhàgé	
Universal unique identifier	通用唯一标识	Tōngyòng wéiyī biāozhì	UUID
Universal Wireless Communication Council	全球无线通信协会	Quánqiú wúxiàn tōngxìn xiéhuì	UWCC
Universal wireless communications	通用无线通信	Tōngyòng wúxiàn tōngxìn	UWC
Universal wireless communications consortium	通用无线通信协议	Tōngyòng wúxiàn tōngxìn xiéyì	UWCC
Universe polygon	边界多边形	Biānjiè duōbiānxíng	
Unknown subscriber	不认识的用户	Bùrènshide yònghù	
Unload cable	非加感电缆	Fēijiāgǎn diànlǎn	
Unlocked frequency	失锁频率	Shīsuǒ pínlǜ	
Unmanaged code	非受控代码	Fēishòukòng dàimǎ	
Unmanaged code	非托管代码	Fēituōguǎn dàimǎ	
Unmodified	非更改	Fēigēnggǎi	NO-MODIFY
Unnumbered acknowledge	无编号确认	Wúbiānhào quèrèn	UA
Unnumbered acknowledge	无编号证实	Wúbiānhào zhèngshí	UA
Unnumbered frames	无编号帧	Wúbiānhào zhèng	UF
Unnumbered frames	无计数帧	Wújìshù zhèng	
Unnumbered information	无编号信息	Wúbiānhào xìnxī	UI
Unnumbered information (frame)	无序信息（帧）	Wúxù xìnxī (zhèng)	UI
Unnumbered information frame	通用信息帧	Tōngyòng xìnxī zhèng	UI
Unnumbered information frame	无编号信息帧	Wúbiānhào xìnxī zhèng	UI
Unordered pair	无序对	Wúxù duì	
Unordered tree	无序数	Wúxù shù	
Unperturbed orbit (of a satellite)	未扰轨道	Wèirǎo guǐdào	
Unprotected network	未保护网洛	Wèibǎohù wǎngluò	
Unqualified	未经限定的	Wèijīng xiàndìngde	

Unqualified	未经修饰的	Wèijīng xiūshìde	
Unreasonable message	不合理信息	Bùhélǐ xìnxī	
Unregistration confirmed (packet protocol)	注销确认	Zhùxiāo quèrèn	UCF
Unregistration reject (packet protocol)	注销拒绝	Zhùxiāo jùjué	URJ
Unregistration request (packet protocol)	注销请求	Zhùxiāo qǐngqiú	URQ
Unreliable frame rate	不可靠帧率	Bùkěkào zhèng lǜ	UFR
Unrestricted digital information	不受限制数字信息	Bùshòuxiànzhì shùzì xìnxī	UDI
Unrestricted digital information	无限制的数字信息	Wúxiànzhìde shùzì xìnxī	UDI
Unsafe temperature	不安全温度	Bù'ānquán wēndù	
Unscheduled maintenance	非定期维护	Fēidìngqī wéihù	
Unshielded twisted pair	非屏蔽双绞线	Fēipíngbì shuāngjiǎo xiàn	UTP
Unshielded twisted pair	无屏蔽双绞线	Wúpíngbì shuāngjiǎoxiàn	UTP
Unshielded twisted pair cable	非屏蔽对线电缆	Fēipíngbì duìxiàn diànlǎn	UTP
Unshielded twisted pair cables	非屏蔽对绞电缆	Fēipíngbì duìjiǎo diànlǎn	
Unsolicited grant service	主动授权业务	Zhǔdòng shòuquán yèwù	UGS
Unsolicited grant service with activity detection	带活动检测的主动授权业务	Dài huódòng jiǎncède zhǔdòng shòuquán yèwù	UGS-AD
Unsolicited grant synchronization header	主动授权同步包头	Zhǔdòng shòuquán tóngbù bāotóu	UGSH
Unsolicited message handler	非请求消息处理器	Fēiqǐngqiú xiāoxi chǔlǐqì	UMH
Unspecified bit rate	未规定比特率	Wèiguīdìng bǐtèlǜ	UBR
Unspecified bit rate	未指定比特率	Wèizhǐdìng bǐtèlǜ	UBR
Unsteady varied flow	不稳定流	Bùwěndìng liú	
Unstructured supplementary service data	非结构补充业务数据	Fēijiégòu bǔchōng yèwù shùjù	USSD
Unstructured supplementary service data	非结构化补充数据业务	Fēijiégòuhuà bǔchōng shùjù yèwù	USSD
Unstructured supplementary services data	非结构化补充服务数据	Fēijiégòuhuà bǔchōng fúwù shùjù	USSD
Unstructured supplementary services notification	非结构化补充服务通知	Fēijiégòuhuà bǔchōng fúwù tōngzhī	USSN
Unstructured supplementary services request	非结构化补充服务请求	Fēijiégòuhuà bǔchōng fúwù qǐngqiú	USSR
Unsuccessful backward set-up information message	后向建立不成功消息	Hòuxiàng jiànlì bùchéng gōng xiāoxi	UBM
Unsuccessful call	未完成呼叫	Wèiwánchéng hūjiào	
Unsupervised classification (GIS)	非监督分类	Fēijiāndū fēnlèi	
Unsupported certificate message (IPsec TLS)	不支持的证书消息	Bùzhīchíde zhèngshū xiāoxi	
Un-themed	无主题	Wúzhǔtí	
Unvoiced sounds	清音	Qīngyīn	
Unwanted emission	无用发射	Wúyòng fāshè	
Unwanted signal	无用信号	Wúyòng xìnhào	
Unweighted circuit noise	电路非衡重杂音	Diànlù fēihéngzhòng záyīn	
Unweighted noise	非衡重杂音	Fēihéngzhòng záyīn	
Up converter	上变频器	Shàng biànpínqì	
Up state	可用状态	Kěyòng zhuàngtài	
Up time	可用时间	Kěyòng shíjiān	
Up-casing	大写转换	Dàxiě zhuǎnhuàn	
Up-converter	上变频器	Shàng biànpínqì	
Update	更新	Gēngxīn	
Update information	最新信息	Zuìxīn xìnxī	
Update location	更新位置	Gēngxīn wèizhì	
Update lock	更新锁	Gēngxīn suǒ	

Update query	更新查询	Gēngxīn cháxún	
Update rate	刷新率	Shuāxīn lǜ	
Update statistics	更新统计	Gēngxīn tǒngjì	
Up-down marker	上下标志	Shàngxià biāozhì	
Upgrade wizard (in SQL Server)	升级向导	Shēngjí xiàngdǎo	
Uplink	上衔	Shàng xián	
Uplink	上行	Shàngxíng	
Uplink	上行链路	Shàngxíng liànlù	UL
Uplink bandwidth allocation message	上行带宽分配消息	Shàngxíng dàikuān fēnpèi xiāoxi	
Uplink beam shaping matrix	上行波束成形矩阵	Shàngxíng bōshù chéngxíng jǔzhèn	
Uplink channel change request message	上行信道改变请求消息	Shàngxíng xìndào gǎibiàn qǐngqiú xiāoxi	UCC-REQ
Uplink channel change response message	上行信道改变响应消息	Shàngxíng xìndào gǎibiàn xiǎngyìng xiāoxi	UCC-RSP
Uplink channel descriptor message	上行信道描述符消息	Shàngxíng xìndào miáoshùfú xiāoxi	UCD
Uplink data channel	上行数据信道	Shàngxíng shùjù xìndào	
Uplink measurement	上行测量	Shàngxíng cèliáng	
Uplink pilot time slot	上行导引时隙	Shàngxíng dǎoyǐn shíxì	UpPTS
Uplink pseudo-random data	上行伪随机数据	Shàngxíng wěisuíjī shùjù	UPRD
Uplink pseudo-random sequence	上行伪随机序列	Shàngxíng wěisuíjī xùliè	PRU
Uplink services	卫星上链服务	Wèixīng shàngliàn fúwù	ULS
Uplink shared channel	上行共用信道	Shàngxíng gòngyòng xìndào	USCH
Uplink shared channel	上行链路共享信道	Shàngxíng liànlù gòngxiǎng xìndào	USCH
Uplink state flag	上行链路状态标记	Shàngxíng liànlù zhuàngtài biāojì	USF
Uplink state flag	上行链路状态标志	Shàngxíng liànlù zhuàngtài biāozhì	USF
Uplink state flag	上行状态标记	Shàngxíng zhuàngtài biāojì	USF
Uplink state flag	上行状态标志	Shàngxíng zhuàngtài biāozhì	USF
Uplink synchronization	上行同步	Shàngxíng tóngbù	
Uplink synchronous transmission scheme	上行同步传输计划	Shàngxíng tóngbù chuánshū jìhuà	USTS
Upload	上载	Shàngzài	
Upper address part	高位地址部分	Gāowèi dìzhǐ bùfen	UAP
Upper call attempt threshold	试呼上界	Shìhū shàngjiè	
Upper case	大写字母	Dàxiě zìmǔ	
Upper level protocol	高层协议	Gāocéng xiéyì	ULP
Upper sideband	上边带	Shàngbiandài	USB
Upper tester	高层测试	Gāocéng cèshì	UT
Upsizing	功能上移	Gōngnéng shàngyí	
Upstream	上行传输方向	Shàngxíng chuánshū fāngxiàng	
Upstream	上行方向	Shàngxíng fāngxiàng	
Upstream current	上升气流	Shàngshēng qìliú	
Upstream failure indication	上游故障指示	Shàngyóu gùzhàng zhǐshì	
Upstream failure indication	上游失效指示	Shàngyóu shīxiào zhǐshì	UFI
Upstream label switching router	上流标志交换路由器	Shàngliú biāozhì jiāohuàn lùyóuqì	
Upstream neighbor's address	上游邻站地址	Shàngyóu línzhàn dìzhǐ	UNA
Upstream router	上游路由器	Shàngyóu lùyóuqì	Ru
Urban and Regional Information Systems Association	城市和区域信息系统协会	Chéngshì hé qūyù xìnxī xìtǒng xiéhuì	URISA
Urban call	市话	Shìhuà	
Urban geographic information system	城市地理信息系统	Chéngshì dìlǐ xìnxī xìtǒng	

Urban information system	城市信息系统	Chéngshì xìnxī xìtǒng	
Urban telephone exchange	市内电话局	Shìnèi diànhuàjú	
Urban telephone network	市内电话网	Shìnèi diànhuà wǎng	
Urban telephone switch	市内电话交换机	Shìnèi diànhuà jiāohuànjī	
Urban traffic control system	城市交通管制系统	Chéngshì jiāotōng guǎnzhì xìtǒng	
Usable field strength	可用场强	Kěyòng chǎngqiáng	
Usable power flux density	可用功率通量密度	Kěyòng gōnglǜ tōngliàng mìdù	Pu
Usable sensitivity	可用灵敏度	Kěyòng língmǐndù	
Usage parameter control	使用参数控制	Shǐyòng cānshù kòngzhì	UPC
Usage parameter control	用法参数控制	Yòngfǎ cānshù kòngzhì	
Useful part of timeslot	时隙的有用部分	Shíxìde yǒuyòng bùfen	
Usenet	用户交流网	Yònghù jiāoliú wǎng	
Usenet	用户网	Yònghù wǎng	
User	应用方	Yìngyòng fāng	
User	用户	Yònghù	
User access	用户接入	Yònghù jiērù	
User account	用户帐号	Yònghù zhànghào	
User agent	用户代理	Yònghù dàilǐ	UA
User agent client	用户代理客户	Yònghù dàilǐ kèhù	UAC
User agent server	用户代理服务器	Yònghù dàilǐ fúwùqì	UAS
User authentication (in sense of authorization)	用户鉴权	Yònghù jiànquán	
User authentication (in sense of identification)	用户鉴别	Yònghù jiànbié	
User cancelled message (IPsec TLS)	用户取消消息	Yònghù qǔxiāo xiāoxi	
User channels	使用者通路	Shǐyòngzhě tōnglù	USR
User class of service	用户业务类别	Yònghù yèwù lèibié	
User control	用户控制	Yònghù kòngzhì	UC
User data header indicator	用户数据报头指示	Yònghù shùjù bàotóu zhǐshì	UDHI
User data protocol	用户数据协议	Yònghù shùjù xiéyì	UDP
User database	用户数据库	Yònghù shùjùkù	
User datagram protocol	用户数据报文协议	Yònghù shùjù bàowén xiéyì	UDP
User datagram protocol	用户数据报协议	Yònghù shùjùbào xiéyì	UDP
User defined function	用户定义功能	Yònghù dìngyì gōngnéng	UDF
User defined function	用户定义函数	Yònghù dìngyì hánshù	UDF
User designed data register	用户设计数据寄存器	Yònghù shèjì shùjù jìcúnqì	UDTR
User determined user busy	用户确定用户忙	Yònghù quèdìng yònghù máng	UDUB
User element	用户元素	Yònghù yuánsù	
User encipherment	用户加密	Yònghù jiāmì	
User equipment with ODMA relay operation enabled	用户设备能使用 ODMA 中继	Yònghù shèbèi néng shǐyòng ODMA zhōngjì	Uer
User facility	用户功能	Yònghù gōngnéng	
User identity	用户标识	Yònghù biāozhì	
User identity	用户标识号	Yònghù biāozhì hào	
User information	用户信息	Yònghù xìnxī	
User information protocol (IETF use)	用户信息协议	Yònghù xìnxī xiéyì	
User interactive dialogue	用户交互对话	Yònghù jiāohù duìhuà	UID
User interface	用户接口	Yònghù jiēkǒu	UI

User interface	用户界面	Yònghù jièmiàn	
User interface manager	用户接口管理器	Yònghù jiēkǒu guǎnlǐqì	UIM
User location service	用户定位服务	Yònghù dìngwèi fúwù	ULS
User mobility server	用户移动性服务器	Yònghù yídòngxìng fúwùqì	UMS
User mode	用户模式	Yònghù móshì	
User name	用户名	Yònghù míng	
User network interface	用户网络接口	Yònghù wǎngluò jiēkǒu	UNI
User network interface structure	用户网络接口结构	Yònghù wǎngluò jiēkǒu jiégòu	
User node interface	拥护节点接口	Yōnghù jiédiǎn jiēkǒu	UNI
User parameter control/network parameter control	用户参数控制/网络参数控制	Yònghù cānshù kòngzhì/ wǎngluò cānshù kòngzhì	UPC/NPC
User part	用户部分	Yònghù bùfen	UP
User plane	用户面	Yònghù miàn	
User plane	用户平面	Yònghù píngmiàn	UP
User port	用户端口	Yònghù duānkǒu	
User port function	用户端口功能	Yònghù duānkǒu gōngnéng	UPF
User port function	用户口功能	Yònghù kǒu gōngnéng	UPF
User program	用户程序	Yònghù chéngxù	
User programmable array	用户可编程阵列	Yònghù kěbiānchéng zhènliè	
User registration area	用户注册区域	Yònghù zhùcè qūyù	URA
User requirements analysis	用户需求分析	Yònghù xūqiú fēnxī	
User service	用户业务	Yònghù yèwù	
User service information	用户业务信息	Yònghù yèwù xìnxī	USI
User sessions	访客量	Fǎngkèliàng	
User to user signaling	用户-用户消息	Yònghù—yònghù xiāoxi	UUS
User-defined data type	用户定义数据类型	Yònghù dìngyì shùjù lèixíng	
User-defined event	用户定义事件	Yònghù dìngyì shìjiàn	
User-defined functions (in SQL Server)	用户自定义函数	Yònghù zìdìngyì hánshù	
User-friendly	容易使用	Róngyì shǐyòng	
User-friendly	用户亲和性	Yònghù qīnhéxìng	
User-network access	用户-网络接入	Yònghù—wǎngluò jiērù	
User-network interface	用户-用户接口	Yònghù—yònghù jiēkǒu	UNI
User-network interface only deactivation	仅用户--网络接口的去激活	Jǐn yònghù—wǎngluò jiēkǒude qùjīhuó	
User-network protocol	用户—网络协议	Yònghù— wǎngluò xiéyì	
User-to-service information	用户到业务信息	Yònghù dào yèwù xìnxī	UTSI
User-to-user connection	用户-用户连接	Yònghù—yònghù liánjiē	
User-to-user iindicator	用户到用户指示	Yònghù dào yònghù zhǐshì	
User-to-user information (ISUP message)	用户到用户信息	Yònghù dào yònghù xìnxī	USR
User-to-user interface	用户—用户接口	Yònghù—yònghù jiēkǒu	UUI
User-to-user message (ISUP)	用户到用户消息	Yònghù dào yònghù xiāoxi	USR
User-to-user protocol	用户-用户协议	Yònghù—yònghù xiéyì	
User-to-user service	用户到用户业务	Yònghù dào yònghù yèwù	UUS
User-to-user signaling	用户到用户信令	Yònghù dào yònghù xìnlìng	UUS
User-to-user signaling	用户-用户信令	Yònghù—yònghù xìnlìng	UUS
User-to-user signaling service 1	用户至用户信令业务 1	Yònghù zhì yònghù xìnlìng yèwù 1	UUS1
Usual asymmetric digital subscriber line	通用不对称数字用户线路	Tōngyòng bùduìchèn shùzì yònghù xiànlù	UADSL

Utilities mapping	设施制图	Shèshī zhìtú	
Utility	实用程序	Shíyòng chéngxù	
Utility	实用工具	Shíyòng gōngjù	
Utility management	设施管理	Shèshī guǎnlǐ	
Utility network	公用设施网络	Gōngyòng shèshī wǎngluò	
Utility program	使用程序	Shǐyòng chéngxù	
Utra absolute radio frequency channel number	UTRA 绝对无线电频率信道号码	UTRA juéduì wúxiàndiàn pínlǜ xìndào hàomǎ	UARFCN
Utra absolute radio frequency number	UTRA 绝对无线电频率号码	UTRA juéduì wúxiàndiàn pínlǜ hàomǎ	UARFN
UTRAN radio network temporary identity	UTRAN 无线电网络临时识别	UTRAN wúxiàndiàn wǎngluò línshí shíbié	U-RNTI
UTRAN registration area	UTRAN 注册区域	UTRAN zhùcè qūyù	URA
UTSTARCOM (US company)	UT 斯达康	UT sī-dá-kāng	

V

Vacancy	空房	Kōngfáng	
Vacant-number signal	空号信号	Kōnghào xìnhào	
Vacuum capacitor	真空电容器	Zhēnkōng diànróngqì	
Vacuum electron device	真空电子器件	Zhēnkōng diànzǐ qìjiàn	
Vacuum evaporation chemicals	真空蒸镀化学药品	Zhēnkōng zhēngdù huàxué yàopǐn	
Vacuum evaporation equipment	真空蒸镀设备	Zhēnkōng zhēngdù shèbèi	
Vacuum fluorescent display	真空萤光显示器	Zhēnkōng yíngguāng xiǎnshìqì	VFD
Vacuum pump	真空泵浦	Zhēnkōng bèngpǔ	
Vacuum ultraviolet laser	真空紫外线激光	Zhēnkōng zǐwàixiàn jīguāng	
Vacuum ultraviolet light source	真空紫外线光源	Zhēnkōng zǐwàixiàn guāngyuán	
Valency	价	Jià	
Valency table	价列表	Jià lièbiǎo	
Valid cell	有效信元	Yǒuxiào xìnyuán	
Valid period of payment	有效兑付期	Yǒuxiào duìfù qī	
Valid user address	有效用户地址	Yǒuxiào yònghù dìzhǐ	VUA
Validated user	合法用户	Héfǎ yònghù	
Validation	确认	Quèrèn	
Validation phase	提交阶段	Tíjiāo jiēduàn	
Validity	正确性	Zhèngquèxìng	
Validity check	合法性检查	Héfǎ-xìng jiǎnchá	
Validity direction	有效性方向	Yǒuxiàoxìng fāngxiàng	
Validity period	有效性周期	Yǒuxiàoxìng zhōuqī	
Value	征值	Zhēngzhí	
Value	值	Zhí	
Value added network	加值网络	Jiāzhí wǎngluò	VAN
Value added network	增值网	Zēngzhí wǎng	VAN
Value added reseller	增值转售商	Zēngzhí zhuǎnshòushāng	VAR
Value added resellers	增值分销商	Zēngzhí fēnxiāo shāng	VAR
Value added service	增值业务	Zēngzhí yèwù	VAS
Value added service provider	增值业务提供商	Zēngzhí yèwù tígōngshāng	VASP
Value attribute table	值属性表	Zhí shǔxìng biǎo	VAT

Value domain	值域	Zhí yù	
Value expression	值表达式	Zhí biǎodá shì	
Value insertion attack	插枝攻击	Chāzhī gōngjī	
Value types	值类型	Zhí lèixíng	
Valve regulated	阀控式	Fákòng-shì	
Valve-regulated lead acid battery	阀控式密封型电池	Fákòng-shì mìfēng xíng diànchí	VRLA
Van duuren code	范杜伦码	Fàn-dù-lún mǎ	
Vane attenuator	翼形衰减器	Yìxíng shuāijiǎnqì	
Vane wattmeter	翼形瓦特计	Yìxíng wǎtèjì	
Vanishing moment	消失距	Xiāoshī jù	
Vapor axial deposition	轴向气相沉积法	Zhóuxiàng qìxiàng chénjī fǎ	VAD
Vapor axial deposition (for FOC)	气相轴向沉积法	Qìxiàng zhóuxiàng chénjī fǎ	VAD
Vapor axial deposition (for FOC)	轴向化学气相沉积法	Zhóuxiàng huàxué qìxiàng chénjī fǎ	VAD
Vapor degreaser (in SMT)	汽相去油器	Qìxiāng qùyóuqì	
Vapor deposition (for FOC)	气相沉积法	Qìxiàng chénjī fǎ	
Vapor phase epitaxy	汽相外延	Qìxiāng wàiyán	VPE
Vaporware	蒸汽软件	Zhēngqì ruǎnjiàn	
Variable	变数	Biànshù	
Variable (a quantity)	变量	Biànliàng	
Variable aperture grille pitch	可变间距光栅	Kěbiàn jiānjù guāngshān	VAGP
Variable attenuator	可变衰减器	Kěbiàn shuāijiǎnqì	
Variable authentication code	可变认证码	Kěbiàn rènzhèng mǎ	VAC
Variable bit rate	可变比特率	Kěbiàn bǐtè lǜ	VBR
Variable bit rate service	可变比特率业务	Kěbiàn bǐtè lǜ yèwù	VBR
Variable capacitance (varactor) diode	变容二极管	Biànróng èrjíguǎn	
Variable crystal oscillator	可变晶体振荡器	Kěbiàn jīngtǐ zhèndàngqì	VXO
Variable dimension vector quantization	变维矢量量化	Biànwéi shǐliàng liànghuà	VDVQ
Variable division frequency divider	可变分频器	Kěbiàn fēnpínqì	
Variable division ratio divider	可变分频器	Kěbiàn fēnpínqì	
Variable dot (printer term)	变点式列印	Biàndiǎn-shì liè yìn	VD
Variable frequency oscillator	可变频频率荡器	Kěbiànpín pínlǜ dàngqì	VFO
Variable length coding	可变长编码	Kěbiàn cháng biānmǎ	
Variable length one-way acknowledgement	变长单向确认	Biàncháng dānxiàng quèrèn	
Variable length two-way acknowledgement	变长双向确认	Biàncháng shuāngxiàng quèrèn	
Variable optical attenuator	可变光衰减器	Kěbiàn guāng shuāijiǎnqì	VOA
Variable optical attenuator array	可变光衰减阵列	Kěbiàn guāng shuāijiǎn zhènliè	VAA
Variable picture element	任意图素	Rènyì tú sù	
Variable rate adaptive multiplexing	可变速自适应多路转换	Kěbiàn sù zìshìyìng duōlù zhuǎnhuàn	VRAM
Variable slope delta modulation	可变斜率增量调制	Kěbiàn xiélǜ zēngliàng tiáozhì	VSDM
Variable spacing	可变间距	Kěbiàn jiānjù	
Variable topology random access memory	可变结构随机存取存储器	Kěbiàn jiégòu suíjī cúnqǔ cúnchǔqì	VTRAM
Variable-aggregate data type	可变聚合数据类型	Kěbiàn jùhé shùjù lèixíng	
Variable-length sub-net mask	可变长度子网掩码	Kěbiàn chángdù zǐwǎng yǎnmǎ	VLSM
Variable-rate	变速率	Biànsù lǜ	
Variance	方差	Fāngchà	
Variance component estimation	方差元素估计	Fāngchà yuánsù gūjì	

Variogram	变异函数	Biànyì hánshù	
V-beam radar	V 形波束雷达	V-xíng bōshù léidá	
VC cross connect	VC 交叉连接	VC jiāochā liánjiē	
Vector	矢量	Shǐliàng	
Vector (in Java)	向量	Xiàngliàng	
Vector algorithms	矢量算法	Shǐliàng suànfǎ	
Vector arithmetic logic unit	向量算术逻辑单元	Xiàngliàng suànshù luóji dānyuán	VALU
Vector canceller	矢量对消器	Shǐliàng duìxiāoqì	
Vector control	矢量控制	Shǐliàng kòngzhì	VC
Vector correlation (radar term)	航向相关	Hángxiàng xiāngguān	
Vector data	矢量数据	Shǐliàng shùjù	
Vector data model	矢量数据模型	Shǐliàng shùjù móxíng	
Vector font	失量字库	Shǐliáng zìkù	
Vector font	向量字库	Xiàngliàng zìkù	
Vector geometry	向量几何特征	Xiàngliàng jǐhé tèzhēng	
Vector identifier	向量标识符	Xiàngliàng biāozhì fú	VI
Vector interrupt mechanism	矢量中断机构	Shǐliàng zhōngduàn jīgòu	VIM
Vector interrupt mechanism	向量中断机构	Xiàngliàng zhōngduàn jīgòu	VIM
Vector length	向量长度	Xiàngliàng chángdù	VL
Vector load index	自量负载指数	Zìliàng fùzài zhǐshù	
Vector map	矢量地图	Shǐliàng dìtú	
Vector optimization problem	向量最优化问题	Xiàngliàng zuìyōuhuà wèntí	VOP
Vector permutate unit	向量排列单元	Xiàngliàng páiliè dānyuán	VPU
Vector processing element	向量处理单元	Xiàngliàng chǔlǐ dānyuán	VPE
Vector processing unit	向量处理单元	Xiàngliàng chǔlǐ dānyuán	VPU
Vector product format	矢量产品格式	Shǐliàng chǎnpǐn géshi	VPF
Vector quantization	矢量和量化	Shǐliàng hé liànghuà	
Vector quantization	矢量量化	Shǐliàng liànghuà	VQ
Vector relational format	矢量关系格式	Shǐliàng guānxi géshi	VRF
Vector sum excited linear predictive coding	矢量和激励线性预测编码	Shǐliàng hé jīlì xiànxìng yùcè biānmǎ	VSELP
Vector symbol set	向量符号集	Xiàngliàng fúhào jí	VSS
Vectorization	矢量化	Shǐliàng huà	
Vector-quantization texture compression	向量纹理压缩	Xiàngliàng wénlǐ yāsuō	VQTC
Vector-to-raster conversion	矢量-栅格转换	Shǐliàng—zhàgé zhuǎnhuàn	
Vehicle equipment	载体设备	Zàitǐ shèbèi	
Vehicle location	车辆定位	Chēliàng dìngwèi	
Vehicle navigation system	汽车导引系统	Qìchē dǎoyǐn xìtǒng	
Vehicle station	车载电台	Chēzài diàntái	
Veitch diagram	维持图	Wéi-chí tú	
Velocity	速度	Sùdù	
Velocity correlation	速度相关	Sùdù xiāngguān	
Velocity discrimination	速度鉴别	Sùdù jiànbié	
Velocity distribution	流速分布	Liúsù fēnbù	
Velocity response spectrum	速度反应谱	Sùdù fǎnyìng pǔ	
Vendor	厂商	Chǎngshāng	
Vendor managed inventory	供应商管理的库存	Gōngyìngshāng guǎnlǐde kùcún	VMI

Venn diagram	文式图	Wén-shì tú	
Ventilating carriage	通风车	Tōngfēng chē	
Venture capital company	风险投资公司	Fēngxiǎn tóuzī gōngsī	
Venturi forced convection (semiconductor mfg)	文氏强制对流	Wén-shì qiángzhì duìliú	
Verbal communication	口头传媒	Kǒutóu chuánméi	
Verifiability	可核查性	Kěhécháxìng	
Verification of account	对账	Duìzhàng	
Verification test	检验试验	Jiǎnyàn shìyàn	
Verification tone	证实音	Zhèngshí yīn	
Verisimilitude	地图现势性	Dìtú xiànshìxìng	
Veronica search	维洛尼卡检索	Wéi-luò-ní-kǎ jiǎnsuǒ	
Versatile interface processor	通用接口处理器	Tōngyòng jiēkǒu chǔlǐqì	VIP
Versatile interior multiplex system	通用内部多路转换系统	Tōngyòng nèibù duōlù zhuǎnhuàn xìtǒng	VIMS
Versatile message transaction protocol	通用消息事务处理协议	Tōngyòng xiāoxi shìwù chǔlǐ xiéyì	VMTP
Versioned data	版本数据	Bǎnběn shùjù	
Vertex	顶点	Dǐngdiǎn	
Vertex aggregation (CAD/CAM)	顶点聚合	Dǐngdiǎn jùhé	VA
Vertex coloring	点染色	Diǎn rǎnsè	
Vertex cover	点覆盖	Diǎn fùgài	
Vertex expansion (CAM/CAM)	顶点展开	Dǐngdiǎn zhǎnkāi	VE
Vertex plate (of a paraboloidal reflector)	顶板	Dǐngbǎn	
Vertical aggregation	垂直压缩	Chuízhí yāsuō	
Vertical bearing capacity	垂直支承力	Chuízhí zhīchénglì	
Vertical blanking interval	垂直空白间隔	Chuízhí kòngbái jiàngé	VBI
Vertical blanking interval (video)	垂直空白间隙	Chuízhí kòngbái jiànxì	VBI
Vertical cavity surface emitting laser	垂直表面激光发射器	Chuízhí biǎomiàn jīguāng fāshèqì	VCSEL
Vertical cavity surface emitting laser diode	垂直共振腔面射型	Chuízhí gòngzhènqiāng miàn shè xíng	VCSEL
Vertical component	垂直成分	Chuízhí chéngfèn	
Vertical datum	垂直基准	Chuízhí jīzhǔn	
Vertical directivity pattern	垂直方向性图	Chuízhí fāngxiàngxìng tú	
Vertical filtering	垂直筛选	Chuízhí shāixuǎn	
Vertical flow	垂直流	Chuízhí liú	
Vertical interpolation	垂直调变	Chuízhí tiáo biàn	
Vertical interval data transmission	垂直区间数据传输	Chuízhí qūjiān shùjù chuánshū	VIDT
Vertical monopole, vertical unipole (antenna)	垂直单极子	Chuízhí dānjízi	
Vertical movement	垂直移动	Chuízhí yídòng	
Vertical partitioning	垂直分区	Chuízhí fēnqū	
Vertical redundancy check	垂直冗余检验	Chuízhí rǒngyú jiǎnyàn	VRC
Vertical refresh rate (video)	垂直扫描频率	Chuízhí sǎomiáo pínlǜ	VRR
Vertical scan rate	垂直扫描频率	Chuízhí sǎomiáo pínlǜ	
Vertical sounding	垂直探测法	Chuízhí tàncèfǎ	
Vertical tabulation	直列制表	Zhíliè zhìbiǎo	VT
Vertical transport	垂直输送	Chuízhí shūsòng	
Very early allocation	很早分配	Hěnzǎo fēnpèi	VEA
Very high frequency	甚高频	Shèngāopín	VHF
Very high frequency (VHF) radio wave propagation	甚高频传播	Shèngāopín chuánbō	

Very high speed digital subscriber line (downlink 12.9Mb/s to 52.8Mb/s, uplink 1.6Mb/s to 2.3Mb/s)	甚高速数字用户线	Shèngāosù shùzì yònghù xiàn	VDSL
Very high speed integrated circuit	超高速集成电路	Chāogāosù jíchéng diànlù	
Very high-speed digital subscriber line	超高速数字用户线	Chāogāosù shùzì yònghù xiàn	VDSL
Very large dimension	超大型维度	Chāodàxíng wéidù	
Very large scale integrated circuit	超大规模集成电路	Chāodàguīmó jíchéng diànlù	VLSI
Very large scale integration	超大规模集成	Chāodàguīmó jíchéng	VLSI
Very long instruction word	超长指令字	Chāocháng zhǐlìng zì	VLIW
Very low frequency	甚低频	Shèndīpín	VLF
Very low frequency (VLF) radio wave propagation	甚低频无线电波传输	Shèndīpín wúxiàndiànbō chuánshū	
Very small aperture satellite terminal	超小型天线终端	Chāoxiǎoxíng tiānxiàn zhōngduān	VSAT
Very small aperture terminal	甚小口径天线地球站	Shènxiǎo kǒujìng tiānxiàn dìqiú zhàn	VSAT
Very small aperture terminal	甚小口径终端	Shènxiǎo kǒujìng zhōngduān	VSAT
Very-high-data-rate digital subscriber line	超高数据传输速率的数字用户线路	Chāogāo shùjù chuánshū sùlǜde shùzì yònghù xiànlù	VDSL
Vestigial sideband	残留边带	Cánliú biāndài	VSB
Vestigial sideband amplitude modulation	残留边带调幅	Cánliú biāndài tiáofú	VSBAM
Vestigial sideband modulation	残余边带调制	Cányú biāndài tiáozhì	
Vestigial-sideband emission	残余边带发射	Cányú biāndài fāshè	
Viable	可行的	Kěxíngde	
Viaduct, overpass	立交桥	Lìjiāoqiáo	
Vibration	振动	Zhèndòng	
Vibration (suppression) methods	制振对策、	Zhìzhèn duìcè	
Vibration isolator	除震台	Chúzhèntái	
Vibration isolator	防震台	Fángzhèntái	
Vibration test	振动实验	Zhèndòng shíyàn	
Video amplifier	视频放大器	Shìpín fàngdàqì	
Video and rendering graphics engine	视频描写图形引擎	Shìpín miáoxiě túxíng yǐnqíng	ViRGE
Video canceller	视频对消器	Shìpín duìxiāoqì	
Video CD	视频 CD	Shìpín CD	VCD
Video channel bandwidth	视频通道带宽	Shìpín tōngdào dàikuān	
Video codec	视频编解码	Shìpín biānjiěmǎ	
Video command	视频命令	Shìpín mìnglìng	
Video command "Fast update request"	视频命令"快速更新请求"	Shìpín mìnglìng "kuàisù gēngxīn qǐngqiú"	VCU
Video command "Freeze picture request"	视频命令"静态画请求"	Shìpín mìnglìng "jìngtài huà qǐngqiú"	VCF
Video compact disc	视频光盘	Shìpín guāngpán	VCD
Video conference	电视会议	Diànshì huìyì	
Video conference	会议电视	Huìyì diànshì	
Video conference	视频会议	Shìpín huìyì	VC
Video conference service	电视会议服务	Diànshì huìyì fúwù	
VIdeo conference system	会议电视系统	Huìyì diànshì xìtǒng	VCS
Video conference system	视讯會议系统	Shìxùn hùiyì xìtǒng	VCS
Video conference terminal	电视会议终端	Diànshì huìyì zhōngduān	
Video conferencing	视讯會议	Shìxùn hùiyi	
Video decoder	视频译码器	Shìpín yìmǎqì	VD
Video display terminal	视频显示终端	Shìpín xiǎnshì zhōngduān	VDT

Video display terminal	图像显示终端	Túxiàng xiǎnshì zhōngduān	VDT
Video display unit	视频显示单元	Shìpín xiǎnshì dānyuán	VDU
Video display unit	视频显示器	Shìpín xiǎnshìqì	VDU
Video encoding	视频编码	Shìpín biānmǎ	
Video frequency (VF)	视频	Shìpín	
Video graphic adapter	视频图形显示适配器	Shìpín túxíng xiǎnshì shìpèiqì	VGA
Video handoff controller	图象切换控制器	Túxiàng qiēhuàn kòngzhìqì	
Video image freezing	视频图象冻结	Shìpín túxiàng dòngjié	
Video image unfreezing	视频图象解结	Shìpín túxiàng jiě jié	
Video interface port	视频接口	Shìpín jiēkǒu	VIP
Video interphone	可视对讲门铃	Kěshì duìjiǎng ménlíng	VI
Video messaging	视频电子信函	Shìpín diànzi xìnhán	
Video messaging	视频消息业务	Shìpín xiāoxi yèwù	
Video messaging service	视频消息处理业务	Shìpín xiāoxi chǔlǐ yèwù	
Video on demand	点播电视	Diǎnbō diànshì	VOD
Video on demand	视频点播	Shìpín diǎnbō	VoD
Video on demand	影视点播	Yǐngshì diǎnbō	VOD
Video optical transmission system	视频光传输系统	Shìpín guāng chuánshū xìtǒng	
Video phone	视讯电话	Shìxùn diànhuà	
Video segmentation	视频分割	Shìpín fēngē	
Video signal standard	视频信号标准	Shìpín xìnhào biāozhǔn	VSIS
Video switched network	活动图象交换网	Huódòng túxiàng jiāohuàn wǎng	VSN
Video system	影像系统	Yǐngxiàng xìtǒng	
Video telephone	可视电话	Kěshì diànhuà	
Video terminal	视频终端	Shìpín zhōngduān	VT
Video transmission unit	视频传输单元	Shìpín chuánshū dānyuán	VTU
Video-frequency protection ratio	视频保护比	Shìpín bǎohù bǐ	
Video-frequency signal-to-interference ratio	视频信号干扰比	Shìpín xìnhào gānrǎo bǐ	
Videography	可视图文	Kěshì túwén	
Videography	图文视传	Túwén shìchuán	
Video-on-demand	按需点播视频	Ànxū diǎnbō shìpín	VOD
Videophone	电视电话	Diànshì diànhuà	
Videophone	视话机	Shìhuàjī	
Videotex	可视图文	Kěshì túwén	
Videotex	用户图问通信	Yònghù túwèn tōngxìn	
Videotex access point	可视图文接入点	Kěshì túwén jiērùdiǎn	VAP
Videotex application	可视图文应用	Kěshì túwén yìngyòng	
Videotex application provider	可视图文应用提供者	Kěshì túwén yìngyòng tígòngzhě	
Videotex closed user group	可视图文闭合用户群	Kěshì túwén bìhé yònghù qún	
Videotex communication network provider	可视图文通信网提供者	Kěshì túwén tōngxìnwǎng tígòngzhě	
Videotex conferencing	可视图文会议	Kěshì túwén huìyì	
Videotex data processing	可视图文数据处理	Kěshì túwén shùjù chǔlǐ	
Videotex database	可视图文数据库	Kěshì túwén shùjùkù	
Videotex form	可视图文证询单	Kěshì túwén zhèng xúndān	
Videotex frame	可视图文帧	Kěshì túwén zhèng	
Videotex host computer	可视图文主机	Kěshì túwén zhǔjī	

Videotex interface unit	可视图文接口单元	Kěshì túwén jiēkǒu dānyuán	
Videotex messaging	可视图文消息传递	Kěshì túwén xiāoxi chuándì	
Videotex page	可视图文页	Kěshì túwén yè	
Videotex service	可视图文业务	Kěshì túwén yèwù	
Videotex service center	可视图文业务中心	Kěshì túwén yèwù zhōngxīn	
Videotex service center	可视图文中心	Kěshì túwén zhōngxīn	VSC
Videotex service facilities	可视图文业务性能	Kěshì túwén yèwù xìngnéng	
Videotex service profile	可视图文业务轮廓	Kěshì túwén yèwù lúnkuò	
Videotex service provider	可视图文业务提供者	Kěshì túwén yèwù tígòngzhě	
Videotex service unit	可视图文业务单元	Kěshì túwén yèwù dānyuán	
Videotex system	可视图文系统	Kěshì túwén xìtǒng	
Videotex system field	可视图文系统域	Kěshì túwén xìtǒng yù	
Videotex telesoftware	可视图文软件遥装	Kěshì túwén ruǎnjiàn yáozhuāng	
Videotex terminal	可视图文终端	Kěshì túwén zhōngduān	
Videotex transaction	可视图文事务处理	Kěshì túwén shìwù chǔlǐ	
Videotex transaction	可视图文信息检索	Kěshì túwén xìnxī jiǎnsuǒ	
Videotex user	可视图文用户	Kěshì túwén yònghù	
Videotex user/terminal identification facility	可视图文用户或终端标识性能	Kěshì túwén yònghù huò zhōngduān biāozhì xìngnéng	
Videotex; interactive videography	交互可视图文	Jiāohù kěshì túwén	
Videotext	可视报文	Kěshì bàowén	
View	视图	Shìtú	
View generation	视图生成	Shìtú shēngchéng	
View menu (WP command)	显示菜单	Xiǎnshì càidān	
Viewdata system	可视数据系统	Kěshì shùjù xìtǒng	
Viewpoint	视点	Shìdiǎn	
Virtual call	虚拟呼叫	Xūnǐ hūjiào	VC
Virtual call (computer software term)	虚调用	Xū diàoyòng	VC
Virtual call (telecom term)	虚呼叫	Xū hūjiào	VC
Virtual call connection	虚呼叫连接	Xū hūjiào liánjiē	VCC
Virtual call control	虚呼叫控制	Xū hūjiào kòngzhì	VCC
Virtual channel	虚信道	Xū xìndào	VC
Virtual channel connection	虚通路连接	Xū tōnglù liánjiē	VCC
Virtual channel connection	虚信道连接	Xū xìndào liánjiē	
Virtual channel connection	虚拟信道连接	Xūnǐ xìndào liánjiē	VCC
Virtual channel connection endpoint	虚信道连接端点	Xū xìndào liánjiē duāndiǎn	VCCE
Virtual channel connection related function	虚信道连接的有关功能	Xū xìndào liánjiēde yǒuguān gōngnéng	CRF(VC)
Virtual channel connection termination	虚通路连接终接	Xū tōnglù liánjiē zhōngjiē	VCCT
Virtual channel entity	虚通路实体	Xū tōnglù shítǐ	VCE
Virtual channel identifier	虚通道标志	Xū tōngdào biāozhì	VCI
Virtual channel identifier	虚通道识别码	Xū tōngdào shíbié mǎ	VCI
Virtual channel identifier	虚通路标识	Xū tōnglù biāozhì	VCI
Virtual channel identifier	虚信道标志	Xū xìndào biāozhì	VCI
Virtual channel identifier	虚信道标识	Xū xìndào biāozhì	VCI
Virtual channel identifier	虚信道识别幅	Xū xìndào shíbié fú	VCI
Virtual channel identifier	虚拟通道标识符	Xūnǐ tōngdào biāozhìfú	VCI

Virtual channel identifier	虚拟信道标识符	Xūnǐ xìndào biāozhì fú	VCI
Virtual channel indicator	虚通路识别码	Xū tōnglù shíbié mǎ	VCI
Virtual channel level	虚通路级	Xū tōnglù jí	
Virtual channel level	虚信道级	Xū xìndào jí	
Virtual channel link	虚通路链路	Xū tōnglù liànlù	
Virtual channel link	虚信道链路	Xū xìndào liànlù	VCL
Virtual channel memory architecture	虚拟通道内存结构	Xūnǐ tōngdào nèicún jiégòu	VCMA
Virtual channel multiplex entity	虚通路复用实体	Xū tōnglù fùyòng shítǐ	VCME
Virtual channel trail termination point	虚通路路径终接点	Xū tōnglù lùjìng zhōng jiēdiǎn	vcTTP
Virtual channel--alarm indication signal	虚通路告警指示信号	Xū tōnglù gàojǐng zhǐshì xìnhào	VC-AIS
Virtual channel--remote defect indication	虚通路远端故障指示	Xū tōnglù yuǎn duān gùzhàng zhǐshì	VC-RDI
Virtual circuit	虚电路	Xū diànlù	
Virtual concatenation	虚级联	Xū jílián	
Virtual connect	虚连接	Xū liánjiē	VC
Virtual connection	虚拟连接	Xūnǐ liánjiē	VC
Virtual connection tree	虚拟连接树	Xūnǐ liánjiē shù	
Virtual connection tree handoff	虚拟连接树切换	Xūnǐ liánjiē shù qiēhuàn	
Virtual container	虚容器	Xū róngqì	VC
Virtual container	虚通路包	Xū tōnglù bāo	VC
Virtual container path overhead	虚容器通道开销	Xū róngqì tōngdào kāixiao	VC POH
Virtual datacube	虚拟多维数据集	Xūnǐ duōwéi shùjùjí	
Virtual decision values	虚判决值	Xū pànjué zhí	
Virtual destination	虚拟终点	Xūnǐ zhōngdiǎn	VD
Virtual device drivers	虚拟设备驱动程序	Xūnǐ shèbèi qūdòng chéngxù	VxD
Virtual dimension	虚拟维度	Xūnǐ wéidù	
Virtual DOS machine	虚拟 DOS 机	Xūnǐ DOS jī	VDM
Virtual enterprise	虚拟企业	Xūnǐ qǐyè	
Virtual execution engine	虚拟执行引擎	Xūnǐ zhíxíng yǐnqíng	VEE
Virtual fetch	虚取	Xū qǔ	VF
Virtual fetch vector table	虚取向量表	Xū qǔ xiàngliáng biǎo	VFVT
Virtual file allocation table	虚拟文件分配表	Xūnǐ wénjiàn fēnpèi biǎo	VFAT
Virtual function	虚函数	Xū hánshù	
Virtual hardware description language	虚拟硬件描述语言	Xūnǐ yìngjiàn miáoshù yǔyán	VHDL
Virtual home environment	虚拟归属环境	Xūnǐ guīshǔ huánjìng	VHE
Virtual home environment	虚拟家区环境	Xūnǐ jiāqū huánjìng	VHE
Virtual home environment	虚拟家庭环境	Xūnǐ jiātíng huánjìng	VHE
Virtual integrated communications access method	虚拟综合通信存取法	Xūnǐ zōnghé tōngxìn cúnqǔ fǎ	VICAM
Virtual interaction controller	虚拟交互控制器	Xūnǐ jiāohù kòngzhìqì	VIC
Virtual interface architecture	虚拟接口体系	Xūnǐ jiēkǒu tǐxì	VIA
Virtual interface template	虚拟接口模板	Xūnǐ jiēkǒu múbǎn	
Virtual leased line	虚拟专线	Xūnǐ zhuānxiàn	VLL
Virtual leased line	虚拟租用线路	Xūnǐ zūyòng xiànlù	VLL
Virtual leased lines	租用虚线路	Zūyòng xū xiànlù	VLL
Virtual line switching ring	虚拟线交换环	Xūnǐ xiàn jiāohuàn huán	VLSR
Virtual local area network	虚拟局域网	Xūnǐ júyù wǎng	VLAN
Virtual local area network (LAN) identifier	虚拟局域网标识符	Xūnǐ júyù wǎng biāozhìfú	VID

Virtual machine	虚拟机	Xūnǐ jī	
Virtual machine	虚拟机器	Xūnǐ jīqì	
Virtual memory	虚拟存储	Xūnǐ cúnchǔ	
Virtual memory	虚拟内存	Xūnǐ nèicún	
Virtual memory allocation	虚拟存储器分配	Xūnǐ cúnchǔqì fēnpèi	VMA
Virtual memory environment	虚拟存储环境	Xūnǐ cúnchǔ huánjìng	VME
Virtual network address translation	虚拟网络地址转换	Xūnǐ wǎngluò dìzhǐ zhuǎnhuàn	VNAT
Virtual network element	虚拟网元	Xūnǐ wǎngyuán	
Virtual network service	虚拟网	Xūnǐ wǎng	VNS
Virtual operating system	虚拟操作系统	Xūnǐ cāozuò xìtǒng	VOS
Virtual optical path	虚光路	Xū guāng lù	
Virtual organization	虚拟组织	Xūnǐ zǔzhī	
Virtual output queue	虚拟输出排队	Xūnǐ shūchū páiduì	VOQ
Virtual packet terminal	虚拟分组终端	Xūnǐ fēnzǔ zhōngduān	VPT
Virtual path	虚路径	Xū lùjìng	
Virtual path	虚通道	Xū tōngdào	
Virtual path (preferred)	虚通路	Xū tōnglù	VP
Virtual path connection	虚通道连接	Xū tōngdào liánjiē	VPC
Virtual path connection (preferred)	虚通路连接	Xū tōnglù liánjiē	VPC
Virtual path connection endpoint	虚通路连接端点	Xū tōnglù liánjiē duāndiǎn	VPCE
Virtual path connection identifier--continuous checking	虚通道连接标识符--连续性检验	Xū tōngdào liánjiē biāozhì fú--liánxùxìng jiǎnyàn	VPCI-CC
Virtual path connection related function	虚通路连接的有关功能	Xū tōnglù liánjiēde yǒuguān gōngnéng	CRF(VP)
Virtual path connection termination	虚通道连接终接	Xū tōngdào liánjiē zhōngjiē	VPCT
Virtual path entity	虚通道实体	Xū tōngdào shítǐ	VPE
Virtual path group	虚通道组	Xū tōngdào zǔ	VPG
Virtual path identifier	虚电路标志	Xū diànlù biāozhì	VPI
Virtual path identifier	虚通道标识	Xū tōngdào biāozhì	VPI
Virtual path identifier	虚通道识别码	Xū tōngdào shíbié mǎ	VPI
Virtual path identifier	虚通路标志	Xū tōnglù biāozhì	VPI
Virtual path identifier	虚通路标识符	Xū tōnglù biāozhì fú	VPI
Virtual path identifier	虚拟路径标识符	Xūnǐ lùjìng biāozhì fú	VPI
Virtual path level	虚通道级	Xū tōngdào jí	
Virtual path level	虚通路级	Xū tōnglù jí	
Virtual path link	虚通道链路	Xū tōngdào liànlù	
Virtual path link	虚通路链路	Xū tōnglù liànlù	VPL
Virtual path multiplex entity	虚通道复用实体	Xū tōngdào fùyòng shítǐ	VPME
Virtual path--alarm indication signal	虚通道告警指示信号	Xū tōngdào gàojǐng zhǐshì xìnhào	VP-AIS
Virtual path--remote defect indicator	虚通道远端故障指示	Xū tōngdào yuǎnduān gùzhàng zhǐshì	VP-RDI
Virtual private dial network	虚拟私有拨号网络	Xūnǐ sīyǒu bōhào wǎngluò	VPDN
Virtual private dial network	虚拟专用拨号网络	Xūnǐ zhuānyòng bōhào wǎngluò	VPDN
Virtual private dial-up network	虚拟拨号专网	Xūnǐ bōhào zhuānwǎng	VPDN
Virtual private dial-up network	虚拟拨号专用网络	Xūnǐ bōhào zhuānyòng wǎngluò	VPDN
Virtual private LAN segment	虚拟专用 LAN 网段	Xūnǐ zhuānyòng LAN wǎngduàn	VPLS
Virtual private LAN segment	虚拟专用 LAN 子网段	Xūnǐ zhuānyòng LAN ziwǎng duàn	VPLS
Virtual private LAN service	虚拟专用局域网业务	Xūnǐ zhuānyòng júyùwǎng yèwù	VPLS

Virtual private mobile network	虚拟专用移动网	Xūnǐ zhuānyòng yídòng wǎng	VPMN
Virtual private network	虚拟用户专网	Xūnǐ yònghù zhuānwǎng	VPN
Virtual private network	虚拟专网	Xūnǐ zhuānwǎng	VPN
Virtual private network	虚拟专用网	Xūnǐ zhuānyòng wǎng	VPN
Virtual private network service	虚拟专用网业务	Xūnǐ zhuānyòng wǎng yèwù	VPNS
Virtual private routed network	虚拟专用路由网络	Xūnǐ zhuānyòng lùyóu wǎngluò	VPRN
Virtual private wire service	虚拟专用线业务	Xūnǐ zhuānyòng xiàn yèwù	VPWS
Virtual program status word	虚拟程序状态字	Xūnǐ chéngxù zhuàngtài zì	VPSW
Virtual prototype	虚拟原型	Xūnǐ yuánxíng	
Virtual prototype modeling language (CAD/CAM)	虚拟原型建模语言	Xūnǐ yuánxíng jiànmó yǔyán	VPML
Virtual provisioned network	虚拟配置网	Xūnǐ pèizhì wǎng	VPrN
Virtual provisioned pipe	虚拟配置管道	Xūnǐ pèizhì guǎndào	VPrP
Virtual reality	虚拟实境	Xūnǐ shíjìng	
Virtual reality	虚拟现实	Xūnǐ xiànshí	VR
Virtual reality mark-up language	虚拟现实标记语言	Xūnǐ xiànshí biāojì yǔyán	VRML
Virtual reality modeling language	虚拟现实建模语言	Xūnǐ xiànshí jiànmó yǔyán	VRML
Virtual reality modeling language	虚拟现实模型语言	Xūnǐ xiànshí móxíng yǔyán	VRML
Virtual redundant router protocol	虚拟冗余路由器协议	Xūnǐ rǒngyú lùyóuqì xiéyì	VRRP
Virtual root	虚拟根	Xūnǐ gēn	
Virtual route identifier	虚拟路由标识符	Xūnǐ lùyóu biāozhì fú	VRID
Virtual router	虚拟路由器	Xūnǐ lùyóuqì	VR
Virtual router redundancy protocol (in LINUX and an IETF protocol)	虚拟路由器冗余协议	Xūnǐ lùyóuqì rǒngyú xiéyì	VRRP
Virtual server	虚拟服务器	Xūnǐ fúwùqì	
Virtual source	虚拟源点	Xūnǐ yuándiǎn	VS
Virtual space teleconferencing system	虚拟空间会议系统	Xūnǐ kōngjiān huìyì xìtǒng	VST
Virtual storage	虚拟存储	Xūnǐ cúnchǔ	VS
Virtual storage management	虚拟存储管理	Xūnǐ cúnchǔ guǎnlǐ	VSM
Virtual table	虚拟表	Xūnǐ biǎo	
Virtual telecommunication access method	虚拟远程通信存取法	Xūnǐ yuǎnchéng tōngxìn cúnqǔ fǎ	VTAM
Virtual terminal	虚拟终端	Xūnǐ zhōngduān	VT
Virtual terminal clients and servers	虚终端客户和服务器	Xū zhōngduān kèhù hé fúwùqì	
Virtual terminal clients and servers	虚终端客户机和服务器	Xū zhōngduān kèhùjī hé fúwùqì	
Virtual terminal protocol	虚拟终端规约	Xūnǐ zhōngduān guīyuē	VTP
Virtual terminal protocol (a Cisco protocol)	虚拟终端协议	Xūnǐ zhōngduān xiéyì	VTP
Virtual trunk	虚中继	Xū zhōngjì	
Virtual user port	虚拟用户端口	Xūnǐ yònghù duānkǒu	VUP
Virtual workplace	虚拟工作场所	Xūnǐ gōngzuò chángsuǒ	
Virtuality	虚境	Xū jìng	
Virtualization	虚拟化	Xūnǐhuà	
Virus	病毒	Bìngdú	
Virus resistant domain (Linux)	病毒防护区	Bìngdú fánghù qū	
Virus software	病毒软件	Bìngdú ruǎnjiàn	
Visibility analysis	可视分析	Kěshì fēnxī	
Visibility map	可视图	Kěshì tú	
Visibiliy	可见度	Kějiàndù	
Visible arc	可见弧	Kějiàn hú	

Visible photodiode	可见光二极体	Kějiàn guāng èrjítǐ	
Visited mobile service switching center	被访移动业务交换中心	Bèifǎng yídòng yèwù jiāohuàn zhōngxīn	VMSC
Visited mobile services switching centre	受访移动无线局	Shòufǎng yídòng wúxiàn jú	VMSC
Visited mobile switching center	拜访移动业务交换中心	Bàifǎng yídòng yèwù jiāohuàn zhōngxīn	VMSC
Visited MSC	拜访 MSC	Bàifǎng MSC	VMSC
Visited PLMN	拜访 PLMN	Bàifǎng PLMN	VPLMN
Visited public land mobile network	拜访公用陆地移动通信网络	Bàifǎng gōngyòng lùdì yídòng tōngxìn wǎngluò	VPLMN
Visited public land mobile network (PLMN)	受访公众陆地移动网	Shòufǎng gōngzhòng lùdì yídòng wǎng	VPLMN
Visiting mobile subscriber	来访移动用户	Láifǎng yídòng yònghù	
Visitor location register	拜访位置寄存器	Bàifǎng wèizhì jìcúnqì	VLR
Visitor location register	访问位置寄存器	Fǎngwèn wèizhì jìcúnqì	VLR
Visitor location register	访问用户位置寄存器	Fǎngwèn yònghù wèizhì jìcúnqì	VLR
Visitor location register	来访位置登记器	Láifǎng wèizhì dēngjìqì	VLR
Visitor location register	来访位置注册处	Láifǎng wèizhì zhùcèchù	VLR
Visitor register	来访登记	Láifǎng dēngjì	
Vista point	视点	Shìdiǎn	
Visual check	目标检查	Mùbiāo jiǎnchá	
Visual display unit	视觉显示器	Shìjué xiǎnshìqì	
Visual interactive modeling	可视交互式建模	Kěshì jiāohù-shì jiànmó	
Visual interpretation (GIS)	目视判读	Mùshì pàndú	
Visual mask	视觉掩模	Shìjué yǎnmó	
Visual perception	视觉感知	Shìjué gǎnzhī	
Visual perception	视觉理解	Shìjué lǐjiě	
Visual teleconference; videoconference	可视电话会议	Kěshì diànhuà huìyì	
Visual total	直观合计	Zhíguān héjì	
Visualization	可视化	Kěshìhuà	
Visualized geometry engine	可视化几何引擎	Kěshìhuà jǐhé yǐnqíng	
Viterbi algorithm	维特比算法	Wéi-tè-bǐ suànfǎ	VA
Vocoder	声码器	Shēngmǎqì	
Vodatel (UK company)	爱达利公司	Ài-dá-lì gōngsī	
Voice access to content	语音接入信息	Yǔyīn jiērù xìnxī	
Voice access unit	语言接入单元	Yǔyán jiērù dānyuán	VAU
Voice activity detection	话音活动检测	Huàyīn huódòng jiǎncè	VAD
Voice activity detection	话音激活检波	Huàyīn jīhuó jiǎnbō	VAD
Voice activity detection	话音激活检测	Huàyīn jīhuó jiǎncè	VAD
Voice activity detector	话音激活检波器	Huàyīn jīhuó jiǎnbōqì	VAD
Voice activity factor	语音激活因子	Yǔyīn jīhuó yīnzǐ	VA
Voice announcement fixed type	话音广播固定类型	Huàyīn guǎngbō gùdìng lèixíng	VAFX
Voice announcement mixed type	话音广播混合类型	Huàyīn guǎngbō hùnhé lèixíng	VAMX
Voice application service provider	语音应用服务提供商	Yǔyīn yìngyòng fúwù tígōngshāng	VASP
Voice broadcast	电话通知系统	Diànhuà tōngzhī xìtǒng	
Voice broadcast service	话音广播业务	Huàyīn guǎngbō yèwù	VBS
Voice broadcast service	语音广播业务	Yǔyīn guǎngbō yèwù	VBS
Voice browser	语音导航	Yǔyīn dǎoháng	VB
Voice channel	话路	Huàlù	VC
Voice channel	话音信道	Huàyīn xìndào	VC

Voice channel controller	话音信道控制器	Huàyīn xìndào kòngzhìqì	VCC
Voice channel unit	话音信道单元	Huàyīn xìndào dānyuán	VCU
Voice circuit	话音电路	Huàyīn diànlù	VC
Voice circuit input level	话路输入电平	Huàlù shūrù diànpíng	
Voice circuit input level difference	话路输入电平差异	Huàlù shūrù diànpíng chāyì	
Voice code	话音编码	Huàyīn biānmǎ	VC
Voice coder	话音编码器	Huàyīn biānmǎqì	VOCODER
Voice coder	音频编码器	Yīnpín biānmǎqì	VOCODER
Voice coding	音频编码	Yīnpín biānmǎ	
Voice commerce	语音商务	Yǔyīn shāngwù	VC
Voice compression algorithm	语音压缩算法	Yǔyīn yāsuō suànfǎ	
Voice control	话音控制	Huàyīn kòngzhì	VC
Voice control	声控	Shēngkòng	
Voice control sensitivity	声控灵敏度	Shēngkòng língmǐndù	
Voice data multiplexer	音频数据复用板	Yīnpín shùjù fùyòng bǎn	VDM
Voice data multiplexer (literally "voice frequency digital overlay board")	音频数字叠加板	Yīnpín shùzì diéjiā bǎn	VDM
Voice digitization	语音数字化	Yǔyīn shùzìhuà	
Voice digitization rate	话音数字化速率	Huàyīn shùzìhuà sùlǜ	VDR
Voice distribution frame	音频配线	Yīnpín pèixiàn	VDF
Voice dropout rate	掉话率	Diàohuà lǜ	
Voice exciting	话音激活	Huàyīn jīhuó	
Voice eXtensible markup language	语音扩展标记语言	Yǔyīn kuòzhǎn biāojì yǔyán	VXML
Voice feature	话音业务	Huàyīn yèwù	
Voice frequency board	音频板	Yīnpín bǎn	VFB
Voice frequency channel	音频信道	Yīnpín xìndào	VFC
Voice group call service	话音组呼叫业务	Huàyīn zǔ hūjiào yèwù	VGCS
Voice group call service	语音群呼叫业务	Yǔyīn qún hūjiào yèwù	VGCS
Voice group call service	语音组呼业务	Yǔyīn zǔ hū yèwù	VGCS
Voice group call service	语音组呼叫业务	Yǔyīn zǔ hūjiào yèwù	VGCS
Voice mail	语音信箱	Yǔyīn xìnxiāng	
Voice mail service	语音信箱业务	Yǔyīn xìnxiāng yèwù	VMS
Voice mail service	语音邮箱业务	Yǔyīn yóuxiāng yèwù	VMS
Voice mail system	话音邮件系统	Huàyīn yóujiàn xìtǒng	
Voice mail system	语音信箱系统	Yǔyīn xìnxiāng xìtǒng	VMS
Voice mailbox	语音邮箱	Yǔyīn yóuxiāng	VM
Voice message exchange	声音信息交换	Shēngyīn xìnxī jiāohuàn	VME
Voice message handling point	语音信息处理点	Yǔyīn xìnxī chǔlǐ diǎn	VMHP
Voice message retrieval system	声音信息检索系统	Shēngyīn xìnxī jiǎnsuǒ xìtǒng	VMRS
Voice messaging	话音讯息交流	Huàyīn xùnxī jiāoliú	
Voice module	语音模块	Yǔyīn mókuài	VM
Voice over ATM	在 ATM 上的话音	Zài ATM-shàngde huà yīn	VOATM
Voice over DSL	DSL 传话音	DSL chuánhuà yīn	VoDSL
Voice over DSL	在 DSL 上传话音	Zài DSL-shàng chuán huàyīn	VoDSL
Voice over internet protocol	IP 网上传输话音	IP wǎngshàng chuánshū huàyīn	VOIP
Voice over Internet protocol	网络电话	Wǎngluò diànhuà	VOIP
Voice over Internet protocol	网上传输话音	Wǎngshàng chuánshū huàyīn	VOIP

Voice over Internet protocol (VoIP) gateway	因特网语音网关	Yīntèwǎng yǔyīn wǎngguān	
Voice over internet protocol (ITU-T protocol)	IP 上的语音协议	IP-shàngde yǔyīn xiéyì	VOIP
Voice over IP	IP 话音	IP huàyīn	VoIP
Voice over IP	IP 上的话音	IP-shàngde huàyīn	VoIP
Voice over IP	在 IP 上的话音	Zài IP-shàngde huàyīn	VOIP
Voice overlaying digital (data)	音频数字叠加	Yīnpín shùzì diéjiā	
Voice phone card	人声电话卡	Rénshēng diànhuà kǎ	
Voice portal	语音门户	Yǔyīn ménhù	VP
Voice processing system	语音处理系统	Yǔyīn chǔlǐ xìtǒng	VPS
Voice recognition	语音辨识	Yǔyīn biànshí	
Voice recording	话音记录	Huàyīn jìlù	
Voice switching unit	语言交换单元	Yǔyán jiāohuàn dānyuán	VSU
Voice/data integration	话音/数据综合	Huàyīn/shùjù zōnghé	
Voiced sounds	浊音	Zhuóyīn	
Voice-frequency multiplex telegraphy	音频复用电报	Yīnpín fùyòng diànbào	VFT
Voice-frequency signaling	音频信令	Yīnpín xìnlìng	
Voicemail alert	语音邮件提示	Yǔyīn yóujiàn tíshì	VMA
Voicemail, voice message	口信	Kǒuxìn	
Voicemail; voice message	音邮	Yīnyóu	
Void polygon	无效多边形	Wúxiào duōbiānxíng	
Void ratio	孔隙比	Kǒngxì bǐ	
Voigt model	沃格特模型	Wò-gé-tè móxíng	
Volatile fault	间歇故障	Jiànxiē gùzhàng	
Volatile memory	易失存储器	Yìshī cúnchǔqì	
Volatile memory	易矢性存储器	Yìshǐxìng cúnchǔqì	
Volcano profile ovens (semiconductor mfg)	火山剖面炉	Huǒshān pōumiàn lú	
Voltage change	电压变化	Diànyā biànhuà	
Voltage change interval	电压变化时间间隔	Diànyā biànhuà shíjiān jiàngé	
Voltage controlled crystal oscillator	电压控制晶体振荡器	Diànyā kòngzhì jīngtǐ zhèndàngqì	VCXO
Voltage controlled crystal oscillator (short for 电压控制晶体振荡器)	压控晶振	Yākòng jīngzhèn	VCXO
Voltage controlled oscillator	压控振荡器	Yākòng zhèndàngqì	VCO
Voltage controlled oscillator input control voltage	压控振荡器输入控制电压	Yākòng zhèndàngqì shūrù kòngzhì diànyā	
Voltage dip	电压瞬时跌落	Diànyā shùnshí diēluò	
Voltage dip	电压骤降	Diànyā zhòujiàng	
Voltage fluctuation	电压波动	Diànyā bōdòng	
Voltage fluctuation magnitude	电压波动量	Diànyā bōdòng liáng	
Voltage fluctuation waveform	电压波动波形	Diànyā bōdòng bōxíng	
Voltage identification definition	电压识别认证	Diànyā shíbié rènzhèng	VID
Voltage imbalance	电压不平衡	Diànyā bùpínghéng	
Voltage measured with a psophometer conforming to ITU-T Recommendation O.41	用符合 ITU-T 建议 O.41 定的噪声计测量到的电压	Yòng fúhé ITU-T jiànyì O.41 guīdìngde zàoshēng jì cèliáng dàode diànyā	Upso
Voltage reflection coefficient	电压反射系数	Diànyā fǎnshè xìshù	
Voltage regulator	稳压器	Wěnyāqì	VR
Voltage regulator module	电压调整模块	Diànyā tiáozhěng mókuài	VRM
Voltage resolving	电压分解	Diànyā fēnjiě	

Voltage standing wave ratio	电压驻波比	Diànyā zhùbōbǐ	VSWR
Voltage surge	电压浪涌	Diànyā làngyǒng	
Voltage to current converter	电压-电流变换器	Diànyā/diànliú biànhuànqì	V/I
Voltage to ground	对地电压	Duìdì diànyā	
Voltage-to-frequency conversion	电压 / 频率转换	Diànyā/pínlǜ zhuǎnhuàn	V/F
Voltmeter	电压表	Diànyābiǎo	
Volume control	音量控制	Yīnliàng kòngzhì	
Volume distributive target	体分布目标	Tǐ fēnbù mùbiāo	
Volume label	卷标	Juàn biāo	
Volume method	容积法	Róngjī fǎ	
Volume of data	数据量	Shùjù liàng	
Volume pixel	立体像素	Lìtǐ xiàngsù	Voxel
Volume shrinkage	体积收缩率	Tǐjī shōusuō lǜ	
Volume texture compression	体积纹理压缩	Tǐjī wénlǐ yāsuō	
Volumetric spatial function	体积测定空间函数	Tǐjī cèdìng kōngjiān hánshù	
Volumetric strain-meter	容积应变仪	Róngjī yìngbiànyí	
Voluntary tunnel	自主隧道	Zìzhǔ suìdào	
Volygon (in 3D modelling, a three-dimensional polygon)	三维多边形	Sānwéi duōbiānxíng	
Vowels	元音	Yuányīn	
Voxel (volume element) (in 3D modelling)	三维像素	Sānwéi xiàngsù	
VP-VC switch	VP-VC 交换机	VP-VC jiāohuànjī	
V-slot	三角形槽	Sānjiǎoxíng cáo	
V-terminal voltage	V 端子电压	V duānzi diànyā	
Vulnerability	脆弱性	Cuìruòxìng	
Vulnerability (in IPSec)	漏洞	Lòudòng	

W

Wafer	晶片圆盘	Jīngpiàn yuánpán	
Wafer	晶圆	Jīngyuán	
Wafer (semiconductor mfg)	芯片	Xìnpiàn	
Wafer packaging system (semiconductor mfg)	芯片封装系统	Xìnpiàn fēngzhuāng xìtǒng	
Wafer stepper (semiconductor mfg)	缩小投影曝光设备	Suōxiǎo tóuyǐng bàoguāng shèbèi	
Wait indicator	等待指示	Děngdài zhǐshì	
Wait to restoration	恢复等待时间	Huīfù děngdài shíjiān	WTR
Wait to restore	等待恢复	Děngdài huīfù	WTR
Wait to restore time	等待恢复时间	Děngdài huīfù shíjiān	WTR
Waiting time	等待时间	Děngdài shíjiān	
Waiting time extension	扩展等待时间	Kuòzhǎn děngdài shíjiān	WTX
Wake	尾流	Wěiliú	
Wake on LAN	局域网唤醒	Júyùwǎng huànxǐng	WOL
Walkie-talkie	步话机	Bùhuàjī	
Wall mounted type	壁装式	Bìzhuāng shì	W
Wall niche type	壁龛式	Bìkān shì	
Wall-mounted mail box	挂式邮政信箱	Guàshì yóuzhèng xìnxiāng	
Wallpaper (computer screen background)	墙纸	Qiángzhǐ	
Walsh function	沃尔什函数	Wò-ěr-shí hánshù	

Walsh-Hadamard transform	沃尔什-哈达码变换	Wò-ěr-shí—Hǎ-dá-mǎ biànhuàn	WHT
Wand	光笔	Guāngbǐ	
Wand bar code scanner	光笔式条码扫描器	Guāngbǐ-shì tiáomǎ sǎomiáoqì	
Wander	漂动	Piāodòng	
Wander, sloshing, rocking	摇动	Yáodòng	
Wang Computers (US company)	王安电脑	Wáng ān diànnǎo	
Warm boot; warm start	热启动	Rè qǐdòng	
Warm-standby	温备用	Wēn bèiyòng	
Warning and its communication	警报及传递	Jǐngbào jí chuándì	
Warning receiver	告警接收机	Gàojǐng jiēshōujī	
Warning statement	警报公布	Jǐngbào gōngbù	
Warning, alarm	警报	Jǐngbào	
Watch receiver	监视接收机	Jiānshì jiēshōujī	
Watchdata System Corp (Beijing)	握奇数据系统有限公司	Wòjī shùjù xìtǒng yǒuxiàn gōngsī	
Watchdog packet	监视狗数据包	Jiānshìgǒu shùjù bāo	
Watchdog timer	监视时钟	Jiānshì shízhōng	WDT
Watchdog timer	监视狗定时器	Jiānshìgǒu dìngshíqì	
Water load	水负载	Shuǐ fùzài	
Water swelling heat melting (FOC)	水胀热融	Shuǐzhàng rèróng	WSHM
Waterblock tape (FOC mfg)	阻水带	Zǔshuǐ dài	
Watt-hour meter	电度表	Diàndùbiǎo	
Wave	波	Bō	
Wave channel interval	波道间隔	Bōdào jiàngé	
Wave coverage	波段覆盖	Bōduàn fùgài	
Wave equation	波动方程式	Bōdòng fāngchéngshì	
Wave gauge	测波高仪	Cè bōgāoyí	
Wave grouping	波群	Bōqún	
Wave guide synthesis	波导合成	Bōdǎo héchéng	WG
Wave impedance	波阻抗	Bō zǔkàng	
Wave interference	波干涉	Bō gānshè	
Wave number	波数	Bōshù	
Wave polarization	波极化	Bō jíhuà	
Wave pressure	波压	Bōyā	
Wave rotation circulator	波旋转式环行器	Bō xuánzhuǎnshì huánxíngqì	
Wave rotation isolator	波旋转式隔离器	Bō xuánzhuǎnshì gélíqì	
Wave soldering	波峰焊	Bōfēnghàn	
Wave table synthesis	波表合成	Bōbiǎo héchéng	WT
Wave transformation	波变形	Bō biànxíng	
Waveform	波形	Bōxíng	
Waveform coding	波形编码	Bōxíng biānmǎ	
Waveform interpolation	波形插值	Bōxíng chāzhí	
Waveform interpolation	波形内插	Bōxíng nèichā	WI
Waveform monitor	波形监视器	Bōxíng jiānshìqì	WFM
Waveguide	波导	Bōdǎo	
Waveguide below cut-off	截止波导	Jiézhǐ bōdǎo	
Waveguide bend	弯波导	Wān bōdǎo	

Waveguide cavity	波导空腔	Bōdǎo kōngqiāng	
Waveguide CO_2 laser	波导型二氧化碳激光	Bōdǎo xíng èryǎnghuàtàn jīguāng	
Waveguide corner	波导弯头	Bōdǎo wāntóu	
Waveguide cut-off frequency	波导截止频率	Bōdǎo jiézhǐ pínlǜ	
Waveguide dispersion	波导色散	Bōdǎo sèsàn	
Waveguide filter	波导滤波器	Bōdǎo lǜbōqì	
Waveguide flange	波导法兰	Bōdǎo fǎlán	
Waveguide gasket	波导垫片	Bōdǎo diànpiàn	
Waveguide grating router	波导光栅选路器	Bōdǎo guāngshān xuǎnlùqì	WGR
Waveguide mode	波导模	Bōdǎo mó	
Waveguide photo diode	波导光探测二极管	Bōdǎo guāng tàncè èrjíguǎn	WGPD
Waveguide post	波导棒	Bōdǎo bàng	
Waveguide shim	波导垫圈	Bōdǎo diànquān	
Waveguide switch	波导开关	Bōdǎo kāiguān	
Waveguide terminating slot antenna	波导端缝隙天线	Bōdǎo duān fèngxì tiānxiàn	
Waveguide tuner	波导调节器	Bōdǎo tiáojiéqì	
Waveguide twist	扭波导	Niǔ bōdǎo	
Waveguide wavelength	波导波长	Bōdǎo bōcháng	
Waveguide window	波导窗	Bōdǎo chuāng	
Wavelength	波长	Bōcháng	
Wavelength allocation	波长分配	Bōcháng fēnpèi	WA
Wavelength continuity constraint	波长连续限制	Bōcháng liánxù xiànzhì	
Wavelength conversion	波长变换	Bōcháng biànhuàn	WC
Wavelength converter	波长变换器	Bōcháng biànhuànqì	
Wavelength converter	波长转换板	Bōcháng zhuǎnhuàn bǎn	
Wavelength cross-connect	波长交叉连接	Bōcháng jiāochā liánjiē	WXC
Wavelength division multiplex	波分多路复用	Bōfēn duōlù fùyòng	WDM
Wavelength division multiplexer	波分复用器	Bōfēn fùyòngqì	WDM
Wavelength division multiplexing	波长分割多路复用	Bōcháng fēngē duōlù fùyòng	WDM
Wavelength division multiplexing	波分复用	Bōfēn fùyòng	WDM
Wavelength interchanging optical cross-connect	波长变换交叉连接器	Bōcháng biànhuàn jiāochā liánjiēqì	
Wavelength isolation	波长隔离度	Bōcháng gélídù	I
Wavelength path connect	波长通道连接	Bōcháng tōngdào liánjiē	WPC
Wavelength path ID	波长通道值	Bōcháng tōngdào zhí	WPI
Wavelength path link	波长通道链路	Bōcháng tōngdào liànlù	WPL
Wavelength reduction factor	波长缩短因子	Bōcháng suōduǎn yīnzǐ	
Wavelength repeatability	波长重复度	Bōcháng chóngfùdù	
Wavelength reuse	波长重用	Bōcháng zhòngyòng	
Wavelength routed network	波长路由网	Bōcháng lùyóu wǎng	
Wavelength routed network	波长选路网	Bōcháng xuǎnlù wǎng	
Wavelength router switch	波长选路开关	Bōcháng xuǎnlù kāiguān	WRS
Wavelength-dependent loss	波长相关损耗	Bōcháng xiāngguān sǔnhào	WDL
Wavelength-selective optical cross-connect	波长选择光交叉连接器	Bōcháng xuǎnzé guāng jiāochā liánjiēqì	
Wavelet	小波	Xiǎobō	
Wavelet decomposition	小波分解	Xiǎobō fēnjiě	
Wavelet packet	小波包	Xiǎobō bāo	WP

Wavelet transform	小波变换	Xiǎobō biànhuàn	
Wave-trap	陷波器	Xiànbōqì	
Weak current system	弱电系统	Ruòdiàn xìtǒng	RD
Weak fair dependence relation (in Petri nets)	弱公平依赖关系	Ruò gōngping yīlài guānxi	
Weak Markovian bisimulation	弱马尔科夫相似	Ruò mǎ-ěr-kē-fū xiāngsì	
Weak password	弱口令	Ruò kǒuling	
Weakly connected graph	弱连通图	Ruò liántōng tú	
Weakness failure	弱点失效	Ruòdiǎn shīxiào	
Weakness fault	弱点故障	Ruòdiǎn gùzhàng	
Wearable computing	可穿戴计算	Kěchuāndài jìsuàn	
Wearnes Computers (Singapore company)	维信电脑	Wéi-xin diànnǎo	
Wear-out failure	耗损失效	Hàosǔn shīxiào	
Wear-out failure period	耗损失效其	Hàosǔn shīxiàoqí	
Wear-out failure rate	终止失效率	Zhōngzhǐ shīxiào lǜ	
Wear-out fault	耗损故障	Hàosǔn gùzhàng	
Weather radar	气象雷达	Qìxiàng léidá	
Web crawler	网络搜索器	Wǎngluò sōusuǒqì	
Web distributed data exchange	Web 分布式数据交换	Web Fēnbùshì shùjù jiāohuàn	WDDX
Web hosting	主机托管	Zhǔjī tuōguǎn	
Web mistress	网上女杰	Wǎngshàng nǚjié	
Web page	网页	Wǎngyè	WEB
Web server	互联网网站	Hùliánwǎng wǎngzhàn	
Web services description language	网络服务描述语言	Wǎngluò fúwù miáoshù yǔyán	WSDL
Web services description language	Web 服务描述语言	Web fúwù miáoshù yǔyán	WSDL
Webaholic	网虫	Wǎngchóng	
Web-based enterprise management	基于 Web 的企业管理	Jīyú Web de qǐyè guǎnlǐ	WBEM
Web-based training	基于网络的训练	Jīyú wǎngluòde xùnliàn	WBT
Webcasting	网播	Wǎngbō	
WebGIS	万维网 GIS	Wànwéiwǎng GIS	
Website	网站	Wǎngzhàn	
Webtop publishing	网上出版	Wǎngshàng chūbǎn	
Weed tolerance	Weed 容差	Weed róngchā	
Weekly Fiberoptics Newsbrief Service (from KMI - Kinder Morgan Inc.)	纤维光学每周新闻简报服务	Xiānwéi guāngxué měizhōu xīnwén jiǎnbào fúwù	FNB
Weibull distribution	韦伯分布	Wéibó fēnbù	
Weibull distribution	威布分布	Wēi-bù fēnbù	
Weight, weighted	权重	Quánzhòng	
Weighted average	加权平均	Jiāquán píngjūn	
Weighted dynamic matching algorithm	加权动态匹配算法	Jiāquán dòngtài pǐpèi suànfǎ	
Weighted fair queuing	加权公平队列	Jiāquán gōngping duìliè	WFQ
Weighted fair queuing	加权公平排队	Jiāquán gōngping páiduì	WFQ
Weighted fair queuing	加权的公平排队算法	Jiāquánde gōngping páiduì suànfǎ	WFQ
Weighted graph	加权图	Jiāquán tú	
Weighted noise	衡重杂音	Héngzhòng záyīn	
Weighted noise	加权噪声	Jiāquán zàoshēng	
Weighted random early detection	加权随机早期检测	Jiāquán suíjī zǎoqī jiǎncè	WRED
Weighted random early detection	加权随机早期侦测	Jiāquán suíjī zǎoqī zhēncè	WRED

English	Chinese	Pinyin	Abbreviation
Weighted random early detection	加权的随机早期控测	Jiāquánde suíjī zǎoqī kòngcè	WRED
Weighted Random Early Detection	加权的随机早期探测	Jiāquánde suíjī zǎoqī tàncè	WRED
Weighted round robin	加权往返算法	Jiāquán wǎngfǎn suànfǎ	WRR
Weighted translation	加权平移	Jiāquán píngyí	
Weighting	加权	Jiāquán	
Western Digital (US disk drive maker)	西部数子	Xībù shùzǐ	
Wetted contact	降阻触点	Jiàngzǔ chùdiǎn	
What you see is what you get	见得相一	Jiàn de xiāng yī	WYSIWYG
What you see is what you get	所见即所得	Suǒjiàn jí suǒdé	WYSIWYG
What you see is what you get	直接可视数据	Zhíjiē kěshì shùjù	WYSIWYG
Wheatstone automatic system	惠斯登自动系统	Huì-sī-dēng zìdòng xìtǒng	
Whip antenna	鞭天线	Biān tiānxiàn	
Whip antenna	鞭状天线	Biānzhuàng tiānxiàn	
Whistler	啸声	Xiàoshēng	
Whistling (in telecommunications)	啸声	Xiàoshēng	
White balance (digital photography)	白平衡	Bái pínghéng	
White edge	白边	Bái biān	
White noise	白噪声	Bái zàoshēng	
White noise generator	白噪声发生器	Bái zàoshēng fāshēngqì	
White page	白页	Báiyè	
Whiteboard	白板	Báibǎn	
Whoever, whenever, wherever, whomever, whatever communication	任何人,与在任何时候任何地方的任何人进行的任何形式的通信	Rènhé rén yǔ zài rènhé shíhou rènhé dìfangde rènhé rén jìnxíngde rènhé xíngshìde tōngxìn	W5
Whois (computer query)	地址查询	Dìzhǐ cháxún	
Whois (Internet tool)	名目项	Míngmù xiàng	
Wholesaler	批发商	Pīfāshāng	
Wholly foreign owned/funded enterprise	独资企业	Dúzī qǐyè	
Wide aperture antenna	宽孔径天线	Kuān kǒngjìng tiānxiàn	WAA
Wide area augmentation system	广域加强系统	Guǎngyù jiāqiáng xìtǒng	WAAS
Wide area information service	广域信息服务系统	Guǎngyù xìnxī fúwù xìtǒng	WAIS
Wide area information service	广域信息服务系统	Guǎngyù xìnxī fúwù xìtǒng	WAIS
Wide area information service	广域资讯服务	Guǎngyù zīxùn fúwù	WAIS
Wide area network	广域网	Guǎngyùwǎng	WAN
Wide area paging system	联网寻呼系统	Liánwǎng xúnhū xìtǒng	
Wide area telecommunications/telephone service	宽域通信/电话服务	Kuānyù tōngxìn/diànhuà fúwù	WATS
Wide dynamic range	宽动态范围	Kuān dòngtài fànwéi	
Wideband channel	宽带信道	Kuāndài xìndào	
Wideband code division multiple access	宽带码分多址	Kuāndài mǎfēn duōzhǐ	WCDMA
Wideband data peak frequency deviation	宽带数据峰值频偏	Kuāndài shùjù fēngzhí pínpiān	
Wideband laser diode	宽带激光器	Kuāndài jīguāngqì	
Wideband passive optical network	宽带无源光网络	Kuāndài wúyuán guāng wǎngluò	BPON
Wideband radio frequency power amplifier	宽带射频功率放大器	Kuāndài shèpín gōnglǜ fàngdàqì	
Wideband station	宽频段电台	Kuānpínduàn diàntái	
Wideband time division multiple access	宽带时分多路存取	Kuāndài shífēn duōlù cúnqǔ	WBTDMA
Wide-sense stationary	宽平稳	Kuān píngwěn	WSS

Widow (in word processing)	寡行	Guǎxíng	
Wiener filter	维纳滤波器	Wéi-nà lǜbōqì	
Wiggler (mm wave device)	磁波荡器	Cí bōdàngqì	
Wild card	通用字元	Tōngyòng zìyuán	
Wild card	万用字元	Wànyòng zìyuán	
Wildcard	通配符	Tōngpèifú	
Wildcard characters (for database)	通配符字符	Tōngpèifú zìfú	
Wildcard mask	通配符掩码	Tōngpèifú yǎnmǎ	
Wildcard search (for database)	通配符搜索	Tōngpèifú sōusuǒ	
Winchester disk	温盘	Wēn pán	
Winchester disk drive	温彻斯特磁盘机	Wēn-chè-sī-tè cípánjī	
Window	窗口	Chuāngkǒu	
Window	视窗	Shìchuāng	
Window function	窗口函数	Chuāngkǒu hánshù	
Window procedure	窗口过程	Chuāngkǒu guòchéng	
Windowing (GIS)	开窗	Kāichuāng	
Windows accelerator	视窗加速器	Shìchuāng jiāsùqì	
Windows driver model	视窗驱动程序模块	Shìchuāng qūdòng chéngxù mókuài	WDM
Windows hardware Engineering conference	视窗硬件工程会议	Shìchuāng yìngjiàn gōngchéng huìyì	WinHEC
Windows menu (WP command)	视窗菜单	Shìchuāng càidān	
Windows multimedia extensions	Windows 多媒体扩充板	Windows duōméitǐ kuòchōng bǎn	WME
Windows NT (operating system)	视窗新技	Shìchuāng xīn jì	
Windows open service architecture	Windows 开放服务结构	Windows kāifàng fúwù jiégòu	WOSA
Windows scripting host	视窗脚本程序	Shìchuāng jiǎoběn chéngxù	WSH
Windows size	窗口尺寸	Chuāngkǒu chǐcùn	
Windows socket	视窗套接口	Shìchuāng tào jiēkǒu	Winsock
Windows socket; Winsock	视窗套接	Shìchuāng tàojiē	
Windows, icons, menu and cursor	窗户,图标,菜单,光标	Chuānghu, túbiāo, càidān, guāngbiāo	WIMC
Windows, icons, menu and pointer	窗户,图标,菜单,光标	Chuānghu, túbiāo, càidān, guāngbiāo	WIMP
Winfast (US company)	丽台	Lì-tái	
Wintone pen (product of a Qinghua University subsidiary company, used as input device for an electronic tablet)	文通笔	Wéntōng bǐ	
Wiper (of a selector)	弧刷	Húshuā	
Wire communication	有线电通信	Yǒuxiàndiàn tōngxìn	
Wire drawing (noun)	拉丝	Lāsī	
Wire harness	接线头	Jiēxiàntóu	
Wire map	线路映射	Xiànlù yìngshè	
Wire speed	线速	Xiànsù	
Wire-core matrix	线心矩阵	Xiànxīn jǔzhèn	WCM
Wired broadcasting	有线广播	Yǒuxiàn guǎngbō	
Wired equivalent privacy	有线等价保密	Yǒuxiàn děngjià bǎomì	WEP
Wired equivalent privacy	有线对等保密	Yǒuxiàn duìděng bǎomì	WEP
Wired equivalent protocol	有线等效协议	Yǒuxiàn děngxiào xiéyì	WEP
Wired for management	有线管理	Yǒuxiàn guǎnlǐ	WfM
Wired for management initiative	主动式管理线路	Zhǔdòngshì guǎnlǐ xiànlù	WMI
Wired Magazine ©	联线杂志	Liánxiàn zázhì	

Wired telecommunications	有线电	Yǒuxiàndiàn	
Wired/wireless switcher	有线/无线转接器	Yǒuxiàn/wúxiàn zhuǎnjiēqì	
Wired-program control	布线程序控制	Bùxiàn chéngxù kòngzhì	
Wireless access	无线接入	Wúxiàn jiērù	WA
Wireless access gateway	无线接入网关	Wúxiàn jiērù wǎngguān	WAG
Wireless access point	无线接入站	Wúxiàn jiērùzhàn	
Wireless access server	无线接入服务器	Wúxiàn jiērù fúwùqì	WAS
Wireless access technology	无线接入技术	Wúxiàn jiērù jìshù	
Wireless advertisement	无线广告业务	Wúxiàn guǎnggào yèwù	WAD
Wireless application environment	无线应用环境	Wúxiàn yìngyòng huánjìng	WAE
Wireless application protocol	无线应用协议	Wúxiàn yìngyòng xiéyì	WAP
Wireless asymmetrical transmission system	无线非对称传输模式	Wúxiàn fēiduìchèn chuánshū móshì	WATS
Wireless both-way trunk	无线双向中继	Wúxiàn shuāngxiàng zhōngjì	WBWT
Wireless channel	无线信道	Wúxiàn xìndào	
Wireless control message protocol	无线控制消息协议	Wúxiàn kòngzhì xiāoxi xiéyì	WCMP
Wireless coverage area network	无线覆盖域网络	Wúxiàn fùgài yù wǎngluò	WCAN
Wireless data link	无线数据传输链路	Wúxiàn shùjù chuánshū liànlù	WDL
Wireless data protocol	无线数据协议	Wúxiàn shùjù xiéyì	WDP
Wireless datagram protocol	无线数据报文协议	Wúxiàn shùjù bàowén xiéyì	WDP
Wireless datagram protocol	无线数据报协议	Wúxiàn shùjùbào xiéyì	WDP
Wireless Ethernet Compatibility Alliance	无线以太网兼容联盟	Wúxiàn yǐtàiwǎng jiānróng liánméng	WECA
Wireless fidelity	无线保真	Wúxiàn bǎozhēn	Wi-Fi
Wireless hearing aid system	无线助听系统	Wúxiàn zhùtīng xìtǒng	
Wireless home network	无线家庭网	Wúxiàn jiātíng wǎng	
Wireless intelligent network	无线智能网络	Wúxiàn zhìnéng wǎngluò	WIN
Wireless link connection timer	无线链路连接定时器	Wúxiàn liànlù liánjiē dìngshíqì	
Wireless local area network	无线本地网	Wúxiàn běndì wǎng	WLAN
Wireless local area network	无线局域网	Wúxiàn júyùwǎng	WLAN
Wireless local area network	无线区域网路	Wúxiàn qūyù wǎnglù	WLAN
Wireless local loop	无线本地环路	Wúxiàn běndì huánlù	WLL
Wireless markup language	无线标记语言	Wúxiàn biāojì yǔyán	WML
Wireless markup language	无线标志语言	Wúxiàn biāozhì yǔyán	WML
Wireless microphone	无线传声器	Wúxiàn chuánshēngqì	
Wireless personal area network	无线个人域网	Wúxiàn gèrén yù wǎng	WPAN
Wireless personal communication	无线个人通信	Wúxiàn gèrén tōngxìn	WPC
Wireless presentation gateway	无线演示文稿机	Wúxiàn yǎnshì wéngǎojī	
Wireless private branch exchange	无线专用交换机	Wúxiàn zhuānyòng jiāohuànjī	WPBX
Wireless receiver equipment	无线接收设备	Wúxiàn jiēshōu shèbèi	WS
Wireless revolution	无线革命	Wúxiàn gémìng	
Wireless session protocol	无线会话协议	Wúxiàn huìhuà xiéyì	WSP
Wireless speech protocol	无线会话协议	Wúxiàn huìhuà xiéyì	WSP
Wireless subscriber access	无线用户接入	Wúxiàn yònghù jiērù	WSA
Wireless telephone exchange	无线电话交换机	Wúxiàn diànhuà jiāohuànjī	WTX
Wireless telephony application	无线电话应用	Wúxiàn diànhuà yìngyòng	WTA
Wireless telephony applications interface	无线电话应用接口	Wúxiàn diànhuà yìngyòng jiēkǒu	WTAI
Wireless terminal	无线终端	Wúxiàn zhōngduān	WT

English	Chinese	Pinyin	Abbr.
Wireless transaction protocol	无线事务处理协议	Wúxiàn shìwù chǔlǐ xiéyì	WTP
Wireless transaction protocol	无线事务协议	Wúxiàn shìwù xiéyì	WTP
Wireless transmission equipment	无线发射设备	Wúxiàn fāshè shèbèi	WF
Wireless transmission level security	无线传输层安全	Wúxiàn chuánshū céng ānquán	WTLS
Wireless transport layer security	无线传送层安全性	Wúxiàn chuánsòng céng ānquánxing	WTLS
Wireless trunking system	无线集群系统	Wúxiàn jíqún xitǒng	
Wireless user group	无线用户组	Wúxiàn yònghù zǔ	WUG
Wireless virtual private network	无线虚拟专用网络	Wúxiàn xūnǐ zhuānyòng wǎngluò	WVPN
Wiretap	搭线法	Dāxiàn fǎ	
Wiretap channel	窃密信道	Qièmì xìndào	
Wiretapping (for wired communications), interception	窃听	Qiètīng	
Wiring	配电	Pèidiàn	PD
Wiring closet	配线室	Pèixiàn shì	
Wiring on porcelain insulator	瓷珠敷设	Cízhū fūshè	K
Wiring on porcelain knob	瓷瓶敷设	Cípíng fūshè	K
Wiring, cabling	布线	Bùxiàn	
Withdrawal	撤消	Chèxiāo	
Withdrawal of analog frequencies	模拟退频	Mónǐ tuìpín	
Withdrawal of undeliverable remittance	无法退还汇款撤回	Wúfǎ tuìhuán huìkuǎn chèhuí	
Within-type optical fiber (cable) connector adapter	同型号光纤（缆）连接器转接座	Tóng xínghào guāngxiān (lǎn) liánjiēqì zhuǎnjiēzuò	
Wizard	精灵程序	Jīnglíng chéngxù	
Wizard, guide	向导	Xiàngdǎo	
Word	单词	Dāncí	
Word articulation	单词清晰度	Dāncí qīngxīdù	
Word error probability	误差概率	Wùchā gàilǜ	
Word generation	字生成	Zì shēngchéng	
Word length	字长	Zìcháng	
Word processing software	词处理软件	Cí chǔlǐ ruǎnjiàn	WP
Word processor	字处理器	Zì chǔlǐqì	
Word Wide Web	环球网	Huánqiú wǎng	www
Word Wide Web Committee	环球网委员会	Huánqiú wǎng wěiyuánhuì	W3C
Word wrap	整字换行	Zhěngzì huànháng	
WordPerfect ©	完美文书	Wánměi wénshū	
WordStar © (software)	字星	Zìxīng	
Work area	工作区	Gōngzuòqū	WA
Work area cable	工作区电缆	Gōngzuòqū diànlǎn	
Work area cord	工作区软线	Gōngzuòqū ruǎnxiàn	
Work area optical cable	工作区光缆	Gōngzuòqū guānglǎn	
Work factor	代价因子	Dàijià yīnzǐ	
Work station	工作站	Gōngzuòzhàn	WS
Work station function block	工作站功能块	Gōngzuòzhàn gōngnéng kuài	WSF
Work station server	工作站服务器	Gōngzuòzhàn fúwùqì	WSS
Work waiting time	工作等待时间	Gōngzuò děngdài shíjiān	WWT
Workflow engine interchange	工作流引擎交换	Gōngzuòliú yǐnqing jiāohuàn	
Workflow management coalition	工作流管理联盟	Gōngzuòliú guǎnlǐ liánméng	WfMC

Workflow management system	工作流管理系统	Gōngzuòliú guǎnlǐ xìtǒng	WfMS
Workflow meta-model	工作流元模型	Gōngzuòliú yuán móxíng	
Workflow model	工作流模型	Gōngzuòliú móxíng	
Workflow net	工作流网	Gōngzuòliú wǎng	
Workflow process definition language	工作流过程定义语言	Gōngzuòliú guòchéng dìngyì yǔyán	WPDL
Workflow relevant data	工作流相关数据	Gōngzuòliú xiāngguān shùjù	
Workflow type definition	工作流类型定义	Gōngzuòliú lèixíng dìngyì	
Workgroup	工作组	Gōngzuòzǔ	
Workgroup software	工作组软件	Gōngzuòzǔ ruǎnjiàn	
Working ground	工作接地	Gōngzuò jiēdì	
Working range	工作范围	Gōngzuò fànwéi	
Working register	工作寄存器	Gōngzuò jìcúnqì	WK
Working stress design	工作应力设计	Gōngzuò yìnglì shèjì	
Workspace	工作空间	Gōngzuò kōngjiān	
Workstation function block	工作站功能块	Gōngzuòzhàn gōngnéng kuài	WSF
World Administrative Radio Conference	世界无线电管理大会	Shìjiè wúxiàndiàn guǎnlǐ dàhuì	WARC
World Administrative Radio Conference	世界无线电行政大会	Shìjiè wúxiàndiàn xíngzhèng dàhuì	WARC
World Association of Industrial and Technological Research Organizations	世界工业与技术研究组织协会	Shìjiè gōngyè yǔ jìshù yánjiū zǔzhī xiéhuì	WAITRO
World Center for Scientific Information	世界科学信息中心	Shìjiè kēxué xìnxī zhōngxīn	WCSI
World Radio-communication Conference	世界无线电通信大会	Shìjiè wúxiàndiàn tōngxìn dàhuì	WRC
World wide web	全球网	Quánqiú wǎng	www
World Wide Web	万维网	Wànwéiwǎng	WWW
World Wide Web Consortium	万维网协会	Wànwéiwǎng xiéhuì	W3C
World Wide Web Consortium	英特网协议组织	Yīng-tè-wǎng xiéyì zǔzhī	W3C
Worldnet	全球视像会议网	Quánqiú shìxiàng huìyì wǎng	
Worldwide Military Command and Control System	全球军事指挥系统控制系统	Quánqiú jūnshì zhǐhuī xìtǒng kòngzhì xìtǒng	WWMCCS
Worm	虫毒	Chóngdú	
Wormhole routing	虫蚀寻径	Chóngshí xúnjìng	
Worst-case fairness index	恶劣公平系数	Èliè gōngping xìshù	
Wrap	自动分行	Zìdòng fēnháng	
Wrapper	包装器	Bāozhuāng qì	
Wrapping	环回	Huánhuí	
Wrist rest	护腕架	Hùwàn jià	
Write data	写数据	Xiě shùjù	WD
Write enable (for database)	写启用	Xiě qǐyòng	
Write once	一次性写入	Yīcìxìng xiěrù	WO
Write one read many	一写多读机	Yīxiě duōdú jī	WORM
Write only	只写	Zhǐ xiě	WO
Write only read many (optical disk)	一次写入多次读出(光盘)	Yīcì xiěrù duōcì dú chū (guāngpán)	WORM
Write-ahead log (for database)	预写日志	Yùxiě rìzhì	
Write-back	写回	Xiěhuí	
Write-behind (in SAMBA)	迟后写	Chíhòu xiě	
Write-once optical disk	一次写入光盘	Yīcì xiěrù guāngpán	
Write-one read many	单写多读	Dānxiě duōdú	WORM
Write-protect	防写保护	Fángxiě bǎohù	

Write-through	写通	Xiětōng	
Wrong attempt counter	非法尝试次数	Fēifǎ chángshì cìshù	WAC
Wuhan Research Institute of Posts & telecommunications	武汉邮电科学研究院	Wǔhàn yóudiàn kēxué yánjiūyuàn	WRI
Wyse Corp.	惠智	Huì-zhì	

X

X display manager control protocol	X 显示管理器控制协议	X xiǎnshì guǎnlǐqì kòngzhì xiéyì	XDMCP
X.400 message handling system	X.400 消息处理系统	X.400 xiāoxi chǔlǐ xìtǒng	
Xenon flashlamp	氙灯	Xiāndēng	
Xenon laser	氙分子激光	Xiānfènzi jīguāng	
Xerox (US corp.)	施乐	Shī-lè	
Xi'an Jiaotong University	西安交通大学	Xī'ān Jiāotōng Dàxué	
Xi'an University of Science and Engineering	西安理工大学	Xī'ān lǐgōng dàxué	
X-Windows	X 窗口	X-chuāngkǒu	
X-Windows graphical user interface	X 窗口图形用户接口	X-chuāngkǒu túxíng yònghù jiēkǒu	

Y

Yagi antenna	八木天线	Bāmù tiānxiàn	
Yahoo! ©	雅虎	Yǎhǔ	
Yahoo! Messenger ©	雅虎通	Yǎhǔ tōng	
Yamaha (Japanese company)	雅马哈	Yǎ-mǎ-hā	
Yellow page	黄页	Huángyè	
Yellow page service	黄页服务	Huángyè fúwù	YP
Yes or no test	是或否测试	Shì huò fǒu cèshì	
Yield (in SMT)	产出率	Chǎnchūlǜ	
Young's modulus	杨氏模量	Yáng-shì móliàng	

Z

Zeeman effect	塞曼效应	Sāi-màn xiàoyìng	
Zehnder fiber optic sensor	策恩德光纤传感器	Cè-ēn-dé guāngxiān chuángǎnqì	
Zentralverband der Electrotechnischen Industrie (Germany)	电气工业中央协会	Diànqì gōngyè zhōngyāng xiéhuì	ZVEI
Zero administration for Windows	零管理视窗系统	Líng guǎnlǐ shìchuāng xìtǒng	ZAM
Zero and add	清零和加	Qīng líng hé jiā	ZA
Zero day exploit	零时间漏洞利用	Líng shíjiān lòudòng lìyòng	
Zero dimension	零维	Líng wéi	
Zero dispersion	零色散	Líng sèsàn	
Zero dispersion point slope	零色散点斜率	Líng sèsàn diǎn xiélǜ	
Zero dispersion slope	零色散斜率	Líng sèsàn xiélǜ	
Zero dispersion wavelength	零色散波长	Líng sèsàn bōcháng	
Zero input	零输入	Líng shūrù	ZI
Zero insertion force	零插力	Líng chālì	ZIF
Zero insertion force	零插入力	Líng chārùlì	ZIF
Zero justification	零码速调整	Líng mǎsù tiáozhěng	
Zero knowledge proof (in cryptography)	零知识证明	Líng zhīshi zhèngmíng	
Zero material dispersion wavelength	零材料色散波长	Líng cáiliào sèsàn bōcháng	
Zero meridian	零度经线	Língdù jīngxiàn	

Zero meridian plane	零度经线平面	Língdù jīngxiàn píngmiàn	
Zero output	零输出	Líng shūchū	ZO
Zero relative level point	零相对电平点	Líng xiāngduì diànpíng diǎn	
Zero remaining lifetime	剩余生存时间为 0	Shèngyú shēngcún shíjiān wéi 0	ZRLT
Zero sequence	零序	Líng xù	
Zero wait state	零等待状态	Líng děngdài zhuàngtài	
Zero-cell	零单元	Líng dānyuán	
Zero-intermediate frequency receiver	零中频接收机	Líng zhōngpín jiēshōujī	
Zerotree coding	零树编码	Líng shù biānmǎ	
Zerotree wavelet coder	零树小波编码器	Líng shù xiǎobō biānmǎqì	
Zerotree wavelet coding algorithm	零树小波编码算法	Líng shù xiǎobō biānmǎ suànfǎ	
Zhongxing Telecommunications Enterprise (Chinese company)	中兴通讯	Zhōngxīng tōngxùn	ZTE
Zhuhai Comleader Information Science & Technology Co. Ltd.	珠海高凌信息科技有限公司	Zhūhǎi gāolíng xìnxī kējì yǒuxiàn gōngsī	
Zip	压缩	Yāsuō	
Zip disk	极碟	Jí dié	
Zip disk drive	极碟驱动器	Jí dié qūdòngqì	
Zirconia ceramic	氧化锆陶瓷	Yǎnghuàgào táocí	
Zirconia induction furnace	氧化锆高频感应炉	Yǎnghuàgào gāopín gǎnyìng lú	
Zirconium oxide	氧化锆	Yǎnghuàgào	ZrO_2
Zone access node	小区接入节点	Xiǎoqū jiērù jiédiǎn	ZAN
Zone bit code	区位码	Qūwèi mǎ	
Zone definition (semiconductor mfg)	区域精确度	Qūyù jīngquèdù	
Zone information protocol (an Apple protocol)	区域信息协议	Qūyù xìnxī xiéyì	ZIP
Zone routing protocol	区域路由协议	Qūyù lùyóu xiéyì	ZRP
Zoned lens; stepped lens	分区透镜	Fēnqū tòujìng	
Zoning	分区	Fēnqū	
Zoom	缩放格	Suō fàng gé	
Zoom in	移前	Yíqián	

Part 3

Alphabetically by English Abbreviation (sometimes Pinyin Abbreviation) with Egnlish, Chinese Characters and Pinyin

A

A	Address identification bit	地址识别比特	Dìzhǐ shíbié bǐtè
A	Agent, proxy	代理	Dàilǐ
A	Amplifier	放大器	Fàngdàqì
A	Amplitude	幅度	Fúdù
A	Asymptotic availability	渐近可用性	Jiànjìn kěyòngxìng
A(t)	Instantaneous availability	瞬时可用性	Shùnshí kěyòngxìng
A/D	Analog/digital conversion	模/数转换	Mó/shù zhuǎnhuàn
A/D	Analog/digital converter	模/数变换器	Mó/shù biànhuànqì
A/D	Analog/digital converter	模/数转换器	Mó/shù zhuǎnhuànqì
A/D/A	Analog/digital/analog (conversion)	模/数/模（变换）	Mó/shù/mó (biànhuàn)
A3	Authentication algorithm A3	认证算法 A3	Rènzhèng suànfǎ A3
A38	A single algorithm performing the functions of A3 and A8	执行 A3 和 A8 功能的一个单一算法	Zhíxíng A3 hé A8 gōngnéngde yīgè dānyī suànfǎ
A5	Communication automation, office automation, building management automation, fire automation and safety automation	通信自动化，办公自动化，建筑管理自动化，消防自动化和安全自动化	Tōngxìn zìdònghuà, Bàngōng zìdònghuà, jiànzhù guǎnlǐ zìdònghuà, xiāofáng zìdònghuà hé ānquán zìdònghuà
AA	Abbreviated address	短缩地址	Duǎnsuō dìzhǐ
AA	Absolute assembler	绝对汇编程序	Juéduì huìbiān chéngxù
AA	Activation analysis	激动分析	Jīdòng fēnxī
AA	Activation analysis	激活分析	Jīhuó fēnxī
AA	Adaptive amplifier	自适应放大器	Zìshìyìng fàngdàqì
AA	Adaptive antenna	自适应天线	Zìshìyìng tiānxiàn
AA	Administrative area	管理区	Guǎnlǐqū
AA	Agent advertisement	代理通告	Dàilǐ tōnggào
AA	Anonymous access	匿名接入	Nìmíng jiērù
AA	Antenna amplifier	天线放大器	Tiānxiàn fàngdàqì
AA	Anycast addressing	任意广播地址	Rènyì guǎngbō dìzhǐ
AA	Aperiodic antenna	非调谐天线	Fēitiáoxié tiānxiàn
AA	Architectural acoustics	建筑声学	Jiànzhù shēngxué
AA	Assert acknowledge	断言应答	Duànyán yìngdá
AA	Auto-answer	自动应答	Zìdòng yìngdá
AA	Automatically answer	自动应答	Zìdòng yìngdá
AAA	Authentication, authorization, accounting	认证、授权、计费	Rènzhèng、shòuquán、jì fèi
AAA	Authentication, authorization, accounting	验证、授权、计费	Yànzhèng、shòuquán、jìfèi
AAAC, A3C	Automatic answering automatic calling	自动应答自动呼叫	Zìdòng yìngdá zìdòng hūjiào
AAAI	American Association for Artificial Intelligence	美国人工智能协会	Měiguó réngōng zhìnéng xiéhuì
AAAS	Active array antenna system	有源天线阵系统	Yǒuyuán tiānxiàn zhèn xìtǒng
AAB	Application anchor block	应用链指针控制块	Yìngyòng liàn zhǐzhēn kòngzhì kuài
AAB	Automatic answerback	自动应答	Zìdòng yìngdá
AAC	Abort advisory channel	有故障的咨询信道	Yǒu gùzhàngde zīxún xìndào
AAC	Acoustical absorption coefficient	声吸收系数	Shēng xīshōu xìshù
AAC	Advanced audio coding	先进音频编码	Xiānjìn yīnpín biānmǎ
AAC	Automatic alarm call	自动警报呼叫	Zìdòng jǐngbào hūjiào

AAC	Automatic amplitude control	自动振幅控制	Zìdòng zhènfú kòngzhì
AACA	Alarm access control board assembly	告警接入控制集成板	Gàojǐng jiērù kòngzhì jíchéngbǎn
AACS	Asynchronous address communications system	异步地址通信系统	Yìbù dìzhǐ tōngxìn xìtǒng
AAD	Address adder	地址加法器	Dìzhǐ jiāfǎqì
AADR	Alternate address	替代地址	Tìdài dìzhǐ
AADS	Automatic applications development system	自动应用开发系统	Zìdòng yìngyòng kāifā xìtǒng
AAE	Agent advertisement extension	代理广播扩展	Dàilǐ guǎngbō kuòzhǎn
AAF	Access adaptation function	接入适配功能	Jiērù shìpèi gōngnéng
AAG	Attributed adjacency graph (CAD/CAM)	属性邻接图	Shǔxìng línjiē tú
AAL	Absolute assembly language	绝对汇编语言	Juéduì huìbiān yǔyán
AAL	Asynchronous transfer mode adaptation layer	异步传送方式适配层	Yìbù chuánsòng fāngshì shìpèi céng
AAL	Asynchronous transfer mode adaptation layer	异步传送模式适配层	Yìbù chuánsòng móshì shìpèi céng
AAL	ATM adaptation layer	ATM 匹配层	ATM pǐpèi céng
AAL	ATM adaptation layer	ATM 适配层	ATM shìpèi céng
AAL2	ATM adaptation layer type 2	ATM 匹配层类型 2	ATM pǐpèi céng lèixíng 2
AAL-PCI	AAL protocol control information	AAL 协议控制信息	AAL xiéyì kòngzhì xìnxī
AAL-PDU	AAL protocol data unit	AAL 协议数据单元	AAL xiéyì shùjù dānyuán
AAL-SAP	AAL service access point	AAL 业务接入点	AAL yèwù jiērù diǎn
AAL-SDU	AAL service data unit	AAL 业务数据单元	AAL yèwù shùjù dānyuán
AAM	Asymmetric amplitude modulation	不对称调幅	Bùduìchèn tiáofú
AAP	Address allocation plan	地址分配方案	Dìzhǐ fēnpèi fāng'àn
AAP	Antenna aspect processor	天线方位处理机	Tiānxiàn fāngwèi chǔlǐjī
AAP	Associative array processor	相连阵列处理机	Xiānglián zhènliè chǔlǐjī
AARP	AppleTalk address resolution protocol	AppleTalk 地址解析协议	AppleTalk dìzhǐ jiěxī xiéyì
AARR	Allow additional register range bit	允许附加寄存器的范围位	Yǔnxǔ fùjiā jìcúnqìde fànwéi wèi
AAS	Adaptive antenna system	自适应天线系统	Zìshìyìng tiānxiàn xìtǒng
AAS	Automatic audio switching	自动音频交换	Zìdòng yīnpín jiāohuàn
AASP	Advanced acoustic signal processor	先进声信号处理器	Xiānjìn shēng xìnhào chǔlǐqì
AAT	Arc attribute table	弧属性表	Hú shǔxìng biǎo
AAT	Automatic answer trunk	自动应答干线	Zìdòng yìngdá gànxiàn
AAT	Average access time (computer disk)	平均存取时间	Píngjūn cúnqǔ shíjiān
AAU	Address arithmetic unit	地址运算器	Dìzhǐ yùnsuànqì
AB	Access burst	接入猝发比特群	Jiērù cùfā bǐtè qún
AB	Access burst	接入突发脉冲序列	Jiērù tūfā màichōng xùliè
AB	Across beam (in telecom installation)	跨梁敷设	Kuà liáng fūshè
AB	Active bit	有效位	Yǒuxiào wèi
AB	Active bit	运行位	Yùnxíng wèi
AB	Address byte	地址字节	Dìzhǐ zìjié
AB	Along beam (telecom installation)	沿梁敷设	Yán liáng fūshè
AB	Arithmetic bus	运算总线	Yùnsuàn zǒngxiàn
AB	Assembly buffer	汇编程序缓冲器	Huìbiān chéngxù huǎnchōngqì
ABB	Automatic back bias	自动反偏压	Zìdòng fǎnpiānyā
ABC	Abstract base class	抽象基类	Chōuxiàng jī lèi
ABC	American Broadcasting Corp. (US company)	美国广播公司	Měiguó guǎngbō gōngsī
ABC	Amplifier bias current	放大器偏压电流	Fàngdàqì piānyā diànliú
ABC	Answer back code	应答电码	Yìngdá diànmǎ

ABC	Automation of bibliography through computerization	计算机化自动编目	Jìsuànjīhuà zìdòng biānmù
ABCDIC	Advanced binary-coded decimal interchange code	高级二-十进制交换代码	Gāojí èr-shíjìnzhì jiāohuàn dàimǎ
ABCS	Automatic base communication system	基地自动通信系统	Jīdì zìdòng tōngxìn xìtǒng
ABD	Abbreviated dialing	简明拨号	Jiǎnmíng bōhào
ABDL	Automatic binary data link	自动二进制数据链路	Zìdòng èrjìnzhì shùjù liànlù
ABF	Air blown fiber	气吹光纤	Qìchuī guāngxiān
ABF	Audio bandpass filter	音频带通滤波器	Yīnpín dàitōng lǜbōqì
ABI	Adjacent bit interference	邻位干扰	Línwèi gānrǎo
ABL	Automatic bootstrap loader	自动引导装入程序	Zìdòng yǐndǎo zhuāngrù chéngxù
ABM	Asynchronous balanced mode	异步平衡方式	Yìbù pínghéng fāngshì
ABM	Asynchronous balanced mode	异步平衡模式	Yìbù pínghéng móshì
ABP	Address bit permutating	地址位序列改变	Dìzhǐ wèi xùliè gǎibiàn
ABR	Answer bid ratio	应答试占比	Yìngdá shìzhàn bǐ
ABR	Area border router	区域边界路由器	Qūyù biānjiè lùyóuqì
ABR	Associativity-based routing	基于关联性的路由算法	Jīyú guānlián xìngde lùyóu suànfǎ
ABR	Available bit rate	可获得比特率	Kěhuòdé bǐtèlǜ
ABR	Available bit rate	可用比特率	Kěyòng bǐtè lǜ
ABRS	Automatic bit rate selection	自动比特率选择	Zìdòng bǐtè lǜ xuǎnzé
ABS	Alternate billing service	可选记帐业务	Kěxuǎn jìzhàng yèwù
ABS	Auto balance system (computer disk)	自动平衡系统	Zìdòng pínghéng xìtǒng
ABT	ATM block transfer	ATM 块传送	ATM kuài chuánsòng
ABT	Auto-build tool	自动生成工具	Zìdòng shēngchéng gōngjù
AC	Access class	接入分类	Jiērù fēnlèi
AC	Access code (to computer memory)	存储码	Cúnchǔ mǎ
AC	Access condition	接入条件	Jiērù tiáojiàn
AC	Access control	访问控制	Fǎngwèn kòngzhì
AC	Access control (to computer memory)	存储控制	Cúnchǔ kòngzhì
AC	Access cycle (to computer memory)	存储周期	Cúnchǔ zhōuqī
AC	Acoustic coupler	声耦合器	Shēng ǒuhéqì
AC	Across column (in telecom installation)	跨珠敷设	Kuà zhū fūshè
AC	Add carry	加法进位	Jiāfǎ jìnwèi
AC	Address carry	地址进位	Dìzhǐ jìnwèi
AC	Along column (telecom installation)	沿珠敷设	Yán zhū fūshè
AC	Alternating current	交流	Jiāoliú
AC	Analog controller	模拟控制器	Mónǐ kòngzhìqì
AC	Application context	应用范围	Yìngyòng fànwéi
AC	Application context	应用上下文	Yìngyòng shàngxiàwén
AC	Apply charging	申请计费	Shēnqǐng jìfèi
AC	Armored cable	铠装电缆	Kǎizhuāng diànlǎn
AC	Asymmetric communications	非对称双路通信	Fēiduìchèn shuānglù tōngxìn
AC	Atlantic cable	大西洋海底电缆	Dàxīyáng hǎidǐ diànlǎn
AC	Audio codec	音频多媒体数字信号编解码器	Yīnpín duōméitǐ shùzì xìnhào biān jiěmǎqì
AC, AUC	Authentication center	鉴权中心	Jiànquán zhōngxīn
ACA	Adaptive channel allocation	自适应通道分配	Zìshìyìng tōngdào fēnpèi
ACA	Adaptive clutter attenuator	自适应散射干扰衰减器	Zìshìyìng sǎnshè gānrǎo shuāijiǎnqì
ACA	Adjacent channel attenuation	相邻信道衰减	Xiānglín xìndào shuāijiǎn

ACA	Asynchronous communications adapter	异步通信适配	Yìbù tōngxìn shìpèi
ACA	Automatic call acceptance	自动呼叫应答	Zìdòng hūjiào yìngdá
ACA	Automatic call accounting	电话自动计费系统	Diànhuà zìdòng jìfèi xìtǒng
ACAM	Associative content addressable memory	相关内容可寻止存储器	Xiāngguān nèiróng kěxúnzhǐ cúnchǔqì
ACAM	Augmented content-addressed memory	可扩充的内容定止存储器	Kěkuòchōngde nèiróng dìngzhǐ cúnchǔqì
ACAP	Automatic circuit analysis program	自动电路分析程序	Zìdòng diànlù fēnxī chéngxù
ACB	Access barred signal	接入拒绝信号	Jiērù jùjué xìnhào
ACB	Automatic camp-on busy	自动忙时保留呼叫装置	Zìdòng mángshí bǎoliú hūjiào zhuāngzhì
ACC	Access control center	接入控制中心	Jiērù kòngzhì zhōngxīn
ACC	Account credit card	记帐信用卡	Jìzhàng xìnyòngkǎ
ACC	Accounting card call	记帐卡呼叫	Jìzhàng kǎ hūjiào
ACC	Asynchronous communication control	异步通信控制	Yìbù tōngxìn kòngzhì
ACC	Automatic congestion control	自动拥塞控制	Zìdòng yōngsè kòngzhì
ACC	Automatic congestion control information message	自动拥塞控制信息消息	Zìdòng yōngsè kòngzhì xìnxī xiāoxi
ACCA	Analog common channel assembly	模拟公共信道集成板	Mónǐ gōnggòng xìndào jíchéngbǎn
ACCH	Associated control channel	辅助控制信道	Fǔzhù kòngzhì xìndào
ACCH	Associated control channel	随路控制信道	Suílù kòngzhì xìndào
ACCM	Asynchronous control character map	异步控制字符影射	Yìbù kòngzhì zìfú yǐngshè
ACCOLC	Access overload class	访问过载等级	Fǎngwèn guòzài děngjí
ACCP	Analog common channel processor	模拟公共信道处理器	Mónǐ gōnggòng xìndào chǔlǐqì
ACD	Automatic call distribution	自动分配话务	Zìdòng fēnpèi huàwù
ACD	Automatic call distribution	自动呼叫分配	Zìdòng hūjiào fēnpèi
ACD	Automatic call distributor	自动呼叫分配器	Zìdòng hūjiào fēnpèiqì
ACDK	Apple Chinese Dictation Kit ©	苹果中文译写器	Píngguǒ zhōngwén yìxiěqì
A-CDMA	Asynchronous code division multiple access	异步码分多址	Yìbù mǎfēn duōzhǐ
ACE	Access connection element	接入连接单元	Jiērù liánjiē dānyuán
ACE	Access control entry	访问控制项	Fǎngwèn kòngzhì xiàng
ACE	Automatic calling equipment	自动呼叫装置	Zìdòng hūjiào zhuāngzhì
ACE	Auxiliary control element	辅助控制单元	Fǔzhù kòngzhì dānyuán
ACEIS	Alcatel Carrier Environment Internet System	阿尔卡特运营环境因特网系统	Ā-ěr-kǎ-tè yùnyíng huánjìng Yīntèwǎng xìtǒng
ACELP	Algebraic code excited linear prediction	代数码激励线性预测	Dàishù mǎ jīlì xiànxìng yùcè
ACELP	Algebraic code excited linear prediction	代数码本激励线性预测编码	Dàishù mǎběn jīlì xiànxìng yùcè biānmǎ
ACF	Admission confirm	接入确认	Jiērù quèrèn
ACF	Admissions confirmed (packet network protocol message)	接主确认	Jiēzhǔ quèrèn
ACF	Advanced communications function	高级通信功能	Gāojí tōngxìn gōngnéng
ACF	Advanced communications function	先进通信功能	Xiānjìn tōngxìn gōngnéng
ACG	Asymptotic coding gain	渐进编码增益	Jiànjìn biānmǎ zēngyì
A-CH	Access channel	接续信道	Jiēxù xìndào
ACI	Access control information	访问控制信息	Fǎngwèn kòngzhì xìnxī
ACI	Access control information	接入控制信息	Jiērù kòngzhì xìnxī
ACI	Adjacent cell interference	邻小区干扰	Línxiǎoqū gānrǎo
ACI	Adjacent cell interference	相临小区干扰	Xiānglín xiǎoqū gānrǎo
ACI	Adjacent channel interference	邻频干扰	Línpín gānrǎo
ACIR	Adjacent channel interference ratio	邻信道干扰比	Línxìndào gānrǎobǐ
ACK	Acknowledge	肯定字符	Kěndìng zìfú

ACK	Acknowledge	确认	Quèrèn
ACK	Acknowledgement	肯定应答	Kěndìng yìngdá
ACK	Acknowledgement	确认	Quèrèn
ACK	Acknowledgement	应答	Yìngdá
ACK	Acknowledgement	应答信号	Yìngdá xìnhào
ACK	Acknowledgement message	认可消息	Rènkě xiāoxi
ACK	Auxiliary clock board	辅助时钟板	Fǔzhù shízhōng bǎn
ACL	Access control list	存取控制表	Cúnqǔ kòngzhì biǎo
ACL	Access control list	访问控制表	Fǎngwèn kòngzhì biǎo
ACL	Access control list	接入控制列表	Jiērù kòngzhì lièbiǎo
ACL	Asynchronous connecting link	异步链路	Yìbù liànlù
ACLR	Adjacent channel leakage power ratio	邻信道泄漏功率比	Línxìndào xièlòu gōnglǜ bǐ
ACLR	Adjacent channel leakage ratio	邻信道泄漏比	Línxìndào xièlòubǐ
ACM	Accumulated call meter	累积呼叫计量器	Lěijī hūjiào jìliàngqì
ACM	Accumulated call meter	累积呼叫计数	Lěijī hūjiào jìshù
ACM	Accumulated call meter	累计呼叫表	Lěijì hūjiàobiǎo
ACM	Address complete message	地址全消息	Dìzhǐ quán xiāoxi
ACM	Address complete message (ISUP message)	地址接收完毕	Dìzhǐ jiēshōu wánbì
ACM	Address completion message	地址收全消息	Dìzhǐ shōuquán xiāoxi
ACM	Asynchronous communication control module	异步通信控制模块	Yìbù tōngxìn kòngzhì mókuài
ACM	Automatic color monitor	自动色彩监视器	Zìdòng sècǎi jiānshìqì
ACMM	Accumulated call meter max	累积呼叫计量器最大值	Lěijī hūjiào jìliàngqì zuìdàzhí
ACN	Application context name	应用上下文名称	Yìngyòng shàngxiàwén míngchēng
ACN	Area communications network	地区通信网	Dìqū tōngxìnwǎng
ACNI	Automatic called number identification	自动呼叫号识别	Zìdòng hūjiào hào shíbié
ACO	Adaptive control optimization	自适应控制优化	Zìshìyìng kòngzhì yōuhuà
ACOM	Algebraic compiler	代数编译程序	Dàishù biānyì chéngxù
ACOM	Antenna combiner	天线合路器	Tiānxiàn hélùqì
ACOPS	Automatic central processor unit overheat prevention system	自动 CPU 过热保护	Zìdòng CPU guòrè bǎohù
ACOPS	Automatic central processor unit overheat prevention system	自动 CPU 过热预防系统	Zìdòng CPU guòrè yùfáng xìtǒng
ACOPS	Automatic CPU overheat prevention system	CPU 过热预防系统	CPU guòrè yùfáng xìtǒng
ACOS	Application control operating system	应用控制操作系统	Yìngyòng kòngzhì cāozuò xìtǒng
ACP	Adjacent channel power	邻道功率	Líndào gōnglǜ
ACP	Alarm control process	告警控制处理	Gàojǐng kòngzhì chǔlǐ
ACPI	Advanced configuration and power interface	高级配置和电源接口	Gāojí pèizhì hé diànyuán jiēkǒu
ACPI	Advanced configuration and power interface	先进设置和电源管理	Xiānjìn shèzhì hé diànyuán guǎnlǐ
ACPM	Association control protocol machine	联系控制协议机	Liánxì kòngzhì xiéyìjī
ACQM	Automatic circuit quality monitoring	自动电路质量监视	Zìdòng diànlù zhìliàng jiānshì
ACR	Address compare register	地址比较寄存器	Dìzhǐ bǐjiào jìcúnqì
ACR	Allowed cell rate	允许信元速率	Yǔnxǔ xìnyuán sùlǜ
ACR	Allowed cell rate	允许的信元率	Yǔnxǔde xìnyuán lǜ
ACR	Allowed cell rate	允许的信元速率	Yǔnxǔde xìnyuán sùlǜ
ACR	Alternating current relay	交流继电器	Jiāoliú jìdiànqì
ACR	Apply charging report	申请计费报告	Shēnqǐng jìfèi bàogào
ACR	Attenuation crosstalk ratio	衰减串扰比	Shuāijiǎn chuànrǎo bǐ

ACR	Attenuation crosstalk ratio	衰减串音比	Shuāijiǎn chuànyīn bǐ
ACR	Attenuation to crosstalk ratio	衰减与串扰比	Shuāijiǎn yǔ chuànrǎo bǐ
ACR	Attenuation to crosstalk ratio	衰减-串音比率	Shuāijiǎn—chuànyīn bǐlǜ
ACR	Automatic call recording	自动呼叫记录	Zìdòng hūjiào jìlù
ACR	Automatic circuit restoration	自动电路恢复	Zìdòng diànlù huīfù
ACR	Avalanche controlled rectifier	雪崩可控整流器	Xuěbēng kěkòng zhěngliúqì
ACR	Average cell rate	平均信元率	Píngjūn xìnyuán lǜ
ACROM	Associative capacitive read-only memory	关联电容只读存储器	Guānlián diànróng zhǐ dú cúnchǔqì
ACS	Access control system	出入控制系统	Chūrù kòngzhì xìtǒng
ACS	Add-compare-select	加选比	Jiā xuǎn bǐ
ACS	Add-compare-select	相加-比较-选择，加选比	Xiāngjiā-bǐjiào-xuǎnzé, jiā xuǎn bǐ
ACS	Adjacent-channel selectivity	邻信道选择性	Línxìndào xuǎnzéxìng
ACS	All channel signaling	全部信道传输信令	Quánbù xìndào chuánshū xìnlìng
ACSE	Association control service element	关联控制服务单元	Guānlián kòngzhì fúwù dānyuán
ACSE	Association control service element	连接控制服务单元	Liánjiē kòngzhì fúwù dānyuán
ACSE	Association control service element	连接控制服务元素	Liánjiē kòngzhì fúwù yuánsù
ACSE	Association control service element	联系控制服务单元	Liánxì kòngzhì fúwù dānyuán
ACSE	Association control service element	联系控制服务要素	Liánxì kòngzhì fúwù yàosù
ACSE	Association control service element (an ISO standard)	关联控制服务元素	Guānlián kòngzhì fúwù yuánsù
ACSL	Advanced continuous simulation language	高级连续仿真语言	Gāojí liánxù fǎngzhēn yǔyán
ACSM	American Congress on Surveying and Mapping	美国测绘委员会	Měiguó cèhuì wěiyuánhuì
ACSSB	Amplitude companded single sideband	振幅压扩单边带	Zhènfú yākuò dānbiāndài
ACT	Algebraic coding theory	代数编码理论	Dàishù biānmǎ lǐlùn
ACTS	Advanced communication technologies and services	现代通信技术和业务	Xiàndài tōngxìn jìshù hé yèwù
ACU	Add control unit	加法控制器	Jiāfǎ kòngzhìqì
ACU	Address control unit	地址控制器	Dìzhǐ kòngzhìqì
ACU	Antenna combining unit	天线组合单元	Tiānxiàn zǔhé dānyuán
ACU	Antenna control unit	天线控制部件	Tiānxiàn kòngzhì bùjiàn
ACU	Antenna control unit	天线控制器	Tiānxiàn kòngzhìqì
ACU	Antenna coupler unit	天线耦合器单元	Tiānxiàn ǒuhéqì dānyuán
ACU	Arithmetic control unit	运算控制器	Yùnsuàn kòngzhìqì
ACUA	Automatic calling unit adapter	自动呼叫设备转接器	Zìdòng hūjiào shèbèi zhuǎnjiēqì
ACV	Address control vector	地址控制向量	Dìzhǐ kòngzhì xiàngliàng
ACV	Automatic correlation vocoder	自动相关声码器	Zìdòng xiāngguān shēngmǎqì
AD	Abbreviated dialing	缩位拨号	Suōwèi bōhào
AD	Address decoder	地址译码器	Dìzhǐ yìmǎqì
AD	Address detector	地址探测器	Dìzhǐ tàncèqì
AD	Addressable detector	地址探测器	Dìzhǐ tàncèqì
AD	Administrative domain	管理域	Guǎnlǐ yù
AD	Avalanche diode	雪崩二极管	Xuěbēng èrjíguǎn
AD	Avalanche diode	雪崩光电二极管	Xuěbēng guāngdiàn èrjíguǎn
ADAPt	Adaptive digital access protocol	自适应数字接入协议	Zìshìyìng shùzì jiērù xiéyì
Adaptive MTI	Adaptive mobile target indicator	自适应动目标显示	Zìshìyìng dòng mùbiāo xiǎnshì
ADAT	Authentication/security data (in FTP)	认证/安全数据	Rènzhèng/ānquán shùjù
ADC	Administration center	管理中心	Guǎnlǐ zhōngxīn

ADC	Analog to digital converter	模数转换器	Móshù zhuǎnhuànqì
ADC；DAMPS	North America Digital cellular System	北美数字蜂窝系统	Běiměi shùzì fēngwō xìtǒng
ADCC	Asynchronous data communication channel	异步数据通信信道	Yìbù shùjù tōngxìn xìndào
ADCCP	Advanced data communication control protocol	高级数据通信控制协议	Gāojí shùjù tōngxìn kòngzhì xiéyì
ADCCP	Advanced data communications procedure	先进数据通信规程	Xiānjìn shùjù tōngxìn guīchéng
ADDDS	Automatic direct distance dialing system	远程直接自动拨号系统	Yuǎnchéng zhíjiē zìdòng bōhào xìtǒng
ADDMD	Administration directory management domain	公用号码簿管理域	Gōngyòng hàomǎbù guǎnlǐ yù
ADDMD	Administration directory management domain	主管部门号码簿管理域	Zhǔguǎn bùmén hàomǎbù guǎnlǐ yù
ADDNR	Add network resource	增配网络资源	Zēngpèi wǎngluò zīyuán
ADDR	Address function	地址函数	Dìzhǐ hánshù
ADEM	Automatic data equalizer modem	自动数据均衡电路调制解调器	Zìdòng shùjù jūnhéng diànlù tiáozhì jiětiáoqì
ADEV	Allan deviation	艾伦偏差	Ài-lún piānchā
ADF	Adaptive digital filtering	自适应数字滤波	Zìshìyìng shùzì lǜbō
ADF	Application dedicated file	应用专用文件	Yìngyòng zhuānyòng wénjiàn
ADFE	Adaptive decree feedback equalizer	自适应判决反馈均衡器	Zìshìyìng pànjué fǎnkuì jūnhéngqì
ADFE	Automatic decision feedback equalizer	自适应判决反馈均衡器	Zìshìyìng pànjué fǎnkuì jūnhéngqì
ADH	Arbitrary device handler	任意设备处理程序	Rènyì shèbèi chǔlǐ chéngxù
ADHOC	Advanced data handler for on-line control	联机控制用先进数据处理程序	Liánjī kòngzhì-yòng xiānjìn shùjùchǔlǐ chéngxù
ADI	Address incomplete signal	地址不全信号	Dìzhǐ bùquán xìnhào
ADI	Alternate digital inversion coding	数字交替反转码	Shùzì jiāotì fǎnzhuǎn mǎ
ADIMM	Advanced dual in-line memory modules	高级双重内嵌式内存模块	Gāojí shuāngchóng nèiqiàn-shì nèicún mókuài
ADL	Acceptable defect level	允许的缺陷标准	Yǔnxǔde quēxiàn biāozhǔn
ADL	Acoustical delay line	声延迟线	Shēng yánchíxiàn
ADL	All dielectric lashed cable (FOC)	全介质捆绑光缆	Quán jièzhì kǔnbǎng guānglǎn
ADL	Asynchronous delay line	异步延迟线	Yìbù yánchí xiàn
ADL-Net	Autonomous decentralized loop network	独立分散循环网络	Dúlì fēnsàn xúnhuán wǎngluò
ADM	Adaptive delta modulation	自适应增量调制	Zìshìyìng zēngliàng tiáozhì
ADM	Add drop multiplexer	插/分复用器	Chā/fēn fùyòngqì
ADM	Add/drop multiplexer	插入/分出复接设备	Chārù/fēnchū fù jiē shèbèi
ADM	Add/drop multiplexer	分/插复用设备	Fēn/chā fùyòng shèbèi
ADM	Add/drop multiplexer	分插复用器	Fēnchā fùyòngqì
ADM	Add/drop multiplexer	上/下复用器	Shàng/xià fùyòngqì
ADM	Add/drop multiplexer	上/下路复用器	Shàng/xià lù fùyòngqì
ADM	Asynchronous disconnected mode	异步拆线方式	Yìbù chāixiàn fāngshì
ADM	Asynchronous disconnected mode	异步断开方式	Yìbù duànkāi fāngshì
ADMD	Administration management domain	公用管理域	Gōngyòng guǎnlǐ yù
ADMS	Asynchronous data multiplexer synchronizer	异步数据多路复用同步器	Yìbù shùjù duōlù fùyòng tóngbùqì
ADN	Abbreviated dialling numbers	数位拨号	Shùwèi bōhào
ADN	Asynchronous transfer mode data network	异步转移模式数据网络	Yìbù zhuǎnyí móshì shùjù wǎngluò
ADNS	Automated digital network system	自动化数字网络系统	Zìdònghuà shùzì wǎngluò xìtǒng
ADO	ActiveX data object	访问服务器专用对象集	Fǎngwèn fúwùqì zhuānyòng duìxiàng jí
ADOCS	Advanced digital opticai control system	高级数据光控制系统	Gāojí shùjù guāng kòngzhì xìtǒng
ADOM	Add/drop optical module	上/下路光模块	Shàng/xià lù guāng mókuài
ADOW	Automatic dial order wire	自动拨号传号线	Zìdòng bōhào chuánhàoxiàn
ADP	Advanced data processing	高级数据处理	Gāojí shùjù chǔlǐ

ADP	Analog-digital processor	模-数处理器	Mó-shù chǔlǐqì
ADP	Answer detection pattern	应答检测图形	Yìngdá jiǎncè túxíng
ADP	Associative data processing	相关数据处理	Xiāngguān shùjù chǔlǐ
ADP	Automatic data processing	自动数据处理	Zìdòng shùjù chǔlǐ
ADPCM	Adaptive differential pulse code modulation	自适应差分脉冲编码调制	Zìshìyìng chāfēn màichōng biānmǎ tiáozhì
ADPCM	Adaptive differential pulse code modulation	自适应差分脉码调制	Zìshìyìng chāfēn màimǎ tiáozhì
ADPCM	Adaptive differential pulse code modulation	自适应脉冲编码调制	Zìshìyìng màichōng biānmǎ tiáozhì
ADPE	Automatic data processing equpment	自动数据处理设备	Zìdòng shùjù chǔlǐ shèbèi
ADPE	Auxiliary data processing equipment	辅助数据处理设备	Fǔzhù shùjù chǔlǐ shèbèi
ADPLL	All digital phase-locked loop	全数子锁相环	Quán shùzi suǒxiàng huán
ADPLL	All digital phase-locked loop	全数子锁相环	Quánshùzĭ suǒxiānghuán
ADPP	Automatic data processing program	自动数据处理程序	Zìdòng shùjù chǔlǐ chéngxù
ADPS	Automatic data processing system	自动数据处理系统	Zìdòng shùjù chǔlǐ xìtǒng
ADPS	Auxiliary data processing system	辅助数据处理系统	Fǔzhù shùjù chǔlǐ xìtǒng
ADR	Address digital receiver	数字地址接收器	Shùzì dìzhǐ jiēshōuqì
ADR	Advisory route	建议路由	Jiànyì lùyóu
ADR	Analog data recognition	模拟数据识别	Mónǐ shùjù shíbié
ADR	Analog-digital recorder	模拟-数字记录器	Mónǐ/shùzì jìlù qì
ADR	Analog-digital recorder	模拟-数字记录器	Mónǐ-shùzì jìlùqì
ADRC	Automatic call distribution remote capture	自动呼叫分布远程截获	Zìdòng hūjiào fēnbù yuǎnchéng jiéhuò
ADRC	Automatic call distribution remote capture	自动呼叫分配远程截获	Zìdòng hūjiào fēnpèi yuǎnchéng jiéhuò
ADRC	Automatic data rate changer	自动数据速率变换器	Zìdòng shùjù sùlǜ biànhuànqì
ADS	Address data strobe	地址数据选通	Dìzhǐ shùjù xuǎntōng
ADS	Address display sub-system	地址显示子系统	Dìzhǐ xiǎnshì zixìtǒng
ADS	Advanced data system	高级数据系统	Gāojí shùjù xìtǒng
ADS	Arc digitizing system	弧段数字化系统	Húduàn shùzìhuà xìtǒng
ADS	Asynchronous data service	异步数据业务	Yìbù shùjù yèwù
ADS	Automatic dependent surveillance (civil air)	自动相关监视	Zìdòng xiāngguān jiānshì
ADSEL	Address selection	地址选择	Dìzhǐ xuǎnzé
ADSL	Asymmetric digital subscriber line	不对称数字订阅线路	Bùduìchèn shùzì dìngyuè xiànlù
ADSL	Asymmetric digital subscriber line	不对称数字用户线	Bùduìchèn shùzì yònghù xiàn
ADSL	Asymmetric digital subscriber line	非对称数字用户线路	Fēiduìchèn shùzì yònghù xiànlù
ADSL	Asymmetric digital subscriber loop	非对称数字用户环路	Fēiduìchèn shùzì yònghù huánlù
ADSL	Asynchronous digital subscriber line	异步数字用户线	Yìbù shùzì yònghù xiàn
ADSL.lite	Low speed-rate asynchronous digital subscriber line without voice splitter	无话音分离器的低速不对称数字用户线	Wúhuàyīn fēnlíqìde dīsù bùduìchèn shùzì yònghù xiàn
ADSP	AppleTalk data stream protocol	AppleTalk 数据流协议	AppleTalk shùjù liú xiéyì
ADSS	All dielectric self-supporting fiber optic cable	全介质自乘式光缆	Quán jièzhì zìchéng-shì guānglǎn
ADSS	Automatic data switching system	自动数据交换系统	Zìdòng shùjù jiāohuàn xìtǒng
ADT	Application dedicated terminal	专用终端设备	Zhuānyòng zhōngduān shèbèi
ADT	Asynchronous data transceiver	异步数据收发机	Yìbù shùjù shōufājī
ADT	Asynchronous data transfer	异步数据传递	Yìbù shùjù chuándì
ADT	Asynchronous data transfer	异步数据转移	Yìbù shùjù zhuǎnyí
ADT	Automatic data tracking	自动数据跟踪	Zìdòng shùjù gēnzōng
ADT	Automatic data translator	自动数据变换器	Zìdòng shùjù biànhuànqì
ADT	Automatic data translator	自动译码器	Zìdòng yìmǎqì

ADTS	Automated data and telecommunications service	自动数据远程通信服务	Zìdòng shùjù yuǎnchéng tōngxìn fúwù
ADTX	Advanced technology storage	先进技术存储	Xiānjìn jìshù cúnchǔ
ADU	Analog delay unit	模拟延迟装置	Mónǐ yánchí zhuāngzhì
ADU	Application data unit	应用数据单元	Yìngyòng shùjù dānyuán
ADU	Asynchronous data unit	异步数据单元	Yìbù shùjù dānyuán
ADU	Automatic dialing unit	自动拨号装置	Zìdòng bōhào zhuāngzhì
ADU	Auxiliary display unit	辅助显示装置（单元）	Fǔzhù xiǎnshì zhuāngzhì (dānyuán)
ADV	Adaptive digital vocoder	自适应数字声码器	Zìshìyìng shùzì shēngmǎqì
ADX	Asymmetric data exchange	非对称数据交换	Fēiduìchèn shùjù jiāohuàn
ADX	Automatic data exchange	自动数据交换	Zìdòng shùjù jiāohuàn
ADXS	Automatic data exchange system	自动数据交换系统	Zìdòng shùjù jiāohuàn xìtǒng
AE	Actinoelectric effect	光化电效应	Guānghuà diàn xiàoyìng
AE	Ancillary equipment	辅助设备	Fǔzhù shèbèi
AE	Aperture effect	孔径效应	Kǒngjìng xiàoyìng
AE	Application entity	应用实体	Yìngyòng shítǐ
AE	Atmospheric effects	雾化效果	Wùhuà xiàoguǒ
AEA	Automatic error analysis	自动误差分析	Zìdòng wùchā fēnxī
AEB	Analog expansion bus	模拟扩展总线	Mónǐ kuòzhǎn zǒngxiàn
AEC	Acoustic echo canceler	回波消除器	Huíbō xiāochúqì
AEC	Acoustic echo controller	回波控制器	Huíbō kòngzhìqì
AEC	Automatic error correction system	自动纠错系统	Zìdòng jiūcuò xìtǒng
AEF	Additional elementary functions	补充基本功能	Bǔchōng jīběn gōngnéng
AEI	Application entity invocation	应用实体调用	Yìngyòng shítǐ diàoyòng
AEI	Automatic error interrogation	自动错误询问	Zìdòng cuòwù xúnwèn
AEIR	Application entity installer and remover	应用实体安装和拆除	Yìngyòng shítǐ ānzhuāng hé chāichú
AEM	Application software element manager	应用软件单元管理	Yìngyòng ruǎnjiàn dānyuán guǎnlǐ
AEP	Acoustic echo path	回波通道	Huíbō tōngdào
AEP	AppleTalk echo protocol	AppleTalk 回声协议	AppleTalk huíshēng xiéyì
AEP	AppleTalk echo protocol	AppleTalk 回应协议	AppleTalk huíyìng xiéyì
AEQ	Automatic equalizer	自动均衡器	Zìdòng jūnhéngqì
AERM	Alignment error rate monitor	定位差错率监视	Dìngwèi chācuòlǜ jiānshì
AES	Advanced encryption standard	高级加密标准	Gāojí jiāmì biāozhǔn
AES	Advanced encryption standard	先进加密标准	Xiānjìn jiāmì biāozhǔn
AES	Advanced encryption system	先进的加密系统	Xiānjìnde jiāmì xìtǒng
AESA	ATM end system address	ATM 终端系统地址	ATM zhōngduān xìtǒng dìzhǐ
AF	Access facility	接入设施	Jiērù shèshī
AF	Acoustic feedback	声反馈	Shēng fǎnkuì
AF	Adaptation function	适配功能	Shìpèi gōngnéng
AF	Address field	地址字段	Dìzhǐ zìduàn
AF	Arithmetic flag	算术标志	Suànshù biāozhì
AF	Assured forwarding	确保转发	Quèbǎo zhuǎnfā
AF	Audio frequency	声频	Shēngpín
AF	Audio frequency	音频	Yīnpín
AF	Audio frequency, voice frequency	音频	Yīnpín
AFC	Abnormal frame count	非正常帧计数	Fēizhèngcháng zhèng jìshù
AFC	Asymmetric flow control	不对称流量控制	Bùduìchèn liúliàng kòngzhì

AFC	Automatic frequency control	自动频率控制	Zìdòng pínlǜ kòngzhì
AFC	Automatic frequency fine control	自动频率微调	Zìdòng pínlǜ wēitiáo
AFD	Amplitude-frequency distortion	幅频失真	Fú-pín shīzhēn
AFD	Amplitude-frequency distortion	振幅频率失真	Zhènfú pínlǜ shīzhēn
AFD	Arithmetic function designator	运算函数标志符	Yùnsuàn hánshù biāozhìfú
AFD	Average fade duration	平均衰落时间	Píngjūn shuāiluò shíjiān
AFE	Analog front-end	模拟前端	Mónǐ qiánduān
AFEB	Antenna front end block	天线前端模块	Tiānxiàn qiánduān mókuài
AFEU	Antenna front end unit	天线前端单元	Tiānxiàn qiánduān dānyuán
AFF	Automatic fault finding	自动故障查找	Zìdòng gùzhàng cházhǎo
AFI	Authority and format identifier	授权和格式标识符	Shòuquán hé géshi biāozhìfú
AFI	Authority frame identifier	规范帧标识	Guīfàn zhèng biāozhì
AFIN	Association Francaise des Informaticiens (French association of persons in the information industry)	法国信息工作人员协会	Fǎguó xìnxī gōngzuò rényuán xiéhuì
AFIPS	American Federation of Information processing Societies	美国信息处理学会联合会	Měiguó xìnxī chǔlǐ xuéhuì liánhéhuì
AFK	Away from the keyboard (computer chat)	离开键盘	Líkāi jiànpán
AFL	Anti-symmetric filter	非对称滤波器	Fēiduìchèn lǜbōqì
AFL	Automatic fault location	自动故障定位	Zìdòng gùzhàng dìngwèi
AFM	Access network fault manager	接入网故障管理	Jiērùwǎng gùzhàng guǎnlǐ
AFMS	Advanced flexible access multiplex system	高级灵活接入复用系统	Gāojí línghuó jiērù fùyòng xìtǒng
AFN	Active filter network	有源滤波器网络	Yǒuyuán lǜbōqì wǎngluò
AFN	Average failure number	平均故障数	Píngjūn gùzhàng shù
AFP	AppleTalk filing protocol	AppleTalk 文件协议	AppleTalk wénjiàn xiéyì
AFPA	Automatic flow process analysis	自动流程分析	Zìdòng liúchéng fēnxī
AFR	Absolute frequency reference	绝对参考频率	Juéduì cānkǎo pínlǜ
AFR	Absolute frequency reference	绝对基准频率	Juéduì jīzhǔn pínlǜ
AFR	Absolute frequency reference	绝对频率参考	Juéduì pínlǜ cānkǎo
AFR	Alternate frame rendering (video)	交替渲染技术	Jiāotì xuànrǎn jìshù
AFR	Amplitude-frequency response	幅频响应	Fú-pín xiǎngyìng
AFS	Active function set	有效功能组	Yǒuxiào gōngnéng zǔ
AFS	Advanced freephone service	高级免费电话业务	Gāojí miǎnfèi diànhuà yèwù
AFSK	Audio frequency shift keying	音频移频键控	Yīnpín yípín jiànkòng
AFT	Automatic file transfer	自动文件传递	Zìdòng wénjiàn chuándì
AFT	Automatic frequency tuning	自动频率调谐	Zìdòng pínlǜ tiáoxié
AFTP	Anonymous file transfer protocol	匿名文件传送协议	Nìmíng wénjiàn chuánsòng xiéyì
AG	Application generator	应用程序生成器	Yìngyòng chéngxù shēngchéngqì
AG	Audio gateway	语音网关	Yǔyīn wǎngguān
AGC	Automatic gain control	自动增益控制	Zìdòng zēngyì kòngzhì
AGCH	Access grant channel	接入允许信道	Jiērù yǔnxǔ xìndào
AGCH	Access grant channel	接入准许信道	Jiērù zhǔnxǔ xìndào
AGCH	Access grant channel	允许接入信道	Yǔnxǔ jiērù xìndào
AGCH	Access grant channel	允许接续信道	Yǔnxǔ jiēxù xìndào
AGCH	Access grant channel	准予接入信道	Zhǔnyǔ jiērù xìndào
AGCH	Access grant channel	准予接续信道	Zhǔnyǔ jiēxù xìndào
AGF	Additional global function	附加的全局功能	Fùjiāde quánjú gōngnéng
AGK	Access gatekeeper	接入网守	Jiērù wǎngshǒu

AGP	Accelerated graphics port	加速图形端口	Jiāsù túxíng duānkǒu
AGP	Accelerated graphics port	图形加速接口	Túxíng jiāsù jiēkǒu
AGP	Advanced graphics port	高级图形端口	Gāojí túxíng duānkǒu
AGS	Advanced graphics system	高级图形系统	Gāojí túxíng xìtǒng
AGS	Advanced guidance system	高级制导系统	Gāojí zhìdǎo xìtǒng
AGW	Access gateway	接入网关	Jiērù wǎngguān
AH	Active homing	主动追踪	Zhǔdòng zhuīzōng
AH	Authentication header	鉴定文件头	Jiàndìng wénjiàn tóu
AH	Authentication header (in IPsec)	认证头	Rènzhèng tóu
AHA	Accelerated hub architecture	加速中心架构	Jiāsù zhōngxīn jiàgòu
AHLF	Additional high layer function	附加的高层功能	Fùjiāde gāocéng gōngnéng
AHT	Average handling time	平均处理时间	Píngjūn chǔlǐ shíjiān
AHT	Average holding time	平均保持时间	Píngjūn bǎochí shíjiān
AHT	Average holding time	平均占用时间	Píngjūn zhànyòng shíjiān
AHU	Air handling unit	空气处理机组	Kōngqì chǔlǐjī zǔ
AI	Acquisition indicator	扑获指示器	Pūhuò zhǐshìqì
Ai	Action indicator	动作指示符	Dòngzuò zhǐshì fú
AI	Action indicator	作用指示器	Zuòyòng zhǐshìqì
AI	Activate indication	激活指示	Jīhuó zhǐshì
AI	Adaptation information	适配信息	Shìpèi xìnxī
AI	Artificial intelligence	人工智能	Réngōng zhìnéng
AI	Error indication	错误指示	Cuòwù zhǐshì
A-I	Auto-iris	自动光圈	Zìdòng guāngquān
AIBI	American Intelligent Building Institute	美国智能建筑学会	Měiguó zhìnéng jiànzhù xuéhuì
AIC	Asian Info-Communications Committee	亚洲信息通信委员会	Yàzhōu xìnxī tōngxìn wěiyuánhuì
AICH	Acquisition indicator channel	扑获指示信道	Pūhuò zhǐshì xìndào
AID	Application identifier	应用标识符	Yìngyòng biāozhì fú
AIE	Antenna illumination efficiency	天线照射效率	Tiānxiàn zhàoshè xiàolǜ
AIMUX	ATM inverse multiplexing	ATM 反向复用	ATM fǎnxiàng fùyòng
AIN	Advanced intelligent network	高级智能网	Gāojí zhìnéng wǎng
AIP	Access interface platform	接入接口平台	Jiērù jiēkǒu píngtái
AIS	Alarm indication signal	告警指示信号	Gàojǐng zhǐshì xìnhào
AIS	Alarm indicator signal	故障警报信号	Gùzhàng jǐngbào xìnhào
AIS3	Asia Information System Security Service	亚洲信息系统安全服务	Yàzhōu xìnxī xìtǒng ānquán fúwù
AISD	Automatic interpretation of structural drawings (CAD/CAM)	建筑结构图自动识别系统	Jiànzhù jiégòutú zìdòng shíbié xìtǒng
AITS	Acknowledged information transfer service	确认式信息传送服务	Quèrèn-shì xìnxī chuánsòng fúwù
AIUR	Air interface user rate	空中接口用户速率	Kōngzhōng jiēkǒu yònghù sùlǜ
AJ	Alignment jitter	校正抖动	Jiàozhèng dǒudòng
AJ	Anti-jamming	抗干扰	Kànggānrǎo
AJF	Anti-jamming frequency	抗干扰频率	Kànggānrǎo pínlǜ
AK	Anonymity key	无名键	Wúmíng jiàn
AKA	Authentication and key agreement	鉴权和密钥同意	Jiànquán hé mìyuè tóngyì
AKEY	Access key	存取键	Cúnqǔ jiàn
AKI	Acknowledge interrupt	肯定中断	Kěndìng zhōngduàn
AL	Access link	接入链路	Jiērù liànlù
AL	Alignment	校准	Jiàozhǔn

AL	Amplitude limiter	限幅器	Xiànfúqì
AL	Artificial life	人工生命	Réngōng shēngmìng
ALAN	Advanced local area network	高级局域网	Gāojí júyùwǎng
ALC	Automatic level control	自动电平控制	Zìdòng diànpíng kòngzhì
ALC	Automatic level control	自动平衡控制	Zìdòng pínghéng kòngzhì
ALC	Automatic light compensation	自动亮度补偿	Zìdòng liàngdù bǔcháng
ALC	Automatic light control	自动光控制	Zìdòng guāng kòngzhì
ALCAP	Access link control application protocol	接入链路控制应用协议	Jiērù liànlù kòngzhì yìngyòng xiéyì
$AlCl_3$	Aluminum trichloride	三氯化铝	Sānlǜhuàlǚ
ALD	Alarm display	告警显示	Gàojǐng xiǎnshì
ALE	Average life expectancy	平均寿命预期值	Píngjūn shòumìng yùqīzhí
ALF	Application level framing	应用层帧协议	Yìngyòng céng zhèng xiéyì
ALF	Application-level framing	应用层分帧	Yìngyòng céng fēnzhèng
ALG	Application-level gateway	应用级网关	Yìngyòng jí wǎngguān
AlGaN	Aluminum gallium nitride	铝镓氮	Lǚjiādàn
ALGOL	Algorithmic language	算法语言	Suànfǎ yǔyán
ALI	Automatic line identification	自动线路识别	Zìdòng xiànlù shíbié
ALI	Automatic location identification	自动位置识别	Zìdòng wèizhì shíbié
ALLF	Additional low layer function	附加的低层功能	Fùjiāde dīcéng gōngnéng
ALM	Alarm	告警	Gàojǐng
AlN	Aluminum nitride	氮化铝	Dànhuà lǚ
ALPD	Axial and linear plasma [Chemical vapor] deposition	轴向和横向等离子化学汽相沉积法	Zhóuxiàng hé héngxiàng děnglízǐ huàxué qìxiàng chénjī fǎ
ALR	Application location register	应用位置登记	Yìngyòng wèizhì dēngjì
ALS	Alarm seconds	告警秒	Gàojǐng miǎo
ALS	Application layer structure	应用层结构	Yìngyòng céng jiégòu
ALS	Automatic laser shutdown	激光器自动关闭	Jīguāngqì zìdòng guānbì
ALS	Automatic laser shutdown	自动激光关闭	Zìdòng jīguāng guānbì
ALS	Automatic laser shutdown	自动激光关断	Zìdòng jīguāng guānduàn
ALSI	Application level subscriber identity	应用层用户标示	Yìngyòng céng yònghù biāoshì
ALT	Automatic link transfer	自动链路转移	Zìdòng liànlù zhuǎnyí
ALU	Analog lines unit	模拟用户线单元	Mónǐ yònghùxiàn dānyuán
ALU	Arithmetic and logic unit	算术及逻辑运算部件	Suànshù jí luóji yùnsuàn bùjiàn
ALU	Arithmetic logic unit	算术逻辑单元	Suànshù luóji dānyuán
AM	Accounting management	帐号管理	Zhànghào guǎnlǐ
AM	Acknowledged mode	应答模式	Yìngdá móshì
AM	Administration module	管理模块	Guǎnlǐ mókuài
AM	Agile manufacturing (British concept)	敏捷制造	Mǐnjié zhìzào
AM	Amplitude modulation	幅度调制	Fúdù tiáozhì
AM	Amplitude modulation	调幅	Tiáofú
AM	Amplitude modulation	振幅调制	Zhènfú tiáozhì
am	Automatic maintenance	自动维护	Zìdòng wéihù
AM/CM	Administration module/communication module	管理/通信模块	Guǎnlǐ/Tōngxìn mókuài
AM/FM	Automated mapping and facilities management	自动制图/设施管理	Zìdòng zhìtú/shèshī guǎnlǐ
AM-ADDR	Active member address	活动的成员地址	Huódòngde chéngyuán dìzhǐ
AMBB	Applications management building block	应用管理构件	Yìngyòng guǎnlǐ gòujiàn

AMC	Adaptive modulation and coding	自适应调制编码	Zìshìyìng tiáozhì biānmǎ
AMC	Adaptive motion compensation algorithm	自适应运动补偿算法	Zìshìyìng yùndòng bǔcháng suànfǎ
AMD	Advanced Micro Devices	超微科技	Chāowēi kējì
AMD	Advanced Micro Devices (US computer company)	超微半导体	Chāowēi bàndǎotǐ
AME	Amplified spontaneous emission	放大自激辐射信号	Fàngdà zìjī fúshè xìnhào
AME	Automatic message exchange	自动信息交换	Zìdòng xìnxī jiāohuàn
AMF	Authentication management field	认证管理范围	Rènzhèng guǎnlǐ fànwéi
AMGUI	Applications manager graphical user interface	应用管理用户图形接口	Yìngyòng guǎnlǐ yònghù túxíng jiēkǒu
AMI	Alternate mark inversion	传号交替变换码	Chuánhào jiāotì biànhuàn mǎ
AMI	Alternate mark inversion	信号交替变换	Xìnhào jiāotì biànhuàn
AMI	Alternate mark inversion	信号交替反转码	Xìnhào jiāotì fǎnzhuǎn mǎ
AMI	Alternate mark inversion	信号交替翻转码	Xìnhào jiāotì fǎnzhuǎn mǎ
AMI	Alternate mark inversion code	交替传号反转码	Jiāotì chuánhào fǎnzhuǎn mǎ
AMI	Alternate mark inversion coding	交替极性翻转码	Jiāotì jíxìng fǎnzhuǎn mǎ
AMI	Alternate mark inversion coding	极性交替反转双极性码	Jíxìng jiāotì fǎnzhuǎn shuāng jíxìng mǎ
AMI	Application management interface	应用管理接口	Yìngyòng guǎnlǐ jiēkǒu
AML	Active mode lock	活动模锁定	Huódòng mó suǒdìng
AML	Address mapping list	地址映射表	Dìzhǐ yìngshè biǎo
AML	Arc/Info macro language	Arc/Info 宏语言	Arc/Info hóng yǔyán
AML	Asymptotic maximum likelihood	渐进最大似然	Zhèjìn zuìdà sìrán
AMLC	Asynchronous multi-line controller	异步多线路控制器	Yìbù duō xiànlù kòngzhìqì
AMN	Artificial mains network	人工电源网络	Réngōng diànyuán wǎngluò
AMO	Automatic maintenance operation	自动维护运行（操作）	Zìdòng wéihù yùnxíng (cāozuò)
AMOS	Anodized metal-oxide semiconductor	阳极化金属-氧化物-半导体	Yángjíhuà jīnshǔ—yǎnghuàwù bàndǎotǐ
AMP	Advanced macro processor	宏指令处理程序	Hóng zhǐlìng chǔlǐ chéngxù
AMPS	Advanced mobile phone service	高级移动电话服务	Gāojí yídòng diànhuà fúwù
AMPS	Advanced mobile phone service	高级移动电话业务	Gāojí yídòng diànhuà yèwù
AMPS	Advanced mobile phone service	先进移动电话业务	Xiānjìn yídòng diànhuà yèwù
AMPS	Advanced mobile phone system	高极移动电话系统	Gāojí yídòng diànhuà xìtǒng
AMPS	Advanced mobile phone system	先进的移动电话系统	Xiānjìnde yídòng diànhuà xìtǒng
AMQ	Analog multiplexer quantizer	模拟复用器量化器	Mónǐ fùyòngqì liànghuàqì
AMR	Adaptive multirate	自适应多速率	Zìshìyìng duōsùlǜ
AMR	Arithmetic mask register	运算屏蔽寄存器	Yùnsuàn píngbì jìcúnqì
AMR	Audio/modem riser	音效调制解调器主机板附加直立插卡	Yīnxiào tiáozhì jiětiáoqì zhǔjī bǎn fùjiā zhílì chā kǎ
AMR	Audio/modem riser	音效/数据主机板附加直立插卡	Yīnxiào/shùjù zhǔjī bǎn fùjiā zhílì chā kǎ
AMR	Audio/modem riser	音效/调制解调器主机板附加直立插卡	Yīnxiào/tiáozhì jiětiáoqì zhǔjī bǎn fùjiā zhílì chā qiǎ
AMR	Automatic meter reading	自动抄表	Zìdòng chāo biǎo
AMRC	Adaptive multirate codec	自适应多码率编译码器	Zìshìyìng duōmǎlǜ biānyìmǎqì
AMS	Adaptive modulation system	自适应调制系统	Zìshìyìng tiáozhì xìtǒng
AMS	Administration and maintenance sub-system	管理维护子系统	Guǎnlǐ wéihù zixìtǒng
AMS	Application management specification	应用管理规范	Yìngyòng guǎnlǐ guīfàn
AMSA	Advanced mobile security architecture	先进移动安全体系结构	Xiānjìn yídòng ānquán tǐxì jiégòu
AMSIA	Audio-visual multimedia service implementation agreement	音像多媒体业务执行协议	Yīnxiàng duōméitǐ yèwù zhíxíng xiéyì

AMSS	Aeronautical mobile satellite service	航空移动卫星通信	Hángkōng yídòng wèixīng tōngxìn
AMT	Address mapping table	地址映射表	Dìzhǐ yìngshè biǎo
AMTS	Advanced mobile telephone system	高级移动电话系统	Gāojí yídòng diànhuà xìtǒng
AN	Access network	接入网	Jiērù wǎng
AN	Active network	有源网络	Yǒuyuán wǎngluò
AN	Alignment network	校正网络	Jiàozhèng wǎngluò
ANA	Assign network address	分配网络地址	Fēnpèi wǎngluò dìzhǐ
ANA	Automatic number analysis	自动号码分析	Zìdòng hàomǎ fēnxī
ANAS	Asynchronous transfer mode network access sub-system	异步传递模式网络接入子系统	Yìbù chuándì móshì wǎngluò jiērù zixìtǒng
ANAS	Asynchronous transfer mode network access sub-system	异步转移模式网络接入子系统	Yìbù zhuǎnyí móshì wǎngluò jiērù zixìtǒng
ANATEL	Agencia Nacional de Telecomunicaoes (Brazil)	国家电信管理局	Guójiā diànxìn guǎnlǐjú
ANC	Adaptive noise cancellation	自适应噪声消除	Zìshìying zàoshēng xiāochú
ANC	All number calling	全号码呼叫	Quán hàomǎ hūjiào
ANC	Answer charging	应答计费	Yìngdá jìfèi
ANC	Answer signal, charge	应答信号、计费	Yìngdá xìnhào、jìfèi
ANC	Automatic noise canceller	自动杂波消除电路	Zìdòng zábō xiāochú diànlù
AND	And circuit (usually “与”)	与电路	Yǔ diànlù
AND	Automatic network dialing	自动网络拨号	Zìdòng wǎngluò bōhào
ANI	Advanced network integration	高级网络集成	Gāojí wǎngluò jíchéng
ANI	Advanced network integration	高级网络综合	Gāojí wǎngluò zōnghé
ANI	Automatic number identification	自动号码识别	Zìdòng hàomǎ shíbié
ANLE	Adaptive non-linear enhancer	自适应非线性增强器	Zìshìying fēixiànxìng zēngqiángqì
ANM	Answer message (SS7 ISUP message)	应答消息	Yìngdá xiāoxi
ANM	Answer message (ISUP message)	被较应答	Bèijiào yìngdá
ANMS	Access network management system	接入网管理系统	Jiērùwǎng guǎnlǐ xìtǒng
ANN	Answer no charge	应答免费	Yìngdá miǎnfèi
ANN	Answer signal, no charge	应答不计费信号	Yìngdá bùjìfèi xìnhào
ANN	Answer signal, no charge	应答信号、免费	Yìngdá xìnhào、miǎnfèi
ANN	Artificial neural network	人工神经网络	Réngōng shénjīng wǎngluò
AN-NMS	Access network –network management system	接入网网管系统	Jiērùwǎng wǎngguǎn xìtǒng
ANRZ	Alternating non-return to zero	交替不归零制	Jiāotì bù guī líng zhì
ANS	Access network system	接入网系统	Jiērùwǎng xìtǒng
ANS	Advanced networks and services	高级网络和服务	Gāojí wǎngluò hé fúwù
ANS	Area networking system	区域网络系统	Qūyù wǎngluò xìtǒng
ANSA	Advanced network system architecture	高级网络系统结构	Gāojí wǎngluò xìtǒng jiégòu
ANSI	American National Standard for Information Systems	美国信息系统国家标准	Měiguó xìnxī xìtǒng guójiā biāozhǔn
ANSI	American National Standards Institute	美国国家标准协会	Měiguó guójiā biāozhǔn xiéhuì
ANSI	American National Standards Institute	美国国家标准研究所	Měiguó guójiā biāozhǔn yánjiūsuǒ
ANSI	American National Standards Institute	美国国家标准组织	Měiguó guójiā biāozhǔn zǔzhī
ANSI	American National Standards Institute	美国国家标准局	Měiguó guójiā biāozhǔnjú
AN-SMF	Access network system management function	接入网系统管理功能	Jiērùwǎng xìtǒng guǎnlǐ gōngnéng
ANU	Answer signal, unqualified	应当信号、计费未说明	Yīngdāng xìnhào、jìfèi wèi shuōmíng
ANX	Automotive network eXchange	汽车网络交换中心	Qìchē wǎngluò jiāohuàn zhōngxīn
AO	Always on	始终保持	Shǐzhōng bǎochí
AO	Associated object	相关目标	Xiāngguān mùbiāo

AOA	Angle of arrival	到达角度	Dàodá jiǎodù
AOB	Adder output buffer	加法器输出缓冲器	Jiāfǎqì shūchū huǎnchōngqì
AOB	Adder output bus	加法器输出总线	Jiāfǎqì shūchū zǒngxiàn
AOC	ADSL overhead control channel	ADSL 开销控制信道	ADSL kāixiao kòngzhì xìndào
AOC	Advice of charge	计费通知	Jìfèi tōngzhī
AOC	Advice of charge	收费通知	Shōufèi tōngzhī
AoC	Advice of charge charging	计费收费通知	Jìfèi shōufèi tōngzhī
AOC	All-optical communication	全光通信	Quán guāng tōngxìn
AOC	Automated operator console	自动操作台	Zìdòng cāozuò tái
AOC	Automated operator control	自动操作控制	Zìdòng cāozuò kòngzhì
AOC	Automated output control	自动输出控制	Zìdòng shūchū kòngzhì
AOC	Automated overload control	自动过载控制	Zìdòng guòzài kòngzhì
AoCC	Advice of charge charging supplementary service	计费通知（记费）补充业务	Jìfèi tōngzhī (jìfèi) bǔchōng yèwù
AoCc	Advice of charge for charging	计费通知(计费)	Jìfèi tōngzhī (jìfèi)
AoCC	Advice of charge, charging level	计费通知，计费类	Jìfèi tōngzhī, jìfèi lèi
AoCi	Advice of charge for information	计费通知(信息)	Jìfèi tōngzhī (xìnxī)
AoCI	Advice of charge information	信息计费通知	Xìnxī jìfèi tōngzhī
AoCI	Advice of charge information supplementary service	计费通知（信息）补充业务	Jìfèi tōngzhī (xìnxī) bǔchōng yèwù
AoCI	Advice of charge, information level	计费通知，信息类	Jìfèi tōngzhī, xìnxī lèi
AOD	Active optical device	有源光器件	Yǒuyuán guāng qìjiàn
AOD	Audio-on-demand	按需点播音频	Ànxū diǎnbō yīnpín
AODV	Ad hoc on-demand distance vector	按序距离矢量	Ànxù jùlí shǐliàng
AOF	Acousto-optic filter	声光率波器	Shēngguāng lǜbōqì
AOF	Active optical fiber	有源光纤	Yǒuyuán guāngxiān
AOF	Attenuation optimized fiber	优化衰减光纤	Yōuhuà shuāijiǎn guāngxiān
AOFC	Aerial fiber optic cable	架空光缆	Jiàkōng guānglǎn
AOH	Add-on header	添加标题	Tiānjiā biāotí
AOI	Automatic optical inspection equipment	自动光学检测设备	Zìdòng guāngxué jiǎncè shèbèi
AOL	America Online	美国线上	Měiguó xiànshàng
AOL	America On-Line	美国在线服务	Měiguó zàixiàn fúwù
AOL	America Online ® (US company)	线上美国	Xiànshàng Měiguó
AOM	Acousto-optic modulator	声光调制器	Shēngguāng tiáozhìqì
AOM	Automatic operation monitor	自动操作监控器	Zìdòng cāozuò jiānkòngqì
AON	Active optical network	有源光网络	Yǒuyuán guāng wǎngluò
AON	All optical network	全光网络	Quán guāng wǎngluò
AOS	Acousto-optic switch	声光开关	Shēngguāng kāiguān
AOS	Acquisition of signal	信号捕获	Xìnhào bǔhuò
AOS	Always on server	始终保持服务器	Shǐzhōng bǎochí fúwùqì
AOTA	All-optical towed array	全光牵引阵列	Quán guāng qiānyǐn zhènliè
AOTF	Acoustic-optic tunable filter	声光可调滤波器	Shēngguāng kětiáo lǜbōqì
AOWC	All optical wave converter	全光波长转换器	Quán guāng bōcháng zhuǎnhuànqì
AP	Access point	接入站	Jiērùzhàn
AP	Access point (database usage)	访问点	Fǎngwèn diǎn
AP	Access point (telecom network usage)	接入点	Jiērùdiǎn
AP	Access preamble	接入段首标记	Jiērùduàn shǒubiāojì
AP	Access protocol	访问协议	Fǎngwèn xiéyì

AP	Administrative point	管理点	Guǎnlǐ diǎn
AP	Administrative processor	管理处理器	Guǎnlǐ chùlǐqì
AP	Anomalous propagation	异常传播	Yìcháng chuánbō
AP	Application process or program	应用进程	Yìngyòng jìnchéng
AP	Argument pointer	自变量指针	Zìbiànliàng zhǐzhēn
AP	Array processor	阵列处理机	Zhènliè chǔlǐjī
AP	Auto-correlation prediction	自相关预测	Zìxiāngguān yùcè
APA	Archive parser agent (in Java)	文档解析代理	Wéndàng jiěxī dàilǐ
APB	All-path-busy	通路全忙	Tōnglù quánmáng
APBX	Automatic private branch exchange	自动专用分路交换机	Zìdòng zhuānyòng fēnlù jiāohuànjī
APC	Adaptive power control	自适应功率控制	Zìshìyìng gōnglǜ kòngzhì
APC	Adaptive predictive coder	自适应预测编码器	Zìshìyìng yùcè biānmǎqì
APC	Adaptive predictive coding	自适应预测编码	Zìshìyìng yùcè biānmǎ
APC	Alarm panel control block	告警面板控制模块	Gàojǐng miànbǎn kòngzhì mókuài
APC	Amplitude phase conversion	幅度相位变换	Fúdù xiāngwèi biànhuàn
APC	Amplitude phase conversion	幅相变换	Fú-xiāng biànhuàn
APC	Angle plane connection	斜角平面连接	Xiéjiǎo píngmiàn liánjiē
APC	Augmented parity check	扩充的奇偶校验	Kuòchōngde jī'ǒu jiàoyàn
APC	Automatic phase compensation	自动相位补偿	Zìdòng xiàngwèi bǔcháng
APC	Automatic phase control	自动相位控制	Zìdòng xiàngwèi kòngzhì
APC	Automatic picture control	自动图象控制	Zìdòng túxiàng kòngzhì
APC	Automatic polarization control	自动偏振控制	Zìdòng piānzhèn kòngzhì
APC	Automatic program control	自动程序控制	Zìdòng chéngxù kòngzhì
APC	Avalanche photodiode coupler	雪崩光电二极管耦合器	Xuěbēng guāngdiàn èrjíguǎn ǒuhéqì
APC-AB	Adaptive predictive coding with adaptive bit allocation	具有自适应比特分配的自适应预测编码	Jùyǒu zìshìyìng bǐtè fēnpèide zìshìyìng yùcè biānmǎ
APCI	Application protocol control information	应用协议控制信息	Yìngyòng xiéyì kòngzhì xìnxī
APCM	Adaptive phase code modulation	自适应相位代码调制	Zìshìyìng xiàngwèi dàimǎ tiáozhì
APCM	Adaptive pulse code modulation	自适应脉码调制	Zìshìyìng màimǎ tiáozhì
APCN	Asia-Pacific Cable Network	亚太电缆网络	Yàtài diànlǎn wǎngluò
APCO	Association of public safety communication officials international	国际公共安全通信官方协议	Guójì gōnggòng ānquán tōngxìn guānfāng xiéyì
APCS	Advanced personal communication system	高级个人通信系统	Gāojí gèrén tōngxìn xìtǒng
APCS	Associative processor computer system	相联处理机计算系统	Xiānglián chǔlǐjī jìsuàn xìtǒng
APCU	Alarm panel control unit assembly	告警面板控制集成单元	Gàojǐng miànbǎn kòngzhì jíchéng dānyuán
APD	Amplitude probability distribution	幅度概率分布	Fúdù gàilǜ fēnbù
APD	Amplitude probability distribution	振幅概率分布	Zhènfú gàilǜ fēnbù
APD	Avalanche photo detector	雪崩光电检测器	Xuěbēng guāngdiàn jiǎncè qì
APD	Avalanche photo detector	雪崩光电探测器	Xuěbēng guāngdiàn tàncèqì
APD	Avalanche photodiode	雪崩光二极管	Xuěbēng guāng èrjíguǎn
APDU	Application protocol data unit	应用协议数据单元	Yìngyòng xiéyì shùjù dānyuán
API	Accurate position indicator	精确位置指示器	Jīngquè wèizhì zhǐshìqì
API	Advanced programming interface	高级编程接口	Gāojí biānchéng jiēkǒu
API	Application process invocation	应用程序请求	Yìngyòng chéngxù qǐngqiú
API	Application program interface	应用程序接口	Yìngyòng chéngxù jiēkǒu
API	Application program interface	应用软件介面	Yìngyòng ruǎnjiàn jièmiàn
API	Application programming interface	应用编程接口	Yìngyòng biānchéng jiēkǒu

APIC	Advanced programmable interrupt controller	高级程序中断控制器	Gāojí chéngxù zhōngduàn kòngzhìqì
APID	Access point identifier	接入点标识符	Jiērùdiǎn biāozhìfú
APID	Access point identifier	接入点识别符	Jiērùdiǎn shíbié fú
APIPA	Automatic private IP addressing	自动专用 IP 寻址	Zìdòng zhuānyòng IP xúnzhǐ
APIS	Array processing instruction set	数组处理指令系统	Shùzǔ chǔlǐ zhǐlìng xìtǒng
APK	Amplitude and phase keying	振幅与相位键控	Zhènfú yǔ xiàngwèi jiànkòng
APK	Amplitude phase keying	幅相键控	Fú-xiāng jiànkòng
APK	Amplitude phase keying	振幅相位键控	Zhènfú xiàngwèi jiànkòng
APL	Automatic phase lock	自动锁相	Zìdòng suǒxiāng
APL	Average picture level	平均图象电平	Píngjūn túxiàng diànpíng
APLL	Analog phase-locked loop	模拟锁相环	Mónǐ suǒxiàng huán
APM	Advanced power management	高级能源管理	Gāojí néngyuán guǎnlǐ
APM	Amplitude-phase modulation	振幅-相位调制	Zhènfú/xiàngwèi tiáozhì
APM	Application transport mechanism	应用传送机制	Yìngyòng chuánsòng jīzhì
APN	Access point name	接入点名	Jiērùdiǎn míng
APN	Access point name	接入点名	Jiērùdiǎn míng
APNA-CC	Asian Pacific Networking Group-Chinese characters	亚太地区网络-中文分组	Yàtài dìqū wǎngluò--zhōngwén fēnzǔ
APOC	Advanced paging operator code	先进寻呼操作码	Xiānjìn xúnhū cāozuòmǎ
APOF	All plastic optical fiber	全塑光纤	Quánsù guāngxiān
APON	All passive optical network	全无源光网络	Quán wúyuán guāng wǎngluò
APON	Asynchronous transfer mode passive optical network	异步传递方式无源光网络	Yìbù chuándì fāngshì wúyuán guāng wǎngluò
APON	ATM passive optical network	ATM 无源光网络	ATM wúyuán guāng wǎngluò
A-PON	Passive optical network based on ATM	基于 ATM 的无源光网络	Jīyú ATM de wúyuán guāng wǎngluò
APP	*a posteriori* probability	后验概率	Hòuyàn gàilǜ
APP	Application transport parameter	应用传送参数	Yìngyòng chuánsòng cānshù
APPC	Advanced peer-to-peer communications	先进的同层通信	Xiānjìnde tóngcéng tōngxìn
APPC	Advanced program-to-program communication	高级程序间通信	Gāojí chéngxù-jiān tōngxìn
APPE	Advanced packet parsing engine	增强形帧解析引擎	Zēngqiáng-xíng zhèng jiěxī yǐnqíng
APPI	Advanced peer-to-peer internetworking	先进的同层互联网	Xiānjìnde tóngcéng hùliánwǎng
APPN	Advanced peer to peer networking	高级对等网络	Gāojí duìděng wǎngluò
APR	Active page register	有效页寄存器	Yǒuxiào yè jìcúnqì
APR	Automatic (optical) power reduction	自动光功率减少	Zìdòng guāng gōnglǜ jiǎnshǎo
APR	Automatic position reporting	自动位置报告	Zìdòng wèizhì bàogào
APR	Automatic power reduction	自动功率降低	Zìdòng gōnglǜ jiàngdī
APR	Automatic power reduction	自动功率减少	Zìdòng gōnglǜ jiǎnshǎo
APR	Automatic programming and recording	自动程序设计与记录	Zìdòng chéngxù shèjì yǔ jìlù
APS	Addressed packet system	编址分组系统	Biānzhǐ fēnzǔ xìtǒng
APS	Application program system	应用程序系统	Yìngyòng chéngxù xìtǒng
APS	Automatic phase shifter	自动移相器	Zìdòng yíxiàngqì
APS	Automatic phase synchronization	自动相位同步	Zìdòng xiàngwèi tóngbù
APS	Automatic protection switching	自动保护倒换	Zìdòng bǎohù dǎohuàn
APS	Automatic protection switching	自动保护切换	Zìdòng bǎohù qiēhuàn
APS	Auxiliary power source	辅助电源	Fǔzhù diànyuán
APSD	Automatic (optical) power shut down	自动光功率关断	Zìdòng guāng gōnglǜ guānduàn
APSD	Automatic power shutdown	自动功率切断	Zìdòng gōnglǜ qiēduàn

APSK	Absolute phase shift keying	绝对相移键控	Juéduì xiāngyí jiànkòng
APSK	Amplitude phase shift keying	振幅移相键控	Zhènfú yíxiāng jiànkòng
APTS	Automatic picture transmission system	自动图象传输系统	Zìdòng túxiàng chuánshū xìtǒng
APU	Audio processor unit	音频处理器单元	Yīnpín chǔlǐqì dānyuán
APU	Automatic program unit	自动程序设计装置	Zìdòng chéngxù shèjì zhuāngzhì
AQ	Adaptive quantization	自适应量化	Zìshìyìng liànghuà
AQBE	Adaptive quantization with backward estimation	采用反向估计的自适应量化	Cǎiyòng fǎnxiàng gūjìde zìshìyìng liànghuà
AQFE	Adaptive quantization with forward estimation	采用正向评判的自适应量化	Cǎiyòng zhèngxiàng píngpànde zìshìyìng liànghuà
AQL	Acceptable quality level (in quality standards)	可接收质量水平	Kějiēshōu zhìliàng shuǐpíng
AR	Access rate	接入率	Jiērù lǜ
AR	Access rate	接入速率	Jiērù sùlǜ
AR	Activate request	激活请求	Jīhuó qǐngqiú
AR	Agent request	代理请求	Dàilǐ qǐngqiú
AR	Alternative routing	迂回路由选择	Yūhuí lùyóu xuǎnzé
ARA	AppleTalk remote access	AppleTalk 远程访问	AppleTalk yuǎnchéng fǎngwèn
ARA	Average response amplitude	平均响应幅度	Píngjūn xiǎngyìng fúdù
AR-ADDR	Access request address	访问请求地址	Fǎngwèn qǐngqiú dìzhǐ
ARB	All routes busy	路由全忙	Lùyóu quán máng
ARC	Alternative route cancel	消除迂回路由	Xiāochú yūhuí lùyóu
ARC	Automatic remote control	自动遥控	Zìdòng yáokòng
ArcFM	Arc/Info facility manager	Arc/Info 公共设施管理器	Arc/Info gōnggòng shèshī guǎnlǐqì
ARCnet	Attached resource computer net	资源附加网络	Zīyuán fùjiā wǎngluò
ARCnet	Attached resource computer network	附加资源计算机网络	Fùjiā zīyuán jìsuànjī wǎngluò
ArcSDE	Arc spatial database engine	Arc 空间数据库引擎	Arc kōngjiān shùjùkù yǐnqíng
ARDB	Address range definition block	地址范围定义块	Dìzhǐ fànwéi dìngyì kuài
ARDT	Automatic remote data terminal	自动远端数据终端	Zìdòng yuǎnduān shùjù zhōngduān
ARF	Access to the resources function	资源访问功能	Zīyuán fǎngwèn gōngnéng
ARF	Alternative routing from	从迂回路由来	Cóng yūhuí lùyóu lái
ARF	Alternative routing from	迂回来路选择	Yūhuí láilù xuǎnzé
ARFCN	Absolute radio frequency channel number	绝对频道号	Juéduì píndào hào
ARFCN	Absolute radio frequency channel number	绝对射频频道号	Juéduì shèpín píndào hào
ARFCN	Absolute radio frequency channel number	绝对无线载频号	Juéduì wúxiàn zàipín hào
ARFCN	Absolute radio frequency channel number	完全的无线频率信道号码	Wánquánde wúxiàn pínlǜ xìndào hàomǎ
ARI	Access rights identity	存取权识别	Cúnqǔ quán shíbié
ARI	Assist request instruction	辅助请求指令	Fǔzhù qǐngqiú zhǐlìng
ARI	Assist request instruction	辅助请求指示	Fǔzhù qǐngqiú zhǐshì
ARIB	Association of Radio Industry Businesses (Japan)	无线行业企业协会	Wúxiàn hángyè qǐyè xiéhuì
ARIS	Aggregate route-based IP switching	集中式基于路由的 IP 交换	Jízhōng-shì jīyú lùyóude IP jiāohuàn
ARIS	Attack Registry & intelligence service	攻击事件注册及智能服务	Gōngjī shìjiàn zhùcè jí zhìnéng fúwù
ARJ	Admissions rejected	接入拒绝	Jiērù jùjué
ARL	Acceptable reliability level	合格的可靠性	Hégéde kěkàoxìng
ARM	Anti-radiation missile	反复射导弹	Fǎnfùshè dǎodàn
ARM	Asynchronous response mode	异步响应方式	Yìbù xiǎngyìng fāngshì
ARM	Asynchronous response mode	异步应答方式	Yìbù yìngdá fāngshì
ARN	Authentication random number	身份验证随机号	Shēnfen yànzhèng suíjī hào
ARP	Address recoding protocol	地址解析协议	Dìzhǐ jiěxī xiéyì

ARP	Address relief protocol	地址解折协议	Dìzhǐ jiězhé xiéyì
ARP	Address resolution protocol	地址解析协议	Dìzhǐ jiěxī xiéyì
ARPA	Advanced Research Project Agency	先进研究计划局	Xiānjìn yánjiū jìhuàjú
ARPA	Advanced Research Projects Agency (US)	高级研究计划局	Gāojí yánjiū jìhuàjú
ARPA	Advanced Research Projects Agency (US)	高级研究计划署	Gāojí yánjiū jìhuàshǔ
ARPAnet	Advanced Research Projects Agency Network	高级研究计划局网络	Gāojí yánjiū jìhuàjú wǎngluò
ARPANET	Advanced Research Projects Agency network (US)	阿帕网	Ā-pà wǎng
ARPANET	Advanced Research Projects Agency network (US)	高级研究规划局网络	Gāojí yánjiū guīhuàjú wǎngluò
ARPANET	Advanced Research Projects Agency network (US)	高级研究计划署网络	Gāojí yánjiū jìhuàshǔ wǎngluò
ARPG	Action role play games (computer game)	动作角色扮演游戏	Dòngzuò juésè bànyǎn yóuxì
ARQ	Admissions request	接入请求	Jiērù qǐngqiú
ARQ	Automatic repeat request	自动重发请求	Zìdòng chóngfā qǐngqiú
ARQ	Automatic repeat request	自动重复请求	Zìdòng chóngfù qǐngqiú
ARQ	Automatic repeat request	自动请求重传	Zìdòng qǐngqiú chóngchuán
ARQ	Automatic repeat request	自动请求重发	Zìdòng qǐngqiú chóngfā
ARQ	Error detecting and feedback system	检错及反馈重发系统	Jiǎncuò jí fǎnkuì chóngfā xìtǒng
ARS	Address resolution server	地址解析服务器	Dìzhǐ jiěxī fúwùqì
ARS	Automatic route selection	自动路由选择	Zìdòng lùyóu xuǎnzé
ART	Alarm reporting telephone	报警电话	Bàojǐng diànhuà
ART	Alternative routing to	从迂回路由去	Cóng yūhuí lùyóu qù
ART	Alternative routing to	迂回去路选择	Yūhuí qùlù xuǎnzé
ART	Average restoration time	平均恢复时间	Píngjūn huīfù shíjiān
ARTCC	Air route traffic control center (civil aviation)	航路交管中心	Háng lù jiāo guǎn zhōngxīn
ARTCC	Air route traffic control center (civil aviation)	航空路途交通管理中心	Hángkōng lùtú jiāotōng guǎnlǐ zhōngxīn
ARX	Automatic retransmission service	自动转发服务	Zìdòng zhuǎnfā fúwù
AS	Access server	接入服务器	Jiērù fúwùqì
AS	Access signaling	存取信令	Cúnqǔ xìnlìng
AS	Access signaling	接入信令	Jiērù xìnlìng
AS	Alarm statement	告警语句	Gàojǐng yǔjù
AS	Alarm surveillance	告警监视	Gàojǐng jiānshì
AS	Application server	应用服务器	Yìngyòng fúwùqì
AS	Auto system	自动台	Zìdòng tái
AS	Autonomous system	自治系统	Zìzhì xìtǒng
ASA	American Standards Association	美国标准协会	Měiguó biāozhǔn xiéhuì
ASA	Annular slot antenna	环状缝隙天线	Huánzhuàng fèngxì tiānxiàn
ASAP	Application service access point	应用业务接入点	Yìngyòng yèwù jiērù diǎn
ASAP	As soon as possible (computer chat)	尽快	Jǐnkuài
ASBR	Autonomous system border router	自治系统边界路由器	Zìzhì xìtǒng biānjiè lùyóuqì
ASBR	Autonomous system boundary router	自治区系统边界路由器	Zìzhìqū xìtǒng biānjiè lùyóuqì
ASBR	Autonomous system boundary router	自主系统边界路由器	Zìzhǔ xìtǒng biānjiè lùyóuqì
ASC	Access service class	接入业务分类	Jiērù yèwù fēnlèi
ASC	Assistance service control	辅助业务控制	Fǔzhù yèwù kòngzhì
ASC	Automatic digital network switching center	自动数字网络交换中心	Zìdòng shùzì wǎngluò jiāohuàn zhōngxīn
ASC	Automatic selectivity control	自动选择性控制	Zìdòng xuǎnzéxìng kòngzhì
ASC	Automatic sensitivity control	自动灵敏度控制	Zìdòng língmǐndù kòngzhì
ASC	Automatic slope control	自动斜率控制	Zìdòng xiélǜ kòngzhì

ASC	Auto-sizing and centering (video term)	自动调效屏幕尺寸和中心位置	Zìdòng tiáoxiào píngmù chǐcùn hé zhōngxīn wèizhì
ASCI	Advanced speech call items	先进的语音呼叫项目	Xiānjìnde yǔyīn hūjiào xiàngmù
ASCII	American standard code	美标码	Měi biāo mǎ
ASCII	American Standard Code for Information Interchange	美国国家标准信息交换代码	Měiguó guójiā biāozhǔn xìnxī jiāohuàn dàimǎ
ASCII	American Standard Code for Information Interchange	美国信息交换标准代码	Měiguó xìnxī jiāohuàn biāozhǔn dàimǎ
ASCII	American Standard Code for Information Interchange	美国信息交换标准码	Měiguó xìnxī jiāohuàn biāozhǔn mǎ
ASCS	Access switching control sub-system	接入交换控制子系统	Jiērù jiāohuàn kòngzhì zìxìtǒng
ASD	Automatic service discovery	自动业务发现	Zìdòng yèwù fāxiàn
ASE	Amplified spontaneous emission	放大自发辐射	Fàngdà zìfā fúshè
ASE	Application service element	应用服务单元	Yìngyòng fúwù dānyuán
ASE	Application service element	应用服务元素	Yìngyòng fúwù yuánsù
ASE	Application service element	应用业务单元	Yìngyòng yèwù dānyuán
ASE	Application service element	应用业务元素	Yìngyòng yèwù yuánsù
ASEAT	Autoregressive spectral estimation acquisition technique	自回归频谱估计捕获技术	Zìhuíguī pínpǔ gūjì bǔhuò jìshù
ASEN	Amplified spontaneous emission noise	放大自激发射噪声	Fàngdà zìjīfāshè zàoshēng
ASES	ASE sub-system	ASE 子系统	ASE zìxìtǒng
ASF	Access to the services function	业务访问功能	Yèwù fǎngwèn gōngnéng
ASF	Advanced streaming (media) format	先进流媒体格式	Xiānjìn liúméitǐ géshì
ASF	Agent-based software service framework	基于代理软件服务框架	Jīyú dàilǐ ruǎnjiàn fúwù kuàngjià
ASFB	Application specific functional block	专用功能块	Zhuānyòng gōngnéng kuài
ASIC	Application specific integrated circuit	特殊应用集成电路	Tèshū yìngyòng jíchéng diànlù
ASIC	Application specific integrated circuit/chip	专用集成电路/芯片	Zhuānyòng jíchéng diànlù/xìnpiàn
ASIM	Asynchronous interface module	异步接口模块	Yìbù jiēkǒu mókuài
ASIP	Application specific integrated processor	专用综合处理器	Zhuānyòng zōnghé chǔlǐqì
ASK	Amplitude shift keying	幅移键控	Fúyí jiànkòng
ASK	Amplitude shift keying	移幅键控	Yífú jiànkòng
ASK	Amplitude shift keying	振幅键控	Zhènfú jiànkòng
ASK IR	Amplitude shift keyed infrared	长波形可移动输入红外线	Chángbō-xíng kěyídòng shūrù hóngwàixiàn
ASL	Analog subscriber line board	模拟用户电路板	Mónǐ yònghù diànlù bǎn
ASL	Average sidelobe level	平均旁瓣电平	Píngjūn pángbàn diànpíng
ASLC	Analog subscriber line circuit	模拟用户线电路	Mónǐ yònghùxiàn diànlù
ASLTE	Automatic subscriber line test equipment	用户线自动测试装置	Yònghù xiàn zìdòng cèshì zhuāngzhì
ASM	Airspace management (civil aviation)	空域管理	Kōngyù guǎnlǐ
ASM	Algorithm state machine	算法状态机	Suànfǎ zhuàngtài jī
ASM	Analog subscriber module	模拟用户模块	Mónǐ yònghù mókuài
ASM	Association for System Management	系统管理协会	Xìtǒng guǎnlǐ xiéhuì
ASMO	Advanced storage magneto-optical	增强形光学存储器	Zēngqiáng-xíng guāngxué cúnchǔqì
ASMP	Access switching management processor	接入交换管理处理器	Jiērù jiāohuàn guǎnlǐ chùlǐqì
ASMS	Access switching maintenance sub-system	接入交换维护子系统	Jiērù jiāohuàn wéihù zìxìtǒng
ASN	Abstract syntax notation	抽象句表记法	Chōuxiàng jùbiǎo jìfǎ
ASN	Abstract syntax notation	抽象句法符号	Chōuxiàng jùfǎ fúhào
ASN	Abstract syntax notation	抽象语法编码	Chōuxiàng yǔfǎ biānmǎ
ASN	Abstract syntax notation	抽象语法标记	Chōuxiàng yǔfǎ biāojì
ASN	Abstract syntax notation	抽象语法定义	Chōuxiàng yǔfǎ dìngyì

ASN	Abstract syntax notation	抽象语法记法	Chōuxiàng yǔfǎ jìfǎ
ASN	Asynchronous sequential network	异步时序网络	Yìbù shíxù wǎngluò
ASN	Asynchronous sequential network	异步序列网络	Yìbù xùliè wǎngluò
ASN	Authentication sequence number	身份验证序列号	Shēnfen yànzhèng xùlièhào
ASN	Automatic switching node	自动交换节点	Zìdòng jiāohuàn jiédiǎn
ASN.1	Abstract syntax notation 1	抽象句法表示法 1	Chōuxiàng jùfǎ biǎoshì fǎ 1
ASO	Application service object	应用服务目标	Yìngyòng fúwù mùbiāo
ASOI	Application service object invocation	应用服务目标请求	Yìngyòng fúwù mùbiāo qǐngqiú
ASON	Automatic switched optical network	自动交换光网络	Zìdòng jiāohuàn guāng wǎngluò
ASP	Abstract service primitive	抽象服务原语	Chōuxiàng fúwù yuányǔ
ASP	Abstract service primitive	抽象业务原语	Chōuxiàng yèwù yuányǔ
ASP	Active server page	激活服务器页	Jīhuó fúwùqì yè
ASP	Adapter signal processing	适配器信号处理	Shìpèiqì xìnhào chǔlǐ
ASP	Advanced signal processing	高级信号处理	Gāojí xìnhào chǔlǐ
ASP	Analog signal processing	模拟信号处理	Mónǐ xìnhào chǔlǐ
ASP	AppleTalk session protocol	AppleTalk 会话协议	AppleTalk huìhuà xiéyì
ASP	Application server process	应用服务器进程	Yìngyòng fúwùqì jìnchéng
ASP	Application service provider	应用服务提供商	Yìngyòng fúwù tígōngshāng
ASP	Application service provider	应用服务提供商	Yìngyòng fúwù tígōngshāng
ASP	Application service provider	应用服务提供者	Yìngyòng fúwù tígòngzhě
ASP	Application service provider	应用服务商	Yìngyòng fúwùshāng
ASP	Application service provider	应用业务提供商	Yìngyòng yèwù tígōng shāng
ASP	Application software package	应用软件包	Yìngyòng ruǎnjiànbāo
ASP	Assignment source point	分配资源点	Fēnpèi zīyuán diǎn
ASPI	Advanced SCSI program interface	高级 SCSI 编程接口	Gāojí SCSI biānchéng jiēkǒu
ASPM	Application server process maintenance	应用服务器进程维护	Yìngyòng fúwùqì jìnchéng wéihù
ASR	Access service request	访问业务请求	Fǎngwèn yèwù qǐngqiú
ASR	Answer-seizure ratio	应答占用率	Yìngdá zhànyòng lǜ
ASR	Automatic send and receive	自动收发	Zìdòng shōufā
ASR	Automatic send-receiver	自动收发机	Zìdòng shōufājī
ASR	Automatic speech recognition	自动声音识别	Zìdòng shēngyīn shíbié
ASR	Automatic speech recognition	自动语音识别	Zìdòng yǔyīn shíbié
ASRG	Arc standard raster graph	Arc 标准栅格图	Arc biāozhǔn zhàgé tú
ASRM	Application-level semantics-reliable multicast	应用层语义可靠的自适应多播体系	Yìngyòng céng yǔyì kěkàode zìshìyìng duōbō tǐxì
ASRTE	Alternative select route	迂回选择路由	Yūhuí xuǎnzé lùyóu
ASS	Administrative support system	管理支持系统	Guǎnlǐ zhīchí xìtǒng
ASS	Analog switching sub-system	模拟交换子系统	Mónǐ jiāohuàn zixìtǒng
ASS	Audio sub-system	音频子系统	Yīnpín zixìtǒng
ASTA	Advanced software technology and algorithms	高级软件技术与算法	Gāojí ruǎnjiàn jìshù yǔ suànfǎ
ASTN	Automatic switched transport network	自动交换传送网络	Zìdòng jiāohuàn chuánsòng wǎngluò
ASU	Acknowledgement signal unit	确认信号单元	Quèrèn xìnhào dānyuán
ASU	Asynchronous transfer mode subscriber unit	异步转移模式用户单元	Yìbù zhuǎnyí móshì yònghù dānyuán
ASU	Automatic synchronizing unit	自动同步设备（单元）	Zìdòng tóngbù shèbèi (dānyuán)
ASU	Auxiliary storage unit	辅助存储单元	Fǔzhù cúnchǔ dānyuán
ASUSP	All suspend	全部中止	Quánbù zhōngzhǐ

ASW	Auxiliary switch	辅助开关	Fǔzhù kāiguān
AT	Access trunk	接入中继线	Jiērù zhōngjìxiàn
AT	Address template	地址模板	Dìzhǐ múbǎn
AT	Automated tunneling	自动隧道	Zìdòng suìdào
ATA	American Translators Association	美国翻译协会	Měiguó fānyì xiéhuì
ATA	Analog terminal adapter	模拟终端适配器	Mónǐ zhōngduān shìpèiqì
ATA	Asynchronous terminal adapter	异步终端转接器	Yìbù zhōngduān zhuǎnjiēqì
ATA	Automatic trouble analysis	自动障碍分析	Zìdòng zhàng'ài fēnxī
ATAPI	Advanced technology attachment packet interface	AT 封包連接介面	AT fēngbāo liánjiē jièmiàn
ATB	Address translation buffer	地址转换缓冲器	Dìzhǐ zhuǎnhuàn huǎnchōngqì
ATB	All trunks busy	中继线全忙	Zhōngjìxiàn quánmáng
ATBM	Average time between maintenance	平均维修间隔时间	Píngjūn wéixiū jiàngé shíjiān
ATC	Access time from clock (in RAM or ROM)	时钟存取时间	Shízhōng cúnqǔshíjiān
ATC	Adaptive threshold control	自适应阈值控制	Zìshìyìng yùzhí kòngzhì
ATC	Adaptive transform coding	自适应变换编码	Zìshìyìng biànhuàn biānmǎ
ATC	Air traffic control (civil aviation)	空中交通管制	Kōngzhōng jiāotōng guǎnzhì
ATC	ATM transfer capability	ATM 传送功能	ATM chuánsòng gōngnéng
ATC	Automatic telephone call	自动电话呼叫	Zìdòng diànhuà hūjiào
ATC	Automatic timing control	自动定时控制	Zìdòng dìngshí kòngzhì
ATC	Automatic timing corrector	自动时间校正器	Zìdòng shíjiān jiàozhèngqì
ATC	Automatic tone control	自动音调控制	Zìdòng yīndiào kòngzhì
ATC	Automatic tone correction	自动音调校正	Zìdòng yīndiào jiàozhèng
ATC	Automatic tracking correction	自动跟踪校正	Zìdòng gēnzōng jiàozhèng
ATC	Automatic tuning control	自动调谐控制	Zìdòng tiáoxié kòngzhì
ATC	Auto-threshold control	自动阈值控制	Zìdòng yùzhí kòngzhì
ATCP	Asynchronous transaction control program	异步事物控制程序	Yìbù shìwù kòngzhì chéngxù
ATCS	Advanced communication technologies and services	先进的通信技术业务	Xiānjìnde tōngxìn jìshù yèwù
ATD	Asynchronous time division	异步时分	Yìbù shífèn
ATD	Audio tone decoder	声调译码器	Shēngdiào yìmǎqì
ATD	Average time delay	平均时延	Píngjūn shíyán
ATDE	Adaptive time domain equalizer	自适应时域均衡器	Zìshìyìng shíyù jūnhéngqì
ATDL	Army Tactical Data Link (US military)	陆军战术数据链	Lùjūn zhànshù shùjù liàn
ATDM	Asynchronous time division multiplexer	异步时分多路复用器	Yìbù shífèn duōlù fùyòngqì
ATDMS	Analog time division multiplexing system	模拟时分复用系统	Mónǐ shífèn fùyòng xìtǒng
ATE	Automatic test equipment	自动测试设备	Zìdòng cèshì shèbèi
ATF	Adaptive transversal filter	自适应横向滤波器	Zìshìyìng héngxiàng lǜbōqì
ATF	Automatic track following	自动跟踪	Zìdòng gēnzōng
ATFM	Air traffic flow management (civil aviation)	空中交通量管理	Kōngzhōng jiāotōngliàng guǎnlǐ
ATI	Automatic transmitter identification	自动发射机识别	Zìdòng fāshèjī shíbié
ATII	Application transport instruction indicator	应用传送指导指示语	Yìngyòng chuánsòng zhǐdǎo zhǐshì yǔ
ATL	Active template library	有源模板库	Yǒuyuán múbǎn kù
ATM	Abstract test method	抽象测试法	Chōuxiàng cèshì fǎ
ATM	Address translation memory	地址翻译存储器	Dìzhǐ fānyì cúnchǔqì
ATM	Air traffic management (civil aviation)	空中交通管理	Kōngzhōng jiāotōng guǎnlǐ
ATM	Alternative test method	替代测试法	Tìdài cèshì fǎ
ATM	Alternative test method	替代试验方法	Tìdài shìyàn fāngfǎ

ATM	Asynchronous transfer mode	异步传递方式	Yìbù chuándì fāngshì
ATM	Asynchronous transfer mode	异步传递模式	Yìbù chuándì móshì
ATM	Asynchronous transfer mode	异步传输模式	Yìbù chuánshū móshì
ATM	Asynchronous transfer mode	异步传送方式	Yìbù chuánsòng fāngshì
ATM	Asynchronous transfer mode	异步传送模式	Yìbù chuánsòng móshì
ATM	Asynchronous transfer mode	异步转换模式	Yìbù zhuǎnhuàn móshì
ATM	Asynchronous transfer mode	异步转移模式	Yìbù zhuǎnyí móshì
ATM	Automatic teller machine	自动柜员机	Zìdòng guìyuánjī
ATME	Automatic call measuring (equipment)	自动传输测量	Zìdòng chuánshū cèliáng
ATME	Automatic transmission measuring and signaling test equipment	自动传输测量和信令测试设备	Zìdòng chuánshū cèliáng hé xìnlìng cèshì shèbèi
ATM-NIC	Asynchronous transfer mode-netwrk interface card	异步转移模式-网络接口卡	Yìbù zhuǎnyí móshì -wǎngluò jiēkǒu kǎ
ATMS	Advanced text management system	高级文本管理系统	Gāojí wénběn guǎnlǐ xìtǒng
ATMS	Automatic teletype message switching (system)	电传电报自动报文交换系统	Diànchuán diànbào zìdòng bàowén jiāohuàn xìtǒng
ATM-SAP	Asynchronous transfer mode -service access point	异步转移模式 - 业务接入点	Yìbù zhuǎnyí móshì- yèwù jiērù diǎn
ATM-SDU	Asynchronous transfer mode service data unit	异步传递模式业务数据单元	Yìbù chuándì móshì yèwù shùjù dānyuán
ATM-SDU	Asynchronous transfer mode service data unit	异步转移模式业务数据单元	Yìbù zhuǎnyí móshì yèwù shùjù dānyuán
ATM-SDU	ATM service data unit	ATM 业务数据单元	ATM yèwù shùjù dānyuán
ATM-SLIC	Asynchronous transfer mode subscriber line interface circuit	异步传递模式用户线接口电路	Yìbù chuándì móshì yònghùxiàn jiēkǒu diànlù
ATM-SLIC	Asynchronous transfer mode subscriber line interface circuit	异步转移模式用户线接口电路	Yìbù zhuǎnyí móshì yònghùxiàn jiēkǒu diànlù
ATM-SW	Asynchronous transfer mode switch	异步传递模式交换	Yìbù chuándì móshì jiāohuàn
ATM-SW	Asynchronous transfer mode switch	异步转移模式交换	Yìbù zhuǎnyí móshì jiāohuàn
ATM-UNI	Asynchronous transfer mode user network interface	异步传递模式用户网络接口	Yìbù chuándì móshì yònghù wǎngluò jiēkǒu
ATM-UNI	Asynchronous transfer mode user network interface	异步转移模式用户网络接口	Yìbù zhuǎnyí móshì yònghù wǎngluò jiēkǒu
ATM-XC	Asynchronous transfer mode -cross-connect	异步传递模式-交叉连接	Yìbù chuándì móshì - jiāochā liánjiē
ATM-XC	Asynchronous transfer mode -cross-connect	异步转移模式-交叉连接	Yìbù zhuǎnyí móshì - jiāochā liánjiē
AtoM	Arbitrary transmission on MPLS	MPLS 上的任意传输	MPLS-shàngde rènyì chuánshū
ATOMM	Advanced super thin-layer and high-output metal media	增强形超薄高速金属媒体	Zēngqiáng-xíng chāobáo gāosù jīnshǔ méitǐ
ATP	AppleTalk transaction protocol	AppleTalk 事务协议	AppleTalk shìwù xiéyì
ATP	Array transform processor	数组变换处理机	Shùzǔ biànhuàn chǔlǐjī
ATPC	Automatic transmission power control	自动发射功率控制	Zìdòng fāshè gōnglǜ kòngzhì
ATPC	Automatic transmission power control	自动发信功率控制	Zìdòng fāxìn gōnglǜ kòngzhì
ATPC	Automatic transmit power control	自动发送功率控制	Zìdòng fāsòng gōnglǜ kòngzhì
ATR	Answer to reset	复位响应	Fùwèi xiǎngyìng
ATR	Answer to reset	复位应答	Fùwèi yìngdá
ATR	Answer to reset	回答到复位	Huídá dào fùwèi
ATR	Answering time recorder	应答时间记录器	Yìngdá shíjiān jìlùqì
ATR	Asynchronous transfer region	异步传递区	Yìbù chuándì qū
ATR	Asynchronous transfer region	异步转移区	Yìbù zhuǎnyí qū
ATR	Automatic target recognition	目标自动识别	Mùbiāo zìdòng shíbié
ATR	Automatic traffic recorder	自动话务量记录器	Zìdòng huàwùliáng jìlùqì
ATS	Abstract test suite	抽象测试套	Chōuxiàng cèshì tào
ATS	Administrative terminal system	管理终端系统	Guǎnlǐ zhōngduān xìtǒng
ATS	Advanced teleprocessing system	高级远程信息处理系统	Gāojí yuǎnchéng xìnxī chǔlǐ xìtǒng
ATS	Air traffic services (civil aviation)	空中交通服务	Kōngzhōng jiāotōng fúwù

ATT	American Telephone and Telegraph (AT&T) (US company)	美国电报电话公司	Měiguó diànbào diànhuà gōngsī
ATT	Attach	附着	Fùzhuó
ATT	Automatic toll ticketing	自动长途电话记录	Zìdòng chángtú diànhuà jìlù
ATT	Automatic trunk testing	自动中继线测试	Zìdòng zhōngjìxiàn cèshì
ATU	ADSL transceiver unit	ADSL 收发单元	ADSL shōufā dānyuán
ATU	Analog trunk unit	模拟中继单元	Mónǐ zhōngjì dānyuán
ATU	Audio terminal unit	音频终端设备	Yīnpín zhōngduān shèbèi
ATU-C	ADSL transceiver unit, central office end	ADSL 局端发送接收单元	ADSL júduān fāsòng jiēshōu dānyuán
ATU-C	ADSL transmission unit-central	ADSL 中央传输单元	ADSL zhōngyāng chuánshū dānyuán
ATU-C	Central office ADSL transmission unit	局端 ADSL 收发单元	Júduān ADSL shōufā dānyuán
ATU-R	ADSL Transciever unit-recever end	用户端 ADSL 收发单元	Yònghù duān ADSL shōufā dānyuán
ATU-R	ADSL transmission unit-remote	ADSL 远端传输单元	ADSL yuǎnduān chuánshū dānyuán
ATU-T	ADSL transceiver unit, remote terminal end	ADSL 远端发送接收单元	ADSL yuǎnduān fāsòng jiēshōu dānyuán
ATWR	Aircraft tail warning radar	护尾雷达	Hùwěi léidá
AU	Access unit	访问单元	Fǎngwèn dānyuán
AU	Access unit	接入单元	Jiērù dānyuán
AU	Access unit	入口单元	Rùkǒu dānyuán
AU	Adaptation unit	适配单元	Shìpèi dānyuán
AU	Administrative unit	管理单元	Guǎnlǐ dānyuán
AU PTR	Administrative unit pointer	管理单元指针	Guǎnlǐ dānyuán zhǐzhēn
AU-AIS	Administrative unit alarm indication signal	管理单元告警指示信号	Guǎnlǐ dānyuán gàojǐng zhǐshì xìnhào
AUAP	Access unit's access point	接入单元的接入点	Jiērù dānyuánde jiērùdiǎn
AUC	Authentication center	验证中心	Yànzhèng zhōngxīn
AUG	Administrative unit group	管理单元组	Guǎnlǐ dānyuán zǔ
AUI	Attachment unit interface	附加单元接口	Fùjiā dānyuán jiēkǒu
AUI	Attachment unit interface	连接单元接口	Liánjiē dānyuán jiēkǒu
AUL	Average useful life	平均使用寿命	Píngjūn shǐyòng shòumìng
AU-LOP	Administrative unit loss of pointer	管理单元指针丢失	Guǎnlǐ dānyuán zhǐzhēn diūshī
AUM	Asynchronous user module	异步用户模块	Yìbù yònghù mókuài
AU-NPJE	Administrative unit pointer negative justification	管理单元负指针调整	Guǎnlǐ dānyuán fù zhǐzhēn tiáozhěng
AUP	Acceptable use policy	可接受使用政策	Kějiēshòu shǐyòng zhèngcè
AUP	Administrative unit pointer	管理单元指针	Guǎnlǐ dānyuán zhǐzhēn
AUPJE	Administrative unit pointer justification event	AU 指针调整事件	AU zhǐzhēn tiáozhěng shìjiàn
AU-PPJE	Administrative unit pointer positive justification	管理单元正指针调整	Guǎnlǐ dānyuán zhèng zhǐzhēn tiáozhěng
AURP	AppleTalk update-based routing protocol	AppleTalk 基于更新的路由选择协议	AppleTalk jīyú gēngxīnde lùyóu xuǎnzé xiéyì
AUTH	Authentication/security mechanism (in FTP)	认证/安全机制	Rènzhèng/ānquán jīzhì
AUTHR	Authentication response	验证响应	Yànzhèng xiǎngyìng
AUTN	Authentication token	认证标记	Rènzhèng biāojì
AV	Analog video	模拟电视	Mónǐ diànshì
AV	Analog video	模拟视频	Mónǐ shìpín
AV	Analog video	模拟视频	Mónǐ shìpín
AV	Audio-visual	声视	Shēng shì
AV	Audio-visual	视听	Shìtīng
AV	Average value	平均值	Píngjūnzhí
AVA	Attribute value assertion	属性值判断语	Shǔxìng zhí pànduàn yǔ

AVC	Aural and visual code	听觉和视觉信号编码	Tīngjué hé shìjué xìnhào biānmǎ
AVC	Automatic voltage clamp	自动电压箝位	Zìdòng diànyā qiánwèi
AVC	Automatic volume control	自动音量控制	Zìdòng yīnliàng kòngzhì
AVCD	Audio and video control device	音像控制装置	Yīnxiàng kòngzhì zhuāngzhì
AVCR	Available cell rate	可用的信元率	Kěyòngde xìnyuán lǜ
AVG	Adventure genre (computer game)	冒险类游戏	Màoxiǎn lèi yóuxì
AVHRR	Advanced very high resolution radiometer	其它分辨率辐射计	Qítā fēnbiànlǜ fúshèjì
AVI	Audio video interleave	音频视频插入	Yīnpín shìpín chārù
AVL	Automatic vehicle location system	自动车辆定位系统	Zìdòng chēliàng dìngwèi xìtǒng
AVRS	Automatic voice response system	自动语音应答系统	Zìdòng yǔyīn yìngdá xìtǒng
AVSS	Audio-video support system	音频-视频支持系统	Yīnpín-shìpín zhīchí xìtǒng
AW	Administrative weight	管理加权	Guǎnlǐ jiāquán
AWA	All wave antenna	全波天线	Quánbō tiānxiàn
AWACS	Airborne warning and control system aircraft	预警飞机	Yùjǐng fēijī
AWACS	ATM wireless access communication system	ATM 无线接入通信系统	ATM wúxiàn jiērù tōngxìn xìtǒng
AWACS	Early warning aircraft	预警机	Yùjǐng jī
AWG	American Wire Gauge	美国线规	Měiguó xiànguī
AWG	American Wire Gauge	美国线缆规格	Měiguó xiànlǎn guīgé
AWG	Array waveguide grating	阵列波导光栅	Zhènliè bōdǎo guāngshān
AWG	Arrayed waveguide grating	列阵波导光栅	Lièzhèn bōdǎo guāngshān
AWGN	Additive white Gaussian noise	附加白高斯噪声	Fùjiā bái gāo-sī zàoshēng
AWGN	Additive white Gaussian noise	附加高斯白噪声	Fùjiā gāo-sī bái zàoshēng
AWGN	Additive white Gaussian noise	加性高斯白噪声	Jiāxìng gāo-sī bái zàoshēng
AWS	Aviation weather service (civil aviation)	航空气象服务	Hángkōng qìxiàng fúwù
AWT	Actual work time	实际占用时间	Shíjì zhànyòng shíjiān
AXC	Asynchronous transfer mode cross connect	异步传递模式交叉连接	Yìbù chuándì móshì jiāochā liánjiē
AXC	Asynchronous transfer mode cross connect	异步转移模式交叉连接	Yìbù zhuǎnyí móshì jiāochā liánjiē
AXFR	Full zone transfer	完整区域传送	Wánzhěng qūyù chuánsòng

B

B	Bel	贝	Bèi
B tag	Beginning tag	开始标签	Kāishǐ biāoqiān
B/L	Bill of lading	提单	Tídān
B2B	Business-to-business	企业对企业	Qǐyè duì qǐyè
B3ZS	Bipolar with three-zero substitution	三零取代双极性码	Sān líng qǔdài shuāng jíxìng mǎ
BA	Basic access	基本接入	Jīběn jiērù
BA	BCCH allocation	BCCH 配置	BCCH pèizhì
BA	Beam axis (of an antenna)	射束轴	Shèshù zhóu
BA	Binding acknowledgement	绑定应答	Bǎngdìng yìngdá
BA	Biometric authentication	生物特性认证	Shēngwù tèxìng rènzhèng
BA	Booster (power) amplifier (for optical fiber)	光功率放大器	Guāng gōnglǜ fàngdàqì
BA	Booster amplifier	功率放大器	Gōnglǜ fàngdàqì
BA	Branch amplifier	分路放大器	Fēnlù fàngdàqì
BA	Bridge amplifier	桥接放大器	Qiáojiē fàngdàqì
BA	Bridging amplifier	桥式放大器	Qiáo-shì fàngdàqì
BA	Buffer address	缓冲地址	Huǎnchōng dìzhǐ

BA	Building automation	楼宇自动化	Lóuyǔ zìdònghuà
BA	Bus adapter	总线适配器	Zǒngxiàn shìpèiqì
BA	Optical booster amplifier	功率光放大器	Gōnglǜ guāng fàngdàqì
BAA	Block adaptive algorithm	块字适应算法	Kuài zìshìyìng suànfǎ
BAA	Broadside array antenna	垂射天线阵	Chuíshè tiānxiànzhèn
BAC	Balanced asynchronous class	异步平衡类别	Yìbù pínghéng lèibié
BAC	Binary asymmetric channel	二进制不对称通道	Èrjìnzhì bùduìchèn tōngdào
BAC	Building automation and control net	建筑物自动化和控制网络	Jiànzhùwù zìdònghuà hé kòngzhì wǎngluò
BACP	Bandwidth allocation control protocol	带宽分配控制协议	Dàikuān fēnpèi kòngzhì xiéyì
BAIC	Barring of all incoming calls	闭锁所有呼入业务	Bìsuǒ suǒyǒu hūrù yèwù
BAIC	Barring of all incoming calls	闭锁所有入呼叫	Bìsuǒ suǒyǒu rù hūjiào
BAIC	Barring of all incoming calls	闭锁所有入局呼叫	Bìsuǒ suǒyǒu rùjú hūjiào
BAIC	Barring of all incoming calls	禁止所有入局呼叫	Jìnzhǐ suǒyǒu rùjú hūjiào
BAIC	Barring of all incoming calls supplementary service	闭锁所有附加业务入呼叫	Bìsuǒ suǒyǒu fùjiā yèwù rù hūjiào
BAIC-Roam	Barring of all incoming calls roam	当漫游出归属 PLMN 国家后，闭锁所有入局呼叫	Dāng mànyóu chū guīshǔ PLMN guójiā hòu, bìsuǒ suǒyǒu rùjú hūjiào
BAK	Back at the keyboard (computer chat)	回到键盘	Huídào jiànpán
BAL	Branch and link	转移和连接	Zhuǎnyí hé liánjiē
Balun	Balance-unbalance switch	平衡 - 不平衡转换器	Pínghéng-bùpínghéng zhuǎnhuànqì
BAM	Back (or background) administrative module	后管理模块	Hòu guǎnlǐ mókuài
BAM	Basic arithmetic module	基本算术模块	Jīběn suànshù mókuài
BAN	Broadband access network	宽带接入网	Kuāndài jiērù wǎng
BANCS	Bell Administrative Network Communications System	贝尔行政管理网络通信系统	Bèi'ěr xíngzhèng guǎnlǐ wǎngluò tōngxìn xìtǒng
BAOC	Barring of all outgoing calls	闭锁所有出呼叫	Bìsuǒ suǒyǒu chū hūjiào
BAOC	Barring of all outgoing calls	闭锁所有出局呼叫	Bìsuǒ suǒyǒu chūjú hūjiào
BAOC	Barring of all outgoing calls supplementary service	闭锁所有附加业务出呼叫	Bìsuǒ suǒyǒu fùjiā yèwù chū hūjiào
BAOC	Barring of all outgoing calls supplementary service	禁止所有出局呼叫补充业务	Jìnzhǐ suǒyǒu chūjú hūjiào bǔchōng yèwù
BAP	Bandwidth allocation protocol	带宽分配协议	Dàikuān fēnpèi xiéyì
BAP	Bluetooth access point	蓝牙接入点	Lányá jiērù diǎn
BARG	Billing and account rapporteurs group (GSM MoU)	计费核算组	Jìfèi hésuàn zǔ
BARRNet	Bay Area Regional Research Network (US)	海湾地区的区域性研究网络	Hǎiwān dìqūde qūyùxìng yánjiū wǎngluò
BAS	Bit-rate allocation signal	比特率定位信号	Bǐtè lǜ dìngwèi xìnhào
BAS	Boolean assignment statement	布尔赋值语句	Bù-ěr fùzhí yǔjù
BAS	Broadband access server	带宽接入服务器	Dàikuān jiērù fúwùqì
BAS	Building automatic system	楼宇自动化系统	Lóuyǔ zìdònghuà xìtǒng
BASIC	Beginner's All-purpose Symbolic Instruction Code	初学者通用符号指令码	Chūxuézhě tōngyòng fúhào zhǐlìng mǎ
BAT	Bearer association transport	承载偶联传送	Chéngzài ǒulián chuánsòng
BAU	Broadband access unit	宽带接入单元	Kuāndài jiērù dānyuán
BAW	Bulk acoustic wave	体声波	Tǐ shēngbō
BB	Backbone bearer	骨干网载体	Gǔgànwǎng zàitǐ
BB	Baseband protocol	基带协议	Jīdài xiéyì
BB	Bus bar	汇流条母线	Huìliútiáo mǔxiàn
BB_Credit	Buffer-to-buffer credit	缓冲区到缓冲区信用数	Huǎnchōng qū dào huǎnchōng qū xìnyòng shù
BBA	Baseband arragement	基带安排	Jīdài ānpái
BBA	Broadband adapter	宽带适配器	Kuāndài shìpèiqì

BBC	Broadband coupler	宽带耦合器	Kuāndài ǒuhéqì
BBE	Background block error	背景差错块	Bèijǐng chācuò kuài
BBE	Background block error	背景块误码	Bèijǐng kuài wùmǎ
BBE	Background block error	背景误块	Bèijǐng wùkuài
BBER	Background bit error ratio	背景误块秒比	Bèijǐng wùkuài miǎo bǐ
BBER	Background block error ratio	背景差错块比	Bèijǐng chācuò kuài bǐ
BBER	Background block error ratio	背景块误码比	Bèijǐng kuài wùmǎ bǐ
BBER	Background block error ratio	背景误块比	Bèijǐng wùkuài bǐ
BBESR	Background block errored second ratio	背景块差错秒比	Bèijǐng kuài chācuò miǎo bǐ
BBF	Baseband filter	基带滤波器	Jīdài lǜbōqì
BBOC	Broadband operation center	宽带运行中心	Kuāndài yùnxíng zhōngxīn
BBr_3	Boron bromide	溴化硼	Xiùhuàpéng
BBS	Bulletin board service	布告板服务	Bùgàobǎn fúwù
BBS	Bulletin board service	公告板服务	Gōnggào bǎn fúwù
BBS	Bulletin board service	公告板业务	Gōnggào bǎn yèwù
BBS	Bulletin board system	布告栏系统	Bùgàolán xìtǒng
BBS	Bulletin board system	电子公告栏	Diànzǐ gōnggào lán
BBSIG	Baseband and signal processing	基带和信号处理	Jīdài hé xìnhào chǔlǐ
BBSP	Building block signal processor	积木块信号处理机	Jīmù kuài xìnhào chǔlǐjī
BC	Backbone cable (in building)	垂直电缆	Chuízhí diànlǎn
BC	Backbone cable (in building)	主干电缆	Zhǔgàn diànlǎn
BC	Bearer capability	承载能力	Chéngzài nénglì
BC	Bearer capability	传递能力	Chuándì nénglì
BC	Billing center	计费中心	Jìfèi zhōngxīn
Bc	Committed burst size	承诺突发量	Chéngnuò tūfā liàng
Bc	Committed burst size	承诺的突发大小	Chéngnuòde tūfā dàxiǎo
BC	Concealed in beam	暗敷设在梁内	Àn fūshè zài liáng-nèi
BC_IE	Bearer capability identity element	承载能力标示单元	Chéngzài nénglì biāoshì dānyuán
BCA	Bisynchronous communications adapter	双同步通信转接器	Shuāng tóngbù tōngxìn zhuǎnjiēqì
BCAM	Basic communication access method	基本通信存取法	Jīběn tōngxìn cúnqǔ fǎ
BCB	Bit control block	位控制序块	Wèi kòngzhì xùkuài
BCBB	Back board	后面板	Hòumian bǎn
BCBB	BCP back board	BCP 后面板	BCP hòumian bǎn
BCBP	BSC clock rack panel	BSC 时钟机架面板	BSCshízhōng jījià miànbǎn
BCBP	Clock rack panel	时钟机架面板	Shízhōng jījià miànbǎn
BCBR	Base rack	基本架	Jīběn jià
BCBR	BTS CDMA base rack	CDMA BTS 基本架	CDMA BTS jīběn jià
BCC	Base transceiver station color code	基站色码	Jīzhàn sèmǎ
BCC	Base transceiver station color code	基站收发信机色码	Jīzhàn shōufāxìnjī sèmǎ
BCC	Bearer channel connection	承载通道连接	Chéngzài tōngdào liánjiē
BCC	Bearer channel connection	承载通路连接	Chéngzài tōnglù liánjiē
BCC	Bearer channel connection control	承载通路连接控制	Chéngzài tōnglù liánjiē kòngzhì
BCC	Binary check character	二进制校验字符	Èrjìnzhì jiàoyàn zìfú
BCC	Blind carbon copy	密件抄送	Mìjiàn chāosòng
BCC	Block check character	块检验字符	Kuài jiǎnyàn zìfú
BCCH	Broadcast control channel	广播控制信道	Guǎngbō kòngzhì xìndào

BCD	Binary coded decimal	二/十进制代码	Èr/shíjìnzhì dàimǎ
BCD	Binary coded decimal	二进制编码的十进制	Èrjìnzhì biānmǎde shíjìnzhì
BCD	Binary coded decimal	十进制数的二进制编码	Shíjìnzhì shùde èrjìnzhì biānmǎ
BCDA	BSC clock distribution board assembly	BSC 时钟分配集成板	BSC shízhōng fēnpèi jíchéngbǎn
BCDA	Clock distribution board assembly	时钟分配集成板	Shízhōng fēnpèi jíchéngbǎn
BCE	Beam collimation error	射束准直误差	Shèshù zhǔnzhí wùchā
BCER	BTS CDMA extended rack	CDMA BTS 扩展架	CDMA BTS kuòzhǎn jià
BCER	Extended rack	扩展架	Kuòzhǎn jià
BCF	Base station control function (module)	基站控制功能（模块）	Jīzhàn kòngzhì gōngnéng (mókuài)
BCF	Basic control function	基本控制功能	Jīběn kòngzhì gōngnéng
BCF	Basic control function	基本控制功能	Jīběn kòngzhì gōngnéng
BCF	Bearer control function	承载控制功能	Chéngzài kòngzhì gōngnéng
BCF	Boot catalog file	启动目录文件	Qǐdòng mùlù wénjiàn
BCF	Broadband confirmed	宽带确认	Kuāndài quèrèn
BCFE	Broadcast control functional entity	广播控制功能实体	Guǎngbō kòngzhì gōngnéng shítǐ
BCF-G	Bearer gateway control function	承载控制网关功能	Chéngzài kòngzhì wǎng guān gōngnéng
BCF-N	Bearer node control function	承载控制节点功能	Chéngzài kòngzhì jiédiǎn gōngnéng
BCFSK	Binary code frequency shift keying	二进制码频移键控	Èrjìnzhì mǎ pínyí jiànkòng
BCF-T	Bearer transmission control function	承载控制转接功能	Chéngzài kòngzhì zhuǎnjiē gōngnéng
BCH	Bids per circuit hour	没电路每小时的试占次数	Méi diànlù měi xiǎoshíde shìzhàn cìshù
BCH	Binary coded Hollerith	何勒内四二进制代码	Hé-lè-nèi-sì èrjìnzhì dàimǎ
BCH	Bose-Chaudhuri-Hocquenghem code	博斯-乔赫里-霍克文黑木码	Bó-sī—Qiáo-hè-lǐ—Huò-kè-wén-hēi-mù mǎ
BCH	Bose-Chaudhuri-Hocquenghem code	以三人之姓所名的码	Yǐ sānrénzhīxìng suǒmíngde mǎ
BCH	Broadcast channel	广播信道	Guǎngbō xìndào
B-channel	Bearer channel	承载信道	Chéngzài xìndào
BCHO	Base station-controlled handoff	基站控制切换	Jīzhàn kòngzhì qiēhuàn
BCI	Basic command interpreter	基本命令解调程序	Jīběn mìnglìng jiětiáo chéngxù
BCIA	BTS control and interface board assembly	BTS 控制和接口集成板	BTS kòngzhì hé jiēkǒu jíchéngbǎn
BCIA	Control and interface board assembly	控制和接口集成板	Kòngzhì hé jiēkǒu jíchéngbǎn
BCIE	Bearer capability information element	承载能力信息单元	Chéngzài nénglì xìnxī dānyuán
BCIE	Bearer capacity information element	承载容量信息单元	Chéngzài róngliàng xìnxī dānyuán
BCIN	BTS communication interconnect network	BTS 通信互联网络	BTS tōngxìn hùliánwǎng luò
BCIN	Communication interconnect network	通信互联网络	Tōngxìn hùlián wǎngluò
BCL	Base class library	基类库	Jī lèi kù
BCl_3	Boron trichloride	三氯化硼	Sānlǜhuàpéng
BCM	BTS control and maintenance	BTS 控制和维护	BTS kòngzhì hé wéihù
BCM	Control and maintenance	控制和维护	Kòngzhì hé wéihù
BCMB	BTS control and maintenance block	BTS 控制和维护模块	BTS kòngzhì hé wéihù mókuài
BCMB	Control and maintenance block	控制和维护模块	Kòngzhì hé wéihù mókuài
BCO	Binary coded octal	二进制编码的八进制	Èrjìnzhì biānmǎde bājìnzhì
BCO	BTS call control	BTS 呼叫控制	BTS hūjiào kòngzhì
BCP	Bridge control protocol	桥式控制协议	Qiáo-shì kòngzhì xiéyì
BCP	Bridging control protocol (in PPP)	桥接控制协议	Qiáojiē kòngzhì xiéyì
BCP	BTS control processor	BTS 控制处理器	BTS kòngzhì chǔlǐ qì
BCP	Control processor	控制处理器	Kòngzhì chǔlǐqì
BCPF	Basic clock pulse frequency	基本时钟脉冲频率	Jīběn shízhōng màichōng pínlǜ

BCPSK	Binary coherent phase shift keying	二进制相干相移键控	Èrjìnzhì xiānggān xiāngyí jiànkòng
BCR	Block cell rate	块信元速率	Kuài xìnyuán sùlǜ
BCR	Buffer counter reset	缓冲计数器	Huǎnchōng jìshùqì
BCRA	Clock relay board assembly	时延集成板	Shíyán jíchéngbǎn
BCS	Block check sequence	数据块检查序列	Shùjù kuài jiǎnchá xùliè
BCS	Block check sequence	字块检验序列	Zìkuài jiǎnyàn xùliè
BCS	British Computer Society	英国电脑学会	Yīngguó diànnǎo xuéhuì
BCSM	Basic call state model	基本呼叫状态模型	Jīběn hūjiào zhuàngtài móxíng
BCSM	Basic call status model	基本呼叫状态模型	Jīběn hūjiào zhuàngtài móxíng
BCT	Bandwidth compression technique	带宽压缩技术	Dàikuān yāsuō jìshù
BCTDR	Bit-load condition-based traffic distortion rate	基于比特的符合条件的业务量失真率	Jīyú bǐtède fúhé tiáojiànde yèwù liáng shīzhēn lǜ
BCUG	Bilateral closed user group	双边闭合用户群	Shuāngbiān bìhé yònghù qún
BCUG	Bilateral closed user group	双向封闭用户集团	Shuāngxiàng fēngbì yònghù jítuán
BCUSM	Basic call unrelated state model	基本呼叫不相关状态模型	Jīběn hūjiào bùxiāngguān zhuàngtài móxíng
BCUSM	Basic call unrelated state model	基本呼叫无关状态模型	Jīběn hūjiào wúguān zhuàngtài móxíng
BD	Bhattacharyya distance	巴特查里亚距离	Bā-tè-chá-lǐ-yà jùlí
BD	Bhattacharyya distance	B 距离	B-jùlí
BD	Building distributor	建筑物配线架	Jiànzhùwù pèixiànjià
BDA	Booster-distribution amplifier	升压器-分布放大器	Shēngyāqì—fēnbù fàngdàqì
BDA	BTS data access	BTS 数据存取	BTS shùjù cúnqǔ
BDB	Bidirectional data bus	双向数据总线	Shuāngxiàng shùjù zǒngxiàn
BDC	Backup domain controller	备份域控制器	Bèifèn yù kòngzhìqì
BDC	Binary-decimal converter	二-十进制交换器	Èr-shíjìnzhì jiāohuànqì
BDCM	Block data check mode	块数据校验方式	Kuài shùjù jiàoyàn fāngshì
BDES	Batch data exchange service	成批数据交换业务	Chéngpī shùjù jiāohuàn yèwù
BDIA	BTS diagnosis	BTS 诊断	BTS zhěnduàn
BDM	Binary delta modulation	二进制增量调制	Èrjìnzhì zēngliàng tiáozhì
BDM	Broadband data multipexer	宽带数据复用器	Kuāndài shùjù fùyòngqì
BDN	Barred dialling number	禁止拨号	Jìnzhǐ bōhào
BDP	Bandwidth delay product	带宽时延乘积	Dàikuān shíyán chéngjī
BDPSK	Binary differential phase shift keying	二相差分相移键控	Èrxiāng chàfēn xiàngyí jiànkòng
BDT	Bidirectional data transfer	双向数据传送	Shuāngxiàng shùjù chuánsòng
BE	Best effort	尽力而为	Jìnlì ér wéi
BE	Border element	边缘设备	Biānyuán shèbèi
Be	Excess burst	超量突发	Chāoliàng tūfā
Be	Excess burst size	超额突发量	Chāo'é tūfā liáng
Be	Excess burst size	超诺突发量	Chāonuò tūfāliàng
BEAS	Building Ethernet access system	数字以太网接入系统	Shùzì yǐtàiwǎng jiērù xìtǒng
BEC	Burst error channel	猝发错误通道	Cùfā cuòwù tōngdào
BECN	Backward explicit congestion notification	后向显式拥塞通知	Hòuxiàng xiǎnshì yōngsè tōngzhī
BECN	Backward explicit congestion notification	后向显示拥塞指示	Hòuxiàng xiǎnshì yōngsè zhǐshì
BECN	Backward explicit congestion notification	向后显式拥挤通告	Xiànghòu xiǎn-shì yōngjǐ tōnggào
BEF	Building entrance facility	建筑物入口设施	Jiànzhùwù rùkǒu shèshī
BEL	Bell	告警	Gàojǐng
BEL	Bus exchange line	总线交换线路	Zǒngxiàn jiāohuàn xiànlù

BELLCORE	Bell Communications Research Lab	贝尔通信研究所	Bèi'ěr tōngxìn yánjiūsuǒ
BEP	Back-end processor	后端处理机	Hòuduān chǔlǐjī
BEP	Burst-error processor	突发错误处理程序	Tūfā cuòwù chǔlǐ chéngxù
BER	Basic encoding rules	基本编码规则	Jīběn biānmǎ guīzé
BER	Bit error rate	比特差错率	Bǐtè chācuò lǜ
BER	Bit error rate	比特错误率	Bǐtè cuòwù lǜ
BER	Bit error rate	比特误码率	Bǐtè wùmǎ lǜ
BER	Bit error rate	误比特率	Wù bǐtè lǜ
BER	Bit error rate	误码率	Wùmǎlǜ
BER	Bit error ratio	比特差错比	Bǐtè chācuò bǐ
BERT	Bit error rate tester	误码率测试仪	Wùmǎlǜ cèshìyí
BES	Broadband exchange service	宽带交换业务	Kuāndài jiāohuàn yèwù
B-ET	Broadband exchange termination	宽带交换终接	Kuāndài jiāohuàn zhōngjiē
BF	Bandpass filter	带通滤波器	Dàitōng lǜbōqì
BF	Reporting office	报室	Bào shì
BFD	Block floating-point distributed	块浮点分布式	Kuài fúdiǎn fēnbù-shì
BFI	Bad frame identity	坏帧标识	Huàizhèng biāozhì
BFI	Bad frame identity	坏帧识别	Huàizhèng shíbié
BFI	Bad frame indication	坏帧标志	Huàizhèng biāozhì
BFI	Bad frame indication	坏帧指示	Huàizhèng zhǐshì
BFM	BTS fault management	BTS 故障管理	BTS gùzhàng guǎnlǐ
BFM	Fault management	故障管理	Gùzhàng guǎnlǐ
B-FMDCPSK	Binary frequency modulated differentially coherent phase shift keying	二进制调频差动相干相移键控	Èrjìnzhì tiáopín chādòng xiānggān xiāngyí jiànkòng
BFO	Beat-frequency oscillator	拍频振荡器	Pāipín zhèndàngqì
BFOC	Bayonet fiber optic connector	大口式光纤连接器	Dàkǒushì guāngxiān liánjiēqì
BFOC	Beijing Lucent Technologies Fiber Optic Co. Ltd.	北京朗讯科技光缆有限公司	Běijīng Lǎng-xùn kējì guānglǎn yǒuxiàn gōngsī
BFPA	Binary floating point arithmetic	二进制浮点运算	Èrjìnzhì fúdiǎn yùnsuàn
BFSK	Binary frequency shift keying	二进制频移键控	Èrjìnzhì pínyí jiànkòng
BFWA	Broadband fixed wireless access	宽带固定无线接入	Kuāndài gùdìng wúxiàn jiērù
BG	Border gateway	边界网关	Biānjiè wǎngguān
BG	Border gateway	边沿网关	Biānyán wǎngguān
BG	Business group	商业组群	Shāngyè zǔqún
BGA	Ball grid array	球状矩阵排列	Qiúzhuàng jǔzhèn páiliè
BGA	Ball grid array	球状网格阵列	Qiúzhuàng wǎnggé zhènliè
BGA	Ball grid array (electronics mfg)	球栅阵列	Qiú zhà zhènliè
BGC	Business group complex	复合商业组群	Fùhé shāngyè zǔ qún
BGF	Basic global function	基本的全局功能	Jīběnde quánjú gōngnéng
BGIWP	Barring of GPRS interworking profile(s)	闭锁 GPRS 互通文件	Bìsuǒ GPRS hùtōng wénjiàn
BGMP	Border gateway multicast protocol	边界网关组播协议	Biānjiè wǎngguān zǔbō xiéyì
BGN	Background noise	背景噪声	Bèijǐng zàoshēng
BGP	Border gateway protocol	边界路由协议	Biānjiè lùyóu xiéyì
BGP	Border gateway protocol	边界网关协议	Biānjiè wǎngguān xiéyì
BGP-MP	Multi-protocol extension for BGP-4	多协议扩展的 BGP 协议	Duōxiéyì kuòzhǎnde BGP xiéyì
BGRAN	Broadband generalized radio access network	通用宽带无线接入网络	Tōngyòng kuāndài wúxiàn jiērù wǎngluò
BGS	Background sound	背景音响	Bèijǐng yīnxiǎng

BGT	Block guard time	块保护时间	Kuài bǎohù shíjiān
BH	Buried heterogeneous (fiber or cable)	掩埋异质结	Yǎnmái yìzhìjié
BHC	Busy hour calls	忙时呼叫	Mángshí hūjiào
BHCA	Busy hour call attempts	忙时话务量	Mángshí huàwùliàng
BHCA	Busy hour calling attempts	忙时呼叫尝试	Mángshí hūjiào chángshì
BHCA	Busy hour calling attempts	忙时试呼次数	Mángshí-shì hū cìshù
BHCC	Busy hour call completed	忙时呼叫完成	Mángshí hūjiào wánchéng
BHIP	BTS high capacity IPC processor	BTS 高容量 IPC 处理器	BTS gāo róngliàng IPC chǔlǐqì
BHIP	High capacity IPC processor	高容量 IPC 处理器	Gāoróngliàng IPC chǔlǐqì
BHL	Busy hour load	忙时负载	Mángshí fùzài
BHLF	Basic high layer function	基本的高层功能	Jīběnde gāocéng gōngnéng
BHU	Busy hour usage	忙时应用	Mángshí yìngyòng
BI	Barring of all incoming calls	全闭锁入呼叫	Quán bìsuǒ rùhūjiào
BI	Barring of all incoming calls supplementary service	所有入局禁止补充业务	Suǒyǒu rùjú jìnzhǐ bǔchōng yèwù
BI	Business intelligence	商业智能化	Shāngyè zhìnénghuà
BIB	Backward indicator bit	后向指示比特	Hòuxiàng zhǐshì bǐtè
BIB	Backward indicator bit	后向指示位	Hòuxiàng zhǐshì wèi
BIBB	BTS interconnect back board	BTS 互联后面板	BTS hù lián hòumian bǎn
BIBB	Interconnect backboard	互联后面板	Hùlián hòumian bǎn
BIC	Baseline implementation capabilities	设备能力底线	Shèbèi nénglì dǐxiàn
BIC	Baseline implementation capabilities	设备能力基线	Shèbèi nénglì jīxiàn
BIC	Bayesian information criterion	贝叶斯信息准则	Bèi-yè-sī xìnxī zhǔnzé
BICC	Bearer independent call control	独立于承载的呼叫控制	Dúlì yú chéngzàide hūjiào kòngzhì
BICC	Bearer Independent Call Control protocol	承载独立呼叫控制协议	Chéngzài dúlì hūjiào kòngzhì xiéyì
BICC	Bearer-independent call control	承载无关的呼叫控制	Chéngzài wúguānde hūjiào kòngzhì
BICC	Bearer-independent call control	与承载无关呼叫控制	Yǔ chéngzài wúguān hūjiào kòngzhì
BIC-Roam	Barring of incoming calls when roaming outside the home PLMN country	闭锁在 PLMN 归属国家外漫游时的入呼叫	Bìsuǒ zài PLMN guīshǔ guójiā wài mànyóu shíde rù hūjiào
BIC-Roam	Barring of incoming calls when roaming outside the home PLMN country supplementary service	当漫游出归属 PLMN 国家后，闭锁入呼叫	Dāng mànyóu chū guīshǔ PLMN guójiā hòu, bìsuǒ rù hūjiào
BIC-Roam	Barring of incoming calls when roaming outside the home PLMN country	当漫游出归属 PLMN 国家时，闭锁入呼叫	Dāng mànyóu chū guīshǔ PLMN guójiā shí, bìsuǒ rù hūjiào
BID	Binding identity	包装识别	Bāozhuāng shíbié
BID	Board inward dialing	板自动拨入	Bǎn zìdòng bōrù
BIE	Base station interface equipment	基站接口设备	Jīzhàn jiēkǒu shèbèi
BIF	Boot image file	启动映像文件	Qǐdòng yìngxiàng wénjiàn
BIM	BSM initialization and maintenance	BSM 初始化和维护	BSM chūshǐhuà hé wéihù
BIM	Initialization and maintenance	初始化和维护	Chūshǐhuà hé wéihù
BINDS	Berkeley Internet Naming Domain Service (software)	柏克利因特网名域服务	Bǎi-kè-lì Yīntèwǎng míngyù fúwù
BINL	Boot information negotiation layer	启动信息协商层	Qǐdòng xìnxī xiéshāng céng
BIOS	Basic input/output system	基本输入输出系统	Jīběn shūrù shūchū xìtǒng
BIP	Bit interleaved parity	比特间插奇偶校验	Bǐtè jiānchā jī'ǒu jiàoyàn
BIP	Bit interleaved parity	比特间插奇偶性	Bǐtè jiānchā jī'ǒu xìng
BIP	Bit interleaved parity	比特交织奇偶性	Bǐtè jiāozhī jī'ǒu xìng
BIP	Bit interleaved parity	比特间插奇偶性	Bǐtè-jiān chā jī'ǒu xìng
BIP	Bit interleaved parity check	比特交叉奇偶校验	Bǐtè jiāochā jī'ǒu jiàoyàn

BIP	Bit interleaved parity check	比特奇偶校验码	Bǐtè jī'ǒu jiàoyàn mǎ
BIP	Bit interleaved parity check	比特间插奇偶校验	Bǐtè-jiān chā jī'ǒu jiàoyàn
BIP-N	Bit interleaved parity check N code	比特间插奇偶校验 N 位码	Bǐtè-jiān chā jī'ǒu jiàoyàn N wèi mǎ
BIS	Border intermediate system	边界中介系统	Biānjiè zhōngjiè xìtǒng
B-ISDN	Broadband integrated services digital network	广带综合业务数字网	Guǎngdài zōnghé yèwù shùzì wǎng
B-ISDN	Broadband integrated services digital network	宽带综合业务数字网	Kuāndài zōnghé yèwù shùzì wǎng
B-ISDN PBX	Private branch exchange for B-ISDN	B-ISDN 专用小交换机	B-ISDN zhuānyòng xiǎo jiāohuànjī
B-ISDN PRM	Protocol reference model of broadband ISDN	宽带 ISDN 协议参考模型	Kuāndài ISDN xiéyì cānkǎo móxíng
BISPO	Bring into service performance objective	投入业务性能指标	Tóurù yèwù xìngnéng zhǐbiāo
BISUP	Broadband ISDN user part	宽带 ISDN 用户部分	Kuāndài ISDN yònghù bùfen
B-ISUP	Broadband integrated services digital network-user part	宽带综合业务数字网用户部分	Kuāndài zōnghé yèwù shùzìwǎng yònghù bùfen
B-ISUP	Broadband ISDN user part	宽带 ISDN 用户部分	Kuāndài ISDN yònghù bùfen
BIT	Basic interconnection test	基本互连测试	Jīběn hùlián cèshì
BIT	Built-in test	内置测试	Nèizhì cèshì
BITEs	Backward interworking telephone events	后向互通电话事件	Hòuxiàng hùtōng diànhuà shìjiàn
BITNET	Because it's Time Network	因为它是时代网络	Yīnwei tā shì shídài wǎngluò
BITS	Binary Intersystem transmission standard	二进制系统间传输标准	Èrjìnzhì xìtǒng-jiān chuánshū biāozhǔn
BITS	Building integrated time supply	楼内综合定时供给设备	Lóunèi zōnghé dìngshí gōngjǐ shèbèi
BITS	Building integrated timing supply	大楼综合定时供给设备	Dàlóu zōnghé dìngshí gōngjǐ shèbèi
BITS	Building integrated timing supply	大楼内综合定时源	Dàlóu-nèi zōnghé dìngshí yuán
BITS	Building integrated timing supply	局内综合定时供给系统	Jú-nèi zōnghé dìngshí gōngjǐ xìtǒng
BITS	Building integrated timing system	大楼综合定时供给系统	Dàlóu zōnghé dìngshí gōngjǐ xìtǒng
BITS	Building integrated timing system	通信楼综合定时供给系统	Tōngxìn lóu zōnghé dìngshí gōngjǐ xìtǒng
BIWF	Bearer interworking function	承载互通功能	Chéngzài hùtōng gōngnéng
BLA	Beam landing area (video term)	电子束落区	Diànzǐshù luò qū
BLA	Blocking-acknowledgement signal	闭塞证实信号	Bìsè zhèngshí xìnhào
BLADES	Buffalo Laboratories application of digitally exact spectra	数字化精确谱 Buffalo 实验室应用（系统）	Shùzìhuà jīngquè pǔ Buffalo shíyànshì yìngyòng (xìtǒng)
BLAST	Bell layered space-time architecture	分层空时结构	Fēncéng kōng shí jiégòu
BLEC	Building local exchange carrier	数字本地交换运营	Shùzì běndì jiāohuàn yùnyíng
BLER	Block error rate	块误码率	Kuài wùmǎ lǜ
BLER	Block error rate	码组差错率	Mǎzǔ chācuò lǜ
B-LEX	Broadband local exchange	宽带本地交换	Kuāndài běndì jiāohuàn
Blit	Bit block transfer	位块传输	Wèikuài chuánshū
BLLF	Basic low layer function	基本的底层功能	Jīběnde dǐcéng gōngnéng
BLO	Blocking signal	闭塞信号	Bìsè xìnhào
BLOB	Binary large object	大块二进制数据目标	Dàkuài èrjìnzhì shùjù mùbiāo
BLOB	Binary large object	二进制大目标	Èrjìnzhì dà mùbiāo
BLOBID	Binary large object identifier	大块二进制数据目标标识	Dàkuài èrjìnzhì shùjù mùbiāo biāozhì
BLOS	Beyond line of sight	超视距	Chāoshìjù
BLP	Bit loss probability	位损耗概率	Wèi sǔnhào gàilǜ
BLR	Bit loss rate	比特丢失率	Bǐtè diūshī lǜ
BLSR	Bidirectional line switching ring	双向线路倒换环	Shuāngxiàng xiànlù dǎohuàn huán
BLUE	Best linear unbiased estimate	最优线性无偏估计	Zuìyōu xiànxìng wúpiān gūjì
BM	Baseband modem	基带调制解调器	Jīdài tiáozhì jiětiáoqì
BM	Baseband modem	基带调制解调制器	Jīdài tiáozhì jiětiáozhìqì

BM	Business management	商业管理	Shāngyè guǎnlǐ
Bm	Full rate traffic channel	全速率业务信道	Quánsùlǜ yèwù xìndào
BMBP	BSC main processor back panel	BSC 主处理器后面板	BSC zhǔ chǔlǐ qì hòumian bǎn
BMC	Background memory controller	后台存储控制器	Hòutái cúnchǔ kòngzhìqì
BMC	Broadcast/multicast control	广播/多播控制	Guǎngbō/duōbō kòngzhì
BMC	Burst-mode controller	突发模式控制器	Tūfā móshì kòngzhìqì
BMCP	Basic mode control procedure	基本型控制规程	Jīběn-xíng kòngzhì guīchéng
BMEA	BTS measurement	BTS 测量	BTS cèliáng
BML	Business management layer	商业管理层	Shāngyè guǎnlǐ céng
BML	Business management layer	事务管理层	Shìwù guǎnlǐ céng
BMP	Basic multilingual plane	基本多文种平面	Jīběn duō wénzhǒng píngmiàn
BMP	Bill management platform	计费管理平台	Jìfèi guǎnlǐ píngtái
BMP	Billing management point	记帐管理点	Jìzhàng guǎnlǐ diǎn
BMP	Bit mapping protocol	位映射协议	Wèi yìngshè xiéyì
BMR	BTS message router	BTS 消息路由器	BTS xiāoxi lùyóu qì
BMR	Message router	消息路由器	Xiāoxi lùyóuqì
BMS	Billing and management system	计费和管理系统	Jìfèi hé guǎnlǐ xìtǒng
BMS	Building management system	建筑管理系统	Jiànzhù guǎnlǐ xìtǒng
BMU	Basic measurement unit	基本测量单位	Jīběn cèliáng dānwèi
BN	Bit number	比特号码	Bǐtè hàomǎ
BNAS	Broadband network access server	宽带网络接入服务器	Kuāndài wǎngluò jiērù fúwùqì
BNC	Backbone network connection	骨干网连接	Gǔgànwǎng liánjiē
BNC	Background noise conditioning	背景噪音调节	Bèijǐng zàoyīn tiáojié
BNC-ID	Backbone network connection identifier	骨干网连接识别符	Gǔgànwǎng liánjiē shíbiéfú
BNCL	Backbone network connection link	骨干网连接链路	Gǔgànwǎng liánjiē liànlù
BNR	Background noise reduction	背景噪音降低	Bèijǐng zàoyīn jiàngdī
B-NT	Network termination for B-ISDN	B-ISDN 网络终端	B-ISDN wǎngluò zhōngduān
BO	All barring of outgoing call	闭锁全部出呼叫	Bìsuǒ quánbù chū hūjiào
BO	Barring of all outgoing calls supplementary service	所有出局禁止补充业务	Suǒyǒu chūjú jìnzhǐ bǔchōng yèwù
BO	Base station originating	基站主叫	Jīzhàn zhǔ jiào
BOC	Bell operating company	贝尔运营公司	Bèi'ěr yùnyíng gōngsī
BOD	Bandwidth on demand	弹性带宽运用	Tánxìng dàikuān yùnyòng
BoD	Bandwidth-on-demand	按需分配带宽	Ànxū fēnpèi dàikuān
BOFA	Broadband optical fiber amplifier	宽带光放大器	Kuāndài guāng fàngdàqì
BOFSN	Broadband optical full service network	宽带光全业务接入网	Kuāndài guāng quán yèwù jiērù wǎng
BOIC	Barring of all outgoing international calls	闭锁所有国际呼出业务	Bìsuǒ suǒyǒu guójì hūchū yèwù
BOIC	Barring of outgoing international calls	闭锁出局国际呼叫	Bìsuǒ chūjú guójì hūjiào
BOIC	Barring of outgoing international calls	闭锁国际出呼叫	Bìsuǒ guójì chū hūjiào
BOIC	Barring of outgoing international calls supplementary service	禁止国际出局呼叫补充业务	Jìnzhǐ guójì chūjú hūjiào bǔchōng yèwù
BOIC-exHC	Barring of outgoing international calls except those direct to the home PLMN	闭锁除直接到归属 PLMN 国家外国际呼叫	Bìsuǒ chú zhíjiē dào guīshǔ PLMN guójiā-wài guójì hūjiào
BOIC-exHC	Barring of outgoing international calls except those directed to the home PLMN country	闭锁除直接到 PLMN 归属国以外的国际出呼叫	Bìsuǒ chú zhíjiē dào PLMN guīshǔ guó yǐwàide guójì chū hūjiào
BOIC-exHC	Barring of outgoing international calls except those directed to the home PLMN country	除至归属公共陆地移动通信网国家外,闭锁国际出呼叫	Chú zhì guīshǔ gōnggòng lùdì yídòng tōngxìnwǎng guójiā wài, bìsuǒ guójì chū hūjiào

BOIC-exHC	Barring of outgoing international calls except those directed to the home PLMN country	除至归属 PLMN 国家外，闭锁国际出呼叫	Chú zhì guīshǔ PLMN guójiā wài, bìsuǒ guójì chū hūjiào
BOIC-exHC	Barring of outgoing international calls except those directed to the home PLMN country supplementary service	禁止所有除归属国外的国际出局呼叫补充业务	Jìnzhǐ suǒyǒu chú guīshǔ guówàide guójì chūjú hūjiào bǔchōng yèwù
BOIC-exHC	Barring of outgoing international calls except those directed towards the home PLMN country	除直接到归属 PLMN 国家外的呼叫外，闭锁国际出呼叫	Chú zhíjiē dào guīshǔ PLMN guójiā wàide hūjiào wài, bìsuǒ guójì chū hūjiào
BOIC-exHC	BOIC except those directed to the home PLMN country	除了指向本地 PLMN 国家之外的 BOIC	Chúle zhǐxiàng běndì PLMN guójiā zhīwàide BOIC
BOM	Beginning of message	消息开始	Xiāoxi kāishǐ
BoM	Bill of materials	材料清单	Cáiliào qīngdān
BOOTP	Bootstrap protocol	自陷协议	Zìxiàn xiéyì
BOPS	Billion operations per second	十亿次运算/秒	Shíyì cì yùnsuàn/miǎo
BOSS	Business operation supporting system	业务运营支援系统	Yèwù yùnyíng zhīyuán xìtǒng
BP	Burst period	突发脉冲序列周期	Tūfā màichōng xùliè zhōuqī
BPA	Burst packet attribute	突发包特征	Tūfā bāo tèzhēng
BPB	Baseband processor mother board	基带处理框背板	Jīdài chǔlǐ kuàng bèibǎn
BPDU	Bridge protocol data unit	桥接协议数据单元	Qiáojiē xiéyì shùjù dānyuán
BPDU	Bridge protocol data unit	网桥协议数据单元	Wǎngqiáo xiéyì shùjù dānyuán
BPFI	Bandpass filter isolator	带通滤波器/隔离器	Dàitōng lǜbōqì/gélíqì
BPI	Baseline protocol indicator	保密协议标识符	Bǎomì xiéyì biāozhì fú
BPIM	Basic primitive interface model	基本的简单接口模型	Jīběnde jiǎndān jiēkǒu móxíng
BPKM-REQ	Baseline privacy key management-request	保密协议密钥管理请求消息	Bǎomì xiéyì mìyào guǎnlǐ qǐngqiú xiāoxi
BPKM-RSP	Baseline privacy key management -response	保密协议密钥管理响应消息	Bǎomì xiéyì mìyào guǎnlǐ xiǎngyìng xiāoxi
BPON	Wideband passive optical network	宽带无源光网络	Kuāndài wúyuán guāng wǎngluò
B-PON	Broadband passive optical network	宽带无源光网络	Kuāndài wúyuán guāng wǎngluò
BPR	Business process re-engineering	业务流程重组	Yèwù liúchéng chóngzǔ
bps	Bits per second	位每秒	Wèi měi miǎo
Bps	Bits per second	位/秒	Wèi/miǎo
BPSK	Binary phase shift keying	二进制相移键控	Èrjìnzhì xiāngyí jiànkòng
BPSK	Binary phase shift keying	二相相移键控	Èrxiàng xiāngyí jiànkòng
BPSK	Binary phase shift keying	二相移相键控	Èrxiàng yíxiàng jiànkòng
BPT	British Posts and Telecommunications Standard	英国邮政与电信标准	Yīngguó yóuzhèng yǔ diànxìn biāozhǔn
BPU	Baseband processing unit	基带处理单元	Jīdài chǔlǐ dānyuán
BPU	Basic processing unit	基本处理装置	Jīběn chǔlǐ zhuāngzhì
BPU	Branch processing unit	分支处理单元	Fēnzhī chǔlǐ dānyuán
BPV	Bipolar violation	双极性破坏	Shuāng jíxìng pòhuài
BR	Base register	基地址寄存器	Jī dìzhǐ jìcúnqì
BRA	Basic rate access	基本速率接入	Jīběn sùlǜ jiērù
BRA	BTS resource allocation	BTS 资源分配	BTS zīyuán fēnpèi
BRAS	Broadband access server	宽带接入服务器	Kuāndài jiērù fúwùqì
BRAS	Broadband remote access server	宽带远程接入服务器	Kuāndài yuǎnchéng jiērù fúwùqì
BREW	Binary running environment for wireless	无线二进制运行环境	Wúxiàn èrjìnzhì yùnxíng huánjìng
BREW	Binary running environment for wireless platforms	无线平台二进制运行环境	Wúxiàn píngtái èrjìnzhì yùnxíng huánjìng
BRI	Basic rate integrated services digital network	基本速率的综合业务数字网	Jīběn sùlǜde zōnghé yèwù shùzì wǎng
BRI	Basic rate interface	基本速率接口	Jīběn sùlǜ jiēkǒu
BRI	Basic rate interface	基群速率接口	Jīqún sùlǜ jiēkǒu

BRIE	Bus request interrupt enable	总线请求中断	Zǒngxiàn qǐngqiú zhōngduàn
BRJ	Bandwidth reject	带宽请求拒绝	Dàikuān qǐngqiú jùjué
BRJ	Broadband rejected	宽带拒绝	Kuāndài jùjué
BRM	Bit rate multiplier	位速率乘法器	Wèi sùlǜ chéngfǎqì
BRM	BTS configure and resource management	BTS 配置和资源管理	BTS pèizhì hé zīyuán guǎnlǐ
BRQ	Broadband request	宽带请求	Kuāndài qǐngqiú
BS	Backspace	退格	Tuìgé
BS	Base station	基站	Jīzhàn
BS	Bearer service	承载业务	Chéngzài yèwù
BS	Billing system	计费系统	Jìfèi xìtǒng
BSA	Beam solid angle	射束立体角	Shèshù lìtǐjiǎo
BSA	Business Software Alliance	商业软件联盟	Shāngyè ruǎnjiàn liánméng
BSC	Base station controller	基站控制器	Jīzhàn kòngzhìqì
BSC	Binary symmetric channel	二进制对称信道	Èrjìnzhì duìchèn xìndào
BSC	Binary synchronous communication	二进制同步通信	Èrjìnzhì tóngbù tōngxìn
BSC	Binary synchronous control	二进制同步控制	Èrjìnzhì tóngbù kòngzhì
BSD	Berkeley software distribution	伯克利软件分配代号	Bó-kè-lì ruǎnjiàn fēnpèi dàihào
BSG	Basic service group	基本业务群	Jīběn yèwù qún
BSG	Basic service group	基本业务组	Jīběn yèwù zǔ
BSG	Boundary state gelatinization (FOC mfg)	界面凝胶法	Jièmiàn níngjiāo fǎ
BSH	BTS status handling	BTS 状态处理	BTS zhuàngtài chǔlǐ
BSI	Base station interface	基站接口	Jīzhàn jiēkǒu
BSI	British Standards Institute	英国标准所	Yīngguó biāozhǔn suǒ
BSIC	Base station identity code	基站标识码	Jīzhàn biāozhì mǎ
BSIC	Base transceiver station identity code	基站收发信机识别码	Jīzhàn shōufāxìnjī shíbié mǎ
BSID	Base station identification	基站识别码	Jīzhàn shíbié mǎ
BSL	Buried service lightguide (cable)	直埋式光缆	Zhímái-shì guānglǎn
BSM	Backward set-up message	后向建立消息	Hòuxiàng jiànlì xiāoxi
BSM	Backward setup signal	后向建立信号	Hòuxiàng jiànlì xìnhào
BSM	Base station manager	基站管理器	Jīzhàn guǎnlǐqì
BSM	Base station module	基站模块	Jīzhàn mókuài
BSMAP	Base station mobile application part	基站移动应用部分	Jīzhàn yídòng yìngyòng bùfen
BSMN	BTS sanity management	BTS 正常运行管理器	BTS zhèngcháng yùnxíng guǎnlǐqì
BSN	Backward sequence number	后向顺序号	Hòuxiàng shùnxù hào
BSNT	Backward sequence number to be transmitted	要传送的后向序号	Yào chuánsòngde hòuxiàng xùhào
BSR	Bootstrap router	引导路由器	Yǐndǎo lùyóuqì
BSR	Bootstrap router	自举路由器	Zìjǔ lùyóuqì
BSR	Border scanning register	边界扫描寄存器	Biānjiè sǎomiáo jìcúnqì
BSRAM	Burst pipelined synchronous static RAM	突发式管道同步静态存储器	Tūfā-shì guǎndào tóngbù jìngtài cúnchǔqì
BSS	Base station sub-system	基站子系统	Jīzhàn zìxìtǒng
BSS	Base station sub-system	基站子系统	Jīzhàn zìxìtǒng
BSS	Base station system	基站系统	Jīzhàn xìtǒng
BSS	Basic spectral subtraction	基本谱减法	Jīběn pǔ jiǎnfǎ
BSS	Broad band switching system	宽带交换系统	Kuāndài jiāohuàn xìtǒng
BSS	Broadcasting satellite service	广播卫星业务	Guǎngbō wèixīng yèwù
BSSAP	Base station application part	基站应用部分	Jīzhàn yìngyòng bùfen

BSSAP	Base station sub-system application part	基站子系统应用部分	Jīzhàn zixìtǒng yìngyòng bùfen
BSSAP	Base station system application part	基站系统应用部分	Jīzhàn xìtǒng yìngyòng bùfen
BSSAP+	Base station system application part+	基站应用部分加	Jīzhàn yìngyòng bùfen jiā
BSSGP	Base station system GPRS protocol	基站子系统 GPRS 协议	Jīzhàn zixìtǒng GPRS xiéyì
BSSMAP	Base station management application part	基站管理应用部分	Jīzhàn guǎnlǐ yìngyòng bùfen
BSSMAP	Base station sub-system management application part	基站子系统管理应用部分	Jīzhàn zixìtǒng guǎnlǐ yìngyòng bùfen
BSSMAP	Base station system management application part	基站系统管理应用部分	Jīzhàn xìtǒng guǎnlǐ yìngyòng bùfen
BSSOMAP	Base station operation and maintenance application part	BSS 操作维护应用部分	BSS cāozuò wéihù yìngyòng bùfen
BSSOMAP	Base station system operation and maintenance application part	基站系统运营和维护应用部分	Jīzhàn xìtǒng yùnyíng hé wéihù yìngyòng bùfen
BSSOMAP	Base station system operation and maintenance application part	基站子系统操作与维护应用部分	Jīzhàn zixìtǒng cāozuò yǔ wéihù yìngyòng bùfen
BSSTE	Base station sub-system test equipment	基站测试设备	Jīzhàn cèshì shèbèi
BSTA	Base station test assembly	基站测试集成件	Jīzhàn cèshì jíchéng jiàn
BSTB	Base station test block	基站测试模块	Jīzhàn cèshì mókuài
BSTCE	Base station telephonic control element	基站电话控制单元	Jīzhàn diànhuà kòngzhì dānyuán
BSTM	BTS system time	BTS 系统时间	BTS xìtǒng shíjiān
BSTU	Base station test unit	基站测试单元	Jīzhàn cèshì dānyuán
BSTXPWR	Base station transmitter power	基站发射器功率	Jīzhàn fāshèqì gōnglǜ
BSU	Backward signal unit	后向信令单元	Hòuxiàng xìnlìng dānyuán
BSU	Basic spatial unit	基本空间单元	Jīběn kōngjiān dānyuán
BSU	Broadband switching unit	宽带交换单元	Kuāndài jiāohuàn dānyuán
BT	Bandwidth time	带宽时间	Dàikuān shíjiān
BT	Base station terminating	基站被叫	Jīzhàn bèi jiào
BT	Burst tolerance	突发容限	Tūfā róngxiàn
B-TA	Terminal adaptor for B-ISDN	B-ISDN 终端适配器	B-ISDN zhōngduān shìpèiqì
BTB/C	Branch target buffer/cache	分支目标缓冲	Fēnzhī mùbiāo huǎnchōng
BTC	Block turbo codes	分组 turbo 码	Fēnzǔ turbo mǎ
BT-CCD	Thin backside illuminated charge coupled device	薄型背照式电荷耦合器件	Báoxíng bèizhàoshì diànhè ǒuhé qìjiàn
B-TE	Terminal equipment for B-ISDN	B-ISDN 终端设备	B-ISDN zhōngduānshèbèi
BTEQ	Bridged tap equalizer	桥接抽头均衡器	Qiáojiē chōutóu jūnhéngqì
BTFD	Blind transport format detection	盲目传输格式检测	Mángmù chuánshū géshi jiǎncè
BTH	Basic transmission header	基本传输标题	Jīběn chuánshū biāotí
BTI	Block transfer instruction	字组传送指令	Zìzǔ chuánsòng zhǐlìng
BTO	Blocking-tube oscillator	电子管间歇振荡器	Diànzǐguǎn jiànxiē zhèndàngqì
BTP	BTS test processor	BTS 测试处理器	BTS cèshì chǔlǐqì
BTS	Base station transceiver system	基站收发信机系统	Jīzhàn shōufāxìnjī xìtǒng
BTS	Base station transmission sub-system	基站传输子系统	Jīzhàn chuánshū zixìtǒng
BTS	Base transceiver station	基站收发信机	Jīzhàn shōufā xìn jī
BTS	Base transceiver station	基站收发信台	Jīzhàn shōufāxìntái
BTS	Base transmitter station	基站	Jīzhàn
BTSM	Base transceiver station management	基站收发信台管理	Jīzhàn shōufāxìntái guǎnlǐ
BTT	Busy tone trunk	忙音中继线	Mángyīn zhōngjìxiàn
BUL	Backup lighting	备用照明	Bèiyòng zhàomíng
BUNI	Basic user-network interface	基本的用户－网络接口	Jīběnde yònghù—wǎngluò jiēkǒu
B-UNI	Broadband user-network interface	宽带用户 - 网络接口	Kuāndài yònghù-wǎngluò jiēkǒu

BUS	Broadcast and unknown server	广播和未知地址服务器	Guǎngbō hé wèizhī dìzhǐ fúwùqì
BUS	Broadcast and unknown server	广播和未知服务器	Guǎngbō hé wèizhī fúwùqì
BW	Broadband, wideband	宽带	Kuāndài
BW	Burial in wall (telecom installation)	墙内埋设	Qiáng-nèi máishè
BWAN	Broadband wireless ATM system	宽带无线 ATM 系统	Kuāndài wúxiàn ATM xìtǒng
BWG	Birmingham Wire gauge (UK)	英国伯明翰线规	Yīngguó bó-míng-hàn xiànguī
BWr	Reference bandwidth	参考带宽	Cānkǎo dàikuān
BWr	Reference broadband	参考宽带	Cānkǎo kuāndài
BWT	Block waiting time	块等待时间	Kuài děngdài shíjiān
BWT	Both-ways trunk	双方中继	Shuāngfāng zhōngjì
BZ	Buzzer	蜂鸣器	Fēngmíngqì
BZ	Buzzer	蜂音器	Fēngyīnqì

C

C	Ceiling mounted type	吸顶式	Xīdǐng-shì
C	Combiner	混合器	Hùnhéqì
C	Connection function	连接功能	Liánjiē gōngnéng
C	Container (SDH term)	容器	Róngqì
C	Convergence	收敛	Shōuliǎn
C, CHR	Chrominance	色度	Sèdù
C/A, AC	Adjacent channel	相邻频道	Xiānglín píndào
C/B GF	Call/bearer gateway function	呼叫/承载网关功能	Hūjiào/chéngzài wǎngguān gōngnéng
C/B/S	Client/browser/server	客户机/浏览器/服务器	Kèhùjī/liúlǎnqì/fúwùqì
C/BGF	Call/bearer gateway function	呼叫/承网关功能	Hūjiào/chéng wǎngguān gōngnéng
C/CSO	Carrier/composite second order beat	载波复合二次差拍比	Zàibō fùhé èrcì chāpāi bǐ
C/CTB	Carrier/composite triple beat	载波复合三次差拍比	Zàibō fùhé sāncì chāpāi bǐ
C/F	Cost and freight	成本加运费	Chéngběn jiā yùnfèi
C/I	Co-channel	共频道	Gòng píndào
C/N	Carrier to noise ratio	载噪比	Zài zào bǐ
C/P	Card punch	卡片穿孔机	Kǎpiàn chuānkǒngjī
C/R	Card reader	卡片阅读机	Kǎpiàn yuèdújī
C/R	Command/response	命令/响应	Mìnglìng/xiǎngyìng
C/R	Command/response field bit	命令/响应比特	Mìnglìng/xiǎngyìng bǐtè
C/R	Command/response field bit	命令/响应字段比特	Mìnglìng/xiǎngyìng zìduàn bǐtè
C/S	Client/server	客户机/服务器	Kèhùjī/fúwùqì
COLR	Connected line identification restriction	连接号码识别限制	Liánjiē hàomǎ shíbié xiànzhì
C2C	Card-to-card interleaving	卡到卡交错存取	Kǎ dào kǎ jiāocuò cúnqǔ
C3	Computer, command and control	计算机，指挥和控制	Jìsuànjī, zhǐhuī hé kòngzhì
CA	Capacity allocation	容量配置	Róngliàng pèizhì
CA	Cascade amplifier	级联放大器	Jílián fàngdàqì
CA	Cell (frequency) allocation	小区（频率）分配	Xiǎoqū (pínlǜ) fēnpèi
CA	Cell allocation	蜂窝配置	Fēngwō pèizhì
CA	Cell allocation	小区配置	Xiǎoqū pèizhì
CA	Cellular automata	单元自动机	Dānyuán zìdòngjī
CA	Cellular automata	细胞自动机	Xìbāo zìdòngjī
CA	Certificate authority	认证管理机构	Rènzhèng guǎnlǐ jīgòu

CA	Certificate authority	证书授权	Zhèngshū shòuquán
CA	Certification authority	认证当局	Rènzhèng dāngjú
CA	Certification authority	认证管理部门	Rènzhèng guǎnlǐ bùmén
CA	Certification authority	认证职权	Rènzhèng zhíquán
CA	Certification authority	认证中心	Rènzhèng zhōngxīn
CA	Certification authority	证件授权机构	Zhèngjiàn shòuquán jīgòu
CA	Certification authority	证书管理机构	Zhèngshū guǎnlǐ jīgòu
CA	Chained addressing	链式寻址	Liàn-shì xúnzhǐ
CA	Character attribute	字符属性	Zìfú shǔxìng
CA	Coaxial	同轴的	Tóngzhóude
CA	Communication automation	通信自动化	Tōngxìn zìdònghuà
CA	Computer Associate	电脑友伴	Diànnǎo yǒubàn
CA	Conditional access	条件接入	Tiáojiàn jiērù
CAA	Capacity allocation acknowledgement	容量配置认可	Róngliàng pèizhì rènkě
CAA	Collinear array antenna	直排天线阵	Zhípái tiānxiàn zhèn
CAA	Computer-assisted accounting	计算机辅助会计计算	Jìsuànjī fǔzhù kuàijì jìsuàn
CAAD	Computer-aided architectural design	计算机辅助建筑设计	Jìsuànjī fǔzhù jiànzhù shèjì
CAB	Appointed certification body	指定的认证机构	Zhǐdìngde rènzhèng jīgòu
CAB	Computer address bus	计算机地址总线	Jìsuànjī dìzhǐ zǒngxiàn
CABA	Clock monitoring and distribution /AGC bank assembly	时钟监测和分配/AGC 集成板	Shízhōng jiāncè hé fēnpèi/AGC jíchéngbǎn
CAC	Channel access code	信道访问码	Xìndào fǎngwèn mǎ
CAC	Connection admission control	接纳允许控制	Jiēnà yǔnxǔ kòngzhì
CAC	Connection admission control	连接接纳控制	Liánjiē jiēnà kòngzhì
CAC	Connection admission control	连接允许控制	Liánjiē yǔnxǔ kòngzhì
CACD	Computer-aided conceptual design	计算机辅助概念设计	Jìsuànjī fǔzhù gàiniàn shèjì
CACE	China Association of Communications Enterprises	中国通信企业协会	Zhōngguó tōngxìn qǐyè xiéhuì
CAD	Computer-aided design	计算机辅助设计	Jìsuànjī fǔzhù shèjì
CAD/CAM	Computer-aided design/computer-aided manufacturing	计算机辅助设计/计算机辅助制造	Jìsuànjī fǔzhù shèjì/jìsuànjī fǔzhù zhìzào
CADD	Computer-aided design drawing	计算机辅助制图	Jìsuànjī fǔzhù zhìtú
CADF	Commutated antenna direction finder	换向天线测向仪	Huànxiàng tiānxiàn cèxiàngyí
CAE	Computer-aided engineering	计算机辅助工程	Jìsuànjī fǔzhù gōngchéng
CAFS	Content addressable file store	可按内容寻址的文件存储	Kě àn nèiróng xúnzhǐde wénjiàn cúnchǔ
CAGD	Computer-aided geometric design	计算机辅助几何设计	Jìsuànjī fǔzhù jǐhé shèjì
CAGR	Combined annual growth rate	综合年度增长率	Zōnghé niándù zēngzhǎnglǜ
CAI	Charge advice information	计费建议信息	Jìfèi jiànyì xìnxī
CAI	Charge advice information	收费通知信息	Shōufèi tōngzhī xìnxī
CAI	Common air interface	公共空中接口	Gōnggòng kōngzhōng jiēkǒu
CAI	Common air interface (CDMA)	通用空中接口	Tōngyòng kōngzhōng jiēkǒu
CAI	Computer analog input	计算机模拟输入	Jìsuànjī mónǐ shūrù
CAI	Computer-aided instruction	计算机辅助教学	Jìsuànjī fǔzhù jiàoxué
CAINONET	China Advanced Info-optical Network	中国高速信息示范网	Zhōngguó gāosù xìnxī shìfàn wǎng
C-ALG	Data confidentiality algorithm	数据保密算法	Shùjù bǎomì suànfǎ
CALI	Compact analog line interface	小型模拟用户线接口	Xiǎoxíng mónǐ yònghù xiàn jiēkǒu
CALL PROC	Call process	呼叫进程	Hūjiào jìnchéng
CAM	Computer-aided manufacturing	计算机辅助制造	Jìsuànjī fǔzhù zhìzào

CAM	Content addressable memory	按内容编址的存储器	Àn nèiróng biānzhǐde cúnchǔqì
CAM	Content-addressable memory	内容定址存储器	Nèiróng dìngzhǐ cúnchǔqì
CAM	Content-addressable memory	内容寻址存储器	Nèiróng xúnzhǐ cúnchǔqì
CAMA	Centralized automatic message accounting	集中自动处理记帐	Jízhōng zìdòng chǔlǐ jìzhàng
CAMA	Centralized automatic message accounting	集中式自动电报计费	Jízhōng-shì zìdòng diànbào jìfèi
CAMA	Centralized automatic message accounting system	集中式自动通话记帐系统	Jízhōng-shì zìdòng tōnghuà jìzhàng xìtǒng
CAMA	Computer-assisted mass appraisal	计算机辅助群体评估	Jìsuànjī fǔzhù qúntǐ pínggū
CAMC	Customer access maintenance center	用户接入维护中心	Yònghù jiērù wéihù zhōngxīn
CAMEL	Customized application for mobile network enhanced logic	移动网增强逻辑定制应用	Yídòng wǎng zēngqiáng luóji dìngzhì yìngyòng
CAMEL	Customized applications for mobil network enhanced logic	移动网增强逻辑的定做应用	Yídòng wǎng zēngqiáng luójide dìngzuò yìngyòng
CAMEL	Customized applications for mobile network enhanced logic	GSM 的移动智能业务	GSM-de yídòng zhìnéng yèwù
CAMEL	Customized applications for mobile network enhanced logic	移动网络增强逻辑的客户化应用	Yídòng wǎngluò zēngqiáng luójide kèhùhuà yìngyòng
CAMP	Common access monitor program	通用存取监控程序	Tōngyòng cúnqǔ jiānkòng chéngxù
CAMR	Channel adapter mode register	通道适配器方式寄存器	Tōngdào shìpèiqì fāngshì jìcúnqì
CAMS	Communication area master station	通信区主控站	Tōngxìn qū zhǔkòngzhàn
CAN	Cellular network administrator	蜂窝网络管理器	Fēngwō wǎngluò guǎnlǐqì
CAN	Changing number acknowledge	改号通知	Gǎihào tōngzhī
CAO	Channel assignment order	通道分配命令	Tōngdào fēnpèi mìnglìng
CAO	Circuit activation order	线路启用命令	Xiànlù qǐyòng mìnglìng
CAO	Circuit allocation order	线路分配命令	Xiànlù fēnpèi mìnglìng
CAP	Cable access point	电缆接入点	Diànlǎn jiērù diǎn
CAP	Cable phone	电缆电话	Diànlǎn diànhuà
CAP	Call analysis program	呼叫分析程序	Hūjiào fēnxī chéngxù
CAP	Carrierless amplitude and phase modulation	无线波调幅与调相	Wúxiànbō tiáofú yǔ tiáoxiàng
CAP	Carrierless amplitude and phase modulation	无载波幅相调制	Wúzàibō fú xiāng tiáozhì
CAP	Carrierless amplitude/phase modulation	无载波调幅/调相	Wúzàibō tiáofú/tiáoxiàng
CAP	Channel access protocol	通道存取协议	Tōngdào cúnqǔ xiéyì
CAP	Channel access protocol	信道访问协议	Xìndào fǎngwèn xiéyì
CAP	Computer-aided planning	计算机辅助规划	Jìsuànjī fǔzhù guīhuà
CAP CAMEL	CAMEL application part	CAMEL 应用部分	CAMEL yìngyòng bùfen
CAP/DSDL	Concurrent algorithmic programming language/digital system design language	并行算法程序设计语言/数字系统设计语言	Bìngxíng suànfǎ chéngxù shèjì yǔyán/shùzì xìtǒng shèjì yǔyán
C-APDU	Command APDU	APDU 命令	APDU mìnglìng
CAPE	Communications automatic processing equipment	通信自动处理设备	Tōngxìn zìdòng chǔlǐ shèbèi
CAPEX	Capital expenses	投资成本	Tóuzī chéngběn
CAPP	Computer-aided process planning (CMM)	计算机辅助工艺过程设计	Jìsuànjī fǔzhù gōngyì guòchéng shèjì
CAPS	Call attempts per second	每秒试呼数	Měi miǎo shìhūshù
CAPS	Call attempts per second	每移试呼数	Měi yíshì hūshù
CAPS	Compact assembler programming system	紧致汇编程序程序设计系统	Jǐnzhì huìbiānchéngxù chéngxù shèjì xìtǒng
CAR	Card adapter register	卡片适配器寄存器	Kǎpiàn shìpèiqì jìcúnqì
CAR	Carry (mathematical term)	进位	Jìnwèi
CAR	Channel address register	通道地址寄存器	Tōngdào dìzhǐ jìcúnqì
CARP	Cache array routing protocol	缓存集群路由协议	Huǎncún jíqún lùyóu xiéyì
CARRS	Close-in automatic route-restoral system	闭合自动路由恢复系统	Bìhé zìdòng lùyóu huīfùxì tǒng

CAS	Channel associated signaling	随路信令	Suílù xìnlìng
CAS	Channel associated signaling	相联通道信号传输	Xiānglián tōngdào xìnhào chuánshū
CAS	Charging accounting sub-system	计费子系统	Jìfèi zìxìtǒng
CAS	Chinese Academy of Sciences	中国科学院	Zhōngguó Kēxuéyuàn
CAS	Coexistent addess solution	混合地址解决方案	Hùnhé dìzhǐ jiějué fāng'àn
CAS	Column address selection	列地址选定	Liè dìzhǐ xuǎndìng
CAS	Column address strobe	列地址控制器	Liè dìzhǐ kòngzhìqì
CAS	Conditional access system	条件接收系统	Tiáojiàn jiēshōu xìtǒng
CAS	Content addressable storage	按内容的寻址的存储器	Àn nèiróngde xúnzhǐde cúnchǔqì
CAS	Customer premises equipment (CPE) alerting signal	用户终端设备提示信号	Yònghù zhōngduān shèbèi tíshì xìnhào
CAS	Customer premises equipment alert signal	终端设备提示信号	Zhōngduān shèbèi tíshì xìnhào
CAS IOS	China Academy of Sciences, Institute of Software	中国科学院软件所	Zhōngguó Kēxuéyuàn ruǎnjiàn suǒ
CASE	Common access switching equipment	共用入口转接设备	Gòngyòng rùkǒu zhuǎnjiē shèbèi
CASE	Common application service	公共应用服务要素	Gōnggòng yìngyòng fúwù yàosù
CASE	Computer-aided software engineering	计算机辅助软件工程	Jìsuànjī fǔzhù ruǎnjiàn gōngchéng
CASSM	Context addressed segment sequential memory	按上下文编址的分段顺序存储器	Àn shàngxiàwén biānzhǐde fēnduàn shùnxù cúnchǔqì
CAT	Channel address translator	通道地址翻译器	Tōngdào dìzhǐ fānyìqì
CAT	Channel availability table	通道可用性表	Tōngdào kěyòngxìng biǎo
Cat-1	Category 1 cabling	第一类电缆	Dìyīlèi diànlǎn
Cat-2	Category 2 cabling	第二类电缆	Dì'èrlèi diànlǎn
Cat-3	Category 3 cabling	第三类电缆	Dìsānlèi diànlǎn
Cat-4	Category 4 cabling	第四类电缆	Dìsìlèi diànlǎn
CATA	Control and transmit assembly	控制和传输集成件	Kòngzhì hé chuánshū jíchéng jiàn
CATS	Common access telecommunications system	共用存取远程通信系统	Gòngyòng cúnqǔ yuǎnchéng tōngxìn xìtǒng
CATT	China Academy of Telecommunications Technology	电信科学技术研究院	Diànxìn kēxué jìshù yánjiūyuàn
CATV	Cable television	有线电视	Yǒuxiàn diànshì
CATV	Cable television	电缆电视	Diànlǎn diànshì
CATV	Community antenna television	共用天线电视	Gòngyòng tiānxiàn diànshì
CAU	Cell antenna unit	小区天线单元	Xiǎoqū tiānxiàn dānyuán
CAU	Control arithmetic unit	控制运算单元	Kòngzhì yùnsuàn dānyuán
CAU	Crypto auxiliary unit	加密辅助单元	Jiāmì fǔzhù dānyuán
CAVE	Cellular authentication and voice encryption	蜂窝鉴权及话音加密	Fēngwō jiànquán jí huàyīn jiāmì
CAW	Character address word	字符地址字	Zìfú dìzhǐ zì
CAW	Command address word	指令地址字	Zhǐlìng dìzhǐ zì
CAX	Community automatic exchange	共用自动交换机	Gòngyòng zìdòng jiāohuànjī
CB	Cell broadcast	小区广播	Xiǎoqū guǎngbō
CB	Check bit	较验位	Jiàoyàn wèi
CB	Citizens band	民用频带	Mínyòng píndài
CB	Code buffer	代码缓冲器	Dàimǎ huǎnchōngqì
CB	Common battery telephone	共电电话	Gòngdiàn diànhuà
CB	Communication bus	通信总线	Tōngxìn zǒngxiàn
CB	Communications buffer	通信缓冲器	Tōngxìn huǎnchōngqì
CB	Condition bit	条件位	Tiáojiàn wèi
CBA	Call back apparatus	应答装置	Yìngdá zhuāngzhì

CBA	Change back acknowledgement	返回正常信道应答	Fǎnhuí zhèngcháng xìndào yìngdá
CBBA	Common bus branch adapter	通用总线分支适配器	Tōngyòng zǒngxiàn fēnzhī shìpèiqì
CBC	Canadian Broadcasting Corp.	加拿大广播公司	Jiā-ná-dà Guǎngbō Gōngsī
CBC	Cell broadcast center	小区广播短消息中心	Xiǎoqū guǎngbō duǎn xiāoxi zhōngxīn
CBC	Cell broadcast center	小区广播中心	Xiǎoqū guǎngbō zhōngxīn
CBC	Cipher block chaining (IPsec)	密码块链	Mìmǎ kuài liàn
CBC	Connectionless bearer control	无连接承载控制	Wúliánjiē chéngzài kòngzhì
CBCH	Cell broadcast control channel	小区广播控制信道	Xiǎoqū guǎngbō kòngzhì xìndào
CBD	Change back declaration signal	返回正常通道说明信号	Fǎnhuí zhèngcháng tōngdào shuōmíng xìnhào
CBDS	Connectionless broadband data service	无连接宽带数据服务	Wúliánjiē kuāndài shùjù fúwù
CBDS	Connectionless broadband data service	无连接型宽带数据业务	Wúliánjiēxíng kuāndài shùjù yèwù
CBE	Cell broadcast entity	小区广播实体	Xiǎoqū guǎngbō shítǐ
CBF	Cable broadband forum	电缆宽带论坛	Diànlǎn kuāndài lùntán
CBG	Check bit generator	校验位发生器	Jiàoyàn wèi fāshēngqì
CBIR	Content-based image retrieval	基于内容的图像检索技术	Jīyú nèiróngde túxiàng jiǎnsuǒ jìshù
CBK	Clear back signal	后向挂机信号	Hòuxiàng guàjī xìnhào
CBK	Clear-back signal	拆除信号	Chāichú xìnhào
CBK	Clear-back signal	挂机信号	Guàjī xìnhào
CBM	Communications buffer memory	通信缓冲存储器	Tōngxìn huǎnchōng cúnchǔqì
CBMI	Cell broadcast message identifier	小区广播消息识别符	Xiǎoqū guǎngbō xiāoxi shíbiéfú
CBMS	Computer-based message system	计算机信息系统	Jìsuànjī xìnxī xìtǒng
CBP	Channel buffer pointer	通道缓冲器指针	Tōngdào huǎnchōngqì zhǐzhēn
CBQ	Cell bar qualify	小区禁止限制	Xiǎoqū jìnzhǐ xiànzhì
CBR	Case-based reasoning	案例推理	Ànlì tuīlǐ
CBR	Case-based reasoning	基于范例推理	Jīyú fànlì tuīlǐ
CBR	Committed burst rate	约定突发速率	Yuēdìng tūfā sùlǜ
CBR	Constant bit rate	固定比特率	Gùdìng bǐtèlǜ
CBR	Constant bit rate	恒定比特率	Héngdìng bǐtè lǜ
CBR	Constant bit rate service	恒定比特率业务	Héngdìng bǐtè lǜ yèwù
CBRA	Conditionality branch address	条件转移地址	Tiáojiàn zhuǎnyí dìzhǐ
CBS	Cell broadcast service	小区广播业务	Xiǎoqū guǎngbō yèwù
CBS	Channel buffer storage	通道缓冲存储器	Tōngdào huǎnchōng cúnchǔqì
CBS	Columbia Broadcasting Corp. (US)	哥伦比亚广播公司	Gē-lún-bǐ-yà guǎngbō gōngsī
CBS	Crossbar switch	纵横机	Zònghéng jī
CBSDT	Component-based software development technology	基于构件的软件开发技术	Jīyú gòujiànde ruǎnjiàn kāifā jìshù
CBSM	Cell broadcast short message	小区广播短消息	Xiǎoqū guǎngbō duǎn xiāoxi
CBSMS	Cell broadcast short message service	小区广播短消息业务	Xiǎoqū guǎngbō duǎnxiāoxi yèwù
CBSR	Candidate bootstrap router	候选自举路由器	Hòuxuǎn zìjǔ lùyóuqì
CBST	Character-byte serial transmission	字符-字节串行传输	Zìfú—zìjié chuànháng chuánshū
CBT	Channel buffer table	通道缓冲区表	Tōngdào huǎnchōngqū biǎo
CBT	Communication bus translator	通信总线转换器	Tōngxìn zǒngxiàn zhuǎnhuànqì
CBT	Computer-based training	电脑辅助培训	Diànnǎo fǔzhù péixùn
CBT	Computer-based training	基于计算机的训练	Jīyú jìsuànjīde xùnliàn
CBT	Core-based tree	核树	Hé shù
CBT	Core-based tree multicast routing protocol	有核树组播路由协议	Yǒuhéshù zǔbō lùyóu xiéyì

C-BTMA	Conservative busy tone multiple access	保护性忙音多路存取	Bǎohù-xìng mángyīn duōlù cúnqǔ
CBU	Coefficient of beam utilization	波束利用系数	Bōshù lìyòng xìshù
CBUF	Control block update facility	控制块更新设施	Kòngzhì kuài gēngxīn shèshī
CBX	Computerized branch exchange	计算机化交换分机	Jìsuànjīhuà jiāohuàn fēnjī
CC	Call control	呼叫控制	Hūjiào kòngzhì
CC	Coaxial cable	同轴电缆	Tóngzhóu diànlǎn
CC	Command center	指挥中心	Zhǐhuī zhōngxīn
CC	Concealed in ceiling	暗敷设在室面内	Àn fūshè zài shìmiàn-nèi
CC	Concealed in roof slab	暗敷设在顶板内	Àn fūshè zài dǐngbǎn-nèi
CC	Condition code	状态码	Zhuàngtài mǎ
CC	Connection confirm	连接证实	Liánjiē zhèngshí
CC	Connection controller	连接控制器	Liánjiē kòngzhìqì
CC	Connectivity check	连续性检测	Liánxùxìng jiǎncè
CC	Copper cable	铜线电缆	Tóngxiàn diànlǎn
CC	Country code	国家代码	Guójiā dàimǎ
CC	Country code	国家号码	Guójiā hàomǎ
CC	Country code	国家码	Guójiā mǎ
CC	Cross coupling	互耦	Hù'ou
CC	Cross coupling	交叉耦合	Jiāochā ǒuhé
CC	Cyber carrier	网络空间运营商	Wǎngluò kōngjiān yùnyíng shāng
CCAF	Call control access function	呼叫控制接入功能	Hūjiào kòngzhì jiērù gōngnéng
CCAF	Call control agent functioning	呼叫控制代理功能	Hūjiào kòngzhì dàilǐ gōngnéng
CCAMP	Common control and measurement plane	公共控制和测量平面	Gōnggòng kòngzhì hé cèliáng píngmiàn
CCB	Call control block	呼叫控制块	Hūjiào kòngzhì kuài
CCB	Cyclic check byte	循环校正字节	Xúnhuán jiàozhèng zìjié
CCBS	Call completed to busy subscriber	忙用户的呼叫完成	Máng yònghùde hūjiào wánchéng
CCBS	Completion of call busy subscriber	对遇忙用户完成呼叫	Duì yùmáng yònghù wánchéng hūjiào
CCBS	Completion of call to busy subscribers	对忙时用户的再呼叫	Duì mángshí yònghùde zài hūjiào
CCBS	Completion of calls to busy subscriber	完成到遇忙用户的呼叫	Wánchéng dào yùmáng yònghùde hūjiào
CCBS	Completion of calls to busy subscriber	遇忙回叫	Yù máng huíjiào
CCBS	Completion of calls to busy subscriber supplementary service	完成对状态忙用户的呼叫补充业务	Wánchéng duì zhuàngtài máng yònghùde hūjiào bǔchōng yèwù
CCBS	Completion of calls to busy subscribers	到忙用户的呼叫完成	Dào máng yònghùde hūjiào wánchéng
CCBS	Completion of calls to busy subscribers	遇忙呼叫完成	Yùmáng hujiào wánchéng
CCBS	Completion of calls to busy subscribers	至忙用户的呼叫的完成	Zhì máng yònghùde hūjiàode wánchéng
CCC	CCP call control	CCP 呼叫控制	CCP hūjiào kòngzhì
CCC	Clear command channel (in FTP)	清除命令信道	Qīngchú mìnglìng xìndào
CCC	Command control center	指挥控制中心	Zhǐhuī kòngzhì zhōngxīn
CCC	Communications control center	通信控制中心	Tōngxìn kòngzhì zhōngxīn
CCC	Customer care center	客户服务中心	Kèhù fúwù zhōngxīn
CCCG	Crystal-controlled clock generator	晶体控制时钟脉冲发生器	Jīngtǐ kòngzhì shízhōng màichōng fāshēngqì
CCCH	Common control channel	公共控制信道	Gōnggòng kòngzhì xìndào
CCD	Charge coupled device	电荷连接设备	Diànhè liánjiē shèbèi
CCD	Charge coupled device	电荷耦合器件	Diànhè ǒuhé qìjiàn
CCDOS	Chinese character DOS	汉字操作系统	Hànzì cāozuò xìtǒng
CCEA	CDMA channel element assembly	CDMA 信道元件	CDMA xìndào yuánjiàn

CCF	Call control function	呼叫控制功能	Hūjiào kòngzhì gōngnéng
CCF	Carbon coated fiber	碳涂层光纤	Tàntúcéng guāngxiān
CCF	Circular core fiber	圆芯光纤	Yuán xīn guāngxiān
CCF	Cluster control function	簇控制功能	Cù kòngzhì gōngnéng
CCF	Conditional call forwarding	条件呼叫前转	Tiáojiàn hūjiào qiánzhuǎn
CCF	Conditional call forwarding	条件呼叫转移	Tiáojiàn hūjiào zhuǎnyí
CCF	Continuity-failure signal	导通故障信号	Dǎotōng gùzhàng xìnhào
CCH	Control channel (ISDN usage)	控制信道	Kòngzhì xìndào
CCI	Circuit condition indicator	电路状态指示器	Diànlù zhuàngtài zhǐshìqì
CCI	Co-channel interference	同波道干扰	Tóngbōdào gānrǎo
CCI	Connection control interface	连接控制接口	Liánjiē kòngzhì jiēkǒu
CCI	Continuity-check incoming (signal)	连续性检验输入（信号）	Liánxù-xìng jiǎnyàn shūrù (xìnhào)
CCIR	Consultative Committee on International Radio (a division of ITU)	国际无线电咨询委员会	Guójì wúxiàndiàn zīxún wěiyuánhuì
CCIR	International Radio Consultative Committee	国际无线电咨询委员会	Guójì wúxiàndiàn zīxún wěiyuánhuì
CCIRN	Coordinating Committee for Intercontinental Research Networking	洲际研究网络协调委员会	Zhōujì yánjiū wǎngluò xiétiáo wěiyuánhuì
CCITT	International Telegraph and Telephone Consultative Committee	国际电报电话咨询委员会	Guójì diànbào diànhuà zīxún wěiyuánhuì
CCITT	International Telegraph and Telephone Consultative Committee	国际电话电报咨询委员会	Guójì diànhuà diànbào zīxún wěiyuánhuì
CCJ	Program controlled toll switch	程控长话交换	Chéngkòng chánghuà jiāohuàn
CCK	Coherent carrier keying	相干载波键控	Xiānggān zàibō jiànkòng
CCK	Corporate control key	共同的控制键	Gòngtóngde kòngzhì jiàn
CCL	Calling party clear signal	主叫用户挂机信号	Zhǔjiào yònghù guàjī xìnhào
CCM	Call center manager	呼叫中心管理	Hūjiào zhōngxīn guǎnlǐ
CCM	Call control manager	拨号控制管理	Bōhào kòngzhì guǎnlǐ
CCM	Certificate configuration message	检验机构消息	Jiǎnyàn jīgòu xiāoxi
CCM	Certificate configuration message	认证机构消息	Rènzhèng jīgòu xiāoxi
CCM	Channel card manager	信道卡管理器	Xìndào kǎ guǎnlǐqì
CCM	Circuit configuration monitor	电路配置监测器	Diànlù pèizhì jiāncèqì
CCM	Circuit supervision message	电路监视消息	Diànlù jiānshì xiāoxi
CCM	Common channel module	公共信道模块	Gōnggòng xìndào mókuài
CCM	Current call meter	通用的呼叫表	Tōngyòngde hūjiào biǎo
CCMS	Central control maintenance sub-system	中央控制维护子系统	Zhōngyāng kòngzhì wéihù zixìtǒng
CCMX	Conference call mix	会议电话呼叫混合	Huìyì diànhuà hūjiào hùnhé
CCNC	Common channel network controller	公共信道网络控制器	Gōnggòng xìndào wǎngluò kòngzhìqì
CCNR	Completion of calls on no reply	未应答的呼叫完成	Wèiyìngdáde hūjiào wánchéng
cc-NUMA	Cache-coherent non-uniform memory access	连贯缓冲非统一内存寻址	Liánguàn huǎnchōng fēi tǒngyī nèicún xúnzhǐ
CCP	Call confirmation protocol	呼叫确认协议	Hūjiào quèrèn xiéyì
CCP	Call control processor	呼叫控制处理器	Hūjiào kòngzhì chǔlǐqì
CCP	Callback control protocol	回叫控制协议	Huíjiào kòngzhì xiéyì
CCP	Capability/configuration parameter	能力配置参数	Nénglì pèizhì cānshù
CCP	Capability/configuration parameter	性能/结构参数	Xìngnéng/jiégòu cānshù
CCP	Compression control protocol	压缩控制协议	Yāsuō kòngzhì xiéyì
CCPA	Call control processor board assembly	呼叫控制处理集成板	Hūjiào kòngzhì chǔlǐ jíchéngbǎn
CCPA	Call control processor board assembly	呼叫控制处理器集成板	Hūjiào kòngzhì chǔlǐqì jíchéngbǎn
CCPC	City-level clearance and processing center	城市级清算和处理中心	Chéngshì jí qīngsuàn hé chǔlǐ zhōngxīn

CCPCH	Common control physical channel	公共控制物理信道	Gōnggòng kòngzhì wùlǐ xìndào
CCPCH	Common control physical channel	共用控制物理信道	Gòngyòng kòngzhì wùlǐ xìndào
CCPF	Classified minimum cost path first	分类的最小代价路径优先	Fēnlèide zuìxiǎo dàijià lùjìng yōuxiān
CCR	Continuity-check-request signal	请求导通检验信号	Qǐngqiú dǎotōng jiǎnyàn xìnhào
CCR	Current cell rate	当前信元速率	Dāngqián xìnyuán sùlǜ
CCS	Central control station	中心控制站	Zhōngxīn kòngzhì zhàn
CCS	Central control station	中心控制站	Zhōngxīn kòngzhì zhàn
CCS	Circuit supervision signal	电路监视信号	Diànlù jiānshì xìnhào
CCS	Common channel signaling	公共信道信令	Gōnggòng xìndào xìnlìng
CCS	Common command set	通用指令集	Tōngyòng zhǐlìng jí
CCS	Program controlled combined city/toll office	程控长市合一	Chéngkòng cháng shì héyī
CCSDS	Consultative Committee on Space Data Systems	空间数据系统咨询委宴会	Kōngjiān shùjù xìtǒng zīxún wěiyànhuì
CCSK	Cyclic code-shift keying	循环码移键控	Xúnhuán mǎyí jiànkòng
CCSN	Common channel signaling network	共路信令网	Gònglù xìnlìng wǎng
CCSP	Common channel signal protocol	公共通道信号协议	Gōnggòng tōngdào xìnhào xiéyì
CCSS	Call completion service setup	呼叫完成业务建立	Hūjiào wánchéng yèwù jiànlì
CCSS	Common channel signaling system	公共信道信号系统	Gōnggòng xìndào xìnhào xìtǒng
CCSS	Common channel signaling system	共路信令系统	Gònglù xìnlìng xìtǒng
CCT	Channel check test	通道检测	Tōngdào jiǎncè
CCT	Clock cycle time	时钟周期	Shízhōng zhōuqī
CCT	Computer compatible tape	计算机兼容磁带	Jìsuànjī jiānróng cídài
CCTrCH	Coded composite transport channel	编码合成传输信道	Biānmǎ héchéng chuánshū xìndào
CCTV	Closed circuit television	闭路电视	Bìlù diànshì
CCU	Channel coding unit	信道编解码单元	Xìndào biānjiěmǎ dānyuán
CCU	Communication control unit	通信控制单元	Tōngxìn kòngzhì dānyuán
CCU	Communication control unit	通信控制器	Tōngxìn kòngzhìqì
CCW	Channel command word	通道命令字	Tōngdào mìnglìng zì
CCW	Control command word	控制命令字	Kòngzhì mìnglìng zì
CD	Call deflection	呼叫改向	Hūjiào gǎixiàng
CD	Call deflection	呼叫转向	Hūjiào zhuǎnxiàng
CD	Campus distributor	建筑群配线架	Jiànzhùqún pèixiànjià
CD	Capacity deallocation	容量重新分配	Róngliàng chóngxīn fēnpèi
CD	Carrier detect	载波检测	Zàibō jiǎncè
CD	Carrier detector	载波检测器	Zàibō jiǎncèqì
CD	Carrier digits	运营商数字	Yùnyíngshāng shùzì
CD	Collision detection	碰撞检波	Pèngzhuàng jiǎnbō
CD	Compact disc	光碟	Guāngdié
CD	Compact disk	激光唱片	Jīguāngchàngpiàn
CD	Configuration daemon (in VPN)	配置精灵	Pèizhì jīnglíng
CD + G	Compact disk plus graphics	CD 盘加图形	CD pán jiā túxíng
CDA	Asynchronous data circuit	异步数据电路	Yìbù shùjù diànlù
CDA	Capacity deallocation acknowledgement	容量重新分配认可	Róngliàng chóngxīn fēnpèi rènkě
CDA	CCP data access	CCP 数据存取	CCP shùjù cúnqǔ
CDB	Centralized database	集中式数据库	Jízhōng-shì shùjùkù
CDB	Command data buffer	命令数据缓冲器	Mìnglìng shùjù huǎnchōngqì
CDB	Current data bit	现行数据位	Xiànxíng shùjù wèi

CDC	Call-directing character	定向呼叫字符	Dìngxiàng hūjiào zìfú
CDC	Call-directing character	定向调入字符	Dìngxiàng tiáorù zìfú
CDCA	Continuous dynamic channel assign	连续的动态信道分配	Liánxùde dòngtài xìndào fēnpèi
CDCS	CDMA digital channel sub-system	CDMA 数字信道子系统	CDMA shùzì xìndào zixìtǒng
CDDI	Copper distributed data interface	铜线分布式数据接口	Tóngxiàn fēnbù-shì shùjù jiēkǒu
CDES	Carbon dioxide extinguishing system	二氧化碳系统	Èryǎnghuàtàn xìtǒng
CDF	Carrier distribution frame	载波分配架	Zàibō fēnpèi jià
CDFS	Compact disk file system	光盘文件系统	Guāngpán wénjiàn xìtǒng
CDG	CDMA development group	CDMA 发展组织	CDMA fāzhǎn zǔzhī
CDG	CDMA Development Group (North America)	CDMA 发展集团	CDMA fāzhǎn jítuán
CDG	Control dependence graph	控制依赖图	Kòngzhì yīlài tú
CD-I	Compact disk interactive	交互式 CD 盘	Jiāohùshì CD pán
CD-I	Compact disk-interactive	互动式光碟	Hùdòngshì guāngdié
CDIA	CCP diagnostics	CCP 诊断	CCP zhěnduàn
CDIT	CEPT digital trunk interface	CEPT 数字中继接口	CEPT shùzì zhōngjì jiēkǒu
CDM	Channel division multiplexer	通道分组多路器	Tōngdào fēnzǔ duōlùqì
CDM	Code division multiplex	码分多路复用	Mǎfēn duōlù fùyòng
CDM	Code division multiplexing	码分复用	Mǎfēn fùyòng
CDM	Compressed delta modulation	压缩增量调制	Yāsuō zēngliàng tiáozhì
CDM	Configuration data manager	配置数据管理器	Pèizhì shùjù guǎnlǐqì
CDMA	Code division multiple access	码分多址	Mǎfēn duōzhǐ
CDMA	Code division multiple access	码分多址接入	Mǎfēn duōzhǐ jiērù
CDMA PCN	Code division multiple access personal communications network	码分多址个人通信网	Mǎfēn duōzhǐ gèrén tōngxìnwǎng
CDN	Content delivery network	内容分发网络	Nèiróng fēnfā wǎngluò
CDN	Content distribution network	内容分发网络	Nèiróng fēnfā wǎngluò
CDN	Coupling and decoupling networks	耦合/去耦合网络	Ǒuhé/qù'ǒuhé wǎngluò
CDP	Cisco discovery protocol	思科发现协议	Sī-kē fāxiàn xiéyì
CDP	Conditional dual phase coding	条件二相码	Tiáojiàn èr xiàng mǎ
CDPD	Cellular digital packet data	蜂窝数字分组数据	Fēngwō shùzì fēnzǔ shùjù
CDPD	Cellular digital packet data	数字蜂窝分组数据	Shùzì fēngwō fēnzǔ shùjù
CD-PLUS	Compact disk-PLUS	增强光盘	Zēngqiáng guāngpán
CDR	Call detail record	呼叫详细记录	Hūjiào xiángxì jìlù
CDR	Call detail record charging identifier	呼叫详细记录计费标识（话单）	Hūjiào xiángxì jìlù jìfèi biāozhì (huà dān)
CDR	Call detail recording	呼叫细节记录	Hūjiào xìjié jìlù
CDR	Call detail recording	通话明细记录	Tōnghuà míngxì jìlù
CDR	CD recordable	可记录光盘	Kějìlù guāngpán
CD-R	Compact disk recordable	可刻录光盘	Kěkèlù guāngpán
CD-R	Compact disk-recordable	可录写光碟	Kělùxiě guāngdié
CDROM	Compact disk read-only memory	密盘只读存储器	Mìpán zhǐ dú cúnchǔqì
CD-ROM	Compact disk read only memory	压缩光盘只读存储器	Yāsuō guāngpán zhǐ dú cúnchǔqì
CD-ROM	Compact disk read only memory	只读 CD 存储器	Zhǐ dú CD cúnchǔqì
CD-ROM	Compact disk read only memory	只读光盘存储器	Zhǐ dú guāngpán cúnchǔqì
CD-ROM	Compact disk-read only memory	唯读光碟	Wéidú guāngdié
CD-ROM	Compact disk-read only memory	影音光碟	Yǐngyīn guāngdié

CD-ROM/XA	Compact disk-read only memory eXtended architecture	唯读光盘增强形架构	Wéidú guāngpán zēngqiáng-xíng jiàgòu
CDRW	Compact disk-rewritable	可重复刻录光盘	Kěchóngfù kèlù guāngpán
CD-RW	Compact disk/read-write	光刻机	Guāngkèjī
CDS	Compatible duplex system	兼容的双工系统	Jiānróngde shuānggōng xìtǒng
CDS	Configuration data set	配置数据集	Pèizhì shùjùjí
CDS	Content delivery services	内容分发业务	Nèiróng fēnfā yèwù
CDS	Content delivery services	内容配送业务	Nèiróng pèisòng yèwù
CDS	Content distribution service	内容分发服务	Nèiróng fēnfā fúwù
CDS	Synchronous data circuit	同步数据电路	Tóngbù shùjù diànlù
CDSA	Common data security architecture	公共数据安全架构	Gōnggòng shùjù ānquán jiàgòu
CDSA	Common data security architecture	公用数据安全框架	Gōngyòng shùjù ānquán kuàngjià
CDSL	Consumer digital subscriber line	消费者数字订阅线路	Xiāofèizhě shùzì dìngyuè xiànlù
CDSS	Computerized digital switching system	计算机化数字交换系统	Jìsuànjīhuà shùzì jiāohuàn xìtǒng
CDTS	Command and data transmission system	指令与数据发射系统	Zhǐlìng yǔ shùjù fāshè xìtǒng
CDTSWG	China Digital Tetra Standards Working Group	中国数字集群标准工作小组	Zhōngguó shùzì jíqún biāozhǔn gōngzuò xiǎozǔ
CDTV	Commodore dynamic total vision	Commodore 公司的动态全视视盘	Commodore gōngsīde dòngtài quánshì shìpán
CDV	Cell delay variation	信元时延变化	Xìnyuán shíyán biànhuà
CDV	Cell delay variation	信元延迟变化	Xìnyuán yánchí biànhuà
CDVT	Cell delay variation tolerance	信元时延变化容限	Xìnyuán shíyán biànhuà róngxiàn
CDVT	Cell delay variation tolerance	信元延迟变化容限	Xìnyuán yánchí biànhuà róngxiàn
CE	Along ceiling (telecom installation)	沿天棚面敷设	Yán tiānpéngmiàn fūshè
CE	Channel element	信道元件	Xìndào yuánjiàn
CE	Concurrent engineering	并行工程	Bìngxíng gōngchéng
CE	Connection element	连接单元	Liánjiē dānyuán
CE	Control electronics	控制电路	Kòngzhì diànlù
CE	Control system	控制系统	Kòngzhì xìtǒng
CE	Customer edge	用户边缘	Yònghù biānyuán
CEA	Circular error average	平均循环误差	Píngjūn xúnhuán wùchā
CEA	Conventional evolutionary algorithm	传统进化类算法	Chuántǒng jìnhuà lèi suànfǎ
CEB	Command execution byte	命令执行字节	Mìnglìng zhíxíng zìjié
CEBB	Channel element back board	信道元件后面板	Xìndào yuánjiàn hòumian bǎn
CEBus	Consumer electronics bus	用户电子总线	Yònghù diànzǐ zǒngxiàn
CECM	Channel element control manager	信道元件控制管理器	Xìndào yuánjiàn kòngzhì guǎnlǐqì
CED	Called station identifier	被呼叫站标识符	Bèihūjiào zhàn biāoshífú
CEI	Connection endpoint identifier	连接端点标识符	Liánjiē duāndiǎn biāozhìfú
CEIEC	China Electronics Import and Export Corp.	中国电子技术进出口公司	Zhōngguó diànzǐ jìshù jìnchūkǒu gōngsī
CEIR	Central equipment identity register	中心设备识别寄存器	Zhōngxīn shèbèi shíbié jìcúnqì
CEIR	Central equipment identity register	中央设备识别寄存器	Zhōngyāng shèbèi shíbié jìcúnqì
CELP	Code excited linear prediction	代码激励线性预测	Dàimǎ jīlì xiànxìng yùcè
CELP	Code excited linear prediction	码激线性预测	M-jī xiànxìng yùcè
CELP	Code-excited linear prediction	码激励线性预测	Mǎjīlì xiànxìng yùcè
CEMA	Cellular message encryption algorithm	蜂窝信息加密算法	Fēngwō xìnxī jiāmì suànfǎ
CEMA	Communication Equipment Manufacturers Association	通信设备制造商协会	Tōngxìn shèbèi zhìzàoshāng xiéhuì
CEMA	Consumer Electronics Manufacturing Association	消费者电子制造业协会	Xiāofèizhě diànzǐ zhìzàoyè xiéhuì

CEMAC	Circuit emulation access card	电路模拟接入卡	Diànlù mónǐ jiērù kǎ
CEN	Commité Européenne de Normalisation, European Committee for Standardization	欧洲标准化委员会	Oūzhōu biāozhǔnhuà wěiyuánhuì
CEND	End of charge point	收费点的末端	Shōufèi diǎnde mòduān
CEO	Chief executive officer	首席执行官	Shǒuxí zhíxíng guān
CEOT	Circuit emulation over transport	传送电路仿真	Chuánsòng diànlù fǎngzhēn
CEP	Circular error probability	循环误差概率	Xúnhuán wùchā gàilǜ
CEP	Circular error probable	圆概率误差	Yuán gàilǜ wùchā
CEP	Connection end point	连接端点	Liánjiē duāndiǎn
CEP	Connection establishment error probability	连接建立错误概率	Liánjiē jiànlì cuòwù gàilǜ
CEP	Connection establishment protocol	建立联系协议	Jiànlì liánxì xiéyì
CEPT	Conference of European Post and Telecommunication Administrations	欧洲邮电行政大会	Oūzhōu yóudiàn xíngzhèng dàhuì
CEPT	Conference of European Post and Telecommunication Administrations	欧洲邮政和电信行政会议	Oūzhōu yóuzhèng hé diànxìn xíngzhèng huìyì
CEPT	Conference of European Posts and Telecommunications	欧洲邮政和通信会议	Oūzhōu yóuzhèng hé tōngxìn huìyì
CEPT	Conference of European Posts and Telecommunications Administrations	欧洲邮电行政会议	Oūzhōu yóudiàn xíngzhèng huìyì
CEQ	Customer equipment	用户设备	Yònghù shèbèi
CER	Cell error rate	误信元率	Wùxìnyuán lǜ
CER	Cell error rate	信元差错率	Xìnyuán chācuò lǜ
CER	Cell error rate	信元错误率	Xìnyuán cuòwù lǜ
CERCO	European Committee of Representatives of Official Cartography	欧洲官方地图学代表委员会	Oūzhōu guānfāng dìtúxué dàibiǎo wěiyuánhuì
CERFnet	California Education and Research Federation Network	加州教育与研究协会网	Jiāzhōu jiàoyù yǔ yánjiū xiéhuì wǎng
CERN	European Particle Physics Laboratory	欧洲量子物理试验室	Oūzhōu liàngzǐ wùlǐ shìyànshì
CERnet	China Education and Research Network	中国教育和科研网	Zhōngguó jiàoyù hé kēyán wǎng
CERT	Character error rate test	字符出错误率测试	Zìfú chū cuòwùlǜ cèshì
CERT	Character error rate tester	字符出错误率测试器	Zìfú chū cuòwùlǜ cèshìqì
CERT	Computer emergency response team	计算机应急响应小组	Jìsuànjī yìngjí xiǎngyìng xiǎozǔ
CES	Circuit emulation service	电路仿真业务	Diànlù fǎngzhēn yèwù
CES	Consumer electronics show	民用设备展览会	Mínyòng shèbèi zhǎnlǎnhuì
CEUR	Channel element unit rack	信道元件单元机架	Xìndào yuánjiàn dānyuán jījià
CF	All call forwarding services	全呼叫前转业务	Quán hūjiào qiánzhuǎn yèwù
CF	All call forwarding services	所有的呼叫前转业务	Suǒyǒude hūjiào qiánzhuǎn yèwù
CF	Call forwarding	呼叫前向转移	Hūjiào qiánxiàng zhuǎnyí
CF	Call forwarding	呼叫转送	Hūjiào zhuǎnsòng
CF	Central frequency	中心频率	Zhōngxīn pínlǜ
CF	Connection fragment	连接段	Liánjiē duàn
CF	Conversion facility	转换功能	Zhuǎnhuàn gōngnéng
CF	Conversion facility	转换设备	Zhuǎnhuàn shèbèi
CF	Core function	核心功能	Héxīn gōngnéng
CFAR	Constant false alarm receiver	恒虚警接收机	Héng xūjǐng jiēshōujī
CFB	Call forward on busy	遇忙呼叫前转	Yùmáng hujiào qiánzhuǎn
CFB	Call forwarding busy	遇忙呼叫前转	Yù máng hujiào qiánzhuǎn
CFB	Call forwarding busy	遇忙呼叫转发	Yùmáng hujiào zhuǎnfā
CFB	Call forwarding busy	遇忙呼叫转送	Yùmáng hujiào zhuǎnsòng
CFB	Call forwarding on busy	遇忙前转	Yùmáng qiánzhuǎn

CFB	Call forwarding on mobile subscriber busy	当移动用户忙时呼叫转发	Dāng yídòng yònghù mángshí hūjiào zhuǎnfā
CFB	Call forwarding on mobile subscriber busy	移动用户忙呼叫前转	Yídòng yònghù máng hujiào qiánzhuǎn
CFB	Call forwarding on mobile subscriber busy	遇移动用户忙呼叫前向转移	Yù yídòng yònghù máng hujiào qiánxiàng zhuǎnyí
CFB	Call forwarding on mobile subscriber busy	遇移动用户忙呼叫前转	Yù yídòng yònghù máng hujiào qiánzhuǎn
CFB	Call forwarding on subscriber busy	当用户忙时呼叫转发	Dāng yònghù mángshí hūjiào zhuǎnfā
CFB	Cipher feedback	密文反馈	Mìwén fǎnkuì
CFC	Call forwarding conditional	有条件前向转移	Yǒu tiáojiàn qiánxiàng zhuǎnyí
CFC	Channel flow control	通道信息流控制	Tōngdào xìnxī liú kòngzhì
CFCA	China Financial Certification Authority	中国金融认证中心	Zhōngguó jīnróng rènzhèng zhōngxīn
CFCB	Communications file control block	通信文件控制块	Tōngxìn wénjiàn kòngzhì kuài
CFD	Computational fluid dynamics	计算流体力学	Jìsuàn liútǐ lìxué
CFG	Control flow graph	控制流图	Kòngzhì liú tú
CFI	Canonical format indicator	经典格式指示符	Jīngdiǎn géshi zhǐshìfú
CFL	Cable fault locator	电缆故障探测器	Diànlǎn gùzhàng tàncèqì
CFL	Call failure signal	呼叫故障信号	Hūjiào gùzhàng xìnhào
CFL	Call-failure loop	呼叫故障循环	Hūjiào gùzhàng xúnhuán
CFM	CCP fault manager	CCP 故障管理	CCP gùzhàng guǎnlǐ
CFM	Companded frequency modulation	压扩调频繁	Yākuò tiáopín fán
CFM	Companding and frequency modulation	压伸与调频	Yāshēn yǔ tiáopín
CFMA	Collision-free multiple access	无冲突多路存取	Wúchōngtū duōlù cúnqǔ
CFMA	Collision-free multiple access	无碰头多路存取	Wúpèngtóu duōlù cúnqǔ
CFN	Connection frame number	接续帧号	Jiēxù zhènghào
CFN	Connection frame number	连接帧号	Liánjiē zhènghào
CFNR	Call forwarding on no reply	无应答呼叫前转	Wúyìngdá hūjiào qiánzhuǎn
CFNR	Call forwarding on no reply	无应答呼叫转发	Wúyìngdá hūjiào zhuǎnfā
CFNR	Call forwarding on no reply	无应答呼叫转送	Wúyìngdá hūjiào zhuǎnsòng
CFNRA	Call forwarding on not reachable	呼叫不可及前转	Hūjiào bùkě jí qiánzhuǎn
CFNRc	Call forwarding not reachable	不可及呼叫前转	Bùkějí hūjiào qiánzhuǎn
CFNRc	Call forwarding on mobile subscriber not reachable	对找不到移动用户的呼叫转移	Duì zhǎobudào yídòng yònghùde hūjiào zhuǎnyí
CFNRc	Call forwarding on mobile subscriber not reachable	在移动用户不可达到时转发	Zài yídòng yònghù bùkě dádào shí zhuǎnfā
CFNRc	Call forwarding on mobile subscriber not reachable supplementary service	不可及呼叫前转补充业务	Bùkě jí hūjiào qiánzhuǎn bǔchōng yèwù
CFNRc	Call forwarding on mobile subscriber not reachable supplementary service	当移动用户不可及前转补充业务	Dāng yídòng yònghù bùkějí qiánzhuǎn bǔchōng yèwù
CFNRk	Call forwarding on mobile subscriber not reachable	移动用户不可及呼叫前转	Yídòng yònghù bùkějí hūjiào qiánzhuǎn
CFNRP	Call forwarding on no reply	无应答前转	Wúyìngdá qiánzhuǎn
CFNRy	Call forwarding on no reply	在无回答时呼叫转发	Zài wúhuídá shí hūjiào zhuǎnfā
CFNRy	Call forwarding on no reply supplementary service	补充业务无应答呼叫前转	Bǔchōng yèwù wú yìngdá hūjiào qián zhuǎn
CFNRy, CFNREP	Call forwarding on no reply	无应答呼叫前向转移	Wúyìngdá hūjiào qiánxiàng zhuǎnyí
CFO	Chief financial officer	首席财务官	Shǒuxí cáiwù guān
CFP	Connection establishment failure probability	连接建立失败概率	Liánjiē jiànlì shībài gàilǜ
CFP	Cordless fixed part (telephone)	无绳座机	Wúshéng zuòjī
CFT	Carrier frequency telephony	载波电话	Zàibō diànhuà
CFT	Conference trunk	会议电话总线	Huìyì diànhuà zǒngxiàn
CFT	Continuous Fourier transform	连续傅里叶变换	Liánxù fùlǐyè biànhuàn

CFU	Call forward unconditionally	无条件呼叫前转	Wútiáojiàn hūjiào qián zhuǎn
CFU	Call forwarding on no reply supplementary service	无应答前转补充业务	Wúyìngdá qiánzhuǎn bǔchōng yèwù
CFU	Call forwarding unconditional	无条件呼叫前向转移	Wútiáojiàn hūjiào qiánxiàng zhuǎnyí
CFU	Call forwarding unconditional	无条件呼叫前转	Wútiáojiàn hūjiào qiánzhuǎn
CFU	Call forwarding unconditional	无条件呼叫转发	Wútiáojiàn hūjiào zhuǎnfā
CFU	Call forwarding unconditional	无条件呼叫转送	Wútiáojiàn hūjiào zhuǎnsòng
CFU	Call forwarding unconditional	无条件前转	Wútiáojiàn qiánzhuǎn
CFU	Call forwarding unconditional supplementary service	无条件呼叫前转补充业务	Wútiáojiàn hūjiào qiánzhuǎn bǔchōng yèwù
CG	Cathode grid	阴极栅	Yīnjí zhà
CG	Channel grant	通道许可	Tōngdào xǔkě
CG	Charging gateway	计费网关	Jìfèi wǎngguān
CG	Clock generator	时钟发生器	Shízhōng fāshēngqì
CGA	Color graphic adapter	彩色图像监控器	Cǎisè túxiàng jiānkòngqì
CGA	Color graphic adapter	彩色图形适配器	Cǎisè túxíng shìpèiqì
CGB	Circuit group blocking request (ISUP message)	电路群闭塞请求	Diànlù qún bìsè qǐngqiú
CGBA	Circuit group blocking acknowledgement (ISUP message)	电路群闭塞认可	Diànlù qún bìsè rènkě
CGC	Circuit group congestion signal	电路群拥塞信号	Diànlù qún yōngsè xìnhào
CGEM	Computable general equilibrium model	一般可计算均衡模型	Yībān kějìsuàn jūnhéng móxíng
CGF	Charging gateway function	计费网关功能	Jìfèi wǎngguān gōngnéng
CGF	Charging gateway functionality	计费网关功能性	Jìfèi wǎngguān gōngnéngxìng
CGG	Computer generated graphics	计算机生成图像	Jìsuànjī shēngchéng túxiàng
CGI	Cell global identification	全球小区识别	Quánqiú xiǎoqū shíbié
CGI	Cell global identification	小区全球识别	Xiǎoqū quánqiú shíbié
CGI	Common gateway interface	公共网关接口	Gōnggòng wǎngguān jiēkǒu
CGI	Common gateway interface	共用网关接口	Gòngyòng wǎngguān jiēkǒu
CGI	Common gateway interface	通用网关接口	Tōngyòng wǎngguān jiēkǒu
CGIS	Canadian Geography Information System	加拿大地理信息系统	Jiā-ná-dà dìlǐ xìnxī xìtǒng
CGM	Computer graphics metafile	计算机图形元文件	Jìsuànjī túxíng yuán wénjiàn
CGM	Conjugate graduation method	共轭梯度法	Gòng'è tīdù fǎ
CGM	Cross-gain modulation	交叉增益调制	Jiāochā zēngyì tiáozhì
CGMP	Cisco group management protocol	思科组管理协议	Sī-kē zǔ guǎnlǐ xiéyì
CGSA	Cellular geographic service area	蜂窝地理服务区	Fēngwō dìlǐ fúwùqū
CGU	Circuit group unblocking request (ISUP message)	解除电路群闭塞请求	Jiěchú diànlùqún bìsè qǐngqiú
CGUA	Circuit group unblocking acknowledgement (ISUP message)	解除电路群闭塞认可	Jiěchú diànlùqún bìsè rènkě
CH	Common HINA	公共 HINA	Gōnggòng HINA
CHAP	Challenge handshake authentication protocol	质询握手验证协议	Zhìxún wòshǒu yànzhèng xiéyì
CHAP	Challenge handshake authentication protocol (IPsec)	挑战握手认证协议	Tiǎozhàn wòshǒu rènzhèng xiéyì
CHAP	Challenge-handshake authentication protocol	盘问握手认证协议	Pánwèn wòshǒu rènzhèng xiéyì
CHAP	Challenge-handshake authentication protocol	握手认证协议	Wòshǒu rènzhèng xiéyì
CHD	Channel decoder	信道解码器	Xìndào jiěmǎqì
CHE	Channel encoder	信道编码器	Xìndào biānmǎqì
CHEC	Channel evaluation and call	通道坚定和呼叫	Tōngdào jiāndìng hé hūjiào
CHESS	Correlated hopping enhanced spread spectrum	增强型相关跳频扩频	Zēngqiáng-xíng xiāngguān tiàopín kuòpín
CHG	Charging message	计费消息	Jìfèi xiāoxi

CHILL	International Telegraph and Telephone Consultative Committee's high-level language	国际电话电报咨询委员会高级语言	Guójì diànhuà diànbào zīxún wěiyuánhuì gāojí yǔyán
ChinaDDN	China Digital Data Network	中国公用数字数据网	Zhōngguó gōngyòng shùzì shùjù wǎng
ChinaGBN	China Golden Bridge Network	中国金桥信息网络	Zhōngguó jīnqiáo xìnxī wǎngluò
ChinaPAC	China Packet Switched Data Network	中国公用分组交换数据网	Zhōngguó gōngyòng fēnzǔ jiāohuàn shùjù wǎng
CHIPS	Chinese information processing system	汉字信息处理系统	Hànzì xìnxī chǔlǐ xìtǒng
CHIPS	Chinese Information Processing system	中文信息处理系统	Zhōngwén xìnxī chǔlǐ xìtǒng
Chirp	Chirp	啁啾	Zhōujiū
CHP	Charging point	收费点	Shōufèi diǎn
CHR	Manual toll switch	人工长话交换	Réngōng chánghuà jiāohuàn
CHRP	Common hardware reference platform	共用硬件参考平台	Gòngyòng yìngjiàn cānkǎo píngtái
CHS	Cylinder/head/sector (of a computer hard disk)	柱面 / 磁头 / 扇区	Zhùmiàn/cítóu/shàn qū
CHV	Card holder verification	持卡人校验信息	Chíkǎrén jiàoyàn xìnxī
CHV	Card holder verification information	卡支持器检验信息	Kǎ zhīchíqì jiǎnyàn xìnxī
CHZ	Automatic toll switch	自动长话交换	Zìdòng chánghuà jiāohuàn
CI	Cell identity	小区标识号	Xiǎoqū biāozhì hào
CI	Cell identity	小区识别	Xiǎoqū shíbié
CI	Characteristic information	标识信息	Biāozhì xìnxī
CI	Characteristic information	特征信息	Tèzhēng xìnxī
CI	Circuit interrupter	电路中断器	Diànlù zhōngduànqì
CI	Command identifier	命令标识符	Mìnglìng biāozhìfú
CI	Command interpreter	命令解释程序	Mìnglìng jiěshì chéngxù
CI	Congestion indication	拥塞指示	Yōngsè zhǐshì
CIB	Command input buffer	命令输入缓冲器	Mìnglìng shūrù huǎnchōngqì
CIB	Console interface board	控制台接口板	Kòngzhìtái jiēkǒu bǎn
CIBP	Control interworking back panel	控制互通后面板	Kòngzhì hùtōng hòumian bǎn
CIC	Call instance code	呼叫实例码	Hūjiào shílì mǎ
CIC	Carrier identification code	承载者标识码	Chéngzàizhě biāozhì mǎ
CIC	Carrier identification code	营商标识码	Yíngshāng biāoshí mǎ
CIC	Carrier identification code	运营商标识码	Yùnyíngshāng biāoshí mǎ
CIC	Carrier interface controller	载频接口控制器	Zàipín jiēkǒu kòngzhìqì
CIC	Channel card interface controller	信道卡接口控制器	Xìndào kǎ jiēkǒu kòngzhìqì
CIC	China Institute of Communications	中国通信学会	Zhōngguó tōngxìn xuéhuì
CIC	Circuit identification code	电路识别码	Diànlù shíbié mǎ
CIC	Coded interrupt cause	代码化中断原因	Dàimǎhuà zhōngduàn yuányīn
CICA	Center for Innovative Computer Application	计算机应用开发中心	Jìsuànjī yìngyòng kāifā zhōngxīn
CICC	Center of International Cooperation for Computerization (Japan)	计算机化国际合作中心	Jìsuànjīhuà guójì hézuò zhōngxīn
CICS	Customer information control system	用户信息控制系统	Yònghù xìnxī kòngzhì xìtǒng
CID	Call identification display	主叫识别信息显示	Zhǔjiào shíbié xìnxī xiǎnshì
CID	Caller identification	主叫识别	Zhǔjiào shíbié
CID	Caller identity delivery	主叫识别信息传送	Zhǔjiào shíbié xìnxī chuánsòng
CID	Connection identifier	连接标识符	Liánjiē biāozhì fú
CID	Consecutive identical digit	连续相同数字	Liánxù xiāngtóng shùzì
CID	Consecutive identical digits	连接相同数字	Liánjiē xiāngtóng shùzì
CID	Consecutive identical digits	连续恒等数字	Liánxù héngděng shùzì

CIDF	Common intrusion detection framework	通用入侵检测框架	Tōngyòng rùqīn jiǎncè kuàngjià
CIDR	Classless inter-domain routing	无类域间路由选择	Wúlèi yùjiān lùyóu xuǎnzé
CIDR	Classless inter-domain routing	无类别域际路由选择	Wúlèibié yùjì lùyóu xuǎnzé
CIDR	Classless inter-domain routing	无类别域间选路	Wúlèibié yù-jiān xuǎnlù
CIEA	Commercial Internet Exchange Association	商业因特网交易协会	Shāngyè Yīntèwǎng jiāoyì xiéhuì
CIF	Common intermediate format	公共中介格式	Gōnggòng zhōngjiè géshi
CIF	Cost, insurance and freight	成本保险加运费付至	Chéngběn bǎoxiǎn jiā yùnfèi fù zhì
CIF	Cost, insurance and freight	成本加运保费	Chéngběn jiā yùnbǎo fèi
CIFS	Common Internet file system	通用 Internet 文件系统	Tōngyòng Internet wénjiàn xìtǒng
CIG	Canadian Institute of Geomatics	加拿大测量工程研究所	Jiā-ná-dà cèliáng gōngchéng yánjiūsuǒ
CIITA	China Information Industry Trade Association	中国信息产业商会	Zhōngguó xìnxī chǎnyè shānghuì
CIL	Common intermediate language	通用中间语言	Tōngyòng zhōngjiān yǔyán
CIL	Common intermediate language	通用中介语言	Tōngyòng zhōngjiè yǔyán
CIL	Component interconnection language	部件互连语言	Bùjiàn hùlián yǔyán
CIM	Common information model	公共信息模型	Gōnggòng xìnxī móxíng
CIM	Common information model	通用信息模型	Tōngyòng xìnxī móxíng
CIME	Customer installation maintenance entities	用户安装维护实体	Yònghù ānzhuāng wéihù shítǐ
CIMS	Computer integrated manufacturing system	计算机集成制造系统	Jìsuànjī jíchéng zhìzào xìtǒng
CIN	Communication interconnection network	通信互联网	Tōngxìn hùliánwǎng
CINI	Control interworking node interface	控制互通节点接口	Kòngzhì hùtōng jiédiǎn jiēkǒu
CINM	Control interworking node manager	控制互通节点管理器	Kòngzhì hùtōng jiédiǎn guǎnlǐqì
CIO	Chief information officer	首席信息官	Shǒuxí xìnxī guān
CIO	Circular input-output routine	循环输入输出程序	Xúnhuán shūrù shūchū chéngxù
CIOM	Communications input/output multiplexer	通信输入/输出多路复用期	Tōngxìn shūrù/shūchū duōlù fùyòngqī
CIOP	Combined input/output queuing	结合输入，输出排队	Jiéhé shūrù, shūchū páiduì
CIOQ	Combined input/output queuing	输入输出结合排队	Shūrù shūchū jiéhé páiduì
CIP	Call information processing	调用信息处理	Diàoyòng xìnxī chǔlǐ
CIP	Call information processing	呼叫信息处理	Hūjiào xìnxī chǔlǐ
CIP	Carriage and insurance paid	运费、保险费付至	Yùnfèi、bǎoxiǎnfèi fù zhì
CIP	Channel interface processor	信道接口处理器	Xìndào jiēkǒu chǔlǐqì
CIP	Communications interrupt program	通信中断程序	Tōngxìn zhōngduàn chéngxù
CIPOA	Common internet protocol (IP) over asynchronous transfer mode (ATM)	ATM 上支持传统 IP 及地址解析协议	ATM-shàng zhīchí chuántǒng IP-jí dìzhǐ jiěxī xiéyì
CIR	Carrier to interference ratio	载干比	Zài gān bǐ
CIR	Carrier to interference ratio	载波干扰比	Zàibō gānrǎo bǐ
CIR	Committed information rate	承诺信息速率	Chéngnuò xìnxī sùlǜ
CIR	Committed information rate	约定信息率	Yuēdìng xìnxī lǜ
CIR	Committed information rate	约定信息速率	Yuēdìng xìnxī sùlǜ
CIRC	Cross-interleave Reed-Solomon code	交叉交织里德-所罗门编码	Jiāochā jiāozhī Lǐdé-Suǒluómén biānmǎ
CIRT	Computer incident response team	计算机事件响应小组	Jìsuànjī shìjiàn xiǎngyìng xiǎozǔ
CIS	Call information system	呼叫信息系统	Hūjiào xìnxī xìtǒng
CIS	Communication interconnection sub-system	通信互联子系统	Tōngxìn hùlián zixìtǒng
CISC	Complex instruction set computer	复杂指令集计算机	Fùzá zhǐlìng jí jìsuànjī
CISC	Complex instruction set computer	复杂指令系统计算机	Fùzá zhǐlìng xìtǒng jìsuànjī
CISC	Complex instruction set computing	复杂指令集计算	Fùzá zhǐlìng jí jìsuàn
CISL	Common intrusion specification language	通用入侵规范语言	Tōngyòng rùqīn guīfàn yǔyán

CISPR	International Electromagnetic Interference Commission	国际电磁干扰委员会	Guójì diàncí gānrǎo wěiyuánhuì
CISPR	International Special Committee on Radio Interference	国际无线电干扰专门委员会	Guójì wúxiàndiàn gānrǎo zhuānmén wěiyuánhuì
CISR	Communication interconnection sub-system rack	通信互联子系统机架	Tōngxìn hùlián zixìtǒng jījià
CIU	Cable interface unit	电缆接口组件	Diànlǎn jiēkǒu zǔjiàn
CIX	Commercial Internet exchange	商业因特网交换中心	Shāngyè Yīntèwǎng jiāohuàn zhōngxīn
CIX	Commercial Internet exchange	商用因特网交换中心	Shāngyòng Yīntèwǎng jiāohuàn zhōngxīn
CK	Check (in SS7)	标验码	Biāoyàn mǎ
CK	Check bit	检查比特	Jiǎnchá bǐtè
CK	Check bit	校验比特	Jiàoyàn bǐtè
CK	Clock signal (timing information)	时钟信号	Shízhōng xìnhào
CKD	Clock device	时钟设备	Shízhōng shèbèi
CKSN	Cipher key sequence/number	加密键序列数/号	Jiāmì jiàn xùliè shù/hào
CKSN	Ciphering key sequence number	密码本序列号	Mìmǎ běn xùlièhào
CKSN	Ciphering key sequence number	密码索引序列号	Mìmǎ suǒyǐn xùlièhào
CL	Certificate library	证书库	Zhèngshū kù
CL	Connectionless	无连接	Wúliánjiē
CLAS	Communication link analysis system	通信链路分析系统	Tōngxìn liànlù fēnxī xìtǒng
CLAW	Common link access for workstations	工作站的通用连接访问	Gōngzuòzhànde tōngyòng liánjiē fǎngwèn
CLB	Configurable logic block	可配置逻辑模块	Kěpèizhì luóji mókuài
CLB	County level branch (of the financial network)	县级处理中心	Xiànjí chǔlǐ zhōngxīn
CLC	Close logical channel	关闭逻辑通道	Guānbì luóji tōngdào
CLC	Communication linkage controller	通信连接控制器	Tōngxìn liánjiē kòngzhìqì
CLC	Concealed in column	暗敷设在珠内	Àn fūshè zài zhū-nèi
CLCA	Close logical channel acknowledge	关闭逻辑通道确认	Guānbì luóji tōngdào quèrèn
CLCR	Close logical channel reject	关闭逻辑通道拒绝	Guānbì luóji tōngdào jùjué
CLDA	Connectionless data acknowledged (SS7 message)	无连接数据确认	Wúliánjiē shùjù quèrèn
CLDT	Connectionless data transfer (SS7 message)	无连接数据传送	Wúliánjiē shùjù chuánsòng
CLEOS	Conference on laser electro-optical systems	激光器与光电系统会议	Jīguāngqì yǔ guāngdiàn xìtǒng huìyì
CLF	Clear forward	前向拆线	Qiánxiàng chāixiàn
CLF	Clear forward signal	前向拆线信号	Qiánxiàng chāixiàn xìnhào
CLF	Clear-forward signal	拆线信号	Chāixiàn xìnhào
CLF	Common log format	公共日志格式	Gōnggòng rìzhì géshi
CLFM	Coherent linear frequency modulation	相干线性调频	Xiānggān xiànxìng tiáopín
CLI	Called line identity	被叫线路标识	Bèijiào xiànlù biāozhì
CLI	Calling line identification	主叫线路识别	Zhǔjiào xiànlù shíbié
CLI	Calling line identity	呼叫消息（线）识别	Hūjiào xiāoxi (xiàn) shíbié
CLI	Calling line identity	主叫识别	Zhǔjiào shíbié
CLI	Call-level interface	调用级接口	Diàoyòng jí jiēkǒu
CLI	Command line interface	命令行界面	Mìnglìng háng jièmiàn
CLI	Common language infrastructure	通用语言基础设施	Tōngyòng yǔyán jīchǔ shèshī
CLIP	Calling line identification presentation	呼叫线标识显示	Hūjiào xiàn biāozhì xiǎnshì
CLIP	Calling line identification presentation	呼叫消息（线）识别显示	Hūjiào xiāoxi (xiàn) shíbié xiǎnshì
CLIP	Calling line identification presentation	主叫号码通知	Zhǔjiào hàomǎ tōngzhī
CLIP	Calling line identification presentation	主叫线路识别显示	Zhǔjiào xiànlù shíbié xiǎnshì
CLIP	Calling line identification presentation	主叫线识别	Zhǔjiàoxiàn shíbié

CLIP	Calling line identification presentation	主叫线识别提供	Zhǔjiàoxiàn shíbié tígōng
CLIP	Calling line identification presentation	主叫线识别显示	Zhǔjiàoxiàn shíbié xiǎnshì
CLIP	Calling line identification presentation supplementary service	主叫识别提供补充业务	Zhǔjiào shíbié tígōng bǔchōng yèwù
CLIR	Calling line identification restriction	呼叫线标识限制	Hūjiào xiàn biāozhì xiànzhì
CLIR	Calling line identification restriction	呼叫消息（线）识别限制	Hūjiào xiāoxi (xiàn) shíbié xiànzhì
CLIR	Calling line identification restriction	主叫号码识别限制	Zhǔjiào hàomǎ shíbié xiànzhì
CLIR	Calling line identification restriction	主叫线路识别限制	Zhǔjiào xiànlù shíbié xiànzhì
CLIR	Calling line identification restriction	主叫线识别限制	Zhǔjiàoxiàn shíbié xiànzhì
CLIR	Calling line identification restriction supplementary service	主叫识别限制补充业务	Zhǔjiào shíbié xiànzhì bǔchōng yèwù
CLLM	Consolidated link layer management	加强的链路层管理	Jiāqiángde liànlùcéng guǎnlǐ
CLLM	Consolidated link layer management	综合链路层管理	Zōnghé liànlù céng guǎnlǐ
CLMA	Component library management agent (in Java)	构件库管理代理	Gòujiàn kù guǎnlǐ dàilǐ
CLNP	Connectionless network layer protocol	无连接的网络层协议	Wúliánjiēde wǎngluò céng xiéyì
CLNP	Connectionless network protocol	无连接模式网络层协议	Wúliánjiē móshì wǎngluò céng xiéyì
CLNP	Connectionless network protocol	无连接网络协议	Wúliánjiē wǎngluò xiéyì
CLNS	Connectionless network layer service	无连接的网络层服务	Wúliánjiēde wǎngluò céng fúwù
CLNS	Connectionless network service	五连接网络服务	Wǔliánjiē wǎngluò fúwù
CLOAX	Corrugated laminated coaxial	多层皱纹金属带被覆同轴对	Duōcéng zhòuwén jīnshǔdài bèifù tóngzhóu duì
CLP	Cell loss priority	信元标明丢失优先度	Xìnyuán biāomíng diūshī yōuxiān dù
CLP	Cell loss priority	信元丢弃优先级	Xìnyuán diūqì yōuxiān jí
CLP	Cell loss priority	信元丢失优先	Xìnyuán diūshī yōuxiān
CLP	Cell loss priority	信元丢失优先级	Xìnyuán diūshī yōuxiān jí
CLP	Cell loss priority	信元丢失优先权	Xìnyuán diūshī yōuxiānquán
CLP	Command line processor	命令行处理器	Mìnglìng háng chǔlǐqì
CLR	Cell loss rate	信元丢失率	Xìnyuán diūshī lǜ
CLR	Clear point	清除点	Qīngchú diǎn
CLR0	Cell loss rate (CLR) for high priority cells (only those with CLP=0)	CLP 为 0 信元的信元丢失率	CLP wéi 0 xìnyuánde xìnyuán diūshī lǜ
CLR0+1	Cell loss rate (CLR) for the aggregate cell stream containing both cell loss priority (CLP)=0 and CLP=1 cells	CLP 为 0 和 1 的总的信元丢失率	CLP wéi 0 hé 1de zǒngde xìnyuán diūshī lǜ
CLS	Common language specification	通用语言规范	Tōngyòng yǔyán guīfàn
CLS	Connectionless server	无连接服务器	Wúliánjiē fúwùqì
CLS	Controlled load service	受控负载业务	Shòukòng fùzài yèwù
CLSF	Connectionless service function	无连接业务功能	Wúliánjiē yèwù gōngnéng
CLT	Communication line terminal	通信线路终端	Tōngxìnliànlù zhōngduān
CLV	Constant linear velocity (optical disk)	恒定线速度	Héngdìng xiànsùdù
CLW	Long distance unmanned cable station	长途电缆无人站	Chángtú diànlǎn wúrénzhàn
CM	Cable modem	缆调制解调器	Lǎn tiáozhì jiětiáoqì
CM	Call management	呼叫管理	Hūjiào guǎnlǐ
CM	Call manager	呼叫管理器	Hūjiào guǎnlǐqì
CM	China Mobile	中国移动通信	Zhōngguó yídòng tōngxìn
CM	Communication management	通信管理	Tōngxìn guǎnlǐ
CM	Communication module	通信模块	Tōngxìn mókuài
CM	Comparators	比较器	Bǐjiào qì
CM	Compatibility mode	兼容方式	Jiānróng fāngshì
CM	Compatibility mode	相容方式	Xiāngróng fāngshì

CM	Compressed mode	压缩方式	Yāsuō fāngshì
CM	Connection management	接续管理	Jiēxù guǎnlǐ
CM	Connection management	连接管理	Liánjiē guǎnlǐ
CM	Connection matrix	连接矩阵	Liánjiē jǔzhèn
CM	Connection module	通信模块	Tōngxìn mókuài
CM	Connectivity manager	连通管理器	Liántōng guǎnlǐqì
CM	Cross-connect matrix	交叉连接矩阵	Jiāochā liánjiē jǔzhèn
CMA	Constant modulus algorithm	恒模算法	Héngmó suànfǎ
CMBR	Combined rack	混合架	Hùnhé jià
CMBS	Circuit mode bearer service	电路方式承载业务	Diànlù fāngshì chéngzài yèwù
CMC	Call modification completed (ISUP message)	呼叫特性改变完毕	Hūjiào tèxìng gǎibiàn wánbì
CMCA	Character mode communications adapter	字符方式通信适配器	Zìfú fāngshì tōngxìn shìpèiqì
CMDB	CDMA modulation and demodulation block	CDMA 调制与解调模块	CDMA tiáozhì yǔ jiětiáo mókuài
CME	Conformant management entity	一致管理项目	Yīzhì guǎnlǐ xiàngmù
CMEA	CCP measurement	CCP 测量	CCP cèliáng
CMF	Cross-modulation factor	交叉调制因子	Jiāochā tiáozhì yīnzǐ
CMF	Cymomotive force; field strength-distance product	场强-距离乘积	Chǎngqiáng--jùlí chéngjī
CMF	Field strength-distance product; cymomotive force	场强-距离乘积	Chǎngqiáng--jùlí chéngjī
CMG	Code modulus generator	代码模数发生器	Dàimǎ móshù fāshēngqì
CMH	CCP message handling	CCP 消息处理	CCP xiāoxi chǔlǐ
CMI	Code mark inversion	代码标记转换	Dàimǎ biāojì zhuǎnhuàn
CMI	Coded mark inversion	编码标记变换	Biānmǎ biāojì biànhuàn
CMI	Coded mark inversion	编码传号反转码	Biānmǎ chuánhào fǎnzhuǎn ma
CMI	Coded mark inversion	传号反转码	Chuánhào fǎnzhuǎn mǎ
CMIP	Common management information protocol	公共管理信息协议	Gōnggòng guǎnlǐ xìnxī xiéyì
CMIP	Common management information protocol	通用管理信息协议	Tōngyòng guǎnlǐ xìnxī xiéyì
CMIP	Common management interface protocol	公共管理接口协议	Gōnggòng guǎnlǐ jiēkǒu xiéyì
CMIP	Customer management information port	用户管理信息接口	Yònghù guǎnlǐ xìnxī jiēkǒu
CMIS	China Mobile Internet Application Protocol special group	中国移动互联网应用协议特别组	Zhōngguó yídòng hùliánwǎng yìngyòng xiéyì tèbiézǔ
CMIS	Common management information service	公共管理信息服务	Gōnggòng guǎnlǐ xìnxī fúwù
CMIS	Common management information service	公共管理信息业务	Gōnggòng guǎnlǐ xìnxī yèwù
CMIS	Common management information service	公用管理信息服务	Gōngyòng guǎnlǐ xìnxī fúwù
CMIS	Common management interface service	公共管理接口服务	Gōnggòng guǎnlǐ jiēkǒu fúwù
CMIS	Common management information service (IETF standard)	通用管理信息服务	Tōngyòng guǎnlǐ xìnxī fúwù
CMISE	Command management information service element	命令管理信息业务元素	Mìnglìng guǎnlǐ xìnxī yèwù yuánsù
CMISE	Common management information service element	公共管理信息服务单元	Gōnggòng guǎnlǐ xìnxī fúwù dānyuán
CMISE	Common management information service element	公共管理信息服务要素	Gōnggòng guǎnlǐ xìnxī fúwù yàosù
CMISE	Common management information service element	公共管理信息服务元素	Gōnggòng guǎnlǐ xìnxī fúwù yuánsù
CMISE	Common management information service element	公共管理信息业务单元	Gōnggòng guǎnlǐ xìnxī yèwù dānyuán
CMISE	Common management information service element	公用管理信息服务单元	Gōngyòng guǎnlǐ xìnxī fúwù dānyuán
CMISE	Common management information service element	公用管理信息协议服务单元	Gōngyòng guǎnlǐ xìnxī xiéyì fúwù dānyuán
CMISE	Common management information service element	公用管理信息业务单元	Gōngyòng guǎnlǐ xìnxī yèwù dānyuán

CML	Current mode logic	电流型逻辑电路	Diànliú-xíng luóji diànlù
CMLE	Conditional maximum likelihood estimate	有条件的最大似然估计	Yǒu tiáojiànde zuìdà sìrán gūjì
CMM	Capability Maturity Model	能力成熟模型	Nénglì chéngshú móxíng
CMMS	Conceptual model of the mission space	任务空间概念模型	Rènwu kōngjiān gàiniàn móxíng
CMN	Call mediation node	呼叫协调功能	Hūjiào xiétiáo gōngnéng
CMN	Call mediation node	呼叫协调节点	Hūjiào xiétiáo jiédiǎn
CMnet	China Mobile Net	中国移动互联网	Zhōngguó yídòng hùliánwǎng
CMNET	China Mobile Network	中国移动通信网络	Zhōngguó yídòng tōngxìn wǎngluò
CMNS	Connection-mode network service	连接方式网络服务	Liánjiē fāngshì wǎngluò fúwù
CMOS	Complementary metal oxide semiconductor	互补金属氧化物半导体	Hùbǔ jīnshǔ yǎnghuàwù bàndǎotǐ
CMP	Common channel signaling MTP processor	公共信道信号 MTP 处理器	Gōnggòng xìndào xìnhào MTP chǔlǐqì
CMP	Costomer management plateform	客户管理平台	Kèhù guǎnlǐ píngtái
CMP	Customer management plane	用户管理平面	Yònghù guǎnlǐ píngmiàn
CMP	Customer management point	用户管理点	Yònghù guǎnlǐ diǎn
CMPP	China Mobile Peer to Peer Protocol	中国移动点对点协议	Zhōngguó yídòng diǎn duì diǎn xiéyì
CMR	Call modification request (ISUP message)	改变呼叫特性请求	Gǎibiàn hūjiào tèxìng qǐngqiú
CMR	Cell mis-insertion rate	信元误插率	Xìnyuán wùchā lǜ
CMR	Cellular mobile radio	蜂窝式移动通信系统	Fēngwō-shì yídòng tōngxìn xìtǒng
CMR	Common mobile radio	公用移动无线电	Gōngyòng yídòng wúxiàndiàn
CMRD	Matsushita Electric Research and Development (China) Corp. (subsidiary of Matsushita Japan)	松下电器研究发展(中国)有限公司	Sōngxià diànqì yánjiū fāzhǎn (Zhōngguó) yǒuxiàn gōngsī
CMRJ	Call modification reject (ISUP message)	拒绝改变呼叫特性	Jùjué gǎibiàn hūjiào tèxìng
CMRS	Cellular mobile radiotelephone service	蜂窝式移动无线电话业务	Fēngwō-shì yídòng wúxiàn diànhuà yèwù
CMS	Cellular mobile system	蜂窝式移动通信系统	Fēngwō-shì yídòng tōngxìn xìtǒng
CMS	Cryptographic message syntax	密码消息语法	Mìmǎ xiāoxi yǔfǎ
CMTS	Cable modem termination system	电缆调制解调器终端系统	Diànlǎn tiáozhì jiětiáoqì zhōngduān xìtǒng
CMTS	Cable MODEM termination system	线缆调制解调器终端系统	Xiànlǎn tiáozhì jiětiáoqì zhōngduān xìtǒng
CN	Congestion notification	拥塞通知	Yōngsè tōngzhī
CN	Core network	核心网络	Héxīn wǎngluò
CN	Customer network	用户网络	Yònghù wǎngluò
CNA	Communication network architecture	通信网络结构	Tōngxìn wǎngluò jiégòu
CNAI	Cellular network administrator interface	蜂窝网络管理器界面	Fēngwō wǎngluò guǎnlǐqì jièmiàn
CNAP	Calling name presentation	呼叫名显示	Hūjiào míng xiǎnshì
CNAP	Communication network analysis program	通信网络分析程序	Tōngxìn wǎngluò fēnxī chéngxù
CNA-P	CDPD network entity identifier authentication protocol	CDPD 网络实体标识符证实协议	CDPD wǎngluò shítǐ biāozhìfú zhèngshí xiéyì
CNAPS	China National Advanced Payment System	中国国家现代支付系统	Zhōngguó guójiā xiàndài zhīfù xìtǒng
CNAPS	Chinese National Advanced Payment System	中国国家现代化支持系统	Zhōngguó guójiā xiàndàihuà zhīchí xìtǒng
CNA-SU	CDPD network entity identifier authentication service user	CDPD 网络实体标识符服务用户证实	CDPD wǎngluò shítǐ biāozhìfú fúwù yònghù zhèngshí
CNAT	Computing network architecture technology	计算机网络结构技术	Jìsuànjī wǎngluò jiégòu jìshù
CNB	Core network bearer service	核心网承载业务	Héxīn wǎng chéngzài yèwù
CNC	China Netcom	网通	Wǎngtōng
CNC	China Network Communications Corp.,	中国网络通信有限公司	Zhōngguó wǎngluò tōngxìn yǒuxiàn gōngsī
CNC	China Network Communications Corp., China Netcom	中国网通	Zhōngguó wǎngtōng
CNC	China Networking Corp.	中国网通公司	Zhōngguó wǎngtōng gōngsī

Abbreviation	English	Chinese	Pinyin
CNC	Coefficient of network complexity	网络复杂性系数	Wǎngluò fùzáxìng xìshù
CNCnet	China Networking Corp. Highspeed Interactive Network	中国网通高速互联网	Zhōngguó wǎngtōng gāosù hùliánwǎng
CNFN	China National Financial Network	中国国家金融网络	Zhōngguó guójiā jīnróng wǎngluò
CNI	Communications, navigation and identification (avionics)	通信导航识别	Tōngxìn dǎoháng shíbié
CNII	China National Information Infrastructure	中国信息基础设施	Zhōngguó xìnxī jīchǔ shèshī
CNIP	Calling number identification presentation	主叫号码识别显示	Zhǔjiào hàomǎ shíbié xiǎnshì
CNIR	Calling number presentation restriction	主叫号码识别限制	Zhǔjiào hàomǎ shíbié xiànzhì
CNITSEC	China National Information Technology Security Certification Center	中国信息安全产品测评认证中心	Zhōngguó xìnxī ānquán chǎnpǐn cèpíng rènzhèng zhōngxīn
CNL	Cooperative network list	协作网络清单	Xiézuò wǎngluò qīngdān
CNM	Circuit network management message group	电路网管理消息	Diànlù wǎng guǎnlǐ xiāoxi
CNM	Communication network manager	通信网络管理程序	Tōngxìn wǎngluò guǎnlǐ chéngxù
CNMA	Communication network management application	通信网络管理应用	Tōngxìn wǎngluò guǎnlǐ yìngyòng
CNMc	Customer network management interface using common management information protocol	使用通用管理信息协议的用户网络管理接口	Shǐyòng tōngyòng guǎnlǐ xìnxī xiéyìde yònghù wǎngluò guǎnlǐ jiēkǒu
CNMc	Open systems interconnect (OSI) management-based interface realization for customer cetwork management service	用户网络管理业务的基于开放式系统互连参考模型管理的接口实现	Yònghù wǎngluò guǎnlǐ yèwùde jīyú kāifàngshì xìtǒng hùlián cānkǎo móxíng guǎnlǐde jiēkǒu shíxiàn
CNMe	Customer network management interface using EDI/MHS	使用电子数据交换/消息处理系统的用户网络管理接口	Shǐyòng diànzi shùjù jiāohuàn/Xiāoxi chǔlǐ xìtǒngde yònghù wǎngluò guǎnlǐ jiēkǒu
CNMe	Electronic data interchange (EDI) management-based interface realization for customer network management service	用户网络管理业务的基于电子数据交换管理的接口实现	Yònghù wǎngluò guǎnlǐ yèwùde jīyú diànzi shùjù jiāohuàn guǎnlǐde jiēkǒu shíxiàn
CNNIC	China National Network Information Center	中国国家网络信息中心	Zhōngguó guójiā wǎngluò xìnxī zhōngxīn
CNNIC	China Network Information Center	中国网络信息中心	Zhōngguó wǎngluò xìnxī zhōngxīn
CNS	Communications, navigation and surveillance (GPS)	同心、导航、监视	Tóngxīn、dǎoháng、jiānshì
CNTIN	China Engineering and Technology Information Network	中国工程技术信息网	Zhōngguó gōngchéng jìshù xìnxīwǎng
CO	Central office	中心局	Zhōngxīn jú
CO	Computing object	计算对象	Jìsuàn duìxiàng
CO	Connection overhead	连接开销	Liánjiē kāixiao
CO	Connection-oriented	面向连接	Miànxiàng liánjiē
COA	Changeover acknowledge signal	倒换证实信号	Dǎohuàn zhèngshí xìnhào
COAK, CC	Connection acknowledged (SS7 message)	连接确认	Liánjiē quèrèn
COB	Cache on board	板上集成缓存	Bǎn-shàng jíchéng huǎncún
COBOL	Common business-oriented language	面向商业的通用语言	Miànxiàng shāngyède tōngyòng yǔyán
COBOL	Common business-oriented language	通用商业语言	Tōngyòng shāngyè yǔyán
COC	Central office code	总局代码	Zǒngjú dàimǎ
COC	Character-oriented communications controller	面向字符的通信控制器	Miànxiàng zìfúde tōngxìn kòngzhìqì
COD	Cache on die	芯片内集成缓存	Xìnpiàn-nèi jíchéng huǎncún
CODA	Connection-oriented data acknowledge	面向连接数据确认	Miànxiàng liánjiē shùjù quèrèn
CODATA	Committee on Data for Science and Technology	科技数据委员会	Kējì shùjù wěiyuánhuì
CODEC	Coder-decoder	编码解码器	Biānmǎ jiěmǎqì
CODIPHASE	Coherent digital phased array system	相干数字相控阵列系统	Xiānggān shùzì xiàng kòng zhènliè xìtǒng
CODT	Connection-oriented data transport	面向连接数据传送	Miànxiàng liánjiē shùjù chuánsòng
COE	Common operating environment	公共操作环境	Gōnggòng cāozuò huánjìng
CoEA	Coevolutionary algorithm	共同进化算法	Gòngtóng jìnhuà suànfǎ

COF	Ciphering offset	加密补偿	Jiāmì bǔcháng
COF	Cursor off	光标隐匿	Guāngbiāo yǐnnì
COFDM	Coded orthogonal frequency division multiplexing	编码正交频分复用	Biānmǎ zhèngjiāo pínfēn fùyòng
COFF	Common object file format	通用对象文件格式	Tōngyòng duìxiàng wénjiàn géshi
COFI	Checkout and fault isolation	检查与故障隔离	Jiǎnchá yǔ gùzhàng gélí
COGO	Coordinate geometry	坐标几何	Zuòbiāo jǐhé
COH	Command handling	命令处理	Mìnglìng chǔlǐ
Coherent MTI	Coherent mobile target indicator	相干动目标显示	Xiānggān dòngmùbiāo xiǎnshì
COIH	Communication output interrupt handler	通信输出中断(信息)处理机	Tōngxìn shūchū zhōngduàn (xìnxī) chǔlǐjī
COINS	International Symposium on Computer and Information Service	国际计算机与信息学论专题讨论会	Guójì jìsuànjī yǔ xìnxīxué lùn zhuāntí tǎolùn huì
COLI	Connected line identity	被叫识别	Bèijiào shíbié
COLI	Connected line identity	连接线识别	Liánjiēxiàn shíbié
COLIPS	Chinese and Oriental Languages Information Processing Society	中文与东方语言信息处理学会	Zhōngwén yǔ Dōngfāng yǔyán xìnxī chǔlǐ xuéhuì
COLM	Column mode	列方式	Liè fāngshì
COLP	Connected line identification presentation	被叫线识别显示	Bèijiào xiàn shíbié xiǎnshì
COLP	Connected line identification presentation	被接线路识别显示	Bèijiē xiànlù shíbié xiǎnshì
COLP	Connected line identification presentation	连接线标识显示	Liánjiēxiàn biāozhì xiǎnshì
COLP	Connected line identification presentation	连接线识别显示	Liánjiēxiàn shíbié xiǎnshì
COLP	Connected line identification presentation supplementary service	被叫识别提供补充业务	Bèijiào shíbié tígōng bǔchōng yèwù
COLR	Connected line identification restriction	被叫线识别限制	Bèijiào xiàn shíbié xiànzhì
COLR	Connected line identification restriction	被接线路识别限制	Bèijiē xiànlù shíbié xiànzhì
COLR	Connected line identification restriction	连接线标识限制	Liánjiēxiàn biāozhì xiànzhì
COLR	Connected line identification restriction	连接线识别限制	Liánjiēxiàn shíbié xiànzhì
COLR	Connected line identification restriction supplementary service	被叫识别限制补充业务	Bèijiào shíbié xiànzhì bǔchōng yèwù
COLTS	Communication on-line testing system	通信联机测试系统	Tōngxìn liánjī cèshì xìtǒng
COM	Common management	公共管理	Gōnggòng guǎnlǐ
COM	Common object model	公用对象模型	Gōngyòng duìxiàng móxíng
COM	Common object modeling	通用对象模型	Tōngyòng duìxiàng móxíng
COM	Communications port (computers)	通讯端口	Tōngxùn duānkǒu
COM	Component object model	部件目标模型	Bùjiàn mùbiāo móxíng
COM	Component object model	组合对象模型	Zǔhé duìxiàng móxíng
COM	Component object model	组件对象模式	Zǔjiàn duìxiàng móshì
COM	Component object model	组件对象模型	Zǔjiàn duìxiàng móxíng
COM	Computer output microfilm	计算机输出缩微胶片	Jìsuànjī shūchū suōwēijiāopiàn
COM	Continuation of message	消息继续	Xiāoxi jìxù
Com.CM	Computing configuration management	计算组成管理	Jìsuàn zǔchéng guǎnlǐ
COMDEX	Computer distributors exposition	计算机代理分销业展览会	Jìsuànjī dàilǐ fēnxiāo yè zhǎnlǎnhuì
COMP	Compiler (computer program)	编译程序	Biānyì chéngxù
COMPAC	Commonwealth Pacific Cable	联邦太平洋电缆	Liánbāng tàipíngyáng diànlǎn
COMPUSEC	Computer security	计算机安全	Jìsuànjī ānquán
COMR	Common rack	公共机架	Gōnggòng jījià
COMSAT	Communications Satellite Corp.	通信卫星公司	Tōngxìn wèixīng gōngsī
COMSEC	Communications secrecy	通信保密	Tōngxìn bǎomì
COMSEC	Communications security	通信安全	Tōngxìn ānquán

CON	Connect message (ISUP)	连接消息	Liánjiē xiāoxi
CON	Control console	控制台	Kòngzhìtái
CON	Cursor on	光标显现	Guāngbiāo xiǎnxiàn
Con.CM	Connection configuration management	连接组成管理	Liánjiē zǔchéng guǎnlǐ
CONF	Conference call	会议电话	Huìyì diànhuà
CONF	Conference calling	会议呼叫	Huìyì hūjiào
CONF	Confidentiality protected command (in FTP)	机密性保护命令	Jīmìxìng bǎohù mìnglìng
CONN	Connection	连接	Liánjiē
CONNACK	Connect acknowledgement	连接认可	Liánjiē rènkě
CONNACK	Connect acknowledgement	连接证实	Liánjiē zhèngshí
CONP	Connection-oriented network layer protocol	面向连接的网络层协议	Miànxiàng liánjiēde wǎngluò céng xiéyì
CONP	Connection-oriented network protocol	定向连接网络协议	Dìngxiàng liánjiē wǎngluò xiéyì
CONP	Connection-oriented network protocol (ISO use)	面向连接的网络协议	Miànxiàng liánjiēde wǎngluò xiéyì
CONS	Connection oriented network service	面向连接网络业务	Miànxiàng liánjiē wǎngluò yèwù
CONS	Connection-oriented network (layer) service	面向连接的网络层服务	Miànxiàng liánjiēde wǎngluò céng fúwù
CONS	Connection-oriented network service	定向连接网络业务	Dìngxiàng liánjiē wǎngluò yèwù
COO	Cell of origin	源小区	Yuán xiǎoqū
COO	Changeover signal	倒换信号	Dǎohuàn xìnhào
COO	Chief operating officer	首席运营官	Shǒuxí yùnyíng guān
COO	Chief organizing officer	首席管理官	Shǒuxí guǎnlǐ guān
COPS	Common open policy service	公共开放策略业务	Gōnggòng kāifàng cèlüè yèwù
COPS	Common open policy service	公共开放政策服务	Gōnggòng kāifàng zhèngcè fúwù
COPS	Common open policy service	通用开放策略服务	Tōngyòng kāifàng cèlüè fúwù
CORBA	Common object request broker	通用对象请求中间件	Tōngyòng duìxiàng qǐngqiú zhōngjiān jiàn
CORBA	Common object request broker architecture	公共对象请求代里体系结构	Gōnggòng duìxiàng qǐngqiú dàilǐ tǐxì jiégòu
CORBA	Common object request broker architecture	公共对象请求中介器体系结构	Gōnggòng duìxiàng qǐngqiú zhōngjièqì tǐxì jiégòu
CORBA	Common object request broker architecture	公共客体请求代理体系	Gōnggòng kètǐ qǐngqiú dàilǐ tǐxì
CORBA	Common object request broker architecture	公共目标请求掮客结构	Gōnggòng mùbiāo qǐngqiú qiánkè jiégòu
CORBA	Common object request broker architecture	通用对象请求代理结构	Tōngyòng duìxiàng qǐngqiú dàilǐ jiégòu
CORBA	Common object request broker architecture	通用对象请求中介架构	Tōngyòng duìxiàng qǐngqiú zhōngjiè jiàgòu
CORBA	Common object request broker architecture	通用对象申请代理结构	Tōngyòng duìxiàng shēnqǐng dàilǐ jiégòu
CORBA	Common object request broker architecture	通用客体请求代理体系结构	Tōngyòng kètǐ qǐngqiú dàilǐ tǐxì jiégòu
CORBA	Common object request broker architecture	通用对象请求代理体系结构	Tōngyòng duìxiàng qǐngqiú dàilǐ tǐxì jiégòu
CORE, CR	Connection request (SS7 message)	连接请求	Liánjiē qǐngqiú
CORENET	Construction and real estate network	建筑与房地产网络	Jiànzhù yǔ fángdìchǎn wǎngluò
CORPSK	Correlative phase shift keying	相关相移键控	Xiāngguān xiàngyí jiànkòng
CORPSK	Correlative phase shift keying	相关移相键控	Xiāngguān yíxiàng jiànkòng
CoS	Class of service	服务类别	Fúwù lèibié
COS	Class of service	业务类型	Yèwù lèixíng
COSIX	Chinese Unix Operating system	中文操作系统	Zhōngwén cāozuò xìtǒng
COSS	Common object services specification	公共对象服务规范	Gōnggòng duìxiàng fúwù guīfàn
COT	Central office terminal	局端机	Júduānjī
COT	Central office termination	局端	Júduān
COT	Continuity signal	导通消息	Dǎotōng xiāoxi
COT	Continuity signal	导通信号	Dǎotōng xìnhào
COTS	Commercial off-the-shelf products	商业成品	Shāngyè chéngpǐn

COTS	Connection-oriented transport service	面向连接的运输服务	Miànxiàng liánjiēde yùnshū fúwù
CP	Channel parameter	信道参数	Xìndào cānshù
CP	Common part	公共部分	Gōnggòng bùfen
CP	Connection point	连接点	Liánjiēdiǎn
CP	Constraint programming (CAD/CAM)	约束规划	Yuēshù guīhuà
CP	Control plane	控制平面	Kòngzhì píngmiàn
CP	Coordination processor	协调处理机	Xiétiáo chǔlǐjī
CP	Core protocol	核心协议	Héxīn xiéyì
CPA	Class parser agent (in Java)	种类解析代理	Zhǒnglèi jiěxī dàilǐ
CPA	Cylindrical parabola antenna	圆筒形抛物面天线	Yuántǒngxíng pāowùmiàn tiānxiàn
CP-AAL	ATM adaptation layer common part	ATM 适配层公用部分	ATM shìpèi céng gōngyòng bùfen
CP-AAL	ATM adaptation layer,common part	ATM 适配层公共部分	ATM shìpèicéng gōnggòng bùfen
CPAR	Control bus parity check error	控制总线寄偶校验错	Kòngzhì zǒngxiàn jì'ǒu jiàoyàn cuò
CPB	Cipher block chaining	密码分组链接	Mìmǎ fēnzǔ liàn jiē
CPC	Code path connect	码字通道连接	Mǎzì tōngdào liánjiē
CPC	Collaborative product commerce	协同产品商务	Xiétóng chǎnpǐn shāngwù
CPCCH	Common power control channel	公共功率控制信道	Gōnggòng gōnglǜ kòngzhì xìndào
CPCH	Common packet channel	公用分组信道	Gōngyòng fēnzǔ xìndào
CPCS	Call processing control system	呼叫处理控制系统	Hūjiào chǔlǐ kòngzhì xìtǒng
CPCS	Common part convergence sub-layer	公共部分会聚子层	Gōnggòng bùfen huìjù zi céng
CPCS	Common part convergence sub-layer	公共会聚子层	Gōnggòng huìjù zicéng
CPCS	Common part convergence sub-layer	通用部分会聚子层	Tōngyòng bùfen huìjù zicéng
CPDM	Companded predictive delta modulation	压扩预测增量调制	Yākuò yùcè zēngliàng tiáozhì
CPE	Circular probable error	循环概率误差	Xúnhuán gàilǜ wùchā
CPE	Convergence protocol entity	会聚协议实体	Huìjù xiéyì shítǐ
CPE	Customer premises equipment	客户端设备	Kèhù duān shèbèi
CPE	Customer premises equipment	用户端设备	Yònghù duān shèbèi
CPE	Customer premises equipment	用户室内设备	Yònghù shìnèi shèbèi
CPE	Customer premises equipment	用户驻地设备	Yònghù zhùdì shèbèi
CPFSK	Continuous phase frequency shift keying	连续相位频移键控	Liánxù xiàngwèi pínyí jiànkòng
CPFSK	Continuous-phase frequency shift keying	连续相位移频键控	Liánxù xiàngwèi yípín jiànkòng
CPG	Call progress (ISUP message)	呼叫过程	Hūjiào guòchéng
CPG	Call progress message (ISUP)	呼叫进程消息	Hūjiào jìnchéng xiāoxi
CPG	Call progressing (message)	呼叫进展消息	Hūjiào jìnzhǎn xiāoxi
CPG	Clock pulse generator	时钟脉冲发生器	Shízhōng màichōng fāshēngqì
CPGA	Ceramic pin grid array	陶瓷针型栅格阵列	Táocí zhēn-xíng zhàgé zhènliè
CPH	Calling party handling	呼叫方控制	Hūjiào fāng kòngzhì
CPI	Characters per inch	每寸多少字	Měi cùn duōshao zì
CPI	Code path ID	码字通道值	Mǎzì tōngdào zhí
CPI	Common part indicator	公共部分指示	Gōnggòng bùfen zhǐshì
CPI	Complete path index (in XML)	全部路径索引	Quánbù lùjìng suǒyǐn
CPICH	Common pilot channel	公共导引信道	Gōnggòng dǎoyǐn xìndào
CPL	Call processing language	呼叫处理语言	Hūjiào chǔlǐ yǔyán
CPL	CCP processor loader	CCP 处理器承载器	CCP chǔlǐqì chéngzàiqì
CPL	Code path link	码字通道链路	Mǎzì tōngdào liànlù
CPLD	Compound phase locked demodulator	复合锁相解调器	Fùhé suǒxiàng jiětiáoqì

CPM	Computer peripheral module	计算机外设模块	Jìsuànjī wàishè mókuài
CPM	Continuous phase modulation	连续相位调制	Liánxù xiàngwèi tiáozhì
CPM	Continuous-phase modulation	连续调相	Liánxù tiáoxiàng
CPM, XPM	Cross-phase modulation	交叉相位调制	Jiāochā xiàngwèi tiáozhì
C-PMS	Central-level management center	中央级管理中心	Zhōngyāng jí guǎnlǐ zhōngxīn
CPN	Colored Petri net	着色 Petri 网	Zhuósè Petri wǎng
CPN	Customer premises network	用户驻地网	Yònghù zhùdì wǎng
CPOL	Communications procedure-oriented language	面向通信过程的语言	Miànxiàng tōngxìn guòchéngde yǔyán
CPP	Cordless portable part (telephone)	无绳手机	Wúshéng shǒujī
CPPW	Circularly polarized plane wave	圆极化平面波	Yuán jíhuà píngmiànbō
CPS	Certification practice statement	使用证明书	Shǐyòng zhèngmíngshū
CPS	Characters per second	每秒多少字	Měi miǎo duōshao zì
CPS	Characters per second	每秒字符数	Měi miǎo zìfúshù
CPS	Common part sub-layer	公共部分字层	Gōnggòng bùfen zìcéng
CPSK	Coherent phase shift keying modulation	相干相移键控调制	Xiānggān xiàngyí jiànkòng tiáozhì
CPT	Carriage paid to	运费付至	Yùnfèi fù zhì
CPT	Compatibility testing	兼容性测试	Jiānróngxìng cèshì
CPU	Central processor unit	中央处理器	Zhōngyāng chǔlǐqì
CPW	Circular polarization wave	圆极化波	Yuán jíhuà bō
CQ	Custom queue	用户定制队列	Yònghù dìngzhì duìliè
CQ	Custom queuing	自定义排队	Zìdìngyì páiduì
CQM	Circuit group query message (ISUP message)	询问电路群信息	Xúnwèn diànlù qún xìnxī
CQM	Complex quaternary phase shift modulation	复四相调制	Fù sìxiāng tiáozhì
CQM	Core [Network] QoS manager	核心网服务质量管理器	Héxīn wǎng fúwù zhìliàng guǎnlǐqì
CQMS	Circuit quality monitoring system	电路质量监测系统	Diànlù zhìliàng jiāncè xìtǒng
CQT	Call quality test	呼叫质量拨打测试	Hūjiào zhìliàng bōdǎ cèshì
CR	Call reference	呼叫参考	Hūjiào cānkǎo
CR	Cambridge ring	剑桥环	Jiànqiáo huán
CR	Carriage return	回车	Huíchē
CR	Channel rate	信道速率	Xìndào sùlǜ
CR	Core router	核心路由器	Héxīn lùyóuqì
CR	Coupling ratio	分光比	Fēnguāng bǐ
CR	Receiver continuous disturbance	收信机的连续骚扰	Shōuxìnjīde liánxù sāorǎo
CR/E	Card reader/encoder	卡读写器/编码器	Kǎ dúxiěqì/biānmǎqì
CRA	CCP resource allocation	CCP 资源分配	CCP zīyuán fēnpèi
CRC	Cyclic redundancy code	循环冗余校验码	Xúnhuán rǒngyú jiàoyàn mǎ
CRC	Cyclical redundancy check	循环冗余检查	Xúnhuán rǒngyú jiǎnchá
CRC	Cyclical redundancy check	循环冗余检验	Xúnhuán rǒngyú jiǎnyàn
CRC	Cyclical redundancy check/correction	循环冗余校验	Xúnhuán rǒngyú jiàoyàn
CRC	Cyclical redundancy code	循环冗余编码	Xúnhuán rǒngyú biānmǎ
CRE	Corrosion resistant	抗蚀	Kàngshí
CRE	Cyclical redundancy error	循环冗余差错	Xúnhuán rǒngyú chācuò
CRED	Credit card calling	信用卡呼叫	Xìnyòngkǎ hūjiào
CREF	Connection refused (in SS7)	拒绝连接	Jùjué liánjiē
CRF	Carrier frequency telephone repeater	载波电话中继器	Zàibō diànhuà zhōngjìqì
CRF	Carrier frequency telephone repeater	载频电话中继器	Zàipín diànhuà zhōngjìqì

CRF	Connection related function	连接相关功能	Liánjiē xiāngguān gōngnéng
CRF	Connection related function	连接有关功能	Liánjiē yǒuguān gōngnéng
CRF	Connection-related function	连接的有关功能	Liánjiēde yǒuguān gōngnéng
CRF(VC)	Virtual channel connection related function	虚信道连接的有关功能	Xū xìndào liánjiēde yǒuguān gōngnéng
CRF(VP)	Virtual path connection related function	虚通路连接的有关功能	Xū tōnglù liánjiēde yǒuguān gōngnéng
CRF-S	Subscriber-side CRF	用户侧的 CRF	Yònghù cede CRF
CRG	Charge information (ISUP message)	计费信息	Jìfèi xìnxī
CRH	Channel reconfiguration hardware	通道重配置硬件	Tōngdào chóng pèizhì yìngjiàn
CRI	Collective routing indicator	成组路由选择指示符	Chéngzǔ lùyóu xuǎnzé zhǐshìfú
CRI	Continuity-recheck incoming	连续性重复检验输入信号	Liánxùxìng chóngfù jiǎnyàn shūrù xìnhào
CRIS	China Railway Information System	中国铁路信息系统	Zhōngguó tiělù xìnxī xìtǒng
CRIS	China Railway Information System	中国铁路综合信息系统	Zhōngguó tiělù zōnghé xìnxī xìtǒng
CRL	Carrier recovery loop	载波恢复环路	Zàibō huīfù huánlù
CRL	Certificate revocation list	证书废除列表	Zhèngshū fèichú lièbiǎo
CRL	Certificate revocation list	证书作废表	Zhèngshū zuòfèi biǎo
CRL	Certificate revocation list (IPsec)	证书撤销列表	Zhèngshū chèxiāo lièbiǎo
CR-LDP	Common route-label distribution protocol	局部路由标记分配协议	Júbù lùyóu biāojì fēnpèi xiéyì
CR-LDP	Constraint-based label distribution protocol	受限标签分配协议	Shòuxiàn biāoqiān fēnpèi xiéyì
CR-LSP	Constraint-based LSP (label switching path)	基于约束 LSP	Jīyú yuēshù LSP
CRM	CCP resource manager	CCP 资源管理器	CCP zīyuán guǎnlǐqì
CRM	Cell rate margin	信元速率边际	Xìnyuán sùlù biānjì
CRM	Configuration and resource management	配置和资源管理	Pèizhì hé zīyuán guǎnlǐ
CRM	Customer relations manager	客户关系管理	Kèhù guānxi guǎnlǐ
CRn	Conformance requirement 'n'	一致性需求"n"	Yīzhìxing xūqiú "n"
CRNC	Controlling radio network controller	控制无线网络的控制器	Kòngzhì wúxiàn wǎngluòde kòngzhìqì
C-RNTI	Cell radio network temporary identity	无线蜂窝网络临时识别	Wúxiàn fēngwō wǎngluò línshí shíbié
CRO	Cell re-select offset	小区重选偏移量	Xiǎoqū chóngxuǎn piānyí liáng
CRO	Cell reselection offset	小区重先偏置	Xiǎoqū chóngxiān piānzhì
CROS	Concurrent real time operating system	并行实时操作系统	Bìngxíng shíshí cāozuò xìtǒng
CRP	Cable replacement protocol	电缆替代协议	Diànlǎn tìdài xiéyì
CRP	Channel request priority	通道请求优先	Tōngdào qǐngqiú yōuxiān
CRP	Continuous replenishment program	连续库存补充计划	Liánxù kùcún bǔchōng jìhuà
CRptr	Performance criteria for continuous phenomena applied to repeaters and ancillary RF amplifiers	中继器和辅助射频放大器的连续骚扰性能判据	Zhōngjìqì hé fǔzhù shèpín fàngdàqìde liánxù sāorǎo xìngnéng pànjù
CRS	Cellular radiotelephone service	蜂窝无线电话服务	Fēngwō wúxiàn diànhuà fúwù
CRS	Central radio station	中心射频站	Zhōngxīn shèpínzhàn
CRS	Configuration report server	配置报告服务器	Pèizhì bàogào fúwùqì
CRT	Cathode ray tube	阴极射线管	Yīnjí shèxiàn guǎn
CRT	Cathode ray tube	阴极线管	Yīnjí xiàn guǎn
CRTDB	Centralized real-time database	集中式实时数据库	Jízhōng-shì shíshí shùjùkù
CRU	Capsule resource unit	包装资源单位	Bāozhuāng zīyuán dānwèi
CRV	Call reference value	呼叫参考值	Hūjiào cānkǎo zhí
CrySTINA	Cryptographically secure TINA	密码安全 TINA	Mìmǎ ānquán TINA
CS	Cabletron Spectrum (description of this network management software)	旧纳档块化技术	Jiù nà dàng kuàihuà jìshù
CS	Campus sub-system	建筑群子系统	Jiànzhùqún zixìtǒng
CS	Capability set	能力集	Nénglì jí

CS	Central station	中心站	Zhōngxīnzhàn
CS	Channel separation	声道分离	Shēngdào fēnlí
CS	Circuit switched service	电路交换业务	Diànlù jiāohuàn yèwù
CS	Circuit switching	电路交换	Diànlù jiāohuàn
CS	Clock source (timing information)	时钟源	Shízhōng yuán
CS	Communication satellite	通信卫星	Tōngxìn wèixīng
CS	Communications server	通信服务器	Tōngxìn fúwùqì
CS	Convergence service	会聚服务	Huìjù fúwù
CS	Convergence sub-layer	会聚子层	Huìjù zicéng
CS	Cryptographic system	加密系统	Jiāmì xìtǒng
CS1	Capability set 1	能力集 1	Nénglì jí 1
CS2	Capability set 2	能力集 2	Nénglì jí 2
CSA	Canadian Standards Association	加拿大标准联合会	Jiā-ná-dà biāozhǔn liánhéhuì
CSA	Canadian Standards Association	加拿大标准协会	Jiā-ná-dà biāozhǔn xiéhuì
CSA	Carrier service area	电信公司服务区	Diànxìn gōngsī fúwùqū
CSA	Carrier service area	电信公司营运服务区	Diànxìn gōngsī yíngyùn fúwùqū
CSA	Carrier service area	营运服务区	Yíngyùn fúwùqū
CSAA	Cell site alarm assembly	小区告警集成件	Xiǎoqū gàojǐng jíchéng jiàn
CS-ACELP	Conjugate structure-algebraic code excited linear prediction	共轭结构-代数码激励线性预测	Gòng'è jiégòu—dàishù mǎ jīlì xiànxìng yùcè
CSB	Channel status byte	通道状态字节	Tōngdào zhuàngtài zìjié
CSB	Communication switch-board	通信交换机台	Tōngxìn jiāohuànjī tái
CSB	Complementary straight binary code	标准二进制补码	Biāozhǔn èrjìnzhì bǔ mǎ
CSBP	Common channel signaling back panel	公共信道信号后面板	Gōnggòng xìndào xìnhào hòumian bǎn
CSBS	China State Bureau of Standards	中国国家标准局	Zhōngguó Guójiā Biāozhǔnjú
CSC	Cell site controller	小区控制器	Xiǎoqū kòngzhìqì
CSC	Central switching-network control	集中交换网络控制	Jízhōng jiāohuàn wǎngluò kòngzhì
CSC	Centralized service control	集中业务控制	Jízhōng yèwù kòngzhì
CSC	Centralized supervisory and control equipment	集中监控设备	Jízhōng jiānkòng shèbèi
CSC	Centralized supervisory and control equipment	集中监视和控制设备	Jízhōng jiānshì hé kòngzhì shèbèi
CSC	Clock start command	时钟起动命令	Shízhōng qǐdòng mìnglìng
CSC	Combined speaker cabinet	组合音响	Zǔhé yīnxiǎng
CSC	Common channel signaling controller	公共通道信号控制器	Gōnggòng tōngdào xìnhào kòngzhìqì
CSC	Common signal channel	公用信号信道	Gōngyòng xìnhào xìndào
CSC	Common signaling channel	公共信令信道	Gōnggòng xìnlìng xìndào
CSC	Communication service center	通信业务中心	Tōngxìn yèwù zhōngxīn
CSC	Computer sub-system controller	计算机子系统控制器	Jìsuànjī zixìtǒng kòngzhìqì
CSC	Control signaling code	控制信令码	Kòngzhì xìnlìng mǎ
CSCA	Common signaling control board assembly	公共信号控制集成板	Gōnggòng xìnhào kòngzhì jíchéngbǎn
CSCB	Cycle steal control buffer	周期挪用缓冲器	Zhōuqī nuóyòng huǎnchōngqì
CSCD	Common signal channel demodulator	公用信号通道解调器	Gōngyòng xìnhào tōngdào jiětiáoqì
CSCF	Call server control function	呼叫服务器控制功能	Hūjiào fúwùqì kòngzhì gōngnéng
CSCF	Call state control function	呼叫状态控制功能	Hūjiào zhuàngtài kòngzhì gōngnéng
CSCI	Computer software configuration item	计算机软件配置项	Jìsuànjī ruǎnjiàn pèizhì xiàng
CSCW	Computer supported collaborative work	计算机支持的协同工作	Jìsuànjī zhīchíde xiétóng gōngzuò
CSCW	Computer supported cooperative work	计算机协同工作支持系统	Jìsuànjī xiétóng gōngzuò zhīchí xìtǒng

CSCW	Computer supported cooperative work	计算机支持协同工作	Jìsuànjī zhīchí xiétóng gōngzuò
CSD	Circuit switched data	电路交换数据	Diànlù jiāohuàn shùjù
CSD	Composite signal dialing	复合信号拨号	Fùhé xìnhào bōhào
CSDC	Circuit switched digital circuitry	线路交换数字电路	Xiànlù jiāohuàn shùzì diànlù
CSDM	Continuous slope delta modulation	连续斜率 Δ 调制	Liánxù xiélǜ Δ tiáozhì
CSDN	Circuit-switched data network	线路转接数据网络	Xiànlù zhuǎnjiē shùjù wǎngluò
CSDS	Communication signal distribution system	通信信号分配系统	Tōngxìn xìnhào fēnpèi xìtǒng
CSE	CAMEL service environment	CAMEL 业务环境	CAMEL yèwù huánjìng
CSE	Check sum error	检查和错误	Jiǎnchá hé cuòwù
CSE	Configuration space enable	可分配空间	Kěfēnpèi kōngjiān
CSES	Consecutive severely errored second	连续严重误块秒	Liánxù yánzhòng wùkuài miǎo
CSES	Continuous severely errored second	连续严重误码秒	Liánxù yánzhòng wùmǎ miǎo
CSF	Call service function	呼叫业务功能	Hūjiào yèwù gōngnéng
CSF	Channel separating filter	分路滤波器	Fēnlù lǜbōqì
CSF	Cut-off wavelength shifted optical fiber	截止波长位移光纤	Jiézhǐ bōcháng wèiyí guāngxiān
CSF-C	Call service mediation function	呼叫业务协调功能	Hūjiào yèwù xiétiáo gōngnéng
CSF-G	Call service gateway function	呼叫业务网关功能	Hūjiào yèwù wǎngguān gōngnéng
CSF-N	Call service node function	呼叫业务节点功能	Hūjiào yèwù jiédiǎn gōngnéng
CSF-T	Call service transit function	呼叫业务转接功能	Hūjiào yèwù zhuǎnjiē gōngnéng
CSGH	Cycle steal grant high	周期挪用许可高	Zhōuqī nuóyòng xǔkě gāo
CSGL	Cycle steal grant low	周期挪用许可低	Zhōuqī nuóyòng xǔkě dī
CS-GW	Circuit switched gateway	电路交换网关	Diànlù jiāohuàn wǎngguān
CSH	Called subscriber held signal	被叫拥护不挂机信号	Bèijiào yōnghù bùguàjī xìnhào
CSH	CCP status handling	CCP 状态处理	CCP zhuàngtài chǔlǐ
CSH	Central switching hub	中央交换式集线器	Zhōngyāng jiāohuànshì jíxiànqì
CSI	Channel status indicator	通道状态指示器	Tōngdào zhuàngtài zhǐshìqì
CSI	Channel stream identifier	信道流标识符	Xìndào liú biāozhì fú
CSI	Cubic spline interpolation	三次样条插值	Sāncì yàngtiáo chāzhí
Csid	Clock source identifier	时钟源指示器	Shízhōng yuán zhǐshìqì
CSJ	Program controlled city switch	程控市话交换	Chéngkòng shìhuà jiāohuàn
CSK	Compatible shift keying	兼容频移键控	Jiānróng pínyí jiànkòng
CSL	CCP system loader	CCP 系统承载器	CCP xìtǒng chéngzàiqì
CSLC	Coherent sidelobe cancellation	相干旁瓣消除法	Xiānggān pángbàn xiāochú fǎ
CSLIP	Compressed serial link Internet protocol	压缩串联因特网协议	Yāsuō chuànlián Yīntèwǎng xiéyì
CSM	Call supervision message	呼叫监视消息	Hūjiào jiānshì xiāoxi
CSM	CCP sanity loader	CCP 正常运行承载器	CCP zhèngcháng yùnxíng chéngzàiqì
CSM	Central strength member (FOC)	中心加强件	Zhōngxīn jiāqiáng jiàn
CSM	Communication system manager	通信系统管理程序	Tōngxìn xìtǒng guǎnlǐ chéngxù
CSM	Communication system monitoring	通信系统监视	Tōngxìn xìtǒng jiānshì
CSMA	Carrier sense multiple access	载波检测多址	Zàibō jiǎncè duōzhǐ
CSMA	Carrier sense multiple access	载波控制多路存取	Zàibō kòngzhì duōlù cúnqǔ
CSMA	Carrier sense multiple access	载波侦听多址访问	Zàibō zhēntīng duōzhǐ fǎngwèn
CSMA/CA	Carrier sense multiple access with collision avoidance	载波侦听多址接入/避免冲撞协议	Zàibō zhēntīng duōzhǐ jiērù/ bìmiǎn chōngzhuàng xiéyì
CSMA/CD	Carrier sense multiple access with collision detection	载波侦听多址接入/碰撞检测协议	Zàibō zhēntīng duōzhǐ jiērù/ pèngzhuàng jiǎncè xiéyì

CSMA/CD	Carrier-sense multiple access with collision detection	带碰撞检测的载波侦听多址访问	Dài pèngzhuàng jiǎncède zàibō zhēntīng duōzhǐ fǎngwèn
CSMC	Cycle stealing message counter	周期挪用信息计数器	Zhōuqī nuóyòng xìnxī jìshùqì
CSMI	Communication system manager interface	通信系统管理程序接口	Tōngxìn xìtǒng guǎnlǐ chéngxù jiēkǒu
CSML	Control system message log	控制系统信息日志	Kòngzhì xìtǒng xìnxī rìzhì
CSMN	CCP sanity manager	CCP 正常运行管理器	CCP zhèngcháng yùnxíng guǎnlǐqì
CSMS	Cell site modem software	小区调制解调软件	Xiǎoqū tiáozhì jiětiáo ruǎnjiàn
CSN	Circuit switched network	电路交换网	Diànlù jiāohuàn wǎng
CSN	Cyclically symmetric network	循环对称网络	Xúnhuán duìchèn wǎngluò
CSNAP	Communications statistical network analysis procedure	通信统计网络分析过程	Tōngxìn tǒngjì wǎngluò fēnxī guòchéng
CSNP	Complete sequence numbers protocol data unit	完全序列号协议数据单元	Wánquán xùlièhào xiéyì shùjù dānyuán
CSP	Channeled substrate planar structure	沟道衬底平面结构	Gōudào chèndǐ píngmiàn jiégòu
CSP	Coder sequential pulse	编码器时序脉冲	Biānmǎqì shíxù màichōng
CSP	Coherent signal processor	相干信号处理机	Xiānggān xìnhào chǔlǐjī
CSP	Common channel signaling processor	公共信道信号处理器	Gōnggòng xìndào xìnhào chǔlǐqì
CSP	Communication satellite program	通信卫星计划	Tōngxìn wèixīng jìhuà
CSP	Constraint satisfaction problem	约束满足问题	Yuēshù mǎnzú wèntí
CSP	Content service provider	内容服务提供者	Nèiróng fúwù tígòngzhě
CSP	Cryptographic service provider	加密服务提供者	Jiāmì fúwù tígòngzhě
CSPA	Chinese Software Professionals Association	中国软件专业协会	Zhōngguó ruǎnjiàn zhuānyè xiéhuì
CSPDN	Circuit switched public data network	电路交换公共数据网	Diànlù jiāohuàn gōnggòng shùjù wǎng
CSPDN	Circuit switched public data network	电路交换公用数据网	Diànlù jiāohuàn gōngyòng shùjù wǎng
CS-PDU	Convergence sub-layer protocol data unit	会聚子层协议数据单元	Huìjù zicéng xiéyì shùjù dānyuán
CSPE	Communication system planning element	通信系统计划环节	Tōngxin xìtǒng jìhuà huánjié
CSPF	Constrained shortest path first	制约最短路径优选	Zhìyuē zuìduǎn lùjìng yōuxuǎn
CSPS	Coherent signal processing system	相干信号处理系统	Xiānggān xìnhào chǔlǐ xìtǒng
CSR	Cell switching router	信元交换路由器	Xìnyuán jiāohuàn lùyóuqì
CSR	Clock shift register	时钟移位寄存器	Shízhōng yíwèi jìcúnqì
CSR	Communications status register	通信状态寄存器	Tōngxìn zhuàngtài jìcúnqì
CSR	Complete spatial randomness	完全空间随机性	Wánquán kōngjiān suíjīxìng
CSR	Customer service representative	客户服务代表	Kèhù fúwù dàibiǎo
CSR	Cycle steal request	周期挪用请求	Zhōuqī nuóyòng qǐngqiú
CSS	Cascading style sheets	层叠格式表	Céngdié géshi biǎo
CSS	Central switching sub-system	中央交换子系统	Zhōngyāng jiāohuàn zixìtǒng
CSS	Common security service	公共安全服务	Gōnggòng ānquán fúwù
CSSB-AM	Companded single sideband amplitude modulation	压扩单边带调幅	Yākuò dānbiāndài tiáofú
CSSHR	Cluster system simulator of heterogeneous resources	资源异构集群系统模拟器	Zīyuán yìgòu jíqún xìtǒng mónǐqì
CSSM	Content standard for spatial metadata	空间元数据的内容标准	Kōngjiān yuánshùjùde nèiróng biāozhǔn
CSTnet	China Science and Technology Network	中国科技网	Zhōngguó kējì wǎng
CSU	Channel selection unit	信道选配单板	Xìndào xuǎnpèi dānbǎn
CSU	Channel service unit	信道服务单元	Xìndào fúwù dānyuán
CSUI	Common session user information	公用会化期用户信息	Gōngyòng huìhuà qī yònghù xìnxī
CSV	Circuit switched voice	线路交换声	Xiànlù jiāohuàn shēng
CT	Call transfer	呼叫转送	Hūjiào zhuǎnsòng
CT	Call transfer	呼叫转移	Hūjiào zhuǎnyí

CT	Call transfer supplementary service	呼叫传送补充业务	Hūjiào chuánsòng bǔchōng yèwù
CT	Channel tester	信道测试仪	Xìndào cèshìyí
CT	Configured tunneling	配置隧道	Pèizhì suìdào
CT	Conformance test	一致性测试	Yīzhìxìng cèshì
CT	Installed in cable tray	电缆桥架敷设	Diànlǎn qiáojià fūshè
CT	Long distance console	长途台	Chángtútái
CT	Transmitter continuous disturbance	发信机的连续骚扰	Fāxìnjīde liánxù sāorǎo
CT, ZH	Carrier telephone	载波电话	Zàibō diànhuà
CT-2	Digital cordless telephone system second generation	第二代数字无绳电话系统	Dì'èrdài shùzì wúshéng diànhuà xìtǒng
CTB	Composite triple beat	复合三价差拍	Fùhé sān jiàchā pāi
CTCA	China Telecommunications Certificate Authority	中国电信认证中心	Zhōngguó diànxìn rènzhèng zhōngxīn
CTCH	Common traffic channel	公共业务信道	Gōnggòng yèwù xìndào
CTD	Cable thermal detector	缆式线型感温探测器	Lǎnshìxiànxíng gǎnwēn tàncèqì
CTD	Cell transfer delay	信元传输时延	Xìnyuán chuánshū shíyán
CTD	Cell transfer delay	信元传送时延	Xìnyuán chuánsòng shíyán
CTD	Cell transfer delay	信元传送延迟	Xìnyuán chuánsòng yánchí
CTD	Cell transfer delay	信元转移时延	Xìnyuán zhuǎnyí shí yán
CTDH	Command and telemetry data handling	命令与遥测数据处理	Mìnglìng yǔ yáocè shùjùchǔlǐ
CTDMA	Code and time division multiple access	码时分多址	Mǎ shífèn duōzhǐ
CTDMA	Concurrent time domain multiple access	并行时域多路存取算法	Bìngxíng shíyù duōlù cúnqǔ suànfǎ
CTE	Coefficient of thermal expansion	热膨胀系数	Rè péngzhàng xìshù
CTERM	Command terminal (in DECnet)	命令终端	Mìnglìng zhōngduān
CTF	Cable termination frame	电缆终端配线架	Diànlǎn zhōngduān pèixiànjià
CTF	Click to fax	点击传真	Diǎnjī chuánzhēn
CTF	Click to fax	点击发送传真	Diǎnjī fāsòng chuánzhēn
CTI	Computer telecommunication integration	计算机电信集成	Jìsuànjī diànxìn jíchéng
CTI	Computer telephony integration	电脑电话集成	Diànnǎo diànhuà jíchéng
CTI	Computer telephony integration	计算机通信技术	Jìsuànjī tōngxìn jìshù
CTI	Computer-telephone integration	计算机电话综合技术	Jìsuànjī diànhuà zōnghé jìshù
CTI	Computer-telephony integration	计算机电话集成	Jìsuànjī diànhuà jíchéng
CTIA	Cellular Telecommunications Industry Association	蜂窝通信工业协会	Fēngwō tōngxìn gōngyè xiéhuì
CTIA	Cellular Telecommunications Industry Association (US)	蜂窝电信工业协会	Fēngwō diànxìn gōngyè xiéhuì
CTL	Certificate trust list	证书信任列表	Zhèngshū xìnrèn lièbiǎo
CTL	Complementary transistor logic circuit	互补晶体管逻辑电路	Hùbǔ jīngtǐguǎn luójì diànlù
CTM	Clock tone module	时钟与信号音模块	Shízhōng yǔ xìnhào yīn mókuài
CTNR	Carrier-to-noise ratio	载波比	Zàibō bǐ
CTNR	Carrier-to-thermal noise ratio	载波-热噪声比	Zàibō—rè zàoshēng bǐ
CTO	Chief technical officer	首席技术官	Shǒuxí jìshù guān
CTO	Chief technology officer	首席技术官	Shǒuxí jìshù guān
Ctor	Constructor	构造函数	Gòuzào hánshù
ctor	Constructor	构造器	Gòuzào qì
CTP	Computer to print	计算机直接印刷	Jìsuànjī zhíjiē yìnshuā
CTP	Connection termination point	连接终结点	Liánjiē zhōngjiédiǎn
C-TPDU	Command TPDU	TPDU 命令	TPDU mìnglìng
CTR	Common technical regulation	公共工程细则	Gōnggòng gōngchéng xìzé

CTR	Common technical regulation	通用技术规定	Tōngyòng jìshù guīdìng
CTR	Connect to resource	连接到资源	Liánjiē dào zīyuán
CTS	Carpal tunnel sydrome	计算机腕管综合症	Jìsuànjī wànguǎn zōnghézhèng
CTS	Clear to send	清除发送	Qīngchú fāsòng
CTS	Clear to send	允许发送协议	Yǔnxǔ fāsòng xiéyì
CTS	Common transport semantic	通用传输语义	Tōngyòng chuánshū yǔyì
CTS	Common type system	通用类型系统	Tōngyòng lèixíng xìtǒng
CTS	Communications and tracking sub-system	通信与跟踪子系统	Tōngxìn yǔ gēnzōng zixìtǒng
CTTE	Common TDMA terminal	公用时分多址终端	Gōngyòng shífēn duōzhǐ zhōngduān
CTX	Customer telephone exchange	用户电话交换机	Yònghù diànhuà jiāohuànjī
CUB	Carrier unit mother board	载频单元框背板	Zàipín dānyuán kuàngbèibǎn
CUC	Common user circuit	公共用户线路	Gōnggòng yònghù xiànlù
CUDN	Common user data network	公共用户数据网络	Gōnggòng yònghù shùjù wǎngluò
CUG	Close user group	闭合用户群	Bìhé yònghù qún
CUG	Closed user group	闭合用户群组	Bìhé yònghù qúnzǔ
CUG	Closed user group	闭锁用户群	Bìsuǒ yònghù qún
CUG SS	Closed user group supplementary service	闭合用户群补充业务	Bìhé yònghù qún bǔchōng yèwù
CUL	See you later (computer chat)	以后见	Yǐhòu jiàn
CuPc	Copper phthalo-cyanine	铜酞菁	Tóngtàijīng
CUSF	Call unrelated service function	与呼叫无关的业务功能	Yǔ hūjiào wúguānde yèwù gōngnéng
CV	Channel vocoder	通道音码器	Tōngdào yīnmǎqì
CV	Code violation	码违例	Mǎ wéilì
CV	Coding violation	编码违列	Biānmǎ wéiliè
CV	Computer virus	计算机病毒	Jìsuànjī bìngdú
CV	Connection view	连接可视	Liánjiē kěshì
CVBS	Color video broadcast signal	彩色全电视信号	Cǎisè quán diànshì xìnhào
CVC	Carrier virtual circuit	载波虚拟电路	Zàibō xūnǐ diànlù
CVE	Common vulnerabilities and exposures	通用漏洞披露	Tōngyòng lòudòng pīlù
CVPE	Collaborative virtual prototyping environment (CAD/CAM)	协作虚拟原型环境	Xiézuò xūnǐ yuánxíng huánjìng
CVS	Computer vision syndrome	计算机视觉综合症	Jìsuànjī shìjué zōnghézhèng
CVS	Connection view state	连接可视状态	Liánjiē kěshì zhuàngtài
CVSD	Continuously variable slope delta modulation	连续可变斜率增量调制	Liánxù kěbiàn xiélǜ zēngliàng tiáozhì
CVSD	Continuously variable slope delta modulation	连续可变斜率 △ 调制	Liánxù kěbiàn xiélǜ Δ tiáozhì
CVSDM	Continuously variable slope delta modulation	连续可变斜率增量方式	Liánxù kěbiàn xiélǜ zēngliàng fāngshì
CVSDM	Continuously variable slope delta modulation	连续可变的角变增量调制	Liánxù kěbiànde jiǎobiàn zēngliàng tiáozhì
CVT	Circuit validation test	电路有效测试	Diànlù yǒuxiào cèshì
CW	Call waiting	呼叫待时	Hūjiào dàishí
CW	Call waiting	呼叫等待	Hūjiào děngdài
CW	Call waiting supplementary service	呼叫等待补充业务	Hūjiào děngdài bǔchōng yèwù
CW	Carrier wave	载波	Zàibō
CW	Continuous wave	连续波	Liánxù bō
CW	Continuous wave transmission	连续波传输	Liánxù bō chuánshū
CW	Control word	控制字	Kòngzhì zì
CWDM	Coarse wavelength division multiplexing	粗波分复用	Cū bōfēn fùyòng
CWG	Chinese Wire Gauge	中国线规	Zhōngguó xiànguī
CWI	Character waiting integer	字符等待整体	Zìfú děngdài zhěngtǐ

CWI	Characteristic waveform interpolation	特征波形内插	Tèzhēng bōxíng nèichā
C-Win	Chinese Windows ©	中文视窗	Zhōngwén shìchuāng
CWND	Congestion window	拥塞窗口	Yōngsè chuāngkǒu
CWT	Character waiting time	字符等待时间	Zìfú děngdài shíjiān
CWTS	China Wireless Telecommunication Standards Research Group	中国无线通信标准研究组	Zhōngguó wúxiàn tōngxìn biāozhǔn yánjiū zǔ
CWTS	China Wireless Telecommunications Standards Group	中国无线通信标准组织	Zhōngguó wúxiàn tōngxìn biāozhǔn zǔzhī
CXD	Long distance cable line	长途电缆线路	Chángtú diànlǎn xiànlù
CXG	Long distance optical cable line	长途光缆线路	Chángtú guānglǎn xiànlù
CXM	Long distance open line	长途明线线路	Chángtú míngxiàn xiànlù
CZ	Facsimile communication	传真通信	Chuánzhēn tōngxìn

D

D	Data	数据	Shùjù
D	Demodulator	解调器	Jiětiáoqì
D	Dial (noun)	拔号盘	Bōhàopán
D	Diode	二极管	Èrjíguǎn
D	Dispatch telephone	调度电话	Diàodù diànhuà
D/A	Digital/analog conversion	数字模拟转换	Shùzì mónǐ zhuǎnhuàn
D/A	Digital/analog converter	数/模转换器	Shù/mó zhuǎnhuànqì
D/P	Document against payment	付款交单	Fùkuǎn jiāodān
DA	Data access	数据存取	Shùjù cúnqǔ
DA	Data address	数据地址	Shùjù dìzhǐ
DA	Debugging aids	调试工具	Tiáoshì gōngjù
DA	Decimal adder	十进制加法器	Shíjìnzhì jiāfǎqì
DA	Design algorithm	设计算法	Shèjì suànfǎ
DA	Destination address	目的地址	Mùdì dìzhì
DA	Dielectric anisotropy	介电性能各向异性	Jièdiàn xìngnéng gèxiàng yìxìng
DA	Dipole antenna	偶极子天线	Ǒujízi tiānxiàn
DA	Directional (antenna) array	定向天线阵	Dìngxiàng tiānxiàn zhèn
DA	Discrete address	离散地址	Lísàn dìzhǐ
DA	Dispersion accommodation	色散容纳	Sèsàn róngnà
DA	Dispersion accommodation	色散容纳技术	Sèsàn róngnà jìshù
DA	Dispersion accommodation	色散调节	Sèsàn tiáojié
Da	Displacement adder	移位加法器	Yíwèi jiāfǎqì
DA	Distribution amplifier	分配放大器	Fēnpèi fàngdàqì
DAB	Digital audio broadcast	数字音频广播	Shùzì yīnpín guǎngbō
DAC	Demand assignment controller	按需分配控制器	Ànxū fēnpèi kòngzhìqì
DAC	Digital to analog converter	数模传换器	Shù mó chuánhuànqì
DAC	Digital to analog converter	数模转换器	Shù mó zhuǎnhuànqì
DAC	Discretionary access control (Linux)	自主存取控制	Zìzhǔ cúnqǔ kòngzhì
DAC	Dual address cycle	双重地址周期	Shuāngchóng dìzhǐ zhōuqī
DAC	Dual-attached concentrator	双连接集中器	Shuāng liánjiē jízhōngqì
DAC	Point to multipoint multicast	点对多点组播业务	Diǎn duì duōdiǎn zǔbō yèwù
DACC	Direct access communication channel	直接存取通信信道	Zhíjiē cúnqǔ tōngxìn xìndào
DACD	Digital to analog conversion daughter board assembly	数模转换子集成板	Shù mó zhuǎnhuàn zǐjíchéng bǎn

DACD	Directory access control domain	号码簿访问控制域	Hàomǎbù fǎngwèn kòngzhì yù
DACEMS	Data communication equipment monitoring and switching	数据通信设备监控与转换	Shùjù tōngxìn shèbèi jiānkòng yǔ zhuǎnhuàn
DACI	Direct adjacent channel interference	直接相邻信道干扰	Zhíjiē xiānglín xìndào gānrǎo
DACL	Discretionary access control list	任意访问控制列表	Rènyì fǎngwèn kòngzhì lièbiǎo
DACL	Discretionary access control list	自由访问控制列表	Zìyóu fǎngwèn kòngzhì lièbiǎo
DACS	Digital access and cross-connect system	数字存取和交叉连接系统	Shùzì cúnqǔ hé jiāochā liánjiē xìtǒng
DACS	Discrete address communication system	离散地址通信系统	Lísàn dìzhǐ tōngxìn xìtǒng
DAD	Distributed array descriptor (Fortran)	分布数组描述	Fēnbù shù zǔ miáoshù
DADC	Direct access data channel	直接存取数据通道	Zhíjiē cúnqǔ shùjù tōngdào
DADPCM	Delay adaptive differential pulse code modulation	延迟自适应差分脉码调制	Yánchí zìshìyìng chāfēn màimǎ tiáozhì
DADSI	Demand assignment-digital speech interpolation	请求分配-数字式语音插入	Qǐngqiú fēnpèi—shùzì-shì yǔyīn chārù
DAE	Digital audio extraction	数子音频抓取	Shùzi yīnpín zhuāqǔ
DAE	Distributed agent environment	分布式代理环境	Fēnbù-shì dàilǐ huánjìng
DAEMON	Data adaptive evaluator and monitor	数据自适应鉴别器与监视器	Shùjù zìshìyìng jiànbiéqì yǔ jiānshìqì
DAFC	Double-adaptive file compression	双重自适应文卷压缩	Shuāngchóng zìshìyìng wénjuàn yāsuō
DAFDTA	Dipole antenna with feed points displaced transverse to dipole axis	馈电点沿轴的横向移动的偶极天线	Kuìdiàn diǎn yán zhóude héngxiàng yídòngde ǒují tiānxiàn
DAG	Directed acyclic graph	有向无环图	Yǒuxiàng wúhuán tú
DAG	Directed acyclic graph	有向无循环图	Yǒuxiàng wúxúnhuán tú
DAIRS	Dial access Information retrieval system	拨号存取信息检索系统	Bōhào cúnqǔ xìnxī jiǎnsuǒ xìtǒng
DAL	Data access language	数据访问语言	Shùjù fǎngwèn yǔyán
DAM	DECT authentication module	DECT 认证模型	DECT rènzhèng móxíng
DAM	Direct access method	直接存取法	Zhíjiē cúnqǔ fǎ
DAMA	Demand assignment multiple access	按申请分配-多址联接	Àn shēnqǐng fēnpèi-duō zhǐ liánjiē
DAMA	Demand assignment multiple access	按需分配多址	Ànxū fēnpèi duōzhǐ
DAMPS	Digital access protocol	数字访问协议	Shùzì fǎngwèn xiéyì
DAMPS	Digital advanced mobile phone service	数字化高级移动电话系统	Shùzìhuà gāojí yídòng diànhuà xìtǒng
D-AMPS	Digital advanced mobile phone service	数字先进移动电话业务	Shùzì xiānjìn yídòng diànhuà yèwù
D-AMPS	Digital-advanced mobile phone system	数字式现代移动电话系统	Shùzì-shì xiàndài yídòng diànhuà xìtǒng
DAMSYS	Directory assistance and messaging system	电话查号与通告系统	Diànhuà cháhào yǔ tōnggào xìtǒng
DAO	Data access object	数据访问对象	Shùjù fǎngwèn duìxiàng
DAO	Defense Acquisition Office (US)	国防采办	Guófáng cǎibàn
DAP	Data access protocol (in DECnet)	数据访问协议	Shùjù fǎngwèn xiéyì
DAP	Demand assignment protocol	按需分配协议	Ànxū fēnpèi xiéyì
DAP	Directory access protocol	号码簿访问协议	Hàomǎbù fǎngwèn xiéyì
DAR	Data address register	数据地址寄存器	Shùjù dìzhǐ jìcúnqì
DART	Dual-channel asynchronous receiver/transmitter	双信道异步接受器/发射器	Shuāng xìndào yìbù jiēshòuqì/ fāshèqì
DARTDB	Distributed active real-time database	分布式主动实时数据库	Fēnbù-shì zhǔdòng shíshí shùjùkù
DAS	Dual attachment station	双向连接站	Shuāngxiàng liánjiē zhàn
DAS	Dual-attachment station	双连接工作站	Shuāng liánjiē gōngzuòzhàn
DASS	Demand assignment signaling and switching (unit)	按需分配信令传送和交换（设备）	Ànxū fēnpèi xìnlìng chuánsòng hé jiāohuàn (shèbèi)
DAST	Direct analog storage technology	直接模拟存储技术	Zhíjiē mónǐ cúnchǔ jìshù
DATA	Data initialization (in FORTRAN)	数据初值语句	Shùjù chūzhí yǔjù
DATAPAC	Packet switched digital data network	分组交换数字数据网	Fēnzǔ jiāohuàn shùzì shùjù wǎng
DA-TDMA	Demand-assignment time division multiple access	按需求分配时分多重存取	Àn xūqiú fēnpèi shífēn duōzhòng cúnqǔ

DAUD	Destination audit	目的地状态查询	Mùdìdì zhuàngtài cháxún
DAV	Data above voice	话上数据	Huà-shàng shùjù
DAVA	Destination available (SS7)	目的地可用	Mùdìdì kěyòng
DAVIC	Digital Audio Video committee	数字音频视频委员会	Shùzì yīnpín shìpín wěiyuánhuì
DAVIC	Digital Audio Video committee	数字音像委员会	Shùzì yīnxiàng wěiyuánhuì
DAVID	Digital advanced mobile phone system	数字先进移动电话系统	Shùzì xiānjìn yídòng diànhuà xìtǒng
DB	Database	数据库	Shùjùkù
dB	Decibel	分贝	Fēnbèi
DB	Deep buffer (in RAM or ROM)	深度缓冲	Shēndù huǎnchōng
DB	Device bay	设备插架	Shèbèi chājià
DB	Direct burial	直接埋设	Zhíjiē máishè
DB	Dummy burst	虚拟脉冲串	Xūnǐ màichōng chuàn
DB	Dummy burst	虚拟突发脉冲序列	Xūnǐ tūfā màichōng xùliè
DB	Telegram, telegraph	电报	Diànbào
dB/m	Decibels per milliwatt	分贝/毫瓦	Fēnbèi/háowǎ
DB2M	Digital branching board (2Mb/s)	数字分支板	Shùzì fēnzhī bǎn
dBA	Adjusted decibels	调准分贝	Tiáozhǔn fēnbèi
DBA	Database administrator	数据库管理者	Shùjùkù guǎnlǐzhě
DBA	Dynamic bandwidth allocation	动态带宽分配	Dòngtài dàikuān fēnpèi
DBAAU	Dial backup auto answer unit	拨号盘备用自动应答设备	Bōhàopán bèiyòng zìdòng yìngdá shèbèi
DBAD	Data block address (in ORACLE)	数据块地址	Shùjù kuài dìzhǐ
DBCC	Database consistency checker (in SQL Server)	数据库一致性检查程序	Shùjùkù yīzhìxìng jiǎnchá chéngxù
DBCS	Double-byte character set	双字节字符集	Shuāng zìjié zìfú jí
DBF	Digital audio/video interactive decoder	数字音频/视频交互式译码器	Shùzì yīnpín/shìpín jiāohùshì yìmǎqì
DBFA	Dual band fiber amplifier	双波段光纤放大器	Shuāng bōduàn guāngxiān fàngdàqì
DBFA	Dual band fiber amplifier	双带光纤放大器	Shuāngdài guāngxiān fàngdàqì
DB-FM	Database fault management	数据库故障管理	Shùjùkù gùzhàng guǎnlǐ
DBH	Database handling	数据库处理	Shùjùkù chǔlǐ
DBMS	Database management system	数据库管理系统	Shùjùkù guǎnlǐ xìtǒng
DBOL	Database overload	数据库溢出	Shùjùkù yìchū
DBOS	Database organizing system	数据库组织系统	Shùjùkù zǔzhī xìtǒng
DBPSK	Differential binary phase shift keying	差动二进制移相键控	Chādòng èrjìnzhì yíxiāng jiànkòng
DBR	Deterministic bit rate	固定比特率	Gùdìng bǐtèlǜ
DBR	Deterministic bit rate	确定比特率	Quèdìng bǐtè lǜ
DBR	Digital control channel	数字控制信道	Shùzì kòngzhì xìndào
DBS	Digital broadcast satellite	数字广播卫星	Shùzì guǎngbō wèixīng
DBS	Direct broadcast satellite	直播卫星	Zhíbō wèixīng
DBS	Direct broadcast satellite	直接广播卫星	Zhíjiē guǎngbō wèixīng
DBS	Direct broadcasting by satellite	卫星直播	Wèixīng zhíbō
DBS-PC	Direct broadcast satellite PC	人造卫星直接广播式 PC	Rénzào wèixīng zhíjiē guǎngbō shì PC
DBSS	Database security system	数据库安全系统	Shùjùkù ānquán xìtǒng
DBU	Dial backup unit	拨号辅助设备	Bōhào fǔzhù shèbèi
D-BUS	Data bus	数据总线	Shùjù zǒngxiàn
DBX	Digital branch exchange	数字小型交换机	Shùzì xiǎoxíng jiāohuànjī
DC	Dedicated control	专用控制	Zhuānyòng kòngzhì
DC	Define constant (assembler term)	定义常数	Dìngyì chángshù

DC	Destination category	目的类	Mùdì lèi
DC	Device control	设备控制	Shèbèi kòngzhì
DC	Digital center	数字中心	Shùzì zhōngxīn
DC	Direct current	直流	Zhíliú
DC	Display console	显示控制台	Xiǎnshì kòngzhìtái
DC	Door contacts	大门传感器	Dàmén chuángǎnqì
DCA	Defense Communication Agency (US)	国防部通信局	Guófángbù tōngxìn jú
DCA	Distributed Bragg reflection	分布布拉格反射	Fēnbù Bùlāgé fǎnshè
DCA	Distributed communication architecture	分布式通信体系	Fēnbù-shì tōngxìn tǐxì
DCA	Distributed communication architecture	公布式通信体系	Gōngbùshì tōngxìn tǐxì
DCA	Dynamic channel allocation	动态波道配置	Dòngtài bōdào pèizhì
DCAA	Dolph-Chebyshev array antenna	多尔夫-契比舍夫天线阵	Duō-ěr-fū—Qì-bǐ-shè-fū tiānxiàn zhèn
DCAP	Data link switching client access protocol (IETF use)	数据转接客户访问协议	Shùjù zhuǎnjiē kèhù fǎngwèn xiéyì
DCB	Digital channel block	数字信道模块	Shùzì xìndào mókuài
DCC	Data circuit concentrator	数据电路集中器	Shùjù diànlù jízhōngqì
DCC	Data communication channel	数据通信通路	Shùjù tōngxìn tōnglù
DCC	Data communication channel	数据通信信道	Shùjù tōngxìn xìndào
DCC	Data communications channel	数据通信通道	Shùjù tōngxìn tōngdào
DCC	Data country code	数据国家代码	Shùjù guójiā dàimǎ
DCC	Define constant character	定义常数字符	Dìngyì chángshù zìfú
DCC	Digital color code	数字色码	Shùzì sèmǎ
DCC	Digital communication channel	数字通信通路	Shùzì tōngxìn tōnglù
DCC	Digital cross-correct	数字交叉校正	Shùzì jiāochā jiàozhèng
DCC	Direct cable connect	直接电缆连接	Zhíjiē diànlǎn liánjiē
DCCA	Duplication communication control board assembly	双重通信控制集成板	Shuāngchóng tōngxìn kòngzhì jíchéngbǎn
DCCH	Dedicated control channel	专用控制信道	Zhuānyòng kòngzhì xìndào
DCCP	Data communication control procedure	数据通信控制规程	Shùjù tōngxìn kòngzhì guīchéng
DCD	Data carrier detect	数据载体监测	Shùjù zàitǐ jiāncè
DCD	Define constant double	定义常数二字	Dìngyì chángshù èr zì
DCD	Document content description (in XML)	文件内容描述	Wénjiàn nèiróng miáoshù
DCDM	Digitally controlled delta modulation	数字控制增量调制	Shùzì kòngzhì zēngliàng tiáozhì
DCE	Data circuit (terminating) equipment	数据电路终接设备	Shùjù diànlù zhōngjiē shèbèi
DCE	Data circuit equipment	数据电路设备	Shùjù diànlù shèbèi
DCE	Data circuit terminating equipment	数据电路终端设备	Shùjù diànlù zhōngduān shèbèi
DCE	Data circuit terminating equipment	数字电路终接设备	Shùzì diànlù zhōngjiē shèbèi
DCE	Data communication equipment	数据通信设备	Shùjù tōngxìn shèbèi
DCE	Device access code	设备访问码	Shèbèi fǎngwèn mǎ
DCE	Distributed computing environment	分布式计算环境	Fēnbù-shì jìsuàn huánjìng
DCEA	Digital channel element assembly	数字信道集成件	Shùzì xìndào jíchéng jiàn
DCF	Data carrier failure detector	数据载波故障检测器	Shùjù zàibō gùzhàng jiǎncèqì
DCF	Data communication function	数据通信功能	Shùjù tōngxìn gōngnéng
DCF	Define constant floating	定义常数浮动	Dìngyì chángshù fúdòng
DCF	Disengage confirm	脱离确认	Tuōlí quèrèn
DCF	Disengage confirmed	退出确认	Tuìchū quèrèn
DCF	Dispersion compensation fiber	色散补偿光纤	Sèsàn bǔcháng guāngxiān

DCF	Distributed coordination function (IEEE 802.11 protocol)	分布协调功能	Fēnbù xiétiáo gōngnéng
DCFG	Fixed dispersion compensator	固定色散补偿器	Gùdìng sèsàn bǔchángqì
DCH	Dedicated channel	专用信道	Zhuānyòng xìndào
DCI	Data circuit terminating equipment	数据电路端接设备	Shùjù diànlù duānjiē shèbèi
DCI	Data communication interface	数据通信接口	Shùjù tōngxìn jiēkǒu
DCL	Data control language (for database)	数据控制语言	Shùjù kòngzhì yǔyán
DCL	Digital channel link	数字信道连接	Shùzì xìndào liánjiē
DCLMTS	Digital cellular land mobile telecommunication system	数字蜂窝陆地移动通信系统	Shùzì fēngwō lùdì yídòng tōngxìn xìtǒng
DCM	Data communication multiplexer	数据通信多路复用器	Shùjù tōngxìn duōlù fùyòngqì
DCM	Data conversion module	数据转换模块	Shùjù zhuǎnhuàn mókuài
DCM	Dispersion compensation module	色散补偿模块	Sèsàn bǔcháng mókuài
DCM	Distributed connection management	分布式连接管理	Fēnbù-shì liánjiē guǎnlǐ
DCM	Dynamic connection management	动态连接管理	Dòngtài liánjiē guǎnlǐ
DCME	Digital circuit multiplication equipment	数字电路倍增设备	Shùzì diànlù bèizēng shèbèi
DCME-ADPCM	Digital circuit multiplication equipment- adaptive differential pulse code modulation	数字电路倍增设备—自适应差分脉冲编码调制	Shùzì diànlù bèizēng shèbèi— zìshìyìng chāfēn màichōng biānmǎ tiáozhì
DCML	Data center markup language	数据中心标记语言	Shùjù zhōngxīn biāojì yǔyán
DCN	Data communication network	数据通信网	Shùjù tōngxìnwǎng
DCN	Digital circuit network	数字电路网	Shùzì diànlù wǎng
DCOM	Distributed component object model	分布式组件对象模型	Fēnbù-shì zǔjiàn duìxiàng móxíng
DCP	Data collection PC	数据收集 PC 机	Shùjù shōují PC-jī
DCP	Debugging computer program	调试计算机程序	Tiáoshì jìsuànjī chéngxù
DCP	Dedicated control program	专用控制程序	Zhuānyòng kòngzhì chéngxù
DCP	Diagnostic control program	诊断控制程序	Zhěnduàn kòngzhì chéngxù
DCP	Digital communication protocol	数字通信协议	Shùzì tōngxìn xiéyì
DCPCM	Differentially coherent pulse code modulation	差分相干脉码调制	Chāfēn xiānggān màimǎ tiáozhì
DCP-I	Distributed control panel - intelligent	智能型分散控制器	Zhìnéng-xíng fēnsàn kòngzhìqì
DCPSK	Differentially coherent phase shift keying	差分相干移相键控	Chāfēn xiānggān yíxiāng jiànkòng
DCRB	Diversity cell receiver board	分集小区接收板	Fēnjí xiǎoqū jiēshōu bǎn
DCS	Data coding scheme	数据编码方案	Shùjù biānmǎ fāng'àn
DCS	Digital cellular system	数字蜂窝系统	Shùzì fēngwō xìtǒng
DCS	Digital cross-connect system	数据交叉连接系统	Shùjù jiāochā liánjiē xìtǒng
DCS	Digital cross-connect system	数字交叉连接系统	Shùzì jiāochā liánjiē xìtǒng
DCS	Dispatch station controller	调度台控制器	Diàodùtái kòngzhìqì
DCS	Distributed control system	集散型控制系统	Jísàn xíng kòngzhì xìtǒng
DCSM	Dispersion compensation single mode optical fiber	色散补偿单模光纤	Sèsàn bǔcháng dānmó guāngxiān
D-CSMA	Directional carrier sense multiple access	定向载波控制多路存取	Dìngxiàng zàibō kòngzhì duōlù cúnqǔ
DCSN	Database control system nucleus	数据库控制系统核心	Shùjùkù kòngzhì xìtǒng héxīn
DCT	Discrete cosine transform	离散余弦变换	Lísàn yúxián biànhuàn
DCTE	Digital communication terminal equipment	数字通信终端设备	Shùzì tōngxìn zhōngduān shèbèi
DCU	Data channel unit	数据信道单元	Shùjù xìndào dānyuán
DCU	Diversity control unit	分集控制单元	Fēnjí kòngzhì dānyuán
DCV	Digitally coded voice	数字编码语音	Shùzì biānmǎ yǔyīn
DCW	Device control word	装置控制字	Zhuāngzhì kòngzhì zì
DCW	Digital chart of the world	世界数字化图	Shìjiè shùzìhuà tú

DD	Double density	双密度	Shuāng mìdù
DDA	Dipole-disk antenna	偶极子盘形天线	Ǒujízi pánxíng tiānxiàn
DDC	Digital down converter	数字下变频	Shùzì xiàbiànpín
DDC	Direct digital control	直接数字控制	Zhíjiē shùzì kòngzhì
DDC	Direct digital controller	直接数字控制器	Zhíjiē shùzì kòngzhìqì
DDC	Display data channel (video term)	显示数据通道	Xiǎnshì shùjù tōngdào
DDCMP	Digital data communications message protocol (in DECnet)	数字数据通信报文协议	Shùzì shùjù tōngxìn bàowén xiéyì
DDD	Direct distance dialing	长途直拨	Chángtú zhíbō
DDD	Direct distance dialing	远程直接拨号	Yuǎnchéng zhíjiē bōhào
DDD	Direct distance dialing	直接通话拨号	Zhíjiē tōnghuà bōhào
DDF	Digital distribution frame	数字分配架	Shùzì fēnpèijià
DDF	Digital distribution frame	数字配线架	Shùzì pèixiàn jià
DDG	Data dependence graph	数据依赖图	Shùjù yīlài tú
DDI	Direct dialing in	直接拨号	Zhíjiē bōhào
DDI	Direct dialing in	直接拨入	Zhíjiē bōrù
DDKTS	Department of Defense (DOD) kernel transition strategy	国防部总体过渡策略	Guófángbù zǒngtǐ guòdù cèlüè
DDL	Data definition language	数据定义语言	Shùjù dìngyì yǔyán
DDL	Data description language	数据描述语言	Shùjù miáoshù yǔyán
DDL	Distortion detection loop	失真检测环路	Shīzhēn jiǎncè huánlù
DDL	Distortion detection loop	失真指示器	Shīzhēn zhǐshìqì
DDL	Double dither loop	双抖动环	Shuāng dǒudòng huán
DDLCN	Distributed double-loop computer network	分布式双环路计算机网络	Fēnbù-shì shuāng huánlù jìsuànjī wǎngluò
DDM	Derived delta modulation	导出增量调制	Dǎochū zēngliàng tiáozhì
DDM	Derived delta modulation	二次增量调制	Èrcì zēngliàng tiáozhì
DDM	Digital data multiplexer	数字数据多路复用器	Shùzì shùjù duōlù fùyòngqì
DDM	Direction division multiplexing	方向分割复用	Fāngxiàng fēngē fùyòng
DDM	Distributed data management	分布式数据管理	Fēnbù-shì shùjù guǎnlǐ
DDMS	Digital data measuring system	数字数据测量系统	Shùzì shùjù cèliáng xìtǒng
DDN	Defense data network	防卫数据网	Fángwèi shùjù wǎng
DDN	Digital data network	数字数据网	Shùzì shùjù wǎng
DDN	Distributed data network	分布式数据网	Fēnbù-shì shùjù wǎng
DDO	Direct dialing overseas	直接对外拨号	Zhíjiē duìwài bōhào
DDOC	Directly dialed outgoing call	直接拨号去话呼叫	Zhíjiē bōhào qùhuà hūjiào
DDoS	Distributed denial of service attack	分布拒绝服务攻击	Fēnbù jùjué fúwù gōngjī
DDoS	Distributed denial of service attack	分布式拒绝服务攻击	Fēnbù-shì jùjué fúwù gōngjī
DDP	Datagram delivery protocol (Apple use)	数据报传送协议	Shùjùbào chuánsòng xiéyì
DDR	Dial-on-demand routing	按需拨号路由	Ànxū bōhào lùyóu
DDR	Dial-on-demand routing	拨号请求路由	Bōhào qǐngqiú lùyóu
DDR	Dial-on-demand routing	拨号选路	Bōhào xuǎnlù
DDR	Double data rate	双倍数据速率	Shuāngbèi shùjù sùlǜ
DDR-SDRAM	Double data rate SDRAM	双数据率 SDRAM	Shuāng shùjù lǜ SDRAM
DDS	Digital data service	数字数据业务	Shùzì shùjù yèwù
DDS	Direct dialing system	直接拨号系统	Zhíjiē bōhào xìtǒng
DDS	Direct digital (frequency) synthesizer	直接数字频率合成器	Zhíjiē shùzì pínlǜ héchéngqì
DDS	Direct digital synthesizer	直接数字式频率合成器	Zhíjiē shùzìshì pínlǜ héchéngqì

DDS	Dynamic debugging system	动态调式系统	Dòngtài diàoshì xìtǒng
DDSE	Digital data switching exchange	数字数据交换局	Shùzì shùjù jiāohuànjú
DDSM	Digital data switching matrix	数字数据开关矩阵	Shùzì shùjù kāiguān jǔzhèn
DDSMS	Digital dispatch security monitoring system	数字发送保密监控系统	Shùzì fāsòng bǎomì jiānkòng xìtǒng
DDSS	Double dynamic suspension system	双悬浮动态减震系统	Shuāng xuánfú dòngtài jiǎnzhèn xìtǒng
DDT	Device descriptor table	设备描述符表	Shèbèi miáoshùfú biǎo
DDTE	Digital data terminal equipment	数字数据终端设备	Shùzì shùjù zhōngduān shèbèi
DDTESM	Digital data terminal equipment service module	数字数据终端设备服务模块	Shùzì shùjù zhōngduān shèbèi fúwù mókuài
DDTS	Digital data transmission system	数字数据转输系统	Shùzì shùjù zhuǎnshū xìtǒng
DDTS	Direct dialing telephone system	直拨电话系统	Zhíbō diànhuà xìtǒng
DDTS	Direct dialing telephone system	直接电话系统	Zhíjiē diànhuà xìtǒng
DDU	Data interface board	数据接口板	Shùjù jiēkǒu bǎn
DDU	Delivered duty unpaid	完税前交货	Wánshuì-qián jiāohuò
DDW	Data descripition word	数据描述字	Shùjù miáoshù zì
DDX	Digital data exchange	数字数据交换局	Shùzì shùjù jiāohuànjú
DDX	Digital data packet switching network	数字数据分组交换网络	Shùzì shùjù fēnzǔ jiāohuàn wǎngluò
DDX	Digital data packet switching network	数字数据信包交换网络	Shùzì shùjù xìnbāo jiāohuàn wǎngluò
DDX	Dynamic data exchange	动态数据交换	Dòngtài shùjù jiāohuàn
DDXS	Digital data switching service	数字数据交换业务	Shùzì shùjù jiāohuàn yèwù
DE	Discard eligibility	丢弃指示	Diūqì zhǐshì
DE	Discard eligibility (in frame relay)	丢弃许可	Diūqì xǔkě
DE	Discard eligibility (in frame relay)	丢失指示	Diūshī zhǐshì
DEA	Data encryption algorithm	数据加密算法	Shùjù jiāmì suànfǎ
DEC	Declination	偏差	Piānchā
DEC	Decoder	译码器	Yìmǎqì
DECA	Digital echo canceler board (A)	数字回波抑制器 A	Shùzì huíbō yìzhìqì A
DECC	Digital echo-canceling chip	回波消除数字电路芯片	Huíbō xiāochú shùzì diànlù xìnpiàn
DECPSK	Differential encoded coherent phase shift keying	微分编码相干移相键控	Wēifēn biānmǎ xiānggān yíxiàng jiànkòng
DECT	Digital enhanced cordless telecommunication	增强数字无绳通讯	Zēngqiáng shùzì wúshéng tōngxùn
DECT	Digital enhanced cordless telecommunications	数字增强型无绳通信	Shùzì zēngqiáng-xíng wúshéng tōngxìn
DECT	Digital enhanced cordless telephone	数字增强无绳电话	Shùzì zēngqiáng wúshéng diànhuà
DECT	Digital European Cordless Telecommunication	欧洲数字无绳电信	Oūzhōu shùzì wúshéng diànxìn
DECT	Digital European Cordless Telecommunication	欧洲数字无绳通信	Oūzhōu shùzì wúshéng tōngxìn
DECT	Digital European Cordless Telecommunication system	泛欧数字无绳通信系统	Fàn'ōu shùzì wúshéng tōngxìn xìtǒng
DECT	Digital European cordless telephone	泛欧数字无绳电话系统	Fàn'ōu shùzì wúshéng diànhuà xìtǒng
DECT	Digital European Cordless Telephone	数位式欧洲无绳电话	Shùwèi-shì Oūzhōu wúshéng diànhuà
DEK	Data encryption key	数据加密键	Shùjù jiāmì jiàn
DEL	Delete character	删除字符	Shānchú zìfú
DELAY	Delay	延迟	Yánchí
DEM	Digital elevation model	数字高程模型	Shùzì gāochéng móxíng
DEM	Dynamic enterprise modeling	动态企业建模	Dòngtài qǐyè jiànmó
DEMS	Digital electronic message service	数字电子报文业务	Shùzì diànzǐ bàowén yèwù
DEMS	Digital error monitor sub-system	数字式误差监控子系统	Shùzì-shì wùchā jiānkòng zìxìtǒng
DEMUX	Demultiplexer	解复用器	Jiěfùyòngqì
DEOT	Disconnect end of transmission	传输结束断开	Chuánshū jiéshù duànkāi
DEPSK	Differential-encoded phase shift keying	差分编码移相键控	Chāfēn biānmǎ yíxiāng jiànkòng

DER	Distinguished encoding rules	唯一编码规则	Wéiyī biānmǎ guīzé
DES	Data encryption standard	数据加密标准	Shùjù jiāmì biāozhǔn
DES	Delivered ex-ship	船上交货	Chuánshàng jiāohuò
DESS	Digital electronic switching system	数字式电子交换系统	Shùzì-shì diànzǐ jiāohuàn xìtǒng
DET	Detach	分开	Fēnkāi
DET	Detach	分离	Fēnlí
DEW	Directed energy weapon	定向能武器	Dìngxiàng néng wǔqì
DF	Data frame	数据帧	Shùjù zhèng
DF	Dedicated file	专用文件	Zhuānyòng wénjiàn
DF	Designated forwarder	指定转发路由器	Zhǐdìng zhuǎnfā lùyóuqì
DF	Dissipation factor	耗散因数	Hàosàn yīnshù
DF	Distortion factor	失真因数	Shīzhēn yīnshù
DF	Distribution frame, distributor	配线架	Pèixiàn jià
DF^2Q	Distributed feedback fair queuing	分布反馈公平排队算法	Fēnbù fǎnkuì gōngping páiduì suànfǎ
DFB	Distributed feedback laser	分布反馈激光器	Fēnbù fǎnkuì jīguāngqì
DFB-LD	Distributed feedback laser diode	分布反馈型激光器	Fēnbù fǎnkuìxíng jīguāngqì
DFC	Detail flowchart	详细流程图	Xiángxì liúchéngtú
DFC	Disconnect forward connection	切断前向连接	Qiēduàn qiánxiàng liánjiē
DFECB	Define event control block	定义事件控制字组	Dìngyì shìjiàn kòngzhì zì zǔ
DFF	Dispersion flattened optical fiber	色散平坦光纤	Sèsàn píngtǎn guāngxiān
DFFMS	Digital feedback frequency modulation system	数字反馈调频系统	Shùzì fǎnkuì tiáopín xìtǒng
DFH	Differential frequency hopping	差分跳频	Chāfēn tiàopín
DFIS	Digital facsimile interface system	数字传真接口系统	Shùzì chuánzhēn jiēkǒu xìtǒng
DFL	Dynamic focus lens (video term)	动态聚焦	Dòngtài jùjiāo
DFM	Direct frequency modulation	直接调频	Zhíjiē tiáopín
DFP	Digital flat panel	数字式平面显示器	Shùzì-shì píngmiàn xiǎnshìqì
DFP	Dipole flat plane (antenna)	偶极子平面（天线）	Ǒujízi píngmiàn (tiānxiàn)
DFP	Distributed functional plane	分布式功能平面	Fēnbù-shì gōngnéng píngmiàn
DFPS	Digital ferrite phase shifter	数字式铁氧体移相器	Shùzì-shì tiěyǎngtǐ yíxiàngqì
DFS	Digital flex scan (video term)	数字伸缩扫描	Shùzì shēnsuō sǎomiáo
DFS	Dynamic flat shading (video term)	动态平面描影	Dòngtài píngmiàn miáoyǐng
DFSK	Double frequency shift keying	双移频键控	Shuāng yípín jiànkòng
DFSM	Dispersion flattened single mode optical fiber	色散平坦单模光纤	Sèsàn píngtǎn dānmó guāngxiān
DF-SS-CDMA	Direct frequency spread spectrum code division multiple access	直接扩频的码分多址	Zhíjiē kuòpínde mǎfēn duōzhǐ
DFT	Diagnostic function test	诊断功能测试	Zhěnduàn gōngnéng cèshì
DFT	Discrete Fourier transform	离散傅立叶变换	Lísàn fù-lì-yè biànhuàn
DFT	Discrete Fourier transform	离散傅氏变换	Lísàn fù-shì biànhuàn
DFW	Data freeway	数据自由路	Shùjù zìyóu lù
DFW	Data freeway	数据自由通道	Shùjù zìyóu tōngdào
DG	Differential gain	微分增益	Wēifēn zēngyì
DGD	Differential group delay	差分群迟延	Chāfēn qún chíyán
DGD	Differential group delay	差分群时延	Chāfēn qún shíyán
DGD	Differential group delay	微分群时延	Wēifēn qún shíyán
DGE	Dynamic gain equalizer	动态增益均衡器	Dòngtài zēngyì jūnhéngqì
DGM	Digital geospatial metadata	数字地理空间元数据	Shùzì dìlǐ kōngjiān yuán shùjù
DGNSS	Differential global navigation satellite system	差分全球卫星导航系统	Chāfēn quánqiú wèixīng dǎoháng xìtǒng

DGP	Directional gyroscope position	定向陀螺仪位置	Dìngxiàng tuóluóyí wèizhì
DGPS	Difference global positioning system	差分全球定位系统	Chāfēn quánqiú dìngwèi xìtǒng
DGS	Display generating software	显示发生软件	Xiǎnshì fāshēng ruǎnjiàn
DHCP	Dynamic host configuration protocol	动态宿主配置协议	Dòngtài sùzhǔ pèizhì xiéyì
DHCP	Dynamic host configuration protocol	动态主机分配协议	Dòngtài zhǔjī fēnpèi xiéyì
DHCP	Dynamic host configuration protocol	动态主机配置协议	Dòngtài zhǔjī pèizhì xiéyì
DHCP	Dynamic host control protocol	动态主机控制协议	Dòngtài zhǔjī kòngzhì xiéyì
DHO	Diversity handover	分集切换	Fēnjí qiēhuàn
DHP	Debugging helper	调试帮助程序	Tiáoshì bāngzhù chéngxù
DHS	Data handling sub-system	数据处理子系统	Shùjù chǔlǐ zixìtǒng
DHTML	Dynamic hypertext markup language	动态超文本标记语言	Dòngtài chāowénběn biāojì yǔyán
DHTML	Dynamic hypertext markup language	动态超文本置标语言	Dòngtài chāowénběn zhìbiāo yǔyán
DI	Deactivate indication	解除激活指示	Jiěchú jīhuó zhǐshì
DI	Decision intelligence	决策智能化	Juécè zhìnénghuà
DI	Digital input	数字输入	Shùzì shūrù
DIA	Document interchange architecture	文件交换体系结构	Wénjiàn jiāohuàn tǐxì jiégòu
DIAC	Dedicated inquiry access code	专用查询识别码	Zhuānyòng cháxún shíbié mǎ
DIAG	Diagnosis and monitoring	诊断和监测	Zhěnduàn hé jiāncè
DIB	Device-independent bitmap	设备无关性位图	Shèbèi wúguānxìng wèi tú
DIB	Directory information base	号码簿信息库	Hàomǎbù xìnxīkù
DIB	Dual independent bus	双独立总线	Shuāng dúlì zǒngxiàn
DIC	Digital image control (video term)	数字图像控制	Shùzì túxiàng kòngzhì
DID	Direct inward dialing	呼入直拨到分机用户	Hūrù zhíbō dào fēnjī yònghù
DID	Direct inward dialing	直接拨入	Zhíjiē bōrù
DID	Direct inward dialing	直接中继方式	Zhíjiē zhōngjì fāngshì
DIDS	Distributed intrusion detection system	分布式入侵检测系统	Fēnbù-shì rùqīn jiǎncè xìtǒng
DiffServ	Difference service model	差分服务模型	Chāfēn fúwù móxíng
DiffServ	Differentiated service (IETF use)	区分服务体系结构	Qūfēn fúwù tǐxì jiégòu
DiffServ	Differentiated service model (CAD/CAM)	区分服务模型	Qūfēn fúwù móxíng
DiffServ	Differentiated services	区别业务	Qūbié yèwù
Diff-serv	Differentiated services	区别服务	Qūbié fúwù
DIG	Digital imaging group	数字成图组织	Shùzì chéngtú zǔzhī
DIGEST	Digital Geographic Information exchange Standard	数字化地理信息交换标准	Shùzìhuà dìlǐ xìnxī jiāohuàn biāozhǔn
DII	Dynamic invocation interface (CORBA term)	动态调用接口	Dòngtài diàoyòng jiēkǒu
DIME	Direct Internet message encapsulation	直接因特网消息封装	Zhíjiē Yīntèwǎng xiāoxi fēngzhuāng
DIME	Dual independent map encoding	双重独立地图编码文件	Shuāngchóng dúlì dìtú biānmǎ wénjiàn
DIMM	Dual inline memory module	双边接触内存模组	Shuāngbiān jiēchù nèicún mózǔ
DIMM	Dual in-line memory module	双重内嵌式内存模块	Shuāngchóng nèiqiàn-shì nèicún mókuài
DIN	Deutsche Industrie Norm	德国工业标准	Déguó gōngyè biāozhǔn
DIP	Digital image processing	数字图象处理	Shùzì túxiàng chǔlǐ
DIP	Dual in-line package	双列直插式封装	Shuāng liè zhíchā-shì fēngzhuāng
DIP	Dual in-line package	双列直插	Shuāngliè zhíchā
DIR	Direct rendering infrastructure (video term)	基层直接渲染	Jīcéng zhíjiē xuànrǎn
DIS	Distributed interactive simulation	分布交互仿真	Fēnbù jiāohù fǎngzhēn
DISA	Data Interchange Standard Association	数据交换标准协会	Shùjù jiāohuàn biāozhǔn xiéhuì
DISA	Defense Information Systems Agency (US)	国防信息系统局	Guófáng xìnxī xìtǒngjú

DISC	Disconnect	拆开	Chāikāi
DISC	Disconnect	断开	Duànkāi
DISC	Disconnect	断连	Duànlián
DISC	Disconnect	切断	Qiēduàn
DISP	Displacement	位移	Wèiyí
DISPID	Dispatch identifier	分派标识符	Fēnpài biāozhì fú
DISS	Distribution shelf	分配架	Fēnpèi jià
DIT	Directory information tree	号码簿信息树	Hàomǎbù xìnxī shù
DIT	Directory information tree	目录信息树	Mùlù xìnxī shù
DITS	Digital information transmission system	数字信息传输系统	Shùzì xìnxī chuánshū xìtǒng
DIVA	Digital input voice answer block	数字输入声音应答部件	Shùzì shūrù shēngyīn yìngdá bùjiàn
DIVOTS	Data input voice output telephone system	数据输入话音输出电话系统	Shùjù shūrù huàyīn shūchū diànhuà xìtǒng
DIY	Do it yourself	自己动手作	Zìjǐ dòngshǒu zuò
DK	Data key	数据密钥	Shùjù mìyào
DKBP	Disk unit back panel	磁盘单元后面板	Cípán dānyuán hòumian bǎn
DKU	Disk unit	磁盘单元	Cípán dānyuán
DL	Data layer	数据层	Shùjù céng
DL	Data link	数据链路	Shùjù liànlù
DL	Data storage library	数据存储库	Shùjù cúnchǔkù
DL	Directionality	方向性	Fāngxiàngxìng
DL	Distribution list	分发表	Fēnfā biǎo
DL	Downlink	下行线路	Xiàxíng xiànlù
DLBP	Data link back panel	数据链路后面板	Shùjù liànlù hòumian bǎn
DLC	Data link connection	数据链路连接	Shùjù liànlù liánjiē
DLC	Digital loop carrier	数字环路载波	Shùzì huánlù zàibō
DLCI	Data link connection identifier	数据链路连接标志	Shùjù liànlù liánjiē biāozhì
DLCI	Data link connection identifier	数据链路连接标识	Shùjù liànlù liánjiē biāozhì
DLCI	Data link connection identifier	数据链路连接标识符	Shùjù liànlù liánjiē biāozhìfú
DLCI	Data link connection identity	数据链路连接识别	Shùjù liànlù liánjiē shíbié
DLCI	Data link connection identity	数据链路连接证实	Shùjù liànlù liánjiē zhèngshí
DLCN	Distributed loop computer network	分布式环形计算机网络	Fēnbù-shì huánxíng jìsuànjī wǎngluò
DL-Control	Data link control	数据链路控制	Shùjù liànlù kòngzhì
DL-CORE	Data link core	数据链路核心层	Shùjù liànlù héxīn céng
DLD	Data link discriminator	数据链路鉴别器	Shùjù liànlù jiànbiéqì
DLE	Data link escape	数据链转义	Shùjù liàn zhuǎnyì
DLE	Data link escape character	数据链路转义字符	Shùjù liànlù zhuǎnyì zìfú
DLE	Destination local exchange	目的地端局交换机	Mùdìdì duānjú jiāohuànjī
DLG	Digital line graph	数字线划图	Shùzì xiàn huàtú
DLINK	Downward link	下行线路	Xiàxíng xiànlù
DLL	Data link layer	数据链路层	Shùjù liànlù céng
DLL	Delay-locked loop	延迟锁定环	Yánchí suǒdìng huán
DLL	Digital leased line service	数字租用线业务	Shùzì zūyòng xiàn yèwù
DLL	Dynamic link library	动态链接库	Dòngtài liànjiēkù
DLL	Dynamic link library	动态链路库	Dòngtài liànlùkù
DLM	Data line multiplexer	数据线路复用器	Shùjù xiànlù fùyòngqì
DLM	Digital landscape model	数字景观模型	Shùzì jǐngguān móxíng

DLMCP	Distributed loop message communication protocol	分布式环形信息通信规约	Fēnbù-shì huánxíng xìnxī tōngxìn guīyuē
dLOS	Loss of signal defect	信号丢失缺陷	Xìnhào diūshī quēxiàn
DLP	Digital light processing (video term)	数字光处理	Shùzì guāng chǔlǐ
DLP	Discrete logarithm problem	离散对数问题	Lísàn duìshù wèntí
DLS	Damped least square method	阻尼最小二乘法	Zǔní zuìxiǎo èrchéngfǎ
DLS	Data link service	数据链路服务	Shùjù liànlù fúwù
DLS-2	Downloadable sounds level 2	第二代可下载音色	Dì'èrdài kěxiàzài yīnsè
DLSAP	Data link service access point	数据链路服务访问点	Shùjù liànlù fúwù fǎngwèndiǎn
DLSDU	Data link service data unit	数据链路服务数据单元	Shùjù liànlù fúwù shùjù dānyuán
DLSw	Data link switching protocol	数据链路交换协议	Shùjù liànlù jiāohuàn xiéyì
DLSw	Data-link switching	数据链路交换	Shùjù liànlù jiāohuàn
DLU	Digital line unit	数字线单元	Shùzì xiàn dānyuán
DLU	Digitizer logic unit	数字化逻辑单元	Shùzìhuà luóji dānyuán
DM	Deflection modulation	偏转调制	Piānzhuǎn tiáozhì
DM	Dense mode	密集模式	Mìjí móshì
DM	Direct melt method (fiber optic mfg)	直接熔融法	Zhíjiē róngróng fǎ
DM	Disconnected mode	断开方式	Duànkāi fāngshì
DM	Medium rate data	中速率数据	Zhōng sùlǜ shùjù
DMA	Deferred maintenance alarm	延缓维护告警	Yánhuǎn wéihù gàojǐng
DMA	Direct memory access	直接存储器存取	Zhíjiē cúnchǔqì cúnqǔ
DMA	Direct memory access	直接内存存取	Zhíjiē nèicún cúnqǔ
DMA	Direct memory access	直接内存访问	Zhíjiē nèicún fǎngwèn
DMA	Direct memory address	直接存储器地址	Zhíjiē cúnchǔqì dìzhǐ
DMA	Dynamic memory allocation	动态存储分配	Dòngtài cúnchǔ fēnpèi
DMAC	Direct memory access channel	直接存储器存取通道	Zhíjiē cúnchǔqì cúnqǔ tōngdào
DMAR	Direct memory access request	直接存储器存取请求	Zhíjiē cúnchǔqì cúnqǔ qǐngqiú
DMAT	Direct memory access transfer	直接存储器存取传送	Zhíjiē cúnchǔqì cúnqǔ chuánsòng
DMC	Discrete memoryless channel	离散无记忆信道	Lísàn wújìyì xìndào
DMCSS	Data mining for customer service and sales	客户服务和客户行销的资料探测	Kèhù fúwù hé kèhù xíngxiāode zīliào tàncè
DMD	Directory management domain	号码簿管理域	Hàomǎbù guǎnlǐ yù
DME	Direct memory execute	直接内存执行	Zhíjiē nèicún zhíxíng
DMF	Dispersion managed fiber	色散管理光纤	Sèsàn guǎnlǐ guāngxiān
DMG	Document maintenance Group (in CMM)	文档支持组	Wéndàng zhīchí zǔ
DMH	Data message handler	数据消息处理器	Shùjù xiāoxi chǔlǐqì
DMH	Data message handling	数据消息处理	Shùjù xiāoxi chǔlǐ
DMI	Definition of management information	管理信息定义	Guǎnlǐ xìnxī dìngyì
DMI	Desktop management interface	桌面管理接口	Zhuōmiàn guǎnlǐ jiēkǒu
DMI	Differential mode inversion (modulation)	微分反模调制	Wēifēn fǎnmó tiáozhì
DMI	Dynamic memory interface	动态存储器接口	Dòngtài cúnchǔqì jiēkǒu
DMIF	Delivery media integrated framework	传送媒体综合框架	Chuánsòng méitǐ zōnghé kuàngjià
DML	Data manipulation language	数据操纵语言	Shùjù cāozòng yǔyán
DML	Data manipulation language	数据操作语言	Shùjù cāozuò yǔyán
DMQ	Distributed message queue	分布式消息队列	Fēnbù-shì xiāoxi duìliè
DMR	Digital microwave radio	数字微波传输设备	Shùzì wēibō chuánshū shèbèi
DMR	Digital mobile radio	数字无线移动	Shùzì wúxiàn yídòng

DMR	Digital modularized radio	数字模块化无线电	Shùzì mókuàihuà wúxiàndiàn
DMS	Digital microwave system	数字微波系统	Shùzì wēibō xìtǒng
DMSE	Digital mean square error (criteria)	数字均方误差（标准）	Shùzì jūn fāng wùchā (biāozhǔn)
DMSO	Defense Modeling and Simulation Office (US)	国防建模和仿真办公室	Guófáng jiànmó hé fǎngzhēn bàngōngshì
DMT	Data message transmission	数据消息传送	Shùjù xiāoxi chuánsòng
DMT	Discrete multitone	不连续多基频模式	Bùliánxù duōjīpín móshì
DMT	Discrete multitone	离散多音	Lísàn duōyīn
DMT	Discrete multitone	离散多载波	Lísàn duōzàibō
DMT	Dispersion multitone	离散多音	Lísàn duōyīn
DMTF	Distributed management task force	分布管理程序	Fēnbù guǎnlǐ chéngxù
DMTF	Distributed management task force	公布式管理任务组	Gōngbùshì guǎnlǐ rènwuzǔ
DMZ	Demilitarized zone	隔离区	Gélí qū
DN	Destination network	终点网络	Zhōngdiǎn wǎngluò
DN	Directory number	电话号码	Diànhuà hàomǎ
DN	Directory number	号码簿号码	Hàomǎbù hàomǎ
DN	Distinguished name	可识别名	Kěshíbié míng
DN	Distinguished name	识别名	Shíbié míng
DN	Mobile subscriber directory number	移动用户电话码	Yídòng yònghù diànhuà mǎ
DN	Mobile user directory number	移动用户号码簿号码	Yídòng yònghù hàomǎbù hàomǎ
DNA	Digital network architecture	数字网络体系结构	Shùzì wǎngluò tǐxì jiégòu
DNA	Distributed interNet application	分布式网间应用程序	Fēnbù-shì wǎngjiān yìngyòng chéngxù
DNA	Distributed Internet application	分布式因特网应用程序	Fēnbù-shì Yīntèwǎng yìngyòng chéngxù
DNA	Distributed internet application architecture	分布式互联网应用结构	Fēnbù-shì hùliánwǎng yìngyòng jiégòu
DNIC	Data network identification code	数据网标别码	Shùjù wǎng biāobiémǎ
DNIC	Data network identification code	数据网标识码	Shùjù wǎng biāozhìmǎ
DNIC	Data network identification code	数据网络识别码	Shùjù wǎngluò shíbiéma
DNIC	Digital network identification code	数字网标识码	Shùzì wǎng biāozhì mǎ
DNID	Data network identifier	数据网络标识符	Shùjù wǎngluò biāozhìfú
DNL	Dynamic noise limiter	动态噪声限制器	Dòngtài zàoshēng xiànzhìqì
DNS	Directory name service	查号业务	Cháhào yèwù
DNS	Domain name server	域名服务器	Yù míng fúwùqì
DNS	Domain name service	域名服务	Yùmíng fúwù
DNS	Domain name system	域名系统	Yùmíng xìtǒng
DNS	Domain name system server	域名服务器	Yùmíng fúwùqì
DNV	Data number value	数字码值	Shùzì mǎ zhí
DO	Data object	数据目标	Shùjù mùbiāo
DO	Digital output	数字输出	Shùzì shūchū
DOA	Direction of arrival	到达方向	Dàodá fāngxiàng
DOA	Direction of arrival	入射方向	Rùshè fāngxiàng
DoCoMo	Do Communication More (Japanese telecom provider)	沟通更多	Gōutōng gèng duō
DOCSIS	Data over cable service interface specification	电缆数据业务接口规范	Diànlǎn shùjù yèwù jiēkǒu guīfàn
DOCSIS	Data over cable service interface specification	有线电视网络上的数据接口规格	Yǒuxiàn diànshì wǎngluò-shàngde shùjù jiēkǒu guīgé
DOCSIS	Data over cable service interface specification	有线电缆数据服务接口规范	Yǒuxiàn diànlǎn shùjù fúwù jiēkǒu guīfàn
DOCSIS	Data over cable service interface specifications	线缆服务接口数据规格	Xiànlǎn fúwù jiēkǒu shùjù guīgé
DOCSIS	Data over cable system interface standard	电缆网上的数据接口规范	Diànlǎn wǎngshàngde shùjù jiēkǒu guīfàn

DOD	Direct outward dialing	出局直接拨号	Chūjú zhíjiē bōhào
DOD	Direct outward dialing	直接拨出	Zhíjiē bōchū
DOD-1	Direct outward dialing one	一次拨号音	Yīcì bōhào yīn
DOF	Depth of field	多重境深	Duōzhòng jing shēn
DOM	Document object model	文档对象模型	Wéndàng duìxiàng móxíng
Domsat	Domestic communications satellite	国内通信卫星	Guónèi tōngxìn wèixīng
DOP	Degree of polarization	偏振度	Piānzhèndù
DOP	Dilution of precision	精度的降额	Jīngdùde jiàng'é
DoS	Denial of service attack	拒绝服务攻击	Jùjué fúwù gōngjī
DOS	Disk operating system	磁盘操作系统	Cípán cāozuò xìtǒng
DOSD	Digital on-screen display	同屏数字化显示	Tóngpíng shùzìhuà xiǎnshì
DOV	Data over voice	话上数据	Huà-shàng shùjù
DP	Detection point	检测点	Jiǎncè diǎn
DP	Dial pulse	号盘脉冲	Hàopán màichōng
DP	Dial/dialed pulse	拨号脉冲	Bōhào màichōng
DP	Distribution point	配线点	Pèixiàn diǎn
DP	Dynamic programming	动态规划	Dòngtài guīhuà
DPBX	Digital private branch exchange	数字式专用小交换机	Shùzì-shì zhuānyòng xiǎo jiāohuànjī
DPC	Data packet communications	数据分组通信	Shùjù fēnzǔ tōngxìn
DPC	Desktop personal computer	桌面个人计算机	Zhuōmiàn gèrén jìsuànjī
DPC	Destination point code	目的点编码	Mùdì diǎn biānmǎ
DPC	Destination point code	目的地址编码	Mùdì dìzhǐ biānmǎ
DPC	Destination point code	目的信令点编码	Mùdì xìnlìng diǎn biānmǎ
DPC	Destination point code	目的地点码	Mùdìdì diǎnmǎ
DPC	Destination point code	目的地信令点编码	Mùdìdì xìnlìngdiǎn biānmǎ
DPCA	Displaced phase center antenna	相移中心天线	Xiàngyí zhōngxīn tiānxiàn
DPCCH	Dedicated physical control channel	专用物理控制信道	Zhuānyòng wùlǐ kòngzhì xìndào
DPCCH/D	Dedicated physical control channel/downlink	下行专用物理控制信道	Xiàxíng zhuānyòng wùlǐ kòngzhì xìndào
DPCH/D	Dedicated physical channel/downlink	下行专用物理信道	Xiàxíng zhuānyòng wùlǐ xìndào
DPCM	Delta pulse code modulation	增量脉码调制	Zēngliàng màimǎ tiáozhì
DPCM	Differential pulse code modulation	差分脉冲编码调制	Chāfēn màichōng biānmǎ tiáozhì
DPCM	Differential pulse code modulation	差分脉码调制	Chāfēn màimǎ tiáozhì
DPCS	Distributed process control system	分布过程控制系统	Fēnbù guòchéng kòngzhì xìtǒng
DPDCH	Dedicated physical data channel	专用物理数据信道	Zhuānyòng wùlǐ shùjù xìndào
DPDCH/D	Dedicated physical data channel/downlink	下行专用物理数据信道	Xiàxíng zhuānyòng wùlǐ shùjù xìn dào
DPE	Distributed processing environment	分布式处理环境	Fēnbù-shì chǔlǐ huánjìng
DPFM	Discrete-time-pulse-frequency modulation	离散时间脉冲频率调制	Lísàn shíjiān màichōng pínlǜ tiáozhì
Dpi	Dots per inch	每英寸点数	Měi yīngcùn diǎnshù
dpi	Dots per inch (printer term)	每英寸的打印像素	Měi yīngcùnde dǎyìn xiàngsù
DPIR	Dial pulse incoming register	拨号脉冲入局记发器	Bōhào màichōng rùjú jìfāqì
DPLE	Digital principal local exchange	数字式市内主交换机	Shùzì-shì shìnèi zhǔ jiāohuànjī
DPLF	Dataphone line formatter	数据电话编制器	Shùjù diànhuà biānzhìqì
DPLL	Digital phase lock loop	数字式锁相环	Shùzì-shì suǒxiàng huán
DPM	Dual port memory	双端口存储器	Shuāng duānkǒu cúnchǔqì
DPMS	Display power management signalling	显示能源管理信号	Xiǎnshì néngyuán guǎnlǐ xìnhào
DPN	Data path not provided signal	不提供数据通路信号	Bù tígōng shùjù tōnglù xìnhào

DPN	Digital packet network	数字分组网	Shùzì fēnzǔ wǎng
DPN	Digital path not provided signal	不提供数字通路信号	Bùtígōng shùzì tōnglù xìnhào
DPN	Distributed processing network	分布处理网络	Fēnbù chǔlǐ wǎngluò
DPPM	Differential phase pulse modulation	微分相位脉冲调制	Wēifēn xiàngwèi màichōng tiáozhì
DPPS	Data post-processing system	数据后处理系统	Shùjù hòuchǔlǐ xìtǒng
DPR	Dedicated protection ring (optical network term)	专用保护环	Zhuānyòng bǎohù huán
DPRAM	Dual port RAM	双端口 RAM	Shuāng duānkǒu RAM
DPRD	Downlink pseudo-random data	下行伪随机数据	Xiàxíng wěisuíjī shùjù
DPS	Distributed processor sub-system	分配处理器子系统	Fēnpèi chǔlǐqì zixìtǒng
DPSK	Differential phase shift keying	差分相移键控	Chāfēn xiāngyí jiànkòng
DPSK	Differential phase shift keying	差分移相键控	Chāfēn yíxiāng jiànkòng
DPST	Double-pole, single-throw switch	双刀单掷开关	Shuāngdāo dānzhì kāiguān
DPT	Dynamic packet transmission	动态分组传送	Dòngtài fēnzǔ chuánsòng
DPT	Dynamic packet transport	动态包传输	Dòngtài bāo chuánshū
DPU	Digital patch unit	数字插入装置	Shùzì chārù zhuāngzhì
DPX	Diplexer	双工器	Shuānggōngqì
DQDB	Distributed queue dual bus	分布排队双总线	Fēnbù páiduì shuāng zǒngxiàn
DQDB	Distributed queue dual bus	分布式队列双总线	Fēnbù-shì duìliè shuāng zǒngxiàn
DQDB	Distributed queue, dual bus	分散队列双总线	Fēnsàn duìliè shuāng zǒngxiàn
DQL	Dynamic quadrapole lens	动态四极镜	Dòngtài sìjí jìng
DQM	Double quaternary modulation	双四相调制	Shuāng sìxiāng tiáozhì
DQPSK	Differential quadrature phase shift keying	差分正交相移键控	Chāfēn zhèngjiāo xiāngyí jiànkòng
DQPSK	Differential quadriphase shift keying	差分四相相移键控	Chāfēn sìxiāng xiāngyí jiànkòng
DQPSK	Differential quaternary phase shift keying	差分正交移相键控	Chāfēn zhèngjiāo yíxiāng jiànkòng
DQPSK	Differentially encoded quadrature phase-shift keying	差分编码正交移相键控	Chāfēn biānmǎ zhèngjiāo yíxiāng jiànkòng
DQPSK	Differentially encoded, quadriphase shift keying	差分编码四相相移键控	Chāfēn biānmǎ sìxiāng xiāngyí jiànkòng
DQU	Data accumulation unit	数据采集器	Shùjù cǎijíqì
DR	Deactivate request	解除激活请求	Jiěchú jīhuó qǐngqiú
DR	Designated router	指定路由器	Zhǐdìng lùyóuqì
DR	Designated router	指定转发者	Zhǐdìng zhuǎnfā zhě
DR	Designated router	指派路由器	Zhǐpài lùyóuqì
DR	Digital radio	数字无线电	Shùzì wúxiàndiàn
DR	Drift, wander	漂移	Piāoyí
DR	Drive	激动	Jīdòng
DR	Drive	驱动	Qūdòng
DRA	Dielectric rod antenna	棒状介质天线	Bàngzhuàng jièzhì tiānxiàn
DRAC	Dynamic resource allocation control	动态资源分配控制	Dòngtài zīyuán fēnpèi kòngzhì
DRAM	Dynamic random access memory	动态随机存储器	Dòngtài suíjī cúnchǔqì
DRAM	Dynamic random access memory	动态随机存取存储器	Dòngtài suíjī cúnqǔ cúnchǔqì
DRC	Directional response characteristics	指向性响应特性	Zhǐxiàng-xìng xiǎngyìng tèxìng
DRCS	Dynamically redefinable character set	动态再定义字符集	Dòngtài zàidìngyì zìfú jí
DRDBMS	Distributed relational DBMS	分布式关系数据库管理系统	Fēnbù-shì guānxì shùjùkù guǎnlǐ xìtǒng
DRDRAM	Direct RAMbus DRAM	直接 RAMbus 内存	Zhíjiē Rambus nèicún
DRDS	Distributed relational database structure	分布式关系数据库结构	Fēnbù-shì guānxì shùjùkù jiégòu
DRFS	Digital cellular radio frequency sub-system	数字蜂窝无线频率子系统	Shùzì fēngwō wúxiàn pínlǜ zixìtǒng
DRI	Declarative referential integrity (for database)	声明引用完整性	Shēngmíng yǐnyòng wánzhěng xìng

DRJ	Disengage reject	脱离拒绝	Tuōlí jùjué
DRJ	Disengage rejected	退出拒绝	Tuìchū jùjué
DRM	Digital rights management	数字权限管理	Shùzì quánxiàn guǎnlǐ
DRNC	Drift radio network controller	无线漂移网络控制器	Wúxiàn piāoyí wǎngluò kòngzhìqì
DRNS	Drift RNS [radio network sub-system]	RNS 漂移	RNS piāoyí
DRP	DECnet routing protocol	DECnet 路由选择协议	DECnet lùyóu xuǎnzé xiéyì
DRP	Distribution requirements planning	配送需求计划	Pèisòng xūqiú jìhuà
DRP	Distribution resource planning	配送资源计划	Pèisòng zīyuán jìhuà
DRQ	Disengage request	退出请求	Tuìchū qǐngqiú
DRQ	Disengage request	脱离请求	Tuōlí qǐngqiú
DRRS	Digital [Microwave] radio relay system	数字微波接力系统	Shùzì wēibō jiēlì xìtǒng
DRS	Delayed release (ISUP message)	延迟释放	Yánchí shìfàng
DRS	Digital reference sequence	数字参考序列	Shùzì cānkǎo xùliè
DRTDB	Distributed real-time database	分布式实时数据库	Fēnbù-shì shíshí shùjùkù
DRX	Discontinuous reception	非连续接收	Fēiliánxù jiēshōu
DRX	Discontinuous reception (mechanism)	不连续接收（机制）	Bùliánxù jiēshōu (jīzhì)
DS	Conduit suspension type	管吊式	Guǎndiào-shì
DS	Defect second	缺陷秒	Quēxiàn miǎo
DS	Dial service	自动电话业务	Zìdòng diànhuà yèwù
DS	Dial system	拨号系统	Bōhào xìtǒng
DS	Differentiated service	差分业务	Chāfēn yèwù
DS	Digital section or segment	数字段	Shùzì duàn
DS	Digital synchronization	数字同步	Shùzì tóngbù
DS	Diode switch	二极管开关	Èrjíguǎn kāiguān
DS	Direct spread spectrum	直接扩频	Zhíjiē kuòpín
DS	Direct synchronization (in CORBA)	直接同步协议	Zhíjiē tóngbù xiéyì
DS	Directory system	号码簿系统	Hàomǎbù xìtǒng
DS	Directory system	目录服务系统	Mùlù fúwù xìtǒng
DS	Disconnecting switch	切断开关	Qiēduàn kāiguān
DS	Distant surveillance	远距离监视	Yuǎnjùlí jiānshì
DS/DD	Double side/double density (disk)	双面双密度（磁盘）	Shuāngmiàn shuāng mìdù (cípán)
DS-1	Digital standard one (lowest data rate = 2Mbps)	一次群	Yīcì qún
DS-3	Digital standard 3 (3rd level digital standard transmission rate = 34Mbps)	三次群	Sāncì qún
DS-4	Digital standard 4 (4th digital standard rate =140Mbps)	四次群	Sìcì qún
DSA	Digital signature algorithm	数字签名算法	Shùzì qiānmíng suànfǎ
DSA	Directory system agent	号码簿系统代理	Hàomǎbù xìtǒng dàilǐ
DSA	Directory system agent (program)	目录系统代理（程序）	Mùlù xìtǒng dàilǐ (chéngxù)
DSA-ACK	Dynamic service addition acknowledgement request message	动态业务增加确认消息	Dòngtài yèwù zēngjiā quèrèn xiāoxi
DSA-REQ	Dynamic service addition request message	动态业务增加请求消息	Dòngtài yèwù zēngjiā qǐngqiú xiāoxi
DSA-RSP	Dynamic service addition response message	动态业务增加响应消息	Dòngtài yèwù zēngjiā xiǎngyìng xiāoxi
DSB	Device status bit	设备状态位	Shèbèi zhuàngtài wèi
DSB	Dial system B-switchboard	拨号制 B 交换台	Bōhào zhì B jiāohuàntái
DSB	Distribution switchboard	分配交换台	Fēnpèi jiāohuàntái
DSB	Double sideband	双边带	Shuāng biāndài
DSB	Double sideband	双边带	Shuāngbiāndài

DSBAM	Double sideband amplitude modulation	双边带幅度调制	Shuāng biāndài fúdù tiáozhì
DSC	Dedicated signaling channel	专用信令信道	Zhuānyòng xìnlìng xìndào
DSC	Digital satellite center	数字卫星中心	Shùzì wèixīng zhōngxīn
DSC	Digital service channel	数字公务通道	Shùzì gōngwù tōngdào
DSC	Digital service channels	数字业务信道	Shùzì yèwù xìndào
DSC	Digital service circuit	数字业务电路	Shùzì yèwù diànlù
DSC	Digital subscriber controller	数字用户控制器	Shùzì yònghù kòngzhìqì
DSC	Distant station connected	远端站连接	Yuǎnduān zhàn liánjiē
DSC	District switching center	区域交换中心	Qūyù jiāohuàn zhōngxīn
DSCA	European Digital Cordless Telephone (DECT) standard cipher algorithm	欧洲数字无绳电话标准密码算法	Oūzhōu shùzì wúshéng diànhuà biāozhǔn mìmǎ suànfǎ
DSC-ACK	Dynamic service change acknowledgement message	动态业务改变确认消息	Dòngtài yèwù gǎibiàn quèrèn xiāoxi
DS-CDMA	Direct sequence code division multiple access	直接序列码分多址	Zhíjiē xùliè mǎfēn duōzhǐ
DS-CDMA	Direct-sequence code division multiple access	直扩码分多址	Zhíkuò mǎfēn duōzhǐ
DSCF	Dispersion slope compensating fiber	色散斜率补偿光纤	Sèsàn xiélǜ bǔcháng guāngxiān
DSCH	Downlink shared channel	下行共用信道	Xiàxíng gòngyòng xìndào
DSCH	Downlink shared channel	下行链路共享信道	Xiàxíng liànlù gòngxiǎng xìndào
DSC-REQ	Dynamic service change request message (for data over cable- docsis)	动态业务改变请求消息	Dòngtài yèwù gǎibiàn qǐngqiú xiāoxi
DSC-RSP	Dynamic service change response message	动态业务改变响应消息	Dòngtài yèwù gǎibiàn xiǎngyìng xiāoxi
DSCS	Digital simulator computer system	数字模拟计算机系统	Shùzì mónǐ jìsuànjī xìtǒng
DSD	Data service division	数据服务部门	Shùjù fúwù bùmén
DSD	Data storage device	数据存储器	Shùjù cúnchǔqì
DSD	Direct stream digital	直接数字信号流	Zhíjiē shùzì xìnhào liú
DSD	Disk storage device	磁盘存储器	Cípán cúnchǔqì
DSD	Dynamic separation of duties	动态取责分离	Dòngtài qǔzé fēnlí
DSD-REQ	Dynamic service deletion request message	动态业务删除请求消息	Dòngtài yèwù shānchú qǐngqiú xiāoxi
DSD-RSP	Dynamic service deletion response message	动态业务删除响应消息	Dòngtài yèwù shānchú xiǎngyìng xiāoxi
DSDS	Dataphone switched digital service	数据电话交换数字业务	Shùjù diànhuà jiāohuàn shùzì yèwù
DSDV	Destination-sequenced distance vector	目的序列距离矢量	Mùdì xùliè jùlí shǐliàng
DSE	Data switch exchange	数据交换机	Shùjù jiāohuànjī
DSE	Data switching equipment	数据交换设备	Shùjù jiāohuàn shèbèi
DSE	Data switching exchange	数据传接交换台	Shùjù chuánjiē jiāohuàntái
DSE	Data switching exchange	数据转换交换机	Shùjù zhuǎnhuàn jiāohuànjī
DSF	Decode status flag	解码状态标志	Jiěmǎ zhuàngtài biāozhì
DSF	Dispersion-shift fiber	色散移位光纤	Sèsàn yíwèi guāngxiān
DSF	Dispersion-shifted optical fiber	色散漂移光纤	Sèsàn piāoyí guāngxiān
DSF	Dispersion-shifted optical fiber	色散位移光纤	Sèsàn wèiyí guāngxiān
DSI	Data serial interface	数据串行接口	Shùjù chuànháng jiēkǒu
DSI	Digit sequence integrity	数字序列完整性	Shùzì xùliè wánzhěngxìng
DSI	Digital speech interpolation	数字话音插空	Shùzì huàyīn chākōng
DSI	Digital speech interpolation	数字话音插入	Shùzì huàyīn chārù
DSI	Dynamic skeleton interface (CORBA term)	动态框架接口	Dòngtài kuàngjià jiēkǒu
DSI	Dynamic skeleton invocation (CORBA term)	动态骨架调用	Dòngtài gǔjià diàoyòng
DSK	Delay shift keying	延迟移位键控	Yánchí yíwèi jiànkòng
DSL	Data strobe link	数据选通连接	Shùjù xuǎntōng liánjiē

DSL	Digital subscriber line	数字用户线	Shùzì yònghù xiàn
DSL	Digital subscriber line board	数字用户电路板	Shùzì yònghù diànlù bǎn
DSL	Digital subscriber loop	数字用户环路	Shùzì yònghù huánlù
DSLAM	Digital subscriber line access multiplexer	数字用户线接入复用器	Shùzì yònghù xiàn jiērù fùyòngqì
DSLM	Dynamic single-longitudinal mode	动态单纵模	Dòngtài dānzòngmó
DSMA	Distributed scheduling multiple access	分布调度多路存取	Fēnbù diàodù duōlù cúnqǔ
DSMA/CD	Digital sense multiple access with collision detection	带碰撞检测的数字侦听多址访问	Dài pèngzhuàng jiǎncède shùzì zhēntīng duōzhǐ fǎngwèn
DSM-CC	Digital storage media-control command	数字存储媒体–控制命令	Shùzì cúnchǔ méitǐ—kòngzhì mìnglìng
DSM - CC	Digital storage media - control command	数字存储媒体 - 控制命令	Shùzì cúnchǔ méitǐ-kòngzhì mìnglìng
DSM-CC U-U	Digital storage media - control command, user-to-user	数字存储媒体 - 控制命令用户至用户	Shùzì cúnchǔ méitǐ-kòngzhì mìnglìng yònghù zhì yònghù
DSN	Data source name (for database)	数据源名称	Shùjù yuán míngchēng
DSN	Digital switch network	数字交换网络	Shùzì jiāohuàn wǎngluò
DSN	Distributed star network	星形分配网	Xīngxíng fēnpèi wǎng
DSP	Data signal processor	数据信号处理器	Shùjù xìnhào chǔlǐqì
DSP	Delivery service partner	交付服务合伙人	Jiāofù fúwù héhuǒrén
DSP	Device stop	设备停止	Shèbèi tíngzhǐ
DSP	Digital signal processing	数字信号处理	Shùzì xìnhào chǔlǐ
DSP	Digital signal processor	数字信号处理器	Shùzì xìnhào chǔlǐqì
DSP	Directory system protocol	号码簿系统协议	Hàomǎbù xìtǒng xiéyì
DSP	Domain specific part	域特定部分	Yù tèdìng bùfen
DSPN	Deterministic and stochastic Petri net	确定与随机 Petri 网	Quèdìng yǔ suíjī Petri wǎng
DSPU	Downstream physical unit	下游物理部件	Xiàyóu wùlǐ bùjiàn
DSR	Data set ready	数据集就绪	Shùjù jí jiùxù
DSR	Dynamic source routing	动态源路由	Dòngtài yuán lùyóu
DSRS	Data signal rate selection (signal)	数据信号率选择（信号）	Shùjù xìnhào lǜ xuǎnzé (xìnhào)
DSS	Decision and support system	决策和支持系统	Juécè hé zhīchí xìtǒng
DSS	Decision support system	决策支持系统	Juécè zhīchí xìtǒng
DSS	Digital satellite standard	数字卫星标准	Shùzì wèixīng biāozhǔn
DSS	Digital speech signal	数字话音信号	Shùzì huàyīn xìnhào
DSS	Digital switching system	数字交换系统	Shùzì jiāohuàn xìtǒng
DSS	Display support software	显示支援软件	Xiǎnshì zhīyuán ruǎnjiàn
DSS1	Digital subscriber signaling no1	1 号数字用户信令	Yihào shùzì yònghù xìnling
DSS1	Digital subscriber signaling system no. one	数字用户信令系统 1	Shùzì yònghù xìnling xìtǒng 1
DSS1	Digital subscriber signaling system one	一号数字用户信令系统	Yīhào shùzì yònghù xìnlìng xìtǒng
DSSM	Dispersion-shifted single mode optical fiber	色散位移单模光纤	Sèsàn wèiyí dānmó guāngxiān
DSSS	Demand-assigned signaling and switching unit sub-system	请求分配信号发送与转换子系统	Qǐngqiú fēnpèi xìnhào fāsòng yǔ zhuǎnhuàn zixìtǒng
DSSS	Direct sequence spread spectrum	直接时序扩展频谱	Zhíjiē shíxù kuòzhǎn pínpǔ
DSSS	Direct sequence spread spectrum	直接序列扩频	Zhíjiē xùliè kuòpín
DSSS	Direct sequence spread spectrum	直接序列展频技术	Zhíjiē xùliè zhǎnpín jìshù
DS-SS-CDMA	Direct sequence spread spectrum code division multiple access	直接序列扩频码分多址接入	Zhíjiē xùliè kuòpín mǎfēn duōzhǐ jiērù
DST	Destination host	目标主机	Mùbiāo zhǔjī
DST	Device start	设备启动	Shèbèi qǐdòng
DST	Dispersion supported transmission	色散支持传输	Sèsàn zhīchí chuánshū

DST	Drive self test	磁盘自检程序	Cípán zìjiǎn chéngxù
DSTE	Data subscriber terminal equipment	数据用户终端设备	Shùjù yònghù zhōngduān shèbèi
DSTM	Dual stack transition mechanism (in IPv6)	双栈过渡机制	Shuāng zhàn guòdù jīzhì
DSU	Data service unit	数据服务单元	Shùjù fúwù dānyuán
DSU	Data services unit	数据业务单元	Shùjù yèwù dānyuán
DSU	Digital service unit	数字业务单元	Shùzì yèwù dānyuán
DSU-R	Digital service unit-radio	用户无线数字业务单元	Yònghù wúxiàn shùzì yèwù dānyuán
DSVD	Digital simultaneous voice and data (ITU-T Recommendation H.320)	声音和数据同时传输协议	Shēngyīn hé shùjù tóngshí chuánshū xiéyì
DSVT	Digital secure voice terminal	保密数字通信音频终端	Bǎomì shùzì tōngxìn yīnpín zhōngduān
DSVT	Digital subscriber voice terminal	数字通信用户音频终端	Shùzì tōngxìn yònghù yīnpín zhōngduān
DSW	Device status word	设备状态字	Shèbèi zhuàngtài zì
DT	Delay transmission	延迟传输	Yánchí chuánshū
DT	Dial tone	拨号音	Bōhào yīn
DT/ECM	Digital trunk/echo canceler module	数字中继/回波抑制模块	Shùzì zhōngjì/huíbō yìzhì mókuài
DT1	Data form1	数据形式 1	Shùjù xíngshì 1
DTAM	Document transfer and manipulation user	文件传送和管理操作用户	Wénjiàn chuánsòng hé guǎnlǐ cāozuò yònghù
DTAP	Direct transfer application part	直接传递应用部分	Zhíjiē chuándì yìngyòng bùfen
DTAP	Direct transfer application part	直接转换应用部分	Zhíjiē zhuǎnhuàn yìngyòng bùfen
DTAP	Direct transmission application part	直接传输应用部分	Zhíjiē chuánshū yìngyòng bùfen
DTASI	Digital time assignment speech interpolation	数字时间分配语言内插入	Shùzì shíjiān fēnpèi yǔyán nèichārù
DTBP	Digital trunk back panel	数字中继后面板	Shùzì zhōngjì hòumian bǎn
DTC	Distributed transaction coordinator (in SQL Server)	分布式事务协调器	Fēnbùshì shìwù xiétiáo qì
DTCH	Dedicated traffic channel	专用业务信道	Zhuānyòng yèwù xìndào
DTD	Data time-slot distribution (board)	数据时隙分配板	Shùjù shíxì fēnpèi bǎn
DTD	Delay transmission diversity	延迟发送分集	Yánchí fāsòng fēnjí
DTD	Document type definition	文档类型定义	Wéndàng lèixíng dìngyì
DTD	Document type definition (in XML)	文件类型定义	Wénjiàn lèixíng dìngyì
DTDMA	Distributed time division multiple access	分布时分多重存取	Fēnbù shífēn duōzhòng cúnqǔ
DTDS	Digital television display system	数子电视显示系统	Shùzi diànshì xiǎnshì xìtǒng
DTE	Data terminal (or termination) equipment	数据终端设备	Shùjù zhōngduān shèbèi
DTE	Data terminal equipment	数字终端设备	Shùzì zhōngduān shèbèi
DTE	Data transmission equipment	数据传输设备	Shùjù chuánshū shèbèi
DTF	Data transmission function	数据传输函数	Shùjù chuánshū hánshù
DTH	Digitally compressed direct satellite broadcast	数字压缩卫星直播	Shùzì yāsuō wèixīng zhíbō
DTH	Direct to home	直接至家庭	Zhíjiē zhì jiātíng
DTI	Digital trunk interface	数字中继接口	Shùzì zhōngjì jiēkǒu
DTI	Domestic trunk interface	国内干线接口	Guónèi gànxiàn jiēkǒu
DTL	Designated transit list	指定转接列表	Zhǐdìng zhuǎnjiē lièbiǎo
DTL	Designated transit list	指定转接序列	Zhǐdìng zhuǎnjiē xùliè
DTL	Designated transit list	指定的转接一览表	Zhǐdìngde zhuǎnjiē yīlǎnbiǎo
DTL	Diode transistor logic circuit	二机管晶体管逻辑电路	Erjīguǎn jīngtǐguǎn luóji diànlù
DTm	Digital tandem	数字汇接局	Shùzì huìjiējú
DTM	Digital terrain model	数字地形模型	Shùzì dìxíng móxíng
DTM	Digital trunk board (module)	数字中继板(块)	Shùzì zhōngjì bǎn (kuài)
DTM	Digital trunk module	数字中继板	Shùzì zhōngjì bǎn

DTM	Duration time modulation	持续时间调制	Chíxù shíjiān tiáozhì
DTM	Dynamic synchronous transfer mode	动态同步传送模式	Dòngtài tóngbù chuánsòng móshì
DTMF	Dual tone multi-frequency	双音多频	Shuāngyīn duōpín
DTMU	Digital termination multiplex unit	数字终端多路复用装置	Shùzì zhōngduān duōlù fùyòng zhuāngzhì
Dtor	Destructor	析构器	Xīgòuqì
dtor	Destructor (function in software)	析构函数	Xīgòu hánshù
DTP	Data transfer protocol	数据传送协议	Shùjù chuánsòng xiéyì
DTP	Data transmission protocol	数据传输协议	Shùjù chuánshū xiéyì
DTP	Dynamic trunk protocol	思科动态中继协议	Sī-kē dòngtài zhōngjì xiéyì
DTR	Data transmission rate	数据传送速率	Shùjù chuánsòng sùlǜ
DTS	Data transformation services (in SQL Server)	数据转换服务	Shùjù zhuǎnhuàn fúwù
DTS	Digital theater system	数字影院系统	Shùzì yǐngyuàn xìtǒng
DTS	Dual -technology sensor	双鉴传感器	Shuāng jiàn chuángǎnqì
DTSTLS	Double time-stamp transaction-level synchronization	双时间印的事各级同步	Shuāng shíjiān yìnde shì gèjí tóngbù
DTX	Discontinous transmission	间断传输	Jiànduàn chuánshū
DTX	Discontinuous transmission	非连续传输	Fēiliánxù chuánshū
DTX	Discontinuous transmission	非连续发射	Fēiliánxù fāshè
DTX	Discontinuous transmission	非连续发信	Fēiliánxù fāxìn
DTX	Discontinuous transmission (mechanism)	不连续发送（机制）	Bùliánxù fāsòng (jīzhì)
DU	Digital unit	数字单元	Shùzì dānyuán
DUA	Directory user agent	号码簿用户代理	Hàomǎbù yònghù dàilǐ
DUA	Directory user agent	目录用户代理	Mùlù yònghù dàilǐ
DUAL	Diffusing update algorithm	扩散修正算法	Kuòsàn xiūzhèng suànfǎ
DUBB	Digital unit back board	数字单元后面板	Shùzì dānyuán hòumian bǎn
DUBB-A	Digital unit backplane board	数字单元底版	Shùzì dānyuán dǐbǎn
DUC	Digital up-converter	数字上变频	Shùzì shàngbiànpín
DUN	Dial-up networking	拨号上网	Bōhào shangwǎng
DUNA	Destination unavailable (SS7)	目的地不可用	Mùdìdì bùkěyòng
DUP	Data user part	数据用户部分	Shùjù yònghù bùfen
DUPU	Destination user part unavailable (SS7)	目的地用户部分不可用	Mùdìdì yònghù bùfen bùkěyòng
DUT	Device under test	被测设备	Bèicè shèbèi
DUT	Device under test	被测器件	Bèicè qìjiàn
DUV	Data under voice	话下数据	Huà-xià shùjù
DUV	Data under voice transmission	话下数据传输	Huà-xià shùjù chuánshū
DV	Digital video	数字视频	Shùzì shìpín
DVA	Device address	装置地址	Zhuāngzhì dìzhǐ
DVB	Digital video broadcast	数字电视广播	Shùzì diànshì guǎngbō
DVB	Digital video broadcast	数字视频广播	Shùzì shìpín guǎngbō
DVD	Digital video disk	数字视频光盘	Shùzì shìpín guāngpán
DVD	Digital video disk	数字式影视光盘	Shùzì-shì yǐngshì guāngpán
DVI	Digital video interface	数字视频接口	Shùzì shìpín jiēkǒu
DVMRP	Distance vector multicast routing protocol	距离矢量组播路由协议	Jùlí shǐliàng zǔbō lùyóu xiéyì
DVMRP	Distance vector multicast routing protocol	距离向量多点广播路由选择协议	Jùlí xiàngliàng duō diǎn guǎngbō lùyóu xuǎnzé xiéyì
DVMRP	Distance vector multicast routing protocol	距离向量组播路由协议	Jùlí xiàngliàng zǔbō lùyóu xiéyì
DVR	Digital video recorder	数字录像机	Shùzì lùxiàngjī

DW	Data warehouse	数据仓库	Shùjù cāngkù
DW	Device wait	设备等待	Shèbèi děngdài
DWDM	Dense wavelength division multiplexing	密集型波分复用	Mìjíxíng bōfēn fùyòng
DWDM	Dense wavelength division multiplex	波长密集型复用技术	Bōcháng mìjíxíng fùyòng jìshù
DWDM	Dense wavelength division multiplexer	密集波分复用器	Mìjí bōfēn fùyòngqì
DWDM	Dense wavelength division multiplexing	密集波分复用	Mìjí bōfēn fùyòng
DWF	Double window fiber	双窗孔纤维	Shuāng chuāngkǒng xiānwéi
DWFI	Dense wavelength division multiplexer filter	密集波分复用滤波器	Mìjí bōfēn fùyòng lǜbōqì
DWL	Dominant wavelength	主波长	Zhǔ bōcháng
DWMT	Discrete wavelet multiTone	离散小波多音	Lísàn xiǎobō duō yīn
DwPTS	Downlink pilot time slot	下行导引时隙	Xiàxíng dǎoyǐn shíxì
DWTS	Digital multi-wavelength transmission system	数字多波段传输系统	Shùzì duōbōduàn chuánshū xìtǒng
DX	Demultiplex	多路分用	Duōlù fēnyòng
DX2M	Digital cross-connect board (2Mb/s)	数字交换板	Shùzì jiāohuàn bǎn
DXC	Digital cross-connect	数字交叉连接	Shùzì jiāochā liánjiē
DXC	Digital cross-connect equipment	数字交叉连接设备	Shùzì jiāochā liánjiē shèbèi
DXC	Digital cross-connect equipment	数字交叉连接器	Shùzì jiāochā liánjiēqì
DXF	Data exchange format	数据交换格式	Shùjù jiāohuàn géshì
DXI	Data exchange interface	数据交换接口	Shùjù jiāohuàn jiēkǒu
DXIO	Data exchange input-output device	数据交换输入输出设备	Shùjù jiāohuàn shūrù shūchū shèbèi
DxR	Dynamic extended resolution	动态可扩展分辨率	Dòngtài kě kuòzhǎn fēnbiànlǜ
DXTC	Direct X texture compression (video term)	DirectX 纹理压缩	DirectX wénlǐ yāsuō
DY	Power supply	电源	Diànyuán
DYNATACS	Dynamic Total Area Communications System (UK)	动态全地区通信系统	Dòngtài quán dìqū tōngxìn xìtǒng
DYNET	Dynamic network planning technique	动态网络规划技术	Dòngtài wǎngluò guīhuà jìshù
DZ	One-point multiple access communications	一点多址通信	Yīdiǎn duōzhǐ tōngxìn

E

E	Emitter	发射机	Fāshèjī
E	Emitter	发射器	Fāshèqì
E	Emitter	发送器	Fāsòngqì
E	Error check bit	差错检测比特	Chācuò jiǎncè bǐtè
E	Execute	执行	Zhíxíng
E tag	End tag	结束标签	Jiéshù biāoqiān
E/O	Electrical/optical conversion	电/光转变	Diàn/guāng zhuǎnbiàn
E/O	Electrical/optical signal converter	电光信号转换器	Diànguāng xìnhào zhuǎnhuànqì
E/O	Electronic/optical conversion	电/光转换	Diàn/guāng zhuǎnhuàn
E0S	Electronic order system	在线订货体系	Zàixiàn dìnghuò tǐxì
E3	Electronic entertainment expo	电子娱乐展览会	Diànzǐ yúlè zhǎnlǎnhuì
EA	Address field extension	地址字段扩展	Dìzhǐ zìduàn kuòzhǎn
EA	Early allocation	预分配	Yùfēnpèi
EA	Edge aggregation (CAD/CAM)	边聚合	Biān jùhé
EA	Effective address	有效地址	Yǒuxiào dìzhǐ
EA	Electronic attack (IW)	电子攻击	Diànzǐ gōngjī
EA	Elementary assignment	基本分配	Jīběn fēnpèi
EA	Extended address	扩展地址	Kuòzhǎn dìzhǐ

EA	Extended addressing	扩充编址	Kuòchōng biānzhǐ
EA	External access equipment	外部接入设备	Wàibù jiērù shèbèi
EA	External alarms	外部报警	Wàibù bàojǐng
EAAG	Extended attribute adjacency graph (CAD/CAM)	扩展属性邻接图	Kuòzhǎn shǔxìng línjiē tú
EACP	E-business advanced communication platform	先进的电子商务通信平台	Xiānjìnde diànzǐ shāngwù tōngxìn píngtái
EACP	European Area communications Plan	欧洲地区通信计划	Oūzhōu dìqū tōngxìn jìhuà
EA-DFB	Electricity absorption - distributed feedback	电吸收分布反馈	Diànxīshōu fēnbù fǎnkuì
E-ADPCM	Embedded adaptive differential pulse code modulation	嵌入式自适应差分脉冲编码调制	Qiànrù-shì zìshìyìng chāfēn màichōng biānmǎ tiáozhì
EAF	Effective attenuation factor	有效衰减系数	Yǒuxiào shuāijiǎn xìshù
EAI	Enterprise application integration	企业应用程序集成	Qǐyè yìngyòng chéngxù jíchéng
EAI	Enterprise application integration	企业应用集成	Qǐyè yìngyòng jíchéng
EAM	Electricity absorption modulation	电吸收调制	Diànxīshōu tiáozhì
EAM	Electroabsorption modulator	电吸收调制器	Diànxīshōu tiáozhìqì
EAM	Extended answer message indication	扩充应答信息指示	Kuòchōng yìngdá xìnxī zhǐshì
EAM	Extended arithmetic module	扩充运算模块	Kuòchōng yùnsuàn mókuài
EAMC	Enhanced adaptive motion compensation algorithm	增强自适应运动补偿算法	Zēngqiáng zìshìyìng yùndòng bǔcháng suànfǎ
EAP	Extensible authentication protocol	可扩展身份验证协议	Kěkuòzhǎn shēnfen yànzhèng xiéyì
EAP	Extensible authentication protocol (in PPP)	扩展认证协议	Kuòzhǎn rènzhèng xiéyì
EAR	Electronically agile radar	机载相控阵天线雷达	Jīzài xiàngkòng zhèn tiānxiàn léidá
EARN	European Academic and Research Network	欧洲科学与研究网	Oūzhōu kēxué yǔ yánjiū wǎng
EAS	Extended area service (telephony term)	扩大区域服务	Kuòdà qūyù fúwù
EASI	Elastic asynchronous-to-synchronous interface	弹性异步-同步接口	Tánxìng yìbù—tóngbù jiēkǒu
EAT	Engineering acceptance test	工程验收测试	Gōngchéng yànshōu cèshì
EAT	Error alert task	错误报警任务	Cuòwù bàojǐng rènwu
EAX	Environmental audio extensions	环境音效扩展技术	Huánjìng yīn xiào kuòzhǎn jìshù
EB	Errored block	差错块	Chācuò kuài
EB	Errored block	误块	Wùkuài
EB	Expansion bus	扩展总线	Kuòzhǎn zǒngxiàn
EBC	Errored block count	误块计数	Wùkuài jìshù
EBCDIC	Extended binary coded decimal code	扩充的二-十进制交换码	Kuòchōngde èr-shíjìnzhì jiāohuàn mǎ
EBCDIC	Extended binary coded decimal interchange code	扩展二进制编码的十进制交换格式	Kuòzhǎn èrjìnzhì biānmǎde shíjìnzhì jiāohuàn géshi
EBCO	Empty base class optimization	空基类优化	Kōng jīlèi yōuhuà
EBFA	Extended band fiber amplifier	扩展带光纤放大器	Kuòzhǎn dài guāngxiān fàngdàqì
EBMT	Example-based machine translation	基于实例的机器翻译	Jīyú shílìde jīqì fānyì
EBR	Excess burst rate	超额突发速率	Chāo'é tūfā sùlǜ
EBSG	Elementary basic service group	基础单元业务群	Jīchǔ dānyuán yèwù qún
EBU	European Broadcasting Union	欧洲广播联盟	Oūzhōu guǎngbō liánméng
EC	Echo canceling	回波抵消	Huíbō dǐxiāo
EC	Echo cancellation	回声消除	Huíshēng xiāochú
EC	Echo canceller	回声抑制单元	Huíshēng yìzhì dānyuán
EC	Electronic commerce, e-commerce	电子商务	Diànzǐ shāngwù
EC	Embedded controller	嵌入式控制器	Qiànrù-shì kòngzhìqì
EC	Embedded controller	微型控制器	Wēixíng kòngzhìqì
EC	Extreme counting	极值计数	Jízhí jìshù

Ec/No	Ratio of energy per modulating bit to noise spectral density	每调制比特的射频能量对噪声频谱密度比	Měi tiáozhì bǐtède shèpín néngliàng duì zàoshēng pínpǔ mìdùbǐ
ECAN	Network echo cancellation	网络回音消除	Wǎngluò huíyīn xiāochú
ECB	Electronic code book	电子密本	Diànzǐ mìběn
ECB	Event control block	事件控制块	Shìjiàn kòngzhì kuài
ECB	Event control block	事件控制字组	Shìjiàn kòngzhì zìzǔ
ECC	Edge card control	边缘卡控制	Biānyuán kǎ kòngzhì
ECC	Elliptic curve crypto	椭圆曲线加密	Tuǒyuán qūxiàn jiāmì
ECC	Embedded control channel	嵌入控制通道	Qiànrù kòngzhì tōngdào
ECC	Embedded control channel	嵌入控制通路	Qiànrù kòngzhì tōnglù
ECC	Error checking (or correcting) code	纠错码	Jiūcuò mǎ
ECC	Error checking and correction	错误检查修正	Cuòwù jiǎnchá xiūzhèng
ECC	Error checking and correction	错误检验与校正	Cuòwù jiǎnyàn yǔ jiàozhèng
ECC	Error correcting (or checking) code	错误校正码	Cuòwù jiàozhèng mǎ
ECC	Error correction code	纠错校正码	Jiūcuò jiàozhèng mǎ
ECCC	European Communications Coordinating Committee	欧洲通信协调委员会	Oūzhōu tōngxìn xiétiáo wěiyuánhuì
ECD	Electrochromic display	电铬显示器	Diàngè xiǎnshìqì
ECDC	Ericsson cellular data converter	爱立信蜂窝数据转换器	Ài-lì-xìn fēngwō shùjù zhuǎnhuànqì
ECDLP	Elliptical curve discrete logarithm problem	椭圆曲线离散对数问题	Tuǒyuán qūxiàn lísàn duìshù wèntí
ECF	Eccentric core fiber	偏心光纤	Piānxīn guāngxiān
ECH	Echo cancellation hybrid	回波抵消四端网络	Huíbō dǐxiāo sìduān wǎngluò
ECL	Emitter coupled logic	射极耦合逻辑	Shè jí ǒuhé luóji
ECM	Electronic countermeasures	电子对抗	Diànzǐ duìkàng
ECM	Empowering control message	授权控制消息	Shòuquán kòngzhì xiāoxi
ECM	Enterprise content management	企业内容管理	Qǐyè nèiróng guǎnlǐ
ECM	Error correction mode (for facsimile)	错误校正模式	Cuòwù jiàozhèng móshì
ECMA	European Computer Manufacturers Association	欧洲计算机制造商协会	Oūzhōu jìsuànjī zhìzàoshāng xiéhuì
ECN	Electronic serial number	电子序列号	Diànzǐ xùlièhào
ECN	Explicit congestion notification	明确拥塞通知	Míngquè yōngsè tōngzhī
ECN	Explicit congestion notification	显示拥塞指标	Xiǎnshì yōngsè zhǐbiāo
ECO	Engineering computing object	工程计算对象	Gōngchéng jìsuàn duìxiàng
ECoI	Electronic commerce over Internet	因特网电子商务	Yīntèwǎng diànzǐ shāngwù
ECOM	Electronic computer originated mail	面向计算机电子邮件	Miànxiàng jìsuànjī diànzi yóujiàn
ECP	Encryption control protocol	保密控制协议	Bǎomì kòngzhì xiéyì
ECP	Encryption control protocol	加密控制协议	Jiāmì kòngzhì xiéyì
ECP	Extended capabilities port	扩充能力端口	Kuòchōng nénglì duān kǒu
ECPT	European Conference of Posts and Telecommunications	欧洲邮政电信会议	Oūzhōu yóuzhèng diànxìn huìyì
ECR	Efficient customer response	有效客户反应	Yǒuxiào kèhù fǎnyìng
ECR	Enhanced call routing	增强型呼叫选路	Zēngqiáng-xíng hūjiào xuǎnlù
ECS	Encryption control signal	加密控制信号	Jiāmì kòngzhì xìnhào
ECS	Error correction Signal	纠错信号	Jiūcuò xìnhào
ECS	European communications Satellite	欧洲通信卫星	Oūzhōu tōngxìn wèixīng
ECS	Expanded character set	扩展的字符组	Kuòzhǎnde zìfú zǔ
ECSA	Extended common service area	扩充的公共服务区	Kuòchōngde gōnggòng fúwùqū
ECSC	Early classmark sending control	尽早类别发送控制	Jǐnzǎo lèibié fāsòng kòngzhì

ECSD	EDGE circuit switched data	EDGE 电路交换传输 模式	EDGE diànlù jiāohuàn chuánshū móshì
ECSD	Enhanced circuit switched data	增强电路交换数据	Zēngqiáng diànlù jiāohuàn shùjù
ECSD	Enhanced circuit switched data	增强的电路交换数据	Zēngqiángde diànlù jiāohuàn shùjù
ECSO	European Communications Satellite Organization	欧洲通信卫星组织	Oūzhōu tōngxìn wèixīng zǔzhī
ECT	Explicit call transfer supplementary service	显呼叫传送附加业务	Xiǎn hūjiào chuánsòng fùjiā yèwù
ECT	Explict call transfer	显式呼叫转接	Xiǎnshì hūjiào zhuǎnjiē
ECTRA	European Committee of Telecommunication Regulatory Affairs	欧洲通信事务管理委员会	Oūzhōu tōngxìn shìwù guǎnlǐ wěiyuánhuì
ECX	Electronically-controlled telephone exchange	电子控制的电话交换局	Diànzǐ kòngzhìde diànhuà jiāohuànjú
ED	Edge deletion (CAD/CAM)	边删除	Biān shānchú
ED	Edge device	边缘设备	Biānyuán shèbèi
ED	End delimiter	结束定界符	Jiéshù dìngjiè fú
EDACS	Enhanced digital access communications system	加强的数字接入通信系统	Jiāqiángde shùzì jiērù tōngxìn xìtǒng
EDC	Error detection code	差错检测码	Chācuò jiǎncè mǎ
EDC	Error detection code byte	错误检波码字节	Cuòwù jiǎnbō mǎ zìjié
E-DDC	Enhanced display data channel	增强形视频数据通道协议	Zēngqiáng-xíng shìpín shùjù tōngdào xiéyì
EDF	Earliest deadline first	最早的限优选算法	Zuìzǎode xiàn yōuxuǎn suànfǎ
EDFA	Erbium-doped fiber amplifier	掺铒光纤放大器	Chān'ěr guāngxiān fàngdàqì
EDFFA	Erbium-doped fluoridized fiber amplifier	掺铒氟化光纤放大器	Chān'ěr fúhuà guāngxiān fàngdàqì
EDGE	Enhanced data rate service (enhanced data rate for GSM evolution)	增强数据速率业务	Zēngqiáng shùjù sùlǜ yèwù
EDGE	Enhanced data rates for global evalution	全球演进增强数据速率	Quánqiú yǎnjìn zēngqiáng shùjù sùlǜ
EDGE	Enhanced data rates for global evolution	GSM 增强数据率改进	GSM zēngqiáng shùjù lǜ gǎijìn
EDGE	Enhanced data rates for GSM evalution	GSM 演进增强数据速率	GSM yǎnjìn zēngqiáng shùjù sùlǜ
EDGE	Enhanced data rates for GSM evolution	全球移动通信系统(GSM)演进的增强型数据率	Quánqiú yídòng tōngxìn xìtǒng (GSM) yǎnjìnde zēngqiángxíng shùjùlǜ
EDI	Electronic data interchange	电子数据交换	Diànzi shùjù jiāohuàn
EDM	Engineering data management	工程数据管理	Gōngchéng shùjù guǎnlǐ
EDMA	Extended direct memory access	扩充的直接存储器存取	Kuòchōngde zhíjiē cúnchǔqì cúnqǔ
EDMD	Electronic distance measuring device	电子距离测量设备	Diànzǐ jùlí cèliáng shèbèi
EDP	Event detection point	事件检出点	Shìjiàn jiǎnchū diǎn
EDPC	Electronic data processing center	电子数据处理器	Diànzǐ shùjù chǔlǐqì
EDP-N	Event detection point-notification	事件检测点 - 通知	Shìjiàn jiǎncè diǎn-tōngzhī
EDP-N	Event detection point-notification	事件检出点-通知	Shìjiàn jiǎnchū diǎn - tōngzhī
EDP-R	Event detection point-request	事件检测点 - 请求	Shìjiàn jiǎncè diǎn-qǐngqiú
EDP-R	Event detection point-request	事件检出点-请求	Shìjiàn jiǎnchū diǎn -qǐngqiú
EDSL	Ethernet digital subscriber line	以太数字用户线	Yǐtài shùzì yònghù xiàn
EDTV	Enhanced definition television	增强清晰度电视	Zēngqiáng qīngxīdù diànshì
EEA	Electronic Engineers Association	电子工程师协会	Diànzǐ gōngchéngshī xiéhuì
E-EDID	Enhanced extended identification data	增强形扩充身份辨识数据	Zēngqiáng-xíng kuòchōng shēnfen biànshí shùjù
EEL	Electric echo loss	电回波损耗	Diàn huíbō sǔnhào
EEP	Equal error protection	同等的错误保护	Tóngděngde cuòwù bǎohù
EEPROM	Electrically erasable programmable read only memory	电可擦可编程序的只读存储器	Diàn kěcā kěbiān chéngxùde zhǐdú cúnchǔqì
EEPROM	Electrically erasable programmable read-only memory	电可擦可编程只读存储器	Diàn kěcā kěbiānchéng zhǐdú cúnchǔqì
EEPROM	Electrically erasable programmable ROM	电擦写可编程只读存储器	Diàn cāxiě kěbiānchéng zhǐdú cúnchǔqì
EET	Ericsson Engineering Tool	爱立信工程工具	Ài-lì-xìn gōngchéng gōngjù

EF	Elementary file	基本文件	Jīběn wénjiàn
EF	Elementary file	基础文件	Jīchǔ wénjiàn
EF	Expedited forwarding	加速转发	Jiāsù zhuǎnfā
EFCC	Existing-frame capacity count	现存帧总量计数	Xiàncún zhèng zǒngliàng jìshù
EFCI	Explicit forward congestion indication	显示前向拥塞指示	Xiǎnshì qiánxiàng yōngsè zhǐshi
EFCI	Explicit forward congestion indication	显式前向阻塞指示	Xiǎnshì qiánxiàng zǔsè zhǐshì
EFCI	Explicit forward congestion indicator	明确前向拥塞指示	Míngquè qiánxiàng yōngsè zhǐshi
EFCI	Explicit forward congestion indicator	显式前向拥塞指示符	Xiǎnshì qiánxiàng yōngsè zhǐshìfú
EFCL	Error-free communication link	无误通信线路	Wúwù tōngxìn xiànlù
EFD	Event forwarding discrimination	事件前向判别	Shìjiàn qiánxiàng pànbié
EFD	Event forwarding discriminator	事件黑心发鉴别器	Shìjiàn hēixīnfā jiànbiéqì
EFEAL	Extended field elliptical aperture lens	可扩展扫描椭圆孔镜头	Kěkuòzhǎn sǎomiáo tuǒyuán kǒng jìngtóu
EFF	Electronic Frontier Foundation	电子前线基金会	Diànzǐ qiánxiàn jījīnhuì
EFL	Excess fiber length	光纤余长	Guāngxiān yú cháng
EFR	Enhanced full rate	增强型全速率	Zēngqiáng-xíng quánsùlǜ
EFR	Extra frame rate	额外帧速率	Éwài zhèng sùlǜ
EFR	Extra frame rate	额外帧率	Éwài zhènglǜ
EFS	End frame series	帧结束序列	Zhèng jiéshù xùliè
EFS	Error free seconds	无差错秒	Wúchācuò miǎo
EFS	Error-free seconds	无误码秒	Wúwùmǎ miǎo
EFT/B	Electrical fast transient/burst	电快速瞬变脉冲群	Diàn kuàisù shùnbiàn màichōng qún
EFTP	Ethernet file transfer protocol	以太网文件传送协议	Yǐtàiwǎng wénjiàn chuánsòng xiéyì
EFWS	Equivalent four-wire system	等效四线系统	Děngxiào sìxiàn xìtǒng
EG	Edge generation (CAD/CAM)	边生成	Biān shēngchéng
EGA	Enhanced graphics adapter	扩展的彩色图形显示适配器	Kuòzhǎnde cǎisè túxíng xiǎnshì shìpèiqì
EGA	Enhanced graphics adapter	增强型图形适配器	Zēngqiáng-xíng túxíng shìpèiqì
EGB	Exterior gateway protocol	外部路由协议	Wàibù lùyóu xiéyì
EGC	Equality gain control	等增益控制	Děngzēngyì kòngzhì
EGC	Equivalent gain consolidation	等增益合并	Děngzēngyì hébìng
E-GGSN	Enhanced GGSN	增强型 GGSN	Zēngqiáng-xíng GGSN
EGP	Exterior gateway protocol	外部网点协议	Wàibù wǎngdiǎn xiéyì
EGP	Exterior gateway protocol	外部网关协议	Wàibù wǎngguān xiéyì
EGPRS	EDGE general packet radio service	EDGE 分组交换传输 模式	EDGE fēnzǔ jiāohuàn chuánshū móshì
EH	Error handling	差错处理	Chācuò chǔlǐ
EHDR	Extended header	扩展帧头	Kuòzhǎn zhèngtóu
EHF	Extra-high frequency	极高频	Jígāopín
E-HLR	Enhanced HLR	增强型 HLR	Zēngqiáng-xíng HLR
EIA	Electronic Industries Association	电子工业协会	Diànzǐ gōngyè xiéhuì
EIA	Electronic Industries Association	电子工业联合会	Diànzǐ gōngyè liánhéhuì
EIA	Electronic Industries Association (US)	美国电子工业协会	Měiguó diànzǐ gōngyè xiéhuì
EIA	Extended interaction amplifier	分布作用放大器	Fēnbù zuòyòng fàngdàqì
EIC	Electrical impedance characteristics	电阻抗特性	Diànzǔkàng tèxìng
EID	End point identifier	端点标识符	Duāndiǎn biāozhìfú
EID	Equipment identifier	设备标识符	Shèbèi biāozhìfú
EIDE	Enhanced integrated drive electronics	增强形电子集成驱动器	Zēngqiáng-xíng diànzǐ jíchéng qūdòngqì
EIFOV	Effective instantaneous field of view	有效瞬时视野	Yǒuxiào shùnshí shìyě

EIGRP	Enhanced interior gateway routing protocol	增强内部网关路由协议	Zēngqiáng nèibù wǎngguān lùyóu xiéyì
EIGRP	Enhanced interior gateway routing protocol	增强的内部网关路由选择协议	Zēngqiángde nèibù wǎngguān lùyóu xuǎnzé xiéyì
EIM	Enterprise information management	企业信息管理	Qǐyè xìnxī guǎnlǐ
EIM	Error interval monitor	差错时间段监视	Chācuò shíjiānduàn jiānshì
EIM	Error interval monitor	错误时段监视器	Cuòwù shíduàn jiānshìqì
EIO	Extended interaction oscillator	分布作振荡器	Fēnbù zuò zhèndàngqì
EIP	Ethernet interface processor	以太网接口处理器	Yǐtàiwǎng jiēkǒu chǔlǐqì
EIR	Equipment identification register	设备识别登记器	Shèbèi shíbié dēngjìqì
EIR	Equipment identity center	设备识别中心	Shèbèi shíbié zhōngxīn
EIR	Equipment identity register	设备标示寄存器	Shèbèi biāoshì jìcúnqì
EIR	Equipment identity register	设备身份寄存器	Shèbèi shēnfen jìcúnqì
EIR	Equipment identity register	设备识别寄存器	Shèbèi shíbié jìcúnqì
EIR	Equipment identity register	设备识别注册处	Shèbèi shíbié zhùcèchù
EIR	Excess information rate	超额信息速率	Chāo'é xìnxī sùlǜ
EIR	Excess information rate	超越信息速率	Chāoyuè xìnxī sùlǜ
EIR	Mobile equipment identity register	移动设备识别寄存器	Yídòng shèbèi shíbié jìcúnqì
EiRP	Effective isotropic radiated power	有效全向辐射功率	Yǒuxiào quánxiàng fúshè gōnglǜ
EIRP	Effective isotropically radiated power	有效各向同性辐射功率	Yǒuxiào gèxiàng tóngxìng fúshè gōnglǜ
EIRP	Equivalent isotropic radiated power	等效全向辐射功率	Děngxiào quánxiàng fúshè gōnglǜ
EIRP	Equivalent isotropically radiated power (in a given direction)	等效各向同性辐射功率	Děngxiào gèxiàng tóngxìng fúshè gōnglǜ
EISA	Enhanced industry standard architecture	增强形工业标准架构	Zēngqiáng-xíng gōngyè biāozhǔn jiàgòu
EISA	Extended industry standard architecture	扩充工业标准体系结构	Kuòchōng gōngyè biāozhǔn tǐxì jiégòu
EISA	Extended industry standard architecture	扩充的工业标准结构	Kuòchōngde gōngyè biāozhǔn jiégòu
E-ISS	Enhanced internal sub-layer service	增强的内部子层服务	Zēngqiángde nèibù zicéng fúwù
EIT	Encoded information type	编码信息类型	Biānmǎ xìnxī lèixíng
EKTS	Electronic key telephone system	电子按键电话系统	Diànzǐ ànjiàn diànhuà xìtǒng
EL	Extra loss	附加损耗	Fùjiā sǔnhào
ELD	Electroluminescence display	电激发光显示器	Diànjī fāguāng xiǎnshìqì
ELED	Edge light emitting diode	边发射发光管	Biān fāshè fāguāng guǎn
ELF	Extremely low frequency	极低频	Jídīpín
ELFEXT	Equal level far end crosstalk	等电平远端串音	Děngdiànpíng yuǎnduān chuànyīn
ELFEXT	Equal level far end crosstalk	等电位远端串扰	Děngdiànwèi yuǎnduān chuànrǎo
ELMCFI	Ethernet in the last mile call for interest	最后一英里以太网呼叫兴趣	Zuìhòu yīyīnglǐ yǐtàiwǎng hūjiào xìngqu
ELMI	Enhanced local management interface	增强型局部管理接口	Zēngqiáng-xíng júbù guǎnlǐ jiēkǒu
EM	Element management	网元管理	Wǎngyuán guǎnlǐ
EM	Element manager	单元管理者	Dānyuán guǎnlǐzhě
EM	End of media	媒体结束	Méitǐ jiéshù
EM	Expansion measurement	扩展测量	Kuòzhǎn cèliáng
EM	Extended memory	扩充存储器	Kuòchōng cúnchǔqì
E-mail	Electronic mail	电子信箱	Diànzǐ xìnxiāng
EMATS	Emergency message automatic transmission system	应急信息自动传输系统	Yìngjí xìnxī zìdòng chuánshū xìtǒng
EMC	Electromagnetic compatibility	电磁兼容性	Diàncí jiānróngxìng
EMDB	Embedded mobile database	嵌入移动数据库	Qiànrù yídòng shùjùkù
emf	Electromotive force	电动势	Diàndòngshì
EMF	Equipment management function	设备管理功能	Shèbèi guǎnlǐ gōngnéng

EMH	Expedited message handling	加速信息处理	Jiāsù xìnxī chǔlǐ
EMHB	Expedited message handler buffer	加速报文处理器缓冲器	Jiāsù bàowén chǔlǐqì huǎnchōngqì
EMI	Electromagnetic interference	电磁干扰	Diàncí gānrǎo
EMIL	Expected measured loss	期望的测量损耗	Qīwàngde cèliáng sǔnhào
EML	Electroabsorption modulated laser	电吸收调制激光器	Diànxīshōu tiáozhì jīguāngqì
EML	Element management layer	网元管理层	Wǎngyuán guǎnlǐ céng
EMLPP	Enhanced multilevel precedence and preemption service	增强型多级优先和先占业务	Zēngqiáng-xíng duōjí yōuxiān hé xiānzhàn yèwù
eMLPP	Enhanced multi-level precedence and pre-emption service	增强型多级优先和占先业务	Zēngqiáng-xíng duōjí yōuxiān hé zhànxiān yèwù
EML-TC	Element management layer topology configurator	单元管理层拓扑结构	Dānyuán guǎnlǐcéng tuòpū jiégòu
EMM	Empowering management message	授权管理消息	Shòuquán guǎnlǐ xiāoxi
EMMI	Electrical man machine interface	电的人机接口	Diànde rénjī jiēkǒu
EMP	Emergency incident management port	紧急事件管理端口	Jǐnjí shìjiàn guǎnlǐ duānkǒu
EMPA	Extended Markovian process algebra	扩展马尔科夫进程代数	Kuòzhǎn mǎ-ěr-kē-fū jìnchéng dàishù
EMRP	Effective monopole radiated power	有效单极辐射功率	Yǒuxiào dānjí fúshè gōnglǜ
EMS	Electromagnetic sensibility	电磁敏感性	Diàncí mǐngǎnxìng
EMS	Element management system	单元管理系统	Dānyuán guǎnlǐ xìtǒng
EMS	Element management system	网元管理系统	Wǎngyuán guǎnlǐ xìtǒng
EMS	Expanded memory specification	扩展内存规范	Kuòzhǎn nèicún guīfàn
EMU	Expanded memory unit	扩展存储器	Kuòzhǎn cúnchǔqì
EMU	Extended memory unit	扩充的存储器	Kuòchōngde cúnchǔqì
EMX	Electronic mobile exchange	移动式电子电话交换局	Yídòng-shì diànzǐ diànhuà jiāohuànjú
EN	Equivalent noise	等效噪声	Děngxiào zàoshēng
ENB	Effective noise bandwidth	有效噪声带宽	Yǒuxiào zàoshēng dàikuān
ENG	Electronic news gathering	电子新闻收集	Diànzǐ xīnwén shōují
ENI	Equivalent noise input	等效噪声输入	Děngxiào zàoshēng shūrù
ENIAC	Electrical numerical integrator & calculator	电子数字综合计算机	Diànzǐ shùzì zōnghé jìsuànjī
ENL	Equivalent number of looks (radar)	等效视数	Děngxiào shìshù
E-NNI	External network-node interface	外部网络节点接口	Wàibù wǎngluò jiédiǎn jiēkǒu
ENQ	Enquiry (inquiry), interrogate	询问	Xúnwèn
ENRZ	Enhanced non-return-to-zero	增强型不归零制	Zēngqiáng-xíng bùguīlíng zhì
ENUM	Electronic numbering	电子号码	Diànzǐ hàomǎ
EO	Elementary operation	基本操作	Jīběn cāozuò
EO	End office	端局	Duān jú
EO	End office	市话端局	Shìhuà duān jú
EOC	Embedded operating channel	嵌入操作通道	Qiànrù cāozuò tōngdào
EOC	Embedded operations channel	嵌入操作通路	Qiànrù cāozuò tōnglù
EOC	Embedded operations channel	嵌入操作信道	Qiànrù cāozuò xìndào
EOC	End of conversion	转换结束	Zhuǎnhuàn jiéshù
EOD	End of dialing	拨号结束	Bōhào jiéshù
EOEM	Extensible object exchange model	可扩展对象交换模型	Kěkuòzhǎn duìxiàng jiāohuàn móxíng
EOF	End of frame	帧终止符	Zhèng zhōngzhǐfú
EOF	End-of-file mark	文件结束标志	Wénjiàn jiéshù biāozhì
EOG	Engineering object group	工程对象组	Gōngchéng duìxiàngzǔ
EOM	End of message	消息结束	Xiāoxi jiéshù
EOS	Earth observation system	对地观测系统	Duìdì guāncè xìtǒng

EOT	End of transmission	传输结束	Chuánshū jiéshù
EOT	End of transmission	发送结束	Fāsòng jiéshù
EOTD	Enhanced observation time difference	增强观察时间差定位	Zēngqiáng guānchá shíjiān chà dìngwèi
EOTD	Enhanced observed time difference	高级时差检测技术	Gāojí shíchā jiǎncè jìshù
EP	Emergency power	应急电源	Yìngjí diànyuán
EPA	Environmental Protection Agency (US)	环境保护局	Huánjìng bǎohù jú
EPABX	Electronic private automatic branch exchange	专用电子自动交换分机	Zhuānyòng diànzǐ zìdòng jiāohuàn fēnjī
EPBX	Electronic private branch exchange	专用支线电子交换机	Zhuānyòng zhīxiàn diànzǐ jiāohuànjī
EPD	Early packet discard	早期报文丢弃	Zǎoqī bàowén diūqì
EPFU	Enhanced performance fiber unit	高性能光线单元	Gāoxìngnéng guāngxiàn dānyuán
EPIC	Explicitly parallel instruction code	显示并行指令代码	Xiǎnshì bìngxíng zhǐlìng dàimǎ
EPIRB	Emergency position-indicating radio beacon	应急示位无线电信标	Yìngjí shìwèi wúxiàndiàn xìnbiāo
EPLA	Erasable programmable logic array	可擦程序控制逻辑阵列	Kěcā chéngxù kòngzhì luójì zhènliè
EPLRS	Enhanced position location reporting system	增强型定位报告系统	Zēngqiáng-xíng dìngwèi bàogào xìtǒng
EPMS	Enterprise process modeling system	企业过程模型系统	Qǐyè guòchéng móxíng xìtǒng
EPOC	Enhanced paging operators code	增强型寻呼码	Zēngqiáng-xíng xúnhū mǎ
EPON	Ethernet passive optical network	以太网无源光网络	Yǐtàiwǎng wúyuán guāng wǎngluò
EPP	Enhanced parallel port	增强形平行端口	Zēngqiáng-xíng píngxíng duānkǒu
EPROM	Erasable programmable read only memory	可擦除的可编程只读存储器	Kěcāchúde kěbiānchéng zhǐdú cúnchǔqì
EPROM	Erasable programmable read only memory	可擦掉的可编程只读存储器	Kěcādiàode kěbiānchéng zhǐdú cúnchǔqì
EPSCS	Enhanced private switched communications service	增强型专用交换通信业务	Zēngqiáng-xíng zhuānyòng jiāohuàn tōngxìn yèwù
EPSN	Experimental packet switching network	实验包交换系统	Shíyàn bāo jiāohuàn xìtǒng
EPSN	Extended packet sequence numbering	扩充包顺序编号	Kuòchōng bāo shùnxù biānhào
EPSS	Experimental packet switched system	实验分组交换系统	Shíyàn fēnzǔ jiāohuàn xìtǒng
EQ	Equalize	均衡	Jūnhéng
ER	Edge router	边缘路由器	Biānyuán lùyóuqì
ER	Equipment room	设备间	Shèbèi jiān
ER	Explicit rate	显式率	Xiǎnshì lǜ
ER	External repository	外部仓库	Wàibù cāngkù
ERCIST	Engineering Research Center of Information Security Technology	信息安全技术工程研究中心	Xìnxī ānquán jìshù gōngchéng yánjiū zhōngxīn
ERD	Emergency repair disk	紧急修复磁盘	Jǐnjí xiūfù cípán
ERDISWIN	Episode rule discovery by sliding windows	基于滑动窗口的情景规则挖掘算法	Jīyú huádòng chuāngkǒude qíngjǐng guīzé wājué suànfǎ
erf	Error function	误差函数	Wùchā hánshù
erfc	Complementary error function	互补误差函数	Hùbǔ wùchā hánshù
ERMES	European Radio Messaging System	欧洲无线电信息系统	Ōuzhōu wúxiàndiàn xìnxī xìtǒng
EROM	Erasable read only memory	可擦只读存储器	Kěcā zhǐ dú cúnchǔqì
ERP	Ear reference point	耳参考点	Ěr cānkǎo diǎn
ERP	Echo return loss	回波损耗	Huíbō sǔnhào
ERP	Effective radiated power	有效辐射功率	Yǒuxiào fúshè gōnglǜ
ERP	Enterprise requirement planning	企业需求计划	Qǐyè xūqiú jìhuà
ERP	Enterprise resource plan	企业资源规划	Qǐyè zīyuán guīhuà
ERP	Enterprise resource planning	企业资源计划	Qǐyè zīyuán jìhuà
ERP	Enterprise resources program	企业资源规划	Qǐyè zīyuán guīhuà
ERP	Equivalent radiated power	等效辐射功率	Děngxiào fúshè gōnglǜ

ERP	Estimated retail price	估计零售价	Gūjì língshòujià
ERR	Error	差错	Chācuò
ES	Element stream	单元流	Dānyuán liú
ES	End system	端系统	Duān xìtǒng
ES	End system	终端系统	Zhōngduān xìtǒng
ES	Errored second	差错秒	Chācuò miǎo
ES	Errored second	误块秒	Wùkuài miǎo
ES	Errored second	误码秒	Wùmǎ miǎo
ES	Errored second (in-service condition)	差错秒（开业务状态）	Chācuò miǎo (kāiyè wù zhuàngtài)
ESA	Error second A	误码秒类型 A	Wùmǎ miǎo lèixíng A
ESA	European Space Agency	欧洲航天局	Oūzhōu hángtiān jú
ESB	Error second B	误码秒类型 B	Wùmǎ miǎo lèixíng B
ESB	External service broker (in VPN)	外部服务代理	Wàibù fúwù dàilǐ
ESC	End session command	结束会话命令	Jiéshù huìhuà mìnglìng
ESC	Environmental [and power supply] supervision and control (board)	环境电源监控（板）	Huánjìng diànyuán jiānkòng (bǎn)
ESC	Escape	转义	Zhuǎnyì
ESC	Escape character	换码子复	Huàn mǎzìfù
ESC	Escape character	换义子复	Huàn yìzìfù
ESCD	Extended system configuration data	可扩展系统配置数据	Kěkuòzhǎn xìtǒng pèizhì shùjù
ESCD	Extended system configuration data	扩展系统配置数据	Kuòzhǎn xìtǒng pèizhì shùjù
ESCON	Enterprise systems connection	企业系统互联	Qǐyè xìtǒng hùlián
ESCR	Environmental stress cracking resistance	耐环境应力开裂	Nài huánjìng yìnglì kāiliè
ESD	Electrostatic discharge	静电放电	Jìngdiàn fàngdiàn
ESD	Electrostatic discharge	静电释放	Jìngdiàn shìfàng
ESD	Energy spectral density	能量谱密度	Néngliàng pǔ mìdù
ESDI	Enhanced small device interface	增强小型设备接口	Zēngqiáng xiǎoxíng shèbèi jiēkǒu
ESDJ	Easy setting CPU dual jumper	简化 CPU 双重跳线法	Jiǎnhuà CPU shuāngchóng tiàoxiànfǎ
ESDJ	Easy setting dual jumper	简化双重跳线法	Jiǎnhuà shuāngchóng tiàoxiàn fǎ
ESG	Electronic sweep generator	电子扫描振荡器	Diànzǐ sǎomiáo zhèndàngqì
ESI	End system identifier	端系统标识符	Duān xìtǒng biāozhìfú
ESIDR	Erased silence descriptor rate	擦除的 SID 帧率	Cāchúde SID zhèng lǜ
ES-IS	End system to intermediate system routing exchange protocol	终端系统和中间系统路由交换协议	Zhōngduān xìtǒng hé zhōngjiān xìtǒng lùyóu jiāohuàn xiéyì
ES-IS	End system to intermediate system routing exchange protocol	终端系统对中间系统路由选择交换协议	Zhōngduān xìtǒng duì zhōngjiān xìtǒng lùyóu xuǎnzé jiāohuàn xiéyì
ES-IS	End system-to-intermediate system	终端系统到中间系统	Zhōngduān xìtǒng dào zhōngjiān xìtǒng
ESME	Expanded short message entity	扩展短消息实体	Kuòzhǎn duǎnxiāoxi shítǐ
ESME Agent	Extended short message entity agent	扩展短消息试题代理	Kuòzhǎn duǎnxiāoxi shìtí dàilǐ
ESMTP	Extended simple mail transfer protocol	扩展型简单邮件传输协议	Kuòzhǎn-xíng jiǎndān yóujiàn chuánshū xiéyì
ESN	Electric sequence number	电子序号	Diànzǐ xùhào
ESN	Electronic sequence number	电子串号	Diànzǐ chuànhào
ESN	Electronic serial number	电子串号	Diànzǐ chuànhào
Esnet	Energy Sciences Network	能源科学网	Néngyuán kēxué wǎng
ESP	Embedded standard products	嵌入标准产品	Qiànrù biāozhǔn chǎnpǐn
ESP	Encapsulating security payload	封装安全荷	Fēngzhuāng ānquán hé

ESP	Encapsulating security payload	封装安全净荷	Fēngzhuāng ānquán jìnghé
ESP	Encapsulating security payload (in IPSec)	封装安全负载	Fēngzhuāng ānquán fùzài
ESP	Encapsulating security payload (protocol)	封装安全载荷（协议）	Fēngzhuāng ānquán zàihè (xiéyì)
ESPL	Electronic switching programming language	电子交换程序设计语言	Diànzǐ jiāohuàn chéngxù shèjì yǔyán
ESR	Errored second ratio	差错秒比	Chācuò miǎo bǐ
ESR	Errored second ratio	误块秒比	Wùkuài miǎo bǐ
ESR	Errored second ratio	误码秒比	Wùmǎ miǎo bǐ
ESR	Errored second ratio	误码秒比率	Wùmǎ miǎo bǐlǜ
ESRI	Environmental Sciences Research Institute (US GIS organization)	环境科学研究所	Huánjìng kēxué yánjiūsuǒ
ESSA	Environmental Sciences Services Administration (US)	环境科学管理局	Huánjìng kēxué guǎnlǐjú
ET	Exchange termination	交换终端	Jiāohuàn zhōngduān
ET	Exchange termination	交换终接	Jiāohuàn zhōngjiē
ET	Exchange termination	交换机终接	Jiāohuànjī zhōngjiē
ET	Exchange termination	交换局终端	Jiāohuànjú zhōngduān
ETACS	European Total Access Communication System	欧洲全向接入通信系统	Oūzhōu quánxiàng jiērù tōngxìn xìtǒng
ETB	End of transmission block	码组传输结束	Mazǔ chuánshū jiéshù
ETC	Establish temporary connection	建立临时连接	Jiànlì línshí liánjiē
ETDM	Electrical time division multiplexing	电时分复用	Diàn shífēn fùyòng
EtherTalk	AppleTalk Ethernet interface	AppleTalk 以太网接口	AppleTalk yǐtàiwǎng jiēkǒu
ETNS	European telecommunications numbering space	欧洲通信编号空间	Oūzhōu tōngxìn biānhào kōngjiān
ETR	Early token release	早期令牌释放	Zǎoqī lìngpái shìfàng
ETR	ETSI technical report	ETSI 技术报告	ETSI jìshù bàogào
ETS	European Telecommunications Standard	欧洲电信标准	Oūzhōu diànxìn biāozhǔn
ETS	European Telecommunications Standard	欧洲通信标准	Oūzhōu tōngxìn biāozhǔn
ETS	Executable test suite	可执行测试套	Kězhíxíng cèshì tào
ETSI	European Telecommunication Standards Institute	欧洲电信标准化委员会	Oūzhōu diànxìn biāozhǔnhuà wěiyuánhuì
ETSI	European Telecommunication Standards Institute	欧洲远程通信标准学会	Oūzhōu yuǎnchéng tōngxìn biāozhǔn xuéhuì
ETSI	European Telecommunications Standards Institute	欧洲电信标准组织／协会	Oūzhōu diànxìn biāozhǔn zǔzhī/xiéhuì
ETSI	European Telecommunications Standards Institute	欧洲通信标准研究院	Oūzhōu tōngxìn biāozhǔn yánjiūyuàn
ETSPL	Extended telephone systems programming language	扩充的电话系统程序语言	Kuòchōngde diànhuà xìtǒng chéngxù yǔyán
ETSS	Electronic telephone switching system	电子电话交换系统	Diànzǐ diànhuà jiāohuàn xìtǒng
ETU	Elementary time unit	基本时间单元	Jīběn shíjiān dānyuán
ETX	End of text	正文结束	Zhèngwén jiéshù
EUM	Extended unsuccessful backward setup information message	扩充后向建立不成功消息	Kuòchōng hòuxiàng jiànlì bùchénggōng xiāoxi
EUT	Equipment under test	受试设备	Shòushì shèbèi
EUT	Equipment under test (ITU-T Recommendation O.161)	被测设备	Bèicè shèbèi
EVOA	Electrically variable optical attenuator	电控可变光衰减器	Diànkòng kěbiàn guāng shuāijiǎnqì
EVRC	Enhanced variable rate coder	增强型可变速率编码器	Zēngqiáng-xíng kěbiàn sùlǜ biānmǎqì
EVSIDR	Erased valid silence descriptor rate	擦除的有效 SID 帧率	Cāchúde yǒuxiào SID zhèng lǜ
EW	Electronic warfare	电子战	Diànzǐzhàn
EXLEV	Received signal level	接收信号电平	Jiēshōu xìnhào diànpíng
EXTCMD	External command	外部命令	Wàibù mìnglìng
EXW	Ex-works	工厂交货	Gōngchǎng jiāohuò
EZW	Embedded zerotree wavelet coding method	嵌入式零树小波编码方法	Qiànrù-shì líng shù xiǎobō biānmǎ fāngfǎ

F

F	Fixed-length records	定长记录	Dìngcháng jìlù
F	Flag (in a data packet)	标志段	Biāozhì duàn
F	Flag (in SS7)	标志码	Biāozhì mǎ
F	Frequency	频率	Pínlǜ
F	Fuse	保险丝	Bǎoxiǎnsī
F(f)	Spot noise factor (of a linear two-port network)	点噪声系数（线性双端口网络的）	Diǎn zàoshēng xìshù (xiànxìng shuāng duānkǒu wǎngluòde)
f/D	Focal-length-to–diameter ratio of a satellite parabolic reflector	卫星抛物反射面焦距对天线口径之比	Wèixīng pāowù fǎnshè miàn jiāojù duì tiānxiàn kǒujìng zhī bǐ
F / V	Frequency to voltage converter	频率 / 电压转换	Pínlǜ/diànyā zhuǎnhuàn
F_RJT	Fabric port reject frame	架构端口拒绝帧	Jiàgòu duānkǒu jùjué zhèng
FA	Fax adaptor	传真适配器	Chuánzhēn shìpèiqì
FA	Field address (computer term)	字段地址	Zìduàn dìzhǐ
FA	Field address (of a computer program)	区段地址	Qūduàn dìzhǐ
FA	Field address (telecom term)	通信组地址	Tōngxìn zǔ dìzhǐ
FA	Fixed analyzer	固定分析器	Gùdìng fēnxīqì
FA	Flat-gain amplifier	平坦增益放大器	Píngtǎn zēngyì fàngdàqì
FA	Flexible access system	灵活接入系统	Línghuó jiērù xìtǒng
FA	Foreign agent	外部代理	Wàibù dàilǐ
FA	Foreign agent	外地代理	Wàidì dàilǐ
FA	Foreign agent	外区代理	Wàiqū dàilǐ
FA	Frequency assignment	频率分配	Pínlǜ fēnpèi
FA	Full adder	全加法器	Quán jiāfǎqì
FA	Full adder	全加器	Quán jiāqì
FA	Full allocation	全配置	Quán pèizhì
FA	Function address	功能地址	Gōngnéng dìzhǐ
FAA	Facility accepted (ISUP message)	网络性能请求许可	Wǎngluò xìngnéng qǐngqiú xǔkě
FAB	File access block	文件存取块	Wénjiàn cúnqǔ kuài
FAB	Fire alarm bell	火警警铃	Huǒjǐng jǐnglíng
FAB	Fuse assembly board	熔丝集成板	Róngsī jíchéngbǎn
FAC	Final assembly code	最后的组合码	Zuìhòude zǔhé mǎ
FACCH	Fast associated control channel	快速随路控制信道	Kuàisù suílù kòngzhì xìndào
FACCH/F	Fast associated control channel/full rate	快速随路控制信道 / 全速率	Kuàisù suílù kòngzhì xìndào/quánsùlǜ
FACCH/F	Fast associated control channel/full rate	快速相关控制信道 / 全速率	Kuàisù xiāngguān kòngzhì xìndào/quánsùlǜ
FACCH/H	Fast associated control channel/half rate	快速随路控制信道 / 半速率	Kuàisù suílù kòngzhì xìndào/bàn sùlǜ
FACH	Forward access channel	前向接入信道	Qiánxiàng jiērù xìndào
FACT	Factor	原因	Yuányīn
FACU	Fire alarm automatic control unit	火灾自动报警控制装置	Huǒzāi zìdòng bàojǐng kòngzhì zhuāngzhì
FADD	Floating point addition	浮点加	Fúdiǎn jiā
FAI	Function address indicator	功能地址指示符	Gōngnéng dìzhǐ zhǐshì fú
FAM	Forward address message	前向地址消息	Qiánxiàng dìzhǐ xiāoxi
FAM	Frequency-amplitude modulation	频率振幅调制	Pínlǜ zhènfú tiáozhì
FAM	Front administrative module	前管理模块	Qián guǎnlǐ mókuài
FAN	Fabric address notification	架构地址通知	Jiàgòu dìzhǐ tōngzhī

FANP	Flow attribute notification protocol (Toshiba)	流属性通知协议	Liú shǔxìng tōngzhī xiéyì
FAQ	Frequently asked questions	常见问题	Chángjiàn wèntí
FAR	Facility request (ISUP message)	网络性能请求	Wǎngluò xìngnéng qǐngqiú
FAR	Facility request message (ISUP)	性能请求消息	Xìngnéng qǐngqiú xiāoxi
FAR	File address register	文件地址寄存器	Wénjiàn dìzhǐ jìcúnqì
FAS	Frame alignment signal	帧定位信号	Zhèng dìngwèi xìnhào
FASC	Four-channel additional sequence control	四通道附加序列控制	Sì tōngdào fùjiā xùliè kòngzhì
FAT	File allocation table	文件分配表	Wénjiàn fēnpèi biǎo
FAT	Flexible access termination	灵活接入终端	Línghuó jiērù zhōngduān
FAT	Mode field	模场	Móchǎng
FAUSCH	Fast uplink signaling channel	上行链路快速信令信道	Shàngxíng liànlù kuàisù xìnlìng xìndào
FAX	Facsimile	传真	Chuánzhēn
FB	Frequency correction burst	频率校正短脉冲串	Pínlǜ jiàozhèng duǎnmàichōng chuàn
FB	Frequency correction burst	频率校正突发	Pínlǜ jiàozhèng tūfā
FB	Frequency correction burst	突发频率校正	Tūfā pínlǜ jiàozhèng
FBBE	Far-end background block error	远端背景块差错	Yuǎnduān bèijǐng kuài chācuò
FBBE	Far-end background block error	远端背景误块	Yuǎnduān bèijǐng wù kuài
FBC	Frame buffer cache	帧缓冲缓存	Zhèng huǎnchōng huǎncún
FBFM	Feedback frequency modulation	反馈调频	Fǎnkuì tiáopín
FBG	Fiber Bragg grating	光纤布拉格光栅	Guāngxiān Bù-lā-gé guāngshān
FBI	Feedback information	反馈信息	Fǎnkuì xìnxī
FBR	Fixed bit rate	固定比特率	Gùdìng bǐtèlǜ
FBT	Fused biconic taper (FOC)	熔融拉锥式	Róngróng lāzhuī-shì
FBTD	Feedback transmit diversity	反馈发射分集	Fǎnkuì fāshè fēnjí
FC	Failure count	失效次数	Shīxiào cìshù
FC	Fault control	故障控制	Gùzhàng kòngzhì
FC	Feature code	业务码	Yèwù mǎ
FC	Fiber channel	光纤信道	Guāngxiān xìndào
FC	Find calling party	寻找呼叫信号	Xúnzhǎo hūjiào xìnhào
FC	Frame control	帧控制	Zhèng kòngzhì
FC	Frame control	帧控制	Zhèng kòngzhì
FC	Frequency converter	频率变换器	Pínlǜ biànhuànqì
FC & FCP	Fiber channel and fiber channel protocol (ANSI use)	光纤信道和光纤信道协议	Guāngxiān xìndào hé guāngxiān xìndào xiéyì
FC_SB	Fiber channel single bytes	光纤通道单字节	Guāngxiān tōngdào dānzì jié
FCA	Fiber Channel Association	光纤通道协会	Guāngxiān tōngdào xiéhuì
FCA	Fixed channel allocation	固定信道分配	Gùdìng xìndào fēnpèi
FC-AL	Fiber channel - arbitrated loop	光纤通道仲裁环路	Guāngxiān tōngdào zhòngcái huán lù
FCAPS	Fault configuration accounting performance security	故障组成计算性能安全	Gùzhàng zǔchéng jìsuàn xìngnéng ānquán
FCB	File control block	文件控制块	Wénjiàn kòngzhì kuài
FCC	Federal Communications Commission (US)	联邦通信委员会	Liánbāng tōngxìn wěiyuánhuì
FCC	Fire alarm system	火灾报警系统	Huǒzāi bàojǐng xìtǒng
FCCH	Frequency correction channel	频率校正信道	Pínlǜ jiàozhèng xìndào
FCCH	Frequency correction channel	频率纠正信道	Pínlǜ jiūzhèng xìndào
FC-CT	Fiber channel - common transport	光纤通道通用传输	Guāngxiān tōngdào tōngyòng chuánshū
FCD	Frequency compression demodulator	频率压缩解调器	Pínlǜ yāsuō jiětiáoqì

FC-FG	Fiber channel - fabric generic requirements	光纤通道一般要求	Guāngxiān tōngdào yībān yāoqiú
FC-FLA	Fiber channel - fabric loop attachment	光纤通道环路接入	Guāngxiān tōngdào huánlù jiērù
FCFS	First come first service	先到先服务	Xiān dào xiān fúwù
FC-GS	Fiber channel - generic services	光纤通道通用服务	Guāngxiān tōngdào tōngyòng fúwù
FC-GS-2	Fiber channel second-generation generic services	光纤通道第二代通用服务	Guāngxiān tōngdào dì' èr dài tōngyòng fúwù
FC-GS-3	Fiber channel third-generation generic services	光纤通道第三代通用服务	Guāngxiān tōngdào dì sān dài tōngyòng fúwù
FCH	Frequency chirp	频率啁啾	Pínlǜ zhōujiū
FCI	File control information	行控制信息	Háng kòngzhì xìnxī
FCI	Furnish charging information	提供计费信息	Tígōng jìfèi xìnxī
FCIA	Fiber Channel Industry Association	光纤通道工业协会	Guāngxiān tōngdào gōngyè xiéhuì
FCIP	Entire fiber channel frame over IP (IETF use)	在 IP 上传输的光纤信道数据帧	Zài IP-shàng chuánshūde guāngxiān xìndào shùjùzhèng
FCIP	Fibre channel over IP	在 IP 上的光纤信道	Zài IP-shàngde guāngxiān xìndào
FC-IP	Fiber channel over IP protocol	用于 IP 协议的光纤通道	Yòng yú IP xiéyìde guāngxiān tōngdào
FCLC	Fiber channel loop community	光纤通道环路社团	Guāngxiān tōngdào huánlù shètuán
fcload	Function card load	功能卡装载	Gōngnéng kǎ zhuāngzài
FCP	Fiber channel protocol	光纤通道协议	Guāngxiān tōngdào xiéyì
FCPGA	Flip chip pin grid array	反转芯片针脚栅格阵列	Fǎnzhuǎn xìnpiàn zhēnjiao zhàgé zhènliè
FCRC	Cyclical redundancy check for fragmented data load (in DOCSIS)	对分段数据净荷的 CRC	Duì fēnduàn shùjù jìnghéde CRC
FCS	Fast cell selection	快速小区选择	Kuàisù xiǎoqū xuǎnzé
FCS	Fast circuit switching	快速电路交换	Kuàisù diànlù jiāohuàn
FCS	Fieldbus control system	现场总线控制系统	Xiànchǎng zǒngxiàn kòngzhì xìtǒng
FCS	Frame check sequence	帧检序列	Zhèng jiǎn xùliè
FCS	Frame check sequence	帧检测序列	Zhèng jiǎncè xùliè
FCS	Frame check sequence	帧检查序列	Zhèng jiǎnchá xùliè
FCS	Frame check sequence	帧检验顺序	Zhèng jiǎnyàn shùnxù
FCS	Frame check sequence	帧检验序列	Zhèng jiǎnyàn xùliè
FCS	Frame check sequence	帧校验序列	Zhèng jiàoyàn xùliè
FCSN	Fiber channel storage network	光纤通道存储网络	Guāngxiān tōngdào cúnchǔ wǎngluò
FC-SW	Fiber channel switch fabric	光纤通道交换架构	Guāngxiān tōngdào jiāohuàn jiàgòu
FCTDR	Frame-based compliant traffic distortion ratio	基于帧和符合条件的业务量失真比	Jīyú zhèng hé fúhé tiáojiànde yèwùliàng shīzhēn bǐ
FCU	Fan coil unit	风机盘管	Fēngjī pánguǎn
FC-VI	Fiber channel virtual interface	光纤通道虚拟接口	Guāngxiān tōngdào xūnǐ jiēkǒu
FD	Electrical installation	电气装置	Diànqì zhuāngzhì
FD	Flame detector	火焰探测器	Huǒyàn tàncèqì
FD	Floor distributor	楼层配线架	Lóucéng pèixiànjià
FD	Frequency divider	分频器	Fēnpínqì
FD/SSMA	Frequency diversity/spread spectrum multiple access	频率分集扩展频谱码分多址	Pínlǜ fēnjí kuòzhǎn pínpǔ mǎfēn duōzhǐ
FDBM	Fluid dynamic bearing motor	液态轴承马达	Yètài zhóuchéng mǎdá
FDC	Floppy disk controller	软盘驱动器控制装置	Ruǎnpán qūdòngqì kòngzhì zhuāngzhì
FDD	Floppy disk driver	软盘驱动器	Ruǎnpán qūdòngqì
FDD	Frequency division duplex	频分双工	Pínfēn shuānggōng
FDDI	Fiber distributed data interface	光导数据介面	Guāngdǎo shùjù jièmiàn
FDDI	Fiber distributed data interface	光缆分配式数据接口	Guānglǎn fēnpèishì shùjù jiēkǒu

FDDI	Fiber distributed data interface	光纤分布数据接口	Guāngxiān fēnbù shùjù jiēkǒu
FDDI	Fiber distributed data interface	光纤分布式数据接口	Guāngxiān fēnbù-shì shùjù jiēkǒu
FDDI	Fiber distributed data interface	光纤缆分布式数据接口	Guāngxiānlǎn fēnbù-shì shùjù jiēkǒu
FDDI	Fiber-based distributed data interface	基于光纤的分布数据接口	Jīyú guāngxiānde fēnbù shùjù jiēkǒu
FDDIF	Fiber distributed data interface	光缆分布数据接口	Guānglǎn fēnbù shùjù jiēkǒu
FDDL	Frequency division data link	频分数据键	Pínfēn shùjù jiàn
FDIV	Floating point division	浮点除	Fúdiǎn chú
FDL	Field bus datalink	现场总线数据链路	Xiànchǎng zǒngxiàn shùjù liànlù
FDM	Frequency division multiplexer	频分多路复用器	Pínfēn duōlù fùyòngqì
FDM	Frequency division multiplexing	频分多路复用	Pínfēn duōlù fùyòng
FDM	Frequency division multiplexing	频分复用	Pínfēn fùyòng
FDM	Fused deposition modeling	熔融沉积法	Róngróng chénjī fǎ
FDMA	Frequency division multiple access	频分多路存取	Pínfēn duōlù cúnqǔ
FDMA	Frequency division multiple access	频分多址	Pínfēn duōzhǐ
FDMA	Frequency division multiple access	频分多址	Pínfēn duōzhǐ
FDN	Fixed dialing number	固定拨号	Gùdìng bōhào
FDR	False transmit format detection ratio	假传送格式检波比率	Jiǎ chuánsòng géshi jiǎnbō bǐlǜ
FDS	Far-end defective second	远端缺陷秒	Yuǎnduān quēxiàn miǎo
FDT	Fault detection test	故障检测	Gùzhàng jiǎncè
FDT	Formal description technology	形式化描述技术	Xíngshì huà miáoshù jìshù
FDX	Full duplex data flow	全双工数据流	Quánshuānggōng shùjùliú
FE	Frame-layer reference event	帧层参考事件	Zhèng céng cānkǎo shìjiàn
FE	Function element	功能单元	Gōngnéng dānyuán
FE	Functional entity	功能实体	Gōngnéng shítǐ
FEAM	Functional entity access manager	功能实体接入管理	Gōngnéng shítǐ jiērù guǎnlǐ
FEBC	Far-end error block counter	远端误块计数	Yuǎnduān wùkuài jìshù
FEBE	Far-end block error	远端块差错	Yuǎnduān kuài chācuò
FEBE	Far-end block error	远端块误码	Yuǎnduān kuài wùmǎ
FEBE	Far-end block error	远端码组差错	Yuǎnduān mǎzǔ chācuò
FEBE	Far-end block error	远端模块错误	Yuǎnduān mókuài cuòwù
FEC	Forward equivalence class	转发等效类	Zhuǎnfā děngxiào lèi
FEC	Forward equivalent classification	前向等效类	Qiánxiàng děngxiào lèi
FEC	Forward error control	前向差错控制	Qiánxiàng chācuò kòngzhì
FEC	Forward error control	正向误差控制	Zhèngxiàng wùchā kòngzhì
FEC	Forward error correction	前向纠错	Qiánxiàng jiūcuò
FEC	Forward error correction code	前向纠错码	Qiánxiàng jiūcuò mǎ
FEC	Forwarding equivalence class	转发等价类	Zhuǎnfā děngjià lèi
FECC	Far-end echo cancellation	远端回声消除	Yuǎnduān huíshēng xiāochú
FECN	Forward explicit congestion notification	前向显式拥塞通知	Qiánxiàng xiǎnshì yōngsè tōngzhī
FECN	Forward explicit congestion notification	显式正向阻塞通知	Xiǎnshì zhèngxiàng zǔsè tōngzhī
FECP	Front-end communications processor	前端通信处理机	Qiánduān tōngxìn chùlǐjī
FED	Federation execution data (in MSMP)	联邦执行数据	Liánbāng zhíxíng shùjù
FED	Field emitter display	场发射显示器	Cháng fāshè xiǎnshìqì
FEI	Frame erase identifier	帧删除标识	Zhèng shānchú biāozhì
FEI	Frame erase identity	帧擦除标识	Zhèng cāchú biāozhì
FEI	Frame erase identity	帧控除标识码	Zhèng kòngchú biāozhì mǎ

FEIP	Fast ethernet interface processor	快速以太网接口处理器	Kuàisù yǐtàiwǎng jiēkǒu chǔlǐqì
FEMMS	Fast entry/exit multimedia state	快速进入/退出多媒体状态	Kuàisù jìnrù/tuìchū duōméitǐ zhuàngtài
FEP	Front-end processor	前端处理机	Qiánduān chǔlǐjī
FEP	Front-end processor	前端处理器	Qiánduān chǔlǐqì
FER	Frame erase rate	帧擦除率	Zhèng cāchú lǜ
FER	Frame erase rate	帧删除率	Zhèng shānchú lǜ
FER	Frame error rate	误帧率	Wùzhèng lǜ
FER	Frame error rate	帧差错率	Zhèng chācuò lǜ
FERF	Far-end receive failure	远端接收失败	Yuǎnduān jiēshōu shībài
FERF	Far-end receive fault	远端接收故障	Yuǎnduān jiēshōu gùzhàng
FES	Far-end errored second	远端误块秒	Yuǎnduān wùkuài miǎo
FET	Field effect transistor	场效应晶体管	Cháng xiàoyìng jīngtǐguǎn
FETD	Front-end target driver	前端目标设备驱动	Qiánduān mùbiāo shèbèi qūdòng
FEXT	Far-end crosstalk	远端串话	Yuǎnduān chuànhuà
FEXT	Far-end crosstalk	远端串扰	Yuǎnduān chuànrǎo
FEXT	Far-end crosstalk	远端串音	Yuǎnduān chuànyīn
FF	Flip-flop	触发器	Chùfāqì
FF	Fluoride fiber	氟化物光纤	Fúhuàwù guāngxiān
FF	Form feed	换页	Huàn yè
FFES	Foam fire extinguishing system	泡沫灭火系统	Pàomò mièhuǒ xìtǒng
FFH	Fast frequency hopping	快跳频	Kuài tiàopín
FFH	Fast frequency hopping	快速跳频	Kuàisù tiàopín
FFJ	Force feedback joystick	力量反匮式操纵杆	Lìliang fǎnkuì-shì cāozònggǎn
FFOL	FDDI follow-on LAN	更高速率的 FDDI 网络	Gènggāo sùlǜde FDDI wǎngluò
FFP	Far field pattern	远场图	Yuǎncháng tú
FFS	For further study	进一步研究	Jìnyībù yánjiū
FFS	For further study	为以后研究	Wéi yǐhòu yánjiū
FFS	For further study	作进一步研究	Zuò jìnyībù yánjiū
FFSK	Fast frequency shift keying	快速移频键控	Kuàisù yípín jiànkòng
FFSK	Fast frequency-shift keying	快速频移键控	Kuàisù pínyí jiànkòng
FFT	Fast Fourier transform	快速傅利叶变换	Kuàisù fù-lì-yè biànhuàn
FFT	Fast Fourier transform	快速付里叶变换	Kuàisù fù-lǐ-yè biànhuàn
FFT	Fast Fourier transform	快速傅氏变换	Kuàisù fù-shì biànhuàn
FFT	Fast Fourier transform	快速热欧姆转换	Kuàisù rè Oū-mǔ zhuǎnhuàn
FG	Building structure	房室结构	Fángshì jiégòu
FG	Finance group (CMM)	财务组	Cáiwù zǔ
FGCC	Federal Geodetic Control Committee	联邦测量控制委员会	Liánbāng cèliáng kòngzhì wěiyuánhuì
F-GCRA	Frame-based generic cell rate algorithm	基于帧的通用信元速率算法	Jīyú zhèngde tōngyòng xìnyuán sùlǜ suànfǎ
FH	Fire hydrant	消火栓	Xiāohuǒshuān
FH	Frame handler	帧处理器	Zhèng chǔlǐqì
FH	Frequency hopping	跳频	Tiàopín
FH/DQPSK	Frequency hopping/differential quadriphase shift keying	跳频/差分四相移相键控	Tiàopín/chāfēn sìxiāng yíxiāng jiànkòng
FH-CDMA	Frequency hopping code division multiple access	跳频码分多址	Tiàopín mǎfēn duōzhǐ
FHEC	Far-end header error control	远端信头差错控制	Yuǎnduān xìntóu chācuò kòngzhì
FHMA	Frequency hopping multiple access	跳频多重存取	Tiàopín duōzhòng cúnqǔ
FHS	Frequency hop synchronization	跳频同步	Tiàopín tóngbù

FHSS	Frequency hopping spread spectrum	跳频扩频	Tiàopín kuòpín
FHT	Fast Hadamard transform	快速哈达码变换	Kuàisù hǎ-dá-mǎ biànhuàn
FI	Fault interface	故障接口	Gùzhàng jiēkǒu
FI	Fee indicator	费用显示器	Fèiyòng xiǎnshìqì
FI	Format identifier	格式标识符	Géshì biāozhì fú
FIB	Forward indicator bit	前向指示比特	Qiánxiàng zhǐshì bǐtè
FIB	Forwarding information base	转发信息表	Zhuǎnfā xìnxī biǎo
FIB	Forwarding information base	转发信息库	Zhuǎnfā xìnxī kù
FICCDC	Federal Interagency Coordinating Committee on Digital Cartography	联邦数字制图协调委员会	Liánbāng shùzì zhìtú xiétiáo wěiyuánhuì
FICON	Fiber connection	光纤互联	Guāngxiān hùlián
Ficon	Fiber connection	光纤连接	Guāngxiān liánjiē
FID	Filter identifer	滤波器标识符	Lǜbōqì biāozhìfú
FID	Filter identifier	过滤标识符	Guòlǜ biāozhìfú
FID	Frequency identity	频率鉴别号码	Pínlǜ jiànbié hàomǎ
FIFO	First in, first out	先进先出	Xiān jìn xiān chū
FIFO	First input first output	先入先出队列	Xiān rù xiān chū duìliè
FIM	Fiber interface module	光纤接口模块	Guāngxiān jiēkǒu mókuài
FIN	Fibernet inbuilding network	光纤网络	Guāngxiān wǎngluò
FIPS	Federal Information Processing Standard (US)	联邦信息处理标准	Liánbāng xìnxī chǔlǐ biāozhǔn
FIR	Finite impulse response	有限推进响应	Yǒuxiàn tuījìn xiǎngyìng
FIR-SRDF	Stored response FIR digital filter	存贮响应 FIR 数字滤波器	Cúnzhù xiǎngyìng FIR shùzì lǜbōqì
FIRST	Forum of Incident Response and Security Teams	事件响应和安全团队论坛	Shìjiàn xiǎngyìng hé ānquán tuánduì lùntán
FIS	Fiber Instrument Sales, Inc (US)	光纤仪表销售公司	Guāngxiān yíbiǎo xiāoshòu gōngsī
FIS	Flight information service (civil aviation)	飞行情报服务	Fēixíng qíngbào fúwù
FISU	Fill-in signal unit	填充信号单元	Tiánchōng xìnhào dānyuán
FITEs	Forward interworking telephone events	前向互通电话事件	Qiánxiàng hùtōng diànhuà shìjiàn
FITL	Fiber in the loop	光纤环路系统	Guāngxiān huánlù xìtǒng
FIX	Federal Information Exchange (US)	联邦信息交换	Liánbāng xìnxī jiāohuàn
FJ	Building construction	房室建筑	Fángshì jiànzhù
FJ	Fiber jack	光纤插孔	Guāngxiān chākǒng
FK	Air conditioning ducting	空调通风	Kōngtiáo tōngfēng
FK	Foreign key (for database)	外键	Wàijiàn
F-km	Fiber-kilometer	光纤-公里	Guāngxiān--gōnglǐ
FL	Fiber laser	光纤激光器	Guāngxiān jīguāngqì
FL	Flatness	均匀性	Jūnyúnxìng
FL	Focal length	焦距	Jiāojù
FLAG	Fiber Link around the Globe	国际海底光缆系统	Guójì hǎidǐ guānglǎn xìtǒng
FLAG	Fiber-optic link around the globe	环球光纤链路	Huánqiú guāngxiān liànlù
Flash	Flash memory	闪存	Shǎn cún
FLASH-PROM	Flash programmable read only memory	块闪可编程只读存储器	Kuàishǎn kěbiānchéng zhǐdú cúnchǔqì
FLCD	Far-end loss of cell delineation	远端信元定界丢失	Yuǎnduān xìnyuán dìngjiè diūshī
FLEX	Flexible paging system	可变速寻呼系统	Kěbiànsù xúnhū xìtǒng
FLEX	High-speed pager coding standard (in the PRC)	高速寻呼编码体制	Gāosù xúnhū biānmǎ tǐzhì
FLIH	First level interrupt handler	第一级中断处理程序	Dìyījí zhōngduàn chùlǐ chéngxù
FLL	Frequency locked loop	频率锁定环	Pínlǜ suǒdìng huán
FLL	Frequency locked loop	频率同步环路	Pínlǜ tóngbù huánlù

FLNPs	Fiber link negotiation pulses	光纤链路协商脉冲	Guāngxiān liànlù xiéshāng màichōng
FLOP	Floating point operations per second	浮点操作/秒	Fúdiǎn cāozuò/ miǎo
FLOPS	Floating point operations per second	每秒浮点运算次数	Měi miǎo fúdiǎn yùnsuàn cìshù
FLP	Fast link pulse	快链路脉冲	Kuài liànlù màichōng
FLR	Frame loss rate	帧丢失率	Zhèng diūshī lǜ
FLR	Frame loss rate	帧丢失率	Zhèng diūshī lǜ
FLS	Frame loss second	帧丢失秒	Zhèng diūshī miǎo
FM	Fault management	失效管理	Shīxiào guǎnlǐ
FM	Fault manager	故障管理器	Gùzhàng guǎnlǐqì
FM	Flash memory	快闪存储器	Kuàishǎn cúnchǔqì
FM	Flexible multiplexer	灵活复用设备	Línghuó fùyòng shèbèi
FM	Flexible multiplexer	灵活复用器	Línghuó fùyòngqì
FM	Frequency modulation	频率调制	Pínlǜ tiáozhì
FM	Frequency modulation	调频	Tiáopín
FM	Frequency shift mode	频率改变方式	Pínlǜ gǎibiàn fāngshì
FM/FDMA	Frequency modulation/frequency division multiple access	调频/频分多路存取	Tiáopín/pínfēn duōlù cúnqǔ
FMBB	Fault management building block	故障管理构件	Gùzhàng guǎnlǐ gòujiàn
FMBS	Frame mode bearer service	帧方式承载业务	Zhèng fāngshì chéngzài yèwù
FMBS	Frame mode bearer service	帧模式承载业务	Zhèng móshì chéngzài yèwù
FMC	Fixed/mobile convergence	固定通信与移动通信相互靠拢	Gùdìng tōngxìn yǔ yídòng tōngxìn xiānghù kàolǒng
FMC	Fixed-mobile convergence	固定与移动通信融合	Gùdìng yǔ yídòng tōngxìn rónghé
FMC	Run in flexible metal conduit	穿蛇皮管敷设	Chuān shépíguǎn fūshè
FMCH	Firmware channel	固件通道	Gùjiàn tōngdào
FMCW	Frequency modulated continuous wave	调频连续波	Tiáopín liánxù bō
FMCW	Frequency modulated continuous wave	调频连续波	Tiáopín liánxù bō
FMD ROM	Fluorescent material read only memory	荧光质只读存储器	Yíngguāng zhì zhǐ dú cúnchǔqì
FM-DCPSK	Frequency modulation and differentially coherent PSK	调频差动相干相移键控	Tiáopín chādòng xiānggān xiàngyí jiànkòng
FMEA	Fault modes and effects analysis	故障模式和影响分析	Gùzhàng móshì hé yǐngxiǎng fēnxī
FMECA	Fault modes, effects and criticality analysis	故障模式、影响和严重性分析	Gùzhàng móshì、yǐngxiǎng hé yánzhòngxìng fēnxī
FMI	Fiberoptics Marketing Intelligence (from KMI - Kinder Morgan Inc.)	纤维光学市场情报	Xiānwéi guāngxué shìchǎng qíngbào
FMM	Finite message machine	有限消息机器	Yǒuxiàn xiāoxi jīqì
FMRS	Fiberoptics Market Research Service (from KMI - Kinder Morgan Inc.)	纤维光学市场研究服务	Xiānwéi guāngxué shìchǎng yánjiū fúwù
FMS	File management system	文件管理系统	Wénjiàn guǎnlǐ xìtǒng
FMS	Financial management system	财务管理系统	Cáiwù guǎnlǐ xìtǒng
FMT	Fiber management trays	光纤管理箱（碟）	Guāngxiān guǎnlǐ xiāng (dié)
FMUL	Floating point multiplication	浮点乘	Fúdiǎn chéng
FMX	Frequency modulated transmitter	调频发射机	Tiáopín fāshèjī
FN	Fiber node	光节点	Guāng jiédiǎn
FN	Frame number	帧号	Zhèng hào
FNA	Financial network association (China)	金融网络协会	Jīnróng wǎngluò xiéhuì
FNB	Weekly Fiberoptics Newsbrief Service (from KMI - Kinder Morgan Inc.)	纤维光学每周新闻简报服务	Xiānwéi guāngxué měizhōu xīnwén jiǎnbào fúwù
FNC	Federal Networking Council (US)	联邦网络技术委员会	Liánbāng wǎngluò jìshù wěiyuánhuì
FNC	Federal Networking Council (US)	联邦网络委员会	Liánbāng wǎngluò wěiyuánhuì

FNS	Fixed network services	固定网络通讯服务	Gùdìng wǎnglùo tōngxùn fúwù
FNS	Fujitsu Network Switching (Japan)	富士通网络交换	Fùshìtōng wǎngluò jiāohuàn
FNTS	Fujitsu Network Transmission Systems Inc. (Japan)	富士通网络传输系统公司	Fùshìtōng wǎngluò chuánshū xìtǒng gōngsī
FNUR	Fixed network user rate	固定网用户率	Gùdìng wǎng yònghùlǜ
FOB	Free on board	船上交货	Chuánshàng jiāohuò
FOC	Fiber optic cable	纤维光缆	Xiānwéi guānglǎn
FOC	Fiber optic cable strand	光缆线	Guānglǎn xiàn
FOCC	Forward control channel	前向控制信道	Qiánxiàng kòngzhì xìndào
FOCI	Fiber Optic Communication, Inc (Taiwan)	光纤通信公司	Guāngxiān tōngxìn gōngsī
FOCIS	Fiber optic connector intermateability standards	可互相配对的光纤连接器标准	Kěhùxiāng pèiduìde guāngxiān liánjiēqì biāozhǔn
FOD	Fax on demand	随选传真	Suíxuǎn chuánzhēn
FOFP	Fiber optic faceplate	光纤面板	Guāngxiān miànbǎn
FOG	Fiber-optic ground	光纤地线	Guāngxiān dìxiàn
FOI	Freedom of information	信息自由	Xìnxī zìyóu
FoIP	Fax over Internet protocol	在网际协议上传输传真	Zài wǎngjì xiéyì-shàng chuánshū chuánzhēn
FOIRL	Fiber optic inter-repeater link	光纤中继器连接	Guāngxiān zhōngjìqì liánjiē
FOIRL	Fiber optic inter-repeater link	光纤中继站间连接	Guāngxiān zhōngjìzhàn-jiān liánjiē
FOIS	Fiber optic interferometric sensor	光纤干扰测量传感器	Guāngxiān gānrǎo cèliáng chuángǎnqì
FOLS	Fiber optics lan section (of TIA, US)	光纤局域网委员会	Guāngxiān júyùwǎng wěiyuánhuì
FOM	Fiber optic modem	光纤调制解调器	Guāngxiān tiáozhì jiětiáoqì
FOMC	Federal Open Market Committee (US)	联邦开放市场委员会	Liánbāng kāifàng shìchǎng wěiyuánhuì
FOMS	Fiber-optic microscope	光纤显微镜	Guāngxiān xiǎnwēijìng
FON	Fiber optic net	光纤网	Guāngxiān wǎng
FONS Corp	Fiber Optic Network Solutions Corp. (US)	光纤网络承包公司	Guāngxiān wǎngluò chéngbāo gōngsī
FORTRAN	Format translator programming language	公式翻译程序语言	Gōngshì fānyì chéngxù yǔyán
FORTRAN	Formula translator	公式翻译语言	Gōngshì fānyì yǔyán
FOT	Forward transfer message (ISUP)	前向转移消息	Qiánxiàng zhuǎnyí xiāoxi
FOT	Forward-transfer signal	前向转移信号	Qiánxiàng zhuǎnyí xìnhào
FOT	Free of tax	免税	Miǎnshuì
FOTA	Fiber organizer tape application	光纤编织带涂敷机	Guāngxiān biānzhīdài túfūjī
FOTP	Fiber optic test equipment and procedures	光纤测试设备与测试方法	Guāngxiān cèshì shèbèi yǔ cèshì fāngfǎ
FOTS	Fiber optic transmission system	光导纤维传输系统	Guāngdǎo xiānwéi chuánshū xìtǒng
FP	Flexible point	灵活点	Línghuó diǎn
FP	Format prefix	格式前缀	Géshi qiánzhuì
FP	Frame protocol	帧协议	Zhèng xiéyì
FPA	Fire public address	火灾事故广播	Huǒzāi shìgù guǎngbō
FPAD	Facsimile packet assembly/disassembly	传真分组装拆设施	Chuánzhēn fēnzǔ zhuāngchāi shèshī
FPC	Full phase correlation	全相关	Quánxiāng guān
FPC	Run in flame-retardant semi-rigid PVC conduit	穿阻燃半硬聚乙烯管敷设	Chuān zǔrán bànyìng jùyǐxī guǎn fūshè
FPD	Flat-panel-display	平板显示	Píngbǎn xiǎnshì
FPGA	Field programmable gate array	现场可编程门阵列	Xiànchǎng kěbiānchéng mén zhènliè
FPGAs	Field-programmable gate arrays	现场可编程序门阵列	Xiànchǎng kěbiān chéngxù mén zhènliè
FPH	Free phone	免费业务	Miǎnfèi yèwù
FPH	Freephone	被叫集中付费业务	Bèijiào jízhōng fùfèi yèwù
FPL	Functional programming language	函数程序设计语言	Hánshù chéngxù shèjì yǔyán

FPLA	Field programmable logic array	现场可编程逻辑阵列	Xiànchǎng kěbiānchéng luóji zhènliè
FP-LD	Fabry-Perot cavity laser device	法布里 - 泊罗腔激光器	Fǎ-bù-lǐ--pó-luó qiāng jīguāngqì
FP-LD	Fabry-Perot laser diode	法布里--珀罗激光二极管	Fǎ-bù-lǐ--pò-luó jīguāng èrjíguǎn
FPLL	Frequency phase locked loop	频率相位同步环路	Pínlǜ xiàngwèi tóngbù huánlù
FPLMTS	Future public land mobile telecommunication system	未来公用陆地移动通信系统	Wèilái gōngyòng lùdì yídòng tōngxìn xìtǒng
FPLMTS	Future public land mobile telecommunication system	未来公众移动通信系统	Wèilái gōngzhòng yídòng tōngxìn xìtǒng
FPM	Foundation for Performance Measurement	性能测试基金会	Xìngnéng cèshì jījīnhuì
FPOL	Fiber polisher	光纤抛光机	Guāngxiān pāoguāngjī
FPP	Fast pattern processor	快速模式处理机	Kuàisù móshì chǔlǐjī
FPP	First person game (computer game)	第一人称游戏	Dìyīrénchēng yóuxì
FPR	Fixed point representation	定点表示法	Dìngdiǎn biǎoshì fǎ
FPRP	Five-phase reservation protocol	五阶段预留协议	Wǔ jiēduàn yùliú xiéyì
FPS	Fast packet switching	快速分组交换	Kuàisù fēnzǔ jiāohuàn
Fps	Frames per second	帧/秒	Zhèng/miǎo
FPS	Frames per second (video term)	每秒多少画面	Měi miǎo duōshao huàmiàn
FPSA	Fabry-Perot saturable absorber	发布里-珀罗饱和吸收器	Fā-bù-lǐ--pò-luó bǎohé xīshōu qì
FPSA	Fiber-to-the power supply serving area	光纤到供电服务区	Guāngxiān dào gōngdiàn fúwùqū
FPSC	Field programmable systems chip	现场可编程序系统芯片	Xiànchǎng kěbiān chéngxù xìtǒng xìnpiàn
FPTA	Fully polynomial time approximation	完全多项式时间近似	Wánquán duōxiàngshì shíjiān jìnsì
FPU	Floating point unit	浮点运算单元	Fúdiǎn yùnsuàn dānyuán
FPU	Frame processing unit (board)	帧处理单元（板）	Zhèng chǔlǐ dānyuán (bǎn)
FQ	Fair queuing	公平排队	Gōngping páiduì
FQDN	Fully qualified domain name	全限定域名	Quán xiàndìng yùmíng
FQDN	Fully qualified domain name	完全合格域名	Wánquán hégé yùmíng
FR	Frame	帧	Zhèng
FR	Frame relay	帧中继	Zhèng zhōngjì
FR	Frequency response	频率响应	Pínlǜ xiǎngyìng
FR	Frequency response	频响	Pínxiǎng
FR	Full rate	全速率	Quán sùlǜ
FR	Full rate	全速	Quánsù
FR	Function register	指令寄存器	Zhǐlìng jìcúnqì
FRA	Fiber optic Raman amplifier	光纤拉曼放大器	Guāngxiān lā-màn fàngdàqì
FRA	Fiber optic Raman amplifier	拉曼光纤放大器	Lā-màn guāngxiān fàngdàqì
FRA	Fixed radio access	固定无线接入	Gùdìng wúxiàn jiērù
FRAD	Frame relay access device	帧中继访问设备	Zhèng zhōngjì fǎngwèn shèbèi
FRAD	Frame relay access device	帧中继接入器件	Zhèng zhōngjì jiērù qìjiàn
FRAD	Frame relay assembly disassembly	帧中继装拆	Zhèng zhōngjì zhuāngchāi
FRAG	Fragmented frame	分段帧	Fēnduàn zhèng
FRBS	Frame relay bearer service	帧中继承载业务	Zhèng zhōngjì chéngzài yèwù
FRC	Frame rate control	帧比率控制	Zhèng bǐlǜ kòngzhì
FRD	Fire resistant damper	防火阀	Fánghuǒ fá
FRDP	Frequency reference divide panel	频率参数分配面板	Pínlǜ cānshù fēnpèi miànbǎn
FRDTS	Frame relay data transmission service	帧中继数据传输业务	Zhèng zhōngjì shùjù chuánshū yèwù
FRF	Frame relay forum	帧中继论坛	Zhèng zhōngjì lùntán
FRICC	Federal Research Internet Coordinating Committee	联邦调查因特网协调委员会	Liánbāng diàochá yīntèwǎng xiétiáo wěiyuánhuì

FRIF	Frame relay information field	帧中继信息字段	Zhèng zhōngjì xìnxī zìduàn
FRJ	Facility reject (ISUP message)	网络性能请求拒绝	Wǎngluò xìngnéng qǐngqiú jùjué
FRJ	Facility reject (ISUP)	性能拒绝	Xìngnéng jùjué
FRL	Facility restriction level	功能限制等级	Gōngnéng xiànzhì děngjí
FRL	Finland-Russia optical cable line (built 1993)	芬（兰）俄（国）光缆线路	Fēn (lán) é (guó) guānglǎn xiànlù
FRLME	Frame relay layer management entity	帧中继层管理实体	Zhèng zhōngjì céng guǎnlǐ shítǐ
FRMR	Frame reject	帧拒收	Zhèng jùshōu
FROG	Finland-Russia optical gateway	芬俄光通路	Fēn é guāng tōnglù
FROG	Finland-Russia optical gateway	芬兰俄国光通路	Fēnlán éguó guāng tōnglù
FRP	Fiberglass reinforced plastic	玻璃纤维增强塑胶	Bōli xiānwéi zēngqiáng sùjiāo
FRP	Fiberglass rodent protection	玻璃光纤齿咬防护	Bōli guāngxiān chǐyǎo fánghù
FRS	Fire resistant shutter	防火卷帘	Fánghuǒ juànlián
FR-SSCS	Frame relay-service-specific convergence sub-layer	帧中继业务特定会聚子层	Zhèng zhōngjì yèwù tèdìng huìjù zicéng
FRU	Field replaceable unit	可实地替换单元	Kěshídì tìhuan dānyuán
FRU	Field replaceable unit	现场可换件	Xiànchǎng kěhuàn jiàn
FRU	Field replaceable unit	现场可替换部件	Xiànchǎng kětìhuan bùjiàn
FS	Building plumbing	房室给排水	Fángshì gěi páishuǐ
FS	File separator	文件分隔	Wénjiàn fēngé
FS	Fixed subscriber	固定用户	Gùdìng yònghù
FS	Frame segment	帧字段	Zhèng zìduàn
FS	Frame start signal	帧起始信号	Zhèng qǐshǐ xìnhào
FS	Frame status	帧状态	Zhèng zhuàngtài
FS	Full scale	满量程	Mǎn liángchéng
FSA	Fiber to the serving area	光纤到服务区	Guāngxiān dào fúwùqū
FSAA	Full scene anti-aliasing (video term)	全景抗锯齿失真	Quánjǐng kàng jùchǐ shīzhēn
FSAN	Full service access network	全业务接入网络	Quán yèwù jiērù wǎngluò
FSB	Front side bus	前置总线	Qiánzhì zǒngxiàn
FSBS	Frame switching bearer service	帧交换承载业务	Zhèng jiāohuàn chéngzài yèwù
FSC	Fiber storage center	光纤存储中心	Guāngxiān cúnchǔ zhōngxīn
FSC	Fixed satellite communications	固定卫星通讯	Gùdìng wèixīng tōngxùn
FSE	Frequency shifter effect	频率转换效果	Pínlǜ zhuǎnhuàn xiàoguǒ
FSES	Far-end severely errored second	远端严重误块秒	Yuǎnduān yánzhòng wùkuài miǎo
FSF	Free Software Foundation	免费软件基金会	Miǎnfèi ruǎnjiàn jījīnhuì
FSI	FLIR Systems, Inc	FLIR 系统公司	FLIR xìtǒng gōngsī
FSIP	Fast serial interface processor	快速串行接口处理器	Kuàisù chuànháng jiēkǒu chǔlǐqì
FSK	Frequency-shift keying	频移键控	Pínyí jiànkòng
FSK	Frequency-shift keying	移频键控	Yípín jiànkòng
FSLT	Fiber optic subscriber line terminal	光纤用户线路终端	Guāngxiān yònghù xiànlù zhōngduān
FSM	Field strength meter	场强计	Chǎngqiáng jì
FSM	Finite state machine	有限状态机	Yǒuxiàn zhuàngtài jī
FSM	Finite state module	有限状态模型	Yǒuxiàn zhuàngtài móxíng
FSM	Forward setup message	前向建立信号	Qiánxiàng jiànlì xìnhào
FSM	Forward setup message (TUP)	前向建立消息	Qiánxiàng jiànlì xiāoxi
FSM	Frequency-shift modulation	频移调制	Pínyí tiáozhì
FSN	Forward sequence number	前向顺序号	Qiánxiàng shùnxù hào
FSN	Full service network	全信息网络	Quán xìnxī wǎngluò

FSNC	Forward sequence number of last message accepted by remote level 2	由远端第二级接受的最后一个消息的前向序号	Yóu yuǎnduān dì'èrjí jiēshòude zuìhòu yīgè xiāoxide qiánxiàng xùhào
FSO	Free space optical communications	自由空间光学通信	Zìyóu kōngjiān guāngxué tōngxìn
FSO	Free space optics	自由空间光纤	Zìyóu kōngjiān guāngxiān
FSP	Fiber channel service protocol	光纤通道服务协议	Guāngxiān tōngdào fúwù xiéyì
FSP	Fiber service platform	光纤服务平台	Guāngxiān fúwù píngtái
FSPF	Fabric shortest path first	光纤最短路径优先协议	Guāngxiān zuìduǎn lùjìng yōuxiān xiéyì
FSR	Frequency shift repeater	移频直防站	Yípín zhífángzhàn
FSS	Fixed satellite service	静止卫星业务	Jìngzhǐ wèixīng yèwù
FSS	Fixed satellite services	固定卫星业务	Gùdìng wèixīng yèwù
FSS	Full service set	全业务集	Quán yèwù jí
FSS	Full service set (of equipment)	全业务台	Quán yèwù tái
FST	Fast sequenced transport	快速连续传送	Kuàisù liánxù chuánsòng
FST	Fast sequenced transport (protocol)	快速有序运输（协议）	Kuàisù yǒuxù yùnshū (xiéyì)
FST	Fast switching thyristor	快速晶闸管	Kuàisù jīngzháguǎn
FST	Frequency-shift telegraphy	频移电报	Pínyí diànbào
FSTC	Financial Services Technology Consortium	金融服务技术联盟	Jīnróng fúwù jìshù liánméng
FSTS	Finite state transition system	有限状态转换系统	Yǒuxiàn zhuàngtài zhuǎnhuàn xìtǒng
FSU	Final signaling unit	最终信号单元	Zuìzhōng xìnhào dānyuán
FSU	Fixed subscriber unit	单用户固定台	Dānyònghù gùdìng tái
FSU	Fixed subscriber unit	固定用户单元	Gùdìng yònghù dānyuán
FSU	From switch unit	源于交换机单元	Yuán yú jiāohuànjī dānyuán
FSUB	Floating point subtraction	浮点减	Fúdiǎn jiǎn
FSW	Forced switch	强制倒换	Qiángzhì dǎohuàn
FSw	Forced switchover	强制切换	Qiángzhì qiēhuàn
FSW	Frame synchronization word	帧同步字	Zhèng tóngbù zì
FT	Fixed terminal	固定终端	Gùdìng zhōngduān
FTA	Fault tree analysis	故障述分析	Gùzhàng shù fēnxī
FTA	Final type approval	最终全面型号认证	Zuìzhōng quánmiàn xínghào rènzhèng
FTA	Full type approval	全面型号认证	Quánmiàn xínghào rènzhèng
FTAM	File transfer access and management (ISO use)	文件传输访问和管理	Wénjiàn chuánshū fǎngwèn hé guǎnlǐ
FTAM	File transfer access management	文件传送存放与管理	Wénjiàn chuánsòng cúnfàng yǔ guǎnlǐ
FTAM	File transfer addressing and management	文件传送地址和管理	Wénjiàn chuánsòng dìzhǐ hé guǎnlǐ
FTAM	File transfer, access and management	文件传输、存取和管理	Wénjiàn chuánshū、cúnqǔ hé guǎnlǐ
FTAM	File transfer, access and management protocol	文件传送接入及管理协议	Wénjiàn chuánsòng jiērù jí guǎnlǐ xiéyì
FTAM	File transfer, access and manipulation	文件传输，接入和使用	Wénjiàn chuánshū, jiērù hé shǐyòng
FTAM	File transmission, access and management	文件传输访问管理	Wénjiàn chuánshū fǎngwèn guǎnlǐ
FTAP	Filter tap coupler	滤波型分路器	Lǜbō-xíng fēnlùqì
FTC	Fast time constant circuit	快时间常数电路	Kuài shíjiān chángshù diànlù
FTC	Federal Trade Commission (US)	联邦贸易委员会	Liánbāng màoyì wěiyuánhuì
FTC	Federal Trade Commission (US)	联邦商业委员会	Liánbāng shāngyè wěiyuánhuì
FTD	Frame transfer delay	帧传送延迟	Zhèng chuánsòng yánchí
FTDL	Flexible topology data link	灵活拓扑数据链路	Línghuó tuòpū shùjù liànlù
FTDMA	Frequency and time division multiple access	频分和时分多址	Pínfēn hé shífēn duōzhǐ
FTF	Face to face	面对面	Miàn duì miàn
FTF	Fiber to feeder	光纤到馈线	Guāngxiān dào kuìxiàn

FTG	Fighting game (computer game)	格斗类游戏	Gédòu-lèi yóuxì
FTHD	Fixed temperature heat detector	定温控测器	Dìngwēn kòngcèqì
FTHMA	Frequency time hopping multiple access	频率时间跳跃多路存取	Pínlǜ shíjiān tiàoyuè duōlù cúnqǔ
FTLA	Fiber to the last amplifier	光纤到最后一个放大器	Guāngxiān dào zuìhòu yīgè fàngdàqì
FTM	FDM transmitter module	FDM 发送器组件	FDM fāsòngqì zǔjiàn
FTM	Fiber transmission module	光传输模块	Guāng chuánshū mókuài
FTMB	Flamethrower mini-bridger	小型桥接器	Xiǎoxíng qiáojiēqì
FTN	FEC to NHLFE map	FEC 至 NHLFE 的映射	FEC zhì NHLFE de yìngshè
Ftn	Forwarded-to number	前转号码	Qiánzhuǎn hàomǎ
ftn	Forward-to number	转送号码	Zhuǎnsòng hàomǎ
FTP	File transfer protocol	文件传输协议	Wénjiàn chuánshū xiéyì
FTP	File transfer protocol	文件传送协议	Wénjiàn chuánsòng xiéyì
FTP	File transfer protocol	远程存取	Yuǎnchéng cúnqǔ
FTP	Foil twisted pair	金属箔对线	Jīnshǔ bó duìxiàn
FTP	Foil twisted pair	金属箔双绞电缆	Jīnshǔ bó shuāngjiǎo diànlǎn
FTP site	File transfer protocol site (Internet location for downloading files using FTP)	文件传送点	Wénjiàn chuánsòng diǎn
FTPC	Fiber-to-the passive coaxial (network)	光纤到无源同轴（网络）	Guāngxiān dào wúyuán tóngzhóu (wǎngluò)
FTP-CONS PTP	Connection-mode network service	点对点面向连接网络业务	Diǎn duì diǎn miànxiàng liánjiē wǎngluò yèwù
FTSE100	Financial Times Stock Exchange top 100 companies	泰晤士金融股票交易 100 家顶级公司	Tàiwùshì jīnróng gǔpiào jiāoyì 100 jiā dǐngjí gōngsī
FTTB	Fiber to the building	光纤到大楼	Guāngxiān dào dàlóu
FTTB	Fiber to the building	光纤到楼	Guāngxiān dào lóu
FTTC	Fiber to the curb	光纤到近邻	Guāngxiān dào jìnlín
FTTC	Fiber to the curb	光纤到路边	Guāngxiān dào lùbiān
FTTC	Fiber to the customer	光纤到用户	Guāngxiān dào yònghù
FTTCab	Fiber to the cabinet	光纤到机柜	Guāngxiān dào jī guì
FTTCab	Fiber to the cabinet	光纤到接线柜箱	Guāngxiān dào jiēxiàn guìxiāng
FTTD	Fiber to the desk	光纤到办公桌	Guāngxiān dào bàngōngzhuō
FTTD	Fiber to the desk	光纤到桌面	Guāngxiān dào zhuōmiàn
FTTH	Fiber to the home	光纤到户	Guāngxiān dào hù
FTTH	Fiber to the home	光纤到家	Guāngxiān dào jiā
FTTH	Fiber to the home	光纤到家庭	Guāngxiān dào jiātíng
FTTL	Fiber in the loop	光纤用户环路	Guāngxiān yònghù huánlù
FTTL	Fiber to the loop	光纤用户环路	Guāngxiān yònghù huánlù
FTTN	Fiber to the node	光纤到节点	Guāngxiān dào jiédiǎn
FTTN	Fiber to the node	光纤到节点	Guāngxiān dào jiédiǎn
FTTO	Fiber to the office	光纤到办公室	Guāngxiān dào bàngōngshì
FTTP	Fiber to the premises	光纤到住地	Guāngxiān dào zhùdì
FTTSA	Fiber to the service area	光纤到小区	Guāngxiān dào xiǎoqū
FTTZ	Fiber to the zone	光纤到小区	Guāngxiān dào xiǎoqū
FTZ	Foreign trade zone	对外贸易区	Duìwài màoyì qū
FU	Frame unit	帧单元	Zhèng dānyuán
FU	Function unit	功能单元	Gōngnéng dānyuán
FU	Fuse unit	保险丝装置	Bǎoxiǎnsī zhuāngzhì
Fubar	Fouled up beyound all recognition	混乱透顶，糟极了	Hùnluàn tòudǐng, zāo jíle

FUC	Frame unit controller	帧单元控制器	Zhèng dānyuán kòngzhìqì
FULPI	Fluorated polyimide (FOC mfg)	氟化聚酸亚胺材料	Fúhuà jùsuān yà'àn cáiliào
FUN	Function	功能	Gōngnéng
FUNI	Frame-based user-to-network interface	帧用户网络接口	Zhèng yònghù wǎngluò jiēkǒu
FUS	Fiberoptic undersea systems	海底光缆系统	Hǎidǐ guānglǎn xìtǒng
FV	Forward validation	向前验证	Xiàngqián yànzhèng
FVC	Forward voice channel	前向话音信道	Qiánxiàng huàyīn xìndào
FW	Jitter and wander	抖动和漂移	Dǒudòng hé piāoyí
FWA	Fixed wireless access	固定无线接入	Gùdìng wúxiàn jiērù
FWD	Free world dial-up	全球随意拨号	Quánqiú suíyì bōhào
FWD	Free world dial-up	世界随意拨号	Shìjiè suíyì bōhào
FWDM	Filter wavelength division multiplexer	滤波型波分复用器	Lǜbō-xíng bōfēn fùyòngqì
FWFS	First Wiener filter solution	第一维纳滤波器解	Dìyī wéinà lǜbōqì jiě
FWH	Firmware hub	固件中心	Gùjiàn zhōngxīn
FWHM	Full width at half maximum	半幅全宽	Bànfú quán kuān
FWHM	Full width half maximum	半幅值全宽	Bànfúzhí quán kuān
FWHM	Full width half maximum (pulse)	脉冲的半高宽度	Màichōngde bàngāo kuāndù
FWM	Four wave mixing	四波混频	Sìbō hùnpín
FWN	Fixed wireless network	固定无线网络	Gùdìng wúxiàn wǎngluò
FWS	Free wavelength solution	自由波长解决方案	Zìyóu bōcháng jiějué fāng'àn
FWT	Fast Walsh transform	快速沃尔什变换	Kuàisù wò-ěr-shí biànhuàn
FXO	Foreign exchange office	外部交换局	Wàibù jiāohuànjú
FXS	Foreign exchange station	外部交换站	Wàibù jiāohuàn zhàn
FYI	For your information	供参考	Gōng cānkǎo
FYI	For your information	供你用的信息	Gōng nǐ yòngde xìnxī
FYI	For your information	为您提供信息	Wéi nín tígōng xìnxī
FYR	For your reference (computer chat)	供你参考	Gōng nǐ cānkǎo

G

G	Gain	增益	Zēngyì
G	Generator	发电机	Fādiànjī
G	Giga- (prefix meaning 10^9)	千兆	Qiānzhào
G	Grid (as a grating)	栅极	Shānjí
G	Grid (as network); lattice; mesh	网格	Wǎnggé
G/IW MSC	Gateway/interworking MSC	关口互连 MSC	Guānkǒu hùlián MSC
G/T	Figure of merit	品质因数	Pǐnzhì yīnshù
G3 FAX	Group 3 facsimile	三类传真	Sānlèi chuánzhēn
GA	Gate array	门阵列	Mén zhènliè
GAAP	Generally accepted accounting principles	公认会计原则	Gōngrèn kuàijì yuánzé
GaAs	Gallium arsenide	砷化镓	Shēnhuàjiā
GAC	Global assembly cache	全局配件缓存	Quánjú pèijiàn huǎncún
GAC	Global assembly cache	全局装配件缓存	Quánjú zhuāngpèijiàn huǎncún
GAC	Government advisory committee	政府顾问委员会	Zhèngfǔ gùwèn wěiyuánhuì
GAINS	Growth and income securities	增长收益债卷	Zēngzhǎng shōuyì zhàijuàn
GAL	Global Access Ltd.	全球接入有限公司	Quánqiú jiērù yǒuxiàn gōngsī
GaN	Gallium nitride	氮化镓	Dànhuà jiā

GAP	Applied physics group	应用物理组	Yìngyòng wùlǐ zǔ
GAP	Gaussian frequency shift keying	高斯滤波频移键控	Gāo-sī lǜbō pínyí jiànkòng
GAP	Generic access profile	通用访问应用	Tōngyòng fǎngwèn yìngyòng
GAP	Generic access profile	通用接口配置	Tōngyòng jiēkǒu pèizhì
GAP	Generic access profile	通用接入图	Tōngyòng jiērù tú
GARP	General attribute registration protocol	一般属性注册协议	Yībān shǔxìng zhùcè xiéyì
GARP	Generic attribute registration protocol	通用属性注册协议	Tōngyòng shǔxìng zhùcè xiéyì
GARP PDU	GARP protocol data unit	GARP 协议数据单元	GARP xiéyì shùjù dānyuán
GART	Graphic address remapping table	图形地址重绘表	Túxíng dìzhǐ chónghuì biǎo
GATM	Global aviation traffic manager	全球航空管制系统	Quánqiú hángkōng guǎnzhì xìtǒng
GATS	General acceptance test software	通用验收测试软件	Tōngyòng yànshōu cèshì ruǎnjiàn
GATS	General Agreement on Trade in Services	服务贸易总协定	Fúwù màoyì zǒng xiédìng
GATS	General Agreement on Trade in Services	贸易服务总协定	Màoyì fúwù zǒngxiédìng
GATT	General Agreement on Tariffs and Trade	关税和贸易总协定	Guānshuì hé màoyì zǒngxiédìng
Gb	Gigabits	吉比特	Jíbǐtè
GB	Gigabyte	吉咖字节	Jígāzìjié,
GB	Gigabyte	吉字节	Jízìjié
GB	Gigabyte	千兆字节	Qiānzhào zìjié
Gb/s	Gigabits per second	吉比特每秒	Jíbǐtè měi miǎo
GB_W,GBW	Gain bandwidth	增益带宽	Zēngyì dàikuān
GBd	Gigabaud	吉波特	Jíbōtè
GBd	Gigabaud	吉咖波特	Jígābōtè
GBd	Gigabaud	千兆波特	Qiānzhào bōtè
GbE	Gigabit Ethernet	千兆比以太网	Qiānzhàobì yǐtàiwǎng
GbE	Gigabit Ethernet	千兆位以太网	Qiānzhàowèi yǐtàiwǎng
GbE,Gbe	Gigabit ethernet	吉比特级以太网	Jíbǐtè jí yǐtàiwǎng
GBIC	Gigabit interface converter	吉比特接口转换器	Jíbǐtè jiēkǒu zhuǎnhuànqì
GBIC	Gigabit interface converter	千兆比特接口转换器	Qiānzhào bǐtè jiēkǒu zhuǎnhuànqì
Gbit/s; Gbps	Gigabits per second	吉位秒	Jíwèi miǎo
GB-Net	Golden Bridge Network (China)	金桥网	Jīnqiáo wǎng
GBR	Global base register	共用基址寄存器	Gòngyòng jīzhǐ jìcúnqì
GBR	Guaranteed bit rate	保证比特率	Bǎozhèng bǐtè lǜ
GBS	Glass break sensor	玻璃破碎传感器	Bōli pòsuì chuángǎnqì
GBSVC	General broadcast signaling virtual channel	通用广播信令虚信道	Tōngyòng guǎngbō xìnlìng xū xìndào
GC	Garbage collection	垃圾回收	Lājī huíshōu
GC	Garbage collection	垃圾收集	Lājī shōují
GC	General control	通用控制	Tōngyòng kòngzhì
GC	Global control	全局控制	Quánjú kòngzhì
GCAC	Generic connection acceptance control	通用连接接纳控制	Tōngyòng liánjiē jiēnà kòngzhì
GCBP	Gateway communication back panel	关口通信后面板	Guānkǒu tōngxìn hòumian bǎn
Gcc	General conference control	通用会议控制	Tōngyòng huìyì kòngzhì
GccSAP	General conference control- service access point	通用会议控制服务接入点	Tōngyòng huìyì kòngzhì fúwù jiērù diǎn
GCF	Gatekeeper confirm	网守发现确认	Wǎngshǒu fāxiàn quèrèn
GCF	Gatekeeper confirm (packet protocol)	关守确认	Guānshǒu quèrèn
GCF	Glass-ceramic ferrules	玻璃陶瓷陶管	Bōli táocí táoguǎn
GCF	GSM certification forum	GSM 认可论坛	GSM rènkě lùntán

GCI	Global cell identity	全球小区识别码	Quánqiú xiǎoqū shíbiémǎ
GCI	Global connection ID	全局连接 ID	Quánjú liánjiē ID
GCIN	Gateway communication interconnection network	关口通信互联网	Guānkǒu tōngxìn hùliánwǎng
GCR	Group call record	组呼叫寄存器	Zǔhūjiào jìcúnqì
GCR	Group call register	呼叫寄发器群	Hūjiào jìfāqì qún
GCRA	Generic cell rate algorithm	通用信元速率算法	Tōngyòng xìnyuán sùlǜ suànfǎ
GCRA	Generic cell rate algorithm	通用信元率算法	Tōngyòng xìnyuánlǜ suànfǎ
GCS	Generic cabling system	一般的布线系统	Yībānde bùxiàn xìtǒng
GCS	Global Communication Semiconductors Inc.	全球通信半导体公司	Quánqiú tōngxìn bàndǎotǐ gōngsī
GCSR	Grating coupler sampled reflector	光栅耦合取样反射器	Guāngshān ǒuhé qǔyàng fǎnshèqì
GCSS	Global Communications Satellite System	全球通信卫星系统	Quánqiú tōngxìn wèixīng xìtǒng
GCT	Graphics communications terminal	图形通信终端	Túxíng tōngxìn zhōngduān
GD	Conduit	管道	Guǎndào
GDC	Game developer conference	游戏发展商会议	Yóuxì fāzhǎn shāng huìyì
GDCP	Global data collection PC	全球数据收集 PC 机	Quánqiú shùjù shōují PC-jī
GDI	Graphics device interface	图形设备接口	Túxíng shèbèi jiēkǒu
GDMO	Guidelines for the definition of managed objects	被管对象定义指南	Bèiguǎn duìxiàng dìngyì zhǐnán
GDMO	Guidelines for the definition of managed objects	对管理目标定义的指南	Duì guǎnlǐ mùbiāo dìngyìde zhǐnán
GDMO	Guidelines for the definition of managed objects	管理对象定义规范	Guǎnlǐ duìxiàng dìngyì guīfàn
GDMO	Guidelines for the definition of managed objects	管理目标定义指南	Guǎnlǐ mùbiāo dìngyì zhǐnán
GDP	Gateway discovery protocol	网关查找协议	Wǎngguān cházhǎo xiéyì
GDP	Gateway discovery protocol	网关发现协议	Wǎngguān fāxiàn xiéyì
GDP	Global data table	全局数据表	Quánjú shùjù biǎo
GDP	Global descriptor table	全局描述表	Quánjú miáoshù biǎo
GDSU	Global digital service unit	全球数字单元	Quánqiú shùzì dānyuán
GDT	Global descriptor table	全局描述符表	Quánjú miáoshùfú biǎo
GE	Gateway exchange	国际出口局	Guójì chūkǒujú
GE	Gigabit Ethernet	千兆比特以太网	Qiānzhào bǐtè yǐtàiwǎng
GE	Gigabit Ethernet	千兆以太网	Qiānzhào yǐtàiwǎng
GE, GbE	Gigabit ethernet	Gb 以太网	Gb Yǐtàiwǎng
GE=GbE	Gigabit ethernet	吉比特以太网	Jíbǐtè yǐtàiwǎng
$GeCl_4$	Germanium chlorate orTetrachloride	四氯化锗	Sìlǜhuàzhě
GEF	Gain equilibrium filter	增益均衡滤波器	Zēngyì jūnhéng lǜbōqì
GEN	Global European network	全球欧网络	Quánqiú ōu wǎngluò
GEO	Geostationary earth orbit	对地静止轨道	Duìdì jìngzhǐ guǐdào
GEO	Geostationary earth orbit	静止地球轨道	Jìngzhǐ dìqiú guǐdào
GEO	Geosynchronous earth orbit	同步地球轨道	Tóngbù dìqiú guǐdào
Geos	Geostationary satellite	同步卫星	Tóngbù wèixīng
GEOS	Geosynchronous earth orbit satellite	同步地球轨道卫星	Tóngbù dìqiú guǐdào wèixīng
GEQ	Fiber grating-type gain equalizer	光纤光栅型增益均衡器	Guāngxiān guāngshānxíng zēngyì jūnhéngqì
GEQ	Gain equalizer	增益均衡器	Zēngyì jūnhéngqì
GEQ	Gain equilibrium	增益均衡	Zēngyì jūnhéng
GERAN	GSM/EDGE radio access network	GSM/EDGE 无线接入网	GSM/EDGE wúxiàn jiērù wǎng
GES	Gateway earth station	网关地球站	Wǎngguān dìqiúzhàn
GES	Graphics exchange specification	图形数据互换说明	Túxíng shùjù hùhuàn shuōmíng
GeT	Greenwich electronic time	格林尼治电子时间	Gé-lín-ní-zhì diànzǐ shíjiān

GF	Galois field	伽罗华域	Jiāluóhuá yù
GF	General flow chart	综合流程图	Zōnghé liúchéngtú
GF	Germanium content fiber	含锗光纤	Hánzhě guāngxiān
GF	Global function	全局功能	Quánjú gōngnéng
GFC	Gas filled cable	充气电缆	Chōngqì diànlǎn
GFC	General flow control	基本流量控制	Jīběn liúliàng kòngzhì
GFC	Generic flow control	通用流量控制	Tōngyòng liúliàng kòngzhì
GFC	Generic flow control	一般流量控制码	Yībān liúliàng kòngzhì mǎ
GFC	Global flow control	总流量控制	Zǒng liúliàng kòngzhì
GFCA	Gridded crossed-field amplifier	栅控正交场放大器	Zhàkòng zhèngjiāo cháng fàngdàqì
GFCI	Ground fault circuit interrupter	接地故障电路中级器	Jiēdì gùzhàng diànlù zhōngjíqì
GFFs	Gain flattening filters	增益平坦滤波器	Zēngyì píngtǎn lǜbōqì
GFI	General format identifier	通用格式标识符	Tōngyòng géshi biāozhìfú
GFP	Generic framing procedure	通用成帧规程	Tōngyòng chéngzhèng guīchéng
GFP	Generic framing protocol	通用成帧协议	Tōngyòng chéng zhèng xiéyì
GFPM	Gated frequency position modulation	手控频率位置调制	Shǒukòng pínlǜ wèizhì tiáozhì
GFR	Guaranteed frame rate	有保证帧速率	Yǒu bǎozhèng zhèng sùlǜ
GFSK	Gaussian frequency shift keying	高斯频移键控	Gāo-sī pínyí jiànkòng
GFT	Gauss-Fourier transform	高斯-傅里叶变换	Gāo-sī—Fù-lǐ-yè biànhuàn
GGP	Gateway-to-gateway protocol	网关到网关连接协议	Wǎngguān dào wǎngguān liánjiē xiéyì
GGPM	Grid-gated photomultiplier	控制栅光电培增器	Kòngzhì zhà guāngdiàn péizēngqì
GGRF	GSM global roaming forum	GSM 全球漫游论坛	GSM quánqiú mànyóu lùntán
GGSN	Gateway GPRS support node	GPRS 网关支持节点	GPRS wǎngguān zhīchí jiédiǎn
GGSN	Gateway GPRS support node	网关 GPRS 支持节点	Wǎngguān GPRS zhīchí jiédiǎn
GHIP	Global high capacity IPC processor	全球高容量 IPC 处理器	Quánqiú gāoróngliàng IPC chǔlǐqì
GHOST	General hardware oriented system transfer	全面硬件导向系统转移	Quánmiàn yìngjiàn dǎoxiàng xìtǒng zhuǎnyí
GHS	Green Hills Software Co.	绿色希尔斯软件公司	Lǜsè Xī-ěr-sī ruǎnjiàn gōngsī
GI	Graded index fiber	渐变折射率光纤	Jiànbiàn zhéshèlǜ guāngxiān
GI	Group identification	群识别	Qún shíbié
GI	Group identifier	群标识符	Qún biāozhì fú
GIAC	General inquiry access code	通用查询访问码	Tōngyòng cháxún fǎngwèn mǎ
GIB	Generic information block	通用信息模块	Tōngyòng xìnxī mókuài
GID	GARP information declaration	GARP 信息发布	GARP xìnxī fābù
GID	Global information distribution	全局信息发布	Quánjú xìnxī fābù
GID1	Group identifier (level 1)	鉴别器群（电平 1）	Jiànbiéqì qún (diànpíng 1)
GID2	Group identifier (level 1)	鉴别器群（电平 2）	Jiànbiéqì qún (diànpíng 2)
GIDO	Generalized intrusion detection objects	通用入侵检测对象	Tōngyòng rùqīn jiǎncè duìxiàng
GIE	Global information exchange	全球信息交换	Quánqiú xìnxī jiāohuàn
GIF	Graded index fiber	渐变梯度光纤	Jiànbiàn tīdù guāngxiān
GIF	Graded index fiber	渐变型多模光纤	Jiànbiànxíng duōmó guāngxiān
GIF	Graded index fiber	浙变梯度光纤	Zhèbiàn tīdù guāngxiān
GIF	Graphic interchange format	图形交换格式	Túxíng jiāohuàn géshi
GIG	Global information grid	全球信息网格	Quánqiú xìnxī wǎnggé
GIGO	Garbage in, garbage out	无用输入无用输出	Wúyòng shūrù wúyòng shūchū
GigSTAR	Gigabit/sec serial transmitter and receiver	Gb/s 系列发射机与接收机	Gb/s xìliè fāshèjī yǔ jiēshōujī
GII	Global information infrastructure	全球信息基础结构	Quánqiú xìnxī jīchǔ jiégòu

GII	Global information infrastructure	全球信息基础设施	Quánqiú xìnxī jīchǔ shèshī
GIK	Group interchange key (IPsec)	组交换密钥	Zǔ jiāohuàn mìyào
GIOC	Guilin Institute of Optical Communications	桂林光通信研究所	Guìlín guāngtōngxìn yánjiūsuǒ
GIOP	General inter-ORB protocol (CORBA term)	通用 ORB 间协议	Tōngyòng ORB-jiān xiéyì
GIP	GARP information propagation	GARP 信息广播	GARP xìnxī guǎngbō
GI-POF	Graded index polymer optical fiber	梯度折射率塑料光纤	Tīdù zhéshèlǜ sùliào guāngxiān
GI-POF	Graded index polymer optical fiber	渐变折射率聚合物光纤	Zhèbiàn zhéshèlǜ jùhéwù guāngxiān
GIS	Geographical information system	地里信息系统	Dìlì xìnxī xìtǒng
GIS	Graphical information system	图形信息系统	Túxíng xìnxī xìtǒng
GK	Gatekeeper	关守	Guānshǒu
GK	Gatekeeper	网闸	Wǎngzhá
GKc	Gatekeeper for service control	业务控制网守	Yèwù kòngzhì wǎngshǒu
GKF	Gatekeeper function	网守功能	Wǎngshǒu gōngnéng
GKMP	Group key management protocol	组密钥管理协议	Zǔ mìyào guǎnlǐ xiéyì
GKS	Graphical kernel system	计算机图形核心系统	Jìsuànjī túxíng héxīn xìtǒng
GLM	Gigabit link module	千兆比特链路模块	Qiānzhào bǐtè liànlù mókuài
GLONASS	Global Navigation Satellite System	全球导航卫星系统	Quánqiú dǎoháng wèixīng xìtǒng
GLONASS	Global Orbiting Navigation Satellite System	全球定轨导航卫星系统	Quánqiú dìngguǐ dǎoháng wèixīng xìtǒng
GLR	Generalized likelihood ratio	一般似然比	Yībān sìrán bǐ
GLVs	Grating light valves	光栅光阀	Guāngshān guāngfá
GM	General Motors Corporation (US company)	通用汽车公司	Tōngyòng qìchē gōngsī
GM	Group management	组管理	Zǔ guǎnlǐ
GMC	General monitoring center	总监测中心	Zǒng jiāncè zhōngxīn
GMCH	Graphics and memory controller hub	图形和内存控制中心	Túxíng hé nèicún kòngzhì zhōngxīn
GMII	Gigabit media-independent interface	千兆比特媒体无关接口	Qiānzhào bǐtè méitǐ wúguān jiēkǒu
GML	Geography markup language	地理标记语言	Dìlǐ biāojì yǔyán
GMM	Gaussian mixture model	高斯混合模型	Gāo-sī hùnhé móxíng
GMM	GPRS mobility management	GPRS 移动性管理	GPRS yídòngxìng guǎnlǐ
GMPCS	Global mobile personal communications by satellite	全球移动个人卫星通信	Quánqiú yídòng gèrén wèixīng tōngxìn
GMPCS	Global mobile personal communications services	全球移动个人通信业务	Quánqiú yídòng gèrén tōngxìn yèwù
GMPLS	Generalized multi-protocol label switching	通用多协议标志交换协议	Tōngyòng duōxiéyì biāozhì jiāohuàn xiéyì
GMR	Giant magnetoresistive	巨型磁阻	Jù-xíng cízǔ
GMRP	GARP multicast registration protocol	GARP 组播注册协议	GARP zǔbō zhùcè xiéyì
GMS	General message security	一般信息安全	Yībān xìnxī ānquán
GMS	General MicroSystems Corp.	通用微波系统公司	Tōngyòng wēibō xìtǒng gōngsī
GMSA	Gateway mobile switching center (MSC)	入口 MSC	Rùkǒu MSC
GMSC	Gateway mobile services switching center	关口移动交换中心	Guānkǒu yídòng jiāohuàn zhōngxīn
GMSC	Gateway mobile services switching center	网关移动业务交换中心	Wǎngguān yídòng yèwù jiāohuàn zhōngxīn
GMSC	Gateway mobile switch center	入口移动交换中心	Rùkǒu yídòng jiāohuàn zhōngxīn
GMSC	Gateway mobile switching center	关口移动业务交换中心	Guānkǒu yídòng yèwù jiāohuàn zhōngxīn
GMSC	Gateway mobile switching center	网关移动交换中心	Wǎngguān yídòng jiāohuàn zhōngxīn
GMSC	Gateway MSC	关口 MSC	Guānkǒu MSC
GMSK	Gaussian filtered minimum-shift keying	高斯滤波最小移频键控	Gāo-sī lǜbō zuìxiǎo yípín jiànkòng
GMSK	Gaussian minimum shift keying	高斯最小频移键控	Gāo-sī zuìxiǎo pínyí jiànkòng
GMSK	Gaussian minimum-shift keying	高斯最小键移	Gāo-sī zuìxiǎo jiànyí
GMSK	Gaussian minimum-shift keying	高斯最小移频键控	Gāo-sī zuìxiǎo yípín jiànkòng

GMSK	Premodulation Gaussian filtered MSK	调前高斯滤波的 MSK	Tiáoqián gāo-sī lǜbōde MSK
GMT	Greenwich mean time	格林尼治时间	Gé-lín-ní-zhì shíjiān
GNB	Graphic network browser	图形网浏览	Túxíng wǎng liúlǎn
GNE	Gateway network element	网关网元	Wǎngguān wǎngyuán
GNE	Gateway network element	网间接口单元	Wǎngjiàn jiēkǒu dānyuán
GNE	Graphic network editor	图形网编辑	Túxíng wǎng biānjí
GNL	Global network locator	全球网络探测器	Quánqiú wǎngluò tàncèqì
GNM	Generic network information model	通用网络信息模型	Tōngyòng wǎngluò xìnxī móxíng
GNOME	GNU's network object model environment	GNU 网络对象模型环境	GNU wǎngluò duìxiàng móxíng huánjìng
GNS	Get nearest server	获取最近服务器	Huòqǔ zuìjìn fúwùqì
GNS	Global network service	全球网络服务	Quánqiú wǎngluò fúwù
GNS	Global network service	全球网络业务	Quánqiú wǎngluò yèwù
GNSS	Global navigation satellite system	全球卫星导航系统	Quánqiú wèixīng dǎoháng xìtǒng
GNTPDN	Grant power down	授权掉电	Shòuquán diàodiàn
GOB	Group of blocks	块群	Kuài qún
GOCAP	Graphic output circuit analysis program	图形输出电路分析程序	Túxíng shūchū diànlù fēnxī chéngxù
GOEP	Generic object exchange profile	通用对象交换应用	Tōngyòng duìxiàng jiāohuàn yìngyòng
GOF	Glass optical fiber	玻璃光纤	Bōli guāngxiān
GOLF	Green, oxygen, light and foot	绿色、氧气、阳光与漫步	Lǜsè、yǎngqì、yángguāng yǔ mànbù
GOS	Grade of service	服务等级	Fúwù děngjí
GOSIP	Government Open system interconnection protocol	政府开放系统互连协议	Zhèngfǔ kāifàng xìtǒng hùlián xiéyì
GOTS	Government off-the-shelf products	政府成品	Zhèngfǔ chéngpǐn
GOTV	Go on TV	上电视	Shàng diànshì
GP	Genetic programming	遗传规划	Yíchuán guīhuà
GP	Guard period	保护时隙	Bǎohù shíxì
GP	Guard period	防护周期	Fánghù zhōuqī
Gpa	GSM PLMN area	GSM 公用陆地移动通信网覆盖面积	GSM gōngyòng lùdì yídòng tōngxìnwǎng fùgài miànjī
GPCS	Global personal communication system	全球个人通信系统	Quánqiú gèrén tōngxìn xìtǒng
GPF	General protection fault	一般保护性错误	Yībān bǎohùxìng cuòwù
GPH	Graphic handler	图形处理器	Túxíng chǔlǐqì
GPI	General purpose input	普通操作输入	Pǔtōng cāozuò shūrù
GPI	Global path index (in XML)	全局路径索引	Quánjú lùjìng suǒyǐn
GPRS	General packet radio service	通用分组无线业务	Tōngyòng fēnzǔ wúxiàn yèwù
GPRS	General packet radio service	通用无线分组业务	Tōngyòng wúxiàn fēnzǔ yèwù
GPRS	General packet radio service	无线分组业务	Wúxiàn fēnzǔ yèwù
GPRSSSF	General packet radio service- service switch function	通用分组无线业务交换功能	Tōngyòng fēnzǔ wúxiàn yèwù jiāohuàn gōngnéng
GPS	General processor sharing	广义处理器共享	Guǎngyì chǔlǐqì gòngxiǎng
GPS	Global positioning system	全球定位系统	Quánqiú dìngwèi xìtǒng
GPSR	GPS receiver	GPS 接收机	GPS jiēshōujī
GPSS	Global positioning satellite system	全球卫星定位系统	Quánqiú wèixīng dìngwèi xìtǒng
GPSU	General power supply unit	通用功率电源单元	Tōngyòng gōnglǜ diànyuán dānyuán
GPU	Graphics processing unit	图形处理器	Túxíng chǔlǐqì
GRA	Circuit group reset-acknowledgement message	电路群复原证实消息	Diànlù qún fùyuán zhèngshí xiāoxi
GRACE	Group routing and charging equipment	群路由选择和计价设备	Qún lùyóu xuǎnzé hé jìjià shèbèi
GRE	Generic routing encapsulation	通用路由封装	Tōngyòng lùyóu fēngzhuāng

GRE	Generic routing encapsulation	通用路由选择封装	Tōngyòng lùyóu xuǎnzé fēngzhuāng
GRE	Generic routing encapsulation	通用选路封装	Tōngyòng xuǎnlù fēngzhuāng
GRE	Graduate record examination	学位等级记录审验考试	Xuéwèi děngjí jìlù shěnyàn kǎoshì
GRIC	Global reach internet connection	可通达全球因特网路连接	Kětōngdá quánqiú Yīntèwǎng lù liánjiē
GRJ	Gatekeeper reject	关守拒绝	Guānshǒu jùjué
GRJ	Gatekeeper reject	网守发现拒绝	Wǎngshǒu fāxiàn jùjué
GRM	Circuit group supervision message	电路群监视消息	Diànlù qún jiānshì xiāoxi
GRQ	Gatekeeper request	关守请求	Guānshǒu qǐngqiú
GRQ	Gatekeeper request	网守发现请求	Wǎngshǒu fāxiàn qǐngqiú
GRQ	General request message	一般请求消息	Yībān qǐngqiú xiāoxi
GRS	Circuit group reset message	电路群复原消息	Diànlù qún fùyuán xiāoxi
GRS	General register stack	通用寄存器堆栈	Tōngyòng jìcúnqì duīzhàn
GS	Fiber optic cable digital equipment	光缆数字设备	Guānglǎn shùzì shèbèi
GSA	Ground-state absorption	基态吸收	Jītài xīshōu
GSA	GSM system area	GSM 系统区域	GSM xìtǒng qūyù
GSAL	Global Security Analysis Lab	全球安全性分析实验室	Quánqiú ānquánxìng fēnxī shíyànshì
GSBP	Global service back panel	全球服务后面板	Quánqiú fúwù hòumian bǎn
GSC	Group security controller	组安全控制器	Zǔ ānquán kòngzhìqì
GSC	Group switching center	分组交换中心	Fēnzǔ jiāohuàn zhōngxīn
GSC	Group switching center	群交换中心	Qún jiāohuàn zhōngxīn
GS-EDFA	Gain shifted erbium-doped fiber amplifier	增益平移掺饵光纤放大器	Zēngyì píngyí chān'ěr guāngxiān fàngdàqì
GSI	Grid security infrastructure	网格安全基础设施	Wǎnggé ānquán jīchǔ shèshī
GSIM	GSM service identity module	GSM 业务识别模块	GSM yèwù shíbié mókuài
GSL	Gigabit serial logic products	吉比特系列产品	Jíbǐtè xìliè chǎnpǐn
GSM	General forward set-up information message	一般前向建立信息消息	Yībān qiánxiàng jiànlì xìnxī xiāoxi
GSM	Global System for Mobile Communications	全球移动通信系统	Quánqiú yídòng tōngxìn xìtǒng
GSM	Groupe Special Mobile (est. 1982)	移动通信特别小组	Yídòng tōngxìn tèbié xiǎozǔ
GSM PLMN	GSM public land mobile network	GSM 公共陆地移动网络	GSM gōnggòng lùdì yídòng wǎngluò
GSM TAAB	GSM type approval advisory board	GSM 型号认证咨询委员会	GSM xínghào rènzhèng zīxún wěiyuánhuì
GSMA	Global scheduling multiple access	全局调度多路存取	Quánjú diàodù duōlù cúnqǔ
GSMP	General switch management protocol	通用交换管理协议	Tōngyòng jiāohuàn guǎnlǐ xiéyì
GSN	Gateway service node	关口服务节点	Guānkǒu fúwù jiédiǎn
GSN	Gateway services node	网关服务节点	Wǎngguān fúwù jiédiǎn
GSN	GPRS support node	GPRS 支持节点	GPRS zhīchí jiédiǎn
GSP	Generalized system of acceptance	普惠制	Pǔhuìzhì
GSR	Gigabit switch router	千兆位交换路油器	Qiānzhàowèi jiāohuàn lùyóuqì
GSS-API	Generic security service application program interface	通用安全服务应用程序接口	Tōngyòng ānquán fúwù yìngyòng chéngxù jiēkǒu
GSTN	General switch telephone network	同用电话交换网	Tóngyòng diànhuà jiāohuàn wǎng
GSTN	General switched telephone network	普通电话交换网	Pǔtōng diànhuà jiāohuàn wǎng
GSTN	General switched telephone network	同用交换电话网	Tóngyòng jiāohuàn diànhuà wǎng
GT	Global title	全局码	Quánjú mǎ
GT	Global title	全球名称	Quánqiú míngchēng
GT	Global title	全球题目	Quánqiú tímù
GT	Global title	全球寻址码	Quánqiú xúnzhǐ mǎ
GTF	Generalized timing formula	一般程序时间公式	Yībān chéngxù shíjiān gōngshì
GTFM	Generalized tamed frequency modulation	通用平滑调频	Tōngyòng pínghuá tiáopín

GTFM	Generalized tamed frequency modulation	通用于滑调频	Tōngyòng yúhuá tiáopín
GTI	Global title indicator	全局码表示语	Quánjú mǎ biǎoshì yǔ
GTO	Gate turnoff thyristor	门极可关断晶体管	Ménjí kěguānduàn jīngtǐguǎn
GTO	Government Telecommunications Organization	政府电信组织	Zhèngfǔ diànxìn zǔzhī
GTP	Group terminal point	群终接点	Qún zhōngjiēdiǎn
GTP	Tunneling protocol (in GPRS)	隧道协议	Suìdào xiéyì
GTP-U	GPRS tunneling protocol for user plane	GPRS 隧道协议用户平面	GPRS suìdào xiéyì yònghù píngmiàn
GTT	Globe text telephone	全球文本电话	Quánqiú wénběn diànhuà
GTW	Global trading web	全球网上电子贸易市场	Quánqiú wǎngshàng diànzǐ màoyì shìcháng
GUI	Graphical user interface	图象使用者介面	Túxiàng shǐyòngzhě jièmiàn
GUI	Graphical user interface	图象用户介面	Túxiàng yònghù jièmiàn
GUI	Graphical user interface	图形界面	Túxíng jièmiàn
GUI	Graphical user interface	图形用户接口	Túxíng yònghù jiēkǒu
GUI	Graphical user interface	图形用户界面	Túxíng yònghù jièmiàn
GUID	Globally uniform identifier	全局统一标识	Quánjú tǒngyī biāozhì
GUID	Globally unique identifier	全局唯一标识符	Quánjú wéiyī biāozhìfú
GUID	Globally unique identifier	全球唯一标识符	Quánqiú wéiyī biāozhì fú
GULS	Generic upper layer security	通用上层安全性	Tōngyòng shàngcéng ānquánxìng
GVC	Global validity condition (CAD/CAM)	全球有效性条件	Quánqiú yǒuxiàoxìng tiáojiàn
GVD	Group velocity dispersion	群速度色散	Qúnsùdù sèsàn
GVNS	Global virtual network service	全局虚拟网业务	Quánjú xūnǐ wǎng yèwù
GVPP	Generic visual perception processor	常规视觉处理器	Chángguī shìjué chǔlǐqì
GVRP	GARP VLAN registration protocol	GARP VLAN 注册协议	GARP VLAN zhùcè xiéyì
GW	Gateway	关口	Guānkǒu
GW	Gateway	关口局	Guānkǒujú
GW	Gateway (exchange)	关口局	Guānkǒu jú
GW	Gateway (on a network)	网关	Wǎngguān
GW	Gateway router	网关路由器	Wǎngguān lùyóuqì
GWWOP	Ground wire wound optical fiber cable	接地线缠绕光缆	Jiēdìxiàn chánrǎo guānglǎn
GXLU	Guoxin Lucent Network Technologies Co. Ltd. (Sino-US joint venture)	国信朗讯科技网络技术有限公司	Guóxìn Lǎngxùn Kējì wǎngluò jìshù yǒuxiàn gōngsī

H

H	Henry (unit of inductance)	亨利	Hēnglì
H	Hexadecimal	十六进制的	Shíliùjìnzhìde
HA	Half adder	半加器	Bànjiāqì
HA	Helical antenna	螺旋型天线	Luóxuán-xíng tiānxiàn
HA	Heterodyne amplifier	外差放大器	Wàichāi fàngdàqì
HA	Hogg horn antenna	喇叭型天线	Lǎba-xíng tiānxiàn
HA	Home address	归属地址	Guīshǔ dìzhǐ
HA	Home agent	本地代理	Běndì dàilǐ
HA	Home agent	归属代理	Guīshǔ dàilǐ
HA	Home automation	家用电器智能化	Jiāyòng diànqì zhìnénghuà
HAC	Hardware address control	机器地址控制	Jīqì dìzhǐ kòngzhì
HAC	Hierarchical abstract computer	分级抽象计算机	Fēnjí chōuxiàng jìsuànjī
HACMP	High availability cluster multi-processor	高可用集群多处理机	Gāokěyòng jíqún duō chǔlǐjī

HADM	Hybrid analog and digital modulation	混合模拟和数字调制	Hùnhé mónǐ hé shùzì tiáozhì
HAL	Hardware abstraction layer	硬件抽象层	Yìngjiàn chōuxiàng céng
HAL	Hardware abstraction layer	硬件抽像化层	Yìngjiàn chōuxiànghuà céng
HAL	Hot air leveller (PCB manufacturing)	热风整平机	Rèfēng zhěng píng jī
HALO	High altitude large optics	极高大型光学计划	Jígāo dà-xíng guāngxué jìhuà
HAPS	High altitude platform station	平流层高空气艇平台	Píngliúcéng gāokōng qìtǐng píngtái
HARF	Hyperstable adaptive recursive filter	超稳定自适应递归滤波器	Chāowěndìng zìshìyìng dìguī lǜbōqì
HARQ	Hybrid automatic repeat request	混合自动重传	Hùnhé zìdòng chóngchuán
HARQ	Hybrid automatic repeat request	混合自动请求重传	Hùnhé zìdòng qǐngqiú chóngchuán
HART	Highway addressable remote transducer	可寻址远程传感器高速通道	Kěxúnzhǐ yuǎnchéng chuángǎnqì gāosù tōngdào
HART	Highway addressable remote transducer (used in process controls)	可寻址远程传感器数据公路	Kěxúnzhǐ yuǎnchéng chuángǎnqì shùjù gōnglù
HATS	Hybrid automatic test system	混合自动测试系统	Hùnhé zìdòng cèshì xìtǒng
HBA	Hardware failure-oriented group blocking acknowledgement message	面向硬件故障的群闭塞证实消息	Miànxiàng yìngjiàn gùzhàngde qún bìsè zhèngshí xiāoxi
HBA	Host bus adapter	主机总线适配器	Zhǔjī zǒngxiàn shìpèiqì
HC/HY-COM	Hybrid combiner	混合瞧型合路器	Hùnhé qiáo-xíng hélùqì
HCA	Hybrid channel assignment	混合信道指配方式	Hùnhé xìndào zhǐpèi fāngshì
HCBS	High-speed C bus service unit	高速 C 总线服务单元	Gāosù C zǒngxiàn fúwù dānyuán
HCC	Horizontal cross connect	水平交叉连接	Shuǐpíng jiāochā liánjiē
HCDM	Hybrid companding delta modulation	混合压扩增量调制	Hùnhé yākuò zēngliàng tiáozhì
HCI	Host controller interface	主控制器接口	Zhǔ kòngzhìqì jiēkǒu
HCI	Host controller interface	主机控制接口	Zhǔjī kòngzhì jiēkǒu
HCL	Hardware compatibility list	硬件兼容性列表	Yìngjiàn jiānróngxìng lièbiǎo
HCMOS	High density complementary metal oxide semiconductor (CMOS)	高密度互补金属氧化物半导体	Gāomìdù hùbǔ jīnshǔ yǎnghuàwù bàndǎotǐ
HCMTS	High capacity mobile telephone system (Japan)	大容量移动电话系统	Dàróngliàng yídòng diànhuà xìtǒng
HCR	Hybrid communication routing	混合通行路由选择	Hùnhé tōngxíng lùyóu xuǎnzé
HCS	Frame header check sequence	帧头校验序列	Zhèng tóu jiàoyàn xùliè
HCS	Hierarchical cell structure	分层小区结构	Fēncéng xiǎoqū jiégòu
HCS	Hierarchical cell structure	分层小区技术	Fēncéng xiǎoqū jìshù
HCS	Higher order connection supervision	高阶连接监控	Gāojiē liánjiē jiānkòng
HCS	Higher order connection supervision	高阶连接监视	Gāojiē liánjiē jiānshì
HCSD	High-speed circuit switched data	高速率电路交换数据	Gāosùlǜ diànlù jiāohuàn shùjù
HCT	Hardware compatibility test	硬件兼容性测试	Yìngjiàn jiānróngxìng cèshì
HCTR	High capacity trunk radio	高容量干线无线电	Gāoróngliàng gànxiàn wúxiàndiàn
HCTR	High capacity trunk radio	高容量中继无线电	Gāoróngliàng zhōngjì wúxiàndiàn
HD	Conference telephone	会议电话	Huìyì diànhuà
HD	Harmonic distortion	谐波失真	Xiébō shīzhēn
HD	Heat detector	感温探测器	Gǎnwēn tàncèqì
HD	High density	高密	Gāomì
HD	High density	高密度	Gāomìdù
HD	Horizontal deflection	水平偏转	Shuǐpíng piānzhuǎn
HDA	Head disk assembly	磁头集合	Cítóu jíhé
HDAM	Hierarchical direct access method	分级直接存取法	Fēnjí zhíjiē cúnqǔ fǎ
HDB	High density bipolar coding	高密度双极性码	Gāomìdù shuāngjíxìng mǎ
HDB3	High density binary-3	高密度二进制 3 型码	Gāomìdù èrjìnzhì san xíng mǎ

HDB3	Third order high density bipolar code	三阶高密度双极性码	Sānjiē gāomìdù shuāng jíxìng mǎ
HDC	Half duplex channel	半双工通道	Bànshuānggōng tōngdào
HDC	Hard disk controller	硬盘控制器	Yìngpán kòngzhìqì
HDCD	High definition compatible digital	高密兼容数码	Gāomì jiānróng shùmǎ
HDD	High density data	高密度数据	Gāomìdù shujù
HDDS	High density data system	高密度数据系统	Gāomìdù shujù xìtǒng
HDFS	High density fixed service	高密度固定业务	Gāomìdù gùdìng yèwù
HDL	Hardware description language	硬件描述语言	Yìngjiàn miáoshù yǔyán
HDLC	High level data link channel	高级数据链路通道	Gāojí shùjù liànlù tōngdào
HDLC	High level data link control	高阶数据链路（连接）控制	Gāojiē shùjù liànlù (liánjiē) kòngzhì
HDLC	High-level data link control	高层数据链路控制	Gāocéng shùjù liànlù kòngzhì
HDLC	High-level data link control	高级数据链路控制规程	Gāojí shùjù liànchí kòngzhì guīchéng
HDLC	High-level data link control	高级数据链路控制	Gāojí shùjù liànlù kòngzhì
HDLC	High-level data link control	高级数据链路控制规程	Gāojí shùjù liànlù kòngzhì guīchéng
HDLC	High-level data link control protocol	高级数据链路控制协议	Gāojí shùjù liànlù kòngzhì xiéyì
HDLC	High-level link control	高层链路控制	Gāocéng liànlù kòngzhì
HDLC	High-speed data link control	高速数据链路规程	Gāosù shùjù liànlù guīchéng
HDLC	High-speed data link control	高速数据链路控制	Gāosù shùjù liànlù kòngzhì
HDLR	Hexadecimal symbolic loader	十六进制符号装入程序	Shíliùjìnzhì fúhào zhuāngrù chéngxù
HDPCM	Hybrid differential pulse code modulation	混合差动脉码调制	Hùnhé chādòng màimǎ tiáozhì
HDPE	High density polyethylene	高密聚乙烯	Gāomì jùyǐxī
HDRC	Hypothetical digital reference connection	假设数字参考连接	Jiǎshè shùzì cānkǎo liánjiē
HDRP	Hypothetical reference digital path	假设参考数字通道	Jiǎshè cānkǎo shùzì tōngdào
HDS	High-speed digital switch	高速数字交换机	Gāosù shùzì jiāohuànjī
HDSL	High bit rate DSL	高比特率数字订阅线路	Gāobǐtèlǜ shùzì dìngyuè xiànlù
HDSL	High bit-rate digital subscriber line	高比特率数字用户线	Gāobǐtèlǜ shùzì yònghù xiàn
HDSL	High bit-rate digital subscriber line	高速数字用户回路	Gāosù shùzì yònghù huílù
HDSL	High data-rate digital subscriber line	高速数字用户线	Gāosù shùzì yònghù xiàn
HDSL	High-bit-rate digital subscriber link	高比特数字用户链路	Gāobǐtè shùzì yònghù liànlù
HDSL	High-data-rate digital subscriber line	高数据速率数字用户线	Gāoshùjùsùlǜ shùzì yònghù xiàn
HDT	Host digital terminal	局用数字终端	Jú-yòng shùzì zhōngduān
HDTM	Half duplex transmission module	半双工传输模块	Bànshuānggōng chuánshū mókuài
HDTS	Half duplex transmission system	半双工传输系统	Bànshuānggōng chuánshū xìtǒng
HDTV	High definition television	高密电视	Gāomì diànshì
HDTV	High definition television	高清晰度电视	Gāoqīngxīdù diànshì
HDTV	High definition TV	高分瓣率电视	Gāofēnbànlǜ diànshì
HDX	Half duplex	半双工	Bànshuānggōng
HE	Home environment	归属环境	Guīshǔ huánjìng
HEADER	Message header	消息报头	Xiāoxi bàotóu
HEC	Header error check	头校验码	Tóu jiàoyàn mǎ
HEC	Header error check	信头差错校验	Xìntóu chācuò jiàoyàn
HEC	Header error control	报头错误控制	Bàotóu cuòwù kòngzhì
HEC	Header error control	头部差错控制	Tóubù chācuò kòngzhì
HEC	Header error control	信头差错控制码	Xìntóu chācuò kòngzhì mǎ
HEC	Header error control	信头差错控制域	Xìntóu chācuò kòngzhì yù

HEC	Header error control	信头误码控制	Xìntóu wùmǎ kòngzhì
HEC	Hybrid error control	混合差错控制	Hùnhé chācuò kòngzhì
HEC	Hybrid error correction	混合纠错	Hùnhé jiūcuò
HEL	Hardware emulation layer	硬件仿真层	Yìngjiàn fǎngzhēn céng
HEL	Hardware emulation layer	硬件模拟层	Yìngjiàn mónǐ céng
HEL	Header extension length	扩展头部长度	Kuòzhǎn tóubù chángdù
HEMS	High-level entity management system	高级实体管理系统	Gāojí shítǐ guǎnlǐ xìtǒng
HEMT	High electron mobility transistor	高电子迁移率晶体管	Gāo diànzǐ qiānyílǜ jīngtǐguǎn
HEO	High earth orbit	高地球轨道	Gāo dìqiú guǐdào
HEO	Highly elliptical orbit	高椭圆轨道（高轨）	Gāotuǒyuán guǐdào (gāo guǐ)
HEO	Highly elliptical orbit	椭圆轨道	Tuǒyuán guǐdào
HEROS	Highly efficient router operating system	高性能路由器操作系统	Gāoxìngnéng lùyóuqì cāozuò xìtǒng
HE-VASP	Home environment value added service provider	归属环境附加值业务提供者	Guīshǔ huánjìng fùjiāzhí yèwù tígòngzhě
HF	High frequency	高频	Gāopín
HF	Human factors	人为因素	Rénwéi yīnsù
HFA	High frequency amplifier	高频放大器	Gāopín fàngdàqì
HFC	Hybrid fiber coax	光纤-同轴电缆混合系统	Guāngxiān –tóngzhóu diànlǎn hùnhé xìtǒng
HFC	Hybrid fiber/coaxial cable	混合光纤/同轴电缆	Hùnhé guāngxiān/tóngzhóu diànlǎn
HFC	Hybrid fiber-coaxial network	光纤铜轴混合网	Guāngxiān tóngzhóu hùnhé wǎng
HFDL	High frequency data link	高频数据链	Gāopín shùjù liàn
HFFR	Halogen-free, flame retardant jacket (FOC)	无卤阻燃护套	Wúlǔ zǔrán hùtào
HFRDF	High frequency repeater distribution frame	高频中继配线架	Gāopín zhōngjì pèixiànjià
H-FSC	Hierarchical fair service curve	优先级的公平服务曲线	Yōuxiān jíde gōngping fúwù qūxiàn
HFW	Hybrid fiber wireless system	混合光纤无线系统	Hùnhé guāngxiān wúxiàn xìtǒng
HG	Hunt group	搜寻组	Sōuxún zǔ
HGA	High gain amplifier	高增益放大器	Gāozēngyì fàngdàqì
HGB	Hardware failure-oriented group blocking message	面向硬件故障的群闭塞消息	Miànxiàng yìngjiàn gùzhàngde qún bìsè xiāoxi
HGL	Submarine optical cable	海底光缆	Hǎidǐ guānglǎn
HGU	Hardware failure-oriented group unblocking message	面向硬件故障的群闭塞解除消息	Miànxiàng yìngjiàn gùzhàngde qún bìsè jiěchú xiāoxi
HHO	Hard handover	硬切换	Yìng qiēhuàn
HIB	High integrated bus	高集成总线	Gāojíchéng zǒngxiàn
HIBP	High capacity IPC back panel	高容量 IPC 后面板	Gāoróngliàng IPC hòumian bǎn
HICAI	Hypermedia intelligent computer-based instruction	基于超媒体的职能计算机辅助教学	Jīyú chāoméitǐde zhínéng jisuànjī fǔzhù jiàoxué
HID	Human interface device	人机接口设备	Rén jī jiēkǒu shèbèi
HIFAM	High fidelity amplitude modulation	高保真度调幅	Gāobǎozhēndù tiáofú
HiFD	High-capacity floppy disk	高容量软盘	Gāoróngliàng ruǎnpán
HIFI	High fidelity	高保真度	Gāobǎozhēndù
HINA	High-speed IPC node board assembly	高速 IPC 节点集成板	Gāosù IPC jiédiǎn jíchéngbǎn
HIPA	High-speed IPC processor assembly	高速 IPC 处理器集成板	Gāosù IPC chǔlǐqì jíchéngbǎn
HIPERLAN	High performance European radio LAN	欧洲高性能无线 LAN	Oūzhōu gāoxìngnéng wúxiàn LAN
HIPPI	High performance parallel interface	高性能并行接口	Gāoxìngnéng bìngxíng jiēkǒu
HIPS	High speed international packet switching	国际通信网络的高速分组交换	Guójì tōngxìn wǎngluòde gāosù fēnzǔ jiāohuàn
HISAM	Hierarchical indexed sequential access method	分级编址按序存取法	Fēnjí biānzhǐ ànxù cúnqǔ fǎ

HKIX	Hong Kong Internet Exchange	香港因特网交换中心	Xiānggǎng Yīntèwǎng jiāohuàn zhōngxīn
HL	Horizontal length	水平长度	Shuǐpíng chángdù
HL	Submarine cable	海底电缆	Hǎidǐ diànlǎn
HLA	High-level architecture	高级体系结构	Gāojí tǐxì jiégòu
HLB	Hybrid load balancing algorithm	混合负载均衡算法	Hùnhé fùzài jūnhéng suànfǎ
HLC	High layer compatibility	高层兼容性	Gāocéng jiānróngxìng
HLDC	High level data control	高级数据控制	Gāojí shùjù kòngzhì
HLF	High layer function	高层功能	Gāocéng gōngnéng
HLIR	High level interface request	高级接口请求	Gāojí jiēkǒu qǐngqiú
HL-PBGA	High thermal, low profile, plastic ball grid array	高耐热、轻薄型塑胶球状矩阵封装	Gāonàirè、qīngbó-xíng sùjiāo qiúzhuàng jǔzhèn fēngzhuāng
HLR	Home location register	归属寄存位置寄存器	Guīshǔ jìcún wèizhì jìcúnqì
HLR	Home location register	归属位置寄存器	Guīshǔ wèizhì jìcúnqì
HLR	Home location register	归属用户位置寄存器	Guīshǔ yònghù wèizhì jìcúnqì
HLR	Home location register	原籍位置注册处	Yuánjí wèizhì zhùcèchù
HMA	Human-machine adaption	人机适配	Rén jī shìpèi
HMAC	Hash-based message authentication code	基于散列的消息验证代码	Jīyú sànliède xiāoxi yànzhèng dàimǎ
HMAC	Hashed message authentication code	哈希消息认证代码	Hā-xī xiāoxi rènzhèng dàimǎ
HMD	Head mounted display	头戴式显示器	Tóudài-shì xiǎnshìqì
HMD	Horizontal magnetic dipole	水平磁偶极子	Shuǐpíng cí ǒujízi
HMGF	High modulus glass fiber	高模数玻璃纤维	Gāomóshù bōli xiānwéi
H-MLP	High-speed multi-layer protocol	高速多层协议	Gāosù duō céng xiéyì
HMM	Hidden Markovian model	隐马尔科夫模型	Yǐn mǎ-ěr-kē-fū móxíng
HMMP	Hypermedia management protocol (in common information model)	超媒体管理协议	Chāoméitǐ guǎnlǐ xiéyì
HMMS	Hypermedia management schema (in common information model)	超媒体管理模式	Chāoméitǐ guǎnlǐ móshì
HMMWV	High Mobility Multi-purpose Wheeled Vehicle (US military vehicle popularly called Humvee)	高机动多用途轮试车	Gāojīdòng duōyòngtú lúnshìchē
HMOM	Hypermedia object management (in common information model)	超媒体对象管理	Chāoméitǐ duìxiàng guǎnlǐ
HMP	Host monitoring protocol	宿主机监视协议	Sùzhǔ jī jiānshì xiéyì
HMSC	Home mobile services switching center	原籍移动无线局	Yuánjí yídòng wúxiàn jú
HMSDC	Hybrid multiplexed synchronous digital converter	混合多路复用同步数字转换器	Hùnhé duōlù fùyòng tóngbù shùzì zhuǎnhuànqì
HN	Homenet	家庭网络	Jiātíng wǎngluò
HNA	Hierarchical network architecture	分级网络结构	Fēnjí wǎngluò jiégòu
HNTD	Heterogeneous nucleating thermochemical reaction (FOC mfg)	非均匀成核热化学反应	Fēijūnyún chénghé rèhuàxué fǎnyìng
HO	Handover, handoff	切换	Qiēhuàn
HO	Handover, handoff (inter-cell)	越区切换	Yuèqū qiēhuàn
HO	High order, higher order	高阶	Gāojiē
HO	Hold off time	挂起时间	Guàqǐ shíjiān
Ho	Holdover mode	保持模式	Bǎochí móshì
Ho	Holdover mode	保持状态	Bǎochí zhuàngtài
HOA	Higher order assembler	高阶组装器	Gāojiē zǔzhuāngqì
HOAPID	Higher order path access point identifier	高阶通道接入点标识符	Gāojiē tōngdào jiērùdiǎn biāozhì fú
HOI	Higher order interface	高阶接口	Gāojiē jiēkǒu
HOLAP	Hybrid online analytical processing	混合联机分析处理	Hùnhé liánjī fēnxī chǔlǐ
HOLD	Call hold	呼叫保持	Hūjiào bǎochí

HOLD	Call hold supplementary service	呼叫保持补充业务	Hūjiào bǎochí bǔchōng yèwù
HONET	Huawei Integrated Services Optical access Network (trademark)	华为综合业务接入网商标	Huáwéi zōnghé yèwù jiērù wǎng shāngbiāo
HOP NC	Higher order path network connection	高阶通道网络连接	Gāojiē tōngdào wǎngluò liánjiē
HOPL	Higher order path layer	高阶通道层	Gāojiē tōngdào céng
HOT	Hypergraph-based outlier test	基于超图模型的离群点检测方法	Jīyú chāo tú móxíngde líqún diǎn jiǎncè fāngfǎ
HOT	Temporary handover number	越局切换号码	Yuèjú qiēhuàn hàomǎ
HO-TCM	Higher order tandem connection monitor	高阶通道串联连接监控	Gāojiē tōngdào chuànlián liánjiē jiānkòng
HOVC	Higher order virtual container	高阶虚容器	Gāojiē xūróngqì
HP	Hewlett-Packard Corp. (US company)	惠普有限公司	Huì-pǔ yǒuxiàn gōngsī
HP	Higher order path	高阶通道	Gāojiē tōngdào
HPA	High gain power amplifier board	高增益功放板	Gāozēngyì gōngfàng bǎn
HPA	Higher order path adaptation	高阶通道适配	Gāojiē tōngdào shìpèi
HPAB	High power amplifier block	高功率放大器	Gāogōnglǜ fàngdàqì
HPAU	High power amplifier unit	高功率放大单元	Gāogōnglǜ fàngdà dānyuán
HPBW	Half-power bandwidth	半功率波束	Bàngōnglǜ bōshù
HPBW	Horizontal plane bandWidth	水平面波束宽度	Shuǐpíngmiàn bōshù kuāndù
HPC	Hand-held PC	手持式电脑	Shǒuchí-shì diànnǎo
HPC	Higher order path connection	高阶通道连接	Gāojiē tōngdào liánjiē
HPCA	High performance communications adapter	高性能通信适配器	Gāoxìngnéng tōngxìn shìpèiqì
HPCC	High performance computing and communication	高性能计算和通信	Gāoxìngnéng jìsuàn hé tōngxìn
HPDU	High power duplexer unit	高功率耦合器	Gāogōnglǜ ǒuhéqì
HPF	High pass filter	高通滤波器	Gāotōng lǜbōqì
HPK	High power klystron	大功率速调管	Dàgōnglǜ sùtiáoguǎn
HPLL	Hybrid phase locked loop	混合锁相环	Hùnhé suǒxiàng huán
HPLMN	Home PLMN	归属 PLMN	Guīshǔ PLMN
HPLMN	Home public land mobile network	归属公用陆地移动通信网	Guīshǔ gōngyòng lùdì yídòng tōngxìnwǎng
HPM	Hybrid phase modulation	混合调相	Hùnhé tiáoxiàng
HPMA	High power microwave assembly	大功率微波部件	Dàgōnglǜ wēibō bùjiàn
HPNA	Home Phoneline Networking Alliance	家庭电话线网络集团	Jiātíng diànhuà xiàn wǎngluò jítuán
HPNA	Home Phoneline Networking Alliance	家用电话线网络联盟	Jiāyòng diànhuà xiàn wǎngluò liánméng
HPOH	Higher order path overhead	高阶通道开销	Gāojiē tōngdào kāixiao
HPOM	Higher order path overhead monitor	高阶通道开销监视	Gāojiē tōngdào kāixiao jiānshì
HPP	Higher order path protection	高阶通道保护	Gāojiē tōngdào bǎohù
HP-PLM	Higher order path payload label mismatch	高阶通道净荷标记失配	Gāojiē tōngdào jìnghé biāojì shīpèi
HP-RDI	Higher order path remote defect indication	高阶通道远端缺陷指示	Gāojiē tōngdào yuǎnduān quēxiàn zhǐshì
HP-RDI	High-level path receive defect indicator	高阶通道接收缺陷指示	Gāojiē tōngdào jiēshōu quēxiàn zhǐshì
HP-REI	Higher order path remote error indication	高阶通道远端误码指示	Gāojiē tōngdào yuǎnduān wùmǎ zhǐshì
HP-REI	Higher order path-remote error indication	高阶通道远端错误指示	Gāojiē tōngdào yuǎnduān cuòwù zhǐshì
HPS	Handover path switching	切换路径开关	Qiēhuàn lùjìng kāiguān
HPS	High performance server	高性能服务器	Gāoxìngnéng fúwùqì
HPT	Higher order path termination	高阶通道终端	Gāojiē tōngdào zhōngduān
HP-TIM	Higher order path trace identification mismatch	高阶通道路踪识别失配	Gāojiē tōngdào lùzōng shíbié shīpèi
HPU	Hand portable unit	手提单元	Shǒutí dānyuán
HP-UNEQ	Higher order path unequipped	高阶通道未装载	Gāojiē tōngdào wèizhuāngzài
HPW	High-performance workstation	高性能工作站	Gāoxìngnéng gōngzuòzhàn

HR	Half rate	半速率	Bàn sùlǜ
HR	Half-rate	半速	Bànsù
HRC	Header vertical redundancy check error	头标垂向冗余校验错	Tóubiāo chuíxiàng rǒngyú jiàoyàn cuò
HRC	Horizontal redundancy check	横向冗余检验	Héngxiàng rǒngyú jiǎnyàn
HRC	Hybrid receiver circuit	混合接收电路	Hùnhé jiēshōu diànlù
HRDL	Hypothetical reference digital link	假设参考数字链路	Jiǎshè cānkǎo shùzì liànlù
HRDS	Hypothetical reference digital section	假设参考数字段	Jiǎshè cānkǎo shùzì duàn
HRE	Hypothetical reference endpoint	假想参考点	Jiǎxiǎng cānkǎodiǎn
HRFWG	Home Radio Frequency Working Group	家用射频工作组	Jiāyòng shèpín gōngzuòzǔ
HRP	Hypothetical reference path	假设参考通道	Jiǎshè cānkǎo tōngdào
HRR	Handover resource reservation	切换资源预留	Qiēhuàn zīyuán yùliú
HrT	Haar transform	哈尔变换	Hā-ěr biànhuàn
HRTF	Head related transfer function	头部关联传输功能	Tóubù guānlián chuánshū gōngnéng
HRVIS	High resolution visible image system	高分辨率可见光影像系统	Gāofēnbiànlǜ kějiàn guāng yǐngxiàng xìtǒng
HRX	Hypothetical reference connection	假设参考连接	Jiǎshè cānkǎo liánjiē
HS	Headset	戴在头上的耳机或听筒	Dài zài tóushàngde ěrjī huò tīngtǒng
HSCP	High-level service control point	高等级业务控制点	Gāoděngjí yèwù kòngzhìdiǎn
HSCSD	High-speed circuit switched data	高速电路交换数据	Gāosù diànlù jiāohuàn shùjù
HSD	High-speed data	高速数据	Gāosù shùjù
HSDPA	High speed downlink packet access	高速下行链路分组接入	Gāosù xiàxíng liànlù fēnzǔ jiērù
HSDPA	High-speed downlink packet access	高速下行分组接入	Gāosù xiàxíng fēnzǔ jiērù
HSL	High-speed-rate data interface board	超速率数据接口板	Chāosùlǜ shùjù jiēkǒu bǎn
HSLAN	High-speed local area network	高速局域网	Gāosù júyùwǎng
HSN	Frequency hopping sequence number	跳频序列号	Tiàopín xùlièhào
HSN	Hierarchically synchronized network	分级同步网络	Fēnjí tóngbù wǎngluò
HSN	Hopping sequence number	跳频序列号码	Tiàopín xùliè hàomǎ
HSP	Host service provider	宿主业务提供商	Sùzhǔ yèwù tígōng shāng
HSPDA	High-speed downlink packet access	高速下行包数据接入	Gāosù xiàxíng bāo shùjù jiērù
HSRM	Hierarchical scalable reliable multicast	层次化可扩展可靠组播	Céngcìhuà kěkuòzhǎn kěkào zǔbō
HSRP	Hot standby routing protocol	热备份路由协议	Rè bèifèn lùyóu xiéyì
HSRP	Hot standby routing protocol	热备份路由器协议	Rè bèifèn lùyóuqì xiéyì
HSS	Home subscriber server	本地用户服务器	Běndì yònghù fúwùqì
HSS	Home subscriber server	归属用户服务器	Guīshǔ yònghù fúwùqì
HSS	Home subscriber server	家庭用户服务器	Jiātíng yònghù fúwùqì
HSSDC	High-speed serial data connection	高速串行数据连接	Gāosù chuànháng shùjù liánjiē
HSSI	High-speed serial interface	高速串行接口	Gāosù chuànháng jiēkǒu
HST	Host station	主站	Zhǔ zhàn
HSTP	High-level signal transfer point	高级信令转换点	Gāojí xìnlìng zhuǎnhuàn diǎn
HSTP	High-level signaling transfer point	高级信令转接点	Gāojí xìnlìng zhuǎnjiēdiǎn
HSUT	Higher order path supervision unequipped termination	高阶通道监控未装装载终	Gāojiē tōngdào jiānkòng wèizhuāng zhuāngzài zhōng
HSUT	Higher order path supervisory unequipped termination	高阶通道监控未装载终端	Gāojiē tōngdào jiānkòng wèizhuāngzài zhōngduān
HT	High terrain	山区	Shānqū
HT	Horizontal tabulation	横向制表	Héngxiàng zhìbiǎo
HTA	Hypertext application	超文本应用程序	Chāowénběn yìngyòng chéngxù
HTCA	Higher order path tandem connection adaptation	高阶通道串联连接适配	Gāojiē tōngdào chuànlián liánjiē shìpèi

HTCM	Higher order path tandem connection monitor	高阶通道串联连接监视	Gāojiē tōngdào chuànlián liánjiē jiānshì
HTCP	Hypertext cache protocol	超文本缓存协议	Chāowénběn huǎncún xiéyì
HTCT	Higher order path tandem connection termination	高阶通道串联连接终端	Gāojiē tōngdào chuànlián liánjiē zhōngduān
HTL	High threshold logic	高阈值逻辑电路	Gāo yù zhí luójidiànlù
HTML	Hypertext markup language	超文本标记语言	Chāowénběn biāojì yǔyán
HTML	Hypertext markup language	超文本标识语言	Chāowénběn biāozhì yǔyán
HTML	Hypertext markup language	超文本组合语言	Chāowénběn zǔhé yǔyán
HTML	Hypertext markup language (in SQL Server)	超文本链接标示语	Chāowénběn liànjiē biāoshì yǔ
HTS	Heat temperature sensor	热温度传感器	Rè wēndù chuángǎnqì
HTTP	Hypertext transfer protocol	超文本传输协议	Chāowénběn chuánshū xiéyì
http	Hypertext transfer protocol	超文本传送协议	Chāowénběn chuánsòng xiéyì
HTTPS	Hypertext transfer protocol server	超文本传送协议服务器	Chāowénběn chuánsòng xiéyì fúwùqì
HTTPS	Secure hypertext transfer protocol	安全超文本传输协议	Ānquán chāowénběn chuánshū xiéyì
HU	Home unit	归属单元	Guīshǔ dānyuán
HU	Home unit	家庭单元	Jiātíng dānyuán
HUA	Hardware failure-oriented group unblocking-acknowledgement message	面向硬件故障的群闭塞解除证实消息	Miànxiàng yìngjiàn gùzhàngde qún bìsè jiěchú zhèngshí xiāoxi
HUB	Hub	集线器	Jíxiànqì
HUD	Head-up display	抬头显示器	Táitóu xiǎnshìqì
HU-PCM	Hybrid uni-digit pulse code modulation	混合单数字脉码调制	Hùnhé dānshùzì màimǎ tiáozhì
HUT	High usage inter-toll trunk	高利用率长途台间中继线	Gāolìyòng lǜ chángtútái-jiān zhōngjìxiàn
HV	Hardware virtualizer	硬件虚拟器	Yìngjiàn xūnǐqì
HV	High quality voice	高保真语音	Gāobǎozhēn yǔyīn
HVAC	Heating ventilation air conditioning	暖通空调	Nuǎn tōng kōngtiáo
HVP	High-video pass circuit	极窄视频脉冲通过电路	Jízhǎi shìpín màichōng tōngguò diànlù
HW	Highway	高速公路	Gāosù gōnglù
HWBR	Half-wave bridge rectifier	半波桥式整流器	Bànbō qiáoshì zhěngliúqì
HWD	Half-wave dipole	半波偶极子	Bànbō ǒujízi
HWS	Hot water supply	热水供应系统	Rèshuǐ gōngyìng xìtǒng
HYCOM	Hybrid combiner board	合路器板	Hélùqì bǎn

I

I	Head disk assembly	头盘部件	Tóu pán bùjiàn
I	Information frame	信息帧	Xìnxī zhèng
I	Intermediate frame bit	中间帧比特	Zhōngjiān zhèng bǐtè
I	Wavelength isolation	波长隔离度	Bōcháng gélídù
I&D	Integrate-and-dump	积分冲洗	Jīfēn chōngxǐ
I/O	Input/output	输入/输出	Shūrù/shūchū
I/O	Input/output device	输入/输出设备	Shūrù/shūchū shèbèi
I / V	Current to voltage converter	电流-电压变换器	Diànliú/diànyā biànhuànqì
IA	Information assurance	信息保障	Xìnxī bǎozhàng
IA	Input acknowledge	输入认可	Shūrù rènkě
IA	Intel ® architecture	英特尔架构	Yīng-tè-ěr jiàgòu
IA	Internet adapter	因特网适配器	Yīntèwǎng shìpèiqì
IA	Internet address	因特网网络地址	Yīntèwǎng wǎngluò dìzhǐ
IA	Intruder alarm	防盗报警	Fángdào bàojǐng

IA5	International alphabet no. 5	国际 5 号电码表	Guójì wǔhào diànmǎ biǎo
IA5	International alphabet no.5 (ISO 7-bit code)	国际五号电码	Guójì wǔhào diànmǎ
IAA	Instruction address A-register	指令地址 A 寄存器	Zhǐlìng dìzhǐ A jìcúnqì
IAB	Internet Activities Board	因特网工作委员会	Yīntèwǎng gōngzuò wěiyuánhuì
IAB	Internet activities board	因特网活动委员会	Yīntèwǎng huódòng wěiyuánhuì
IAB	Internet Architecture Board	国际互联网体系结构委员会	Guójì hùliánwǎng tǐxì jiégòu wěiyuánhuì
IAB	Internet Architecture Board	国际互联网网络体系技术委员会	Guójì hùliánwǎng wǎngluò tǐxì jìshù wěiyuánhuì
IAB	Internet Architecture Board	因特网结构委员会	Yīntèwǎng jiégòu wěiyuánhuì
IAB	Internet Architecture Board	因特网体系结构委员会	Yīntèwǎng tǐxì jiégòu wěiyuánhuì
IABS	International alternative billing service	国际可选记帐业务	Guójì kěxuǎn jìzhàng yèwù
IAC	Inquiry access code	查询访问码	Cháxún fǎngwèn mǎ
IAC	Interactive application communication	交互式应用程序通讯	Jiāohù-shì yìngyòng chéngxù tōngxùn
IAC	Inter-application communication	内部应用程序通讯	Nèibù yìngyòng chéngxù tōngxùn
IACK	Information request acknowledge	信息查询确认	Xìnxī cháxún quèrèn
IACK	Information request acknowledged	信息请求证实	Xìnxī qǐngqiú zhèngshí
IACR	Input access control register	输入访问控制寄存器	Shūrù fǎngwèn kòngzhì jìcúnqì
IACS	Intermediate altitude communication satellite	中高空通信卫星	Zhōng gāokōng tōngxìn wèixīng
IAD	Integrated access device	综合接入设备	Zōnghé jiērù shèbèi
IAD	Interactive debug	交互调式	Jiāohù diàoshì
IADA	Amplifier/divider assembly	放大/分配集成件	Fàngdà/fēnpèi jíchéngjiàn
IAF	Intelligent access function	智能接入功能	Zhìnéng jiērù gōngnéng
IAF	Internet aware fax	能直接连在 IP 网上的传真机	Néng zhíjiē liánzài IP wǎngshàngde chuánzhēnjī
IAF	Interworking agent function	互联代理功能	Hùlián dàilǐ gōngnéng
IAGC	Instantaneous automatic gain control	瞬时自动增益控制	Shùnshí zìdòng zēngyì kòngzhì
IAI	Initial address information	起始地址信息	Qǐshǐ dìzhǐ xìnxī
IAI	Initial address message with additional information	带有附加信息的初始地址消息	Dàiyǒu fùjiā xìnxīde chūshǐ dìzhǐ xiāoxi
IAI	Initial address with additional information	带附加信息的初始地址消息	Dài fùjiā xìnxīde chūshǐ dìzhǐ xiāoxi
IAL	Intel® Architecture Labs	Intel 公司构架实验室	Intel gōngsī gòujià shíyànshì
I-ALG	Data integrity algorithm	数据完整性算法	Shùjù wánzhěngxìng suànfǎ
IAM	Initial address message	初始地址消息	Chūshǐ dìzhǐ xiāoxi
IANA	Internet Assigned Numbers Authority	因特网编号分配委员会	Yīntèwǎng biānhào fēnpèi wěiyuánhuì
IANA	Internet Assigned Numbers Authority	因特网编号管理局	Yīntèwǎng biānhào guǎnlǐjú
IANA	Internet Assigned Numbers Authority	因特网编号收授权委员会	Yīntèwǎng biānhào shōu shòuquán wěiyuánhuì
IANA	Internet Assigned Numbers Authority	因特网号码分配部门	Yīntèwǎng hàomǎ fēnpèi bùmén
IAP	Internet access provider	因特网接入提供者	Yīntèwǎng jiērù tígòngzhě
IAS	Interactive around-sound	交互式环绕声	Jiāohù-shì huánrào shēng
IAS	International alphabet set	国际字母	Guójì zìmǔ
IATF	Information assurance technical framework	信息保障技术框架	Xìnxī bǎozhàng jìshù kuàngjià
IB	Indicator bit	指示比特	Zhǐshì bǐtè
IB	Intelligent building	智能大厦	Zhìnéng dàshà
IB	Intelligent building	智能建筑	Zhìnéng jiànzhù
IBAS	Integrated broadband access system	综合宽带接入系统	Zōnghé kuāndài jiērù xìtǒng
IBASIC	Instrument BASIC language	仪器 BASIC 语言	Yíqì BASIC yǔyán
IBC	Internet business center	因特网商业中心	Yīntèwǎng shāngyè zhōngxīn

IBDN	Integrated building distribution network	建筑物综合分布网络	Jiànzhùwù zōnghé fēnbù wǎngluò
I-Block	Information block	信息码组	Xìnxī mǎzǔ
IBM	International Business Machines (US company)	国际商业机器公司	Guójì shāngyè jīqì gōngsī
IBMS	Intelligent building management system	智能建筑管理系统	Zhìnéng jiànzhù guǎnlǐ xìtǒng
IBS	Intelligent building system	智能大楼布线系统	Zhìnéng dàlóu bùxiàn xìtǒng
IBT	Instrumented bend test	采用仪表的弯曲实验	Cǎiyòng yíbiǎode wānqū shíyàn
IBT	Intrinsic burst tolerance	固有突发容限	Gùyǒu tūfā róngxiàn
I-BTMA	Ideal busy tone multiple access	理想忙音信好多路存取	Lǐxiǎng mángyīn xìnhǎo duōlù cúnqǔ
IC	Idling circuit	空载电路	Kōngzài diànlù
IC	Impedance coupling	阻抗耦合	Zǔkàng ǒuhé
IC	Integrated circuit	集成电路	Jíchéng diànlù
IC	Interlock code (CUG SS)	闭锁码	Bìsuǒ mǎ
IC	Interlock code (CUG SS)	连锁码	Liánsuǒ mǎ
IC(pref)	Interlock code of the preferential CUG (closed user group)	优先的 CUG 连锁码	Yōuxiānde CUG liánsuǒ mǎ
ICA	Initiate call attempt	启动试呼	Qǐdòng shìhū
ICAO	International Civil Aviation Organization	国际民航组织	Guójì mínháng zǔzhī
ICB	Incoming calls barred	来话呼叫限制	Láihuà hūjiào xiànzhì
ICB	Incoming calls barred (within the CUG)	入局呼叫禁止（限于闭合用户群）	Rùjú hūjiào jìnzhǐ (xiànyú bìhé yònghù qún)
ICC	Inbound control channel	入境控制信道	Rùjìng kòngzhì xìndào
ICC	Intermediate cross connect	中介交叉联接	Zhōngjiè jiāochā liánjiē
ICC	Internet call center	因特网呼叫中心	Yīntèwǎng hūjiào zhōngxīn
ICCID	Integrated circuit identity	集成电路识别码	Jíchéng diànlù shíbié mǎ
ICCP	Integrated communications control panel	综合通信控制板	Zōnghé tōngxìn kòngzhì bǎn
ICD	Installable client driver	可安装客户端驱动程序	Kě'ānzhuāng kèhù duān qūdòng chéngxù
ICD	International code designator	国际编码设计	Guójì biānmǎ shèjì
ICF	Incoming frame	入帧	Rù zhèng
ICF	Information conversion function	信息转换功能	Xìnxī zhuǎnhuàn gōngnéng
ICG	Interim coordination group	中间协调组	Zhōngjiān xiétiáo zǔ
ICGW	Incoming call gateway	来话呼叫网关	Láihuà hūjiào wǎngguān
ICH	Input/output controller hub	输入/输出控制中心	Shūrù/shūchū kòngzhì zhōngxīn
ICI	Inter-channel interference	路际串扰	Lùjì chuànrǎo
ICI	Inter-channel interference	信道间干扰	Xìndào-jiān gānrǎo
ICL	Inter-computer communication link	计算机间通信链路	Jìsuànjī-jiān tōngxìn liànlù
ICM	Incoming call modification	入呼叫变更	Rù hūjiào biàngēng
ICMB	Internal chassis management bus	内部管理总线	Nèibù guǎnlǐ zǒngxiàn
ICMP	Internet control message protocol	互联网控制消息协议	Hùliánwǎng kòngzhì xiāoxi xiéyì
ICMP	Internet control message protocol	互联网消息协议	Hùliánwǎng xiāoxi xiéyì
ICMP	Internet control message protocol	网际控制消息协议	Wǎngjì kòngzhì xiāoxi xiéyì
ICMP	Internet control message protocol	因特网控制报文协议	Yīntèwǎng kòngzhì bàowén xiéyì
ICMP	Internet control message protocol	因特网控制信息协议	Yīntèwǎng kòngzhì xìnxī xiéyì
ICMP	Internet control message protocol	因特网信息控制协议	Yīntèwǎng xìnxī kòngzhì xiéyì
ICNIA	Integrated communication, navigation and identification avionics	综合化通信导航识别航空电子系统	Zōnghéhuà tōngxìn dǎoháng shíbié hángkōng diànzǐ xìtǒng
ICP	Internet cache protocol	英特网缓存协议	Yīng-tè-wǎng huǎncún xiéyì
ICP	Internet content provider	互联网内容提供商	Hùliánwǎng nèiróng tígōng shāng

ICP	Internet content provider	因特网内容提供商	Yīntèwǎng nèiróng tígōngshāng
ICP	Internet content provider	因特网内容提供者	Yīntèwǎng nèiróng tígòngzhě
ICQ	I seek you	网络呼叫器	Wǎngluò hūjiàoqì
ICS	Implementation conformance statement	实现一致性声明	Shíxiàn yīzhìxìng shēngmíng
ICS	Incoming call screening service	来话呼叫筛选业务	Láihuà hūjiào shāixuǎn yèwù
ICS	Infrared communications system	红外线通信系统	Hóngwàixiàn tōngxìn xìtǒng
ICS	Interference cancellation system	干扰消除系统	Gānrǎo xiāochú xìtǒng
ICS	Internet connection server	因特网连接服务器	Yīntèwǎng liánjiē fúwùqì
ICS	Inter-network circuit section	网间电路段	Wǎngjiān diànlù duàn
ICSA	International Computer Security Association	国际计算机安全协会	Guójì jìsuànjī ānquán xiéhuì
ICT	Incoming trunk	入局中继	Rùjú zhōngjì
ICT	Information and communications technology	信息与通信技术	Xìnxī yǔ tōngxìn jìshù
ICT	Interference compliance test	干扰顺从度测试	Gānrǎo shùncóngdù cèshì
ICU	Instruction control unit	指令控制单元	Zhǐlìng kòngzhì dānyuán
ICU	Interrupt control unit	中断控制器	Zhōngduàn kòngzhìqì
ICV	Integrity check value	集成校验值	Jíchéng jiàoyàn zhí
ICV	Integrity check value	完整性检测值	Wánzhěngxìng jiǎncè zhí
ICV	Integrity check value	完整性检查值	Wánzhěngxìng jiǎnchá zhí
ICV	Integrity check vector	完整性检测向量	Wánzhěngxìng jiǎncè xiàngliàng
ID	Identification/Identity	身份标识	Shēnfen biāozhì
ID	Identification/identity, recognition	识别	Shíbié
ID	Identifier	标识	Biāozhì
ID	Identifier	识别器	Shíbiéqì
ID	Identity	标识	Biāozhì
ID	Identity	鉴别号码	Jiànbié hàomǎ
ID	Internet draft	因特网草案	Yīntèwǎng cǎo'àn
ID SEQ	Identification sequence field	识别序列字段	Shíbié xùliè zìduàn
IDC	Instantaneous deviation control	瞬时频偏控制	Shùnshí pínpiān kòngzhì
IDC	Instantaneous deviation controller	瞬时频偏控制器	Shùnshí pínpiān kòngzhìqì
IDC	Insulation displacement connection	绝缘层信移连接件	Juéyuán céng xìnyí liánjiē jiàn
IDC	International Data Corporation	国际数据机构	Guójì shùjù jīgòu
IDC	Internet data center	互联网数据中心	Hùliánwǎng shùjù zhōngxīn
IDC	Internet data center	因特网数据中心	Yīntèwǎng shùjù zhōngxīn
IDCS	Integrated digital communication system	综合数字通信系统	Zōnghé shùzì tōngxìn xìtǒng
IDCT	Inverse discrete cosine transform	反转离散余弦变换	Fǎnzhuǎn lísàn yúxián biànhuàn
IDCT	Inverse discrete cosine transform	非连续反余弦变换	Fēiliánxù fǎnyúxián biànhuàn
IDD	International direct dialing	国际直拨	Guójì zhíbō
IDDD	International direct distance dialing	国际长途自动电话	Guójì chángtú zìdòngdiànhuà
IDE	Integrated development environment	集成开发环境	Jíchéng kāifā huánjìng
IDE	Integrated devices electronics	综合电器介面	Zōnghé diànqì jièmiàn
IDE	Integrated drive electronics	电子集成驱动器	Diànzǐ jíchéng qūdòngqì
IDE	Intelligent drive electronics	智能驱动电子仪器	Zhìnéng qūdòng diànzǐyíqì
IDEA	International data encryption algorithm	国际数据加密算法	Guójì shùjù jiāmì suànfǎ
IDEF	Intrusion detection system exchange format	入侵检测系统交换格式	Rùqīn jiǎncè xìtǒng jiāohuàn géshi
iDEN	Integrated digital enhanced network	数字集群调度专网	Shùzì jíqún diàodù zhuānwǎng
IDF	Intel Developer forum	英特尔开发者论坛	Yīng-tè-ěr kāifāzhě lùntán

IDF	Intermediate distributing frame	中级配线架	Zhōngjí pèixiànjià
IDF	Intermediate distribution facility	中介分布设备	Zhōngjiè fēnbù shèbèi
IDF	Intermediate distribution frame	中间配线架	Zhōngjiān pèixiànjià
IDFT	Inverse discrete fourier transform	离散傅里叶反变换	Lísàn fù-lǐ-yè fǎnbiànhuàn
IDG	International Data Group	国际数据集团	Guójì shùjù jítuán
IDG	International Data Group	国际数据组织	Guójì shùjù zǔzhī
IDGS	Interactive graphics design software	交互式图形设计软件	Jiāohù-shì túxíng shèjì ruǎnjiàn
IDI	Initial domain identifier	初始域标识	Chūshǐ yù biāozhì
IDL	Interface definition language	接口定义语言	Jiēkǒu dìngyì yǔyán
IDL	Interface description language	接口描述语言	Jiēkǒu miáoshù yǔyán
IDLC	Integrated digital loop carrier	综合数字环路载波	Zōnghé shùzì huánlù zàibō
IDM	Integrating delta modulation	积分增量调制	Jīfēn zēngliàng tiáozhì
IDN	Integrated data network	综合数据网	Zōnghé shùjù wǎng
IDN	Integrated digital network	数字综合网	Shùzì zōnghé wǎng
IDN	Integrated digital network	综合数字网	Zōnghé shùzì wǎng
IDNet	Inter-departmental net	部门联网	Bùmén liánwǎng
IDNS	Integrated distribution network system	综合布线网络系统	Zōnghé bùxiàn wǎngluò xìtǒng
IDP	Initial detection point	启动检出点	Qǐdòng jiǎnchū diǎn
IDP	Initial domain part	初始域部分	Chūshǐ yù bùfen
IDP	Inter-network datagram protocol	网间互通数据报协议	Wǎngjiān hùtōng shùjùbào xiéyì
IDPR	Inter-domain policy routing	域际策略路由选择	Yùjì cèlüè lùyóu xuǎnzé
IDPR	Inter-domain policy routing	域间策略路由选择	Yùjiān cèlüè lùyóu xuǎnzé
IDR	Information descriptor record	信息描述符记录	Xìnxī miáoshù fú jìlù
IDR	Intermediate data rate	中速率	Zhōng sùlǜ
IDR	Intermediate data rate (between 64kbps and 44.763Mbps)	中等数据率	Zhōngděng shùjù lǜ
IDRP	Inter-domain routing protocol	域间路由协议	Yùjiān lùyóu xiéyì
IDRP	Inter-domain routing protocol	域间选路协议	Yùjiān xuǎnlù xiéyì
IDRP	Inter-domain routing protocol (ISO use)	域间路由选择协议	Yùjiān lùyóu xuǎnzé xiéyì
IDS	Industrial distribution system	工业布线系统	Gōngyè bùxiàn xìtǒng
IDS	Intrusion detection system	入侵监测系统	Rùqīn jiāncè xìtǒng
IDSE	Internetworking data switching exchange	网络互连数据交换机	Wǎngluò hùlián shùjù jiāohuànjī
IDSL	ISDN digital subscriber line	ISDN 数字用户线路	ISDN shùzì yònghù xiànlù
IDSS	Intelligent decision support system	智能决策支持系统	Zhìnéng juécè zhīchí xìtǒng
IDT Base Address	Interrupt descriptor table base address	中断描述符表基地址	Zhōngduàn miáoshùfú biǎo jī dìzhǐ
IDU	Idle signal unit	空闲信号系统	Kòngxián xìnhào xìtǒng
IDU	Idle signal unit	闲置信号单元	Xiánzhì xìnhào dānyuán
IDU	Indoor unit	室内单元	Shìnèi dānyuán
IDU	Interface data unit	接口数据单元	Jiēkǒu shùjù dānyuán
IDWG	Intrusion detection working group	入侵检测工作组	Rùqīn jiǎncè gōngzuòzǔ
IDWG	Intrusion detection working group	入侵检测任务组	Rùqīn jiǎncè rènwuzǔ
IE	Information element	信息单元	Xìnxī dānyuán
IE	Information element	信息元素	Xìnxī yuánsù
IE	Internet explorer	因特网测试员	Yīntèwǎng cèshìyuán
IE	Signaling information element	信令信息元素	Xìnlìng xìnxī yuánsù
IEC	Incoming error count	输入误码计数	Shūrù wùma jìshù

IEC	International Electrotechnical Commission	国际电工技术委员会	Guójì diàngōng jìshù wěiyuánhuì
IEC	International Electrotechnical Commission	国际电工委员会	Guójì diàngōng wěiyuánhuì
IEC	International Electrotechnical Commission	国际电子技术委员会	Guójì diànzǐ jìshù wěiyuánhuì
IEE	Institution of Electrical Engineers (UK)	电气工程师协会	Diànqì gōngchéngshī xiéhuì
IEEE	Institute of Electrical and Electronic Engineers	电气与电子工程师协会	Diànqì yǔ diànzǐ gōngchéngshī xiéhuì
IEEE	Institute of Electrical and Electronics Engineers	电子电气工程学会	Diànzǐ diànqì gōngchéng xuéhuì
IEEE	Institute of Electrical and Electronics Engineers	美国电气及电子工程师协会	Měiguó diànqì jí diànzǐ gōngchéngshī xiéhuì
IEI	Information element identifier	信息单元标识符	Xìnxī dānyuán biāozhìfú
IEI	Information element identity	信息单元识别	Xìnxī dānyuán shíbié
IEN	Internet Engineering Note	因特网工程备忘录	Yīntèwǎng gōngchéng bèiwànglù
IEN	Internet experiment note	因特网实验备忘录	Yīntèwǎng shíyàn bèiwànglù
IES	Incoming echo suppressor	输入回波抑制器	Shūrù huíbō yìzhìqì
IESG	Internet Engineering Steering group	因特网工程管理组	Yīntèwǎng gōngchéng guǎnlǐ zǔ
IESP	Integrated electronic signal processor	综合电子信号处理机	Zōnghé diànzi xìnhào chǔlǐjī
IETF	Internet Engineering Task Force	互联网工程任务组	Hùliánwǎng gōngchéng rènwu zǔ
IETF	Internet Engineering Task Force	Internet 工程任务组	Internet gōngchéng rènwu zǔ
IETF	Internet Engineering Task Force	英特网工程任务阻	Yīng-tè-wǎng gōngchéng rènwu zǔ
IETF	Internet Engineering Task Force	因特网工程部	Yīntèwǎng gōngchéng bù
IETF	Internet Engineering Task Force	因特网工程任务组	Yīntèwǎng gōngchéng rènwu zǔ
IETF	Internet Engineering Task Force	因特网工程作业推动	Yīntèwǎng gōngchéng zuòyè tuīdòng
I-ETS	Interim European Telecommunications Standard	欧洲通信临时（中间）标准	Oūzhōu tōngxìn línshí (zhōngjiān) biāozhǔn
IEU	Integer execution unit	整数执行单元	Zhěngshù zhíxíng dānyuán
IF	Information flow	信息流	Xìnxī liú
IF	In-frame (SDH)	定帧	Dìngzhèng
IF	Infrastructure	底层结构	Dǐcéng jiégòu
IF	Interferometer (noun) , interferometric (adj)	干涉仪	Gānshèyí
IF	Intermediate frequency	中频	Zhōngpín
IFC	Intelligent fire controller	照明智能控制器	Zhàomíng zhìnéng kòngzhìqì
iFCP	Internet fiber channel protocol (IETF use)	Internet 光纤信道协议	Internet guāngxiān xìndào xiéyì
IFF	Identifier friend or foe	敌我识别雷达	Díwǒ shíbié léidá
IFFT	Inverse fast Fourier transform	逆快速傅立叶变换	Nì kuàisù fù-lì-yè biànhuàn
IFIP	International Federation for Information Processing	国际信息处理联合会	Guójì xìnxī chǔlǐ liánhéhuì
IFS	Information field sizes	信息字段大小	Xìnxī zìduàn dàxiǎo
IFS	Iteration function system	迭代函数系统	Diédài hánshù xìtǒng
IFSC	Information field sizes for the UICC	UICC 信息字段大小	UICC xìnxī zìduàn dàxiǎo
I-FSK/FH	Independent frequency shift keying/frequency hopping	独立频移键控/跳频	Dúlì pínyí jiànkòng/tiàopín
IF-SM	Intermediate frequency switching matrix	中频交换矩阵	Zhōngpín jiāohuàn jǔzhèn
IFST	Information field sizes for the terminal	终端信息字段大小	Zhōngduān xìnxī zìduàn dàxiǎo
IFT	Interceptor flight tool (software)	拦截飞行工具	Lánjié fēixíng gōngjù
IFU	Interworking function unit	互通功能单元	Hùtōng gōngnéng dānyuán
IFWP	International forum white paper	国际白皮书论坛	Guójì báipíshū lùntán
IG	Information group	信息组	Xìnxī zǔ
IG	International gateway	国际接口局	Guójì jiēkǒu jú
IGBT	Insulated gate bipolar transistor	绝缘栅双极型晶体管	Juéyuán zhà shuāngjíxíng jīngtǐguǎn
IGES	Initial graphics exchange specification	初始化图形交换规程	Chūshǐhuà túxíng jiāohuàn guīchéng

IGES	International Graphics Exchange System (US company)	国际图形交换系统	Guójì túxíng jiāohuàn xìtǒng
IGFET	Insulated gate field effect transistor	绝缘栅场效应晶体管	Juéyuán zhà cháng xiàoyìng jīngtǐguǎn
IGMP	Internet group management protocol	互联网组管理协议	Hùliánwǎng zǔ guǎnlǐ xiéyì
IGMP	Internet group management protocol (IPsec)	网际群组管理协议	Wǎngjì qúnzǔ guǎnlǐ xiéyì
IGMP	Internet group membership protocol	因特网组成员协议	Yīntèwǎng zǔchéngyuán xiéyì
IGMP	Internet group message protocol	互联网组消息协议	Hùliánwǎng zǔ xiāoxi xiéyì
IGMP	Internet group message protocol	互联网组播成员管理协议	Hùliánwǎng zǔbō chéngyuán guǎnlǐ xiéyì
IGOSS	Industry/Government Open System Specification	工业，政府部门开放系统技术规范	Gōngyè, zhèngfǔ bùmén kāifàng xìtǒng jìshù guīfàn
IGP	Interior gateway protocol	内部路由协议	Nèibù lùyóu xiéyì
IGP	Internal gateway protocol	内部网关协议	Nèibù wǎngguān xiéyì
IGRP	Interior gateway routing protocol	内部网关路由选择协议	Nèibù wǎngguān lùyóu xuǎnzé xiéyì
IGRP	Interior gateway routing protocol (Cisco use)	内部网关路由协议	Nèibù wǎngguān lùyóu xiéyì
IGW	Integrated gateway boards	综合网关模块	Zōnghé wǎng guān mókuài
IGW	Interface gateway	接口网关	Jiēkǒu wǎngguān
IHOSS	Internet hosted octet stream service	因特网提供的八比特组流量业务	Yīntèwǎng tígōngde bābǐtèzǔ liúliàng yèwù
IHV	Independent hardware vendor	独立硬件购买者	Dúlì yìngjiàn gòumǎizhě
IID	Inter-aural intensity difference	两侧声音强度差别	Liǎngcè shēngyīn qiángdù chābié
iif	Incoming interface	入接口	Rù jiēkǒu
IIOP	Internet inter-ORB protocol	互联网 ORB 间通信协议	Hùliánwǎng ORB-jiān tōngxìn xiéyì
IIOP	Internet inter-ORB protocol (CORBA term)	因特网 ORB 间协议	Yīntèwǎng ORB-jiān xiéyì
IIP	Internet imaging protocol	因特网图像协议	Yīntèwǎng túxiàng xiéyì
IIQ	Improved in-phase quadrature modulation	改进同相正交调制	Gǎijìn tóngxiàng zhèngjiāo tiáozhì
IIR	Infinite duration impulse response	无限区间脉冲响应	Wúxiàn qūjiān màichōng xiǎngyìng
IIR	Institute for International Research	国际会议机构	Guójì huìyì jīgòu
IIS	Internet information server	互联网信息服务器	Hùliánwǎng xìnxī fúwùqì
IIS	Internet information server	因特网信息服务器	Yīntèwǎng xìnxī fúwùqì
IIS	Internet information services (in SQL Server)	因特网信息服务	Yīntèwǎng xìnxī fúwù
iisp	Interim inter-switch signaling protocol	中期交换机间的信令协议	Zhōngqī jiāohuànjī jiānde xìnlìng xiéyì
IISP	Interim-interswitch signaling protocol	交换机间临时信令系统	Jiāohuànjī-jiān línshí xìnlìng xìtǒng
IKE	Internet key exchange	网络钥匙交换	Wǎngluò yàoshi jiāohuàn
IKE	Internet key exchange	因特网密钥交换	Yīntèwǎng mìyào jiāohuàn
IKE	Internet key exchange protocol	因特网密钥交换协议	Yīntèwǎng mìyào jiāohuàn xiéyì
IL	Insertion loss	插入损耗	Chārù sǔnhào
IL	Insertion loss (FOC)	介入损耗	Jièrù sǔnhào
IL	Intermediate language	中间语言	Zhōngjiān yǔyán
IL	Intermediate language	中介语言	Zhōngjiè yǔyán
ILD	Inject light diode	注入式激光二极管	Zhùrùshì jīguāng èrjíguǎn
ILM	Incoming label map	入标记映射	Rù biāojì yìngshè
ILMI	Integrated local management interface	集成本地管理接口	Jíchéng běndì guǎnlǐ jiēkǒu
ILMI	Interim local management interface	过度期本地管理接口	Guòdùqī běndì guǎnlǐ jiēkǒu
ILMI	Interim local management interface	临时的局部管理接口	Línshíde júbù guǎnlǐ jiēkǒu
ILRP	Improved Land Radio Phone (Japan)	改进的陆地无线电话系统	Gǎijìnde lùdì wúxiàn diànhuà xìtǒng
ILS	Instrument landing system	仪表着陆系统	Yíbiǎo zhuólù xìtǒng
ILSA	Intelligent local search algorithm	智能本地搜索算法	Zhìnéng běndì sōusuǒ suànfǎ

ILST	Interrupt level status table	中断级状态表	Zhōngduàn jí zhuàngtài biǎo
IM	Impedance matching	阻抗匹配	Zǔkàng pǐpèi
IM	In-call modification	呼叫变更	Hūjiào biàngēng
IM	Information model	信息模型	Xìnxī móxíng
IM	Integrated model	集成模式	Jíchéng móshì
IM	Intermodulation	互调	Hùtiáo
IM	Intermodulation	互相调制	Hùxiāng tiáozhì
IMA	Interactive Multimedia Association	交互式多媒体协议	Jiāohù-shì duōméitǐ xiéyì
IMA	Inverse multiplexing access	反向复用板	Fǎnxiàng fùyòng bǎn
IMA	Inverse multiplexing on ATM	在 ATM 上逆多路复用	Zài ATM-shàng nì duōlù fùyòng
IMAP	Internet message access protocol	因特网信息访问协议	Yīntèwǎng xìnxī fǎngwèn xiéyì
IMAP4	Internet message access protocol version 4	第四版因特网信息存取协议	Dìsìbǎn Yīntèwǎng xìnxī cúnqǔ xiéyì
IMBE	Improved multi-band excitation	改进多频带激励	Gǎijìn duō píndài jīlì
IMBE	Improved multi-band excitation	改进的多带激励编码	Gǎijìnde duōdài jīlì biānmǎ
IMC	Internet mail consortium	因特网邮件组织	Yīntèwǎng yóujiàn zǔzhī
IMD	Intermodulation distortion	互调失真	Hùtiáo shīzhēn
IM-DM	Intensity modulation-direction modulation	直接强度调制	Zhíjiē qiángdù tiáozhì
IME	Input method editor	输入法编辑器	Shūrù fǎ biānjíqì
IMEI	International mobile equipment identity	国际移动设备识别码	Guójì yídòng shèbèi shíbié mǎ
IMEI	International mobile station equipment identity	国际移动设备识别号码	Guójì yídòng shèbèi shíbié hàomǎ
IMEI	International mobile terminal equipment identity	国际移动终端设备标识	Guójì yídòng zhōngduān shèbèi biāozhì
IMEISV	International mobile equipment identity software version	国际移动设备识别软件版本	Guójì yídòng shèbèi shíbié ruǎnjiàn bǎnběn
IMEISV	International mobile equipment identity software version	国际移动台识别软件版本号	Guójì yídòngtái shíbié ruǎnjiàn bǎnběn hào
IMGI	International mobile group identity	国际移动群识别	Guójì yídòngqún shíbié
IMHO	In my humble opinion (computer chat)	我的浅见	Wǒde qiǎnjiàn
IMHO	In my humble opinion (computer chat)	依比人之见	Yī bǐ rén zhī jiàn
IMM	Intel ® mobile module	英特尔移动模块	Yīng-tè-ěr yídòng mókuài
IMR	Internet monthly report	因特网月度报告	Yīntèwǎng yuèdù bàogào
IMR	Interrupt mask register	中断屏弊寄存器	Zhōngduàn píngbì jìcúnqì
IMS	Internet multiedia sub-system	因特网多媒体子网	Yīntèwǎng duōméitǐ zìwǎng
IMSI	International mobile station identity	国际移动台标识符	Guójì yídòngtái biāozhìfú
IMSI	International mobile station identity	国际移动台识别号码	Guójì yídòngtái shíbié hàomǎ
IMSI	International mobile subscriber ID code	国际移动用户识别码	Guójì yídòng yònghù shíbié mǎ
IMSI	International mobile subscriber identity	国际移动用户标识	Guójì yídòng yònghù biāozhì
IMSI	International mobile subscriber identity	国际移动用户识别号码	Guójì yídòng yònghù shíbié hàomǎ
IMT	International mobile telecommunications	国际移动通信	Guójì yídòng tōngxìn
IMT-2000	International mobile telecommnications 2000	国际移动通信 2000	Guójì yídòng tōngxìn 2000
IMT-2000	Internet mobile/multimedia telecommunication	因特网移动/多媒体通信	Yīntèwǎng yídòng/duōméitǐ tōngxìn
IMTC	International Multimedia Teleconferencing Consortium	国际多媒体电子会议协会	Guójì duōméitǐ diànzǐ huìyì xiéhuì
IMTP	Intelligent multi-service transport platform	智能多业务光传送平台	Zhìnéng duō yèwù guāng chuánsòng píngtái
IMUN	International mobile user number	国际移动用户号码	Guójì yídòng yònghù hàomǎ
IMX	Inquiry message exchange	询问信息交换	Xúnwèn xìnxī jiāohuàn
IN	Information network	信息网	Xìnxīwǎng
IN	Intelligent network	智能网	Zhìnéng wǎng
IN	Intelligent network	智能网络	Zhìnéng wǎngluò

IN	Interrogating node	咨询节点	Zīxún jiédiǎn
INAK	Information request negative acknowledge	信息查询否认	Xìnxī cháxún fǒurèn
INAK	Information request negative acknowledge	信息请求否认	Xìnxī qǐngqiú fǒurèn
INAP	Intelligent network application part	职能网应用部分	Zhínéng wǎng yìngyòng bùfen
INAP	Intelligent network application procedure	职能网应用规程	Zhínéng wǎng yìngyòng guīchéng
INAP	Intelligent network application protocol	职能网应用协议	Zhínéng wǎng yìngyòng xiéyì
INC	Internet controller	互相网控制器	Hùxiāngwǎng kòngzhìqì
INCR	Interrupt control register	中断控制寄存器	Zhōngduàn kòngzhì jìcúnqì
INCS	Interconnection network control sub-system	互联网控制子系统	Hùliánwǎng kòngzhì zixìtǒng
Indosat	Indonesian Satellite Corp.	印尼卫星公司	Yìnní wèixīng gōngsī
INF	Information (ISUP message)	信息	Xìnxī
INF	Information field	信息字段	Xìnxī zìduàn
INF	Information message (ISUP)	信息消息	Xìnxī xiāoxi
INF File	Information file	信息文件	Xìnxī wénjiàn
INFOSEC	Information security	信息安全	Xìnxī ānquán
INIT	Initialize	初始化	Chūshǐhuà
INIT_PWR	Initialization power	初始功率	Chūshǐ gōnglǜ
INM	Integrated network management	综合网络管理	Zōnghé wǎngluò guǎnlǐ
INMARSAT	International Maritime Satellite Organization	国际海事卫星组织	Guójì hǎishì wèixīng zǔzhī
INMARSAT	International Maritime Satellite Telecommunications Organization	国际海事卫星通信组织	Guójì hǎishì wèixīng tōngxìn zǔzhī
INMS	Integrated network management system	综合网络管理系统	Zōnghé wǎngluò guǎnlǐ xìtǒng
INMS	Interconnection network maintenance sub-system	互联网维护子系统	Hùliánwǎng wéihù zìxìtǒng
INN	Intermediate network node	中间网络节点	Zhōngjiān wǎngluò jiédiǎn
I-NNI	Internal network-node interface	内部网络节点接口	Nèibù wǎngluò jiédiǎn jiēkǒu
INOHYC	Integrated optical hybrid circuit	混合光集成电路	Hùnhé guāng jíchéng diànlù
INOP	Inoperable	不可操作	Bùkěcāozuò
InP	Indium phosphide	磷化铟	Línhuàyīn
INR	Information request (ISUP message)	信息请求	Xìnxī qǐngqiú
INR	Information request message (ISUP)	信息请求消息	Xìnxī qǐngqiú xiāoxi
INS	Information network system	信息通信系统	Xìnxī tōngxìn xìtǒng
Ins	Insert key	加插键	Jiāchā jiàn
INTBWT	International both way trunk	国际双向中继线	Guójì shuāngxiàng zhōngjìxiàn
INTCCB	Interrupt channel control block	中断通道控制块	Zhōngduàn tōngdào kòngzhì kuài
INTE	Interrupt enable	中断启动	Zhōngduàn qǐdòng
INTELSAT	International Telecommunications satellite	国际电信卫星组织	Guójì diànxìn wèixīng zǔzhī
InterNIC	Internet network information center	国际互联网网络信息中心	Guójì hùliánwǎng wǎngluò xìnxī zhōngxīn
InterNIC	Internet network information center	网际网络信息中心	Wǎngjì wǎngluò xìnxī zhōngxīn
INTS	International transit switch	国际转接交换局	Guójì zhuǎnjiē jiāohuànjú
IntServ	Integrated service model	集成服务模型	Jíchéng fúwù móxíng
IO	Information outlet	信息插座	Xìnxī chāzuò
IO	Iterative operation	迭代运算	Diédài yùnsuàn
IOB	Input-output block	输出输入模块	Shūchū shūrù mókuài
IOC	Inter-office communication	室内通信	Shìnèi tōngxìn
IOEC	Integrated opto-electronic circuit	光电子集成电路	Guāng diànzǐ jíchéng diànlù
ION	Integrated on-demand network	按需要集成的网络	Àn xūyào jíchéngde wǎngluò
ION	Integrated on-demand network	一体化按需网络	Yītǐhuà ànxū wǎngluò

IOP	Input optical power	输入光功率	Shūrù guāng gōnglǜ
IOP	Input/output processor	输入/输出处理机	Shūrù/shūchū chǔlǐjī
IOPT	Incoming call option	入局呼叫选项	Rùjú hūjiào xuǎnxiàng
IOR	Interoperable object reference	可互操作的对象引用	Kěhùcāozuòde duìxiàng yǐnyòng
IOS	Intelligent optical switching	智能光交换	Zhìnéng guāng jiāohuàn
IOS	Intelligent out station	智能外围站	Zhìnéng wàiwéizhàn
IOTP	Internet open trading protocol	互联网开放贸易协议	Hùliánwǎng kāifàng màoyì xiéyì
IP	Intelligent peripheral	智能外设	Zhìnéng wàishè
IP	Intelligent peripheral	智能外围设备	Zhìnéng wàiwéi shèbèi
IP	Internet protocol	互联网规程	Hùliánwǎng guīchéng
IP	Internet protocol	互联网协议	Hùliánwǎng xiéyì
IP	Internet protocol	联网协议	Liánwǎng xiéyì
IP	Internet protocol	网际互联协议	Wǎngjì hùlián xiéyì
IP	Internet protocol	网际协议	Wǎngjì xiéyì
IP	Internet protocol	因特网协议	Yīntèwǎng xiéyì
IP	Internetworking protocol	组网协议	Zǔwǎng xiéyì
IP	Interpersonal	人际	Rénjì
IP	Interworking protocol	互通协议	Hùtōng xiéyì
IP over SDH	Internet protocol over synchronous digital hierarchy	同步数字系列上的因特网协议	Tóngbù shùzì xìliè shàngde Yīntèwǎng xiéyì
IPBUS	Inter-processor common bus	处理机间共用总线	Chǔlǐjī-jiān gòngyòng zǒngxiàn
IPC	Instructions per clock cycle	指令/时钟周期	Zhǐlìng/sízhōng zhōuqī
IPC	Interprocess communication	进程间通信	Jìnchéng-jiān tōngxìn
IPC	Interprocess communication	进程间通讯	Jìnchéng-jiān tōngxùn
IPC	Inter-processor communication	处理器间通信	Chǔlǐqì-jiān tōngxìn
IPCP	IP control protocol	IP 控制协议	IP kòngzhì xiéyì
IPDC	Internet protocol device control	IP 设备控制	IP shèbèi kòngzhì
IPDS	Intelligent printer data stream (IBM use)	智能打印机数据流	Zhìnéng dǎyìnjī shùjùliú
IPDU	Inter-network protocol data unit	互联网协议数据单元	Hùliánwǎng xiéyì shùjù dānyuán
IPEI	International portable equipment identifier	国际移动设备标识号	Guójì yídòng shèbèi biāozhì hào
IPFM	Integral pulse frequency modulation	积分脉冲调制	Jīfēn màichōng iáozhì
Iphone	IP phone	IP 电话	IP diànhuà
IPI	Information protocol identifier	信息协议识别符	Xìnxī xiéyì shíbiéfú
IPI	Intelligent peripheral interface	智能外设接口	Zhìnéng wàishè jiēkǒu
IPL	Initial program loader	初始程序输入器	Chūshǐ chéngxù shūrùqì
IPL	Initial program loader	初始程序装入程序	Chūshǐ chéngxù zhuāngrù chéngxù
IPL	Primary link for interactive services	交互型业务的基群链路	Jiāohù-xíng yèwùde jīqún liànlù
IPM	Incidental phase modulation	附带的相位调制	Fùdàide xiàngwèi tiáozhì
IPM	Incremental phase modulation	增量相位调制	Zēngliàng xiàngwèi tiáozhì
IPM	Interpersonal message	人际消息	Rénjì xiāoxi
IPM	Interpersonal messaging service	人际消息传递业务	Rénjì xiāoxi chuándì yèwù
IP-M	IP multicast	IP 多播	IP duōbō
IP-M	IP-multicast	IP 组播业务	IP zǔbō yèwù
IPM-MS	Interpersonal messaging - message store	个人间通信-消息存储	Gèrén-jiān tōngxìn- xiāoxi cúnchǔ
IPMS	Interpersonal messaging system	人际消息通信系统	Rénjì xiāoxi tōngxìn xìtǒng
IPNP	Inter-paging networking protocol	高速寻呼联网协议	Gāosù xúnhū liánwǎng xiéyì
IPO	Initial public offering	上市	Shàngshì

IPOA	Classical IP over ATM	ATM 上的经典 IP 规范	ATM-shàngde jīngdiǎn IP guīfàn
IPoA	IP over ATM	ATM 上的网际协议	ATM-shàngde wǎngjì xiéyì
IPOT	Octet-based IP packet throughput	基于字节的 IP 包吞吐量	Jīyú zìjiéde IP bāo tūntǔliàng
IPP	Internet payment provider	因特网支付提供商	Yīntèwǎng zhīfù tígōng shāng
IPP	Internet presence provider	因特网平台提供者	Yīntèwǎng píngtái tígòngzhě
IPP	Internet printing protocol	因特网打印协议	Yīntèwǎng dǎyin xiéyì
IPPR	Image processing and pattern recognition	图像处理和模式识别	Túxiàng chǔlǐ hé móshì shíbié
IPR	Improved packet radio network	改进的分组交换无线电网络	Gǎijìnde fēnzǔ jiāohuàn wúxiàndiàn wǎngluò
IPS	Interactive programming system	会话形式程序设计系统	Huìhuà xíngshì chéngxù shèjì xìtǒng
IPSC	Information processing standard for computer	计算机信息处理标准	Jìsuànjī xìnxī chǔlǐ biāozhǔn
IPSec	Internet protocol security	网际协议安全	Wǎngjì xiéyì ānquán
IPSEC	Internet protocol security protocol	IP 网络安全协议	IP wǎngluò ānquán xiéyì
IPSec	IP security	IP 安全协议	IP ānquán xiéyì
IPsec	Security architecture for IP network	IP 层协议安全结构	IP céng xiéyì ānquán jiégòu
IPSO	IP security option	IP 安全选项	IP ānquán xuǎnxiàng
IPSS	International Packet Switching Service (BPO)	国际信息包交换业务	Guójì xìnxī bāojiāohuàn yèwù
IPTU	Indoor pan and tilt unit	室内水平俯仰云台	Shìnèi shuǐpíng fǔyǎng yúntái
IPUI	International portable user identity	国际移动用户标识号	Guójì yídòng yònghù biāozhì hào
Ipv4	Internet protocol version 4	互联网协议-第 4 版	Hùliánwǎng xiéyì--dì 4 bǎn
Ipv4	Internet protocol version 4	因特网协议版本 4	Yīntèwǎng xiéyì bǎnběn 4
IPv6	Internet protocol version 6	互联网协议-第 6 版	Hùliánwǎng xiéyì--dì 6 bǎn
IPv6	Internet protocol version 6	因特网协议版本 6	Yīntèwǎng xiéyì bǎnběn 6
IPX	Inter-network packet exchange	包交换协议	Bāo jiāohuàn xiéyì
IPX	Inter-network packet exchange	交互网络信息包交换	Jiāohù wǎngluò xìnxī bāo jiāohuàn
IPX	Inter-network packet exchange	网际数据包(分组)交换	Wǎngjì shùjù bāo (fēnzǔ) jiāohuàn
IPX	Internetwork packet exchange protocol (Novell usage)	网络分组交换协议	Wǎngluò fēnzǔ jiāohuàn xiéyì
IPXCP	Inter-network packet exchange control protocol	网间数据包交换控制协议	Wǎngjiān shùjù bāo jiāohuàn kòngzhì xiéyì
IQ	In-phase + quadrature	同相+正交	Tóngxiàng+zhèngjiāo
IQ-DS-SS	In-phase + quadrature direct sequence spread spectrum	同相+正交直接序列扩展频谱	Tóngxiàng+zhèngjiāo zhíjiē xùliè kuòzhǎn pínpǔ
IQL	In-phase + quadrature channel loop	同相+正交信道环路	Tóngxiàng+zhèngjiāo xìndào huánlù
IR	Infrared	红外线	Hóngwàixiàn
IR	Isotropic radiator	各向同性辐射体	Gèxiàng tóngxìng fúshètǐ
IRC	Internet relay chat	网际清淡	Wǎngjì qīngdàn
IRC	Internet relay chat	网络聊天	Wǎngluò liáotiān
IRC	Internet relay chat	网络中继聊天	Wǎngluò zhōngjì liáotiān
IRC	Internet relay chat	因特网接力闲谈	Yīntèwǎng jiēlì xiántán
IRC	Internet relay chat	因特网中继闲谈	Yīntèwǎng zhōngjì xiántán
IrCOMM	Infrared communications	红外通信	Hóngwài tōngxìn
IRCP	Internet relay chat protocol (IETF usage)	网际转发闲聊协议	Wǎngjì zhuǎnfā xiánliáo xiéyì
IRD	Internet control message protocol router discovery	因特网控制报文协议发现路由器	Yīntèwǎng kòngzhì bàowén xiéyì fāxiàn lùyóuqì
IrDA	Infrared Data Association	红外数据联合会	Hóngwài shùjù liánhéhuì
IrDA	Infrared Data Association	红外数据联盟	Hóngwài shùjù liánméng
IrDA	Infrared Data Association	红外数据协会	Hóngwài shùjù xiéhuì
IrDA	Infrared Data Association	红外线数据标准协会	Hóngwàixiàn shùjù biāozhǔn xiéhuì

IRDP	ICMP router discovery protocol	ICMP 路由发现协议	ICMP lùyóu fāxiàn xiéyì
IRDP	ICMP router discovery protocol (IETF usage)	ICMP 路由器发现协议	ICMP lùyóuqì fāxiàn xiéyì
IREG	International Roaming Experts Group (GSM MoU)	国际漫游组	Guójì mànyóu zǔ
IRG	Inter-record gap	记录间间隔	Jìlù-jiān jiàngé
IRIS	Inland Revenue Integrated System	艾丽斯	Ài-lì-sī
IRIS	Inland Revenue integrated system	综合税务系统	Zōnghé shuìwù xìtǒng
IRL	Incoming register link	入局记发链路	Rùjú jìfā liànlù
IrMC	Infrared mobile communications	红外移动通信	Hóngwài yídòng tōngxìn
IRN	Intermediate routing node	中介路由选择节点	Zhōngjiè lùyóu xuǎnzé jiédiǎn
IrOBEX	Infrared object exchange	红外对象交换协议	Hóngwài duìxiàng jiāohuàn xiéyì
IRP	Integrated reference point	集成参考点	Jíchéng cānkǎo diǎn
IRP	Integrated reference point	综合参考点	Zōnghé cānkǎo diǎn
IRP	Internal reference point	内部参考点	Nèibù cānkǎo diǎn
IRP	International routing plan	国际线路选定计划	Guójì xiànlù xuǎndìng jìhuà
IRQ	Information request	信息查询	Xìnxī cháxún
IRQ	Information request (computer term)	信息请求	Xìnxī qǐngqiú
IRQ	Interrupt request	中断请求	Zhōngduàn qǐngqiú
IRR	Information request reason	信息请求原因	Xìnxī qǐngqiú yuányīn
IRR	Information request response	信息查询响应	Xìnxī cháxún xiǎngyìng
IRR	Information request response	信息请求响应	Xìnxī qǐngqiú xiǎngyìng
IRS	Intelligent railway system	智能铁路系统	Zhìnéng tiělù xìtǒng
IRSG	Internet Research Steering group	因特网研究管理组	Yīntèwǎng yánjiū guǎnlǐ zǔ
IRSG	Internet Research Steering group	因特网研究指导组	Yīntèwǎng yánjiū zhǐdǎo zǔ
IRTF	Internet Research Task Force	因特网研究部	Yīntèwǎng yánjiū bù
IRV	Interrupt request vector	中断请求向量	Zhōngduàn qǐngqiú xiàngliàng
IS	Intermediate system	中间系统	Zhōngjiān xìtǒng
IS	Intermediate system	中介系统	Zhōngjiè xìtǒng
IS	Internal stack	内置堆栈	Nèizhì duīzhàn
ISA	Industry standard architecture	工业标准架构	Gōngyè biāozhǔn jiàgòu
ISA	Instruction set architecture	指令集架构	Zhǐlìng jí jiàgòu
ISA	Instrument Society of America	美国仪表协会	Měiguó yíbiǎo xiéhuì
ISAKMP	Internet security association and key management protocol	因特网安全连接和密钥管理协议	Yīntèwǎng ānquán liánjiē hé mìyào guǎnlǐ xiéyì
ISAM	Indexed sequential access method	索引顺序访问方法	Suǒyǐn shùnxù fǎngwèn fāngfǎ
ISAN	Integrated service access network	综合业务接入网	Zōnghé yèwù jiērù wǎng
ISB	Independent sideband	独立边带	Dúlì biāndài
ISB	Internal service broker (in VPN)	内部服务代理	Nèibù fúwù dàilǐ
ISBX	Integrated services business exchange	综合业务企业交换	Zōnghé yèwù qǐyè jiāohuàn
ISC	International Science Committee	国际科学委员会	Guójì kēxué wěiyuánhuì
ISC	International Softswitch Consortium	国际软交换协会	Guójì ruǎn jiāohuàn xiéhuì
ISC	International switching center	国际交换中心	Guójì jiāohuàn zhōngxīn
ISC	International switching center	国际局	Guójì jú
ISC	International switching center	国际软交换中心	Guójì ruǎnjiāohuàn zhōngxīn
ISCEP	Integrated service creation environment point	综合业务生成环境点	Zōnghé yèwù shēngchéng huánjìng diǎn
ISCF	Integrated service control function	综合业务控制功能	Zōnghé yèwù kòngzhì gōngnéng
ISCII	International Standard Code for Information Interchange	信息交换用国际标准代码	Xìnxī jiāohuàn-yòng guójì biāozhǔn dàimǎ

ISCP	Integrated services control point	综合业务控制点	Zōnghé yèwù kòngzhì diǎn
ISCP	Interference signal code power	干扰信号码功率	Gānrǎo xìnhào mǎ gōnglǜ
ISCP	International service control point	国际业务控制点	Guójì yèwù kòngzhìdiǎn
iSCSI	Internet small computer system interface (IETF usage)	Internet 小型计算机系统接口	Internet xiǎoxíng jìsuànjī xìtǒng jiēkǒu
ISD	Integrated symbolic debugger	综合符号调试程序	Zōnghé fúhào diàoshì chéngxù
ISD	International subscriber dialing	国际用户拨号	Guójì yònghù bōhào
ISD	Ionization smoke detector	离子感烟探测器	Lízǐ gǎnyān tàncèqì
ISDN	Integrated service data network	综合业务数据网络	Zōnghé yèwù shùjù wǎngluò
ISDN	Integrated service data point	综合业务数据点	Zōnghé yèwù shùjù diǎn
ISDN	Integrated services digital network	一体化服务数字网络	Yītǐhuà fúwù shùzì wǎngluò
ISDN	Integrated services digital network	一线通	Yīxiàn tōng
ISDN	Integrated services digital network	综合服务数字网络	Zōnghé fúwù shùzì wǎngluò
ISDN	Integrated services digital network	综合业务数字网	Zōnghé yèwù shùzì wǎng
ISDN-PRM	ISDN protocol reference mode	ISDN 协议参考模型	ISDN xiéyì cānkǎo móxíng
ISDN-SN	ISDN subscriber number	ISDN 用户号码	ISDN yònghù hàomǎ
ISDT	Integrated services digital terminal	综合服务数字终端	Zōnghé fúwù shùzì zhōngduān
ISE	Integrated switching element	集成交换单元	Jíchéng jiāohuàn dānyuán
ISF	Incoming signal failure	输入信号失效	Shūrù xìnhào shīxiào
ISF	Individual store and forward readout	单独存储与正向读出	Dāndú cúnchǔ yǔ zhèngxiàng dúchū
ISI	Inter-symbol interference	符号间干扰	Fúhào-jiān gānrǎo
ISI	Inter-symbol interference	码间干扰	Mǎ-jiān gānrǎo
ISID	Idle signal identification	空闲信号识别	Kòngxián xìnhào shíbié
IS-IS	Intermediate system to intermediate system protocol (ISO, IETF usage)	中间系统到中间系统协议	Zhōngjiān xìtǒng dào zhōngjiān xìtǒng xiéyì
IS-IS	Intermediate system to intermediate system routing exchange protocol	中间系统到中间系统路由交换协议	Zhōngjiān xìtǒng dào zhōngjiān xìtǒng lùyóu jiāohuàn xiéyì
IS-IS	Intermediate system-to-intermediate system	中介系统到中介系统	Zhōngjiè xìtǒng dào zhōngjiè xìtǒng
ISL	Cisco inter-switch link protocol	思科交换链路内协议	Sī-kē jiāohuàn liànlù-nèi xiéyì
ISL	Inter-switch link	交换机间连接	Jiāohuànjī-jiān liánjiē
ISLE	Integral square linear error	积累平房线性误差	Jīlěi píngfáng xiànxìng wùchā
ISLS	Improved sidelobe suppression	改进的旁瓣抑制	Gǎijìnde pángbàn yìzhì
ISM	Industrial, scientific and medical apparatus	工业，科学，医疗设备	Gōngyè, kēxué, yīliáo shèbèi
ISM	Industrial, scientific and medical applications (of radio frequency energy)	工业，科学和医疗应用	Gōngyè, kēxué hé yīliáo yìngyòng
ISM	Interface subscriber module	接口用户模块	Jiēkǒu yònghù mókuài
ISM	Inter-site messaging service	站间消息传递服务	Zhàn-jiān xiāoxi chuándì fúwù
ISM	ISDN subscriber module	ISDN 用户模块	ISDN yònghù mókuài
ISMA	Idle signal multiple access	空线信号多路存取	Kōng xiàn xìnhào duōlù cúnqǔ
ISMAP	Integrated service management access point	综合业务管理接入点	Zōnghé yèwù guǎnlǐ jiērù diǎn
ISMAP	Integrated service management access point	综合业务管理接入点	Zōnghé yèwù guǎnlǐ jiērù diǎn
ISMC	International Switching Maintenance Center	国际电话交换维护中心	Guójì diànhuà jiāohuàn wéihù zhōngxīn
ISMF	Integrated service management function	综合业务管理功能	Zōnghé yèwù guǎnlǐ gōngnéng
ISMG	Internet short message gateway	互联网短信网关	Hùliánwǎng duǎnxìn wǎngguān
ISMG	Internet short message gateway	因特网短消息网关	Yīntèwǎng duǎn xiāoxi wǎngguān
ISMP	Integrated service management point	综合业务管理点	Zōnghé yèwù guǎnlǐ diǎn
ISN	Interface service node	接口服务节点	Jiēkǒu fúwù jiédiǎn

iSNS	Internet storage name service (IETF usage)	Internet 存储名称服务	Internet cúnchǔ míngchēng fúwù
ISO	International Organization for Standardization	国际标准化组织	Guójì Biāozhǔnhuà Zǔzhī
ISO	International Standardization Organization	国际标准化组织	Guójì Biāozhǔnhuà Zǔzhī
ISO DCC	ISO data and country code	ISO 数据和国家代码	ISO shùjù hé guójiā dàimǎ
ISO/MPEG	International Standard Organization's Moving Picture Expert group	国际标准化组织的活动图片专家组	Guójì Biāozhǔnhuà Zǔzhīde huódòng túpiàn zhuānjiāzǔ
ISOC	Internet Society	因特网协会	Yīntèwǎng xiéhuì
ISOC	Internet Society	因特网学会	Yīntèwǎng xuéhuì
ISOID	Isotropic identification	各向同性识别	Gèxiàng tóngxìng shíbié
ISP	Intermediate services part	中间业务部分	Zhōngjiān yèwù bùfen
ISP	International signaling point	国际信令点	Guójì xìnlìng diǎn
ISP	Internet service provider	互联网业务提供商	Hùliánwǎng yèwù tígōng shāng
ISP	Internet service provider	Internet 服务提供商	Internet fúwù tígōngshāng
ISP	Internet service provider	英特网业务提供者	Yīng-tè-wǎng yèwù tígòngzhě
ISP	Internet service provider	因特网服务提供商	Yīntèwǎng fúwù tígōngshāng
ISP	Internet service provider	因特网服务提供者	Yīntèwǎng fúwù tígòngzhě
ISP	Internet service provider	因特网业务提供商	Yīntèwǎng yèwù tígōngshāng
ISP	Internet service provider	因特网业务提供者	Yīntèwǎng yèwù tígòngzhě
ISPBX	Integrated services private branch exchange	综合业务用户交换机	Zōnghé yèwù yònghù jiāohuànjī
ISPL	Instruction set processor language	指令集处理机语言	Zhǐlìng jí chǔlǐjī yǔyán
ISQL	Interactive structured query language	交互式结构化查询语言	Jiāohù-shì jiégòuhuà cháxún yǔyán
ISR	Intermediate session routing	中介会话路由选择	Zhōngjiè huìhuà lùyóu xuǎnzé
ISR	Interrupt service routine	中断服务程序	Zhōngduàn fúwù chéngxù
ISS	Improved spectral subtraction	改进谱减法	Gǎijìn pǔ jiǎnfǎ
ISS	Internal sub-layer service	内部子层服务	Nèibù zicéng fúwù
ISSC	Information Security Sub-Committee (of CIITA)	西安全产业分会	Xī'ān quán chǎnyè fēnhuì
ISSCC	International Solid-State Circuits Conference	国际晶体管电路讨论会	Guójì jīngtīguǎn diànlù tǎolùnhuì
ISSE	Information systems security engineering	信息系统安全工程	Xìnxī xìtǒng ānquán gōngchéng
ISSP	International service switching point	国际业务交换点	Guójì yèwù jiāohuàndiǎn
ISTN	Integrated switching and transmission network	综合交换和传输网络	Zōnghé jiāohuàn hé chuánshū wǎngluò
ISTP	International signal transfer point	国际信令转接点	Guójì xìnlìng zhuǎnjiē diǎn
ISU	Initial signal unit	初始信号单元	Chūshǐ xìnhào dānyuán
ISU	Instruction storage unit	指令存储器	Zhǐlìng cúnchǔqì
ISU	Integrated services unit	综合业务单元	Zōnghé yèwù dānyuán
ISUP	Integrated services digital network user part	综合业务数字网用户部分	Zōnghé yèwù shùzì wǎng yònghù bùfen
ISUP	ISDN user part	ISDN 用户部分	ISDN yònghù bùfen
ISV	Independent software vendor	独立软件提供者	Dúlì ruǎnjiàn tígòngzhě
ISV	Independent software vendors	独立软件购买者	Dúlì ruǎnjiàn gòumǎizhě
ISVs	Independent software vendors	独立软件供应商	Dúlì ruǎnjiàn gōngyìngshāng
ISW	Interrupt status word	中断状态字	Zhōngduàn zhuàngtài zì
ISWA	Switch assembly	交换集成件	Jiāohuàn jíchéng jiàn
IT	Immediate transmission	立即传输	Lìjí chuánshū
IT	Information technology	信息技术	Xìnxī jìshù
ITA	Interim type approval	中间型号批准	Zhōngjiān xínghào pīzhǔn
ITAA	Information Technology Association of America	美国信息技术协会	Měiguó xìnxī jìshù xiéhuì
ITBE	Inter-channel time base error	通道间时基误差	Tōngdào-jiān shíjī wùchā

ITC	Independent telephone company	独立电话公司	Dúlì diànhuà gōngsī
ITC	Information transfer capability	信息传送容量	Xìnxī chuánsòng róngliàng
ITC	Information transfer channel	信息传送通道	Xìnxī chuánsòng tōngdào
ITCP	Integrated test and checkout procedures	综合测试和检查程序	Zōnghé cèshì hé jiǎnchá chéngxù
ITDM	Intelligent time division multiplexer	智能时分多路复用器	Zhìnéng shífèn duōlù fùyòngqì
ITE	Information technology equipment	信息技术设备	Xìnxī jìshù shèbèi
ITG	Internet telephone gateway	因特网电话网关	Yīntèwǎng diànhuà wǎngguān
ITMX	Isolator/tap coupler/wavelength division multiplexer	隔离器/分路器/滤波型波分复用器	Gélíqì/fēnlùqì/lǜbō-xíng bōfēn fùyòngqì
ITO	Indium-tin-oxide	氧化铟锡	Yǎnghuàyīnxī
ITP	Integrated terminal plan or program	综合终端计划	Zōnghé zhōngduān jìhuà
ITP	Interactive terminal protocol	交互终端规约	Jiāohù zhōngduān guīyuē
ITP	International transit part	国际转接部分	Guójì zhuǎnjiē bùfen
ITR	Implicit token register	隐含令牌寄存器	Yǐnhán lìngpái jìcúnqì
ITR	Internet talk radio	网际广播	Wǎngjì guǎngbō
ITS	Intelligent transportation system	智能运输系统	Zhìnéng yùnshū xìtǒng
ITSC	International transit switching center	国际转换中心	Guójì zhuǎnhuàn zhōngxīn
ITSO	International Telecommunications Satellite Organization	国际远程通信卫星组织	Guójì yuǎnchéng tōngxìn wèixīng zǔzhī
ITT	International Telephone and Telegraph Co. ITT (UK)	国际电话电报公司	Guójì diànhuà diànbào gōngsī
ITT	Intertoll trunk	长途电话中继线	Chángtú diànhuà zhōngjìxiàn
ITU	International Telecommunications Union (UN)	国际电信联盟	Guójì Diànxìn Liánméng
ITUM	Integrated terrain unit mapping	综合地形单元制图	Zōnghé dìxíng dānyuán zhìtú
ITU-R	International Telecommunication Union – Radiocommunication Sector	国际电信联盟 – 无线通讯分册	Guójì Diànxìn Liánméng - wúxiàn tōngxùn fēncè
ITU-T	International Telecommunication Union-Telecommunication Standardization Sector	国际电信联盟-电信标准部门	Guójì Diànxìn Liánméng-- Diànxìn biāozhǔn bùmén
ITU-T	International Telecommunications Union - Telecommunications Standardization Sector	国际电信联盟-电信标准化部门	Guójì Diànxìn Liánméng—diànxìn biāozhǔnhua bùmén
ITV	Interactive teleVision	互动电视	Hùdòng diànshì
ITV	Interactive tevevision	交互式电视	Jiāohù-shì diànshì
IUC	Interval usage coding	间隔使用编码	Jiàngé shǐyòng biānmǎ
IUI	International user identification module identifier	国际 USIM 标识符	Guójì USIM biāozhìfú
IUO	Intelligent underlay overlay	智能分层覆盖	Zhìnéng fēncéng fùgài
IUO	Intelligent underlay-overlay (network)	智能双层网	Zhìnéng shuāngcéng wǎng
IUT	Implementation under test	测试中的实现	Cèshì zhòngdì shíxiàn
IUT	Implementation under test	测试下的实现	Cèshì-xiàde shíxiàn
IUT	Implementation under test	经测试实现	Jīng cèshì shíxiàn
IUT	Implementation under test	在测试实现	Zài cèshì shíxiàn
IUT	Implication under test	被测实现	Bèicè shíxiàn
IUT	Instrument under test	被测试实现体	Bèi cèshì shíxiàn tǐ
IUT	Instrument under test	被测对象	Bèicè duìxiàng
IV	Initial vector	初始向量	Chūshǐ xiàngliàng
IVMO	Initial value managed object	管理目标初始值	Guǎnlǐ mùbiāo chūshǐ zhí
IVMS	Integrated voice-messaging system	综合声音信息系统	Zōnghé shēngyīn xìnxī xìtǒng
IVOD-d	Interactive video on demand with delayed access	延时交互式视频点播	Yánshí jiāohùshì shìpín diǎnbō
IVOD-i	Interactive voice over data with instantaneous access	即时交互式视频点播	Jíshí jiāohùshì shìpín diǎnbō

IVPD	Inside vapor phase deposition (FOC mfg)	内汽相沉积法	Nèi qìxiàng chénjī fǎ
IVPN	International virtual private network service	国际虚拟专网业务	Guójì xūnǐ zhuān wǎng yèwù
IVR	Interactive voice response	交互语音响应	Jiāohù yǔyīn xiǎngyìng
IVR	Interactive voice response	交互语音应答	Jiāohù yǔyīn yìngdá
IVR	Interactive voice response (equipment)	语音交互设备	Yǔyīn jiāohù shèbèi
IVR	Interactive voice response system	交互语音应答系统	Jiāohù yǔyīn yìngdá xìtǒng
IWCS	Integrated wideband communication system	综合宽带通信系统	Zōnghé kuāndài tōngxìn xìtǒng
IWDM	Fiber isolator/wavelength division multiplexer	光隔离器/波分复用器	Guāng gélíqì/bōfēn fùyòngqì
IWE	Interworking equipment	互联设备	Hùlián shèbèi
IWF	Interworking function	互配功能	Hùpèi gōngnéng
IWF	Interworking function	互通功能	Hùtōng gōngnéng
IWF	Interworking function	互通功能模块	Hùtōng gōngnéng mókuài
IWGW	Interworking gateway	互联网关	Hùlián wǎngguān
IWM	Interworking module	互通模块	Hùtōng mókuài
IWMSC	Interworking MSC	互通功能装备的 MSC	Hùtōng gōngnéng zhuāngbèide MSC
IWS	Intelligent workstation	智能工作台	Zhìnéng gōngzuòtái
IWS	Intelligent workstation	智能工作站	Zhìnéng gōngzuòzhàn
IWU	Interworking unit	互通单元	Hùtōng dānyuán
IXFR	Incremental zone transfer	增量区域传送	Zēngliàng qūyù chuánsòng
IXIT	Implementation extra information	执行额外信息	Zhíxíng éwài xìnxī
IXR	Index register	变址寄存器	Biànzhǐ jìcúnqì

J

JAIN	Java APIs for integrated networks	综合网络的 Java API	Zōnghé wǎngluòde Java API
JANET	Joint academic network	联合科研网	Liánhé kēyán wǎng
JAPS	Java automatic paralleling system	Java 自动并行化系统	Java zìdòng bìngxínghuà xìtǒng
JAR file	Java archive file	Java 归档文件	Java guīdàng wénjiàn
JBIG	Joint bi-level Image Experts Group	联合两级图象专家组	Liánhé liǎngjí túxiàng zhuānjiāzǔ
JBIG	Joint bi-level Imaging Group	联合双态成像组	Liánhé shuāngtài chéngxiàngzǔ
JBOD	Just a bunch of disks	磁盘束	Cípán shù
JCA	Java cryptographic architecture	Java 密码体系结构	Java mìmǎ tǐxì jiégòu
JCE	Java cryptographic extension	Java 密码扩展	Java mìmǎ kuòzhǎn
JCOS	Java chip operating system	Java 芯片操作系统	Java xìnpiàn cāozuò xìtǒng
JD	Joint detection	联合检波	Liánhé jiǎnbō
JDC	Japan digital cellular system	日本数字蜂窝系统	Rìběn shùzì fēngwō xìtǒng
JDK	Java development kit	Java 开发包	Java kāifā bāo
JEDEC	Joint Electronic Device Engineering Council	联合电子设备工程委员会	Liánhé diànzǐ shèbèi gōngchéng wěiyuánhuì
JEPI	Joint Electronic payment initiative	联合电子支付联盟	Liánhé diànzǐ zhīfù liánméng
JERS	Japanese earth resources satellite	日本地球资源卫星	Rìběn dìqiú zīyuán wèixīng
JFET	Junction field effect transistor	结型场效应晶体管	Jiéxíng cháng xiàoyìng jīngtǐguǎn
JIDS	Joint intrusion detection system	捷普入侵检测系统	Jiépǔ rùqīn jiǎncè xìtǒng
JIT	Just in time	准时制生产	Zhǔnshí zhì shēngchǎn
JMCOMS	Joint Maritime Communications Strategy	联合海上通信系统策略	Liánhé hǎishàng tōngxìn xìtǒng cèlüè
JME	Jones matrix eigenanalysis	琼斯矩阵本征分析	Qióng-sī jǔzhèn běnzhēng fēnxī
JNDI	Java naming directory interface	Java 命名索引薄接口	Java mìngmíng suǒyǐn báo jiēkǒu
JP	Joint pre-distortion	接头预失真	Jiētóu yùshīzhēn

JPEG	Joint Photographic Experts Group	联合摄影专家组	Liánhé shèyǐng zhuānjiāzǔ
JPEG	Joint Photographic Experts Group	联合图象专家组	Liánhé túxiàng zhuānjiāzǔ
JPEG	Joint Photographic Experts Group	联合照相专家组	Liánhé zhàoxiàng zhuānjiāzǔ
JPL	Jet Propulsion Laboratory (US)	喷气推进实验室	Pēnqì tuījìn shíyànshì
JSSE	Java secure socket extension	Java 安全套接字扩展	Java ānquán tàojiēzì kuòzhǎn
JSTARS	Joint Surveillance and Target Attack Radar System (US military)	联合监视和目标攻击雷达系统	Liánhé jiānshì hé mùbiāo gōngjī léidá xìtǒng
JTAPI	Java telephony application programming interface	Java 电话应用程序设计接口	Java diànhuà yìngyòng chéngxù shèjì jiēkǒu
JTIDS	Joint Tactical Information Distribution System (U.S.)	联合战术信息分发系统	Liánhé zhànshù xìnxī fēnfā xìtǒng
JTRS	Joint Tactical Radio System (US military usage)	联合战术无线电系统	Liánhé zhànshù wúxiàndiàn xìtǒng
JUNET	Japan Unix Network	日本 UNIX 网络	Rìběn UNIX wǎngluò
JVM	Java virtual machine	Java 虚拟机	Java xūnǐjī
JWL	Computer network	计算机网络	Jìsuànjī wǎngluò

K

K	Constraint length of the convolutional code	卷积码的约束长度	Juànjī mǎde yuēshù chángdù
K	Wiring on porcelain insulator	瓷珠敷设	Cízhū fūshè
K	Wiring on porcelain knob	瓷瓶敷设	Cípíng fūshè
K-ALG	Key management algorithm	密钥管理算法	Mìyào guǎnlǐ suànfǎ
KB	Keyboard	键盘	Jiànpán
KB	Kilobyte (1024 bytes)	千字节	Qiānzìjié
KBC	Keyboard controller	键盘控制器	Jiànpán kòngzhìqì
Kbps	Kilobits per second	每秒千比特	Měi miǎo qiānbǐtè
Kc	Ciphering key	密码本	Mìmǎ běn
KCMC	Cipher key certificate management center	密钥证书管理中心	Mìyào zhèngshū guǎnlǐ zhōngxīn
KDC	Cipher key distribution center	密钥分配中心	Mìyào fēnpèi zhōngxīn
KDD	Knowledge discovery in databases	数据库中的知识发现	Shùjùkù-zhōngde zhīshi fāxiàn
KDD	Kokusai Denshin Denwa Co. Ltd. (Japan)	国际电信电话有限公司	Guójì diànxìn diànhuà yǒuxiàn gōngsī
KDE	K desktop environment (in UNIX)	K 桌面环境	K zhuōmiàn huánjìng
KEA	Cipher key exchange algorithm	密钥交换算法	Mìyào jiāohuàn suànfǎ
KES	Cipher key escrow system (cryptology)	密钥托管系统	Mìyào tuōguǎn xìtǒng
KEY	Key protection	键保护	Jiàn bǎohù
Ki	Individual subscriber authentication key	单个用户的鉴别钥匙	Dāngè yònghùde jiànbié yàoshi
Ki	Individual subscriber authentication key	个人身份鉴权键	Gèrén shēnfen jiànquán jiàn
Ki	Subscriber authentication key	用户鉴权密码	Yònghù jiànquán mìmǎ
Ki	Subscriber authentication key	用户鉴权密钥	Yònghù jiànquán mìyào
KID	Cipher key injection device, key injector	密钥注入器	Mìyào zhùrùqì
KK	Key enciphering key	密钥加密密钥	Mìyào jiāmì mìyào
KKM	Master key enciphering key	主密钥	Zhǔ mìyào
KLA	Klystron amplifier	速调管放大器	Sùtiáoguǎn fàngdàqì
KLT	Karhunen Loeve transform	KL 变换	KL Biànhuàn
KMC	Cipher key management center	密钥管理中心	Mìyào guǎnlǐ zhōngxīn
KMI	Cipher key management infrastructure	密钥管理基础设施	Mìyào guǎnlǐ jīchǔ shèshī
KMT	Korea Mobile Telecom	韩国移动通信	Hánguó yídòng tōngxìn
KNI	Katmai new instructions	Katmai 新指令集	Katmai xīn zhǐlìng jí
KQML	Knowledge query management language	知识查询管理语言	Zhīshi cháxún guǎnlǐ yǔyán

Ksps	Kilo-symbols per second	每秒千符号（码元）	Měi miǎo qiānfúhào (mǎ yuán)
KTN	Kernel transport network	核心传送网络	Héxīn chuánsòng wǎngluò
KTN.CM	KTN configuration management	KTN 组成管理	KTN zǔchéng guǎnlǐ
KTN-Com.CM	KTN computing configuration management	KTN 计算组成管理	KTN jìsuàn zǔchéng guǎnlǐ
KTN-Con.CM	KTN connection configuration management	KTN 连接组成管理	KTN liánjiē zǔchéng guǎnlǐ
KTN-Pro.CM	KTN protocol configuration management	KTN 协议组成管理	KTN xiéyì zǔchéng guǎnlǐ
KTN-TCM	KTN topology configuration management	KTN 拓扑组成管理	KTN tuòpū zǔchéng guǎnlǐ
KTS	Key telephone system	按键电话系统	Ànjiàn diànhuà xìtǒng
KVAH	Kilovolt ampere-hour	千伏安小时	Qiānfú'ān xiǎoshí
KW	Keyword	关键词	Guānjiàn cí
KWh	Kilowatt hour	千瓦小时	Qiānwǎ xiǎoshí

L

L&G	Legal and Regulatory Group (GSM MoU)	政策法规组	Zhèngcè fǎguī zǔ
L/P	Line printer	行式打印机	Hángshì dǎyìnjī
L1	Layer 1	层 1	Céng yī
L1	Layer 1 (physical layer)	第一层（物理层）	Dìyīcéng (wùlǐ céng)
L2	Layer 2 (data link later)	第二层（数据链路层）	Dì'èrcéng (shùjù liànlù céng)
L2CAP	Logical link control and adaptation protocol	逻辑链路控制和适配协议	Luójí liànlù kòngzhì hé shìpèi xiéyì
L2F	Layer 2 forwarding protocol	第二层转发协议	Dì'èrcéng zhuǎnfā xiéyì
L2ML	Layer 2 management link	层 2 管理连接	Céng èr guǎnlǐ liánjiē
L2ML	Layer 2 management link	第二层链路管理	Dì'èrcéng liànlù guǎnlǐ
L2ML	Layer 2 management link (OSI data link layer)	第二层管理链路	Dì'èrcéng guǎnlǐ liànlù
L2R	Layer 2 relay	层 2 中继	Céng èr zhōngjì
L2R	Layer 2 relay	第二层中继	Dì'èrcéng zhōngjì
L2TP	Layer 2 transport protocol	二层传送协议	Èrcéng chuánsòng xiéyì
L2TP	Layer 2 tunneling protocol	二级通道协议	Èrjí tōngdào xiéyì
L2TP	Layer 2 tunneling protocol	层二隧道协议	Céng èr suìdào xiéyì
L2TP	Layer 2 tunneling protocol	第二层隧道协议	Dì'èrcéng suìdào xiéyì
L3	Layer 3	第三层	Dìsāncéng
LA	Lens antenna	透镜天线	Tòujìng tiānxiàn
LA	Lightning arrester	避雷计	Bì léi jì
LA	Line amplifier	线路放大器	Xiànlù fàngdàqì
LA	Location area	位置区	Wèizhì qū
LA	Location area	位置区域	Wèizhì qūyù
LAA	Laser attenuator assembly	激光衰减控制器	Jīguāng shuāijiǎn kòngzhìqì
LAA	Linear array antenna	线性天线阵	Xiànxìng tiānxiàn zhèn
LAA	Linear array antenna	线性阵列天线	Xiànxìng zhènliè tiānxiàn
LAAS	Local area augmentation system	局域加强系统	Júyù jiāqiáng xìtǒng
LAC	L2TP access concentrator	L2TP 接入聚合器	L2TP jiērù jùhéqì
LAC	Laser amplifier chain	激光放大器电路	Jīguāng fàngdàqì diànlù
LAC	Link access control	链路接入控制	Liànlù jiērù kòngzhì
LAC	Location area code	位置区域码	Wèizhì qūyù mǎ
LAC	Location area code	位置区码	Wèizhì qū mǎ
LACE	Local automatic circuit exchange	市内自动线路交换机	Shìnèi zìdòng xiànlù jiāohuànjī
LACN	Local area communications network	局部通信网络	Júbù tōngxìn wǎngluò

LADM	Linear add/drop multiplexer	线性分叉复用器	Xiànxìng fēnchā fùyòngqì
LAI	Location area identification	位置区域识别	Wèizhì qūyù shíbié
LAI	Location area identity	位置区号	Wèizhì qū hào
LAI	Location area information	位置区信息	Wèizhì qū xìnxī
LAMA	Local automatic message accounting	本端自动消息记帐	Běnduān zìdòng xiāoxi jìzhàng
LAN	Local area network	区域网络	Qūyù wǎngluò
LAN	Local area network	局域网	Júyùwǎng
LAN	Local area network	局域网络	Júyù wǎngluò
LAN	Local area network	本地网	Běndì wǎng
LANE	Local area network emulation	局域网仿真	Júyùwǎng fǎngzhēn
LANE-NNI	LAN emulation - network to network interface	LAN 仿真-网间接口	LAN fǎngzhēn- wǎngjiān jiēkǒu
LANE-UNI	Local area network (LAN) emulation - user to network interface	LAN 仿真-用户与网络间接口	LAN fǎngzhēn– yònghù yǔ wǎngluòjiān jiēkǒu
LAP	Link access procedure	链路接入规程	Liànlù jiērù guīchéng
LAP	Link access protocol	链路接入协议	Liànlù jiērù xiéyì
LAP	Link access protocol	链路访问协议	Liànlù fǎngwèn xiéyì
LAP	Local area network access point	局域网接入点	Júyùwǎng jiērù diǎn
LAP	Low address part	低地址段	Dīdìzhǐ duàn
LAPB	Link access procedure - balanced	链路接入规程 - 平衡	Liànlù jiērù guīchéng –pínghéng
LAPB	Link access procedure balanced (ISO usage)	链路访问过程平衡	Liànlù fǎngwèn guòchéng pínghéng
LAPB	Link access procedure, balanced	平衡链路接入规程	Pínghéng liànlù jiērù guīchéng
LAPB	Link access procedure-balanced	平衡型链路接入规程	Pínghéng-xíng liànlù jiērù guīchéng
LAPB	Link access protocol balanced	平衡链路接入协议	Pínghéng liànlù jiērù xiéyì
LAPB	Link access protocol balanced	链路接入平衡协议	Liànlù jiērù pínghéng xiéyì
LAPD	Link access procedure on D channel	D 信道链路接入规程	D xìndào liànlù jiērù guīchéng
LAPD	Link access procedure on the D-channel	D 通路上的链路接入规程	D-tōnglù-shàngde liànlù jiērù guīchéng
LAPD	Link access procedures on the D-channel	D 通路上的链路接入程序	D-tōnglù shàngde liànlù jiērù chéngxù
LAPD	Link access protocol on D channel	D 信道上的链路接入协议	D-xìndào shàngde liànlù jiērù xiéyì
LAP-D	Link access procedure D-channel	链路接入过程 D-信道	Liànlù jiērù guòchéng D-xìndào
LAP-D	Link access protocol channel D	链路访问协议 D 信道	Liànlù fǎngwèn xiéyì D xìndào
LAP-D	Link access protocol D	链路接入规程 D	Liànlù jiērù guīchéng D
LAP-D	Link access protocol on the D channel	D 信道上的链路访问协议	D-xìndào-shàngde liànlù fǎngwèn xiéyì
LAPDm	Link access protocol on Dm channel	Dm 信道上链路接入协议	Dm xìndàoshàng liànlù jiērù xiéyì
LAPDm	Link access protocol on the Dm channel	在 Dm 信道上链路接入协议	Zài Dm xìndàoshàng liànlù jiērù xiéyì
LAP-Dm	Link access protocol on the Dm channel	Dm 信道上的链路访问协议	Dm-xìndào-shàngde liànlù fǎngwèn xiéyì
LAPF	Link access procedure to frame mode bearer service	帧模式承载业务链路接入规程	Zhèng móshì chéngzài yèwù liànlù jiērù guīchéng
LAPF	Link access protocol frame	链路接入协议帧	Liànlù jiērù xiéyì zhèng
LAPM	Link access procedure for modem	调制解调器的链路接入规程	Tiáozhì jiětiáoqìde liànlù jiērù guīchéng
LAPOSH®	LAPOSH® single mode optical fiber	大保实®单模光纤	Dàbǎoshí® dānmó guāngxiān
LAPS	Link access procedure-SDH	链路接入规程-SDH	Liànlù jiērù guīchéng-SDH
LAPS	Link access protocol-SDH	链路接入协议-SDH	Liànlù jiērù xiéyì-SDH
LAPX	Link access procedure- half-duplex	半双工链路接入规程	Bànshuānggōng liànlù jiērù guīchéng
LAS-CDMA	Large area synchronous code division multiple access	大区域同步码分多址接入	Dàqūyù tóngbù mǎfēn duōzhǐ jiērù
LASCS	Light activated silicon controlled switch	光控可控硅开关	Guāng kòng kěkòngguī kāiguān
LASER	Light amplification by stimulated emission of radiation	辐射激发的光线放大	Fúshè jīfāde guāngxiàn fàngdà
LATA	Local access and transport area	本地接入及传动区	Běndì jiērù jí chuánsòng qū

LATA	Local access and transport area	本地访问和传输区域	Běndì fǎngwèn hé chuánshū qūyù
LAU	Location area update	位置区域更新	Wèizhì qūyù gēngxīn
LB	Laser bias current	激光器偏置电流	Jīguāngqì piānzhì diànliú
LB	Local bus	局部总线	Júbù zǒngxiàn
LBA	Logical block addressing	逻辑块寻址	Luójì kuài xúnzhǐ
LBOP	Laser backface optical power	激光器背光功率	Jīguāngqì bèiguāng gōnglǜ
LBP	Laser beam printer, laser printer	激光打印机	Jīguāng dǎyìnjī
LBTA	Link bit error rate test board assembly	链路误码率测试集成板	Liànlù wùmǎlǜ cèshì jíchéngbǎn
LC	Layer clock	等级钟	Děngjí zhōng
LC	Link connection	链路连接	Liànlù liánjiē
LC	Link controller	链路控制器	Liànlù kòngzhìqì
LC	Local control	本地控制	Běndì kòngzhì
LC	Logical channel	逻辑信道	Luójì xìndào
LCA	Logic cell array (FPGA term)	逻辑单元阵列	Luójì dānyuán zhènliè
LCAS	Link capacity adjusting scheme	链路容量调整方案	Liànlù róngliàng tiáozhěng fāng'àn
LCAS	Link capacity adjustment scheme	链路容量调节方案	Liànlù róngliàng tiáojié fāng'àn
LCC	Line card control	线路卡控制	Xiànlù kǎ kòngzhì
LCC	Lost call cleared	丢失呼叫清除	Diūshī hūjiào qīngchú
LCCW	Logical channel command word	逻辑通道命令字	Luójì tōngdào mìnglìng zì
LCD	Liquid crystal display	液晶显示器	Yèjīng xiǎnshìqì
LCD	Liquid crystal display	液晶显示屏	Yèjīng xiǎnshì píng
LCD	Loss of cell delineation	信元定界丢失	Xìnyuán dìngjiè diūshī
LCD	Low constrained delay	低约束时延	Dīyuēshù shíyán
LCF	Laser control field	激光器控制域	Jīguāngqì kòngzhì yù
LCF	Least connection first algorithm	链接最小优先算法	Liànjiē zuìxiǎo yōuxiān suànfǎ
LCF	Location confirm	地址解析回答	Dìzhǐ jiěxī huídá
LCF	Location confirm	地址解析确认	Dìzhǐ jiěxī quèrèn
LCF	Location confirm	定位确认	Dìngwèi quèrèn
LCG	Local charging generator software	本地计费生成软件	Běndì jìfèi shēngchéng ruǎnjiàn
LCH	Lost call hold	丢失呼叫保持	Diūshī hūjiào bǎochí
LCI	Local cell identifier	本地小区标识符	Běndì xiǎoqū biāozhì fú
LCI	Logical channel identifier	逻辑通路标识符	Luójì tōnglù biāozhìfú
LCID	Locale identifier	区域设置标识符	Qūyù shèzhì biāozhì fú
LCIN	Local communication interconnection network	本地通信互联网	Běndì tōngxìn hùliánwǎng
LCL	Longitudinal conversion loss	纵向变换损耗	Zòngxiàng biànhuàn sǔnhào
LCL	Longitudinal conversion loss	纵向转换损耗	Zòngxiàng zhuǎnhuàn sǔnhào
LCL	Longitudinal conversion loss	纵向转换衰减	Zòngxiàng zhuǎnhuàn shuāijiǎn
LCL	Longitudinal conversion loss	纵模变换损耗	Zòngmó biànhuàn sǔnhào
LCM	Line concentrator module	线路集线器模块	Xiànlù jíxiànqì mókuài
LCN	Local communication network	本地通信网络	Běndì tōngxìn wǎngluò
LCN	Local communications network	本地通信网	Běndì tōngxìnwǎng
LCO	Local central office	本地交换局	Běndì jiāohuàn jú
LCOS	Liquid crystal on silicon	硅上液晶	Guī-shàng yèjīng
LCP	Line card processor	用户板处理机	Yònghù bǎn chǔlǐjī
LCP	Link control protocol	链路控制协议	Liànlù kòngzhì xiéyì
LCPA	Lower command packet address	命令包地区地址	Mìnglìng bāo dìqū dìzhǐ

LCS	Large complicated systems	大型复杂系统	Dàxíng fùzá xìtǒng
LCS	Line card to switch	线卡到交换机	Xiànkǎ dào jiāohuànjī
LCS	Localization service	定位业务	Dìngwèi yèwù
LCS	Location services	定位业务	Dìngwèi yèwù
LCS	Lower order connection supervision	低阶连接监控	Dījiē liánjiē jiānkòng
LCS	Lower order connection supervision	低阶连接监视	Dījiē liánjiē jiānshì
LCSC	Location services client	定位业务客户	Dìngwèi yèwù kèhù
LCSP	Link controller service signaling	链路控制器服务信令	Liànlù kòngzhìqì fúwù xìnlìng
LCSS	Location services server	定位业务服务器	Dìngwèi yèwù fúwùqì
LCT	Local craft terminal	本地维护终端	Běndì wéihù zhōngduān
LCTI	Line and circuit test interface	线性电路测试接口	Xiànxìng diànlù cèshì jiēkǒu
LCTL	Longitudinal conversion transfer loss	纵向变换转移损耗	Zòngxiàng biànhuàn zhuǎnyí sǔnhào
LD	Laser device	激光器	Jīguāngqì
LD	Laser diode	激光二极管	Jīguāng èrjíguǎn
LD	Link disconnect	链路断开	Liànlù duànkāi
LD	Loading	装载	Zhuāngzài
LD	Location directory	位置目绿	Wèizhì mùlǜ
LDAP	Lightweight directory access protocol	轻型目录存取协议	Qīngxíng mùlù cúnqǔ xiéyì
LDAP	Lightweight directory access protocol	轻权目录访问协议	Qīngquán mùlù fǎngwèn xiéyì
LDAP	Lightweight directory access protocol	轻量目录访问协议	Qīngliàng mùlù fǎngwèn xiéyì
LDAP	Lightweight directory access protocol	轻量级目录访问协议	Qīngliàngjí mùlù fǎngwèn xiéyì
LDC	Low-speed data channel	低速数据通道	Dīsù shùjù tōngdào
LD-CELP	Low-delay - code excited linear prediction coding	低时延码激励线性预测编码	Dīshíyán mǎ jīlì xiànxìng yùcè biānmǎ
LD-CELP	Low-delay - code excited linear prediction	低时延码激励线性预测	Dīshíyán mǎ jīlì xiànxìng yùcè
LDM	Linear delta modulation	线性增量调制	Xiànxìng zēngliàng tiáozhì
LDMA	Location division multiple access	位置划分多路存取	Wèizhì huàfēn duōlù cúnqǔ
LDME	Local digital message exchange	局部数字信息交换	Júbù shùzì xìnxī jiāohuàn
LDN	Local distinguished name	本地识别名	Běndì shíbié míng
LDP	Label distribution protocol	标志分配协议	Biāozhì fēnpèi xiéyì
LDP	Label distribution protocol	标签分配协议	Biāoqiān fēnpèi xiéyì
LDP	Label distribution protocol	标记分发协议	Biāojì fēnfā xiéyì
LDP	Label distribution protocol (IETF usage)	标记分配协议	Biāojì fēnpèi xiéyì
LDPE	Low density polyethylene	低密聚乙烯	Dīmì jùyǐxī
LDR	Light dependent resistor	光敏电阻	Guāng mǐndiànzǔ
LDRT	Low data rate transmission	低数据率传输	Dīshùjùlǜ chuánshū
LDT	Lightning data transport	闪电数据传输总线	Shǎndiàn shùjù chuánshū zǒngxiàn
LE	Large enterprises	大型企业	Dàxíng qǐyè
LE	Local exchange	本地交换局	Běndì jiāohuànjú
LE	Local exchange	本地交换机	Běndì jiāohuànjī
LE	Local exchange	本地交换网	Běndì jiāohuàn wǎng
LE-ARP	LAN emulation address resolution protocol	局域网仿真地址解析协议	Júyùwǎng fǎngzhēn dìzhǐ jiěxī xiéyì
LEB	Lost error bit	丢失错误位	Diūshī cuòwù wèi
LEC	Local area network emulation client	局域网仿真客户机	Júyùwǎng fǎngzhēn kèhùjī
LEC	Local exchange carrier	本地交换公司	Běndì jiāohuàn gōngsī
LEC	Local exchange carrier	本地交换运营商	Běndì jiāohuàn yùnyíngshāng
LECC	Linear error correcting code	线性误差校正码	Xiànxìng wùchā jiàozhèng mǎ

LED	Light emitting diode	发光二极体	Fāguāng èrjítǐ
LED	Light emitting diode	发光二极管	Fāguāng èrjíguǎn
LED	Light emitting diode	发光管	Fāguāng guǎn
LEDT	Linkage editor	连接编辑程序	Liánjiē biānjí chéngxù
LEM	Line expansion module	线路扩展模块	Xiànlù kuòzhǎn mókuài
LEMP	Lightning electromagnetic pulse	闪电电磁脉冲	Shǎndiàn diàncí màichōng
LEN node	Low-entry networking node	低输入网络连接节点	Dīshūrù wǎngluò liánjiē jiédiǎn
LEO	Low earth orbit	低地球轨道	Dīdìqiú guǐdào
LEO	Low earth orbit	低轨道	Dīguǐdào
LEO	Low earth orbit satellites	地球低轨卫星	Dìqiú dīguǐ wèixīng
LE-OpS	Local exchange operation system	本地交换运行系统	Běndì jiāohuàn yùnxíng xìtǒng
LER	Label edge router	标签交换边沿路由器	Biāoqiān jiāohuàn biānyán lùyóuqì
LER	Label edge router	标签边缘路由器	Biāoqiān biānyuán lùyóuqì
LES	Local area network emulation server	局域网仿真服务器	Júyùwǎng fǎngzhēn fúwùqì
LF	Line feed	换行	Huànháng
LF	Linear filtering	线性过滤	Xiànxìng guòlǜ
LF	Load factor	负载因子	Fùzài yīnzǐ
LF	Low frequency	低频	Dīpín
LFA	Low frequency amplifier	低频放大器	Dīpín fàngdàqì
LFAR	Last frame address register	最后帧地址寄存器	Zuìhòu zhèng dìzhǐ jìcúnqì
LFC	Laminated flat cable	层状绝缘扁平电缆	Céngzhuàng juéyuán biǎnpíng diànlǎn
LFC	Local function capabilities	本地功能能力	Běndì gōngnéng nénglì
LFM	Linear frequency modulation	线性频率调制	Xiànxìng pínlǜ tiáozhì
LFSR	Linear feedback shift register	现行反馈移位寄存器	Xiànxíng fǎnkuì yíwèi jìcúnqì
LGN	Logical group node	逻辑群节点	Luóji qún jiédiǎn
LGTH	Data cell length	数据单元的长度	Shùjù dānyuánde chángdù
LH	Line hunting	寻线	Xúnxiàn
LH	Line hunting	连续寻线	Liánxù xúnxiàn
LHCP	Left hand circular polarization	左漩圆极化	Zuǒxuán yuán jíhuà
LHIP	Local high capacity IPC processor	本地高容量 IPC 处理器	Běndì gāo róngliàng IPC chǔlǐqì
LHOTS	Long-haul optical transmission set	远程光传输设备	Yuǎnchéng guāng chuánshū shèbèi
LI	Length indicator	长度指示	Chángdù zhǐshì
LI	Line identity	线路识别	Xiànlù shíbié
LIAC	Limited inquiry access code	有限查询访问码	Yǒuxiàn cháxún fǎngwèn mǎ
LIB	Label information base	标记信息库	Biāojì xìnxīkù
LIC	Line interface circuit	线路接口电路	Xiànlù jiēkǒu diànlù
LIC	Line interface coupler	线路接口耦合器	Xiànlù jiēkǒu ǒuhéqì
LIC	Link identification code	链路标识符	Liànlù biāozhì fú
LID	Local injection and detection (FOC)	局部通光检测	Júbù tōngguāng jiǎncè
LIEA	Line interface E1 link assembly	线路 E1 接口链路集成件	Xiànlù E1 jiēkǒu liànlù jíchéngjiàn
LIEA	Link interface E1 board assembly	链路 E1 接口集成板	Liànlù E1 jiēkǒu jíchéngbǎn
LIF	Low insertion force	小插接力	Xiǎo chājiēlì
LIFA	Loop initialization fabric assigned frame	环路初始化架构分配帧	Huánlù chūshǐhuà jiàgòu fēnpèi zhèng
LIHA	Loop initialization hard assigned frame	环路初始化硬分配帧	Huánlù chūshǐhuà yìng fēnpèi zhèng
LIM	Line interface module	线路接口模块	Xiànlù jiēkǒu mókuài
$LiNbO_3$	Lithium niobate	铌酸锂	Nísuānlǐ

LIP	Loop initialization primitive sequence	环路初始化进程	Huánlù chūshǐhuà jìnchéng
LIPA	Link interface IPC processor assembly	链路接口 IPC 处理器集成件	Liànlù jiēkǒu IPC chǔlǐqì jíchéng jiàn
LIPA	Loop initialization previously assigned	环路初始化预分配	Huánlù chūshǐhuà yùfēnpèi
LIRP	Loop initialization report position frame	环路初始化位置报告帧	Huánlù chūshǐhuà wèizhì bàogào zhèng
LIS	Land information system	土地信息系统	Tǔdì xìnxī xìtǒng
LIS	Logical Internet protocol (IP) sub-network	逻辑因特网协议子网	Luóji Yīntèwǎng xiéyì zìwǎng
LIS	Logical IP sub-network	逻辑 IP 子网	Luóji IP zìwǎng
LISA	Loop initialization soft assigned frame	环路初始化软分配帧	Huánlù chūshǐhuà ruǎn fēnpèi zhèng
LISM	Loop initialization select master frame	环路初始化主控制器选择帧	Huánlù chūshǐhuà zhǔ kòngzhìqì xuǎnzé zhèng
LISN	Line impedance stability network	线路阻抗稳定网络	Xiànlù zǔkàng wěndìng wǎngluò
LIT	Light interface technology	光接口计数	Guāng jiēkǒu jìshù
LIT	Local inter-office trunking	市内局间中继线	Shìnèi jú-jiān zhōngjìxiàn
LITA	Link interface T1 board assembly	链路 T1 接口集成板	Liànlù T1 jiēkǒu jíchéngbǎn
LITA-A/D	Line interface T1 link assembly	线路 T1 接口链路集成件	Xiànlù T1 jiēkǒu liànlù jíchéngjiàn
LIU	Laser interconnection unit	激光互连装置	Jīguāng hùlián zhuāngzhì
LIU	Lightguide interconnection unit	光纤互连装置	Guāngxiān hùlián zhuāngzhì
LK2M	Link board (2Mb/s)	链路板	Liànlù bǎn
LL	Latitude / longitude	纬度/经度	Wěidù/jīngdù
LL	Link layer	链路层	Liànlù céng
LLA	Leased line adapter	租用线路转换器	Zūyòng xiànlù zhuǎnhuànqì
LLA	Luneburg lens antenna	楞勃透镜天线	Léng-bó tòujìng tiānxiàn
LLAP	LocalTalk link access protocol (Apple use)	AppleTalk 链路访问协议	AppleTalk liànlù fǎngwèn xiéyì
LLAR	Local line automatic (testing) routine	本地线路自动检验列行程序	Běndì xiànlù zìdòng jiǎnyàn lièxíng chéngxù
LLC	Logic link control layer	逻辑链路控制层	Luóji liànlù kòngzhì céng
LLC	Logical link control (sub-layer)	逻辑链路控制（子层）	Luóji liànlù kòngzhì (zǐcéng)
LLC	Low layer compatibility	低层兼容性	Dīcéng jiānróngxìng
LLC	Lower layer compatibility	低层兼容	Dīcéng jiānróng
LLC2	Logical link control, type 2	第二类逻辑链路控制	Dì'èrlèi luóji liànlù kòngzhì
LLCK	Local line clock distribution	本地线路时钟分配	Běndì xiànlù shízhōng fēnpèi
LLDPE	Linear low density polyethylene	线性低密聚乙烯	Xiànxìng dīmì jùyǐxī
LLF	Least load first algorithm	负载最小优先算法	Fùzài zuìxiǎo yōuxiān suànfǎ
LLF	Low layer function	低层功能	Dīcéng gōngnéng
LLFM	Landline frequency modulation	陆线调频	Lùxiàn tiáopín
LLG	Logical line code	逻辑线路组	Luóji xiànlù zǔ
LLIR	Low level interrupt request	低级中断请求	Dījí zhōngduàn qǐngqiú
LLME	Low layer management entity	低层管理实体	Dīcéng guǎnlǐ shítǐ
LLR	Last level register	末级寄存器	Mòjí jìcúnqì
LLSU	Link layer service unit	链路层服务单元	Liànlù céng fúwù dānyuán
Lm	Half-rate traffic channel	半速率信道	Bànsùlǜ xìndào
LM	Level modulation	电平调节	Diànpíng tiáojié
LM	Link manager	链路管理	Liànlù guǎnlǐ
LM	Logic module	逻辑模块	Luóji mókuài
LM	Loop multiplexer	环路复用器	Huánlù fùyòngqì
Lm	Lumen (unit of measure for the flow of light)	流明	Liúmíng
Lm	Traffic channel with capacity lower than a full rate channel	容量比全速率业务信道低的业务信道	Róngliàng bǐ quánsùlǜ yèwù xìndào dīde yèwù xìndào

LMCS	Local multipoint communication system (Canadian term for LMDS)	本地多点通信系统	Běndì duōdiǎn tōngxìn xìtǒng
LMDS	Local multipoint distributed system	局域多点分布式系统	Júyù duōdiǎn fēnbù-shì xìtǒng
LMDS	Local multipoint distribution service	本地多点分配业务	Běndì duōdiǎn fēnpèi yèwù
LME	Layer management entity	层管理实体	Céng guǎnlǐ shítǐ
LMEI	Layer management entity identifier	层的管理实体标识符	Céngde guǎnlǐ shítǐ biāozhìfú
LMF	Loss of maintenance flow	维护流丢失	Wéihù liú diūshī
LMM	Local message metering system	局部信息计费	Júbù xìnxī jìfèi
LMP	Link management protocol	链路管理协议	Liànlù guǎnlǐ xiéyì
LMR	Land mobile radio	陆地移动无线电	Lùdì yídòng wúxiàndiàn
LMS	Label management (system)	标记管理	Biāojì guǎnlǐ
LMS	Least mean square	最小均芳	Zuìxiǎo jūn fāng
LMS	Least mean square (algorithm)	最小均方（算法）	Zuìxiǎo jūn fāng (suànfǎ)
LMS	Least mean squares	最小均方根	Zuìxiǎo jūn fānggēn
LMS	Least median square	最小中值法	Zuìxiǎo zhōng zhí fǎ
LMSI	Local mobile station identity	本地移动台识别	Běndì yídòngtái shíbié
LMSI	Local mobile station identity	本地移动台识别码	Běndì yídòngtái shíbié mǎ
LMSI	Local mobile subscriber identity	本地移动用户识别号	Běndì yídòng yònghù shíbié hào
LMSP	Local management service point	本地管理业务点	Běndì guǎnlǐ yèwù diǎn
LMT	Local maintenance terminal	本地维护终端	Běndì wéihù zhōngduān
LMU	Location measurement unit	定位测量单元	Dìngwèi cèliáng dānyuán
LN	Logical name	逻辑名	Luóji míng
LNA	Low-noise amplifier	低噪声放大器	Dīzàoshēng fàngdàqì
LNA	Low-noise amplifier	低噪音放大器	Dīzàoyīn fàngdàqì
LNC	Local node clock	本地节点时钟	Běndì jiédiǎn shízhōng
LNC	Low-noise cable	低噪声电缆	Dīzàoshēng diànlǎn
LND	Last number dialed	拔最后的号码	Bō zuìhòude hàomǎ
LND	Last number dialed	最后拔号存储	Zuìhòu bōhào cúnchǔ
LNMC	Local network management center	本地网络管理中心	Běndì wǎngluò guǎnlǐ zhōngxīn
LO	Lock out (used for computer login or malfunction)	暂停	Zàntíng
Lo	Locked mode	锁定状态	Suǒdìng zhuàngtài
LO	Lower order	低阶	Dījiē
LOA	Loss of alignment	帧失位	Zhèng shīwèi
LOC	Local operations control station	本地操作控制台	Běndì cāozuò kòngzhìtái
LOC	Loss of continuity	连续性丢失	Liánxùxìng diūshī
LOC-OTS	Loss of continuity on optical transmission section	光传送段连续性丢失	Guāng chuánsòng duàn liánxùxìng diūshī
LOF	Loss of frame	帧丢失	Zhèng diūshī
LOF	Loss of frame alarm	帧丢失告警	Zhèng diūshī gàojǐng
LOI	Lower order interface	低阶接口	Dījiē jiēkǒu
LOM	Laminated object manufacturing	叠层工艺法	Diécéng gōngyì fǎ
LOM	Loss of multi-frame	复帧丢失	Fùzhèng diūshī
LOP	Loss of pointer	指针丢失	Zhǐzhēn diūshī
LOP	Low power oscillator	低功率振荡器	Dīgōnglǜ zhèndàngqì
LOP NC	Lower order path network connection	低阶通道网络连接	Dījiē tōngdào wǎngluò liánjiē
LOPL	Lower order path layer	低阶通道层	Dījiē tōngdào céng
LoS	Line of sight	视距	Shìjù
LOS	Line of sites	站点线路	Zhàndiǎn xiànlù

LOS	Line-out-of-service signal	线路不工作信号	Xiànlù bùgōngzuò xìnhào
LOS	Loss of signal	信号丢失	Xìnhào diūshī
LOS	Loss of signal	失去信号	Shīqù xìnhào
LOS	Loss of signal (optical)	光信号丢失	Guāng xìnhào diūshī
LOS	Loss of signal alarm	信号丢失告警	Xìnhào diūshī gàojǐng
LOSRRL	Line-of-sight radio-relay link	视距无线电中继链路	Shìjù wúxiàndiàn zhōngjì liànlù
LOSRRL	Line-of-sight radio-relay system	视距无线电中继系统	Shìjù wúxiàndiàn zhōngjì xìtǒng
LOSW	Loss of sync word	同步字丢失	Tóngbù zì diūshī
LO-TCM	Lower order tandem connection monitor	低阶通道串联连接监视器	Dījiē tōngdào chuànlián liánjiē jiānshìqì
LOTOS	Language of temporal ordering specification	时序描述语言	Shíxù miáoshù yǔyán
LOVC	Lower order virtual container	低阶虚容器	Dījiē xūróngqì
LP	Language processor (device)	语言处理器	Yǔyán chǔlǐqì
LP	Lean production (Japanese concept)	精良生产	Jīngliáng shēngchǎn
LP	Linear prediction coefficient	线性预测系数	Xiànxìng yùcè xìshù
LP	Logic port	逻辑端口	Luóji duānkǒu
LP	Lower order path	低阶通道	Dījiē tōngdào
LPA	Log periodic antenna	对数周期天线	Duìshù zhōuqī tiānxiàn
LPA	Loop-back acknowledgement (ISUP message)	环路已接通	Huánlù yǐ jiētōng
LPA	Lower order path adaptation	低阶通道适配	Dījiē tōngdào shìpèi
LPAR	Linear power amplifier rack	线性功率放大器机架	Xiànxìng gōnglǜ fàngdàqì jījià
LPAS	Linear power amplifier shelf	线性功率放大器架子	Xiànxìng gōnglǜ fàngdàqì jiàzi
LPB	Loop port bypass	环路端口旁路	Huánlù duānkǒu pánglù
LPC	Linear predictive coding	线性预测编码	Xiànxìng yùcè biānmǎ
LPC	Lower order path connection	低阶通道连接	Dījiē tōngdào liánjiē
LPCM	Linear phase code modulation	线性相码调制	Xiànxìng xiàngmǎ tiáozhì
LPD	Line printer daemon	行式打印机程序	Hángshì dǎyìnjī chéngxù
LPD	Low probability of detection	低检测概率	Dījiǎncè gàilǜ
LPDA	Log periodic dipole array	对数周期偶极子天线阵	Duìshù zhōuqī ǒujízi tiānxiàn zhèn
LPDU	Link protocol data unit	链路协议数据单元	Liànlù xiéyì shùjù dānyuán
LPE	Liquid phase epitaxy	液相外延	Yèxiàng wàiyán
LPE	Loop port enable	环路端口启用	Huánlù duānkǒu qǐyòng
LPF	Low pass filter	低通滤波器	Dītōng lǜbōqì
LPF	Low pass function	低通功能	Dītōng gōngnéng
LPH	Line printer handler	行式打印机处理器	Hángshì dǎyìnjī chǔlǐ qì
LPI	Local path index (in XML)	局部路径索引	Júbù lùjìng suǒyǐn
LPI	Low probability of intercept	低截获概率	Dījiéhuò gàilǜ
LPLMN	Local public land mobile communications network	本地公用陆地移动通信网络	Běndì gōngyòng lùdì yídòng tōngxìnwǎng luò
LPLMN	Location PLMN	本地 PLMN	Běndì PLMN
LPOH	Lower order path overhead	低阶通道开销	Dījiē tōngdào kāixiao
LPOM	Lower order path overhead monitor	低阶通道开销监视器	Dījiē tōngdào kāixiao jiānshìqì
LPOM	Lower order path overhead monitoring	低阶通道开销监视	Dījiē tōngdào kāixiao jiānshì
LPP	Lightweight presentation protocol (IETF usage)	轻量级表示协议	Qīngliàngjí biǎoshì xiéyì
LPP	Lower order path protection	低阶通道保护	Dījiē tōngdào bǎohù
LPPF	Low probability of position fix	低定位概率	Dīdìngwèi gàilǜ
LPR	Local primary reference	区域基准时钟	Qūyù jīzhǔn shízhōng
LPR	Local primary reference	区域基准钟	Qūyù jīzhǔn zhōng

LPR	Local primary reference	本地基准参考	Běndì jīzhǔn cānkǎo
LPR	Local primary reference source	本地主基准源	Běndì zhǔ jīzhǔn yuán
LPR	Power loss, outage	掉电	Diàodiàn
LP-RDI	Lower order path receive defect indicator	低阶通道接收缺陷指示	Dījiē tōngdào jiēshōu quēxiàn zhǐshì
LP-RDI	Lower order path remote defect indication	低阶通道远端缺陷指示	Dījiē tōngdào yuǎnduān quēxiàn zhǐshì
LP-REI	Remote error indication of lower order path	低阶通道远端误码指示	Dījiē tōngdào yuǎnduān wùmǎ zhǐshì
LP-RFI	Remote failure indication of lower order path	低阶通道远端失效指示	Dījiē tōngdào yuǎnduān shīxiào zhǐshì
LPR-PCW	Linear predictive residual - pitch-cycle waveform	线性预测残差-基音周期波形	Xiànxìng yùcè cánchā—jīyīn zhōuqī bōxíng
LPSE	Low probability of signal exploitation	低溯源概率	Dīsùyuán gàilǜ
LPSM	Loop port state machine	环路端口状态机	Huánlù duānkǒu zhuàngtài jī
LPT	Lower order path termination	低阶通道终端	Dījiē tōngdào zhōngduān
LP-TIM	Lower order path trace identification mismatch	低阶通道路踪识别失配	Dījiē tōngdào lùzōng shíbié shīpèi
LP-UNEQ	Lower order path unequipped	低阶通道未装载	Dījiē tōngdào wèizhuāngzài
LQM	Link quality monitor	链路质量监视	Liànlù zhìliàng jiānshì
LQR	Link quality report	链路质量报告	Liànlù zhìliàng bàogào
LR	Link reset	链路重启	Liànlù chóngqǐ
LR	Location register	位置寄存器	Wèizhì jìcúnqì
LRC	Longitudinal redundancy check	纵向冗余(码)校验	Zòngxiàng rǒngyú (mǎ) jiàoyàn
LRJ	Location reject	定位拒绝	Dìngwèi jùjué
LRJ	Location reject (packet protocol)	地址解析拒绝	Dìzhǐ jiěxī jùjué
LRJ	Location reject message	拒绝地址解析	Jùjué dìzhǐ jiěxī
LRM	Link resource manager	链路资源管理器	Liànlù zīyuán guǎnlǐqì
LRP	Logistics resource planning	物流资源计划	Wùliú zīyuán jìhuà
LRQ	Location request	地址解析请求	Dìzhǐ jiěxī qǐngqiú
LRQ	Location request	定位请求	Dìngwèi qǐngqiú
LRR	Link reset response	链路重启应答	Liànlù chóngqǐ yìngdá
LRRP	Lowest required radiated power	所需最小辐射功率	Suǒxū zuìxiǎo fúshè gōnglǜ
LRS	Location registration sub-system	位置登记子系统	Wèizhì dēngjì zixìtǒng
LRSACE	Location register system ACE	位置寄存器系统 ACE	Wèizhì jìcúnqì xìtǒng ACE
LS	Label stack	标记堆栈	Biāojì duīzhàn
LS	Label switching	标签交换	Biāoqiān jiāohuàn
LS	Local switch	本地交换局	Běndì jiāohuànjú
LS	Local switch	本地交换机	Běndì jiāohuànjī
LS	Local switch	本地端局	Běndì duānjú
LS	Local switch	端局交换机	Duān jú jiāohuànjī
LSA	Link state advertisement	链路状态通告	Liànlù zhuàngtài tōnggào
LSA	Localized service area	局部业务区域	Júbù yèwù qūyù
LSA	Loop stick antenna	环棒天线	Huánbàng tiānxiàn
L-SAGIC	Low voltage small aperture grid with impregnated cathode	低电压光圈阴极管	Dīdiànyā guāngquān yīnjíguǎn
LSB	Least significant bit	最低位	Zuìdī wèi
LSB	Least significant bit	最低有效位	Zuìdī yǒuxiào wèi
LSB	Least significant bit	最低有效比特	Zuìdī yǒuxiào bǐtè
LSB	Lower sideband	下边带	Xiàbiandài
LSBCM	Laser base current monitor	激光器偏流监视	Jīguāngqì piānliú jiānshì
LSBS	Location sensitive billing system	用户位置的灵活计账系统	Yònghù wèizhìde línghuó jìzhàng xìtǒng
LSC	Low-speed line card	低速线路卡	Dīsù xiànlù qiǎ

LSCP	Low order service control point	低等级业务控制点	Dīděngjí yèwù kòngzhìdiǎn
LSD	Least significant digit	最低有效位	Zuìdī yǒuxiào wèi
LSD	Low-speed data	低速数据	Dīsù shùjù
LSE	Local system environment	本地系统环境	Běndì xìtǒng huánjìng
LSI	Large scale integrated circuit	大规模集成电路	Dàguīmó jíchéng diànlù
LSI	Large scale integration	大规模集成电路	Dàguīmó jíchéng diànlù
LSP	Label switch path	标签交换路径	Biāoqiān jiāohuàn lùjìng
LSP	Label switching path	标志交换路径	Biāozhì jiāohuàn lùjìng
LSP	Label switching path	标记交换路径	Biāojì jiāohuàn lùjìng
LSP	Laddered siloxane polymer (FOC mfg)	梯型硅氧烷聚合物	Tī-xíng guīyǎng wán jùhéwù
LSP	Link selector parameter	链路选择器参数	Liànlù xuǎnzéqì cānshù
LSP	Link state packet	链路状态包	Liànlù zhuàngtài bāo
LSP	Logical sub-fiber protection	逻辑子光纤保护	Luóji ziguāngxiān bǎohù
LSR	Label switch router	标签交换路由器	Biāoqiān jiāohuàn lùyóuqì
LSR	Label switch router	标记交换路由器	Biāojì jiāohuàn lùyóuqì
LSR	Label switching router	标志交换路由器	Biāozhì jiāohuàn lùyóuqì
LSS	Local switching sub-system	本地交换子系统	Běndì jiāohuàn zixìtǒng
LSSU	Link status signal unit	链路状态信号单元	Liànlù zhuàngtài xìnhào dānyuán
LSSU	Link status Signaling unit	链路状态信令单元	Liànlù zhuàngtài xìnlìng dānyuán
LSTP	Low level signal transfer point	低级信令转换点	Dījí xìnlìng zhuǎnhuàn diǎn
LSTP	Low level signal transfer point	低级信令转接点	Dījí xìnlìng zhuǎnjiē diǎn
LSU	Lone signal unit	单一信号单元	Dānyī xìnhào dānyuán
LSUT	Lower order path supervisory unequipped termination	低阶通道监控未装载终端	Dījiē tōngdào jiānkòng wèizhuāngzài zhōngduān
LSZH	Low smoke zero halogen (FOC)	低烟无卤阻燃	Dīyān wúlǔ zǔrán
LT	Laser temperature	激光器温度	Jīguāngqì wēndù
LT	Line terminal	线路终端	Xiànlù zhōngduān
LT	Line termination	线路终接	Xiànlù zhōngjiē
LT	Line termination	线路终端	Xiànlù zhōngduān
LT	Line termination equipment	线路终端设备	Xiànlù zhōngduān shèbèi
LT	Local terminal	局侧终端	Júcè zhōngduān
LTA	Line and trunk access	线路和中继通路	Xiànlù hé zhōngjì tōnglù
LTAS	Line and trunk access sub-system	线路和中继通路子系统	Xiànlù hé zhōngjì tōnglù zixìtǒng
LTB	Line test block	线路测试模块	Xiànlù cèshì mókuài
LTC	Landline trunk controller	有线线路分配器	Yǒuxiàn xiànlù fēnpèiqì
LTCA	Lower order path tandem connection adaptation	低阶通道串联连接适配	Dījiē tōngdào chuànlián liánjiē shìpèi
LTCM	Lower order path tandem connection monitor	低阶通道串联连接监视	Dījiē tōngdào chuànlián liánjiē jiānshì
LTCT	Lower order path tandem connection termination	低阶通道串联连接终端	Dījiē tōngdào chuànlián liánjiē zhōngduān
LTE	Local terminal emulator	本地终端仿真器	Běndì zhōngduān fǎngzhēnqì
LTG	Line/trunk group	用户中继群	Yònghù zhōngjì qún
LTH	Length bit	长度比特	Chángdù bǐtè
LTI	Loss of timing information	失去定时信息	Shīqù dìngshí xìnxī
LTL	Linear temporal logic	线性时序逻辑	Xiànxìng shíxù luóji
LTLC	Linear temporal logic with clocks	带有时钟变量的线性时序逻辑	Dàiyǒu shízhōng biànliàngde xiànxìng shíxù luóji
LTP	Logical terminal profile	逻辑终端轮廓	Luóji zhōngduān lúnkuò
LTR	Local time reference	本地时钟参考	Běndì shízhōng cānkǎo

LTS	Line transient suppression	线路瞬时抑制	Xiànlù shùnshí yìzhì
LTZ	Local time zone	本地时区	Běndì shíqū
LU	Line unit	线路单元	Xiànlù dānyuán
LU	Local unit	本地单元	Běndì dānyuán
LU	Location update	位置更新	Wèizhì gēngxīn
LU	Logic units (ITU-T usage)	逻辑单元	Luóji dānyuán
LUDT	Long unit data (in SS7)	长单位数据	Cháng dānwèi shùjù
LUDT	Long unit data transmission	长单位数据传输	Cháng dānwèi shùjù chuánshū
LUDTS	Long unit data transmission service	长单位数据传输业务	Cháng dānwèi shùjù chuánshū yèwù
LUF	Lowest useful frequency	最低可用频率	Zuìdī kěyòng pínlǜ
LUP	Logical user port	逻辑用户端口	Luóji yònghù duānkǒu
LUT	Look up table	查询表	Cháxúnbiǎo
LVDS	Low voltage differential signal	低电压差动信号	Dīdiànyā chādòng xìnhào
LWL	Long wavelength optical fiber	长波光纤	Chángbō guāngxiān
LXL	Link by link	逐段转接	Zhúduàn zhuǎnjiē
LZ	Cable carrier wave	电缆载波	Diànlǎn zàibō

M

M	Magnetic moment	磁矩	Cíjǔ
M	Manager	管理者	Guǎnlǐzhě
M	Mandatory	强制性的	Qiángzhìxìngde
M	Monitor bit	监视器比特	Jiānshìqì bǐtè
M	Supported by messenger wire	钢索敷设	Gāngsuǒ fūshè
M/D	Magnetic drum	磁鼓	Cígǔ
M2PA	Message transfer protocol 2 (MTP2) peer-to-peer adaptation layer	消息传递部分第二级对等适配层	Xiāoxi chuándì bùfen dì'èrjí duìděng shìpèi céng
M2UA	MTP2-user adaptation layer	MTP 第二级用户适配层	MTP dì'èrjí yònghù shìpèi céng
M3UA	Message transport protocol 3 (MTP3) user adaptation layer	消息传递部分第三级用户适配层	Xiāoxi chuándì bùfen dìsānjí yònghù shìpèi céng
M3UA	MTP3-user adaptation layer	MTP 第三级用户适配层	MTP dìsānjí yònghù shìpèi céng
MA	Machine address	机器地址	Jīqì dìzhǐ
MA	Maintenance and adaptation	维护和适配	Wéihù hé shìpèi
MA	Media adapter	媒体适配器	Méitǐ shìpèiqì
MA	Microstrip array	微带阵列	Wēidài zhènliè
MA	Mobile (frequency) allocation	移动台（频率）分配	Yídòngtái (pínlǜ) fēnpèi
MA	Mobile access	移动接入	Yídòng jiērù
MA	Mobile address allocation	移动通信地址分配	Yídòng tōngxìn dìzhǐ fēnpèi
MA	Mobile agent	移动代理	Yídòng dàilǐ
MA	Mobile allocation	移动分配	Yídòng fēnpèi
MA	Multicast addressing	多播地址	Duōbō dìzhǐ
MA	Multiple access	多路接入	Duōlù jiērù
MA, MSA	Microstrip antenna	微带天线	Wēidài tiānxiàn
MAAS	Multiplicative array antenna system	乘积阵天线系统	Chéngjī zhèn tiānxiàn xìtǒng
MAC	Macro assembler	宏功能汇编语言	Hóng gōngnéng huìbiān yǔyán
MAC	Manchester auto-code	曼彻斯特自动带码	Màn-chè-sī-tè zìdòng dàimǎ
MAC	Mandatory access control (IPsec)	强制访问控制	Qiángzhì fǎngwèn kòngzhì

MAC	Mandatory access control (Linux)	强制存取控制	Qiángzhì cúnqǔ kòngzhì
MAC	Media access control	介质访问控制	Jièzhì fǎngwèn kòngzhì
MAC	Media access control	媒介接入控制	Méijiè jiērù kòngzhì
MAC	Media access control	媒介访问控制	Méijiè fǎngwèn kòngzhì
MAC	Media access control	媒体接入控制	Méitǐ jiērù kòngzhì
MAC	Media access control	媒体控制访问	Méitǐ kòngzhì fǎngwèn
MAC	Media access control	媒体访问控制	Méitǐ fǎngwèn kòngzhì
MAC	Media access control	媒质接入控制	Méizhì jiērù kòngzhì
MAC	Media access control layer	媒体访问控制层	Méitǐ fǎngwèn kòngzhì céng
MAC	Media access control sub-layer	媒体接入控制子层	Méitǐ jiērù kòngzhì zicéng
MAC	Media access control sub-layer	媒体访问控制子层	Méitǐ fǎngwèn kòngzhì zicéng
MAC	Medium access control	媒质接入控制层	Méizhì jiērù kòngzhì céng
MAC	Medium access control layer	介质访问控制层	Jièzhì fǎngwèn kòngzhì céng
MAC	Memory access controller	存储器存取控制器	Cúnchǔqì cúnqǔ kòngzhìqì
MAC	Message authentication code	报文认证码	Bàowén rènzhèng mǎ
MAC	Message authentication code	报文鉴别代码	Bàowén jiànbié dàimǎ
MAC	Message authentication code	消息校验码	Xiāoxi jiàoyàn mǎ
MAC	Message authentication code	消息认证码	Xiāoxi rènzhèng mǎ
MAC	Message authentication code	消息鉴权码	Xiāoxi jiànquán mǎ
MAC	Message authentication code	消息验证码	Xiāoxi yànzhèng mǎ
MAC	Message authentication code	认证消息码	Rènzhèng xiāoxi mǎ
MAC	Mobile attenuation code	移动衰减码	Yídòng shuāijiǎn mǎ
MACF	Multiple association control function	多偶联控制功能	Duō'ǒulián kòngzhì gōngnéng
MACF	Multiple association control function	多相关控制功能	Duōxiàngguān kòngzhì gōngnéng
MACN	Mobile allocation channel number	移动分配信道号	Yídòng fēnpèi xìndàohào
MACN	Mobile allocation channel number	移动通信指配信道号码	Yídòng tōngxìn zhǐpèi xìndào hàomǎ
MACS	Medium altitude communication satellite	中高空通信卫星	Zhōng gāokōng tōngxìn wèixīng
MACS	Multi-line automatic calling system	复式线路自动呼叫系统	Fùshì xiànlù zìdòng hūjiào xìtǒng
MAD	Mean administrative delay	平均管理耽误	Píngjūn guǎnlǐ dānwù
MADCAP	Multicast address dynamic client allocation protocol	多播地址动态客户端分配协议	Duōbō dìzhǐ dòngtài kèhùduān fēnpèi xiéyì
MADEV	Modified Allan deviation	修正艾伦偏差	Xiūzhèng ài-lún piānchā
MADT	Mean accumulated down time	平均累积不可用时间	Píngjūn lěijī bùkěyòng shíjiān
MAF	Management application function	管理应用功能	Guǎnlǐ yìngyòng gōngnéng
MAF	Mobile additional function	移动通信附加功能	Yídòng tōngxìn fùjiā gōngnéng
MAH	Mobile access hunting	移动访问捕获	Yídòng fǎngwèn bǔhuò
MAH	Mobile access hunting supplementary service	移动地址搜索附加业务	Yídòng dìzhǐ sōusuǒ fùjiā yèwù
MAHO	Mobile assisted handover	移动台辅助切换	Yídòngtái fǔzhù qiēhuàn
MAI	Macro assembler instruction	宏汇编程序指令	Hóng huìbiān chéngxù zhǐlìng
MAI	Mobile allocation index	移动分配索引	Yídòng fēnpèi suǒyǐn
MAI	Multiple access interference	多址干扰	Duōzhǐ gānrǎo
MAIO	Mobile allocation index offset	移动分配索引偏移	Yídòng fēnpèi suǒyǐn piānyí
MALS	Multi-astigmatism lens system (video term)	多重散光聚焦系统	Duōzhòng sǎnguāng jùjiāo xìtǒng
MAM	Memory allocation manager	存储分配管理程序	Cúnchǔ fēnpèi guǎnlǐ chéngxù
MAMSK	Multi-amplitude minimum shift keying	多振幅最小移位键控	Duōzhènfú zuìxiǎo yíwèi jiànkòng
MAN	Metropolitan area network	城域网	Chéngyù wǎng
MAN	Multi-service access nodes	多业务接入节点	Duōyèwù jiērù jiédiǎn

MANET	Mobile ad hoc network	移动特设网络	Yídòng tèshè wǎngluò
MAP	Maintenance and administration personal computer	维护和管理 PC 机	Wéihù hé guǎnlǐ PC-jī
MAP	Manufacturing automation protocol	制造自动化协议	Zhìzào zìdònghuà xiéyì
MAP	Manufacturing automation protocol	生产自动化协议	Shēngchǎn zìdònghuà xiéyì
MAP	Maximum *a posteriori*	最大后验概率	Zuìdà hòuyàn gàilǜ
Map	Maximum *a posteriori* probability	最大后验概率	Zuìdà hòuyàn gàilǜ
MAP	Mobile application part	移动应用单元	Yídòng yìngyòng dānyuán
MAP	Mobile application part	移动应用部分	Yídòng yìngyòng bùfen
MAP	Mobile application part	移动通信应用部分	Yídòng tōngxìn yìngyòng bùfen
MAP	Mobility application part	移动性应用部分	Yídòngxìng yìngyòng bùfen
MAP	Multicast adaptation protocol	组播适配协议	Zǔbō shìpèi xiéyì
MAPI	Messaging application procedure interface	信息应用过程接口	Xìnxī yìngyòng guòchéng jiēkǒu
MAPI	Messaging application programming interface	消息应用程序接口	Xiāoxi yìngyòng chéngxù jiēkǒu
MAPI	Messaging application programming interface	信报传递应用程序接口	Xìnbào chuándì yìngyòng chéngxù jiēkǒu
MAPPDU	Multicast adaptation protocol/protocol data unit	组播适配协议-协议数据单元	Zǔbō shìpèi xiéyì/xiéyì shùjù dānyuán
MAPSAP	Multicast adaptation protocol/service access point	组播适配协议--服务接入点	Zǔbō shìpèi xiéyì/fúwù jiērù diǎn
MAR	Memory address register	存储地址寄存器	Cúnchǔ dìzhǐ jìcúnqì
MARS	Multicast address resolution server (IETF usage)	组播地址解析服务	Zǔbō dìzhǐ jiěxī fúwù
MARS	Multicast address resolution service	多播地址解析服务	Duōbō dìzhǐ jiěxī fúwù
MAS	Mass call	大众呼叫	Dàzhòng hūjiào
MAS	Mass calling service	大众呼叫业务	Dàzhòng hūjiào yèwù
MAS	Mobile application sub-system	移动应用子系统	Yídòng yìngyòng zixìtǒng
MAS	Multi-agent system	多代理系统	Duōdàilǐ xìtǒng
MAS	Multicast aware level 2 switch	组播敏感的第二层交换机	Zǔbō mǐngǎnde dì'èrcéng jiāohuànjī
MASE	Message administration service element	消息管理服务要素	Xiāoxi guǎnlǐ fúwù yàosù
MASK	Multiple amplitude shift keying	多幅移键控	Duōfúyí jiànkòng
MASS	Metallic aerial self-supporting (FOC)	金属自承光缆	Jīnshǔ zì chéng guānglǎn
MASS	Multiple access switching system	多路进入交换系统	Duōlù jìnrù jiāohuàn xìtǒng
MAT	Maximum allowable tension	最大充许使用张力	Zuìdà chōngxǔ shǐyòng zhānglì
MAT	Maximum allowed tension	最大充许拉力	Zuìdà chōngxǔ lālì
MAU	Media attachment unit	介质链接单元	Jièzhì liànjiē dānyuán
MAU	Media attachment unit	媒体附加接口	Méitǐ fùjiā jiēkǒu
MAU	Multi-station access unit	多站访问单元	Duōzhàn fǎngwèn dānyuán
MAVAR	Mixer amplification by variable reactance	脉伐，可变电抗混频放大	Mài fá, kěbiàn diànkàng hùnpín fàngdà
maxCR	Maximum cell rate	最大的信元率	Zuìdàde xìnyuán lǜ
MB	Macro-block	宏块	Hóng kuài
MB	Megabit (10^6 bit)	兆位	Zhàowèi
MB, mb	Megabyte (10^6 bytes)	兆字节	Zhàozìjié
Mb/s	Megabits per second	兆比特每秒	Zhàobǐtè měi miǎo
MBA	Maintenance-oriented group blocking acknowledgement message	面向维护的群闭塞证实消息	Miànxiàng wéihùde qún bìsè zhèngshí xiāoxi
MBA	Multi-beam antenna	多波束天线	Duōbōshù tiānxiàn
MBC	Main beam clutter	主波束杂波	Zhǔ bōshù zábō
MBCR	Multi-band cell reporting	多频小区报告	Duōpín xiǎoqū bàogào
MBCS	Multi-function broadband communication system	多功能宽带通信系统	Duōgōngnéng kuāndài tōngxìn xìtǒng
MBDL	Missile battery data link (US military)	导弹连数据链	Dǎodàn lián shùjù liàn

MBE	Molecular beam epitaxy	分子束外延	Fènzi shù wàiyán
MBE	Multiband excitation	多频带激励	Duōpíndài jīlì
MBE	Multi-band excitation	多带激励	Duōdài jīlì
MBE	Multi-band excitation	多带激励编码	Duōdài jīlì biānmǎ
MBE	Multi-byte expansion	多字节扩展	Duōzìjié kuòzhǎn
MBFR	Maximum bit forwarding rate	最大位转发率	Zuìdà wèi zhuǎnfā lǜ
MBG	Multi-business group	多种商业组群	Duōzhǒng shāngyè zǔqún
MBGP	Multicast border gateway protocol	多目广播边界网关协议	Duōmù guǎngbō biānjiè wǎngguān xiéyì
MBGP	Multicast border gateway protocol	组播边界网关协议	Zǔbō biānjiè wǎngguān xiéyì
MBGP	Multiprotocol border gateway protocol	多协议边缘网关协议	Duōxiéyì biānyuán wǎngguān xiéyì
MBK	Multi-beam klystron	多束速调管	Duōshù sùtiáoguǎn
MBMC	Multiple burst mode controller	多突发模式控制器	Duōtūfā móshì kòngzhìqì
MBMMR	Multiband multimode radio (a US system)	多频段多模式无线电台	Duōpínduàn duōmóshì wúxiàndiàntái
MBONE	Multicast backbone	多播主干网	Duōbō zhǔgàn wǎng
MBONE	Multicast backbone network	组播主干网	Zǔbō zhǔgàn wǎng
MBR	Master boot record	主引导记录	Zhǔ yǐndǎo jìlù
MBR	Memory buffer register	存储器缓冲寄存器	Cúnchǔqì huǎnchōng jìcúnqì
MBR	Minimum bounding rectangle	最小矩形	Zuìxiǎo jǔxíng
MBS	Maximum burst size	最大突发量	Zuìdà tūfāliàng
MBS	Mobile broadband service	移动宽带业务	Yídòng kuāndài yèwù
MBS	Mobile broadband system	移动宽带系统	Yídòng kuāndài xìtǒng
M-BUS	Maintenance bus	维护总线	Wéihù zǒngxiàn
MC	Message center	消息中心	Xiāoxi zhōngxīn
MC	Microcell	微小组	Wēixiǎo zǔ
MC	Mixed character string type	混合字符串型	Hùnhé zìfú chuànxíng
MC	Mobile commerce	移动商务	Yídòng shāngwù
MC	Monitoring center	监测中心	Jiāncè zhōngxīn
MC	Motion compensation (video term)	运动补偿	Yùndòng bǔcháng
MC	Multipoint controller	多点控制器	Duōdiǎn kòngzhìqì
MCA	Micro channel architecture	微信道结构	Wēixìndào jiégòu
MCA	Micro channel architecture	微渠道架构	Wēiqúdào jiàgòu
MCA	Micro channel architecture	微通道体系结构	Wēitōngdào tǐxì jiégòu
MCA	Multi-channel access	多信道选取	Duōxìndào xuǎnqǔ
MCAS	Merchandise counterfeit authentication solution	商品防伪认证解决方案	Shāngpǐn fángwěi rènzhèng jiějué fāng'àn
MCC	Main cross connect	主交叉连接	Zhǔ jiāochā liánjiē
MCC	Meter counts collector	计费汇总计数收集器	Jìfèi huìzǒng jìshù shōujíqì
MCC	Microcell controller	微小组控制器	Wēixiǎo zǔ kòngzhìqì
MCC	Mobile country code	国家移动代码	Guójiā yídòng dàimǎ
MCC	Mobile country code	移动国家号码	Yídòng guójiā hàomǎ
MCC	Mobile country code	移动国家码	Yídòng guójiā mǎ
MCC	Mobile country code	移动通信国家码	Yídòng tōngxìn guójiā mǎ
MCC	Multipoint command conference	多点命令会议	Duōdiǎn mìnglìng huìyì
MCCTS	Multi-channel carrier telephone system	多信道载波电话系统	Duōxìndào zàibō diànhuà xìtǒng
MCD	Maintenance cell description	维护信元描述	Wéihù xìnyuán miáoshù
MCD	Mobile computing device	移动计算设备	Yídòng jìsuàn shèbèi
MCEF	Mobile station memory capacity exceeded flag	移动台存储能力溢出标志	Yídòngtái cúnchǔ nénglì yìchū biāozhì

Abbreviation	English	Chinese	Pinyin
MCF	Message communications function	消息通信功能	Xiāoxi tōngxìn gōngnéng
MCG	Master clock generator	主时钟发生器	Zhǔ shízhōng fāshēngqì
MCGA	Multi-color graphics array	多色图像阵列	Duōsè túxiàng zhènliè
MCH	Multi-channel	多信道	Duōxìndào
MCH	Multi-channel	多通道	Duōtōngdào
MCHB	Maintenance channel buffer register	维护通道缓冲寄存器	Wéihù tōngdào huǎnchōng jìcúnqì
MCHC	Maintenance channel command register	维护通道指令寄存器	Wéihù tōngdào zhǐlìng jìcúnqì
MCHO	Mobile-controlled handoff	移动台控制切换	Yídòngtái kòngzhì qiēhuàn
MCHR	Minimum-conflict heuristic repair	最小冲突启发式修补	Zuìxiǎo chōngtū qǐfāshì xiūbǔ
MCI	Malicious call identification	恶意呼叫识别	Èyì hūjiào shíbié
MCI	Malicious call identification	捣乱呼叫识别	Dǎoluàn hūjiào shíbié
MCI	Malicious call identification supplementary service	恶意呼叫检验补充业务	Èyì hūjiào jiǎnyàn bǔchōng yèwù
MCI	Media control interface	媒体控制介面	Méitǐ kòngzhì jièmiàn
MCK	Main clock board	主时钟板	Zhǔ shízhōng bǎn
MCM	Multi-carrier modulation	多载波调制	Duōzàibō tiáozhì
MCM	Multi-chip module (electronics mfg)	多芯片模块	Duōxìnpiàn mókuài
MCML	Multi-class multi-link point to point protocol	多级多链路 ppp	Duōjí duōliànlù PPP
MCN	Multipoint command negotiation	多点命令协商	Duōdiǎn mìnglìng xiéshāng
MCP	Monitoring and control panel	监控维护盘	Jiānkòng wéihù pán
MCPA	Main control board assembly	主控制集成板	Zhǔ kòngzhì jíchéngbǎn
MCPC	Multi-channel per carrier	每载波多信道	Měi zàibō duō xìndào
MCPC	Multiple channel per carrier	每载波多路	Měi zàibō duōlù
MCPU	Multiple call processing unit	多呼叫处理装置	Duōhūjiào chǔlǐ zhuāngzhì
MCR	Minimum cell rate	最小信元速率	Zuìxiǎo xìnyuán sùlǜ
MCS	Maintenance control sub-system	维护控制子系统	Wéihù kòngzhì zixìtǒng
MCS	Microcellular system	微蜂窝系统	Wēifēngwō xìtǒng
MCS	Mobile control station	移动控制站	Yídòng kòngzhìzhàn
MCS	Monte Carlo simulation	蒙特卡洛模拟	Méng-tè-kǎ-luò mónǐ
MCS	Multi-channel system (optical)	多波长系统	Duōbōcháng xìtǒng
MCS	Multipoint command service	多点命令服务	Duōdiǎn mìnglìng fúwù
MCS	Multipoint command symmetrical data transmission	多点命令相称性数据传输	Duōdiǎn mìnglìng xiāngchènxìng shùjù chuánshū
MCS	Multipoint communication service	多点通信服务	Duōdiǎn tōngxìn fúwù
MCSAP	Multipoint communication service access point	多点通信服务接入点	Duōdiǎn tōngxìn fúwù jiērùdiǎn
MCSM	Matched coaxial single mode optical fiber	匹配包层单模光纤	Pǐpèi bāo céng dānmó guāngxiān
MCSP	Microsoft Certified Solution Providers	微软认证解决方案供应商	Wēiruǎn rènzhèng jiějué fāng'àn gōngyìngshāng
MCT	Master configuration table	主配置表	Zhǔ pèizhì biǎo
MCU	Media control unit	媒体控制单元	Méitǐ kòngzhì dānyuán
MCU	Memory control unit	存储控制装置	Cúnchǔ kòngzhì zhuāngzhì
MCU	Multipoint conferencing unit	多点会议单元	Duōdiǎn huìyì dānyuán
MCU	Multipoint control unit	多点控制单元	Duōdiǎn kòngzhì dānyuán
MCUR	Main control unit rack	主控制单元机架	Zhǔ kòngzhì dānyuán jījià
MCVD	Modified chemical vapor deposition	改进化学汽相沉积法	Gǎijìn huàxué qìxiàng chénjī fǎ
MCVF	Multi-channel voice frequency	多路语音频率	Duōlù yǔyīn pínlǜ
MCVFT	Multi-channel voice-frequency telegraphy	多路音频电报	Duōlù yīnpín diànbào
MCWLA	Minimum-conflict weight learning algorithm	最小冲突权值学习算法	Zuìxiǎo chōngtū quán zhí xuéxí suànfǎ

MD	Management domain	管理域	Guǎnlǐ yù
MD	Management domains	管理区域	Guǎnlǐ qūyù
MD	Mediation device	中介装置	Zhōngjiè zhuāngzhì
MD	Mediation device	中介设备	Zhōngjiè shèbèi
MD	Mediation device	协调设备	Xiétiáo shèbèi
MD	Mediation device	调停手段	Tiáoting shǒuduàn
MD5	Message digest 5	第 5 类报文摘要	Diwǔlèi bàowén zhāiyào
MD5	Message digest version 5	消息摘要版本 5	Xiāoxi zhāiyào bǎnběn 5
MDA	Message digest algorithm	报文摘要算法	Bàowén zhāiyào suànfǎ
MDA	Monochrome adapter (video term)	单色适配器	Dānsè shìpèiqì
MDA	Monochrome display adapter	单色显示监控器	Dānsè xiǎnshì jiānkòngqì
MDBS	Mobile data base station	移动数据基站	Yídòng shùjù jīzhàn
MDC	Mobile daughter card	移动式子卡	Yídòng-shì zikǎ
MDI	Media dependent interface	媒体依赖接口	Méitǐ yīlài jiēkǒu
MDI	Media dependent interface	媒体相关接口	Méitǐ xiāngguān jiēkǒu
MDI	Multi-documentation interface	多文档界面	Duōwéndàng jièmiàn
MD-IS	Mobile data intermediate system	移动数据中介系统	Yídòng shùjù zhōngjiè xìtǒng
MDL	Minimum description length	最小描述长度	Zuìxiǎo miáoshù chángdù
MDL	Mobile management entity - data link layer	移动管理实体–数据链路层	Yídòng guǎnlǐ shítǐ - shùjù liànlù céng
MDLC	Mobile data link connection	移动数据链路连接	Yídòng shùjù liànlù liánjiē
MDLC	Multiple data link controller	多路数据链接控制器	Duōlù shùjù liànjiē kòngzhìqì
MDLCI	Mobile data link connection identifier	移动数据链路连接标识符	Yídòng shùjù liànlù liánjiē biāozhìfú
MDLP	Mobile data link protocol	移动数据链路协议	Yídòng shùjù liànlù xiéyì
MDMF	Multiple data message format	复合数据消息格式	Fùhé shùjù xiāoxi géshi
MDN	Mobile directory number	移动目录号码	Yídòng mùlù hàomǎ
MDPE	Medium density polyethylene	中密集聚乙烯	Zhōng mìjí jùyǐxī
MDPU	Minimum delay protocol for unicast	基于单播的最小延时	Jīyú dānbōde zuìxiǎo yánshí
MDRS	Multi-frequency dial register sender	多频拨号记存发送器	Duōpín bōhào jìcún fāsòngqì
MDS	Minimum detectable signal	最小可探测信号	Zuìxiǎo kětàncè xìnhào
MDS	Multimedia distribution service	多媒体业务分布	Duōméitǐ yèwù fēnbù
MDSE	Message delivery service element	消息投递服务要素	Xiāoxi tóudì fúwù yàosù
MDSS	Multi-function digital signaling service	多功能数字信号服务	Duōgōngnéng shùzì xìnhào fúwù
MDT	Mean down time	平均不可用时间	Píngjūn bùkěyòng shíjiān
MDT	Mean down time	平均停机时间	Píngjūn tíngjī shíjiān
MDTI	Multi-stream data transmission interface	多路数据传输接口	Duōlù shùjù chuánshū jiēkǒu
MDTS	Mobile dial telephone system	移动拨号电话系统	Yídòng bōhào diànhuà xìtǒng
MDX	Multi-dimensional expressions	多维表达式	Duōwéi biǎodá shì
ME	Maintenance entity	维护实体	Wéihù shítǐ
ME	Mobile equipment	移动设备	Yídòng shèbèi
MEA	Maintenance entity assembly	维护实体组	Wéihù shítǐ zǔ
MEA	Measurement	测量	Cèliáng
MEC	Mobile echo control	移动回音控制	Yídòng huíyīn kòngzhì
MED	Message entry device	消息输入设备	Xiāoxi shūrù shèbèi
MEF	Maintenance entity function	维护实体功能	Wéihù shítǐ gōngnéng
MEGACO	Media gateway control	媒体网关控制	Méitǐ wǎngguān kòngzhì
Megaco	Media gateway control protocol	媒体网关控制协议	Méitǐ wǎngguān kòngzhì xiéyì

MEGAFLOP	One million floating point operations per second	百万次浮点运算/秒	Bǎiwàncì fúdiǎn yùnsuàn/miǎo
MEHO	Mobile evaluated handover	移动切换估算	Yídòng qiēhuàn gūsuàn
MEI	Maintenance event information	维护事件信息	Wéihù shìjiàn xìnxī
MELP	Mixed excitation linear prediction	混合激励线性预测	Hùnhé jīlì xiànxìng yùcè
MELP	Mixed excitation linear predictive coder	混合激励线性预测编码器	Hùnhé jīlì xiànxìng yùcè biānmǎqì
MEM	Maximum envelope method	最大包络法	Zuìdà bāoluò fǎ
MEMMA	Microelectromechanical mirror arrays	微电机镜阵列	Wēidiànjī jìng zhènliè
MEMS	Micro electronic mechanical system	微电 - 机系统	Wēidiànjī xìtǒng
MEMS	MicroElectroMechanical switch	微电子机械开关	Wēidiànzǐ jīxiè kāiguān
MEMS	Microelectronic mechanical system	微电子机械系统	Wēidiànzǐ jīxiè xìtǒng
MEO	Medium earth orbit	中地球轨道	Zhōng dìqiú guǐdào
MEO	Medium earth orbit	中轨	Zhōngguǐ
MER	Message error rate	消息差错率	Xiāoxi chācuò lǜ
MES	Mobile satellite earth station	移动地球站	Yídòng dìqiúzhàn
M-ES	Mobile end system	移动端系统	Yídòng duān xìtǒng
MESI	Modified, exclusive, shared, invalid	修改，排除，共享，废弃	Xiūgǎi, páichú, gòngxiǎng, fèiqì
MexE	Mobile execution environment	移动运行环境	Yídòng yùnxíng huánjìng
MF	Master file	主文件	Zhǔ wénjiàn
MF	Master file	主要文件	Zhǔyào wénjiàn
MF	Mediation function block	中介功能块	Zhōngjiè gōngnéng kuài
MF	Medium frequency	中频	Zhōngpín
MF	Multi-frame	多帧	Duōzhèng
MFA	Multi-feed antenna	多馈线天线	Duōkuìxiàn tiānxiàn
MFBP	Maintenance and fault back panel	维护和故障后面板	Wéihù hé gùzhàng hòumianbǎn
MFC	Microsoft foundation classes	微软基础类库	Wēiruǎn jīchǔ lèi kù
MFC	Multi-frequency control board	多频互控板	Duōpín hùkòngbǎn
MFD	Mode field diameter (of FOC)	模场直径	Móchǎng zhíjìng
MFD	Multi function device	多功能设备	Duōgōngnéng shèbèi
MFD	Multi-frequency dialing	多频拨号	Duōpín bōhào
MFLOPS	Million floating point operations per second	每秒百万个浮点操作	Měi miǎo bǎiwàngè fúdiǎn cāozuò
MFLOPS	Million floating point operations per second	每秒百万次浮点运算	Měi miǎo bǎiwàncì fúdiǎn yùnsuàn
MFOS	Multi-frequency output sender	多频输出发送器	Duōpín shūchū fāsòngqì
MFP	Multi-function peripheral	多功能外围设备	Duōgōngnéng wàiwéi shèbèi
MFP	Multi-function product	多功能复合事务机	Duōgōngnéng fùhé shìwùjī
MFPB	Multi-frequency press button	多频按键	Duōpín ànjiàn
MFSK	Multiple frequency shift keying	多路移频键控	Duōlù yípín jiànkòng
MFSK	Multiple frequency shift keying	多频移频键控	Duōpín yípín jiànkòng
MFT	Master file table	主文件表	Zhǔ wénjiàn biǎo
MFT	Missile flight tool (software)	导弹飞行工具	Dǎodàn fēixíng gōngjù
MG	Media gateway	媒体网关	Méitǐ wǎngguān
MGB	Maintenance-oriented group blocking message	面向维护的群闭塞消息	Miànxiàng wéihùde qún bìsè xiāoxi
MGC	Media gateway controller	媒体网关控制器	Méitǐ wǎngguān kòngzhìqì
MGCF	Media gateway control function	媒体网关控制功能	Méitǐ wǎngguān kòngzhì gōngnéng
MGCP	Media gateway control part	媒体网关控制部分	Méitǐ wǎngguān kòngzhì bùfen
MGCP	Media gateway control protocol	媒体网关控制器协议	Méitǐ wǎngguān kòngzhìqì xiéyì
MGCP	Media gateway control protocol	媒体网关控制协议	Méitǐ wǎngguān kòngzhì xiéyì

MGCU	Media gateway control unit	媒体网关控制单元	Méitǐ wǎngguān kòngzhì dānyuán
MGF	Management gateway function	管理网关功能	Guǎnlǐ wǎngguān gōngnéng
MGF	Media gateway function	媒体网关功能	Méitǐ wǎngguān gōngnéng
MGT	Mobile global title	全球移动通信名称	Quánqiú yídòng tōngxìn míngchēng
MGT	Mobile global title	全球移动通信图标	Quánqiú yídòng tōngxìn túbiāo
MGU	Maintenance-oriented group unblocking message	面向维护的群闭塞解除消息	Miànxiàng wéihùde qún bìsè jiěchú xiāoxi
MGU	Media gateway unit	媒体网关单元	Méitǐ wǎngguān dānyuán
MHC	Modified Huffman code	变形赫夫门码	Biànxíng hè-fū-mén mǎ
MHEG	Multimedia and hypermedia information coding expert group	多媒体和超媒体信息编码专家组	Duōméitǐ hé chāoméitǐ xìnxī biānmǎ zhuānjiāzǔ
MHF	Mobile home function	移动归属功能	Yídòng guīshǔ gōngnéng
MHI	Mitsubishi Heavy Industries (Japan)	三菱重工	Sān-líng zhònggōng
MHS	Message handling system	消息处理系统	Xiāoxi chǔlǐ xìtǒng
MHV	Modified Hadama variance	修正哈达玛方差	Xiūzhèng hǎ-dá-mǎ fāngchà
MHZ	MegaHertz	兆赫	Zhàohè
MHz	MegaHertz	兆赫兹	Zhàohè-zī
MI	Management information	管理信息	Guǎnlǐ xìnxī
MI	Modulation instability	调制不稳定性	Tiáozhì bùwěndìngxìng
MIA	Media interface adapter	介质接口适配器	Jièzhì jiēkǒu shìpèiqì
MIA	Multiplex interface adapter	多路转换接口适配器	Duōlù zhuǎnhuàn jiēkǒu shìpèiqì
MIB	Management information base	管理信息基	Guǎnlǐ xìnxījī
MIB	Management information base	管理信息库	Guǎnlǐ xìnxīkù
MIC	Integrity protected command (in FTP)	完整性保护命令	Wánzhěngxìng bǎohù mìnglìng
MIC	Machine instruction code	机器指令码	Jīqì zhǐlìng mǎ
MIC	Management information catalogue	管理信息目录	Guǎnlǐ xìnxī mùlù
MIC	Media interface connector	介质接口连接器	Jièzhì jiēkǒu liánjiēqì
MIC	Media interface connector	媒体接口连接器	Méitǐ jiēkǒu liánjiēqì
MIC	Message integrity code	信息完整性编码	Xìnxī wánzhěngxìng biānmǎ
MIC	Message integrity code	消息完整性编码	Xiāoxi wánzhěngxìng biānmǎ
MIC	Microphone	微音器	Wēiyīnqì
MIC	Microphone	麦克风	Màikèfēng
MIC	Mineral-insulated cable	无机物绝缘电缆	Wújīwù juéyuán diànlǎn
MIC	Mobile interface controller	移动接口控制器	Yídòng jiēkǒu kòngzhìqì
MICE	Mobile interwork control element	移动互通控制单元	Yídòng hùtōng kòngzhì dānyuán
MID	Message identifier	消息标识符	Xiāoxi biāozhìfú
MID	Message identifier	消息识别码	Xiāoxi shíbié mǎ
MID	Multiplexing identification	复用标志	Fùyòng biāozhì
MID	Multiplexing identification	复用标识	Fùyòng biāozhì
MIDI	Musical instrument digital interface	乐器数位介面	Yuèqì shùwèi jièmiàn
MIDI	Musical instrument digital interface	乐器数字接口	Yuèqì shùzì jiēkǒu
MIFR	Master international frequency register	国际频率登记总表	Guójì pínlǜ dēngjì zǒngbiǎo
MII	Media independent interface	媒体无关接口	Méitǐ wúguān jiēkǒu
MII	Ministry of Information Industry (China)	信息产业部	Xìnxī chǎnyè bù
MIL	Management information library	管理信息定义库	Guǎnlǐ xìnxī dìngyìkù
MIL	Module interconnection language	模块互连语言	Mókuài hùlián yǔyán
MIM	Management information model	管理信息模型	Guǎnlǐ xìnxī móxíng

MIM	Management information model	管理信息模式	Guǎnlǐ xìnxī móshì
MIM	Mobile interwork module	移动互通模块	Yídòng hùtōng mókuài
MIME	Multi-purpose internet mail extension	多用途因特网邮件扩展	Duōyòngtú Yīntèwǎng yóujiàn kuòzhǎn
MIME	Multipurpose Internet mail extensions	多用途的网际邮件扩充协议	Duōyòngtúde wǎngjì yóujiàn kuòchōng xiéyì
MIMIC	Millimeter wave monolithic integrated circuit	毫米波单片集成电路	Háomǐbō dānpiàn jíchéng diànlù
MIMO	Multi-input multi-output	多输入多输出	Duōshūrù duō shūchū
MIMO	Multi-input multi-output	多输入输出	Duōshūrù shūchū
MIMOS	Malaysian Institute of Microelectronic Systems	马来西亚微电子学院	Mǎ-lái-xī-yà wēidiànzǐ xuéyuàn
MIN	Mobile identification number	移动标识号码	Yídòng biāozhì hàomǎ
MIN	Mobile identification number	移动识别码	Yídòng shíbié mǎ
MIN	Mobile user identification number	移动用户识别码	Yídòng yònghù shíbié mǎ
MIN	Multi-stage interconnection network	多级互连网络	Duōjí hùlián wǎngluò
MIO	Multi-user information outlet	多用户信息插座	Duōyònghù xìnxī chāzuò
MIOC	Memory and I/O bridge controller (chip)	内存和 I/O 桥控制器	Nèicún hé I/O qiáo kòngzhìqì
MIP	Microwave interference protection	微波干扰防护	Wēibō gānrǎo fánghù
MIP	Multicast internet protocol	组播互联网协议	Zǔbō hùliánwǎng xiéyì
MIPS	Million instructions per second	每秒百万条指令	Měi miǎo bǎiwàntiáo zhǐlìng
MIPS	Million instructions per second	每秒百万次指令	Měi miǎo bǎiwàncì zhǐlìng
MIPS	Million instructions per second	百万条指令/秒	Bǎiwàn tiáo zhǐlìng/miǎo
MIPS	Millions of instructions per second	每秒多少百万个指令	Měi miǎo duōshao bǎiwàngè zhǐlìng
MIS	Management information service	管理信息业务	Guǎnlǐ xìnxī yèwù
MIS	Management information system	管理信息系统	Guǎnlǐ xìnxī xìtǒng
MIT	Management information tree	管理信息树	Guǎnlǐ xìnxīshù
MITA	Mobile internet technical architecture	移动因特网技术的体系结构	Yídòng Yīntèwǎng jìshùde tǐxì jiégòu
MITATT	Mixed tunnel and avalanche transit-time diode	混合型隧道和雪崩度起时间二极管	Hùnhé-xíng suìdào hé xuěbēng dùqǐ shíjiān èrjíguǎn
MJPEG	Motion Joint Photographic Experts Group	移动式连续图像专家组	Yídòng-shì liánxù túxiàng zhuānjiāzǔ
MKMP	Multicast key management protocol	多播密钥管理协议	Duōbō mìyào guǎnlǐ xiéyì
MKR	Marker	标志器	Biāozhìqì
ML	Maximum likelihood	最大似然	Zuìdà sìrán
MLA	Microstrip linear antenna	微带线性天线	Wēidài xiànxìng tiānxiàn
MLAN	Multi-channel local area network	多通道局域网	Duōtōngdào júyùwǎng
MLC	Mobile terminal locating center	移动终端定位中心	Yídòng zhōngduān dìngwèi zhōngxīn
MLC	Multi-layer ceramic capacitor	陶瓷多层电容器	Táocí duōcéng diànróngqì
MLCM	Multi-level coded modulation	多电平编码调制	Duōdiànpíng biānmǎ tiáozhì
MLD	Mean logistic delay	平均后勤耽误	Píngjūn hòuqín dānwù
MLE	Microsoft Learning and Entertainment	微软教学与娱乐公司	Wēiruǎn jiàoxué yǔ yúlè gōngsī
MLM	Multi-longitude mode	多纵模	Duōzòngmó
MLM	Multi-longitudinal mode laser	多纵模激光器	Duōzòngmó jīguāngqì
MLP	Machine language program	机器语言程序	Jīqì yǔyán chéngxù
MLP	Multi-layer protocol	多层协议	Duōcéng xiéyì
MLP	Multi-link procedure	多链路规程	Duōliànlù guīchéng
MLPP	Multi-level precedence and preemption	多等级优先占用	Duō děngjí yōuxiān zhànyòng
MLS	Microwave landing system	微波着陆系统	Wēibō zhuólù xìtǒng
MLSE	Maximum likelihood sequence estimation	最大似然序列估值	Zuìdà sìrán xùliè gūzhí
MLSE	Maximum likelihood sequence estimation	最大似然序列估计	Zuìdà sìrán xùliè gūjì

MLSR	Maximum-length shift register	最大长度移位寄存器	Zuìdà chángdù yíwèi jìcúnqì
MLSR	Maximum-length shift register	最长移位寄存器	Zuìcháng yíwèi jìcúnqì
MM	Media manager	媒体管理	Méitǐ guǎnlǐ
MM	Mobility management	移动性管理	Yídòngxìng guǎnlǐ
MM	Pulse code equipment	脉码设备	Màimǎ shèbèi
MMA	Master management agent	主管理代理	Zhǔ guǎnlǐ dàilǐ
MMB	Motherboard	母板	Mǔbǎn
MMBP	Man-machine interface back panel	人机接口后面板	Rén jī jiēkǒu hòumian bǎn
MMC	Man-machine command	人机命令	Rén jī mìnglìng
MMDS	Microwave multipoint distribution system	微波多点分配系统	Wēibō duōdiǎn fēnpèi xìtǒng
MMDS	Multi-channel microwave distribution system	多信道微波分配系统	Duōxìndào wēibō fēnpèi xìtǒng
MMDS	Multi-channel microwave distribution system	多路微波分配系统	Duōlù wēibō fēnpèi xìtǒng
MMDS	Multi-channel multipoint distribution service	多信道多点分配业务	Duōxìndào duōdiǎn fēnpèi yèwù
MMDS	Multi-channel multipoint distribution service	多波段多点分发服务	Duōbōduàn duōdiǎn fēnfā fúwù
MMDS	Multi-channel multipoint distribution service	多路多点分配业务	Duōlù duōdiǎn fēnpèi yèwù
MME	Mobile management entity	移动管理实体	Yídòng guǎnlǐ shítǐ
MMF	Multimode optical fiber	多模光纤	Duōmó guāngxiān
MMG	Multimedia message gateway	多媒体信息网关	Duōméitǐ xìnxī wǎngguān
MMH	Maintenance man-hours	维护工时	Wéihù gōngshí
MMI	Man-machine interface	人机接口	Rén jī jiēkǒu
MML	Man-machine language	人机语言	Rén jī yǔyán
MMM	Multimedia mailing	多媒体邮件	Duōméitǐ yóujiàn
MMO	Multimedia outlet	多媒体插座	Duōméitǐ chāzuò
MMS	Microsoft® media server	微软媒体服务器	Wēiruǎn méitǐ fúwùqì
MMS	Multimedia messaging service	多媒体信息服务	Duōméitǐ xìnxī fúwù
MMS	Multiplex modulation system	多路复用调制系统	Duōlù fùyòng tiáozhì xìtǒng
MMSE	Minimum (root) mean square error	最小均方根差	Zuìxiǎo jūn fānggēn chà
MMSE	Minimum mean square error	最小均方误差	Zuìxiǎo jūn fāng wùchā
MMTP	Multimedia mail transfer protocol	多媒体邮件传送协议	Duōméitǐ yóujiàn chuánsòng xiéyì
MMU	Multimedia unit	多媒体单元	Duōméitǐ dānyuán
MMUSIC	Multi-party multimedia session control	多方多媒体会话控制	Duōfāng duōméitǐ huìhuà kòngzhì
MMVF	Multimedia video file	多媒体视频文件	Duōméitǐ shìpín wénjiàn
MMX	Multimedia extensions	多媒体扩展指令集	Duōméitǐ kuòzhǎn zhǐlìng jí
MN	Mobile node	移动节点	Yídòng jiédiǎn
MNC	Mobile network code	移动电话网号码	Yídòng diànhuà wǎng hàomǎ
MNC	Mobile network code	移动网号	Yídòng wǎng hào
MNC	Mobile network code	移动网络码	Yídòng wǎngluò mǎ
MNC	Mobile network code	移动网编号	Yídòng wǎng biānhào
MNLP	Mobile network location protocol	移动网位置协议	Yídòng wǎng wèizhì xiéyì
MNP	Mobile number portability	移动号码可携	Yídòng hàomǎ kěxié
MNP	Mobile number portability	移动号码可携带性	Yídòng hàomǎ kěxiédàixìng
MNRP	Mobile network registration protocol	移动网登记协议	Yídòng wǎng dēngjì xiéyì
MNT	Major node earth terminal	主要结点地面终端	Zhǔyào jiédiǎn dìmiàn zhōngduān
MO	Managed object	管理对象	Guǎnlǐ duìxiàng
MO	Managed object	管理目标	Guǎnlǐ mùbiāo
MO	Message origination	上传消息	Shàngchuán xiāoxi

MO	Mobile originated	移动发起	Yídòng fāqǐ
MO	Mobile originated	移动台发起的	Yídòngtái fāqǐde
MO	Mobile originating	移动始发呼叫	Yídòng shǐfā hūjiào
MOA	Managed-object agent	被管目标代理	Bèiguǎn mùbiāo dàilǐ
MOC	Managed object class	管理对象类	Guǎnlǐ duìxiàng lèi
MOC	Managed-object class	被管对象类	Bèiguǎn duìxiàng lèi
MOC	Mobile originating call	移动主叫	Yídòng zhǔjiào
MOC	Mobile originating call	移动发端呼叫	Yídòng fāduān hūjiào
MOC	Mobile originating call	移动台主叫	Yídòngtái zhǔ jiào
MOCS	Managed object conformance statement	管理目标一致性句法	Guǎnlǐ mùbiāo yīzhìxìng jùfǎ
MOCVD	Metallo-organic chemical vapor deposition	金属有机化学汽相沉积法	Jīnshǔ yǒujī huàxué qìxiàng chénjī fǎ
MOD	Message on demand	点播消息	Diǎnbō xiāoxi
MOD	Message output descriptor	报文输出描述符	Bàowén shūchū miáoshùfú
MOD	Movie on demand	点播电影	Diǎnbō diànyǐng
MODEM	Modem, modulator/demodulator	调制/解调器	Tiáozhì/jiětiáoqì
MODEM	Modulator demodulator	调制解调器	Tiáozhì jiětiáoqì
MOFI	Miniature free space optical isolator	微型自由空间光隔离器	Wēixíng zìyóu kōngjiān guāng gélíqì
MOGENT	Mobile agent system	移动代理系统	Yídòng dàilǐ xìtǒng
MOGP	Multi-objective genetic programming	多目标遗传规划	Duōmùbiāo yíchuán guīhuà
MOHO	Mobile originated handover	开始移动切换	Kāishǐ yídòng qiēhuàn
MOI	Managed object instance	管理对象实例	Guǎnlǐ duìxiàng shílì
MOLAP	Multi-dimensional online analytical processing	多维联机分析处理	Duōwéi liánjī fēnxī chǔlǐ
MO-LR	Mobile originating location request	移动发起定位请求	Yídòng fāqǐ dìngwèi qǐngqiú
MOM	Message-oriented middleware	定向信息中间件	Dìngxiàng xìnxī zhōngjiān jiàn
MOM	Message-oriented middleware	面向消息的中间件	Miànxiàng xiāoxide zhōngjiān jiàn
MON	Monitored	被检测的	Bèijiǎncède
MOP	Maintenance operation protocol	维护操作协议	Wéihù cāozuò xiéyì
MOPA	Master oscillator power amplifier transmitter	主振放大式发射机	Zhǔ zhèn fàngdàshì fāshèjī
MOS	Mean opinion score	主观平均得分	Zhǔguān píngjūn défēn
MOS	Mean opinion score	平均主管得分	Píngjūn zhǔguǎn défēn
MOS	Mean opinion score	平均评价得分	Píngjūn píngjià défēn
MOS	Mean opinion score	平均鉴定分数	Píngjūn jiàndìng fēnshù
MOS	Metal oxide semiconductor	金属氧化物半导体	Jīnshǔ yǎnghuàwù bàndǎotǐ
MOSFET	Metal oxide semiconductor field effect transistor	金属氧化物半导体场效应晶体管	Jīnshǔ yǎnghuàwù bàndǎotǐ cháng xiàoying jīngtǐguǎn
MOSPF	Multicast open shortest path first protocol	开最短路径优先组播路由协议	Kāi zuìduǎn lùjìng yōuxiān zǔbō lùyóu xiéyì
MOT	Means of test	测试方式	Cèshì fāngshì
MoU	Memorandum of understanding	备忘录	Bèiwànglù
MoU	Memorandum of understanding	谅解备忘录	Liàngjiě bèiwànglù
MOV	Metal oxide varister	金属氧化物变阻器	Jīnshǔ yǎnghuàwù biànzǔqì
MOVPE	Metal organic vapor phase epitaxy	金属有机化学汽相沉积	Jīnshǔ yǒujī huàxué qìxiāng chénjī
MP	Management plane	管理平面	Guǎnlǐ píngmiàn
MP	Management point	管理点	Guǎnlǐ diǎn
MP	Marketing Planning group (GSM MoU)	市场规划组	Shìchǎng guīhuà zǔ
MP	Measurement point	测量点	Cèliáng diǎn
MP	Message push	推信息	Tuī xìnxī

MP	Multilink PPP	PPP 多链路协议	PPP duō liànlù xiéyì
MP	Multipoint processor	多点处理器	Duōdiǎn chǔlǐqì
MP	Multi-service platform	多业务平台	Duōyèwù píngtái
MP&MCU	Multi-processor and multi-control unit	多点处理器及多点控制单元	Duōdiǎn chǔlǐqì jí duōdiǎn kòngzhì dānyuán
MPA	Multi-processor architecture	多重处理器架构	Duōzhòng chǔlǐqì jiàgòu
MPBP	Main processor back panel	主处理器后面板	Zhǔ chǔlǐqì hòumianbǎn
MPCC	Multi-protocol communications controller	多协议通信控制器	Duōxiéyì tōngxìn kòngzhìqì
MPCI	Multi-port programmable communications interface	多端口可编程序通信接口	Duōduānkǒu kěbiān chéngxù tōngxìn jiēkǒu
M-PCM-IM(PS)	Multi-level pulse code modulation, intensity modulated (pulse source)	多级脉码调制，强度 调制（脉冲源）	Duōjí màimǎ tiáozhì, qiángdù tiáozhì (màichōng yuán)
M-PCM-PM(PS)	Multi-level pulse code modulation, polarization modulated (pulse source)	多级脉码调制，极化 调制（脉冲源）	Duōjí màimǎ tiáozhì, jíhuà tiáozhì (màichōng yuán)
MPD	Maximum phase deviation	最大相位偏移	Zuìdà xiàngwèi piānyí
MPD	Mean packet delay	平均包延迟	Píngjūn bāo yánchí
MPDM	Main processor duplication manager	主处理器复制管理器	Zhǔ chǔlǐqì fùzhì guǎnlǐqì
MPDU	MAC protocol data unit	MAC 协议数据单元	MAC xiéyì shùjù dānyuán
MPE	Multimedia signal processing equipment	多媒体信号处理装置	Duōméitǐ xìnhào chǔlǐ zhuāngzhì
MPEG	Motion Picture Experts Group	动画专家组	Dònghuà zhuānjiāzǔ
MPEG	Motion Picture Experts Group	活动图像专家组	Huódòng túxiàng zhuānjiāzǔ
MPEG	Motion Picture Experts Group	运动图像专家组	Yùndòng túxiàng zhuānjiāzǔ
MPEG	Moving Picture Coding Experts Group	活动图像编码专家组	Huódòng túxiàng biānmǎ zhuānjiāzǔ
MPEG	Moving Pictures Experts Group	移动图象专家组	Yídòng túxiàng zhuānjiāzǔ
MPEG TS	MPEG transmission stream	MPEG 传输流	MPEG chuánshū liú
MPEG-TS	MPEG transmission stream	MPEG 传送流	MPEG chuánsòng liú
MPE-LPC	Multi-pulse excitation linear predictive coding	多脉冲激励线性预测编码	Duōmàichōng jīlì xiànxìng yùcè biānmǎ
MPF	Multi-path fading distortion	多路径衰落失真	Duōlùjìng shuāiluò shīzhēn
MPH	Management entity – physical layer (primitive)	管理实体 - 物理层原语	Guǎnlǐ shítǐ-wùlǐ céng yuányǔ
MPH	Mobile management entity - physical layer	移动管理实体–物理层	Yídòng guǎnlǐ shítǐ - wùlǐ céng
MPI	Main path interface	主通路接口	Zhǔ tōnglù jiēkǒu
MPI	Main path interface	主通道接口	Zhǔ tōngdào jiēkǒu
MPI	Minimum picture interval	最小画面间隔	Zuìxiǎo huàmiàn jiàngé
MPI-R	Main path interface at the receiver	主通道接收参考点	Zhǔ tōngdào jiēshōu cānkǎo diǎn
MPI-R	Main path interface at the receiver	主通道接收端	Zhǔ tōngdào jiēshōu duān
MPI-R	Receive main path interface reference point	接收主通道接口参考点	Jiēshōu zhǔtōngdào jiēkǒu cānkǎodiǎn
MPIS	Multi-protocol wavelength switching	多协议波长交换	Duōxiéyì bōcháng jiāohuàn
MPI-S	Main path interface at the transmitter	主通道发送参考点	Zhǔ tōngdào fāsòng cānkǎo diǎn
MPI-S	Main path interface at the transmitter	主通道发送端	Zhǔ tōngdào fāsòng duān
MPI-S	Source main path interface reference point	发射主通道接口参考点	Fāshè zhǔtōngdào jiēkǒu cānkǎodiǎn
MPL	Maximum packet lifetime	最大包寿命时间	Zuìdà bāo shòumìng shíjiān
MPLambdaS	Multi-protocol wavelength switching	多协议 λ 交换	Duōxiéyì λ jiāohuàn
MPLPC	Multi-pulse linear prediction code	多脉冲线性预测编码	Duōmàichōng xiànxìng yùcè biānmǎ
MPLS	Multi-protocol label switching	多协议标号交换	Duōxiéyì biāohào jiāohuàn
MPLS	Multi-protocol label switching	多协议标志交换	Duōxiéyì biāozhì jiāohuàn
MPLS	Multi-protocol label switching	多协议标答交换	Duōxiéyì biāodá jiāohuàn
MPLS	Multi-protocol label switching	多协议标签交换	Duōxiéyì biāoqiān jiāohuàn
MPLS	Multi-protocol label switching	多协议标签协议	Duōxiéyì biāoqiān xiéyì

MPLS	Multi-protocol label switching	多协议标记交换	Duōxiéyì biāojì jiāohuàn
MPLSF	MPLS forum	MPLS 论坛	MPLS lùntán
MPM	Meter pulse message	计次脉冲消息	Jìcì màichōng xiāoxi
MPM	Modified phase modification synchronization (in CORBA)	改进的相位修改协议	Gǎijìnde xiàngwèi xiūgǎi xiéyì
MPN	Mode partition noise	模分配噪声	Mó fēnpèi zàoshēng
MPN	Multiplexed packet network	多路传输包网络	Duōlù chuánshū bāo wǎngluò
MPN	Multiplexed packet network	多路复用分组网络	Duōlù fùyòng fēnzǔ wǎngluò
MPOA	Multi-protocol over asynchronous transfer mode	ATM 上的多协议	ATM-shàngde duō xiéyì
MPOA	Multi-protocol over ATM	ATM 上的多协议规范	ATM-shàngde duō xiéyì guīfàn
MPoA	Multi-protocol over ATM (technology)	ATM 上的多协议(技术)	ATM-shàngde duō xiéyì (jìshù)
MPOF	Micro-structured polymer optical fiber	聚合物微结构光纤	Jùhéwù wēi jiégòu guāngxiān
MPP	Massive parallel processing	巨量平行处理架构	Jùliàng píngxíng chǔlǐ jiàgòu
MPPM	Multi-carrier pulse position modulation	多载波脉冲位置调制	Duōzàibō màichōng wèizhì tiáozhì
MPPS	Message processing procedure specification	报文处理过程说明	Bàowén chǔlǐ guòchéng shuōmíng
MPPS	Million pixels per second	百万个像素/秒	Bǎiwàn gè xiàngsù/miǎo
MPQ	Multiple priority queue	多优先队列	Duōyōuxiān duìliè
MPR	Multi-service packet ring	多业务分组环	Duōyèwù fēnzǔ huán
MPRN	Mobile packet radio network	移动式信包无线电通信网	Yídòng-shì xìnbāo wúxiàndiàn tōngxìn wǎng
MPRouter	Multimedia periphery router	多媒体外设路由器	Duōméitǐ wàishè lùyóuqì
MPS	Multi-processor specification	多处理器规范	Duōchǔlǐqì guīfàn
MPS	Multi-processor specification	多重处理器规范	Duōzhòng chǔlǐqì guīfàn
MPSK	Multi-level phase shift keying	多级相移键控	Duōjí xiāngyí jiànkòng
MPSK	Multiple phase shift keying	多值相移键控	Duōzhí xiāngyí jiànkòng
MPSK	Multiple phase shift keying	多相移相键控	Duōxiàng yíxiāng jiànkòng
MPSN	Microwave pulse shaping network	微波脉冲整形网络	Wēibō màichōng zhěngxíng wǎngluò
MPSR	Multi-path self-routing	多路径自选路由	Duōlùjìng zìxuǎn lùyóu
MPT	Ministry of Post and Telecommunications (PRC)	邮政与电信部	Yóuzhèng yǔ diànxìn bù
MPT	Multipoint to point tree	多点到点树	Duōdiǎn dào diǎn shù
MPTP	Micro payment transfer protocol	小额支付传输协议	Xiǎo'é zhīfù chuánshū xiéyì
MPTP	Micro-payment transport protocol	微支付传输协议	Wēizhīfù chuánshū xiéyì
MPTy	Multi-party	多方会话	Duōfāng huìhuà
MPTY	Multi-party	多用户	Duōyònghù
MPTY	Multi-party call	多方呼叫	Duōfāng hūjiào
MPTY	Multi-party telecommunication	多方通话	Duōfāng tōnghuà
MPU	Main processor unit	主处理单元	Zhǔ chǔlǐ dānyuán
MPX	Multiplexer	多路转换器	Duōlù zhuǎnhuànqì
MQAM	Multinary quadrature amplitude modulation	多进制正交幅度调制	Duōjìnzhì zhèngjiāo fúdù tiáozhì
MQAM	Multiple quadrature amplitude modulation	多重星座调制	Duōzhòng xīngzuò tiáozhì
MQI	Message queuing interface	报文排队接口	Bàowén páiduì jiēkǒu
MQORC	Modified quadrature overlapped raised-cosine modulation	修正的正交重叠基座余弦调制	Xiūzhèngde zhèngjiāo chóngdié jīzuò yúxián tiáozhì
MQW	Multiple quantum well device	多量子阱器件	Duōliàngzǐ jǐng qìjiàn
MQW	Multi-quantum well	多量子阱	Duōliàngzǐ jǐng
MQW-DFB-LD	Multiple quantum well distributed feedback laser device	多量子阱分布反馈激光器	Duōliàngzǐ jǐng fēnbù fǎnkuì jīguāngqì
MQW-LD	Multiple quantum well laser device	多量子阱激光器	Duōliàngzǐ jǐng jīguāngqì
MR	Measurement report	测量报告	Cèliáng bàogào

MR	Memory register	存储寄存器	Cúnchǔ jìcúnqì
MR	Modified relative element address designator code	修正的相对元素位置指示编码	Xiūzhèngde xiāngduì yuánsù wèizhì zhǐshì biānmǎ
MRA	Mutual recognition agreements	相互认可协议	Xiānghù rènkě xiéyì
MRC	Maximal ratio combining	最大比值合并	Zuìdà bǐzhí hébìng
MRC	Maximum ratio consolidation	最大比合并	Zuìdà bǐ hébìng
MRE	Memory register exponent	存储器寄存器指数	Cúnchǔqì jìcúnqì zhǐshù
MRF	Media resource function	媒体资源功能	Méitǐ zīyuán gōngnéng
MRFC	Media resources function control	媒体资源功能控制	Méitǐ zīyuán gōngnéng kòngzhì
MRFP	Media resources function processing	媒体资源功能处理	Méitǐ zīyuán gōngnéng chǔlǐ
MRH	Memory repeater hub	内存数据处理中心	Nèicún shùjù chǔlǐ zhōngxīn
MRP	Manufacturing resource planning	制造资源规划系统	Zhìzào zīyuán guīhuà xìtǒng
MRP	Manufacturing resource planning	制造资源计划	Zhìzào zīyuán jìhuà
MRP	Material requirement planning	物料需求计划	Wùliào xūqiú jìhuà
MRP	Mouth reference point	口参考点	Kǒu cānkǎo diǎn
MRP	Mouth reference point	嘴参考点	Zuǐ cānkǎo diǎn
MRP	Multiple frequency reuse pattern	多重复用方式	Duōchóng fùyòng fāngshì
MRP	Multi-reuse patterns	多复用模式	Duōfùyòng móshì
MRS	Midrange server	中型服务器	Zhōngxíng fúwùqì
MRSACE	Mobile radio system ACE	移动无线系统 ACE	Yídòng wúxiàn xìtǒng ACE
MRSE	Message retrieval service element	消息检索服务要素	Xiāoxi jiǎnsuǒ fúwù yàosù
MRSLL	Maximum relative side lobe level	最大相对旁瓣电平	Zuìdà xiāngduì pángbàn diànpíng
MRT	Mean repair time	平均修理时间	Píngjūn xiūlǐ shíjiān
MRTIE	Maximum relative time interval error	最大相对时间间隔误差	Zuìdà xiāngduì shíjiān jiàngé wùchā
MRU	Maximum receive unit	最大接收单元	Zuìdà jiēshōu dānyuán
MRU	Microwave relay unit	微波中继装置	Wēibō zhōngjì zhuāngzhì
MRW	Midrange workstation	中型工作站	Zhōngxíng gōngzuòzhàn
MRWD	Morphological representation of wavelet data	小波数据的形态学表示	Xiǎobo shùjùde xíngtàixué biǎoshì
MS	Magnetic sensors	磁场感应器	Cíchǎng gǎnyìngqì
MS	Managed solution	管理方案	Guǎnlǐ fāng'àn
MS	Message store	消息存储	Xiāoxi cúnchǔ
MS	Microsoft (US company)	微软公司	Wēiruǎn gōngsī
ms	Millisecond	毫秒	Háomiǎo
MS	Mobile station	移动台	Yídòngtái
MS	Mobile station	移动电台	Yídòng diàntái
MS	Mobile station	移动站	Yídòngzhàn
MS	Mobile subscriber	移动用户	Yídòng yònghù
MS	More segments	多程序段	Duōchéngxù duàn
MS	Multiplex section	复接段	Fùjiē duàn
MS	Multiplex section	复用段	Fùyòng duàn
MSA	Multiplex section adaptation	复用段适配	Fùyòng duàn shìpèi
MSA	Multi-service access module	多业务接入模块	Duōyèwù jiērù mókuài
MS-AIS	Multiplex section alarm indication signal	复用段告警指示	Fùyòng duàn gàojǐng zhǐshì
MS-AIS	Multiplex section alarm indication signal	复用段告警指示信号	Fùyòng duàn gàojǐng zhǐshì xìnhào
MSAN	Multi-service access network	多业务接入网	Duōyèwù jiērù wǎng
MSAP	MAC service access point	MAC 服务访问点	MAC fúwù fǎngwèn diǎn
MSAP	Multi-service access platform	多业务接入平台	Duōyèwù jiērù píngtái

MSAP	Multi-service access point	多业务接入点	Duōyèwù jiērùdiǎn
MS-APS	Multiplex section automatic protection switching	复用段自动保护倒换	Fùyòng duàn zìdòng bǎohù dǎohuàn
MSAT	Ultra small terminal mobile satellite communication system	超小型终端移动卫星通信系统	Chāoxiǎoxíng zhōngduān yídòng wèixīng tōngxìn xìtǒng
MSB	Most significant bit	最高位	Zuìgāo wèi
MSB	Most significant bit	最高有效位	Zuìgāo yǒuxiào wèi
MSB	Most significant bit	最高有效比特	Zuìgāo yǒuxiào bǐtè
MSB	Most significant byte	最高有效字节	Zuìgāo yǒuxiào zìjié
MSBD	Media streaming broadcast and distribution	媒体流广播和分发	Méitǐ liú guǎngbō hé fēnfā
MSBI	Main processor SCSI BUS interface	主处理器 SCSI BUS 接口	Zhǔ chǔlǐqì SCSI Bus jiēkǒu
MSC	Main switching center	主要的交换中心	Zhǔyàode jiāohuàn zhōngxīn
MSC	Maintenance and supply center	维护和供应中心	Wéihù hé gōngyìng zhōngxīn
MSC	Mass storage controller	大容量存储控制器	Dàróngliàng cúnchǔ kòngzhìqì
MSC	Message sequence chart	信息顺序图	Xìnxī shùnxù tú
MSC	Message sequence chart	消息序列表	Xiāoxi xùliè biǎo
MSC	Message sequence chart	消息顺序表	Xiāoxi shùnxù biǎo
MSC	Message switching center	信息交换中心	Xìnxī jiāohuàn zhōngxīn
MSC	Mobile satellite communications	移动卫星通讯	Yídòng wèixīng tōngxùn
MSC	Mobile switching center	移动交换中心	Yídòng jiāohuàn zhōngxīn
MSC	Mobile switching center	移动交换局	Yídòng jiāohuànjú
MSC	Mobile switching center	移动交换机	Yídòng jiāohuànjī
MSC	Mobile switching center	移动无线局	Yídòng wúxiàn jú
MSC, MSSC	Mobile service switching center	移动业务交换中心	Yídòng yèwù jiāohuàn zhōngxīn
MSC-A	The controlling MSC on which the call was originally established	发起切换的主控 MSC	Fāqǐ qiēhuànde zhǔkòng MSC
MSC-B	The MSC to which the MS is handed over in a basic handover	被切换到的 MSC	Bèiqiēhuàn dàode MSC
MSC-B'	The MSC to which the MS is handed over in a subsequent handover	被切换到的第三方 MSC	Bèiqiēhuàn dàode dìsānfāng MSC
MSCM	Mobile station class mark	移动台等级标	Yídòngtái děngjí biāo
MSCP	Multi-service confluence point	多业务汇接点	Duōyèwù huìjiēdiǎn
MSCU	Mobile station control unit	移动台控制单元	Yídòngtái kòngzhì dānyuán
MSCW	Marker stack control word	标记栈控制字	Biāojì zhàn kòngzhì zì
MSD	Microsoft diagnostics	微软诊断程序	Wēiruǎn zhěnduàn chéngxù
MS-DCC	Multiplex section data communications channel	复用段数据通信通道	Fùyòng duàn shùjù tōngxìn tōngdào
MSDIO	Measurements and statistics data I/O block	测量和统计数据 I/O 模块	Cèliáng hé tǒngjì shùjù I/O mókuài
MSDP	Multicast source discovery protocol	组播源发现协议	Zǔbō yuán fāxiàn xiéyì
MSDR	Main storage data register	主存储器数据寄存器	Zhǔ cúnchǔqì shùjù jìcúnqì
MSDS	Message switching data service	报文交换数据服务	Bàowén jiāohuàn shùjù fúwù
MSDSL	Multirate single pair digital subscriber loop	多速率单一线对数字用户环路	Duōsùlǜ dānyī xiànduì shùzì yònghù huánlù
MSDSL	Multirate symmetrical digital subscriber line	多速率对称数字用户线	Duōsùlǜ duìchèn shùzì yònghù xiàn
MSDSL	Multirate symmetrical digital subscriber loop	多速率对称数字用户环路	Duōsùlǜ duìchèn shùzì yònghù huánlù
MSDU	MAC service data unit	MAC 服务数据单元	MAC fúwù shùjù dānyuán
MSE	Maintenance sub-entity	维护子实体	Wéihù zǐshítǐ
MSE	MexE service environment	MExE 业务环境	MexE yèwù huánjìng
MSF	Media switching function	媒体交换模块	Méitǐ jiāohuàn mókuài
MSF	Mobile serving function	移动业务功能	Yídòng yèwù gōngnéng
MSF	Multi-service switching forum	多业务交换论坛	Duōyèwù jiāohuàn lùntán
MS-FERE	Multiplex segment far-end receive expiration	复用段远端接收失效	Fùyòng duàn yuǎnduān jiēshōu shīxiào

MSFF	Master-slave flip-flop	主从触发器	Zhǔ cóng chùfāqì
MSG	Multi-service gateway	多业务网关	Duōyèwù wǎngguān
MSI	Medium-scale integrated circuit	中规模集成电路	Zhōng guīmó jíchéng diànlù
MSID	Mobile station identifier	移动台标识符	Yídòngtái biāozhìfú
MSIN	Mobile station identification number	移动台识别号码	Yídòngtái shíbié hàomǎ
MSIN	Mobile station identification number	移动站识别号	Yídòngzhàn shíbié hào
MSISDN	Mobile station International ISDN number	移动台国际 ISDN 号码	Yídòngtái guójì ISDN hàomǎ
MSISDN	Mobile station international ISDN number	移动站国际 ISDN 号	Yídòngzhàn guójì ISDN hào
MSISDN	Mobile station ISDN number	移动台 ISDN 号码	Yídòngtái ISDN hàomǎ
MSISDN	Mobile subscriber ISDN number	移动用户 ISDN 号码	Yídòng yònghù ISDN hàomǎ
MSK	Minimal shift keying	最小频移键控	Zuìxiǎo pínyí jiànkòng
MSK	Minimum (frequency) shift keying	最小移频键控	Zuìxiǎo yípín jiànkòng
MSK	Minimum-phase frequency shift keying	最小相位频移键控	Zuìxiǎo xiàngwèi pínyí jiànkòng
MSL	Maximum segment lifetime	最大段寿命	Zuìdà duàn shòumìng
MSLC	Multiple sidelobe cancellation system	多旁瓣抑制系统	Duōpángbàn yìzhì xìtǒng
MSLL	Mean sidelobe level	平均旁瓣电平	Píngjūn pángbàn diànpíng
MSM	Message switching multiplexer	报文转发多路复用器	Bàowén zhuǎnfā duōlù fù yòngqì
MSMP	Modeling and Simulation Master Plan (US)	建模与仿真主计划	Jiànmó yǔ fǎngzhēn zhǔ jìhuà
MSN	Microsoft Network ©	微软网络	Wēiruǎn wǎngluò
MSN	Multiple subscriber number	多重用户号码	Duōchóng yònghù hàomǎ
MSN	Multi-subscriber number	多用户号码	Duōyònghù hàomǎ
MS-NC	Multiplex section network connection	复用段网络连接	Fùyòng duàn wǎngluò liánjiē
MSO	Management support object	管理支持目标	Guǎnlǐ zhīchí mùbiāo
MSOH	Multiplex section overhead	复接段开销	Fùjiē duàn kāixiao
MSOH	Multiplex section overhead	复用段开销	Fùyòng duàn kāixiao
MSP	Maintenance service provider	维护业务提供者	Wéihù yèwù tígōngzhě
MSP	Management service provider	管理业务提供者	Guǎnlǐ yèwù tígōngzhě
MSP	Mechanical extrusion forming (FOC mfg)	机械挤压法	Jīxiè jǐyā fǎ
MSP	Media stream processor	媒体流处理器	Méitǐ liú chǔlǐqì
MSP	Media stream provider	媒体流提供程序	Méitǐ liú tígōng chéngxù
MSP	Message security protocol	信息安全协议	Xìnxī ānquán xiéyì
MSP	Multiple subscriber profile	多用户分布	Duōyònghù fēnbù
MSP	Multiplex section protection	复用段保护	Fùyòng duàn bǎohù
MSP	Multiplex stage protection	复用段保护	Fùyòng duàn bǎohù
MSP	Multi-subscriber profile	多用户线路	Duōyònghù xiànlù
MSP-MF	MSP management function	MSP 管理功能	MSP guǎnlǐ gōngnéng
MSP-OpS	MSP operation system	MSP 运行系统	MSP yùnxíng xìtǒng
MSPP	Multiple service provisioning platform	多业务配置平台	Duōyèwù pèizhì píngtái
MSPP	Multi-service provider platform	多业务提供平台	Duōyèwù tígōng píngtái
MSPring	Multiplex segment shared protection ring	复用段保护环	Fùyòng duàn bǎohù huán
MSR	Magnetically shielded room	磁场屏蔽室	Cíchǎng píngbìshì
MSR	Mode status register	方式状态寄存器	Fāngshì zhuàngtài jìcúnqì
MSR	Model-specific register	模型特定寄存器	Móxíng tèdìng jìcúnqì
MSRD	Multi-speed-rate data (type of interface board)	多速率同步数据	Duōsùlǜ tóngbù shùjù
MS-RDI	Multiplex section remote defect indication	复用段远端缺陷指示	Fùyòng duàn yuǎnduān quēxiàn zhǐshì
MS-RDI	Multiplex segment receive defect indicator	复用段接收缺陷指示	Fùyòng duàn jiēshōu quēxiàn zhǐshì

MS-REI	Multiplex section remote error indication	复用段远端差错指示	Fù yòng duàn yuǎnduān chācuò zhǐshì
MS-REI	Multiplex section remote error indication	复用段远端误码指示	Fùyòng duàn yuǎnduān wùmǎ zhǐshì
MS-REI	Multiplex section remote error indicator	复用段远端差错指针	Fùyòng duàn yuǎnduān chācuò zhǐzhēn
MSRN	Mobile station roaming number	移动台漫游号码	Yídòngtái mànyóu hàomǎ
MSRN	Mobile subscriber roaming number	移动用户漫游号码	Yídòng yònghù mànyóu hàomǎ
MSS	Mobile satellite service	移动卫星业务	Yídòng wèixīng yèwù
MSSE	Message submission service element	消息提文服务要素	Xiāoxi tíwén fúwù yàosù
MSSF	Monitoring and system support facilities	监控和系统支持设施	Jiānkòng hé xìtǒng zhīchí shèshī
MSSN	Mean square signal-to-noise	均方信噪比	Jūn fāng xìn zào bǐ
MS-SPRing	Multiplex section-shared protection ring	复用段共享保护环	Fùyòng duàn gòngxiǎng bǎohù huán
MST	Ministry of science and technology	科学技术部	Kēxué jìshù bù
MST	Multiplex section termination	复用段终端	Fùyòng duàn zhōngduān
MST	Multiplex section termination	复用段终结	Fùyòng duàn zhōngjié
MST	Multiplex section termination function	复用段终端功能	Fùyòng duàn zhōngduān gōngnéng
MSTDM	Movable-slot time-division multiplexing	活动槽口时分多路复用	Huódòng cáokǒu shífèn duōlù fùyòng
MSTE	Multiplex section terminating element	复用段终端元	Fùyòng duàn zhōngduān yuán
MSTF	Mail-safe transfer format	邮件安全传输格式	Yóujiàn ānquán chuánshū géshi
MSTP	Multi-service transmission platform	多业务传输节点	Duōyèwù chuánshū jiédiǎn
MSTP	Multi-service transport platform	多业务传输平台	Duōyèwù chuánshū píngtái
MSTS	Multi-subscriber time shared (computer system)	多用户分时（计算机系统）	Duōyònghù fēnshí (jìsuànjī xìtǒng)
MSU	Message signal unit	消息信号单元	Xiāoxi xìnhào dānyuán
MSU	Message signaling unit	消息信令单元	Xiāoxi xìnlìng dānyuán
MSU	Mobile subscriber unit	移动用户单元	Yídòng yònghù dānyuán
MSw	Manual switch	人工切换	Réngōng qiēhuàn
MSW	Micro-switch	微型开关	Wēixíng kāiguān
MT	Machine translation	机器翻译	Jīqì fānyì
MT	Message termination	下传消息	Xiàchuán xiāoxi
MT	Message transfer	消息传送	Xiāoxi chuánsòng
MT	Mobile (station) terminating	移动台被叫	Yídòngtái bèijiào
MT	Mobile terminal	移动终端	Yídòng zhōngduān
MT	Mobile terminated	移动台终止的	Yídòngtái zhōngzhǐde
MT	Mobile terminated	移动终接	Yídòng zhōngjiē
MT	Mobile terminated	移动终止	Yídòng zhōngzhǐ
MT	Mobile terminated call	移动终止呼叫	Yídòng zhōngzhǐ hūjiào
MT	Run in metallic tubing	穿金属管敷设	Chuān jīnshǔguǎn fūshè
MTA	Mail transfer agent	邮件传输代理	Yóujiàn chuánshū dàilǐ
MTA	Message transfer agent	文电传递代理	Wéndiàn chuándì dàilǐ
MTA	Message transfer agent	消息传送代理	Xiāoxi chuánsòng dàilǐ
MTA	Multi-function terminal adapter	多功能终端适配器	Duōgōngnéng zhōngduān shìpèiqì
MTA	Multiple-tuned antenna	复调谐天线	Fù tiáoxié tiānxian
MTAM	Multi-leaving telecommunications access method	多点传送远程通信存取方法	Duōdiǎn chuánsòng yuǎnchéng tōngxìn cúnqǔ fāngfǎ
MTB	Maximum theoretical bandwidth	最大理论带宽	Zuìdà lǐlùn dàikuān
MTBF	Mean operating time between failures	平均失效间工作时间	Píngjūn shīxiào-jiān gōngzuò shíjiān
MTBF	Mean operating time between failures	平均无故障工作时间	Píngjūn wúgùzhàng gōngzuò shíjiān
MTBF	Mean time between failure	平均无故障时间	Píngjūn wúgùzhàng shíjiān
MTBF	Mean time between failures	平均失效间隔时间	Píngjūn shīxiào jiàngé shíjiān

MTBF	Mean time between failures	平均故障时间	Píngjūn gùzhàng shíjiān
MTBF	Mean time between failures	平均故障间隔时间	Píngjūn gùzhàng jiàngé shíjiān
MTBF	Mean time between failures	连续无故障时间	Liánxù wúgùzhàng shíjiān
MTBI	Mean time between interrupts	平均中断（间隔）时间	Píngjūn zhōngduàn (jiàngé) shíjiān
MTBM	Mean time between maintenance	平均维护（间隔）时间	Píngjūn wéihù (jiàngé) shíjiān
MTBSO	Mean time between service outages	平均业务运行中断间隔时间	Píngjūn yèwù yùnxíng zhōngduàn jiàngé shíjiān
MTC	Mobile terminating call	移动台被叫	Yídòngtái bèijiào
MTC	Mobile terminating call	移动被叫	Yídòng bèijiào
MTC	Mobile termination call	移动终端呼叫	Yídòng zhōngduān hūjiào
MTCS	Mobile traffic control sub-system	移动业务控制子系统	Yídòng yèwù kòngzhì zixìtǒng
MTD	Moving target detector	动目标检测器	Dòng mùbiāo jiǎncèqì
MTE	Microwave transport equipment	微波传输设备	Wēibō chuánshū shèbèi
MTH	Memory transfer hub	内存转换中心	Nèicún zhuǎnhuàn zhōngxīn
MTI	Moving target indicator	动目标显示	Dòng mùbiāo xiǎnshì
MTI	Moving targets indication radar	动目标显示雷达	Dòng mùbiāo xiǎnshì léidá
MTIE	Maximum timing interval error	最大时间间隔误差	Zuìdà shíjiān jiàngé wùchā
MT-LR	Mobile terminal location request	移动终端定位请求	Yídòng zhōngduān dìngwèi qǐngqiú
MTM	Mobile-to-mobile (call)	移动到移动（呼叫）	Yídòng dào yídòng (hūjiào)
MTP	Message transfer part	消息传输部分	Xiāoxi chuánshū bùfen
MTP	Message transfer part	消息传送部分	Xiāoxi chuánsòng bùfen
MTP	Message transfer part	消息传递部分	Xiāoxi chuándì bùfen
MTP	Message transfer part	信息传输部分	Xìnxī chuánshū bùfen
MTP	Message transport part	信息传递部分	Xìnxī chuándì bùfen
MTP/SO	Multicast transmission protocol/self-ordering	组播传送协议/自组织	Zǔbō chuánsòng xiéyì/zìzǔzhī
MTPL2	Message transfer part level 2 (in SS7)	消息传递部二层	Xiāoxi chuándìbù èrcéng
MTPL3-b	Broadband message transfer part level 3 (in SS7)	宽带消息传递部三层	Kuāndài xiāoxi chuándì bù sāncéng
MTRS	Mean time to restore service	恢复业务平均时间	Huīfù yèwù píngjūn shíjiān
MTS	Message transfer system	消息传送系统	Xiāoxi chuánsòng xìtǒng
MTS	Mobile Telephone System (Canada)	移动电话系统	Yídòng diànhuà xìtǒng
MTS	Module test system	模块试验系统	Mókuài shìyàn xìtǒng
MTS	Multi-thread server	多线路服务器	Duōxiànlù fúwùqì
M-TS	Manual-toll switch office	人工长途局	Réngōng chángtújú
MTSE	Message transfer service element	消息传送服务要素	Xiāoxi chuánsòng fúwù yàosù
MTSO	Mobile telephone switching office	移动电话交换局	Yídòng diànhuà jiāohuànjú
MTTF	Mean time to failure	平均失效前时间	Píngjūn shīxiào qián shíjiān
MTTF	Mean time to failure	平均无故障时间	Píngjūn wúgùzhàng shíjiān
MTTFF	Mean time to first failure	平均首次失效前时间	Píngjūn shǒucì shīxiào qián shíjiān
MTTR	Mean time to recovery	平均恢复时间	Píngjūn huīfù shíjiān
MTTR	Mean time to repair	平均修复时间	Píngjūn xiūfù shíjiān
MTTR	Mean time to repair	平均故障修理时间	Píngjūn gùzhàng xiūlǐ shíjiān
MTTR	Mean time to restoration	平均恢复时间	Píngjūn huīfù shíjiān
MTTSR	Mean time to service restoration	平均业务恢复时间	Píngjūn yèwù huīfù shíjiān
MTU	Maximum transmission unit	最大传输单元	Zuìdà chuánshū dānyuán
MTU	Maximum transmission unit	最大的传输单元	Zuìdàde chuánshū dānyuán
MTU	Maximum transmission unit	最大的传送单元	Zuìdàde chuánsòng dānyuán
MTVPAK	Microsoft TV Platform adaptation kit	微软 TV 平台适配套件	Wēiruǎn TV píngtái-shì pèitào jiàn

MU	Mark up (in price) (verb and noun)	标高	Biāogāo
MU	Mark up (in price) (verb and noun)	涨价	Zhǎngjià
MU	Mark up (in price) (verb and noun)	记账	Jìzhàng
MU	Miniature unit-coupling (FOC term)	小型单元耦合型	Xiǎoxíng dānyuán ǒuhéxíng
MUA	Maintenance-oriented group unblocking acknowledgement message	面向维护的群解除闭塞证实消息	Miànxiàng wéihùde qún jiěchú bìsè zhèngshí xiāoxi
MUD	Multiple user dimension	多用户	Duōyònghù
MUD	Multi-user detection	多用户检测	Duōyònghù jiǎncè
MUI	Mobile user identifier	移动用户标识符	Yídòng yònghù biāozhìfú
MULDEX	Multiplex and demultiplex	多路复用和多路分用	Duōlù fùyòng hé duōlù fēnyòng
Muldex	Multiplexer-demultiplexer	复用分用器	Fùyòng fēnyòngqì
MultiPPP	Mult-link point-to-point protocol	多重链路点对点协议	Duōzhòng liànlù diǎn duì diǎn xiéyì
MUM	Multi-unit message	多单元消息	Duōdānyuán xiāoxi
MUMS	Multi-user mobile station	多用户移动台	Duōyònghù yídòngtái
MuPS	Multicast service policy server	组播策略服务器	Zǔbō cèlüè fúwùqì
MUSA	Multiple-unit steerable array (antenna)	多元可控阵	Duōyuán kěkòng zhèn
MUSA	Multi-unit steerable antenna	多单元可控天线	Duōdānyuán kěkòng tiānxiàn
MUSE	Multiple sub-Nyquist sampling encoding	多重子奈奎斯特抽样编码	Duōzhòng ziNài-kuí-sī-tè chōuyàng biānmǎ
MUSIC	Multiple signal classification	多信号类级	Duōxìnhào lèijí
MUSICAM	Masking-pattern universal sub-band integrated coding and multiplexing	掩蔽模型通用子带综合编码和复用	Yǎnbì móxíng tōngyòng zidài zōnghé biānmǎ hé fùyòng
MUT	Mean up time	平均可用时间	Píngjūn kěyòng shíjiān
MUX	Flexible multiplexer	灵活复接器	Línghuó fùjiēqì
MUX	Multiplex	多路复用	Duōlù fùyòng
MUX	Multiplexer	复接设备	Fùjiē shèbèi
MUX	Multiplexer	复用器	Fùyòngqì
MUX	Multiplexer	多路复用器	Duōlù fùyòngqì
MUX/DEMUX	Multiplexer/demultiplexer	复接器 / 分接器	Fùjiēqì/fēnjiēqì
MVDS	Microwave video distribution system (European term for LMDS)	微波视像分配系统	Wēibō shìxiàng fēnpèi xìtǒng
MVDS	Multipoint video distribution service	多点视频分配业务	Duōdiǎn shìpín fēnpèi yèwù
MVDS	Multipoint video distribution system	多点视频分配系统	Duōdiǎn shìpín fēnpèi xìtǒng
MVID	Main vector identifier	主向量标示	Zhǔ xiàngliàng biāoshì
MVNO	Mobile virtual network operator	移动虚拟网络运营商	Yídòng xūnǐ wǎngluò yùnyíngshāng
MVPD	Modified vapor phase deposition (FOC mfg)	改良式汽相沉积法	Gǎiliáng-shì qìxiàng chénjī fǎ
MVPN	Mobile virtual private network	移动虚拟专用网	Yídòng xūnǐ zhuānyòng wǎng
MVSDLIB	Multiple virtual storage distribution library	多虚拟存储器分布库	Duōxūnǐ cúnchǔqì fēnbù kù
MWA	Mobile wireless access	移动无线接入	Yídòng wúxiàn jiērù
MWD	Maximum waiting delay	最大等待时延	Zuìdà děngdài shíyán
MWD	Message waiting data	消息等待数据	Xiāoxi děngdài shùjù
MWI	Message waiting indication	消息等待指示	Xiāoxi děngdài zhǐshì
MWI	Message-waiting indication	报文等待指示	Bàowén děngdài zhǐshì
MWS	Multiple wavelength solution	多波长解决方案	Duōbōcháng jiějué fāng'àn
MXP	Multi-service packet transmission platform	多业务分组传输平台	Duōyèwù fēnzǔ chuánshū píngtái
MZ	Open line carrier	明线载波	Míngxiàn zàibō
MZAP	Multicast scope zone announcement protocol (IETF usage)	组播区域范围公告协议	Zǔbō qūyù fànwéi gōnggào xiéyì

N

N	Nano- (prefix meaning 10^{-9})	毫微	Háowēi
N/A	Not used, not applicable	不适用	Bùshiyòng
N64	Nintendo 64 (computer game)	任天堂 64 位游戏机	Rèntiāntáng 64 wèi yóuxìjī
NA	Network adapter	网络适配器	Wǎngluò shìpèiqì
NA	No answer	无答应	Wúdáying
NA	Numerical aperture (of FOC)	数值孔径	Shùzhí kǒngjìng
NAB	Network address block	网络地址块	Wǎngluò dìzhǐ kuài
NAC	Network access controller	网络接入控制器	Wǎngluò jiērù kòngzhìqì
NACK	Negative acknowledgement	错误应答	Cuòwù yìngdá
NAD	Node address byte	节点地址字节	Jiédiǎn dìzhǐ zìjié
NAD	North American Datum (GIS)	北美大地基准面	Běiměi dàdì jīzhǔnmiàn
NAEA	North American equal access	北美平等接入	Běiměi píngděng jiērù
NAI	Nature of address indicator	地址性质表示语	Dìzhǐ xìngzhì biǎoshì yǔ
NAI	Nature of address indicator	地址指示器的特性	Dìzhǐ zhǐshìqìde tèxìng
NAI	Network access identifier	网络接入标识符	Wǎngluò jiērù biāozhì fú
NAK	Negative acknowledge	否认字符	Fǒurèn zìfú
NAK	Negative acknowledge	消极确认	Xiāojí quèrèn
NAM	National area message	国内地区使用消息	Guónèi dìqū shǐyòng xiāoxi
NAM	Number assignment module	号码分配模块	Hàomǎ fēnpèi mókuài
NAMAX.TH	Maximum theoretical numerical aperture	最大理论数值孔径	Zuìdà lǐlùn shùzhí kǒngjìng
NAMC	Non-adaptive motion compensation algorithm	非自适应运动补偿算法	Fēizìshìyìng yùndòng bǔcháng suànfǎ
NAMTS	Nippon Electric Company Advanced Mobile Telephone System	日本电气公司先进移动电话系统	Rìběn Diànqì Gōngsī xiānjìn yídòng diànhuà xìtǒng
NAND	Not and (a logical operator)	与非	Yǔ fēi
NAOC	No-account overclock	无效超频	Wúxiào chāopín
NAP	Network access point	网络访问点	Wǎngluò fǎngwèn diǎn
NAP	Non-significant address part	不重要的地址部分	Bùzhòngyàode dìzhǐ bùfen
NAPT	Network address port translation	网络地址及端口转换	Wǎngluò dìzhǐ jí duānkǒu zhuǎnhuàn
NAPT	Network address port translation	网络地址端口转换	Wǎngluò dìzhǐ duānkǒu zhuǎnhuàn
NARP	NBMA address resolution protocol (IETF use)	NBMA 地址解析协议	NBMA dìzhǐ jiěxī xiéyì
NAS	Network access server	网络接入服务器	Wǎngluò jiērù fúwùqì
NAS	Network access server	网络访问服务器	Wǎngluò fǎngwèn fúwùqì
NAS	Network attached storage	网络存储设备	Wǎngluò cúnchǔ shèbèi
NAS	Network attached storage	网络连接存储	Wǎngluò liánjiē cúnchǔ
NAS	Network attached storage	网络附加存储	Wǎngluò fùjiā cúnchǔ
NAS	Network attached storage	附网存储	Fùwǎng cúnchǔ
NAS	Network-attached storage	直接挂网的存储器	Zhíjiē guàwǎngde cúnchǔqì
NAS	Non-access stage	非接入层	Fēijiērù céng
NASA	National Aeronautics and Space Administration (US)	国家航空航天局	Guójiā hángkōng hángtiān jú
NAT	Network addess transform	网址变换	Wǎngzhǐ biànhuàn
NAT	Network address translation	网络地址解析	Wǎngluò dìzhǐ jiěxī
NAT	Network address translation	网络地址转换	Wǎngluò dìzhǐ zhuǎnhuàn
NAT	Network address translator	网络地址翻译器	Wǎngluò dìzhǐ fānyìqì
NAT	Network address translator	网络地址转换器	Wǎngluò dìzhǐ zhuǎnhuànqì

NAT-PT	Network address translation/protocol translation (in IPv6)	网络地址转换/协议转换技术	Wǎngluò dìzhǐ zhuǎnhuàn/ xiéyì zhuǎnhuàn jìshù
NAU	Network addressable unit	网络可寻址单元	Wǎngluò kěxúnzhǐ dānyuán
NAUM	Nearest active upstream neighbor	最近的，运行着的上行邻居	Zuìjìnde, yùnxíngzhede shàngxíng línjū
NAWS	Network management work station	网管工作站	Wǎngguǎn gōngzuòzhàn
NB	Normal burst	常规突发脉冲序列	Chángguī tūfā màichōng xùliè
NB	Normal burst	普通信息分组	Pǔtōng xìnxī fēnzǔ
NBAP	Node B application part	节点 B 应用部分	Jiédiǎn B yìngyòng bùfen
NBBE	Near-end background block error	近端背景误块	Jìnduān bèijǐng wùkuài
NBC	North Bridge chip	北桥芯片	Běiqiáo xìnpiàn
NBCD	Natural binary-coded decimal	自然二进制编码的十进制	Zìrán èrjìnzhì biānmǎde shíjìnzhì
NBCH	Natural binary-coded hexadecimal	自然二进制编码的十六进制	Zìrán èrjìnzhì biānmǎde shíliùjìnzhì
NBDL	Narrowband data link (line)	窄带数据链（线路）	Zhǎidài shùjù liàn (xiànlù)
NBFM	Narrowband frequency modulation	窄带调制	Zhǎidài tiáozhì
NBITD	National Board for Industrial and Technical Development (Sweden)	瑞典国立工业和技术发展委员会制订	Ruìdiǎn guólì gōngyè hé jìshù fāzhǎn wěiyuánhuì zhìdìng
NBMA	Non-broadcast multi-access	非广播式多路访问	Fēiguǎngbō-shì duōlù fǎngwèn
NBMA	Non-broadcast multiple access	非广播多接入	Fēiguǎngbō duōjiērù
NBP	Name binding protocol	名字绑定协议	Míngzì bǎngdìng xiéyì
NBP	Name binding protocol (Apple usage)	名称绑定协议	Míngchēng bǎngdìng xiéyì
NBPM	Narrowband phase modulation	窄带调相	Zhǎidài tiáoxiàng
NBS	National Bureau of Standards (US)	国家标准局	Guójiā Biāozhǔnjú
NBTDMA	Narrowband time division multiple access	窄频带时分多路存取	Zhǎipíndài shífēn duōlù cúnqǔ
NC	Network computer	网络计算机	Wǎngluò jìsuànjī
NC	Network connection	网络连接	Wǎngluò liánjiē
NC	Node control	节点控制	Jiédiǎn kòngzhì
NCAM	Network communication access method	网络通信访问法	Wǎngluò tōngxìn fǎngwèn fǎ
NCB	National call supervision message	国内呼叫监视消息	Guónèi hūjiào jiānshì xiāoxi
NCB	National Computer Board	国家电脑局	Guójiā diànnǎo jú
NCB	Network connect block	网络连接块	Wǎngluò liánjiē kuài
NCC	Network call controller	网络呼叫控制器	Wǎngluò hūjiào kòngzhìqì
NCC	Network color code	网络色码	Wǎngluò sèmǎ
NCCK	Non-coherent carrier keying	非相干载波键控	Fēixiānggān zàibō jiànkòng
NCD	No cell defined	无信元定界	Wúxìnyuán dìngjiè
NCDCDS	National Committee for Digital Cartographic Data Standards	数字制图数据标准国家委员会	Shùzì zhìtú shùjù biāozhǔn guójiā wěiyuánhuì
NCELL	Neighboring cell	相邻小区	Xiānglín xiǎoqū
NCFI	Non-canonical format indication	新规范的格式表示	Xīn guīfànde géshi biǎoshì
NCFI	Non-canonical format indication	非规范的格式标识符	Fēiguīfànde géshi biāozhì fú
NCFSK	Non-coherent frequency shift keyed modulation	非相干频移键控调制	Fēixiānggān pínyí jiànkòng tiáozhì
NCGIA	National Center for Geographic Information and Analysis	国家地理信息与分析中心	Guójiā dìlǐ xìnxī yǔ fēnxī zhōngxīn
NCH	Notification channel	通知信道	Tōngzhī xìndào
NCHO	Network control hand-off	网络控制切换	Wǎngluò kòngzhì qiēhuàn
NCI	North China Institute of Computing Technology	华北计算技术研究所	Huáběi Jìsuàn Jìshù Yánjiūsuǒ
NCIA	Native client interface architecture	本地客户接口结构	Běndì kèhù jiēkǒu jiégòu
NCIC	National Center for Intelligent Computing	国家智能计算机研究开发中心	Guójiā zhìnéng jìsuànjī yánjiū kāifā zhōngxīn
NCK	Network control key	网络控制键	Wǎngluò kòngzhì jiàn

NCM	Network configuration management	网络组成管理	Wăngluò zŭchéng guănlĭ
NCO	Numerically controlled oscillator	数控振荡器	Shùkòng zhèndàngqì
NCP	Network control protocol	网络控制协议	Wăngluò kòngzhì xiéyì
NCP	Network core protocol (Novell usage)	网络核心协议	Wăngluò héxīn xiéyì
NCP	Network layer control protocol	网络层控制协议	Wăngluò céng kòngzhì xiéyì
NCPA	Network synchronization control processor board assembly	网络同步控制处理器集成板	Wăngluò tóngbù kòngzhì chŭlĭqì jíchéngbăn
NCSA	National Center for Supercomputing Applications (US)	国家超级计算应用中心	Guójiā chāojí jìsuàn yìngyòng zhōngxīn
NCSA	National Computer Security Association	国家计算机安全协会	Guójiā jìsuànjī ānquán xiéhuì
NCSC	National Computer Security Center (US)	国家计算机安全中心	Guójiā jìsuànjī ānquán zhōngxīn
NCSMA	Non-persistent carrier sensing multiple access	非持续载波传感多路存取	Fēichíxù zàibō chuángăn duōlù cúnqŭ
NCSMA-CD	Non-persistent carrier sensing multiple access with collision detection	碰撞检测非持续载波传感多路存取	Pèngzhuàng jiăncè fēichíxù zàibō chuán găn duōlù cúnqŭ
NCSP	Network compiler simulation program	网络编译程序的仿真程序	Wăngluò biānyì chéngxùde făngzhēn chéngxù
NCTA	National Cable Television Association (US)	美国电缆电视协会	Mĕiguó diànlăn diànshì xiéhuì
NCU	Network control unit	网络控制单元	Wăngluò kòngzhì dānyuán
ND	Neighborhood discovery	寻找邻居	Xúnzhăo línjū
ND	Network default	网络默认值	Wăngluò mòrèn zhí
ND	Network defense	网络防卫	Wăngluò fángwèi
ND	Network digit	网络数字	Wăngluò shùzì
NDA	Non-DWORD-aligned (audio term)	非 DWORD 排列	Fēi DWORD páiliè
NDBP	Network synchronization distributor back panel	网络同步分配器后面板	Wăngluò tóngbù fēnpèiqì hòumianbăn
NDC	National destination code	国内目的地码	Guónèi mùdìdì mă
NDC	National destination code	国内终点号码	Guónèi zhōngdiăn hàomă
NDC	National destination code	国家目的码	Guójiā mùdì mă
NDC	National destination code	国家终点局代码	Guójiā zhōngdiănjú dàimă
NDCDB	National Digital Cartographic Data Base	国家数字制图数据库	Guójiā shùzì zhìtú shùjùkù
NDD	Norton Disk Doctor ©	诺顿磁盘医生	Nuò-dùn cípán yīshēng
NDE	Non-linear differential equation	非线性微分方程	Fēixiànxìng wēifēn fāngchéng
NDF	New data flag	新数据标帜	Xīn shùjù biāozhì
NDF	New data flag	新数据标识	Xīn shùjù biāozhì
NDF	New data flag (in SDH)	新数据标志	Xīn shùjù biāozhì
NDFA	Niobium-doped fiber amplifier	掺铌光纤放大器	Chānní guāngxiān fàngdàqì
NDI	Non-developmental item	非发展项目	Fēifāzhăn xiàngmù
NDIS	Network driver interface specification	网络驱动器接口规范	Wăngluò qūdòngqì jiēkŏu guīfàn
NDIS	Network driver interface specification	网络驱动程序接口规范	Wăngluò qūdòng chéngxù jiēkŏu guīfàn
NDLC	Network data link control	网络数据链控制	Wăngluò shùjù liàn kòngzhì
NDM	Normal disconnected mode	正常断开方式	Zhèngcháng duànkāi fāngshì
NDMP	Network data management protocol	网络数据管理协议	Wăngluò shùjù guănlĭ xiéyì
NDMS	Network design and management system	网络设计和管理系统	Wăngluò shèjì hé guănlĭ xìtŏng
NDP	Neighbor discovery protocol	邻机发现协议	Línjī fāxiàn xiéyì
NDRO	Non-destructive read-only	无损只读	Wúsŭn zhĭdú
NDRO	Non-destructive read-only	非破坏只读	Fēipòhuài zhĭ dú
NDRS	Non-algorithmic digital record systems	非规则数字记录系统	Fēiguīzé shùzì jìlù xìtŏng
NDS	Near-end defective second	近端缺陷秒	Jìnduān quēxiàn miăo
NDSC	Non-data-set clocking	非数据集时钟	Fēishùjùjí shízhōng

NDSS	Network directed system selection	网络指示的系统选择	Wǎngluò zhǐshìde xìtǒng xuǎnzé
NDUB	Network determined user busy	网络决定用户忙	Wǎngluò juédìng yònghù máng
NDUB	Network determined user busy	网络确定用户忙	Wǎngluò quèdìng yònghù máng
NDUP	Network determited user busy	确定网络用户忙	Quèdìng wǎngluò yònghù máng
NE	Network element	网元	Wǎngyuán
NE	Network element	网络单元	Wǎngluò dānyuán
NE	Network equipment	网络设备	Wǎngluò shèbèi
NE	Not equal	不等于	Bùděngyú
NEAM	Non-volatile electrically alterable memory	永久性电可变存储器	Yǒngjiǔxìng diàn kěbiàn cúnchǔqì
NEB	Noise equivalent bandwidth	噪声等效带宽	Zàoshēng děngxiào dàikuān
NEBC	Near-end error block counter	近端误块计数	Jìnduān wùkuài jìshù
NEC	Near-end crosstalk	近端串话	Jìnduān chuànhuà
NEC	Nippon Electronics Corporation	日电	Rì diàn
NEF	Network element function	网元功能	Wǎngyuán gōngnéng
NEF	Network element function	网络单元功能	Wǎngluò dānyuán gōngnéng
NEF	Network element function block	网络单元功能块	Wǎngluò dānyuán gōngnéng kuài
NEF	Noise equivalent flux	噪声等效通量	Zàoshēng děngxiào tōngliàng
NEFD	Noise equivalent flux density	噪声等效流密度	Zàoshēng děngxiào liú mìdù
NEHO	Network evaluated handover	判断网络切换	Pànduàn wǎngluò qiēhuàn
NEI	Network entity identifier	网络实体标识符	Wǎngluò shítǐ biāozhìfú
NEI	Noise equivalent intensity	噪声等效强度	Zàoshēng děngxiào qiángdù
NEL	Network element layer	网元层	Wǎngyuán céng
NEL	Network element level	网元层	Wǎngyuán céng
NEMF	Network error management facilities	网络错误管理设施	Wǎngluò cuòwù guǎnlǐ shèshī
NEMS	Network element management system	网元管理系统	Wǎngyuán guǎnlǐ xìtǒng
NEP	Noise equivalent power	噪声等效功率	Zàoshēng děngxiào gōnglǜ
NEPD	Noise equivalent power density	噪声等效功率密度	Zàoshēng děngxiào gōnglǜ mìdù
NER	Noise equivalent radiance	噪声等效辐射率	Zàoshēng děngxiào fúshè lǜ
NES	Near-end echo suppressor	近端回波抑制器	Jìnduān huíbō yìzhìqì
NES	Near-end errored second	近端误块秒	Jìnduān wùkuài miǎo
NES	Noise equivalent input signal	噪声等效输入信号	Zàoshēng děngxiào shūrù xìnhào
NET	Network entity title	网络实体名称	Wǎngluò shítǐ míngchēng
NET	Noise equivalent temperature	噪声等效温度	Zàoshēng děngxiào wēndù
NET	Northern Eagle Technology Corp. (US company)	北鹰科技有限公司	Běiyīng kējì yǒuxiàn gōngsī
NetBEUI	NetBIOS extended user interface	网络基本输入/输出系统扩展用户接口	Wǎngluò jīběn shūrù/shūchū xìtǒng kuòzhǎn yònghù jiēkǒu
NetBEUI	NetBIOS extended user interface (IBM usage)	NetBIOS 扩展用户接口	NetBIOS kuòzhǎn yònghù jiēkǒu
NetBIOS	Network basic input output system (IBM usage)	网络基本输入输出系统	Wǎngluò jīběn shūrù shūchū xìtǒng
NetBIOS	Network basic input/output system	网络基本输入/输出系统	Wǎngluò jīběn shūrù/shūchū xìtǒng
NETD	Noise equivalent temperature difference	噪声等效温差	Zàoshēng děngxiào wēnchā
NetDDE	Network dynamic data exchange	网络动态数据交换	Wǎngluò dòngtài shùjù jiāohuàn
NEXT	Near-end cross talk	近端串音	Jìnduān chuànyīn
NEXT	Near-end crosstalk	近端串扰	Jìnduān chuànrǎo
NF	Network function	网络功能	Wǎngluò gōngnéng
NF	Noise figure	噪声系数	Zàoshēng xìshù
NF	Norme Francaise (French standards organization)	法国标准	Fǎguó biāozhǔn

NFA	Non-forwarding address	非转发地址	Fēizhuǎnfā dìzhǐ
NFAP	Network file access protocol	网络文件访问存取协议	Wǎngluò wénjiàn fǎngwèn cúnqǔ xiéyì
NFC	Noise feedback control	噪声反馈控制	Zàoshēng fǎnkuì kòngzhì
NFE	Network facility extensions	网络设施扩展	Wǎngluò shèshī kuòzhǎn
NFL	Nearest feature line (CAD/CAM)	最近特征线	Zuìjìn tèzhēng xiàn
NFM	Narrowband frequency modulation	窄带调频	Zhǎidài tiáopín
NFP	Near-field pattern	近场图	Jìncháng tú
NFS	Network file system	网络文件系统	Wǎngluò wénjiàn xìtǒng
n-FSK	N-condition frequency shift keying	n 态频移键控	n-tài pínyí jiànkòng
NG	National grid	国家格网	Guójiā géwǎng
NGAF	Non-GPRS alert flag	非 GPRS 提示标志	Fēi GPRS tíshì biāozhì
NGD	National Geographic Directorate	国家地理管理局	Guójiā dìlǐ guǎnlǐjú
NGD	National Geospatial Database	国家地理空间数据库	Guójiā dìlǐ kōngjiān shùjùkù
NGEN	Native image generator	本地映像生成器	Běndì yìngxiàng shēngchéngqì
NGI	Next generation Internet	下一代因特网	Xiàyīdài Yīntèwǎng
NGIO	Next generation input/output	新一代输入/输出标准	Xīn yīdài shūrù/shūchū biāozhǔn
NGL	National Geological Library (China)	国家地质图书馆	Guójiā dìzhì túshūguǎn
NGN	Next generation network	下一代网络	Xiàyīdài wǎngluò
NGOSS	Next generation operating system and software	下一代电信运营系统和软件	Xiàyīdài diànxìn yùnyíng xìtǒng hé ruǎnjiàn
NGP	Network graphics protocol	网络图解协议	Wǎngluò tújiě xiéyì
NGRS	National Geodetic Reference System (US)	国家测量参照系	Guójiā cèliáng cānzhàoxì
NHC	Next hop client	下一跳客户	Xiàyītiào kèhù
NHLFE	Next hop label forwarding entry	下一跳标记转发条目	Xiàyītiào biāojì zhuǎnfā tiáomù
NHRP	Next hop routing protocol	下一跳路由协议	Xiàyītiào lùyóu xiéyì
NHRP	Next-hop (address) resolution protocol	下一跳地址解析协议	Xiàyītiào dìzhǐ jiěxī xiéyì
NHRP	Next-hop resolution protocol	下一跳解析协议	Xiàyītiào jiěxī xiéyì
NHRP	Next-hop routing protocol	下一跳路由协议	Xiàyītiào lùyóu xiéyì
NHS	Next-hop server	下一跳服务器	Xiàyītiào fúwùqì
NHS	Number handling sub-system	编号处理子系统	Biānhào chǔlǐ zixìtǒng
NI	Network indicator	网络表示语	Wǎngluò biǎoshì yǔ
NI	Network integrator	网络综合器	Wǎngluò zōnghéqì
NI	Network interface	网络接口	Wǎngluò jiēkǒu
NI	Non-Intel ®	非英特尔架构	Fēi Yīng-tè-ěr jiàgòu
NIA	Network interface adapter	网络接口传接器	Wǎngluò jiēkǒu chuánjiēqì
NIA	Networking Interoperability Alliance	网络互操作联盟	Wǎngluò hùcāozuò liánméng
NIC	Network independent clocking	网络独立同步	Wǎngluò dúlì tóngbù
NIC	Network information center	网络信息中心	Wǎngluò xìnxī zhōngxīn
NIC	Network interface card	网络接口卡	Wǎngluò jiēkǒu kǎ
NIC	Network interface controller	网络接口控制器	Wǎngluò jiēkǒu kòngzhìqì
NICE	Network information and control exchange protocol (in DECnet)	网络信息和控制交换协议	Wǎngluò xìnxī hé kòngzhì jiāohuàn xiéyì
NICS	Network integrity control system	网络统一控制系统	Wǎngluò tǒngyī kòngzhì xìtǒng
NID	Network identification	网络标识	Wǎngluò biāozhì
NID	Network identity	网络识别码	Wǎngluò shíbié mǎ
NIE	Network interface element	网络接口单元	Wǎngluò jiēkǒu dānyuán
NIF	Neighbor information frame	相邻站点信息帧	Xiānglín zhàndiǎn xìnxī zhèng
NIF	Network information files	网络信息文件	Wǎngluò xìnxī wénjiàn

NIF	Network interconnect function	网络互连功能	Wǎngluò hùlián gōngnéng
NIF	Node interworking function	节点互通功能	Jiédiǎn hùtōng gōngnéng
NII	National Information Infrastructure	全国资讯体系	Quánguó zīxùn tǐxì
NII	National Information Infrastructure	国家信息基础设施	Guójiā xìnxī jīchǔ shèshī
NIKOS	New Internet knowledge system	新因特网智能系统	Xīn Yīntèwǎng zhìnéng xìtǒng
NI-LR	Network induced location request	导致网络定位请求	Dǎozhì wǎngluò dìngwèi qǐngqiú
NIS	Network information system	网络信息服务	Wǎngluò xìnxī fúwù
N-ISDN	Narrowband integrated services digital network	窄带综合业务数字网	Zhǎidài zōnghé yèwù shùzì wǎng
N-ISDN	Narrowband integrated services digital network	窄带综合业务网	Zhǎidài zōnghé yèwù wǎng
NIST	National Institute of Standards and Technology (US)	国家标准技术研究所	Guójiā biāozhǔn jìshù yánjiūsuǒ
N-ISUP	Narrowband ISDN user part	窄带 ISDN 用户部分	Zhǎidài ISDN yònghù bùfen
NITZ	Network identity and time zone	网络识别和时域	Wǎngluò shíbié hé shíyù
NIU	Network interface unit	网络接口单元	Wǎngluò jiēkǒu dānyuán
NLAID	Network level aggregation identifer	网络级聚集标识符	Wǎngluò jí jùjí biāozhìfú
NLCQI	Natural language Chinese query interface	自然语言汉语查询界面	Zìrán yǔyán hànyǔ cháxún jièmiàn
NLD	Non-linear distortion	非线性失真	Fēixiànxìng shīzhēn
NLFM	Non-linear frequency modulation	非线性调频	Fēixiànxìng tiáopín
NLM	NetWare loadable module	NetWare 可装入模块	NetWare kězhuāngrù mókuài
NLMS	Normalized least mean square	归一最小均方	Guī yī zuìxiǎo jūn fāng
NLMS	Normalized least mean squares	归一化最小均方误差	Guīyīhuà zuìxiǎo jūnfāng wùchā
NLOS	Non-line-of-site	非站点线路	Fēizhàndiǎn xiànlù
NLP	Natural language processing	自然语言理解	Zìrán yǔyán lǐjiě
NLP	Non-linear processor	非线性处理器	Fēixiànxìng chǔlǐqì
NLPI	Network layer protocol identifier	网络层协议标识符	Wǎngluò céng xiéyì biāozhì fú
NLPort	Node loop port	节点环端口	Jiédiǎn huán duānkǒu
NLQ	Near letter quality	近打字效果	Jìn dǎzì xiàoguǒ
NLS	National language support	国家语言支持	Guójiā yǔyán zhīchí
NLSP	NetWare link services protocol	NetWare 链路服务协议	NetWare liànlù fúwù xiéyì
NLSP	NetWare link state protocol (Novell usage)	NetWare 链路服务协议	NetWare liànlù fúwù xiéyì
NLTC	Network layer topology configurator	网络层拓扑结构	Wǎngluò céng tuòpū jiégòu
NM	Network management	网管	Wǎngguǎn
NM	Network management	网络管理	Wǎngluò guǎnlǐ
NM	Network manager	网络管理者	Wǎngluò guǎnlǐzhě
NMAC	Network monitor and control	网络监控	Wǎngluò jiānkòng
NMAP	Neighboring mobile access point	相邻移动接入点	Xiānglín yídòng jiērù diǎn
NMAS	National Map Accuracy Standards (US)	国家地图精度标准	Guójiā dìtú jīngdù biāozhǔn
NMC	Network management center	网管中心	Wǎngguǎn zhōngxīn
NMC	Network management center	网络管理中心	Wǎngluò guǎnlǐ zhōngxīn
NMF	Network management forum	网络管理论坛	Wǎngluò guǎnlǐ lùntán
NMI	Network management interface	网管接口	Wǎngguǎn jiēkǒu
NML	Network management layer	网络管理层	Wǎngluò guǎnlǐ céng
NML	Neutral message language	中性消息语言	Zhōngxìng xiāoxi yǔyán
NMLTC	Network management layer topology configurator	网络管理层拓扑结构	Wǎngluò guǎnlǐ céng tuò pū jiégòu
NMR	Network measurement results	网络测量结果	Wǎngluò cèliáng jiéguǒ
NMR	Noise to masking ratio	噪声掩蔽比	Zàoshēng yǎnbì bǐ
NMS	Network management sub-system	网络管理子系统	Wǎngluò guǎnlǐ zixìtǒng

NMS	Network management system	网管系统	Wǎngguǎn xìtǒng
NMS	Network management system	网络管理系统	Wǎngluò guǎnlǐ xìtǒng
NMS/X	Nokia Measurement System for X-Windows	诺基亚基于 X-Windows 平台的测量系统	Nuò-jī-yà jīyú X-Windows píngtáide cèliáng xìtǒng
NMSI	National mobile station identification number	国家移动台识别号	Guójiā yídòngtái shíbiéhào
NMSI	National mobile station identifier	国家移动台标识符	Guójiā yídòngtái biāozhìfú
NMSI	National mobile station identity	国内移动台识别号码	Guónèi yídòngtái shíbié hàomǎ
NMSS	Network maximum segment size	网络最大段长度	Wǎngluò zuìdà duàn chángdù
NMT	Network management terminal	网管终端	Wǎngguǎn zhōngduān
NMT	Nordic Mobile Telephone System	北欧移动电话系统	Běi'ōu yídòng diànhuà xìtǒng
NMU	Native mode usage	本机操作模式	Běnjī cāozuò móshì
NMVT	Network management vector transport	网络管理相量传输	Wǎngluò guǎnlǐ xiāngliáng chuánshū
NN	National number	国内号码	Guónèi hàomǎ
NN	Nearest neighbor (CAD/CAM)	最近邻	Zuìjìn lín
NN	Neighbor station advice	邻站通知	Línzhàn tōngzhī
NNC	National-network-congestion signal	国内网拥塞信号	Guónèi wǎng yōngsè xìnhào
NNE	Non-SDH network element	非 SDH 网元	Fēi SDH wǎng yuán
NNI	Network node interface	网络节点接口	Wǎngluò jiédiǎn jiēkǒu
NNI	Network node interface	网路节点接口	Wǎnglù jiédiǎn jiēkǒu
NNI	Network to network interface	网络间接口	Wǎngluò-jiān jiēkǒu
NNI	Network-to-network interface	网络-网络接口	Wǎngluò—wǎngluò jiēkǒu
NNMC	National (Mobile Communications) Network Management Center	全国(移动通信)操作维护中心	Quánguó (yídòng tōngxìn) cāozuò wéihù zhōngxīn
NNMC	National Network Management Center	全国网络管理中心	Quánguó wǎngluò guǎnlǐ zhōngxīn
NNTP	Network news transfer protocol	网络新闻传输协议	Wǎngluò xīnwén chuánshū xiéyì
NNTP	Network news transfer protocol	网络新闻传送协议	Wǎngluò xīnwén chuánsòng xiéyì
NO	Network operator	网络运营商	Wǎngluò yùnyíngshāng
NOAA	National Oceanic and Atmospheric Administration (US)	国家海洋与大气署	Guójiā hǎiyáng yǔ dàqì shǔ
NOC	Network operating center	网络运行中心	Wǎngluò yùnxíng zhōngxīn
NOC	Network operations center	网络操作中心	Wǎngluò cāozuò zhōngxīn
NOLM	Non-linear optical fiber loop mirror	非线性光纤环路镜	Fēixiànxìng guāngxiān huánlù jìng
NOLM	Non-linear optical loop mirroring	非线性光纤环行镜	Fēixiànxìng guāngxiān huánxíng jìng
NOM_PWR	Nominal power	标称功率	Biāochēng gōnglǜ
NOMC	Network operation and maintenance center	网络操作和维护中心	Wǎngluò cāozuò hé wéihù zhōngxīn
NO-MODIFY	Unmodified	非更改	Fēigēnggǎi
NOR	Not or	或非	Huò fēi
NOS	Network operation system	网络操作系统	Wǎngluò cāozuò xìtǒng
NOT	Not	非	Fēi
NP	Neper (unit of attenuation, =8.686 dB)	奈培	Nài-péi
NP	Network performance	网络性能	Wǎngluò xìngnéng
NP	Network provider	网络提供商	Wǎngluò tígōngshāng
NP	Non-linear programming	非线性规划	Fēixiànxìng guīhuà
NP	Number portability	号码可携带	Hàomǎ kěxiédài
NP	Number portability	号码流动	Hàomǎ liúdòng
NP	Numbering plan	号码规划	Hàomǎ guīhuà
NP	Numbering plan	编号计划	Biānhào jìhuà

NPA	Network performance analyzer	网络性能分析程序	Wǎngluò xìngnéng fēnxī chéngxù
NPA	Numbering plan area	编号计划范围	Biānhào jìhuà fànwéi
NPAI	Network protocol address information	网络协议地址信息	Wǎngluò xiéyì dìzhǐ xìnxī
NPC	National processing Center	国家处理中心	Guójiā chǔlǐ zhōngxīn
NPC	National processing center (in the finance network)	国家处理中心	Guójiā chǔlǐ zhōngxīn
NPC	Network parameter control	网络参数控制	Wǎngluò cānshù kòngzhì
NPDTE	Non-packet digital terminal equipment	非包式数字终端设备	Fēibāo-shì shùzì zhōngduān shèbèi
NPDU	Network protocol data unit	网络协议数据单元	Wǎngluò xiéyì shùjù dānyuán
NPE	Network protection equipment	网络保护设备	Wǎngluò bǎohù shèbèi
NPI	Null point identification	无效指针指示	Wúxiào zhǐzhēn zhǐshì
NPI	Numbering plan identifier	编号计划标识符	Biānhào jìhuà biāozhì fú
NPI	Numbering plan indicator	编号计划指示符	Biānhào jìhuà zhǐshì fú
NPMS	Non-process monitor system	非过程监督系统	Fēiguòchéng jiāndū xìtǒng
NPON	Narrowband passive optical network	窄带无源光网络	Zhǎidài wúyuán guāng wǎngluò
NPR	Noise power ratio	噪声功率比	Zàoshēng gōnglǜ bǐ
NPS/X	Nokia Planning System for X-Windows	诺基亚基于 X-Windows 平台的规划系统	Nuò-jī-yà jīyú X-Windows píngtáide guīhuà xìtǒng
NPSIN	National Public Switched Telecommunications Network	国家公共交换电信网	Guójiā gōnggòng jiāohuàn diànxìn wǎng
N-PSK	N-phase pulse-shift-keying	N 相脉冲移位链控	N-xiàng màichōng yíwèi liànkòng
NPSS	National Packet-Switched Data Transmission System	全国包交换数据传输系统	Quánguó bāo jiāohuàn shùjù chuánshū xìtǒng
NPT	Non-packet Terminal	非分组终端	Fēifēnzǔ zhōngduān
N-QAM	N-state quadrature amplitude modulation	N 态正交调幅	N-tài zhèngjiāo tiáofú
n-QAM	N-state quadrature amplitude modulation	n 状态正交幅度调制	n-zhuàngtài zhèngjiāo fúdù tiáozhì
N-QAM	N-state quadrature amplitude modulation	N 状态正交调幅	N-zhuàngtài zhèngjiāo tiáofú
N-QFSK	Narrowband quadrature frequency shift keying	窄带正交移频键控	Zhǎidài zhèngjiāo yípín jiànkòng
N-QPSK	Narrowband quadrature phase shift keying	窄带正交移相键控	Zhǎidài zhèngjiāo yíxiàng jiànkòng
NR	Network resource	网络资源	Wǎngluò zīyuán
NRA	Network resource architecture	网络资源结构	Wǎngluò zīyuán jiégòu
NRC	Network resources control	网络资源控制	Wǎngluò zīyuán kòngzhì
NREN	National Research and Education Network	国家科研教育网络	Guójiā kēyán jiàoyù wǎngluò
NRIM	Network resource information model	网络资源信息模型	Wǎngluò zīyuán xìnxī móxíng
NRM	Network resource management	网络资源管理	Wǎngluò zīyuán guǎnlǐ
NRM	Network resource model	网络资源模型	Wǎngluò zīyuán móxíng
NRM	Normal response mode	正常响应方式	Zhèngcháng xiǎngyìng fāngshì
NRMS	Nominal root-mean square	标称均方根	Biāochēng jūn fānggēn
NrREP	Non-regenerative repeater	无再生中继器	Wúzàishēng zhōngjìqì
NRT	Non-real time	非实时	Fēishíshí
NrtPS	Non-real time polling service	非实时查询业务	Fēishíshí cháxún yèwù
nrt-VBR	Non-real time variable bit rate	非实时可变比特率	Fēishíshí kěbiàn bǐtè lǜ
NRU	Node resource unit	节点资源单位	Jiédiǎn zīyuán dānwèi
NRZ	Non-return to zero	不归零制	Bùguīlíng zhì
NRZ	Non-return to zero coding	非归零码	Fēiguīlíng mǎ
NRZI	Non-return to zero (inverted)	不归零反相	Bùguīlíng (fǎnxiāng)
NRZL	Non-return to zero-level	不归零电平	Bùguīlíng diànpíng
NS	Nanosecond	毫微秒	Háowēimiǎo

NS	Network service	网络业务	Wǎngluò yèwù
NS	Network service	网络服务	Wǎngluò fúwù
NS	Network synchronization	网同步	Wǎng tóngbù
NS	Non-standard	非标准	Fēibiāozhǔn
NSA	National Security Agency (US)	国家安全局	Guójiā ānquán jú
NSAN	Null-steering antenna	零转向天线	Líng zhuǎnxiàng tiānxiàn
NSAP	Network service access point	网络业务接入点	Wǎngluò yèwù jiērù diǎn
NSAP	Network service access point	网络服务接入点	Wǎngluò fúwù jiērù diǎn
NSAP	Network service access point	网络服务访问点	Wǎngluò fúwù fǎngwèn diǎn
NSAPI	Network layer service access point identifier	网络层业务接入点标识符	Wǎngluò céng yèwù jiērùdiǎn biāozhìfú
NSAPI	Network service access point identifier	网络业务接入点标识符	Wǎngluò yèwù jiērù diǎn biāozhìfú
NSB	National successful backward set-up message	国内后向建立成功消息	Guónèi hòuxiàng jiànlì chénggōng xiāoxi
NSBP	Network synchronization back panel	网络同步后面板	Wǎngluò tóngbù hòumianbǎn
NSC	Network service center	网络服务中心	Wǎngluò fúwù zhōngxīn
NSC	Noise suppression circuit	噪声抑制电路	Zàoshēng yìzhì diànlù
NS-C	Network synchronization connection function module	网同步连接功能模块	Wǎng tóngbù liánjiē gōngnéng mókuài
NSCG	Network synchronization clock generation	网络同步时钟发生器	Wǎngluò tóngbù shízhōng fāshēngqì
NSCK	Network subset control key	网络用户电话机控制键	Wǎngluò yònghù diànhuàjī kòngzhì jiàn
NSCM	Network synchronization clock maintenance	网络同步时钟维护	Wǎngluò tóngbù shízhōng wéihù
NSCR	Network synchronization clock repeater	网络同步时钟中继器	Wǎngluò tóngbù shízhōng zhōngjìqì
NSDU	Network service data unit	网络业务数据单元	Wǎngluò yèwù shùjù dānyuán
NSDU	Network service data unit	网络服务数据单元	Wǎngluò fúwù shùjù dānyuán
NSE	Network section ensemble	网络段集合	Wǎngluò duàn jíhé
NSE	Network service entity	网络业务实体	Wǎngluò yèwù shítǐ
NSEI	Network service entity identifier	网络业务实体标识符	Wǎngluò yèwù shítǐ biāozhìfú
NSES	Near-end severely errored second	近端严重误块秒	Jìnduān yánzhòng wùkuài miǎo
NSF	National Science Foundation (US)	国家科学基金会	Guójiā Kēxué Jījīnhuì
NSFnet	National Science Foundation Network (US)	国家科学基金会网络	Guójiā Kēxué Jījīnhuì wǎngluò
NSM	Network and switch management	网络与交换管理	Wǎngluò yǔ jiāohuàn guǎnlǐ
NSP	National signaling point	国内信令点	Guónèi xìnlìng diǎn
NSP	Network service part	网络服务部分	Wǎngluò fúwù bùfen
NSP	Network service protocol (in DECnet)	网络服务协议	Wǎngluò fúwù xiéyì
NSP	Network service provider	网络业务提供者	Wǎngluò yèwù tígòngzhě
NSP	Network service provider	网络服务提供商	Wǎngluò fúwù tígōngshāng
NSS	Network sub-system	网络子系统	Wǎngluò zixìtǒng
NSS	Network switching sub-system	网络交换子系统	Wǎngluò jiāohuàn zixìtǒng
NS-VC	Network service virtual connection	网络业务虚连接	Wǎngluò yèwù xū liánjiē
NS-VCI	Network service virtual connection identifier	网络业务虚连接标识符	Wǎngluò yèwù xū liánjiē biāozhìfú
NS-VL	Network service virtual link	网络业务虚链路	Wǎngluò yèwù xū liànlù
NS-VLI	Network service virtual link identifier	网络业务虚链路标识符	Wǎngluò yèwù xū liànlù biāozhìfú
NT	Network terminal, termination	网络终端	Wǎngluò zhōngduān
NT	Network termination	网络终接	Wǎngluò zhōngjiē
NT	Not transparent	不透明的	Bùtòumíngde
NT1	Network terminal type 1	第一类网络终端	Dìyīlèi wǎngluò zhōngduān
NT-1	Network termination 1	网络终端设备 1	Wǎngluò zhōngduān shèbèi 1
NTA	Noise temperature of antenna	天线噪声温度	Tiānxiàn zàoshēng wēndù

NTAAB	New type approval advisory board	新定型咨询台	Xīn dìngxíng zīxún tái
NTC	Negative temperature coefficient	负温度系数	Fù wēndù xìshù
NTC	Network and trunk control	网络及总线控制	Wǎngluò jí zǒngxiàn kòngzhì
NTCM	Network topology configuration management	网络拓扑组成管理	Wǎngluò tuòpū zǔchéng guǎnlǐ
NTF	National transfer format	国家传输格式	Guójiā chuánshū géshi
NTF	Navy technological forecast	海军技术预测	Hǎijūn jìshù yùcè
NTMS	Network traffic management system	网络话务管理系统	Wǎngluò huàwù guǎnlǐ xìtǒng
NTN	Network terminal number	网络终端号码	Wǎngluò zhōngduān hàomǎ
NTP	Network termination point	网络终端端点	Wǎngluò zhōngduān duāndiǎn
NTP	Network time protocol	网络时间协议	Wǎngluò shíjiān xiéyì
NTP	Network time protocol	网络时间同步协议	Wǎngluò shíjiān tóngbù xiéyì
NTP	Network timing protocol	网络定时协议	Wǎngluò dìngshí xiéyì
NTR	Network time reference	网络时钟参考	Wǎngluò shízhōng cānkǎo
NTR	Noise-temperature ratio	噪声温度比	Zàoshēng wēndù bǐ
NTSC	National Television Standard Committee	国家电视标准委员会	Guójiā diànshì biāozhǔn wěiyuánhuì
NTSC	National Television Systems Committee (US television broadcast standard)	全国电视系统委员会制式	Quánguó diànshì xìtǒng wěiyuánhuì zhìshì
NTT	Nippon Telegraph & Telephone	日本电报电话	Rìběn Diànbào Diànhuà
NTU	Network terminal unit	网络终端单元	Wǎngluò zhōngduān dānyuán
NU	National use	国内使用	Guónèi shǐyòng
NUA	Network user access	网络用户地址	Wǎngluò yònghù dìzhǐ
NUB	National unsuccessful backward set-up message	国内后向建立不成功消息	Guónèi hòuxiàng jiànlì bùchénggōng xiāoxi
NUI	National user/user identification module identifier	国家用户/普通用户识别模块标识符	Guójiā yònghù/pǔtōng yònghù shíbié mókuài biāozhì fú
NUI	Network user identification	网络用户标示	Wǎngluò yònghù biāoshì
NUI	Network user identification	网络用户识别	Wǎngluò yònghù shíbié
NUL	Null	空白	Kòngbái
NumLock	Number lock key	数字键位	Shùzì jiàn wèi
NUP	Network user part	网络用户部分	Wǎngluò yònghù bùfen
NURBS	Non-uniform rational B-splines	非均匀有理 B 样条	Fēijūnyún yǒulǐ B-yàng tiáo
NVI	Non-vectored interrupt	非向量中断	Fēixiàngliàng zhōngduàn
NVM	Non-volatile memory	不挥发存储器	Bùhuīfā cúnchǔqì
NVOD	Near video on demand	准影视点播	Zhǔn yǐngshì diǎnbō
NVOD	Near video on demand	准点播电视	Zhǔn diǎnbō diànshì
NVRAM	Non-volatile random access memory	非易失随机存取存储器	Fēiyìshī suíjī cúnqǔ cúnchǔqì
NZ	Normalization type	标准型	Biāozhǔn xíng
NZDF	Non-zero dispersion fiber	非零色散光纤	Fēilíng sèsàn guāngxiān
NZDSF	Non-zero dispersion-shifted optical fiber	非零色散位移光纤	Fēilíng sèsàn wèiyí guāngxiān
NZ-DSF	Non-zero-dispersion shift fiber	非零散位移光纤	Fēiíngsǎn wèiyí guāngxiān

O

O	Oxide-coated	敷氧化层的	Fūyǎnghuà céngde
O&M	Operation and maintenance	运行与维护	Yùnxíng yǔ wéihù
O&M; OM	Operations and maintenance	操作和维护	Cāozuò hé wéihù
O, OSC	Oscillator	振荡器	Zhèndàngqì
O/E	Optical/electronic converter	光/电转换器	Guāng/diàn zhuǎnhuànqì
O/R	Originator/recipient	始发者/接收者	Shǐfāzhě/jiēshōuzhě

O/T-CSI	Origination/termination-CAMEL subscription information	始发 / 终接 CAMEL 用户签约信息	Shǐfā/zhōngjiē CAMEL yònghù qiānyuē xìnxī
OA	Office automation	办公自动化	Bàngōng zìdònghuà
OA	Online access	联机访问	Liánjī fǎngwèn
OA	Operational analysis	操作分析	Cāozuò fēnxī
OA	Optical amplifier	光放大器	Guāng fàngdàqì
OA	Organization authority (CMM)	组织主管	Zǔzhī zhǔguǎn
OA	Outgoing access	向外访问	Xiàngwài fǎngwèn
OA	Output acknowledged	输出认可	Shūchū rènkě
OA&M	Operations, administration and maintenance	操作、维护和管理	Cāozuò, wéihù hé guǎnlǐ
OA, ODA	Omni-directional antenna	全向天线	Quánxiàng tiānxiàn
OAA	Open applications architecture	开放应用体系结构	Kāifàng yìngyòng tǐxì jiégòu
OAAF	Open Arcade Architecture Forum	开放式 Arcade 体系论坛	Kāifàngshì Arcade tǐxì lùntán
OACSU	Off-air call setup	不占用空中通道的呼叫启动	Bùzhànyòng kōngzhōng tōngdàode hūjiào qǐdòng
OACSU	Off-air call setup	非占空呼叫建立	Fēizhànkōng hūjiào jiànlì
OAD	Optically active device	光有源器件	Guāng yǒuyuán qìjiàn
OADG	Open Architecture Developers Group	开放结构开发组织	Kāifàng jiégòu kāifā zǔzhī
OADM	Optical add and drop multiplexer	光分插复用器	Guāng fēnchā fùyòngqì
OADM	Optical add drop multiplexer	光波分插复用器	Guāngbō fēn chā fùyòngqì
OADM	Optical add/drop multiplexer	光上/下路复用器	Guāng shàng/xià lù fùyòngqì
OADM	Optical add/drop multiplexer	光分插复用设备	Guāng fēn/chā fùyòng shèbèi
OAF	Origin address field	源地址段	Yuán dìzhǐ duàn
OAI	Operational-address instruction	运算地址指令	Yùnsuàn dìzhǐ zhǐlìng
O-ALG	One-way function algorithm	单向功能算法	Dānxiàng gōngnéng suànfǎ
OALM	Optically addressed light modulator	光选址光调制器	Guāng xuǎnzhǐ guāng tiáozhìqì
OAM	Operation and maintenance	运行和维护	Yùnxíng hé wéihù
OAM	Operation and management	操作与管理	Cāozuò yǔ guǎnlǐ
OAM	Operation, administration and maintenance	运行，管理和维护	Yùnxíng, guǎnlǐ hé wéihù
OAM	Operations, administration and maintenance	操作管理和维护	Cāozuò guǎnlǐ hé wéihù
OAM&P	Operation, administration, maintenance, and provisioning	运行管理维护和预置	Yùnxíng guǎnlǐ wéihù hé yùzhì
OAM&P	Operations, administration, maintenance and provisioning	操作管理维护和指配	Cāozuò guǎnlǐ wéihù hé zhǐpèi
OAMC	Operation, administration and maintenance center	运行、管理和维护中心	Yùnxíng、guǎnlǐ hé wéihù zhōngxīn
OAMC	Operations, administration and maintenance center	操作,管理和维护中心	Cāozuò, guǎnlǐ hé wéihù zhōngxīn
OAMC-MF	OAMC management function	OAMC 管理功能	OAMC guǎnlǐ gōngnéng
OAMC-OpS	OAMC operation system	OAMC 运行系统	OAMC yùnxíng xìtǒng
OAN	Optical access network	光接入网	Guāng jiērù wǎng
OAN	Optical access network	光纤接入网	Guāngxiān jiērùwǎng
OAO	Online analog output	在线模拟量输出	Zàixiàn mónǐliàng shūchū
OAP	Online analysis and processing	在线分析与处理	Zàixiàn fēnxī yǔ chǔlǐ
OAP	Orthogonal array processor	正交数组处理程序	Zhèngjiāo shùzǔ chǔlǐ chéngxù
OAPM	Optimal amplitude and phase modulation	最佳调幅和调相	Zuìjiā tiáofú hétiáo xiāng
OAPSK	Offset amplitude-phase shift keying	补偿幅-相偏移键控	Bǔcháng fú—xiāng piānyí jiànkòng
OAR	Operand address register	操作数据地址寄存器	Cāozuò shùjù dìzhǐ jìcúnqì
OAR	Optically amplified receiver	光放大接收机	Guāng fàngdà jiēshōujī
OAR	Optically amplified receiver	带光放大器的接收机	Dài guāng fàngdàqìde jiēshōujī

OAS	Optical amplifier section	光放大段	Guāng fàngdà duàn
OAS	Optical amplifier span	光放段	Guāng fàng duàn
OASA	Optical amplifer section adapter	光放大段适配	Guāng fàngdà duàn shìpèi
OASOH	Optical amplifier section overhead handling	光放大段开销处理	Guāng fàngdà duàn kāixiao chǔlǐ
OAST	Optical amplifier section termination	光放大段终结	Guāng fàngdà duàn zhōngjié
OAT	Optically amplified transmitter	光放大发射机	Guāng fàngdà fāshèjī
OAT	Optically amplified transmitter	带光放大器的发送机	Dài guāng fàngdàqìde fāsòngjī
OAT	Oxide aligned transistor (product of TRW)	氧化物对准晶体管	Yǎnghuàwù duìzhǔn jīngtǐguǎn
OBA	Off-boresight angle	脱离瞄视角	Tuōlí miáo shijiǎo
OBA	Optical booster amplifier	光攻放	Guāng gōng fàng
OBASC	Object-based analysis-synthesis coding	基于对象分析合成编码	Jīyú duìxiàng fēnxī héchéng biānmǎ
OBC	On-board controller	板上控制器	Bǎn-shàng kòngzhìqì
O-BCSM	Originating basic call state model	始发基本呼叫状态模型	Shǐfā jīběn hūjiào zhuàngtài móxíng
OBD	Optical branching device	光分路器	Guāng fēnlùqì
OBD	Output bus driver	输出总线驱动器	Shūchū zǒngxiàn qūdòngqì
OBE	Out-of-band emission	带外辐射	Dài-wài fúshè
OBEX	Object exchange	对象交换	Duìxiàng jiāohuàn
OBEX	Object exchange protocol (in Bluetooth)	对象交换协议	Duìxiàng jiāohuàn xiéyì
OBFD	Optical beam flame detector	线型光速火焰探测器	Xiànxíng guāngsù huǒyàn tàncèqì
OBR	Optical barcode reader	光条形码阅读器	Guāng tiáoxíng mǎ yuèdúqì
OBR	Optical barcode recognition	光学条码识读	Guāngxué tiáomǎ shídú
OBR	Output buffer register	输出缓冲寄存器	Shūchū huǎnchōng jìcúnqì
OBS	Online billing server	在线计费服务器	Zàixiàn jìfèi fúwùqì
OBW	Occupied bandwidth	占有带宽	Zhànyǒu dàikuān
OBW	Occupied bandwidth	射频占有带宽	Shèpín zhànyǒu dàikuān
OC	Optical carrier	光载波	Guāng zàibō
OC	Optical channel	光通道	Guāng tōngdào
OC	Originating call	主叫	Zhǔjiào
OC-1	Optical carrier level 1	光运载第 1 级	Guāng yùnzài dì yī jí
OCA	Optical channel adapter	光通道转接器	Guāng tōngdào zhuǎnjiēqì
OCA	Optical channel adapter	光通道适配器	Guāng tōngdào shìpèiqì
OCB	Outgoing call barred within the closed user group	在闭锁用户群中禁止出局呼叫	Zài bìsuǒ yònghù qún zhōng jìnzhǐ chūjú hūjiào
OCB	Overload circuit breaker	过载断路器	Guòzài duànlùqì
OCC	Optical connection controller	光连接控制器	Guāng liánjiē kòngzhìqì
OCC	Outbound control channel	出境控制信道	Chūjìng kòngzhì xìndào
OCCA	Open cooperative computing architecture	开放式协作运算体系	Kāifàng-shì xiézuò yùnsuàn tǐxì
OCCCH	OADM common control channel	OADM 公共控制信道	OADM gōnggòng kòngzhì xìndào
OCCRUI	Out-channel call related user interaction	与呼叫相关的通路外的用户交互作用	Yǔ hūjiào xiāngguānde tōnglù wàide yònghù jiāohù zuòyòng
OCD	Optical core device	光核心设备	Guāng héxīn shèbèi
OCD	Out of cell delineation	信元定界失同步	Xìnyuán dìngjiè shī tóngbù
OCD	Out of cell delineation	信元定界失步	Xìnyuán dìngjiè shībù
OCDS	Output command data set	输出指令数据装置	Shūchū zhǐlìng shùjù zhuāngzhì
OCDU	Optics coupling display unit	光纤耦合显示器	Guāngxiān ǒuhé xiǎnshìqì
OCEPL	Optical cables along electrical power lines	电力线架空光缆	Diànlìxiàn jiàkōng guānglǎn
Och	Optical channel	光信道	Guāng xìndào

OCh	Optical channel	光通路	Guāng tōnglù
OCH	Optical channel layer	光通道层	Guāng tōngdào céng
OCM	On-chip memory	片上存储器	Piàn-shàng cúnchǔqì
OC-N	Optical carrier level-N	光载波级 N	Guāng zàibō jí N
OCNS	Orthogonal channel noise simulator	正交信道噪声仿真器	Zhèngjiāo xìndào zàoshēng fǎngzhēnqì
OCOH	Optical channel overhead handling	光通路开销处理	Guāng tōnglù kāixiao chǔlǐ
OCPD	Open connection port dialog	打开连接端口对话	Dǎkāi liánjiē duānkǒu duìhuà
OCR	Optical character recognition	光学字符识别	Guāngxué zìfú shíbié
OCR	Optical character recognition	光学字符识读	Guāngxué zìfú shídú
OCR	Optical character recognition equipment	光学字元阅读机	Guāngxué zìyuán yuèdújī
OCR	Over consolidation ratio	超固结比	Chāogùjié bǐ
O - CSI	Originating CAMEL subscription information	发端 CAMEL 签约信息	Fāduān CAMEL qiānyuē xìnxī
O-CSI	Originating camel subscription information	始发 CAMEL 签约信息	Shǐfā CAMEL qiānyuē xìnxī
OCSK	Orthogonal code-shift keying	正交码偏移键控	Zhèngjiāo mǎ piānyí jiànkòng
OCSR	Output control shift register	输出控制移位寄存器	Shūchū kòngzhì yíwèi jìcúnqì
OCT	Optical channel termination	光通路终结	Guāng tōnglù zhōngjié
OCT	Optical channel termination	光通道终结	Guāng tōngdào zhōngjié
OD	Optical demultiplexer	光分波器	Guāng fēnbōqì
OD	Optical multiplexer/demultiplexer	光解复用器	Guāng jiě/fùyòngqì
ODA	Office document architecture	办公文档结构	Bàngōng wéndàng jiégòu
ODA	Operational design and analysis	操作设计与分析	Cāozuò shèjì yǔ fēnxī
ODB	Operator determined barring	操作员确定闭锁	Cāozuòyuán quèdìng bìsuǒ
Odb	Operator determined barring	运营者决定的闭锁业务	Yùnyíngzhě juédìngde bìsuǒ yèwù
ODBC	Open database communication	开放式数据库互连	Kāifàng-shì shùjùkù hùlián
ODBC	Open database connectivity	开放式数据库链接	Kāifàng-shì shùjùkù liànjiē
ODBC	Open database connectivity	开放数据库互连	Kāifàng shùjùkù hùlián
ODBC	Open database connectivity	开放数据库连通性	Kāifàng shùjùkù liántōngxìng
ODBR	Output data buffer	输出数据缓冲器	Shūchū shùjù huǎnchōngqì
ODCCH	ODMA dedicated control channel	ODMA 专用控制信道	ODMA zhuānyòng kòngzhì xìndào
ODCH	Dedicated ODMA channel	ODMA 专用信道	ODMA zhuānyòng xìndào
ODD	Operator distance dialing	操作员远程拨号	Cāozuòyuán yuǎnchéng bōhào
ODD	Optical data disk	数据记录光盘	Shùjù jìlù guāngpán
ODF	Optical distribution frame	光纤分配架	Guāngxiān fēnpèijià
ODF	Optical distribution frame	光配线架	Guāng pèixiànjià
ODG	Object dataflow graph	对象数据流图	Duìxiàng shùjùliú tú
ODI	Open data link interface	开放数据链路接口	Kāifàng shùjù liànlù jiēkǒu
ODI	Outgoing defect indication	输出缺陷指示	Shūchū quēxiàn zhǐshì
ODL	Object definition language	对象定义语言	Duìxiàng dìngyì yǔyán
ODL	Overlay description language	覆盖描述语言	Fùgài miáoshù yǔyán
ODMA	Open (system) distributed management architecture	开放分布管理体系	Kāifàng fēnbù guǎnlǐ tǐxì
ODMA	Open document management architecture	开放式文件管理结构	Kāifàng-shì wénjiàn guǎnlǐ jiégòu
ODMA	Opportunity driven multiple access	驱动多接入机会	Qūdòng duō jiērù jīhuì
ODN	Optical distributed network	光分配网络	Guāng fēnpèi wǎngluò
ODN	Optical distribution network	光配线网	Guāng pèixiànwǎng
ODP	Open (system) distributed processing	开放分布处理	Kāifàng fēnbù chǔlǐ
ODS	Open data services (for database)	开放式数据服务	Kāifàng-shì shùjù fúwù

ODSI	Optical domain service interconnect	光域业务互连	Guāngyù yèwù hùlián
ODSI	Optical domain service interconnect	光域业务内部连接	Guāngyù yèwù nèibù liánjiē
ODSI	Optical domain service interworking	光域业务互联	Guāngyù yèwù hùlián
ODSI	Optical Domain Services Internetworking Federation	光域业务互连联盟	Guāngyù yèwù hùlián liánméng
ODTA	Open distribution telecom architecture	分布式开放的电信结构	Fēnbù-shì kāifàngde diànxìn jiégòu
ODTCH	ODMA dedicated traffic channel	ODMA 专用业务信道	ODMA zhuānyòng yèwù xìndào
ODU	Optical data unit	光数据单元	Guāng shùjù dānyuán
ODU	Outdoor unit	室外单元	Shìwài dānyuán
ODVP	Optical digital voice processor	光学数字音频信息处理机	Guāngxué shùzì yīnpín xìnxī chǔlǐjī
OEI	Outgoing error indication	输出误码指示	Shūchū wùmǎ zhǐshì
OEIC	Opto-electronic integrated circuit	光电子集成	Guāng diànzǐ jíchéng
OEIC	Opto-electronic integrated circuit	光电集成电路	Guāngdiàn jíchéng diànlù
OEM	Object exchange model	对象交换模型	Duìxiàng jiāohuàn móxíng
OEM	Original equipment manufacturer	初始设备制造厂	Chūshǐ shèbèi zhìzàochǎng
OEM	Original equipment manufacturer	原始设备制造厂家	Yuánshǐ shèbèi zhìzào chǎngjiā
OEM	Original equipment manufacturer	原始设备制造商	Yuánshǐ shèbèi zhìzàoshāng
OEO	Optical-electrical-optical converter	光/电/光转换器	Guāng/diàn/guāng zhuǎnhuànqì
OFA	Object file area	目标文件区	Mùbiāo wénjiàn qū
OFA	Optical fiber amplifer	光纤放大器	Guāngxiān fàngdàqì
OFB	Output feedback	输出反馈	Shūchū fǎnkuì
OFC	Oil-filled cable	充油电缆	Chōng yóu diànlǎn
OFC	Optical fiber cable	光纤电缆	Guāngxiān diànlǎn
OFC	Optical fiber communication conference	光纤通信国际会议	Guāngxiān tōngxìn guójì huìyì
OFC	Optical fiber communications	光纤通信	Guāngxiān tōngxìn
OFDM	Optical frequency division multiplexing	光频分复用	Guāng pínfēn fùyòng
OFDM	Orthogonal frequency division modulation	正交频分调制	Zhèngjiāo pínfēn tiáozhì
OFDM	Orthogonal frequency division multiplexing	正交频分复用	Zhèngjiāo pínfēn fùyòng
OFDM	Orthogonal frequency division multiplexing	直角频率部分多路复用	Zhíjiǎo pínlǜ bùfen duōlù fùyòng
OFDMF	Orthogonal frequency division multiplexing forum	正交频分复用论坛	Zhèngjiāo pínfēn fùyòng lùntán
OFH	Output format handler	输出格式处理器	Shūchū géshi chǔlǐqì
OFHC	Oxygen-free high conductivity copper	无氧高电导铜	Wúyǎng gāodiàndǎo tóng
OFNP	Optical fiber with no plenum layer	无导体天花板隔层光缆	Wúdǎotǐ tiānhuābǎn gécéng guānglǎn
OFNR	Optical fiber cable with no riser	无导体竖井光缆	Wúdǎotǐ shùjǐng guānglǎn
OFS	Optical fiber sensor	光纤传感器	Guāngxiān chuángǎnqì
OFS	Out-of-frame second	帧失步秒	Zhèng shībù miǎo
OFTF	Optical fiber transfer function	光导纤维传送功能	Guāngdǎo xiānwéi chuánsòng gōngnéng
OFTL	Optical fiber transmission line	光纤传输线	Guāngxiān chuánshūxiàn
OFTS	Optical fiber transmission system	光纤传输系统	Guāngxiān chuánshū xìtǒng
OG	Object group	对象组	Duìxiàng zǔ
OG, OR	OR gate	"或"门	Huò mén
OGC	Online grid control	在线格网控制	Zàixiàn géwǎng kòngzhì
OGC	Open GIS consortium	开放式 GIS 协会	Kāifàng-shì GIS xiéhuì
OGIS	Open geodata interoperability specification	开放式地学数据互操作规范	Kāifàng-shì dìxué shùjù hùcāozuò guīfàn
OGPSWF	Outgoing primary switch frame	出局初级接线器架	Chūjú chūjí jiēxiànqì jià
OGR	Outgoing repeater	输出转换器	Shūchū zhuǎnhuànqì
OGR	Outgoing repeater or relay	输出中继器	Shūchū zhōngjìqì

OGRL	Outgoing rural line	农村去话电话线	Nóngcūn qùhuà diànhuà xiàn
OGT	Outgoing trunk	出中继	Chūzhōngjì
OGTC	Outgoing trunk call circuit	打出去的长途电话电路	Dǎchūqùde chángtú diànhuà diànlù
OGW	Optical guided wave	光导波	Guāngdǎobō
OHA	Overhead access	开销接入	Kāixiao jiērù
OHG	Operators harmonization group	运营者融合组	Yùnyíngzhě rónghé zǔ
OHP	Overhead processing	开销处理	Kāixiao chǔlǐ
OHP	Overhead processor (unit)	开销处理单元	Kāixiao chǔlǐ dānyuán
OI	Optimal interpolation	最优内插	Zuìyōu nèichā
OI	Origination indicator	主叫标识	Zhǔjiào biāozhì
OIA	Optical interface adapter	光接口适配器	Guāng jiēkǒu shìpèiqì
OIC	Oh, I see (computer chat)	哦，我明白了	Ó, wǒ míngbai le
OIF	Optical Internetworking Forum	光互联网络论坛	Guāng hùlián wǎngluò lùntán
OIF	Optical internetworking Forum	光因特网论坛	Guāng Yīntèwǎng lùntán
OIF	Optical internetworking forum	光纤互连网络论坛	Guāngxiān hùlián wǎngluò lùntán
OIF	Optical internetworking Forum	光联网论坛	Guāng liánwǎng lùntán
oif	Outgoing interface	出接口	Chū jiēkǒu
OIL	Outgoing interface list	输出接口列表	Shūchū jiēkǒu lièbiǎo
OIM	Open information model	开放信息模型	Kāifàng xìnxī móxíng
OIN	Intelligent optical network	智能光网络	Zhìnéng guāng wǎngluò
OIR	Online insertion and removal	在线插入和拆卸	Zàixiàn chārù hé chāixiè
OJI	Open Java virtual machine interface	开放 JAVA 虚拟机接口	Kāifàng JAVA xūnǐ jī jiēkǒu
OL	Optimal location	最优区位	Zuìyōu qūwèi
OLA	Optical line amplifier	光线路放大器	Guāng xiànlù fàngdàqì
OLA	Optical line amplifier	线路光放大器	Xiànlù guāng fàngdàqì
OLAP	Online analytical processing	联机分析处理	Liánjī fēnxī chǔlǐ
OLBP	Optic line back panel	光线路后面板	Guāng xiànlù hòumian bǎn
OLC	Open logical channel	打开逻辑通道	Dǎkāi luóji tōngdào
OLCA	Open logical channel acknowledge	打开逻辑通道确认	Dǎkāi luóji tōngdào quèrèn
OLCR	Open logical channel reject	打开逻辑通道拒绝	Dǎkāi luóji tōngdào jùjué
OLD	On-line diagnostics	联线诊断	Liánxiàn zhěnduàn
OLE	Object linking and embedding	对象的连接与嵌入	Duìxiàng liánjiē yǔ qiànrù
OLE	Object linking and embedding	目标连接与嵌入	Mùbiāo liánjiē yǔ qiànrù
OLE	Originating local exchange	发端端局交换机	Fāduān duānjú jiāohuànjī
OLED	Organic light-emitting diode	有机发光二极管	Yǒujī fāguāng èrjíguǎn
OLGA	Organic land grid array	基板栅格阵列	Jībǎn zhàgé zhènliè
OLM	Overload message	过载信息	Guòzài xìnxī
OLR	Overall loudness rating	总额定响度	Zǒng'é dìngxiǎngdù
OLS	Off-line primitive sequence	离线原语序列	Líxiàn yuányǔ xùliè
OLS	Optical label switch	光标记交换	Guāng biāojì jiāohuàn
OLSI	Optic link switch interface	光链路交换接口	Guāng liànlù jiāohuàn jiēkǒu
OLT	Optical line terminal	光纤线路终端	Guāngxiān xiànlù zhōngduān
OLT	Optical line terminal	光线路终端	Guāng xiànlù zhōngduān
OLTP	Online transaction processing	在线事务进程	Zàixiàn shìwù jìnchéng
OLTP	Online transaction processing (for database)	联机事务处理	Liánjī shìwù chǔlǐ
OLXC	Optical layer cross connection	光层交叉连接	Guāng céng jiāochā liánjiē

OM	Optical multiplexer	光合波器	Guāng hébōqì
OM	Optical multiplexer	光复用器	Guāng fùyòngqì
OM	Optical multiplexing	光复用	Guāng fùyòng
OM	Overlay model	重叠模式	Chóngdié móshì
OM/DM	Optical multiplexer/demultiplexer	光复用器/解复用器	Guāng fùyòngqì/jiě fùyòngqì
OMA	Object management architecture	对象管理体系结构	Duìxiàng guǎnlǐ tǐxì jiégòu
OMA	Object management architecture	对象管理结构	Duìxiàng guǎnlǐ jiégòu
OMAP	Object module assembly program	目标模块汇编程序	Mùbiāo mókuài huìbiān chéngxù
OMAP	Operations and maintenance application part	操作维护应用部分	Cāozuò wéihù yìngyòng bùfen
OMBP	Operating and maintenance back panel	操作维护后面板	Cāozuò wéihù hòumian bǎn
OMC	Operation and maintenance center	操作维护中心	Cāozuò wéihù zhōngxīn
OMC	Operations and maintenance center	操作与维护中心	Cāozuò yǔ wéihù zhōngxīn
OMC	Operations management center	操作管理中心	Cāozuò guǎnlǐ zhōngxīn
OMDT	Object model development tool	对象模型开发工具	Duìxiàng móxíng kāifā gōngjù
OMG	Object management group	对象管理组	Duìxiàng guǎnlǐ zǔ
OMG	Object management group	对象管理组织	Duìxiàng guǎnlǐ zǔzhī
OMG-CDR	Object management group-common data representation	客体管理组 - 通用数据表示	Kètǐ guǎnlǐ zǔ-tōng yòng shùjù biǎoshì
OMG-GIOP	Object management group-general internal object request broker (ORB) protocol	客体管理组 - 一般内部 ORB 协议	Kètǐ guǎnlǐ zǔ-yībān nèibù ORB xiéyì
OML	Object module library	目标模块库	Mùbiāo mókuài kù
OML	Operation and maintenance link	操作维护链路	Cāozuò wéihù liànlù
OML	Operations and maintenance link	操作与维护链路	Cāozuò yǔ wéihù liànlù
OMLU	Object module library update	目标模块库修改	Mùbiāo mókuài kù xiūgǎi
OMN	Optical transport management network	光传送网管理网	Guāng chuánsòng wǎng guǎnlǐ wǎng
OM-QPSK	Offset-keying quadrature phase shift keying	偏移键控正交相移键控	Piānyí jiànkòng zhèngjiāo xiàngyí jiànkòng
OMS	Operations and maintenance sub-system	操作维护分系统	Cāozuò wéihù fēn xìtǒng
OMS	Optical multiplex segment layer	光复用段层	Guāng fùyòng duàn céng
OMS	Optical multiplex stage	光复用段	Guāng fùyòng duàn
OMS	Opto-electronic multiplex switch	光电多路复用开关	Guāngdiàn duōlù fùyòng kāiguān
OMS	Output multiplex synchronizer	输出多路复用同步装置	Shūchū duōlù fùyòng tóngbù zhuāngzhì
OMSA	Optical multiplex section adapter	光复用段适配	Guāng fùyòng duàn shì pèi
OMSN	Optical multi-service node	光多业务节点设备	Guāng duō yèwù jiédiǎn shèbèi
OMSOH	Optical multiplex section overhead handling	光复用段开销处理	Guāng fùyòng duàn kāixiao chǔlǐ
OMSP	Optical multiplex stage protection	光复用段保护	Guāng fùyòng duàn bǎohù
OMST	Optical multiplex section termination	光复用段终结	Guāng fùyòng duàn zhōngjié
OMT	Object model template	对象模型模板	Duìxiàng móxíng múbǎn
OMT	Object modeling technique	对象模型技术	Duìxiàng móxíng jìshù
OMT	Optical multiplexing terminal	光复用终端	Guāng fùyòng zhōngduān
OMT	Orthomode transducer	正交模耦合器	Zhèngjiāo mó ǒuhéqì
OMU	Operations and maintenance unit (board)	操作维护单元（板）	Cāozuò wéihù dānyuán (bǎn)
ONR	Originating number register	发端（信息）编号寄存器	Fāduān (xìnxī) biānhào jìcúnqì
ONS	Originating number sender	发端（信息）编号发送器	Fāduān (xìnxī) biānhào fāsòngqì
ONT	Optical network termination	光网络终端	Guāng wǎngluò zhōngduān
ONU	Optical network unit	光纤网络单元	Guāngxiān wǎngluò dānyuán
ONU	Optical network unit	光网络单元	Guāng wǎngluò dānyuán
OOA	Object-oriented analysis	面向对象分析	Miànxiàng duìxiàng fēnxī

OOC	Optical orthogonal code	光正交码	Guāng zhèngjiāo mǎ
OOD	Object-oriented design	面向对象设计	Miànxiàng duìxiàng shèjì
OOD	Object-oriented design	面向目标的设计	Miànxiàng mùbiāode shèjì
OODB	Object-oriented database	面向对象数据库	Miànxiàng duìxiàng shùjùkù
OODS	Object-oriented database system	面向对象数据库系统	Miànxiàng duìxiàng shùjùkù xìtǒng
OOF	Out-of-frame	帧失步	Zhèng shībù
OOK	On-off keying	开关键控	Kāiguān jiànkòng
OOK	On-off keying	通断键控	Tōng duàn jiànkòng
OOK	On-off keying	通断键控	Tōngduàn jiànkòng
OOL	Operator-oriented language	面向操作员的语言	Miànxiàng cāozuòyuánde yǔyán
OOM	One to one marketing	一对一行销	Yī duì yī xíngxiāo
OOMT	Object management-oriented modeling tools	面向管理对象建模工具	Miànxiàng guǎnlǐ duìxiàng jiànmo gōngjù
OoO	Out of order	乱序执行	Luànxù zhíxíng
OOP	Object-oriented programming	面向对象的程序设计	Miànxiàng duìxiàngde chéngxù shèjì
OOP	Object-oriented programming	面向对象程序设计	Miànxiàng duìxiàng chéngxù shèjì
OOP	Object-oriented programming	面向对象编程	Miànxiàng duìxiàng biānchéng
OP	Operation code	操作码	Cāozuòmǎ
OP	Optical probe	光学探头	Guāngxué tàntóu
OP	Orthogonal polarization	正交极化	Zhèngjiāo jíhuà
OP	Output printer	输出打印机	Shūchū dǎyìnjī
OPA	Origin port address	始点端口地址	Shǐdiǎn duānkǒu dìzhǐ
OPAC	Optical attached aerial cable	附属式架空光缆	Fùshǔ-shì jiàkōng guānglǎn
OPC	Odd-parity check	奇数奇偶校验	Jīshù jīǒu jiàoyàn
OPC	Original point code	起始信令点编码	Qǐshǐ xìnlìngdiǎn biānmǎ
OPC	Originating point code	始点码	Shǐdiǎn mǎ
OPC	Originating point code	起源点编码	Qǐyuándiǎn biānmǎ
OPC	Origination point code	发源点编码	Fāyuándiǎn biānmǎ
OPC	Origination point code	源信令点	Yuán xìnlìng diǎn
OPC	Origination point code	源信令点编码	Yuán xìnlìng diǎn biānmǎ
OPD	Object-process diagram	对象过程图	Duìxiàng guòchéng tú
OPD	Optically passive device	光无源器件	Guāng wúyuán qìjiàn
OPDU	Optical packet data unit	光分组数据单元	Guāng fēnzǔ shùjù dānyuán
OPEX	Operating expenses	运营成本	Yùnyíng chéngběn
OPGW	Optical fiber composite ground wire	光纤复合接地线	Guāngxiān fùhé jiēdìxiàn
OPGW	Optical fiber composite ground wire	复合地线光缆	Fùhé dìxiàn guānglǎn
OPGW	Optical fiber composite ground wire	接地线复合光缆	Jiēdìxiàn fùhé guānglǎn
OPGW	Optical fiber pole-mounted composite ground wire	光纤复合架空地线	Guāngxiān fùhé jiàkōng dìxiàn
OPGW	Optical power grounded waveguide optical fiber	光纤架空地线	Guāngxiān jiàkōng dìxiàn
OPGW	Optical power grounded waveguide optical fiber	地线复合光缆	Dìxiàn fùhéguāng lǎn
OPH	Output handler	输出处理器	Shūchū chǔlǐqì
OPL	Object program loader	目标程序装入器	Mùbiāo chéngxù zhuāngrùqì
OPM	Object-process methodology	对象过程方法	Duìxiàng guòchéng fāngfǎ
OPM	Optical performance monitor	光性能监测器	Guāng xìngnéng jiāncèqì
OPM	Optical performance monitoring	光性能监控	Guāng xìngnéng jiānkòng
OPN	Open primitive signal	连接建立原语信号	Liánjiē jiànlì yuányǔ xìnhào
OPPC	Optical phase conductor (FOC)	光纤复合相导线	Guāngxiān fùhé xiāng dǎoxiàn

OPR	Operator signal	话务员信号	Huàwùyuán xìnhào
OPS	Optical packet switch	光包交换	Guāng bāo jiāohuàn
OPS	Optical packet switching	光分组交换	Guāng fēnzǔ jiāohuàn
OPS	Optical positioning system	光学定位系统	Guāngxué dìngwèi xìtǒng
OPT	Optimized production technology	优化生产技术	Yōuhuà shēngchǎn jìshù
OPTIS	Overlapped PAM transmission with interlocking spectra	频谱互锁重叠的 PAM 传输	Pínpǔ hùsuǒ chóngdiéde PAM chuánshū
OQASK	Offset quadrature amplitude shift keying	偏移正交幅移键控	Piānyí zhèngjiāo fúyí jiànkòng
OQPSK	Offset quadrature phase shift keying	偏移四相移相键控	Piānyí sìxiāng yíxiāng jiànkòng
OQPSK	Offset quadrature phase shift keying	偏移正交相移键控	Piānyí zhèngjiāo xiàngyí jiànkòng
OQPSK	Offset quadriphase phase shift keying	偏移四相相移键控	Piānyí sìxiàng xiàngyí jiànkòng
OQPSK	Offset quadriphase shift keying	偏置四相相移键控	Piānzhì sìxiāng xiāngyí jiànkòng
OQPSK	Offset-keyed quadriphase phase shift keying	参差四相相移键控	Cēncī sìxiāng xiāngyí jiànkòng
OQPSK	Orthogonal quaternary phase shift keying	正交四相相移键控	Zhèngjiāo sìxiàng xiàngyí jiànkòng
OR	Optimal routing	最佳路由选择	Zuìjiā lùyóu xuǎnzé
OR	OR function	"或"功能	Huò gōngnéng
OR	OR logic circuit	或逻辑电路	Huò luójidiànlù
OR	Output register	输出寄存器	Shūchū jìcúnqì
OR	Overrun bit	超（负荷）运行位	Chāo (fùhè) yùnxíng wèi
ORACH	ODMA random access channel	ODMA 随机接入信道	ODMA suíjī jiērù xìndào
ORB	Object request broker	对象请求代理	Duìxiàng qǐngqiú dàilǐ
ORB	Object request broker	对象请求代理器	Duìxiàng qǐngqiú dàilǐqì
ORB	Object request broker	目标请求掮客	Mùbiāo qǐngqiú qiánkè
ORE	Optical repeater equipment	光学中继设备	Guāngxué zhōngjì shèbèi
ORL	Optical retun loss	光回波损耗	Guāng huíbō sǔnhào
ORL	Optical return loss	光回呼损耗	Guāng huíhū sǔnhào
ORLCF	Optimal routing for late call forwarding	对滞后呼叫前转的最佳路由选择	Duì zhìhòu hūjiào qiánzhuǎnde zuìjiā lùyóu xuǎnzé
ORP	Optional response poll (bit protocol control)	任选响应轮询（位协议控制）	Rènxuǎn xiǎngyìng lúnxún (wèi xiéyì kòngzhì)
OS	Object supports	对象支持	Duìxiàng zhīchí
OS	Operating system	操作系统	Cāozuò xìtǒng
OS	Operation system	运行系统	Yùnxíng xìtǒng
OS	Optical section	光信号段	Guāng xìnhào duàn
OS	Optical section	光纤段	Guāngxiān duàn
OS	Originating subscriber	始发用户	Shǐfā yònghù
OS	Outgoing sender	出局发码器	Chūjú fāmǎqì
OS/MD	Operation system or mediation device	操作系统或协调装置	Cāozuò xìtǒng huò xiétiáo zhuāngzhì
OSA	Open service access	开放业务接入	Kāifàng yèwù jiērù
OSA	Open service architecture	开放的业务结构	Kāifàngde yèwù jiégòu
OSA	Open systems architecture	开放系统体系结构	Kāifàng xìtǒng tǐxì jiégòu
OSA	Optical spectrum analyzer	光频谱分析单元	Guāng pínpǔ fēnxī dānyuán
OSB	Operational status bit	操作状态位	Cāozuò zhuàngtài wèi
OSB	Output signal balance	输出口信号平衡	Shūchūkǒu xìnhào pínghéng
OSC	Optical supervisory channel	光监控信道	Guāng jiānkòng xìndào
OSC	Optical supervisory channel	光监控通路	Guāng jiānkòng tōnglù
OSC	Optical supervisory channel	光监控通道	Guāng jiānkòng tōngdào

OSC	Optical surveillance channel	光监控信道	Guāng jiānkòng xìndào
OSCA	Optical supervisory channel adapter	光监控通路适配	Guāng jiānkòng tōnglù shìpèi
OSCL	Operating system command languages	操作系统命令语言	Cāozuò xìtǒng mìnglìng yǔyán
OSDM	Optical space-division multiplexing	光空分复用	Guāng kōngfēn fùyòng
OSDM	Optical space-division multiplexing	光空分多路复用	Guāng kōngfēn duōlù fùyòng
OSDP	On-site data processing	现场数据处理	Xiànchǎng shùjù chǔlǐ
OSDS	Operating system for distributed switching	分散交换的操作系统	Fēnsàn jiāohuànde cāozuò xìtǒng
OSF	Open Software Foundation	开放软件基金会	Kāifàng ruǎnjiàn jījīnhuì
OSF	Operating system function	操作系统功能	Cāozuò xìtǒng gōngnéng
OSF	Operation system function	运行系统功能	Yùnxíng xìtǒng gōngnéng
OSF	Operation system function block	运行系统功能块	Yùnxíng xìtǒng gōngnéng kuài
OSF/MF	Operation system function or mediation function	操作系统功能或协调功能	Cāozuò xìtǒng gōngnéng huò xiétiáo gōngnéng
OSI	Open system interchange	开放系统互联	Kāifàng xìtǒng hùlián
OSI	Open system interconnection	开放系统互连	Kāifàng xìtǒng hùlián
OSI	Open systems interconnection (reference model)	开放系统互连(参考模型)	Kāifàng xìtǒng hùlián (cānkǎo móxíng)
OSI RM	OSI reference model	OSI 参考模型	OSI cānkǎo móxíng
OSIM	Open system interconnection model	开放式系统互连模型	Kāifàng-shì xìtǒng hùlián móxíng
OSIP	Open system interconnection plan	开放型系统互连计划	Kāifàng-xíng xìtǒng hùlián jìhuà
OSL	Outgoing sending link	出局发送链路	Chūjú fāsòng liànlù
O-SNCP	Optical sub-network connection protection	光子网连接保护	Guāng zǐwǎng liánjiē bǎohù
O-SNCP	Optical sub-network connection protection	光子网连接保护	Guāngzǐ wǎng liánjiē bǎohù
OSNR	Optical signal to noise ratio	光信噪比	Guāng xìn zào bǐ
OSNR	Optical signal-to-noise ratio	光信号-噪声比	Guāng xìnhào-zàoshēng bǐ
OSP	Octet stream protocol	八比特组数据流协议	Bā bǐtè zǔ shùjùliú xiéyì
OSP	Online service provider	在线服务提供者	Zàixiàn fúwù tígòngzhě
OSP	Optical signal processing	光学信号处理	Guāngxué xìnhào chǔlǐ
OSP	Optical surge protection	光浪涌保护	Guāng làngyǒng bǎohù
OSP:IHOSS	Octet stream protocol for Internet-hosted octet stream service	字节流协议用于因特网的主机字节流业务	Zìjié liú xiéyì yòng yú Yīntèwǎngde zhǔjī zìjié liú yèwù
OSPF	Open shortest path first	开放最短路径优先	Kāifàng zuìduǎn lùjìng yōuxiān
OSPF	Open shortest path first [Protocol]	最短路径先开协议	Zuìduǎn lùjìng xiān kāi xiéyì
OSPF	Open shortest path first protocol	开放式最短路径优先协议	Kāifàngshì zuìduǎn lùjìng yōuxiān xiéyì
OSPF	Open shortest path first protocol	开放最短路经优先协议	Kāifàng zuìduǎn lùjīng yōuxiān xiéyì
OSRP	Optical signaling and routing protocol	光信令路由协议	Guāng xìnlìng lùyóu xiéyì
OSS	Operating support system	运行支持系统	Yùnxíng zhīchí xìtǒng
OSS	Operation sub-system	操作子系统	Cāozuò zixìtǒng
OSS	Operation support system	操作支援系统	Cāozuò zhīyuán xìtǒng
OSS	Operation support system	运营支持系统	Yùnyíng zhīchí xìtǒng
OSS	Operation support system	运营支撑系统	Yùnyíng zhīchēng xìtǒng
OSS	Operations support system	操作支持系统	Cāozuò zhīchí xìtǒng
OSS	Operator specific service	运营者特定业务	Yùnyíngzhě tèdìng yèwù
OSS	Optional service sub-system	任选服务子系统	Rènxuǎn fúwù zixìtǒng
OSS/BSS, BOSS	Operation support system/business support system	业务运营支撑系统	Yèwù yùnyíng zhīchēng xìtǒng
OSTF	Ordnance Survey Transfer Format (UK)	陆地测量部传输格式	Lùdì cèliángbù chuánshū géshi
OT	Optical transponder	光转换器	Guāng zhuǎnhuànqì

OTAF	Over-the-air service provisioning function	空中下载业务准备操作	Kōngzhōng xiàzài yèwù zhǔnbèi cāozuò
OTASP	Over-the-air parameter administration	空中下载业务准备	Kōngzhōng xiàzài yèwù zhǔnbèi
OTC	Originating toll center	去话长途电话中心局	Qù huà chángtú diànhuà zhōngxīnjú
OTD	Observed time difference	观察时间差异	Guānchá shíjiān chāyì
OTD	Orthogonal transmission diversity	正交发送分集	Zhèngjiāo fāsòng fēnjí
OTDM	Optical time-division multiplexing	光时分复用	Guāng shífēn fùyòng
OTDR	Optical time domain reflectometer	光时域反射仪	Guāng shíyù fǎnshèyí
OTDR	Optical time domain reflectometer	光时域反射器	Guāng shíyù fǎnshèqì
OTDR	Optical time domain reflectometer	光时域反射计	Guāng shíyù fǎnshèjì
OTDR	Optical time domain reflectometry	光时域反射法	Guāng shíyù fǎnshèfǎ
OTDR	Optical time domain reflectometry	光时域反射测量法	Guāng shíyù fǎnshè cèliángfǎ
OTFT	Organic thin-film field effect transistor	有机薄膜场效晶体管	Yǒujī bómó cháng xiào jīngtǐguǎn
OTH	Optical transport hierarchy	光传送体制	Guāng chuánsòng tǐzhì
O-TIME	Optical technology for Internet with multi-wavelength environment (Chinese term based on English abbreviation)	光时代	Guāng shídài
OTM	Optical terminal multiplexer	光终端复用单元	Guāng zhōngduān fùyòng dānyuán
OTM	Optical terminal multiplexer	光终端复用器	Guāng zhōngduān fùyòngqì
OTM	Optical transport module	光传送模块	Guāng chuánsòng mókuài
OTN	Optical transmission network	光传输网	Guāng chuánshū wǎng
OTN	Optical transport network	光传送网络	Guāng chuánsòng wǎngluò
OTP	Office of Telecommunications Policy (US)	电信政策办公室	Diànxìn zhèngcè bàngōngshì
OTP	One-time password (crypto)	一次性口令	Yīcìxìng kǒulìng
OTP	Optical transmission protection	光信道监控保护	Guāng xìndào jiānkòng bǎohù
OTS	Optical transmission section	光传送段	Guāng chuánsòng duàn
OTS	Optical transport segment layer	光传送段层	Guāng chuánsòng duàn céng
OTS	Ordinal time scale	有序时间标度	Yǒuxù shíjiān biāodù
OTTS	Outgoing trunk transmission system	去中继传输系统	Qù zhōngjì chuánshū xìtǒng
OTU	Optical transform unit	光转化单元	Guāng zhuǎnhuà dānyuán
OTU	Optical transponder unit	光转发器	Guāng zhuǎnfāqì
OTU	Optical transponder unit	光转换单元	Guāng zhuǎnhuàn dānyuán
OTU	Optical transponder unit	光转换器单元	Guāng zhuǎnhuànqì dānyuán
OTU	Optical transponder unit	波长转换器	Bōcháng zhuǎnhuànqì
OTU-A	Optical transponder unit-add	上路波长转换器	Shànglù bōcháng zhuǎnhuànqì
OTU-D	Optical transponder unit-drop	下路波长转换器	Xiàlù bōcháng zhuǎnhuànqì
OUF	Optimum usable frequency	最佳可用频率	Zuìjiā kěyòng pínlǜ
OUF	Optional user facility	任选用户设施	Rènxuǎn yònghù shèshī
OUI	Organizational unique identifier	组织性唯一标示符	Zǔzhīxìng wéiyī biāoshìfú
OVD	Outside vapor deposition (FOC mfg)	外部汽相沉积法	Wàibù qìxiàng chénjī fǎ
OVD	Outside-tube [chemical] vapor deposition (for FOC)	外部化学气相沉积法	Wàibù huàxué qìxiàng chénjī fǎ
OVD	Outside-tube vapor deposition (for FOC)	管外气相沉积法	Guǎn-wài qìxiàng chénjī fǎ
OVF	Overflow	上溢	Shàng yì
OVF	Overflow	溢出	Yìchū
OVPD	Outside vapor phase deposition (FOC mfg)	外汽相沉积法	Wài qìxiàng chénjī fǎ
OVPN	Optical virtual private network	光虚拟专用网	Guāng xūnǐ zhuānyòng wǎng
OVPN	Optical virtual private network	光虚拟专网	Guāng xūnǐ zhuān wǎng
OVSF	Orthogonal variable spread factor codes	正交可变扩频系数码	Zhèngjiāo kěbiàn kuòpín xìshù mǎ

OVSF	Orthogonal variable spreading factor	正交可变扩频因子	Zhèngjiāo kěbiàn kuòpín yīnzǐ
OW	Orderwire	公务电话	Gōngwù diànhuà
OWC	One-way communication	单向通信	Dānxiàng tōngxìn
OWF	Optimum working frequency	最佳工作频率	Zuìjiā gōngzuò pínlǜ
OWU	Order wire unit	公务单元	Gōngwù dānyuán
OXC	Optical cross-connect	光交叉连接器	Guāng jiāochā liánjiēqì
OXC	Optical cross-connection	光交叉连接	Guāng jiāochā liánjiē
OXCN	Optical cross-connect node	光交叉连接节点	Guāng jiāochā liánjiē jiédiǎn

P

P	Pico- (prefix meaning 10^{-12})	微微	Wēiwēi
P	Program	程序	Chéngxù
P	Program counter	程序记数器	Chéngxù jìshùqì
P	Provider router	运营商路由器	Yùnyíngshāng lùyóuqì
P	Pulse	脉冲	Màichōng
P&C	Prompt and collect user information	提示并收集用户信息	Tíshì bìng shōují yònghù xìnxī
p/4DQPSK	p/4 shifted, differentially encoded quadrature phase-shift keying	p/4 相移的差分编码正交移相键控	p/4 xiàngyíde chāfēn biānmǎ zhèngjiāo yíxiàng jiànkòng
P/F	Poll/final	探询，终止	Tànxún, zhōngzhǐ
P/L	Packing list	明细表	Míngxìbiǎo
P/L	Packing list	装箱单	Zhuāngxiāng dān
P2DR	Policy, protection, detection, response	策略，保护，检测，响应	Cèlüè, bǎohù, jiǎncè, xiǎngyìng
P3	People, price and product	人员，价格和产品	Rényuán, jiàgé hé chǎnpǐn
P3P	Privacy preference project	个人私隐安全平台	Gèrén sīyǐn ānquán píngtái
PA	Packet assembly	组装	Zǔzhuāng
PA	Packet assembly (data communications)	包装	Bāozhuāng
PA	Pixel address	象素地址	Xiàngsù dìzhǐ
PA	Planar array	平面阵列	Píngmiàn zhènliè
PA	Play announcement	播送通知	Bōsòng tōngzhī
PA	Pre-amplifier	前置放大器	Qiánzhì fàngdàqì
PA	Pre-amplifier	预放	Yùfàng
PA	Pre-amplifier	预放大器	Yùfàngdàqì
PA	Project authority (CMM)	项目主管	Xiàngmù zhǔguǎn
PABX	Private automatic branch exchange	专用自动交换分机	Zhuānyòng zìdòng jiāohuàn fēnjī
PABX	Private automatic branch exchange	专用自动小交换机	Zhuānyòng zìdòng xiǎo jiāohuànjī
PABX	Private automatic branch exchange	专用自动用户交换机	Zhuānyòng zìdòng yònghù jiāohuànjī
PABX	Private automatic branch exchange	用户自动交换机	Yònghù zìdòng jiāohuànjī
PABX	Private automatic branch exchange	用户自动小交换机	Yònghù zìdòng xiǎo jiāohuànjī
PAC	Packet switch	分组交换机	Fēnzǔ jiāohuànjī
PAC	Pan unit and controller	云台及云台控制器	Yúntái jí yúntái kòngzhìqì
PAC	Pilot synchronization/access channel	导频同步/接入信道	Dǎopín tóngbù/jiērù xìndào
PAC	Primary address code	原址代码	Yuánzhǐ dàimǎ
PAC	Privileged access control (in Linux)	特权存取控制	Tèquán cúnqǔ kòngzhì
PACA	Priority access and channel assignment	优先接入及信道指配	Yōuxiān jiērù jí xìndào zhǐpèi
PACCH	Packet access grant channel	分组接入应答信道	Fēnzǔ jiērù yìngdá xìndào
PACCH	Packet accompanying control channel	分组伴随控制信道	Fēnzǔ bànsuí kòngzhì xìndào

PACCH	Packet associated control channel	分组随路控制信道	Fēnzǔ suílù kòngzhì xìndào
PACE	Phased array control electronics	相位阵控制电子设备	Xiàngwèi zhèn kòngzhì diànzǐ shèbèi
PACE	Product Assurance Confidence Evaluator (TRW Inc.)	产品保证可信度评估程序	Chǎnpǐn bǎozhèng kěxìndù pínggū chéngxù
PACM	Pulse-amplitude-code modulation	脉冲幅度编码调制	Màichōng fúdù biānmǎ tiáozhì
PACORE	Parabolic corner reflector	抛物面角型反射器	Pāowùmiàn jiǎo-xíng fǎnshèqì
PACT	Project for advancement of coding technique	改进编码技术的研究计划	Gǎijìn biānmǎ jìshùde yánjiū jìhuà
PAD	Data packet assembly/disassembly function	数据包分组/重组功能	Shùjù bāo fēnzǔ/chóngzǔ gōngnéng
PAD	Packet assembler/disassembler	分组组装/分解设备	Fēnzǔ zǔzhuāng/fēnjiě shèbèi
PAD	Packet assembler/disassembler	分组装/卸	Fēnzǔ zhuāng/xiè
PAD	Packet assembler/disassembler	报文分组组装器/拆卸器	Bàowén fēnzǔ zǔzhuāngqì/chāixièqì
PAD	Packet assembly and disassembly	包装配与拆卸	Bāo zhuāngpèi yǔ chāixiè
PAD	Packet assembly and disassembly	打包和拆包	Dǎbāo hé chāibāo
PAD	Packet assembly/disassembly	分组拆装	Fēnzǔ chāizhuāng
PAD	Packet assembly/disassembly	分组装拆包	Fēnzǔ zhuāngchāi bāo
PAD	Packet assembly/disassembly equipment	分组装拆设备	Fēnzǔ zhuāngchāi shèbèi
PAD	Peoples Air Defense telephone post	人防电话站	Rénfáng diànhuàzhàn
PADIL	Patriot digital information link (US military)	爱国者数字信息链	Àiguózhě shùzì xìnxī liàn
PADLA	Programmable asynchronous dual line adapter	可编程序异步双线适配器	Kěbiān chéngxù yìbù shuāngxiàn shìpèiqì
PADS	Performance analysis display system	性能分析显示系统	Xìngnéng fēnxī xiǎnshì xìtǒng
PAE	Port access entity	端口访问实体	Duānkǒu fǎngwèn shítǐ
PAGC	Private automatic branch eXchange access for GSM extension	全球移动通信系统分机用专用自动小交换机接入	Quánqiú yídòng tōngxin xìtǒng fēnjī yòng zhuānyòng zìdòng xiǎo jiāohuànjī jiērù
PAGCH	Packet access grant channel	分组接入允许信道	Fēnzǔ jiērù yǔnxǔ xìndào
PAGCH	Packet access grant channel	分组接入准许信道	Fēnzǔ jiērù zhǔnxǔ xìndào
PAL	Phase alternating line (European television broadcast standard)	逐行倒相制式	Zhúháng dǎoxiāng zhìshì
PAL	Pinhole automatic light compensation (ALC) lens	针孔型自动亮度补偿镜头	Zhēnkǒng-xíng zìdòng liàngdù bǔcháng jìngtóu
PAM	Pass-along message (ISUP message)	传送信息	Chuánsòng xìnxī
PAM	Pulse amplitude modulation	脉冲幅度	Màichōng fúdù
PAM	Pulse amplitude modulation	脉冲幅度调制	Màichōng fúdù tiáozhì
PAM	Pulse amplitude modulation	脉冲振幅调制	Màichōng zhènfú tiáozhì
PAMR	Public access mobile radio	公用调度集群通信网	Gōngyòng diàodù jíqún tōngxìnwǎng
PAN	Personal area network	个人域网	Gèrén yù wǎng
PAN	Publicly accessed node	公共被寻址节点	Gōnggòng bèi xúnzhǐ jiédiǎn
PanAmSat	Pan American Satellite Corp. (US)	泛美卫星公司	Fànměi wèixīng gōngsī
PANDA	Polarization maintaining and absorption reducing (fiber)	偏振保持和吸收衰减（纤维）	Piānzhèn bǎochí hé xīshōu shuāijiǎn (xiānwéi)
PAP	Password authentication protocol	口令认证协议	Kǒulìng rènzhèng xiéyì
PAP	Password authentication protocol	密码认证协议	Mìmǎ rènzhèng xiéyì
PAP	Password authentication protocol	密码验证协议	Mìmǎ yànzhèng xiéyì
PAP	Printer access protocol (Apple usage)	打印机访问协议	Dǎyìnjī fǎngwèn xiéyì
PAP	Privacy (?) authentication protocol	密码鉴权协议	Mìmǎ jiànquán xiéyì
PAPM	Pulse amplitude and phase modulation	脉冲调幅调相	Màichōng tiáofú tiáoxiàng
PAR	Packet adaptive routing	包自适应路径选择	Bāo zìshìyìng lùjìng xuǎnzé
PAR	Parity check	寄偶校验	Jì'ǒu jiàoyàn
PAR	Peak to average ratio	峰值对平均值比率	Fēngzhí duì píngjūnzhí bǐlǜ
PAR	Positive acknowledgment with retransmission	用于重发的肯定应答	Yòng yú chóngfāde kěndìng yìngdá

PARK	Portable access rights key	移动用户接入权限识别码	Yídòng yònghù jiērù quánxiàn shíbié mǎ
PAS	Personal access system	个人接入系统	Gèrén jiērù xìtǒng
PAS	Public address system	公共广播音响系统	Gōnggòng guǎngbō yīnxiǎng xìtǒng
PASLA	Programmable asynchronous line adapter	可编程序异步线路转换器	Kěbiān chéngxù yìbù xiànlù zhuǎnhuànqì
PA-TDMA	Preassigned time division multiple access	预分配分时多路存取	Yùfēnpèi fēnshí duōlù cúnqǔ
PAU	Picture access unit	图像接入单元	Túxiàng jiērù dānyuán
PBA	Pencil beam antenna	笔形波束天线	Bǐxíng bōshù tiānxiàn
PBA	Printed circuit board assembly	印制电路集成板	Yìnzhì diànlù jíchéngbǎn
PBBI	Priority-based block and inheritance	基于优先级封锁-继承	Jīyú yōuxiānjí fēngsuǒ—jìchéng
PBC	Peripheral board controller	外设板控制器	Wàishèbǎn kòngzhìqì
PBC	Port bypass circuit	端口旁路电路	Duānkǒu pánglù diànlù
PBCCH	Packet broadcast control channel	分组广播控制信道	Fēnzǔ guǎngbō kòngzhì xìndào
PBG	Photonic band gap	光子带隙	Guāngzǐ dàixì
PBG	Photonic band gap	光子禁带	Guāngzǐ jìndài
PBMI	Packet bus management interface	包总线管理接口	Bāo zǒngxiàn guǎnlǐ jiēkǒu
PBNM	Policy-based network management	基于政策的网络管理	Jīyú zhèngcède wǎngluò guǎnlǐ
PBP	Paging block periodicity	寻呼闭塞周期性	Xúnhū bìsè zhōuqīxìng
PBSZ	Protection buffer size	保护缓冲容量	Bǎohù huǎnchōng róngliàng
PBT	Polybutylene terephthalate	聚对苯二甲酸丁二醇酯	Jùduìběn èrjiǎsuān dīng'èrchúnzhǐ
PBTS	Priority-based transaction restart	基于优先级的事务重启	Jīyú yōuxiānjíde shìwù chòngqǐ
PBX	Private branch exchange	专用交换机	Zhuānyòng jiāohuànjī
PBX	Private branch exchange	专用小交换机	Zhuānyòng xiǎo jiāohuànjī
PBX	Private branch exchange	用户交换机	Yònghù jiāohuànjī
PBX	Private branch exchange	用户小交换机	Yònghù xiǎo jiāohuànjī
PC	Personal computer	个人电脑	Gèrén diànnǎo
PC	Personal computer	个人计算机	Gèrén jìsuànjī
PC	Perspective correction	透视纠正	Tòushì jiūzhèng
PC	Phase coherence	相位相干	Xiàngwèi xiānggān
PC	Plane connection	平面连接	Píngmiàn liánjiē
PC	Plane connection	平面连接	Píngmiàn liánjiē
PC	Polycarbonate	聚碳酸酯	Jùtànsuānzhǐ
PC	Power control	功率控制	Gōnglǜ kòngzhì
PC	Priority control	优先级控制	Yōuxiān jí kòngzhì
PC	Protocol controller	协议控制器	Xiéyì kòngzhìqì
PC	Proximity card	接近卡	Jiējìn kǎ
PC	Run in rigid PVC conduit	穿硬聚乙烯管敷设	Chuān yìng jùyǐxī guǎn fūshè
PC, PCH	Paging channel	寻呼信道	Xúnhū xìndào
PCA	Printed circuit antenna	印制电路天线	Yìnzhì diànlù tiānxiàn
PCA	Programmable cellular automata (crypt,)	可编程细胞自动机	Kěbiānchéng xìbāo zìdòngjī
PCAV	Partial constant angular velocity	部分恒定角速度	Bùfen héngdìng jiǎosùdù
PCB	Printed circuit board	印制板	Yìnzhì bǎn
PCB	Printed circuit board	印刷电路板	Yìnshuā diànlù bǎn
PCB	Protocol control byte	协议控制字节	Xiéyì kòngzhì zìjié
PCBA	Printed circuit board assembly	印制电路板组件	Yìnzhì diànlù bǎn zǔjiàn
PCBA	Printed circuit board assembly	印刷电路板装配	Yìnshuā diànlù bǎn zhuāngpèi
PC-based PBX	Personal computer-based private branch exchange	基于电脑的小型用户交换机	Jīyú diànnǎode xiǎoxíng yònghù jiāohuànjī

PCC	Common coupling point	公共耦合点	Gōnggòng ǒuhédiǎn
PCCA	Processor communication control board assembly	处理器通信控制集成板	Chǔlǐqì tōngxìn kòngzhì jíchéngbǎn
PCCC	Parallel concatenated convolutional code	并联链接卷积码	Bìnglián liànjiē juànjīmǎ
PCCCH	Packet common control channel	分组公共控制信道	Fēnzǔ gōnggòng kòngzhì xìndào
PCCH	Paging control channel	寻呼控制信道	Xúnhū kòngzhì xìndào
P-CCPCH	Primary common control physical channel	基本公共控制物理信道	Jīběn gōnggòng kòngzhì wùlǐ xìndào
PCDDS	Private circuit digital data service	专用电路数字数据业务	Zhuānyòng diànlù shùzì shùjù yèwù
PCDE	Peak code domain error	峰值码域误差	Fēngzhí mǎyù wùchā
PC-DOS	Personal computer-disk operating system	个人计算机磁盘操作系统	Gèrén jìsuànjī cípán cāozuò xìtǒng
PCE	Packet centralization equipment	分组集中器	Fēnzǔ jízhōngqì
PCEP	Presentation connection end point	表示连接端点	Biǎoshì liánjiē duāndiǎn
PCET	Personal computer extended technology bus	个人计算机扩充技术总线	Gèrén jìsuànjī kuòchōng jìshù zǒngxiàn
PCF	Packet controlled function	分组控制功能	Fēnzǔ kòngzhì gōngnéng
PCF	Packet data control function	分组数据控制功能	Fēnzǔ shùjù kòngzhì gōngnéng
PCF	Photonic crystal fiber	光子晶体光纤	Guāngzǐ jīngtǐ guāngxiān
PCF	Port and core function	端口及核心功能	Duānkǒu jí héxīn gōngnéng
PCF-OS	Port and core function-operating system	端口及核心功能-运行系统	Duānkǒu jí héxīn gōngnéng--yùnxíng xìtǒng
PCF-OSF	Port and core function-operating system function	端口及核心功能-运行系统功能	Duānkǒu jí héxīn gōngnéng--yùnxíng xìtǒng gōngnéng
PCG	Project coordination group	项目协调组	Xiàngmù xiétiáo zǔ
PCH	Pre-chirp	预啁啾	Yùzhōujiū
PCI	Parallel communication interface	并行通信接口	Bìngxíng tōngxìn jiēkǒu
PCI	Peripheral component interconnect	互连外围设备	Hùlián wàiwéi shèbèi
PCI	Peripheral component interconnect	周边器材互联	Zhōubiān qìcái hùlián
PCI	Peripheral component interconnect	外围设备互联	Wàiwéi shèbèi hùlián
PCI	Peripheral component interconnect	外部部件互连	Wàibù bùjiàn hùlián
PCI	Peripheral component interface	外围设备接口	Wàiwéi shèbèi jiēkǒu
PCI	Protocol control information	协议控制信息	Xiéyì kòngzhì xìnxī
PCI SIG	Peripheral component interconnect special interest group	互连外围设备专业组	Hùlián wàiwéi shèbèi zhuānyè zǔ
PCIA	Packet communication I/F card assembly	分组通信 I/F 集成卡	Fēnzǔ tōngxìn I/F jíchéng kǎ
PCIMG	PCI Industry Computer Manufacturers group	PCI 工业计算机制造商协会	PCI gōngyè jìsuànjī zhìzàoshāng xiéhuì
PCK	Personalization control key	个性化控制键	Gèxìnghuà kòngzhì jiàn
PCL	Printer control language	打印机控制语言	Dǎyìnjī kòngzhì yǔyán
PCL	Process control language	过程控制语言	Guòchéng kòngzhì yǔyán
PCL	Secured by pVC clip	塑料夹敷设	Sùliào jiā fūshè
PCM	Pulse code modulation	脉冲码调制	Màichōng mǎ tiáozhì
PCM	Pulse code modulation	脉冲编码调制	Màichōng biānmǎ tiáozhì
PCM	Pulse code modulation	脉码调制	Màimǎ tiáozhì
PCMA	Processor controlled memory access	处理机控制存储存取	Chǔlǐjī kòngzhì cúnchǔ cúnqǔ
PCMCIA	Personal computer memory card international	国际个人计算机存储卡协会	Guójì gèrén jìsuànjī cúnchǔ qiǎ xiéhuì
PCMCIA	Personal Computer Memory Card International Association	个人计算机内存卡国际标准协会	Gèrén jìsuànjī nèicúnkǎ guójì biāozhǔn xiéhuì
PCMCIA	Personal Computer Memory Card International Association	个人计算机存储卡国际联合会	Gèrén jìsuànjī cúnchǔkǎ Guójì liánhéhuì
PCME	Packet circuit multiplication equipment	分组电路倍增设备	Fēnzǔ diànlù bèizēng shèbèi
PCM-IM (PS)	Pulse code modulation intensity modulated (pulse source)	强调制的脉码调制（脉冲源）	Qiáng tiáozhìde màimǎ tiáozhì (màichōng yuán)

PCM-LIN	Pulse code modulation-linear	线性脉码调制	Xiànxìng màimǎ tiáozhì
PCM-LOG	Pulse code modulation-logarithmic companded	对数压缩扩展脉码调制	Duìshù yāsuō kuòzhǎn màimǎ tiáozhì
PCM-PM (PS)	Pulse code modulation-polarization modulation (pulse source)	极化调制脉码调制（脉冲源）	Jíhuà tiáozhì màimǎ tiáozhì (màichōng yuán)
PCN	Personal communication network	个人通信网	Gèrén tōngxìnwǎng
PCO	Point of control and observation	控制和观察点	Kòngzhì hé guānchá diǎn
PCO	Point of control and observation	控制和观测点	Kòngzhì hé guāncèdiǎn
PCO	Point of control and observation	控制观察点	Kòngzhì guānchádiǎn
PCPCH	Physical common packet channel	物理公共分组信道	Wùlǐ gōnggòng fēnzǔ xìndào
PCPG	Primary clock pulse generator	主时钟脉冲发生器	Zhǔ shízhōng màichōng fāshēngqì
P-CPIH	Primary common pilot channel	基本公共导频信道	Jīběn gōnggòng dǎopín xìndào
PCR	Peak cell rate	峰值信元速率	Fēngzhí xìnyuán sùlǜ
PCS	Personal communication service	个人通讯服务	Gèrén tōngxùn fúwù
PCS	Personal communication services	个人通信	Gèrén tōngxìn
PCS	Personal communications service	个人通信业务	Gèrén tōngxìn yèwù
PCS	Personal communications systems	个人通信系统	Gèrén tōngxìn xìtǒng
PCS	Personalization center	个人化中心	Gèrénhuà zhōngxīn
PCS	Physical coding sub-layer	物理编码子层	Wùlǐ biānmǎ zicéng
PCS	Plastic clad silica fiber	塑包石英光纤	Sùbāo shíyīng guāngxiān
PCS	Plesiochronous connection supervision	准同步连接监督	Zhǔn tóngbù liánjiē jiāndū
PCS	Plesiochronous connection supervision	准同步连接管理	Zhǔn tóngbù liánjiē guǎnlǐ
PCS	Program counter save register	程序记数器保存积存器	Chéngxù jìshùqì bǎocún jīcúnqì
PCSFSK	Phase comparison sinusoidal frequency shift keying	相位比较正弦移频键控	Xiàngwèi bǐjiào zhèngxián yípín jiànkòng
PCSMA/CD	Prioritized carrier-sense multiple access with collision detection	带有碰撞检测的优先载波读出多路存取	Dàiyǒu pèngzhuàng jiǎncède yōuxiān zàibō dúchū duōlù cúnqǔ
PCS-MSC	Personal communication system – mobile switching center	个人通信系统-移动交换中心	Gèrén tōngxìn xìtǒng—yídòng jiāohuàn zhōngxīn
PCSS	Phase-coded spread-spectrum signal	相位编码扩展频谱信号	Xiàngwèi biānmǎ kuòzhǎn pínpǔ xìnhào
PCSSM	Phase-coded spread-spectrum modulation	相位编码扩展频谱调制	Xiàngwèi biānmǎ kuòzhǎn pínpǔ tiáozhì
PCTR	Protocol conformance test report	协议一致性测试报告	Xiéyì yīzhìxìng cèshì bàogào
PCU	Packet control unit	分组控制单元	Fēnzǔ kòngzhì dānyuán
PCU	Packet data unit	分组数据单元	Fēnzǔ shùjù dānyuán
PCU	Power control unit	功率控制单元	Gōnglǜ kòngzhì dānyuán
PCVD	Plasma chemical vapor deposition (FOC mfg)	等离子体化学汽相沉积法	Děnglízǐtǐ huàxué qìxiāng chénjīfǎ
PCVD	Plasma-activated chemical vapor deposition (for FOC)	等离子体激活化学气相沉积	Děnglízǐtǐ jīhuó huàxué qìxiāng chénjī
PCW	Pitch-cycle waveform	基音周期波形	Jīyīn zhōuqī bōxíng
PD	Photo detector	光电探测器	Guāngdiàn tàncèqì
PD	Physical delivery	物理投递	Wùlǐ tóudì
PD	Project delivery (CMM term)	项目交付	Xiàngmù jiāofù
PD	Protocol discriminator	协议标识符	Xiéyì biāozhì fú
PD	Protocol discriminator	协议鉴别器	Xiéyì jiànbiéqì
PD	Public data	公用数据	Gōngyòng shùjù
PD	Wiring	配电	Pèidiàn
PDA	Personal digital assistant	个人数字助理	Gèrén shùzì zhùlǐ
PDA	Personal digital assistant	个人数字辅助器	Gèrén shùzì fǔzhùqì
PDAU	Physical delivery access unit	物理投递访问单元	Wùlǐ tóudì fǎngwèn dānyuán
PDB	Per domain behavior	每域行为	Měi yù xíngwéi

PDBM	Pulse delay binary modulation	脉冲延迟二进制调制	Màichōng yánchí èrjìnzhì tiáozhì
PDC	Passive dispersion compensator	无源色散补偿器	Wúyuán sèsàn bǔchángqì
PDC	Personal digital cellular system (Japan)	个人数字蜂窝系统	Gèrén shùzì fēngwō xìtǒng
PDC	Personal digital cellular telecommunications system (Japan)	个人数字蜂窝通信系统	Gèrén shùzì fēngwō tōngxìn xìtǒng
PDC	Primary domain controller	主域控制器	Zhǔ yù kòngzhìqì
PDCH	Packet data channel	分组数据信道	Fēnzǔ shùjù xìndào
PDCH	Physical dedicated channel	专用物理信道	Zhuānyòng wùlǐ xìndào
PDCP	Packet data convergence protocol	分组数据会聚协议	Fēnzǔ shùjù huìjù xiéyì
PDE	Position determining entity	位置确定实体	Wèizhì quèdìng shítǐ
PDEF	Physical design exchange format	物理设计交换格式	Wùlǐ shèjì jiāohuàn géshì
PDF	Portable document format	轻便文档格式	Qīngbiàn wéndàng géshì
PDF	Power supply distribution frame	电原配电架	Diànyuán pèidiànjià
PDFA	Praseodymium-doped fiber amplifier	掺镨光纤放大器	Chān pǔ guāngxiān fàngdàqì
PDFI	Polarization-dependent fiber isolator (FOC)	偏振相关光隔离器	Piānzhèn xiāngguān guāng gélíqì
PDG	Polarization-dependent gain	偏振相关增益	Piānzhèn xiāngguān zēngyì
PDG	Primary digital group	数字基群	Shùzì jīqún
PDH	Plesiochronous digital hierarchy	准同步数字体系	Zhǔn tóngbù shùzì tǐxì
PDH	Plesiochronous digital hierarchy	准同步数字系列	Zhǔn tóngbù shùzì xìliè
PDH	Pseudo-synchronous digital hierarchy	伪同步数字网	Wěitóngbù shùzì wǎng
PDH	Pseudo-synchronous digital hierarchy	准同步数字体系	Zhǔn tóngbù shùzì tǐxì
PDH	Pseudo-synchronous digital hierarchy	准同步数字分级	Zhǔn tóngbù shùzì fēnjí
PDL	Polarization-dependent loss (FOC)	偏振相关损耗	Piānzhèn xiāngguān sǔnhào
PDM	Phase division multiplexing	相分多路复用	Xiàngfēn duōlù fùyòng
PDM	Physical delivery message	物理投递消息	Wùlǐ tóudì xiāoxi
PDM	Product data management	产品数据管理	Chǎnpǐn shùjù guǎnlǐ
PDM	Pulse delta modulation	脉冲增量调制	Màichōng zēngliàng tiáozhì
PDM	Pulse duration modulation	脉冲宽度调制	Màichōng kuāndù tiáozhì
PDM	Pulse duration modulation, pulse width modulation	脉冲持续时间调制	Màichōng chíxù shíjiān tiáozhì
PDM	Pulse width modulation	脉冲宽度调制	Màichōng kuāndù tiáozhì
PDMA	Polarization division multiple access	极化分割多路存取	Jíhuà fēngē duōlù cúnqǔ
PDM-FM	Pulse-duration modulation frequency modulation	脉宽调制-调制	Màikuān tiáozhì—tiáozhì
PDN	Packet data network	分组数据网络	Fēnzǔ shùjù wǎngluò
PDN	Public data network	公用数据网	Gōngyòng shùjù wǎng
PDN	Public data network	共用数据网	Gòngyòng shùjù wǎng
PDP	Packet data protocol	分组数据协议	Fēnzǔ shùjù xiéyì
PDP	Plasma display panel	电浆显示器	Diànjiāng xiǎnshìqì
PDP	Policy decision point	策略决定点	Cèlüè juédìng diǎn
PDQ	Predictive differential quantizer	预测差分量化器	Yùcè chāfēn liànghuàqì
PDR	Programmable digital radio	可编程数字无线电	Kěbiānchéng shùzì wúxiàndiàn
PDS	Physical delivery system	物理投递系统	Wùlǐ tóudì xìtǒng
PDS	Premises distribution system	建筑物布线系统	Jiànzhùwù bùxiàn xìtǒng
PDS	Premises distribution system	建筑物结构化综合布线系统	Jiànzhùwù jiégòuhuà zōnghé bùxiàn xìtǒng
PDS	Premises distribution system	建筑综合布线系统	Jiànzhù zōnghé bùxiàn xìtǒng
PDS	Premises distribution system	综合布线系统	Zōnghé bùxiàn xìtǒng
PDS	Program debugging system	程序调试系统	Chéngxù tiáoshì xìtǒng
PDS	Public directory support	公众目录支持	Gōngzhòng mùlù zhīchí

PDSCH	Physical downlink shared channel	下行链路共享物理信道	Xiàxíng liànlù gòngxiǎng wùlǐ xìndào
PDSCH	Physical downlink shared channel	物理下行共享信道	Wùlǐ xiàxíng gòngxiǎng xìndào
PDSN	Packet data service network	分组数据业务网络	Fēnzǔ shùjù yèwù wǎngluò
PDSN	Packet data serving node	分组数据服务节点	Fēnzǔ shùjù fúwù jiédiǎn
PDTCH	Packet data traffic channel	分组数据业务信道	Fēnzǔ shùjù yèwù xìndào
PDTCH	Packet data traffic channel	分组数据传输信道	Fēnzǔ shùjù chuánshū xìndào
PDTCH	Packet data transfer channel	分组数据传递信道	Fēnzǔ shùjù chuándì xìndào
PDU	Protocol data unit	协商数据单元	Xiéshāng shùjù dānyuán
PDU,PDY	Protocol data unit	协议数据单元	Xiéyì shùjù dānyuán
PDX	Processor-controlled digital exchange	处理机控制的数字交换机	Chǔlǐjī kòngzhìde shùzì jiāohuànjī
PE	Packet layer reference event	分组层参考事件	Fēnzǔ céng cānkǎo shìjiàn
PE	Phase encoding	相位编码	Xiàngwèi biānmǎ
PE	Physical entity	物理实体	Wùlǐ shítǐ
PE	Polyethylene	聚乙烯	Jùyǐxī
PE	Portable executable file	可移植可执行文件	Kěyízhí kě zhíxíng wénjiàn
PE	Probability of error	差错（误码）概率	Chācuò (wù mǎ) gàilǜ
PE	Protection earth wire	保护线	Bǎohù xiàn
PE	Protocol entity	协议实体	Xiéyì shítǐ
PE	Protocol event	协议事件	Xiéyì shìjiàn
PE	Proton exchange	质子交换	Zhìzǐ jiāohuàn
PE	Provider edge	提供商边缘	Tígōng shāng biānyuán
PE	Provider edge router	运营商边缘路由器	Yùnyíngshāng biānyuán lùyóuqì
PECVD	Plasma enhanced chemical vapor deposition	等离子体增强化学汽相沉积	Děnglízǐtǐ zēngqiáng huàxué qìxiāng chénjī
PED	Protocol encoder/decoder	协议编译码器	Xiéyì biānyìmǎqì
PELPC	Pitch excited linear productive coding	高度激励线性生产编码	Gāodù jīlì xiànxìng shēngchǎn biānmǎ
PEM	Privacy enhanced mail	私有加强邮件	Sīyǒu jiāqiáng yóujiàn
PEM	Pulse encoded modulation	脉冲编码调制	Màichōng biānmǎ tiáozhì
PEN	Protection earth and neutral	保护和中性公用线	Bǎohù hé zhōngxìng gōngyòng xiàn
PEP	Path end point	通道端点	Tōngdào duāndiǎn
PEP	Path end point	通道端点	Tōngdào duāndiǎn
PEP	Personal equity plan	个人股东投资计划	Gèrén gǔdōng tóuzī jìhuà
PEP	Policy enhancement point	策略强加点	Cèlüè qiángjiā diǎn
PER	Packet encoding rules	分组编码规则	Fēnzǔ biānmǎ guīzé
PER	Packet error rate	分组差错率	Fēnzǔ chācuò lǜ
PER	Packet error rate	分组错误率	Fēnzǔ cuòwù lǜ
PER	Packet error rate	包出错率	Bāo chūcuò lǜ
PERL	Practical extraction and report language	实用摘录与报告语言	Shíyòng zhāilù yǔ bàogào yǔyán
PESY	Peripheral exchange synchronization	外围交换同步化	Wàiwéi jiāohuàn tóngbùhuà
PF	Power factor	功率因数	Gōnglǜ yīnshù
PF	Presentation function	表示功能	Biǎoshì gōngnéng
PF	Pressurization fan	加压风机	Jiāyā fēngjī
PFDL	Packet format description language	报文格式描述语言	Bàowén géshi miáoshù yǔyán
PFEP	Programmable front end processor	可编程前端处理机	Kěbiānchéng qiánduān chǔlǐjī
PFH	Parallel frequency hopping	并行频率跳变	Bìngxíng pínlǜ tiàobiàn
PFM	Pulse frequency modulation	脉冲频率调制	Màichōng pínlǜ tiáozhì
PFQ	Packet fair queuing	分组公平排队算法	Fēnzǔ gōngpíng páiduì suànfǎ

PFS	Product form solution	乘积形式解	Chéngjī xíngshì jiě
PFSK	Permutation frequency shift keying	置换频移键控	Zhìhuàn pínyí jiànkòng
PFT	Pulsed Fourier transform	脉冲傅氏转换	Màichōng fù-shì zhuǎnhuàn
PG	Pressure gradient	压差式	Yāchā-shì
PG	Processing gain	处理增益	Chǔlǐ zēngyì
PG	Protective ground	保护接地	Bǎohù jiēdì
PGA	Pin grid array	引脚网格阵列	Yǐnjiǎo wǎnggé zhènliè
PGA	Pin grid array (electronics mfg)	针栅阵列	Zhēn zhà zhènliè
PGA	Professional graphics adapter	专用图形适配器	Zhuānyòng túxíng shìpèiqì
PGC	Parallel graphics configuration	并行图像配置	Bìngxíng túxiàng pèizhì
PGI	Parameter group identifier	参数组标识符	Cānshù zǔ biāozhì fú
PGM	Pragmatic general multicast protocol (IETF usage)	实用通用组播协议	Shíyòng tōngyòng zǔbō xiéyì
PGP	Pretty good privacy	优良保密协议	Yōuliáng bǎomì xiéyì
PH	Packet handler	分组处理器	Fēnzǔ chǔlǐqì
PH	Packet header	包标题	Bāo biāotí
PH, PHY	Physical layer	物理层	Wùlǐ céng
PHB	Per-hop behavior	每跳行为	Měi tiào xíngwéi
PHB	Per-hop behavior	逐跳转发行为	Zhútiào zhuǎnfā xíngwéi
PHC	Physical connection	物理连接	Wùlǐ liánjiē
PHDSL	Pair high bit-rate digital subscriber line	双线制高比特率数字用户线	Shuāngxiàn zhìgāo bǐtèlǜ shùzì yònghù xiàn
PHF	Packet handler function	分组处理器功能	Fēnzǔ chǔlǐqì gōngnéng
PHI	Packet handler interface	分组处理器接口	Fēnzǔ chǔlǐqì jiēkǒu
PHI	Packet handling interface	分组处理接口	Fēnzǔ chǔlǐ jiēkǒu
PHIGS	Programmer's hierarchical interactive graphics standard	程序员用分极较糊图形标准	Chéngxùyuán-yòng fēnjí jiàohú túxíng biāozhǔn
Philcomsat	Philippine Communications Satellite Corp.	菲律宾卫星公司	Fēi-lǜ-bīn wèixīng gōngsī
PHM	Packet handler module	分组处理模块	Fēnzǔ chǔlǐ mókuài
PHPDU	Physical protocol data unit	物理协议数据单元	Wùlǐ xiéyì shùjù dānyuán
PHS	Payload header suppression	净荷包头抑制	Jìnghé bāotóu yìzhì
PHS	Personal handy-phone system	个人手持电话系统	Gèrén shǒuchí diànhuà xìtǒng
PHS	Personal handy-phone system	个人无绳电话系统	Gèrén wúshéng diànhuà xìtǒng
PhS	Physical service	物理服务	Wùlǐ fúwù
PHS Rule	Payload header suppression rule	净荷包头抑制规则	Jìnghé bāotóu yìzhì guīzé
PhSAP	Physical service access point	物理业务访问点	Wùlǐ yèwù fǎngwèn diǎn
PhSDU	Physical service data unit	物理服务数据单元	Wùlǐ fúwù shùjù dānyuán
PHSF	Payload header suppression field	净荷包头抑制域	Jìnghé bāotóu yìzhì yù
PHSI	Payload header suppression index	净荷包头抑制索引	Jìnghé bāotóu yìzhì suǒyǐn
PHSM	Payload header suppression marker	净荷包头抑制校验	Jìnghé bāotóu yìzhì jiàoyàn
PHSS	Payload header suppression size	净荷包头抑制长度	Jìnghé bāotóu yìzhì chángdù
PHSV	Payload header suppression valid	净荷包头抑制校验	Jìnghé bāotóu yìzhì jiàoyàn
PHV	Packet handler for voice	语音分组处理程序（器）	Yǔyīn fēnzǔ chǔlǐ chéngxù (qì)
PHY	Physical layer device	物理层设备	Wùlǐ céng shèbèi
PI	Page indicator	寻呼指示器	Xúnhū zhǐshìqì
PI	Parameter identifier	参数标识符	Cānshù biāozhì fú
PI	Presentation indicator	展示指示器	Zhǎnshì zhǐshìqì
PI	Proportional-integral (controller)	比例积分（控制器）	Bǐlì jīfēn (kòngzhìqì)
PI	Protocol identifier	协议标识符	Xiéyì biāozhì fú

PI	Protocol sub-tree identification	协议子树标识	Xiéyì zishù biāozhì
PI/O	Process input/output device	过程输入/输出装置	Guòchéng shūrù/shūchū zhuāngzhì
PIA	Personal information assistant	个人信息助理	Gèrén xìnxī zhùlǐ
PIA	Point in association	相关点	Xiāngguān diǎn
PIAFS	Personal (handset system) Internet access forum standard	个人手机系统因特网接入论坛标准	Gèrén shǒujī xìtǒng Yīntèwǎng jiērù lùntán biāozhǔn
PIB	Processor-in-a-box	盒装处理器	Hézhuāng chǔlǐqì
PIC	Parallel instruction code	并行指令代码	Bìngxíng zhǐlìng dàimǎ
PIC	Parallel interference cancellation	并行干扰消除	Bìngxíng gānrǎo xiāochú
PIC	Photonic integrated circuit	光子集成电路	Guāngzǐ jíchéng diànlù
PIC	Programmable interrupt controller	可编程中断控制器	Kěbiānchéng zhōngduàn kòngzhìqì
PICH	Paging indicator channel	寻呼指示信道	Xúnhū zhǐshì xìndào
PICI	Processor inter-communication interface	处理器内部通信接口	Chǔlǐqì nèibù tōngxìn jiēkǒu
PICP	Power amplifier interconnection panel	功率放大器互联面板	Gōnglǜ fàngdàqì hùlián miànbǎn
PICS	Platform for Internet content selection	因特网内容选择平台	Yīntèwǎng nèiróng xuǎnzé píngtái
PICS	Protocol implementation conformance statement	协议实现一致性声明	Xiéyì shíxiàn yīzhìxìng shēngmíng
PICS	Protocol implementation conformance statement	协议实现的一致性陈述	Xiéyì shíxiànde yīzhìxìng chénshù
PICS	Protocol implementation conformity statement	协议实现一致性说明	Xiéyì shíxiàn yīzhìxìng shuōmíng
PID	Packet identification	分组包识别	Fēnzǔbāo shíbié
PID	Partial ID number type	局部 ID 号码类型	Júbù ID hàomǎ lèixíng
PID	Passive infrared detector	被动式红外传感器	Bèidòngshì hóngwài chuángǎnqì
pid	Process ID (Unix)	进程标识	Jìnchéng biāozhì
PID	Process identifier	进程标识符	Jìnchéng biāozhìfú
PID	Proportional-integral-differential (controller)	比例积分微分(控制器)	Bǐlì jīfēn wēifēn (kòngzhìqì)
PIF	Partial information feedback	部分信息反馈	Bùfen xìnxī fǎnkuì
PIFI	Polarization-insensitive fiber isolator (FOC)	偏振无关光隔离器	Piānzhèn wúguān guāng gélíqì
PIM	Parallel iterative matching	并行迭代匹配	Bìngxíng diédài pǐpèi
PIM	Personal information management	个人信息管理系统	Gèrén xìnxī guǎnlǐ xìtǒng
PIM	Product information management	产品信息管理	Chǎnpǐn xìnxī guǎnlǐ
PIM	Protocol-independent multicast	协议无关多点广播	Xiéyì wúguān duōdiǎn guǎngbō
PIM	Protocol-independent multicast	独立于协议的组播协议	Dúlì yú xiéyìde zǔbō xiéyì
PIM	Protocol-independent muticast	独立组播协议	Dúlì zǔbō xiéyì
PIM	Pulse interval modulation	脉冲区间调制	Màichōng qūjiān tiáozhì
PIM DM	Protocol-independent multicast dense mode	独立组播协议密集模式	Dúlì zǔbō xiéyì mìjí móshì
PIM SM	Protocol-independent multicast sparse mode	独立组播协议稀疏模式	Dúlì zǔbō xiéyì xīshū móshì
PIM-DM	Protocol-independent multicast dense mode	协议独立稠密模式组播	Xiéyì dúlì chóumì móshì zǔbō
PIM-DM	Protocol-independent multicast--dense mode	协议无关组播-密集模式	Xiéyì wúguān zǔbō--mìjí móshì
PIM-SM	Protocol-independent multicast sparse mode	协议独立稀疏模式组播	Xiéyì dúlì xīshū móshì zǔbō
PIM-SM	Protocol-independent multicast--sparse mode	协议无关组播-稀疏模式	Xiéyì wúguān zǔ bō--xīshū móshì
PIN	Personal identification number	个人识别号码	Gèrén shíbié hàomǎ
PIN	Personal identification number	个人识别码	Gèrén shíbié mǎ
PIN	Personal identification number	个人身份识别号	Gèrén shēnfen shíbié hào
PIN	Personal identification number	用户个人资料识别码	Yònghù gèrén zīliào shíbié mǎ
PIN	Personal identification number	身份识别码	Shēnfen shíbié mǎ
PIN	Photo-intrinsic diode	光电二极管	Guāngdiàn èrjíguǎn
PIN	Public initialization node	公共发起节点	Gōnggòng fāqǐ jiédiǎn

PING	Packet Internet groper	分组因特网探索程序	Fēnzǔ Yīntèwǎng tànsuǒ chéngxù
PING	Packet Internet groper	分组因特网查询进程	Fēnzǔ Yīntèwǎng cháxún jìnchéng
PING	Packet Internet groper	网际包探测器	Wǎngjì bāo tàncèqì
PInvoke	Platform invoke service	平台调用服务	Píngtái diàoyòng fúwù
PIO	Parallel input output	并行输入输出	Bìngxíng shūrù shūchū
PIO	Programmable input output	可编程输入输出模式	Kěbiānchéng shūrù shūchū móshì
PIP	Private intelligent peripheral	专用智能外设	Zhuānyòng zhìnéng wài shè
PIR	Packet insertion rate	分组插入率	Fēnzǔ chārù lǜ
PIR	Project initiation request (CMM)	项目启动申请	Xiàngmù qǐdòng shēnqǐng
PIROM	Processor information ROM	处理器信息 ROM	Chǔlǐqì xìnxī ROM
PIT	Partition information table	分区信息表	Fēnqū xìnxī biǎo
PITS	Protocol integrated test system	协议集成测试系统	Xiéyì jíchéng cèshì xìtǒng
PIXIT	Protocol implementation extra information for testing	协议实现的测试补充材料	Xiéyì shíxiànde cèshì bǔchōng cáiliào
PIXIT	Protocol implementation extra information for testing	协议实现附加测试信息	Xiéyì shíxiàn fùjiā cèshì xìnxī
PJC	Pointer justification count	指针调整记数	Zhǐzhēn tiáozhěng jìshù
PJE	Pointer justification event	指针调整事件	Zhǐzhēn tiáozhěng shìjiàn
PJL	Printer job language	打印机作业语言	Dǎyìnjī zuòyè yǔyán
PK	Primary keyword (for database)	主键	Zhǔ jiàn
PKA	Public key algorithm	公用密钥算法	Gōngyòng mìyào suànfǎ
PKI	Public key infrastructure	公共密钥基础设施	Gōnggòng mìyào jīchǔ shèshī
PKI	Public key infrastructure	公共键构	Gōnggòng jiàn gòu
PKI	Public key infrastructure	公用关键基础设施	Gōngyòng guānjiàn jīchǔ shèshī
PKI	Public key infrastructure	公钥基础结构	Gōngyào jīchǔ jiégòu
PKI	Public key infrastructure	公钥基础设施	Gōngyào jīchǔ shèshī
PKI	Public key infrastructure	公钥机制	Gōngyào jīzhì
Pk-Pk	Peak to peak	峰峰值	Fēng-fēng zhí
PL	Mobile station power level	移动台功率电平	Yídòngtái gōnglǜ diànpíng
PL	Power level	功率电平	Gōnglǜ diànpíng
PL	Private line	专用线路	Zhuānyòng xiànlù
PL	Processor loader	处理器承载器	Chǔlǐqì chéngzàiqì
PL	Secured by porcelain clip	瓷夹敷设	Cíjiā fūshè
PLA	Powerline access	电力线接入	Diànlìxiàn jiērù
PLA	Programmable logic array	可编程序的逻辑阵列	Kěbiān chéngxùde luóji zhènliè
PLAN	Token passing network	令牌网	Lìngpái wǎng
PLB	Powerline broadband	电力线宽带	Diànlìxiàn kuāndài
PLC	Packet line card	分组线路板	Fēnzǔ xiànlù bǎn
PLC	Planar lightwave circuit	平面光波电路	Píngmiàn guāngbō diànlù
PLC	Planar lightwave circuit	平面波导线路	Píngmiàn bōdǎo xiànlù
PLC	Powerline carrier	电力线载波	Diànlìxiàn zàibō
PLC	Programmable logic controller	可编程逻辑控制器	Kěbiānchéng luóji kòngzhìqì
PLCF	Powerline carrier forum	电力线载波论坛	Diànlìxiàn zàibō lùntán
PLCP	Packet layer control processor	分组层控制处理器	Fēnzǔ céng kòngzhì chǔlǐqì
PLD	Phase-locked detector	同相检波	Tóngxiāng jiǎnbō
PLD	Processor load data	处理器装载数据	Chǔlǐqì zhuāngzài shùjù
PLD	Programmable logic device	可变程逻辑器件	Kěbiànchéng luóji qìjiàn

PLDA	Private loop direct attached	私有环路直接连接	Sīyǒu huánlù zhíjiē liánjiē
PLEDM	Phase-state low electron (hole)-number drive memory	相位态低电子驱动存储器	Xiàngwèi tài dīdiànzǐ qūdòng cúnchǔqì
PLK	Primary link	基群链路	Jīqún liànlù
PLL	Permanent link layer	永久链路层	Yǒngjiǔ liànlù céng
PLL	Permanent logical link	永久逻辑链路	Yǒngjiǔ luójí liànlù
PLL	Phase locked loop	锁相环	Suǒxiàng huán
PLL	Phase locked loop	锁相环路	Suǒxiàng huánlù
PLL-QPSK	Phase-locked loop quadrature phase shift keying	锁相环四相相移键控	Suǒxiāng huán sìxiāng xiāngyí jiànkòng
PLM	Payload mismatch	净荷失配	Jìnghé shīpèi
PLM	Port level manager	端口级管理程序	Duānkǒu-jí guǎnlǐ chéngxù
PLMN	Public land cellular mobile network	公用陆地蜂窝移动通信网	Gōngyòng lùdì fēngwō yídòng tōngxìnwǎng
PLMN	Public land mobile communications network	公用陆地移动通信网	Gōngyòng lùdì yídòng tōngxìnwǎng
PLMN	Public land mobile network	公众陆地移动电话网	Gōngzhòng lùdì yídòng diànhuà wǎng
PLMN	Public land mobile network	公共陆地移动网络	Gōnggòng lùdì yídòng wǎngluò
PLMN	Public land mobile network	公共陆地移动通信网	Gōnggòng lùdì yídòng tōngxìnwǎng
PLMN	Public land mobile network	公共陆基移动网	Gōnggòng lùjī yídòngwǎng
PLMN	Public land mobile network	公用陆地移动网络	Gōngyòng lùdì yídòng wǎngluò
PLMTS	Public land mobile telecommunications system	共用陆地移动通信系统	Gòngyòng lùdì yídòng tōngxìn xìtǒng
PL-OAM	Physical layer-operation and maintenance (cell)	物理层-操作和维护（信元）	Wùlǐ céng—cāozuò hé wéihù (xìnyuán)
PLP	Packet layer protocol	分组层协议	Fēnzǔ céng xiéyì
PLP	Packet-level protocol	包级协议	Bāo jí xiéyì
PLR	Packet loss rate	分组丢失率	Fēnzǔ diūshī lǜ
PLS	Physical layer signaling	物理层信令	Wùlǐ céng xìnlìng
PLS	Public Land System (US)	国家土地系统	Guójiā tǔdì xìtǒng
PLSS	Public Land Survey System (US)	国家土地调查体系	Guójiā tǔdì diàochá tǐxì
PLT	Powerline telecommunications	电力线通信	Diànlìxiàn tōngxìn
PLZT	Lead-zirconium titanate wafer	钛酸锆酸铅晶圆	Tàisuān gàosuān qiān jīngyuán
PM	Market penetration	市场普及率	Shìchǎng pǔjílǜ
PM	Packet mode	包方式	Bāo fāngshì
PM	Phase modification synchronization (in CORBA)	相位修改同步协议	Xiàngwèi xiūgǎi tóngbù xiéyì
PM	Phase modulation	相位调制	Xiàngwèi tiáozhì
PM	Phase modulation	调相	Tiáoxiàng
PM	Physical media	物理媒体	Wùlǐ méitǐ
PM	Physical medium sub-layer	物理媒体子层	Wùlǐ méitǐ zicéng
PM	Power matching	功率匹配	Gōnglǜ pǐpèi
PM	Preventive maintenance	预防性维护	Yùfángxìng wéihù
PM	Private memory	专用存储器	Zhuānyòng cúnchǔqì
PM1	Processable mode number one	一号可处理方式	Yīhào kěchǔlǐ fāngshì
PMA	Physical media access	物理介质接入	Wùlǐ jièzhì jiērù
PMA	Physical media attachment	物理介质接入	Wùlǐ jièzhì jiērù
PMA	Prompt maintenance alarm	即时维护告警	Jíshí wéihù gàojǐng
PMBB	Properties management building block	性能管理构件	Xìngnéng guǎnlǐ gòujiàn
PMBR	Protocol-independent multicast (PIM) multicast border router	协议无关组播协议组播边界路由器	Xiéyì wúguān zǔbō xiéyì zǔbō biānjiè lùyóuqì
PMBS	Packet mode bearer service	分组承载业务	Fēnzǔ chéngzài yèwù
PMBS	Packet mode bearer service	分组模式承载业务	Fēnzǔ móshì chéngzài yèwù

PMC	Physical media dependent	物理媒体有关	Wùlǐ méitǐ yǒuguān
PMC	Provincial monitoring center	省监测中心	Shěng jiāncè zhōngxīn
PMCVD	Plasma modified chemical vapor deposition	等离子改良的化学汽相沉积法	Děnglízǐ gǎiliángde huàxué qìxiāng chénjīfǎ
PMD	Physical media dependent	物理媒体相关	Wùlǐ méitǐ xiāngguān
PMD	Physical media dependent	物理媒质相关	Wùlǐ méizhì xiāngguān
PMD	Physical medium dependent	物理介质相关	Wùlǐ jièzhì xiāngguān
PMD	Physical medium dependent	物理介质相关子层	Wùlǐ jièzhì xiāngguān zicéng
PMD	Polarization mode dispersion	偏振模式色散	Piānzhèn móshì sèsàn
PMD	Polarization mode dispersion	极化模色散	Jíhuà mó sèsàn
PMD	Polarization mode dispersion (FOC)	偏振模色散	Piānzhèn mó sèsàn
PMD/TC	Physical medium dependent/transmission channel	物理媒体相关/传输会聚	Wùlǐ méitǐ xiāngguān/chuánshū huìjù
PMDC	Polarization mode dispersion compensator (FOC)	偏振模色散补偿器	Piānzhèn mó sèsàn bǔchángqì
PMD-DGD	Polarization mode dispersion (PMD) differential group delay	偏振模色散差分群时延	Piānzhèn mó sèsàn chāfēn qún shíyán
PMF	Parameter management frame	参数管理帧	Cānshù guǎnlǐ zhèng
PMF	Polarization maintaining fiber	偏振保持光纤	Piānzhèn bǎochí guāngxiān
PMI	Physical media independent	物理媒体无关	Wùlǐ méitǐ wúguān
PMI	Privilege management infrastructure	特权管理基础设施	Tèquán guǎnlǐ jīchǔ shèshī
PMJI	Pardon my jumping in (computer chat)	原谅我的参与	Yuánliàng wǒde cānyù
PMLC	Programmed multi-line controller	程序多线控制器	Chéngxù duōxiàn kòngzhìqì
PMM	Packet mobile management	分组移动管理	Fēnzǔ yídòng guǎnlǐ
PMMA	Polymethyl methacrylate	聚甲基丙烯酸甲酯	Jùjiǎjī bǐngxīsuān jiǎzhǐ
PMR	Personal mobile radio	个人移动无线电	Gèrén yídòng wúxiàndiàn
PMR	Private mobile radio	专用移动无线电	Zhuānyòng yídòng wúxiàndiàn
PMR	Private mobile radio	专用调度集群移动通信网	Zhuānyòng diàodù jíqún yídòng tōngxìnwǎng
PMR	Private mobile radio	专用集群移动通信网	Zhuānyòng jíqún yídòng tōngxìnwǎng
PMR	Private mobile radio	集群移动通信	Jíqún yídòng tōngxìn
PMS	Picture messaging service	图像短信息传送服务	Túxiàng duǎn xìnxī chuánsòng fúwù
PMS	Power management system	电源管理系统	Diànyuán guǎnlǐ xìtǒng
PMS	Process monitor system	过程监督系统	Guòchéng jiāndū xìtǒng
PMS	Property management system	资源管理系统	Zīyuán guǎnlǐ xìtǒng
PMSE	Process model simulating environment	过程模型模拟环境	Guòchéng móxíng mónǐ huánjìng
PMS-TC	Physical media-specific transmission channel layer	物理媒质特定传输汇聚层	Wùlǐ méizhì tèdìng chuánshū huìjù céng
PMT	Packet-mode terminal	分组方式终端	Fēnzǔ fāngshì zhōngduān
PMT	Packet-mode terminal	包方式终端	Bāo fāngshì zhōngduān
PMT	Photomultiplier	光电子增倍管	Guāngdiànzǐ zēngbèiguǎn
PMX	Packet multiplexer	包多路复用器	Bāo duōlù fùyòngqì
PN	Permanent nucleus (the European GSM standards setting group)	核心小组	Héxīn xiǎozǔ
PN	Pseudo-noise	伪噪声	Wěizàoshēng
PN	Pseudo-random noise	伪随机噪声	Wěisuíjī zàoshēng
PNA	Progressive network audio	渐进网络音频	Jiànjìn wǎngluò yīnpín
PNAP	Private network access point	私人网路接入节点	Sīrén wǎnglù jiērù jiédiǎn
PNCH	Packet notification channel	分组通知信道	Fēnzǔ tōngzhī xìndào
PNMC	Provincial (mobile communications net) network management center	省移动通信网网络管理中心	Shěng yídòng tōngxìnwǎng wǎngluò guǎnlǐ zhōngxīn
PNNI	Private network-network interface	专用网络－网络接口	Zhuānyòng wǎngluò—wǎngluò jiēkǒu
PNNI	Private network-to-network interface	专用网间接口	Zhuānyòng wǎngjiān jiēkǒu

PnP	Plug and play	即插即用	Jíchā jíyòng
PNP	Plug-and-play	即装即用	Jízhuāng jíyòng
PNP	Private numbering plan	专用编号计划	Zhuānyòng biānhào jìhuà
PNP	Private numbering plan	专用网编号计划	Zhuānyòng wǎng biānhào jìhuà
PNP	Private numbering plan	用户编号计划	Yònghù biānhào jìhuà
PNT	Phoneline network transceiver	电话线网络收发器	Diànhuàxiàn wǎngluò shōufāqì
PO	Pressure operated	压强式	Yāqiáng-shì
POC	Proof-of-concept (for hardware)	概念验证	Gàiniàn yànzhèng
$POCl_3$	Phosphorous oxychloride	三氯化氧磷	Sānlǜhuàyǎnglín
POCSAG	Post Office Code Standardization Advisory Group (UK)	邮政总局寻码标准化咨询组	Yóuzhèng zǒngjú xúnmǎ biāozhǔnhuà zīxúnzǔ
PODS	Precision orbit determination system	经确定轨系统	Jīngquè dìngguǐ xìtǒng
POF	Polymer optical fiber	聚合体光纤	Jùhétǐ guāngxiān
POF	Polymer optical fiber	聚合物光纤	Jùhéwù guāngxiān
POH	Path overhead	通路开销	Tōnglù kāixiao
POH	Path overhead	通道开销	Tōngdào kāixiao
POI	Point of interconnection	互连点	Hùliándiǎn
PON	Passive optical network	无源光纤网	Wúyuán guāngxiān wǎng
PON	Passive optical network	无源光网络	Wúyuán guāng wǎngluò
PoP	Point of presence	业务提供点	Yèwù tígōng diǎn
POP	Point of presence	存在点	Cúnzài diǎn
POP	Post office protocol	邮局协议	Yóujú xiéyì
POP3	Post office protocol 3	第三号邮局协议	Dìsānhào yóujú xiéyì
POP3	Post office protocol 3	邮局协议的第 3 个版本	Yóujú xiéyìde dìsangè bǎnběn
POP3	Post office protocol version 3	第三版电子邮局协议	Dìsānbǎn diànzǐ yóujú xiéyì
POS	Internet protocol (IP) over synchronous digital hierarchy (SDH)	SDH 上传送 IP	SDH-shàng chuansòng IP
POS	Packet over SDH	承载分组信号的 SDH	Chéngzài fēnzǔ xìnhàode SDH
PoS	Packet over synchronous digital hierarchy	在同步数字系统上传输分组	Zài tóngbù shùzì xìtǒng-shàng chuánshū fēnzǔ
POS	Packet over synchronous digital hierarchy (SDH)	分组按同步数字体系传送	Fēnzǔ àn tóngbù shùzì tǐxì chuánsòng
POS	Point of sale	销售点	Xiāoshòu diǎn
POS	Point of sale system	销售点系统	Xiāoshòu diǎn xìtǒng
POS	Point of sales	销售点终端	Xiāoshòu diǎn zhōngduān
POSH®	POSH® single mode optical fiber	保实®单模光纤	Bǎo-shí ® dānmó guāngxiān
POSIX	Portable operating system interface for UNIX	轻便操作系统界面	Qīngbiàn cāozuò xìtǒng jièmiàn
POST	Power-on self test	上电自检	Shàngdiàn zì jiǎn
POST	Power-on self test	加电自检	Jiādiàn zìjiǎn
POST	Power-on self test	加电自测试	Jiādiàn zìcèshì
POST	Power-on self test	开机自动测试	Kāijī zìdòng cèshì
POST	Power-on self-test	通电自检	Tōngdiàn zì jiǎn
POTS	Plain old telephone service	普通电话业务	Pǔtōng diànhuà yèwù
POTS	Plain old telephone service	普通老式电话业务	Pǔtōng lǎoshì diànhuà yèwù
POTS	Plain old telephone service	老式普通电话业务	Lǎoshì pǔtōng diànhuà yèwù
POTS	Plain old telephone system	简易老式电话系统	Jiǎnyì lǎoshì diànhuà xìtǒng
POW	Power	功率	Gōnglǜ
PP	Presentation layer protocol (in ISO's OSI)	表示层协议	Biǎoshì céng xiéyì
PP, P2P	Point-to-point	点到点	Diǎn dào diǎn

PPC	Partial period correlation	部分相关	Bùfen xiāngguān
PPC	Prepaid charging	预付费业务	Yùfùfèi yèwù
PPCF	Polymer photonic crystal optical fiber	聚合物光子晶体光纤	Jùhéwù guāngzǐ jīngtǐ guāngxiān
PPCH	Packet paging channel	分组寻呼信道	Fēnzǔ xúnhū xìndào
PPCI	Presentation protocol control information	表示协议控制信息	Biǎoshì xiéyì kòngzhì xìnxī
PPDU	Presentation protocol data unit	表示协议数据单元	Biǎoshì xiéyì shùjù dānyuán
PPE	Programmable priority encoder	可编程优选译码器	Kěbiānchéng yōuxuǎn yìmǎqì
PPF	Paging proceed flag	进行寻呼标志	Jìnxíng xúnhū biāozhì
PPGA	Plastic pin grid array	塑胶针状矩阵封装	Sùjiāo zhēnzhuàng jǔzhèn fēngzhuāng
PPI	Constant altitude plane position indicator	等高平面位置显示器	Děnggāo píngmiàn wèizhì xiǎnshìqì
PPI	Partial path index (in XML)	部分路径索引	Bùfen lùjìng suǒyǐn
PPM	Pages per minute	每分钟多少页	Měi fēnzhōng duōshao yè
ppm	Pages per minute (printer term)	页/分	Yè/ fēn
Ppm	Parts per million	百万分之一	Bǎiwàn fēn zhī yī
PPM	Parts per million	百万分之几	Bǎiwàn fēn zhī jǐ
PPm	Parts per million	百万分率	Bǎiwàn fēnlǜ
PPM	Presentation protocol machine	表示协议机	Biǎoshì xiéyì jī
PPM	Pulse phase modulation	脉冲相位洲制	Màichōng xiàngwèi zhōuzhì
PPM	Pulse position modulation	脉位调制	Màiwèi tiáozhì
PPM	Pulse position modulation	脉冲位置调制	Màichōng wèizhì tiáozhì
PPM	Pulse position modulation	脉冲位调制	Màichōng wèi tiáozhì
P-PMS	Provincial management center	省级管理中心	Shěngjí guǎnlǐ zhōngxīn
PPNI	Public packet network interface	公用包网络接口	Gōngyòng bāo wǎngluò jiēkǒu
PPP	Multi-link point-to-point protocol	多链接点到点协议	Duōliànjiē diǎn dào diǎn xiéyì
PPP	Peer-to-peer protocol	端对端协议	Duān duì duān xiéyì
PPP	Point to point protocol	点对点通信协议	Diǎn duì diǎn tōngxìn xiéyì
PPP	Point-to-point protocol	点到点协议	Diǎn dào diǎn xiéyì
PPP	Point-to-point protocol	点对点传输协议	Diǎn duì diǎn chuánshū xiéyì
PPP	Point-to-point protocol	点对点协议	Diǎn duì diǎn xiéyì
PPPIFR	Point-to-point protocol in frame relay	帧中继中的点到点协议	Zhèng zhōngjì zhòngde diǎn dàodiǎn xiéyì
PPPOA	Point-to-point protocol over AAL5	AAL5 上的点到点协议	AAL5-shàngde diǎn dàodiǎn xiéyì
PPPoA	Point-to-point protocol over asynchronous transfer mode	ATM 上的 PPP	ATM-shàngde PPP
PPPoE	Point-to-point protocol over Ethernet	以太网上 PPP 协议	Yǐtàiwǎng-shàng PPP xiéyì
PPPOE	Point-to-point protocol over Ethernet	以太网上传送 PPP 协议	Yǐtàiwǎng-shàng chuánsòng PPP xiéyì
PPPoE	Point-to-point protocol over Ethernet	以太网上点到点协议	Yǐtàiwǎng-shàng diǎn dàodiǎn xiéyì
PPPOE	Point-to-point protocol over Ethernet	以太网上点到点链路协议	Yǐtàiwǎng-shàng diǎn dàodiǎn liànlù xiéyì
PPS	Precision positioning service	精密定位业务	Jīngmì dìngwèi yèwù
PPS	Precision positioning service (in GPS)	精密定位服务	Jīngmì dìngwèi fúwù
PPS	Protocol and parameter select	协议和参数选择	Xiéyì hé cānshù xuǎnzé
PPS	Pulse per second	脉冲/秒	Màichōng/miǎo
PPS	Pulses per second	每秒脉冲数	Měi miǎo màichōng shù
PPSN	Public packet switched network	公用分租接转网络	Gōngyòng fēnzū jiēzhuǎn wǎngluò
PPTP	Point to point tunneling protocol	点对点通道协议	Diǎn duì diǎn tōngdào xiéyì
PPTP	Point-to-point tunneling protocol	点到点隧道协议	Diǎn dào diǎn suìdào xiéyì
PPTP	Point-to-point tunneling protocol	点对点隧道协议	Diǎn duì diǎn suìdào xiéyì
PQ	Priority queuing	优先权排队	Yōuxiānquán páiduì

PQ	Priority queuing	优先队列	Yōuxiān duìliè
PQFP	Plastic quad flat package	塑料方块平面封装	Sùliào fāngkuài píngmiàn fēngzhuāng
PR	Paging request	寻呼请求	Xúnhū qǐngqiú
PR	Performance rate	性能比率	Xìngnéng bǐlǜ
PRA	Packet routing address	分组路由选择地址	Fēnzǔ lùyóu xuǎnzé dìzhǐ
PRA	Primary rate access	一次群速率入口	Yīcì qún sùlǜ rùkǒu
PRA	Primary rate access	一次群速率接入	Yīcì qún sùlǜ jiērù
PRA	Primary rate access	主群速率	Zhǔ qún sùlǜ
PRA	Primary rate access	基群速率接入	Jīqún sùlǜ jiērù
PRACH	Packet random access channel	分组随机接入信道	Fēnzǔ suíjī jiērù xìndào
PRACH	Physical random access channel	随机接入物理信道	Suíjī jiērù wùlǐ xìndào
PRACH	Physical random access channels	物理随机接入信道	Wùlǐ suíjī jiērù xìndào
PRBS	Pseudo-random binary sequence	伪随机二元序列	Wěisuíjī èryuán xùliè
PRBS	Pseudo-random binary sequence	伪随机二进制序列	Wěisuíjī èrjìnzhì xùliè
PRBS	Pseudo-random binary sequence	伪随机码序列	Wěisuíjī mǎ xùliè
PRBS	Pseudo-random bit sequence	伪随机比特序列	Wěisuíjī bǐtè xùliè
PRC	Primary reference clock	主参考时钟	Zhǔ cānkǎo shízhōng
PRC	Primary reference clock	主基准时钟	Zhǔ jīzhǔn shízhōng
PRC	Primary reference clock	全国基准时钟	Quánguó jīzhǔn shízhōng
PRC	Primary reference clock	全网基准钟	Quán wǎng jīzhǔn zhōng
PRC	Primary reference clock	基准参考时钟	Jīzhǔn cānkǎo shízhōng
PRC	Primary reference clock	基准时钟	Jīzhǔn shízhōng
PRC	Primary reference clock	基准钟	Jīzhǔn zhōng
PRC	Primary resource clock	基准主时钟	Jīzhǔn zhǔ shízhōng
PRD	Periodic resource distribution	周期资源分配	Zhōuqī zīyuán fēnpèi
PRD	Piezoelectric radiation detector	热电辐射控测器	Rèdiàn fúshè kòngcèqì
PRD	Pseudo-random downlink sequence	下行伪随机序列	Xiàxíng wěi suíjī xùliè
PRDMD	Private directory management domain	专用号码簿管理域	Zhuānyòng hàomǎbù guǎnlǐ yù
PRF	Parallel resonant frequency	并联谐振频率	Bìnglián xiézhèn pínlǜ
PRFM	Partial response frequency modulation	部分响应频率调制	Bùfen xiǎngyìng pínlǜ tiáozhì
PRI	Primary rate interface	一次群接口	Yīcì qún jiēkǒu
PRI	Primary rate interface	原级速率界面	Yuánjí sùlǜ jièmiàn
PRI	Primary rate interface	基群速率接口	Jīqún sùlǜ jiēkǒu
PRI	Primary rate interface (North America and Japan)	主群速率接口	Zhǔ qún sùlǜ jiēkǒu
PR-IJF-OQPSK	Partial response inter-symbol-interference and jitter free offset quadrature phase shift keying	部分响应符号间干扰和无跳动编移正交相移键控	Bùfen xiǎngyìng fúhào jiān gānrǎo hé wú tiàodòng biānyí zhèngjiāo xiāngyí jiànkòng
PRM	Pattern recogniton method	模式识别法	Móshì shíbié fǎ
PRM	Phase reversal modulation	倒相调制	Dǎoxiàng tiáozhì
PRM	Protocol reference model	协议参考模型	Xiéyì cānkǎo móxíng
PRMA	Packet reservation multiple access	分组预约多址	Fēnzǔ yùyuē duō zhǐ
PRMD	Private management domain	专用管理域	Zhuānyòng guǎnlǐ yù
PRML	Partial response maximum likelihood	最大可能部分反应	Zuìdà kěnéng bùfen fǎnyìng
PRNG	Pseudo-random noise generation	伪随机噪声生成	Wěisuíjī zàoshēng shēngchéng
PROM	Programmable read-only memory	可编只读存储器	Kěbiān zhǐ dú cúnchǔqì
PROT	Data channel protection level (in FTP)	数据信道保护级别	Shùjù xìndào bǎohù jíbié
PRR	Potential round robin	势轮转算法	Shì lúnzhuàn suànfǎ

PRS	Primary reference source	基准参考源	Jīzhǔn cānkǎoyuán
PRS	Primary reference source (timing)	时间基准	Shíjiān jīzhǔn
PRT	Platinum resistance thermometer	铂电阻温度计	Bó diànzǔ wēndùjì
PRT	Protection register	保护寄存器	Bǎohù jìcúnqì
PRT	Pulse recurrent time	脉冲周期时间	Màichōng zhōuqī shíjiān
PRU	Uplink pseudo-random sequence	上行伪随机序列	Shàngxíng wěisuíjī xùliè
PRUNI	Primary rate user-network interface	基群速率用户-网络接口	Jīqún sùlǜ yònghù—wǎngluò jiēkǒu
PS	Packet switched or switching	分组交换	Fēnzǔ jiāohuàn
PS	Password	密码	Mìmǎ
PS	Personal (radio) station	个人电台	Gèrén diàntái
PS	Poincare sphere	邦加球	Bāng-jiā qiú
PS	Polystyrene	聚苯乙烯	Jùběnyǐxī
PS	Precise serialization	精确串行化	Jīngquè chuànhánghuà
PS	Presentation service	表示服务	Biǎoshì fúwù
PS	Sony Play Station (computer game)	索尼 32 位游戏机	Suǒní 32 wèi yóuxìjī
PS	Sony Pocket Station (computer game)	索尼手提游戏机	Suǒní shǒutí yóuxìjī
PS2	Personal system 2	个人系统二型	Gèrén xìtǒng èr xíng
PSACR	Attenuation crosstalk ratio power sum	衰减串音功率和	Shuāijiǎn chuànyīn gōnglǜ hé
PSAP	Presentation service access point	表示服务访问点	Biǎoshì fúwù fǎngwèn diǎn
PSAP	Public secure answer point	公众安全应答服务机构	Gōngzhòng ānquán yìngdá fúwù jīgòu
PSC	Primary synchronization code	主同步码	Zhǔ tóngbù mǎ
PSC	Protection switching count	保护倒换计数	Bǎohù dǎohuàn jìshù
PSCH	Physical shared channel	物理共享信道	Wùlǐ gòngxiǎng xìndào
PSD	Packet switched data	包交换数据	Bāo jiāohuàn shùjù
PSD	Photoelectric smoke detector	光电感烟探测器	Guāngdiàn gǎnyān tàncèqì
PSD	Platform security division	平台安全部分	Píngtái ānquán bùfen
PSD	Power spectrum density	功率谱密度	Gōnglǜ pǔ mìdù
PSD	Protection switching duration	保护倒换持续时间	Bǎohù dǎohuàn chíxù shíjiān
PSD	Protection switching duration	保护倒换间隔时间	Bǎohù dǎohuàn jiàngé shíjiān
PSDMASK	Power spectrum density mask	功率谱密度模板	Gōnglǜ pǔ mìdù múbǎn
PSDN	Packet switched data network	分组交换数据网	Fēnzǔ jiāohuàn shùjù wǎng
PSDN	Public switched data network	共用数据交换网	Gòngyòng shùjù jiāohuàn wǎng
PSDU	Presentation service data unit	表示服务数据单元	Biǎoshì fúwù shùjù dānyuán
PSE	Page size extension	页面尺寸扩展模式	Yèmiàn chǐcùn kuòzhǎn móshì
PSE	Personal service environment	个人服务环境	Gèrén fúwù huánjìng
PSE	Protection switching event	保护倒换事件	Bǎohù dǎohuàn shìjiàn
PSE36	Page size extension 36-bit (chip)	页面尺寸扩展模式， 36 位	Yèmiàn chǐcùn kuòzhǎn móshì, 36 wèi
PSELFEXT	Equal level far end crosstalk attenuation power sum	等电平远端串音衰减功率和	Děngdiànpíng yuǎnduān chuànyīn shuāijiǎn gōnglǜ hé
PSEUDO	Pseudo instruction	伪指令	Wěizhǐlìng
PSG	Phase separated glass (FOC mfg)	玻璃分相法	Bōli fēnxiàng fǎ
PSGVQ	Product [codeform] state gain vector quantization	乘积码形状增益矢量量化	Chéngjī mǎxíngzhuàng zēngyì shǐliàng liànghuà
PSI-CELP	Pitch synchronous innovation-code excited linear prediction	基音同步更新码激励线性预测	Jīyīn tóngbù gēngxīn mǎ jīlì xiànxìng yùcè
PSK	Phase shift keying	移相键控	Yíxiāng jiànkòng
PSK	Phase-shift keying	相移键控	Xiàngyí jiànkòng
PS-MGW	Packet switched media gateway	分组域媒体网关	Fēnzǔ yù méitǐ wǎngguān

PSN	Packet switched network	分组交换网络	Fēnzǔ jiāohuàn wǎngluò
PSN	Packet-switching node	分组交换节点	Fēnzǔ jiāohuàn jiédiǎn
PSN	Processor serial number	处理器序列号	Chǔlǐqì xù lièhào
PSN	Public switched network	公用交换网	Gōngyòng jiāohuàn wǎng
PSNEXT	Near-end crosstalk attenuation power sum	近端串音衰减功率和	Jìnduān chuànyīn shuāijiǎn gōnglǜ hé
PSNEXT	Near-end crosstalk power sum	近端串音功率和	Jìnduān chuànyīn gōnglǜ hé
PS-NEXT	Power sum near-end crosstalk	综合近端串扰	Zōnghé jìnduān chuànrǎo
PSNP	Partial sequence numbers protocol data unit	部分序列号协议数据单元	Bùfen xùlièhào xiéyì shùjù dānyuán
PSNR	Peak signal-to-noise ratio	峰值信噪比	Fēngzhí xìn zào bǐ
PSO	Particle swarm optimization	粒子群优化	Lìzi qún yōuhuà
PSP	Packet switching protocol	分组交换协议	Fēnzǔ jiāohuàn xiéyì
PSP	Peak sideband power	边带峰值功率	Biāndài fēngzhí gōnglǜ
PSP	Physical service port	物理业务端口	Wùlǐ yèwù duānkǒu
PSP	Principal state of polarization	主偏振态	Zhǔ piānzhèn tài
PSPDN	Packet switched public data network	公众分组交换数据网	Gōngzhòng fēnzǔ jiāohuàn shùjù wǎng
PSPDN	Packet switched public data network	公众分组交换网	Gōngzhòng fēnzǔ jiāohuàn wǎng
PSPDN	Packet switched public data network	分组交换公共数据网	Fēnzǔ jiāohuàn gōnggòng shùjù wǎng
PSPDN	Packet switched public data network	分组交换共用数据网	Fēnzǔ jiāohuàn gòngyòng shùjù wǎng
PSPDN	Packet switched public data network	包交换公众数据网	Bāo jiāohuàn gōngzhòng shùjù wǎng
PSPDN	Packet switched public data network	包交换公共数据网	Bāo jiāohuàn gōnggòng shùjù wǎng
PSPDN	Public switched packet data network	公用交换分组数据网	Gōngyòng jiāohuàn fēnzǔ shùjù wǎng
PSPDN	Public switching packet data network	公共交换分组数据网	Gōnggòng jiāohuàn fēnzǔ shùjù wǎng
PSQM	Perceptual speech quality measure	知觉话音质量度量	Zhījué huàyīn zhìliàng dùliàng
PSQM	Perceptual speech quality measure	知觉语言质量度量	Zhījué yǔyán zhìliàng dùliàng
PSS	Private network Q reference point signaling system	专用网络 Q 参考点信令系统	Zhuānyòng wǎngluò Q cānkǎodiǎn xìnlìng xìtǒng
PSSD	Process unstructured supplementary services data	过程非结构化补充服务数据	Guòchéng fēijiégòuhuà bǔchōng fúwù shùjù
PSSR	Process unstructured SS data request	处理 USSD 请求	Chǔlǐ USSD qǐngqiú
PSSR	Process unstructured supplementary services request	过程非结构化补充服务请求	Guòchéng fēijiégòuhuà bǔchōng fúwù qǐngqiú
PSTN	Public switched telecommunication network	公共交换电信网	Gōnggòng jiāohuàn diànxìn wǎng
PSTN	Public switched telephone network	公众交换电话网	Gōngzhòng jiāohuàn diànhuà wǎng
PSTN	Public switched telephone network	公众电话交换网	Gōngzhòng diànhuà jiāohuàn wǎng
PSTN	Public switched telephone network	公共交换式电话网络	Gōnggòng jiāohuànshì diànhuà wǎngluò
PSTN	Public switched telephone network	公共交换电话网	Gōnggòng jiāohuàn diànhuà wǎng
PSTN	Public switched telephone network	公共电话交换网	Gōnggòng diànhuà jiāohuàn wǎng
PSTN	Public switched telephone network	公用交换式电话网	Gōngyòng jiāohuàn-shì diànhuà wǎng
PSTN	Public switched telephone network	公用交换电话网	Gōngyòng jiāohuàn diànhuà wǎng
PSTN	Public switched telephone network	公用电话交换网	Gōngyòng diànhuà jiāohuàn wǎng
PSW	Program status word	程序状态字	Chéngxù zhuàngtài zì
PSWR	Power standing-wave ratio	功率驻波比	Gōnglǜ zhùbōbǐ
PT	Packet terminal	分组终端	Fēnzǔ zhōngduān
PT	Path termination	通道终端	Tōngdào zhōngduān
PT	Path termination	通道终结	Tōngdào zhōngjié
PT	Payload type	净荷类型	Jìnghé lèixíng
PT	Penalty time	惩罚时间	Chéngfá shíjiān
PT	Protocol type	协议类型	Xiéyì lèixíng

PTC	Packet transmission channel	包传输通道	Bāo chuánshū tōngdào
PTCCH	Packet time advance control channel	分组时间提前量控制信道	Fēnzǔ shíjiān tíqiánliàng kòngzhì xìn dào
PTCCH	Packet timing advance control channel	分组时间提前信道	Fēnzǔ shíjiān tíqián xìndào
PTCCH/D	Packet timing control channel/downlink	分组定时控制信道一下行	Fēnzǔ dìngshí kòngzhì xìndào yīxià xíng
PTCCH/U	Packet timing control channel/uplink	分组定时控制信道一上行	Fēnzǔ dìngshí kòngzhì xìndào yī shàngxíng
PTCH	Packet traffic channel	分组业务信道	Fēnzǔ yèwù xìndào
PTE	Path terminating element	通道终端设备	Tōngdào zhōngduān shèbèi
PTEI	Processor and test equipment interface	处理器和测试设备接口	Chǔlǐqì hé cèshì shèbèi jiēkǒu
PTF	Partial transfer function	部分传递函数	Bùfen chuándì hánshù
PTF	Punch-through factor	穿通因数	Chuāntōng yīnshù
PTI	Payload type indication	净荷类型指示	Jìnghé lèixíng zhǐshì
PTIC	China Post and Telecommunications Industry Corporation	中国邮电工业总公司	Zhōngguó yóudiàn gōngyè zǒnggōngsī
PTM	Point to multipoint service	点对多点业务	Diǎn duì duōdiǎn yèwù
PTM	Pulse time modulation	脉冲时间调制	Màichōng shíjiān tiáozhì
PTM	Punch-through modulation	穿通调制	Chuāntōng tiáozhì
PTM-G	Point-to-multipoint group call	点对多点群呼业务	Diǎn duì duōdiǎn qúnhū yèwù
PTM-G	PTM groupcall	PTM 组呼叫	PTM zǔ hūjiào
PTM-M	Point to multipoint multicasting	点对多点广播业务	Diǎn duì duōdiǎn guǎngbō yèwù
PTM-M	PTM multicast	PTM 多播	PTM duōbō
P-TMSI	Packet temporary mobile station identity	分组移动台临时识别号	Fēnzǔ yídòngtái línshí shíbié hào
P-TMSI	Packet temporary mobile subscription identity	分组临时移动用户识别码	Fēnzǔ línshí yídòng yònghù shíbié mǎ
PTN	Personal telecommunication number	个人通信号码	Gèrén tōngxìn hàomǎ
PTN	Personal telephone number	个人电话号码	Gèrén diànhuà hàomǎ
PTN	Private telecommunication network	专用通信网	Zhuānyòng tōngxìnwǎng
PTO	Public telecom operator	公众电信运营者	Gōngzhòng diànxìn yùnyíngzhě
PTP	Packet transfer protocol	包传输协议	Bāo chuánshū xiéyì
PTP	Paper tape punch	纸带穿孔机	Zhǐdài chuānkǒngjī
PTP	Point to point service	点对点业务	Diǎn duì diǎn yèwù
PTP-CLNS	Point-to-point connectionless-mode network service	点对点无连接网络业务	Diǎn duì diǎn wúliánjiē wǎngluò yèwù
PTP-CONS	Point to point-connection network service	点对点面向连接网络业务	Diǎn duì diǎn miànxiàng liánjiē wǎngluò yèwù
PTR	Paper tape reader	纸带阅读机	Zhǐdài yuèdújī
PTR	Pointer	指针	Zhǐzhēn
PTS	Protocol type select	协议类型选择	Xiéyì lèixíng xuǎnzé
PTT	Post and telecommunications	邮政	Yóuzhèng
PU	Payload unit	有效负载单元	Yǒuxiào fùzài dānyuán
PU	Pickup (audio)	拾音器	Shíyīnqì
PU	Programmable unit	可编程单元	Kěbiānchéng dānyuán
PUCT	Price per unit currency table	每单位市场价格表	Měi dānwèi shìchǎng jiàgé biǎo
PUK	Personal identification number (PIN) unblocking key	个人识别码解锁密码	Gèrén shíbié mǎ jiěsuǒ mìmǎ
PUNI	Private user network interface	专用网接口	Zhuānyòng wǎng jiēkǒu
PUP	Physical user port	物理用户端口	Wùlǐ yònghù duān kǒu
PUSCH	Physical uplink shared channel	上行共用物理信道	Shàngxíng gòngyòng wùlǐ xìndào
PUSCH	Physical uplink shared channel	上行链路共享物理信道	Shàngxíng liànlù gòngxiǎng wùlǐ xìndào
PUSI	Payload unit start indicator	净负荷起始标识符	Jìnghè qǐshǐ biāozhì fú
PUT	Programmable unijunction transistor	可编程单结晶体管	Kěbiānchéng dānjié jīngtǐguǎn

PV	Parameter value	参数值	Cānshù zhí
PVC	Packetized virtual circuit	包式虚拟电路	Bāo shì xūnǐ diànlù
PVC	Parameter validity check (CAD/CAM)	参数有效性检查	Cānshù yǒuxiàoxìng jiǎnchá
PVC	Parameter validity condition (CAD/CAM)	参数有效性条件	Cānshù yǒuxiàoxìng tiáojiàn
PVC	Permanent virtual channel	永久虚信道	Yǒngjiǔ xū xìndào
PVC	Permanent virtual circuit	永久虚电路	Yǒngjiǔ xū diànlù
PVC	Permanent virtual connection	永久虚拟连接	Yǒngjiǔ xūnǐ liánjiē
PVC	Permanent virtual connection	永久虚连接	Yǒngjiǔ xū liánjiē
PVC	Polyvinyl chloride	聚氯乙烯	Jùlǜyǐxī
PVCC	Permanent virtual channel connection	永久虚信道连接	Yǒngjiǔ xū xìndào liánjiē
PVCS	Public video conferencing system	公用型会议电视系统	Gōngyòng-xíng huìyì diànshì xìtǒng
PVDF	Polyvinylidene fluoride	聚偏二氟乙烯	Jùpiān èrfúyǐxī
PVM	Parallel virtual machine	并行虚拟计算机	Bìngxíng xūnǐ jìsuànjī
PVP	Permanent virtual path	永久虚电路	Yǒngjiǔ xū diànlù
PVP	Permanent virtual path	永久虚通道	Yǒngjiǔ xū tōngdào
PVPC	Permanent virtual path connection	永久虚通路连接	Yǒngjiǔ xū tōnglù liánjiē
PVT	Packet voice terminal	报文语言终端	Bàowén yǔyán zhōngduān
PW	Password	口令	Kǒulìng
PW	Password	通过字	Tōngguò zì
PWB	Power supply motherboard	电源母	Diànyuán mǔ
PWC	Public power source board	公共电源板	Gōnggòng diànyuán bǎn
PWCM	Pulse width with carrier modulation	带载波调制的脉冲宽度	Dài zàibō tiáozhìde màichōng kuāndù
PWE3	Pseudo wire emulation edge to edge	伪线仿真边缘到边缘	Wěixiàn fǎngzhēn biānyuán dào biānyuán
PWE3	Pseudo wires edge-to-edge emulation	边缘到边缘伪线路仿真	Biānyuán dào biānyuán wěixiànlù fǎngzhēn
PWF	Splitter power supply board	分路器电源板	Fēnlùqì diànyuán bǎn
PWI	Prototype waveform interpolation	典型波形内插	Diǎnxíng bōxíng nèichā
PWM	Pulse width modulation	脉宽调制	Mài kuān tiáozhì
PWR_STEP	Power step	功率步长	Gōnglǜ bùcháng
PWS	Power system	电源系统	Diànyuán xìtǒng
PWT	Transmitter power supply board	发射机电源板	Fāshèjī diànyuán bǎn
PX	Peak envelope power (of a radio transmitter)	峰包功率	Fēng bāo gōnglǜ
PX	Pre-translator	预译码器	Yùyìmǎqì
PXB	PCI expander bridge	PCI 增强桥	PCI zēngqiáng qiáo
PY	Mean power (of a radio transmitter)	平均功率	Píngjūn gōnglǜ
PZ	Carrier power (of a radio transmitter)	载波功率	Zàibō gōnglǜ

Q

Q	Quotient register	扩展累加器	Kuòzhǎn lěijiāqì
Q.1	Service interface V.11	服务接口 V.11	Fúwù jiēkǒu V.11
QAF	Q-adapter function block	Q 适配器功能块	Q-shìpèiqì gōngnéng kuài
QAM	Quadrature amplitude modulation	正交幅度调制	Zhèngjiāo fúdù tiáozhì
QAM	Quadrature amplitude modulation	正交调幅	Zhèngjiāo tiáofú
QAM	Quantized amplitude modulation	量化振幅调制	Liànghuà zhènfú tiáozhì
QAM	Quantized amplitude modulation	量化调幅	Liànghuà tiáofú
QBM	Quad-band memory	四倍边带内存	Sìbèi biāndài nèicún
QC	Quality control	质量控制	Zhìliàng kòngzhì

QCELP	Qualcomm code excited linear prediction	Qualcomm 码激励线性预测编码	Qualcomm mǎjīlì xiànxìng yùcè biānmǎ
QCELP	Qualcomm code excited linear prediction	码激励线性预测编码	Mǎjīlì xiànxìng yùcè biānmǎ
QCIF	Quarter-common intermediate format	四分之一公共中介格式	Sì fēn zhī yī gōnggòng zhōngjiè géshi
QFD	Quality function deployment	质量功能配置	Zhìliàng gōngnéng pèizhì
QFP	Quad flat pack (electronics mfg)	方平包装	Fāngpíng bāozhuāng
QGM	Query graph model	查询图模型	Cháxúntú móxíng
QKD	Quantum key distribution	量子密钥分布	Liàngzǐ mìyào fēnbù
QKD	Quantum key distribution	量子密钥分配	Liàngzǐ mìyào fēnpèi
QL	Quality level	质量等级	Zhìliàng děngjí
QLLC	Qualified logic link control (for SNA over X.25)	限定式逻辑链路控制	Xiàndìngshì luóji liànlù kòngzhì
QM	Quadrature modulation	正交调制	Zhèngjiāo tiáozhì
QMF	Quadrature mirror filter	正交镜象滤波器	Zhèngjiāo jìngxiàng lǜbōqì
QMTP	Quick mail transfer protocol	快速邮件传输协议	Kuàisù yóujiàn chuánshū xiéyì
QN	Queuing network	排队网络	Páiduì wǎngluò
QoA	Quality of access	接入质量	Jiērù zhìliàng
QOP	Quality protection	保护质量	Bǎohù zhìliàng
QoR	Release query	释放查询	Shìfàng cháxún
QoS	Quality of service	业务质量	Yèwù zhìliàng
QOS	Quality of service	服务质量	Fúwù zhìliàng
QP	Quasi-peak	准峰值	Zhǔn fēngzhí
QPA	Quad-port acceleration	四接口加速	Sì jiēkǒu jiāsù
QPSK	Quadrature phase shift keying	正交相移键控	Zhèngjiāo xiāngyí jiànkòng
QPSK	Quadrature phase shift keying	正交移相键控	Zhèngjiāo yíxiàng jiànkòng
QPSK	Quadrature phase-shift keying	四相相移键控	Sìxiāng xiāngyí jiànkòng
QPSK	Quadriphase shift keying	四相相移键控	Sìxiāng xiāngyí jiànkòng
QPSK	Quaternary phase-shift keying	四相移相键控	Sìxiàng yíxiàng jiànkòng
QR	Quick response	快速反应	Kuàisù fǎnyìng
QVSB	Qwest video services for business	Qwest 企业视像业务	Qwest qǐyè shìxiàng yèwù
QW-DFB-LD	Quantum well distributed feedback laser	量子阱分布反馈激光器	Liàngzǐ jǐng fēnbù fǎnkuì jīguāngqì
QWSL	Quantum well semiconductor laser	量子阱半导体激光器	Liàngzǐ jǐng bàndǎotǐ jīguāngqì

R

RA	Random mode request information field	请求信息字段随机模式	Qǐngqiú xìnxī zìduàn suíjī móshì
RA	Rate adaptation	速率适配	Sùlǜ shìpèi
RA	Rate adapter	速率适配器	Sùlǜ shìpèiqì
RA	Receiver attenuation	接收机衰减	Jiēshōujī shuāijiǎn
RA	Request agent	请求代理	Qǐngqiú dàilǐ
RA	Routing area	路由区	Lùyóu qū
RA	Routing area	路由区域	Lùyóu qūyù
RA	Routing area	路由选择范围	Lùyóu xuǎnzé fànwéi
RAB	Radio access bearer	无线接入承载	Wúxiàn jiērù chéngzài
RAB	Radio access bearer service	无线接入承载业务	Wúxiàn jiērù chéngzài yèwù
RAB	Random access burst	随机接入分组	Suíjī jiērù fēnzǔ
RAC	Racing game (computer game)	赛车类游戏	Sàichē lèi yóuxì
RAC	Rambus application specific integrated circuit cell	Rambus 集成电路单元	Rambus jíchéng diànlù dānyuán

RAC	Rectified alternating current	被整流的直流	Bèizhěngliúde zhíliú
RAC	Resource availability confirm	可用资源确认	Kěyòng zīyuán quèrèn
RAC	Resources available confirmation	资源可用性确认	Zīyuán kěyòngxìng quèrèn
RAC	Routing area code	路由区域码	Lùyóu qūyù mǎ
RAC	Routing area code	路由选择区域码	Lùyóu xuǎnzé qūyù mǎ
RACE	Regional automatic circuit exchange	地区自动电路交换机	Dìqū zìdòng diànlù jiāohuànjī
RACE	Research and Development Program on Advanced communications technologies for Europe	欧洲选进通信技术研究和发展规划	Oūzhōu xuǎnjìn tōngxìn jìshù yánjiū hé fāzhǎn guīhuà
RACE	Research in Advanced communication for Europe	欧洲先进通信研究	Oūzhōu xiānjìn tōngxìn yánjiū
RACE	Research on Advanced Communications in Europe	欧洲高级通信研究计划	Ōuzhōu gāojí tōngxìn yánjiū jìhuà
RACE	Response analysis for call evaluation	通话鉴定的响应分析	Tōnghuà jiàndìngde xiǎngyìng fēnxī
RACH	Random access channel	随机接入信道	Suíjī jiērù xìndào
Racon	Radar beacon	雷达信标	Léidá xìnbiāo
RADA	Random access control address	离散用户的随机接入	Lísàn yònghùde suíjī jiērù
RADA	Receive amplifier/divider assembly	接收放大/分集集成件	Jiēshōu fàngdà/ fēnjí jíchéng jiàn
RADIUS	Remote access dial-in user service	拨号用户远程认证服务	Bōhào yònghù yuǎnchéng rènzhèng fúwù
RADIUS	Remote access dial-in user service	远程接入/拨号用户业务	Yuǎnchéng jiērù/bōhào yònghù yèwù
Radius	Remote authentication dial-in user service	远程拨号用户认证服务	Yuǎnchéng bōhào yònghù rènzhèng fúwù
RADIUS	Remote authentication dial-in user service	远程认证拨入用户服务	Yuǎnchéng rènzhèng bōrù yònghù fúwù
RADIUS	Remote authentication dial-in user service	远程身份验证拨入用户服务	Yuǎnchéng shēnfen yànzhèng bōrù yònghù fúwù
RADIUS	Remote authentication dial-in user service	远端拨入用户验证服务	Yuǎnduān bōrù yònghù yànzhèng fúwù
RADIUS	Remote authentication dial-in user service	远端鉴权拨号接入用户业务	Yuǎnduān jiànquán bōhào jiērù yònghù yèwù
RADIUS	Remote authentication dial-in user service	远程用户拨号认证系统	Yuǎnchéng yònghù bōhào rènzhèng xìtǒng
RADIUS	Remote authentication dial--in user service	远程认证拨号用户服务	Yuǎnchéng rènzhèng bōhào yònghù fúwù
RADIUS	Remote authentication dial-in user service (IPsec)	远端认证拨入用户业务	Yuǎnduān rènzhèng bōrù yònghù yèwù
RADIUS	Remote authorization dial in user service	远程授权拨入用户服务	Yuǎnchéng shòuquán bōrù yònghù fúwù
RADSL	Rate adaptive digital subscriber line	速率自适应数字用户线	Sùlǜ zìshìyìng shùzì yònghù xiàn
RADSL	Rate adaptive digital subscriber line	速率自适应数字订阅线路	Sùlǜ zìshìyìng shùzì dìngyuè xiànlù
RADSL	Rate-adjustable digital subscriber line	可调速率数字用户线	Kětiáo sùlǜ shùzì yònghù xiàn
RAFF	Rotary acceleration feed forward (Western Digital Corp. hard drive technology)	旋转加速伺服系统	Xuánzhuǎn jiāsù sìfú xìtǒng
RAGR	Router and GCIN rack	路由器和 GCIN 机架	Lùyóuqì hé GCIN jījià
RAI	Remote alarm indication	远端告警指示	Yuǎnduān gàojǐng zhǐshì
RAI	Resource availability indication	可用资源指示	Kěyòng zīyuán zhǐshì
RAI	Resource availability indication	资源可用性指示	Zīyuán kěyòngxìng zhǐshì
RAI	Routing area identity	路由区识别号	Lùyóu qū shíbiéhào
RAI	Routing area identity	路由选择区域识别	Lùyóu xuǎnzé qūyù shíbié
RAID	Redundant array of inexpensive disks	廉价冗余硬磁盘阵列	Liánjià rǒngyú yìngcípán zhènliè
RAID	Redundant array of inexpensive disks	独立磁盘冗余阵列	Dúlì cípán rǒngyú zhènliè
RAID	Redundant array of inexpensive disks	经济磁盘冗余阵列	Jīngjì cípán rǒngyú zhènliè
RAID	Redundant arrays of inexpensive disks	冗余廉价磁盘阵列	Rǒngyú liánjià cípán zhènliè
RAM	Random access memory	随机存取存储器	Suíjī cúnqǔ cúnchǔqì
RAM	Random access memory	随机存取记存器	Suíjī cúnqǔ jìcúnqì
RAMDAC	Random access memory digital to analog converter	随机存储器数/模转换器	Suíjī cúnchǔqì shù/mó zhuǎnhuànqì
RAN	Radio access network	无线接入网	Wúxiàn jiērù wǎng

RAN	Radio access network	无线接入网络	Wúxiàn jiērù wǎngluò
RAN	Reanswer signal	再应答信号	Zàiyìngdá xìnhào
RANAP	Radio access network application part	无线接入网应用部分	Wúxiàn jiērù wǎng yìngyòng bùfen
RANAP	Radio access network application part	无线接入网络应用部分	Wúxiàn jiērù wǎngluò yìngyòng bùfen
RAND	Random number	随机号码	Suíjī hàomǎ
RAND	Random number (used for authentication)	随机数	Suíjī shù
RAP	Radio access point	无线电接入点	Wúxiàndiàn jiērù diǎn
RAP	Radio adapter port	电台接口	Diàntái jiēkǒu
RARE	Réseaux Associés pour la Recherche Européenne	欧洲大学和研究中心协会	Oūzhōu dàxué hé yánjiū zhōngxīn xiéhuì
RARP	Reverse address resolution protocol	反向地址判别协议	Fǎnxiàng dìzhǐ pànbié xiéyì
RARP	Reverse address resolution protocol	反向地址解析协议	Fǎnxiàng dìzhǐ jiěxī xiéyì
RARP	Reverse address resolution protocol	逆地址解析协议	Nì dìzhǐ jiěxī xiéyì
RARP	Reverse address resolution protocol	逆向地址解析协议	Nìxiàng dìzhǐ jiěxī xiéyì
RAS	Registration, admission and status	注册，接入和状态	Zhùcè, jiērù hé zhuàngtài
RAS	Registration, admission, status	注册,认证,状态	Zhùcè, rènzhèng, zhuàngtài
RAS	Remote access server	远程接入服务器	Yuǎnchéng jiērù fúwùqì
RAS	Remote access server	远端访问服务器	Yuǎnduān fǎngwèn fúwùqì
RAS	Remote access service	远程接入服务	Yuǎnchéng jiērù fúwù
RAS	Row address selection	行地址选定	Háng dìzhǐ xuǎndìng
RAS	Row addressable strobe	行地址控制器	Háng dìzhǐ kòngzhìqì
RASE	Rapid acquisition by sequential estimation	序贯估计快速捕获	Xùguàn gūjì kuàisù bǔhuò
RAT	Route attribute table	路线属性表	Lùxiàn shǔxìng biǎo
RAU	Request acess unit	请求接入单元	Qǐngqiú jiērù dānyuán
RAU	Routing area update	路由选择区域更新	Lùyóu xuǎnzé qūyù gēngxīn
RAVPN	Remote access VPN (virtual private network)	远端接入虚拟专用网	Yuǎnduān jiērù xūnǐ zhuānyòng wǎng
RAW	Read after write	写后读	Xiě hòu dú
RAW	Routing and assignment of wavelength	路由及波长分配	Lùyóu jí bōcháng fēnpèi
Raw PCM	Raw pulse code modulated	元脉码调制	Yuánmàimǎ tiáozhì
RB	Radio bearer	无线承载电路	Wúxiàn chéngzài diànlù
R-B&G	Remote bit and gain information	远端比特和增益信息	Yuǎnduān bǐtè hé zēngyì xìnxī
RBAC	Role-based access control	基于角色访问控制	Jīyú juésè fǎngwèn kòngzhì
RBAR	Most redundant bandwidth adaptive route selecting	最大冗余带宽适应路由选择	Zuìdà rǒngyú dàikuān shìyìng lùyóu xuǎnzé
RBB	Residential broadband network	社区宽带网络	Shèqū kuāndài wǎngluò
RBBP	Router and BIN back panel	路由器和 BIN 后面板	Lùyóuqì hé BIN hòumianbǎn
RBCF	Radio bearer common functionality	无线承载共用功能	Wúxiàn chéngzài gòngyòng gōngnéng
RBER	Residual bit error rate	残余比特差错率	Cányú bǐtè chācuò lǜ
RBER	Residual bit error rate	残余误码率	Cányú wùmǎ lǜ
R-Block	Receive-ready block	接收准备部件	Jiēshōu zhǔnbèi bùjiàn
RBOC	Regional Bell operating company	地方贝尔运营公司	Dìfang Bèi-ěr yùnyíng gōngsī
RBPF	Receiver band pass filter	接收机带宽滤波器	Jiēshōujī dàikuān lǜbōqì
RBQPSK	Reduced bandwidth quadrature phase shift keying	减小带宽正交相移键控	Jiǎnxiǎo dàikuān zhèngjiāo xiāngyí jiànkòng
RBS	Radio base station	无线基站	Wúxiàn jīzhàn
RBS	Riser backbone sub-system	主干子系统	Zhǔgàn zixìtǒng
RBS	Riser backbone sub-system	垂直子系统	Chuízhí zixìtǒng
RBW	Resolution bandwidth	分辨率带宽	Fēnbiànlǜ dàikuān
RC	Radio cell	无线小区	Wúxiàn xiǎoqū

RC	Radio channel	无线电信道	Wúxiàndiàn xìndào
RC	Radio channel	无线电波道	Wúxiàndiàn bōdào
RC	Release call	释放呼叫	Shìfàng hūjiào
RC	Repair center	修理中心	Xiūlǐ zhōngxīn
RC	Room coefficient	房间系数	Fángjiān xìshù
RC	Routing controller	路由控制器	Lùyóu kòngzhìqì
RCF	Registration confirm (packet protocol)	注册确认	Zhùcè quèrèn
RCF	Remote call forwarding	远程呼叫转移	Yuǎnchéng hūjiào zhuǎnyí
RCF	Resource configuration fragment	资源组成段	Zīyuán zǔchéng duàn
RCG	Radio channel group	无线信道群	Wúxiàn xìndào qún
RCG	RAS/CAS generator	RAS/CAS 发生器	RAS/CAS fāshēngqì
RCLK	Route clock	线路时钟	Xiànlù shízhōng
RCne	Network element resources control	网络单元资源控制	Wǎngluò dānyuán zīyuán kòngzhì
RCO	Resource control object	资源控制对象	Zīyuán kòngzhì duìxiàng
RCP	Remote copy program	远端复制程序	Yuǎnduān fùzhì chéngxù
RCP	Remote copy protocol	远程拷贝协议	Yuǎnchéng kǎobèi xiéyì
rcp	Remote copy protocol	远端复制协议	Yuǎnduān fùzhì xiéyì
RCP	Restoration control point	恢复控制点	Huīfù kòngzhì diǎn
RCP	Restoration control point	恢复控制点	Huīfù kòngzhì diǎn
RCP	Right-hand circular polarization	右旋圆极化	Yòuxuán yuán jíhuà
RCP	Routing and control processor	路由和控制处理机	Lùyóu hé kòngzhì chǔlǐjī
RCPN	Rule-based colored Petri net	基于规则约束着色 Petri 网	Jīyú guīzé yuēshù zhuosè Petri wǎng
RCPT	Rate compatible puncturing Turbo code	速率适配凿孔 Turbo 码	Sùlǜ shìpèi záokǒng Turbo mǎ
RCR	Research and Development Center for Radio System (Japan)	无线系统研究开发中心	Wúxiàn xìtǒng yánjiū kāifā zhōngxīn
RCS	Remote computing service	远程计算业务	Yuǎnchéng jìsuàn yèwù
RCT	Radio control terminal	无线电控制终端	Wúxiàndiàn kòngzhì zhōngduān
RCT	Reverse conducting thyristor	逆导晶闸管	Nìdǎo jīngzháguǎn
RCU	Remote control unit	终端控制器	Zhōngduān kòngzhìqì
Rd	Downstream router	下游路由器	Xiàyóu lùyóuqì
RD	Request disconnect	请求断开	Qǐngqiú duànkāi
RD	Routing domain	路由区域	Lùyóu qūyù
RD	Routing domain	路由选择域	Lùyóu xuǎnzé yù
RD	Weak current system	弱电系统	Ruòdiàn xìtǒng
RDA	Remote database access	远端数据库访问	Yuǎnduān shùjùkù fǎngwèn
RDB	Relational database	关系数据库	Guānxì shùjùkù
RDBMS	Relational database management system	关系型数据库管理系统	Guānxi-xíng shùjùkù guǎnlǐ xìtǒng
RDBMS	Relational database management system	关系数据库管理系统	Guānxì shùjùkù guǎnlǐ xìtǒng
RDBMS	Relational database management system	关联式数据库管理系统	Guānlián-shì shùjùkù guǎnlǐ xìtǒng
RDBMS	Remote database management system	远端数据库管理系统	Yuǎnduān shùjùkù guǎnlǐ xìtǒng
RDC	Redirect confirm packet	重定向确认分组	Chóngdìngxiàng quèrèn fēnzǔ
RDF	Resource description format	资源描述方式	Zīyuán miáoshù fāngshì
RDF	Resource description framework	资源描述框架	Zīyuán miáoshù kuàngjià
RDI	Receive defect indicator	接收缺陷指示	Jiēshōu quēxiàn zhǐshì
RDI	Remote defect indication	远端失效指示	Yuǎnduān shīxiào zhǐshì
RDI	Remote defect indication	远端缺陷指示	Yuǎnduān quēxiàn zhǐshì
RDI	Remote defect indication	远端限质指示	Yuǎnduān xiànzhì zhǐshì

RDI	Remote defect indicator	远端故障指示	Yuǎnduān gùzhàng zhǐshì
RDI	Remote degradation indicator	远端降质指示	Yuǎnduān jiàng zhì zhǐshì
RDI	Restricted digital information	禁止的数字信息	Jìnzhǐde shùzì xìnxī
RDI	Restricted digital information	限制的数字信息	Xiànzhìde shùzì xìnxī
RDL	Remote digital loopback	远程数字回送	Yuǎnchéng shùzì huísòng
RDMCS	Real-time and dynamic management and control support	实时动态管控支持	Shíshí dòngtài guǎnkòng zhīchí
RDN	Relative distinguished name	相对可识别名	Xiāngduì kěshíbié míng
RDN	Relative distinguished name	相对识别名	Xiāngduì shíbié míng
RDN	Relative distinguished name	相对辨别名	Xiāngduì biàn biémíng
RDO	Remote data object	远程数据对象	Yuǎnchéng shùjù duìxiàng
RDP	Reliable data protocol	可靠数据协议	Kěkào shùjù xiéyì
RDR	Redirect request packet	重定向请求分组	Chóngdìngxiàng qǐngqiú fēnzǔ
RDRAM	Rambus direct random access memory	直接型 RambusRAM	Zhíjiē-xíng Rambus RAM
RDS	Radio data system transmission	无线数据广播	Wúxiàn shùjù guǎngbō
RDS	Redirect server	重定向服务器	Chóngdìngxiàng fúwùqì
RE	Rationalizing engineering (German concept)	合理化工程	Hélǐhuà gōngchéng
RE	Reference event	参考事件	Cānkǎo shìjiàn
REC	RECommendation	建议	Jiànyì
REC	Recommendation	建议	Jiànyì
REC	Recommendation	推荐	Tuījiàn
REC	Reverse error control	反响误差控制	Fǎnxiǎng wùchā kòngzhì
RECC	Reverse control channel	反向控制信道	Fǎnxiàng kòngzhì xìndào
RED	Random early detection	随机早期侦测	Suíjī zǎoqī zhēncè
RED	Random early detection	随机早期检测	Suíjī zǎoqī jiǎncè
REG	Regenerative repeater	再生中继器	Zàishēng zhōngjìqì
REG	Regenerator	再生器	Zàishēngqì
REG	Trunk regenerator	再生中继设备	Zàishēng zhōngjì shèbèi
REG-ACK	Register acknowledge message	登记确认消息	Dēngjì quèrèn xiāoxi
REGINT	Registration interval	登记周期	Dēngjì zhōuqī
REG-REQ	Register request message	登记请求消息	Dēngjì qǐngqiú xiāoxi
REG-RSP	Register response message	登记响应消息	Dēngjì xiǎngyìng xiāoxi
REI	Remote error indication	远端差错指示	Yuǎnduān chācuò zhǐshì
REI	Remote error indication	远端误码指示	Yuǎnduān wùmǎ zhǐshì
REJ	Reject(ion)	拒绝	Jùjué
REJ	Reject, rejection	阻止	Zǔzhǐ
REJPDN	Reject power down	拒绝掉电	Jùjué diàodiàn
REL	Line release message	线路释放消息	Xiànlù shìfàng xiāoxi
REL	Release	释放	Shìfàng
REL(ISUP)	Release message (ISUP)	释放消息	Shìfàng xiāoxi
RELAK	Release acknowledged (SCCP message)	释放确认	Shìfàng quèrèn
RELP	Residual excitation linear prediction coding	残差激励线性预测编码	Cánchā jīlì xiànxìng yùcè biānmǎ
RELP	Residual excitation linear predictive coding	残余激励线性预测编码	Cányú jīlì xiànxìng yùcè biānmǎ
RELRE	Release request (SS7, SCCP message)	释放请求	Shìfàng qǐngqiú
REM	Ring error monitor	环差错监视器	Huán chācuò jiānshìqì
REMA	Realtime exclusive mode applications	实时高级应用	Shíshí gāojí yìngyòng
REP	Radio equipment	无线设备	Wúxiàn shèbèi

Rep	Repeater station	中继站	Zhōngjìzhàn
REP-LPC	Regular pulse excitation long-term predictive coding	规则脉冲激励长时预测编码	Guīzé màichōng jīlì--chángshí yùcè biānmǎ
REQ	Request frame	请求帧	Qǐngqiú zhèng
REQ, RQ	Request	请求	Qǐngqiú
REQPDN	Request to power down	掉电请求	Diàodiàn qǐngqiú
RES	Reserved	预定	Yùdìng
RES	Resume	恢复	Huīfù
RES	Resume message (ISUP)	恢复消息	Huīfù xiāoxi
RES	Resume request (ISUP message)	呼叫恢复请求	Hūjiào huīfù qǐngqiú
RESCO	Restore confirm	复原证实	Fùyuán zhèngshí
RESRE	Restore request	复原请求	Fùyuán qǐngqiú
RET	Remote access terminal	远端接入终端	Yuǎnduān jiērù zhōngduān
RET	Remote electrical tilt	远程电调	Yuǎnchéng diàntiáo
REV	Reverse charging	对方计费	Duìfāng jìfèi
REV	Reverse charging	被叫计费	Bèijiào jìfèi
REV	Reverse signal	反极信号	Fǎnjí xìnhào
RF	Radio frequency	射频	Shèpín
RF	Radio frequency	无线电频率	Wúxiàndiàn pínlǜ
RFB	Remote file browser	远程文件浏览器	Yuǎnchéng wénjiàn liúlǎnqì
RFC	Radio-frequency channel	无线电频率信道	Wúxiàndiàn pínlǜ xìndào
RFC	Request for comment	征求意见	Zhēngqiú yìjiàn
RFC	Request for comment	请求评议	Qǐngqiú píngyì
RFC	Request for comment	请求评论文档	Qǐngqiú pínglùn wéndàng
RFC	Request for comments	注释请求	Zhùshì qǐngqiú
RFC	Request for connection	要求连接	Yāoqiú liánjiē
RFER	Residual frame error rate	残余错帧率	Cányú cuò zhèng lǜ
RFER	Residual frame error rate	残留错帧率	Cánliú cuòzhèng lǜ
RFES	Receive front end shelf	接收前端架	Jiēshōu qiánduān jià
RFH	Remote frame handler	远端帧处理器	Yuǎnduān zhèng chǔlǐqì
RFHI	Remote frame handler interface	远端帧处理器接口	Yuǎnduān zhèng chǔlǐqì jiēkǒu
RFI	Radio frequency interference	射频干扰	Shèpín gānrǎo
RFI	Radio-frequency interference	无线电频率干扰	Wúxiàndiàn pínlǜ gānrǎo
RFI	Remote failure indication	远端失效指示	Yuǎnduān shīxiào zhǐshì
RFN	Reduced TDMA frame number	简化 TDMA 帧号	Jiǎnhuà TDMA zhènghào
RFP	Request for proposal	建议请求	Jiànyì qǐngqiú
RFSK/FH	Random frequency shift keying/frequency hopping	随机频移键控/频率跳变	Suíjī pínyí jiànkòng/pínlǜ tiàobiàn
RFT	Radio frequency terminal	射频终端	Shèpín zhōngduān
RFT	Remote file transfer	远程文件传送	Yuǎnchéng wénjiàn chuánsòng
RFTE	Radio frequency test equipment	无线频率测试设备	Wúxiàn pínlǜ cèshì shèbèi
RFTE	Radio-frequency test equipment	射频测试设备	Shèpín cèshì shèbèi
RFTS	Remote fiber test system	远程光缆监测系统	Yuǎnchéng guānglǎn jiāncè xìtǒng
RFU	Radio frequency unit	无线频率单元	Wúxiàn pínlǜ dānyuán
RFU	Reserve for future use	保留未用	Bǎoliú wèi yòng
RFU	Reserved for future use	留作将来使用	Liúzuò jiānglái shǐyòng
RFUR	Radio frequency unit rack	无线频率单元机架	Wúxiàn pínlǜ dānyuán jījià
RG	Regenerator	再生设备	Zàishēng shèbèi

RG	Release guard (in CORBA)	启动保护协议	Qǐdòng bǎohù xiéyì
RG	Residential gateway	社区网关	Shèqū wǎngguān
RG	Residential gateway	驻地网关	Zhùdì wǎngguān
RG	Ring group	铃群组	Líng qún zǔ
RGB	Three primary colors (red, green, blue; refers to system for representing colors on a computer display)	三原色	Sānyuánsè
RGBP	Ring generator back panel	震铃产生器后面板	Zhènlíng chǎnshēngqì hòumianbǎn
RGMP	Cisco router port group management protocol	思科路由器端口组管理协议	Sī-kē lùyóuqì duānkǒuzǔ guǎnlǐ xiéyì
RGW	Residential gateway	住户网关	Zhùhù wǎngguān
RHCP	Right hand circular polarized (wave, signal)	右旋圆极化(波,信号)	Yòuxuán yuán jíhuà (bō, xìnhào)
RHE	Remote head end	远地前端	Yuǎndì qiánduān
RHP	Right hand polarization	右旋极化	Yòuxuán jíhuà
RI	Remote information	远程信息	Yuǎnchéng xìnxī
RI	Remote information	远端信息	Yuǎnduān xìnxī
RI	Response identifier	响应标识符	Xiǎngyìng biāozhìfú
RI	Routing information	路由选择信息	Lùyóu xuǎnzé xìnxī
RI/RO	Ring in, ring out	环入/环出	Huán rù/ huán chū
RIAA	Recording Industry Association of America	美国唱片工业协会	Měiguó chàngpiàn gōngyè xiéhuì
RIC	Radio pager identity code	寻呼机标识码	Xúnhūjī biāozhì mǎ
RID	Route intrusion detection	路由入侵检测	Lùyóu rùqīn jiǎncè
RIE	Reactive ion etch	反应式离子蚀刻法	Fǎnyìngshì lízǐ shíkè fǎ
RIF	Routing information field	路由信息域	Lùyóu xìnxī yù
RIF	Routing information field	路由选择信息字段	Lùyóu xuǎnzé xìnxī zìduàn
RII	Routing information indicator	路由选择信息指示符	Lùyóu xuǎnzé xìnxī zhǐshìfú
RIL	Radio interface layer	无线接口层	Wúxiàn jiēkǒu céng
RIMM	RAMBUS in-line memory module	RAMBUS 内嵌式内存模块	RAMBUS nèiqiàn-shì nèicún mókuài
RIP	Received isotropic power	各向同性接收功率	Gèxiàng tóngxìng jiēshōu gōnglǜ
RIP	Request in process	请求处理中	Qǐngqiú chǔlǐ zhōng
RIP	Request in progress	进展请求	Jìnzhǎn qǐngqiú
RIP	Routing information protocol	路由信息协议	Lùyóu xìnxī xiéyì
RIPE	Réseaux IP Européennes	欧洲 IP 网络	Oūzhōu IP wǎngluò
RIPng	Routing information protocol for IPv6	IPv6 的路由信息协议	IPv6-de lùyóu xìnxī xiéyì
RIPX	Routing information protocol over Internet packet exchange	在 IPX 上的路由信息协议	Zài IPX-shàngde lùyóu xìnxī xiéyì
RISC	Reduced instruction set computer	精简指令计算机	Jīngjiǎn zhǐlìng jìsuànjī
RISC	Reduced instruction set computing	精简指令集计算	Jīngjiǎn zhǐlìng jí jìsuàn
RISC	Reduced instruction set computing	精简指令集计算机	Jīngjiǎn zhǐlìng jí jìsuànjī
RISC	Reduced instruction-set computer	简约指令集计算机	Jiǎnyuē zhǐlìngjí jìsuànjī
RJ	Computer software	计算机软件	Jìsuànjī ruǎnjiàn
RJ Connector	Registered jack connector	注册的插座连接器	Zhùcède chāzuò liánjiēqì
RJE	Remote job entry	远端任务入口	Yuǎnduān rènwu rùkǒu
RL	Restriction level (in SS7)	限制等级	Xiànzhì děngjí
RL	Return loss	反射损耗	Fǎnshè sǔnhào
RL	Return loss	反射衰减	Fǎnshè shuāijiǎn
RL	Return loss	反射衰减	Fǎnshè shuāijiǎn
RL	Return loss	回路损耗	Huílù sǔnhào
RL	Return loss	回输损耗	Huíshū sǔnhào

RL	Return loss (radio term)	回波损耗	Huíbō sǔnhào
RLC	Radio link control	无线链路控制	Wúxiàn liànlù kòngzhì
RLC	Radio link control sub-layer	无线链路控制子层	Wúxiàn liànlù kòngzhì zicéng
RLC	Release complete	线路释放完成	Xiànlù shìfàng wánchéng
RLC	Release complete (ISUP message)	释放完成	Shifàng wánchéng
RLC	Release complete message (ISUP)	释放完成消息	Shifàng wánchéng xiāoxi
RLC	Remote line concentrator	远程线路集线器	Yuǎnchéng xiànlù jíxiànqì
RLC	Run-length coding	游程长度编码	Yóuchéng chángdù biānmǎ
RLCP	Radio link control protocol	无线链路控制协议	Wúxiàn liànlù kòngzhì xiéyì
RLDRAM	Reduced latency dynamic random access memory	低延迟动态随机存取存储器	Dīyánchí dòngtài suíjī cúnqǔ cúnchǔqì
RLE	Run length encoding	游程编码	Yóuchéng biānmǎ
RLE	Run length encoding	行程编码	Xíngchéng biānmǎ
RLG	Release guard signal	释放监护信号	Shìfàng jiānhù xìnhào
RLL	Radio in the local loop	本地环路无线电	Běndì huánlù wúxiàndiàn
RLM	Radio link management	无线链路管理	Wúxiàn liànlù guǎnlǐ
RLOGIN	Remote login (in Unix)	远程登录命令	Yuǎnchéng dēnglù mìnglìng
RLP	Radio line protocol	无线电线路规约	Wúxiàndiàn xiànlù guīyuē
RLP	Radio link protocol	无线链路协议	Wúxiàn liànlù xiéyì
RLP	Radio link protocol	无线链路规约	Wúxiàn liànlù guīyuē
RLR	Receiving loudness rating	接收响度评定值	Jiēshōu xiǎngdù píngdìng zhí
RLS	Radio link setup	无线链路建立	Wúxiàn liànlù jiànlì
RLS	Recursive least square	递归最小二乘	Dìguī zuìxiǎo èrshèng
RLS	Recursive least square	递归最小平方	Dìguī zuìxiǎo píngfāng
RLSD	Connection released (in SS7)	释放连接	Shìfàng liánjiē
RM	Relational model (in SQL Server)	关系模型	Guānxi móxíng
RM	Request management (CMM)	需求管理	Xūqiú guǎnlǐ
RM	Resource management	资源管理	Zīyuán guǎnlǐ
RM	Resource manager	资源管理器	Zīyuán guǎnlǐqì
RMA	Rate monotonic analysis (in CORBA)	比率单调分析	Bǐlǜ dāndiào fēnxī
RMA	RealMedia architecture ©	实媒体架构	Shí méitǐ jiàgòu
RMBB	Resource management building block	资源管理构件	Zīyuán guǎnlǐ gòujiàn
RMCSF	Real-time management and control support fragment	实时管控支持段	Shíshí guǎn kòng zhīchí duàn
RMFF	Real media file format	真实媒体文件格式	Zhēnshí méitǐ wénjiàn géshi
RMI	Remote method interface	远程调用接口	Yuǎnchéng diàoyòng jiēkǒu
RMI	Remote method invocation	远程方法调度	Yuǎnchéng fāngfǎ diàodù
RML	Radio microwave link	无线电微波线路	Wúxiàndian wēibō xiànlù
RM-ODP	Reference model of open distributed processing	开放分布式处理的参考模型	Kāifàng fēnbùshì chǔlǐde cānkǎo móxíng
RMON	Remote monitoring	远端监控	Yuǎnduān jiānkòng
RMON	Remote monitoring (in SNMP)	远程监控	Yuǎnchéng jiānkòng
RMOS	Real-time multi-tasking operating system	实时多任务操作系统	Shíshí duō rènwu cāozuò xìtǒng
RMP	Reliable multicast protocol	可靠组播协议	Kěkào zǔbō xiéyì
Rms	Radical mean square	均方根	Jūn fānggēn
RMS	Regional management system	区域管理系统	Qūyù guǎnlǐ xìtǒng
RMS	Reliability, maintainability and safety	可靠性、维修性和安全性	Kěkàoxìng、wéixiūxìng hé ānquánxìng
RMS	Root mean square	均方根	Jūn fānggēn
RMS	Root mean square detector	均方根值检波器	Jūn fānggēn zhí jiǎnbōqì

RMSE	Root mean square error	均方根误差	Jūn fānggēn wùchā
RMTP	Reliable multicast transport protocol	可靠组播传输协议	Kěkào zǔbō chuánshū xiéyì
RMU	Redundancy memory unit	冗余存贮器	Rǒngshé cúnzhùqì
RNC	Radio network controller	无线电网络控制器	Wúxiàndiàn wǎngluò kòngzhìqì
RNC	Radio network controller	无选网络控制器	Wúxuǎn wǎngluò kòngzhìqì
RND	Redirecting name display	改向名字显示	Gǎixiàng míngzì xiǎnshì
RNG	Random number generator	随机数字发生器	Suíjī shùzì fāshēngqì
RNG-RSP	Ranging response message	测距响应消息	Cèjù xiǎngyìng xiāoxi
RNR	Receive not ready	接收未准备好	Jiēshōu wèizhǔnbèi hǎo
RNS	Radio access network system	无线接入网系统	Wúxiàn jiērù wǎng xìtǒng
RNS	Radio network sub-system	无线电网络子系统	Wúxiàndiàn wǎngluò zixìtǒng
RNS	Radio network sub-system	无线网络子系统	Wúxiàn wǎngluò zixìtǒng
RNSAP	Radio network sub-system application part	无线电网络子系统应用部分	Wúxiàndiàn wǎngluò zixìtǒng yìngyòng bùfen
RNSAP	Radio network sub-system application part	无线网络子系统应用部分	Wúxiàn wǎngluò zixìtǒng yìngyòng bùfen
RNTI	Radio network temporary identity	无线电网络临时识别	Wúxiàndiàn wǎngluò línshí shíbié
RNZR	Randomized non-return to zero	随机不归零制	Suíjī bù guī líng zhì
RO	Read only	只读	Zhǐ dú
RO	Ring oscillator	振铃振荡器	Zhènlíng zhèndàngqì
ROA	Recognized operating authority	经认可的运营机构	Jīng rènkěde yùnyíng jīgòu
ROF	Radio over fiber	光纤无线电	Guāngxiān wúxiàndiàn
ROH	Receiver off-hook	接收机脱钩	Jiēshōujī tuōgōu
ROI	Return on investment	投资回报	Tóuzī huíbào
ROL	Reverse oscillation lay (FOC)	反向振荡节距	Fǎnxiàng zhèndàng jiéjù
ROLAP	Relational online analytical processing	关系联机分析处理	Guānxi liánjī fēnxī chǔlǐ
ROLR	Receive objective loudness result	接收客观响度评定值	Jiēshōu kèguān xiǎngdù píngdìng zhí
ROM	Read only memory	只读内储	Zhǐ dú nèichǔ
ROM	Read-only memory	只读存储器	Zhǐ dú cúnchǔqì
ROM	Read-only memory	唯读记忆体	Wéidú jìyìtǐ
RORTD	Rate of rise thermal detector	差温探测器	Chà wēn tàncèqì
ROSA	Recording optical spectrum analyzer	记录光谱分析仪	Jìlù guāngpǔ fēnxīyí
ROSE	Remote operation service element	远程操作服务元素	Yuǎnchéng cāozuò fúwù yuánsù
ROSE	Remote operation service element	远端操作业务单元	Yuǎnduān cāozuò yèwù dānyuán
ROSE	Remote operation service element	远端操作服务要素	Yuǎnduān cāozuò fúwù yàosù
ROSE	Remote operation service element	遥控操作业务单元	Yáokòng cāozuò yèwù dānyuán
ROSE	Remote operations service element	远程操作业务单元	Yuǎnchéng cāozuò yèwù dānyuán
ROSE	Remote operations service element	远端操作业务元素	Yuǎnduān cāozuò yèwù yuánsù
ROSY	Remote operations stub generator	远操作规范数结构生成器	Yuǎn cāozuò guīfàn shù jiégòu shēngchéngqì
ROTDR	Raman optical time-domain reflectometry	拉曼光学时域反射测量术	Lā-màn guāngxué shíyù fǎnshè cèliáng shù
RP	Remote point	远端点	Yuǎnduān diǎn
RP	Rendezvous point	汇聚点	Huìjù diǎn
RP	Rendezvous point	汇集点	Huìjídiǎn
RP	Rendezvous point	聚合点	Jùhé diǎn
RP	Request packet	请求包	Qǐngqiú bāo
RP	Route processor	路由处理器	Lùyóu chǔlǐqì
RPC	Remote packet concentrator	远程数组集中器	Yuǎnchéng shùzǔ jízhōngqì

RPC	Remote procedure call	远程过程调用	Yuǎnchéng guòchéng diàoyòng
RPC	Remote procedure call	远端程序调度	Yuǎnduān chéngxù diàodù
RPC	Remote procedure call	远端程序调用	Yuǎnduān chéngxù diàoyòng
RPC	Remote procedure call protocol (IETF use)	远程过程调用协议	Yuǎnchéng guòchéng diàoyòng xiéyì
RPC	Remote-procedure call	远端过程调用	Yuǎnduān guòchéng diàoyòng
RPE	Radiation pattern envelope	辐射图包络	Fúshè tú bāoluò
RPE	Regular pulse excitation	规则脉冲激励编码	Guīzé màichōng jīlì biānmǎ
RPE-LTP	Regular pulse excitation linear predictive coding with long-term prediction	带有长期预测的规则脉冲激励线性预测编码	Dàiyǒu chángqī yùcède guīzé màichōng jīlì xiànxìng yùcè biānmǎ
RPE-LTP-LPC	Regular pulse excitation - long-term prediction - linear predictive coding	规则脉冲激励-长期预测-线性预测编码	Guīzé màichōng jīlì--chángqī yùcè—xiànxìng yùcè biānmǎ
RPE-LTP-LPC	Regular pulse excited-long term predition-linear predictive coding	规则脉冲激励—长时预测—线性预测编码	Guīzé màichōng jīlì— chángshí yùcè—xiànxìng yùcè biānmǎ
RPF	Reverse path forwarding	反向路径转发	Fǎnxiàng lùjìng zhuǎnfā
RPF	Reverse path forwarding	反向路径转换	Fǎnxiàng lùjìng zhuǎnhuàn
RPF	Reverse path forwarding	反转路径转发	Fǎnzhuǎn lùjìng zhuǎnfā
RPF	Reverse path forwarding	逆向路径转发	Nìxiàng lùjìng zhuǎnfā
RPG	Role playing game (computer game)	角色扮演游戏	Juésè bànyǎn yóuxì
RPLMN	Registered public land mobile network	登记的公用陆地移动通信网	Dēngjìde gōngyòng lùdì yídòng tōngxìnwǎng
RPM	Random phase modulation	随机相位调制	Suíjī xiàngwèi tiáozhì
RPM	Reverse path multicasting	反向路径组播	Fǎnxiàng lùjìng zǔbō
RPM	Rotations per minute	转/分	Zhuǎn/fēn
RPOA	Recognised private operating agency	认可的专用运行代理	Rènkěde zhuānyòng yùnxíng dàilǐ
RPR	Resilient packet ring	弹性分组环	Tánxìng fēnzǔ huán
RPS	Ring parameter server	环参数服务器	Huán cānshù fúwùqì
RPT	RP-rooted share tree	以 RP 为树跟的共享树	Yǐ RP wéi shùgēnde gòngxiǎng shù
RQI	Request for initialization	初始化请求	Chūshǐhuà qǐngqiú
RQI	Request interrupt	请求中断	Qǐngqiú zhōngduàn
RR	Radio resource	无线资源	Wúxiàn zīyuán
RR	Radio resources	无线电资源	Wúxiàndiàn zīyuán
RR	Receive ready	接收准备好	Jiēshōu zhǔnbèi hǎo
RR	Registration reply	注册应答	Zhùcè yìngdá
RR	Resource record	资源记录	Zīyuán jìlù
RR	Reverberation radius	混响半径	Hùnxiǎng bànjìng
RRBE	Request report BCSM event	请求报告 BCSM 事件	Qǐngqiú bàogào BCSM shìjiàn
RRC	Radio resource control	无线资源控制	Wúxiàn zīyuán kòngzhì
RRC	Radio resource control layer	无线资源控制层	Wúxiàn zīyuán kòngzhì céng
RRC	Radio resources control	无线电资源控制	Wúxiàndiàn zīyuán kòngzhì
RR-EI	Radio relay equipment interface (microwave)	微波接力设备接口	Wēibō jiēlì shèbèi jiēkǒu
RRJ	Registration reject (packet protocol)	注册拒绝	Zhùcè jùjué
RRJ	Registration reject message	拒绝注册	Jùjué zhùcè
RRL	Radio relay link	无线电中继链路	Wúxiàndiàn zhōngjì liànlù
RRL	Radio relay system	无线电中继系统	Wúxiàndiàn zhōngjì xìtǒng
RRM	Radio resource management	无线资源管理	Wúxiàn zīyuán guǎnlǐ
RRM	Radio resources management	无线电资源管理	Wúxiàndiàn zīyuán guǎnlǐ
RRM	Round robin matching	轮循匹配	Lúnxún pǐpèi

RRME	Radio resource management entity	无线资源管理实体	Wúxiàn zīyuán guǎnlǐ shítǐ
RRMP	Radio resource management protocol	无线资源管理协议	Wúxiàn zīyuán guǎnlǐ xiéyì
RR-P&C	Return result of prompt and collect user information	提示并收集用户信息的返回结果	Tíshì bìng shōují yònghù xìnxīde fǎnhuí jiéguǒ
RRQ	Registration request (packet protocol)	注册请求	Zhùcè qǐngqiú
RR-RP	Radio relay system reference point	微波接力系统的参考点	Wēibō jiēlì xìtǒngde cānkǎo diǎn
RRT	Resource request table	资源请求表	Zīyuán qǐngqiú biǎo
RRVP	Resource reserVation protocol	资源保留协议	Zīyuán bǎoliú xiéyì
RS	Radio standard	无线电规范	Wúxiàndiàn guīfàn
RS	Radio subscriber	无线用户	Wúxiàn yònghù
RS	Radius server	认证服务器	Rènzhèng fúwùqì
RS	Record separator	记录分隔	Jìlù fēngé
RS	Reed-Solomon code	里德-索洛蒙码	Lǐ-dé—suǒ-luò-méng mǎ
RS	Reflected sound	反射场	Fǎnshè cháng
RS	Regenerator section	再生段	Zàishēng duàn
RS	Relay station	接力站	Jiēlì zhàn
RS NC	Regenerator section network connection	再生段网络连接	Zàishēng duàn wǎngluò liánjiē
RS-232	Recommended Standard 232	第 232 号推荐标准	Dì 232 hào tuījiàn biāozhǔn
RSA	Remote subscriber access	远端用户接入	Yuǎnduān yònghù jiērù
RSA	Rivest-Shamir-Adelman coding	通用关键子密码方法	Tōngyòng guānjiàn zi mìmǎ fāngfǎ
RSC	Circuit reset signal	电路复原消息	Diànlù fùyuán xiāoxi
RSC	Recursive systematic convolutional code	递归系统卷积码	Dìguī xìtǒng juànjīmǎ
RSC	Reed-Solomon code	里德-所罗门码	Lǐ-dé—suǒ-luó-mén mǎ
RSC	Reset circuit signal	电路复原信号	Diànlù fùyuán xìnhào
RSCP	Received signal code power	接收信号码功率	Jiēshōu xìnhào mǎ gōnglǜ
RSCS	Remote spooling communication system	远程假脱机通信系统	Yuǎnchéng jiǎtuōjī tōngxìn xìtǒng
RSD	Removable storage device	移动式存储设备	Yídòng-shì cúnchǔ shèbèi
RSDS	Reduced swing differential signal	小幅度摆动差动信号	Xiǎo fúdù bǎidòng chādòng xìnhào
RSDT	Remote station data terminal	远程站数据终端	Yuǎnchéng zhàn shùjù zhōngduān
RSE	Radio system entity	无线电系统实体	Wúxiàndiàn xìtǒng shítǐ
RSFHMA	Random slow frequency hopping multiple access	随机缓慢跳频变多路存取	Suíjī huǎnmàn tiàopín biàn duōlù cúnqǔ
RSFT	Redundant space and frequency tree	冗余的空间和频率树	Rǒngyúde kōngjiān hé pínlǜ shù
RSGU	Ring signal generate unit	震铃信号产生单元	Zhènlíng xìnhào chǎnshēng dānyuán
R-SGW	Roaming signaling gateway	漫游信令网关	Mànyóu xìnlìng wǎngguān
rsh	Remote shell protocol	远端外壳协议	Yuǎnduān wàiké xiéyì
RSI	Repetitive strain injury	重复动作损伤	Chóngfù dòngzuò sǔnshāng
RSL	Radio signaling link	无线信令链路	Wúxiàn xìnlìng liànlù
RSL	Radio signaling link	无线电信令链路	Wúxiàndiàn xìnlìng liànlù
RSL	Registry size limit	注册表大小限制	Zhùcè biǎo dàxiǎo xiànzhì
RSL	Restriction sub-level (in SS7)	限制子等级	Xiànzhì ziděngjí
RSM	Radio sub-system management	无线子系统管理	Wúxiàn zixìtǒng guǎnlǐ
RSM	Radio system management	无线系统管理	Wúxiàn xìtǒng guǎnlǐ
RSM	Remote subscriber module	远端用户模块	Yuǎnduān yònghù mókuài
RSMF	Real-time security management fragment	实时安全管理段	Shíshí ānquán guǎnlǐ duàn
RSOH	Regenerator section overhead	再生段开销	Zàishēng duàn kāixiao
RSP	Remote subscriber processing	远端用户处理	Yuǎnduān yònghù chǔlǐ

RSQI	Received signal quality indicator	接收信号质量指示	Jiēshōu xìnhào zhìliàng zhǐshì
RSRB	Remote source-route bridging	远端信源路由网桥	Yuǎnduān xìnyuán lùyóu wǎngqiáo
RSS	Really simple syndication	真正简单的整合	Zhēnzhèng jiǎndānde zhěnghé
RSS	Root-sum square	平方和的根	Píngfānghéde gēn
RSSI	Received signal strength indication	接收信号强度指示	Jiēshōu xìnhào qiángdù zhǐshì
RST	Regenerator section termination	再生段终端	Zàishēng duàn zhōngduān
RST	Remote station	远程站	Yuǎnchéng zhàn
RST	Reset	设置	Shèzhì
RST	Reset signal	复位信号	Fùwèi xìnhào
RST	Terminal radio station	终端无线电台	Zhōngduān wúxiàndiàntái
RSTCP	Remote synchronous terminal control program	远程同步终端控制程序	Yuǎnchéng tóngbù zhōngduān kòngzhì chéngxù
RS-TIM	Regenerator section trace identification mismatch	再生段路踪识别失配	Zàishēng duànlù zōng shíbié shīpèi
RSU	Remote subscriber unit	远端用户单元	Yuǎnduān yònghù dānyuán
RSU	Remote switch unit	远端交换模块	Yuǎnduān jiāohuàn mókuài
RSU	Remote switch unit	远端模块局	Yuǎnduān mókuài jú
RSU	Remote switching unit	远端交换单元	Yuǎnduān jiāohuàn dānyuán
RSUP	Route set-up packet	路由设置表	Lùyóu shèzhì biǎo
RSVP	Resource reservation protocol	资源预留协议	Zīyuán yùliú xiéyì
RSVP-TE	Resource reservation protocol-traffic engineering (IETF usage)	基于流量工程扩展的资源预留协议	Jīyú liúliàng gōngchéng kuòzhǎnde zīyuán yùliú xiéyì
RSZI	Regional subscription zone identity	区域使用识别码	Qūyù shǐyòng shíbié mǎ
RSZI	Regional subscription zone identity	区域性签约区域识别号码	Qūyùxìng qiānyuē qūyù shíbié hàomǎ
RSZI	Regional subscription zone identity	区域性预约区标示	Qūyùxìng yùyuēqū biāoshì
RSZI	Regional subscription zone identity	地方的预约信息段识别	Dìfangde yùyuē xìnxī duàn shíbié
RT	Remote terminal	远端机	Yuǎnduān jī
RT	Reverberation time	混响时间	Hùnxiǎng shíjiān
RT	Routing type	路由选择类型	Lùyóu xuǎnzé lèixíng
RTA	Response time approximation	响应时间近似变换	Xiǎngyìng shíjiān jìnsì biànhuàn
RTAC	Real-time adaptive control	实时自适应控制	Shíshí zìshìyìng kòngzhì
RTB	Real-time billing	实时计费	Shíshí jìfèi
RTC	Real-time clock	实时时钟	Shíshí shízhōng
RTC	Real-time communication	实时通信	Shíshí tōngxìn
RTCM	Radio Technology Committee, Marine	海事无线电技术委员会	Hǎishì wúxiàndiàn jìshù wěiyuánhuì
RTCP	Real-time control protocol	实时控制协议	Shíshí kòngzhì xiéyì
RTCP	Real-time transmission control protocol	实时传输控制协议	Shíshí chuánshū kòngzhì xiéyì
RTD	Real-time difference	实际时钟差异	Shíjì shízhōng chāyì
RTD	Resistance temperature detector	电阻温度传感器	Diànzǔ wēndù chuángǎnqì
RTDMA	Random time division multiple access	随机分时多路存取	Suíjī fēnshí duōlù cúnqǔ
RTDMS	Real-time database management system	实时数据库管理系统	Shíshí shùjùkù guǎnlǐ xìtǒng
RTE	Radio test equipment (board)	无线测试设备（板）	Wúxiàn cèshì shèbèi (bǎn)
RTE	Real-time executive	实时执行	Shíshí zhíxíng
RTE	Remote terminal emulator	远程终端仿真器	Yuǎnchéng zhōngduān fǎngzhēnqì
RTF	Radio terminal function	无线电终端功能	Wúxiàndiàn zhōngduān gōngnéng
RTG	Regenerator timing generator	再生器定时发生器	Zàishēngqì dìngshí fāshēngqì
RTI	Remote terminal identification	远程终端识别	Yuǎnchéng zhōngduān shíbié
RTI	Run-time infrastructure	运行时间支撑系统	Yùnxíng shíjiān zhīchēng xìtǒng

RTIM	Repository type information model	知识库类型信息模型	Zhīshikù lèixíng xìnxī móxíng
RTIOP	Real-time inter-ORB (object request broker) protocol	对象请求代理间的实时协议	Duìxiàng qǐngqiú dàilǐ jiānde shíshí xiéyì
RTL	Resistor transistor logic circuit	电阻晶体管逻辑电路	Diànzǔ jīngtǐguǎn luóji diànlù
RTM	Reference test method	基准试验方法	Jīzhǔn shìyàn fāngfǎ
RTMC	Real-time management control function	实时管理协调功能	Shíshí guǎnlǐ xiétiáo gōngnéng
RTMP	Routing table maintenance protocol	路由表维护协议	Lùyóu biǎo wéihù xiéyì
RTMP	Routing table maintenance protocol	路由选择表维护协议	Lùyóu xuǎnzé biǎo wéihù xiéyì
RTO	Repeat timeout	重发超时	Chóngfā chāoshí
RTOS	Real-time operating system	实时操作系统	Shíshí cāozuò xìtǒng
RTP	Rapid thermal processing	快速热处理	Kuàisù rèchǔlǐ
RTP	Rapid transport protocol	快速传输协议	Kuàisù chuánshū xiéyì
RTP	Rapid transport protocol	快速传送协议	Kuàisù chuánsòng xiéyì
RTP	Real-time protocol	实时协议	Shíshí xiéyì
RTP	Real-time transport production	实时传送流	Shíshí chuánsòng liú
RTP	Real-time transport protocol	实时传输协议	Shíshí chuánshū xiéyì
RTP	Real-time transport protocol	实时传送协议	Shíshí chuánsòng xiéyì
RTP	Routing table protocol	路由表协议	Lùyóu biǎo xiéyì
RTP	Routing table protocol	路由选择表协议	Lùyóu xuǎnzé biǎo xiéyì
rtPS	Real-time polling service	实时查询业务	Shíshí cháxún yèwù
RTR	Restore threshold report	门限复位报告	Ménxiàn fùwèi bàogào
RTS	Rated tensile strength	额定抗拉强度	Édìng kànglā qiángdù
RTS	Rated tensile strength	额定拉断力	Édìng lāduànlì
RTS	Real time strategy (computer game)	实时战略	Shíshí zhànlüè
RTS	Request to send	请求发送	Qǐngqiú fāsòng
RTS	Request to send	需求发送	Xūqiú fāsòng
RTS	Residual time stamp	剩余时间标志法	Shèngyú shíjiān biāozhì fǎ
RTS/CTS	Request to send/ clear to send	请求发送/允许发送协议	Qǐngqiú fāsòng/yǔnxǔ fāsòng xiéyì
RTSE	Reliable transfer service element	可靠传送服务要素	Kěkào chuánsòng fúwù yàosù
RTSE	Reliable transfer service element	可靠的传送业务单元	Kěkàode chuánsòng yèwù dānyuán
RTSE	Reliable transfer service element protocol	可靠传输服务元素协议	Kěkào chuánshū fúwù yuánsù xiéyì
RTSec.M	Real-time security management	实时安全管理	Shíshí ānquán guǎnlǐ
RTSF	Radio transmission specific functionality	无线传输特定功能	Wúxiàn chuánshū tèdìng gōngnéng
RTSP	Real-time streaming media protocol	实时流媒体协议	Shíshí liúméitǐ xiéyì
RTSP	Real-time streaming protocol	实时流协议	Shíshí liú xiéyì
RTT	Radio transmission technology	无线电传输技术	Wúxiàndiàn chuánshū jìshù
RTT	Round-trip time	往返时间	Wǎngfǎn shíjiān
RTT	Round-trip time	来往传输时间	Láiwǎng chuánshū shíjiān
RTT	Round-trip transmission time	双向传播时间	Shuāngxiàng chuánbō shíjiān
RTTVAR	Round-trip transmission time variation	双向传播时间变化	Shuāngxiàng chuánbō shíjiān biànhuà
RTU	Remote transmission unit	远程传输单元	Yuǎnchéng chuánshū dānyuán
RT-VBR	Real-time variable bit rate	实时可变比特率	Shíshí kěbiàn bǐtè lǜ
RU	Remote unit	远端单元	Yuǎnduān dānyuán
RU	Resource unit	资源单位	Zīyuán dānwèi
Ru	Upstream router	上游路由器	Shàngyóu lùyóuqì
RUA	Received upstream neighbor station address	收到的上游邻站地址	Shōudàode shàngyóu línzhàn dìzhǐ
RUDP	Reliable user datagram protocol	可靠用户数据报协议	Kěkào yònghù shùjùbào xiéyì

RVC	Return voice channel	反响话音信道	Fǎnxiǎng huàyīn xìndào
RVC	Reverse voice channel	反向话音信道	Fǎnxiàng huàyīn xìndào
RVR	Rendezvous radar	交会雷达	Jiāohuì léidá
RVS	Remote video surveillance	远程视频监视	Yuǎnchéng shìpín jiānshì
RVT	Route verify test	选路验证测试	Xuǎnlù yànzhèng cèshì
RVT	Routing verification test	路由证实测试	Lùyóu zhèngshí cèshì
RWB	Resolution bandwidth	分辨带宽	Fēnbiàn dàikuān
RWC	Real world computing	真实世界电脑	Zhēnshí shìjiè diànnǎo
RWG	Ridge waveguide	脊波导	Jǐ bōdǎo
RWM	Rectangular-wave modulation	矩形波调制	Jǔxíng bō tiáozhì
RWS	Remote workstation	远端工作站	Yuǎnduān gōngzuòzhàn
Rx	Optical receiver	光接收机	Guāng jiēshōujī
Rx	Receiver	接收机	Jiēshōujī
RXCF	Receiver control field	接收机控制域	Jiēshōujī kòngzhì yù
RXLE	Receive level	收信电平值	Shōuxìn diànpíng zhí
RXLEV	Received signal level	接收信号等级	Jiēshōu xìnhào děngjí
RXMOD	Receiver antenna module	接收天线模块	Jiēshōu tiānxiàn mókuài
RXMUCO	Receiver multi-coupler	接收多路藕合器	Jiēshōu duōlù ǒuhéqì
RXQUA	Receive quality	收信质量级	Shōuxìn zhìliàng jí
RXQUAL	Received signal quality	接收信号质量	Jiēshōu xìnhào zhìliàng
RZ	Return to zero	归零制	Guī líng zhì

S

S/C	Sales contract	销售确认书	Xiāoshòu quèrènshū
S/MIME	Secure multi-purpose Internet mail extension	安全多用途因特网邮件扩展协议	Ānquán duōyòngtú Yīntèwǎng yóujiàn kuòzhǎn xiéyì
S/MIME	Secure multi-purpose Internet mail extensions	安全多用途网际邮件扩展协议	Ānquán duōyòngtú wǎngjì yóujiàn kuòzhǎn xiéyì
S/N	Signal to noise ratio	信纳比	Xìn nà bǐ
S/P	Serial/parallel conversion	穿/并变换	Chuān/bìng biànhuàn
S/PDIF	Sony/Phillips digital interface	索尼/飞利普数字接口	Suǒ-ní—fēi-lì-pǔ shùzì jiēkǒu
S/V	Selector/vocoder	选择器/声码器	Xuǎnzéqì/shēngmǎqì
S3	Sight, sound, speed	视频、音频、速度	Shìpín、yīnpín、sùdù
S3TC	S3 texture compression (video term)	S3 纹理压缩	S3 wénlǐ yāsuō
S3TL	S3 transformation and lighting (video term)	S3 多边形转换和光源处理	S3 duōbiānxíng zhuǎnhuàn hé guāngyuán chǔlǐ
SA	Satellite access	卫星接入	Wèixīng jiērù
SA	Sector address	区段地址	Qūduàn dìzhǐ
SA	Sector address type	扇形地址类型	Shànxíng dìzhǐ lèixíng
SA	Security association	安全关联	Ānquán guānlián
SA	Security association	安全联盟	Ānquán liánméng
SA	Selective availability	选择可用性	Xuǎnzé kěyòngxìng
SA	Selective availability	选择性供给	Xuǎnzéxìng gōngjǐ
SA	Service alarm	业务告警	Yèwù gàojǐng
SA	Service assurance	业务保障	Yèwù bǎozhàng
SA	Smart antenna	智能天线	Zhìnéng tiānxiàn
SA	Source address	源地址	Yuán dìzhǐ

SA	Spherical array (antenna)	球星天线阵	Qiúxīng tiānxiàn zhèn
SA	Spiral antenna	螺旋天线	Luóxuán tiānxiàn
SA	Subscriber application	用户应用	Yònghù yìngyòng
SA	Switch assembly	开关组件	Kāiguān zǔjiàn
SA	System analysis	系统分析	Xìtǒng fēnxī
SAA	Sampling adaptive algorithm	采样字适应算法	Cǎiyàng zìshìyìng suànfǎ
SAA	Sound absorption ability	吸声能力	Xīshēng nénglì
SAAL	Signaling asynchronous transfer mode adaptation layer	信令 ATM 适配层	Xìnlìng ATM shìpèi céng
SAAL	Signaling ATM adaptation layer	ATM 信令适配层	ATM xìnlìng shìpèi céng
SAB	Site alarm block	位置告警模块	Wèizhì gàojǐng mókuài
SABM	Set asynchronous balanced mode	设立异步均衡模式	Shèlì yìbù jūnhéng móshì
SABM	Set asynchronous balanced mode	设置异步平衡模式	Shèzhì yìbù pínghéng móshì
SABM	Set asynchronous balanced mode	置异步平衡方式	Zhì yìbù pínghéng fāngshì
SABME	Set asynchronous balanced mode extended	置扩展的异步平衡方式	Zhì kuòzhǎnde yìbù pínghéng fāngshì
SABME	Set asynchronous balanced mode extended	置异步平衡扩展模式	Zhì yìbù pínghéng kuòzhǎn móshì
SAC	Service allowance control	业务容许控制	Yèwù róngxǔ kòngzhì
SAC	Single address code	单地址编码	Dāndìzhǐ biānmǎ
SAC	Single-attached concentrator	单连集线器	Dānlián jíxiànqì
SAC	Single-attached concentrator	单连接集中器	Dānliánjiē jízhōngqì
SACAC	South African Council for Automation and Computation	南非自动化和计算委员会	Nánfēi zìdònghuà hé jìsuàn wěiyuánhuì
SACCH	Slow assisted control channel	慢速辅助控制信道	Mànsù fǔzhù kòngzhì xìndào
SACCH	Slow associated control channel	慢速随路控制信道	Mànsù suílù kòngzhì xìndào
SACCH/T	Slow assisted control channel/traffic channel	慢速辅助控制信道/业务信道	Mànsù fǔzhù kòngzhì xìndào/yèwù xìndào
SACCH/T	Slow associated control channel/traffic channel	慢速随路控制信道/业务信道	Mànsù suílù kòngzhì xìndào/yèwù xìndào
SACCH/TF	Slow assisted control channel/traffic channel full rate	慢速辅助控制信道/全速率业务信道	Mànsù fǔzhù kòngzhì xìndào/quánsùlǜ yèwù xìndào
SACCH/TF	Slow associated control channel/traffic channel full rate	慢速随路控制信道/全速率业务信道	Mànsù suílù kòngzhì xìndào/quán sùlǜ yèwù xìndào
SACCHTH	Slow assisted control channel/traffic channel half rate	慢速辅助控制信道/半速率业务信道	Mànsù fǔzhù kòngzhì xìndào/bàn sùlǜ yèwù xìndào
SACD	Super audio CD	超级音乐 CD	Chāojí yīnyuè CD
SACF	Single association control function	单偶联控制功能	Dān'ǒulián kòngzhì gōngnéng
SACF	Single association control function	单相关控制功能	Dānxiàng guān kòngzhì gōngnéng
SACL	System access control list	系统访问控制列表	Xìtǒng fǎngwèn kòngzhì lièbiǎo
SAD	Security association database	安全关联数据库	Ānquán guānlián shùjùkù
SAD	System-aided design	系统辅助设计	Xìtǒng fǔzhù shèjì
SADL	Software architectural description language	软件构架描述语言	Ruǎnjiàn gòujià miáoshù yǔyán
SADT	Structured analysis and design technique	结构化分析与设计技术	Jiégòuhuà fēnxī yǔ shèjì jìshù
SAF	Specific access function	特定接入功能	Tèdìng jiērù gōngnéng
SA-F	Far-end subscriber access	远端用户接入	Yuǎnduān yònghù jiērù
SAFER	Split access and flexible egress routing	分开存取和灵活发送的路由选择	Fēnkāi cúnqǔ hé línghuó fāsòngde lùyóu xuǎnzé
SAGF	Service application gateway function	业务应用网关功能	Yèwù yìngyòng wǎngguān gōngnéng
SAID	Speech analog input to digitizer	数字转换器的语言模拟输入	Shùzì zhuǎnhuànqìde yǔyán mónǐ shūrù
SAM	Sales available market	可发售市场	Kěfāshòu shìchǎng

SAM	Security account manager	安全帐户管理器	Ānquán zhànghù guǎnlǐqì
SAM	Sequential access method	按序存取方式	Ànxù cúnqǔ fāngshì
SAM	Service access multiplexer	业务接入复用器	Yèwù jiērù fùyòngqì
SAM	Subsequent address message	后继地址消息	Hòujì dìzhǐ xiāoxi
SAM	Subsequent address message	后续地址消息	Hòuxù dìzhǐ xiāoxi
SAMBA	System for advanced mobile broadband applications	先进的移动宽带应用系统	Xiānjìnde yídòng kuāndài yìngyòng xìtǒng
SAMF	Subscriber access management function	用户接入管理功能	Yònghù jiērù guǎnlǐ gōngnéng
SAMI	Service access multiplexer interface	业务接入复用器接口	Yèwù jiērù fùyòngqì jiēkǒu
SAML	Security assertion markup language	安全性断言标记语言	Ānquánxìng duànyán biāojì yǔyán
SAMS	Spatial access methods	空间逼近发	Kōngjiān bījìn fā
SAN	Storage area network	存储局域网络	Cúnchǔ júyù wǎngluò
SAN	Storage area network	存储区域网络	Cúnchǔ qūyù wǎngluò
SAN	Storage area network and SAN protocols (IETF, ANSI and ISO usage)	存储区域网络及其协议	Cúnchǔ qūyù wǎngluò jíqí xiéyì
SAN	Storage network, storage area network	存储器网	Cúnchǔqì wǎng
SAN	Storage-area network	存储域网	Cúnchǔ yù wǎng
SA-N	Near-end subscriber access	近端用户接入	Jìnduān yònghù jiērù
SAO	Single association object	单偶联对象	Dān'ǒulián duìxiàng
SAO	Single association object	单偶联体	Dānǒuliántǐ
SAO	Single association object	单相关对象	Dānxiàng guān duìxiàng
SAO	Subsequent address message with one signal	带有一信号的后续地址消息	Dàiyǒu yī xìnhàode hòuxù dìzhǐ xiāoxi
SAP	Service access point	服务访问点	Fúwù fǎngwèn diǎn
SAP	Service access point	服务接入点	Fúwù jiērù diǎn
SAP	Service access point	业务接入点	Yèwù jiērù diǎn
SAP	Session announcement protocol	会话通知协议	Huìhuà tōngzhī xiéyì
SAP	Session announcement protocol (IETF use)	会话通告协议	Huìhuà tōnggào xiéyì
SAP	Sideband address port	边带寻址端口	Biāndài xúnzhǐ duānkǒu
SAPI	Service access point identifier	服务访问电识别符	Fúwù fǎngwèn diàn shíbiéfú
SAPI	Service access point identifier	服务接入点识别符	Fúwù jiērù diǎn shíbiéfú
SAPI	Service access point identifier	服务接入点识别器	Fúwù jiērù diǎn shíbiéqì
SAPI	Service access point identifier	业务接入点标志	Yèwù jiērù diǎn biāozhì
SAPI	Service access point identifier	业务接入点识符	Yèwù jiērù diǎn shífú
SAPI	Service access point identity	业务接入识别码	Yèwù jiērù shíbié mǎ
SAPI	Service access point indicator	服务访问点标识符	Fúwù fǎngwèn diǎn biāozhì fú
SAPI	Service access point indicator	服务接入点标识	Fúwù jiērù diǎn biāozhì
SAR	Search and rescue	搜索救援	Sōusuǒ jiùyuán
SAR	Segmentation and reassembly	程序分段和重编	Chéngxù fēnduàn hé chóngbiān
SAR	Segmentation and reassembly	分段和重装	Fēnduàn hé chóngzhuāng
SAR	Segmentation and reassembly	分段和重组	Fēnduàn hé chóngzǔ
SAR	Segmentation and reassembly	分段与组装	Fēnduàn yǔ zǔzhuāng
SAR	Segmentation and reassembly	分装段和重组	Fēnzhuāng duàn hé chóngzǔ
SAR	Segmentation and reassembly sub-layer	拆装子层	Chāizhuāng zicéng
SAR	Synthetic aperture radar	合成孔径雷达	Héchéng kǒngjìng léidá
SAR	Synthetic aperture radar	合成口径雷达	Héchéng kǒujìng léidá
SARFT	State Administration of Radio, Film and Television	国家广播电影和电视总局	Guójiā guǎngbō diànyǐng hé diànshì zǒngjú
SARS	Segmentation and reassembly sub-layer	分段和重装子层	Fēnduàn hé chóngzhuāng zicéng

SAS	Safety automation system	保安自动化系统	Bǎo'ān zìdònghuà xìtǒng
SAS	Solid-state array spectroradiometer	固体列阵式光谱辐射计	Gùtǐ lièzhèn-shì guāngpǔ fúshèjì
SAS	Subscriber alerting signal	用户提示音	Yònghù tíshì yīn
SASE	Specialized application service	特定应用服务要素	Tèdìng yìngyòng fúwù yàosù
SASE	Stand alone synchronization equipment	独立型同步设备	Dúlì-xíng tóngbù shèbèi
SASE	Stand-alone synchronization equipment	独立型同步设备	Dúlì-xíng tóngbù shèbèi
SASE	Standalone synchronization supply equipment	独立同步供给设备	Dúlì tóngbù gōngjǐ shèbèi
SAT	Supervisory audio tone	监测单音	Jiāncè dānyīn
SAT	Supervisory audio tone	监测音	Jiāncè yīn
SAT	Supervisory audio tone	监测音频单音	Jiāncè yīnpín dānyīn
SATA	Serial ATA (asynchronous terminal adapter)	串行 ATA	Chuànháng ATA
SATAN	Security administrator tool for analyzing networks	网络安全分析器	Wǎngluò ānquán fēnxīqì
SATIN	TINA service architecture and intelligent network services	TINA 业务结构和或智能网业务	TINA yèwù jiégòu hé zhìnéng wǎng yèwù
SATV	Satellite television	卫星电视	Wèixīng diànshì
SAW	Surface acoustic wave	声表面波	Shēng biǎomiànbō
SB	Synchronization burst	同步脉冲串	Tóngbù màichōng chuàn
SB	Synchronization burst	同步突发脉冲序列	Tóngbù tūfā màichōng xùliè
SB	Synchronization byte	同步字节	Tóngbù zìjié
SBA	Sideband addressing	边带寻址	Biāndài xúnzhǐ
SBAS	Steerable-beam antenna system	波束可控天线系统	Bōshù kěkòng tiānxiàn xìtǒng
SBC	Single board computer	单板计算机	Dānbǎn jìsuànjī
SBC	South Bridge chip	南桥芯片	Nánqiáo xìnpiàn
SBC	Sub-band coding	分波段编码	Fēnbōduàn biānmǎ
SBC	Sub-band coding	子带编码	Zidài biānmǎ
SBC-ADPCM	Sub-band coding for adaptive differential pulse-code modulation	自适应微分脉码调制的部分波段编码	Zìshìyìng wēifēn màimǎ tiáozhìde bùfen bōduàn biānmǎ
SBCE	Synchronous broadband control element	同步宽带控制器	Tóngbù kuāndài kòngzhìqì
SBD	Simulation-based design	基于仿真设计	Jīyú fǎngzhēn shèjì
SBE	Signal byte expansion	信号字节扩展	Xìnhào zìjié kuòzhǎn
SBE	Simple Boolean expression	简单布尔表示式	Jiǎndān Bù-ěr biǎoshì shì
SBE	Single bit error	一位出错	Yīwèi chūcuò
SBE	Single byte expansion	单字节扩展	Dānzìjié kuòzhǎn
SBFS	Simple boot flag specification	简单引导标记规范	Jiǎndān yǐndǎo biāojì guīfàn
SBI	Super bandwidth infrastructure	超级带宽架构	Chāojí dàikuān jiàgòu
SBIA	System bus interface assembly	系统总线接口集成件	Xìtǒng zǒngxiàn jiēkǒu jíchéng jiàn
SBIRS	Space-based infrared surveillance	空基红外监视	Kōngjī hóngwài jiānshì
S-Block	Supervisory block	监测设备	Jiāncè shèbèi
SBM	Shared buffer memory	共享存储器	Gòngxiǎng cúnchǔqì
SBM	Sub-net bandwidth management	子网带宽管理	Zìwǎng dàikuān guǎnlǐ
SBM	Successful backward set-up information message	后向建立成功信息消息	Hòuxiàng jiànlì chénggōng xìnxī xiāoxi
SBR	Statistical bit rate	统计比特率	Tǒngjì bǐtè lǜ
SBS	Selector bank sub-system	选择器子系统	Xuǎnzéqì zìxìtǒng
SBS	Silicon bi-directional switch	硅双向开关	Guī shuāngxiàng kāiguān
SBS	Silicon bi-directional switch	双向硅开关	Shuāngxiàng guī kāiguān
SBS	Stimulated Brillouin scattering	受激布里渊散射	Shòujī bù-lǐ-yuān sǎnshè

SBS	Synchronous backbone system	同步信息骨干系统	Tóngbù xìnxī gǔgàn xìtǒng
SBSR	Selector bank sub-system rack	选择器子系统机架	Xuǎnzéqì zixìtǒng jījià
SBSVC	Selective broadcast signaling virtual channel	选择性广播信令虚信道	Xuǎnzéxìng guǎngbō xìnlìng xū xìndào
SC	Data transmission telecommunication	数据传输通信	Shùjù chuánshū tōngxin
SC	Service center	业务中心	Yèwù zhōngxīn
SC	Service channel	服务信道	Fúwù xìndào
SC	Service code	业务码	Yèwù mǎ
SC	Service code	业务码	Yèwù mǎ
SC	Signaling controller	信令控制器	Xìnlìng kòngzhìqì
SC	Software center	软件中心	Ruǎnjiàn zhōngxīn
SC	Source category	源类	Yuán lèi
SC	Subscriber connector	用户连接器	Yònghù liánjiēqì
SC	Symmetrical communications	双向对称通信	Shuāngxiàng duìchèn tōngxìn
SC	Synchronization code	同步码	Tóngbù mǎ
SCA	Sequential cellular automata (cryptology)	串行细胞自动机	Chuànháng xìbāo zìdòngjī
SCADA	Supervisory control and data acquisition	监控和数据采集	Jiānkòng hé shùjù cǎijí
SCB	Scan control block	浏览控制模块	Liúlǎn kòngzhì mókuài
SCB	Segment control bits	段控制位	Duàn kòngzhì wèi
SCB	System control board	系统控制板	Xìtǒng kòngzhì bǎn
SCC	Serial communication controller	串行通信控制器	Chuànháng tōngxìn kòngzhìqì
SCC	Signaling channel controller	信令信道控制器	Xìnlìng xìndào kòngzhìqì
SCCC	Specialized-communication common carrier	专用通信公共载波	Zhuānyòng tōngxìn gōnggòng zàibō
SCCH	Synchronization control channel	同步控制信道	Tóngbù kòngzhì xìn dào
SCCP	Signaling connection control part	信令连接控制部分	Xìnlìng liánjiē kòngzhì bùfen
SCCP	Skinny client control protocol (Cisco use)	小客户控制协议	Xiǎokèhù kòngzhì xiéyì
S-CCPCH	Secondary common control physical channel	第二公共控制物理信道	Dì'èr gōnggòng kòngzhì wùlǐ xìndào
SCD	Softswitch control device	软交换控制设备	Ruǎn jiāohuàn kòngzhì shèbèi
SCDL	Surveillance and control Data link (US military)	侦察与控制数据链	Zhēnchá yǔ kòngzhì shùjù liàn
SCDMA	Space-code division multiple access	空间码分多址	Kōngjiān mǎfēn duōzhǐ
SCE	Service creation environment	业务创造环境	Yèwù chuàngzào huánjìng
SCE	Service creation environment	业务生成环境	Yèwù shēngchéng huánjìng
SCE	Signal combining equipment	信号组合设备	Xìnhào zǔhé shèbèi
SCE	Signal conversion equipment	信号变换装置	Xìnhào biànhuàn zhuāngzhì
SCE	Sony Computer Entertainment (company)	索尼计算机娱乐部	Suǒní jìsuànjī yúlè bù
SCEA	Silicon Valley Chinese Engineer Association	硅谷中国工程师协会	Guīgǔ Zhōngguó gōngchéngshī xiéhuì
SCEF	Service creation environment function	业务创建环境功能	Yèwù chuàngjiàn huánjìng gōngnéng
SCEF	Service creation environment function	业务生成环境功能	Yèwù shēngchéng huánjìng gōngnéng
SCEP	Service creation environment point	业务生成环境点	Yèwù shēngchéng huánjìng diǎn
SCF	Service capability feature	业务能力特征	Yèwù nénglì tèzhēng
SCF	Service confirmation	业务确认	Yèwù quèrèn
SCF	Service control function	业务控制功能	Yèwù kòngzhì gōngnéng
SCF	Synchronization and convergence function	同步和会聚功能	Tóngbù hé huìjù gōngnéng
SCF	Synchronization and convergence function	同步与会聚功能	Tóngbù yú huìjù gōngnéng
SCF-CUSF	Service control function - call unrelated service function	业务控制功能-不相干呼叫业务功能	Yèwù kòngzhì gōngnéng-bùxiānggān hūjiào yèwù gōngnéng
SCF-SCF	Service control function - service control function	业务控制功能 –业务控制功能	Yèwù kòngzhì gōngnéng - yèwù kòngzhì gōngnéng

SCF-SDF	Service control function - service data function	业务控制功能 – 业务数据功能	Yèwù kòngzhì gōngnéng – yèwù shùjù gōngnéng
SCF-SRF	Service control function - specialized resource function	业务控制功能 专用资源功能	Yèwù kòngzhì gōngnéng-zhuānyòng zīyuán gōngnéng
SCF-SSF	Service control function - service switching function	业务控制功能 – 业务交换功能	Yèwù kòngzhì gōngnéng – yèwù jiāohuàn gōngnéng
SCGF	Service control gateway function	业务控制网关功能	Yèwù kòngzhì wǎngguān gōngnéng
SCH	Synchronization channel	同步信道	Tóngbù xìndào
SCI	Stacker control instruction	栈控制指令	Zhàn kòngzhì zhǐling
SCL	Sequential control logic	顺序控制逻辑	Shùnxù kòngzhì luóji
SCM	Selected communications mode	选择通信模式	Xuǎnzé tōngxìn móshì
SCM	Selector interface card manager	选择器接口卡管理器	Xuǎnzéqì jiēkǒu kǎ guǎnlǐqì
SCM	Service circuit module	服务电路模块	Fúwù diànlù mókuài
SCM	Single channel modem	单路调制解调器	Dānlù tiáozhì jiětiáoqì
SCM	Station class mark	移动台级别标志	Yídòngtái jíbié biāozhì
SCM	Sub-carrier frequency modulation	副载波调制	Fùzàibō tiáozhì
SCM	Sub-carrier multiplex	子载波复用	Zizàibō fùyòng
SCM	Sub-carrier multiplexing	副载波复用	Fùzàibō fùyòng
SCM	Supply chain management	供需链的管理	Gōngxū liànde guǎnlǐ
SCMA	Sub-carrier multiple access	副载波多址接入	Fùzàibō duōzhǐ jiērù
SCMF	Specific field strength-distance product	特定的场强–距离乘积	Tèdìngde chǎngqiáng-jùlí chéngjī
SCN	Satellite control network	卫星控制网	Wèixīng kòngzhìwǎng
SCN	Scanner	扫描器	Sǎomiáoqì
SCN	Self-compensating network	自补偿网络	Zìbǔcháng wǎngluò
SCN	Sub-channel number	子信道号码	Zixìndào hàomǎ
SCN	Subscriber connection network	用户连接网络	Yònghù liánjiē wǎngluò
SCN	Switch control node	交换控制节点	Jiāohuàn kòngzhì jiédiǎn
SCN	Switched circuit network	电路交换网络	Diànlù jiāohuàn wǎngluò
SCN	Switched circuit network	交换电路网	Jiāohuàn diànlù wǎng
SCN	System change number (in ORACLE)	系统变更号码	Xìtǒng biàngēng hàomǎ
SCNA	Sudden cosmic noise absorption	突发宇宙噪声吸收	Tūfā yǔzhòu zàoshēng xīshōu
SCNM	Support centralized network management	支持中心网络管理	Zhīchí zhōngxīn wǎngluò guǎnlǐ
SCO	Sub-carrier oscillator	负载波振荡器	Fùzàibō zhèndàngqì
SCO	Synchronous connecting link	同步连接链路	Tóngbù liánjiē liànlù
SCO	Synchronous connection-oriented	同步面向连接	Tóngbù miànxiàng liánjiē
SCOBA	Silicon Valley Chinese Overseas Business Association	硅谷留美博士企业家协会	Guīgǔ liúměi bóshì qǐyèjiā xiéhuì
SCOT	Small communication terminal	小型通信终端设备	Xiǎoxíng tōngxìn zhōngduān shèbèi
SCOTS	Surveillance and control of transmission system	传输系统的监视与控制	Chuánshū xìtǒngde jiānshì yǔ kòngzhì
SCP	Service control point	业务控制点	Yèwù kòngzhì diǎn
SCP	Session control protocol (in DECnet)	会话控制协议	Huìhuà kòngzhì xiéyì
SCP	Standard communications platform	标准通信平台	Biāozhǔn tōngxìn píngtái
SCP	Subscribers call processing	用户呼叫处理	Yònghù hūjiào chǔlǐ
SCP	Support communication post	支援通信站	Zhīyuán tōngxìn zhàn
SCP	System control panel	系统控制盘	Xìtǒng kòngzhì pán
SCPB	Single channel per burst	单路单突发	Dānlù dāntūfā
SCPC	Single channel per carrier	单路单载波	Dānlù dānzàibō

SCPC	Single channel per carrier	单载波单路	Dānzàibō dānlù
SCPC	Single channel per carrier	每载波单路	Měi zàibō dānlù
S-CPICH	Secondary common pilot channel	第二公共导频信道	Dì'èr gōnggòng dǎopín xìndào
SCPT	Single channel per transponder	每转发器单路	Měi zhuǎnfāqì dānlù
SCR	Signal-to-clutter ratio	信号杂波比	Xìnhào zábō bǐ
SCR	Signal-to-complexity ratio	信杂比	Xìn zá bǐ
SCR	Silicon controlled rectifier	可控硅整流器	Kěkòngguī zhěngliúqì
SCR	State control register	状态控制寄存器	Zhuàngtài kòngzhì jìcúnqì
SCR	Status change registration	状态改变注册	Zhuàngtài gǎibiàn zhùcè
SCR	Sustainable cell rate	持续信元速率	Chíxù xìnyuán sùlǜ
SCR	Sustainable cell rate	可持续信元速率	Kěchíxù xìnyuán sùlǜ
SCR	Sustainable cell rate	可维持信元率	Kěwéichí xìnyuán lǜ
SCR	Sustainable cell rate	可维持信元速率	Kěwéichí xìnyuán sùlǜ
SCRA	Single channel radio access (an Alcatel-Telletra system)	单信道无线电接入	Dānxìndào wúxiàndiàn jiērù
SCREEN	Service creation engineering environment	业务生成工程环境	Yèwù shēngchéng gōngchéng huánjìng
SCS	Safety control switch	安全控制开关	Ānquán kòngzhì kāiguān
SCS	Service capability server	业务能力服务器	Yèwù nénglì fúwùqì
SCS	Service consumer system	业务使用者系统	Yèwù shǐyòngzhě xìtǒng
SCS	Silicon controlled switch	可控硅开关	Kěkòng guī kāiguān
SCS	Single channel system (optical)	单波长系统	Dānbōcháng xìtǒng
SCS	Speed control system	速度控制系统	Sùdù kòngzhì xìtǒng
SCS	Structured cabling system	结构化布线系统	Jiégòuhuà bùxiàn xìtǒng
SCS	Supply control system	电源控制系统	Diànyuán kòngzhì xìtǒng
SCS	System conformance statement	系统一致性陈述	Xìtǒng yīzhìxìng chénshù
SCSI	Small computer system interface	小型电脑系统介面	Xiǎoxíng diànnǎo xìtǒng jièmiàn
SCSI	Small computer system interface	小型计算机系统接口	Xiǎoxíng jìsuànjī xìtǒng jiēkǒu
SCT	Serial clock transmit	串行时标发送	Chuànháng shíbiāo fāsòng
SCT	Single channel transponder	单路转发器	Dānlù zhuǎnfāqì
SCT	Software compatibility test	软件兼容性测试	Ruǎnjiàn jiānróngxìng cèshì
SCT	Sub-routine call table	子程序调用表	Zǐchéngxù diàoyòng biǎo
SCTE	Serial clock transmit external	串行时钟外部传输	Chuànháng shízhōng wàibù chuánshū
SCTP	Stream control transmission protocol	流控传输协议	Liú kòng chuánshū xiéyì
SCTP	Stream control transmission protocol	流控制传输协议	Liú kòngzhì chuánshū xiéyì
SCTP	Stream control transport protocol	流控制传送协议	Liú kòngzhì chuánsòng xiéyì
SCTR	System conformance test report	系统一致性测试报告	Xìtǒng yīzhìxìng cèshì bàogào
SCTS	Standard code test signal	标准码试验信号	Biāozhǔn mǎ shìyàn xìnhào
SCU	Scanner control unit	扫描器控制部件	Sǎomiáoqì kòngzhì bùjiàn
SCUAF	Service control user agent function	业务控制用户代理功能	Yèwù kòngzhì yònghù dàilǐ gōngnéng
SCVFT	Single channel voice frequency telegraphy	单路音频电报	Dānlù yīnpín diànbào
SD	Send data	发送数据	Fāsòng shùjù
SD	Service discovery	服务搜索	Fúwù sōusuǒ
SD	Share disk	共享磁盘	Gòngxiǎng cípán
SD	Signal degrade	信号劣化	Xìnhào lièhuà
SD	Smoke damper	排烟阀	Páiyān fá
SD	Smoke detector	感烟探测器	Gǎnyān tàncèqì
SD	Space diversity doublet	空间分集偶极天线	Kōngjiān fēnjí ǒují tiānxiàn

SD	Start delimiter	起始定界符	Qǐshǐ dìngjièfú
SD	Super density	超密度	Chāomìdù
SD	Sweep driver	扫描驱动器	Sǎomiáo qūdòngqì
SD	Synchronization distribution	同步分配	Tóngbù fēnpèi
SD	System distortion	系统失真	Xìtǒng shīzhēn
SDA	Synchronous data adapter	同步数据转接器	Tóngbù shùjù zhuǎnjiēqì
SDAP	Service discovery and application profile	服务发现和应用配置	Fúwù fāxiàn hé yìngyòng pèizhì
SDB	Segment descriptor block	段描述子块	Duàn miáoshù zikuài
SDB	Site database	现场数据库	Xiànchǎng shùjùkù
SDBMS	Spatial database management system	空间数据库管理系统	Kōngjiān shùjùkù guǎnlǐ xìtǒng
SDC	Secondary digital carrier	二次数字载波	Èrcì shùzì zàibō
SDC	Send data condition	发送数据条件	Fāsòng shùjù tiáojiàn
SDCA	Synchronization data communications adapter	同步数据通讯适配器	Tóngbù shùjù tōngxùn shìpèiqì
SDCCH	Stand-alone dedicated control channel	独立专用控制信道	Dúlì zhuānyòng kòngzhì xìndào
SDCCU	Synchronous data communication control unit	同步数据通信控制器	Tóngbù shùjù tōngxìn kòngzhìqì
SDCS	Satellite digital communications system	卫星数字通信系统	Wèixīng shùzì tōngxìn xìtǒng
SDCU	Satellite delay compensation unit	卫星延迟补偿器	Wèixīng yánchí bǔchángqì
SDDB	Service discovery database	服务搜索数据库	Fúwù sōusuǒ shùjùkù
SDE	Spatial database engine	空间数据库引擎	Kōngjiān shùjùkù yǐnqíng
SDF	Service data function	业务数据功能	Yèwù shùjù gōngnéng
SDH	Synchronous digital hierarchy	同步数字传输体系	Tóngbù shùzì chuánshū tǐxì
SDH	Synchronous digital hierarchy	同步数字体系	Tóngbù shùzì tǐxì
SDH	Synchronous digital hierarchy	同步数字系列	Tóngbù shùzì xìliè
SDH	Synchronous digital hierarchy	同步数字序列	Tóngbù shùzì xùliè
SDI	Strategic Defense Initiative (US)	战略防御计划	Zhànlüè fángyù jìhuà
SDIU	Subscriber's digital interface unit	用户数字接口设备	Yònghù shùzì jiēkǒu shèbèi
SDK	Software development kit	软件开发包	Ruǎnjiàn kāifā bāo
SDK	Software development kit	软件开发工具包	Ruǎnjiàn kāifā gōngjù bāo
SDK	Software development toolkit	软件开发套件	Ruǎnjiàn kāifā tàojiàn
SDL	Simple data link	简单数据通路	Jiǎndān shùjù tōnglù
SDL	Simple data link	简易数据链路	Jiǎnyì shùjù liànlù
SDL	Simplified data link	简单数据链路	Jiǎndān shùjù liànlù
SDL	Simplified data link	简化数据链路	Jiǎnhuà shùjù liànlù
SDL	Specification and description language	规范和描述语言	Guīfàn hé miáoshù yǔyán
SDL	Specification description language	规范描述语言	Guīfàn miáoshù yǔyán
SDL	Specification description language	说明与描述语言	Shuōmíng yǔ miáoshù yǔyán
SDL	System description language	系统描述语言	Xìtǒng miáoshù yǔyán
SDLC	Synchronous data link control	同步数据链路控制	Tóngbù shùjù liànlù kòngzhì
SDLC	Synchronous data link control protocol (IBM use)	同步数据链路控制协议	Tóngbù shùjù liànlù kòngzhì xiéyì
SDM	Space division multiplexing	空分复用	Kōngfēn fùyòng
SDM	Space division multiplexing	空间分割多种复用	Kōngjiān fēngē duōzhǒng fùyòng
SDMA	Sequence division multiple access	顺序分配多路存取	Shùnxù fēnpèi duōlù cúnqǔ
SDMA	Space division multiple access	空分多址	Kōngfēn duōzhǐ
SDMA	Space division multiple access	空间分割多路存取	Kōngjiān fēngē duōlù cúnqǔ
SDMF	Single data message format	单数据消息格式	Dānshùjù xiāoxī géshi
SDML	Spatial data manipulation language	空间数据操作语言	Kōngjiān shùjù cāozuò yǔyán

SDN	Secondary distribution network	二次配线网	Èrcì pèixiànwǎng
SDN	Sybase developer network	Sybase 开发者网络	Sybase kāifāzhě wǎngluò
SdoC	Supplier's declaration of conformity	产品一致性声明	Chǎnpǐn yīzhìxìng shēngmíng
SDP	Sequential disk processor	顺序磁盘处理机	Shùnxù cípán chǔlǐjī
SDP	Service data point	业务数据点	Yèwù shùjù diǎn
SDP	Service discovery protocol	业务搜索协议	Yèwù sōusuǒ xiéyì
SDP	Session description protocol	会话描述协议	Huìhuà miáoshù xiéyì
SDP	Severely disturbed period	严重扰动期	Yánzhòng rǎodòng qī
SDP	Standard description protocol	标准描述协议	Biāozhǔn miáoshù xiéyì
SDPLL	Sampled data phase-locked loop	取样数据锁相环	Qǔyàng shùjù suǒxiàng huán
SDR	Software defined radio	软件定义的无线电	Ruǎnjiàn dìngyìde wúxiàndiàn
SDR	Storage data register	存储器数据寄存器	Cúnchǔqì shùjù jìcúnqì
SDR SDRAM	Single data-rate SDRAM	单数据率 SDRAM	Dānshùjù lǜ SDRAM
SDRAM	Synchronous dynamic random access memory	同步动态随机存储器	Tóngbù dòngtài suíjī cúnchǔqì
SDS	Servo drive system	伺服驱动系统	Sì-fú qūdòng xìtǒng
SDSL	Single digital subscriber line	单线制数字用户线	Dānxiànzhì shùzì yònghù xiàn
SDSL	Single-line digital subscriber line	单线数字用户线路	Dānxiàn shùzì yònghù xiànlù
SDT	SDL development tool	SDL 开发工具	SDL kāifā gōngjù
SDT	Segment descriptor	段描述符	Duàn miáoshùfú
SDT	Serial data transmission	串行数据传输	Chuànháng shùjù chuánshū
SDT	Signal degrade threshold	信号劣化门限	Xìnhào lièhuà ménxiàn
SDT	Structured data transfer	结构数据传送	Jiégòu shùjù chuánsòng
SDTS	Spatial data transform standard	空间数据转换标准	Kōngjiān shùjù zhuǎnhuàn biāozhǔn
SDTS/TVP	Spatial data transfer standard / topologic vector product	空间数据交换标准/拓扑矢量产品	Kōngjiān shùjù jiāohuàn biāozhǔn/ tuòpū shǐliàng chǎnpǐn
SDTV	Standard definition television	标准清晰度电视	Biāozhǔn qīngxīdù diànshì
SDU	Service data unit	服务数据单元	Fúwù shùjù dānyuán
SDU	Service data unit	业务数据单元	Yèwù shùjù dānyuán
SDV	Switched digital video	交换式数字图像	Jiāohuàn-shì shùzì túxiàng
SDVB	Switched digital video broadcast	交换式数字电视广播	Jiāohuàn-shì shùzì diànshì guǎngbō
SDXC	SDH cross-connection	SDH 交叉连接	SDH jiāochā liánjiē
SDXC	Synchronous digital cross connect equipment	同步数字交叉连接设备	Tóngbù shùzì jiāochā liánjiē shèbèi
SDXC	Synchronous digital cross-connector	同步数字交叉连接器	Tóngbù shùzì jiāochā liánjiēqì
SDZW	Subset-division-based zerotree wavelet coding algorithm	基于自集分割的零树小波编码算法	Jīyú zìjí fēngēde língshù xiǎobō biānmǎ suànfǎ
SE	Security environment	安全保密环境	Ānquán bǎomì huánjìng
SE	Share everything	完全共享	Wánquán gòngxiǎng
SE	Sound energy	声能	Shēngnéng
SE	Storage error	存储器错误	Cúnchǔqì cuòwù
SE	Support entity	支持实体	Zhīchí shítǐ
SE	Switching element	交换单元	Jiāohuàn dānyuán
SE	System engineer	系统工程师	Xìtǒng gōngchéng hī
SE	Systems engineering	系统工程	Xìtǒng gōngchéng
SEAL	Simple and efficient AAL	简单和有效的 AAL	Jiǎndān hé yǒuxiàode AAL
SEAL	Simple and efficient adaptation layer	简单有效的适配层	Jiǎndān yǒuxiàode shìpèi céng
SEC	SDH equipment clock	SDH 设备时钟	SDH shèbèi shízhōng

SEC	Single edge connector	单边连接器	Dānbiān liánjiēqì
SEC	Single error correcting (codes)	单错校正（码）	Dāncuò jiàozhèng (mǎ)
SEC	Switching-equipment-congestion signal	交换设备拥塞信号	Jiāohuàn shèbèi yōngsè xìnhào
SEC	Synchronous digital hierarchy equipment clock	同步数字体系设备时钟	Tóngbù shùzì tǐxì shèbèi shízhōng
SECAM	Sequential Couleur avec memoire (French television broadcast standard)	顺序与存储彩色电视系统	Shùnxù yǔ cúnchǔ cǎisè diànshì xìtǒng
SECAM	Sequential Couleur avec Memoire (Middle East television standard)	顺序彩色和存储视频制式	Shùnxù cǎisè hé cúnchǔ shìpín zhìshì
SECB	Severely errored cell block	严重误信元块	Yánzhòng wù xìnyuán kuài
SECBR	Seriously errored cell block ratio	严重误信元块比例	Yánzhòng wùxìn yuán kuài bǐlì
SECBR	Severely errored cell block ratio	严重差错信元块比	Yánzhòng chācuò xìnyuán kuài bǐ
SECBR	Severely errored cell block ratio	严重误信元块比例	Yánzhòng wùxìn yuán kuài bǐlì
SED	Sound energy density	声能密度	Shēngnéng mìdù
SEEF	Smoke extractor exhaust fan	排烟风机	Páiyān fēngjī
SEF	Severely errored frame	严重错误帧	Yánzhòng cuòwù zhèng
SEF	Support entity function	支持实体功能	Zhīchí shítǐ gōngnéng
SEG	System Engineering Group (CMM)	系统工程组	Xìtǒng gōngchéng zǔ
SELV	Safety extra-low voltage	安全特低电压	Ānquán tèdī diànyā
SEM	Strategic enterprise management	企业战略管理	Qǐyè zhànlüè guǎnlǐ
SEM	Structural equation modeling	结构化方程模型	Jiégòuhuà fāngchéng móxíng
SEMF	Synchronous equipment management function	同步设备管理功能	Tóngbù shèbèi guǎnlǐ gōngnéng
SEP	Signaling end point	信令端点	Xìnlìng duāndiǎn
SEP	Signaling end point	信令终结点	Xìnlìng zhōngjié diǎn
SEPP	Secure electronic payment process	安全电子支付过程	Ānquán diànzǐ zhīfù guòchéng
SEPP	Secure electronic payment protocol	安全电子结算协议	Ānquán diànzǐ jiésuàn xiéyì
SEQN	Sequential numbering scheme	序列号码机制	Xùliè hàomǎ jīzhì
SER	Symbol error rate	符号差错率	Fúhào chācuò lǜ
Ser.CM	Service configuration management	服务组成管理	Fúwù zǔchéng guǎnlǐ
SERDES	SERializing/DESerializing circuitry	串行并行转换电路	Chuànháng bìngxíng zhuǎnhuàn diànlù
SERG	Services Experts Rapporteurs Group (GSM MoU)	业务专家组	Yèwù zhuānjiāzǔ
SES	Severely errored second	严重差错秒	Yánzhòng chācuò miǎo
SES	Severely errored second	严重误块秒	Yánzhòng wùkuài miǎo
SES	Severely errored second	严重误码秒	Yánzhòng wùmǎ miǎo
SESE	Security exchange service element	安全交易业务单元	Ānquán jiāoyì yèwù dānyuán
SeSG	Semantic serialization graph	语义串行化图	Yǔyì chuànhánghuà tú
SESR	Severely errored second ratio	严重差错秒比	Yánzhòng chācuò miǎo bǐ
SESR	Severely errored second ratio	严重误块秒比	Yánzhòng wùkuài miǎo bǐ
SESR	Severely errored second ratio	严重误码秒比	Yánzhòng wùmǎ miǎo bǐ
SET	Secure electronic transaction	安全电子事务处理	Ānquán diànzǐ shìwù chǔlǐ
SET	Secure electronic transfer	安全电子交易	Ānquán diànzi jiāoyì
SETG	Synchronous equipment timing generator	同步设备定时发生器	Tóngbù shèbèi dìngshí fāshēngqì
SETI	Search for extra-terrestrial intelligence	地外文明探索	Dìwài wénmíng tànsuǒ
SETPI	Synchronous equipment timing physical interface	同步设备定时物理接口	Tóngbù shèbèi dìngshí wùlǐ jiēkǒu
SETS	Synchronous equipment timing source	同步设备定时源	Tóngbù shèbèi dìngshí yuán
SF	Safety fuse	保险丝	Bǎoxiǎnsī
SF	Service feature	业务特征	Yèwù tèzhēng
SF	Service fulfillment	业务开通	Yèwù kāitōng

SF	Signal fail	信号失效	Xìnhào shīxiào
SF	Spreading factor	扩频因子	Kuòpín yīnzǐ
SF	Stack full	栈满	Zhàn mǎn
SF	Start field	起始字段	Qǐshǐ zìduàn
SF	Status field	状态段	Zhuàngtài duàn
SF	Status field	状态字段	Zhuàngtài zìduàn
SF	Subscriber feeder	用户线	Yònghù xiàn
SF	Switching function	交换功能	Jiāohuàn gōngnéng
SFC	Nintendo Super Famicom (computer game)	超级任天堂 16 位游戏机	Chāojí rèntiāntáng 16 wèi yóuxìjī
SFET	Synchronous frequency encoding technique	同步频率编号技术	Tóngbù pínlǜ biānhào jìshù
SFF	Server signal fail	服务器信号失效	Fúwùqì xìnhào shīxiào
SFH	Slow frequency hopping	慢跳频	Màntiàopín
SFHMA	Slow frequency hopping multiple access	慢频率跳编多路存取	Màn pínlǜ tiàobiān duōlù cúnqǔ
SFID	Service flow identifier	业务流标识符	Yèwùliú biāoshífú
SFL	Sequential fuzzy language	时序模糊语言	Shíxù móhu yǔyán
SFM	Space frequency modulation	空间频率调制	Kōngjiān pínlǜ tiáozhì
SFM	Swept frequency modulation	扫描频率调制	Sǎomiáo pínlǜ tiáozhì
SFN	Sound field non-uniformity	声场不均匀度	Shēngchǎng bùjūnyún dù
SFN	System frame number	系统帧号码	Xìtǒng zhèng hàomǎ
SFP	Sound field processor	声场处进器	Shēngchǎng chùjìnqì
SFS	Start frame sequence	帧起始序列	Zhèng qǐshǐ xùliè
SFS	Stochastic fair sharing	随机公平共享	Suíjī gōngping gòngxiǎng
SFSK	Sinusoidal frequency shift keying	正弦曲线频移键控	Zhèngxián qūxiàn pínyí jiànkòng
SFT	Signal failure threshold	信号失败门限	Xìnhào shībài ménxiàn
SFTP	Shielded foil twisted pair	屏蔽金融箔对线	Píngbì jīnróng bó duìxiàn
SFTS	Standard frequency and time signals	标准频率和时间信号	Biāozhǔn pínlǜ hé shíjiān xìnhào
SFWA	Satellite fixed wireless access	卫星固定无线接入	Wèixīng gùdìng wúxiàn jiērù
SG	Security gateway	安全网关	Ānquán wǎngguān
SG	Security group (GSM MoU)	安全保密组	Ānquán bǎomì zǔ
SG	Serialization graph	串行化图	Chuànhánghuà tú
SG	Signal gateway	信号网关	Xìnhào wǎngguān
SG	Signaling gateway	信令网关	Xìnlìng wǎngguān
SG	Spreading gain	扩频增益	Kuòpín zēngyì
SG	Submerged optical cable	水底光缆	Shuǐdǐ guānglǎn
SG	System gain	系统增益	Xìtǒng zēngyì
SGC	Signal conditioner	信号整形回路	Xìnhào zhěngxíng huílù
SGCP	Service gateway control protocol	业务网关控制协议	Yèwù wǎngguān kòngzhì xiéyì
SGCP	Simple gateway control protocol	简单网关控制协议	Jiǎndān wǎngguān kòngzhì xiéyì
SGF	Signaling gateway function	信令网关功能	Xìnlìng wǎngguān gōngnéng
SGM	Segmentation message (ISUP)	分段消息	Fēnduàn xiāoxi
SGML	Standard general markup language (in SQL Server)	标准通用标示语言	Biāozhǔn tōngyòng biāoshì yǔyán
SGML	Standard generalized markup language	标准规范化标记语言	Biāozhǔn guīfànhuà biāojì yǔyán
SGML	Standard generalized markup language	标准普及标记语言	Biāozhǔn pǔjí biāojì yǔyán
SGML	Standard generalized markup language	标准通用标记语言	Biāozhǔn tōngyòng biāojì yǔyán
SGMP	Simple gateway monitoring protocol	简单网关监视协议	Jiǎndān wǎngguān jiānshì xiéyì
SGP	Signaling gateway process	信令网关进程	Xìnlìng wǎngguān jìnchéng

SGRAM	Synchronous graphics random access memory	同步图形随机储存器	Tóngbù túxíng suíjī chǔcúnqì
SGSC	Sub-group security controller	子组安全控制器	Zizǔ ānquán kòngzhìqì
SGSN	Service GPRS support node	服务 GPRS 支持节点	Fúwù GPRS zhīchí jiédiǎn
SGSN	Serving GPRS supporting node	GPRS 服务支持节点	GPRS fúwù zhīchí jiédiǎn
SGSN	Specific general packet radio service node	特定的通用分组无线电业务节点	Tèdìngde tōngyòng fēnzǔ wúxiàndiàn yèwù jiédiǎn
SGU	Signal gateway unit	信号网关单元	Xìnhào wǎngguān dānyuán
SGU	Signaling gateway unit	信令网关单元	Xìnlìng wǎngguān dānyuán
SH	Supplementary service handling	补充业务处理	Bǔchōng yèwù chǔlǐ
SHA	Secure hash algorithm	安全散列算法	Ānquán sànliè suànfǎ
SHA	Security hash algorithm	安全 Hash 算法	Ānquán hash suànfǎ
SHCCH	Shared channel control channel	共享信道控制信道	Gòngxiǎng xìndào kòngzhì xìndào
SHDSL	Single pair high-speed digital subscriber line	单线对高速数据用户线	Dānxiànduì gāosù shùjù yònghù xiàn
SHDSL	Single-pair high bit-rate digital subscriber line	单线对高比特率数字用户线	Dānxiànduì gāobǐtèlǜ shùzì yònghù xiàn
SHF	Super high frequency	超高频	Chāogāopín
SHLR	Standalone home location register	独立的标识位置寄存器	Dúlìde biāozhì wèizhì jìcúnqì
SHLR	Standalone home location register	独立的原始位置寄存器	Dúlìde yuánshǐ wèizhì jìcúnqì
SHR	Self-healing hybrid ring (SDH term)	自愈环	Zìyù huán
S-HTTP	Secure hypertext transfer protocol (IETF use)	加密的 HTTP 协议	Jiāmìde HTTP xiéyì
SHZ	Digital subscriber loop carrier	数字用户环路载波	Shùzì yònghù huánlù zàibō
SI	Screening indicator	屏蔽指示器	Píngbì zhǐshìqì
SI	Service interworking	业务互通	Yèwù hùtōng
SI	Shift in	移入	Yírù
SI	Sound installation	音响设备	Yīnxiǎng shèbèi
SI	Sound insulation	隔音	Géyīn
SI	Subscriber installation	用户装置	Yònghù zhuāngzhì
SI	Supplementary information	补充信息	Bǔchōng xìnxī
SI	System information	系统信息	Xìtǒng xìnxī
Si02F	Flourided silicon oxide	二氧氟化硅	Èryǎng fúhuà guī
SIA	Semiconductor Industry Association	半导体工业协会	Bàndǎotǐ gōngyè xiéhuì
SIA	Sub-miniature integrated antenna	超小型机成天线	Chāoxiǎoxíng jīchéng tiānxiàn
SIB	Sector interface block	扇区接口模块	Shànqū jiēkǒu mókuài
SIB	Service-independent building blocks	业务独立构件	Yèwù dúlì gòujiàn
SIBH	Semi-insulated buried heterostructure (laser)	半绝缘隐埋式异质结（激光器）	Bàn juéyuán yǐnmáishì yìzhìjié (jīguāngqì)
SIBP	Subscriber interface back panel	用户接口后面板	Yònghù jiēkǒu hòumian bǎn
SIC	Service implementation capabilities	实现业务容量	Shíxiàn yèwù róngliàng
SICA	Sector interface card assembly	扇区接口卡集成件	Shànqū jiēkǒu kǎ jíchéng jiàn
SICE	Still image conference entity	静止图像会议实体	Jìngzhǐ túxiàng huìyì shítǐ
$SiCl_4$	Silicon chlorate (used in FOC manufacture)	四氯化硅	Sìlǜhuàguī
SICP	Sector interface card processor	扇区接口卡处理器	Shànqū jiēkǒu kǎ chǔlǐqì
SICS	Simultaneous interpretation conference system	同声传译系统	Tóngshēng chuányì xìtǒng
SID	Security identifier	安全标识号	Ānquán biāozhì hào
SID	Segment identifier	段识别符	Duàn shíbiéfú
SID	Service identifier	业务标识符	Yèwù biāozhì fú
SID	Silence descriptor	静寂帧	Jìngjì zhèng

SID	Silence descriptor	静音描述	Jìngyīn miáoshù
SID	Silence descriptor	静音指示	Jìngyīn zhǐshì
SID	Sudden ionospheric disturbance	突发电离层骚扰	Tūfā diànlícéng sāorǎo
SID	System identification	系统标识	Xìtǒng biāozhì
SID	System identification	系统识别码	Xìtǒng shíbié mǎ
SIF	Signaling information field	令信息字段	Lìngxìnxī zìduàn
SIF	Signaling information field	信令信息段	Xìnlìng xìnxī duàn
SIF	Standard interchange format	标准交换格式	Biāozhǔn jiāohuàn géshi
SIF	Status information frame	状态信息帧	Zhuàngtài xìnxī zhèng
SIF	Step index fiber	突变型多模光纤	Tūbiànxíng duōmó guāngxiān
SIF	Stress-induced birefringence fiber	应力感应双折射纤维	Yìnglì gǎnyìng shuāngzhéshè xiānwéi
SI-F	Far-end subscriber installation	远端用户设备	Yuǎnduān yònghù shèbèi
SIG	Signature element	签名要素	Qiānmíng yàosù
SIG	Special interest group	特别兴趣小组	Tèbié xìngqu xiǎozǔ
SIG	Special interest group	特殊利益集团	Tèshū lìyì jítuán
SiGe	Silicon germanium	锗硅	Zhěguī
SIGTRAN	Signal transfer	信号传送	Xìnhào chuánsòng
SIGTRAN	Signaling transport	信令传送	Xìnlìng chuánsòng
$SiHCl_3$	Silicon hydrochloride (used in FOC manufacture)	三氯氢硅	Sānlǜqīngguī
Sij	Scattering parameter	散射参数	Sǎnshè cānshù
SILC	Selective incoming load control	选择输入装载控制	Xuǎnzé shūrù zhuāngzài kòngzhì
SILTC	Signaling link terminal control	信令链路终端控制	Xìnlìng liànlù zhōngduān kòngzhì
SIM	GSM subscriber identity module	GSM 用户识别模块	GSM yònghù shíbié mókuài
SIM	Service interaction manager	业务相互作用管理	Yèwù xiānghù zuòyòng guǎnlǐ
SIM	Set initialization mode	设置初始化模式	Shèzhì chūshǐhuà móshì
SIM	Set initialization mode	置初始化方式	Zhì chūshǐhuà fāngshì
SIM	Subscriber identification module	用户识别模块	Yònghù shíbié mókuài
SIM	Subscriber identity module	用户标识模块	Yònghù biāozhì mókuài
SIM	Subscriber identity module	用户身份模块	Yònghù shēnfen mókuài
SIM	Subscriber identity module	用户身份模组	Yònghù shēnfen mózǔ
SIM	Subscriber identity module	用户识别模块	Yònghù shíbié mókuài
SIM	Subscriber identity module	用户识别模组	Yònghù shíbié mózǔ
SIM	Subscriber identity module	用户识别卡	Yònghù shíbiékǎ
SIMD	Single instruction multiple data	单指令多数据流	Dānzhǐlìng duō shùjùliú
SIMF	Subscriber installation management function	用户装置管理功能	Yònghù zhuāngzhì guǎnlǐ gōngnéng
SIMI	Subscriber identity module interface	用户标识模块接口	Yònghù biāozhì mókuài jiēkǒu
SIMM	Single inline memory module	单边接触内存模组	Dānbiān jiēchù nèicún mózǔ
SI-N	Near-end subscriber installation	近端用户设备	Jìnduān yònghù shèbèi
SINES	Spatial information enquiry service	空间信息查询服务	Kōngjiān xìnxī cháxún fúwù
SINR	Signal-to-interference noise ratio	信干噪比	Xìn gānzào bǐ
SIO	Serial input/output	串行输入输出	Chuànháng shūrù shūchū
SIO	Service information octet	业务消息八位位组	Yèwù xiāoxi bāwèi wèizǔ
SIO	Service information octet	业务信息八位位组	Yèwù xìnxī bāwèi wèizǔ
SIOH	Serial input output handler	串行输入输出处理器	Chuànháng shūrù shūchū chǔlǐqì
SI-OpS	Subscriber installation operation system	用户装置运行系统	Yònghù zhuāngzhì yùnxíng xìtǒng
SIP	Sector interface processor	扇区接口处理器	Shànqū jiēkǒu chǔlǐqì

SIP	Segment interface protocol	段接口协议	Duàn jiēkǒu xiéyì
SIP	Session initiation protocol	会话初始协议	Huìhuà chūshǐ xiéyì
SIP	Session initiation protocol	会话发起协议	Huìhuà fāqǐ xiéyì
SIP	Session initiation protocol	会话启动协议	Huìhuà qǐdòng xiéyì
SIP	Session initiation protocol	会话起始协议	Huìhuà qǐshǐ xiéyì
SIP	Session-initiated protocol	起始会话协议	Qǐshǐ huìhuà xiéyì
SIP	Simple internet protocol	简单因特网协议	Jiǎndān Yīntèwǎng xiéyì
SIPDU	Still image protocol data unit	静止图像协商数据单元	Jìngzhǐ túxiàng xiéshāng shùjù dānyuán
SI-POF	Stepped index plastic optical fiber	阶跃型塑胶光纤	Jiēyuèxíng sùjiāo guāngxiān
SIPP	Service interface and protocol processing unit	业务接口和协议处理单元	Yèwù jiēkǒu hé xiéyì chǔlǐ dānyuán
SIPP	Services interface and protocol processing	业务接口和协议处理	Yèwù jiēkǒu hé xiéyì chǔlǐ
SIR	Signal-to-interference ratio	信号对干扰比（信干比）	Xìnhào duì gānrǎo bǐ (xìn gān bǐ)
SIR	Submission information rate	提交信息率	Tíjiāo xìnxī lǜ
SIRR	Software interrupt request register	软件中断请求寄存器	Ruǎnjiàn zhōngduàn qǐngqiú jìcúnqì
SiS	Silicon Integrated Systems Inc.	硅片综合系统公司	Guī piàn zōnghé xìtǒng gōngsī
SIS	Switched inter-networking services	交换式网络互联服务	Jiāohuàn-shì wǎngluò hùlián fúwù
SISO	Soft input soft output (algorithm)	软输入软输出（算法）	Ruǎn shūrù ruǎn shūchū (suànfǎ)
SIT	Static induction transistor	静电感应晶体管	Jìngdiàn gǎnyìng jīngtǐguǎn
SIT	System integration test	系统集成测试	Xìtǒng jíchéng cèshì
SITH	Static induction thyristor	静电感应晶闸管	Jìngdiàn gǎnyìng jīngzháguǎn
SIV	System information viewer	系统信息观察器	Xìtǒng xìnxī guāncháqì
SIWFS	Shared interworking function system	共享互通功能	Gòngxiǎng hùtōng gōngnéng
SK	Socket	插座	Chāzuò
SK Telecom	South Korea Telecom (GSM network operator)	南朝鲜京电信	Nán Cháoxiān jīng diànxìn
SKEY	Storage key	存取键	Cúnqǔ jiàn
SKIP	Simple key exchange Internet protocol	因特网简单密钥交换协议	Yīntèwǎng jiǎndān mìyào jiāohuàn xiéyì
SKMD	Scalable multicast key distribution	可伸缩多播密钥分配	Kěshēnsuō duōbō mìyào fēnpèi
SL	Segments left	剩余段	Shèngyú duàn
SL	Service logic	业务逻辑	Yèwù luóji
SL	Signal label	信号标签	Xìnhào biāoqiān
SL	Stereolithography	光固化法	Guāng gùhuà fǎ
SL	Submerged cable	水底电缆	Shuǐdǐ diànlǎn
SL	System loading	系统加载	Xìtǒng jiāzài
SL	System loss	系统损耗	Xìtǒng sǔnhào
SLA	Semiconductor laser amplifier	半导体光放大器	Bàndǎotǐ guāng fàngdàqì
SLA	Service [quality] level agreement	服务品质协议	Fúwù pǐnzhì xiéyì
SLA	Service level agreement	业务等级协商	Yèwù děngjí xiéshāng
SLA	Service level agreement	业务级别协议	Yèwù jíbié xiéyì
SLA	Service-level agreement	服务等级协议	Fúwù děngjí xiéyì
SLA	Service-level agreement	服务级别协定	Fúwù jíbié xiédìng
SLA	Service-level agreement	服务水平协议	Fúwù shuǐpíng xiéyì
SLA	Service-level agreement	业务等级协议	Yèwù děngjí xiéyì
SLA	Synchronous line adapter	同步线转换器	Tóngbù xiàn zhuǎnhuànqì
SLAC	Subscriber line audio processing circuit	用户线路声频信息处理电路	Yònghù xiànlù shēngpín xìnxī chǔlǐ diànlù
SLAID	Site-level aggregation identifier	站点层次聚集标识符	Zhàndiǎn céngcì jùjí biāozhìfú
SLAP	Subscriber line access protocol	用户线接入协议	Yònghù xiàn jiērù xiéyì

SLB	Subscriber local busy signal	用户本地忙信号	Yònghù běndì máng xìnhào
SLB	Subscriber local busy signal	用户市忙信号	Yònghù shì máng xìnhào
SLC	Sidelobe cancellation	旁瓣消除	Pángbàn xiāochú
SLC	Signaling link code	信令链路码	Xìnlìng liànlù mǎ
SLC	Single layer ceramic capacitor	陶瓷单层电容器	Táocí dāncéng diànróngqì
SLC	Subscriber loop carrier system	用户环路载波系统	Yònghù huánlù zàibō xìtǒng
SLCS	Subscriber line concentration switch	用户线集中交换机	Yònghù xiàn jízhōng jiāohuànjī
SLE	Subscriber's line equipment	用户线路设备	Yònghù xiànlù shèbèi
SLED	Super light emitting diode	超辅射发光管	Chāofúshè fāguāng guǎn
SLEE	Service logic execution environment	业务逻辑执行环境	Yèwù luóji zhíxíng huánjìng
SLG	Simulation game (computer game)	模拟类游戏	Mónǐ lèi yóuxì
SLI	Scanline interleave	扫描线间插	Sǎomiáo xiànjiān chā
SLI	Synchronous line optical interface	同步线路光口板	Tóngbù xiànlù guāng kǒu bǎn
SLIC	Subscriber line interface circuit	用户线接口电路	Yònghù xiàn jiēkǒu diànlù
SLIC	Subscriber line interface controller	用户线接口控制器	Yònghù xiàn jiēkǒu kòngzhìqì
SLIP	Serial line interface protocol	串行线路接口协议	Chuànháng xiànlù jiēkǒu xiéyì
SLIP	Serial line interface protocol (IETF usage)	串形线路接口协议	Chuànxíng xiànlù jiēkǒu xiéyì
SLIP	Serial line Internet protocol	串行线路网际协议	Chuànháng xiànlù wǎngjì xiéyì
SLIP	Serial line internet protocol	互联网串行线协议	Hùliánwǎng chuànxíng xiàn xiéyì
SLK	SDH link termination board	SDH 链路终端板	SDH liànlù zhōngduān bǎn
SLM	Service-level management	服务级管理	Fúwù jí guǎnlǐ
SLM	Signal label mismatch	信号标记失配	Xìnhào biāojì shīpèi
SLM	Single longitudinal mode laser	单纵模激光器	Dānzòngmó jīguāngqì
SLM	Single-longitudinal mode	单纵模	Dānzòngmó
SLM	Synchronization network local manager	同步网本地管理中心	Tóngbù wǎng běndì guǎnlǐ zhōngxīn
SLMA	Subscriber line module, analog	模拟用户线模块	Mónǐ yònghùxiàn mókuài
SLMD	Subscriber line module, digital	数字用户线模块	Shùzì yònghù xiàn mókuài
SLME	Subscriber line measurement equipment	用户线测试设备	Yònghù xiàn cèshì shèbèi
SLMQW	Strained layer multiple quantum well	应变层多量子阶	Yìngbiàn céng duō liàngzǐ jiē
SLO	Service-level objective	服务等级目标	Fúwù děngjí mùbiāo
SLP	Service location protocol	服务定位协议	Fúwù dìngwèi xiéyì
SLP	Service logic program	业务逻辑程序	Yèwù luóji chéngxù
SLP	Service logic program	业务逻辑进程	Yèwù luóji jìnchéng
SLP	Single link procedure	单链路规程	Dānliànlù guīchéng
SLPI	Service logic processing instance	业务逻辑处理实例	Yèwù luóji chǔlǐ shílì
SLPI	Service logic program instance	业务逻辑进程实例	Yèwù luóji jìnchéng shílì
SLPP	Subscriber LCS privacy profile	LCS 用户保密指南	LCS yònghù bǎomì zhǐnán
SLR	Side-looking radar	侧视雷达	Cèshì léidá
SLS	Selective laser sintering	激光选区烧结法	Jīguāng xuǎnqū shāojiéfǎ
SLS	Sidelobe suppression	旁瓣抑制	Pángbàn yìzhì
SLS	Signaling link selection	信令链路选择	Xìnlìng liànlù xuǎnzé
SLT	Signaling link terminal	信令链路终端	Xìnlìng liànlù zhōngduān
SLTA	Signaling link terminal board A	信令链路终端板 A	Xìnlìng liànlù zhōngduān bǎn A
SLTE	Submarine cable line termination equipment	海缆线路终端设备	Hǎilǎn xiànlù zhōngduān shèbèi
SLTM	Signaling link test message	信令链路测试消息	Xìnlìng liànlù cèshì xiāoxi
SLTU	Subscriber loop termination unit	用户环路终端单元	Yònghù huánlù zhōngduān dānyuán

SLU	Secondary logical unit	辅助逻辑设备单元	Fǔzhù luójì shèbèi dānyuán
SLU	Source library update	源程序库更新	Yuán chéngxù kù gēngxīn
SM	Sanity manager	正常化管理器	Zhèngchánghuà guǎnlǐqì
SM	Security management	安全管理	Ānquán guǎnlǐ
SM	Security management	安全性管理	Ānquánxìng guǎnlǐ
SM	Send message	发送消息	Fāsòng xiāoxi
SM	Service management	服务管理	Fúwù guǎnlǐ
SM	Session manager	会话管理	Huìhuà guǎnlǐ
SM	Short message	短消息	Duǎn xiāoxi
SM	Sparse mode	稀疏模式	Xīshū móshì
SM	Switching module	交换模块	Jiāohuàn mókuài
SM	Synchronous multiplexer	同步复用器	Tóngbù fùyòngqì
SM	System margin	系统余量	Xìtǒng yúliàng
SM MO	Short message mobile-originated point-to-point	移动发起的点对点短消息	Yídòng fāqǐde diǎn duì diǎn duǎn xiāoxi
SM MT	Short message mobile-terminated point-to-point	移动终止的点对点短消息	Yídòng zhōngzhǐde diǎn duì diǎn duǎn xiāoxi
SMA	Satellite mobile access	卫星移动接入	Wèixīng yídòng jiērù
SMA	Shared memory architecture	共享内存结构	Gòngxiǎng nèicún jiégòu
SMAC	Source media access control	源媒体接入控制	Yuán méitǐ jiērù kòngzhì
SMAE	System management application entity	系统管理应用实体	Xìtǒng guǎnlǐ yìngyòng shítǐ
SMAF	Service management access function	业务管理接入功能	Yèwù guǎnlǐ jiērù gōngnéng
SM-AL	Short message application layer	短消息应用层	Duǎn xiāoxi yìngyòng céng
SMAP	Service management access point	业务管理接入点	Yèwù guǎnlǐ jiērù diǎn
SMAP	System management application process	系统管理应用程序	Xìtǒng guǎnlǐ yìngyòng chéngxù
SMAPM	System management application protocol machine	系统管理应用协议机	Xìtǒng guǎnlǐ yìngyòng xiéyì jī
SMART	Self-monitoring analysis and report technology	自动检测分析及报告技术	Zìdòng jiǎncè fēnxī jí bàogào jìshù
SMASE	Special management application element	特定管理应用元素	Tèdìng guǎnlǐ yìngyòng yuánsù
SMASE	System management application service element	系统管理应用服务单元	Xìtǒng guǎnlǐ yìngyòng fúwù dānyuán
SMATV/MATV	Satellite master antenna television /master antenna television	卫星共用天线电视/共用天线电视	Wèixīng gòngyòng tiānxiàn diànshì/Gòngyòng tiānxiàn diànshì
SMATV/MATV	Satellite master antenna television /master antenna television	主卫星天线电视/主天线电视	Zhǔ wèixīng tiānxiàn diànshì/zhǔ tiānxiàn diànshì
SMB	Server message block	服务器消息块	Fúwùqì xiāoxi kuài
SMB	Server message block	服务器信息块	Fúwùqì xìnxī kuài
SMB	Server message block protocol (IBM use)	服务器信息块协议	Fúwùqì xìnxī kuài xiéyì
SMB	System management bus	全系统管理总线	Quán xìtǒng guǎnlǐ zǒngxiàn
SMB	System management bus	系统管理总线	Xìtǒng guǎnlǐ zǒngxiàn
SMBS	Sub-multiplexer for base station interface	用于 BS 接口的子复用器	Yòng yú BS jiēkǒude zifùyòngqì
SMC	Security management center	安全管理中心	Ānquán guǎnlǐ zhōngxīn
SMC	Short message control entity	短消息控制实体	Duǎn xiāoxi kòngzhì shítǐ
SMC	Surface mount component (electronics mfg)	表面组装元件	Biǎomiàn zǔzhuāng yuánjiàn
SMC, SC	Short message center	短消息中心	Duǎn xiāoxi zhōngxīn
SMCP	Service management control platform	业务管理控制平台	Yèwù guǎnlǐ kòngzhì píngtái
SMD	Surface mount device	表面安装设备	Biǎomiàn ānzhuāng shèbèi
SMD	Surface mount device (electronics mfg)	表面组装器件	Biǎomiàn zǔzhuāng qìjiàn
SM - DLL	Short message data link layer	短消息数据链路层	Duǎn xiāoxi shùjù liànlù céng
SMDS	Switched muiti-megabit data service	交换多兆比特数据业务	Jiāohuàn duōzhàobǐtè shùjù yèwù

SMDS	Switched multimegabit data service	交换式多兆比特数据业务	Jiāohuàn-shì duō zhàobǐtè shùjù yèwù
SMDS	Switched multimegabit data service	交换式多兆位数据服务	Jiāohuàn-shì duō zhàowèi shùjù fúwù
SMDS	Switched multimegabit data service	几兆比特数据交换业务	Jǐzhào bǐtè shùjù jiāohuàn yèwù
SMDS	Switched multimegabit digital service	交换型多兆位数字式服务	Jiāohuàn-xíng duō zhàowèi shùzì-shì fúwù
SMDX	Sub-highway multiplexer and demultiplexer	子公共信道多路复用和多路分解器	Zigōnggòng xìndào duōlù fùyòng hé duōlù fēnjiěqì
SME	Security management entity	安全管理实体	Ānquán guǎnlǐ shítǐ
SME	Short message entity	段消息实体	Duàn xiāoxi shítǐ
SME	Signaling management equipment	信令管理设备	Xìnlìng guǎnlǐ shèbèi
SME	Small and medium-sized enterprises	中小型企业	Zhōngxiǎoxíng qǐyè
SMF	Service management function	业务管理功能	Yèwù guǎnlǐ gōngnéng
SMF	Single mode fiber	单模纤维	Dānmó xiānwéi
SMF	System management function	系统管理功能	Xìtǒng guǎnlǐ gōngnéng
SMFC	Single mode fiber coupler	单模分光器	Dānmó fēnguāngqì
SMG	Short message gateway	短消息网关	Duǎn xiāoxi wǎng guān
SMG	Special mobile group	特别移动通信组	Tèbié yídòng tōngxìn zǔ
SMG	Subscriber media gateway	用户媒体网关	Yònghù méitǐ wǎngguān
SMHS	Signaling message handling sub-system	信号消息处理子系统	Xìnhào xiāoxi chǔlǐ zixìtǒng
SMHW	Sub-multiplexer highway board	干线子复用器板	Gànxiàn zifùyòngqì bǎn
SMI	Structure of management information	管理信息结构	Guǎnlǐ xìnxī jiégòu
SMI	Sub-multiplexer interface	子复用板	Zifùyòng bǎn
SMI	System management interrupt	系统管理中断	Xìtǒng guǎnlǐ zhōngduàn
SMIB	Security management information base	安全管理信息库	Ānquán guǎnlǐ xìnxīkù
SMIL	Synchronous multimedia integrated language	同步多媒体集成语言	Tóngbù duōméitǐ jíchéng yǔyán
SMIRA	Stepwise maximum interference removal algorithm	分布最大干扰移去算法	Fēnbù zuìdà gānrǎo yíqù suànfǎ
SMISE	Special management information service element	专用管理信息业务单元	Zhuānyòng guǎnlǐ xìnxī yèwù dānyuán
SMK	System management kernel	系统管理内核	Xìtǒng guǎnlǐ nèihé
SML	Service management layer	业务管理层	Yèwù guǎnlǐ céng
SMLC	Synchronous multi-line controller	同步多路控制器	Tóngbù duōlù kòngzhìqì
SMM	Statistics maintenance manager	统计维护管理器	Tǒngjì wéihù guǎnlǐqì
SMM	System management mode	系统管理模式	Xìtǒng guǎnlǐ móshì
SMN	SDH management network	SDH 管理网	SDH guǎnlǐ wǎng
SMN	Synchronous digital hierarchy management network	同步数字体系管理网络	Tóngbù shùzì tǐxì guǎnlǐ wǎngluò
SMO	State machine object	状态机对象	Zhuàngtài jī duìxiàng
SMP	Service management platform	业务管理平台	Yèwù guǎnlǐ píngtái
SMP	Service management point	业务管理点	Yèwù guǎnlǐ diǎn
SMP	Standby monitor presence	备用监视器存在	Bèiyòng jiānshìqì cúnzài
SMP	Symmetric multi-processing	对称多重处理	Duìchèn duōchóng chǔlǐ
SMP	Symmetric multi-processing	对称式多重处理架构	Duìchèn-shì duōchóng chǔlǐ jiàgòu
SMP	Symmetric multi-processing	对称式多处理	Duìchèn-shì duōchǔlǐ
SMPP	Short message peer to peer protocol	短消息点对点协议	Duǎn xiāoxi diǎn duì diǎn xiéyì
SMPP	Short message point to point protocol	短消息点对点协议	Duǎn xiāoxi diǎn duì diǎn xiéyì
SMR	Short message relay entity	短消息中继实体	Duǎn xiāoxi zhōngjì shítǐ
SMR	Signal-to-masking ratio	信号掩蔽比	Xìnhào yǎnbì bǐ
SMR	Special mobile radio	专用移动无线电	Zhuānyòng yídòng wúxiàndiàn
SMR	Specialized mobile radio system	集群移动通信	Jíqún yídòng tōngxìn

SM-RL	Short message relay layer	短消息中继层	Duǎn xiāoxi zhōngjì céng
SM-RP	Short message relay protocol	短消息中继协议	Duǎn xiāoxi zhōngjì xiéyì
SMRS	Specialized mobile radio system	专用移动无线电系统	Zhuānyòng yídòng wúxiàndiàn xìtǒng
SMRT	Single message rate timing	单信号率定时	Dānxìnhào lǜ dìngshí
SMS	Satellite multi-service system	卫星多业务系统	Wèixīng duō yèwù xìtǒng
SMS	SDH management sub-network	SDH 管理子网	SDH guǎnlǐ zìwǎng
SMS	Security management system	安全管理系统	Ānquán guǎnlǐ xìtǒng
SMS	Service management system	业务管理系统	Yèwù guǎnlǐ xìtǒng
SMS	Short message service	短消息业务	Duǎn xiāoxi yèwù
SMS	Short message service	短信业务	Duǎnxìn yèwù
SMS	Subscriber management system	注册用户管理系统	Zhùcè yònghù guǎnlǐ xìtǒng
SMS	Subscriber management systtem	用户管理系统	Yònghù guǎnlǐ xìtǒng
SMS	Synchronous digital hierarchy management sub-network	同步数字体系管理子网	Tóngbù shùzì tǐxì guǎnlǐ zìwǎng
SMS PP	Short message service point to point	点对点短消息业务	Diǎn duì diǎn duǎn xiāoxi yèwù
SMS/PP	Short message service/point-to-point	短消息业务/点到点	Duǎn xiāoxi yèwù/diǎn dàodiǎn
SMSC	Satellite mobile service switching center	卫星移动业务交换中心	Wèixīng yídòng yèwù jiāohuàn zhōngxīn
SMSC	Short message service center	短消息业务中心	Duǎn xiāoxi yèwù zhōngxīn
SMSC	Short message switching center	短消息交换中心	Duǎn xiāoxi jiāohuàn zhōngxīn
SMSC	Single mode star coupler	单模星型分光器	Dānmó xīngxíng fēnguāngqì
SMSCB	Short message service cell broadcast	短消息小区广播	Duǎn xiāoxi xiǎoqū guǎngbō
SMS-CB	Short message service cell broadcast	短消息业务小区广播	Duǎn xiāoxi yèwù xiǎoqū guǎngbō
SMS-CBSC	Short message service-cell broadcast service center	短消息小区广播业务中心	Duǎn xiāoxi xiǎoqū guǎngbō yèwù zhōngxīn
SMSI	System management service interface	系统管理业务接口	Xìtǒng guǎnlǐ yèwù jiēkǒu
SMS-MO/PP	Short message service-mobile originating/point-to-point	移动台起始点对点短消息业务	Yídòngtái qǐshǐ diǎn duì diǎn duǎn xiāoxi yèwù
SMS-MT/PP	Short message service-mobile terminating/point-to-point	移动台终接点对点短消息业务	Yídòngtái zhōngjiēdiǎn duì diǎn duǎn xiāoxi yèwù
SMSR	Side mode suppression ratio	边摸抑制比	Biānmō yìzhìbǐ
SMT	Station management	站管理	Zhàn guǎnlǐ
SMTC	Single mode tree coupler	单模树型分光器	Dānmó shùxíng fēnguāngqì
SMTE	Short message terminal equipment	短消息终端	Duǎn xiāoxi zhōngduān
SMTE	Short message termination	短消息终端	Duǎn xiāoxi zhōngduān
SM-TL	Short message transfer layer	短消息传递层	Duǎn xiāoxi chuándì céng
SM-TL	Short message transport layer	短消息传送层	Duǎn xiāoxi chuánsòng céng
SM - TL	Short message transfer layer	短消息传送层	Duǎn xiāoxi chuánsòng céng
SMTP	Simple mail transfer protocol	简单邮件传输协议	Jiǎndān yóujiàn chuánshū xiéyì
SMTP	Simple mail transfer protocol	简单邮件传送协议	Jiǎndān yóujiàn chuánsòng xiéyì
SMTP	Simple mail transfer protocol	简单的邮件传送协议	Jiǎndānde yóujiàn chuánsòng xiéyì
SMU	Scaled measurement unit	标尺测量单位	Biāochǐ cèliáng dānwèi
SMUX,SM	Sub-multiplexer	子复用器	Zifùyòngqì
SMX	Sub-multiplexer unit	子多路复用器	Ziduōlù fùyòngqì
SN	Sequence number	顺序号	Shùnxù hào
SN	Sequence number	序列号码	Xùliè hàomǎ
SN	Service node	服务节点	Fúwù jiédiǎn
SN	Service node	业务节点	Yèwù jiédiǎn
SN	Serving network	服务网络	Fúwù wǎngluò
SN	Subscriber number	用户号	Yònghù hào

SN	Subscriber number	用户号码	Yònghù hàomǎ
SN	Switching network	交换网络	Jiāohuàn wǎngluò
SN / IP	Service node/intelligent peripheral	服务节点 / 智能外围设备	Fúwù jiédiǎn/zhìnéng wàiwéi shèbèi
SNA	System network architecture	系统网络建筑	Xìtǒng wǎngluò jiànzhù
SNA	System network architecture	系统网络体系结构	Xìtǒng wǎngluò tǐxì jiégòu
SNA	Systems network architecture and protocols (IBM use)	系统网络体系结构及其协议	Xìtǒng wǎngluò tǐxì jiégòu jí qí xiéyì
SNAP	Standard network access protocol	标准网络连接协议	Biāozhǔn wǎngluò liánjiē xiéyì
SNAP	Sub-network access protocol	子网访问协议	Zìwǎng fǎngwèn xiéyì
SNAP	Sub-network access protocol	子网接入协议	Zìwǎng jiērù xiéyì
SNC	Sub-network connection	子网连接	Zìwǎng liánjiē
SNC/I	Sub-network connection with inherent monitoring	带固有监视的子网连接保护	Dài gùyǒu jiānshìde zi wǎng liánjiē bǎohù
SNC/N	Sub-network connection protection with non-intrusive monitoring	带非介入监视的子网连接保护	Dài fēijièrù jiānshìde zìwǎng liánjiē bǎohù
SNCP	Sub-network connection protection	子网连接保护	Zìwǎng liánjiē bǎohù
SND	Short number dialing	简缩拨号	Jiǎnsuō bōhào
SND	Short number dialing	缩位拨号	Suōwèi bōhào
SNDC	Sub-network dependent convergence	子网依赖汇聚	Zìwǎng yīlài huìjù
SNDC	Sub-network dependent convergence layer	子网依赖结合层	Zìwǎng yīlài jiéhé céng
SNDCF	Sub-network dependent convergence function	子网从属会聚功能	Zìwǎng cóngshǔ huìjù gōngnéng
SNDCP	Sub-network dependent convergence protocol	子网相关收敛协议	Zìwǎng xiāngguān shōuliǎn xiéyì
SNDCP	Sub-network dependent convergence protocol	子网依赖汇聚协议	Zìwǎng yīlài huìjù xiéyì
SNDR	Signal power-to-noise power density ratio	信号功率噪声功率密度比	Xìnhào gōnglǜ zàoshēng gōnglǜ mìdù bǐ
SNDR	Signal-to-noise density ratio	信号噪声密度比	Xìnhào zàoshēng mìdù bǐ
SNH	Service request not honored	不能对应传送请求	Bùnéng duìyìng chuánsòng qǐngqiú
SNI	Service network interface	业务网络接口	Yèwù wǎngluò jiēkǒu
SNI	Service node interface	业务节点接口	Yèwù jiédiǎn jiēkǒu
SNI	Subscriber network interface	用户网络接口	Yònghù wǎngluò jiēkǒu
SNI	Subscriber network interface	用户-网络接口	Yònghù—wǎngluò jiēkǒu
SNIA	Storage Networking Industry Association	存储连网行业协会	Cúnchǔ liánwǎng hángyè xiéhuì
SNL	Signaling network layer	信号网络层	Xìnhào wǎngluò céng
SNM	Sub-network management system	子网管理系统	Zìwǎng guǎnlǐ xìtǒng
SNM	Synchronization network manager	同步网全网管理中心	Tóngbù wǎng quánwǎng guǎnlǐ zhōngxīn
SNMP	Simple network management protocol	简单网络管理协议	Jiǎndān wǎngluò guǎnlǐ xiéyì
SNOC	Switched network order code	交换网络命令码	Jiāohuàn wǎngluò mìnglìng mǎ
SNP	Sequence number protection	顺序号码保护	Shùnxù hàomǎ bǎohù
SNP	Sequence number protection	序号保护	Xùhào bǎohù
SNP	Sequence numbers protocol data unit	序列号协议数据单元	Xùlièhào xiéyì shùjù dānyuán
SNPA	Sub-network point of access	子网接入点	Zìwǎng jiērù diǎn
SNPA	Sub-network point of attachment	子网连接点	Zìwǎng liánjiē diǎn
SNPDU	Sub-network protocol data unit	子网协议数据单元	Zìwǎng xiéyì shùjù dānyuán
SN-PDU	Sub-network dependent convergence protocol data unit	子网依赖汇聚协议分组数据单元	Zìwǎng yīlài huìjù xiéyì fēnzǔ shùjù dānyuán
SNR	Serial number	串联号码	Chuànlián hàomǎ
SNR	Serial number	序号	Xùhào
SNR	Set normal response	设置正常应答	Shèzhì zhèngcháng yìngdá
SNR	Signal-to-noise ratio	信噪比	Xìn zào bǐ

SNR	Signal-to-noise ratio	信号噪声比	Xìnhào zàoshēng bǐ
SNRM	Set normal response mode	置正常响应方式	Zhì zhèngcháng xiǎngyìng fāngshì
SNS	Short name server/service	简单名字服务器/服务	Jiǎndān míngzì fúwùqì/fúwù
SNS	Switch network sub-system	交换网络子系统	Jiāohuàn wǎngluò zixìtǒng
SNSDU	Sub-network service data unit	子网服务数据单元	Ziwǎng fúwù shùjù dānyuán
SNTP	Simple network time protocol	简单网络定时协议	Jiǎndān wǎngluò dìngshí xiéyì
SNTP	Simple network time protocol (IETF use)	简单网络时间协议	Jiǎndān wǎngluò shíjiān xiéyì
SO	Shift out	移出	Yíchū
SO	Socket	插口	Chākǒu
SOA	Semiconductor optical amplifier	半导体光放大器	Bàndǎotǐ guāng fàngdàqì
SOA	Suppress outgoing access	压缩出局访问	Yāsuō chūjú fǎngwèn
SOA	Suppress outgoing access	抑制出访	Yìzhì chūfǎng
SOAC	System on a chip	系统集成多功能芯片	Xìtǒng jíchéng duōgōngnéng xìnpiàn
SOAP	Simple object access protocol	简单对象访问协议	Jiǎndān duìxiàng fǎngwèn xiéyì
SOC	System-on-a-chip	片上系统	Piàn-shàng xìtǒng
Socks	Protocol for sessions traversal across firewall securely (IETF usage)	防火墙安全会话转换协议	Fánghuǒqiáng ānquán huìhuà zhuǎnhuàn xiéyì
SOCMA	Second order coherent multiple access	二阶相关多路存取	Èrjiē xiāngguān duōlù cúnqǔ
SODAR	Sound detection and ranging	声雷达	Shēng léidá
SO-DIMM	Small outline dual-inline memory module	小型双重内嵌式内存模块	Xiǎoxíng shuāngchóng nèiqiàn-shì nèicún mókuài
SOF	Start of frame	帧起始符	Zhèng qǐshǐfú
SOFC	Submarine optical fiber cable	水下光缆	Shuǐxià guānglǎn
SOH	Section overhead	段开销	Duàn kāixiao
SOH	Start of header	标题开始	Biāotí kāishǐ
SOHO	Small office home office	小型家庭办公室	Xiǎoxíng jiātíng bàngōngshì
SOHO	Small office/home office	小办公室/家庭办公室	Xiǎo bàngōngshì/Jiātíng bàngōngshì
SOI	Silicon-on-insulator	绝缘体硅片	Juéyuántǐ guīpiàn
SoIP	SCSI over IP	IP 网络上的 SCSI 接口	IP wǎngluò-shàngde SCS jiēkǒu
SOL-GEL	Sol-gel method (FOC mfg)	溶胶-凝胶法	Róngjiāo—níngjiāo fǎ
SOLSA	Support of local service area	位置区服务	Wèizhì qū fúwù
SoLSA	Support of localized service area	固定业务区域的支持	Gùdìng yèwù qūyùde zhīchí
SOM	Start of message	报文开始	Bàowén kāishǐ
SONC	System-on-a-chip	系统集成芯片	Xìtǒng jíchéng xìnpiàn
SONET	Synchronous optical network	同步光网络	Tóngbù guāng wǎngluò
SONET	Synchronous optical network	同步光缆网络	Tóngbù guānglǎn wǎngluò
SONET/SDH	Synchronous optical network (ANSI/ITU-T)	同步光纤网络和同步数字系列	Tóngbù guāngxiān wǎngluò hé tóngbù shùzì xìliè
SOP	Signal operations platforms-provisioning (operating system)	信号操作平台服务提供(操作系统)	Xìnhào cāozuò píngtái fúwù tígōng (cāozuò xìtǒng)
SOP	State of polarization	偏振态	Piānzhèn tài
SOS	Server operating system	服务器操作系统	Fúwùqì cāozuò xìtǒng
SOT	Single operation test	单独操作试验	Dāndú cāozuò shìyàn
SOVA	Soft output Viterbi algorithm	软输出维特比算法	Ruǎn shūchū wéi-tè-bǐ suànfǎ
SP	Service provider	服务提供商	Fúwù tígōng shāng
SP	Service provider	业务提供商	Yèwù tígōngshāng
SP	Service provider	业务提供者	Yèwù tígòngzhě
SP	Session layer protocol (in ISO's OSI)	会话层协议	Huìhuà céng xiéyì

SP	Shift pulse	移位脉冲	Yíwèi màichōng
SP	Signaling point	信令点	Xìnlìng diǎn
SP	Spare	备用	Bèiyòng
SP	Spooling device	段脱机设备	Duàntuōjī shèbèi
SP	Stack pointer	栈指示字	Zhàn zhǐshì zì
SP	Switching point	交换点	Jiāohuàn diǎn
SPA	Software Publishers Association	软件出版商协会	Ruǎnjiàn chūbǎnshāng xiéhuì
SPA	Stochastic process algebra	随机进程代数	Suíjī jìnchéng dàishù
SPADE	Single channel per carrier- pulse code modulation- multiple access- demand assignment	每载波单路-脉码调制-多址联接-按申请分配	Měi zàibō dānlù-mài mǎ tiáozhì- Duō zhǐ liánjiē- Àn shēnqǐng fēnpèi
SPAN	Switched port analyzer	交换端口分析器	Jiāohuàn duānkǒu fēnxīqì
SPC	Service programming code	业务编程代码	Yèwù biānchéng dàimǎ
SPC	Signaling point code	信令点编码	Xìnlìng diǎn biānmǎ
SPC	Soft permanent circuit mode	软永久电路模式	Ruǎn yǒngjiǔ diànlù móshì
SPC	Statistical process control	统计过程控制	Tǒngjì guòchéng kòngzhì
SPC	Stored program control	存储程序控制	Cúnchǔ chéngxù kòngzhì
SPC	Super plane connection	超级平面连接	Chāojí píngmiàn liánjiē
SPC Model	Soft permanent circuit model	软永久电路模型	Ruǎn yǒngjiǔ diànlù móxíng
SPCC	Signal processor card common	信号处理器公用卡	Xìnhào chǔlǐqì gōngyòng kǎ
SPCK	Service provider control key	业务提供者控制键	Yèwù tígòngzhě kòngzhì jiàn
SPCM	Straight pulse-code modulation	直接脉码调制	Zhíjiē màimǎ tiáozhì
SPCS	State plane coordinate system	国家平面坐标系	Guójiā píngmiàn zuòbiāo xì
SPD	Security policy database	安全策略数据库	Ānquán cèlüè shùjùkù
SPD	Serial presence detect	串行存在检查	Chuànháng cúnzài jiǎnchá
SPD	Serial presence detect	内存内部序号检测装置	Nèicún nèibù xùhào jiǎncè zhuāngzhì
SPD	Serial presence detect	序号检测装置	Xùhào jiǎncè zhuāngzhì
SPD	Speech decoder	语音解码器	Yǔyīn jiěmǎqì
SPDL	Standard page description language	标准页面描述语言	Biāozhǔn yèmiàn miáoshù yǔyán
SPDU	Session protocol data unit	会话协议数据单元	Huìhuà xiéyì shùjù dānyuán
SPE	Semi-public environment	半公共环境	Bàngōnggòng huánjìng
SPE	Speech encoder	语音编码器	Yǔyīn biānmǎqì
SPE	Stokes parameter evaluation	斯托克斯参数测定	Sī-tuō-kè-sī cānshù cèdìng
SPEC	Speech predictive encoded communication	话音预测编码通信	Huàyīn yùcè biānmǎ tōngxìn
SPEC	Speech-predictive coding	语言预测编码	Yǔyán yùcè biānmǎ
SPEC	Standard Performance Evaluation Corporation	标准性能评估测试有限公司	Biāozhǔn xìngnéng pínggū cèshì yǒuxiàn gōngsī
SPF	Service port function	业务端口功能	Yèwù duānkǒu gōngnéng
SPF	Service port function	业务口功能	Yèwù kǒu gōngnéng
SPF	Shortest path first	最短路径优先	Zuìduǎn lùjìng yōuxiān
SPF	Shortest path first algorithm	最短路径优先算法	Zuìduǎn lùjìng yōuxiān suànfǎ
SPF	Single-polarization fiber	单极化纤维	Dānjíhuà xiānwéi
SPFI	Single polarization fiber isolator	单偏振隔离器	Dānpiānzhèn gélíqì
SPG	Sports games (computer game)	运动类游戏	Yùndòng lèi yóuxì
SPI	SDH physical interface	SDH 物理接口	SDH wùlǐ jiēkǒu
SPI	Security parameter index (IPsec)	安全参数索引	Ānquán cānshù suǒyǐn
SPI	Serial peripheral interface	串行外围接口	Chuànháng wàiwéi jiēkǒu
SPI	Service provider identifier	业务提供者标识符	Yèwù tígòngzhě biāozhìfú

SPI	Service provider interface	业务提供者接口	Yèwù tígòngzhě jiēkǒu
SPI	Synchronous digital hierarchy physical interface	同步数字体系物理接口	Tóngbù shùzì tǐxì wùlǐ jiēkǒu
SPI	Synchronous physical interface	同步物理接口	Tóngbù wùlǐ jiēkǒu
SPIC	Simulation program with integrated circuit emphasis	用集成电路加强的仿真程序	Yòng jíchéng diànlù jiāqiángde fǎngzhēn chéngxù
SPID	Service profile identifier	服务类型标识	Fúwù lèixíng biāozhì
SPIFF	Still picture interchange file format	静止图象交换文件格式	Jìngzhǐ túxiàng jiāohuàn wénjiàn géshi
SPITEs	Switching processing interface telephone events	交换处理接口电话事件	Jiāohuàn chǔlǐ jiēkǒu diànhuà shìjiàn
SPKM	Simple public key GSS-API mechanism	简单公共密匙 GSS - API 机制	Jiǎndān gōnggòng mìchí GSS-API jīzhì
SPL	Service provider link	业务提供者链路	Yèwù tígòngzhě liànlù
SPL	Software production language	软件生产语言	Ruǎnjiàn shēngchǎn yǔyán
SPL	Sound pressure level	声压级	Shēngyājí
SPL	Splitter board	分路器板	Fēnlùqì bǎn
SPLL	Semi-permanent link layer	半永久链路层	Bàn yǒngjiǔ liànlù céng
SPM	Scratchpad memory	暂时存储器	Zànshí cúnchǔqì
SPM	Self-phase modulation	自相位调制	Zìxiàngwèi tiáozhì
SPM	Service processing module	业务处理模块	Yèwù chǔlǐ mókuài
SPM	Session protocol machine	会话协议机	Huìhuà xiéyìjī
SPMC	Signaling point management cluster	信令点管理簇	Xìnlìng diǎn guǎnlǐ cù
SPN	Service provider network	业务提供者网络	Yèwù tígòngzhě wǎngluò
SPN	Subscriber premises network	用户室内网	Yònghù shìnèi wǎng
SPN	Subscriber premises network	用户住宅网	Yònghù zhùzhái wǎng
SPNI	Service provider network identifier	业务提供者网络标识符	Yèwù tígòngzhě wǎngluò biāozhìfú
SPOF	Single point of failure	单点故障源	Dāndiǎn gùzhàng yuán
SPP	Sequenced packet protocol	顺序分组协议	Shùnxù fēnzǔ xiéyì
SPP	Sequenced packet protocol	顺序信息包协议	Shùnxù xìnxī bāo xiéyì
SPP	Software project plan (CMM)	软件项目计划	Ruǎnjiàn xiàngmù jìhuà
SPP	Standard parallel port	标准并行口	Biāozhǔn bìngxíng kǒu
SPR	Spurious packet ratio	虚假包比例	Xūjiǎ bāo bǐlì
SPS	Shock protection system	抗震保护系统	Kàngzhèn bǎohù xìtǒng
SPS	Standard positioning service	标准定位业务	Biāozhǔn dìngwèi yèwù
SPS	Standard positioning service (in GPS)	标准定位服务	Biāozhǔn dìngwèi fúwù
SPT	Shortest path tree	最短路径树	Zuìduǎn lùjìng shù
SPTO	Software project tracking and oversight (CMM term)	软件项目跟踪和监控	Ruǎnjiàn xiàngmù gēnzōng hé jiānkòng
SPTV	Still-picture television	静止图像电视	Jìngzhǐ túxiàng diànshì
SPVC	Soft permanent virtual channel	软永久虚信道	Ruǎn yǒngjiǔ xū xìndào
SPVC	Switched permanent virtual circuit	交换型永久虚电路	Jiāohuàn-xíng yǒngjiǔ xū diànlù
SPVP	Soft permanent virtual path	软永久虚电路	Ruǎn yǒngjiǔ xū diànlù
SPX	Sequenced packet exchange	顺序分组交换	Shùnxù fēnzǔ jiāohuàn
SPX	Sequenced packet exchange protocol (Novell usage)	序列分组交换协议	Xùliè fēnzǔ jiāohuàn xiéyì
SPX	Simplex circuit	单工线路	Dāngōng xiànlù
SQD	Signal quality detector	信号质量检测器	Xìnhào zhìliàng jiǎncèqì
SQE	Signal quality error	信号特性错误	Xìnhào tèxìng cuòwù
SQE	Signal quality error	信号质量错误	Xìnhào zhìliàng cuòwù
SQFM	Symmetric quadratic frequency modulation	对称二次调制	Duìchèn èrcì tiáozhì
SQL	Structured query language	结构化查询语言	Jiégòuhuà cháxún yǔyán

SQL	Structured query language	结构式询问语言	Jiégòushì xúnwèn yǔyán
SQL/MM	Structured query language / multimedia	多媒体结构化查询语言	Duōméitǐ jiégòuhuà cháxún yǔyán
SQLCH	Squelch	屏蔽	Píngbì
SQORC	Staggered quadrature overlapped raised cosine (modulation)	参差正交重叠上升余弦（调制）	Cēncī zhèngjiāo chóngdié shàngshēng yúxián (tiáozhì)
SQPNM	Staggered quadriphase pseudo-noise modulation	参差四相伪噪声调制	Cēncī sìxiāng wěizàoshēng tiáozhì
SQPR	Staggered quadrature partial response (modulation)	参差正交部分响应调制	Cēncī zhèngjiāo bùfen xiǎngyìng tiáozhì
SQPSK	Staggered quadriphase shift keying	交错四相相移键控	Jiāocuò sìxiāng xiāngyí jiànkòng
SQPSK	Staggered quadriphase shift keying	交错四相移键控	Jiāocuò sìxiāngyí jiànkòng
SQRT	Square root calculation	平方根计算	Píngfānggēn jìsuàn
SR	Sample relay	取样继电器	Qǔyàng jìdiànqì
SR	Saturable reactor	饱和电抗器	Bǎohé diànkàngqì
SR	Segment register	段寄存器	Duàn jìcúnqì
SR	Silicon rectifier	硅整流器	Guī zhěngliúqì
SR	Speaker recognition	人声识别技术	Rénshēng shíbié jìshù
SR	Subscriber register	用户寄存器	Yònghù jìcúnqì
SR/TLB	Source-route translational bridging	源路由平移桥接	Yuán lùyóu píngyí qiáojiē
SRA	Stepwise removal algorithm	分布移去算法	Fēnbù yíqù suànfǎ
SRA	Symmetric rendering architecture	对称渲染架构	Duìchèn xuànrǎn jiàgòu
SRAM	Static random access memory	静态随机存储器	Jìngtài suíjī cúnchǔqì
SRAM	Static random access memory	静态随机存取存储器	Jìngtài suíjī cúnqǔ cúnchǔqì
SRB	Source-route bridging	源路由桥接	Yuán lùyóu qiáojiē
SRC	Source host	源主机	Yuán zhǔjī
SREJ	Selective reject	选择拒绝	Xuǎnzé jùjué
SRES	Signed response	符号响应	Fúhào xiǎngyìng
SRF	Special resource function	专用资源功能	Zhuānyòng zīyuán gōngnéng
SRF	Special resources function	特殊资源功能	Tèshū zīyuán gōngnéng
SRF	Specialized resource function	专用的资源处理函数	Zhuānyòngde zīyuán chǔlǐ hánshù
SRG	Software Relational Group (CMM)	软件相关组	Ruǎnjiàn xiāngguān zǔ
SRG	Standardized raster graphic	标准化栅格图形	Biāozhǔnhuà zhàgé túxíng
SRI	Send routing information	发送路由信息	Fāsòng lùyóu xìnxī
SRJ	Service reject	业务拒绝	Yèwù jùjué
SRL	Structural return loss	结构器波损耗	Jiégòuqì bō sǔnhào
SRlack	Send routing information acknowledgment	发送路由信息证实	Fāsòng lùyóu xìnxī zhèngshí
SRLG	Shared risk link group	共享风险链路组	Gòngxiǎng fēngxiǎn liànlù zǔ
SRM	Scalable reliable multicast	可扩展可靠组播	Kěkuòzhǎn kěkào zǔbō
SRM	Shared resources module	共享资源模块	Gòngxiǎng zīyuán mókuài
SRM	Storage resource management	存储资源管理	Cúnchǔ zīyuán guǎnlǐ
SRM	Synchronization network regional manager	同步网区域管理中心	Tóngbù wǎng qūyù guǎnlǐ zhōngxīn
SRNC	Serving radio network controller	服务无线电网络控制器	Fúwù wúxiàndiàn wǎngluò kòngzhìqì
SRNS	Serving radio network sub-system	服务无线网络分系统	Fúwù wúxiàn wǎngluò fēnxìtǒng
S-RNTI	SRNC radio network temporary identity	SRNC 无线网络临时识别	SRNC wúxiàn wǎngluò línshí shíbié
SRP	Space recycle protocol	空间再利用协议	Kōngjiān zàilìyòng xiéyì
SRP	Spatial reuse protocol	空间复用协议	Kōngjiān fùyòng xiéyì
SRP	Spatial reuse protocol	空间再用协议	Kōngjiān zàiyòng xiéyì
SRP	Speech recognition processor	语言识别处理器	Yǔyán shíbié chǔlǐqì

SRPG	Strategy role play games (computer game)	战略角色扮演游戏	Zhànlüè juésè bànyǎn yóuxì
SRQ	Service request	业务请求	Yèwù qǐngqiú
SRQR	Service request report	业务请求报告	Yèwù qǐngqiú bàogào
SRR	Specialized resource report	专用资源报告	Zhuānyòng zīyuán bàogào
SRRF	Standard resource record format	标准资源记率格式	Biāozhǔn zīyuán jilǜ géshi
SRS	Sound reinforcement system	扩声系统	Kuòshēng xìtǒng
SRS	Sound retrieval system	声音修复系统	Shēngyīn xiūfù xìtǒng
SRS	Stimulated Raman scattering	受激拉曼散射	Shòujī lā-màn sǎnshè
SRT	Source routing and transparency	源路由选择并透明	Yuán lùyóu xuǎnzé bìng tòumíng
SRT	Source-route transparent bridging	源路由透明桥接	Yuán lùyóu tòumíng qiáojiē
SRTLB	Source-route translational bridging	源路由转换桥接	Yuán lùyóu zhuǎnhuàn qiáojiē
SRTP	Sequenced routing update protocol	顺序路由更新协议	Shùnxù lùyóu gēngxīn xiéyì
SRTP	Sequenced routing update protocol	序列路由更新协议	Xùliè lùyóu gēngxīn xiéyì
SRTR	Self routing tag	自选路由标签	Zìxuǎn lùyóu biāoqiān
SRTS	Synchronous residual time stamp	同步剩余时间标志法	Tóngbù shèngyú shíjiān biāozhì fǎ
SRTT	Smoothed round-trip transmission time	平滑的双向传输时间	Pínghuáde shuāngxiàng chuánshū shíjiān
SRVT	SCCP routing verification test	SCCP 路由证实测试	SCCP lùyóu zhèngshí cèshì
SS	Self-sustained (optical fiber cable)	自持(光纤电缆)	Zìchí (guāngxiān diànlǎn)
SS	Session service	会话服务	Huìhuà fúwù
SS	Shock sensor	震动传感器	Zhèndòng chuángǎnqì
SS	Sound source	音源	Yīnyuán
SS	Spread spectrum	扩展频谱	Kuòzhǎn pínpǔ
SS	Sprinkler system	自动喷水灭火系统	Zìdòng pēnshuǐ mièhuǒ xìtǒng
SS	Supplementary service	补充业务	Bǔchōng yèwù
SS	System simulator	系统仿真器	Xìtǒng fǎngzhēnqì
SS	System simulator	系统模拟器	Xìtǒng mónǐqì
SS APDU	Supplement service application protocol data unit	补充业务应用协议数据单元	Bǔchōng yèwù yìngyòng xiéyì shùjù dānyuán
SS/CF	Signal strength on center frequency	中心频率信号强度	Zhōngxīn pínlǜ xìnhào qiángdù
SS7	Common channel signaling system no.7	七号共用信道信令系统	Qīhào gòngyòng xìndào xìnlìng xìtǒng
SS7	Signaling system no.7	七号信令系统	Qīhào xìnlìng xìtǒng
SSAP	Session service access point	话路服务接入点	Huàlù fúwù jiērù diǎn
SSAP	Session service access point	会话服务访问点	Huìhuà fúwù fǎngwèn diǎn
SSB	Single sideband	单边带	Dānbiāndài
SSB	Single sideband modulation	单边带调制	Dānbiāndài tiáozhì
SSB	Subscriber busy (electrical)	用户忙信号(电的)	Yònghù máng xìnhào (diànde)
SSB	Super South Bridge chip	超级南桥芯片	Chāojí nánqiáo xìnpiàn
SSB	Symmetric switched broadband	对称交换宽带	Duìchèn jiāohuàn kuāndài
SSBAM	Single sideband amplitude modulation	单边带调幅	Dānbiāndài tiáofú
SSBF	Signal structure beamforming	信号结构波束成型	Xìnhào jiégòu bōshù chéngxíng
SSBP	Space switch back panel	空分交换后面板	Kōngfēn jiāohuàn hòumian bǎn
SSC	Secondary synchronization code	第二同步码	Dì'èr tóngbùmǎ
SSC	Service switching center	业务交换中心	Yèwù jiāohuàn zhōngxīn
SSC	Spread spectrum communication	扩频通信	Kuòpín tōngxìn
SSC	Sub-system congestion	子系统拥塞	Zixìtǒng yōngsè
SSC	Supplementary service control string	补充业务控制串	Bǔchōng yèwù kòngzhì chuàn
SSC	Supplementary service control string	补充业务控制字符串	Bǔchōng yèwù kòngzhì zìfúchuàn

SSCA	Space switch clock distribution board assembly	空分交换时钟分配集成板	Kōngfēn jiāohuàn shízhōng fēnpèi jíchéngbǎn
SSCF	Service-specific coordination function	特殊业务协调功能	Tèshū yèwù xiétiáo gōngnéng
SSCF	Service-specific coordination function	业务特定的协调功能	Yèwù tèdìngde xiétiáo gōngnéng
SSCF-NNI	Service-specific coordination function-network node interface	特殊业务协调功能-网络节点接口	Tèshū yèwù xiétiáo gōngnéng- wǎngluò jiédiǎn jiēkǒu
SSCF-UNI	Service specific coordination function supporting user-to-network interface	支持用户网络接口的业务特定协调功能	Zhīchí yònghù wǎngluò jiēkǒude yèwù tèdìng xiétiáo gōngnéng
SSCHK	Supplementary service check	补充业务检查	Bǔchōng yèwù jiǎnchá
SSCK	Space switch clock distributor	空分交换时钟分配器	Kōngfēn jiāohuàn shízhōng fēnpèiqì
SSCM	Space switch control and maintenance	空分交换控制和维护	Kōngfēn jiāohuàn kòngzhì hé wéihù
SSCO	Subscriber service control block	用户服务控制模块	Yònghù fúwù kòngzhì mókuài
SSCOF	Service-specific connection-oriented function	业务特定面向连接功能	Yèwù tèdìng miànxiàng liánjiē gōngnéng
SSCOP	Service-specific connection-oriented protocol	面向业务专用连接的协议	Miànxiàng yèwù zhuānyòng liánjiēde xiéyì
SSCOP	Service-specific connection-oriented protocol	特定服务的面向连接协议	Tèdìng fúwùde miànxiàng liánjiē xiéyì
SSCOP	Service-specific connection-oriented protocol	业务特定面向连接协议	Yèwù tèdìng miànxiàng liánjiē xiéyì
SSCOPMCE	Service-specific connection oriented protocol in a multi-link and connectionless environment	在一个多连接和无连接环境中业务特定面向连接协议	Zài yīgè duō liánjiē hé wú liánjiē huánjìng zhōng yèwù tèdìng miànxiàng liánjiē xiéyì
SSCP	System services control point	系统服务控制点	Xìtǒng fúwù kòngzhì diǎn
SSCPFM	System services control point format	系统服务控制点格式	Xìtǒng fúwù kòngzhì diǎn géshi
SSCS	Service-specific convergence layer	业务特有会聚层	Yèwù tèyǒu huìjù céng
SSCS	Service-specific convergence sub-layer	特定服务的汇聚子层	Tèdìng fúwùde huìjù zicéng
SSCS	Service-specific convergence sub-layer	特殊业务会聚子层	Tèshū yèwù huìjù zicéng
SSCS	Service-specific convergence sub-layer	业务特定会聚子层	Yèwù tèdìng huìjù zicéng
SS-CSI	Supplementary service camel subscription	补充业务 CAMEL 签约信息	Bǔchōng yèwù CAMEL qiānyuē xìnxī
SSD	Server signal degrade	服务层信号劣化	Fúwù céng xìnhào lièhuà
SSD	Server signal degrade	服务器信号劣化	Fúwùqì xìnhào lièhuà
SSD	Shared secret data	共享保密数据	Gòngxiǎng bǎomì shùjù
SSD	Shared secret data	共用保密数据	Gòngyòng bǎomì shùjù
SSD	Special service device	特业台	Tèyètái
SSD	Static separation of duties	静态取责分离	Jìngtài qǔzé fēnlí
SSDA	Synchronous serial data adapter	同步串行数据转换器	Tóngbù chuànháng shùjù zhuǎnhuànqì
SSDT	Site selection diversity transmission	选择位置分集发射	Xuǎnzé wèizhì fēnjí fāshè
SSDU	Session service data unit	会话服务数据单元	Huìhuà fúwù shùjù dānyuán
SSE	Silicon switch engine	硅交换机引擎	Guī jiāohuànjī yǐnqíng
SSE	Silicon switching engine	硅交换引擎	Guī jiāohuàn yǐnqíng
SSE	Streaming SIMD extensions	单一指令多数据流扩展	Dānyī zhǐlìng duō shùjùliú kuòzhǎn
SSF	Server signal fail	服务层信号失效	Fúwù céng xìnhào shīxiào
SSF	Service signal failure	业务信号失效	Yèwù xìnhào shīxiào
SSF	Service switching function	业务交换功能	Yèwù jiāohuàn gōngnéng
SSF	Sub-service field	子业务字段	Ziyèwù zìduàn
SSFH	Spread spectrum frequency hopping	扩展频谱频率跳变	Kuòzhǎn pínpǔ pínlǜ tiàobiàn
SSFM, SSBFM	Single sideband frequency modulation	单边带调频	Dānbiāndài tiáopín
SSG	Synchronizing signal generation	同步信号产生	Tóngbù xìnhào chǎnshēng
SSH	Secure shell protocol (ITU-T usage)	安装配置	Ānzhuāng pèizhì
SSI	Server side include	服务器方包含	Fúwùqì fāng bāohán
SSID	Service set identity	业务组标识符	Yèwù zǔ biāozhì fú

SSIO	Space switch input and output	空分交换输入输出	Kōngfēn jiāohuàn shūrù shūchū
SSK-DS-SS	Sequence shift keying-direct sequence spread spectrum	顺序位移键控-直接序列扩展频谱	Shùnxù wèiyí jiànkòng—zhíjiē xùliè kuòzhǎn pínpǔ
SSL	Secure socket layer	安全插座层	Ānquán chāzuò céng
SSL	Secure socket layer	安全套接层	Ānquán tàojiē céng
SSL	Secure socket layer	加密套接字安全层	Jiāmì tàojiēzì ānquán céng
SSL	Secure socket layer (CORBA term)	安全套接字层	Ānquán tàojiē zìcéng
SSL	Synchronization sub-layer	同步子层	Tóngbù zicéng
SSL	System service layer	系统业务层	Xìtǒng yèwù céng
SSM	Single segment message	单段消息	Dānduàn xiāoxi
SSM	Spread spectrum modulation	扩展频谱调制	Kuòzhǎn pínpǔ tiáozhì
SSM	Synchronization status message	同步状态信息	Tóngbù zhuàngtài xìnxī
SSM	Synchronization supervisor module	同步监控模块	Tóngbù jiānkòng mókuài
SSM	System support machine	系统支援机器	Xìtǒng zhīyuán jīqì
SSMA	Satellite switched multiple access	卫星交换多址	Wèixīng jiāohuàn duōzhǐ
SSMA	Spread spectrum multiple access	扩频多址	Kuòpín duōzhǐ
SSMA	Spread spectrum multiple access	扩展频谱多址	Kuòzhǎn pínpǔ duōzhǐ
SSMB	Synchronization status message byte	同步状态消息字节	Tóngbù zhuàngtài xiāoxi zìjié
SSMF	Signaling system multi-frequency	多频信令系统	Duōpín xìnlìng xìtǒng
SSMF	Standard single mode fiber	标准单模光纤	Biāozhǔn dānmó guāngxiān
SSMX	Space switch matrix	空分交换矩阵	Kōngfēn jiāohuàn jǔzhèn
SSN	Send sequence number	发送序列号	Fāsòng xùlièhào
SSN	Signal-satellite network	卫星信号网络	Wèixīng xìnhào wǎngluò
SSN	Stream sequence number	流顺序号码	Liú shùnxù hàomǎ
SSN	Sub-system number	子系统号	Zìxìtǒng hào
SSN	Sub-system number	子系统号码	Zìxìtǒng hàomǎ
SSN	Switched star network	交换式星形网络	Jiāohuàn-shì xīngxíng wǎngluò
SSN	Switching/signaling node	交换/信令节点	Jiāohuàn/xìnlìng jiédiǎn
SSNAP	Stargate satellite network access point	星关卫星网路接入节点	Xīngguān wèixīng wǎnglù jiērù jiédiǎn
SSO	Single sign-on	一次性登录	Yīcìxìng dēnglù
SSP	Service switching point	业务交换点	Yèwù jiāohuàn diǎn
SSP	Service switching point	业务交换眯	Yèwù jiāohuàn mí
SSP	Silicon switch processor	硅交换机处理器	Guī jiāohuànjī chǔlǐqì
SSP	Switch-to-switch protocol	交换机到交换机协议	Jiāohuànjī dào jiāohuànjī xiéyì
SSP	Switch-to-switch protocol	交换机间协议	Jiāohuànjī-jiān xiéyì
SSPA	Solid-state power amplifier	固体功率放大器	Gùtǐ gōnglǜ fàngdàqì
SSP-AAL	ATM adaptation layer service specific part	ATM 适配层业务特定部分	ATM shìpèi céng yèwù tèdìng bùfen
SSPM	Single sideband phase modulation	单边带调相	Dānbiāndài tiáoxiàng
SSPR	System selection for preferred roaming	首选漫游的系统选择	Shǒuxuǎn mànyóude xìtǒng xuǎnzé
SSR	Secondary surveillance radar	二次监视雷达	Èrcì jiānshì léidá
SSR	Signal stability routing	信号稳定度的路由算法	Xìnhào wěndìngdùde lùyóu suànfǎ
SSR	Solid-state relay	固体继电器	Gùtǐ jìdiànqì
SSR	Switching select repeater	中断器开关选择器	Zhōngduànqì kāiguān xuǎnzéqì
SSRA	Spread spectrum random access	扩频随机接入	Kuòpín suíjī jiērù
SSRP	Simple server redundancy protocol	简单服务器冗余协议	Jiǎndān fúwùqì rǒngyú xiéyì
SSS	Service selection server	服务选择服务器	Fúwù xuǎnzé fúwùqì

SSS	Service selection server	业务选择服务器	Yèwù xuǎnzé fúwùqì
SSS	Signaling service sub-system	信令服务子系统	Xìnlìng fúwù zi xìtǒng
SSS	Silicon symmetrical switch	硅对称开关	Guī duìchèn kāiguān
SSS	Silicon symmetrical switch	双向可控硅	Shuāngxiàng kěkòng guī
SSS	Switched star system	交换式星形系统	Jiāohuàn-shì xīngxíng xìtǒng
SSS	Switching sub-system	交换子系统	Jiāohuàn zixìtǒng
SSSAR	Service-specific segmentation and re-assembly sub-layer	特殊业务分段和重新装配子层	Tèshū yèwù fēnduàn hé chóngxīn zhuāngpèi zicéng
SST	Send special-information tone signal	发送专用信息音信号	Fāsòng zhuānyòng xìnxī yīnxìnhào
SSTDMA	Satellite switched time-division multiple access	卫星转接十分多路存取	Wèixīng zhuǎnjiē shífēn duōlù cúnqǔ
SSTF	Shortest searching time first	最短寻道时间优先	Zuìduǎn xúndào shíjiān yōuxiān
sSTM	Sub-STM (synchronous transfer mode)	子类同步传输模式	Zǐlèi tóngbù chuánshū móshì
SSTP	Service support transmission protocol	业务支撑传输协议	Yèwù zhīchēng chuánshū xiéyì
SSU	Scan and signal unit	扫描及信号单元	Sǎomiáo jí xìnhào dānyuán
SSU	Subsequent signal unit	后续信号单元	Hòuxù xìnhào dānyuán
SSU	Synchronous supply unit	同步供给单元	Tóngbù gōngjǐ dānyuán
SSW	Digital data network	数字数据网	Shùzì shùjù wǎng
ST	Segment type	段类型	Duàn lèixíng
ST	Service ticket	服务票据	Fúwù piàojù
ST	Signaling tone	信令音	Xìnlìng yīn
ST	Start	启动	Qǐdòng
ST	Starter	启动器	Qǐdòngqì
ST	Straight tip (optical fiber connector)	直通式光纤连接器	Zhítōng-shì guāngxiān liánjiēqì
ST	Subscriber's tap	用户分支器	Yònghù fēnzhīqì
STA	SCSI trade Association	SCSI 同业公会	SCSI tóngyè gōnghuì
STA	Spanning tree algorithm	生成树算法	Shēngchéng shù suànfǎ
STADIL	Satellite Tactical Data Information Link (US military)	卫星战术数据信息链	Wèixīng zhànshù shùjù xìnxī liàn
STB	Set top box	顶置盒	Dǐngzhìhé
STB	Set-top-box	机顶盒	Jīdǐnghé
STB	Subscriber toll busy signal	用户长忙信号	Yònghù cháng máng xìnhào
STB	Subscriber toll busy signal	用户长途忙信号	Yònghù chángtú máng xìnhào
STBP	Subscriber test back panel	用户测试后面板	Yònghù cèshì hòumian bǎn
ST-BUS	Serial telecommunications Bus	串行通信总线	Chuànháng tōngxìn zǒngxiàn
STC	Satellite telephone switching center	卫星电话交换中心	Wèixīng diànhuà jiāohuàn zhōngxīn
STC	Signaling transport converter	信令传送转换器	Xìnlìng chuánsòng zhuǎnhuànqì
STC	Sine transform coding	正弦变换编码	Zhèngxián biànhuàn biānmǎ
STC	Sinusoidal transfer coder	正弦变换编码奇	Zhèngxián biànhuàn biānmǎqí
STCA	Signaling terminal control board assembly	信令终端控制集成板	Xìnlìng zhōngduān kòngzhì jíchéngbǎn
STD	Selection transmission diversity	选择发送分集	Xuǎnzé fāsòng fēn jí
STD	Space transmit diversity	空间发分集	Kōngjiān fāfēnjí
STD	Subscriber trunk dialing	用户干线拨号	Yònghù gànxiàn bōhào
STD	Suspend to disk	磁盘唤醒	Cípán huànxǐng
STDEVP	Statistical standard deviation for the population (in SQL Server)	函数返回总体标准差	Hánshù fǎnhuí zǒngtǐ biāozhǔn chà
STDM	Statistical time-division multiplexing	统计时分复用	Tǒngjì shífēn fùyòng
STDM	Synchronous time division multiplexing	同步时分复用	Tóngbù shífēn fùyòng
STDMA	Synchronous time division multiple access	同步时分多路存取	Tóngbù shífēn duōlù cúnqǔ

STE	Signaling terminal	信令终端	Xìnlìng zhōng duān
STE	Signaling transfer equipment	信令转换设备	Xìnlìng zhuǎnhuàn shèbèi
STE	Subscriber terminal equipment	用户终端设备	Yònghù zhōngduān shèbèi
STEP	Signaling transfer end point	信令转接终结点	Xìnlìng zhuǎnjiē zhōngjié diǎn
STEP	Standard for the exchange of product model data	产品模型数据交换标准	Chǎnpǐn móxíng shùjù jiāohuàn biāozhǔn
STEP	Standard for the exchange of product model data	产品模型数据转换标准	Chǎnpǐn móxíng shùjù zhuǎnhuàn biāozhǔn
STG	Shooting game (computer game)	射击类游戏	Shèjī lèi yóuxì
STG	Synchronous timing generator	同步定时产生器	Tóngbù dìngshí chǎnshēngqì
STG	Synchronous timing generator	同步定时发生器	Tóngbù dìngshí fāshēngqì
STI	Surface transfer impedance	表面传输阻扰	Biǎomiàn chuánshū zǔrǎo
STK	SimToolKit	用户识别应用发展工具	Yònghù shíbié yìngyòng fāzhǎn gōngjù
STL	Signaling transport layer	信令传送层	Xìnlìng chuánsòng céng
STL-2000	ITU-T Software Tools Library, release 2000	ITU-T 软件工具库 2000 年版	ITU-T ruǎnjiàn gōngjùkù 2000 nián bǎn
STM	Status manager	状态管理	Zhuàngtài guǎnlǐ
STM	Synchronous transfer mode	同步传递方式	Tóngbù chuándì fāngshì
STM	Synchronous transfer mode	同步传递模式	Tóngbù chuándì móshì
STM	Synchronous transfer mode	同步传输模式	Tóngbù chuánshū móshì
STM	Synchronous transfer mode	同步传送模式	Tóngbù chuánsòng móshì
STM	Synchronous transfer mode	同步转移模式	Tóngbù zhuǎnyí móshì
STM	Synchronous transfer module	同步转移模块	Tóngbù zhuǎnyí mókuài
STM	Synchronous transport module	同步传输模块	Tóngbù chuánshū mókuài
STM	Synchronous transport module	同步传送模块	Tóngbù chuánsòng mókuài
STM	Synchronous transport module	同步运输模块	Tóngbù yùnshū mókuài
STM-N	Synchronous transmission mode-N	N 阶同步传送模块	N-jiē tóngbù chuánsòng mókuài
STM-N	Synchronous transport module level-N	同步传送模块等级 N	Tóngbù chuánsòng mókuài děngjí N
STM-N	Synchronous transport module-N	第 N 级同步传送模块	Dì N-jí tóngbù chuánsòng mókuài
STMPX	Statistical time-division multiplexer	统计时分复用器	Tǒngjì shífēn fùyòngqì
STMR	Side tone masking rating	侧音屏蔽平定值	Cèyīn píngbì píngdìng zhí
STNI	Signaling terminal network interface board assembly	信令终端网络接口集成板	Xìnlìng zhōngduān wǎngluò jiēkǒu jíchéngbǎn
STORM	Spatio-temporal object relationship model	时空对象关系模型	Shíkōng duìxiàng guānxi móxíng
STP	Shielded twisted pair	屏幕双绞线	Píngmù shuāngjiǎoxiàn
STP	Shortest path tree	源最短路径树	Yuán zuìduǎn lùjìng shù
STP	Signal transfer point	信号传送点	Xìnhào chuánsòng diǎn
STP	Signaling transfer point	信令传送点	Xìnlìng chuánsòng diǎn
STP	Signaling transfer point	信令转接点	Xìnlìng zhuǎnjiē diǎn
STP	Signaling transfer processor	信令转换处理器	Xìnlìng zhuǎnhuàn chǔlǐqì
STP	Spanning tree protocol	生成树协议	Shēngchéng shù xiéyì
STPID	SNAP-encoded tag protocol identifier	SNAP 编码标记协议标识符	SNAP biānmǎ biāojì xiéyì biāozhìfú
STPID	SNAP-encoded tag protocol identifier snap	编码标记协议标识符	Biānmǎ biāojì xiéyì biāozhìfú
STR	Space and time resource	时空资源	Shíkōng zīyuán
STR	Suspend to RAM	内存唤醒	Nèicún huànxǐng
STS-1	Synchronous transport signal level-1	同步运输信号第 1 层	Tóngbù yùnshū xìnhào dìyīcéng
STT	Secure transaction technology	交易保安技术	Jiāoyì bǎo'ān jìshù
STTD	Space time transmit diversity	空时发射分集	Kōngshí fāshè fēnjí

STTD	Space time transmit diversity (space time block coding based on transmit antenna diversity)	基于发射天线分集的空间时间分组编码分集	Jīyú fāshè tiānxiàn fēnjíde kōngjiān shíjiān fēnzǔ biānmǎ fēnjí
STTD	Space-time transmission diversity	空时发送分集	Kōngshí fāsòng fēnjí
STU	Synchronization traceability unknown	同步信息未知	Tóngbù xìnxī wèizhī
STUI	Service to user information	业务到用户信息	Yèwù dào yònghù xìnxī
STUN	Serial tunnel	串行隧道	Chuànháng suìdào
STX	Start of text	正文开始	Zhèngwén kāishǐ
STX	Start of text	正文开头	Zhèngwén kāitóu
SU	Service usage	业务使用率	Yèwù shǐyònglǜ
SU	Subscriber unit	用户单元	Yònghù dānyuán
SUA	SCCP user adaptation layer	SCCP 用户适配层	SCCP yònghù shìpèi céng
SUA	Signaling connection control part user adaptation layer	信令连接控制部分用户适配层	Xìnlìng liánjiē kòngzhì bùfen yònghù shìpèi céng
SUA	Single user account	单用户帐号	Dānyònghù zhànghào
SUA	Stored upstream neighbor station address	存储的上游邻站地址	Cúnchǔde shàngyóu línzhàn dìzhǐ
SUB	Splitter unit motherboard	分路器框背板	Fēnlùqì kuàng bèibǎn
SUB	Sub-addressing	子地址寻址	Zidìzhǐ xúnzhǐ
SUB	Substitution	取代	Qǔdài
SUERM	Signal unit error rate monitor	信号单元差错率监视	Xìnhào dānyuán chācuò lǜ jiānshì
SUM	System utilization monitor	系统利用率监控器	Xìtǒng lìyònglǜ jiānkòngqì
SUPERNET	Shared unlicenced personal radio network	共用无执照个人无线电网络	Gòngyòng wúzhízhào gèrén wúxiàndiàn wǎngluò
SUS	Suspend	暂停	Zàntíng
SUS	Suspend message (ISUP)	暂停消息	Zàntíng xiāoxi
SUS	Suspend request (ISUP message)	呼叫挂器请求	Hūjiào guàqì qǐngqiú
SUT	System under test	被测试系统	Bèicèshì xìtǒng
SUT	System under test	测试中的系统	Cèshì zhòngdì xìtǒng
SUT	System under test	测试下的系统	Cèshì-xiàde xìtǒng
SUT	System under test	在测试系统	Zài cèshì xìtǒng
SV	Smoke vent	排烟器	Páiyānqì
SV	Sub-vector	子向量	Zixiàngliàng
SVC	Signaling virtual channel	信令虚通路	Xìnlìng xū tōnglù
SVC	Signaling virtual channel	信令虚信道	Xìnlìng xū xìndào
SVC	Switch virtual circuit	交换式虚电路	Jiāohuàn-shì xū diànlù
SVC	Switched virtual channel	交换虚通路	Jiāohuàn xū tōnglù
SVC	Switched virtual circuit	交换虚电路	Jiāohuàn xū diànlù
SVC	Switched virtual circuit	交换虚拟电路	Jiāohuàn xūnǐ diànlù
SVC	Switched virtual circuit	交换型虚电路	Jiāohuàn-xíng xū diànlù
SVC	Switched virtual connection	交换虚连接	Jiāohuàn xū liánjiē
SVCC	Switched virtual channel connection	交换虚信道连接	Jiāohuàn xū xìndào liánjiē
SVD	Serial Viterbi decoder	串行维特比解码器	Chuànháng wéi-tè-bǐ jiěmǎqì
SVI	Sub-vector indicator	子向量标识符	Zixiàngliàng biāozhìfú
SVL	Sub-vector length	子向量长度	Zixiàngliàng chángdù
SVN	Software version number	软件版号	Ruǎnjiàn bǎn hào
SVN	Switched virtual network	交换虚拟网络	Jiāohuàn xūnǐ wǎngluò
SVP	Selector vocoder processor	选择声码处理器	Xuǎnzé shēngmǎ chǔlǐqì
SVP	Switched virtual path	交换式虚通路	Jiāohuàn-shì xū tōnglù

SVR	Switching voltage regulator	交换式电压调节	Jiāohuàn-shì diànyā tiáojié
SVS	Secure voice system	保密音频系统	Bǎomì yīnpín xìtǒng
SW	Status word	状态字	Zhuàngtài zì
SWA	Standing-wave antenna	驻波天线	Zhùbō tiānxiàn
SWA	Surface wave antenna	表面波天线	Biǎomiàn bō tiānxiàn
SWAOM	Standing-wave acousto-optical modulation	驻波声光调制	Zhùbō shēngguāng tiáozhì
SWAP	Shared wireless access protocol	共享无线访问协议	Gòngxiǎng wúxiàn fǎngwèn xiéyì
SWBC	Single mode single window broadband coupler	单模单窗宽带分光器	Dānmó dānchuāng kuāndài fēnguāngqì
SWDM	Single mode wavelength division multiplexer	单模波分复用器	Dānmó bōfēn fùyòngqì
SWEG	Software Engineering Group (CMM)	软件工程组	Ruǎnjiàn gōngchéng zǔ
SWF	Shortwave fade-out	短波信号消逝	Duǎnbō xìnhào xiāoshì
SWFS	Second Wiener filter solution	第二维纳滤波器解	Dì'èr wéinà lǜbōqì jiě
SWG	Standard wire gauge (UK)	标准线规	Biāozhǔn xiànguī
SWIFT	Society for Worldwide Interbank Financial Telecommunications	世界银行间金融电信协会	Shìjiè yínháng-jiān jīnróng diànxìn xiéhuì
SWL	Short wavelength optical fiber	短波光纤	Duǎnbō guāngxiān
SWR	Standing-wave ratio	驻波比	Zhùbōbǐ
SWS	Security work station	安全工作站	Ānquán gōngzuòzhàn
SWS	Short word size type	短句尺寸型	Duǎnjù chǐcùnxíng
SWS	Single wavelength solution	单波长解决方案	Dānbōcháng jiějué fāng'àn
SWSC	Single mode single window broadband star coupler	单模单窗宽带星型分光器	Dānmó dānchuāng kuāndài xīngxíng fēnguāng qì
SWTC	Single mode single window broadband tree coupler	单模单窗宽带树型分光器	Dānmó dānchuāng kuāndài shùxíng fēnguāngqì
SWVR	Standing wave voltage-ratio	驻波电压比	Zhùbō diànyā bǐ
SXD	City telephone cable lines	市话电缆线路	Shìhuà diànlǎn xiànlù
SXG	City telephone optical cable lines	市话光缆线路	Shìhuà guānglǎn xiànlù
SXIA	Selector transcoder interface assembly	选择易码接口集成件	Xuǎnzé yìmǎ jiēkǒu jíchéng jiàn
SXOA	Selector transcoder assembly	选择易码集成件	Xuǎnzé yìmǎ jíchéng jiàn
SXS	Step by step	步进制	Bùjìnzhì
SXS	Step by step switch	步进制交换机	Bùjìnzhì jiāohuànjī
SymDSL	Symmetrical digital subscriber line	对称数字用户线	Duìchèn shùzì yònghù xiàn
SYN	Synchronous idle	同步空闲	Tóngbù kòngxián
SYN	Synchronous idle character	同步空闲字符	Tóngbù kòngxián zìfú
SYNC	Timing synchronization message	定时同步消息	Dìngshí tóngbù xiāoxi
Syncompex	Synchronized compression and expansion	同步压扩	Tóngbù yākuò
SYSGEN	System generation	系统生成	Xìtǒng shēngchéng
SYU	Synchronization signal unit	同步信号单元	Tóngbù xìnhào dānyuán
SZ	Digital terminal	数字终端	Shùzì zhōngduān

T

T	Timer	记时器	Jìshíqì
T	Transparent	简明的	Jiǎnmíngde
T&L	Polygon transformation and lighting (video term)	多边形转换与光源处理	Duōbiānxíng zhuǎnhuàn yǔ guāngyuán chǔlǐ
T, TERA	Tera- (prefix meaning 10^{12})	兆兆	Zhàozhào
t.p.n.d	Theft, pilferage and non-delivery	偷窃提货不着险	Tōuqiè tíhuò bùzháo xiǎn
T/R	Remote T reference point	远端 T 参考点	Yuǎnduān T cānkǎo diǎn
T/S	Remote S reference point	远端 S 参考点	Yuǎnduān S cānkǎo diǎn

T1	Detection time	检测时间	Jiǎncè shíjiān
T4	Restoration transfer time	恢复转移时间	Huīfù zhuǎnyí shíjiān
TA	Terminal adaptation	终端适配	Zhōngduān shìpèi
TA	Terminal adapter	终端适配器	Zhōngduān shìpèiqì
TA	Time advance	提前时间	Tíqián shíjiān
TA	Timing advance	定时提前	Dìngshí tíqián
TA	Timing advance	定时提前量	Dìngshí tíqiánliàng
TA	Timing advance	时间提前	Shíjiān tíqián
TA	Timing advance	时间提前量	Shíjiān tíqiánliàng
TA	Transmission asymmetry	发送非对称性	Fāsòng fēiduìchènxìng
TA	Trunk amplifier	干线放大器	Gànxiàn fàngdàqì
TA	Trunk amplifier	中继放大器	Zhōngjì fàngdàqì
TAA	Thinned array antenna	稀疏天线阵	Xīshū tiānxiàn zhèn
TAAS	Type-annotated assembler	带类型注解的汇编器	Dài lèixíng zhùjiěde huìbiānqì
TAB	Table chess (computer game)	桌棋类游戏	Zhuō qí lèi yóuxì
TA-BUS	Trunk access – bus	中继接入–总线	Zhōngjì jiērù—zǒngxiàn
TAC	Technical assistance center	技术辅助中心	Jìshù fǔzhù zhōngxīn
TAC	Telenet access controller	远程通信网存取控制器	Yuǎnchéng tōngxìnwǎng cúnqǔ kòngzhìqì
TAC	Terminal access controller	终端访问控制器	Zhōngduān fǎngwèn kòngzhìqì
TAC	Type approval code	定型号码	Dìngxíng hàomǎ
TAC	Type approval code	鉴定类型码	Jiàndìng lèixíng mǎ
TAC	Type approval code	型号批准码	Xínghào pīzhǔn mǎ
TACACS	Terminal access controller access control system (Cisco protocol)	终端访问控制器访问控制系统	Zhōngduān fǎngwèn kòngzhìqì fǎngwèn kòngzhì xìtǒng
TACS	Total access communications system	全存取通信系统	Quán cúnqǔ tōngxìn xìtǒng
TACS	Total access communications system	全接入通信系统	Quán jiērù tōngxìn xìtǒng
TACS	Total access communications system	全选址通信系统	Quán xuǎnzhǐ tōngxìn xìtǒng
TACT	Terminal activated channel test	终端启动通信测试	Zhōngduān qǐdòng tōngxìn cèshì
TADIG	Transferred account data interchange group (GSM MoU)	数据交换组	Shùjù jiāohuàn zǔ
TADIL	Tactical Data Information Link (US military)	战术数据信息链	Zhànshù shùjù xìnxī liàn
TADS	Transportable automatic digital switch	可移动式自动数字交换机	Kěyídòng-shì zìdòng shùzì jiāohuànjī
TAE	Terminal adapter equipment	终端适配设备	Zhōngduān shìpèi shèbèi
TAF	Terminal adaptation function	终端适配功能	Zhōngduān shìpèi gōngnéng
TAF	Terminal adapter function	终端适配功能	Zhōngduān shìpèi gōngnéng
TAI	International atomic time	国际原子时	Guójì yuánzǐshí
TALI	Transport adapter layer interface	传输适配层接口	Chuánshū shìpèicéng jiēkǒu
TAM	Telephone answering machine	电话应答机	Diànhuà yìngdájī
TAP	Test access port	测试存取口	Cèshì cúnqǔ kǒu
TAPI	Telephone application programming interface	电话应用程序接口	Diànhuà yìngyòng chéngxù jiēkǒu
TAR	Terminal address register	终端地址寄存器	Zhōngduān dìzhǐ jìcúnqì
TASA	Transcoding and selector board assembly	译码和选择集成件	Yìmǎ hé xuǎnzé jíchéng jiàn
TASI	Time-assigned speech interpolation	话音插空	Huàyīn chā kōng
TAST	Time assigned speech interpolation	时分话音插空	Shífēn huàyīn chākōng
TAT	Transatlantic Telephone (Cable)	横越大西洋海底电话（电缆）	Héngyuè Dàxīyáng hǎidǐ diànhuà (diànlǎn)
TBC	Telecommunication certification body	通信产品认证机构	Tōngxìn chǎnpǐn rènzhèng jīgòu
TBC	Trunk block connector	长途中继线接续设备	Chángtú zhōngjìxiàn jiēxù shèbèi

TBCC	Two byte code character	两字节编码字符	Liǎng zìjié biānmǎ zìfú
T-BCSM	Terminating basic call state model	终接基本呼叫状态模式	Zhōngjiē jīběn hūjiào zhuàngtài móshì
TBD	To be defined	未定义	Wèidìngyì
TBDA	Test bus distributor board assembly	测试总线分配集成板	Cèshì zǒngxiàn fēnpèi jíchéngbǎn
TBEM	Terminal based electronic mail	终端电子邮寄	Zhōngduān diànzǐ yóujì
TBF	Temporary block flow	临时块流	Línshí kuàiliú
TBF	Temporary block flow	临时数据块流	Línshí shùjùkuài liú
TBF	Temporary block flow	临时信息组流量	Línshí xìnxīzǔ liúliàng
TBP	Token bus protocol	令牌总线协议	Lìngpái zǒngxiàn xiéyì
TBPF	Transmit band pass filter	传输带宽滤波器	Chuánshū dàikuān lǜbōqì
TBR	Technical basis for regulation	规章技术基础	Guīzhāng jìshù jīchǔ
TBRL	Terminal balance return loss	终端平衡回波损耗	Zhōngduān pínghéng huíbō sǔnhào
TBRL	Terminal balanced return loss	终端平衡回损	Zhōngduān pínghéng huísǔn
TBUS	Telecommunications bus	电信总线	Diànxìn zǒngxiàn
TBW	Synchronous network	同步网	Tóngbù wǎng
Tc	Committed rate measurement interval	承诺速率测量时间间隔	Chéngnuò sùlǜ cèliáng shíjiān jiàngé
Tc	Committed time interval	承诺的时间间隔	Chéngnuòde shíjiān jiàngé
Tc	Confirmation time	证实时间	Zhèngshí shíjiān
TC	Task control	任务控制	Rènwu kòngzhì
TC	Technical committee	技术委员会	Jìshù wěiyuánhuì
TC	Telecommunications closet	电信间	Diànxìn jiān
TC	Terminating call	被叫	Bèijiào
TC	Termination class	结束类别	Jiéshù lèibié
TC	Terrestrial channel	地面通道	Dìmiàn tōngdào
TC	Test control	测试控制	Cèshì kòngzhì
TC	Timing channel	计时通道	Jìshí tōngdào
TC	Toll center	长途电话交换中心	Chángtú diànhuà jiāohuàn zhōngxīn
TC	Transaction capabilities	事务处理能力	Shìwù chǔlǐ nénglì
TC	Transcoder	代码转换器	Dàimǎ zhuǎnhuànqì
TC	Transcoder	码变换器	Mǎ biànhuànqì
TC	Transient characteristic	瞬间特性	Shùnjiān tèxìng
TC	Transmission convergence	传输会聚	Chuánshū huìjù
TC	Transmission convergence sub-layer	传输会聚子层	Chuánshū huìjù zicéng
TC	Transport connection	运输连接	Yùnshū liánjiē
TC SMG	Technical Committee special mobile Group	技术委员会特别移动通信组	Jìshù wěiyuánhuì tèbié yídòng tōngxìn zǔ
TC/HS	Traffic channel/half-rate speech	业务信道/半速话音	Yèwù xìndào/bànsù huàyīn
TCA	Threshold crossing alarm	门限超越告警	Ménxiàn chāoyuè gàojǐng
TCA	Threshold crossing alarm	越限告警	Yuèxiàn gàojǐng
TCA	Twin cache architecture	双缓存结构	Shuāng huǎncún jiégòu
TCAM	Ternary content-addressable memory	三重按内容寻址存储器	Sānchóng àn nèiróng xúnzhǐ cúnchǔqì
TCAM	Ternary content-addressable memory	三元按内容寻址存储器	Sānyuán àn nèiróng xúnzhǐ cúnchǔqì
TCAM	Ternary content-addressable memory	三元内容寻址存储器	Sānyuán nèiróng xúnzhǐ cúnchǔqì
TCAP	Transaction capabilities application part	事条能力应用部分	Shìtiáo nénglì yìngyòng bùfen
TCAP	Transaction capabilities application part	事务处理部分	Shìwù chǔlǐ bùfen
TCAP	Transaction capabilities application part	事务处理功能应用部	Shìwù chǔlǐ gōngnéng yìngyòng bù
TCAP	Transaction capabilities application part	事务处理应用部分	Shìwù chǔlǐ yingyòng bùfen

TCAP	Transaction capability application part	事务处理能力应用部分	Shìwù chǔlǐ nénglì yìngyòng bùfen
TCAP	Transaction capability application part	事务能力应用部分	Shìwù nénglì yìngyòng bùfen
TCAP	Transmission service access point	传输服务存取点	Chuánshū fúwù cúnqǔdiǎn
TCAS	Transaction capability and application sub-system	交易能力和应用子系统	Jiāoyì nénglì hé yìngyòng zixìtǒng
TCB	Task control block	任务控制块	Rènwu kòngzhì kuài
TCB	Transport control block	传送控制块	Chuánsòng kòngzhì kuài
TCB	Trusted computing base	可信计算基	Kěxìn jìsuàn jī
TCB	Trusted computing base (ISO security)	可信计算库	Kěxìn jìsuàn kù
TCC	Transmission control characters	传输控制字符	Chuánshū kòngzhì zìfú
TCCC	Technical Committee on Computer Communications	计算机通信技术委员会	Jìsuànjī tōngxìn jìshù wěiyuánhuì
TCCD	Total call connection delay	全部呼叫连接时延	Quánbù hūjiào liánjiē shíyán
TCE	Transit connection element	转接连接单元	Zhuǎnjiē liánjiē dānyuán
TCEP	Transport connection endpoint	运输层联接端点	Yùnshū céng liánjiē duāndiǎn
TCF	Terminal configuration facilities	终端配置设备	Zhōngduān pèizhì shèbèi
TCFS	Triple coated fiber structure	三芯光纤结构	Sānxīn guāngxiān jiégòu
TCH	Traffic channel	话务频道	Huàwù píndào
TCH	Traffic channel	话务信道	Huàwù xìndào
TCH	Traffic channel	业务信道	Yèwù xìndào
TCH/F	Full rate traffic channel	全速业务信道	Quánsù yèwù xìndào
TCH/F	Full rate traffic channel	全速率业务信道	Quánsùlǜ yèwù xìndào
TCH/F2.4	Full rate data traffic channel (2.4kbs)	全速率数据业务信道	Quánsùlǜ shùjù yèwù xìndào
TCH/F9.6	Traffic channel/full rate 9.6kbit/s	业务信道/全速 9.6kbit/s	Yèwù xìndào/quánsù 9.6kbit/s
TCH/FS	Full rate speech traffic channel (TCH)	全速率话音业务信道	Quánsùlǜ huàyīn yèwù xìndào
TCH/FS	Traffic channel/full rate speech	业务信道/全速话音	Yèwù xìndào/quánsù huàyīn
TCH/H	Half rate traffic channel	半速率业务信道	Bàn sùlǜ yèwù xìndào
TCH/H2.4	Half rate data traffic channel (2.4kbit/s)	半速率数据业务信道 (2.4kbit/s)	Bàn sùlǜ shùjù yèwù xìndào (2.4kbit/s)
TCH/H4.8	Half rate data traffic channel (4.8kbit/s)	半速率数据业务信道 (4.8kbit/s)	Bàn sùlǜ shùjù yèwù xìndào (4.8kbit/s)
TCH/H4.8	Traffic channel/full rate 4.8kbit/s	业务信道/全速 4.8kbit/s	Yèwù xìndào/quánsù 4.8kbit/s
TCH/H4.8	Traffic channel/half-rate 4.8kbit/s	业务信道/半速 4.8kbit/s	Yèwù xìndào/bànsù 4.8kbit/s
TCH/HS	Half rate speech traffic channel	半速率话音业务信道	Bàn sùlǜ huàyīn yèwù xìndào
TCI	Tag control information	标记控制信息	Biāojì kòngzhì xìnxī
TCI	Test control interface	测试控制接口	Cèshì kòngzhì jiēkǒu
TCI	Transceiver control interface	收发信机控制接口	Shōufāxìnjī kòngzhì jiēkǒu
TCK	Test clock input [bus]	测试时钟输入[总线]	Cèshì shízhōng shūrù (zǒngxiàn)
TCM	Tandem connection monitor	串联连接监视	Chuànlián liánjiē jiānshì
TCM	Terrain contour matching	地形匹配制导	Dìxíng pǐpèi zhìdǎo
TCM	Time compression multiplex	时间压缩多路复用	Shíjiān yāsuō duōlù fùyòng
TCM	Time compression multiplexer	时间压缩复用器	Shíjiān yāsuō fù yòngqì
TCM	Time compression multiplexing	时间压缩复用	Shíjiān yāsuō fùyòng
TCM	Tone code modulation	音调代码调制	Yīndiào dàimǎ tiáozhì
TCM	Trellis coded modulation	格码调制	Gémǎ tiáozhì
TCM	Trellis coded modulation	格形编码调制	Géxíng biānmǎ tiáozhì
TCM	Trellis coded modulation	格栅编码调制	Gézhà biānmǎ tiáozhì
TCM	Trellis coded modulation	格状编码调制	Gézhuàng biānmǎ tiáozhì

TCM	Trellis coded modulation	网格编码调制	Wǎnggé biānmǎ tiáozhì
TCMA	Tunable-channel multi-access	可调信道多址	Kětiáo xìndào duōzhǐ
TCMF	Touch-calling multi-frequency	多频键控呼叫	Duōpín jiànkòng hūjiào
TCMF	Touch-calling multi-frequency	链控呼叫多频	Liàn kòng hūjiào duōpín
TCO	Total cost of ownership	拥有总成本	Yōngyǒu zǒngchéngběn
TCO	TSB control	TSB 控制	TSB kòngzhì
TCOA	Transmit combiner assembly	传输合并器	Chuánshū hébìngqì
TCOH	Tandem connection overhead	串联连接开销	Chuànlián liánjiē kāixiao
TCP	Tape carrier package	薄膜封装	Bómó fēngzhuāng
TCP	Telephone control protocol	电话控制协议	Diànhuà kòngzhì xiéyì
TCP	Termination connection point	终端连接点	Zhōngduān liánjiē diǎn
TCP	Termination connection point	终结连接点	Zhōngjié liánjiē diǎn
TCP	Transmission control protocol	传输控制规程	Chuánshū kòngzhì guīchéng
TCP	Transmission control protocol	传输控制协议	Chuánshū kòngzhì xiéyì
TCP	Transport control protocol	传送控制协议	Chuánsòng kòngzhì xiéyì
TCP/IP	Transmission control protocol/ Internet protocol	传输控制规约/网间规约	Chuánshū kòngzhì guīyuē/wǎng jiān guīyuē
TCP/IP	Transmission control protocol/Internet protocol	传输控制协议/网际互连协议	Chuánshū kòngzhì xiéyì/wǎngjì hùlián xiéyì
TCP/IP	Transmission control protocol/Internet protocol	传输控制协议/网际协议	Chuánshū kòngzhì xiéyì/wǎngjì xiéyì
TCP/IP	Transmission control protocol/Inter-network protocol	传输控制协议/网间协议	Chuánshū kòngzhì xiéyì/wǎng- jiān xiéyì
TCP/IP	Transmission control protocol/Interwork protocol	传输控制协议/互通协议	Chuánshū kòngzhì xiéyì/hùtōng xiéyì
TCP/IP	Transport control protocol/Internet protocol	传输控制协议/互联网协议	Chuánshū kòngzhì xiéyì/hùliánwǎng xiéyì
TCPAM	Trellis coded pulse amplitude modulation	格栅编码脉冲幅度调制	Gézhà biānmǎ màichōng fúdù tiáozhì
TCPDUMP	TCP/IP packet analysis utility	TCP/IP 数据包分析	TCP/IP shùjùbāo fēnxī
TC-RDI	Tandem connection remote defect indicator	串联连接远端缺陷指示	Chuànlián liánjiē yuǎnduān quēxiàn zhǐshì
TC-REI	Tandem connection remote error indicator	串联连接远端误差指示	Chuànlián liánjiē yuǎnduān wùchā zhǐshì
TCRF	Transit connection-related function	有关转接连接功能	Yǒuguān zhuǎnjiē liánjiē gōngnéng
TCS	Telecommunication system	通信系统	Tōngxìn xìtǒng
TCS	Telecommunication system	通讯系统	Tōngxùn xìtǒng
TCS	Telephony control specification	电话控制协议	Diànhuà kòngzhì xiéyì
TCS	Terminal capacity set	终端能力集	Zhōngduān nénglì jí
TCS	Test and control system	测试和控制系统	Cèshì hé kòngzhì xìtǒng
TCS	Traffic control sub-system	业务控制子系统	Yèwù kòngzhì zixìtǒng
TCSA	Terminal capacity set acknowledge	终端能力集确认	Zhōngduān nénglì jí quèrèn
TCSEC	Trusted computer security evaluation criteria	可信计算机安全评级准则	Kěxìn jìsuànjī ānquán píngjí zhǔnzé
T-CSI	T-CAMEL subscription information	终接 CAMEL 签约信息	Zhōngjiē CAMEL qiānyuē xìnxī
T-CSI	Terminating camel subscription information	终端 CAMEL 签约信息	Zhōngduān CAMEL qiānyuē xìnxī
TCSM	Transcoder and sub-multiplex unit	码变换及子复用单元	Mǎ biànhuàn jí zifùyòng dānyuán
TCSM	Transcoder and sub-rate channel multiplexer	码变换器和子复用设备	Mǎ biànhuànqì hé zifùyòng shèbèi
TCSR	Terminal capacity set reject	终端能力集拒绝	Zhōngduān nénglì jí jùjué
TCSSS	Threshold communication secret key sharing system	门限通信密钥分散保管系统	Ménxiàn tōngxìn mìyào fēnsàn bǎoguǎn xìtǒng
TCT	Tandem connection trace	串联连接踪迹	Chuànlián liánjiē zōngjī
TCTE	Tandem connection terminating element	串联连接终端设备	Chuànlián liánjiē zhōngduān shèbèi
TC-TR	Technical committee technical report	技术委员会技术报告	Jìshù wěiyuánhuì jìshù bàogào
TCU	Trunk coupling unit	干线耦合单元	Gànxiàn ǒuhé dānyuán
TCXO	Temperature compensation crystal oscillator	温补晶振	Wēn bǔ jīng zhèn

TCXO	Temperature compensation crystal oscillator	温度补偿晶体振荡器	Wēndù bǔcháng jīngtǐ zhèndàngqì
TD	Ticket dispenser	发卡机	Fākǎ jī
TD	Transmit degrade	发送劣化	Fāsòng lièhuà
TDAN	Time-division analog network	分时模拟网络	Fēnshí mónǐ wǎngluò
TDBS	Trusted database system	可信数据库系统	Kěxin shùjùkù xìtǒng
TD-BUS	Telephony device control bus	电话设备控制总线	Diànhuà shèbèi kòngzhì zǒngxiàn
TDC	Time dependent constellation	时间决定星座	Shíjiān juédìng xīngzuò
TDC	Time domain coding	时域编码	Shíyù biānmǎ
TDC	Tunable dispersion compensator	可调色散补偿器	Kětiáo sèsàn bǔchángqì
TDCD	Transmitter duty cycle distortion	工作周期失真	Gōngzuò zhōuqī shīzhēn
TD-CDMA	Time division – code division multiple access	时分码分多址接入	Shífèn mǎfēn duōzhǐ jiērù
TD-CDMA	Time division-code division multiple access	时分-码分多址	Shífèn-mǎfēn duōzhǐ
TDCM	Telephony device control master	电话设备控制主机	Diànhuà shèbèi kòngzhì zhǔjī
TDCS	Time division circuit switching	时分电路交换	Shífèn diànlù jiāohuàn
TDD	Time division duplex	时分双工	Shífèn shuānggōng
TDD-EDSL	Time division duplex-based ethernet digital subscriber line	基于时分双工的以太数字用户线	Jīyú shífèn shuānggōngde yǐtài shùzì yònghùxiàn
TDDL	Time division data link	时分数据链	Shífèn shùjù liàn
TDDL	Time-division data link	时间分割数据传输器	Shíjiān fēngē shùjù chuánshūqì
TDDN	Time division digital network	时分数字网络	Shífèn shùzì wǎngluò
TDEV	Time deviation	时间编差	Shíjiān biānchà
TDEV	Time deviation, timing deviation	时间偏差	Shíjiān piānchā
TDEV	Timing deviation	时间方差	Shíjiān fāngchà
TDF	Trunk distribution frame	中继线配线架	Zhōngjìxiàn pèixiànjià
TDFA	Thulium doped fiber amplifier	参铥光纤放大器	Cān diū guāngxiān fàngdàqì
TDI	Test data input [bus]	测试数据输入[总线]	Cèshì shùjù shūrù (zǒngxiàn)
TDL	Temperature-dependent loss	温度相关损耗	Wēndù xiāngguān sǔnhào
TDM	Technical data management	技术数据管理	Jìshù shùjù guǎnlǐ
TDM	Technical document management	技术文档管理	Jìshù wéndàng guǎnlǐ
TDM	Time division modulation	时分调制	Shífèn tiáozhì
TDM	Time division multiplex	时分多路复用	Shífèn duōlù fùyòng
TDM	Time division multiplex	时分复用	Shífèn fùyòng
TDM	Time division multiplexer	时分多路复用器	Shífèn duōlù fùyòngqì
TDMA	Time division multiple access	时分多址	Shífèn duōzhǐ
TDMA	Time division multiple access	时分多址访问	Shífèn duōzhǐ fǎngwèn
TDMA	Time division multiple access	时分多址接入	Shífèn duōzhǐ jiērù
TDMC	Time division multiplexed channel	时分复用信道	Shífèn fùyòng xìndào
TDM-PAM	Time division multiplexed-pulse amplitude modulation	时分多路脉冲调幅	Shífèn duōlù màichōng tiáofú
TDM-PCM	Time division multiplexed-pulse code modulation	时分多路脉码调制	Shífèn duōlù màimǎ tiáozhì
TDMS	Time division multiplexing system	时分复用系统	Shífèn fùyòng xìtǒng
TDMUX	Trans-demultiplexer	子速率解复用器	Zisùlǜ jiěfùyòngqì
TDM-VDMA	Time division multiplexed-variable destination multiple access	时分复用变址多路存取	Shífèn fùyòng biànzhǐ duōlù cúnqǔ
TDO	Test data output [bus]	测试数据输出[总线]	Cèshì shùjù shūchū (zǒngxiàn)
TDOA	Time difference of arrival	到达时差	Dàodá shíchā
TDOA	Time-difference of arrival	到达时间差	Dàodá shíjiān chà

TDP	Trigger detection point	触发检出点	Chùfā jiǎnchū diǎn
TDP-N	Trigger detection point-notification	触发检测点 - 通知	Chùfā jiǎncè diǎn-tōngzhī
TDP-N	Trigger detection point-notification	触发检出点—通知	Chùfā jiǎnchū diǎn-tōngzhī
TDP-N	Trigger DP-notification	触发 DP 通知	Chùfā DP tōngzhī
TDP-R	Trigger detection point-request	触发检测点 - 请求	Chùfā jiǎncè diǎn-qǐngqiú
TDP-R	Trigger detection point-request	触发检出点—请求	Chùfā jiǎnchū diǎn-qǐngqiú
TDP-R	Trigger DP-request	触发 DP 请求	Chùfā DP qǐngqiú
TDPSK	Time differential phase-shift keying	时间微分相移键控	Shíjiān wēifēn xiàngyí jiànkòng
TDR	Time domain reflector	时域反射仪	Shíyù fǎnshèyí
TDR	Tone dial receiver	单音拨号的接收机	Dānyīn bōhàode jiēshōujī
TDRSS	Tracking and data relay satellite system	跟踪与数据中继卫星系统	Gēnzōng yǔ shùjù zhōngjì wèixīng xìtǒng
TDS	Tabular data stream	表格格式数据流	Biǎogé géshi shùjù liú
TDS	Time division switching	时分交换结构	Shífēn jiāohuàn jiégòu
TD-SCDMA	Time division synchronous code division multiple access	时分同步码分多址	Shífēn tóngbù mafēn duōzhǐ
TDSL	Telephony device system library block	电话设备系统库模块	Diànhuà shèbèi xìtǒngkù mókuài
TDT	Timing detection table	定时检测表	Dìngshí jiǎncè biǎo
TDTSI	Time division-time slot interchanger	时分时隙交换器	Shífēn shíxì jiāohuànqì
TE	Terminal equipment	用户终端	Yònghù zhōngduān
TE	Terminal equipment	终端设备	Zhōngduān shèbèi
TE	Trace error	路踪误差	Lùzōng wùchā
TE	Traffic engineering	业务工程	Yèwù gōngchéng
TE	Traffic engineering	业务量工程	Yèwùliàng gōngchéng
TE	Traffic engineering	业务流设计	Yèwùliú shèjì
TE	Transit exchange	转接交换机	Zhuǎnjiē jiāohuànjī
TE	Transmission equipment	传输设备	Chuánshū shèbèi
TE	Transverse electric mode	横电模	Héngdiàn mó
TE	Trellis encoding	网格编码	Wǎnggé biānmǎ
TE/CPN	Terminal equipment/customer premises network	终端设备 / 用户驻地网	Zhōngduān shèbèi/yònghù zhùdì wǎng
TEC	Total electron content	总电子含量	Zǒng diànzǐ hánliàng
T-EDFA	Tellurium-doped EDFA	掺碲的 EDFA	Chāndìde EDFA
TEI	Temporary equipment identifier	临时设备标识符	Línshí shèbèi biāozhìfú
TEI	Terminal end point identifier	终端端点标志	Zhōngduān duāndiǎn biāozhì
TEI	Terminal endpoint identifier	终点端点标志	Zhōngdiǎn duāndiǎn biāozhì
Tei	Terminal endpoint identifier	终端标识	Zhōngduān biāozhì
TEID	Tunnel end point identifier	隧道端点标识符	Suìdào duāndiǎn biāozhìfú
TELCO	Telephone company	电话公司	Diànhuà gōngsī
TEM	Transverse electromagnetic mode	横电磁模	Héngdiàncí mó
TEMPEST	Transient electromagnetic pulse emanation standard	瞬变电磁脉冲发射标准	Shùnbiàn diàncí màichōng fāshè biāozhǔn
TEP	Time/event processing software	时间 / 事件处理软件	Shíjiān/shìjiàn chǔlǐ ruǎnjiàn
TEPI	Terminal end point identifier	终端端点标识符	Zhōngduān duāndiǎn biāozhìfú
TES	Telecommunication earth station	通信地球站	Tōngxìn dìqiú zhàn
TES	Telephony earth station (Hughes)	话音小站	Huàyīn xiǎozhàn
TET	Text enhanced technology	文本增强技术	Wénběn zēngqiáng jìshù
TETRA	Terrestrial trunked radio	陆上集群无线电	Lùshàng jíqún wúxiàndiàn
TETRA	Terrestrial trunked radio	数码集群流动通讯	Shùmǎ jíqún liúdòng tōngxùn

TETRA	Trans-European trunked radio	泛欧洲数字集群标准	Fàn'Oūzhōu shùzì jíqún biāozhǔn
Texel	Texture element	纹理像素	Wénlǐ xiàngsù
TF	Transfer function	传送功能	Chuánsòng gōngnéng
TF	Transmit fail	发送失效	Fāsòng shīxiào
TF	Transport format	传送格式	Chuánsòng géshi
TF	Transport function	传送功能	Chuánsòng gōngnéng
TFA	Transfer allowed	允许转接	Yǔnxǔ zhuǎnjiē
TFB	Timing and frequency block	定时和频率模块	Dìngshí hé pínlǜ mókuài
TFC	Transport format combination	传送格式组合	Chuánsòng géshi zǔhé
TFCC	Transmission frequency characteristic	传输频率特性	Chuánshū pínlǜ tèxìng
TFCI	Transport format combination indicator	传送格式组合指示器	Chuánsòng géshi zǔhé zhǐshìqì
TFCMA	Time-frequency coded multiple access	时间频率编码多路存取	Shíjiān pínlǜ biānmǎ duōlù cúnqǔ
TFCS	Transport format combination set	传送格式组合集	Chuánsòng géshi zǔhé jí
TFES	Transmit front end shelf	传输前端架	Chuánshū qiánduānjià
TFF	Thin film filter	薄膜滤波器	Bómó lǜbōqì
TFH	Time-frequency hopping	时间频率跳变	Shíjiān pínlǜ tiàobiàn
TFI	Temporary flow identity	临时流量识别	Línshí liúliàng shíbié
TFI	Transport format indicator	传送格式指示器	Chuánsòng géshi zhǐshìqì
TFM	Tamed frequency modulation	平滑调频	Pínghuá tiáopín
TFM	Timed frequency modulation	时控调频	Shíkòng tiáopín
TFO	Tamed frequency oscillator	平滑振荡器	Pínghuá zhèndàngqì
TFO	Tandem free operation	无二次编解码操作	Wú'èrcì biānjiěmǎ cāozuò
TFO	Tandem free operation	无二次编解码操作	Wú'èrcì biānjiěmǎ cāozuò
TF-OS	Transfer function-operating system	传送功能-运行系统	Chuánsòng gōngnéng--yùnxíng xìtǒng
TF-OSF	Transfer function-operating system function	传送功能-运行系统功能	Chuánsòng gōngnéng--yùnxíng xìtǒng gōngnéng
TFP	Transfer prohibited	禁止传输	Jìnzhǐ chuánshū
TFPMA	Tetrafluoro propyl methyl acrylate (FOC mfg)	四氟丙基丙烯酸甲酸	Sìfúbǐngjī bǐngxīsuān jiǎsuān
TFS	Transport format set	传送格式集	Chuánsòng géshi jí
TFSK	Time-frequency-shift keying	时频偏移键控	Shípín piānyí jiànkòng
TFT	Thin film transistor	薄膜晶体管	Bómó jīngtǐguǎn
TFT	Traffic flow template	业务流样板	Yèwùliú yàngbǎn
TFTP	Trivial file transfer protocol	简单文件传输协议	Jiǎndān wénjiàn chuánshū xiéyì
TFTP	Trivial file transfer protocol	简单文件传送协议	Jiǎndān wénjiàn chuánsòng xiéyì
TFTP	Trivial file transfer protocol	简易文件传输协议	Jiǎnyì wénjiàn chuánshū xiéyì
TFTP	Trivial file transfer protocol	平凡文件传输协议	Píngfán wénjiàn chuánshū xiéyì
TFTP	Trivial file transfer protocol	普通文件传送协议	Pǔtōng wénjiàn chuánsòng xiéyì
TFTP	Trivial file transfer protocol	一般文件传输协议	Yībān wénjiàn chuánshū xiéyì
TFWA	Terrestrial fixed wireless access	地面固定无线接入	Dìmiàn gùdìng wúxiàn jiērù
TGNP	The greatest noise power	最大噪声功率	Zuìdà zàoshēng gōnglǜ
TGS	Token granting server (ISO security)	票证许可服务器	Piàozhèng xǔkě fúwùqì
TGT	Ticket granting ticket	赋予票据的票据	Fùyǔ piàojùde piàojù
TGW	Trunk gateway	中继网关	Zhōngjì wǎngguān
TH	Time hopping	跳时	Tiàoshí
THA	Temporary home agent	临时家乡代理	Línshí jiāxiāng dàilǐ
THD	Total harmonic distortion	总谐波失真	Zǒng xiébō shīzhēn
THD+N	Total harmonic distortion plus noise	总谐波失真加噪音	Zǒng xiébō shīzhēn jiā zàoyīn

TI	Texas Instruments	德州仪器	Dézhōu yíqì
TI	Timestamp interval	时标段	Shíbiāo duàn
TI	Timing information	定时信息	Dìngshí xìnxī
TI	Transaction identifier	交易标识符	Jiāoyì biāozhìfú
TI	Transaction identifier	事务标识	Shìwù biāozhì
TI	Transaction identifier	事务处理标识符	Shìwù chǔlǐ biāozhìfú
TIA	Telecommunication Industries Association (US)	电信工业协会	Diànxìn gōngyè xiéhuì
TIA	Telecommunications Industry Association	通信工业协会	Tōngxìn gōngyè xiéhuì
TIA	Telecommunications Industry Association (US)	美国电信工业协会	Měiguó diànxìn gōngyè xiéhuì
TIC	Terminal international center	终端国际中心	Zhōngduān guójì zhōngxīn
TIC	Token ring interface coupler	令牌环接口耦合器	Lìngpái huán jiēkǒu ǒuhéqì
TICRG	Tungsten impregnated cathode ray gun (video)	钨传输阴级射线枪	Wū chuánshū yīnjí shèxiàn qiāng
TID	Terminal identification	终端标识	Zhōngduān biāozhì
TID	Tunnel identifier	隧道标识符	Suìdào biāozhìfú
TIE	Time interval error	时间间隔误差	Shíjiān jiàngé wùchā
TIEA	TSB interface E1 board assembly	TSB E1 接口集成板	TSB E1 jiēkǒu jíchéngbǎn
TIFF	Tagged image file format	标签图像文件格式	Biāoqiān túxiàng wénjiàn géshi
TIGER	Topologically integrated geographical encoding and reference	一体化拓扑地理编码和参照	Yītǐhuà tuòpū dìlǐ biānmǎ hé cānzhào
TIM	Technical information management	技术信息管理	Jìshù xìnxī guǎnlǐ
TIM	Timing circuit	定时电路	Dìngshí diànlù
TIM	Timing circuit	时间电路	Shíjiān diànlù
TIM	Trace identifier mismatch	追踪识别符失配	Zhuīzōng shíbiéfú shīpèi
TIM	Trace identifier mismatch	踪迹识别符失配	Zōngjī shíbiéfú shīpèi
TIM	Trail identification mismatch	路径识别符失配	Lùjìng shíbiéfú shīpèi
TIN	Triangular irregular network	不规则三角网	Bùguīzé sānjiǎo wǎng
TINA	Telecommunications information networking architecture	电信信息组网结构	Diànxìn xìnxī zǔwǎng jiégòu
TIP	Transceiver interface processor	收发信机接口处理器	Shōufāxìnjī jiēkǒu chǔlǐqì
TIR	Total internal reflection (type of FOC)	全反射导光型	Quánfǎnshè dǎoguāng xíng
TIRB	Timer interrupt request block	时标中断请求块	Shíbiāo zhōngduàn qǐngqiú kuài
TITA	TSB interface T1 board assembly	TSB T1 接口集成板	TSB T1 jiēkǒu jíchéngbǎn
TIU	Trusted interface unit (ISO security)	可信接入单元	Kěxìn jiērù dānyuán
TK	Token	令牌	Lìngpái
TKEQ	Tape deck equipment	放音设备	Fàngyīn shèbèi
TKT	Tape deck trunk	放音中继	Fàngyīn zhōngjì
TL	Transport layer	传送层	Chuánsòng céng
TLA	Transmitted waveform amplitude	输出波形幅度	Shūchū bōxíng fúdù
TLAID	Top level aggregation identifier	顶级聚集标识符	Dǐngjí jùjí biāozhìfú
TLB	Translate look-side buffer	翻译旁视缓冲器	Fānyì pángshì huǎnchōngqì
TLDN	Mobile subscriber temporary local directory number	移动用户临时本地电话号码	Yídòng yònghù línshí běndì diànhuà hàomǎ
TLDN	Temporary local directory number	临时本地号码	Línshí běndì hàomǎ
TLDN	Temporary local directory number	临时本地号码簿号码	Línshí běndì hàomǎbù hàomǎ
TLLI	Temporary link level identity	临时链路电平识别	Línshí liànlù diànpíng shíbié
TLLI	Temporary logic link identity	临时逻辑链路识别	Línshí luóji liànlù shíbié
TLLI	Temporary logical link identity	临时逻辑链路标识	Línshí luóji liànlù biāozhì
TLLI	Temporary logical link identity	临时逻辑链路识别	Línshí luóji liànlù shíbié

TLN	Trunk line network	中继线网络	Zhōngjìxiàn wǎngluò
TLS	Time limited service	时限服务	Shíxiàn fúwù
TLS	Transport layer security	传输层安全	Chuánshū céng ānquán
TLS	Transport layer security	传输层安全性	Chuánshū céng ānquánxìng
TLS	Transport layer security protocol	安全传输层协议	Ānquán chuánshū céng xiéyì
TLSW	Trunk line switch	中继链路开关	Zhōngjì liànlù kāiguān
TLV	Type-length-value	类型长度值	Lèixíng chángdù zhí
TLV	Type-length-value	类型-长度-取值的编码格式	Lèixíng-chángdù-qǔzhíde biānmǎ géshi
TLV	Type-length-value	类型--长度--值	Lèixíng-chángdù-zhí
TM	Tandem switch	汇接交换机	Huìjiē jiāohuànjī
TM	Terminal multiplexer	终端多路复用器	Zhōngduān duōlù fùyòngqì
TM	Terminal multiplexer	终端复用器	Zhōngduān fùyòngqì
TM	Terminal multiplexing	终端复用	Zhōngduān fùyòng
TM	Test management	测试管理	Cèshì guǎnlǐ
TM	Test mobile	测试移动台	Cèshì yídòngtái
TM	Tone modulation	音调调制	Yīndiào tiáozhì
TM	Traffic management	信息量管理	Xìnxīliàng guǎnlǐ
TM	Transaction manager	事务管理器	Shìwù guǎnlǐqì
TM	Transport media	传送媒体	Chuánsòng méitǐ
TM	Transverse magnetic mode	横磁模	Héngcí mó
Tm, TO	Tandem office	汇接局	Huìjiē jú
TMA	Terrestrial mobile access	地面移动接入	Dìmiàn yídòng jiērù
TMBP	Telephony device master back panel	电话设备主机后面板	Diànhuà shèbèi zhǔjī hòumianbǎn
TMC	Telecommunication maintenance center	远程通信维护中心	Yuǎnchéng tōngxìn wéihù zhōngxīn
TMF	Telecommunications Management Forum, TeleManagement Forum	电信管理论坛	Diànxìn guǎnlǐ lùntán
TMG	Tactical multi-net gateway	战术多网网间连接器	Zhànshù duōwǎng wǎng jiān liánjiēqì
TMG	Trunk media gateway	干线媒体网关	Gànxiàn méitǐ wǎngguān
TMIPM	Trilinear MIP mapping	三次线性 MIP 材质贴图	Sāncì xiànxìng MIP cáizhì tiē tú
TMIS	Telephone management information system	电话管理信息系统	Diànhuà guǎnlǐ xìnxī xìtǒng
TMN	Telecommunication management network	通信管理网络	Tōngxìn guǎnlǐ wǎngluò
TMN	Telecommunications management network	电信管理网	Diànxìn guǎnlǐ wǎng
TMN	Telecommunications Management network	电信管理网络	Diànxìn guǎnlǐ wǎngluò
TMN MF	Telecommunications Management network-management function	电信管理网管理功能	Diànxìn guǎnlǐ wǎng guǎnlǐ gōngnéng
TMN MS	Telecommunications Management network-management service	电信管理网管理业务	Diànxìn guǎnlǐ wǎng guǎnlǐ yèwù
TMN MSC	Telecommunications Management network-management service components	电信管理网管理业务成分	Diànxìn guǎnlǐ wǎng guǎnlǐ yèwù chéngfèn
TMO	Time-out	超时	Chāoshí
TMO	Time-out	时间已过	Shíjiān yǐguò
TMP	Test management protocol	测试管理协议	Cèshì guǎnlǐ xiéyì
TMR	Analog trunked mobile radio	模拟集群流动通讯	Mónǐ jíqún liúdòng tōngxùn
TMR	Transmission medium requirement	传输媒介请求	Chuánshū méijiè qǐngqiú
TMS	Test mode selector [bus]	测试模式选择[总线]	Cèshì móshì xuǎnzé (zǒngxiàn)
TMSC	Tandem mobile switching center	移动汇接中心	Yídòng huìjiē zhōngxīn
TMSC	Tandem MSC	汇接 MSC	Huìjiē MSC
TMSI	Temporary mobile station identity	临时移动台识别码	Línshí yídòng tái shíbié mǎ
TMSI	Temporary mobile subscriber identity	临时移动用户标识	Línshí yídòng yònghù biāozhì

TMSI	Temporary mobile subscriber identity	临时移动用户识别号码	Línshí yídòng yònghù shíbié hàomǎ
TMUX	Transmultiplexer	复用转换器	Fùyòng zhuǎnhuànqì
TMUX	Trans-multiplexer	子速率复用器	Zisùlǜ fùyòngqì
TMUX	Transparent multiplexing equipment	透明复用设备	Tòumíng fùyòng shèbèi
TN	Time slot number	时隙号	Shíxì hào
TN	Timeslot number	时隙号码	Shíxì hàomǎ
TN	Transit network	转移网	Zhuǎnyí wǎng
TNC	Terminal national center	终端国内中心	Zhōngduān guónèi zhōngxīn
TNC	Transit node clock	转接节点时钟	Zhuǎnjiē jiédiǎn shízhōng
TNDB	Task number definition block	任务号码定义块	Rènwu hàomǎ dìngyì kuài
TNL	Total noise level	总噪声级	Zǒng zàoshēng jí
Tnotify	Time notify	时间通知	Shíjiān tōngzhī
TNR	Terabit network router	太比特网络路由器	Tài bǐtè wǎngluò lùyóuqì
TNS	Tactical name server	战术名字服务器	Zhànshù míngzì fúwùqì
TNS	Transit network segment	转接网络段	Zhuǎnjiē wǎngluò duàn
TO	Telecommunication outlet	通信引出端	Tōngxìn yǐnchū duān
TO	Telecommunication outlet (as RS-232, RJ-11)	信息插座	Xìnxī chāzuò
TO	Telecommunications operations map	通信运行地址变换	Tōngxìn yùnxíng dìzhǐ biànhuàn
TO	Telecommunications outlet	电信引出端	Diànxìn yǐnchū duān
TO	Telecommunications outlet	通信插座	Tōngxìn chāzuò
TO	Temporary offset	临时偏移	Línshí piānyí
TO	Temporary offset	暂时偏移	Zànshí piānyí
TO	Time-out error	过时错误	Guòshí cuòwù
TOA	Time of arrival	到达时间	Dàodá shíjiān
TOA	Type of address	地址类型	Dìzhǐ lèixíng
TOA/NPI	Type of address /numbering plan identifier	地址类型/编号方案标识符	Dìzhǐ lèixíng/ biānhào fāng'àn biāozhì fú
TOC	Tactical operations center	战术作战中心	Zhànshù zuòzhàn zhōngxīn
TOC	Transfer of control	转移控制	Zhuǎnyí kòngzhì
TOD	Time of day	时刻	Shíkè
TOE	Terminal operation environment	远端运行环境	Yuǎnduān yùnxíng huánjìng
TOG	The Open Group	开发组织	Kāifā zǔzhī
TOLR	Transmit objective loudness result	发送客观响度评定值	Fāsòng kèguān xiǎngdù píngdìngzhí
TON	Type of number	编号方式	Biānhào fāngshì
TON	Type of number	号码类型	Hàomǎ lèixíng
TOP	Task-oriented procedure	面向任务过程	Miànxiàng rènwu guòchéng
TOP	Technical office protocol	技术办公协议	Jìshù bàngōng xiéyì
TORA	Temporary ordered routing algorithm	临时按序路由算法	Línshí ànxù lùyóu suànfǎ
TOS	Type of service	服务类型	Fúwù lèixíng
ToS	Type of service	业务类别	Yèwù lèibié
TOSCA	TINA open service creation architecture	TINA 开放业务生产结构	TINA kāifàng yèwù shēngchǎn jiégòu
TP	Temperature probe	温度传感器	Wēndù chuángǎnqì
TP	Terminal portability	终端可携带性	Zhōngduān kěxiédà xìng
TP	Third party	第三团体	Dìsān tuántǐ
TP	Timing point	定时点	Dìngshí diǎn
TP	Transfer layer protocol	传输层协议	Chuánshū céng xiéyì
TP	Transition point	转接点	Zhuǎnjiēdiǎn

TP	Transmission path	传输通路	Chuánshū tōnglù
TP	Transport layer protocol (in ISO's OSI)	传输层协议	Chuánshū céng xiéyì
TP	Transport path	传送通道	Chuánsòng tōngdào
TP	Transport plane	传送平面	Chuánsòng píngmiàn
TP	Trust policy	信任策略	Xìnrèn cèlüè
TP	Twisted pair	对绞线	Duìjiǎo xiàn
TP4	ISO transport protocol class 4	ISO 运输层协议 4 级	ISO yùnshū céng xiéyì 4 jí
TP4	Transport-level protocol 4	第四类运输层协议	Dìsìlèi yùnshū céng xiéyì
TPC	Third party copy	第三方拷贝	Dìsānfāng kǎobèi
TPC	Transmit power control	发射功率控制	Fāshè gōnglǜ kòngzhì
TPC	Transpacific cable	横渡太平洋的海底电缆	Héngdù Tàipíngyángde hǎidǐ diànlǎn
TPDDI	Twisted pair distributed data interface	双较线分布式数据接口	Shuāng jiàoxiàn fēnbù-shì shùjù jiēkǒu
TPDU	Transfer protocol data unit	传输协议数据单元	Chuánshū xiéyì shùjù dānyuán
TPDU	Transport protocol data unit	传送协议数据单元	Chuánsòng xiéyì shùjù dānyuán
TPDU	Transport protocol data unit	运输协议数据单元	Yùnshū xiéyì shùjù dānyuán
TPE	Thermoplastic polyester elastomer (FOC)	热塑性聚酯弹性体	Rèsùxìng jùzhǐ tánxìngtǐ
TPE	Transmission path endpoint	传输通路端点	Chuánshū tōnglù duāndiǎn
TPF	Termination point fragment	端点段	Duāndiǎn duàn
TPI	Tag protocol information	标记协议信息	Biāojì xiéyì xìnxī
TPID	Tag protocol identifier	标记协议标识符	Biāojì xiéyì biāozhì fú
TPL	Test program language	试验程序语言	Shìyàn chéngxù yǔyán
TPMA	Timed pre-assigned multiple access	定时预分配多路存取	Dìngshí yù fēnpèi duōlù cúnqǔ
TPS	Transactions per second	每秒处理事项数	Měi miǎo chǔlǐ shìxiàng shù
TPS-TC	Transmission protocol-specific TC layer	传输协议特定传输汇聚层	Chuánshū xiéyì tèdìng chuánshū huìjù céng
TPSU	Transceiver power supply unit	收发信机功率供给单元	Shōufāxìnjī gōnglǜ gōngjǐ dānyuán
TQI	Temporary queuing identity	临时排队识别	Línshí páiduì shíbié
TQM	Total quality management	全面质量管理	Quánmiàn zhìliàng guǎnlǐ
TR	Receiver transient disturbance	收信机的瞬态骚扰	Shōuxìnjīde shùntài sāorǎo
Tr	Restoration time	恢复时间	Huīfù shíjiān
TR	Technical report	技术报告	Jìshù bàogào
TR	Threshold report	门限报告	Ménxiàn bàogào
TR	Token ring	令牌环	Lìngpái huán
TR	Token ring	令牌网	Lìngpái wǎng
TR	Token ring	权标环	Quánbiāo huán
TR	Tributary (SDH term)	支路	Zhīlù
TR	Trunked radio	中继式无线电	Zhōngjìshì wúxiàndiàn
Tr/Th	Transient signal rise time	瞬态信号的上升时间	Shùntài xìnhàode shàngshēng shíjiān
TRACE	Toll recording and computing equipment	长途电话记录和计算设备	Chángtú diànhuà jìlù hé jìsuàn shèbèi
TRACE	Total remote assistance center	远程辅助总中心	Yuǎnchéng fǔzhù zǒng zhōngxīn
TRAIM	Timing receiver autonomous integrity monitoring	定时接收机自主完善性监测	Dìngshí jiēshōujī zìzhǔ wánshànxìng jiāncè
TRAU	Transcoder and rate adaptation unit	码型转换和速率适配单元	Mǎ-xíng zhuǎnhuàn hé sùlǜ shìpèi dānyuán
TRAU	Transcoder and rate adapter unit	码变换速率适配单元	Mǎ biànhuàn sùlǜ shìpèi dānyuán
TRB	Time reference beamforming	时间参考波束成型	Shíjiān cānkǎo bōshù chéngxíng
TrCH	Transport channel	传送信道	Chuánsòng xìndào
TRIAC	Triode AC switch	三极管交流开关	Sānjíguǎn jiāoliú kāiguān
TRIP	Telephony routing over IP	IP 网上电话路由选择	IP wǎng-shàng diànhuà lùyóu xuǎnzé

TRIP	Telephony routing over IP	IP 电话路由	IP diànhuà lùyóu
TRIP	Token ring interface processor	令牌环接口处理器	Lìngpái huán jiēkǒu chǔlǐqì
Triple-DES	Triple data encryption standard	三重数字加密标准	Sānchóng shùzì jiāmì biāozhǔn
TRPSK	Transmitted reference-phase shift keying	发送参考相移键控	Fāsòng cānkǎo xiàngyí jiànkòng
TRptr	Performance criteria for transient phenomena applied to repeaters and ancillary RF amplifiers	中继器和辅助射频放大器的瞬态骚扰性能判据	Zhōngjìqì hé fǔzhù shèpín fàngdàqìde shùntài sāorǎo xìngnéng pànjù
TRR	Trouble recorder	故障记录器	Gùzhàng jìlùqì
TRS	Telephone repeater station	电话中继局	Diànhuà zhōngjì jú
TRUP	Transceiver unit processor	收发信机单元处理器	Shōufāxìnjī dānyuán chǔlǐqì
TRX	Transceiver (board)	收发信机（板）	Shōufāxìnjī (bǎn)
TS	Technical specification	技术规范	Jìshù guīfàn
TS	Teleservice	电传业务	Diànchuán yèwù
TS	Teleservice	电信业务	Diànxìn yèwù
TS	Terminal station	终端站	Zhōngduān zhàn
TS	Time slot	时隙	Shíxì
TS	Timestamp	时标	Shíbiāo
TS	Toll switch	长途交换机	Chángtú jiāohuànjī
TS	Toll switch	长途交换局	Chángtú jiāohuànjú
TS	Toll switch	长途局	Chángtújú
TS	Toll switch office	长话交换局	Chánghuà jiāohuànjú
TS	Transport service	运输服务	Yùnshū fúwù
TSA	Time slot access	时隙访问	Shíxì fǎngwèn
TSAC	Time slot assignment circuit	时间片分配电路	Shíjiān piàn fēnpèi diànlù
TSAP	Transport service access point	传输服务存取点	Chuánshū fúwù cúnqǔdiǎn
TSAP	Transport service access point	传送服务接入点	Chuánsòng fúwù jiērù diǎn
TSAP	Transport service access point	运输服务访问点	Yùnshū fúwù fǎngwèn diǎn
TSAPI	Telephony services application programming interface	电话服务应用程序接口	Diànhuà fúwù yìngyòng chéngxù jiēkǒu
TSB	Transcoder and selector bank	译码和选择器	Yìmǎ hé xuǎnzéqì
TSBP	Time switch back panel	时分交换后面板	Shífēn jiāohuàn hòumian bǎn
TSBR	Transcoder and selector bank rack	译码和选择器机架	Yìmǎ hé xuǎnzéqì jījià
TSC	Training sequence code	训练系列号	Xùnliàn xìliè hào
TSC	Training sequence code	训练序列码	Xùnliàn xùliè mǎ
TSC	Transcoder sub-multiplexer controller	码变换子复用控制器	Mǎ biànhuàn zifùyòng kòngzhìqì
TSCM	Time switch control and maintenance	时分交换控制和维护	Shífēn jiāohuàn kòngzhì hé wéihù
TSD	Time scale decomposition	时间数量级分解	Shíjiān shùliàngjí fēnjiě
TSD	Trail signal degrade (ATM term)	路径信号劣化	Lùjìng xìnhào lièhuà
TSDI	Transceiver speech and data interface	收发信机话音和数据接口	Shōufāxìnjī huàyīn hé shùjù jiēkǒu
TSDU	Transport service data unit	运输服务数据单元	Yùnshū fúwù shùjù dānyuán
TSES	Time-sharing executive system	分时执行系统	Fēnshí zhíxíng xìtǒng
TSF	Time series forecasting	时间序列预测	Shíjiān xùliè yùcè
TSF	Trail signal fail	路径信号失效	Lùjìng xìnhào shīxiào
TS-FX	Toll switch-facsimile equipment	长途交换传真设备	Chángtú jiāohuàn chuánzhēn shèbèi
TSG	Technical specification group	技术规范小组	Jìshù guīfàn xiǎozǔ
T-SGW	Transport signaling gateway	传送信令网关	Chuánsòng xìnlìng wǎngguān
TSI	Time slot interchange	时隙交换	Shíxì jiāohuàn
TSI	Time slot interchanging	时隙互换	Shíxì hùhuàn

TSID	Technical support identification number	技术支持代码	Jìshù zhīchí dàimǎ
TSID	Test signal identification	测试信号识别	Cèshì xìnhào shíbié
TSK	Time shift keying	时移键控	Shíyí jiànkòng
TSL	Task specification language	任务定义语言	Rènwu dìngyì yǔyán
TSM	Test manager	测试管理器	Cèshì guǎnlǐqì
TSN	Telecommunications supporting networks	电信支撑网	Diànxìn zhīchēng wǎng
TSN	Transit service node	转接服务节点	Zhuǎnjiē fúwù jiédiǎn
TSN	Transport serial number	传送顺序号	Chuánsòng shùnxù hào
TSOP	Thin small outline package	超小型封装	Chāoxiǎoxing fēngzhuāng
TSP	Third party service provider	第三方业务提供者	Dìsānfāng yèwù tígòngzhě
TSP	Transmission layer security protocol	传输层安全协议	Chuánshū céng ānquán xiéyì
TSP	Traveling salesman problem	旅行商问题	Lǚxíng shāng wèntí
TSR	Tag switch router	标记交换路由器	Biāojì jiāohuàn lùyóuqì
TSR	Terabit switch router	太比特交换路由器	Tài bǐtè jiāohuàn lùyóuqì
TSR	Terminate and stay resident	终结并常驻内存	Zhōngjié bìng chángzhù nèicún
TSR	Terminate-and-stay-resident program	终止并驻留内存程序	Zhōngzhǐ bìng zhùliú nèicún chéngxù
TSS&TP	Test suite structure and test purposes	测试组结构和测试目的	Cèshì zǔ jiégòu hé cèshì mùdì
TSTD	Time switched transmission diversity	时间切换发送分集	Shíjiān qiēhuàn fāsòng fēnjí
TSTD	Time switched transmit diversity	分时发分集	Fēnshí fāfēnjí
TSTS	Temporal status transition system	时序状态转换系统	Shíxù zhuàngtài zhuǎnhuàn xìtǒng
TSU	Time slot switching unit	时隙交换单元	Shíxì jiāohuàn dānyuán
TSU	To switch unit	到交换单元	Dào jiāohuàn dānyuán
TT	Trail termination function	路径终端功能	Lùjìng zhōngduān gōngnéng
TT	Trail termination function	路径终结功能	Lùjìng zhōngjié gōngnéng
TT	Transcode type	译码类型	Yìmǎ lèixíng
TT	Transmitter transient disturbance	发信机的瞬态骚扰	Fāxìnjīde shùntài sāorǎo
Tt	Transfer time	转移时间	Zhuǎnyí shíjiān
TTA	Telecommunication Technology Association	电信技术协会	Diànxìn jìshù xiéhuì
TTC	Terminating toll center	终端长途电话局	Zhōngduān chángtú diànhuàjú
TTCN	Tree and tabular combined notation	树表结合表示	Shù biǎo jiéhé biǎoshì
TTCN	Tree and tabular combined notation	树形和板状的组合标志	Shùxíng hé bǎnzhuàngde zǔhé biāozhì
TTCN	Tree tabular combined notation	数表结合的表示法	Shùbiǎo jiéhéde biǎoshì fǎ
TTF	Transport terminal function	传送终端功能	Chuánsòng zhōngduān gōngnéng
TTFF	Time to first fix (in position location)	首次定位时长	Shǒucì dìngwèi shícháng
TTI	Trail trace identifier	路径踪迹识别符	Lùjìng zōngjī shíbiéfú
TTI	Trail trace identifier multi-frame	路径踪迹识别复帧	Lùjing zōngjī shíbiéfù zhèng
TTI	Transmission time interval	传输时间间隔	Chuánshū shíjiān jiàngé
TTIB	Transparent tone-in-band single sideband	透明带内导频单边带	Tòumíng dàinèi dǎopín dānbiāndài
TTIP	Trail trace identifier processing	路径踪迹标识处理	Lùjìng zōngjī biāozhì chǔlǐ
TTL	Time to live	存活期	Cúnhuóqī
TTL	Time to live	生存时间	Shēngcún shíjiān
TTL	Time to live (SDH term)	生存期	Shēngcún qī
TTL	Transistor-transistor logic circuit	晶体管晶体管逻辑电路	Jīngtǐguǎn jīngtǐguǎn luójidiànlù
TTM	Transit-time modulation	渡越时间调制	Dùyuè shíjiān tiáozhì
TTP	Trail termination point	踪迹终结点	Zōngjī zhōngjié diǎn
TTP	Trusted third party	受托第三方	Shòutuō dìsānfāng

TTP	Trusted third party	中立第三方	Zhōnglì dìsānfāng
TTP	Trusted third party (IPsec)	可信任的第三方	Kěxìnrènde dì sān fāng
TTS	Text-to-speech	文语转换	Wén yǔ zhuǎnhuàn
TTS	Text-to-speech conversion	文本至语音的转换	Wénběn zhì yǔyīnde zhuǎnhuàn
TTS	Tri-technology sensor	三鉴传感器	Sānjiàn chuángǎnqì
TTT	The TINA trial	TINA 试验	TINA shìyàn
TTX	Teletex	智能用户电报	Zhìnéng yònghù diànbào
TTX	Teletext	电视数据	Diànshì shùjù
TU	Terrestrial urban	平坦城市	Píngtǎn chéngshì
TU	Tributary unit	支路单元	Zhīlù dānyuán
TU PTR	Tributary unit pointer	支路单元指针	Zhīlù dānyuán zhǐzhēn
TU/AU	Tributary unit/administrative unit	支路单元/管理单元	Zhīlù dānyuán/guǎnlǐ dānyuán
TU-AIS	Tributary unit alarm indication signal	支路单元告警指示信号	Zhīlù dānyuán gàojǐng zhǐshì xìnhào
TUCB	Transmit up-converter board	传送增频变频器板	Chuánsòng zēngpín biànpínqì bǎn
TUD	Trunk up-down	干线升降	Gànxiàn shēngjiàng
TUG	Tributary unit group	支路单元组	Zhīlù dānyuán zǔ
TU-LOM	Tributary unit-loss of multi-frame	支路单元复帧丢失	Zhīlù dānyuán fù zhèng diūshī
TU-LOP	Tributary unit loss of pointer	支路单元指针丢失	Zhīlù dānyuán zhǐzhēn diūshī
TUNNETT	Tunnel transit time diode	隧道渡越时间二极管	Suìdào dùyuè shíjiān èrjíguǎn
TUP	Telephone user part (SS7)	电话用户部分	Diànhuà yònghù bùfen
TUP	Tributary unit pointer	支路单元指针	Zhīlù dānyuán zhǐzhēn
TUPP	Tributary unit payload processing	支路净荷处理	Zhīlù jìnghé chǔlǐ
TVC	Topologic validity condition (CAD/CAM)	拓扑有效性条件	Tuòpū yǒuxiàoxìng tiáojiàn
TVPC	Television-capable personal computer	电视电脑	Diànshì diànnǎo
TVRO	Television receive only ground station	电视接收地面站	Diànshì jiēshōu dìmiànzhàn
TWA	Terrestrial wireless access	地面无线接入	Dìmiàn wúxiàn jiērù
TWA	Trailing wire antenna	下垂天线	Xiàchuí tiānxiàn
TWA	Traveling wave antenna	行波天线	Xíngbō tiānxiàn
TWA	Two way alternate	双向交替	Shuāngxiàng jiāotì
TWA	Two-way alternate	双向交替	Shuāngxiàng jiāotì
TWBC	Single mode two window broadband coupler	单模双窗宽带分光器	Dānmó shuāngchuāng kuāndài fēnguāngqì
TWDM	Tap coupler/filter wavelength division multiplexer	分光器/滤波型波分复用器	Fēnguāngqì/lǜbōxíng bōfēn fùyòngqì
TWG	Terminal Working Group (GSM MoU)	终端工作组	Zhōngduān gōngzuòzǔ
TWP	Twisted wire pair	双扭线对	Shuāng niǔxiànduì
TWS	Thumb wheel switch	拇指旋转开关	Mǔzhǐ xuánzhuǎn kāiguān
TWS	Two way simultaneous	双向同时	Shuāngxiàng tóngshí
TWS	Two-way simultaneous call	同时双向互发	Tóngshí shuāngxiàng hùfā
TWSC	Single mode two window broadband star coupler	单模双窗宽带星型分光器	Dānmó shuāngchuāng kuāndài xīngxíng fēnguāngqì
TWT	Traveling wave tube	行波管	Xíngbōguǎn
TWTA	Traveling wave tube amplifier	行波管放大器	Xíngbōguǎn fàngdàqì
TWTC	Single mode two window broadband tree coupler	单模双窗宽带树型分光器	Dānmó shuāngchuāng kuāndài shùxíng fēnguāngqì
Tx	Optical transmitter	光发射机	Guāng fāshèjī
Tx	Optical transmitter	光发送机	Guāng fāsòngjī
TX	Short wave antenna	短波天线	Duǎnbō tiānxiàn
TX	Terminating toll operator	长途终局话务员	Chángtú zhōngjú huàwùyuán

TX	Transmit	发射	Fāshè
Tx	Transmit	发送	Fāsòng
Tx	Transmitter	发送机	Fāsòngjī
Tx	Transmitter/transmission	发信机/发射	Fāxìnjī/ Fāshè

U

U	Asymptotic unavailability	渐近不可用性	Jiànjìn bùkěyòngxìng
U(t)	Instantaneous unavailability	瞬时不可用性	Shùnshí bùkěyòngxìng
UA	Unicast addressing	单向广播地址	Dānxiàng guǎngbō dìzhǐ
UA	Unipole antenna	单极天线	Dānjí tiānxiàn
UA	Unnumbered acknowledge	无编号确认	Wúbiānhào quèrèn
UA	Unnumbered acknowledge	无编号证实	Wúbiānhào zhèngshí
UA	User agent	用户代理	Yònghù dàilǐ
UAC	Unbalanced asynchronous class	不平衡操作的异步响应类别	Bùpínghéng cāozuòde yìbù xiǎngyìng lèibié
UAC	User agent client	用户代理客户	Yònghù dàilǐ kèhù
UADSL	Universal asynchronous digital subscriber line	通用非对称数字用户线	Tōngyòng fēiduìchèn shùzì yònghù xiàn
UADSL	Usual asymmetric digital subscriber line	通用不对称数字用户线路	Tōngyòng bùduìchèn shùzì yònghù xiànlù
UAN	Universal access number	通用接入号码	Tōngyòng jiērù hàomǎ
UAP	Upper address part	高位地址部分	Gāowèi dìzhǐ bùfen
UARFCN	Utra absolute radio frequency channel number	UTRA 绝对无线电频率信道号码	UTRA juéduì wúxiàndiàn pínlǜ xìndào hàomǎ
UARFN	Utra absolute radio frequency number	UTRA 绝对无线电频率号码	UTRA juéduì wúxiàndiàn pínlǜ hàomǎ
UART	Universal asynchronous receiver/transmitter	通用异步接收/发送装置	Tōngyòng yìbù jiēshōu/fāsòng zhuāngzhì
UART	Universal asynchronous receiver/transmitter	通用异步收/发器	Tōngyòng yìbù shōu/fāqì
UAS	Unavailable second	不可用秒	Bùkěyòng miǎo
UAS	Unified access server	综合接入服务器	Zōnghé jiērù fúwùqì
UAS	Universal audio server	通用话音服务器	Tōngyòng huàyīn fúwùqì
UAS	User agent server	用户代理服务器	Yònghù dàilǐ fúwùqì
UAT	Ultra aperture terminal	超小口径卫星地面接收站	Chāoxiǎo kǒujìng wèixīng dìmiàn jiēshōu zhàn
UAT	Unavailable time	不可用时间	Bùkěyòng shíjiān
UAWG	Universal ADSL Working Group	通用 ADSL 工作组	Tōngyòng ADSL gōngzuòzǔ
UBA	Unblocking acknowledgement signal	解除闭塞信号	Jiěchú bìsè xìnhào
UBL	Unblocking request (ISUP message)	解除闭塞请求	Jiěchú bìsè qǐngqiú
UBM	Unsuccessful backward set-up information message	后向建立不成功消息	Hòuxiàng jiànlì bùchéng gōng xiāoxi
UBR	Undefined bit rate	未指定比特率	Wèizhǐdìng bǐtèlǜ
UBR	Unspecified bit rate	未规定比特率	Wèiguīdìng bǐtèlǜ
UBR	Unspecified bit rate	未指定比特率	Wèizhǐdìng bǐtèlǜ
UC	User control	用户控制	Yònghù kòngzhì
U-C	Central office line U reference point	局端线路 U 参考点	Júduān xiànlù U cānkǎo diǎn
U-C	Loop interface-central office end	局端环路接口	Júduān huánlù jiēkǒu
U-C2	Central office line U reference point 2	局端线路 U 参考点 2	Júduān xiànlù U cānkǎo diǎn 2
UCC	Unified contact center	统一联络中心	Tǒngyī liánluò zhōngxīn
UCC-REQ	Uplink channel change request message	上行信道改变请求消息	Shàngxíng xìndào gǎibiàn qǐngqiú xiāoxi
UCC-RSP	Uplink channel change response message	上行信道改变响应消息	Shàngxíng xìndào gǎibiàn xiǎngyìng xiāoxi
UCD	Uplink channel descriptor message	上行信道描述符消息	Shàngxíng xìndào miáoshùfú xiāoxi

UCF	Unregistration confirmed (packet protocol)	注销确认	Zhùxiāo quèrèn
UCIC	Unequipped circuit identification code (ISUP message)	未装电路标志码	Wèizhuāng diànlù biāozhìmǎ
UCMM	Unconnected message manager	非连接报文管理器	Fēiliánjiē bàowén guǎnlǐqì
UCS	Universal multiple-octet coded character set	通用多 8 位编码字符集	Tōngyòng duō bāwèi biānmǎ zìfú jí
UCS2	Universal character set 2	集合 2 通用符号	Jíhé er tōngyòng fúhào
UD	Unit driver	装置驱动器	Zhuāngzhì qūdòngqì
UDA	Universal data access	万能数据访问	Wànnéng shùjù fǎngwèn
UDD	Unconstrained delay data	无约束时延的数据	Wúyuēshù shíyánde shùjù
UDDI	Universal description, discovery and integration protocol	通用描述发现和集成协议	Tōngyòng miáoshù fāxiàn hé jíchéng xiéyì
UDF	User defined function	用户定义功能	Yònghù dìngyì gōngnéng
UDF	User defined function	用户定义函数	Yònghù dìngyì hánshù
UDHI	User data header indicator	用户数据报头指示	Yònghù shùjù bàotóu zhǐshì
UDI	Unrestricted digital information	不受限制数字信息	Bùshòuxiànzhì shùzì xìnxī
UDI	Unrestricted digital information	无限制的数字信息	Wúxiànzhìde shùzì xìnxī
UDP	User data protocol	用户数据协议	Yònghù shùjù xiéyì
UDP	User datagram protocol	用户数据报文协议	Yònghù shùjù bàowén xiéyì
UDP	User datagram protocol	用户数据报协议	Yònghù shùjùbào xiéyì
UDSL	Ultra-high-speed digital subscriber line	超高速数字用户线	Chāogāosù shùzì yònghù xiàn
UDTR	User designed data register	用户设计数据寄存器	Yònghù shèjì shùjù jìcúnqì
UDUB	User determined user busy	用户确定用户忙	Yònghù quèdìng yònghù máng
UDWDM	Ultra-dense wavelength division multiplexing	超密集波分复用	Chāomìjí bōfēn fùyòng
UEP	Unequal error protection	非同等错误保护	Fēitóngděng cuòwù bǎohù
Uer	User equipment with ODMA relay operation enabled	用户设备能使用 ODMA 中继	Yònghù shèbèi néng shǐyòng ODMA zhōngjì
UF	Unnumbered frames	无编号帧	Wúbiānhào zhèng
UFI	Upstream failure indication	上游失效指示	Shàngyóu shīxiào zhǐshì
UFR	Unreliable frame rate	不可靠帧率	Bùkěkào zhèng lǜ
UGS	Unsolicited grant service	主动授权业务	Zhǔdòng shòuquán yèwù
UGS-AD	Unsolicited grant service with activity detection	带活动检测的主动授权业务	Dài huódòng jiǎncède zhǔdòng shòuquán yèwù
UGSH	Unsolicited grant synchronization header	主动授权同步包头	Zhǔdòng shòuquán tóngbù bāotóu
UHF	Ultra-high frequency	特高频	Tègāopín
UI	Unit interval	单位间隔	Dānwèi jiàngé
UI	Unit interval	单元间隔	Dānyuán jiàngé
UI	Unnumbered information	无编号信息	Wúbiānhào xìnxī
UI	Unnumbered information (frame)	无序信息（帧）	Wúxù xìnxī (zhèng)
UI	Unnumbered information frame	通用信息帧	Tōngyòng xìnxī zhèng
UI	Unnumbered information frame	无编号信息帧	Wúbiānhào xìnxī zhèng
UI	User interface	用户接口	Yònghù jiēkǒu
UICC	Universal integrated circuit card	通用集成电路卡	Tōngyòng jíchéng diànlù kǎ
UID	User interactive dialogue	用户交互对话	Yònghù jiāohù duìhuà
UIM	User interface manager	用户接口管理器	Yònghù jiēkǒu guǎnlǐqì
UITS	Unacknowledged information transfer service	不确认式信息传送服务	Bùquèrènshì xìnxī chuánsòng fúwù
UL	Underwriters Laboratories Inc. (US)	担保实验室	Dānbǎo shíyànshì
UL	Uplink	上行链路	Shàngxíng liànlù
ULF	Ultra-low frequency	超低频	Chāodīpín
ULH	Ultra long-haul fiber	超长光传输	Chāocháng guāng chuánshū

ULHOTT	Ultra long-haul optical transmission technology	超长光传输技术	Chāocháng guāng chuánshū jìshù
ULP	Upper level protocol	高层协议	Gāocéng xiéyì
ULS	Uplink services	卫星上链服务	Wèixīng shànglián fúwù
ULS	User location service	用户定位服务	Yònghù dìngwèi fúwù
Ultra DMA	Ultra direct memory access	超高速直接内存存取	Chāogāosù zhíjiē nèicún cúnqǔ
UM	Space connector	空中接口	Kōngzhōng jiēkǒu
UM	Unacknowledged mode	无应答模式	Wúyìngdá móshì
UM	Unidirectional microphone	单指向性传声器	Dānzhǐxiàng-xìng chuánshēngqì
UMA	Unified memory architecture	统一内存架构	Tǒngyī nèicún jiàgòu
UMC	United Microelectronics Corp. (Taiwan semiconductor maker)	联华电子公司	Liánhuá diànzǐ gōngsī
UMH	Unsolicited message handler	非请求消息处理器	Fēiqǐngqiú xiāoxi chǔlǐqì
UML	Unified modeling language	标准建模语言	Biāozhǔn jiànmó yǔyán
UML	Unified modeling language	统一建模语言	Tǒngyī jiànmó yǔyán
UML	Unified modeling language	一致性建模语言	Yīzhìxìng jiànmó yǔyán
UML	Unified modelling language	统一模型语言	Tǒngyī móxíng yǔyán
UMS	Unified message service	统一消息	Tǒngyī xiāoxi
UMS	Universal Memory System (Intel Corp.)	通用存储器系统	Tōngyòng cúnchǔqì xìtǒng
UMS	Universal messaging service	通用信息传送服务	Tōngyòng xìnxī chuánsòng fúwù
UMS	User mobility server	用户移动性服务器	Yònghù yídòngxìng fúwùqì
UMSC	UMTS mobile services switching center	UMTS 移动业务交换中心	UMTS yídòng yèwù jiāohuàn zhōngxīn
UMTS	Universal mobile telecommunication system	通用移动通信系统	Tōngyòng yídòng tōngxìn xìtǒng
UMTS	Universal mobile telecommunications system	通用移动电信系统	Tōngyòng yídòng diànxìn xìtǒng
UNA	Unattended answering accessory	无人管理应答辅助设备	Wúrén guǎnlǐ yìngdá fǔzhù shèbèi
UNA	Upstream neighbor's address	上游邻站地址	Shàngyóu línzhàn dìzhǐ
UNC	Unbalanced normal class	不平衡操作的正常响应类别	Bùpínghéng cāozuòde zhèngcháng xiǎngyìng lèibié
UNC	Unconnected	未连接	Wèiliánjiē
UNCITRAL	United Nations Commission on International Trade Law	联合国国际贸易法委员会	Liánhéguó guójì màoyìfǎ wěiyuánhuì
UNEQ	Unequal	未装载	Wèizhuāngzài
UNEQ	Unequipped	未装载	Wèizhuāngzài
UNI	User network interface	用户网络接口	Yònghù wǎngluò jiēkǒu
UNI	User node interface	拥护节点接口	Yōnghù jiédiǎn jiēkǒu
UNI	User-network interface	用户-用户接口	Yònghù—yònghù jiēkǒu
UNN	Unallocated-number, vacant number	空号	Kōnghào
UON	Universal object naming	通用对象命名	Tōngyòng duìxiàng mìngmíng
UP	User part	用户部分	Yònghù bùfen
UP	User plane	用户平面	Yònghù píngmiàn
UPA	Ultra port architecture	超级端口结构	Chāojí duānkǒu jiégòu
UPC	Universal product code	通用产品代码	Tōngyòng chǎnpǐn dàimǎ
UPC	Usage parameter control	使用参数控制	Shǐyòng cānshù kòngzhì
UPC/NPC	User parameter control/network parameter control	用户参数控制/网络参数控制	Yònghù cānshù kòngzhì/ wǎngluò cānshù kòngzhì
UPCMI	Uniform PCM interface	同一标准的 PCM 接口	Tóngyī biāozhǔnde PCM jiēkǒu
UPF	User port function	用户端口功能	Yònghù duānkǒu gōngnéng
UPF	User port function	用户口功能	Yònghù kǒu gōngnéng
UpnP	Universal plug and play	通用即插即用	Tōngyòng jí chā jíyòng
UpPTS	Uplink pilot time slot	上行导引时隙	Shàngxíng dǎoyǐn shíxì

UPRD	Uplink pseudo-random data	上行伪随机数据	Shàngxíng wěisuíjī shùjù
UPS	Uninterruptible power supply	不间断电源设备	Bùjiànduàn diànyuán shèbèi
Upso	Voltage measured with a psophometer conforming to ITU-T Recommendation O.41	用符合 ITU-T 建议 O.41 定的噪声计测量到的电压	Yòng fúhé ITU-T jiànyì O.41 guīdìngde zàoshēng jì cèliáng dàode diànyā
UPSR	Uni-directional path switch ring	单向通道倒换环	Dānxiàng tōngdào dǎohuàn huán
UPT	Universal personal telecommunications	通用个人通信	Tōngyòng gèrén tōngxìn
UPT	Universal private telecommunication	通用专线通信	Tōngyòng zhuānxiàn tōngxìn
UQPSK	Unbalanced quadrature phase shift keying	不平衡正交相移键控	Bùpínghéng zhèngjiāo xiāngyí jiànkòng
U-R	Loop interface-remote terminal end	远端环路接口	Yuǎnduān huánlù jiēkǒu
U-R	Remote circuit U reference point	远端线路 U 参考点	Yuǎnduān xiànlù U cānkǎo diǎn
U-R2	Remote circuit U reference point 2	远端线路 U 参考点 2	Yuǎnduān xiànlù U cānkǎo diǎn 2
URA	User registration area	用户注册区域	Yònghù zhùcè qūyù
URA	UTRAN registration area	UTRAN 注册区域	UTRAN zhùcè qūyù
URAN	UMTS radio access network	UMTS 无线接入网	UMTS wúxiàn jiērù wǎng
URI	Uniform resource identifier	统一资源标识符	Tǒngyī zīyuán biāozhìfú
URISA	Urban and Regional Information Systems Association	城市和区域信息系统协会	Chéngshì hé qūyù xìnxī xìtǒng xiéhuì
URJ	Unregistration reject (packet protocol)	注销拒绝	Zhùxiāo jùjué
URL	Uniform (universal) resource locator	划一资讯位址	Huàyī zīxùn wèizhǐ
URL	Uniform resource locator	统一资源定位地址	Tǒngyī zīyuán dìngwèi dìzhǐ
URL	Uniform resource locator	统一资源定位器(符)	Tǒngyī zīyuán dìngwèiqì (fú)
URL	Uniform resource locator	通用链接定位	Tōngyòng liànjiē dìngwèi
URL	Universal resource locator	全球资源位置符	Quánqiú zīyuán wèizhìfú
URL	Universal resource locator	通用资源定位符	Tōngyòng zīyuán dìngwèifú
URL	Universal resource locator	通用资源定位器	Tōngyòng zīyuán dìngwèiqì
U-RNTI	UTRAN radio network temporary identity	UTRAN 无线电网络临时识别	UTRAN wúxiàndiàn wǎngluò línshí shíbié
URQ	Unregistration request (packet protocol)	注销请求	Zhùxiāo qǐngqiú
US	Unit separator	单元分隔	Dānyuán fēngé
US	Unitary service	统一业务	Tǒngyī yèwù
USB	Universal serial bus	通用串行总线	Tōngyòng chuànháng zǒngxiàn
USB	Universal serial bus	通用串联总线	Tōngyòng chuànlián zǒngxiàn
USB	Upper sideband	上边带	Shàngbiandài
USBDCDPD	Universal serial bus device class definition for printing devices	打印设备的通用串行总线级标准	Dǎyìn shèbèide tōngyòng chuànháng zǒngxiàn jí biāozhǔn
USBP	Universal signaling back panel	通用信号后面板	Tōngyòng xìnhào hòumian bǎn
USC	UE service capabilities	UE 业务容量	UE yèwù róngliàng
USCH	Uplink shared channel	上行共用信道	Shàngxíng gòngyòng xìndào
USCH	Uplink shared channel	上行链路共享信道	Shàngxíng liànlù gòngxiǎng xìndào
USDM	Unified system diagnostic manager	统一系统监测管理器	Tǒngyī xìtǒng jiāncè guǎnlǐqì
USF	Universal Service Fund	普遍服务基金	Pǔbiàn fúwù jījīn
USF	Uplink state flag	上行链路状态标记	Shàngxíng liànlù zhuàngtài biāojì
USF	Uplink state flag	上行链路状态标志	Shàngxíng liànlù zhuàngtài biāozhì
USF	Uplink state flag	上行状态标记	Shàngxíng zhuàngtài biāojì
USF	Uplink state flag	上行状态标志	Shàngxíng zhuàngtài biāozhì
USI	User service information	用户业务信息	Yònghù yèwù xìnxī
USIM	Universal mobile telecommunications system subscriber identity module	通用移动通信系统用户识别模块	Tōngyòng yídòng tōngxìn xìtǒng yònghù shíbié mókuài

USIM	Universal subscriber identity module	普通用户识别模块	Pǔtōng yònghù shíbié mókuài
USNMAS	United States National Map Accuracy Standard	美国国家地图精度标准	Měiguó guójiā dìtú jīngdù biāozhǔn
USNO	United States Naval Observatory	美国海军天文台	Měiguó hǎijūn tiānwéntái
USR	User channels	使用者通路	Shǐyòngzhě tōnglù
USR	User-to-user information (ISUP message)	用户到用户信息	Yònghù dào yònghù xìnxī
USR	User-to-user message (ISUP)	用户到用户消息	Yònghù dào yònghù xiāoxi
USSD	Unstructured supplementary service data	非结构补充业务数据	Fēijiégòu bǔchōng yèwù shùjù
USSD	Unstructured supplementary service data	非结构化补充数据业务	Fēijiégòuhuà bǔchōng shùjù yèwù
USSD	Unstructured supplementary services data	非结构化补充服务数据	Fēijiégòuhuà bǔchōng fúwù shùjù
USSN	Unstructured supplementary services notification	非结构化补充服务通知	Fēijiégòuhuà bǔchōng fúwù tōngzhī
USSR	Unstructured supplementary services request	非结构化补充服务请求	Fēijiégòuhuà bǔchōng fúwù qǐngqiú
UST	United symbol time	组合符号时间	Zǔhé fúhào shíjiān
USTS	Uplink synchronous transmission scheme	上行同步传输计划	Shàngxíng tóngbù chuánshū jìhuà
USWC	Uncached speculative write combining	无缓冲思索联合写操作	Wúhuǎnchōng sīsuǒ liánhé xiě cāozuò
UT	Universal Time	世界时	Shìjiè shí
UT	Universal time	通用时间	Tōngyòng shíjiān
UT	Upper tester	高层测试	Gāocéng cèshì
UTC	Coordinated Universal Time	协调世界时	Xiétiáo shìjièshí
UTC	Unable to comply	无法遵循	Wúfǎ zūnxún
UTC	Universal coordinated time	世界协调时	Shìjiè xiétiáo shí
UTC	Universal time clock	通用时钟	Tōngyòng shízhōng
UTC	Universal time constant	通用世界时	Tōngyòng shìjièshí
UTC	Universal time coordinate	通用时间坐标	Tōngyòng shíjiān zuòbiāo
UTD	Uniform geometric theory of diffraction	一致性几何绕射理论	Yīzhìxìng jǐhé ràoshè lǐlùn
UTM	Universal Transverse Mercator	通用横轴墨卡托	Tōngyòng héngzhóu mò-kǎ-tuō
UTP	Unshielded twisted pair	非屏蔽双绞线	Fēipíngbì shuāngjiǎo xiàn
UTP	Unshielded twisted pair	无屏蔽双绞线	Wúpíngbì shuāngjiǎoxiàn
UTP	Unshielded twisted pair cable	非屏蔽对线电缆	Fēipíngbì duìxiàn diànlǎn
UTRA	Universal mobile telecommunications system-terrestrial radio access	通用移动通信系统地面无线接入	Tōngyòng yídòng tōngxìn xìtǒng dìmiàn wúxiàn jiērù
UTRA	Universal terrestrial radio access	通用地面无线接入	Tōngyòng dìmiàn wúxiàn jiērù
UTRAD	Unified TMN requirement, analysis and design	统一 TMN 需求、分析和设计	Tǒngyī TMN xūqiú、fēnxī hé shèjì
UTRAN	Universal terrestrial radio access network	通用陆地无线接入网络	Tōngyòng lùdì wúxiàn jiērù wǎngluò
UTSI	User-to-service information	用户到业务信息	Yònghù dào yèwù xìnxī
UUI	User-to-user interface	用户–用户接口	Yònghù—yònghù jiēkǒu
UUID	Universal unique identifier	通用唯一标识	Tōngyòng wéiyī biāozhì
UUS	User to user signaling	用户–用户消息	Yònghù—yònghù xiāoxi
UUS	User-to-user service	用户到用户业务	Yònghù dào yònghù yèwù
UUS	User-to-user signaling	用户到用户信令	Yònghù dào yònghù xìnlìng
UUS	User-to-user signaling	用户–用户信令	Yònghù—yònghù xìnlìng
UUS1	User-to-user signaling service 1	用户至用户信令业务 1	Yònghù zhì yònghù xìnlìng yèwù 1
UUT	Under unit test	被测单元	Bèicè dānyuán
UV	Ultraviolet radiation	紫外辐射	Zǐwài fúshè
UWC	Universal wireless communications	通用无线通信	Tōngyòng wúxiàn tōngxìn
UWCC	Universal Wireless Communication Council	全球无线通信协会	Quánqiú wúxiàn tōngxìn xiéhuì
UWCC	Universal wireless communications consortium	通用无线通信协议	Tōngyòng wúxiàn tōngxìn xiéyì

UWOA	Ultra-wideband optical fiber amplifier	超宽带光纤放大器	Chāokuāndài guāngxiān fàngdàqì

V

V/F	Voltage-to-frequency conversion	电压 / 频率转换	Diànyā/pínlǜ zhuǎnhuàn
V/I	Voltage to current converter	电压-电流变换器	Diànyā/diànliú biànhuànqì
VA	Vertex aggregation (CAD/CAM)	顶点聚合	Dǐngdiǎn jùhé
VA	Viterbi algorithm	维特比算法	Wéi-tè-bǐ suànfǎ
VA	Voice activity factor	语音激活因子	Yǔyīn jīhuó yīnzǐ
VAA	Variable optical attenuator array	可变光衰减阵列	Kěbiàn guāng shuāijiǎn zhènliè
VAC	Variable authentication code	可变认证码	Kěbiàn rènzhèng mǎ
VAD	Vapor axial deposition	轴向气相沉积法	Zhóuxiàng qìxiàng chénjī fǎ
VAD	Vapor axial deposition (for FOC)	气相轴向沉积法	Qìxiàng zhóuxiàng chénjī fǎ
VAD	Vapor axial deposition (for FOC)	轴向化学气相沉积法	Zhóuxiàng huàxué qìxiàng chénjī fǎ
VAD	Voice activity detection	话音激活检波	Huàyīn jīhuó jiǎnbō
VAD	Voice activity detection	话音激活检测	Huàyīn jīhuó jiǎncè
VAD	Voice activity detector	话音激活检波器	Huàyīn jīhuó jiǎnbōqì
VAFX	Voice announcement fixed type	话音广播固定类型	Huàyīn guǎngbō gùdìng lèixíng
VAGP	Variable aperture grille pitch	可变间距光栅	Kěbiàn jiānjù guāngshān
VALU	Vector arithmetic logic unit	向量算术逻辑单元	Xiàngliàng suànshù luóji dānyuán
VAMX	Voice announcement mixed type	话音广播混合类型	Huàyīn guǎngbō hùnhé lèixíng
VAN	Value added network	加值网络	Jiāzhí wǎngluò
VAN	Value added network	增值网	Zēngzhí wǎng
VAP	Videotex access point	可视图文接入点	Kěshì túwén jiērùdiǎn
VAR	Value added reseller	增值转售商	Zēngzhí zhuǎnshòushāng
VAR	Value added resellers	增值分销商	Zēngzhí fēnxiāo shāng
VARP	Statistical variance for the population (in SQL Server)	函数返回总体变异数	Hánshù fǎnhuí zǒngtǐ biànyì shù
VAS	Value added service	增值业务	Zēngzhí yèwù
VASP	Value added service provider	增值业务提供商	Zēngzhí yèwù tígōngshāng
VASP	Voice application service provider	语音应用服务提供商	Yǔyīn yìngyòng fúwù tígōngshāng
VAT	Value attribute table	值属性表	Zhí shǔxìng biǎo
VAU	Voice access unit	语言接入单元	Yǔyán jiērù dānyuán
VB	Voice browser	语音导航	Yǔyīn dǎoháng
VBI	Vertical blanking interval	垂直空白间隔	Chuízhí kòngbái jiàngé
VBI	Vertical blanking interval (video)	垂直空白间隙	Chuízhí kòngbái jiànxì
VBR	Variable bit rate	可变比特率	Kěbiàn bǐtè lǜ
VBR	Variable bit rate service	可变比特率业务	Kěbiàn bǐtè lǜ yèwù
VBS	Voice broadcast service	话音广播业务	Huàyīn guǎngbō yèwù
VBS	Voice broadcast service	语音广播业务	Yǔyīn guǎngbō yèwù
VC	Vector control	矢量控制	Shǐliàng kòngzhì
VC	Video conference	视频会议	Shìpín huìyì
VC	Virtual call	虚拟呼叫	Xūnǐ hūjiào
VC	Virtual call (computer software term)	虚调用	Xū diàoyòng
VC	Virtual call (telecom term)	虚呼叫	Xū hūjiào
VC	Virtual channel	虚信道	Xū xìndào
VC	Virtual connect	虚连接	Xū liánjiē
VC	Virtual connection	虚拟连接	Xūnǐ liánjiē

VC	Virtual container	虚容器	Xū róngqì
VC	Virtual container	虚通路包	Xū tōnglù bāo
VC	Voice channel	话路	Huàlù
VC	Voice channel	话音信道	Huàyīn xìndào
VC	Voice circuit	话音电路	Huàyīn diànlù
VC	Voice code	话音编码	Huàyīn biānmǎ
VC	Voice commerce	语音商务	Yǔyīn shāngwù
VC	Voice control	话音控制	Huàyīn kòngzhì
V-C	Central office V reference point	局端 V 参考点	Júduān V cānkǎo diǎn
VC POH	Virtual container path overhead	虚容器通道开销	Xū róngqì tōngdào kāixiao
VC-AIS	Virtual channel--alarm indication signal	虚通路告警指示信号	Xū tōnglù gàojǐng zhǐshì xìnhào
VCC	Virtual call connection	虚呼叫连接	Xū hūjiào liánjiē
VCC	Virtual call control	虚呼叫控制	Xū hūjiào kòngzhì
VCC	Virtual channel connection	虚通路连接	Xū tōnglù liánjiē
VCC	Virtual channel connection	虚拟信道连接	Xūnǐ xìndào liánjiē
VCC	Voice channel controller	话音信道控制器	Huàyīn xìndào kòngzhìqì
VCCE	Virtual channel connection endpoint	虚信道连接端点	Xū xìndào liánjiē duāndiǎn
VCCT	Virtual channel connection termination	虚通路连接终接	Xū tōnglù liánjiē zhōngjiē
VCD	Video CD	视频 CD	Shìpín CD
VCD	Video compact disc	视频光盘	Shìpín guāngpán
VCE	Virtual channel entity	虚通路实体	Xū tōnglù shítǐ
VCF	Video command "Freeze picture request"	视频命令 "静态画请求"	Shìpín mìnglìng "jìngtài huà qǐngqiú"
VCI	Virtual channel identifier	虚通道标志	Xū tōngdào biāozhì
VCI	Virtual channel identifier	虚通道识别码	Xū tōngdào shíbié mǎ
VCI	Virtual channel identifier	虚通路标识	Xū tōnglù biāozhì
VCI	Virtual channel identifier	虚信道标志	Xū xìndào biāozhì
VCI	Virtual channel identifier	虚信道标识	Xū xìndào biāozhì
VCI	Virtual channel identifier	虚信道识别幅	Xū xìndào shíbié fú
VCI	Virtual channel identifier	虚拟通道标识符	Xūnǐ tōngdào biāozhìfú
VCI	Virtual channel identifier	虚拟信道标识符	Xūnǐ xìndào biāozhì fú
VCI	Virtual channel indicator	虚通路识别码	Xū tōnglù shíbié mǎ
VCL	Virtual channel link	虚信道链路	Xū xìndào liànlù
VCMA	Virtual channel memory architecture	虚拟通道内存结构	Xūnǐ tōngdào nèicún jiégòu
VCME	Virtual channel multiplex entity	虚通路复用实体	Xū tōnglù fùyòng shítǐ
VCO	Voltage controlled oscillator	压控振荡器	Yākòng zhèndàngqì
VC-RDI	Virtual channel--remote defect indication	虚通路远端故障指示	Xū tōnglù yuǎn duān gùzhàng zhǐshì
VCS	VIdeo conference system	会议电视系统	Huìyì diànshì xìtǒng
VCS	Video conference system	视讯會议系统	Shìxùn huìyì xìtǒng
VCSEL	Vertical cavity surface emitting laser	垂直表面激光发射器	Chuízhí biǎomiàn jīguāng fāshèqì
VCSEL	Vertical cavity surface emitting laser diode	垂直共振腔面射型	Chuízhí gòngzhènqiāng miàn shè xíng
vcTTP	Virtual channel trail termination point	虚通路路径终接点	Xū tōnglù lùjìng zhōng jiēdiǎn
VCU	Video command "Fast update request"	视频命令 "快速更新请求"	Shìpín mìnglìng "kuàisù gēngxīn qǐngqiú"
VCU	Voice channel unit	话音信道单元	Huàyīn xìndào dānyuán
VCXO	Voltage controlled crystal oscillator	电压控制晶体振荡器	Diànyā kòngzhì jīngtǐ zhèndàngqì
VCXO	Voltage controlled crystal oscillator (short for 电压控制晶体振荡器)	压控晶振	Yākòng jīngzhèn

VD	Variable dot (printer term)	变点式列印	Biàndiǎn-shì liè yìn
VD	Video decoder	视频译码器	Shìpín yìmǎqì
VD	Virtual destination	虚拟终点	Xūnǐ zhōngdiǎn
VDF	Voice distribution frame	音频配线	Yīnpín pèixiàn
VDM	Virtual DOS machine	虚拟 DOS 机	Xūnǐ DOS jī
VDM	Voice data multiplexer	音频数据复用板	Yīnpín shùjù fùyòng bǎn
VDM	Voice data multiplexer (literally "voice frequency digital overlay board")	音频数字叠加板	Yīnpín shùzì diéjiā bǎn
VDR	Voice digitization rate	话音数字化速率	Huàyīn shùzihuà sùlǜ
VDSL	Very high speed digital subscriber line (downlink 12.9Mb/s to 52.8Mb/s, uplink 1.6Mb/s to 2.3Mb/s)	甚高速数字用户线	Shèngāosù shùzì yònghù xiàn
VDSL	Very high-speed digital subscriber line	超高速数字用户线	Chāogāosù shùzì yònghù xiàn
VDSL	Very-high-data-rate digital subscriber line	超高数据传输速率的数字用户线路	Chāogāo shùjù chuánshū sùlǜde shùzì yònghù xiànlù
VDT	Video display terminal	视频显示终端	Shìpín xiǎnshì zhōngduān
VDT	Video display terminal	图像显示终端	Túxiàng xiǎnshì zhōngduān
VDU	Video display unit	视频显示单元	Shìpín xiǎnshì dānyuán
VDU	Video display unit	视频显示器	Shìpín xiǎnshìqì
VDVQ	Variable dimension vector quantization	变维矢量量化	Biànwéi shǐliàng liànghuà
VE	Vertex expansion (CAM/CAM)	顶点展开	Dǐngdiǎn zhǎnkāi
VEA	Very early allocation	很早分配	Hěnzǎo fēnpèi
VEE	Virtual execution engine	虚拟执行引擎	Xūnǐ zhíxíng yǐnqíng
VEMMI	Enhanced man machine interface for videotex and other retrieval services	可视图文和其他可恢复业务的增强人机接口	Kěshì túwén hé qítā kěhuīfù yèwùde zēngqiáng rénjī jiēkǒu
VF	Virtual fetch	虚取	Xū qǔ
VFAT	Virtual file allocation table	虚拟文件分配表	Xūnǐ wénjiàn fēnpèi biǎo
VFB	Voice frequency board	音频板	Yīnpín bǎn
VFC	Voice frequency channel	音频信道	Yīnpín xìndào
VFD	Vacuum fluorescent display	真空萤光显示器	Zhēnkōng yíngguāng xiǎnshìqì
VFT	Voice-frequency multiplex telegraphy	音频复用电报	Yīnpín fùyòng diànbào
VFVT	Virtual fetch vector table	虚取向量表	Xū qǔ xiàngliáng biǎo
VGA	Video graphic adapter	视频图形显示适配器	Shìpín túxíng xiǎnshì shìpèiqì
VGCS	Voice group call service	话音组呼叫业务	Huàyīn zǔ hūjiào yèwù
VGCS	Voice group call service	语音群呼叫业务	Yǔyīn qún hūjiào yèwù
VGCS	Voice group call service	语音组呼业务	Yǔyīn zǔ hū yèwù
VGCS	Voice group call service	语音组呼叫业务	Yǔyīn zǔ hūjiào yèwù
VHDL	Virtual hardware description language	虚拟硬件描述语言	Xūnǐ yìngjiàn miáoshù yǔyán
VHE	Virtual home environment	虚拟归属环境	Xūnǐ guīshǔ huánjìng
VHE	Virtual home environment	虚拟家区环境	Xūnǐ jiāqū huánjìng
VHE	Virtual home environment	虚拟家庭环境	Xūnǐ jiātíng huánjìng
VHF	Very high frequency	甚高频	Shèngāopín
VI	Vector identifier	向量标识符	Xiàngliàng biāozhì fú
VI	Video interphone	可视对讲门铃	Kěshì duìjiǎng ménlíng
VIA	Virtual interface architecture	虚拟接口体系	Xūnǐ jiēkǒu tǐxì
VIC	Virtual interaction controller	虚拟交互控制器	Xūnǐ jiāohù kòngzhìqì
VICAM	Virtual integrated communications access method	虚拟综合通信存取法	Xūnǐ zōnghé tōngxìn cúnqǔ fǎ
VID	Virtual local area network (LAN) identifier	虚拟局域网标识符	Xūnǐ júyù wǎng biāozhìfú

VID	Voltage identification definition	电压识别认证	Diànyā shíbié rènzhèng
VIDT	Vertical interval data transmission	垂直区间数据传输	Chuízhí qūjiān shùjù chuánshū
VIM	Vector interrupt mechanism	矢量中断机构	Shǐliàng zhōngduàn jīgòu
VIM	Vector interrupt mechanism	向量中断机构	Xiàngliàng zhōngduàn jīgòu
VIMS	Versatile interior multiplex system	通用内部多路转换系统	Tōngyòng nèibù duōlù zhuǎnhuàn xìtǒng
VIP	Versatile interface processor	通用接口处理器	Tōngyòng jiēkǒu chǔlǐqì
VIP	Video interface port	视频接口	Shìpín jiēkǒu
ViRGE	Video and rendering graphics engine	视频描写图形引擎	Shìpín miáoxiě túxíng yǐnqíng
VL	Vector length	向量长度	Xiàngliàng chángdù
VLAN	Virtual local area network	虚拟局域网	Xūnǐ júyù wǎng
VLF	Very low frequency	甚低频	Shèndīpín
VLIW	Very long instruction word	超长指令字	Chāocháng zhǐlìng zì
VLL	Virtual leased line	虚拟专线	Xūnǐ zhuānxiàn
VLL	Virtual leased line	虚拟租用线路	Xūnǐ zūyòng xiànlù
VLL	Virtual leased lines	租用虚线路	Zūyòng xū xiànlù
VLR	Visitor location register	拜访位置寄存器	Bàifǎng wèizhì jìcúnqì
VLR	Visitor location register	访问位置寄存器	Fǎngwèn wèizhì jìcúnqì
VLR	Visitor location register	访问用户位置寄存器	Fǎngwèn yònghù wèizhì jìcúnqì
VLR	Visitor location register	来访位置注册处	Láifǎng wèizhì zhùcèchù
VLSI	Very large scale integrated circuit	超大规模集成电路	Chāodàguīmó jíchéng diànlù
VLSI	Very large scale integration	超大规模集成电路	Chāodàguīmó jíchéng diànlù
VLSM	Variable-length sub-net mask	可变长度子网掩码	Kěbiàn chángdù ziwǎng yǎnmǎ
VLSR	Virtual line switching ring	虚拟线交换环	Xūnǐ xiàn jiāohuàn huán
VM	Voice mailbox	语音邮箱	Yǔyīn yóuxiāng
VM	Voice module	语音模块	Yǔyīn mókuài
VMA	Virtual memory allocation	虚拟存储器分配	Xūnǐ cúnchǔqì fēnpèi
VMA	Voicemail alert	语音邮件提示	Yǔyīn yóujiàn tíshì
VME	Virtual memory environment	虚拟存储环境	Xūnǐ cúnchǔ huánjìng
VME	Voice message exchange	声音信息交换	Shēngyīn xìnxī jiāohuàn
VMHP	Voice message handling point	语音信息处理点	Yǔyīn xìnxī chǔlǐ diǎn
VMI	Vendor managed inventory	供应商管理的库存	Gōngyìngshāng guǎnlǐde kùcún
VMRS	Voice message retrieval system	声音信息检索系统	Shēngyīn xìnxī jiǎnsuǒ xìtǒng
VMS	Voice mail service	语音信箱业务	Yǔyīn xìnxiāng yèwù
VMS	Voice mail service	语音邮箱业务	Yǔyīn yóuxiāng yèwù
VMS	Voice mail system	语音信箱系统	Yǔyīn xìnxiāng xìtǒng
VMSC	Visited mobile service switching center	被访移动业务交换中心	Bèifǎng yídòng yèwù jiāohuàn zhōngxīn
VMSC	Visited mobile services switching centre	受访移动无线局	Shòufǎng yídòng wúxiàn jú
VMSC	Visited mobile switching center	拜访移动业务交换中心	Bàifǎng yídòng yèwù jiāohuàn zhōngxīn
VMSC	Visited MSC	拜访 MSC	Bàifǎng MSC
VMTP	Versatile message transaction protocol	通用消息事务处理协议	Tōngyòng xiāoxi shìwù chǔlǐ xiéyì
VNAT	Virtual network address translation	虚拟网络地址转换	Xūnǐ wǎngluò dìzhǐ zhuǎnhuàn
VNS	Virtual network service	虚拟网	Xūnǐ wǎng
VOA	Variable optical attenuator	可变光衰减器	Kěbiàn guāng shuāijiǎnqì
VOATM	Voice over ATM	在 ATM 上的话音	Zài ATM-shàngde huà yīn
VOCODER	Voice coder	话音编码器	Huàyīn biānmǎqì
VOCODER	Voice coder	音频编码器	Yīnpín biānmǎqì

VOD	Video on demand	点播电视	Diǎnbō diànshì
VoD	Video on demand	视频点播	Shìpín diǎnbō
VOD	Video on demand	影视点播	Yǐngshì diǎnbō
VOD	Video-on-demand	按需点播视频	Ànxū diǎnbō shìpín
VoDSL	Voice over DSL	DSL 传话音	DSL chuánhuà yīn
VoDSL	Voice over DSL	在 DSL 上传话音	Zài DSL-shàng chuán huàyīn
VOIP	Voice over internet protocol	IP 网上传输话音	IP wǎngshàng chuánshū huàyīn
VOIP	Voice over Internet protocol	网络电话	Wǎngluò diànhuà
VOIP	Voice over Internet protocol	网上传输话音	Wǎngshàng chuánshū huàyīn
VOIP	Voice over internet protocol (ITU-T protocol)	IP 上的语音协议	IP-shàngde yǔyīn xiéyì
VoIP	Voice over IP	IP 话音	IP huàyīn
VoIP	Voice over IP	IP 上的话音	IP-shàngde huàyīn
VOIP	Voice over IP	在 IP 上的话音	Zài IP-shàngde huàyīn
VOP	Vector optimization problem	向量最优化问题	Xiàngliàng zuìyōuhuà wèntí
VOQ	Virtual output queue	虚拟输出排队	Xūnǐ shūchū páiduì
VOS	Virtual operating system	虚拟操作系统	Xūnǐ cāozuò xìtǒng
VOT	Televoting	电话投票	Diànhuà tóupiào
Voxel	Volume pixel	立体像素	Lìtǐ xiàngsù
VP	Virtual path (preferred)	虚通路	Xū tōnglù
VP	Voice portal	语音门户	Yǔyīn ménhù
VP-AIS	Virtual path--alarm indication signal	虚通道告警指示信号	Xū tōngdào gàojǐng zhǐshì xìnhào
VPC	Virtual path connection	虚通道连接	Xū tōngdào liánjiē
VPC	Virtual path connection (preferred)	虚通路连接	Xū tōnglù liánjiē
VPCE	Virtual path connection endpoint	虚通路连接端点	Xū tōnglù liánjiē duāndiǎn
VPCI-CC	Virtual path connection identifier--continuous checking	虚通道连接标识符--连续性检验	Xū tōngdào liánjiē biāozhì fú--liánxùxìng jiǎnyàn
VPCT	Virtual path connection termination	虚通道连接终接	Xū tōngdào liánjiē zhōngjiē
VPDN	Virtual private dial network	虚拟私有拨号网络	Xūnǐ sīyǒu bōhào wǎngluò
VPDN	Virtual private dial network	虚拟专用拨号网络	Xūnǐ zhuānyòng bōhào wǎngluò
VPDN	Virtual private dialup network	虚拟拨号专用网络	Xūnǐ bōhào zhuānyòng wǎngluò
VPDN	Virtual private dial-up network	虚拟拨号专网	Xūnǐ bōhào zhuānwǎng
VPE	Vapor phase epitaxy	汽相外延	Qìxiāng wàiyán
VPE	Vector processing element	向量处理单元	Xiàngliàng chǔlǐ dānyuán
VPE	Virtual path entity	虚通道实体	Xū tōngdào shítǐ
VPF	Vector product format	矢量产品格式	Shǐliàng chǎnpǐn géshi
VPG	Virtual path group	虚通道组	Xū tōngdào zǔ
VPI	Virtual path identifier	虚电路标志	Xū diànlù biāozhì
VPI	Virtual path identifier	虚通道标识	Xū tōngdào biāozhì
VPI	Virtual path identifier	虚通道识别码	Xū tōngdào shíbié mǎ
VPI	Virtual path identifier	虚通路标志	Xū tōnglù biāozhì
VPI	Virtual path identifier	虚通路标识符	Xū tōnglù biāozhì fú
VPI	Virtual path identifier	虚拟路径标识符	Xūnǐ lùjìng biāozhì fú
VPL	Virtual path link	虚通路链路	Xū tōnglù liànlù
VPLMN	Visited PLMN	拜访 PLMN	Bàifǎng PLMN
VPLMN	Visited public land mobile network	拜访公用陆地移动通信网络	Bàifǎng gōngyòng lùdì yídòng tōngxìn wǎngluò
VPLS	Virtual private LAN segment	虚拟专用 LAN 网段	Xūnǐ zhuānyòng LAN wǎngduàn

VPLS	Virtual private LAN segment	虚拟专用 LAN 子网段	Xūnǐ zhuānyòng LAN ziwǎng duàn
VPLS	Virtual private LAN service	虚拟专用局域网业务	Xūnǐ zhuānyòng júyùwǎng yèwù
VPME	Virtual path multiplex entity	虚通道复用实体	Xū tōngdào fùyòng shítǐ
VPML	Virtual prototype modeling language (CAD/CAM)	虚拟原型建模语言	Xūnǐ yuánxíng jiànmó yǔyán
VPMN	Virtual private mobile network	虚拟专用移动网	Xūnǐ zhuānyòng yídòng wǎng
VPN	Virtual private network	虚拟用户专网	Xūnǐ yònghù zhuānwǎng
VPN	Virtual private network	虚拟专网	Xūnǐ zhuānwǎng
VPN	Virtual private network	虚拟专用网	Xūnǐ zhuānyòng wǎng
VPNS	Virtual private network service	虚拟专用网业务	Xūnǐ zhuānyòng wǎng yèwù
VP-RDI	Virtual path--remote defect indicator	虚通道远端故障指示	Xū tōngdào yuǎnduān gùzhàng zhǐshì
VPRN	Virtual private routed network	虚拟专用路由网络	Xūnǐ zhuānyòng lùyóu wǎngluò
VPrN	Virtual provisioned network	虚拟配置网	Xūnǐ pèizhì wǎng
VPrP	Virtual provisioned pipe	虚拟配置管道	Xūnǐ pèizhì guǎndào
VPS	Voice processing system	语音处理系统	Yǔyīn chǔlǐ xìtǒng
VPSW	Virtual program status word	虚拟程序状态字	Xūnǐ chéngxù zhuàngtài zì
VPT	Virtual packet terminal	虚拟分组终端	Xūnǐ fēnzǔ zhōngduān
VPU	Vector permutate unit	向量排列单元	Xiàngliàng páiliè dānyuán
VPU	Vector processing unit	向量处理单元	Xiàngliàng chǔlǐ dānyuán
VPWS	Virtual private wire service	虚拟专用线业务	Xūnǐ zhuānyòng xiàn yèwù
VQ	Vector quantization	矢量量化	Shǐliàng liànghuà
VQTC	Vector-quantization texture compression	向量纹理压缩	Xiàngliàng wénlǐ yāsuō
VR	Virtual reality	虚拟现实	Xūnǐ xiànshí
VR	Virtual router	虚拟路由器	Xūnǐ lùyóu qì
VR	Voltage regulator	稳压器	Wěnyāqì
VRAM	Variable rate adaptive multiplexing	可变速自适应多路转换	Kěbiàn sù zìshìyìng duōlù zhuǎnhuàn
VRC	Vertical redundancy check	垂直冗余检验	Chuízhí rǒngyú jiǎnyàn
VRF	Vector relational format	矢量关系格式	Shǐliàng guānxi géshi
VRID	Virtual route identifier	虚拟路由标识符	Xūnǐ lùyóu biāozhì fú
VRLA	Valve-regulated lead acid battery	阀控式密封型电池	Fákòng-shì mìfēng xíng diànchí
VRM	Voltage regulator module	电压调整模块	Diànyā tiáozhěng mókuài
VRML	Virtual reality mark-up language	虚拟现实标记语言	Xūnǐ xiànshí biāojì yǔyán
VRML	Virtual reality modeling language	虚拟现实建模语言	Xūnǐ xiànshí jiànmó yǔyán
VRML	Virtual reality modeling language	虚拟现实模型语言	Xūnǐ xiànshí móxíng yǔyán
VRR	Vertical refresh rate (video)	垂直扫描频率	Chuízhí sǎomiáo pínlǜ
VRRP	Virtual redundant router protocol	虚拟冗余路由器协议	Xūnǐ rǒngyú lùyóuqì xiéyì
VRRP	Virtual router redundancy protocol (an IETF protocol)	虚拟路由器冗余协议	Xūnǐ lùyóuqì rǒngyú xiéyì
VRRP	Virtual router redundancy protocol (in LINUX)	虚拟路由器冗余协议	Xūnǐ lùyóuqì rǒngyú xiéyì
VS	Virtual source	虚拟源点	Xūnǐ yuándiǎn
VS	Virtual storage	虚拟存储	Xūnǐ cúnchǔ
VSAT	Very small aperture satellite terminal	超小型天线终端	Chāoxiǎoxíng tiānxiàn zhōngduān
VSAT	Very small aperture terminal	甚小口径天线地球站	Shènxiǎo kǒujìng tiānxiàn dìqiú zhàn
VSAT	Very small aperture terminal	甚小口径终端	Shènxiǎo kǒujìng zhōngduān
VSB	Vestigial sideband	残留边带	Cánliú biāndài
VSBAM	Vestigial sideband amplitude modulation	残留边带调幅	Cánliú biāndài tiáofú
VSC	Videotex service center	可视图文中心	Kěshì túwén zhōngxīn
VSDM	Variable slope delta modulation	可变斜率增量调制	Kěbiàn xiélǜ zēngliàng tiáozhì

VSELP	Vector sum excited linear predictive coding	矢量和激励线性预测编码	Shǐliàng hé jīlì xiànxìng yùcè biānmǎ
VSIS	Video signal standard	视频信号标准	Shìpín xìnhào biāozhǔn
VSM	Virtual storage management	虚拟存储管理	Xūnǐ cúnchǔ guǎnlǐ
VSN	Video switched network	活动图象交换网	Huódòng túxiàng jiāohuàn wǎng
VSS	Vector symbol set	向量符号集	Xiàngliàng fúhào jí
VST	Virtual space teleconferencing system	虚拟空间会议系统	Xūnǐ kōngjiān huìyì xìtǒng
VSU	Voice switching unit	语言交换单元	Yǔyán jiāohuàn dānyuán
VSWR	Voltage standing wave ratio	电压驻波比	Diànyā zhùbōbǐ
VT	Vertical tabulation	直列制表	Zhílìè zhìbiǎo
VT	Video terminal	视频终端	Shìpín zhōngduān
VT	Virtual terminal	虚拟终端	Xūnǐ zhōngduān
VTAM	Virtual telecommunication access method	虚拟远程通信存取法	Xūnǐ yuǎnchéng tōngxìn cúnqǔ fǎ
VTP	Virtual terminal protocol	虚拟终端规约	Xūnǐ zhōngduān guīyuē
VTP	Virtual terminal protocol (a Cisco protocol)	虚拟终端协议	Xūnǐ zhōngduān xiéyì
VTRAM	Variable topology random access memory	可变结构随机存取存储器	Kěbiàn jiégòu suíjī cúnqǔ cúnchǔqì
VTU	Video transmission unit	视频传输单元	Shìpín chuánshū dānyuán
VUA	Valid user address	有效用户地址	Yǒuxiào yònghù dìzhǐ
VUP	Virtual user port	虚拟用户端口	Xūnǐ yònghù duānkǒu
VxD	Virtual device drivers	虚拟设备驱动程序	Xūnǐ shèbèi qūdòng chéngxù
VXML	Voice eXtensible markup language	语音扩展标记语言	Yǔyīn kuòzhǎn biāojì yǔyán
VXO	Variable crystal oscillator	可变晶体振荡器	Kěbiàn jīngtǐ zhèndàngqì

W

W	Wall mounted type	壁装式	Bìzhuāng shì
W3C	Word Wide Web Committee	环球网委员会	Huánqiú wǎng wěiyuánhuì
W3C	World Wide Web Consortium	万维网协会	Wànwéiwǎng xiéhuì
W3C	World Wide Web Consortium	英特网协议组织	Yīng-tè-wǎng xiéyì zǔzhī
W5	Whoever, whenever, wherever, whomever, whatever communication	任何人，与在任何时候任何地方的任何人进行的任何形式的通信	Rènhé rén yǔ zài rènhé shíhou rènhé dìfangde rènhé rén jìnxíngde rènhé xíngshìde tōngxìn
WA	Coaxial wire armored cable	通轴线铠装电缆	Tōngzhóuxiàn kǎizhuāng diànlǎn
WA	Wavelength allocation	波长分配	Bōcháng fēnpèi
WA	Wireless access	无线接入	Wúxiàn jiērù
WA	Work area	工作区	Gōngzuòqū
WAA	Wide aperture antenna	宽孔径天线	Kuān kǒngjìng tiānxiàn
WAAS	Wide area augmentation system	广域加强系统	Guǎngyù jiāqiáng xìtǒng
WAC	Wrong attempt counter	非法尝试次数	Fēifǎ chángshì cìshù
WAD	Wireless advertisement	无线广告业务	Wúxiàn guǎnggào yèwù
WAE	Wireless application environment	无线应用环境	Wúxiàn yìngyòng huánjìng
WAG	Wireless access gateway	无线接入网关	Wúxiàn jiērù wǎngguān
WAIS	Wide area information service	广域信息服务系统	Guǎngyù xìnxī fúwù xìtǒng
WAIS	Wide area information service	广域信息服务系统	Guǎngyù xìnxī fúwù xìtǒng
WAIS	Wide area information service	广域资讯服务	Guǎngyù zīxùn fúwù
WAITRO	World Association of Industrial and Technological Research Organizations	世界工业与技术研究组织协会	Shìjiè gōngyè yǔ jìshù yánjiū zǔzhī xiéhuì
WAN	Wide area network	广域网	Guǎngyùwǎng
WAN	Wide area network	广域网	Guǎngyùwǎng

WAP	Wireless application protocol	无线应用协议	Wúxiàn yìngyòng xiéyì
WARC	World Administrative Radio Conference	世界无线电管理大会	Shìjiè wúxiàndiàn guǎnlǐ dàhuì
WARC	World Administrative Radio Conference	世界无线电行政大会	Shìjiè wúxiàndiàn xíngzhèng dàhuì
WAS	Wireless access server	无线接入服务器	Wúxiàn jiērù fúwùqì
WATS	Wide area telecommunications/telephone service	宽域通信/电话服务	Kuānyù tōngxìn/diànhuà fúwù
WATS	Wireless asymmetrical transmission system	无线非对称传输模式	Wúxiàn fēiduìchèn chuánshū móshì
WBEM	Web-based enterprise management	基于 Web 的企业管理	Jīyú Web de qǐyè guǎnlǐ
WBM	Analog microwave	模拟微波	Mónǐ wēibō
WBS	Digital microwave	数字微波	Shùzì wēibō
WBT	Web-based training	基于网络的训练	Jīyú wǎngluòde xùnliàn
WBTDMA	Wideband time division multiple access	宽带时分多路存取	Kuāndài shífēn duōlù cúnqǔ
WBWT	Wireless both-way trunk	无线双向中继	Wúxiàn shuāngxiàng zhōngjì
WC	Wavelength conversion	波长变换	Bōcháng biànhuàn
WCAN	Wireless coverage area network	无线覆盖域网络	Wúxiàn fùgài yù wǎngluò
WCDMA	Wideband code division multiple access	宽带码分多址	Kuāndài mǎfēn duōzhǐ
WCM	Wire-core matrix	线心矩阵	Xiànxīn jǔzhèn
WCMP	Wireless control message protocol	无线控制消息协议	Wúxiàn kòngzhì xiāoxi xiéyì
WCSI	World Center for Scientific Information	世界科学信息中心	Shìjiè kēxué xìnxī zhōngxīn
WD	Satellite earth station	卫星地球站	Wèixīng dìqiúzhàn
WD	Western Digital (US hard drive maker)	西部数据	Xībù shùjù
WD	Write data	写数据	Xiě shùjù
WDDX	Web distributed data exchange	Web 分布式数据交换	Web fēnbù-shì shùjù jiāohuàn
WDL	Wavelength-dependent loss	波长相关损耗	Bōcháng xiāngguān sǔnhào
WDL	Wireless data link	无线数据传输链路	Wúxiàn shùjù chuánshū liànlù
WDM	Wavelength division multiplex	波分多路复用	Bōfēn duōlù fùyòng
WDM	Wavelength division multiplexer	波分复用器	Bōfēn fùyòngqì
WDM	Wavelength division multiplexing	波长分割多路复用	Bōcháng fēngē duōlù fùyòng
WDM	Wavelength division multiplexing	波分复用	Bōfēn fùyòng
WDM	Windows driver model	视窗驱动程序模块	Shìchuāng qūdòng chéngxù mókuài
WDP	Wireless data protocol	无线数据协议	Wúxiàn shùjù xiéyì
WDP	Wireless data protocol	无线数据报协议	Wúxiàn shùjùbào xiéyì
WDP	Wireless datagram protocol	无线数据报文协议	Wúxiàn shùjù bàowén xiéyì
WDP	Wireless datagram protocol	无线数据报协议	Wúxiàn shùjùbào xiéyì
WDT	Watchdog timer	监视时钟	Jiānshì shízhōng
WEB	Web page	网页	Wǎngyè
WECA	Wireless Ethernet Compatibility Alliance	无线以太网兼容联盟	Wúxiàn yǐtàiwǎng jiānróng liánméng
WEP	Wired equivalent privacy	有线等价保密	Yǒuxiàn děngjià bǎomì
WEP	Wired equivalent privacy	有线对等保密	Yǒuxiàn duìděng bǎomì
WEP	Wired equivalent protocol	有线等效协议	Yǒuxiàn děngxiào xiéyì
WF	Wireless transmission equipment	无线发射设备	Wúxiàn fāshè shèbèi
WFM	Waveform monitor	波形监视器	Bōxíng jiānshìqì
WfM	Wired for management	有线管理	Yǒuxiàn guǎnlǐ
WfMC	Workflow management coalition	工作流管理联盟	Gōngzuòliú guǎnlǐ liánméng
WfMS	Workflow management system	工作流管理系统	Gōngzuòliú guǎnlǐ xìtǒng
WFQ	Weighted fair queuing	加权公平队列	Jiāquán gōngping duìliè
WFQ	Weighted fair queuing	加权公平排队	Jiāquán gōngping páiduì

WFQ	Weighted fair queuing	加权的公平排队算法	Jiāquánde gōngping páiduì suànfǎ
WG	Wave guide synthesis	波导合成	Bōdǎo héchéng
WGPD	Waveguide photo diode	波导光探测二极管	Bōdǎo guāng tàncè èrjíguǎn
WGR	Waveguide grating router	波导光栅选路器	Bōdǎo guāngshān xuǎnlùqì
WHQL	Microsoft Windows Hardware Quality lab	微软公司视窗硬件质量实验室	Wēiruǎn gōngsī shìchuāng yìngjiàn zhìliàng shíyànshì
WHT	Walsh-Hadamard transform	沃尔什-哈达码变换	Wò-ěr-shí—Hǎ-dá-mǎ biànhuàn
WI	Waveform interpolation	波形内插	Bōxíng nèichā
Wi-Fi	Wireless fidelity	无线保真	Wúxiàn bǎozhēn
WiMAX	Broadband wireless MAN standard (IEEE 802.16)	宽带无线 MAN 标准	Kuāndài wúxiàn MAN biāozhǔn
WIMC	Windows, icons, menu and cursor	窗户，图标，菜单，光标	Chuānghu, túbiāo, càidān, guāngbiāo
WIMP	Windows, icons, menu and pointer	窗户，图标，菜单，光标	Chuānghu, túbiāo, càidān, guāngbiāo
WIN	Wireless intelligent network	无线智能网	Wúxiàn zhìnéng wǎng
WIN	Wireless intelligent network	无线智能网络	Wúxiàn zhìnéng wǎngluò
WinHEC	Windows hardware Engineering conference	视窗硬件工程会议	Shìchuāng yìngjiàn gōngchéng huìyì
Winsock	Windows socket	视窗套接口	Shìchuāng tào jiēkǒu
WK	Working register	工作寄存器	Gōngzuò jìcúnqì
WLAN	Wireless local area network	无线本地网	Wúxiàn běndì wǎng
WLAN	Wireless local area network	无线局域网	Wúxiàn júyùwǎng
WLAN	Wireless local area network	无线区域网路	Wúxiàn qūyù wǎnglù
WLL	Wireless local loop	无线本地环路	Wúxiàn běndì huánlù
WME	Windows multimedia extensions	Windows 多媒体扩充板	Windows duōméitǐ kuòchōng bǎn
WMI	Wired for management initiative	主动式管理线路	Zhǔdòngshì guǎnlǐ xiànlù
WML	Wireless markup language	无线标记语言	Wúxiàn biāojì yǔyán
WML	Wireless markup language	无线标志语言	Wúxiàn biāozhì yǔyán
WO	Write once	一次性写入	Yīcìxìng xiěrù
WO	Write only	只写	Zhǐ xiě
WOL	Wake on LAN	局域网唤醒	Júyùwǎng huànxǐng
WORM	Write one read many	一写多读机	Yīxiě duōdú jī
WORM	Write only read many (optical disk)	一次写入多次读出（光盘）	Yīcì xiěrù duōcì dú chū (guāngpán)
WORM	Write-one read many	单写多读	Dānxiě duōdú
WOSA	Windows open service architecture	Windows 开放服务结构	Windows kāifàng fúwù jiégòu
WP	Wavelet packet	小波包	Xiǎobō bāo
WP	Word processing software	词处理软件	Cí chǔlǐ ruǎnjiàn
WPAN	Wireless personal area network	无线个人域网	Wúxiàn gèrén yù wǎng
WPBX	Wireless private branch exchange	无线专用交换机	Wúxiàn zhuānyòng jiāohuànjī
WPC	Wavelength path connect	波长通道连接	Bōcháng tōngdào liánjiē
WPC	Wireless personal communication	无线个人通信	Wúxiàn gèrén tōngxìn
WPDL	Workflow process definition language	工作流过程定义语言	Gōngzuòliú guòchéng dìngyì yǔyán
WPI	Wavelength path ID	波长通道值	Bōcháng tōngdào zhí
WPL	Wavelength path link	波长通道链路	Bōcháng tōngdào liànlù
WRC	World Radio-communication Conference	世界无线电通信大会	Shìjiè wúxiàndiàn tōngxìn dàhuì
WRED	Weighted random early detection	加权随机早期检测	Jiāquán suíjī zǎoqī jiǎncè
WRED	Weighted random early detection	加权随机早期侦测	Jiāquán suíjī zǎoqī zhēncè
WRED	Weighted random early detection	加权的随机早期控测	Jiāquánde suíjī zǎoqī kòngcè
WRED	Weighted Random Early Detection	加权的随机早期探测	Jiāquánde suíjī zǎoqī tàncè

WRI	Wuhan Research Institute of Posts & telecommunications	武汉邮电科学研究院	Wǔhàn yóudiàn kēxué yánjiūyuàn
WRR	Weighted round robin	加权往返算法	Jiāquán wǎngfǎn suànfǎ
WRS	Wavelength router switch	波长选路开关	Bōcháng xuǎnlù kāiguān
WS	On wall surface (telecom installation)	沿墙面敷设	Yán qiángmiàn fūshè
WS	Wireless receiver equipment	无线接收设备	Wúxiàn jiēshōu shèbèi
WS	Work station	工作站	Gōngzuòzhàn
WSA	Wireless subscriber access	无线用户接入	Wúxiàn yònghù jiērù
WSDL	Web services description language	网络服务描述语言	Wǎngluò fúwù miáoshù yǔyán
WSDL	Web services description language	Web 服务描述语言	Web fúwù miáoshù yǔyán
WSF	Work station function block	工作站功能块	Gōngzuòzhàn gōngnéng kuài
WSF	Workstation function block	工作站功能块	Gōngzuòzhàn gōngnéng kuài
WSH	Windows scripting host	视窗脚本程序	Shìchuāng jiǎoběn chéngxù
WSHM	Water swelling heat melting (FOC)	水胀热融	Shuǐzhàng rèróng
WSP	Wireless session protocol	无线会话协议	Wúxiàn huìhuà xiéyì
WSP	Wireless speech protocol	无线会话协议	Wúxiàn huìhuà xiéyì
WSS	Wide-sense stationary	宽平稳	Kuān píngwěn
WSS	Work station server	工作站服务器	Gōngzuòzhàn fúwùqì
WT	Microwave tower	微波铁塔	Wēibō tiětǎ
WT	Wave table synthesis	波表合成	Bōbiǎo héchéng
WT	Wireless terminal	无线终端	Wúxiàn zhōngduān
WTA	Wireless telephony application	无线电话应用	Wúxiàn diànhuà yìngyòng
WTAI	Wireless telephony applications interface	无线电话应用接口	Wúxiàn diànhuà yìngyòng jiēkǒu
WTLS	Wireless transmission level security	无线传输层安全	Wúxiàn chuánshū céng ānquán
WTLS	Wireless transport layer security	无线传送层安全性	Wúxiàn chuánsòng céng ānquánxìng
WTP	Wireless transaction protocol	无线事务处理协议	Wúxiàn shìwù chǔlǐ xiéyì
WTP	Wireless transaction protocol	无线事务协议	Wúxiàn shìwù xiéyì
WTR	Wait to restoration	恢复等待时间	Huīfù děngdài shíjiān
WTR	Wait to restore	等待恢复	Děngdài huīfù
WTR	Wait to restore time	等待恢复时间	Děngdài huīfù shíjiān
WTX	Waiting time extension	扩展等待时间	Kuòzhǎn děngdài shíjiān
WUG	Wireless user group	无线用户组	Wúxiàn yònghù zǔ
WVPN	Wireless virtual private network	无线虚拟专用网络	Wúxiàn xūnǐ zhuānyòng wǎngluò
WWMCCS	Worldwide Military Command and Control System	全球军事指挥系统控制系统	Quánqiú jūnshì zhǐhuī xìtǒng kòngzhì xìtǒng
WWT	Work waiting time	工作等待时间	Gōngzuò děngdài shíjiān
www	Word Wide Web	环球网	Huánqiú wǎng
WWW	World Wide Web	万维网	Wànwéiwǎng
WXC	Wavelength cross-connect	波长交叉连接	Bōcháng jiāochā liánjiē
WYSIWYG	What you see is what you get	见得相一	Jiàn de xiāng yī
WYSIWYG	What you see is what you get	所见即所得	Suǒjiàn jí suǒdé
WYSIWYG	What you see is what you get	直接可视数据	Zhíjiē kěshì shùjù
WZ	Microwave carrier	微波载波	Wēibō zàibō

X

X.25	Public packet data network	公用分组数据网	Gōngyòng fēnzǔ shùjù wǎng
XACML	Extensible access control markup language	扩展访问控制标记语言	Kuòzhǎn fǎngwèn kòngzhì biāojì yǔyán
XALC	Extended assembler language coding	扩充的汇编语言编码	Kuòchōngde huìbiān yǔyán biānmǎ

XB	Crossbar	纵横制	Zònghéng zhì
XBPB	Transceiver back plane board	收发信机后面板	Shōufāxìnjī hòumian bǎn
XC	Cross-connect element	交叉单元	Jiāochā dānyuán
XC	Cross-connect system	交叉连接系统	Jiāochā liánjiē xìtǒng
XCA	Extended changeover acknowledgment	扩展的倒换证实	Kuòzhǎnde dǎohuàn zhèngshí
XCO	Extended changeover order	扩展的倒换命令	Kuòzhǎnde dǎohuàn mìnglìng
XCVA	Transceiver assembly	收发信机集成板	Shōufāxìnjī jíchéngbǎn
XCVB	Transceiver block	收发信机模块	Shōufāxìnjī mókuài
XCVR	Transceiver	收发报机	Shōufābàojī
XCVR	Transceiver rack	收发信机机架	Shōufāxìnjī jījià
XCVS	Transceiver shelf	收发信机架	Shōufāxìnjī jià
XCVU	Transceiver unit	收发信机单元	Shōufāxìnjī dānyuán
XDMCP	X display manager control protocol	X 显示管理器控制协议	X xiǎnshì guǎnlǐqì kòngzhì xiéyì
XDR	External data representation	外部数据表示	Wàibù shùjù biǎoshì
XFSB	Transceiver frequency synthesizer board	收发信机频率同步面板	Shōufāxìnjī pínlǜ tóngbù miànbǎn
XIC	Transmission interface converter	传输接口转换器	Chuánshū jiēkǒu zhuǎnhuànqì
XICP	Interconnect panel	互联面板	Hùlián miànbǎn
XID	Exchange identification	交换标识	Jiāohuàn biāozhì
XID	Exchange identifier	交换标识符	Jiāohuàn biāozhì fú
XKMS	Extensible markup language key management specification	XML 密钥管理规范	XML mìyào guǎnlǐ guīfàn
XLW	Signaling network	信令网	Xìnlìng wǎng
XMCU	Transceiver master control unit	收发信机主机控制单元	Shōufāxìnjī zhǔjī kòngzhì dānyuán
XMI	Extensible markup language message interface	可扩展标记语言消息接口	Kěkuòzhǎn biāojì yǔyán xiāoxi jiēkǒu
XML	Extensible markup language	可扩展标记语言	Kěkuòzhǎn biāojì yǔyán
XML	Extensible markup language	扩充标记语言	Kuòchōng biāojì yǔyán
XML	Extensible markup language	扩展性标识语言	Kuòzhǎn-xìng biāozhì yǔyán
XML	Extensible markup language (in SQL Server)	扩展标示语言支持	Kuòzhǎn biāoshì yǔyán zhīchí
XMS	eXtended memory specification	扩充记忆体	Kuòchōng jìyìtǐ
XPD	Cross polarization discrimination	交叉极化鉴别度	Jiāochā jíhuà jiànbié dù
XPIC	Cross-polarization interference counteracter	交叉极化干扰抵消器	Jiāochā jíhuà gānrǎo dǐxiāoqì
XPM	Super permanent memory	超级永久性存储器	Chāojí yǒngjiǔxìng cúnchǔqì
XPSA	Transceiver power supply assembly	收发信机功率供给集成件	Shōufāxìnjī gōnglǜ gōngjǐ jíchéng jiàn
XPTE	Extended page table entry	扩充的页面表项	Kuòchōngde yèmiàn biǎoxiàng
XRES	Expected user response	期待用户响应	Qīdài yònghù xiǎngyìng
XrML	eXtensible rights markup language	可扩展权限标记语言	Kěkuòzhǎn quánxiàn biāojì yǔyán
XSCB	Transceiver slave controller unit	收发信机从属控制单元	Shōufāxìnjī cóngshǔ kòngzhì dānyuán
XSD	Extensible markup language schema definition	可扩展标记语言模式定义语言	Kěkuòzhǎn biāojì yǔyán móshì dìngyì yǔyán
XSL	Extensible style language (in SQL Server)	可扩展样式语言	Kěkuòzhǎn yàngshì yǔyán
XSL	Extensible stylesheet language	可扩展设计语言	Kěkuòzhǎn shèjì yǔyán
XSL	eXtensible stylesheet language	可扩展样式表语言	Kěkuòzhǎn yàngshì biǎo yǔyán
XSLT	eXtensible stylesheet language transformation	可扩展样式表语言转换	Kěkuòzhǎn yàngshì biǎo yǔyán zhuǎnhuàn
XUDT	Extended unit data (in SS7)	增强单位数据	Zēngqiáng dānwèi shùjù
XUDTS	Extended unit data service (in SS7)	增强单位数据业务	Zēngqiáng dānwèi shùjù yèwù
XWD	Mini-satellite earth station	小卫星地球站	Xiǎo wèixīng dìqiúzhàn

Y

YD	Mobile telecommunication	移动通信	Yídòng tōngxìn
YDK	Post and telecoms electrical control	由政电控	Yóuzhèng diànkòng
YGQ	Subscriber optical network	用户光纤网	Yònghù guāngxiān wǎng
YJ	Diesel generator	油机	Yóujī
YJX	Post and telecoms machinery	邮政电机械	Yóuzhèng diànjīxiè
YP	Yellow page service	黄页服务	Huángyè fúwù
YX	Remote control line	遥控线	Yáokòng xiàn

Z

Z(t)	Instantaneous failure intensity	瞬时失效频度	Shùnshí shīxiào píndù
ZA	Zero and add	清零和加	Qīng líng hé jiā
ZAM	Zero administration for Windows	零管理视窗系统	Líng guǎnlǐ shìchuāng xìtǒng
ZAN	Zone access node	小区接入节点	Xiǎoqū jiērù jiédiǎn
ZB	Automatic transit telegram (Telex)	自动转报	Zìdòng zhuǎnbào
ZD	Terminal machine (telecom term)	终端机	Zhōngduānjī
ZI	Zero input	零输入	Líng shūrù
ZIF	Zero insertion force	零插入力	Líng chārùlì
ZIP	Zone information protocol (an Apple protocol)	区域信息协议	Qūyù xìnxī xiéyì
ZK	Automatic control	自动控制	Zìdòng kòngzhì
ZNL	Intelligent building	智能大楼	Zhìnéng dàlóu
ZO	Zero output	零输出	Líng shūchū
ZRLT	Zero remaining lifetime	剩余生存时间为 0	Shèngyú shēngcún shíjiān wéi 0
ZrO_2	Zirconium oxide	氧化锆	Yǎnghuàgào
ZRP	Zone routing protocol	区域路由协议	Qūyù lùyóu xiéyì
ZTE	Zhongxing Telecommunications Enterprise (Chinese company)	中兴通讯	Zhōngxīng tōngxùn
ZVEI	Zentralverband der Electrotechnischen Industrie (Germany)	电气工业中央协会	Diànqì gōngyè zhōngyāng xiéhuì
ZW	Trunk line unmanned re-amplifier	中继线无人赠音站	Zhōngjìxiàn wúrén zèngyīn zhàn

1East.com.	(Shanghai Web magazine)	经纬网	Jīngwěiwǎng
.bmp	Bitmap file	位图文件	Wèi tú wénjiàn
.exe	Executable file	执行档	Zhíxíng dàng
.pdf	Portable Document Format (Adobe format)	可移植资料格式	Kěyízhí zīliào géshi
.pdf	Portable Document Format (Adobe)	移植资料格式	Yízhí zīliào géshi
©	Copyright	版权	Bǎnquán
μA	Microampere	微安	Wēi'ān
1NF	First normal form	第1范式	Dìyī fànshì
1PPS	One pulse per second	秒脉冲	Miǎo màichōng
1XRTT	First generation radio transmission technology	第一阶段无线传输技术	Dìyī jiēduàn wúxiàn chuánshū jìshù
2B1Q	Two binary one quaternary	两个二进制一个四进制编码	Liǎnggè èrjìnzhì yīgè sìjìnzhì biānmǎ
2-cell	Two-cell	二单元	Èr dānyuán
2D	Two-dimensional	二维	Èrwéi
2G	Second generation	第二代	Dì'èrdài
2NF	Second normal form	第2范式	Dì'èr fànshì
2WPD	Two-way power divider	二路功率分配器	Èrlù gōnglǜ fēnpèiqì
3C	Computer, communication, control	计算机，通讯和控制	Jìsuànjī, tōngxùn hé kòngzhì
3D	Three dimensional	三维	Sānwéi
3D	Three dimensional	三维	Sānwéi
3DPA	Three dimensional (3D) positional audio	三维定位音频	Sānwéi dìngwèi yīnpín
3DS	Three dimensional sub-system (video)	三维子系统	Sānwéi zìxìtǒng
3G	Third generation	第三代	Dì sān dài
3G	Third generation mobile telephone	第三代移动通信）	Dìsāndài yídòng tōngxìn
3GIG	Third generation interest group	第三代兴趣小组	Dìsāndài xìngqu xiǎozǔ
3GPP	Third generation partnership projects	第三代伙伴组织计划	Dìsāndài huǒbàn zǔzhī jìhuà
3GTEG	China 3G Technical Experts Group	第三代移动通信技术试验专家组	Dìsāndài yídòng tōngxìn jìshù shìyàn zhuānjiāzǔ
3NF	Third normal form	第3范式	Dìsān fànshì
3PTY	Three party service	三方通信	Sānfāng tōngxìn
3PTY	Three party communications	三方通信	Sānfāng tōngxìn
3PTY	Three party service	三方业务	Sānfāng yèwù
3R	Regeneration, reshaping, retiming	再生、重整形和重定时	Zàishēng、chóngzhěngxíng hé chóngdìngshí
4GL	Fourth generation language	第四代语言	Dìsìdài yǔyán
4-level FM	Four-level frequency modulation	四电平调频	Sìdiànpíng tiáopín
4WPD	Four-way power divider	四路功率分配器	Sìlù gōnglǜ fēnpèiqì
8PSK	Octal phase shift keying	八进制移相键控	Bājìnzhì yíxiāng jiànkòng
γ	Phase	相位	Xiàngwèi
μs	Microsecond	微妙	Wēimiào
π/4DQPSK	p/4 shifted, differentially encoded quadrature phase-shift keying	π /4相移的差分编码正交移相键控	π /4 xiàngyíde chāfēn biānmǎ zhèngjiāo yíxiàng jiànkòng

τDL	Tau dither loop	τ 抖动环	τ dǒudòng huán
φ	Phase	相位	Xiàngwèi
Ω	Ohm (unit of resistance)	欧姆	Oū-mǔ
ГОСТ	Gosudarstvennui Standart (Russian government standard) (used by the Chinese to indicate the agency	国家标准制定部	Guójiā biāozhǔn zhìdìng bù